PRINCIPAL SUBJECTS

Forming of Steel Sheet, Strip and Plate

Shearing, Slitting, and Gas and Arc Cutting

Forming of Bar, Tube and Wire

Forming of:

METALS HANDBOOK

8th Edition

VOL. 4

Forming

prepared under the direction of the

ASM HANDBOOK COMMITTEE

Taylor Lyman, Editor
Howard E. Boyer, Managing Editor
Edward A. Durand, Senior Editor
Associate Editors: William J. Carnes,
Margaret W. Chevalier, H. C. Doepken,
Philip D. Harvey, Helen Lawton and
Theodore M. Leach. Assistant Editors:
Ian A. Anderson, Helen V. Bukovics,
Barbara A. Caldwell, E. Robin Watkins

AMERICAN SOCIETY FOR METALS
Metals Park, Ohio 44073

First printing, June 1969
Second printing, March 1970

Nothing contained in the Metals Handbook is to be construed as a grant of any right of manufacture, sale, or use in connection with any method, process, apparatus, product, or composition, whether or not covered by letters patent or registered trade mark, nor as a defense against liability for the infringement of letters patent or registered trade mark.

Library of Congress Catalog Card Number: 27-12046

PRINTED IN THE UNITED STATES OF AMERICA

MEMBERS OF ASM HANDBOOK COMMITTEE (1967 to 1969)

PREVIOUS CHAIRMEN OF ASM HANDBOOK COMMITTEE

OFFICERS AND TRUSTEES OF THE AMERICAN SOCIETY FOR METALS

Contributors to This Volume

Numbers refer to the pages where contributors are credited in the volume. Names of committee chairmen are printed in capital letters.

W. E. Allan, 405
CHARLES B. ALLEN, 353
C. V. Anderson, 465
H. L. ANTHONY III, 1
J. W. Archer, 189
Kenneth Armagost, 353
John T. Armstrong, 112
Norbert A. Arnold, 449
ROGER S. BABCOCK, 278
F. L. Banta, 201
M. Glenn Barber, 1
Sidney J. Barber, 353
Donald Bassler, 112
Louis W. Baum, Jr., 449
A. G. Baumgartner, 265
Rudolph K. F. Baumle, 465
Othmar C. Besch, 201
Emil C. Blocks, 194
Harold Bloomfield, 353
Victor J. Boll, 194
Pehr O. Bolling, 1
FRANCIS W. BOULGER, 250, 437
A. J. Boylan, 322
C. R. Bradlee, 475
Robert F. Brandt, 371
N. F. Bratkovich, 437
R. William Breitzig, 432
Norman N. Breyer, 322
Barlow W. Brooks, Jr., 224
David F. Brower, 256
Walton E. Brush, 333
H. T. Burke, 112
Robert L. Callaghan, 465
Roy L. Camp, 371
A. E. Carlile, 78
R. J. Carlson, 250
S. R. Carpenter, 437
John J. Carroll, 194
F. R. Cervarich, 101
George L. Chase, 194, 405
J. C. Chaston, 447
John E. Choate, 101
Henry P. Cipperley, 224
M. L. Clark, 1
Edward J. Clarkin, 101
Richard M. Cogan, 201
A. J. Cook, 112
A. L. Cooper, 278
Eldon Cooperrider, 379
Frank J. Covelli, 201
William T. Cox, 145
James E. Coyne, Jr., 437
R. P. Culbertson, 371
Harold R. Daniels, 1
Russell N. Dean, 405
Ernest Dell, 437
STEWART M. DePOY, 69
Andrew C. Dickson, 305
Paul Dillon, 347
C. Kenneth Divers, 353
W. J. Doelker, 449
Frank Donaldson, 371
V. V. Donaldson, 437
James Durkin, 101
R. E. Eirons, 322
William P. Ekey, 224
W. L. Elliott, 278
Frank Emley, 449
Gene F. Erbin, 437
A. R. Essenberg, 405
S. O. Evans, 322
George F. Farley, 379
D. G. Farnsworth, 112
Glenn Faulkner, 437
Joseph Fekete, 201
Sidney H. Feldman, 305
Eric E. Ferda, 112
M. F. Fireoved, 305
Frank G. Flocke, 101
Roy Flowers, 265
Rex A. Ford, 437
A. G. Forrest, 475
William B. Forsberg, 1
Barry France, 371
W. D. FRANCE, 405
Robert E. Frankenberg, Sr., 353
E. H. Franks, 278
Clark Fredenburg, 224
F. J. Fuchs, 189
W. G. Gaboda, 69
E. GAMMETER, 322
Gerald Garfield, 437
Donald Garrett, 60
Ray J. Gatz, 465
Carl H. Gerlach, 69, 145, 194
D. F. Gerstle, 69
E. G. Gibson, 449
William J. Gilmore, 78
J. H. Golata, 112
Ralph S. Golden, 353
Gorton M. Goodwin, 112
Robert D. Goodwin, 475
Frank Gorsler, 333
Willard B. Green, Jr., 333
Robert L. Haley, 101
J. F. Hamburg, 60
C. H. HANNON, 60
T. Hanson, 154
Robert D. Hargesheimer, 475
R. Harnist, 1
H. B. Hartline, 278
G. S. Hauser, 475
Walter S. Hazlett, 60
Alan K. Hegedus, 371
Fred Heinzelman, Jr., 322
JAMES C. HERR, 379
A. A. Herrada, 1
Walter T. Hiller, 353
J. J. Hines, 405
G. W. Hinkle, 353
A. F. HOFSTATTER, 371
P. J. Hogan, 78
Robert W. Hohl, 112, 145
H. A. Holberson, 145
Louis Hrusovsky, 465
L. W. HUDSON, 424
Robert O. Hughes, 424
K. J. HUMBERSTONE, 101
H. E. Ihle, 192
Raymond J. Imars, 101
W. A. Irvine, 449
L. L. Jaffe, 194
Craig C. Johnson, 305
H. G. Johnstin, 475
Wesley Kalita, 353
Serope Kalpakjian, 201
Joseph I. Karash, 60
S. P. Karnitz, 69
John W. Keegan, 465
George E. Keith, 69
John R. Kelly, 278
Richard T. Kennedy, 379
Kenneth R. Keska, 265
J. F. Kinal, 347
E. C. Kingsland, 305
Larry S. Klass, 437
Joseph Klavon, 112, 145
V. A. Kortesoja, 69
David S. Lambie, 465
J. K. Langfitt, Jr., 449
Armand Laplante, 371
A. Justus Larson, 69, 145
J. D. Lashbrook, 371
E. A. Lauchner, 371
John M. Lee, 405
C. E. Lehnhardt, 424
Burton F. Lewis, 347
Lloyd F. Lockwood, 424
J. M. Lowe, 305
Hugh G. Lusher, 305
J. J. Lynch, 101
L. R. MAITLAND, 78
J. A. Mallen, 424
ELTON MAYHEW, 333
C. R. Mayne, 353
Richard N. McCarten, 353
Cecil J. McClure, 322
Mynard McConnell, 322
R. E. McFarland, 465
Raymond L. McGaughey, 145

FOREWORD

FORMING PROCESSES are among the most important metalworking operations. This Volume 4 of the 8th Edition of METALS HANDBOOK describes and illustrates these processes comprehensively, with accuracy and clarity.

Today, industry must evaluate continuously the costs of competitive materials and of the operations necessary for converting each material into finished products. This book can serve as an invaluable aid to that analysis. The information it contains is drawn from industry experience. Each article on a specific forming process describes advantages and limitations of that process, and discusses suitability of work metals, before presenting a detailed account of the techniques and equipment employed for efficient application of the process. Many of the articles also compare alternative manufacturing processes for the same product. Throughout the book, examples cite actual experience and illustrations clarify the printed word.

The information contained in this book is vital to both suppliers and fabricators of metals. It can assist them in using metals more effectively, and thereby in meeting the challenge of plastics and the other nonmetallics that increasingly compete with metals for the world's expanding markets. Moreover, proper application of this information can permit new metallic materials — many of which are inherently difficult to form — to become competitive.

Long hours of effort have been spent in the preparation of this volume. The Handbook Committee, especially selected for its experience in metalworking, guided the planning of its content. Carefully chosen author committees, made up of experts in metal forming, worked together to prepare their articles and sections — supplying, coordinating and verifying the information presented in these pages. An experienced editorial staff developed the contributions of the author committees and brought the book to its completion. Members of ASM — in fact, *all* users of metals throughout the world — owe these men and women gratitude for compiling a new and practical reference work on the forming of metals.

The American Society for Metals is proud to make this book available to the technical community as a part of ASM's continuing goal of presenting useful information concerning metals.

CARL H. SAMANS
President – American Society for Metals

ALLAN RAY PUTNAM
Managing Director

PREFACE

THIS IS THE FOURTH in a series of volumes that will supersede and expand the single-volume 7th edition of METALS HANDBOOK. In preparing this new volume, the aim of the ASM Handbook Committee and the authors has been to provide the reader with practical information that will help him select and control processes for forming ferrous and nonferrous metals.

The word "forming", as it relates to the title and content of this volume, is used in a broader sense than bending, stretching and drawing of metal in presses and press brakes, but in a narrower sense than would be implied by the term "shaping". Forming here includes the principal mechanical and metallurgical shaping processes other than casting, forging, rolling and machining. Thus, in addition to the common bending and press forming operations, this volume discusses processes such as blanking, shearing, gas cutting, straightening, spinning, contour roll forming, rotary swaging, cold heading, cold (impact) extrusion, coining, and powder metallurgy.

About half of the volume deals with forming low-carbon steel of the common grades and qualities. The remainder is concerned with the full range of commercially formable ferrous and nonferrous alloys, in approximate proportion to the frequency with which they are formed. All common mill products (sheet, strip, plate, bar, rod, extrusions, tube, wire and powder) are dealt with as starting materials for forming.

As it was for the first three volumes of this 8th edition, principal reliance for authorship has again been placed on committees of engineers and production managers from industry, in order to arrive at a balanced presentation of divergent viewpoints and to achieve realism in relation to practice. More than 200 plants, large and small, are represented in the authorship of this fourth volume; 25 committees and 306 individuals are named herein as contributors. In addition to the contributors credited throughout these pages, many other members and friends of ASM — including, especially, numerous colleagues of the authors cited — have supplied valuable information and have reviewed manuscripts for accuracy and clarity.

The table at the foot of this page compares in detail the subject coverage in this fourth volume of the 8th edition with the coverage of corresponding subject matter in the 7th edition. As measured by the number of illustrations and tables, more than 50 times as much numerical information has been included in this volume as in the corresponding subject areas of the 7th edition. Apart from expanded coverage of subjects, this increased emphasis on easily accessible data (as distinguished from descriptive text), together with the closer relation of this volume to industrial practice (demonstrated by the large number of specific examples, applications and comparisons), constitutes the important difference between the 7th edition of METALS HANDBOOK and this 8th edition.

The principal new contribution made in this volume is the multiplicity of examples that describe forming practice. Numbered consecutively from 1 through 705 from the front to the back of the book, these examples deal with methods and tools used, and with improvements made or problems solved, in specific operations and appli-

Comparison of Volume 4 of the 8th Edition With Corresponding Subject Matter on Forming in the 7th Edition

Subject matter (page reference, 8th edition)	Illustrations 8th ed	Illustrations 7th ed	Tables 8th ed	Tables 7th ed	Examples 8th ed	Examples 7th ed	Contributors 8th ed	Contributors 7th ed	Pages 8th ed	Pages 7th ed
Forming of steel sheet, strip and plate (1 to 264)	1588	0	192	0	339	0	130	2	264	2
Shearing, slitting, and gas and arc cutting (265 to 304)	123	18	44	9	27	0	17	7	40	11
Forming of bars, tube and wire (305 to 352)	260	14	51	0	84	0	41	2	48	2
Forming of stainless steel and heat-resisting alloys (353 to 378)	187	0	30	0	59	0	25	1	26	1
Forming of nonferrous metals (379 to 448)	395	7	85	8	113	0	56	11	70	11
Powder metallurgy (449 to 464)	81	5	25	4	24	0	13	10	16	7
Cold heading and cold extrusion (465 to 496)	323	2	50	0	59	0	24	6	32	2
Total	2957	46	477	21	705	0	306	39	496	36

cations; and they emphasize the results obtained in the manufacture of a great variety of metal parts.

To tie the various sections of the book together and make a more unified whole, the editors have used several techniques, the three principal ones of which are as follows:

First, many cross references are given in the text — and in tabulations at the end of some articles — to direct the reader to closely related discussion or examples presented elsewhere in the book.

Second, to make it easy for the reader to find any of the 705 consecutively numbered examples without having to consult the index or the table of contents, the span of example numbers presented on each pair of facing pages is indicated at the tops of those pages, near the inside margins.

Third, the index (printed on colored paper) has been compiled with the reader's needs in mind, and has been organized to help him get quickly to the page that contains the information he wants.

In compiling this new work on forming, and in orienting the subject matter strongly toward industrial practice, the authors have omitted discussions of the underlying fundamentals of the physics of metal deformation. This omission is justified by the need to conserve space and by the availability of the more fundamental physical data in journal articles and other sources.

IN CONCLUDING this preface, we borrow the final words of the Preface to Volume 1: The extensive range of data and examples presented in this book reflects the specialized knowledge of its 306 contributors. Upon the collective experience and high competence of these specialists rest the accuracy and authority of the volume.

TAYLOR LYMAN
Editor – Metals Handbook

Contents of Metals Handbook Volume 4

Forming of Steel Sheet, Strip and Plate

Forming of Steel (cont'd)

Forming of Steel (cont'd)

Shearing, Slitting, and Gas and Arc Cutting

Forming of Bars, Tube and Wire

Forming of Stainless Steel and Heat-Resisting Alloys

Forming of Nonferrous Metals

Powder Metallurgy

Cold Heading and Cold Extrusion

FORMING OF STEEL SHEET, STRIP AND PLATE

CONTENTS

Presses and Auxiliary Equipment for Forming of Sheet Metal

*By the ASM Committee on Forming of Sheet Metal in Presses**

PRESSES described in this article are mechanically or hydraulically powered machines used for producing parts from sheet metal.

Power presses can be classified according to the following characteristics: source of power, type of frame, method of actuation of slides, and number of slides in action. Presses in any of these classes are available in a range of capacities (tonnage or bed area), although the range is not necessarily the same for all types of presses. Characteristics of 18 types of presses are summarized in Table 1.

JIC Identification System. The Joint Industry Conference (JIC) system of identifying press characteristics is in general use. In a typical sample:

S4-750-96-72

the press is identified by the S as a single-action model (D is used for double-action, T for triple-action, and OBI for open-back inclinable); by the 4 as having four-point suspension; by the 750 as being rated at 750-ton capacity; and by the 96 and 72 as having a bed measuring 96 in. left-to-right and 72 in. front-to-back. Any other press can be so identified, by substitution of appropriate numerals for number of suspension points, tonnage rating, and bed dimensions. These characteristics are discussed later in this article.

The JIC also recommends that a metal tag be attached permanently to the press, stating the stroke length, shut height, kind and length of adjustment, strokes per minute, size and weight. If a die cushion is provided, an additional tag should describe it.

Source of Power

Power presses for sheet-metal work can be driven hydraulically or mechanically. The performance characteristics and other operational features of hydraulic and mechanical presses are compared in the following list.

1 Force is exerted constantly throughout the stroke of a hydraulic press. Force developed by a mechanical press varies with the position of the slide.
2 The length of stroke is easily adjusted and controlled in a hydraulic press. In a mechanical press, the stroke is fixed by the throw of the crank or eccentric.
3 The speed of a hydraulic press is adjustable over a wide range, whereas the speed of a mechanical press is limited by the type of drive.
4 A hydraulic press cannot be overloaded. It can deliver only a preset force, and slide motion stops when that force is reached. A mechanical press can be overloaded, resulting in damage to the press, if it is not equipped with overload protection.
5 Mechanical presses cycle faster and are better suited to high production than are hydraulic presses.
6 Because energy is stored in the flywheel, a mechanical press can use a smaller motor. For some applications, the size of the motor in a hydraulic press may be as much as

*H. L. ANTHONY III, *Chairman,* Staff Fellow, Mellon Institute, Carnegie-Mellon University; M. GLENN BARBER, Senior Manufacturing Research Engineer, Michigan Manufacturing & Engineering Div., Burroughs Corp.; PEHR O. BOLLING, Overland-Bolling Co.

M. L. CLARK, Producibility Analyst, Small Aircraft Engine Dept., General Electric Co.; WILLIAM B. FORSBERG, Product Engineer, Carr Fastener Div., United-Carr Fastener Corp.; R. HARNIST, Tool and Design Supervisor, F. H. Lawson Co.; A. A. HERRADA, Supervisor of Tool Design Unit, Manufacturing Engineering Dept., General Parts Div., Ford Motor Co.; ROBERT S. NEILSON, Project Engineer, Fabrication Engineering Dept., Lukens Steel Co.; JOHN E. PARKS, HPM Div., Koehring Co.

J. W. RATH, Supervisor of Tool Engineering, Delco Appliance Div., General Motors Corp.; G. D. REED, Production Engineer, West Bend Co.; MERRILL RIDGWAY, Application Engineer, Minster Machine Co.; STEPHEN K. SZUCK (deceased), formerly Chief Manufacturing Engineer, Ronson Corp. of Pennsylvania.

The assistance of HAROLD R. DANIELS, senior associate editor, *Metalworking* magazine, in preparing this article is gratefully acknowledged.

Table 1. Characteristics of 18 Types of Presses

	Type of frame							Position of frame				Action			Method of actuation								Type of drive				Suspension			Ram		Bed		
Type of press	Open-back	Gap	Straight-side	Arch	Pillar	Solid	Tie rod	Vertical	Horizontal	Inclinable	Inclined	Single	Double	Triple	Crank	Front-to-back crank	Eccentric	Toggle	Screw	Cam	Rack and pinion	Piston	Over direct	Geared, overdrive	Under direct	Geared, underdrive	One-point	Two-point	Four-point	Single	Multiple	Solid	Open	Adjustable
Bench	X	X	..	..	..	X	..	X	..	X	X	X	..	..	X	..	X	..	X	..	X	X	X	..	..	..	X	..	..	X	..	X	X	X
Open-back inclinable	X	X	..	..	..	X	..	X	..	X	..	X	X	..	X	..	X	..	..	X	..	X	X	X	..	..	X	X	..	X	X	..	X	..
Gap-frame	X	X	..	..	..	X	X	X	X	X	X	X	X	..	X	X	X	X	..	..	..	X	X	X	..	..	X	X	X	X	X	X	X	..
Adjustable-bed horn	..	X	..	..	..	X	..	X	..	..	..	X	..	..	X	..	X	..	..	..	..	X	X	X	..	..	X	X	..	X	..	X	X	X
End-wheel	..	X	..	..	..	X	..	X	..	..	..	X	..	..	..	X	X	..	..	..	..	..	X	X	..	..	X	..	..	X	..	X	X	..
Arch-frame	..	..	X	X	..	X	..	X	..	..	X	X	..	..	X	..	..	..	..	..	..	..	X	X	..	..	X	..	..	X	..	..	X	..
Straight-side	..	..	X	X	..	X	X	X	X	..	X	X	X	X	X	X	X	..	..	..	X	X	X	X	X	X	X	X	X	X	X	X	X	..
Reducing	X	X	X	..	..	X	X	X	X	..	..	X	..	..	X	..	..	..	..	..	..	X	X	X	..	..	X	..	..	X	..	..	X	..
Knuckle-lever	..	..	X	..	..	X	X	X	..	..	X	X	X	..	..	..	..	X	..	..	..	..	X	X	..	..	X	X	..	X	X	X	X	..
Toggle-draw	..	..	X	..	..	X	X	X	..	..	..	..	X	X	X	..	X	X	..	..	..	..	..	X	..	X	X	X	X	..	X	..	X	..
Cam-drawing	X	X	X	..	..	X	X	X	..	X	..	..	X	..	X	..	..	..	..	X	..	..	X	X	..	..	X	..	..	..	X	..	X	..
Two-point single-action	..	X	X	..	..	X	X	X	..	..	X	X	..	..	X	..	X	..	..	..	..	..	..	X	..	X	..	X	..	X	..	X	X	..
High-production	..	..	X	..	..	X	X	X	..	..	X	X	..	..	X	..	X	..	..	..	..	..	X	X	..	..	X	X	..	X	..	..	X	..
Dieing machine	..	..	..	..	X	..	..	X	..	..	..	X	..	..	X	..	..	..	..	..	..	..	X	..	X	..	X	X	..	X	..	..	X	..
Transfer	..	X	X	..	..	X	X	X	..	..	..	X	..	..	X	X	X	X	..	..	..	..	X	X	..	..	..	X	..	X	..	..	X	..
Flat-edge trimming	..	..	..	X	..	X	..	X	..	..	..	..	X	..	..	..	..	..	..	X	..	..	..	X	..	..	X	..	..	X	..	..	..	..
Hydraulic	..	X	X	..	X	..	X	X	X	X	..	X	X	X	..	..	..	..	..	..	..	X	..	..	..	..	X	X	..	X	X	X	X	X
Press brake	X	X	..	..	..	X	..	X	..	..	..	X	..	..	X	..	..	..	..	..	..	X	..	X	..	..	..	X	X	X	..	X	..	..

2½ times as large as in an equivalent mechanical press.

7 Ram velocity in a mechanical press is higher, making this equipment more useful in operations such as blanking and piercing, in which a high-impact blow is needed. Blanking and piercing can be done in a hydraulic press, but the shock of the punch breaking through the metal can cause damage to the hydraulic system.

Mechanical Presses. In most mechanical presses, a flywheel is the major source of energy that is applied to the slides by cranks, gears, eccentrics or linkages during the working part of the stroke. During operation, the flywheel runs continuously and is engaged by the clutch only when a press stroke is needed. In some very large mechanical presses the drive motor is connected directly to the press shaft, thus eliminating the need for a flywheel and a clutch.

Two basic types of drive are used to transfer the rotational force of the flywheel to the main shaft of the press — the nongeared drive and the gear drive.

Nongeared Drive. In a nongeared drive (often known as a flywheel drive), the flywheel is on the main shaft (Fig. 1a), and its speed, in revolutions per minute, controls the slide speed. Press speeds with this type of drive usually are high, ranging from 60 to 1000 strokes per minute. The main shaft can have a crankshaft as shown in Fig. 1(a), or an eccentric.

Energy stored in the flywheel should be sufficient to insure that the reduction in the speed of the flywheel will be no greater than 10% per press stroke. If the energy in the flywheel is not sufficient to maintain this minimum in speed reduction, a press with a gear drive should be used.

Gear drives (Fig. 1b, c and d) have the flywheel on an auxiliary shaft that drives the main shaft through one or more gear reductions. Either single-reduction or multiple-reduction gear drives are used, depending on size and tonnage requirements. In gear-driven presses, there is more flywheel energy available for doing work than in the nongeared presses, because the speed of the flywheel is higher than that of the main shaft. The flywheel shaft of a gear-driven press often is connected to the main shaft at both ends, as shown in Fig. 1(c), which results in a more efficient drive.

A single-reduction gear drive develops speeds of 30 to 100 strokes per minute. Speed for a multiple-reduction twin-gear drive (Fig. 1d) usually is 10 to 30 strokes per minute, which provides exceptionally steady pressure.

Hydraulic Presses. Hydrostatic pressure against one or more pistons provides the power for a hydraulic press. Most hydraulic presses have a variable-volume, variable-pressure, concentric-piston pump to provide them with a fast slide opening and closing speed, as well as with a slow working speed at high forming pressure.

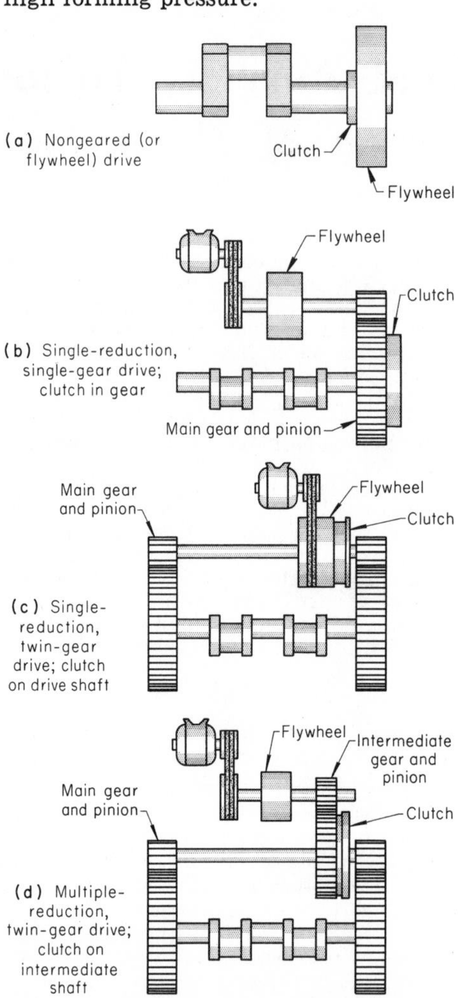

Fig. 1. Four types of drive-and-clutch arrangements for mechanical presses

Pumps, reservoirs and other components of the hydraulic system usually are housed in the frame and in the crown of the press, although in some presses these components are housed below the bed. If all components are readily accessible for maintenance, their location is unimportant. The principal components of a typical hydraulic press are shown in Fig. 2. A bolster plate is attached to the bed to support the dies and to guide the pressure pins between the die cushion and the pressure pad.

The tonnage that a hydraulic press can exert depends on the diameter of the hydraulic pistons and on the rated maximum hydraulic pressure, the latter being a function of the pump pressure and related mechanisms.

Hydraulic presses with capacities up to 50,000 tons have been built, but most have a capacity of less than 15,000 tons. The typical hydraulic press is rated at 100 to 1000 tons. Gap-frame presses are rated at 5 to 50 tons.

Because of their construction, hydraulic presses can be custom designed at relatively low cost. They can be designed with a number of slides and motions, or separate hydraulic circuits can be used for various independent actions.

Side action can be provided also within the frame of the press by separate cylinders. Such side action in a mechanical press usually is provided by cams and is complex and expensive. Most hydraulic presses are straight-side models, but small, fast, gap-type presses designed to compete with mechanical open-back inclinable (OBI) presses have been developed.

Hydraulic press slides, or platens, are actuated by numerous combinations of hydraulic drives. Hydraulic presses usually have a longer stroke than mechanical presses, and force can be constant throughout the stroke. Hydraulic presses have an adjustable stroke for one or more slides. Accumulators or large-volume pumps can provide fast motion for a slide to open and close. High-pressure pumps provide the working force at a slower speed.

Usually all slides are operated by one pumping system. The relation of each action to the others, interaction, and timing all depend on the controls.

Type of Press Frame

Presses are classified broadly according to the type of frame used in their construction, into two main groups — gap-frame presses and straight-side presses. Details of construction vary widely in each group.

Gap-frame presses are sometimes called C-frame presses because the frame resembles the letter "C" when viewed from the side. The gap makes the die area accessible from either side as well as from the front, for ease in die setting or for feeding stock. Coil stock often is supplied to gap-frame presses by feeders from stock reels and straighteners.

Workpieces usually are ejected through an opening in the press bed, or through the back of an open-back press. (A few gap-frame presses with solid backs are in service, but solid-back presses are in increasing disfavor because work cannot be ejected through the back of the press, and because the design in general is less convenient than the open-back type.)

Deep-throat presses are made, but the throat depth (distance from bolster centerline to frame) on standard presses varies from 6 in. in a 22-ton press to 17 in. in a 200-ton press.

Gap-frame construction has one disadvantage — the gap opens under load, thus causing angular deflection. (A straight vertical deflection would be less critical.) Gap deflection resulting from overload causes misalignment of punches and dies, which is a major cause of premature die wear. This condition can be avoided by using a larger press; however, gap-frame presses have sufficient rigidity if not overloaded.

Tie rods extending from the top of the frame to the front corners of the bed can be used to minimize deflection. Since the tie rods close the gap, the accessibility to the die area and the width of parts fed into the die are limited. Tie rods can be removed for die setup.

Gap-frame presses are made in four frame styles, based on frame position:

1 Vertical frame with a fixed or an adjustable-height bed
2 Inclined frame fixed at an angle of 20° to 30° (Inclination can be custom built to any angle.)
3 Inclinable frame that can be tilted to a maximum angle of 20° to 30°, in stepless increments or in two or three increments, depending on design
4 Horizontal frame (not a common design).

Gap-frame presses generally have less over-all height than straight-side presses of the same tonnage rating. This can be important when overhead clearances are low.

Open-back inclinable (OBI) presses are gap-frame presses that can be inclined so that gravity assists in ejection of the workpiece. The smaller OBI presses can be tilted as much as 45°, whereas the larger OBI presses are usually designed to tilt to a maximum of 20°.

The Joint Industry Conference (JIC) has developed standards for eight sizes of OBI presses ranging in capacity from 22 to 200 tons. Larger OBI presses have been built, but most are within this range. Machined surfaces are provided for mounting a die cushion in the press bed. On small presses, die cushions frequently are mounted on the lower side of the bolster plate.

JIC standards include bed dimensions, bolsters, T-slot and mounting-bolt spacing, and the location of the pressure-pin holes in the bolster; thus bolsters and dies can be interchanged between different makes of presses. The dimensions of slide faces, size and location of T-slots and die-anchorage holes and the upper-shoe stem hole, and minimum shut heights also have been standardized.

Inclinable gap-frame presses are made in tonnage ratings other than those standardized by the Joint Industry Conference.

End-wheel presses are gap-frame presses with a deep throat and, usually, a closed back. The crankshaft runs from front to back, with the flywheel and drive in the back of the press. End-wheel presses, sometimes referred to as deep-throat presses, are best suited to hole punching and other blanking or forming applications requiring a deep reach-in of tools from the edge of the workpiece.

Adjustable-bed presses serve much the same function as gap-frame presses, except that instead of being part of a solid "C", the bed is a separate component. The bed, supported by an adjusting screw, can be moved up or down to provide a greater range of shut heights; consequently, the use of die cushions in this press is impractical.

An advantage of the adjustable-bed press is that the bed usually is hinged and can be swung out of the way. A horn or mandrel can be inserted in a hole in the press frame, so that the press can be used as a horn press for cylindrical work. A typical application of an adjustable-bed press is the forming and insertion of flanges on oil drums.

Straight-side presses have a frame made up of a base, or bed, two columns, and a top member (crown). In most straight-side presses, steel tie rods hold the base and crown against the columns. Straight-side presses have either

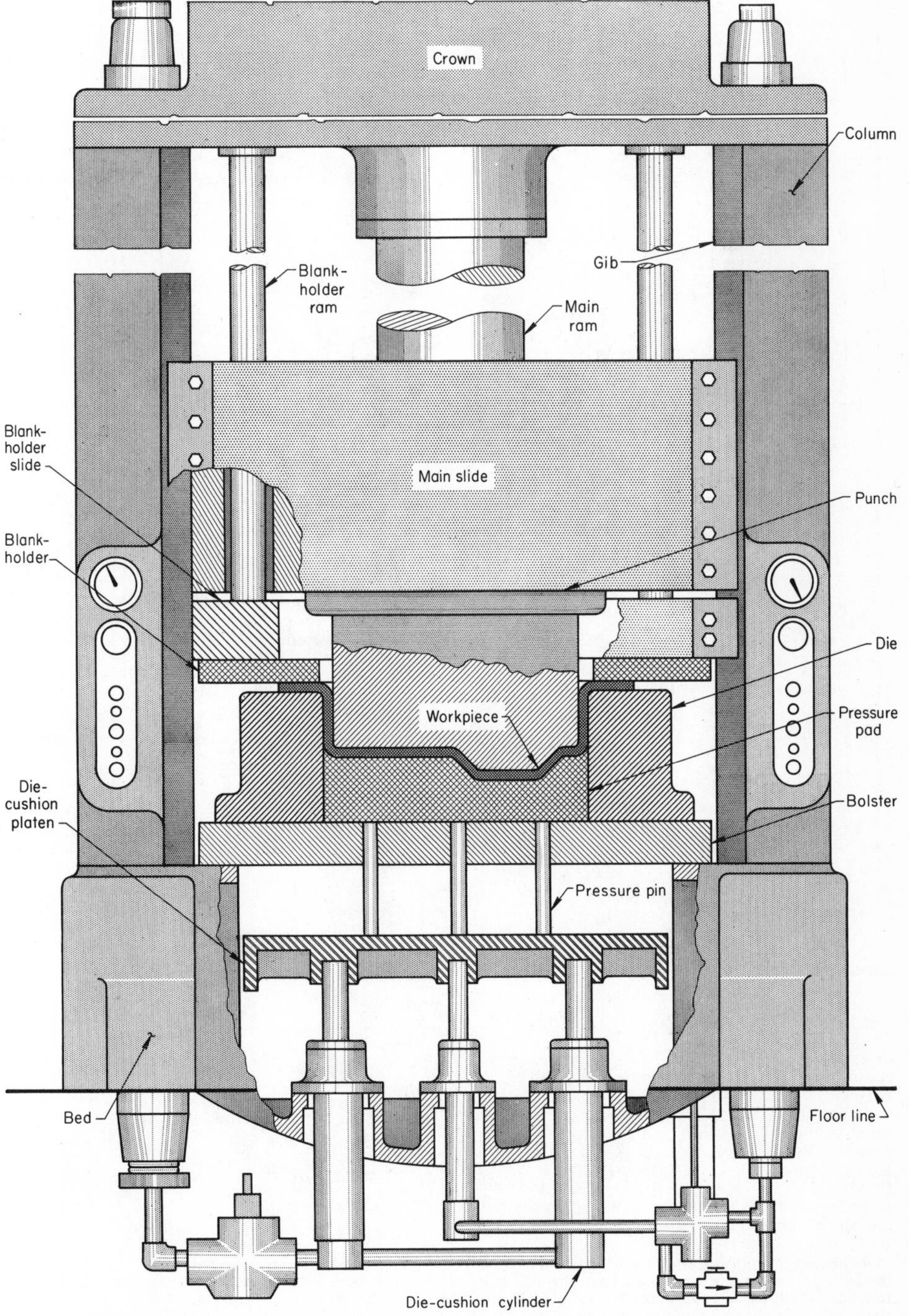

Fig. 2. Principal components of a double-action hydraulic press with a die cushion

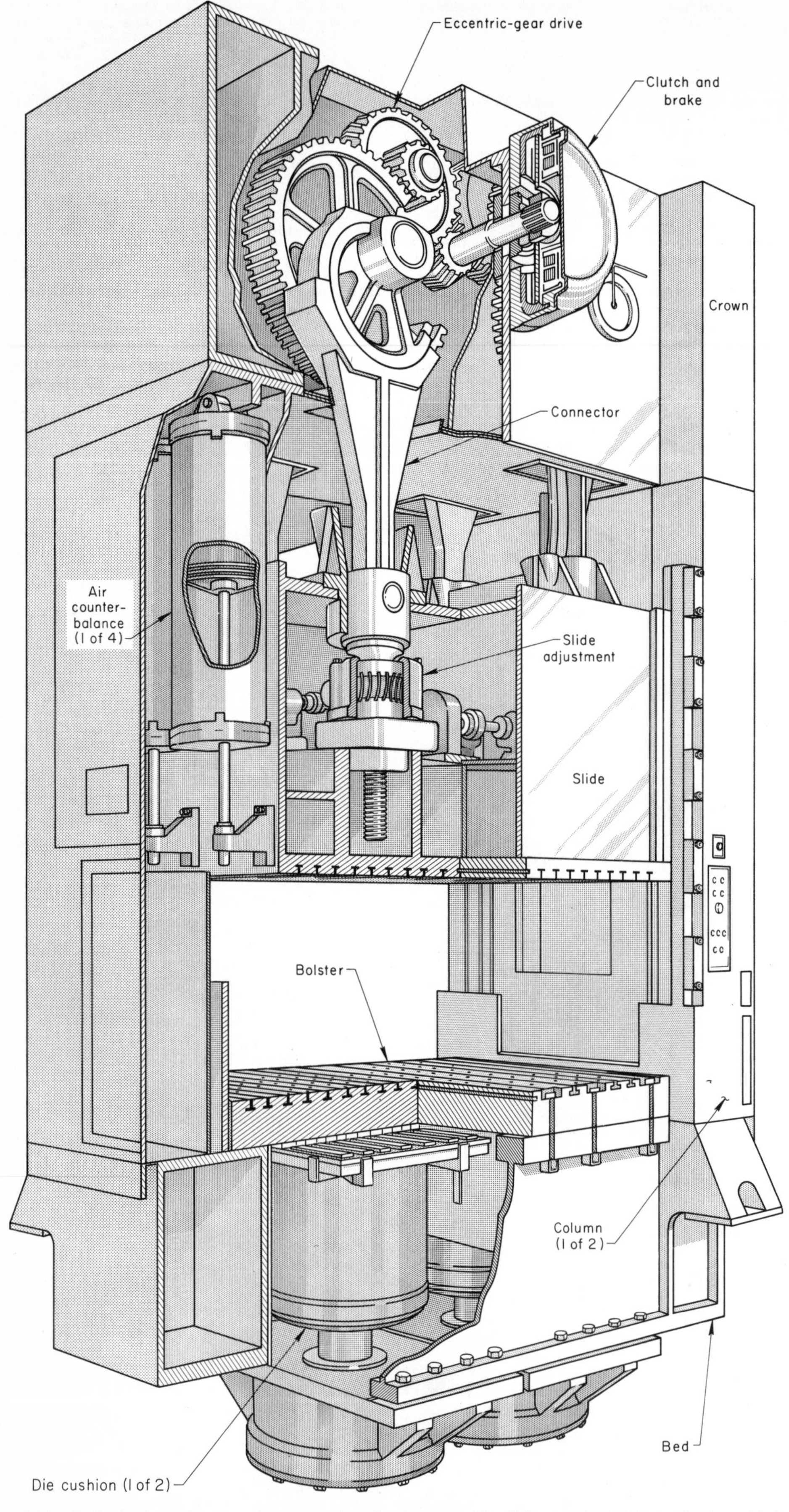

Large-bed, four-point-suspension, eccentric-drive press with slide counterbalance cylinders. Slide adjustment is motorized. Presses with smaller beds have one or two-point suspension and have nongeared (flywheel) or eccentric-shaft drives, but no slide counterbalance cylinders.

Fig. 3. Principal components of a single-action straight-side mechanical press

crankshaft, eccentric-shaft or eccentric-gear drives. (See the section "Slide Actuation in Mechanical Presses", which begins on the next page.)

A single-action straight-side press is shown in Fig. 3. The slide in this illustration is equipped with air counterbalances to assist the drive in lifting the weight of the slide and the upper die to the top of the stroke. Counterbalance cylinders provide a smooth press operation and easy slide adjustment. Die cushions are used in the bed for blankholding and for ejection of the work.

The straight-side design permits the use of an endless variety of bed and slide sizes. Presses range from 20-ton capacity and a bed of 20 by 15 in., to 4000-ton capacity with a bed as large as 360 in. left-to-right by 180 in. front-to-back. The size and shape of the slide usually determine the number of points of suspension, or connections between the main shaft and the slide, that are needed.

The straight-side design also can provide high pressures with minimum deflection. A straight-side press will deflect less under off-center loads than a gap-frame press.

Size and location of anchorage holes and slots, T-slots, and pressure pin holes for the press bed, bolster plate and ram were standardized by JIC.

Rail presses combine the long, narrow bed of a press brake with the construction features of a straight-side press. They are used for forming channels and for operations in progressive or multiple dies or utility tooling.

Tryout presses are straight-side presses used almost exclusively for die tryout. Press capacities range from 50 to 300 tons. The drive is in the bottom of the press. The upper part of the press is a pivoted head that rotates around a horizontal axis at the front of the press. The head, carrying the upper die, swings to the front of the press, so that the tooling can be finished or corrected without removing it from the press. Once corrected, the tooling is installed in a conventional press for production.

Notching presses are small, high-speed, short-stroke presses that have a single-column, closed-back frame like that of a horn press. They are high-production presses, used primarily for notching and piercing of motor laminations. (See the article "Blanking and Piercing of Magnetically Soft Materials", which begins on page 60 in this volume.)

Arch-frame presses (of straight-side design, with bowed-out columns to provide extra die area) are becoming obsolete.

Pillar presses are small, solid-frame, straight-side presses specially built for use with a subpress instead of a die set.

Underdrive presses have the drive mechanism below the bed and pull the slide down, instead of pushing it as in conventional design. They usually are built in capacities of 400 tons or more and have a minimum left-to-right dimension of 72 in. They are driven by rocker arms or eccentric gears and are of single, double or triple-action construction. Because of their large size, they have either double or triple-reduction gearing.

These presses should be installed in a plant with two levels. The upper level is confined to production work, the lower level to maintenance operations. Most of the press mechanism is at the lower level; therefore, underdrive presses require less ceiling height than top-drive presses. The presses are mounted on a network of I-beams, which are supported on the lower-level piers. Because the I-beams are readily accessible, it is fairly simple to relocate both the beams and the presses, when necessary to facilitate production.

Another type of underdrive press is the dieing machine (see the section "Presses for High Production", page 16 in this article). This press is mounted on the floor with the bed at eye level.

Slide Actuation in Mechanical Presses

Rotary motion of the motor shaft on a mechanical press is converted into reciprocating motion of the slides by one of the following:

Crankshaft
Eccentric shaft
Eccentric-gear drive
Knuckle-lever drive
Rocker-arm drive
Toggle mechanism.

Crankshafts. The most common mechanical drive for presses with capacities up to 300 tons is the crankshaft drive (Fig. 4). A crankshaft is used in both gap-frame and straight-side presses. The crankshaft drive is used most often in the single-suspension design, although some double-crank (two-point suspension) presses — particularly in the 100-to-200-ton range — also have crankshafts.

The crankshaft imparts a sine-curve speed relation to the press slide. The stroke of a crankshaft-actuated press can be as short as 1 in., in a small gap-frame press, to as much as 30 in., in a straight-side press. However, most mechanical presses with longer strokes are actuated by an eccentric gear, because it provides greater strength. Crankshaft drives usually are limited to strokes of 6 to 12 in.

The main advantage of a crankshaft-driven press is its lower cost, particularly when capacities do not exceed 300 tons.

Points of suspension refer to the number of connections between the slide and the actuating mechanism. Presses can have single-point, two-point, or four-point suspension, according to the number of points at which the slide is pushed or pulled. The simplest mechanical presses have a pitman that connects the eccentric shaft or the crankshaft to the slide at only one point.

Many wide mechanical presses are built with two-point suspension by connecting the slide to the crankshaft (or eccentric) with two pitmans instead of one, for better distribution of force on the slide.

The largest straight-side mechanical presses usually have four-point suspension, for more uniform loading of large slides. Four-point suspension usually is accomplished by two interconnected crankshafts or eccentrics and four pitmans; each pitman is connected near a corner of the slide.

Hydraulic presses also can have one, two, or more points of suspension, by operating the slide with as many rams as desired.

Eccentric shafts are similar to crankshafts. The eccentric completely fills the space between the supporting bearings of the press crown, thereby eliminating the deflection commonly caused by the unsupported portion where the crank cheeks normally would be. Eccentric drives (Fig. 4) are often used in high-speed short-stroke straight-side presses with progressive dies.

The height of the workpiece is the main limitation of the eccentric-shaft drive, because the stroke always is equal to twice the eccentricity. When eccentricity is increased, the space available in the press crown will determine the maximum stroke that can be used. In most presses of this type, the maximum stroke usually is limited to 6 in. A few presses have been built and used in high-speed operations in which strokes longer than 6 in. were needed. This is accomplished in the press by balancing the eccentric shaft to minimize vibration.

Eccentric-gear drives (Fig. 4) are used almost universally for large straight-side presses that operate at speeds of less than 50 strokes per minute. In place of a crankshaft, an eccentric is built as an integral part of the press drive gear. The eccentric gear permits strokes as long as 50 in.; however, with such long strokes, speeds usually are only 8 to 16 strokes per minute. With the eccentric as part of the gear, accuracy of alignment of the slide is determined by accuracy and alignment of the gears. In a two-point suspension, the parallel condition of the ram is determined by the alignment of the driving gears. The principal advantage of the eccentric gear is that it permits greater torque loads at points above the bottom of the stroke. The eccentric gear also permits multiple-point construction with greater versatility and range of stroke length than is possible with a crankshaft.

The chief limitation of the eccentric-gear design is that usually it requires an overhung flywheel. In addition, a single-gear eccentric press usually costs more than a crankshaft or eccentric-shaft press of equal capacity. A second limitation is that eccentric-gear presses are more likely to stick at the bottom of the stroke than crankshaft presses. Sticking is caused by greater friction in the connector, which is inherent in the large-diameter eccentrics needed for an equal press stroke. Sticking usually will occur during setup, if the press is moved slowly until the bottom of the stroke is reached. At this point, a skilled setup man usually can detect whether the press is likely to stick.

Knuckle-lever drives combine the motions of a crank and a knuckle lever to drive the press slide (Fig. 4). Their use is limited to operations such as coining or embossing, in which the work is done almost entirely at the bottom of a short stroke. The knuckle-lever mechanism permits large capacity in a relatively small press. High mechanical advantage is inherent at the bottom of the stroke. These presses are rated to deliver full tonnage at $\frac{1}{16}$ to $\frac{1}{4}$ in. above the bottom of the stroke. The very quick increase in force as the slide nears the bottom of the stroke is the reason its usefulness is limited to operations performed at the bottom of the stroke. Knuckle-lever presses usually have capacities of 150 to 1000 tons.

Rocker-arm drives apply crank or eccentric motion to a rocker arm that is connected to the press slide (Fig. 4). In this mechanism, the linkage is driven by an eccentric gear and a connecting rod. The rocker-arm drive is a variation of the knuckle-lever drive. However, a press with rocker-arm drive is not limited to coining operations, but can be used also for drawing or forming operations.

The rocker-arm drive is used mainly in large-bed underdrive presses. The linkage operates from below the press bed and pulls the slide into the work by a link running up through each of the press columns. In most rocker-arm

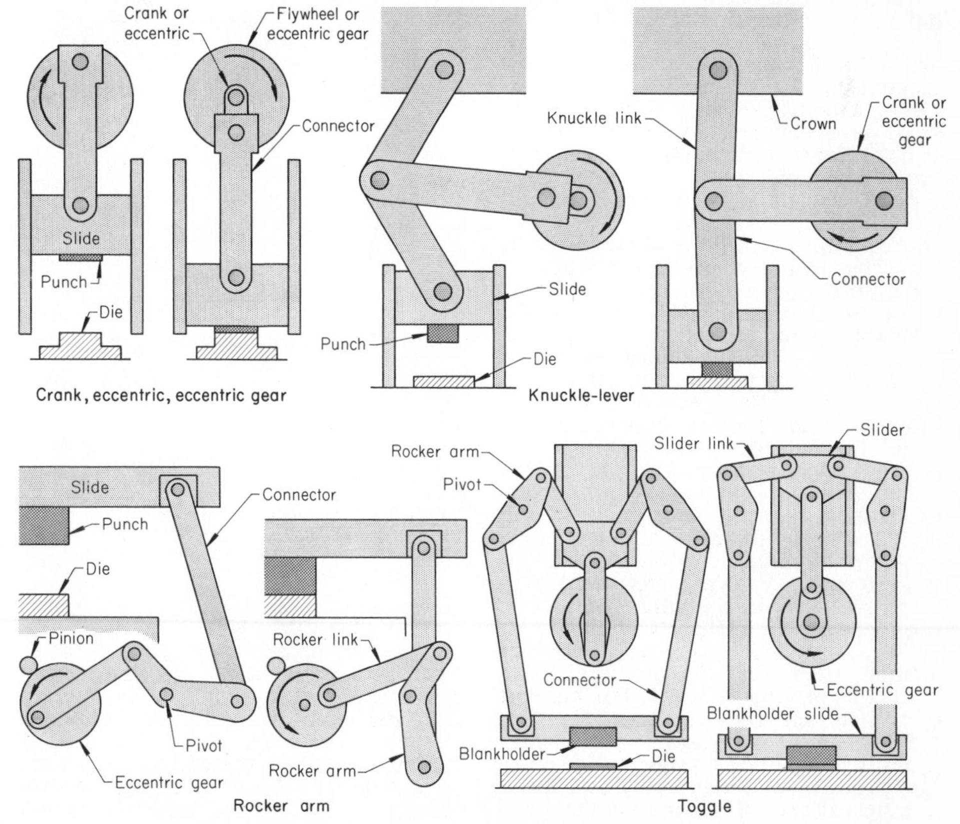

Fig. 4. Principles of operation of drives for mechanical presses

drives, the rocker pin and the connecting eccentric pin do not stop in a vertical plane; thus, the load on the eccentric shaft is relieved at the point where the maximum load on the slide is exerted, and sticking at the bottom of the stroke is prevented. In addition, a high press capacity is obtained because of the mechanical advantage.

Toggle mechanisms are the most widely used means of providing the second action in double-action mechanical presses. The toggles operate an outer slide, which clamps the blank against the die, while the punch, operated by the inner slide directly from the crankshaft, performs the draw operation. Principal components of a toggle mechanism are shown in Fig. 4.

The diagram in Fig. 5 shows relative positions on the stroke during one revolution of the crankshaft for the outer slide (blankholder) and the inner slide (punch holder) in a typical draw operation. As shown in Fig. 5, the blankholder dwells while the punch performs the draw operation. The shaded area of Fig. 5 represents the recommended working portion of the press stroke. By incorporating mechanical slow-down linkages or two-speed clutches to accelerate the slides before and after the actual working stroke, the number of press strokes per minute can be increased without affecting the draw speed. An accelerated-motion curve for one press stroke is shown in Fig. 6.

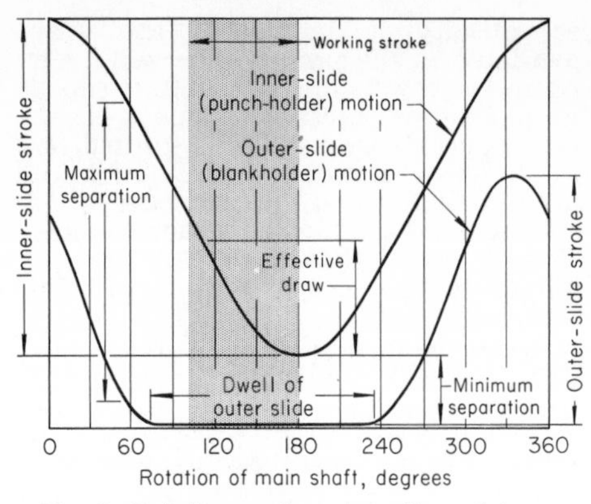

Fig. 5. Relative cycles of motion of inner slide (punch holder) and outer slide (blankholder) during one stroke of a double-action mechanical press

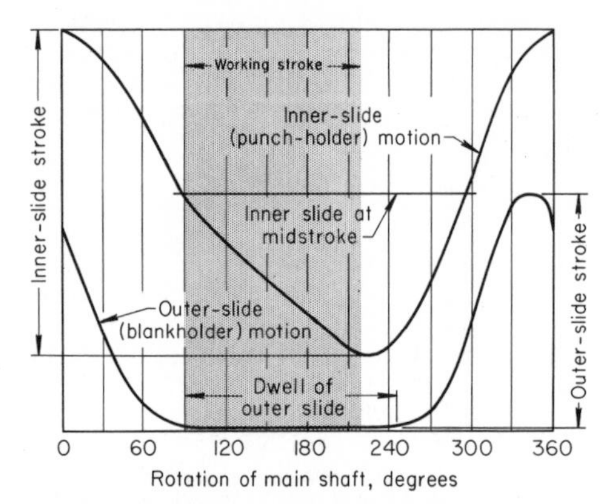

Fig. 6. Accelerated-motion curve for one stroke of a double-action mechanical press. Slides descend to work rapidly, slow down during draw cycle, and return at high speed.

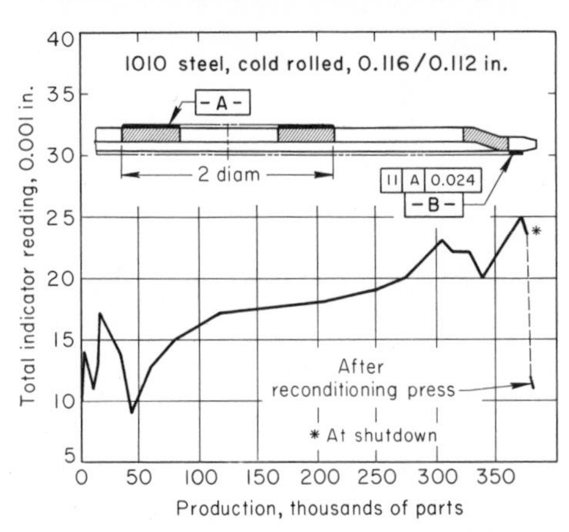

Item	Measurement, in. Original	At shutdown
Slide-to-bolster parallelism:		
Right to left, in. per ft ...	0.001	0.005
Front to back, in. per ft ...	0.001	0.004
Gib clearance, in.	0.002	0.008

Fig. 7. Variation in parallelism between two offset formed surfaces that was attributed to wear of gib surfaces (Example 1)

Number of Slides

Mechanical presses have one, two or three slides and are referred to as single, double or triple-action presses. Each slide can be moved in a separately controlled motion.

Single-action presses (see Fig. 3) have one moving slide that applies force to the workpiece. These presses are built with one, two or four points of suspension, depending on the bed size.

Single-point presses are of the crankshaft, eccentric-shaft, eccentric-gear or knuckle-lever construction. The same drives are used in two and four-point presses, except that a rocker arm is used instead of a knuckle lever. The two and four-point presses may be of top-drive or underdrive construction.

Single-action presses are used for all sheet-metal pressworking operations.

Double-action presses have two slides — an outer, or blankholder, slide, and an inner, or punch-holder, slide. This type of press is generally used for drawing and forming operations in which the outer slide carries the blankholder and the inner slide carries the punch. The outer slide, having a shorter stroke than the inner slide, dwells and holds the blank while the inner slide, which carries the punch, descends to perform the drawing operation. (Relative motions of the inner and outer slides are shown in Fig. 5 and 6.)

The outer slide also can carry one member of a blanking die for cutting blanks from strip or sheet. The blank is then held for the drawing operation.

Triple-action presses have three slides with motions properly synchronized for drawing, redrawing and forming operations. The blankholder and punch-holder slides are located in the crown, as in a double-action press, and a third slide is located in the press bed. The punch-holder slide has a small dwell at the bottom of its stroke. The blankholder slide usually has slightly more dwell than in a comparable double-action press. The lower slide usually is actuated by an eccentric or a crank. As a rule, the lower-slide mechanism develops a long stroke, but only during the top portion of the stroke is work done by the slide. In many triple-action presses the lower-slide mechanisms are synchronized with the upper-slide motions, although separately driven lower motions electrically interlocked to the upper motions are used.

The third slide can be used for reverse drawing, forming, blanking or lancing operations. The lancing or blanking may be done before the drawing is completed, to provide extra metal. Drawing or forming is done when it is not possible to use a bottoming form block in the die.

Press Accuracy

Suggested criteria for the accuracy of a press are:

1 Maximum tolerances for parallelism between slide and bed; 0.001 in. per foot at the bottom of the stroke for all slides; 0.003 in. per foot at midstroke for punch slides; and 0.005 in. per foot at midstroke for blankholder slides.
2 Feed, if used, should be accurate within ±0.003 in. at 900 in. per minute.
3 Gib clearance should be set as close as required to do the job.

For many operations, such as blanking and piercing, the gibs are set with a minimum clearance. On small-bed presses this may be within 0.0015 in. When doing drawing operations with dies fitted with heel blocks, it is better to have the gibs set loose. This allows the heel blocks to function without interference from the gibs. For this reason, provision to adjust the gib surfaces of the inner slide of a double-action press is not commonly found. If minimum gib clearance is desired, the formula $c = ph/w$ can be used as a guide. Where c is the gib clearance; p, the total parallelism of slide to bed; h, the height of slide guides; and w, the left-to-right dimension of the slide. (All dimensions are in inches.)

A press that conforms to these standards is rated as being in good condition. If a press is accurate within half of these tolerances, it is rated in excellent condition. A press that meets only some of these tolerances is rated as being in fair condition.

A running log of the accuracy and condition of each press in a plant is helpful in scheduling maintenance and in routing work.

Press slides that are not parallel with the bed at the bottom of the stroke can result in uneven stock thickness when the punch bottoms against the die surface. (In Example 172 in the article on Press Forming, the parallelism of the slide and bolster was maintained within 0.003 in. per foot to maintain the accuracy specified for the part being formed.)

The gradual decrease in accuracy on formed parts that occurs as slide and bolster become increasingly out-of-parallel, and as gib clearance increases, with continued use of a press is described in the following example. The restoration of the original accuracy on the parts after reconditioning of the press also is discussed.

Example 1. Decrease in Dimensional Accuracy on Formed Parts Caused by Press Wear During Continued Use (Fig. 7)

A press-formed 46-tooth sprocket (a cross section of which is shown in Fig. 7) was not acceptable with out-of-parallelism greater than

0.024 in. TIR (total indicator reading) between offset surfaces A and B indicated on the cross section in Fig. 7. To attain this degree of accuracy, the press used for flattening was rebuilt to the slide-to-bolster parallelism and gib-clearance specifications given in the "Original" column in the table with Fig. 7. After flattening 375,000 pieces (approximate annual output), the press was shut down and measurements were taken of the slide-to-bolster parallelism and gib clearance. Both measurements are given in the table with Fig. 7.

Measurement of workpiece samples that were randomly selected during one year produced the data shown graphically in Fig. 7. Out-of-parallelism approached the permissible maximum at about 315,000 pieces (350 samples), and the frequency of measurement at this point was increased to 200 samples from 60,000 pieces.

At about 370,000 pieces, the rejection rate had increased substantially, but production was continued to a total of 375,000 pieces, salvaging the rejects by restriking.

Then the press was shut down and restored to its original accuracy. As shown in Fig. 7, parallelism on the pieces formed after reconditioning the press was equivalent to that obtained at the beginning of production.

Press Capacity

Capacity, or tonnage rating, of a press is the maximum force that the press can apply. Hydraulic presses can exert maximum force during the full press stroke. Mechanical presses exert maximum force at a specified distance above the bottom of the stroke (see Table 2), and the force decreases to a minimum at midstroke.

The tonnage rating of a press may have little relation to the bed area. This is especially true in the automotive and appliance industries, where presses have large bed area and large die space, but relatively low tonnage rating. Coining presses have small bed area and high tonnage rating.

Overloading of the press can cause damage to the die and the press. Several devices, based on the strain-gage principle, have been developed for accurately measuring the load on a mechanical press with a given die. Misfeeds or double blanks are common causes of press overloading. Detectors built into the die stop the press before overloading occurs.

The capacity of a mechanical press involves consideration of the frame capacity, drive capacity, flywheel energy, and motor size.

Frame Capacity. The press frame must be able to work at its rating without deflecting beyond predetermined standard limits. For general-purpose applications, the bed deflection should not exceed 0.002 in. per foot between tie-rod centers (or per foot of left-to-right bed dimension on presses without tie rods), when the rated load is evenly distributed over the middle 60% of the distance between tie-rod centers (or of left-to-right bed length). Slide deflection should not exceed 0.002 in. per foot between pitman centers, when the rated load is evenly distributed between pitmans. Both bending and shear deflections are considered. These specifications can be revised to suit more precise applications.

Drive capacity is the tonnage a mechanical press develops through the gear train and linkage. The tonnage can vary because of the mechanical advantage developed by different types of press linkage, and generally is expressed in distance above the bottom of the stroke, as shown in Table 2.

Generally, straight-side, twin-drive, geared presses of the crank or eccentric-gear type are rated at ½ in. above the bottom of the stroke, whereas gap-frame gear presses are rated at ¼ in. or less above the bottom of the stroke. The rating point above the bottom of the stroke depends on the press design. However, the values given in Table 2 are generally applicable.

Variation in the capacities of presses with eccentric-gear, crankshaft or eccentric-shaft drive at any point in the stroke is almost equal. However, the capacity decreases between the bottom of the stroke and midstroke. The capacity of both the knuckle-lever drive and the rocker-arm drive, however, is much less above the point of rating on the stroke than that of the crank drives, because the knuckle-lever drive loses mechanical advantage more rapidly than crank drives. In addition to loss in capacity, velocity of the slide in the knuckle-lever drive and the rocker-arm drive is considerably greater at points high above the bottom of the stroke, than in the eccentric-gear or crankshaft drives.

Table 2. Distance From Bottom of Stroke at Which Maximum Rated Tonnage Is Obtained in Mechanical Presses

Capacity of press, tons	Distance from bottom of stroke, in.: Flywheel drive (non-geared)	Single reduction: Single-gear drive	Single reduction: Twin-gear drive	Multiple reduction: Single-gear drive	Multiple reduction: Twin-gear drive
Gap-Frame, Open-Back Inclinable, or Straight-Side Presses					
Up to 32	1/32	⅛	..	..	..
45 to 200	1/16	¼	½	¼	½
Over 200	⅛	¼	½	¼	½
Knuckle-Lever Presses					
Up to 400	1/32	1/16	..	1/16	..
Over 400	1/16	⅛	..	⅛	..
Rocker-Arm Presses					
All sizes	..	..	½	..	½

Figure 8 is a nomograph showing the relation of press capacity and position on the stroke for standard double-gear presses in which tonnage capacity is rated at ½ in. above the bottom of the stroke. The chart may be used to determine the force exerted at specific positions on the stroke for various stroke lengths.

Sample Calculation Using Fig. 8. To find the force exerted 2 in. from the bottom of a 20-in. stroke, first find the point at which the curve for 2-in. working stroke intersects the vertical line for 20-in. stroke length. From this point, project horizontally (broken line) to the 0.5-in. curve (position of rating). From the 0.5-in. curve, project downward to the lower (horizontal) 20-in.-stroke line. As shown in Fig. 8, the intersection occurs at 53%, which means that the press can exert 53% of its rated force at a stroke position 2 in. above the bottom.

Most press manufacturers supply similar curves for determining press capacity at any point, or tables of such capacity data.

Flywheel energy for a given job may be insufficient, although the press frame and shaft may be adequately strong. For a greater working distance or for faster operation, more energy and power must be provided.

Blanking operations are completed in a brief portion of the press cycle. The flywheel instantly supplies practically all of the energy required by its resistance to deceleration. The motor may take the remainder of the press cycle to restore lost energy to the flywheel by bringing it back up to speed. Draw operations may take up to one fourth of the press cycle.

For intermittent operation, 20% is arbitrarily considered the maximum the flywheel may be slowed down when

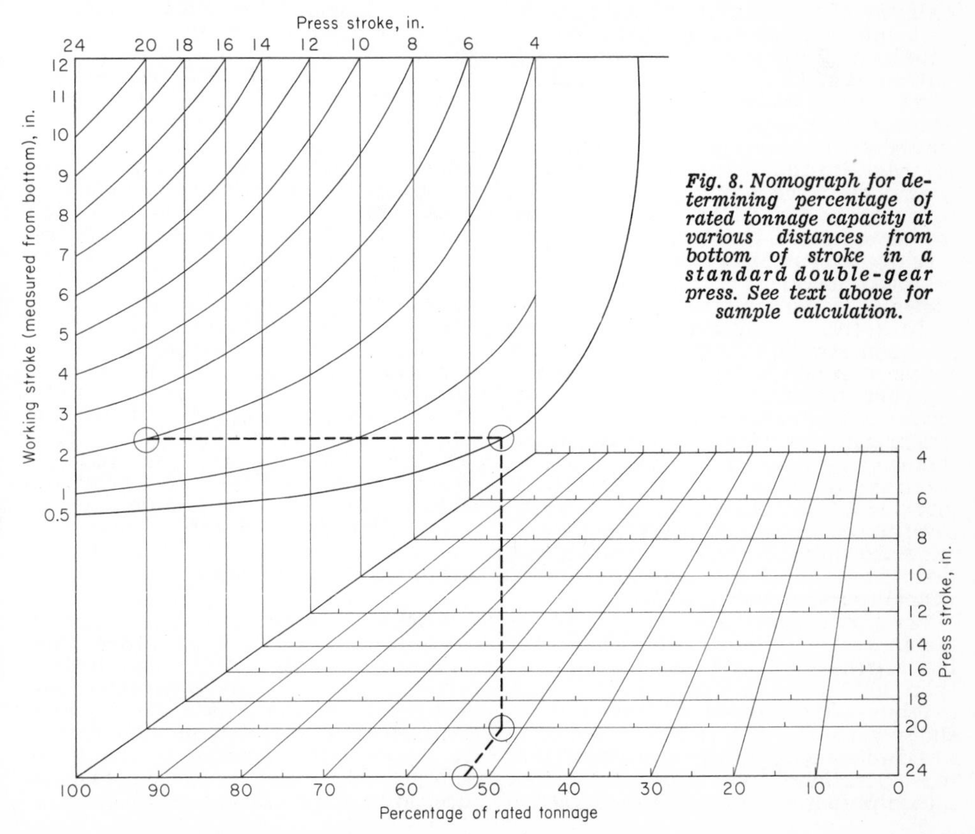

Fig. 8. Nomograph for determining percentage of rated tonnage capacity at various distances from bottom of stroke in a standard double-gear press. See text above for sample calculation.

using energy from it. For continuous operation, 10% is considered the limit, because of the short time available to restore lost energy. The low-speed torque characteristics of the press drive motor will greatly affect how much the flywheel can be safely slowed, because the ability of the motor to restore lost kinetic energy is a function of these characteristics.

The amount of energy available at 10% slowdown can be determined from the following formula:

$$E = N^2D^2 \frac{W}{5.25 \times 10^9}$$

where E is energy, in inch-tons; N is number of flywheel revolutions per minute; D is the outside diameter of the flywheel, in inches; and W is the weight of the flywheel, in pounds. A constant includes necessary conversion factors.

If calculation indicates that the flywheel will not furnish the necessary energy, it may be necessary to increase the weight, diameter or speed of the flywheel, or to use a different type of drive or motor.

For safety with respect to centrifugal force, cast iron flywheels should not have a speed greater than 5500 sfm.

To change the press speed, speed-change devices must change the speed of the flywheel. Energy of the flywheel is directly proportional to the square of its speed of rotation. Therefore, the standard energy of a variable-speed press is calculated at its slowest speed. The intended operating speed should be used in checking the suitability of a press for a specific operation.

Motor sizes specified for punch presses frequently are high for blanking and coining and low for deep drawing. If the flywheel alone can deliver the total energy requirements, the motor need only return the wheel to speed, spreading its delivery of power over the entire cycle. The motor horsepower should be approximately $0.0048E \times$ spm, where E is the energy (in inch-tons) required per stroke, and spm the strokes per minute. Energy here is the force, in tons, required to do the operation, multiplied by the distance, in inches, through which the force acts.

Motors designed for punch presses can be slowed down 10 to 15% without serious overloading. In contrast, a general-purpose motor is limited to a slowdown of 3 to 5%.

In a drawing operation with a long working stroke, the flywheel may slow down as much as 20% in order to give up enough energy to do the job. A general-purpose motor on such a job would resist the slowdown and probably would take on a greater and greater proportion of the load. Unless the motor has considerable capacity, it will become overloaded. A punch-press motor will slow down and let the wheel do the work. Then the motor will return the wheel to speed during the comparatively long period between strokes.

Clutches and Brakes in Mechanical Presses

Clutches and brakes are essential to the operation of mechanical presses. No other part must work more perfectly if the press is to operate successfully. The clutch must deliver and control the surge of force that is required to shape the work metal. When the press runs continuously, the clutch transmits power from the flywheel to the main shaft. In a single-stroke press, the clutch must accelerate the rotating parts of the drive from stop to full speed at each stroke of the press. The brake must decelerate this moving mass in order to stop the slide at the end of each upstroke. The brake must be large and efficient enough to stop the press in an emergency, or during inching.

Clutches and brakes in presses that are stopped at the end of each stroke need more maintenance than those in presses operating continuously or stopped only a few times a day.

Positive clutches are used mainly on presses of less than 100-ton capacity. Positive clutches always are on the main shaft and use pins, keys or jaws to lock the shaft and flywheel together. They usually are engaged by a foot treadle or by an air cylinder.

Positive clutches can be engaged or disengaged only once during each press stroke. Usually a throwout cam disengages the keys, pins or jaws near the top of the stroke. These clutches can be arranged for one-stroke or continuous operation.

Positive clutches accelerate the slide very rapidly, because there is no slip. Because they are shaft mounted, they have a minimum mass to move.

Mechanical positive clutches cost less than other types and are compact and easy to operate, but are limited in many respects and usually require excessive maintenance. They are not recommended for one-stroke work, because wear on the clutch would be severe.

Pneumatic positive clutches are much more efficient than the mechanical types. A pneumatic positive clutch usually is a jaw clutch with 16 or more points of engagement. The jaws are engaged by an air cylinder or a diaphragm, and are disengaged by springs. No throwout cams are used. The clutches have electric controls like those used with friction clutches. A press with a positive pneumatic clutch can be used for a single stroke, operated continuously, jogged in either direction, and stopped for emergencies. The brake used with this type of clutch is usually spring-operated and air-released as a fail-safe measure.

Friction clutches are preferred to positive clutches for most press applications. They are mounted on either the crankshaft, eccentric shaft, intermediate gear shaft, or the drive shaft, as shown in Fig. 1. The location of the clutch-brake unit is determined by factors such as press size, press speed, type of clutch-brake unit, and proper attention to the inertia of the press drive.

Friction clutches use air pressure to force the friction surfaces together; brakes use springs. Brakes are spring-operated rather than air-operated, so the press will stop if the power or air fails. Acceleration and deceleration of the press drive parts is relatively shock-free; thus less maintenance is needed than with positive clutches.

There are three basic types of friction clutches: integral, combination and separate mounting. In the integral type of friction clutch, the clutch and brake are mounted at one point on the shaft, but are not built as a single unit on a common sleeve. In the combination type of friction clutch, the clutch and brake components are assembled on a common sleeve. Both the integral and the combination types use the same air chamber to actuate the clutch and release the brake simultaneously. The brake is actuated by springs as a fail-safe measure. An advantage of these clutches is that clutching and braking are mechanically synchronized. A disadvantage is that most of the clutch and brake parts must be started and stopped each time the press is single-stroked.

For faster single-stroke rates, a third type of friction clutch has been developed, in which the clutch and brake have separate mountings and separate controls. Separate air chambers engage the clutch and disengage the brake. The effect is to reduce the number of rotating parts and consequently to reduce inertia.

Another type of friction clutch uses air or hydraulic pressure to force together two bronze plates, one of which is a driving member. The plates are submerged in oil. This design improves heat dissipation — a problem always present in friction clutches used in high production.

The air chambers for friction clutches may be simple cylinders, diaphragms or tubes. Diaphragms and tubes have some operating advantages and usually are more easily serviced.

One of the greatest advantages of friction clutches is their compatibility with electric and electronic controls. In this respect, they are superior to the positive clutch, with the exception of the pneumatic type.

Some air friction clutches can be used as overload protection devices when mounted on the main shaft. The clutch air pressure is gradually reduced, while making stampings, until the clutch begins to slip. The air pressure is then increased about 5 psi above the slipping point. If a load greater than normal is encountered, the press will not carry through its stroke, because the clutch will slip and stall the press. The air-pressure adjustment must be repeated for every die setup.

Eddy-Current Clutches. A high degree of control over the press is the major advantage of eddy-current clutches, which are, in reality, press drives. Ram speed at any point on the stroke can be programmed.

Eddy-current drives consist of a constant-speed flywheel, a variable-speed clutch-and-brake rotor, and a stationary brake field assembly. The clutch-and-brake rotor is directly connected to the press drive shaft.

Clutching and braking are controlled by the current in the coils. In practice, the press drive usually is controlled automatically to speed up the motion of the slide during the idle portion of the stroke, and to slow it down just before the tooling contacts the work. Figure 6 shows accelerated-motion curves for slides operated in this manner.

Clutch Location. The location of the clutch-brake unit depends on the type and amount of work to be done, press size, slide velocity, and the type of unit. For maximum torque, the clutch should be mounted on the shaft that revolves at the highest speed. However, mounting a friction clutch on the slowest shaft will make it more efficient, in terms of heat generation, because fewer and slower operating parts must be stopped and started.

The torque requirement of the clutch is reduced in direct proportion to its increase in speed. The heat generated by a friction clutch increases as the square of the speed.

In nongeared presses, the clutch usually is in the flywheel. In single-gear drive presses, the clutch is more often in the housing of the main gear, as shown in Fig. 1(b).

In twin-gear drive presses, the clutch is usually in the flywheel, which is mounted on the pinion drive shaft, as shown in Fig. 1(c). In multiple-reduction presses, the clutch is mounted on the intermediate gear (see Fig. 1d).

When the friction clutch is on the pinion drive shaft, overload protection is lost, because the load cannot be sensed through the gear train. Thus, some other form of protection is necessary.

Press Accessories

The setup and operation of a mechanical press are made more versatile through the use of built-in accessories. Included are bolster plates, rolling bolster assemblies, speed-change mechanisms, shut-height adjusters, and slide counterbalances.

Bolster plates are used in most hydraulic and mechanical presses, between the bed and die. They provide a flat surface on which to mount the dies and can be remachined to remove nicks and worn areas. T-slots in the top surface facilitate clamping the die to the bolster plate. Clearance holes through the bolster plate provide for pressure pins extending from the die cushion to the die. Some press beds have a large hole through the top surface for drop-through of parts or for mounting of die cushions. For this reason, bolster plates are thick to minimize deflection and to support the die properly. When parts are ejected through the die, holes of the proper size and location are cut in the bolster.

The width, length and thickness dimensions of bolster plates have been standardized for each bed size, as have the size and location of T-slots, pressure pin holes, and holes for fastening to the bed. Standardization facilitates interchangeability of dies between presses. Filler plates can be used either above or below the bolster to reduce the shut height of the press. This is in addition to the normal slide adjustment.

Rolling bolster assemblies are made for some large straight-side presses, for fast tooling change. Dies are set up on an assembly outside the press. When a press run is finished, the punch and blankholder are unclamped from the slides and the assembly is moved out of the press. Then another assembly is moved into place, the punch and blankholder are clamped to the slides, adjustments are made, auxiliary equipment is set up, and the press is made ready to run.

Speed-change drives are used mostly to change the number of strokes per minute, but some drives also can be used to change speeds during the press stroke for fast approach to the work, slower working stroke, and quick return. Changing speed during the stroke permits an increase in production without increasing the working speed. Press builders commonly supply charts that show the slide speed at any point on the press stroke.

In simple blanking operations the speed of the working stroke is not critical. In drawing and some forming operations, the plastic flow characteristics of the material being formed impose specific speed limitations.

A two-speed drive is combined with clutching and braking in some presses. A clutch can have planetary gears for a two-speed drive. Some two-speed drives have two flywheels with a common brake. With a two-speed gearbox and two speeds from the clutch, a press can have four speeds.

Variable-speed drives may incorporate a speed-change belt with adjustable cone pulleys connecting the motor to the flywheel or a steplessly variable electric drive. The eddy-current drive, originally developed for inching of mechanical presses, also provides variable speed.

Shut-height adjustment is provided in mechanical presses for changing the distance between the slide and the bed to fit dies of different sizes.

Small, single-point presses have a screw arrangement to provide this adjustment. In heavier presses, a gear drive makes it easier for the operator to move the massive slide. As press size increases, this gear drive is motorized. Motorized slide adjustment is used also in many smaller presses. Air counterbalances on most large presses relieve the load of the slide and die from the adjusting mechanism.

Some presses have dials that indicate the shut height in thousandths of an inch. If the dies to be used in the press are similarly marked, die-setting time will be greatly reduced. Other presses have a motorized adjustment with a dial control. The operator sets the desired shut height, and the slide automatically positions itself.

Counterbalances in press slides provide smooth cycling and reduce backlash and gear wear, by:

1. Counteracting the moving weight of slides, components and die members attached to the slides
2. Reducing the load on the press brake, thus providing faster stopping
3. Taking up clearance on the main bearings, reducing the breakthrough shock for cutting operations
4. Reducing backlash in the drive gearing
5. Easing the adjustment of slides by reducing the load on the adjusting screws.

Excessive counterbalance pressure can prevent the normal breathing of bearings and consequently can prevent good lubrication of the bearings.

Most presses manufactured with slide counterbalances use pneumatic cylinders as a counterbalance means, although springs have been used. To prevent too great an increase of pressure through the full range of press stroke, a surge tank is used in conjunction with the cylinders. The tanks are of such size that the pressure does not increase more than 20 to 25%. A pressure control valve allows the counterbalance pressure to be adjusted to take care of variation in die weights.

The counterbalance cylinder is attached to the press frame, and the cylinder rod to the press slide. Usually the cylinders are attached either to the crown or the press uprights.

Die Cushions

A die cushion is a tooling component that provides a reasonably uniform blankholding force in a single-action press (Fig. 9a) or secondary blankholding force in a double-action press (Fig. 9b). Die cushions are used also in stripping finished parts from the punch or the die.

Blankholding and stripping action in blanking and piercing dies and shallow forming and drawing dies for single-action presses can be achieved by springs or rubber pads incorporated in the die design. The force exerted by compression springs increases as they are depressed. For a relatively small increase in force, extremely long springs are required. On deep draws, the increase in blankholding force and the decrease in flange area under the blankholder result in an increase in force per unit area (pressure) on the flange metal. The workpiece will fracture if the force pulling it into the die exceeds the tensile strength of the work metal.

Die cushions are often used in double-action presses to keep a stamping flat, to hold it to shape, or to prevent it from slipping and distorting during drawing. Die cushions are used also to actuate the ejector plates or pins that push the finished part from the die cavity or from the punch.

In a single-action press using a die cushion (Fig. 9a), the punch is on the lower shoe, and the die is on the upper shoe. Through pins, force is applied to the pressure ring by the die cushion to hold the outer portion of the blank against the die during drawing. The force increases a maximum of 20 to 25% throughout the stroke. (If springs were used instead of the die cushion, the force would increase much more during the working stroke.) The die cushion is used also to remove the part from the punch.

In a double-action press (Fig. 9b), the die is on the lower shoe, and the punch is on the inner slide. A blankholder carried by the outer slide holds the blank against the die during drawing. The die cushion is used to hold the blank firmly against the bottom of the punch and to eject the formed workpiece from the die.

The capacity of a die cushion generally is 15 to 20% of the rated capacity of the press; some cushions have a capacity about one-third that of the press. The stroke of the die cushion generally is one-third to one-half the length of the press stroke. The size of the press bed opening limits the size, type and capacity of the cushion.

Pneumatic die cushions are used for short, fast operating strokes and when

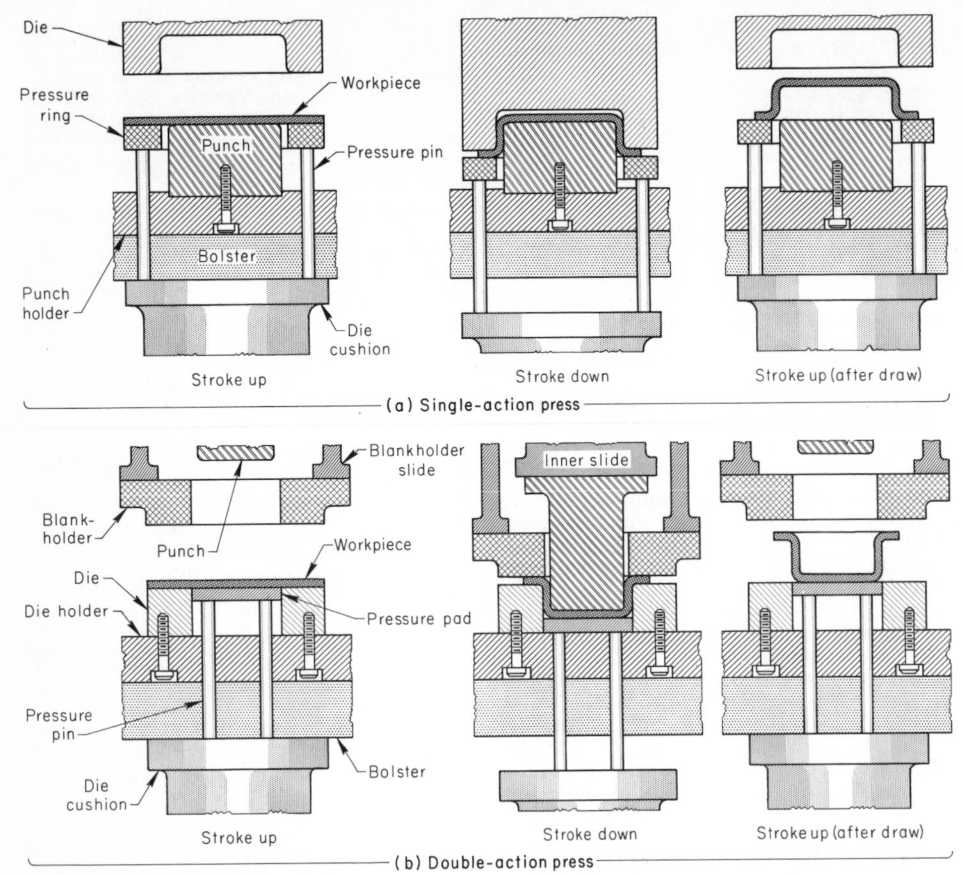

Fig. 9. Setups incorporating die cushions in single-action and double-action presses

the capacity does not need an operating air pressure of more than 100 psi. Hydropneumatic die cushions are recommended when the capacity is greater than can be obtained with 100 psi in a pneumatic cushion. A hydraulic die cushion can be used when hydraulic power is available. Hydropneumatic and hydraulic die cushions are slower acting than pneumatic cushions, and therefore generally are used in larger and slower presses.

A pneumatic die cushion consists basically of a cylinder, a piston and a surge tank. Either the piston or the cylinder is fixed. Downward movement of the blankholder, through pressure pins, forces the movable element against a cushion of air inside the cylinder and moves the air back into the surge tank. On the upstroke, the air in the surge tank forces the movable part back to its original position.

The air in the cushion cylinder and surge tank compresses on the downstroke of the press slide, and the force exerted by the cushion can increase as much as 20 to 25% over a full cushion stroke. This buildup in pressure is not enough to be detrimental to a drawing operation.

Hydropneumatic Die Cushions. Figure 10 shows the essential components of a hydropneumatic die cushion. Two individually controlled air lines are required — one to the operating valve of the cushion, and one to the top of the surge tank. The air pressure supplied to the air-piston assembly determines the tonnage capacity of the cushion on the downstroke. The air pressure in the surge tank determines the stripping pressure on the upstroke.

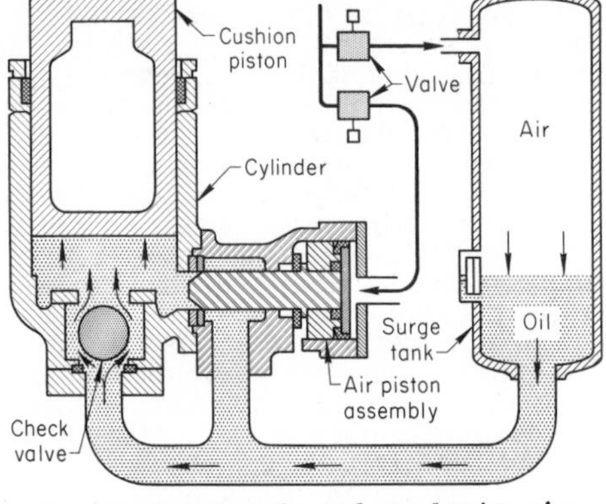

Fig. 10. Components and mechanics of a hydropneumatic die cushion

Auxiliary Equipment

Most primary press operations are automated, so that equipment for feeding and unloading is used even for fairly short runs. Hand feeding, with its attendant hazards, is often confined to second operations on partly completed workpieces.

Planning for automated operations should include the following goals:

1. Maximum safety to the operator and to the equipment
2. High or nearly continuous production
3. Improved quality of the product and minimum scrap
4. Reduction in cost of the finished parts.

The shape and position of the part before and after each operation must be carefully studied to determine whether design changes, such as providing tabs or extra stock on the blank, will facilitate handling.

Automatic handling equipment can be divided into the following categories: feeding equipment, unloading equipment, and equipment for transferring the work from one press operation to the next.

Straighteners are used to remove coil kinks and to flatten stock before feeding into a die. Roller levelers improve formability of the stock by plastic working. Coil-handling equipment moves coiled stock to the press area and uncoils it with a minimum of damage to the stock and danger to the tools and operator.

Feeding Equipment (Feeds)

Mechanical feeds are important for high production, for combined operations, and for operator and press safety. Some feeds supply the presses with stock from a strip or coil; others feed blanks or partly completed workpieces. Either kind, with or without auxiliary hand feeding, can be used with almost any kind of press. For progressive-die work, the feed length should be accurate and repeat within ±0.003 in. The stock must advance accurately so that the pilot pin can easily enter the piloting hole and position the strip. Too great a variation in feed length could result in distorted pilot holes and scrap parts.

Feeds for coil stock feed the work metal from a coil to the press. Choosing the optimum type of feed depends mainly on the type of press, strokes per minute, length of feed per stroke, accuracy needed, and the kind of strip — its width, thickness, stiffness and surface condition. The two most common kinds of feeds are slide and roll feeds.

Slide feeds are made in a variety of sizes and capacities. The basic principle of a slide feed is the use of a feed block that is moved between positive stops to advance the material the distance required at each stroke. Slide feeds are very accurate and are particularly suitable for use with coil stock. When strip stock is used, the ends of the strip must be hand fed into the press.

Some slide feeds are powered by the press through an eccentric mounted on the crankshaft extension. The eccentric can be a simple one-piece unit keyed to the crankshaft, or it can be adjustable to vary the feed in relation to the rotation of the crankshaft. When changes in feed length are frequent, the adjustable type is usually warranted.

The feed block is mounted on hardened slides and either has a feed-blade holder with an adjustable feed blade (usually carbide-tipped), or has a pair of eccentric gripping cylinders. The material is gripped during the feed stroke and released on the return stroke. Accurate control of feed length is obtained by the use of adjustable stops.

The direction of feed — left to right, right to left, or front to back — is governed by the location of the crankshaft extension on the press and the arrangement of the die. A mechanical slide feed, feeding from left to right on a press with a front-to-back crankshaft, can be provided by using an appropriate linkage.

Slide feeds also can be powered by air cylinders or cams on the press slide.

Air-actuated slide feeds are recommended for production jobs involving long feed lengths and small press tonnages. This feed is adaptable to hydraulic presses or other presses without accessible crankshafts, and the feed length can be easily set.

Cam-actuated slide feeds can feed stock in any direction and can be used on presses that do not have accessible crankshafts. The propelling force is generated by one or more springs that are compressed by the action of the cam as the punch slide descends. The springs feed the stock into the die on the upstroke of the press. The mechanical action of a cam feed is shown in Fig. 11.

Cam-actuated feeds are inexpensive devices, and are ordinarily mounted permanently on the dies with which they are used. They are well suited for fast blanking operations and for use with progressive dies. They can feed stock up to 8 in. wide and 0.031 in. thick. (One type can feed stock up to 0.050 in. thick, but only in narrow widths.)

Cam-actuated feeds use gripper blades or rolls to grip the stock during feeding. The feed shown in Fig. 11 has a pair of gripping rolls on the slide, which grip the stock during the feed stroke. A pair of stationary rolls prevents the stock from moving back when the slide is retracted. The rolls are eccentrically mounted so that they grip and release the stock automatically. This feed is not suited to a long feed length. Because of the cam action, the length of feed cannot exceed the approximate length of stroke of the press. The length of the springs also has an effect on feed length.

Another type of spring-powered feed has a rack slide in the body of the feed. With it, a feed length about four times as long as the press stroke is possible. This feed has a stock release that opens the pinch rolls, making the feed suitable for use with dies with pilots. Because only the edge of the material being fed is gripped, wide stock can be used. This feed is particularly suitable for use in draw operations.

Roll feeds are available in sizes suitable for use with almost any width and thickness of stock and are used in every type of presswork, from blanking to complex operations in progressive dies.

A roll feed consists essentially of a pair of rolls that can turn in one direction only. The rolls exert pressure on the stock by the use of springs or some other device. The rolls are rotated by the motion of the press crankshaft.

Roll feeds are suitable for extremely thin material and material with highly polished surfaces. If hard-chromium-plated rolls are substituted for standard ground-steel rolls, polished surfaces will not be scored or marked during feeding. Rubber-coated or plastic-coated rolls can be used on soft finished or prepainted stock.

There are two advantages in using roll feeds for feeding thin stock. With patterned rolls, a flange can be formed on a waste edge of the stock as a stiffener. With a single roll feed, the stock usually is pulled through the die.

The best method of feeding extra-thin stock is the use of double roll feeds (Fig. 12), in which roll feeds at each side of the die are set so that the stock between them is always under slight tension. Double roll feeds eliminate manual feeding of end sections when strip stock is processed, and are suitable only when a substantial scrap skeleton remains.

Rack-and-pinion-actuated roll feeds are available in almost all sizes but are used most in relatively heavy stamping and drawing operations. In larger presses it is common to use double roll feeds of the rack-and-pinion type that are attached to the press bolster.

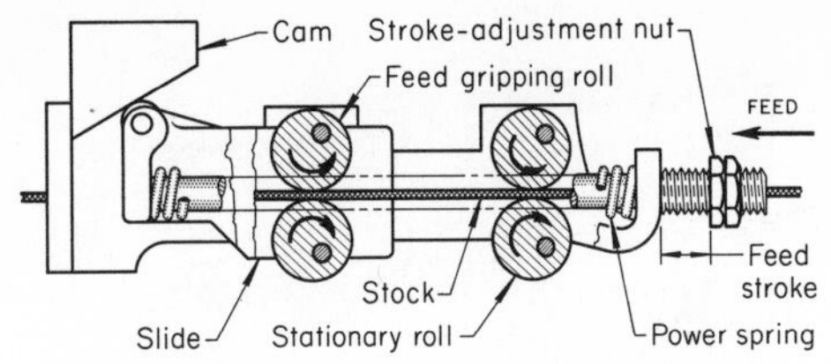

Fig. 11. Cam-actuated slide feed with pinch rolls that grip the stock for feeding. Arrows on the rolls indicate gripping direction. Reverse rotation of rolls releases the stock.

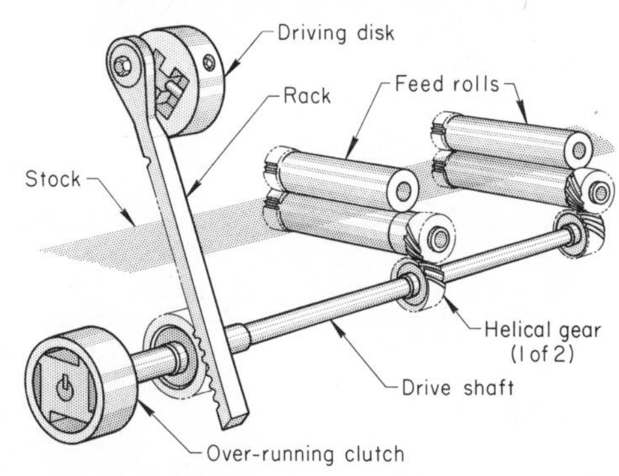

Fig. 12. Components of a double roll feed

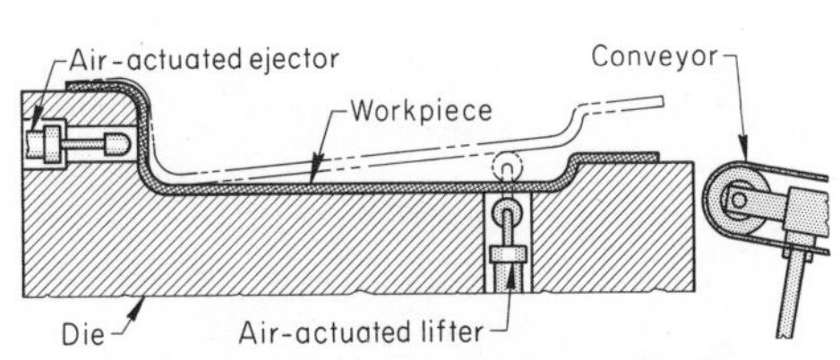

Fig. 13. Air-actuated device for lifting a workpiece from the die cavity and ejecting it onto a conveyor belt

Roll vs Slide Feeds. Roll feeds are the most used because: (*a*) they can feed stock as wide as 72 in. in increments as large as 90 in., (*b*) they are easy to set up and require little maintenance, and (*c*) they run well at high speed, with feeds of 1 to 3 in. per press stroke.

Disadvantages of roll feeds include: (*a*) lower accuracy than slide feeds, especially for longer feed lengths and faster speeds; (*b*) lack of a built-in measuring device; and (*c*) higher cost than slide feeds.

Disadvantages of slide feeds include: (*a*) less versatility than roll feeds, (*b*) greater difficulty in setting up than roll feeds, (*c*) slower feed than roll feeds, and (*d*) more marking of work metal.

Feeds for Blanks. Unlike slide and roll feeds, which are used solely with strip and coil stock, feeds for blanks are used with work metal that has already been blanked from the scrap skeleton, and for feeding partly completed workpieces into a press for secondary operations. The most common types are dial feeds, transfer feeds, and various hopper, chute and magazine feeds. Size and shape of the workpiece, production rate and quantity, and type of press are the principal factors in the choice of a feeding device.

Dial Feeds. Basically, a dial feed is a rotating table. It can either be fixed to the press bed, or be used as a separate piece of equipment. The dial is set up to rotate and index, as required, to deliver the workpiece from station to station. One type of dial takes the work to a series of dies or work stations; another carries the dies beneath a series of rams or punches. Workpieces sometimes are loaded into dial feeds by hand; more often, dial feeds are loaded from hoppers, chutes, vibrator feeders, or feed fingers.

Dial feeds are used for making slots, one at a time, in stator and rotor laminations.

Dial feeds can be applied to blanking, coining, staking, piercing, forming and drawing operations. Their use is limited only by the size of the dies and the workpiece. Dial feeds have been used on presses exceeding 150 tons in capacity.

Transfer feeds are used for multiple-operation stamping when it is impractical to move the blank from station to station by using a strip, as in a progressive die. Coil stock, flat blanks, or preforms are fed to the first station. Transfer of the work material is done by cam-actuated gripping fingers shaped to fit the workpiece. The fingers grip the part, carry it to the next station, return to their initial station, and repeat the cycle.

Feeds for Small Parts. Air-operated feeds for small parts can be mounted on the side of a gap-frame press. Parts are transferred to the die from a magazine or a preload station outside the die area. The feed unit cycles the press, and an air jet ejects the part from the die. Pickup heads are interchangeable and may be actuated mechanically or magnetically, or by vacuum.

Another type of feed for small parts consists of an arm, movable in three planes, with adjustable fingers. The unit has a memory system, and the arm is programmed by manually passing it along the desired path. Once programmed, it will continue to cycle along the same path.

Hopper feeds are widely used for feeding partly completed workpieces or, occasionally, small blanks to the next operation. The workpieces usually are dumped by hand into a hopper, where they are oriented by the feed. There are many kinds of hoppers and hopper feeds; selection depends on the size and shape of the workpiece. They may be driven by the press or by a separate power source. Although most hopper feeds are made up of standard components, some modification is usually needed to suit the specific job.

Chute feeds are simple, gravity-operated feeds that are used almost exclusively with blanks or fairly flat workpieces. They usually have a device at the bottom of the chute that allows the blanks to drop out one at a time.

Magazine feeds are a development of the chute feed. They are gravity fed but have a slide at the bottom with a blade of the same thickness as the workpiece to push the bottom piece out.

Stack feeds can feed blanks and lengths of sheet or strip from the top of the stack by use of vacuum pads or suction cups that grasp the work. A magnetic or air-operated sheet separator almost always is needed with this type of feed, especially when working with thin or oily material. Most stack feeds have an air or mechanically actuated transfer arm capable of simple motions.

Unloading Equipment

Stampings can be removed from dies by falling through the die or sliding down an incline. Those, however, that need special handling must sometimes be removed by hand or by mechanical devices.

A short blast of air can be used to unload small light parts. The air-blast control valve can be operated by a cam on the crankshaft. When the press cycles, the cam opens the valve to permit a jet of air to escape near the top of the stroke, or just before the press stops.

Air-actuated ejectors can be used to remove parts that are too heavy for air-blast removal, particularly if the press cannot be inclined. A simple air-actuated ejector can propel the part onto a conveyor or into a chute after the part has been lifted out of the die cavity, as in the setup shown in Fig. 13.

Mechanical Unloaders. Various linkages, arms, trays, pusher slides, and ram-operated devices are used in dies to unload finished parts automatically. Many of these devices are designed for a specific die and are difficult to adapt to another die.

Commercial unloaders are actuated by air or hydraulic cylinders and are synchronized with the press stroke. These devices have a swinging or horizontal motion to lift and carry the parts from the dies. The finished parts are raised out of the die cavity by lifter units built into the die. From this position, jaws grip the parts and carry them from the press to a conveyor or transfer fixture.

A swinging-arm unloading device is mounted on the press frame above the die space, as shown in Fig. 14. Two air cylinders operate the device — one for swinging the arm and one for opening and closing the jaws. The jaws are opened and closed by a wedge cam, moved by an air cylinder. The locking cam prevents the jaws from opening while carrying a load. In addition, they can close, without adjustment, on stock of any thickness within the span of the jaw opening. The cylinders are controlled by limit switches tripped by the press slide or by the rotary-cam switch of the press. The jaws are replaceable with standard jaws, or jaws designed to suit the part being moved.

The unloader shown in Fig. 14 is mounted on rails and can be easily moved aside to permit die change or die repair. Further, the unloader can be positioned to grip the part at the best point for removal.

The straight-line press-unloader is an air-operated device with adjustable stroke. It uses the same kind of jaws as the swinging-arm type. The unloader reciprocates in a straight line to remove the part, and can be mounted on a portable A-frame, on conveyors, or on the press. Parts can be unloaded from positive-knockout dies, which eject at the top of the stroke, by replacing the jaws with a basket or shovel.

Equipment for Transfer Between Presses

Workpieces that require processing in two or more presses are transported from one press to another by various types of transfer units. Conveyor or shuttle-type machines receive the workpiece from an unloader and move it to the next press, where it is loaded into the die either manually or automatically. The type of transfer equipment used depends on the material, weight, size and shape of the workpieces, on the orientation of the work required at the next station, and on the importance of preventing scratches.

Adjustable flat-belt conveyors can be used for transferring stampings in press-line operations. The conveyor can be lengthened or shortened quickly. The entire conveyor, or one end at a time, can be raised or lowered to suit the die.

Turnover devices (Fig. 15) are used to turn the workpiece over as it moves from one press to another. The workpiece is placed above the arm of the turnover mechanism, the arm raises, the vacuum cups engage the workpiece, and the arm rotates approximately 180°, thus turning the workpiece over. The vacuum is released, and the arm returns and repeats the cycle. The workpiece is positioned above the arm by a press unloader. The arm can turn the part over from a fixed pivot point, or the arm can traverse between the presses to move the part from an unload to a load position. The turned-over workpiece is placed on a table ready for feeding into the next press.

Transfer devices of various designs move workpieces between presses. Some machines incorporate devices for unloading the die, turning the workpiece over, rotating, carrying the workpiece, and loading it into another press. Transfer is done with a shuttle table by reciprocating pusher dogs, or by chain or belt conveyors. The units are driven by pneumatic, hydraulic or electric power, and are synchronized with the presses.

A shuttle transfer, used between presses, is shown in Fig. 16. The oscillating rail removes the part from the die and carries it along the stationary rail to the next press. The transfer machine is supported on casters and can be moved aside for die repair or die change. Adjustable feet make it easy to set the rails to suit the die.

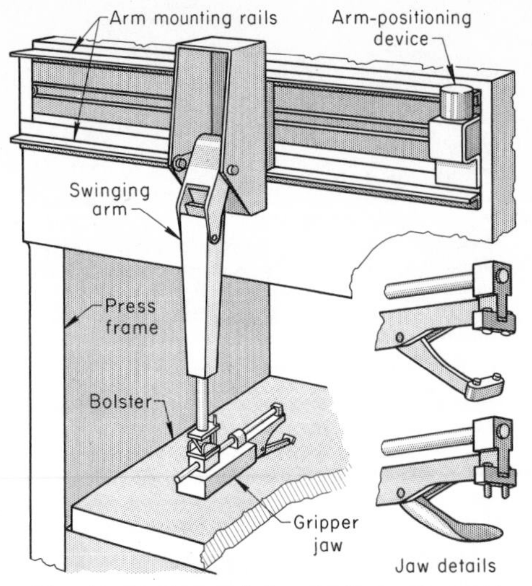

Fig. 14. Rail-mounted swinging-arm press unloader with interchangeable gripper jaws

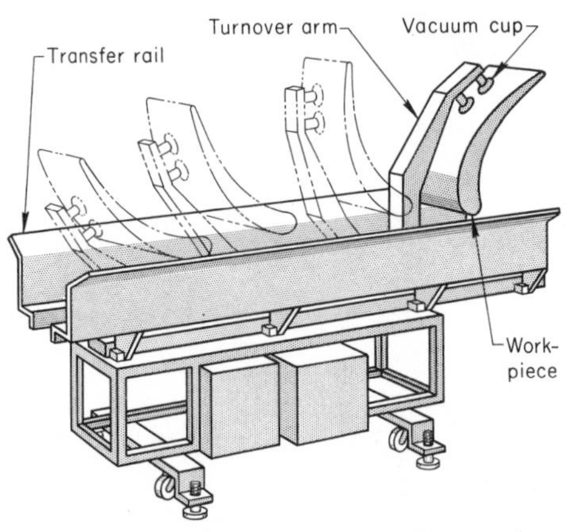

Fig. 15. Turnover machine with vacuum cups to hold workpiece during 180° rotation

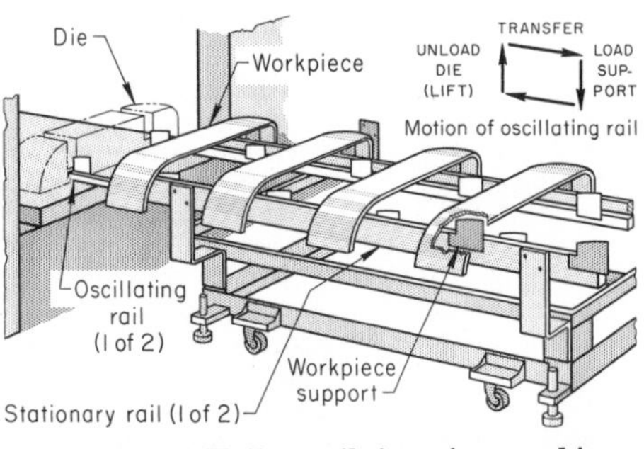

Fig. 16. Oscillating-rail transfer machine

Applicators for Lubricants

In blanking or in forming, a lubricant usually is applied to metal that is fed into the press from coils. The lubricant can be swabbed or brushed on the metal as it leaves the reel, but this is inefficient and wasteful and produces inconsistent results. An automatic applicator improves efficiency and uniformity. The type of applicator used depends on whether the lubricant is a powder or a liquid and, if a liquid, on its viscosity and flow characteristics.

Liquid Lubricants. The simplest automatic applicator is a dropper suspended above the stock as close to the feed as possible. Usually these are manifold-type applicators so that orifices spaced along the stock width can be opened to control the flow of the lubricant. Disadvantages of this method are that only one side of the metal is coated, and that some lubricants for deep drawing are too thick to flow freely.

Wicks made of felt or other absorbent material can be used to apply the lubricant. The wicks are kept wetted with lubricant, and they wipe one or both sides of the metal as it passes between them. Wicks are inefficient with some viscous lubricants, such as chlorinated mineral oils, and the amount of lubricant delivered is limited.

Roller-coating devices, similar to those used for painting, can be used with most lubricants. They are installed just ahead of the feed, and do not waste lubricant. Sometimes the lubricator is placed between the die and feeder so that the lubricant will not affect the accuracy of the feed length.

Dry lubricants, in the form of powder or dried soap solutions, are used where liquid lubricants are unsuitable. An efficient arrangement for applying dry lubricants is described and illustrated on page 68 in the article "Blanking and Piercing of Magnetically Soft Materials", in this volume.

Straighteners

Straighteners have upper and lower rolls alternately mounted in a staggered position. The minimum number of rolls that can be used is three; however, five-roll or seven-roll straighteners are most common for the usual range of stock thickness. Straightening of stock less than 0.020 in. thick requires more rolls; as many as 17 have been used for some thin stock.

When three-roll straighteners are used, frequent adjustment of the center roll is necessary to compensate for the change in curvature of the metal from the outside to the inside of the coil. The metal unrolled from a new coil has a large radius of curvature, and only a small amount of offset between the rolls is necessary to remove the curvature. As the coil is unwound, the roll offset must be increased, because the radius of curvature of the coil has decreased. If the offset is too great, a reverse curvature is put in the stock.

Straighteners with five or more rolls use this principle by bending the stock more than is necessary to remove the smallest radius of curvature. The following set (or sets) of rolls have a smaller offset and straighten the metal, because the induced curvature is the same whether the outer or inner layers of the coils are being straightened. The arrangement of straightener rolls is the same as that of the leveling rolls illustrated in Fig. 17(a).

Some straighteners have a separate screw adjustment for each of the upper rolls; others have one adjustment for the entire series of upper rolls. A straightener should not be overloaded. When stiff, thick metal is passed through a straightener designed for thin metal, it may deflect the rolls permanently or break their shafts. Stiff, thick stock requires larger, stronger rolls spaced well apart. Thin metal requires more straightening rolls than thick metal. These rolls usually are smaller in diameter and more closely spaced.

Stock straighteners are available in a wide range of capacities and speeds, with powered or nonpowered straightening rolls. Either the upper or lower set of rolls, or sometimes both sets, are powered. Nonpowered rolls can be used when there is enough pulling or pushing force to get the stock through the rolls. Powered pinch rolls are used to push or to pull the stock through the straightener.

Thin stock requires more working to straighten than thick stock. For this reason two sets of pinch rolls are used and all straightening rolls are driven.

The speed of powered straighteners can be adjusted so that the material is delivered by the rolls at the rate it is fed into the press, plus 10%. The ideal condition is to have the stock run through the rolls continuously, so that there are no breaks or bends in the stock when it is stopped on the rolls. When straighteners are operated intermittently, breaks or bends occur in the stock and are almost impossible to remove.

The size of the slack loop between the straightener and press can be controlled by several devices. A paddle or roller above or below the stock, and connected to an arm, controls the size of the loop by providing a signal to operate a clutch. A photoelectric cell or proximity switch regulates the loop size without contacting the metal surface. This is an advantage when using a very soft metal, or stock with a polished surface, such as stainless steel, or preplated or prepainted stock. All of these surfaces can be damaged by a rolling or sliding control device.

Straighteners often are combined with reels or cradles, or with feeds, to conserve floor space. Separate units are easily moved from press to press.

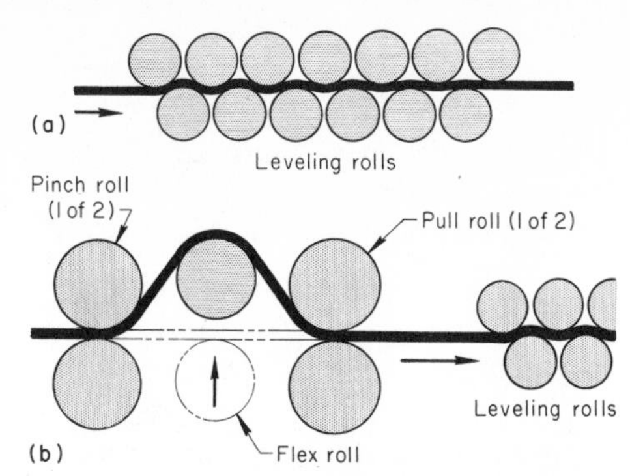

Fig. 17. Arrangement of rolls for roller leveling of sheet or strip with and without flex rolling (see text for discussion)

Roller Levelers

Roller levelers, like straighteners, have staggered pairs of meshing rolls, as shown in Fig. 17(a), but the rolls are smaller and more closely spaced, and as many as 39 rolls are used. All of the rolls are powered and some of the upper and lower working rolls have backup rolls. Levelers with backup rolls can impose strains on the metal to remove slack edges or a crowned center.

To secure good leveling, the material must be worked beyond its yield point. This is done by adjusting the leveling rolls at the entrance end so that the metal is worked beyond the yield point. The exit end of the rolls is set open an amount equal to stock thickness. Very slight adjustment of the exit-end rolls will turn the strip up or down, depending on the roll arrangement. The tops of the lower rolls usually are level or parallel with the material. The leveling rolls in the upper bank are adjusted to achieve the proper cold working.

A more effective type of roller leveling includes a break roll, or flex roll. In this type, the stock is gripped by a pair of pinch rolls and a pair of pull rolls (Fig. 17b). After the sheet is gripped by these rolls, the flex roll moves upward, flexing the sheet as shown in Fig. 17(b). The flex roll is usually actuated by hydraulic or mechanical means and can be adjusted to any height within the limits of the machine. After flex rolling, the metal passes through a series of staggered rolls, as in conventional roller leveling.

Roller levelers can be equipped with washing facilities to provide uniformly clean blanks for feeding into the dies. Brush rolls and high-volume solvent sprays remove dirt, steel slivers, and mill lubricants from the surface of the stock.

Flex rolling is frequently done as a continuous operation in a blanking or shearing line as the metal is uncoiled. As in straightening, the rolls run at a speed slightly greater than the rate at which the metal is fed into the press. This eliminates the need to start and stop the flex roller, prevents bends or breaks in the metal, and assures flexing of the entire strip. Because of the age-hardening phenomenon, scheduling of stock to the drawing operation dictates to what extent in-line flex rolling or roller leveling can be utilized. Timing is important, because the metal will age harden within 24 hr after flex rolling. In the event of die or press breakdown, a sheet flex roll processor may be needed to reroll the stock before it can be formed. Rerolling of cut blanks — that is, turning 180° and flex rolling again — is done on a blank for a critical part where stretcher strains could appear close to the leading and trailing ends of the blank. This is not needed for blanks cut from coil stock that was flex rolled in the shearing line.

The tension type of roller leveler is used to flatten metals too thin (0.020 to 0.005 in.) to be processed on ordinary roller levelers. Flatness is achieved by elongation of the strip, which results from the combination of bending stress and applied tension. The leveler has pre-flex stands and a roller-leveling station. Pre-flex rolls work the metal beyond its elastic limit; elongation, precisely controlled to a preset percentage, takes place, producing a flat, stress-equalized strip. Control of strip elongation is maintained through bridles that are interconnected by a mechanical draw drive.

The function of roller leveling is discussed in the article "Press Forming of Low-Carbon Steel", page 112.

Coil-Handling Equipment

Coil cradles, reels, uncoilers, re-coilers and other types of coil-handling equipment are important to the successful operation of a press.

Coil cradles may be either nonpowered or powered. In the nonpowered type, the stock is pulled from the coil by a powered feed, straightener or pinch rolls, or by the equipment being fed. A powered cradle is preferable for coils that weigh more than 2000 lb or when stock is going directly from the reel to the press feed.

In a powered cradle, the coil is supported by chain-driven or gear-driven rolls, or by a driven steel-slat conveyor belt. The drive should be automatically self-equalizing, to prevent skidding of the coil.

Coil cradles should have motors that can stand frequent starting of inertia loads. A slack loop is created between the coil and straightener or feed devices by starting and stopping the motor intermittently on signal from a dancer roll, paddle or other control. This intermittent operation may cause a standard motor to fail prematurely. With a variable time delay (electronic or adjustable-cam), the motor can overrun to a controllable extent after the control has commanded it to stop.

A variable-speed drive reduces the number of starts and stops, prolongs the life of the motor and drive, and often makes it possible to match the speed of the cradle to that of the machine being fed. A clutch can be used so that the motor will run continuously and the clutch is engaged to drive the slat conveyor or rolls only when stock is required.

Guide plates should extend between the support rolls and should be easily adjustable from either side for coils of different widths. Rotary guide plates are recommended only for tilting cradles, which are generally used to feed OBI presses, and for some heavy-duty shaft-driven cradles.

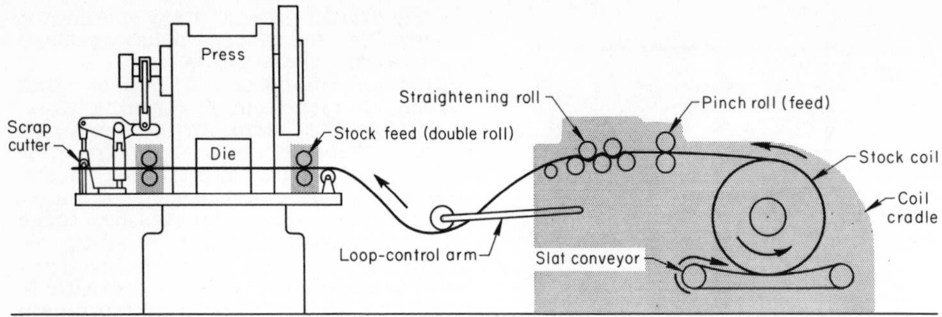

Fig. 18. Power-operated coil cradle, with straightening rolls and a loop-control arm, supplying coil stock to a double roll feed in a gap-frame press

Some cradles have rollers that reduce friction between the side of the rotating coil and the guide plates. These rollers protect the edges of some kinds of material.

Pinch rolls, or take-out rolls, add extra pull to the action of the support rolls, and should be used in cradles for feeding extra-thin or extra-heavy coil, for oily material, for spring-temper or lamination stock, for coils with slitting camber, and for feeding from irregular coils. Some pinch rolls swing out from the cradle to make loading easier. Pinch rolls are provided in some cradles, but they can also be bought as separate items.

Coil catchers, or bumpers, cushion the weight of the coil and lower it gently into position on the support rolls, or conveyor, to prevent shock to the equipment and damage to the coils.

Coil cradles often are combined with straightening heads. This results in a more compact unit requiring less floor space, reduces capital investment, promotes faster loading and adjustment, and reduces power requirements and maintenance. The addition of a straightener requires hold-down rolls to prevent the outer wrap of the coil from unwinding (hold-down rolls are useful even with a plain cradle), coil breakers, and peelers. These devices serve primarily to straighten the leading and trailing edges of the stock for easier feeding into the straightener, or for use with an automatic threader. A combination cradle-and-straightener supplying coil stock to a double roll feed is shown in Fig. 18.

Cradle Limitations. For some applications, a reel or other type of uncoiler is more suitable than a cradle. Ordinarily, cradles are not recommended for use with prefinished stock, thin material, telescoped coils, or soft material.

Prefinished Stock. The scuffing that inevitably occurs when stock is uncoiled from a cradle (even from a cradle with a cleaning and oiling attachment) will mar plated, polished, vinyl-coated and otherwise prefinished material.

Thin Material. When a heavy coil of thin material is unwound from a cradle, the stock may elongate unevenly between the support rolls and drift toward the side guides in a wobbling motion. Some producers of equipment do not recommend a cradle for use with stock less than 0.050 in. thick, but the thickness-to-weight ratio, rather than the thickness alone, is the critical factor.

When thin material is not strong enough to resist the corrective action of the side guides, a flange may be produced that cannot be removed by the straightener. Even slight flanging makes it impossible to feed the material into a die without corrective work.

Telescoped coils rub heavily against the side guides of a coil cradle and may be impossible to control. Such coils can usually be unwound more efficiently from a reel or other type of uncoiler.

Soft material, very loosely wound material, and egg-shaped coils also present problems when unwound from a cradle.

Despite the limitations mentioned, coil cradles and cradle-and-straightener combinations have many uses. If they are selected for the work expected of them, they are a highly efficient means of handling coil stock, especially in the heavier thicknesses. The main advantage of a coil cradle is that it unwinds the stock at a constant rate regardless of the outside diameter of the coil.

Stock Reels and Uncoilers. Commercial stock reels can accept coils weighing as much as 50,000 lb. There are reels of the proper size and type for almost any pressworking application.

Selection of a reel should be based on the maximum coil weight and the widths of stock to be unwound. In selecting a reel, it is better to overestimate future requirements than to underestimate and find that reel capacity limits improvement in equipment and production methods.

Plain or nonpowered reels usually are adequate when the press feed or stock straightener has pinch rolls with enough gripping power to pull the stock from the reel. When stock is going directly from reel to press feed, the reel should be powered so that the feed does not have the job of both feeding the press and unwinding the coil. If the stock becomes taut between the reel and the feed, the feed may start to advance and the stock slip, resulting in a short feed length. If a straightener is used between the press feed and the reel, a plain reel can be used. However, materials with low tensile strength and lightweight materials should be unwound from a powered reel; otherwise, they might be stretched between the reel and the feeding device.

Powered reels with variable speed and a loop control are preferred for smooth operation. Noncontact sensor units, such as photoelectric cells or proximity switches, on the loop control should be used for soft metals, polished surfaces, and prepainted stock. These prevent damage inherent with contact-type (rolling or sliding) sensor units. Without powered reels or loop control a sudden pull can cause the stock feed to slip and mark the work metal. A motor-driven reel with loop control and automatic centering is shown in Fig. 19. The arms expand to grip the inside of the coils, regardless of their inside diameter. Unreeling is smooth, and the coil is always centered.

Automatic centering by adjustable arms is available in plain and powered reels and on both single-head and double-head models. It is recommended for all but the smallest coil-processing applications. (Double-head reels have two reels on a common base. While one side of the reel is feeding the process equipment, the empty side is being loaded, thus minimizing downtime for changing reels.)

Reels for light duty are available in a wide variety of plate and arm reels. A horizontal pan reel feeds stock from either the inside or the outside of the coil. This type requires no centering of the coil, nor does it require a brake. It can be used for stock up to 8 in. wide and coil weights to 300 lb. Its best application is for narrow widths of springy material.

Plate reels, in which the stock is confined between two disks, are suitable for coils with a small inside diameter and a relatively small outside diameter.

Arm reels are used when the inside and outside diameters of the coils and stock widths vary considerably. Arm reels have manual adjustments for these variations. Most arm reels use quick-clamping forks for rapid loading and unloading of the coil. Some can be adjusted for height and can be tilted 90°, primarily for use with OBI presses.

Manual braking is controlled by a drag that can be adjusted to keep the stock from overrunning.

Automatic braking is preferable for pressworking of thin material. Usually, the stock loop between the press feed or stock straightener and the coil contacts an arm that engages and disengages the brake. When stock is being fed into the press, the length of the loop is reduced, causing the loop control to disengage the brake on the stock reel. The brake remains disengaged as long as the stock loop is not too large. When feeding stops, the stock loops down, dropping the loop-control arm, causing the brake to engage and prevent overrunning of the stock.

Medium and Heavy-Duty Reels. Reels with capacities of 2,500 to 10,000 lb are rated as medium-duty. Reels with capacities of 10,000 to 50,000 lb are rated as heavy-duty. Both types are available in plain and powered models. Automatic centering is essential with heavier coils.

Because they must support great weights from one side only, these reels must be massive and must have ample bearing capacity to support overhanging weight. Sometimes these reels are used with outboard supports to help counteract deflection.

Cone-Type and Arbor Reels. The cone-type uncoiler has opposed, steep-angle cones that enter the coil at each end. The greater the angle of the cone, the greater the range of inside diameters that can be handled. Minimum inside diameter is a limitation of cone-type uncoilers. Another limitation is that they are likely to deform the inner layers of the coil. This type of equipment cannot be used for stock less than 9 in. wide.

Stub-arbor uncoilers, which have two opposed stub mandrels, can uncoil stock as narrow as 4 in. in width. Screw-driven mechanical or hydraulic expansion of the jaws does not deform the stock. Stub-arbor uncoilers are loaded and unloaded rapidly.

Other equipment useful for handling coil stock includes re-coilers, turnstiles, downlayers, coil cars, coil grabs, and coil ramps.

Re-coilers are used for winding coil stock after slitting and for winding the scrap skeleton after pressworking.

Turnstiles (or horns) are two-arm or three-arm devices used to store coils temporarily before processing. In function, a turnstile resembles a coil ramp. Turnstiles may be equipped with hydraulic push-off devices, which add to their speed and efficiency.

Downlayers, sometimes called up-enders, are turnover devices for rotating the coil from horizontal to vertical position.

Coil cars are used for transporting heavy coils to the press service area.

Coil grabs, for use with cranes, are devices that can handle stock in the horizontal or vertical position. Some similar devices are available for use with fork-lift trucks. Other devices will pick up a coil and change the position from horizontal to vertical.

Coil ramps are inclined storage units for use with reels or cradles. Most coil ramps operate by gravity.

For additional information on material handling in pressrooms, see "Metalworking Automation", by G. H. De Groat (McGraw-Hill, 1962), and "Techniques of Pressworking Sheet Metal", by D. F. Eary and E. A. Reed (Prentice-Hall, 1958).

Operator Safety and Protection

The safest press is one operating continuously with a stock feeder and part unloader. This type of machine does not require the full attention of an operator, and there is no need for him to reach into the danger area. Flywheels, gears and other moving parts likely to catch an operator or passerby usually are covered.

For hand feeding, shields should be interlocked with press controls, so that the press will not run unless the shields are in place. Best practice is to make the guard or shield a part of the die, so that protection is automatically in place when the setup is made or installed by the setup man. Shields also can be attached to the press frame and adjusted for various kinds of work. These guards should suit all the work done in the press, should be easy for the setup man to adjust, and should give the operator an unobstructed view.

Usually, it is more difficult to guard hand-fed second operations, because the workpiece requires special handling. However, if production rate and quantity warrant the expenditure, standard or special devices can replace hand feeding of presses.

Available safeguards include (*a*) barriers or interlocking guards that keep the operator away from danger, (*b*) sweep and pulling devices that push the operator's hands away, and (*c*) devices that require both hands to trip the press. All safeguards should be inspected and adjusted before and after every press run.

Important considerations in choosing safety devices are: number of operators at the press, size and type of press, size and shape of workpieces, length of press stroke, and number of strokes per minute.

Protective devices cannot do the job by themselves; they should be used with a well-planned and strictly enforced safety program.

Rod or Basket Guards. For primary, strip-feed operations and for use with dies provided with feeds, adjustable barrier guards are used. These are usually attached to the press frame and have adjustable front and side sections that can be made to fit many dies. Some guards can be swung clear of the die area. These are interlocked with the press so that it cannot be tripped when the guard is out of position. The guards can also be attached to the die for operator protection. Operators must be trained not to remove or adjust them under any circumstances; adjustment should be the diesetter's responsibility.

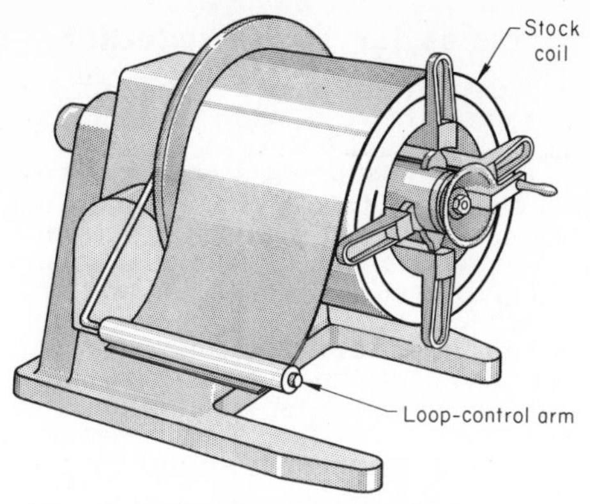

Fig. 19. Motor-driven automatic-centering reel with loop control

Drop gates usually have a barrier or gate that drops when the foot treadle is depressed. If the gate is blocked by the operator's hand or any other object, the press will not cycle. Operators should be trained not to reach around the barrier or tamper with it.

Drop gates can also be used as fixed barriers for strip operations. A deficiency of drop gates that are connected to the trip mechanism is that they do not guard against repeats.

Sweep guards have a single or a double arm that passes across the front of the press between the die and the operator. They are actuated by the press ram and are intended to brush the operator's hands out of the danger area. To be effective, they must sweep the front of the die area during the beginning of the press stroke. Sometimes the whipping action can injure the operator's hands. If an operator has a hand against a guide pin or other obstruction, the sweep guard can hold or trap the operator.

Sweep guards have been most effective on small presses. During slow, long-stroke operations using large dies, the operator may be able to reach over a sweep guard before the ram is at the bottom and be injured.

Pullbacks, attached to the operator's wrists or arms, pull his hands away from the danger area as the ram descends. Properly adjusted, they guard against repeats, major malfunctions that cause the ram to drop, and operator error.

Pullbacks must be adjusted after every change of dies or operator. They should also be checked regularly for wear. The cable must be attached to the operator in such a manner that it cannot wrap around a guide post or other obstruction in front of him; otherwise, his hand will be pulled into the danger area instead of away from it.

Two-hand controls are based on the principle that the operator must engage a control with each hand to operate the press and therefore cannot have either of his hands in the die area.

Three types are in general use: (*a*) mechanical controls that trip the press through a linkage system, (*b*) electric two-hand controls that actuate a solenoid or a solenoid air valve, and (*c*) air-operated two-hand devices that control an air cylinder that actuates the press. A special two-hand system, and one of the safest, has dual valves, pneumatically in series and electrically in parallel, with single-stroke operation and complete monitoring.

Although the principle of two-hand control is sound, many injuries have been caused by presses equipped with these devices. Almost invariably, the cause is inferior components or faulty installation. Merely wiring two switches in series or hooking up two air valves does not make a safe circuit. Nor is the device safe if the operator can tie down one of the switches and still operate, or if he can use his knee or elbow to depress one switch. Also, two-hand controls do not provide foolproof protection on presses with positive clutches at speeds below 200 strokes per minute.

Because of the many protective features that must be included in a truly safe two-hand control circuit, only reliable components should be used. High-reliability valves are made specifically for press control. Generally the design and installation of control circuitry are beyond the capability of the average shop electrician.

Die Protection

Electrical, mechanical or optical sensors can be incorporated in tooling or mounted on the press to detect stock buckling, misfeeds, doubles, failure of the workpiece to eject, and other malfunctions that can damage dies.

Electrical sensors include spring sensors, wire barriers, and proximity switches. A spring sensor basically is a piece of wire attached to an insulated rod. When a grounded metal part (for instance, a piece of buckled stock) touches it, it provides an electrical signal that can be amplified and used to stop the press.

Spring sensors are the least expensive protective devices, but they can be set off by oil droplets and sometimes are difficult to incorporate in progressive tooling.

Wire barriers consist of a grid of fine wires. Every other wire has ground potential. Ejected parts, striking the wires, make a bridge between the ground and the sensor wires and produce a signal. Usually the wires are arranged so that lack of a signal, indicating that a part was not ejected, will stop the press. They are not suitable for small flat work that can fly between the wires without touching them. Another disadvantage is that a part can hit the wires and fall back into the die if the barrier is improperly set up.

Proximity switches function in much the same way as spring sensors. They are easier to install but cost more.

Mechanical sensors include sensitive switches and transducer pickup plates. A sensitive switch functions when a part contacts and deflects a lever arm that closes a circuit. A transducer functions like a phonograph pickup — when an ejected part strikes a transducer control, a minute signal is generated. This signal can be detected by a sensitive circuit and amplified. Transducers are not suited to heavy parts, because of wear of the sensor, nor to press speeds above 250 strokes per minute.

Optical sensors consist of a photoelectric cell and a light source. Usually the light source makes a curtain of light (sometimes infrared) through which the part must pass. In doing so, it makes a signal, which is read by the photocell and is amplified.

Optical sensors are the most expensive. They have a high degree of reliability and flexibility, however, and their usefulness increases directly with the speed of the press.

Press Protection

Mechanical presses should be protected against overloading. (Hydraulic presses are inherently protected against overloading.) A small error on the part of the diesetter in adjusting the slide can result in an overload that can fracture the frame members or the crown. Even when the damage is less severe — sometimes the crankshaft or eccentric shaft will break — bearing damage almost always occurs.

There are two types of overload devices — permanent and replaceable. Both protect against overloads occurring near the bottom of the stroke. (Torque overloads occurring near the top of the stroke are far less severe a problem.) Overloads can be caused by double blanks, misfeeds, or improper die setting, or by trying to do a job in too small a press.

Replaceable overload devices are of either the stretch-link or the shear-washer type. The former, used only on underdrive presses, consists of a link that will stretch if a given load is exceeded. It is more an overload indicator than a protective device.

A shear washer (or collar) is mounted on the slide adjustment. It is designed to shear or fracture when overloaded, leaving sufficient displacement on the adjustment nut to relieve the overload, if it is within ½ in. of the bottom of the stroke (where most overloads occur).

Disadvantages of shear washers are: (*a*) they must be replaced after each overload; (*b*) they will fail under less than rated load after long use; and (*c*) because shear washers on a multiple-point-suspension press do not fail simultaneously, there can be severe side loading, which can damage the gibs.

Permanent overload devices do not require replacement after an overload. In most of these devices, a hydraulic cylinder is mounted in the slide adjustment. A preset pressure is maintained by a hydraulic pump, and a piston in the cylinder trips a limit switch if the preset load is exceeded. Another type uses air cylinders and a linkage attached to the tie rods of the press. It will allow the press crown to lift slightly if the preset pressure is exceeded.

These devices can be used to relieve a stuck press, and then can be quickly reset to the proper tension on the tie rods.

Friction clutches can be used for overload protection by regulating the air pressure or by automatically reducing air pressure near the bottom of the stroke with relief valves. Full air pressure is restored on the upstroke.

Slip couplings can be used with either positive or friction clutches on crankshaft presses. The couplings have a friction disk built into the flywheel and arranged so that the drive will slip under severe overload.

Presses for High Production

Mass-produced parts are often formed in presses that are made especially for high-production operation. High speed, or the highest number of strokes per minute, is not the only factor in a high production rate. The capability of a press to run continuously for several hours without full operator attention and with a minimum of wear and vibration contributes more to high productivity than running at high speed for a short period and then stopping for reconditioning of dies.

The more common types of high-production presses are dieing machines, multiple-slide machines, two principal types of transfer presses, and "high-productivity" presses.

Dieing machines are set up with conventional progressive dies for long-run operation. These machines are used extensively for the blanking of laminations; however, drawing and forming can be done. The height of the bed above the floor makes it easy to install stacking chutes for laminations and other parts.

Dieing machines are single-action underdrive presses. The drive mechanism for a dieing machine is located beneath the press bed. Four guide rods from a guided lower crosshead pass up through bronze bushings in the bed and are fastened to a platen to which the upper die half is attached. The lower crosshead is reciprocated by a crankshaft through connecting rods. By this action, the die halves are pulled together, rather than pushed together as in a conventional press.

The size of the guide rods and bushings results in excellent die alignment and long die life. The underdrive construction keeps the center of gravity of the press low. The progressive dies mounted in the machine are near eye level, and there are no columns or side members to obstruct the operator's view. Ejection chutes for finished parts and scrap are comparatively high above the floor so that containers are easy to position.

Pneumatic cushions, fastened to the top of the platen for better accessibility for service and adjustment, are used as strippers and blankholders.

Stock is fed through the guide rods with either single or double roll feeders. A scrap cutter can be mounted on the end of the machine. Both devices are operated by the upper platen or by a power takeoff on the end of the crankshaft.

Multiple-slide machines are fully automatic machines for mass production of small parts from metal strip or wire in coil form. Detailed information is given in the article on Forming of Steel Strip in Multiple-Slide Machines, page 154 in this volume. Tooling for parts made of wire is discussed in the article on Forming of Wire, page 347.

Transfer Presses. Two types of machines are called transfer presses. One type has single stations in which straight punches, die inserts that fit standard holders, transfer fingers and simple strippers are mounted. This type is the successor to, and often is still called, the eyelet machine. The second type is basically a wide-bed straight-side press with a horizontal slide for transfer-type operations. Individual single-operation or compound dies are used in these presses.

Eyelet-type transfer presses use many of the principles of the eyelet machine, but can form larger parts of heavier material and can perform many secondary operations with appropriate die design or attachments. Such operations include bottom stamping and marking, threading, beading, knurling and side lettering, side forming and piercing, and side slotting. Idle stations may be used (*a*) to provide space for mechanisms serving adjacent stations, (*b*) to position parts for special side marking, (*c*) to heat a part by an induction coil, or (*d*) to avoid moving an attachment already installed, powered and adjusted.

The tooling is mounted in each separate station and is actuated either by individual cam-actuated plungers for each station, or by a single cam-actuated ram acting against individually adjusted plungers. The single-station principle makes servicing and maintenance easy. The tools can be removed for repair or replacement without affecting the rest of the setup or its relationship, because the tooling elements are more nearly independent of other elements within the tool than with progressive dies.

The presses are used primarily for draw work. The first few stations involve blanking, an initial draw, and several redraws. Thus, elements developed for one job are common to many other jobs. In general, tool costs are about 50% of the cost of comparable progressive-die tooling.

The part is blanked in the first station from coil stock running at right angles to the tooling progression. The blank is moved from station to station with cam-actuated slides carrying transfer fingers. Because no stock allowance for pilots or carrying tabs is needed, as much as 30% less material is required than for comparable operations in a progressive die.

Multiple rows of blanks may be cut by using a re-coiling reel at the back of the press. After the stock has been run through the press once, it is transferred to the front and run again. A reversible feed system for multiple-row blanking is available. Another practice is to feed the stock through the first station, then loop the partial skeleton over the press and back through a second set of tools.

Setup time for a previously run job is less than one hour for each station. New jobs require more time, because the transfer fingers must be fitted to each individual station and the punches and dies may need alteration to eliminate wrinkles and draw marks. Tools from other jobs may be used in the initial stations, thus reducing toolmaking and setup time.

The production run needed to justify an eyelet-type transfer press compared to other methods is about 50,000 parts. On complex parts with fairly deep draws, the figure may be less than 25,000 parts. Runs of as few as 5000 parts have been made when anticipated production is not high enough to amortize other tooling, particularly a progressive die. Estimates of break-even point must be made to determine the economical length of run more closely.

Eyelet-type transfer presses have from 7 to 15 stations with a capacity of 15 to 75 tons, depending on the press design. Production rate ranges from 30 to 275 strokes per minute. This can be doubled by using a dual-feed arrangement. The maximum blank diameter ranges from 1½ to 3⅞ in., with a maximum draw depth of 13⁄16 to 3⅛ in., respectively. The maximum press stroke is approximately twice the maximum draw depth plus ¼ in.

Straight-side transfer presses are wide-bed straight-side presses in which a series of dies are set up to produce a finished stamping. Mechanical handling equipment takes a blank from the blanking die in the first station, or from a stack of precut blanks, and simultaneously transfers all stampings from one die to the next until the part is completed.

A straight-side transfer press setup is used when a part cannot be successfully produced on a progressive die and the additional cost above a series of separate dies is justified. Operations that sometimes become difficult or impossible to perform in progressive dies — such as deep drawing, restriking, cam piercing, and trimming — can be done in a transfer press. The transfer press eliminates the need for conveyor systems between presses or storage areas between operations.

The feed or transfer motion is basically the same on all straight-side transfer presses. It can be either press-driven or powered separately by electric motors, hydraulic motors, air or hydraulic cylinders, or a combination of these methods. Most transfer mechanisms are designed so that stampings are fed while the press is running through the top portion of its stroke. As the press closes through the midstroke position, the mechanical fingers are retracted. At the bottom of the working stroke the fingers return unclamped to the pickup position. The fingers clamp on the workpiece and the transfer cycle starts to repeat as the press opens through the midstroke position. All transfer dies in a set are designed to feed at the same level. In each station, the stamping must be elevated to the feed-line height of the die to permit transfer to the next die without interference.

Two basic types of stock feed are used — roll feed and stack feed. The choice of feed type is dictated by the following considerations:

1. Shape of the workpiece
2. Efficient use of roll stock
3. Availability of a blanking press
4. Effect of coil loading and its frequency on production rate
5. Effect of blanking die, if used, on other operations.

The roll feed brings coil stock into a blanking die. A stack feed is used for precut blanks, in which a blanking die is set up in a separate blanking press.

High-productivity presses are precision machines designed to operate continuously at speeds equal to or greater than conventional presses and are equipped with precision automatic feeding devices. They are available in gap-frame design, either fixed or inclinable, for relatively light operations. For work above about a 60-ton rating, straight-side presses are recommended because of their rigidity.

Gibs and slides, designed so that clearance and deflection are minimized, are machined to close tolerances and parallelism, because the alignment of the slide and bed is critical. Crankshafts, connections and bearings have been carefully designed to minimize vibration and cumulative bearing clearances, as both have an adverse effect on die life.

The advantage of carbide progressive dies can be fully utilized, because these presses are precision machines.

Definitions of Terms Relating to Presses

bed. The stationary, lower part of the press that serves as a table or support for the die or bolster plate. The bed in an inclinable press tilts back as the press is inclined, but otherwise the bed of a press is usually horizontal. The die may be bolted to the press bed, but usually is supported by a bolster that is secured to the bed. One or more fillers or risers can be used on the bed to decrease the shut height, putting the bolster atop the fillers, to raise the height of the stationary parts. The bed is sometimes called the lower platen, as in some hydraulic presses. When moving bolsters are used, the bolster, bolster-handling device, and supports replace the conventional press bed.

blankholder slide. The outer or upper slide of a double-action press that moves parallel to the main, or punch-holder, slide. It usually provides force to clamp the outer portion of the workpiece (blank) during drawing, to control metal flow. It may be used for blanking before drawing.

bolster. A plate or structure that holds the die, in some presses. Instead of being bolted to the bed, the die can be fastened to the bolster, thus raising the effective level of the press by the thickness or height of the bolster. JIC has standardized bolster dimensions and size and location of T-slots, pressure-pin holes and anchor holes. Some large, straight-side presses have bolsters that slide or roll out the side of the press for ease of die setup.

crown. The upper part of the press frame or structure, sometimes called the head, or the dome. Most presses have the press drive in the crown.

daylight. See *shut height of a press.*

die. A press tool, a pair of mating tools, or a combination of pairs of mating tools. Sometimes only the female (stationary) tool is called the die, and the mating male (moving) tool is called the punch. In an inverted die assembly, the punch is stationary and the die is movable.

die set. A unit consisting of an upper shoe, a lower shoe, and guide pins and posts. The die elements are attached to the shoes. Alignment and position are maintained with guide pins and bushings.

ejector. The mechanism for ejecting the workpiece from the die. The ejector may be actuated by a crossbar through a slot in the slide, a bell crank worked by a cam, a die cushion, springs or a rubber pad.

frame. The main structure of a press.

knockout. See *ejector.*

pitman. A connecting rod that carries force from a rotating or oscillating member to the slide. This member contains a means for adjusting the slide.

press slide. The part of the press that moves, carrying the punch, or upper part of the die, toward the mating tool part. On a hydraulic press it may be called the platen, or the upper platen.

pressure pad. A general term used for the part of a die that delivers holding pressure to the metal being worked. It can also be used as an ejector.

punch. The male part of a die; usually, the upper and moving part.

punch slide. The inner slide in a double-action press, which usually carries the punch. See also *press slide.*

ram. See *press slide.*

shut height of a press. Distance from the top of the bed to the bottom of the slide with the stroke down and adjustment up. In general, the shut height of a press is the maximum die height that can be accommodated for normal operation, taking the bolster thickness and any fillers into consideration.

slide. See *blankholder slide, press slide* and *punch slide.*

slide adjustment. The distance that the slide of a mechanical press can be moved to lessen the die space, decreasing the shut height. Adjustment may be made by hand or by power.

stroke. Distance the press slide moves from one end of its motion to the other.

strokes per minute. Rating of a press, in cycles of operation, for continuous running. When single-stroking a press (stopping after each stroke), strokes per minute may depend on the type of clutch and on the skill and dexterity of the operator in loading and unloading the die.

working stroke. That portion of the stroke that performs the work or operation (see Fig. 5 and 6). It cannot be greater than half the press stroke. In forming or drawing operations, the relation of the working stroke to the press stroke should be such that the slide velocity at the start of work does not exceed the drawing speed of the work metal.

Selected References

General Sources

Frank W. Wilson (editor in chief), "Die Design Handbook", prepared for the American Society of Tool and Manufacturing Engineers, Second Edition. McGraw-Hill, New York, 1965. [Section 23 (28 p) gives a detailed classification of the available types of press with concise descriptions of their principal features, and discusses the principles of press selection. The standards of the Joint Industry Conference of press users and manufacturers (JIC) for dimensions and markings of the principal types are reproduced. Section 22 (15 p) is an illustrated account of limit stops and safety guards for protecting presses and operators, and Section 19 (26 p) deals with most types of press feeds, with unloading devices, and with transfer equipment between presses.]

Frank W. Wilson (editor in chief), "Tool Engineers Handbook", prepared for the American Society of Tool Engineers, Second Edition. McGraw-Hill, New York, 1959. [Section 56 (24 p) gives a concise, illustrated classification of power presses (distinguishing clearly between knuckle-joint and toggle presses), summarizes the main features of clutches, brakes, controls, die cushions, feeding and unloading devices, and illustrates some special-feature presses. The JIC press standards are summarized, and there are notes on safety provisions.]

Heinrich Mäkelt, "Die mechanischen Pressen", Carl Hanser Verlag, Munich (W. Germany), 1966; 266 p. [A comprehensive textbook dealing with the design, construction, and uses of all types of mechanical presses, fully illustrated with diagrams and photographs. Includes sections on multiple-slide and transfer presses and feeding devices; 188 references. In German.]

Gerhard Oehler, "Die hydraulischen Pressen", Carl Hanser Verlag, Munich (W. Germany), 1962; 294 p. [A systematic account of the construction and characteristics of hydraulic presses of all types; 135 references. In German.]

L. Scherer, "Les Machines à Travailler les Métaux en Feuilles. Tome VI, Emboutissage", La Société des Publications Mécaniques, Paris (France), 1954; 106 p. [An illustrated catalog of presses of French manufacture, with dimensions and capacities. French safety requirements are listed. In French.]

Aldo Berruti, "Stampi e Presse", S. Lattes, Turin (Italy), 1951; 481 p. [The construction and operation of the basic types of press are described, illustrated with clear sketches, and accompanied by a systematic account of the functions of all press and die parts in blanking, bending, and forming operations. In Italian.]

A. Geleji, "Forge Equipment, Rolling Mills, and Accessories" (translated by J. Sivó), Akadémiai Kiadó, Budapest (Hungary), 1967. [A textbook on press design. Chapter 4 (47 p) considers calculations of forces and power requirements in cutting, bending and deep drawing with friction, eccentric, and crank-operated presses.]

C. W. Hinman, "Press Working of Metals", Second Edition, McGraw-Hill, New York, 1950. [Contains chapters outlining press types and their selection with simple computations of pressure and tonnage ratings; die construction; press accessories; the design of feeding equipment; formulas and reference tables with details of methods for developing shells and blanks.]

E. Molloy (editor), "Power Presses", George Newnes Ltd., London (England), 1945. [Includes chapters giving an illustrated survey of power press types (55 p), a brief survey of feed mechanisms (9 p), a useful account of fixed, automatic and interlock guards (21 p), and a discussion of the principles of lubrication (9 p).]

J. Dudley Jevons, "The Metallurgy of Deep Drawing and Pressing", Second Edition, Chapman and Hall, Ltd., London (England), 1941. [Includes chapters describing and illustrating the basic types of press (22 p), surveying press tool design and tool materials (70 p), and discussing in some detail the principles of lubrication (44 p).]

George Sachs, "Principles and Methods of Sheet Metal Fabricating", Second Edition revised and enlarged by Henry E. Voegeli, Reinhold, New York, 1966. [Chapter 16 (19 p) outlines the principles of press and tool construction and of lubrication practice.]

E. V. Crane, "Plastic Working of Metals and Non-Metallic Materials in Presses", Third Edition, John Wiley and Sons Inc., New York, 1944. [Basic press characteristics and some special-purpose modifications are described in Chapter 13 (42 p).]

J. A. Grainger, "Presswork and Presses", Second Edition, Machinery Publishing Co. Ltd., London (England), and The Industrial Press, New York, 1952. [Includes chapters describing and illustrating typical examples of presses (19 p), cushions for single-action presses (7 p), and the design of safety guards (13 p).]

John W. Langton, "Sheet Metal Working Machinery", Sir Isaac Pitman and Sons Ltd., London (England), 1963. [Chapter 4 (57 p) is a simple descriptive introduction to the main features of power presses.]

B. Kurseman, "Economics of Press Selection", ASTME Paper SP 63-68, 15 p, 1963. [Proper choice of press can reduce operating costs. Types considered include gap-frame, OBI (open-back inclinable), straight-side, high-productivity, and transfer presses.]

J. A. Grainger, Modern Trends in Power Press Design, *Sheet Metal Industries,* **39**, Oct 1962, 721-728. [Trend is seen to smaller, not overelaborate presses of greater power. High-speed friction clutches and high-energy-rate forming machines are described as under development.]

"Entwicklungstendenzen bei Stufenpressen", *Blech,* **12**, Aug 1965, 396, 398-400. [Compares design and performance of two 25-ton presses built in 1956 and 1964. Improvements include faster tool changes, higher speed of working, and more sophisticated control systems. Illustrated. In German.]

"Metalworking's Mechanical Press Handbook", Metalworking Publishing Co., Boston, 1960. [Describes the design, construction and use of mechanical presses. Discusses applications of straight-side, gap-frame, transfer and high-productivity presses.]

Special-Purpose Presses

J. H. Hayes, Automatic Presswork on Multi-Slide Machines, *Sheet Metal Industries,* **37**, Apr 1960, 267-276; discussion, 276-278. [Describes the design, operation, tooling, and application of multiple-slide machines, and discusses savings possible by their use.]

D. W. Bonnar, Press Automation with Short Run Flexibility, ASTME Paper 720, 11 p, 1965. [Discusses the use of moving-bolster presses integrated with automatic feeding equipment to give large outputs with quick change-overs.]

R. H. Eshelman, Change Tooling in Minutes on Sliding Bolster Press, *Iron Age,* **182**, Dec 25, 1958, 47-49. [Time of change-over can be reduced from 4-8 hr to 15-30 min.]

L. Schuler and E. E. Michaelis, The Speed of C-Frame Power Presses, *Sheet Metal Industries,* **35**, Sept 1958, 705-709. [A survey of the Schuler range of presses, using fast electromagnetic friction clutches to minimize tool wear at very high operating speeds.]

Feeding Devices

H. F. Hawkins and R. J. L. Lloyd, Development of Roller-Feed Mechanisms for Coiled Strip, *Sheet Metal Industries,* **39**, Feb 1962, 101-123; discussion, 123-126, 135. [Describes research leading to the development of improved mechanisms for positively controlled roller-transport feeds. Methods of combating the ill effects of drag, snatch, lack of flatness, and the presence of oil and dirt on accurate registration are examined.]

W. W. Schug, Dial Feeds Can Boost Your Press Production, *Tooling and Production,* **26**, Oct 1960, 65-68. [Recommendations for efficient use are given.]

A. P. J. Soepnel, Feeding Band and Strip Material to Automatic Presses, *Sheet Metal Industries,* **38**, Aug 1961, 588-594. [Discusses accuracy obtainable by roller and clamp transport and describes a twin-slide feeder.]

Safety

"Safety Code for Power Presses and Hand and Foot Presses", United States Standard USA B11.1-1960, United States of America Standards Institute, New York.

Frank E. McElroy (editor), "Accident Prevention Manual for Industrial Operations", Fifth Edition, National Safety Council, Chicago, 1964. [Chapter 22 (30 p) gives principles, types, methods and materials for guarding, with advantages and limitations of guard method for many machines and auxiliary transmission equipment; relates plant layout to safe practice. Chapter 23 (44 p) lists power press definitions; discusses purpose of operation guarding, auxiliary devices, feeding and ejecting devices for various presses, and handling, setting up, and removing heavy and light dies.]

A. P. J. Soepnel, Safety Devices for Eccentric Power Presses; Some Further Comments on Design of Eccentric Presses, *Sheet Metal Industries,* **35**, Oct 1958, 737-743; **36**, Oct 1959, 647-652, 656. [Constructional details of some safety features and devices are outlined.]

S. Hoffer, Electronic Die Protection Techniques, ASTME Paper SP 65-84, 18 p, Jan 1965. [Outlines the available systems and discusses their applications.]

E. E. Michaelis, Development in Photo-electric Guarding, *Sheet Metal Industries,* **40**, Dec 1963, 894-896, 904. [Describes circuits and guards developed by Institution of Automation, Munich.]

Selection of Presses for Forming of Sheet Metal

*By the ASM Committee on Forming of Sheet Metal in Presses**

SELECTION of press equipment for making a sheet metal part involves three steps:

1 Analyzing the part
2 Determining the type of tooling
3 Relating part and tooling requirements to press features.

Although these steps can be considered individually, the final decision is usually a set of compromises based on costs, lead time, and availability or utilization of equipment.

Analysis of Part

A drawing of the part and a sample part, if available, are carefully studied to determine what basic sheet metal operations, such as blanking, piercing, bending, forming or drawing, are necessary to make the part. The effect of one operation on another, relations of part features to one another, and the dimensional tolerances, influence the sequence of operations and die design. How the basic operations can be combined into a die or die station, size and shape of the part after each die operation, production rate and total quantity, and the composition and thickness of the work metal, all have an effect on the type of press selected.

*For committee list, see page 1.

Operations. Blanking and piercing usually are best done in a short-stroke, high-speed press, whereas longer-stroke presses of slower speed are better suited to forming and drawing operations. Coining and embossing usually need a short-stroke press with high force near the bottom of the stroke.

Drawing and forming operations have a critical slide speed, depending on the type of work metal used. Thus, press selection requires consideration of stroke length, slide velocity at the point the die contacts the metal, and press tonnage. All of these are governed by the type of operation.

Part size generally determines the size of dies used to make the part. The depth of a formed or drawn part affects the over-all height of the die and consequently the shut height and stroke length of the press (see pages 20 and 21). Because the perimeter of the part surface is a variable in the formula for calculating press tonnage, part size influences tonnage.

Work Metal. Each type of work metal has a different nominal drawing speed (see Table 11 on page 175 in the article "Deep Drawing" in this volume). Blanking and piercing generally can be done at any speed. The strength and thickness of the work metal are used to estimate press tonnage.

Production rate and quantity often affect the manner in which operations are combined in dies, the type of die used to make the part, or how complicated the die should be. Depending on part size and the adaptability of the part to a process, parts made at high production rate or in large quantity are produced in tools and equipment that minimize labor cost and utilize material efficiently. These tools and equipment have a high initial cost, but when amortized over total parts made, tool cost is a small fraction of the total cost.

On the other hand, when fewer parts are needed, less expensive tools and equipment are used. This usually results in a higher material and production cost, but the lower tool cost can be amortized over the fewer parts with an acceptable total cost.

The use of automated tooling and handling equipment also is governed by the production rate. This equipment has a major effect on the style of press and accessories selected and must be considered early in the analysis.

Example 604 in the article on Forming of Magnesium Alloys in this volume cites an increase in the production rate of a round cup by changing from three single-operation dies to one compound die, and from a hydraulic draw press to a high-speed mechanical press.

Type of Tooling

The operations necessary to make a part can be incorporated into a series of individual dies, a progressive die or a transfer die. Individual dies may be either single-operation or compound.

Press size and tonnage rating depend on the size of die and how much work it has to perform. The length of a progressive or transfer die is determined by the size of the part and the number of operations to be performed. The number of die stations is not necessarily the same as the number of basic operations, but depends on how these operations are combined and divided when the strip layout is designed. The layout should include the necessary idle stations to make a strong die, provide space for transfer from station to station and provide extra stations, if needed, to make the die function more smoothly. For a difficult part, it is good practice, if time permits, to make temporary dies to determine by trial how the part will form and how many stations are necessary.

The number of stations to be used in a progressive die or a transfer die should be carefully considered, particularly if one or two additional stations would make the die so long that the next-larger press would be required. If a larger press is not available, or if one cannot be purchased, the operations required to make the part must be combined into fewer die stations or the part must be made in more than one die. Also, the next larger press may operate at fewer strokes per minute than the smaller press. Lower production rate and increased part cost could result.

When operations are combined into fewer stations in a progressive or transfer die to accommodate a press bed, the quality of the work metal may require upgrading. Doing more work in a die station usually results in more severe forming than if the work were distributed over more stations.

Parts having a deeper draw at one end than at the other, and large panels of irregular shape, often can be tipped at an angle to the press bed to obtain a more favorable drawing or forming position, or to gain a better blankholding surface (see Example 458).

Small parts can be made two or more per stroke to utilize the press more efficiently. An air blast or gravity is used to unload the die. Larger parts that have a low production rate are loaded and unloaded manually, with some assistance from gravity. High-production parts of any size can be transferred by automatic loading and unloading mechanisms. Manually loaded presses usually are cycled intermittently by the operator. High-production presses are run continuously. When set up as a production line, the presses are synchronized so that all the presses and auxiliary equipment in the line operate as a unit.

Progressive and transfer dies with heavy die shoes, guide posts, bushings, and punch and die elements reduce die wear from vibration and distortion, and promote longer production between regrinding operations. A heavy, precisely built press is necessary to realize maximum production rate and die life.

Table 1. Press Specifications That Should Be Considered When Selecting a Press

Tonnage, inner and outer slides
Bed size, in.
Sizes of inner and outer slides, in.
Bolster size and thickness, in.
Stroke length, inner and outer slides, in.
Strokes per minute
Slide velocity at midstroke, ft per min
Shut height, inner and outer slides, in.(a)
Adjustment, inner and outer slides, in.(b)
Bed opening, in.
Length of cushion stroke, in.
Cushion capacity, tons at specified psi
Upright opening, in., and location above bed
Bed-to-floor height, in.
Need for shaft extensions(b)

(a) Stroke down, adjustment up. (b) Applicable to mechanical presses only.

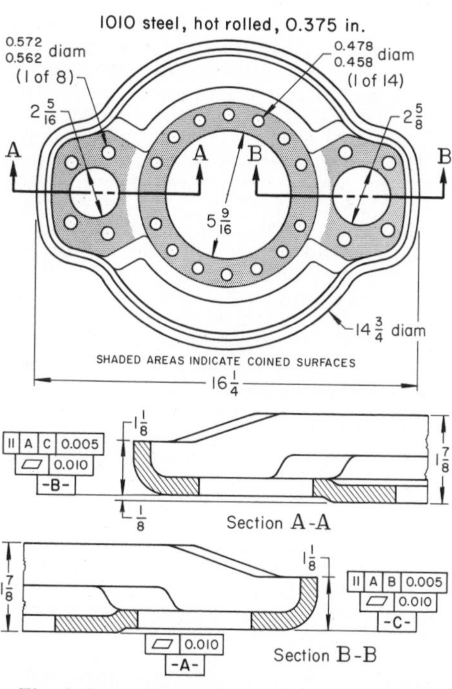

Fig. 1. Large torque plate of 0.375-in.-thick low-carbon steel that was formed in six operations in three different-size presses (Example 2)

A progressive-die strip layout in which the amount of work is unevenly distributed can cause an unbalanced force on the press slide. This condition can cause uneven wear on the gibs and punch breakage. To avoid an unbalanced force on the press slide, the strip can be redesigned to distribute the forces more evenly, or a dummy operation can be added on the scrap skeleton to balance the load.

Press features and dimensions that should be considered when selecting a press are listed in Table 1.

Ceiling and crane-rail heights in the building where the press is to be installed also can affect press selection. Another consideration is the crane capacity and headroom needed to install the new press. Safety of operator, and prevention of damage to tooling and press must always be considered.

Selection of a Mechanical Press

Mechanical presses are suitable for all forming operations, and also for blanking and piercing.

Tonnage Capacity. The force needed to do a given job depends on the strength and thickness of the work metal and on the perimeter of the surfaces to be worked. Forces required to do a given operation can be estimated by the formulas given in the articles in this volume that deal with the specific types of operations.

Mechanical presses develop their rated tonnage at a specific distance above the bottom of the stroke (see Table 2 on page 7, in the preceding article on Presses). Therefore, the point on the stroke at which work begins is important. Forming and drawing begin at a distance above the bottom of the stroke equal to or greater than the depth of draw. At this point the force exerted by the press is less than the rated tonnage, as illustrated by Fig. 8 on page 7, in the article on Presses.

Blanking and piercing are done near the bottom of the stroke, where press tonnage is maximum. Blanking in compound blank-and-form or blank-and-draw dies is done above the bottom of the stroke, where the tonnage is less than the full rating.

Restriking, coining and embossing operations are done at the bottom of the stroke and usually require more press tonnage than forming, because the metal is in compression. Operations using progressive dies require a combination of press tonnage and bed size, particularly left to right. Although some progressive dies are hand fed, most require auxiliary equipment such as stock feeders, scrap choppers, coil reels, and chutes to carry the finished parts to containers.

In a double-action press, the inner and outer slide capacities are stated separately; therefore, the forces required on the punch and the blankholder are calculated and applied separately. When a drawing or forming punch depresses a die cushion at the same time that the part is being formed, this force must be added to the drawing force to obtain the total force on the punch slide.

Single-action presses must have enough capacity to overcome the resistance of the stripping and blankholding force, as well as to provide the force required for the operation.

The following example illustrates several factors in press selection, including the distribution of work among six operations on presses of three different sizes.

Example 2. Use of Three Different-Size Mechanical Presses for Making a Torque Plate From 0.375-In.-Thick Steel (Fig. 1)

The torque plate shown in Fig. 1 was made of hot rolled 1010 steel 0.375 in. thick. This part, used in a brake for a heavy truck, was blanked, formed, pierced, and restruck (coined) in six separate operations, using three presses of different sizes, as follows:

1. The developed shape was blanked from a sheared strip in a 250-ton press at 300 pieces per hour.
2. Flanges and offsets were formed in a 1000-ton press at 300 pieces per hour.
3. The 5⁹⁄₁₆-in.-diam hole was pierced at 300 per hour in a 120-ton straight-side press.
4. Eight 0.562/0.572-in.-diam holes were pierced in a 120-ton press at 300 pieces per hour.
5. The 2⁵⁄₁₆ and 2⅝-in.-diam holes and the fourteen 0.458/0.478-in.-diam holes were pierced in a 250-ton press at 300 pieces per hour.
6. The part was restruck to flatten and coin in a 1000-ton press at 300 pieces per hour.

The above sequence of operations permitted the use of the strongest, least expensive dies, met the production requirements of 5000 to 10,000 pieces per month, and fully utilized the available presses. The work was distributed among the operations as indicated for the following reasons:

1 The same blank was used for several torque plates, and a compound blank-and-form die for one design was not practical.
2 The first forming operation required a large amount of force because of the 0.375-in. thickness of the stock.
3 Doing operations 3, 4 and 5 simultaneously would have required a press capacity of 500 to 600 tons.
4 A die for combining operations 3, 4 and 5 would have been expensive, because of the necessity for machining the dies for the smaller holes in the same piece of tool steel as the die for the large holes. This would have reduced the strength of the die sections and precluded the use of replaceable die buttons.

The presses were loaded and unloaded by hand. Dies were made of D2 tool steel, and no additional lubricant was needed for the hot rolled, pickled and oiled stock as-received.

Frame capacity, drive capacity, flywheel energy and motor size are involved in press capacity and are discussed in the preceding article on Presses.

Bed and Slide Size. The bed must be large enough to accommodate the intended die set without overhang, but not so large that the die covers less than two-thirds of the bed. The operator must be able to see the die easily and, when it is centered on the bed, to load and unload it without any unsafe movements or positions. When material-handling equipment is used, the distance the jaws must travel to load or unload the die should be as short as possible.

The planner must have an understanding of die design to estimate how much die space is necessary (see the section "Type of Tooling", page 19).

Length of stroke is the amount of press stroke necessary to form the part, plus an allowance for unloading the die. For single-stroke deep drawing operations the minimum stroke is usually 2½ to 3 times the depth of draw. For continuous operations, a stroke of at least four times the depth of draw is specified, to permit ample time for the loading and unloading equipment to function.

The ratio of stroke to part depth for blanking, piercing and shallow forming operations may be greater than the ratio for drawing operations, because of the time needed to feed stock and to eject the finished workpiece. A longer stroke is used for continuous operation of a press than for single-stroke operation, because feeding and unloading are done while the slide is in motion.

Most manufacturers have standard stroke lengths that simplify engineering and increase the interchangeability of dies.

Strokes per minute of a mechanical press depends on the revolutions per minute of the flywheel or mainshaft. In geared presses, the gear-reduction ratio also affects strokes per minute. The flywheel speed can be changed by changing sheaves or by a variable-speed drive. Because flywheel speed affects the amount of energy available to do work, the speed range for a specific flywheel is limited (see "Flywheel Energy", on pages 7 and 8 in the preceding article on Presses).

Slide Velocity. The length of stroke and the number of strokes per minute determine the velocity at which the punch slide travels. In a mechanical press, the slide has maximum velocity at midstroke and decreases to zero at the bottom of the stroke. The rate of decrease depends on the type of linkage between the main shaft and the slides.

The slide velocity v in feet per minute at any point on the stroke of a press with a crank or eccentric drive can be approximated by the formula:

$$v = 0.5233S\sqrt{dy - y^2}$$

where S is the maximum strokes per minute, d the full press stroke, in inches, and y the working stroke, in inches. The constant (0.5233) contains the necessary conversion factors.

Slide velocity is an important press characteristic in drawing and forming operations. For successful production, the recommended drawing speed for the work metal should not be exceeded at the point where the punch first contacts the workpiece. For example, if the drawing speed of a low-carbon steel part is 55 ft per min, with a working stroke of 3 in. and an 8-in. press stroke, using the above formula, the maximum number of strokes per minute would be 27. A 3-in. working stroke in a press with a 12-in. stroke would have a maximum of 20 strokes per minute. This is a reduction in strokes per minute of about 25%; however, productivity for the slower press may be greater than for the faster one, because the 12-in.-stroke press could operate continuously at 20 strokes per minute with automatic loading and unloading, whereas the press with an 8-in. stroke would be manually loaded and unloaded and cycled at a rate less than the maximum of 27 strokes per minute (see the section "Length of Stroke", on this page).

In blanking and piercing operations, punch speed is of little consequence; coining and embossing are done near zero velocity.

When using a long-stroke press to accommodate automatic material handling equipment, the slide velocity at the point of contact of punch and work metal may be too fast. Mechanisms to provide different slide motions can be built into the press. The slide velocity during the working stroke can be as required for the operation, but the approach and return portion of the stroke are accelerated to reduce cycle time.

In the following example, the speed at which an embossing punch struck the work metal was too great, resulting in punch loading and breakage. A 9% decrease in slide velocity increased tool life by a factor of six or more.

Example 3. Small Decrease in Press Speed That Increased Tool Life and Net Production Rate

Small rectangular steel workpieces 0.050 by 0.650 by 0.200 in. were embossed, shaved and trimmed in a progressive die mounted in a flywheel or nongeared press. When a flywheel speed of 165 rpm was used, only 7000 to 10,000 pieces were made before tool sharpening was required. Also, the embossing punches loaded up, requiring stoning of the sides, and breakage was high. Total die life was 750,000 pieces.

Reducing the flywheel speed from 165 to 150 rpm (or 150 strokes per minute, as the press was direct-drive) increased punch life between regrinds to 40,000 to 50,000 pieces or a total life of 3 million pieces. Although the reduction in speed decreased the number of parts that could be made per hour, the greater tool life and resulting decrease in downtime caused a net increase in productivity.

The die was made of A2 tool steel and hardened to Rockwell C 58 to 60.

Press Style. The principal factors involved in selecting the style of press are: frame type, number of slides and location of drive members.

Each of the two basic types of press frame (straight-side and gap-frame) has advantages and disadvantages (see the preceding article on Presses).

The size and shape of part and the feeding and unloading requirements affect the type of frame used. Gap-frame presses are single-action, can be equipped with a die cushion and generally have a maximum rating of 200 tons. Gap-frame presses have about the same stroke length as straight-side presses of equal tonnage capacity, but the shut height and over-all height (headroom) are usually less.

Inclined gap-frame presses, either fixed or adjustable, assist in gravity loading of blanks for second operations and in unloading of finished parts by having the bed tilted at an angle. The open sides offer no restriction to length of part, although part width or the distance between the edge of the part and the work area may be restricted by the dimensions of the press throat. Stops supported by bed extensions can be used to locate parts without causing difficulty in loading and unloading the die. Gap-frame presses should not be overloaded, because the frame deflects angularly, which causes misalignment of the punch and die.

Straight-side presses have tonnage ratings and a die area much larger than gap-frame presses. They are available with a die cushion in both the single-action type (one slide) and the double-action type (with a punch slide and a blankholder slide). Single-action presses operate faster than double-action presses and are more suitable for blanking, piercing, forming and shallow drawing operations. In a single-action press, because of the slide velocity near midstroke, the blankholder or the draw ring (if an inverted type of die is being used) may strike the work metal with considerable force and at a high velocity. This can slightly coin the work metal and break the blankholder from repeated impact.

Double-action presses are generally used for deep drawing operations. Because the blankholder slide operates separately from the punch slide, there is no shock as the blankholder touches the work metal. Tonnage on the outer slide is 75 to 100% of that on the inner slide and is not included in the press tonnage rating.

A triple-action press (one with three independent slides) is used when a motion opposite to that of the main slide is needed for operations such as forming, blanking or lancing. These operations usually are done while the punch slide is in motion and cannot be done satisfactorily with a die cushion. Blanking and lancing provide metal for drawing into restricted areas where fracture would otherwise occur. Forming can be done in a controlled manner not possible with a die cushion or a bottoming type of die.

Location of the drive members in the press crown or bed can be influenced by the available headroom. Large underdrive presses (over 400 tons) need open space below the floor level for the drive mechanism and for maintenance. Overdrive presses (those with the drive in the crown) frequently need a pit for the mechanism below the bed, but they extend above the floor further than an underdrive press of similar tonnage capacity. Some high-speed presses for progressive dies are of the floor-mounted underdrive type, but have a low tonnage rating.

Shut height requirement is determined by the height of the die in the closed position plus the thickness of the press bolster. Recent trends toward thicker die shoes and die blocks increase the over-all die height. Thus, older presses may have insufficient shut height, even with the adjustment up, to accommodate the new dies. The shut height of a mechanical press can be varied only by the amount the press slide can be adjusted.

When purchasing new presses with a short stroke and small shut height, the amount of slide adjustment may be increased to provide access for die repair. If dies can be repaired without removing them from the press, downtime will be reduced.

Except in gap-frame presses and some straight-side presses, shut height is engineered to user requirements. Press manufacturers have typical shut heights that serve as a guide.

Die Cushions. The tonnage capacity of a die cushion is one-sixth to one-half that of the press slide. The stroke of the cushion is about one-half the stroke of the press slide. Cushion requirements, as well as press type, are determined by part size and shape, material specifications, and the design of the dies.

For shallow draws in a single-action press, cushion force is used for clamping the blank to prevent wrinkling and control metal flow into the die. On the return stroke, its function is to strip the drawn part from the punch (see Fig. 9a on page 10 in this volume).

For deep drawing and forming of large, irregular shapes in double-action presses, the cushion supports the blank during forming and serves as a means of ejecting the part from the die.

Miscellaneous Features. Coil stock frequently is fed to dies through openings in uprights or columns of the press. The width, height and distance of the openings above the bed may restrict stock width and the use of feeding equipment. Sometimes the scrap skeleton is pulled through the opening and cut into pieces by a scrap cutter on the outside of the press. Finished parts are ejected at the front or back of the press or through the column openings.

Machined pads on the press frame for mounting feeding devices, shaft extensions for power takeoff arms, rotary control cams, and knockout bars can affect the type of auxiliary equipment and die design.

The height of the press bed above the floor may restrict the use of floor-mounted loading and unloading devices or may make it difficult for operators to load and unload the die.

Blank feeders or part ejectors or unloaders are used where safety or production requirements dictate. Some loaders and unloaders can be readily adapted to parts of similar size and shape; thus, production rate can be increased as well as safety to the operator, press, die and part.

When purchasing new presses, consideration should be given to devices and accessories that add to the versatility and efficiency of the equipment. These include:

1. Die-change slides for small presses and moving bolsters for large presses, which reduce setup time by providing a means of presetting the die and then quickly moving it into the press. Hydraulic clamping adapters in the upper slides of large presses permit quick clamping of the dies.
2. Overload devices that protect the press and die against damage due to misfeed or double blanks.
3. Tonnage indicators that show how much force is being used for a given operation, and thus help to prevent overloading the press.
4. Machined pads that make it easier to mount loading and unloading devices to the press frame.
5. Shut-height indicators calibrated in thousandths of an inch, which reduce setup time by providing a positive dimension for resetting the die in the press.
6. Lighting fixtures, mounted within press uprights, to provide extra safety and operator convenience by illuminating the die area.
7. Knockout equipment that has adjustable rods or is cam-actuated for removing finished parts from the upper die.
8. Electrical outlets that are conveniently located on the press frame for operation of accessory devices or power tools used by setup men.
9. Receptacles for plug-in air-operated devices in the die or feeding equipment, to provide a quick means for attaching these devices.
10. Rotary cam arrangements powered by the main shaft, to cycle feeding, ejecting and other mechanisms that require sequence control.

Selection of a Hydraulic Press

Table 1 gives specifications that should be considered in the selection of hydraulic presses.

Hydraulic presses are not used extensively for forming sheet metal, because of high initial and maintenance costs and difficulties in relocating in a press line. Also, cycle time for a hydraulic press is greater than for a comparable mechanical press.

Hydraulic presses, however, are particularly suited for making deep and intricate draws in all types of sheet metal. Although blanking can be done in the press, precut blanks are preferred for better control of the drawing operation and to avoid damaging the hydraulic system as the punch breaks through the metal.

Metal flow is well controlled, because both the force on the slide and the velocity of the slide are constant throughout the working stroke. These features are an advantage when cupping and reverse redrawing in the same press stroke. The amount of impact between the work metal and the blankholder or punch is minimized, because the press ram is slowed automatically before die contact and then does its work at whatever speed and force are needed to produce the best results. This permits the use of a small punch nose radius, thereby eliminating the need for a restriking or sizing operation.

In addition to deep drawing and redrawing, operations such as nosing, coining and embossing are commonly performed in a hydraulic press. The final steady squeeze of the hydraulic press produces the metal-setting action necessary for satisfactory coining and embossing.

In hydraulic presses, the moving member that carries the punch is called a platen or slide. It is guided by gibs in the press frame. The ram is the connection between the slide and the cylinder. Sometimes a slide is not used and the tool is attached directly to the ram.

Tonnage capacity for a hydraulic press usually is stated as the sum of the tonnage capacity of all the rams. Normally, maximum blankholder-slide tonnage is one-third the maximum tonnage of the main press slide. The blankholder force sometimes opposes the force exerted by the main press slide, thus reducing the available force on the main slide by the force on the blankholder slide. However, in some presses half the blankholder force can be counterbalanced and retained for useful drawing work. If, as in some hydraulic presses, the blankholder cylinder is mounted to the crown, the blankholding force does not oppose the main slide force. (See Fig. 2 in the article on Presses, page 3.)

The force on the slides can be readily and accurately adjusted from maximum to 10% of maximum. Thus, the actual force needed to do a job is used and the work metal is never overloaded. Also, the same force is applied to each workpiece, regardless of variation in stock thickness.

Pressure in the main cylinder overcomes the resistance of the forming operation, and the ram continues to advance until a predetermined pressure or ram position is attained. Pressure increase is smooth; the rate of increase depends on pump displacement rate and the resistance encountered. Once the pressure for forming has been developed it is maintained for the entire stroke. If the metal is not being formed properly, the resistance will increase the pressure in the cylinder to the predetermined amount and reverse the motion of the slide.

The slide has a fast traverse rate for advancing to the workpiece and returning to the top of the stroke after the operation is finished. This feature helps to reduce the press cycle time.

Bed and Slide Size. The criteria for selecting the bed size of a hydraulic press are the same as for a mechanical press. The bed must be large enough to accommodate the die and any attachments, but not so large that the die is difficult to see or to load and unload.

Strokes per Minute. The number of strokes per minute for a hydraulic press is not a fixed value, because the stroke length and slide velocity can be changed for each setup. The actual value is also affected by the length of the working stroke and the fast approach.

Stroke length in a hydraulic press depends on the length of the hydraulic cylinder. The length of stroke used for any one setup can be varied between the maximum and minimum positions.

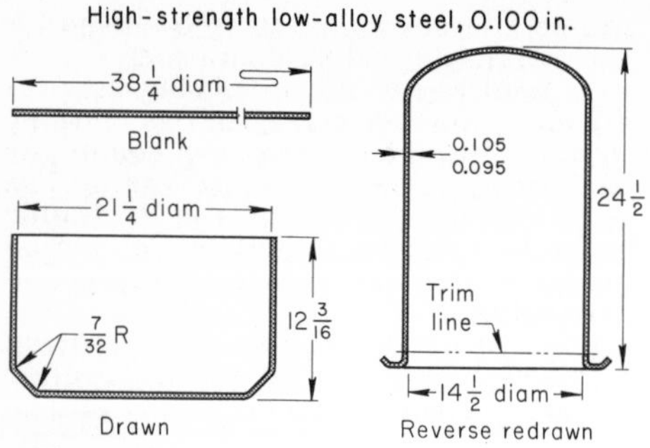

Fig. 2. Steps in deep drawing a shell in one stroke of a hydraulic press (Example 4)

The bottom of stroke is set by slowly lowering the slide with the die in place. The controls on the variable-displacement pump are set so that, when a given pressure is attained, delivery ceases and the ram is reversed. Controls also can be set to reverse the ram when a positive position is reached. The upper limits of the stroke are set so that the workpiece can be removed from the die either by an operator or by automatic unloading equipment. The stroke length is thereby set to suit the workpiece.

Shut height between the slide and bed on a hydraulic press can be varied from the minimum to any practical maximum by reducing the stroke length. Because the stroke length is not fixed there is no need for slide adjustment as in a mechanical press.

Slide velocity during the working stroke of a hydraulic press can be adjusted according to the needs of the work metal and the shape being drawn. Both the main slide and the blankholder slide can advance rapidly to the working position and then, without shock or jerky motion, can shift quickly into a slower speed and a high working pressure. The speed of the slide during the working stroke is constant, but can be easily and accurately adjusted from maximum to 10% of maximum and is rated in inches per minute at maximum velocity.

In the following example, the constant slide velocity and the ability to adjust the slide forces to meet the need eliminated one press operation and an intermediate anneal when deep drawing a pressure vessel. Drawing a similar vessel in two press operations is described in Example 264 in the article on Deep Drawing in this volume.

Example 4. Use of a Hydraulic Press in Deep Drawing a Pressure Vessel (Fig. 2)

The shell shown in Fig. 2 was cupped and reverse redrawn in one stroke of a double-action hydraulic press with a die cushion. Making the shell in one press stroke eliminated a redrawing operation and an intermediate anneal. The combination of reverse redrawing, steady pressure and steady drawing speed enabled the bottom and sidewalls to be held to a thickness of 0.095 to 0.105 in.

The 750-ton hydraulic press had a 60-by-60-in. bed, 135-in. shut height and a maximum stroke of 84 in. Forces used were: 450 to 500 tons on the main slide, 125 to 150 tons on the blankholder slide, and 75 to 100 tons on the die cushion.

A cup 21¼ in. in diameter and 12$\frac{3}{16}$ in. deep was drawn during the first part of the press stroke. As the ram continued to descend, the cup was reverse redrawn over a stationary punch into a shell 14½ in. in diameter and 24½ in. deep with a dome-shape bottom and a flange around the open end. The cupping punch had a 45° bevel instead of a full corner radius. The size of the bevel, blending radii, and die radii for cupping and reverse redrawing were carefully developed so that blanks of various thicknesses from 0.050 to 0.110 in. could be drawn in the same die.

The draw ring, the hollow punch that served as the cupping punch and redrawing die, the pressure ring and the stationary punch had inserts of D2 tool steel. (For illustration of the tooling and press action, see Fig. 38 on page 179 in the article on Deep Drawing.) More than 100,000 parts were made in the dies with no measurable wear.

Various lubricants were tried. Sodium stearate, applied wet in a thin film and then dried, best withstood the pressures and temperatures of the process.

Frame Type. Hydraulic presses are available with gap-frame, straight-side or column construction.

High-speed, gap-frame hydraulic presses are available in the range of 2 to 200 tons. They can be run continuously with automatic stock feeders to perform any sheet forming operation.

The straight-side and column-type presses are either single-action or double-action, and usually have a die cushion. In a double-action press, the blankholder slide can be locked, thus making a single-action press. The die cushion can easily be made inoperative when a blankholder or ejector is not needed, thus increasing the versatility of the hydraulic press.

Number of slides in a hydraulic press is usually one or two, with a die cushion in the bed. However, it is relatively easy to design and build more slides in the crown, in the bed, or from any or all of the four sides. In the following example, 12 rams were used in making a large box-shape part.

Example 5. Forming a Large Box-Shape Part in a 3600-Ton Hydraulic Press (Fig. 3)

The part shown in Fig. 3 was formed, embossed and bent in one cycle of a 3600-ton hydraulic press that had twelve rams and a hydraulic liftout. There were seven rams in the crown and five in the bed: the rams in the crown were controlled by three valves, and the rams in the bed by two valves. The press was cycled manually, because production was not great enough to justify the cost of sequence valves.

By having individually actuated forming punches for the top, sides and ends, the box was bent to shape after forming, in the same press. Standard time for the operation was 3.75 min, of which 2.10 min was actual press time. The remaining 1.65 min was used for loading the blank, and for unloading the formed part and placing it in a fixture for transfer to the welding department.

The controlled pressure in each ram enabled the proper amount of force to be applied to each punch, regardless of the variation in stock thickness.

The blank was pierced and notched from 84$\frac{13}{16}$ in. wide by 119$\frac{11}{16}$ in. long by 0.105 in. thick commercial quality, hot rolled 1010 steel, pickled and oiled, by one stroke of a 750-ton mechanical press using a separate die for each end. The blank width was near the maximum obtainable in one piece.

Forming was done in the following sequence of operations:

1. The blank was loaded into the press using the bend relief notches near each corner as locating points. The hydraulic liftout prevented the blank from sagging at the center.
2. With the four lower corner rams locked in their down positions and the lower center ram in its up position, the seven upper rams descended to form the flat blank. (One center ram formed the semicircular top, two side rams embossed the sides, and four corner rams embossed one-half of each end.)
3. When pressure on the upper corner rams reached 2500 psi, the upper corner rams were raised.
4. The lower corner rams were raised, bending one-half of each end around the side punches.
5. The side rams were raised and both the upper and lower center rams were lowered, bending the sides around the center punch.
6. All rams were returned to open position and the formed part was unloaded.

The hydraulic lifter raised the part so it could be removed more easily.

In step 2, cam-actuated forming bars bent the 1-by-¾-in. U-shape flange around the bottom.

The joints where the end halves met and where the ends met the top were arc welded, both inside and outside, forming an airtight, watertight box. The welds were ground smooth; then the completely formed workpiece was hot dip galvanized with 3 to 5 oz of zinc per square foot.

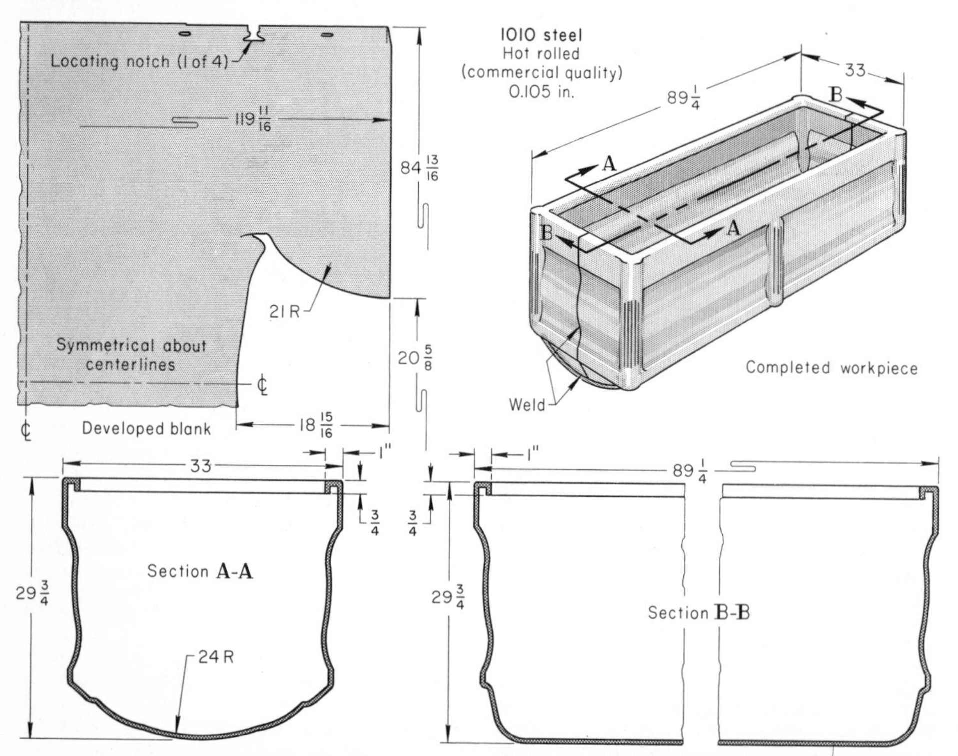

Fig. 3. Large part formed in one cycle of a hydraulic press having 12 rams (Example 5)

The upper center ram had a 1000-ton capacity and 48-in. travel. Each side ram had an 800-ton capacity and 42-in. travel. The capacity of each corner ram was 250 tons, with 42-in. travel. Minimum shut height was 120 in. Each of the five lower rams had a 6-in. stroke. The press had six 12-in.-diam columns. The centerline area defined by the four corner columns was 124 by 111.25 in. The hydraulic pumps were powered by a 100-hp and a 50-hp electric motor. No lubricant other than the residual oil on the blank was used.

If the part had been made by deep drawing, a larger blank would have been needed for blankholding purposes. Unless welded from two pieces, a wider blank would have been difficult to obtain. Also, secondary operations would have been necessary to emboss the sides and ends.

Making the part in a mechanical press would have required a minimum of three forming operations with intermediate handling. Forming the contour of the sides and ends and the six fluted columns would not have been uniform, because of variations in stock thickness. However, for less ornate parts, a mechanical press was used for forming three pieces that were subsequently welded together into a box.

Die cushions are furnished in capacities up to one-third the maximum tonnage of the main ram. The stroke of the die cushion is one-half the main slide travel and can be delayed both at the beginning and end of the working stroke of the main slide. A delay at the end of the stroke permits the punch and blankholder to withdraw before the part is ejected from the die.

The bottom of an irregular part can be formed or embossments made in the bottom of a shell before the side walls are formed, by locking the die bottom in the up position with the die cushion.

Selection and Use of Lubricants in Forming of Sheet Metal

LUBRICATION is of two main types: fluid (hydrodynamic) and boundary. (Extreme-pressure lubrication is a special type of boundary lubrication.) These types are illustrated schematically in Fig. 1.

Fluid lubrication is typified by metal surfaces separated by a continuous film of lubricant having a thickness considerably greater than the height of the surface asperities of the metal (Fig. 1a). This type of lubrication, common in bearing systems, is seldom observed in sheet-metal forming.

Boundary lubrication is typified by metal surfaces separated by a lubricant film only a few molecules thick, with considerable metal-to-metal contact between asperities of the two surfaces (Fig. 1b). In most metal-forming operations, because of the high pressures and low speeds involved, lubrication is of the boundary type.

Nonpolar lubricants (such as mineral oils) that are used for fluid lubrication have insufficient adherence to metal surfaces for effective boundary lubrication. For this reason, polar lubricants, such as fatty oils, fatty acids, soaps and waxes, are used as lubricants in sheet-metal forming. The main function of a boundary lubricant in press forming is to interpose between the work metal and the tools a film that minimizes metallic contact and that is itself easily sheared. In deep drawing, this film also is of major importance in controlling friction of the work metal against the drawing die and the blankholder or pressure ring.

The molecules of polar substances in boundary lubricants have long carbon chains with one or more chemically active (polar) groups at one end. The polar groups adhere strongly to the work metal and the tool metal, causing the long carbon chain to be oriented at approximately a right angle to the metal surfaces. These oriented films of polar substances (sometimes called oiliness agents), which are several molecules thick, minimize metal-to-metal contact and friction. They also retard the plastic flow of asperities and thus minimize galling or welding.

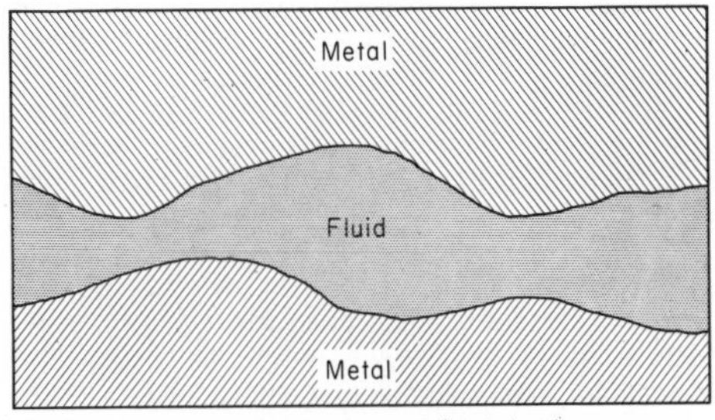

(a) Fluid (hydrodynamic) lubrication

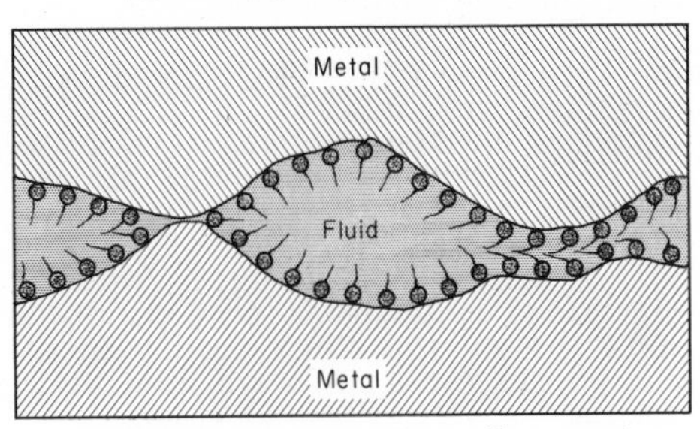

(b) Boundary lubrication with an oiliness agent

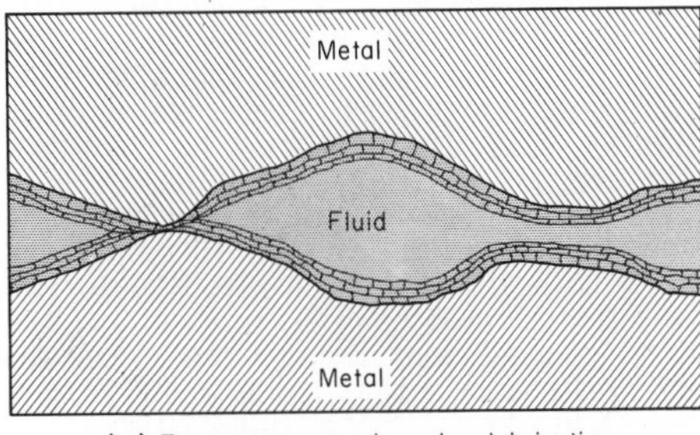

(c) Extreme-pressure boundary lubrication with a pigment (mechanical EP agent)

Fig. 1. Schematic representation of the types of lubrication

The classification of lubricants according to severity of press operations, as presented in this article, was developed by the editorial staff of this Handbook from an analysis of examples in this volume and from severity relations tabulated in the articles that begin on pages 319 and 330 in Volume 1 of this Handbook.

Much of the information on characteristics and compositions of lubricants, as well as on their suitability for press forming of steel, was supplied by Leon Salz, of Fiske Brothers Refining Co., Newark, N. J. Other sources of information concerning lubricants are cited in the list of references at the end of this article.

Extreme-Pressure (EP) Lubrication. Substances that have boundary-lubrication properties in an optimum combination are called extreme-pressure (EP) lubricants. One type contains finely divided inorganic solids (pigments, or mechanical EP agents) that physically separate workpieces from the tools. The use of extreme-pressure boundary lubrication with a pigment is illustrated in Fig. 1(c). When subjected to sufficiently high pressure, the layer of solid particles can be squeezed out from between some of the asperities, permitting metallic contact at those points (as at the left in Fig. 1c). To avoid metal-to-metal contact at asperities where particles of pigment can be squeezed out in forming, phosphate coatings are sometimes applied to the work metal. Besides providing an integrally bonded solid barrier layer, the porous phosphate coating improves the retention of the lubricant.

A second type of EP lubricant contains chemical EP agents. These are chlorinated, sulfurized or phosphated organic materials that react with the metal surface to form firmly bonded chemical compounds of chlorine, sulfur or phosphorus. Lubrication with chemical EP agents can be represented in a form similar to that shown in Fig. 1(b) but with denser packing of the boundary-film molecules.

Components of Lubricants

A lubricant for use in press forming operations may contain:

1 Vehicles or diluents
2 Oiliness agents
3 Pigments (mechanical EP agents)
4 Chemical EP agents
5 Emulsifiers
6 Special-purpose additives.

Vehicles or diluents usually are low-cost materials, such as water or mineral oil, that act as carriers or extenders for the more costly friction-reducing and antigalling components of a lubricant. They also help to dissipate the heat generated in forming; in some applications, this is their most important function. Water is the most effective coolant in common use, being about twice as effective in the removal of heat as mineral oil.

One of the main technical advantages of mineral oil as a vehicle for lubricants is that it is available in a number of viscosity ranges and chemical types. This permits selection of the most suitable grade for a particular forming application.

Oiliness agents are polar organic materials such as fatty oils, fatty acids, soaps, waxes and certain synthetic oils. These polar materials provide boundary lubrication.

Fatty oils include liquid oils and oils that are solid at room temperature. (Solid oils are also called fats.) The fatty oils commonly used include lard oil, castor oil, palm oil, and tallow.

The grades of fatty oils used in lubricants for press operations contain free fatty acids as an impurity, usually in amounts of 2 to 5%, but sometimes as much as 15%. In these amounts, fatty acids slightly increase the lubricating effectiveness of the oil, but when present in amounts of 10% or more, they also slightly increase the rusting of steel workpieces.

Fatty acids are sometimes added to lubricants for press forming of steel, particularly to those based on mineral or fatty oils, or to sulfochlorinated oil blends.

Saturated fatty acids such as stearic and palmitic acids, which are less likely to form varnishlike residues on severely formed parts, are preferred to unsaturated acids such as oleic acid. A free acid content greater than about 5% often results in the formation of a residue of iron soaps that are difficult to remove if allowed to remain on the workpiece for two or three days after application.

Most soaps used in lubricants (usually the fatty acid soaps of sodium or potassium) are soluble in water.

Wax may be a natural type such as beeswax or carnauba wax, or a petroleum derivative, and may be chemically modified to make it emulsifiable.

Synthetic oils, such as polyalkylene glycols and similar compounds, are expensive, but usually are more stable than natural oils at high temperature and are selected for the physical properties desired.

The response of a polar substance to changes in temperature is important in lubrication, not only with regard to suitability for warm or hot forming, but also because forming pressures increase the temperature of the metal surface and the lubricating film. The effectiveness of a polar substance in a boundary lubricant decreases sharply above its melting point, at which temperature the film loses its orientation. As the temperature is increased still further, the effectiveness continues to decrease, until the film is completely desorbed. An effective boundary-lubricant film should have: (*a*) a high melting point, (*b*) strong lateral attraction between molecular chains, (*c*) low shear strength at forming pressures, and (*d*) strong polarity.

Pressure also influences the behavior of lubricants in metal forming. Provided that temperature does not become excessive, liquid lubricants undergo a great increase in viscosity at the high pressures existing at regions of metal-to-metal contact in severe forming, whereas solid lubricants increase greatly in shear strength. These phenomena may explain why mineral oil and some pigmented lubricants provide more effective lubrication in press forming than would be expected from their properties at atmospheric pressure.

Pigments (mechanical EP agents) are chemically inactive solids that physically separate the work metal from the tool surfaces and prevent welding under conditions of extreme pressure. The most widely used of these pigments, or "spacing agents", are chalk, zinc oxide, lithopone, mica, talc, graphite, and molybdenum disulfide. Chalk, zinc oxide, and lithopone are the most commonly used of a number of inexpensive light-colored pigments that are readily available in a finely divided and relatively nonscratching form. Mica, talc, graphite, and molybdenum disulfide have a weak lamellar, or platelike, structure that allows the particles to slide readily over one another.

Pigments may be suspended in either water-base or oil-base diluents. Graphite and molybdenum disulfide are the most suitable pigments for high-temperature forming operations.

In deep drawing, the pigment is compacted by pressure between one side of the work metal and the die, and between the other side of the work metal and the blankholder or pressure ring. In addition to minimizing metal-to-metal contact, the compacted pigment equalizes the pressure exerted by the die and the pressure ring on the work metal. This equalization of pressure over the confined area of the work metal hinders preferential movement of metal in some regions and prevents or minimizes wrinkling.

Chemical EP agents react with the metal surface to form a solid film that is firmly bonded with the metal and that resists welding of the work metal to the punch or die under extreme pressure. The active element usually is sulfur or chlorine. To a lesser extent, phosphorus compounds are used as EP agents.

The most commonly used chemical EP agents are concentrated chlorinated oils and sulfurized oils. The former are chlorinated mineral oils, paraffin oils, fatty oils, or waxes. They are usually liquids, may differ greatly in viscosity, and contain 30 to 50% chlorine.

Sulfurized oils are made by chemically reacting either mineral oil or a fatty oil with sulfur at an elevated temperature. Sulfurized mineral oils, which are light-colored and transparent, contain an approximate maximum of 1.5% sulfur. Sulfurized fatty oils, which are dark brown in color, contain about 12% sulfur ("inactive" grades of oil) or about 16% sulfur ("active" grades). Elemental sulfur ("flowers of sulfur") can be suspended in oils or in water, but it is too corrosive for use in most press operations on steel. To minimize or prevent chemical attack on the work metal and on dies (particularly, dies made from ordinary grades of hardened steel), inactive grades of sulfurized fatty oil are preferred.

Sulfurized and chlorinated oils can be blended to make what are called sulfochlorinated oils. These blends are also used as chemical EP agents.

Chlorinated and sulfurized oils react with steel workpieces to form boundary films of iron chlorides and iron sulfides, respectively. The rate of formation of these boundary films depends on the local temperature, the chemical activity of the metal surface, and the tightness of bonding of chlorine or sulfur in the lubricant molecules. During the forming of metal, the boundary film is reformed almost instantaneously where it is broken, because the sites of damage to the film are also regions where the temperature rises and where a fresh, active metal surface becomes exposed.

The compounds formed by the reaction of chemical EP agents with steel retain their effectiveness as boundary lubricants up to temperatures approaching their melting points (iron chlorides, to about 1100 F; iron sulfides, to about 1800 F), as contrasted with fatty acid soaps, which lose most of their effectiveness above about 210 F.

Emulsifiers are chemicals (such as soaps, organic sulfonates, esters of fatty acids, polyoxyethylene acids, and alcohols) that modify mineral oils, fatty oils and waxes to permit them to form a stable emulsion readily in water. The modified materials are called soluble oils or emulsifiable oils or waxes. A combination of soaps and sulfonates or other emulsifiers is used for rapid dispersion in water, rust resistance, and stability in hard water.

Special-purpose additives are included in lubricants in low concentrations to modify either the chemical or the physical properties of the lubricant. Depending on the type of lubricant and on work-handling procedures, a die lubricant may contain corrosion inhibitors, antifoaming agents or antimicrobial agents.

Corrosion inhibitors may be needed in water-base lubricants to prevent corrosion of work metal and die surfaces, lubricating equipment, and storage containers for lubricants. They are not intended to provide long-term protection of the work metal, but rather to permit the storage of lubricated workpieces for periods ranging from several hours to several weeks without significant damage.

Emulsifiers such as mineral oil sulfonates form sodium salts that function as corrosion inhibitors in emulsions, and sodium or potassium soaps are effective in protecting against corrosion. Sodium nitrite or an organic amine may be used as a corrosion inhibitor in such water-base lubricants as emulsions and diluted soap-fat pastes.

Corrosion inhibitors are not generally used in oil-base lubricants, except to reduce the corrosiveness of concentrated chlorinated oils or blends of chlorinated oils.

Antifoaming agents are sometimes used to prevent excessive buildup of stable foam in water-base lubricants that contain soaps. Soluble-oil emulsions, which ordinarily are the only lubricants used in recirculating systems, present no foaming problem.

Antimicrobial agents (bactericides and fungicides) are used more frequently in water-base than in oil-base lubricants. They prevent the growth of bacteria and fungi, and thus inhibit the production of insoluble matter, frothing, discoloration, odor formation, corrosion and demulsification. Substances commonly used as antimicrobial agents include tarry acids, chlorine-containing compounds, and certain alcohols.

Selection Factors

Table 1 summarizes the characteristics of water-base and oil-base lubricants used on low-carbon sheet steel in the common press forming operations. The formulations shown may be modified by the addition of other lubricants or of component materials. For example, low percentages of chemical EP agents are sometimes added to the water-base or oil-base lubricants that are used in low-severity forming. Also, fatty additives may be introduced into EP lubricants, and occasionally are applied over dry soap or wax films at points of exceptionally severe deformation. The reason for balancing formulations or using more than one lubricant is that polar agents are more effective than EP agents in reducing friction, whereas EP agents are much more effective in producing and maintaining a boundary film between work metal and tools under conditions of severe deformation.

Viscosity has an important influence on the effectiveness and suitability of a lubricant for a specific operation. In general, lubricants of high viscosity are used on thick work metal and for severe deformation of the work metal, and lubricants of low viscosity are used on thin work metal and for mild deformation. Lubricants of a given chemical type are generally available in a range of viscosities, or the viscosity can be modified by blending two or more lubricant materials.

In deep drawing, the adjustment of lubricant viscosity to help obtain an optimum amount of friction between the blank and the restraining surfaces of the die and the blankholder may be as important as the chemical composition of the lubricant.

Viscosity must also be considered in relation to the method of lubricant application, and (together with tackiness or the presence of pigments) in terms of effects on the handling of blanks and formed parts — particularly in automated operations.

Method of Application. When selected in a suitable viscosity range, most lubricants can be applied by spray, roller, drip feed, dip, flood, swab or brush. Pigmented lubricants cannot be sprayed, and are difficult to apply by any method except brushing. Dry soap or wax films are almost always produced by dipping the workpiece in a hot aqueous solution. Recirculation and flooding are seldom used in press operations on sheet metal; these methods are useful primarily for applying soluble oils in high-speed operations on small parts.

Toxicity, Flammability, Odor and Stability. Toxicity and skin-irritation effects should be checked before introducing a lubricant with which the user has no experience. Forced ventilation and other safety precautions may be needed in using lubricants that contain flammable or volatile substances. Some lubricants have objectionable odors.

Fatty oils (including fats) can become rancid on standing, producing foul odors, acidity and gummy deposits.

Table 1. Lubricants Commonly Used in the Press Forming of Low-Carbon Sheet Steel(a)

Type or composition of lubricant	Ease of removal by: Water-base cleaners	Degreasers or solvents	Protection against rusting
Water-Base Lubricants			
Low-Severity Press Operations			
1 Water emulsion of 5 to 20% general-purpose soluble oil or wax	Very good	Good	Fair
Moderate-Severity Press Operations			
2 Water solution of 5 to 20% soap	Very good	Very poor	Fair
3 Water emulsion of heavy-duty soluble oil (contains sulfurized or chlorinated additives)	Very good	Good	Fair
High-Severity Press Operations			
4 Soap-fat paste, diluted with water (may contain wax)	Fair	Poor	Fair
5 Water emulsion of heavy-duty soluble oil (contains a high concentration of sulfurized or chlorinated additives)	Very good	Good	Fair to poor
Maximum-Severity Press Operations			
6 Pigmented soap-fat paste, diluted with water	Poor	Very poor	Good
7 Dry soap or wax (applied from water solution or dispersion); may contain soluble filler such as borax	Good	Very poor	Good
Oil-Base Lubricants			
Low-Severity Press Operations			
8 Mill oil, residual (usually about 100 SUS at 100 F)	Good	Very good	Fair
9 Mineral oil (40 to 300 SUS at 100 F)	Good	Very good	Fair
10 Vanishing oil	Removal not required		...
Moderate-Severity Press Operations			
11 Mineral oil (100 to 300 SUS at 100 F) plus 10 to 30% fatty oil	Good	Very good	Fair
12 Mineral oil plus 2 to 20% sulfurized or chlorinated oil (EP oil)	Good to fair	Good	Fair to poor
High-Severity Press Operations			
13 Fatty oil	Fair	Fair	Fair
14 Mineral oil (100 to 300 SUS at 100 F) plus 5 to 50% of:			
(a) Nonemulsifiable chlorinated oil	Poor	Good	Very poor
(b) Emulsifiable chlorinated oil	Good	Good	Very poor
15 Concentrated phosphated oil	Fair	Fair	Fair
Maximum-Severity Press Operations			
16 Blend of pigmented soap-fat paste with mineral oil	Poor	Poor	Fair
17 Concentrated sulfochlorinated oil (may contain some fatty oil):			
(a) Nonemulsifiable	Very poor	Fair	Poor
(b) Emulsifiable	Good	Fair	Poor
18 Concentrated chlorinated oil:			
(a) Nonemulsifiable	Very poor	Fair	Very poor
(b) Emulsifiable	Good	Fair	Very poor

(a) See text for discussion and for explanation of severity classifications.

Water-base lubricants are susceptible to the growth of bacteria and fungi.

Deterioration is much less troublesome with lubricants for press forming than with the cutting fluids used in machining, because the interval between application and removal of forming lubricants is ordinarily only a few hours to a few weeks. It can be a serious problem in recirculating lubricant systems, but these are used in only a small fraction of press forming applications. Lubricants containing suitable stabilizers and other additives are used in these applications, and the lubricant is changed and the system cleaned thoroughly at regular intervals.

Cost and Final Selection. In general, the cost of lubricants increases with the order of listing in each half of Table 1, or with ability to lubricate effectively under conditions of severe deformation. However, the cost of the lubricant itself is often small in comparison with the effect of lubricant selection on over-all manufacturing cost and capability.

The choice between oil-base and water-base lubricants, and the final selection of one lubricant composition for a given forming application may require consideration of the effect of lubrication on the manufacturing sequence as a whole. Factors to be considered include the condition of the workpiece before forming, the condition required after forming, storage time and environment at various stages of processing, and the type of equipment available for applying and removing the lubricant and for handling the workpiece before, during and after forming.

Sometimes it is necessary to use different lubricants in successive press operations on a single workpiece, as in the application described in the following example from the article on Deep Drawing, in this volume:

Example 265. Multiple-operation drawing and ironing of a shell 8 in. in inside diameter by 62 in. deep from low-carbon steel blanks 0.220 in. thick, with the following lubrication steps:

1 Lubricate with sulfur-containing oil before cold drawing the flat blank to a cup 20 in. in diameter by 15 in. deep in a 1500-ton press.

2 Apply oil plus graphite for hot redrawing in three stages to a shell 8¼ in. in diameter by 29 in. deep in 500-ton presses.

3 Pickle and apply a dry soap film before cold redrawing and ironing to a shell 8$\frac{1}{16}$ in. in diameter by 45 in. deep in a 500-ton press.
4 Pickle and apply a dry soap film before cold redrawing and ironing to a shell 8 in. in diameter by 62 in. deep in a 500-ton press.

Final selection of a lubricant for a specific application is done largely by full-scale trial.

Laboratory tests to assess lubricant performance may sometimes be misleading, but are used in some plants and are of value at least for screening purposes. One technique that has been used is the Parkinson cup test (see E. L. H. Bastian, "Metalworking Lubricants", McGraw-Hill, 1951).

Lubricant stability can be observed readily by prolonged exposure of the lubricant, and corrosion behavior can be assessed by exposure of lubricant-coated test panels under shop conditions or in a humidity chamber.

Severity Classification

The primary factor to be considered in selecting a lubricant is the severity of the press operation, because the forces at the region of contact between work metal and tools are the primary cause of galling or welding, and hence of damage to the workpiece and wear of the tools.

In Table 1, lubricants are arranged according to their suitability for press operations of four categories of severity: low, moderate, high and maximum.

In the four sections of this article that follow, the four severity categories are described in terms of typical blanking, piercing, bending, forming, drawing and deep drawing operations. Types of lubricants suitable for operations of each severity category are given in Table 1, along with ratings of removability and corrosion behavior, and are discussed in the sections that follow. In general, a lubricant can also be used for press forming operations of lower severity than the operations for which it is shown in the table.

Water-base lubricants (No. 1 to 7) are listed in the top half of Table 1, and oil-base lubricants (No. 8 to 18) are listed in the bottom half. In each half of the table, the lubricants are shown in order of increasing suitability for severe press operations, but differences in effectiveness within a severity group are generally small and may vary with the concentration of the active components.

Selection within each of the four severity groups, as discussed in the following sections, often depends primarily on the removability of the lubricant and the protection it provides against rusting or its corrosiveness to steel (see Table 1). Selection also is influenced by the other factors discussed above (viscosity, facilities for application, toxicity, flammability, odor, stability, cost, and effect on other steps in the manufacturing sequence).

Lubricants for Press Operations of Low Severity

Low-severity operations are defined here as those of severity approximately equal to the following, on low-carbon commercial quality sheet steel:

Blanking and piercing of sheet 0.105 in. thick with a punch-to-die clearance of 10% of sheet thickness
Bending 90° around a radius equal to the sheet thickness (t), with a flange width of $25t$ or greater
Forming with maximum localized stretch of 10% in a 1-in. length
Drawing a cup with 10% reduction in diameter.

For such operations, the following four lubricants (numbered as in Table 1) are commonly used:

1 Water emulsion of 5 to 20% general-purpose soluble oil or wax
8 Residual mill oil (usually about 100 SUS at 100 F)
9 Mineral oil (40 to 300 SUS at 100 F)
10 Vanishing oil.

These lubricants are essentially nonpolar in their lubricating behavior. None of them presents any problem in removability or corrosion behavior, as shown by the ratings in the last three columns of Table 1.

Water Emulsion (Lubricant 1). Because of their excellent cooling characteristics, water-base emulsions are well suited for high-speed press operations when applied to work metal and dies by flooding in a recirculating system. They are applied also by drip-feed and spray methods, and are used for a wide variety of operations, including the forming of large parts. The versatility of these emulsions is illustrated by five examples that are presented in this volume:

Example 151. Forming a large, shallow rectangular pan from 0.075-in.-thick sheet.
Example 153. Forming a large dish-shape part from 0.062-in.-thick sheet.
Example 159. Four-operation forming of a 9-in.-diam center disk from 0.028-in.-thick stock.
Example 186. Flattening and crimping 0.028-in.-thick tabs.
Example 187. Forming a small ball socket and staking small projections, using 0.125-in.-thick stock in a progressive die run at about 1000 pieces per hour. The strip was sprayed with lubricant as it entered the die.

Mill Oil (Lubricant 8). Cold rolled steel usually is supplied with a coating of mill oil on the surface, and hot rolled steel is often ordered for delivery in the pickled and oiled condition. Mill oil is ordinarily a mineral oil of low viscosity (about 100 SUS at 100 F), and is intended primarily to provide the steel with resistance against rusting in transit and in storage.

In many applications, residual mill oil provides adequate lubrication for mild forming. For instance, see the following examples in this volume:

Example 149. Forming 0.218 and 0.250-in.-thick backing plates for an automotive brake drum from pickled and oiled stock.
Example 177. Multiple-operation fabrication (notch, trim, cut off and form) of a motor cradle from 0.120-in.-thick strip in a progressive die.
Example 179. In making a deflector in separate dies, residual mill oil was a satisfactory lubricant, but light mineral oil was used also when progressive dies (pierce, notch, form and cut off) were adopted to meet increased demand.

Mineral oil (Lubricant 9) was used in the applications described in the following examples:

Example 51. Blanking and piercing of 0.025-in.-thick laminations. Mineral oil was applied by spraying and by dipping.
Example 135. Press-brake forming (blanking, notching, piercing, forming and embossing comprised the complete production sequence) of a small bracket from 0.089-in.-thick hot rolled steel.
Example 160. Progressive-die forming of a complex lever from 0.075-in.-thick stock at 2400 pieces per hour.
Example 173. Progressive-die forming of an eggbeater side frame from 0.040-in.-thick stock at 360 pieces per hour.
Example 174. Progressive-die piercing, shaving and forming of a shaver-comb support from 0.042-in.-thick stock at 7200 pieces per hour. (Shaving dies lubricated with mineral oil had a short life of 5000 to 10,000 pieces between regrinds, compared with 50,000 pieces per regrind for piercing and forming dies with the same lubricant.)
Example 179. In making a deflector in separate dies, residual mill oil was a satisfactory lubricant, but light mineral oil was used also when progressive dies (pierce, notch, form and cut off) were adopted to meet an increase in production requirements.

Vanishing oil (Lubricant 10) is a low-viscosity, chemically inert, colorless and odorless organic liquid that evaporates completely in about an hour or less. It is a special-purpose lubricant for use when cleaning of the completed part would be impractical, or for use when it will result in a saving in cost or some other production advantage.

Vanishing oil has no effect on the surface of plated, lithographed, painted or plastic-coated metal, and is approved by the U.S. Food and Drug Administration for use on materials that will come into contact with food. In order to realize the advantages of vanishing oil, work metal and die surfaces must be kept free of oil, grease or other contaminants.

Because vanishing oils are usually flammable, they should be handled and used with adequate ventilation, and the customary precautions for flammable liquids should be observed.

Lubricants for Press Operations of Moderate Severity

Moderate-severity operations are defined here as those of severity approximately equal to the following, on low-carbon commercial quality sheet steel:

Blanking and piercing of sheet thicker than 0.125 in.
Bending 90° around a radius less than sheet thickness (t) with a flange width of $15t$
Forming with maximum localized stretch of 20% in a 1-in. length
Drawing a cylindrical shell with 20% reduction in diameter.

For such operations, the following four lubricants (numbered as in Table 1) are commonly used:

2 Water solution of 5 to 20% soap
3 Water emulsion of heavy-duty soluble oil (contains sulfurized or chlorinated additives)
11 Mineral oil (100 to 300 SUS at 100 F) plus 10 to 30% fatty oil
12 Mineral oil plus 2 to 20% sulfurized or chlorinated oil (EP oil).

In contrast to the lubricants for low-severity press operations, which are essentially nonpolar, the lubricants for moderate-severity use contain moderate to high concentrations of polar substances such as soap or fatty oil, or low concentrations of EP agents.

Soap Solution (Lubricant 2). Water solutions containing 5 to 20% of fatty acid soaps of sodium or potassium are commonly used for light-severity work. Potassium soaps have the advantage of being more easily dissolved in water than sodium soaps.

Synthetic soaps made by saponifying a fatty acid with an organic base such as triethanolamine are completely ashless, and need not be removed before annealing or other heat treating operations that are done at temperatures high enough to burn them off (usually, above 1000 F). Also, residues of such soaps often do not interfere with welding operations.

Heavy-Duty Emulsion (Lubricant 3). Water emulsions of heavy-duty soluble oil are preferred for blanking and piercing of thick sheet, particularly in high-speed production where their low foaming and superior performance as coolants are added advantages in recirculating systems.

Mineral Oil Plus Fatty Oil (Lubricant 11). Blends of 10 to 30% fatty oil in mineral oil show excellent friction-reducing characteristics and form polar films of sufficient strength for moderate-severity presswork. These blends are available in a wide range of viscosity, are easily removed in either water-base or solvent cleaning systems, and provide steel with fair protection against rusting.

Mineral Oil Plus EP Oil (Lubricant 12). Blends of 2 to 20% sulfurized or chlorinated EP oils with mineral oil have a wide range of usefulness in moderate-severity operations. Almost any viscosity desired can be obtained by selection of a suitable grade of mineral oil, and the polar or chemical activity can be altered to suit the severity of the operation by adjusting the content of EP additive.

Blends of EP oils in mineral oil are easily removed in solvents; their removability in water-base cleaners depends on the concentration of EP oil in the blend. The sulfur-containing types generally provide fair resistance against rusting; but blends of chlorinated oils have the disadvantage of being corrosive to steel (approximately in proportion to their EP activity), and usually must be removed within a few hours to a few days after application.

The use of oil-base lubricants of these types is illustrated by the following examples in this volume:

Example 19. Blanking, forming and notching of a brake-drum back from 0.097-in.-thick steel at 1050 pieces per hour, with blended chlorinated oil as lubricant.
Example 23. Blanking and piercing of a cam from 0.187-in.-thick stock at 3600 pieces per hour, with blended sulfurized oil as lubricant.
Example 34. Blanking and piercing of a 0.250-in.-thick flyweight at 300 pieces per hour, with roller-applied sulfurized oil as lubricant.

Mineral oils of extremely high viscosity contain significant concentrations of heterocyclic compounds and other polar constituents. Hence they have sufficient boundary-lubrication capability for some moderate-severity operations, even without the addition of oiliness agents or EP agents.

Lubricants for Press Operations of High Severity

High-severity operations are defined here as those of severity approximately equal to the following, on low-carbon drawing quality sheet steel:

Bending stock thicker than 0.125 in. 90°, with flange width of 10*t* or less
Forming with maximum localized stretch of 30% in a 1-in. length
Drawing a cylindrical shell with 30% reduction in diameter.

For such operations, the following five lubricants (numbered as in Table 1) are commonly used:

4 Soap-fat paste diluted with water (may contain wax)
5 Water emulsion of heavy-duty soluble oil (contains a high concentration of sulfurized or chlorinated additives)
13 Fatty oil
14 Mineral oil (100 to 300 SUS at 100 F) plus 5 to 50% of: (*a*) nonemulsifiable chlorinated oil, or (*b*) emulsifiable chlorinated oil
15 Concentrated phosphated oil.

To provide boundary films of sufficient strength and adherence for high-severity press operations, all of these lubricants contain high concentrations of oiliness agents or moderate to high concentrations of EP agents.

Diluted Soap-Fat Paste (Lubricant 4). The water dilutions of soap-fat pastes (nonpigmented) provide excellent lubrication for many high-severity press operations, particularly when these pastes also contain wax. They are frequently used in the deep drawing of products that will be porcelain enameled, such as tubs, sinks, and washer and refrigerator liners.

These materials can be removed by alkaline cleaning in soak tanks or spray washers; when completely saponified, they present no redeposition problems. They are more difficult to remove in a solvent system, especially if they have dried to a hard crust. They give fair protection against rusting.

On some deep drawn parts, residues from soap-fat drawing lubricants need not be removed before welding or annealing, since they yield only a low percentage of ash when burned.

Heavy-Duty Emulsion, Concentrated (Lubricant 5). Emulsions of heavy-duty soluble oils containing a high percentage of sulfur or chlorine are effective where a high rate of cooling is needed in high-speed press operations, in addition to EP activity. Emulsions containing chlorine must be removed shortly after use, to avoid excessive corrosion of the work metal, but those based on sulfur generally give fair resistance against rusting.

The effectiveness of a water emulsion of a chlorinated oil as a coolant is illustrated in the following example, which is presented in the article on Deep Drawing in this volume:

Example 239. Drawing of an oil-filter shell from 0.089-in.-thick steel, using three dies in a 550-ton mechanical press. A pigmented lubricant had been tried for this part, but the work heated up to 400 F during drawing and required handling with asbestos gloves. Changing to a water-soluble chlorinated oil kept the work cool enough to be handled without special gloves and also improved cleanability of the drawn shell.

Fatty Oil (Lubricant 13). Fatty oils, which usually contain from 2 to 5% free fatty acid as an impurity, are extremely effective in reducing friction. However, their removability in either water-base or solvent systems is only fair (unless the oil is modified to make it emulsifiable for easy removal in aqueous cleaners). In removing fatty oils in water-base cleaners, spray washers are preferred to soak tanks, in order to avoid flotation of oil and possible redeposition on the work.

An advantage of fatty oils is that (like organic-base synthetic soaps) they can be burned off in annealing operations where the temperature exceeds 1000 F, leaving no residue. Under these circumstances, the cleaning step usually needed before annealing can be eliminated.

Fatty oils are sometimes applied to blanks over dry soap films to give a further reduction in friction in maximum-severity press operations (see discussion of Dry Soap or Wax Films, Lubricant 7, on the next page).

Mineral Oil Plus Chlorinated Oil (Lubricant 14). Blends of mineral oil and chlorinated oil are readily removed in either water-base or solvent systems, except for nonemulsifiable grades, which are difficult to remove in aqueous cleaners. As with fatty oils, spray washers are preferred to soak tanks for removal with water-base cleaners, in order to avoid flotation of oil and possible redeposition on the work.

Chlorinated blends are corrosive to steel and require removal shortly after use, followed by the application of a rust-preventive film.

Phosphated Oil (Lubricant 15). Concentrated phosphated oils are used to a limited extent for high-severity operations on steel sheet. These lubricants, which contain ester phosphates as EP agents, are much less corrosive than concentrated chlorinated or sulfochlorinated oils, and are readily removable (except for nonemulsifiable grades in aqueous cleaners).

Lubricants for Press Operations of Maximum Severity

Maximum-severity operations are defined as those of severity approximately equal to the following, on low-carbon drawing quality sheet steel:

Forming with maximum localized stretch (about 40% in a 1-in. length)
Deep drawing a cylindrical shell with maximum reduction in diameter (reduction of 40% or more).

For such operations, the following five lubricants (numbered as in Table 1) are commonly used:

6 Pigmented soap-fat paste, diluted with water
7 Dry soap or wax (applied from water solution or dispersion), which may contain soluble filler such as borax
16 Blend of pigmented soap-fat paste with mineral oil
17 Concentrated sulfochlorinated oil (may contain some fatty oil), either nonemulsifiable or emulsifiable
18 Concentrated chlorinated oil, nonemulsifiable or emulsifiable

Each of these lubricants contains a high concentration of either pigments (mechanical EP agents) or chemical EP agents.

Diluted Pigmented Paste (Lubricant 6). Because of the cushioning effect of the pigment, water dilutions of pigmented soap-fat pastes give greater protection than unpigmented pastes against galling of work metal and dies in high-severity press operations. They permit deep draws with sharp radii, even on thick material, and are often used in cupping operations and for break-in of new dies. The extent of dilution is usually slight, and the pastes are sometimes used without dilution. The presence of a pigment in a water-base soap-fat lubricant can sometimes eliminate metal tearing in drawing steel of ductility that is borderline for the application.

A major disadvantage of the pigmented type of lubricant is the difficulty in removing the pigment after forming, especially by degreasers, and in solvent systems that are not supplemented by scrubbing or brushing. The pigment, or spacing agent, frequently remains on the metal after the soap and fat have been removed.

In addition, problems are encountered in keeping the pigment in suspension and avoiding the clogging of small openings. Thus, application by spray is not usually possible, and any type of recirculation is difficult. Also, these materials are likely to build up hard-to-remove accumulations on the tools and press equipment.

Dry soap or wax films (Lubricant 7) elongate with the metal during forming and prevent metal-to-metal contact almost completely, even under high pressure. These dry films are easily removed in water-base cleaners; some types are removable in plain hot water.

The six examples cited below, which appear in the article on Press Forming of Low-Carbon Steel in this volume, illustrate the use of dry soap for press forming operations that involve maximum stretch. In forming these irregularly shaped parts, highly effective cushioning action and uniform flow of metal were needed in the critical regions. As noted in the text of several of these examples, it was also necessary to apply fatty-oil compounds to critical regions or on certain lots of material for further reduction in friction.

Example 146. Severe forming of 0.096-in.-thick steel in a 500-ton double-action toggle press at 720 pieces per hour.

Example 157. Severe forming of an 0.089-in.-thick side rail for an automobile frame in an 800-ton column press at about 600 pieces per hour.

Example 161. Severe forming and edge bending of side rails up to 0.250 in. thick for automobile or truck frames in 500-ton to 4000-ton presses at up to 900 pieces per hour.

Example 165. Severe hole flanging in forming a 0.16-in.-thick automobile control arm at 200 to 325 pieces per hour.

Example 166. Severe forming of a 0.150-in.-thick automobile control arm at 350 to 575 pieces per hour.

Example 167. Severe forming of a 0.179-in.-thick truck frame member in an 1800-ton hydraulic press at 250 to 310 pieces per hour.

The principal use of dry soap or wax films is in drawing large parts such as refrigerator doors, bathtubs and gas cylinders. Illustrations of the use of dry soap films in maximum-severity deep drawing include the following examples, which appear in the article on Deep Drawing in this volume.

Example 241. Drawing a 36-in.-diam by 11½-in.-deep cup from 0.048-in.-thick low-carbon steel in a 700-ton double action mechanical press at 150 pieces per hour.

Example 244. Direct drawing and reverse redrawing in making a 21-in.-diam by 14-in. or 16-in.-deep washing-machine tub from 0.048-in.-thick low-carbon steel.

Example 245. Direct drawing and reverse redrawing in forming a large complex shape for a washing-machine base from 0.060-in.-thick low-carbon steel at a production rate of 220 pieces per hour.

Example 246. Forming a flanged shell 14½ in. in diameter by 24 in. deep from 0.103-in.-thick high-strength low-carbon steel in one step by reverse redrawing.

Example 264. Two-stage drawing of 14½-in.-diam by 24-in.-deep halves for a compressed-gas cylinder from 0.100-in.-thick high-strength low-alloy steel, applying a dry soap film before each draw.

Dry soap films are also used in conjunction with phosphate coatings in cupping and deep drawing of cartridge cases and other cylindrical cups with a high depth-to-diameter ratio (see the section "Special Dry Barrier-Type Films", which follows).

Disadvantages of the use of dry soap films include: (*a*) incompatibility with mill oil; and (*b*) the need to prepare solutions of dry powder in hot water, to apply the solution hot, to control its concentration, and to use ovens or heat lamps to dry the film on the blanks. These films are of little value in high-speed production of small drawn parts.

Pigmented Paste Plus Mineral Oil (Lubricant 16). Concentrated blends of pigmented soap-fat paste containing a small percentage of mineral oil (in addition to their normal water content) perform well in maximum-severity deep drawing and can be used where the corrosiveness of chlorinated or sulfochlorinated oils cannot be tolerated. Lubricants of this type generally resemble water dilutions of pigmented pastes (Lubricant 6) in removability, but the problems are less severe because the oil reduces hard crusting of residues.

Sulfochlorinated Oil (Lubricant 17). Concentrated sulfochlorinated EP oils are also used for maximum-severity press operations, often with additions of fatty oils or other fatty additives. The content of both sulfur and chlorine in these lubricants is high. At equal chlorine content, they would have the same corrosive action as straight chlorinated oils; substituting sulfur for some of the chlorine content reduces corrosivity somewhat.

In viscosity and removability, sulfochlorinated oils resemble the concentrated chlorinated oils (Lubricant 18), which are discussed next.

Chlorinated Oil (Lubricant 18). Concentrated chlorinated oils are unsurpassed in prolonging die life and in enabling maximum-severity press operations without scratching, galling or tearing of metal. They are widely used for maximum-severity deep drawing when their corrosiveness can be tolerated, and are well suited for automated operations.

These lubricants are applied just before forming and are removed within a day or two, after which a rust-preventive compound is applied if needed. In removing chlorinated oils, the use of spray cleaners is preferred to cleaning in soak tanks, in order to avoid redeposition on the work.

Although the original concentrated chlorinated oils were highly viscous and not suitable for pumping and spraying, chemically modified types or formulations that contain small percentages of mineral oil or fatty oil are available at the same level of chemical activity and in viscosities as low as that of SAE 10 motor oil.

Typical parts on which concentrated chlorinated oils have been used include bumper guards, deep drawn automotive parts, and ⅛-in.-thick cages for roller bearings. Other illustrations of the use of these lubricants for maximum-severity forming include the following examples, which are presented in the article on Press Forming of Low-Carbon Steel in this volume:

Example 138. Forming a channel-shape control arm with flanged holes from 0.089-in.-thick stock in a 1600-ton transfer press at 1110 pieces per hour.

Example 145. Forming a panel for a glove compartment door from 0.032-in.-thick stock in a transfer die at 500 pieces per hour.

Example 168. Forming a corner bracket from 0.043-in.-thick stock in a progressive die at 600 pieces per hour.

On each of these parts, maximum-severity deformation was encountered in the critical region. The selection of concentrated chlorinated oils for these three applications was based not only on their effectiveness as EP lubricants, but also on their efficient heat transfer and suitability for automated high-speed press operations.

Special Dry Barrier-Type Films

Phosphate-type chemical conversion coatings are used in conjunction with dry soap films or other lubricants to provide an impervious barrier film between work metal and tools and to improve retention of the lubricant in regions of high forming pressures.

In the following two examples, which appear in the article on Deep Drawing in this volume, the work metal was phosphated and then coated with lubricant before drawing:

Example 243. Drawing a shell 5.76 in. in inside diameter by 21¼ in. deep from 0.075 to 0.089-in.-thick 4130 steel in four stages, including two reverse redraws. The raw stock was lubricated for drawing by phosphating and then applying a dry soap film. The shell was lubricated after each of two anneals (before the third and fourth draws).

Example 249. Drawing a flanged cup 1$^{7}/_{16}$ in. in diameter by 1$^{11}/_{16}$ in. deep from 0.047-in.-thick enameling iron in two draws and a restriking operation.

Example 259. Drawing an 8.872-in.-OD by 3.648/3.618-in.-deep cup with a reverse spherical bottom from 0.188-in.-thick low-carbon steel, in three stages, with drastic thinning of the walls only. The blanks were phosphated and coated with a pigmented lubricant before cupping.

In Volume 2 of this Handbook, a reduction in finishing cost for automobile bumpers was attributed to the use of phosphating before forming:

Example 23 (Vol. 2, page 545). Forming an automobile bumper from blanks that were phosphated before applying a dry soap film. Hand polishing of the bumpers, which was needed when the soap film alone was used, was eliminated when the phosphating operation was added to the cycle.

Widely different types of solid barrier-type films are also used in the press forming of steel.

Organic dry films such as cured vinyl, polyethylene, polypropylene and other resinous organic coatings are sometimes used in drawing highly finished steel sheet that must be protected from scuff marks or scratches. These films can be applied as solutions in an organic solvent or as dispersions in water.

Clear vinyl films are applied to the highly finished side of automobile-bumper stock, and the stock is coated on both sides with a supplementary conventional drawing lubricant, such as a water dilution of a soap-fat paste, before the deep drawing operation. Organic films and adhesive-bonded or loose sheets of paper are also used in drawing decorative chromium plated steel, as described in Examples 211 and 212; the plastic film used in Example 211 was a strippable coating that was removed after drawing.

Example 211. Forming a broiler top from 0.025-in.-thick decorative chromium preplated steel, using strippable plastic and paper in place of a conventional lubricant.

Example 212. Forming a hotplate top from 0.030-in.-thick decorative chromium preplated steel that was coated on the face side with low-tack adhesive paper, using no additional lubricant.

Permanent paint and plastic coatings on sheet steel also function as solid barrier-type lubricants in forming and drawing operations. In addition, electroplating or hot dip coating with a soft ductile metal such as tin, zinc, copper or aluminum provides lubrication in press operations on sheet steel, as described in the article on Forming of Coated Steel, which begins on page 137.

Examples in this volume that describe the forming or deep drawing of steel coated with a soft, ductile metal are:

Example 140. Forming a housing wrapper from unlubricated 0.039-in.-thick galvanized steel in six stages in compound and single-operation dies.

Example 152. Forming a flanged and contoured bracket from unlubricated 0.075-in.-thick galvanized steel in two operations at 2400 pieces per hour.

Example 207. Piercing, notching, cutting off and bending a flame-spreader flange from unlubricated 0.036-in.-thick hot dip aluminum-coated steel.

Example 208. Multiple-operation forming of a burner-body half from 0.037-in.-thick hot dip aluminum-coated steel strip, using an oil-base lubricant that was applied to the strip by roller. Forming was done more easily, and less work was needed to recondition the tools, than with steel that did not have the aluminum coating.

Example 209. Deep drawing a rocker-arm cover from 0.031-in.-thick electrolytic tin-coated steel. The thin, unfused electrolytic tin coating helped retain the dry drawing lubricant used.

Example 210. Forming flat 180° bends and sharp corners on folded-end baking pans made from unlubricated 0.022-in.-thick electrolytic tin plate with a 1.5-lb tin coating.

Lubricants for Stainless Steel

Lubrication needs are more critical with stainless steels than with low-carbon steels, because the higher friction, strength and thermal resistivity of stainless steels means more heat is generated at the surface being formed, and less is being conducted away, than in forming a comparable workpiece from low-carbon steel. Stainless steel is more likely to gall than low-carbon steel. The demand for surface finish is usually more exacting for stainless steel parts than for low-carbon steel parts. The following two examples from the article "Forming of Stainless Steel" demonstrate the typical care exercised in the lubrication of stainless in preparation for forming. In both examples an oil-base lubricant was used.

Example 457. A muffler header of type 321 annealed stainless steel 0.032 in. thick was formed nearly to the limits of formability of the material in two press operations. The dies were brushed with oil between pieces.

Example 458. A dome section was drawn in a blank that had to be held at an angle other than 90° to the motion of the punch in order to accommodate a re-entrant angle in the drawn dome. The blank was clamped on two flanges, an upper and a lower. Blankholder load was evenly divided between the two flanges, but since the upper flange had more area than the lower, material was likely to be drawn from the upper flange and cause wrinkling in the dome. A bead was added to the upper flange, and the lower flange was lubricated with fatty-acid-type, nonpigmented drawing compound, to encourage the drawing of dome material from the lower flange.

Soap solutions and ordinary emulsions of water-soluble oils are not effective in most forming operations on stainless steel. Oils that contain significant concentrations of sulfur are not ordinarily used on stainless steel, because they can permanently stain the metal surface; if used, they should be removed promptly and completely.

The chemical EP activity of chlorinated oils is effective in heavy-duty forming and drawing of stainless, as in the following four examples from the article "Forming of Stainless Steel".

Example 461. A shell was blanked and severely drawn in one operation. Material was 0.037-in.-thick type 302 stainless steel. The formed piece was restruck in the same die to sharpen the draw radius. The lubricant was an emulsified chlorinated concentrate.

Example 463. A small bracket was made of type 302 stainless steel 0.015 in. thick in a seven-station progressive die. A chlorinated, inhibited oil was used as the lubricant.

Example 465. A mounting frame was made of 0.022-in.-thick type 430 stainless in a nine-station progressive die. The lubricant was an emulsifiable chlorinated-oil concentrate.

Example 472. Fountain-pen caps were deep drawn in seven stages in different presses from blanks of 0.011-in.-thick type 302 stainless. The lubricant was sulfur-free chlorinated oil mixed 1 to 3 with inhibited hydraulic oil having a viscosity of 250 SUS. It was furnished to all presses through a central pumping station.

The ability to adjust the chemical EP activity and viscosity of a wide range of chlorinated lubricants and the ease with which they can be formulated for easy removal make them very useful in severe forming and deep drawing of stainless steel. The percentage of active chlorine is adjusted to control chemical EP activity: any viscosity from SAE 10 to liquids that are so thick they barely flow can be obtained by selection of EP concentrate and blending with mineral oil or fatty oils.

In the first of the two examples that follow, both high chlorine content and high viscosity were needed to draw acceptable parts; in the second example, a viscous mineral oil was replaced by a low-viscosity mineral oil containing a chlorinated wax.

Example 459. A wheel cover was drawn from type 302 stainless steel 0.028 in. thick. At first, a lightly chlorinated oil (10% Cl) of medium viscosity (1500 SUS at 100 F) was used. Although the draw was shallow, rejection rate was 12% for splits and scratches. A change was made to a much more highly chlorinated oil (36% Cl) with a much higher viscosity (4000 SUS at 100 F), and rejection rate dropped to less than 1%. After forming, the wheel covers were cleaned in a vapor degreaser.

Example 470. A coffeepot was deep drawn from a type 302 stainless steel blank 0.032 in. thick in two draws and one bulging operation. At first, the blanks were lubricated by brushing both sides with mineral oil having a viscosity of 6000 SUS at 100 F. The workpiece wrinkled in the first draw, and galling and tearing occurred in redrawing and bulging. The lubricant was replaced with a thinner mineral oil (viscosity, 500 SUS at 100 F) that was fortified with a chlorinated wax. The lubricant was brushed on, as before. The modified lubricant not only eliminated wrinkles in the first draw, but also prevented galling in the two other operations.

In some severe drawing applications, there is no substitute for the physical separation and equalization of pressure provided by pigments, as demonstrated in the following example:

Example 471. Chlorinated and sulfochlorinated oils with viscosities of 4000 to 20,000 SUS at 100 F failed to eliminate welding to the dies and splitting at the corners in deep drawing a rectangular shell from 0.035-in.-thick type 304 stainless steel. The oils had been chosen because they could be removed later in a vapor degreaser. The original lubricants were replaced by a highly pigmented water-miscible soap-fat paste diluted with two parts of water. The paste, which was applied by roller to both sides of the blank, eliminated welding and splitting, but it had to be removed later in a hot alkaline solution.

Lubrication of stainless steel for forming is discussed on page 354 in the article "Forming of Stainless Steel", in this volume. Table 3 in that article (page 355) lists lubricants generally used in forming of stainless steels, and indicates their suitability for use in various forming operations.

Lubricants for Heat-Resisting Alloys

Most mild forming of heat-resisting alloys can be done with the use of polar lubricants, such as fatty oils. However, for more severe forming operations, metallic soaps or EP lubricants such as chlorinated, sulfochlorinated or sulfurized oils are used.

Pigments (such as mica) are sometimes added to both these types of lubricant. Pigments containing lead, zinc or sulfur should not be used on workpieces that will be annealed, because of the difficulty of removing pigments and because of the harmful effects of these elements on heat-resisting alloys at high temperature.

In the following example from the article "Forming of Heat-Resisting Alloys" in this volume, a chlorinated oil was used as the lubricant in the press forming of alloy A-286.

Example 496. Aerospace end caps 9 in. in diameter were press formed in two stages from 0.045-in.-thick alloy A-286. The lubricant was a sulfur-free chlorinated oil.

Lubrication during the forming of heat-resisting alloys is discussed on page 373 in the article "Forming of Heat-Resisting Alloys".

Refractory Metals. Lubricants used in forming refractory metals are oils, extreme-pressure (EP) lubricants, soaps, waxes, silicones, graphite, molybdenum disulfide, copper plating, and enamels made by suspending powdered copper in acrylic resin. Columbium and tantalum are often formed with ordinary oils and greases, because they are generally formed at room temperature, as in the following example from the article "Forming of Refractory Metals":

Example 505. A deep drawn shell was produced from 0.010-in.-thick columbium sheet in four operations as follows: draw cup; bulge; draw smaller cup in bottom; pierce. A mixture of graphite and oil was used as lubricant.

For severe forming operations on columbium and tantalum, petrolatum is frequently used.

Solid lubricants and suspensions of suitable pigments such as molybdenum disulfide with or without colloidal graphite are used in hot forming of tungsten and molybdenum.

Lubricants for Aluminum Alloys

In selecting lubricants for forming of aluminum and aluminum alloys, special attention must be given to avoiding staining or corrosion. The following two examples, presented in the article "Forming of Aluminum Alloys", are typical of general practice in lubricating aluminum for severe press forming.

Example 524. A large rectangular box was made in two draws from 0.072-in.-thick aluminum alloy 5052-O. A special drawing lubricant was used: mineral oil containing 10% fatty oil and 10 to 15% EP additive (sulfurized fatty oil).

Example 525. A 22½-in.-deep rectangular bin was drawn in three stages from 0.102-in.-thick alloy 3003-O. A heavy oil-base drawing compound was used to prevent galling.

Table 1 on page 380 in the article on Forming of Aluminum lists ten lubricants used in forming of aluminum alloys, in approximate order of increasing effectiveness. Lubrication in specific processes applied to aluminum is discussed in the sections on Blanking and Piercing, Press-Brake Forming, Contour Roll Forming, Deep Drawing, Hot Drawing, Spinning, Stretch Forming, Drop Hammer Forming, and Bending of Bars and Tubing, in the same article (pages 379 to 402).

Lubricants for Copper Alloys

Avoidance of staining or corrosion is an important consideration in the selection of lubricants for forming of copper and copper alloys.

Because of their effectiveness as coolants, water-base lubricants are favored for high-speed press operations, but they are likely to cause staining and must be removed promptly. Soap-fat pastes have the widest range of usefulness of the water-base lubricants. Use of this type of lubricant for severe drawing is illustrated in the next three examples from the article "Forming of Copper and Copper Alloys". (Soluble-oil emulsions are suitable where forming pressures are less severe, as for redrawing in Examples 590 and 593.)

Example 590. A tapered ferrule was drawn and trimmed in eight stages from 0.021-in.-thick alloy 260 (cartridge brass, 70%) with a grain size of 0.030 to 0.050 mm. The workpiece was annealed after the first drawing operation (cupping). Water-base lubricants were used, in a 1-to-30 mixture with water: for cupping, a dilute soap-plus-fat paste; for redraws, an emulsion of soluble oil.

Example 592. A synchro-converter case was deep drawn from 0.016-in.-thick alloy 752 (nickel silver, 65-18) with a grain size of 0.025 to 0.050 mm. Eleven drawing operations were required for producing this complex, dual-diameter case. The lubricant was diluted soap-plus-fat paste.

Example 593. A rectangular relay body was deep drawn from alloy 735 (nickel silver, 72-18) in four operations. The stock was 0.022 in. thick and had a grain size of 0.020 to 0.040 mm. The body was 1¼ in. deep by ½ in. wide by 1¹⁄₁₆ in. long. Dilute soap-plus-fat paste was used for cupping, and an emulsion of soluble oil and water was used for redraws.

Pigmented soap-fat pastes are used in more severe drawing, as described in the next three examples:

Example 591. A sugar bowl was produced from alloy 230 (red brass, 85%) by deep drawing in one operation and closing in. The blank had a grain size of 0.015 to 0.020 mm. A pigmented soap-plus-fat paste, applied to the workpiece by dipping, was used as the lubricant in drawing.

Example 596. A cup was drawn from alloy 110 (ETP copper) in two stages. The stock was 0.026 in. thick. Reduction was 40% in the first operation and 24% in the second operation. A pigmented soap-plus-fat paste was used as the lubricant.

Example 598. A preform for a spun pillar was made by deep drawing a shell from 0.032-in.-thick alloy 220 (commercial bronze, 90%) with a grain size of 0.010 to 0.020 mm. A 50% reduction in diameter was produced by the draw. Lubricant was a pigmented soap-plus-fat paste.

Oil-base lubricants free from acidity are less likely than water-base lubricants to stain workpieces on prolonged contact. Stabilized chlorinated oils are effective for maximum-severity forming and high-speed operations, as illustrated in the following example:

Example 589. A small cylindrical housing was deep drawn from annealed alloy 230 (red brass, 85%), having a nominal grain size of 0.025 mm, in eight operations (including four redraws) in an eyelet machine. Lubricant was a stabilized chlorinated oil with 30 to 50% combined chlorine.

Information on lubricants used in the forming of copper is presented in the section "Lubrication" on pages 408 and 409 in the article "Forming of Copper and Copper Alloys", where a severity classification and guide for selection of lubricants is given in Table 5. Additional information on the selection of lubricants for the forming of copper and its alloys is given in the same article in the sections on Spinning, Contour Roll Forming, and Coining.

Lubricants for Magnesium Alloys

Lubrication is more important in hot forming than in cold forming of magnesium and magnesium alloys, because these alloys are more likely to gall in hot forming. Dry soap films are satisfactory at forming temperatures below 250 F; graphite and molybdenum disulfide are used at higher temperatures, but may be difficult to remove.

Following are two examples from the article "Forming of Magnesium Alloys" in this volume, in which graphite was used as the lubricant in the forming of heated magnesium alloy.

Example 606. Rectangular boxes 9⅜ in. long by 6⅛ in. wide by 9½ in. deep were drawn from 0.081-in.-thick alloy LA141A. Temperature of the pressure pad was 540 F, of the draw ring, 440 F, and of the punch, 300 F. Clamp pressure was 75 psi. Drawing speed was approximately 2 ft per min.

In the same press, boxes of the same size were drawn from the same thickness of alloy AZ31B or AZ31C. For these boxes, draw-ring and punch temperature was 750 F; clamp pressure was 100 psi, and drawing speed was 1 ft per min. A graphite lubricant was used for all three alloys.

Example 607. A dome-shape piece was drawn from a 0.100-in.-thick blank of alloy ZE10A-H24 that was 38 in. in diameter. Blanks were graphite coated and heated to 400 F. Tools were heated by gas to 400 F. Clamping force varied from 1500 to 2000 lb. The punch had a spherical radius of 29.087 in. It traveled 7⅜ in. to form the dome.

When lubricants cannot be tolerated, thin sheets of paper or fiber glass, depending on forming temperature, are placed between the work metal and the die. Lubrication used in forming of magnesium alloys is discussed in the section on pages 426 to 427 in the article "Forming of Magnesium Alloys".

Lubricants for Nickel Alloys

Nickel alloys, depending on their composition, may gall readily during forming. Fatty oils and blends of fatty oils with mineral oil provide satisfactory lubrication for many mild and moderate forming or drawing operations, but EP lubricants (chlorinated or sulfurized oils) are generally needed for severe forming of nickel alloys. The EP lubricant must be removed completely after forming, as sulfur will cause embrittlement on heating and chlorine causes pitting on long exposure.

Lubrication of nickel alloys during forming is discussed under "Lubricants" on page 432 in the article "Forming of Nickel Alloys", and in the sections in that article that deal with Shearing, Blanking and Piercing; Bending Tube and Pipe; Expanding Heat-Exchanger Tube; Cold Heading and Cold Extrusion; and Straightening.

Lubricants for Titanium Alloys

Lubricants for cold forming of titanium alloys are generally similar to those for severe forming of aluminum.

A dried soap film provided lubrication for forming of titanium in the next two examples from the article "Forming of Titanium Alloys", in this volume:

Example 611. A rectangular blank of commercially pure titanium 0.090 in. thick was formed in two operations to an irregular shape that included two oblong drawn cups that tapered to a depth of 3½ in. Preforming was done at 550 F in a 7000-ton press, using beryllium copper inserts for a draw ring; and the part was then sized at 1000 F in a drop hammer, using zinc alloy dies. Both sets of dies were lubricated with soap.

Example 612. Blanks of alloy Ti-8Al-1Mo-1V or Ti-6Al-4V, 0.050 in. thick, were reduced 50% on diameter to produce 8-in.-diam hemispheres in a rubber-diaphragm press. Maximum forming pressure was 14,000 psi. A disk of 1018 steel, ⅛ in. thick, was used as an overlay on the titanium to protect the diaphragm and prevent wrinkling of the work. The punch side of the blank was coated with wax, which was removed from the workpiece immediately after forming.

Temperature-resistant lubricants for hot forming contain graphite or molybdenum disulfide, and they are often applied over zinc phosphate conversion coatings.

Lubricants used in cold and hot forming of titanium alloys are listed in Table 3 on page 439 in the article "Forming of Titanium Alloys"; additional information on lubricants is presented in the sections "Power Spinning" (page 442) and "Bending of Tubing" (page 446) in that article.

Selected References

Richard L. Jentgen, Lubrication in Metal-Deformation Processes, DMIC Report 234, 10 June 1967, p 74-103.

W. Torkington, Lubricants as Related to Shearing, Blanking and Forming; Technical Paper 150 presented at a symposium sponsored by the Metal Fabricating Institute at Purdue University, Apr 1969.

D. A. Shenton, paper presented to a symposium on metalworking (drawing) lubricants, sponsored by ASTM Committee E-26, at Hamilton, Ontario, Canada, 23 Apr 1966.

Felix M. Giordano, A Critical Review of Die Lubricants in Pressworking, ASTME Technical Paper SP 63-21.

Ferdinand L. Ewald, How to Choose a Lubricant for Stamping Steel Parts, *Metal Progress*, Jan 1966, p 72-75.

E. L. H. Bastian, "Metalworking Lubricants", McGraw-Hill, 1951.

Blanking of Low-Carbon Steel

*By the ASM Committee on Press Forming of Steel**

A BLANK is a shape cut from flat or preformed stock. Ordinarily, a blank serves as a starting workpiece for a formed part; less often, it is a desired end product. This article deals with the production of blanks from low-carbon steel (such as 1008 and 1010) sheet and strip, in dies in a mechanical or hydraulic press. The blanking and piercing of magnetically soft materials and of high-carbon steel are discussed in separate articles in this volume.

Improving the quality of blanked edges by shaving is discussed later in this article. Fine-edge blanking is treated in a separate article beginning on page 56 in this volume. Shearing, a method of making blanks that does not use a die, is dealt with in the articles "Shearing of Plate and Flat Sheet", which begins on page 265, and "Slitting and Shearing of Coiled Sheet and Strip", which begins on page 271.

Methods of Blanking in Presses

Cutting operations that are done by dies in presses to produce blanks include cutoff, parting, blanking, notching and lancing. The first three of these operations can produce a complete blank in a single press stroke. In progressive dies, two or more of these five operations are done in sequence to develop the complete outline of the blank and to separate it from the sheet, strip or coil stock.

Trimming, or cutting off excess material from the periphery of a workpiece, usually is done in dies, and is similar to blanking. Often it is the final operation on a formed or drawn part.

Applications of these methods are described in examples throughout this article. For other examples of the use of these methods of producing blanks, see the articles "Piercing of Low-Carbon Steel" (page 44), "Blanking and Piercing of Magnetically Soft Materials" (page 60), "Press Forming of Low-Carbon Steel" (page 112), "Press Forming of High-Carbon Steel" (page 132), and "Deep Drawing" (page 162).

Cutoff is cutting along a line to produce blanks, without generating any scrap in the cutting operation, most of the part outline having been developed by notching or lancing in preceding stations. The cutoff line may have almost any shape — straight, broken or curved. After being cut off, the blanks fall onto a conveyor or into a chute or container.

A cutoff die may be used to cut the entire outline of blanks whose shape permits nesting in a layout that uses all of the material (except possibly at the ends of the strip), as shown in Fig. 1. Alternating positions can sometimes be used in nesting, as shown in the middle strip in Fig. 1, to avoid the production of scrap except at strip ends.

Cutoff also is used to cut blanks from strip that has already been notched to separate the blanks along part of their periphery, as described in the example that follows.

Example 6. Use of Cutoff to Separate Blanks Partly Outlined by Notching (Fig. 2)

Figure 2 shows the layout for cutoff of blanks for body-bolt brackets of an automobile. The brackets were completed by piercing and forming (see Examples 43 and 152).

The coiled strip, of galvanized hot rolled 1006 steel, was 0.075 in. thick by 19.5 in. wide. This was wide enough for two blanks, as shown in Fig. 2. The blanks were alternated in the layout for greater ease in trimming and piercing.

The strip was fed into a progressive die, in which the first stations notched and seminotched it (making a small amount of scrap). In the stations that followed, straight cutoff punches made four blanks at each stroke, without producing any additional scrap.

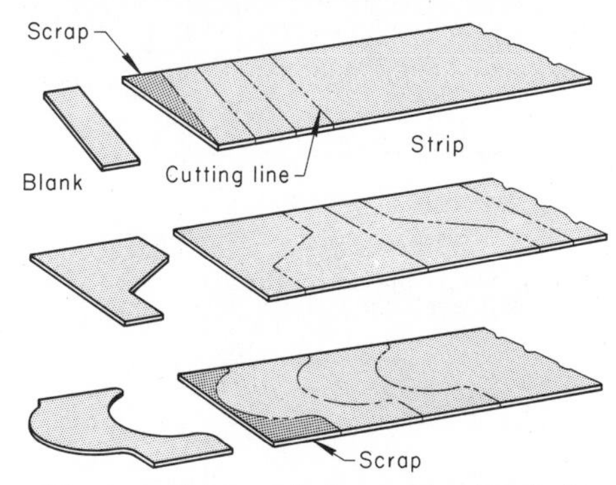

Fig. 1. Nested layouts for making blanks by cutoff

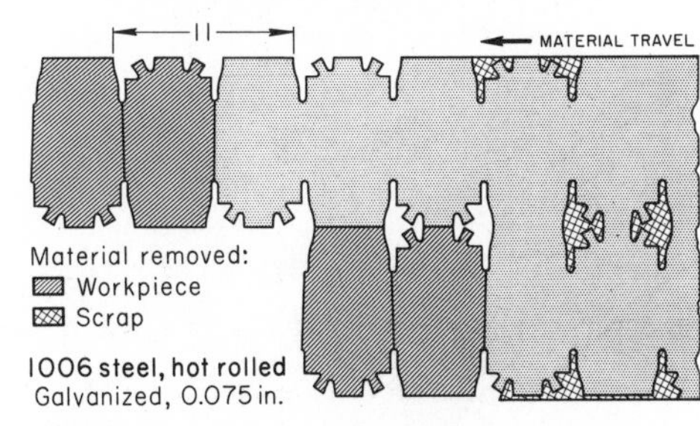

Fig. 2. Layout for cutoff of four blanks at each press stroke from notched and seminotched strip (Example 6)

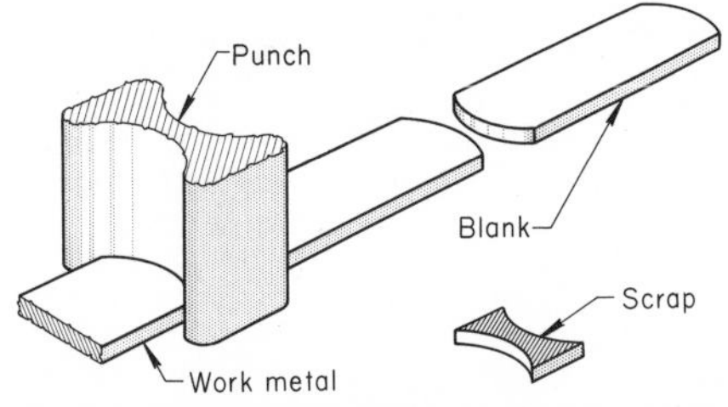

Fig. 3. Use of a parting punch to make blanks not having mating adjacent surfaces

The work was done in a 400-ton single-action mechanical press with an air cushion. The press was equipped with a double roll feed and made 50 strokes (200 blanks) per minute.

Advantages of cutoff in making blanks include:

1 The die has few components and is relatively inexpensive.
2 Waste of material in blanking is minimized or eliminated.
3 The die can be resharpened easily, and maintenance costs are low.

Disadvantages of cutoff include:

1 It can be used only to make blanks that nest in the layout without waste.
2 Cutting on one edge causes one-way deflection and stress.
3 Accuracy may be affected adversely by the method of feeding.

Parting (Fig. 3) is the separation of blanks by cutting away a strip of material between them. Like cutoff, it can be done after most of the part outline has been developed by notching or lancing. It is used to make blanks that do not have mating adjacent surfaces for cutoff (Fig. 3); or blanks that must be spaced for ease of handling, to avoid distortion, or to allow room for sturdy tools. Some scrap is produced in making blanks by parting, which is therefore less efficient than cutoff in the use of material.

Blanking (also called punching) is the cutting of the complete outline of a workpiece in a single press stroke. Usually a scrap skeleton is produced, so that blanking causes some waste of material. However, blanking is usually the fastest and most economical way to make flat parts, particularly in large quantities.

The skeleton left by blanking sometimes has only scrap-metal value, but many shops have organized programs to maximize the use of cutouts and sizable scrap skeletons in making other production parts (see Example 12). Waste of material is avoided completely in the use of the scrap skeleton that remains from certain blanking operations to provide perforated stock for items such as air filters for forced-air furnaces.

Piercing (with a flat-end punch), often also called punching or perforating, is similar to blanking, except that the punched-out (blanked) slug is the waste, and the surrounding metal the workpiece. Piercing is discussed in the article that begins on page 44 in this volume.

Notching is an operation in which the individual punch removes a piece of metal from the edge of the blank or strip (Fig. 4). Reasons for notching include the following:

1 To free some metal for drawing (Fig. 4a) and for forming (Fig. 4b) while the workpiece remains attached to the strip
2 To remove excess metal before forming (Fig. 4c)
3 To cut part of the outline of a blank that would be difficult to cut otherwise (Fig. 2 and 34).

*For committee list, see page 112.

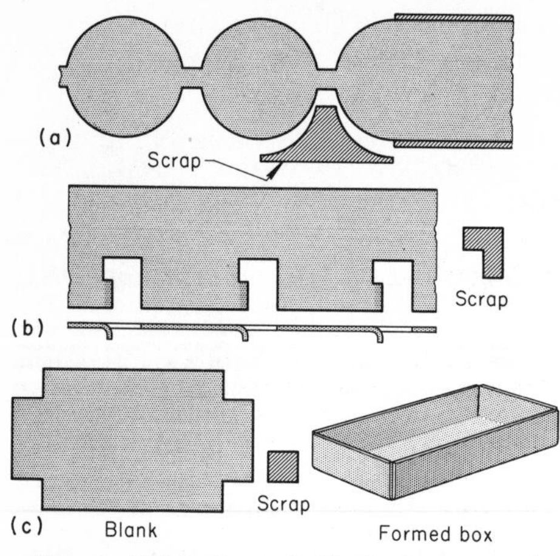

Fig. 4. Notched work illustrating use of notching for freeing of metal before drawing (a) and before forming (b), and for removing excess metal before forming (c)

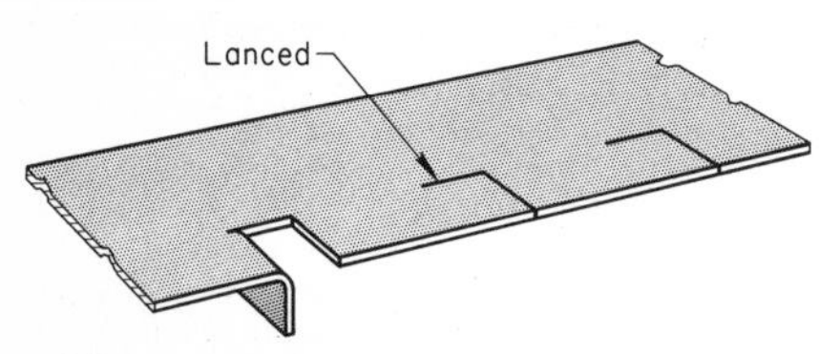

Fig. 5. Strip lanced to free metal for forming

Piercing of holes of any shape in a strip to free metal for subsequent forming, or to produce surfaces that later coincide with the outline of a blanked part, is sometimes called seminotching. The pierced area may outline a portion of one part, or of two or more adjacent parts in a strip. Progressive die layouts incorporating seminotching are illustrated in Fig. 2, 18 and 31.

Lancing is a press operation in which a single-line cut or slit is made part way across the strip stock, without removing any metal. Generally, lancing is done to free metal for forming, as shown in Fig. 5, or as in forming louvers. The cut does not have a closed contour and does not release a blank or a piece of scrap. Besides its use in freeing metal for subsequent forming, lancing also is used to cut partial contours for blanked parts, particularly in progressive dies.

Trimming is an operation for removing excess metal (such as deformed and uneven metal on drawn or formed parts) and metal that has been needed in a previous operation (such as a blankholding flange for a draw operation). Trimming is done in several ways, depending on the shape of the workpiece, on the accuracy required, and on production quantity.

Figure 6 illustrates the tooling for trimming a horizontal flange on a drawn shell in a separate operation. The drawn shell is set on a locating plug for trimming. After scrap from a sufficient number of trimmed shells has accumulated, the piece of scrap at the bottom is severed at each stroke of the press by the scrap cutters shown in Fig. 6, and falls clear. Except that the die must be constructed to accept and locate the drawn shell, the operation is identical with the blanking of a flat workpiece and produces square edges of the same accuracy and quality.

A drawn shell or formed part may be trimmed in a press without leaving a flange on the completed part, by one of three methods: pinch trim, shimmy trim, or trim and wipe-down.

Pinch trimming, shown as a separate operation in a push-through die in Fig. 7, is done only on a part that has at least a narrow flange as-formed. The shell must be free from wrinkles at or near the trimming line. The trimmed edge is not square with the sidewall, but has the general shape shown in the lower right corner of Fig. 7. Accuracy of height resulting from pinch trimming is affected by variation in wall thickness and flange radius. To be sure of an even pinch-off and to avoid sharp or rough edges, clearance between punch and die must be held to a minimum, and the punch must be kept sharp.

Pinch trimming is also done without a blankholder or hold-down, using a die otherwise similar to that shown in Fig. 7. The scrap rings may be blown off the die at each stroke. In another method, the scrap rings climb the punch until they are severed by being compressed against a scrap cutter, after which they are spread apart and allowed to run out along a track for disposal. Pinch trimming without a blankholder is particularly well suited for use in high-volume production of eyelets and other small parts.

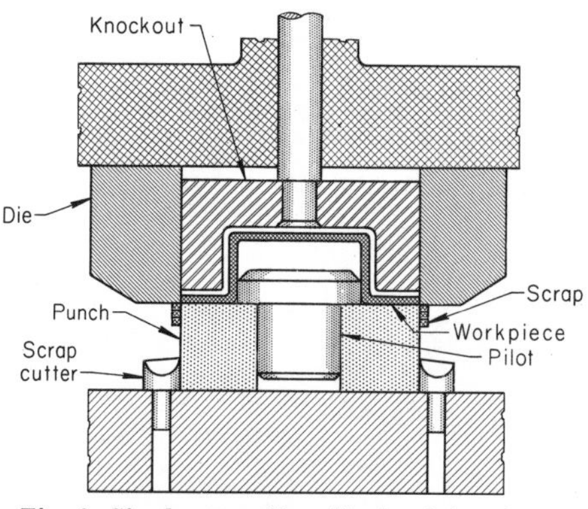

Fig. 6. Single-operation die for trimming a horizontal flange on a drawn shell

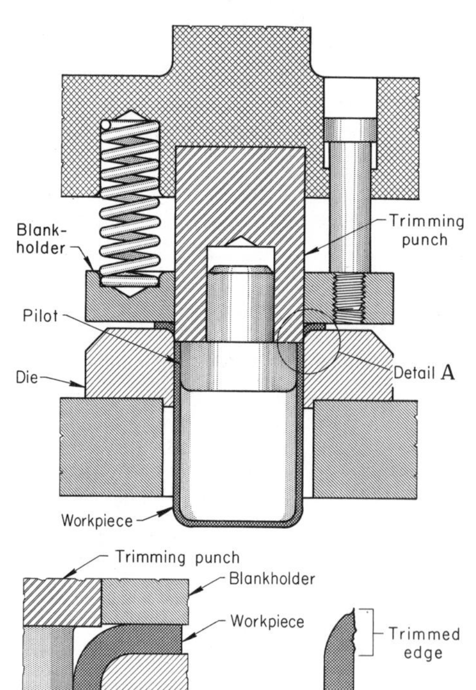

Fig. 7. Pinch trimming a drawn shell in a push-through die

Pinch trimming is primarily a mass production method. The production rate is high, because only one stroke of the press is required to complete the trim. The method often is combined with drawing in a compound draw-and-trim die, to reduce production cost still further.

Disadvantages are excessive burrs, sharp cut edge, and high die maintenance.

Shimmy Trimming. In trimming with a shimmy die (known also as Brehm or model trimming), the drawn shell is held in a close-fitting die of the exact shell height, and is trimmed in segments by successive horizontal oscillations of an internal cam-actuated punch toward the outside of the shell. The resulting trimmed edge is square and closely resembles the conventional blanked edge on a flat part. Shell height is more accurate than with pinch trimming.

Besides its application to shells that must have square, accurate edges, shimmy trimming is used on shells that have a wrinkled or otherwise nonuniform top edge as-drawn (cutoff is done below the defects), and on shells that cannot be produced economically with even the narrow flange needed for pinch trimming.

Tooling cost for shimmy trimming is much higher than for pinch trimming. Also, shimmy trimming is slower, because it requires four or more oscillations of the punch in one press stroke and cannot be combined with other operations in a compound die.

Shimmy dies are inexpensive to maintain, because they remain in alignment and thus are not likely to wear by shearing or chipping.

Trim and Wipe-Down. In this type of trimming, a flange is cut to width with a die such as that shown in Fig. 6, and then wiped or straightened into line with the sidewall of the shell or formed part. Because of narrow flange width, trimming and wiping down may be two operations.

The edge is square with the sidewall, but the shell height may be slightly irregular because of the forming characteristics of the metal. Also, a ring may be visible at the original location of the flange radius.

Trimming, other than shimmy trimming, is frequently combined with one or more other operations in a compound die. Trim stock often is left on a drawn or formed workpiece so that it can be trimmed to size in a second operation. This is done to get the most accurate relation of some other feature, such as a pierced hole, to the trimmed outline of the workpiece.

Characteristics of Blanked Edges

The sheared edges of a blank produced in a conventional die are not smooth and vertical for the entire thickness of the part, but instead show the characteristics represented on an exaggerated scale in Fig. 8. The blank is shown in the position in which it would be cut from the work metal by the downward motion of the punch. A portion of the stock remaining after removal of the blank is shown at the top of the illustration.

Rollover on the lower edges of the blank develops by plastic deformation of the work metal as it is forced into the die by the punch. Compression of the metal above the rollover zone against the walls of the die opening burnishes a portion of the edge of the blank, as shown in Fig. 8. As the punch completes its stroke, the remaining portion of the blank edge is broken away or fractured (resulting in "die break"), and a tensile burr is formed along the top of the blank edge.

The angle of the fractured portion of the edge is identified in Fig. 8 as the breakout angle. The breakout dimension of the blank and the burnish dimension of the hole in the scrap skeleton are approximately equal to the corresponding punch dimension, and the burnish dimension of the blank is very close to the corresponding die dimension. Thus, the punch determines the hole size and the die governs the blank size.

Penetration depth, or the amount of penetration of the punch into the work metal before fracture occurs, is shown on the edge of the remaining stock or scrap skeleton in Fig. 8. This depth is approximately equal to the sum of rollover depth and burnish depth on the blank, except when low die clearance produces secondary burnish. It is usually expressed as a percentage of the work-metal thickness.

The percentage of penetration (before fracture) depends on the properties of the work metal, as shown in Table 1, which gives approximate values for various steels and nonferrous metals under typical blanking conditions. Percentage penetration affects energy consumption and cutting force in blanking, as described under "Calculation of Force Requirements", on this page.

Die Clearance

The terms clearance, die clearance, and punch-to-die clearance are used synonymously to refer to the space between punch and die. Clearance is important for reliable operation of the blanking equipment, quality and type of cut edges, and life of punch and die. In general, the effects of clearance on these factors in blanking are the same as in piercing, and are discussed on page 44 in the article "Piercing of Low-Carbon Steel".

The edge characteristics of slugs produced in piercing holes are described on pages 44 and 45 in the article on Piercing, and are illustrated in Fig. 2 of that article. The data in that illustration can serve as a guide for selecting clearances for blanking.

All clearance values given in this article are per side, except where indicated otherwise.

Optimum blanking clearance may sometimes be less than optimum piercing clearance. This is partly because the blanked edge generally is close to the stock edge, and material expansion therefore is less restricted. A piercing tool must move a great deal of material away from its cutting edge and, for longest life, the clearance should be selected to eliminate as much compressive loading on the work metal as possible.

A part blanked using clearance much greater than normal may show double shear, which ordinarily is evident only with extremely small clearance (see edge types 4 and 5 in Fig. 2 on page 45). Also, a part blanked using large clearance will be smaller than the die opening (except for a deeply dished blank), and it is difficult to correct the tooling to compensate for this. In some applications, retaining the blank becomes almost as great a problem as expelling the slugs into a die cavity after piercing, because of the increased clearance.

Relief in a blanking die (Fig. 9) is the taper that is provided so that the severed blank can fall free. The relief angle may range from ½° to 2° from the vertical wall of the die opening. Sometimes, relief in a die is called draft or angular clearance. In some dies, the relief may start at the top of the die surface and have a taper of only 0.002 in. per inch per side (see page 64 in the article "Blanking and Piercing of Magnetically Soft Materials", in this volume). In other dies, there is a straight, vertical land between the top of the die and the relief.

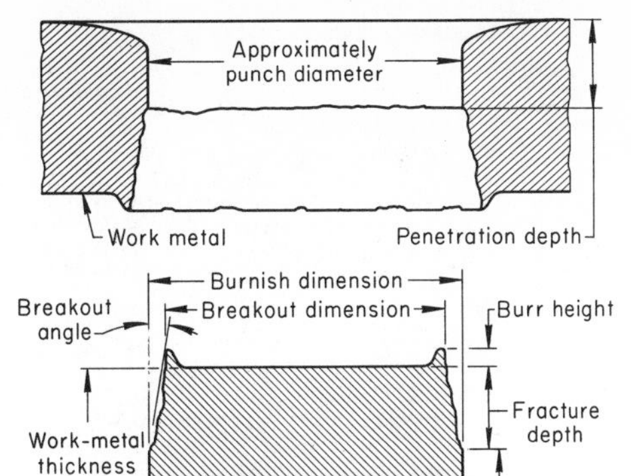

Fig. 8. Characteristics of the sheared edges of a blank. Curvature and angles are exaggerated for emphasis.

Table 1. Approximate Penetration of Sheet Thickness Before Fracture in Blanking

Work metal	Penetration, %	Work metal	Penetration, %
Carbon steels(a):		**Nonferrous Metals**	
0.10% C, Ann	50	Aluminum alloys	60
0.10% C, CR	38	Brass	50
0.20% C, Ann	40	Bronze	25
0.20% C, CR	28	Copper	55
0.30% C, Ann	33	Nickel alloys	55
0.30% C, CR	22	Zinc alloys	50
Silicon steels	30		

(a) Ann = annealed; CR = cold rolled

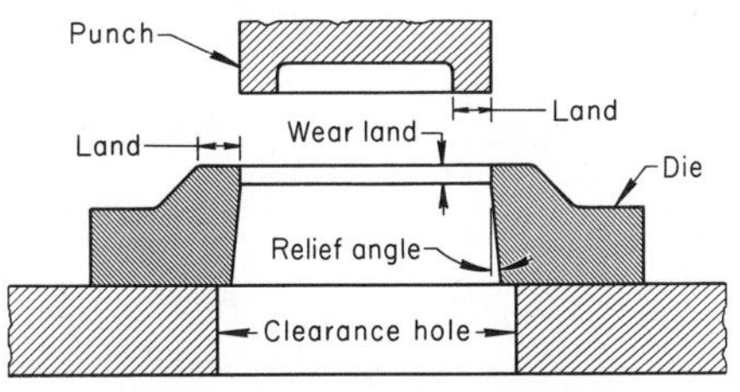

Fig. 9. Relief in a blanking die

Calculation of Force Requirements

Calculation of the forces and the work involved in blanking gives average figures that are applicable only when: (*a*) the correct shear strength for the material is used; and (*b*) the die is sharp and the punch is in good condition, has correct clearance, and is functioning properly.

The total load on the press, or the press capacity required to do a particular job, is the sum of the cutting force and other forces acting at the same time, such as the blankholding force exerted by a die cushion.

Cutting Force: Square-End Punches and Dies. When punch and die surfaces are flat and at right angles to the motion of the punch, cutting force can be found by multiplying the area of the cut section by the shear strength of the work material:

$$L = S_s t l$$

where L is load on the press, lb (cutting force); S_s is shear strength of the stock, psi; t is stock thickness, in.; and l is length or perimeter of cut, in. Shear strengths of various steels and nonferrous metals are given in Table 2.

Cutting Force: Dies With Shear. For cutting large blanks, shear may be applied to the face of the die by grinding it at an angle to the motion of the punch (Fig. 10), but shear is not used in cutting small blanks. Shear reduces shock on the press, blanking noise, and blanking force, but the same amount of work is done as with a flat die surface.

The most common type of shear used on the die is convex (Fig. 10a). The apex of the die face is rounded slightly to avoid initiating a crack in the work metal. Concave shear (Fig. 10b) is somewhat more difficult to grind on the die, but holds the work metal more securely during blanking. A radius approximately equal to that of the grinding wheel is produced where the ground surfaces meet.

A third type of shear, sometimes used on a die for a large blank, consists of a wavy or scalloped surface around the die opening. This technique uses several convex and concave shear surfaces around the die opening. The punch load is distributed over the entire die surface, thus minimizing punch shift.

The amount of shear in a die can be less than or greater than stock thickness. Shear that is equal in depth to the stock thickness (or is greater than the stock thickness) is called full shear.

Table 2. Shear Strengths of Various Steels and Nonferrous Metals at Room Temperature

Metal	Shear strength, psi
Carbon steels:	
0.10% C	35,000 to 43,000
0.20% C	44,000 to 55,000
0.30% C	52,000 to 67,000
High-strength low-alloy steels	45,000 to 63,700
Silicon steels	60,000 to 70,000
Stainless steels	57,000 to 129,000
Nonferrous Metals	
Aluminum alloys	7,000 to 46,000
Copper and bronze	22,000 to 70,000
Lead alloys	1,825 to 5,870
Magnesium alloys	17,000 to 29,000
Nickel alloys	35,000 to 116,000
Tin alloys	2,900 to 11,100
Titanium alloys	60,000 to 70,000
Zinc alloys	14,000 to 38,000

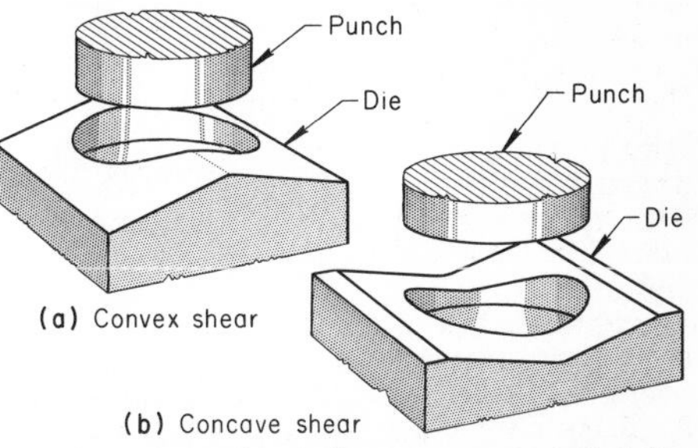

Angle and depth of shear are exaggerated for emphasis. Normally, depth of shear does not greatly exceed stock thickness.

Fig. 10. Convex shear and concave shear on blanking dies

Table 3. Scrap Allowance for Blanking

Work metal	Scrap allowance when length of skeleton segment between blanks or along edge is: 2t or less — Thickness of stock (t), in.	Edge of stock to blank, in.	Between blanks in row, in.	Greater than 2t — Thickness of stock (t), in.	Edge of stock to blank, in.	Between blanks in row, in.
Metals in general:						
Standard strip stock	Up to 0.021 ..	0.050	0.050	Up to 0.044 ..	0.050	0.050
	0.022-0.055 ..	0.040	0.040	Over 0.044 ..	0.9t	0.9t
	Over 0.055 ..	0.7t	0.7t			
Extra-wide stock and weak scrap skeleton	Up to 0.042 ..	0.060	0.050	Up to 0.033 ..	0.060	0.050
	Over 0.042 ..	1.4t	1.2t	Over 0.033 ..	1.8t	1.6t
Stock run thru twice	Up to 0.042 ..	0.060	0.050(a)	Up to 0.033 ..	0.060	0.050(a)
	0.043-0.055 ..	1.4t	0.040	0.034-0.044 ..	1.8t	0.040
	Over 0.055 ..	1.4t	0.7t	Over 0.044 ..	1.8t	0.9t
Stock run thru twice; blanks in rows 1 & 2 interlock	Up to 0.042 ..	0.060	0.050(b)	Up to 0.033 ..	0.060	0.050(b)
	Over 0.042 ..	1.4t	1.4t	Over 0.033 ..	1.8t	1.8t
Stainless, silicon and spring steels	Up to 0.042 ..	0.060 min	0.060 min	Up to 0.033 ..	0.060 min	0.060 min
	Over 0.042 ..	1.4t	1.4t	Over 0.033 ..	1.8t	1.8t
Ni-base magnetically soft alloys	All	0.060	0.060	All	1t(c)	1t(c)

(a) Allowance between blanks in the same row and also between blanks of the first and second rows. (b) Allow 0.060 in. between blanks at first and second rows. (c) When the blank edge is parallel to the edge of the stock, or when the length of the skeleton segment between blanks is more than 4t, scrap allowance is 1.8t.

Cutting force for a die with shear can be calculated after first finding the work done (energy used) in blanking. Work done in blanking equals the force required in blanking (load on the press) multiplied by the distance that the force acted:

$$W = Ls$$

where W is work done in blanking, in.-lb; L is load, lb; and s is distance the load acts (thickness multiplied by percentage of penetration before fracture), in. To obtain accurate work values, percentage penetration must be known accurately.

Cutting or blanking force is reduced by the use of angular shear in the die, the amount of reduction in force depending on the depth of the angular shear. The reduced average cutting force on the press is:

$$L_{sh} = \frac{W}{s + s_1}$$

where L_{sh} is average cutting force, lb, with angular shear; W is work done in blanking, in.-lb; s is the distance, in., that the load acts (thickness multiplied by percentage penetration before fracture); and s_1 is the depth of angular shear, in.

In simplified practice, some plants ignore partial shear in calculating cutting force for blanking. When full shear is used, force is calculated as without shear and then reduced by 30%.

Stripping force is the force that is needed (when drop-through is not used) to free the blank from the die or the strip from the punch when they stick or jam because of springback. Stripping force can be calculated from the following formula:

$$L_{st} = kA$$

where L_{st} is stripping force, lb; k is a stripping constant, psi; and A is area of the cut surface, sq in. (stock thickness, t, in., multiplied by length or perimeter of cut, l, in.). Approximate values for the constant, k (as determined by experiment for low-carbon steel), are: 1500 for sheet metal thinner than 0.062 in., when the cut is near an edge or near a preceding cut; 2100 for other cuts in sheet thinner than 0.062 in.; and 3000 for sheet more than 0.062 in. thick.

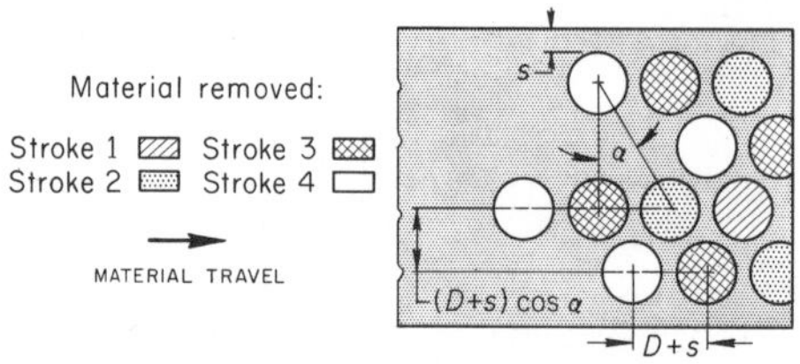

Material removed: Stroke 1, Stroke 2, Stroke 3, Stroke 4. MATERIAL TRAVEL. s, a, $(D+s)\cos a$, $D+s$

Fig. 11. Strip layout for blanking four circles per stroke with minimum waste of material

Factors That Affect Processing

Factors that affect the processing of blanks include the following:

1. Size and shape of the blank
2. Material for blanking
3. Form in which the material is supplied
4. Thickness of the blank
5. Production quantity and schedule
6. Quality specifications
7. Availability of equipment and tools
8. Number and type of subsequent operations required for completing the work.

Size and shape of the blank affect the form and handling of the material blanked, the blanking method, and the handling of the completed blank.

Thickness of the blank affects the press load required (see the preceding section, "Calculation of Force Requirements"), and the selection of equipment and the choice of blanking and handling methods (see the section "Effect of Work-Metal Thickness", on page 42 in this article).

Production quantity and schedule determine the choice of equipment. Usually, a total production of less than 10,000 pieces is considered a short run, 10,000 to 100,000 pieces a medium run, and more than 100,000 pieces is considered a long run.

Quality specifications and tolerances for thickness, camber, width, length, flatness and finish affect the handling of the material.

The availability of single, double or triple-action presses (rated at various tonnages, sizes, speeds, lengths of stroke, strokes per minute, and shut heights) affects the selection of the processing method. The availability and capacity of auxiliary press equipment can have an effect on the selection of a tooling system, and on whether a part can be made in-plant.

Operations that follow blanking also affect the choice of equipment, the processing method and the handling procedures. Such subsequent operations may include piercing, bending, forming, deep drawing, machining, grinding or finishing. Only rarely is the blank a final product.

Selection of Work-Metal Form

Work metal for blanking in presses ordinarily is in the form of flat sheets, strip, or coil stock. Less frequently, steel plate is blanked in presses (see the section "Effect of Work-Metal Thickness", in this article). In some applications, the metal is preformed before blanking.

Special preparation of the work metal ordinarily is not required for the blanking operation itself. However, annealing, leveling or cleaning often is needed because of subsequent forming operations on the blank, as discussed in the article "Press Forming of Low-Carbon Steel", in this volume.

Sheet or Strip. Flat sheet usually is the work metal for large blanks, such as automobile roofs. Square-sheared sheet can be used as a blank, or it can be blanked in a die. Small quantities of blanks, regardless of size, usually are made from straight lengths of sheet or strip.

Coil stock is used for mass production, whenever possible. In continuous production, the use of coil stock can save as much as one-third of the time needed for producing an equal quantity from flat stock. Besides, there are fewer scrap ends when coil stock is used.

Sheet metal is least expensive when it is supplied in large coils from the mill. For most applications, the coil must be slit to the proper width for blanking, and some edge material must be trimmed off. Parts sometimes can be made most economically in a progressive die by using coil stock that is the width of the developed blank, as in Example 28 in the article on Piercing.

Blank Layout

In medium and high production of medium-size blanks, the cost of material is 50 to 75% of the total cost of the blank; for large blanks, it may be more than 95% of the total cost of the blank. Substantial savings in net material cost often can be achieved by coordinating blank layout with the selection of stock form and width to minimize the amount of scrap produced.

Several trial layouts may be needed to find the width of stock and the layout that use the material most efficiently, while taking into account possible effects of orientation of parts on subsequent operations. The layout must include the minimum workable scrap allowance between blanks, providing just enough material to support or hold down the strip during blanking. Scrap allowances, based on the use of well-maintained equipment and good shop practice, are shown in Table 3.

The percentage of scrap in a strip layout can be calculated as:

$$100\ (1 - A_B/A_S)$$

where A_B is area of blanks produced in one press stroke, and A_S is area of strip consumed by one press stroke, or strip width times feed length.

Round blanks can be staggered in rows, at the same spacing as for hexagons (Fig. 11), for the most efficient blanking from a long strip. With such a layout, 20 to 40% more blanks can be made from a given amount of material than by blanking each circle from a separate square. With the layout shown in Fig. 11, each press stroke (after the third stroke) produces four blanks—spaced so as to provide enough room for mounting the punches and dies.

The percentage of scrap loss for the layout of Fig. 11 can be calculated using the general formula given above and the following:

$$A_B = n\,\pi D^2/4$$
$$A_S = wl$$
$$l = D + s$$
$$w = (D + 2s) + (n - 1)(D + s)\cos\alpha$$

where n is number of rows of blanks across strip width; D is blank diameter, in.; l is feed length (one blank made in each row per press stroke), in.; w is strip width, in.; s is scrap allowance from edge of strip to blank and between blanks, in.; and α is angular displacement between blanks, degrees. The area of the holes pierced in a blank is not considered in these calculations, because it does not affect the efficiency of the layout.

Rectangular blanks generally can be laid out more easily than other shapes. The following example compares the cost of producing notched rectangular blanks from two different layouts, by three methods.

Example 7. Reducing Cost by Improving Layout and Blanking Method (Table 4)

Table 4 shows the costs for producing a notched rectangular blank in quantities of 10,000, 100,000 and 500,000 by three different methods and from two different layouts. The blanks were made from cold rolled, commercial quality 1010 steel, 0.036 in. thick (20 gage). The blank and layouts are illustrated in Table 4.

In method A, the blanks were made from sheets purchased to 36½-in. width by 78½-in. length. The sheet was sheared to 36 by 78 in., and then notched and pierced in a punch press. As shown in Table 4, nine blanks were produced from each sheet.

For method B, the blank was turned 90° in relation to the layout for method A, and was produced from a sheet sheared to 60¼-in. length from 26¼-in.-wide coil stock. Five blanks were made from each sheet by notching, trimming ends, piercing and cutoff, in a press. Method A cost less than method B for 10,000 blanks because of lower tool cost; for larger quantities, method B cost less (see Table 4).

The layout for method C was like that of method B, but the blanks were produced continuously from coil stock roll-fed to a blanking-press line, instead of from sheared lengths. The lower cost of labor was the chief reason that method C cost slightly less than method B.

Odd-shape blanks generally are more difficult to lay out for the greatest economy. The following example shows three different layouts, the most economical of which would require a change in the shape of the blank to save material.

Table 4. Comparative Costs for Producing the Same Blanks by Three Different Methods (Example 7)

Cost item	Cost for producing blanks in quantities of: 10,000	100,000	500,000
Method A (Nine Blanks From Sheared Sheet)			
Material	$2,512	$25,120	$125,600
Labor(a)	320	3,205	16,025
Setup(b)	100	100	100
Tool(c)	1,800	1,800	1,800
Total cost	$4,732	$30,225	$143,525
Cost per blank	$0.4732	$0.30225	$0.2870
Method B (Five Blanks From Narrower Sheet)			
Material	$2,437	$24,370	$121,850
Labor(a)	109	1,090	5,450
Setup(d)	75	75	75
Tool(c)	2,500	2,500	2,500
Total cost	$5,121	$28,035	$129,875
Cost per blank	$0.5121	$0.28035	$0.2597
Method C (Blanks From Coil Stock)			
Material	$2,427	$24,270	$121,350
Labor(a)	55	550	2,750
Setup(b)	100	100	100
Tool(c)	2,500	2,500	2,500
Total cost	$5,082	$27,420	$126,700
Cost per blank	$0.5082	$0.2742	$0.2534

1010 steel, cold rolled, commercial quality, 0.036 in.

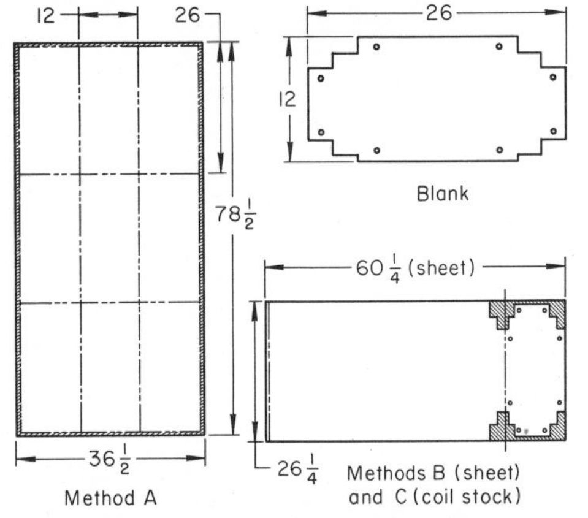

(a) At $5 per hour. (b) Ten setups of 2 hr each, at $5 per hour. (c) Amortized over 1 year. (d) Ten setups of 1.5 hr each, at $5 per hour.

Example 8. Effect of Blank Layout on Cost (Fig. 12)

In determining the most economical procedure for manufacturing a simple odd-shape blank, three different blank layouts were considered (Fig. 12). The strip used was hot rolled, commercial quality 1010 steel, 0.12 in. thick.

Layout A in Fig. 12 was simple but wasteful; a blank could be produced with one stroke of the press.

Layout B would use less material, but the die would have to blank two pieces per stroke, which would increase tooling cost, or the material would have to be passed through the press a second time, which would add to labor cost. For flat lengths of strip, this would add 10 to 15% to labor cost; coil stock would have to be re-coiled for a second pass, causing still higher labor cost.

Layout C would have been the simplest and least expensive. It would make two blanks with one press stroke. Because layout C called for a change in the design of the blank, it could be used only if the shape were not functional.

The table accompanying Fig. 12 summarizes costs for materials for the three layouts.

Nesting (interlocking of blanks in the layout to save material) should be done wherever the shape of the blank permits; this is possible with many irregular blanks.

Figure 13 shows a layout in which irregular blanks are nested so that an appreciable amount of material is saved. With such a layout, a double die may be used, blanking two pieces per stroke. A single die can be used for short runs; the strip is turned around after the first pass and fed through the die again.

Another way of nesting blanks is a layout such as the one illustrated in Fig. 14. With this layout three punches cut four pieces per stroke (after the third press stroke), in a shearing action that produces no scrap except at the ends of the strip.

Other strip layouts in which the blanks have been nested are shown in the articles "Press Bending of Low-Carbon Steel", which begins on page 89, and "Press Forming of Low-Carbon Steel", which begins on page 112.

Use of Full Stock Width. Blanks that have two parallel sides sometimes can be made most economically in a layout that uses the full width of the stock. The remaining outline of the blank is produced by shearing, lancing, notching or parting (or a combination of these operations). (See layout C in Fig. 12, and Example 28, page 51, in the article on Piercing.)

Effect of Rolling Direction. For blanks that must later be bent or formed, consideration must be given in layout to the orientation of the blanks with respect to the direction of rolling (grain direction).

Ideally, blanks should be laid out so that severe bends are made with the bend axis at right angles to the direction of rolling, or, if this is not practical, with the bend axis at an

1010 steel, hot rolled, commercial quality, 0.12 in.

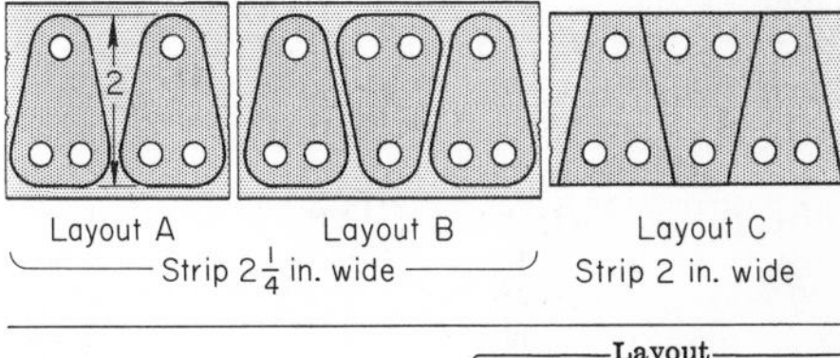

Item	Layout A	B	C
Metal per blank, sq in.	3.105	2.54	2.00
Cost of metal per 1000 blanks (at 10¢/lb)	$10.82	$8.85	$6.97

Fig. 12. Three blank layouts and comparison of metal cost for each (Example 8)

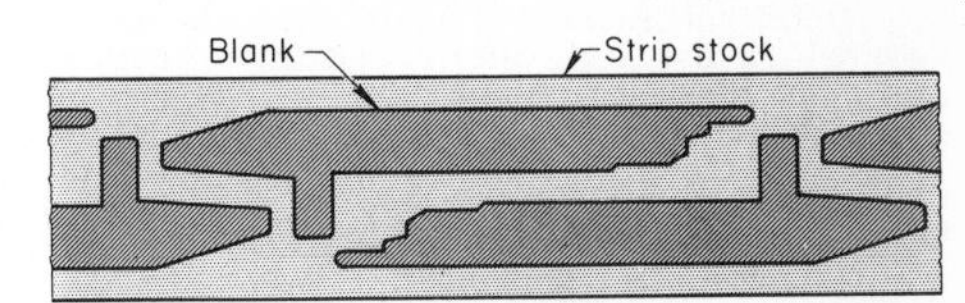

Fig. 13. Nesting of irregular blanks in layout to save material

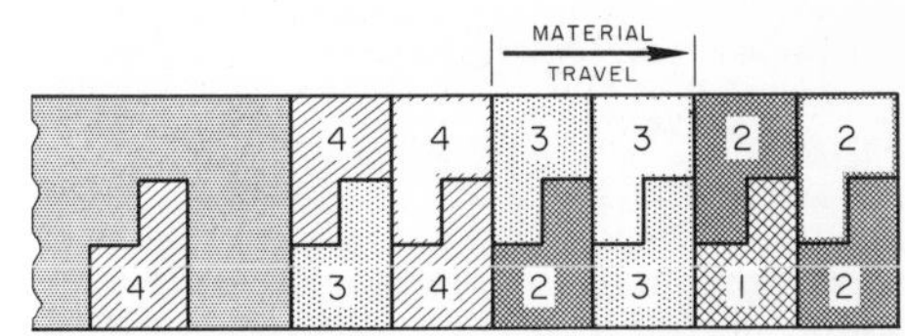

Numbers show order of press strokes.

The three shaded shapes for each press stroke denote the blanks produced directly by the three punches. The unshaded shape for each press stroke denotes a blank produced by the action of adjacent punches.

Fig. 14. Layout for scrapless blanking of four blanks per press stroke, using three punches

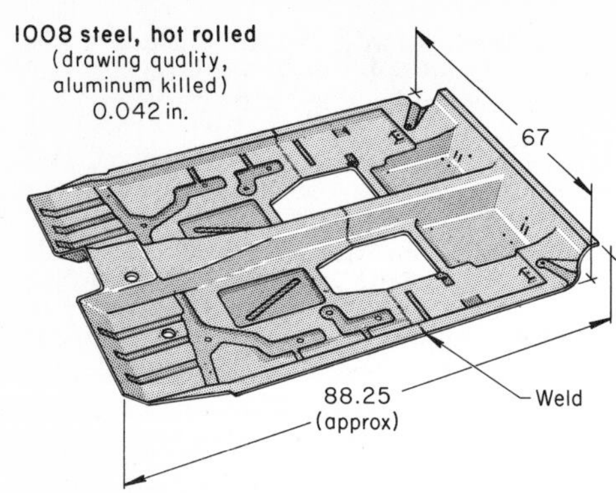

Fig. 15. Floor panel formed from a lap-seam welded two-piece blank at 7% less cost than from a one-piece blank (Example 9)

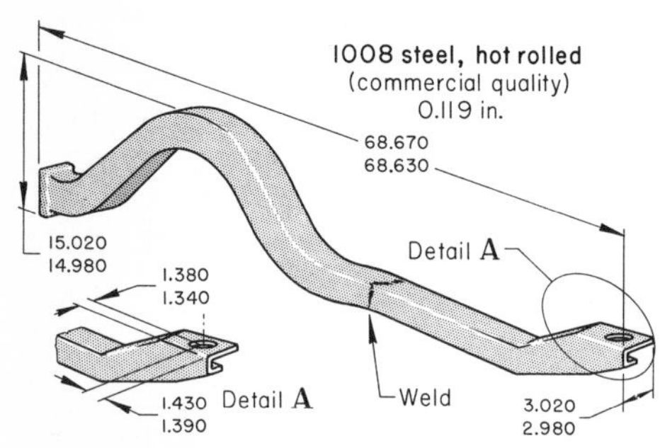

Fig. 16. Automobile-frame side rail that was formed from two blanks joined by MIG *welding* (Example 10)

angle to the direction of rolling. Stretching should be in the direction of rolling, whenever possible. (See the articles "Press Bending of Low-Carbon Steel" and "Press Forming of Low-Carbon Steel" for examples and illustrations of blank layouts made to take advantage of the direction of rolling.)

Welded Blanks

Welded blanks are used when they have advantages over one-piece blanks, as in the following situations:

1 The welded blank may cost less than an equivalent one-piece blank if scrap or other low-cost metal can be used to make the welded blank, or if tooling and production for the one-piece blank cost more than for the welded one.
2 Stock for a welded blank may be more readily available than stock for an equivalent one-piece blank.
3 The blank may have a shape that would waste more material if it were made in one piece instead of being welded. Sometimes material can be saved by welding projecting portions, such as tabs and ears, to simpler shapes.
4 The welded blank, when used in subsequent forming operations, may reduce the cost of tooling. Flat or simple shapes are welded in a layout designed to avoid the presence of seams in certain portions of the blank, and to permit automatic welding, if possible.

Large blanks that would cost extra because of width or for other reasons if they were made in one piece can sometimes be made at less cost by welding, as shown in the following example.

Example 9. Use of a Large Lap-Seam Welded Blank (Fig. 15)

Originally, the blank for a large press-formed floor panel (Fig. 15) was made from a single sheet of hot rolled, drawing quality, aluminum-killed 1008 steel, 0.042 by 75 by 99 in. Because of the large size, the sheets had to be obtained from a distant supplier at extra freight charges.

The added costs for shipping and extra width were saved by making the blank from two pieces of 0.042-in. sheet stock, 56 by 75 in. and 44 by 75 in., joined by lap-seam welding. The weld seam was in a portion of the formed panel that was not subject to severe deformation.

The one-piece blank cost $8.19. Cost of the two-piece blank, including $0.45 for welding, was $7.63 — a saving of $0.56 per blank.

Difficult shapes that would waste a considerable amount of material if they were made in one piece can sometimes be made by welding two or more simple blanks together. In the application described in the following example, two developed blanks were welded and then formed into a bent channel.

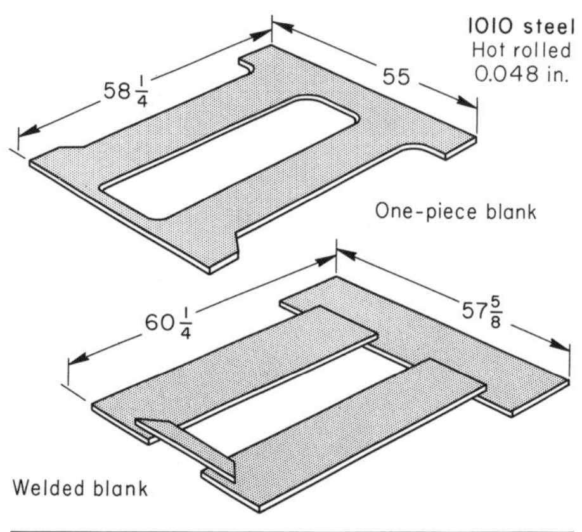

Cost item	Cost per blank One-piece(a)	Welded(b)
Material	$3.6980	$2.6354
Labor and overhead	0.6758	1.0879
Total	$4.3738	$3.7233
Saving		$0.6505

(a) Entire method consisted of shearing sheet, blanking sheared piece, trimming and piercing, and flanging. (b) Entire method consisted of shearing four pieces from sheet, spot welding, blanking weldment, trimming and piercing, and flanging.

Fig. 17. One-piece blank, and more economical spot welded blank, for a truck floor pan (Example 11)

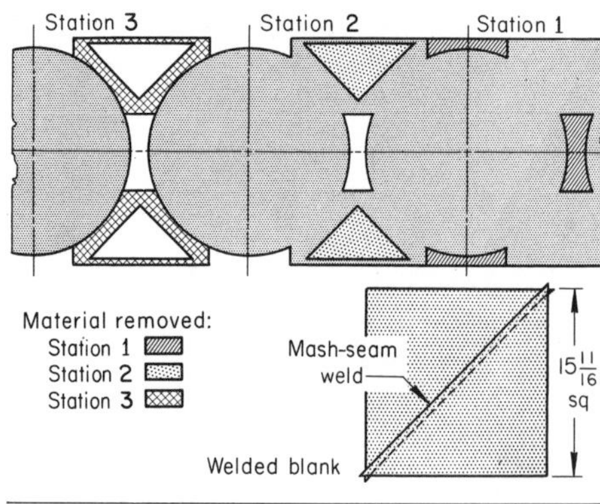

Cost item	Cost per blank One-piece	Welded
Material	$0.2248	$0.0292(a)
Labor	0.0030(b)	0.0337(c)
Total	$0.2278	$0.0629
Saving		$0.1649

(a) Scrap value of metal was 1¢/lb. (b) For slitting and shearing. (c) For welding ($0.0303) and dipping in rust preventive ($0.0034).

Fig. 18. Strip layout that yielded triangular "scrap" pieces from which a square blank was made by mash-seam welding at 28% of the cost of a one-piece blank (Example 12)

Example 10. Use of Two MIG-Welded Blanks to Form an Automobile-Frame Rail (Fig. 16)

Figure 16 shows a side rail for an automobile frame that was formed from 0.119-in.-thick hot rolled, commercial quality 1008 steel. The blank for this rail had a shape that could be made in one piece only with excessive waste of metal in scrap. The two pieces used were blanked from nested layouts with little scrap waste.

Blanking was done in a die that made both pieces in a single press stroke. The two portions were butted and joined by high-speed automatic MIG welding and then formed. Tolerance on all dimensions shown in Fig. 16 was ±0.020 in.

The saving in metal was more than the cost of welding, but if production needs had been fewer than 10,000 pieces, the saving in metal would not have paid for the welding and the blanking dies.

The production quantity was 300,000 rails made in lot sizes of 20,000 pieces.

Open Shapes. A blank with a large cutout can sometimes be made at less cost than a one-piece blank by welding simpler pieces together, as demonstrated in the next example.

Example 11. Use of a Spot Welded Four-Piece Blank to Reduce Cost (Fig. 17)

The blank for a large floor pan used in a truck originally was made in one piece by blanking in the usual manner and then trimming a large inner portion from the middle of the blank. Because the trimmed material was scrap, the method was changed to make the blank at lower cost by spot welding four pieces together, as shown in Fig. 17. Both blanks were completed in the same way — trimming and piercing, and then flanging. Costs for floor pans produced by the two methods are compared in the table accompanying Fig. 17.

Waste metal sometimes can be joined by welding to make a blank that costs less than a one-piece blank, as shown in the following example.

Example 12. Blank Produced by Mash-Seam Welding of Pieces Salvaged From Another Blanking Operation (Fig. 18)

A large circle was blanked from coiled strip in three stations of a progressive die, as shown in Fig. 18. Some of the scrap metal was saved for later use by blanking two triangles in station 2 at each stroke of the press. The triangles then were mash-seam welded to make a 15 11/16-in.-square blank (Fig. 18). This square was drawn and trimmed to make a blower cover. A comparison of costs for producing the square blank from one piece of metal and from two scrap triangles by mash-seam welding is shown in the table with Fig. 18. The metal was cold rolled low-carbon steel or enameling iron.

Welding methods used in making blanks include resistance welding methods (lap-seam, spot, foil butt-seam, mash-seam, flash, and high-frequency butt) and fusion welding.

Lap-seam welding (wheel electrodes) often is used (see Example 9). Tooling is simple, if the components are joined first by tack welding. The disadvantages of lap-seam welding are loose edges, and joints that are double the thickness of the work metal.

Spot welding, which was used in Example 11, is fast, and needs only simple, inexpensive tooling. The disadvantages of spot welding are loose edges, and joints that are not tight and are not as strong as those made by other methods.

Foil butt-seam welding is a fast method that makes smooth, tight joints with no loose edges. Its disadvantages include the cost of adding foil to one or both sides of the seam, and the need for using starting tabs to make strong joints.

Mash-seam welding makes smooth joints that often need no grinding, and tight joints that have no loose edges. It was used in Example 12. Disadvantages include the short life of electrodes, and the high cost of tooling that results from difficulty in maintaining the small overlap.

Flash welding uses simple tooling; the joints are tight and free from loose edges. However, the length of joint that can be produced by flash welding is limited, and the joints are rough and therefore must be ground before the weldment can be worked in a die.

High-frequency butt welding is fast and can be used to join two dissimilar metals. Electrode life is good. It requires costly equipment, however, and is generally suitable only for mass production.

Fusion welding methods include metal-arc inert-gas (MIG) and tungsten-arc inert-gas (TIG). MIG welding was used in Example 10.

Presses

Most blanking is done in single-action mechanical presses.

Some dies can be used only with a particular type of press; usually the die is made to suit a specific press. The capacity or tonnage rating must be adequate for the work, and must be well above the calculated cutting force (see page 33). Press capacities are given in tons at a certain distance above the bottom of the stroke. This distance must suit the die and the operation. Most blanking is done near the bottom of the stroke where the available force is largest. In compound dies, blanking may be done near midstroke, where the available force is much lower than at the bottom.

Size of bed, shut height, stroke length, and speed must all be suitable for the die and the work. Some types of dies can be run at high speeds and some need moderate or slow speeds, as discussed in the section "Construction and Use of Conventional Dies", which starts on the next page.

Construction and Use of Short-Run Dies

Small and medium quantities of blanks often are produced in punch presses by the use of inexpensive short-run dies. These include steel-rule dies, template dies (sometimes called plate dies or continental dies), and subpress dies. Although most applications of such dies are for production quantities of a few hundred to 10,000 pieces, suitably constructed dies of these types have been used for quantities of 100,000 pieces or more.

Short-run dies are used to a limited extent for blanking initial quantities of parts that are to be mass-produced. Because they can be made and put into operation more quickly than conventional dies, short-run dies make it possible to expedite delivery of completed parts.

In addition, short-run dies are used to produce trial lots of parts that may be subject to extensive changes in design. If the trial lots show that die design changes are needed, the changes can be made at less cost before the conventional die is completed. After the conventional die has been set up, either the entire production can be transferred to it, or both dies can be used.

For small quantities (fewer than 100 pieces), even the most inexpensive short-run blanking die may not be justified. Such small quantities of blanks generally are cut at less cost with standard tools, such as a nibbler, a squaring shear, or a rotary shear. Also, small quantities of blanks may be made by contour band sawing, routing, gas cutting, filing or machining.

Steel-rule dies are simple, inexpensive dies that are made by setting thin, bevel-edge strips of high-carbon tool steel on edge to outline the blank. The rule is set tightly into a slot in plain or impregnated plywood, and the plywood is backed by a steel subplate, as shown in Fig. 19. The die plate or template is attached directly to a steel subplate, and both upper and lower subplates are fastened to master die shoes, which are mounted in a conventional press.

Steel-rule dies are used for blanking, piercing, notching, and shallow forming. For work on flat blanks or on flat, sheared stock of low-carbon steel up to about ½ in. thick, a steel-rule die usually can be made more rapidly and at less cost than any other kind of die. Blanks as large as 4 by 7 ft have been made in steel-rule dies.

Die. The steel rule that is used as the die is made of high-carbon steel or of a tool steel such as W1 or W2, in spring temper and other hardnesses. It is available in stock lengths in several thicknesses, from 0.014 to 0.170 in., and in widths of 1.25 in. and narrower. Actual printers' rules of thickness from 1 point (0.014 in.) to 12 points (0.170 in.) are sometimes used. The finished rule usually has a square back edge, and a cutting edge that is ground to a 45° bevel or to a V-edge.

The back edge is fitted tightly into sawed slots in hard plywood as shown in Fig. 19, so that it will cut the outline of the blank. The steel subplate is used to back up the steel rule and support the plywood.

Punch. For blanking low-carbon steel, a die plate (high-carbon or tool steel template), of the same shape as the required blank, is used as the punch, opposing the steel rule. Other punch elements and die parts, as needed, are added to the die for piercing holes and slots at the same time that the blanking is done. Solid steel blocks, instead of a steel rule, may be used in the die to cut sharp corners and notches in the blank.

For some work, including the cutting of paper and other soft materials, the punch may be a block of hard wood, or a thick sheet of rubber or other soft material, with a working surface that extends beyond the area enclosed by the steel rule.

Stripper. For cutting paper and leather, the steel-rule die is stripped by elastic material such as sponge rubber, which is added to the die. In blanking low-carbon steel, blocks of tougher solid rubber may be used as strippers. Positive spring-loaded steel stripper plates are also used.

Accuracy. The accuracy of the blanks produced in steel-rule dies depends mainly on the skill of the diemaker and the care used in their construction. For noncritical parts blanked in steel-rule dies, the tolerance may be as large as ±1⁄32 in.; for more critical parts, the work can be located accurately to maintain a tolerance of ±0.005 in. Closer tolerances on blanks can be obtained at increased cost by using rotary-head millers or jig boring machines in constructing the dies.

Because holes and slots made by steel-rule blanking are pierced with conventional punch and die elements that are added to the steel-rule die, they can be produced to the same tolerances as in conventional blanking.

Steel-rule dies commonly blank laminations with burrs only 0.002 in. high.

Cost. A steel-rule die, made to blank low to moderate quantities of low-carbon steel, generally costs about 20% as much as a conventional die that is made for mass production of similar work.

The following example describes the use of a steel-rule die for stopgap and trial production of an automobile part. A die change was made cheaply; then, after being proved successful in the steel-rule die, the same change was included in the design of the conventional die for production use.

Example 13. Use of a Steel-Rule Die for Temporary Production (Fig. 20)

A steel-rule die was used to blank a part for an automobile frame, to begin production without waiting until the conventional die could be delivered. It was expected that the steel-rule die would have to produce 325 blanks before production could be changed to the conventional die.

The die, shown in Fig. 20, was used in a 250-ton straight-side press to blank annealed cold rolled low-carbon steel, 0.156 in. thick by 9 by 19 in., with three 9⁄16-in.-diam holes and three round-end slots ⅝ by 1½ in. Tolerances were ±1⁄32 in. on the blank outline, and ±0.005 in. on the pierced holes and slots. No burr limits were specified.

The steel rule was made of 12-point rule stock (0.170 in. thick by 1¼ in. wide), set full depth into hard plywood ⅝ in. thick. A die plate of steel, which fitted inside the rule, was used as the punch. The die was made by measuring a developed formed blank.

The ease and low cost of making a change in a steel-rule die proved important in this

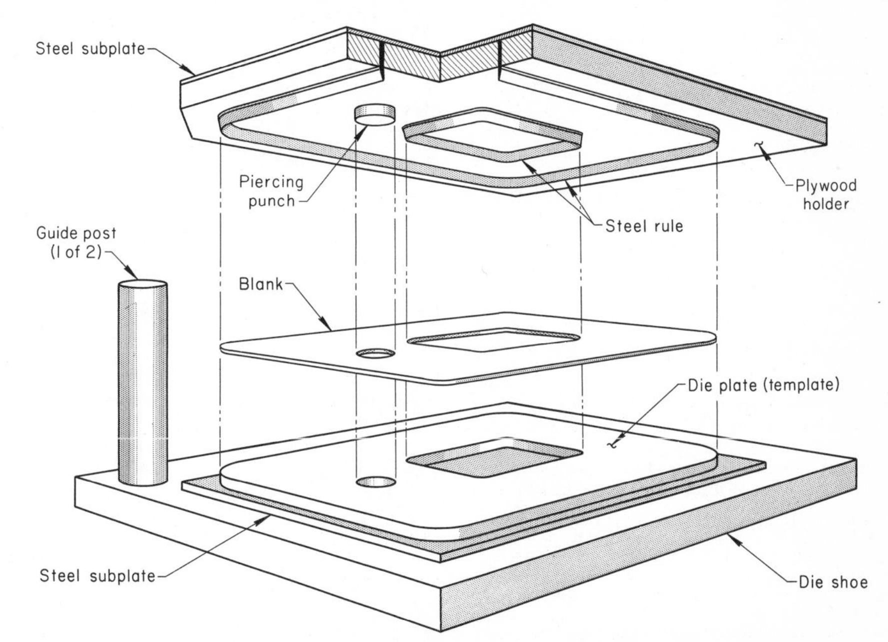

Fig. 19. Exploded view of a steel-rule die. See text for discussion.

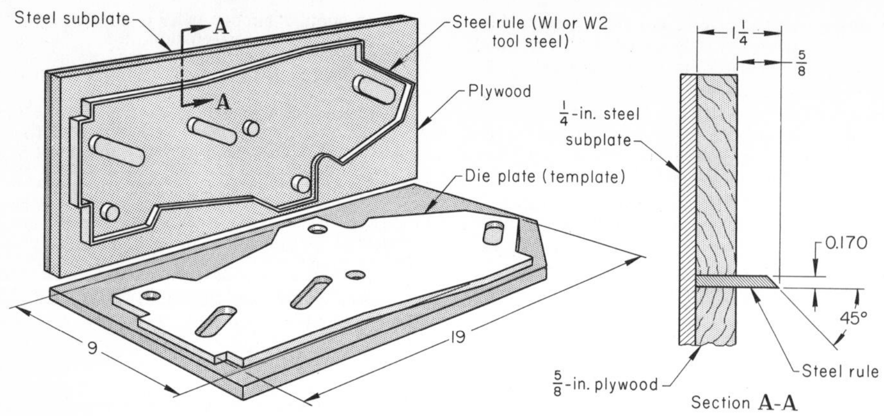

Fig. 20. Steel-rule die that was used as temporary tooling for blanking of low-carbon steel sheet 0.156 in. thick (Example 13)

application, because it was decided that one of the holes would not be needed. The punch that had been added for that hole was simply removed from the steel-rule die. After tryout, that hole was also eliminated in the conventional die before it was completed. The change, if made after the conventional die had been completed, would have cost much more.

The steel-rule die cost less than $800, which was 20% of the cost of the conventional die. The steel-rule die was fed and unloaded by hand, so that production was only a few pieces per minute. More than 1000 blanks were made in this steel-rule die.

Template dies (also called plate dies) are competitive with steel-rule dies, both in cost and in the quantity that they can produce.

An exploded view of the elements of a template die is shown in Fig. 21. Punches and die elements can be added, as in steel-rule dies, to combine piercing with blanking.

Punch. The punch or template (Fig. 21) is made to fit the outline of the blank to be produced. Ordinarily the punch is made of medium-carbon steel plate (1040, 1050 or 4140) or of ground flat stock such as O2 tool steel, on which the edges may be flame hardened. In more difficult applications or where longer life is needed, the punch may be made of D2 or equivalent tool steel and hardened.

Die. The die usually is assembled of doweled hardened blocks of steel, ground to fit the punch with proper clearance. The same materials are used as for the punch.

Construction. Typical clearance for template dies is 0.003 in. The construction shown in Fig. 21 is satisfactory for blanking low-carbon steel in the same types of applications as steel-rule dies. For severe blanking, a template die can be made stronger by using one-piece construction or adding pins to prevent the die blocks from spreading, and by nesting the die or die segments into a recess in the die backing plate (subplate).

Operation. A continuous strip of stock can be fed into a template die, feeding the stock against a stop for each press stroke, using a side guide for the stock.

Usually blocks of tough rubber are used as strippers (Fig. 21), pushing the blank back into the strip, so that the blank is removed from the die by the feed motion of the strip.

Typical applications of template dies are described in the two examples that follow.

Example 14. Blanking 0.060-In.-Thick Laminations in a Template Die

Motor laminations of 0.060-in.-thick pickled hot rolled low-carbon steel were blanked in a template die. The blank was 12.5 by 5.5 in. The punch was made of a one-piece template, except for inserts that were provided where changes might be needed. The die was made with 0.003 in. clearance all around the punch (template).

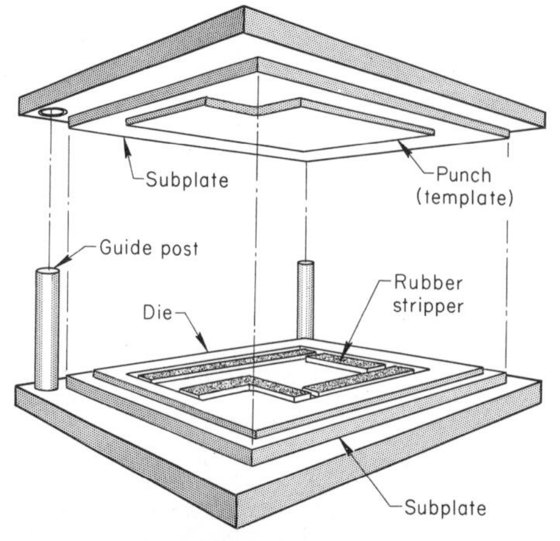

Fig. 21. Exploded view of a template die

The die was made of D2 tool steel. Rubber blocks were used for strippers, which pushed the blank back into the skeleton, in the vertical press, so that the blank was unloaded by the feeding of the stock. Feed by hand produced fewer than ten pieces per minute.

The burr was about 0.002 in., well below the specified limit of 0.004 in. Estimated die life was 100,000 pieces.

Example 15. Blanking Stock 0.130 In. Thick in a Template Die

Small quantities of a blank for a tractor part were made from 0.130-in.-thick hot rolled low-carbon steel in a template die. The blank measured 3½ by 10¾ in.; burr limit was 0.005 in. The die blocks for this heavy-duty blanking were nested into the die backing plate (subplate). The work metal was hand fed to the die. Production rate was a few pieces per minute; annual production was less than a thousand pieces.

Subpress dies are short-run die sets that are attached to the press bed, but in which the punch shoe is not attached to the ram. They require less setup time, but have a lower production rate, than conventional dies. The length of stroke of a subpress die is limited, because springs are used to raise the punch.

Subpress dies sometimes are used to blank the precision parts used in instruments and timepieces.

Self-contained notching tools can be purchased ready to install as subpress tools. Notching units, consisting of both punch and die mounted in individual C-frame units, are available in a variety of standard-corner, V, and square-edge sizes for notching low-carbon steel in thicknesses up to ¼ in. Special shapes of irregular outline can be incorporated in standard notching units. The notching units can be used singly or in groups, and can be used in combination with piercing tools of similar construction.

Each unit is self-contained and self-stripping by means of springs. The punches are held in close alignment and are not attached to the ram of the press. Each unit is located, pinned, and bolted to a die plate, template, or T-slot plate, and mounted on the bed of any type of press or press brake of adequate shut height.

This type of subpress tool can be used to make small blanks, but it is more commonly used to notch and pierce precut blanks. The units can be reused to produce parts of different shapes by relocating the tools.

Construction and Use of Conventional Dies

Conventional blanking dies consist basically of one or more mating pairs of rigid punches and dies, and are the standard tooling for production blanking of sheet metal in a press. Mating pairs of metal punches and dies are combined in various ways; and additional components are added to make up compound, progressive, transfer and multiple dies.

Conventional dies are costly, specialized tools, used generally for only one product, but they are so efficient, accurate, and productive that ordinarily they are the best method of mass production at the lowest cost per piece. Occasionally they are used for short-run production when tolerances are exceptionally stringent, or when other reasons make the use of short-run dies impractical.

Conventional dies are more accurate than most short-run tooling, and they retain their accuracy for a greater number of pieces. Also, they generally can be resharpened after wear has affected their action or the quality of the work. Before dies are worn out, they ordinarily have been resharpened many times. It is common for conventional dies to produce several million blanks before they must be replaced.

Tool materials commonly used for blanking low-carbon steel sheet in conventional dies include, in order of increasing lot size for which they are recommended: 1020 steel; W1, O1, A2 and D2 tool steels; and, for extremely long runs, carbide. For long runs on steel thicker than about ¼ in., M2 tool steel is used instead of carbide, because of the limited shock resistance of carbide. Type D2 tool steel is probably the most commonly used and most widely available tool material for mass-production blanking of steel and other metals.

Cold rolled sheet and hot rolled pickled-and-oiled sheet are far less damaging to tools than grit-blasted or hot rolled unpickled surfaces. Tool materials that have a high resistance to abrasion, such as A2 or D2 tool steel, are recommended for use in tools for the blanking of sizable production lots of hot rolled unpickled steel. (For detailed information on the selection of tool material and on tool life, the reader is referred to the article on Selection of Materials for Blanking and Piercing Dies, which begins on page 69 in this volume.)

Single-Operation Dies. The simplest conventional blanking dies are single-operation dies. They are used as separate units to produce blanks or as parts of more complex dies that do several operations on a workpiece. The separate stations of a progressive die are similar to single-operation dies (although integrally constructed), and transfer presses use many single-operation dies.

One of the commonest types is a drop-through die (Fig. 22), in which the severed blank is forced through the die opening by the downward motion of the punch, and drops through into a chute or container. This type of blanking die has a minimum number of parts and is relatively inexpensive. Another major advantage of drop-through blanking dies is their simple and reliable blank-ejection system, which is usually compatible with the use of this type of construction in progressive or transfer dies. In other types of dies, the ejection system may be more complicated than the die itself.

Disadvantages of drop-through dies for blanking include the following:

1 Unless parallels are placed between die and bolster, blanks must be small enough to go through the hole in the bed.
2 Blanks may distort by dishing.
3 Some shapes make drop-through difficult.
4 The die must be on the lower shoe and the punch on the upper shoe of the die set.

Two other types of single-operation blanking dies can be used when, because of size or susceptibility to damage, blanks or workpieces cannot be unloaded by dropping through the die, but can be removed between the die and punch faces. These are inverted and return dies.

Inverted dies (Fig. 23) have the punch on the lower shoe and the die on the upper shoe. A knockout pin releases the blank from the die, and the blank is removed mechanically or manually from the top of the punch. A scrap cutter is usually included, so that the scrap can be blown or knocked away. Sometimes the scrap is allowed to stack up in successive collars around the punch and is stripped off manually after a number of pieces have been blanked.

Return dies (Fig. 24) are made in the usual way, with the punch on the upper shoe and the die on the lower shoe. The punch shears the blank and presses it into the die cavity, as with other types of blanking dies. A spring-loaded pressure plate or die cushion acts as an ejector for the die, returning the blank to the surface of the die, where it can be picked off manually or mechanically. A spring-loaded plate on the upper shoe acts as a blankholder on the downstroke and as a punch stripper on the upstroke.

Like many inverted dies, a variation of the return die in Fig. 24 includes a scrap cutter (not shown in Fig. 24) that parts the ring of scrap so that it can drop away, be blown away, or be removed mechanically.

Inverted and return dies have the advantage of not needing a clearance hole to let the workpiece or blank drop through. The main disadvantages of inverted and return dies are (*a*) they are more expensive than drop-through dies, because they have more parts; and (*b*) they may require careful adjustment and synchronization of external ejectors and air blasts, which adds to setup costs. Of the two types, inverted dies generally are simpler to construct and have less complicated knockout mechanisms than the pressure-plate or die-cushion ejectors in return dies.

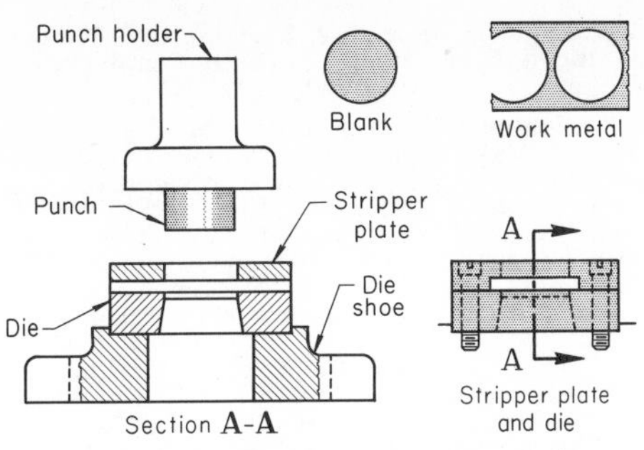

Fig. 22. Elements of a conventional drop-through blanking die

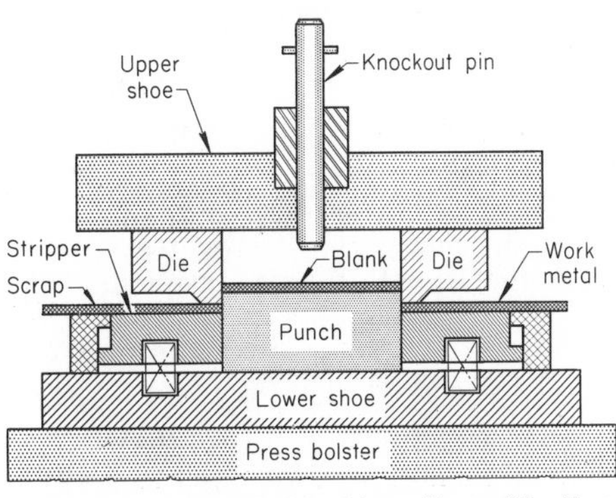

Fig. 23. Inverted blanking die, with the punch on the lower shoe and the die on the upper shoe

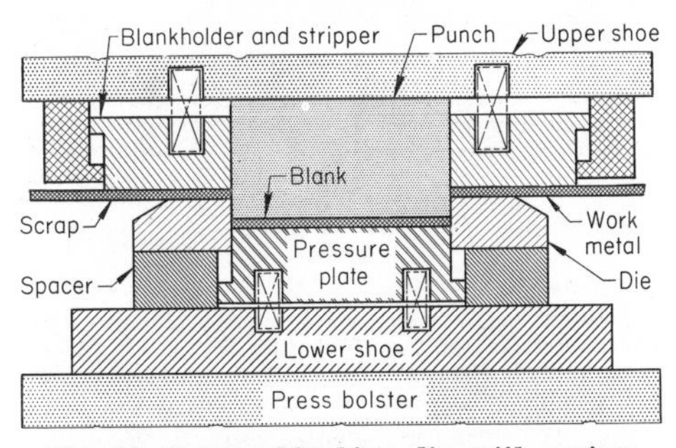

Fig. 24. Return blanking die, with spring-loaded pressure plate that acts both as a die cushion and as an ejector for the die

Return dies are better suited to continuous strip operation, because the strip remains in line and is not pressed down by the die over the punch. If the workpiece must be clamped before blanking, the blankholder or the pressure plate (or both) in a return die holds the workpiece or blank through the entire working stroke.

Instead of being removed by the methods described in the preceding paragraphs, the severed blank sometimes is pushed back (completely or partly) into the strip, to be removed later, as sometimes is done in a progressive die. Pushback also may be used for other purposes, such as to provide knockouts for fitting in electrical panels or junction boxes and in other sheet-metal products. Sometimes a flattening operation is added to help in pushback.

Compound dies do several operations on the same workpiece in the same stroke of the press, such as blank and pierce, or blank, pierce, and form. The elements of a compound die for simultaneous blanking and piercing are shown in Fig. 25. In this die, the blanking punch is in the bottom; a hole in the punch is used as the piercing die. The piercing punch and the blanking die are in the top.

Compound dies generally are more economical in mass production than a series of one-operation dies, and they usually are more accurate. For instance, a compound die that blanks and pierces a workpiece can hold the spacing between pierced holes or the relation of the pierced hole to the edge of the blank more accurately than would be possible if the individual operations were done in separate dies. This is because of possible variation in locating the blank for piercing, or in locating a prepierced strip for blanking.

Because the complexity of operation causes greater difficulties in unloading the workpiece, compound dies usually run slower than single-operation dies; the maximum speed of a compound die is about 250 strokes per minute. Other disadvantages of compound dies in comparison to single-operation dies are that they are more specialized, so that a change in the product is more likely to make the die obsolete; and both initial and maintenance costs are higher. An advantage of compound dies is that, because of their slower operation, they generally produce more pieces per sharpening than do single-operation dies.

Sometimes a complex compound die can be more economical than two simpler compound dies in making the same part. This is illustrated by the application described in the next example.

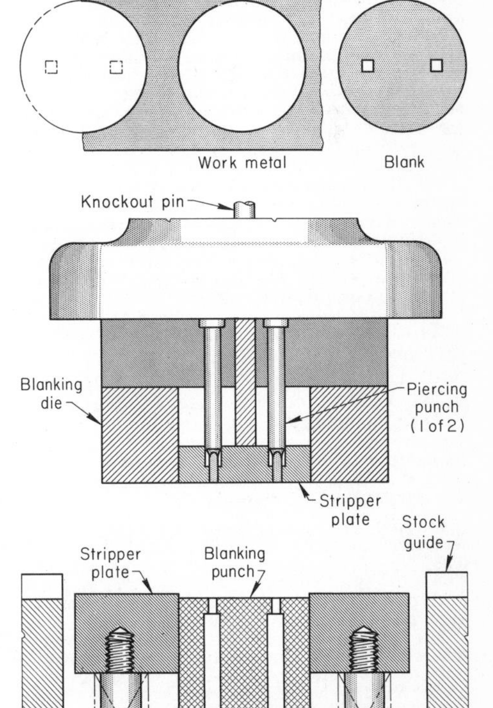

Fig. 25. Elements of a compound die for simultaneous blanking and piercing

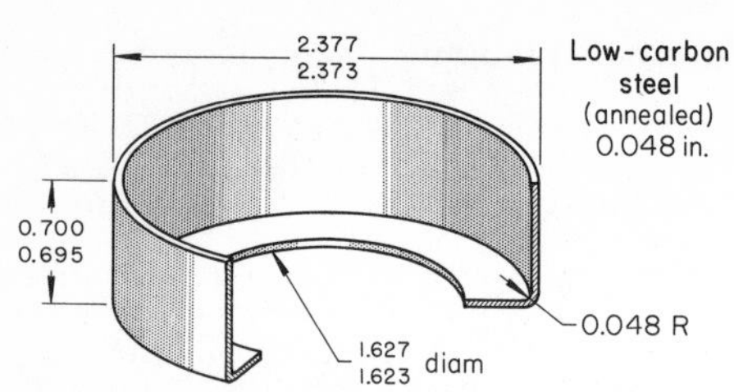

This part was previously made in two compound dies: blank and draw, and trim and pierce.

Fig. 26. Cup that was blanked, drawn, pierced and trimmed in a compound die (Example 16)

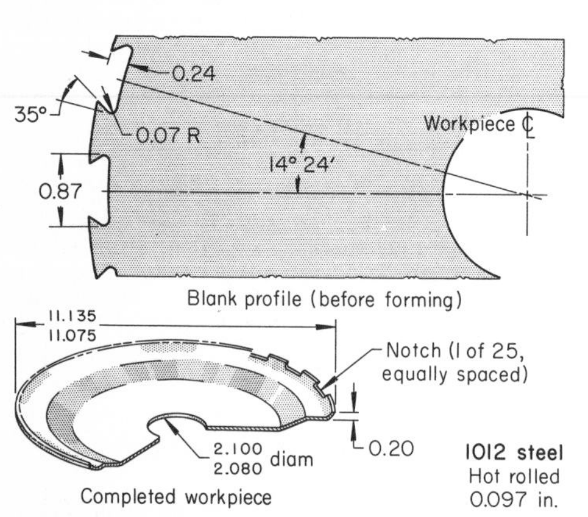

Fig. 27. Brake-drum back that was produced in two press operations, in a blank-and-notch die and in a restrike-and-form die (Example 18)

Example 16. Replacing Two Two-Operation Dies With a Four-Operation Die (Fig. 26)

Originally, the cup shown in Fig. 26 was produced from annealed cold rolled low-carbon steel in two compound dies, in separate press operations. The first die was a blank-and-draw die; the second was a pierce-and-pinch-trim die. Two separate dies had been used on the assumption that the large pierced hole in the cup would not leave enough tool thickness to sustain all four operations. A 45-ton open-back inclinable press was used for each of the two operations, at a production rate of 500 pieces per hour.

A restudy of the procedure led to the design of a die to blank, draw, pierce and trim — all in one press stroke. The same press was used at the same speed, thus cutting the labor cost per piece in half. Tooling cost also was reduced, because the cost of the new die (less than $1000) was less than the combined cost of the original two dies.

The two examples that follow describe production applications in which compound dies were used for blanking and other operations because of their inherent accuracy.

Example 17. Maintaining Extremely Accurate Hole Position in Blanking and Piercing

A part for a business machine was a rectangle of 1008 or 1010 cold rolled steel, 0.093 by 4 by 5 in., with two notched corners. The part was blanked, and six round holes and twenty rectangular holes were pierced, in a blank-and-pierce compound die.

The positions of all the holes were specified within a few thousandths of an inch, both hole-to-hole and hole-to-edge. Most of the holes had to be in accurate position within ±0.002 in. Extreme accuracy of hole position was assured by guiding the piercing punches in the stripper and by trimming the blank in the compound die.

Anticipated demand was 2000 to 3000 pieces per month for an indefinite number of years. The part was case hardened, and ground on both faces to remove burrs. The die was made of D2 tool steel and was designed for a life of 500,000 pieces.

Example 18. Blanking, Forming and Piercing a Brake-Drum Back in Compound Dies (Fig. 27)

An automobile brake-drum back, shown in Fig. 27, was formed from hot rolled 1012 steel in two press operations. A compound die was used to blank and notch the part in a 200-ton press, at the rate of 17½ strokes per minute, making one part per stroke. The tolerances shown in Fig. 27 were maintained in production with ordinary shop practice, as was the tolerance on the 14° 24′ angle (±0° 30′). The die, made of vanadium tool steel, required reworking after 50,000 pieces. Chlorinated oils were used as lubricant.

In the second press operation, a compound die in a 400-ton press formed the workpiece, pierced the center hole, and flattened the workpiece at the notches. This die was made of tungsten oil-hardening tool steel. Production rates, lubrication and die life were the same as in the blank-and-notch operation.

Progressive Dies. In a progressive die, the workpiece, while attached to the strip (or to the scrap skeleton), is fed from station to station at each stroke. At each stroke, the die performs work at some or all of the stations. The workpiece is cut off and unloaded at the last station. Each station may be simple or compound. The principal parts of a two-station blank-and-pierce progressive die are shown in Fig. 28.

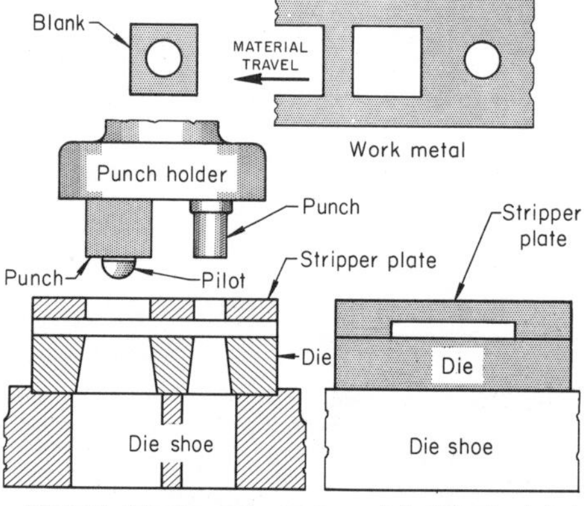

Pierced blank and work metal (steel strip) are shown at the top. The use of a pilot in the pierced hole assures accuracy to within a few thousandths of an inch.

Fig. 28. Principal components of a two-station blank-and-pierce progressive die

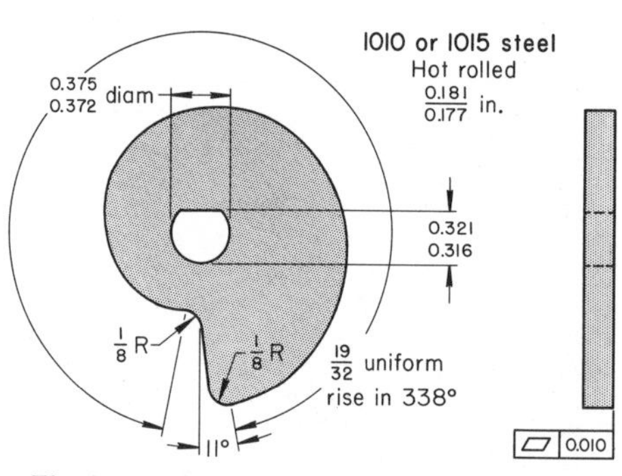

Fig. 29. Brake-shoe adjusting cam that was pierced, shaved and blanked in a progressive die (Example 19)

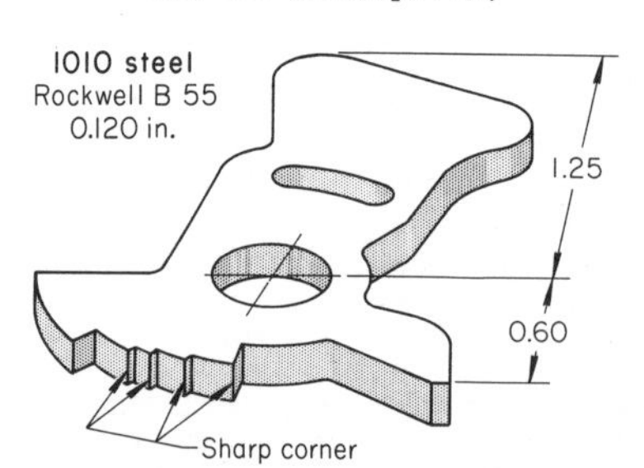

Fig. 30. Fast-idle cam on which sharp corners were cut in a progressive die (Example 20)

In producing the simple blank shown in Fig. 28 from coiled strip in a progressive die, the round hole is pierced at the first station. The strip is then fed left, to the next station. There the pilot enters the hole as the blanking punch moves down to complete the blank. Accurate relation of the hole to the outline of the blank depends on accurate fit of the pilot in the hole. The completed part is not separated from the strip until the last operation, regardless of the number of operations. After the first piece, one piece is completed at each stroke.

The cost of a progressive die is high, and usually it is set up in an automatic press with scrap cutter, feeder, straightener and uncoiler, so that the total cost of auxiliary equipment is also high. Other disadvantages of progressive dies are: (*a*) the part cannot be turned over between operations; and (*b*) material may be wasted, because the workpiece may not nest well in the strip layout.

Coil stock (or, less often, flat strip stock) is used. Many operations on small and medium-size parts can be done in conjunction with blanking in a progressive die, but the planning may be complicated. Soft or thin stock may be troublesome, because the pilot may distort the locating holes. Setup and maintenance may be difficult.

The example that follows describes a high-production application of a progressive die in which piercing and shaving were combined with blanking, to make an adjusting cam for a brake shoe.

Example 19. Piercing, Shaving and Blanking a Cam in a Progressive Die (Fig. 29)

The brake-shoe adjusting cam shown in Fig. 29 was pierced, shaved in two operations, and blanked — all in a progressive die. The work metal was hot rolled 1010 or 1015 steel, pickled and oiled, 0.179 in. thick.

Hole diameter was held within 0.003 in. by shaving. A satisfactory cam surface without shaving was maintained by resharpening the die after blanking 15,000 to 20,000 pieces. The maximum punch-to-die clearance was 10% of stock thickness for piercing, 1% for shaving and 5% for blanking.

The punch and die were made of D2 tool steel and hardened to Rockwell C 59 to 60. The die was run in a 90-ton press at 55 strokes per minute.

The example that follows describes an application in which a progressive die was preferred to a compound die because it was too difficult to cut sharp corners in the compound die.

Example 20. Change From a Compound to a Progressive Die to Cut Sharp Corners (Fig. 30)

Figure 30 shows a fast-idle cam on which the corners had to be sharp. Because it was difficult to make and maintain sharp corners in a compound die, a progressive die was used. The part was blanked from coiled 1010 steel strip, 0.120 by 2⅜ in., with maximum hardness of Rockwell B 55. A seven-station progressive die cut the steps in the cam.

The punches were made of M2 tool steel and hardened to Rockwell C 60 to 63, and the die and the punch holders were made of O1 tool steel and hardened to Rockwell C 56 to 58. About 10,000 to 15,000 cams were made between sharpenings of the progressive die, using a punch-to-die clearance of 0.004 in. This die was mounted in a 60-ton press that was run at 76 strokes per minute.

In another operation, the steps in the cam were shaved to remove die break, so that surfaces were flat across the thickness. Tools were of the same materials as in the progressive die, and had a life of 5000 to 6000 pieces between sharpenings. The shaving was done at 16 strokes per minute in a 40-ton press.

Finally, the cam was liquid carburized 0.003 to 0.006 in. deep and oil quenched to file hardness. Zinc plating (0.0002-in. minimum thickness) and a chromate postplating treatment followed.

In the next example, three blanks were cut from coil stock at each press stroke. The layout resulted in minimum scrap loss and maximum utilization of the press capacity. Less than ½ in. of the coil width (based on minimum coil width), and less than ¼ in. at the end of each blank, was scrap.

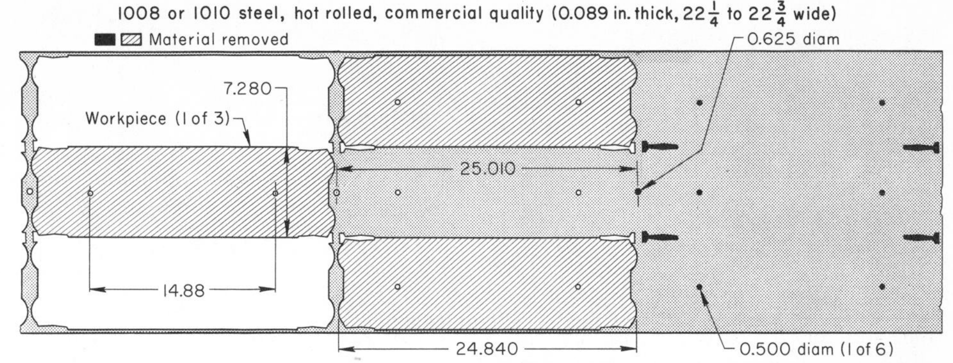

Fig. 31. Strip development in the production of three blanks at a time in a three-stage progressive die (Example 21)

Example 21. Making Three Blanks at Each Press Stroke in a Progressive Die (Fig. 31)

The strip development for making three blanks at a time is shown in Fig. 31. These blanks were formed into parts in a transfer die (see Example 138, in "Press Forming of Low-Carbon Steel"). The blanks were made in a three-station progressive die, from 0.089-in.-thick hot rolled, commercial quality 1008 or 1010 steel coiled strip, pickled and oiled. The coil had a slit edge and was 22¼ to 22¾ in. wide.

In the first station, six 0.500-in.-diam holes, one 0.625-in.-diam pilot hole and four cutouts were pierced. Next, the two side blanks were cut from the strip to fall through the die. The remaining middle strip was the width of the third blank, which was cut off in the third station. The total scrap width was 0.41 to 0.91 in.

The die was made of W2 tool steel and hardened to Rockwell C 60 to 62. The die shoe was 36 by 84 in. A 600-ton mechanical press with a 66-by-120-in. bed, operating at 30 strokes per minute, was used. Clearance per side between the punches and dies was 0.012 in., or 13.5% of stock thickness. Die life was 200,000 strokes for each resharpening.

A hydraulic-actuated roller stock pusher kept the work metal against roller guides in the first station. Hardened tool steel guides were used in stations 2 and 3.

As the blanks were cut, 750 to 900 of them were loaded automatically into containers. The containers were moved to the transfer press, where the blanks were loaded automatically into the transfer die.

Transfer dies, in which separate workpieces are fed from station to station by transfer fingers, are used for blanking only when coil stock is used. Blanking is done at the first station, and is followed by other operations.

Transfer dies ordinarily are used for additional operations on precut blanks made in a separate press (blanks that permitted close nesting for best utilization of the stock). When equally high utilization of stock can be obtained, coil stock may be used in a transfer die, with blanking being done at the first station.

Like progressive dies, transfer dies and their related equipment (presses, special attachments, and feeding devices) are expensive and are best suited for mass production. Production rates are high.

Multiple dies (also called multiple-part dies) make two or more workpieces at each stroke of the press. The workpieces may be pairs of right-hand and left-hand parts, duplicate parts, or unrelated parts. Punch height may be staggered to reduce shock and blanking noise. Such dies are used in mass production.

Multiple dies may be multiples of single-operation dies or multiples of compound dies. They generally cost only a little more than similar dies that make only one part per stroke. (A die that makes two parts per stroke may cost only 5% more than a die that makes only one.)

Such dies are used mostly for blank-and-form sequences. Draw operations are more difficult to combine with blanking or other operations, because of blankholder needs and slower draw operation. Unloading of the work is sometimes difficult.

The use of multiple dies depends on size and shape of the workpiece, size of the press, production quantity, possible savings in material and labor, and costs for setup and maintenance.

Advantages of multiple dies may include savings in material by better blank layout, reduced cost of labor, and increased production. Disadvantages of multiple dies may include an increase in the costs of setup and maintenance.

Often it is better to increase the production of a single-part die by some simple change, such as putting the die in a faster press, rather than to replace the single-part die with a multiple die. Also, a multiple die may have to be run slower than the simpler die, if a press of greater tonnage must be used to provide ample force.

The use of a multiple compound die to blank, pierce and form three pieces per stroke is illustrated in the following example.

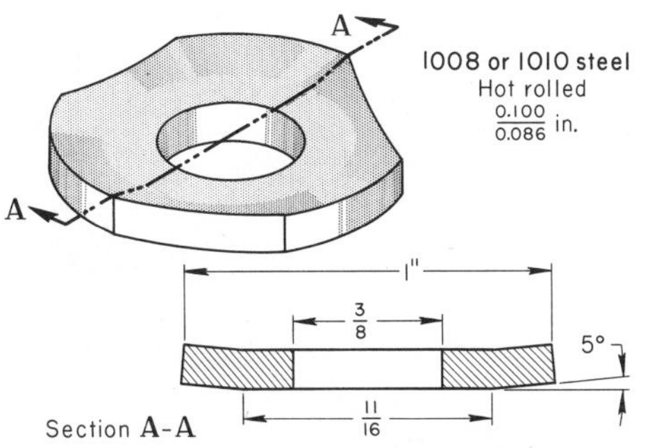

Fig. 32. Dished washer that was blanked, pierced and formed, three pieces per stroke, in a multiple compound die (Example 22)

Example 22. Blanking, Piercing and Forming Three Pieces per Stroke in a Multiple Compound Die (Fig. 32)

A multiple compound die was used to make a thick dished washer with three flats equally spaced on the edge circle, as shown in Fig. 32. The part was made of hot rolled 1008 or 1010 steel, 0.093 ± 0.007 in. thick.

Operations in the compound die were blank, pierce and form. The blanks were nested so closely in the stock layout that the pilot holes (half-circles) had to be notched in the edge of the stock. Three parts were made with each stroke of the die, and the parts were pushed partly back into the scrap skeleton so that they were carried out of the press for unloading.

Production was 500,000 pieces per month. The die, made of D2 tool steel, needed to be resharpened after 150,000 strokes (450,000 pieces), and required reconditioning (replacement of some parts) after 3.5 million pieces.

Operating Conditions

In order to achieve high productivity and low unit cost, most blanking is done in high-speed mechanical presses. Speeds as high as 1200 strokes per minute are used. The equipment for high-speed blanking ordinarily includes a short-stroke press, automatic feed devices, and dies designed for bottom ejection.

In most blanking operations, press speed is limited by the length of feed, which is governed by blank size, or by the relation between press capacity (tonnage) and load. The combination of blanking with forming or drawing in compound dies also restricts press speed. Blanking speed may be as low as ten strokes per minute in producing blanks that are extremely large or that present handling problems for other reasons.

Regardless of the number of strokes per minute, the velocity of the punch always approaches zero near the bottom of the stroke. Within the usual range for production work in conventional blanking dies, the speed of the press has little practical effect on the speed of the punch during the blanking portion of the stroke. This effect, however, is critical for fine-edge blanking, in which punch speed during the interval while the punch is cutting through the work metal is usually about 0.3 to 0.6 in. per second (see "Fine-Edge Blanking and Piercing", which begins on page 56).

Lubrication requirements generally are less critical for blanking than for forming or deep drawing; stock to be blanked is often fed into the press with no lubrication other than the residue remaining on the stock from the lubrication at the mill. Sometimes the stock is coated with a light mineral oil or a light chlorinated oil. However, lubrication is important in dies that have close clearance between punches and stripper. At speeds of 40 strokes and more per minute, such dies must be lubricated constantly with a spray of light mineral oil to prevent galling of the punches in the stripper.

For a more complete discussion of lubrication requirements in blanking, the reader is referred to the article on Selection and Use of Lubricants in Forming of Sheet Metal, which begins on page 23 in this volume.

Effect of Work-Metal Thickness

Stock thickness affects the selection of material for dies and related components, as well as the selection of die type and design. The amount of shear and relief (angular clearance or draft) built into a blanking die, and the amount of clearance between punch and die, all depend on blank thickness.

Work-metal thickness also is a factor in the selection of blanking method, handling procedure and handling equipment. Blanking in a punch press usually is the fastest and most economical way of producing blanks less than about ¼ in. thick, in medium or large quantities.

Plate stock, in thicknesses of ¼ to 1 in., is less frequently blanked in presses than is sheet or strip. Blanks of such thick material are often made by gas cutting, sawing, nibbling or routing, instead of by shearing or by press operations, with the selection of method depending primarily on plate thickness and production quantity.

Nearly all blanks thinner than ⅛ in., except for intricate shapes chemically blanked from foil, are produced with conventional dies in mechanical or hydraulic presses. In only four of the examples of commercial practice presented in this article was work metal thicker than ⅛ in. (Example 13, 0.156 in.; Example 15, 0.130 in.; Example 19, 0.179 in.; and Example 23, 0.187 in.)

Because of its strength and rigidity, material thicker than ⅛ in. seldom is blanked from coil stock or in a progressive die. On the other hand, because of its lack of strength and extreme flexibility, material thinner than 0.020 in. generally requires special handling techniques.

The articles in this volume on Piercing of Low-Carbon Steel (page 44), Blanking and Piercing of Magnetically Soft Materials (page 60), and Press Forming of High-Carbon Steel (page 132) contain additional information on the effect of work-metal thickness on processing. For instance, the blanking and piercing of a perforated comb for an electric shaver from 0.0045-in.-thick steel is described in Example 195 on page 134. The examples that appear in the articles on bending, forming, and deep drawing of low-carbon steel, and on press-brake forming, describe a number of parts that were blanked from thick material.

Example 33 in the article on Piercing describes the blanking of steel shims from thin (0.010-in.) coil stock in a compound die.

In blanking complex shapes from thin low-carbon steel sheet by repeated strokes of a notching die, distortion is often a problem. Distortion of such parts can be minimized by the use of hardened stock and by doing the entire blanking operation in one stroke in a single die.

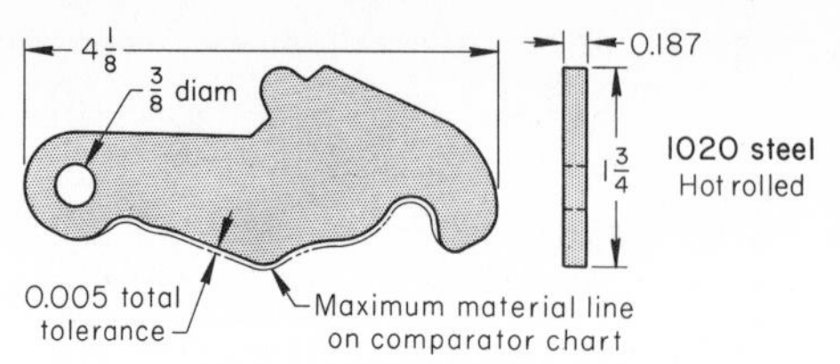

Fig. 33. Cam that was blanked and pierced in a compound die within an envelope tolerance of 0.005 in. TIR (Example 23)

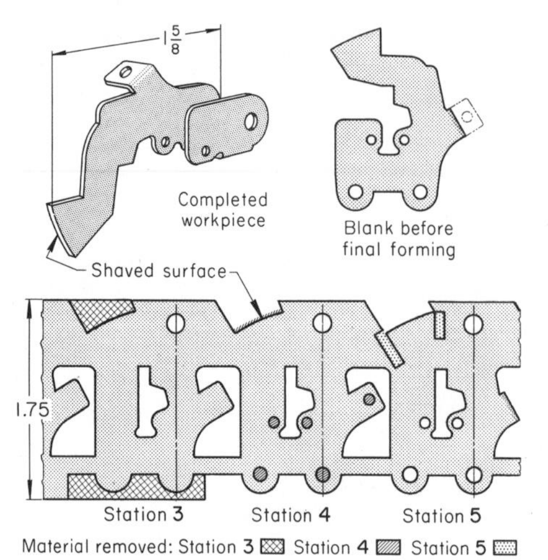

Fig. 34. Formed part on which a blanked edge was made smoother and more accurate by shaving (station 4) after notching (station 3) in a progressive die (Example 24)

Accuracy

Blanking in conventional dies readily produces parts within a total tolerance of 0.002 to 0.010 in., depending on the accuracy of the dies and the condition of the press.

The tolerances given in Table 4 in the article "Piercing of Low-Carbon Steel" (page 51) generally apply also to blanks. The total tolerances listed under the column head "Location" apply to the relation of a point on the periphery of the blank to a hole or other reference feature on the blank; the values listed under "Size" apply to a diameter for round blanks, or to a similar control dimension for other blank shapes.

Production of blanks to these tolerances is illustrated by the examples in this article and the article "Piercing of Low-Carbon Steel". The example that follows describes the use of a compound die to maintain a total (envelope) tolerance of 0.005 in. on the relation of a cam surface to a hole.

Example 23. Blanking and Piercing a Cam to 0.005-In. Total Tolerance on Cam Surface in Relation to Hole Position (Fig. 33)

A compound die was used to blank and pierce the cam shown in Fig. 33, so that the hole would be in accurate relation to the cam surface. The die was made of A2 or equivalent tool steel and hardened to Rockwell C 62, and had a clearance per side equal to 10% of the stock thickness.

The cam, used in the hinge mechanism of an automobile door, was blanked from hot rolled 1020 steel, 0.187 in. thick. Samples of the cam were inspected by means of an optical comparator, which compared the relation of hole and cam surface to an outline that showed the full 0.005-in. tolerance (as illustrated in Fig. 33).

In another operation, the cam surface was machined to remove die break, so that the edge would be square. Then the cam was case hardened.

The part was produced in a 160-ton open-back inclinable press at 60 strokes per minute. A sulfur-base lubricant was used. Die life was 40,000 pieces per sharpening.

Examples 17 and 18 in this article describe other applications of compound dies in blanking and piercing to conventional tolerances.

For parts made in a progressive die, the relation of the blank outline to features of the part produced in other stations of the die depends on the accurate fit of the pilot in the pilot hole. Transfer dies ordinarily give better accuracy than progressive dies, because the positive location of separate parts can be more precise than roll feed of coil stock with pilots.

Holding close tolerances on parts made in a progressive die is particularly difficult on soft or thin material, because distortion of the locating holes by the pilot is more likely. Handling problems that might contribute to excessive variation in location or dimensions are not usually encountered in transfer dies, except with blanks of extremely thin material.

Shaving (see the section that follows) is used to improve the accuracy of blank outlines to meet close tolerances or to improve edge quality.

Short-run dies generally are less accurate than conventional dies. By using more accurate methods of constructing short-run dies, closer tolerances on blanked work can be obtained, but at some increase in die cost (see the section on short-run dies in this article).

Generally, making blanks by methods other than the use of dies in presses, except for machining or grinding, results in a lower level of accuracy.

Shaving

Shaving is an operation that may be used after blanking, to give a smooth, square edge and greater accuracy than can be achieved in ordinary blanking.

Shaving removes only the blanked edge — cutting away the deformed, broken and burred edge that was left in blanking. The elimination of these irregularities and the removal of locally work-hardened metal minimizes breakage of the work metal during subsequent flanging, particularly flanging of holes. The scrap produced in shaving is so thin that it resembles the chips produced in finish machining, rather than the usual scrap that is produced in a press.

When shaving is planned, a small amount of extra stock is left on the workpiece, to be removed in shaving. Shaving can be done in a separate operation, or it can be included in one station of a progressive die.

The shaving operation produces a straight, square edge, generally to about 75% of the metal thickness. Two shaves make a better, straighter edge (to about 90% of the metal thickness) than does a single shaving operation. To eliminate rollover from blank edges, which requires the removal of a greater amount of stock, it may be better to consider machining the workpiece rather than shaving.

Punch-to-die clearances range from zero to 1½% of stock thickness per side. Sturdy guideposts in a heavy die set are necessary to maintain the close alignment needed to prevent damage to the punch and die.

Shaving causes more wear on a die than ordinary blanking, so that the die produces fewer parts per grind and needs more frequent maintenance. Slivers of shaving scrap (chips) can jam feeding mechanisms, become embedded in workpieces or mar the punch and die surfaces if not removed after each press stroke.

Because of the problems described in the preceding paragraph, special attention must be given to die design when shaving is included among the operations done in a progressive die, as illustrated in the example that follows.

Example 24. Shaving in a Progressive Die (Fig. 34)

In evaluating methods for high-volume production of the shaved low-carbon steel part shown in Fig. 34, the use of a single progressive die for all cutting and forming operations was projected as the most economical method, principally because this method would entail fewer operations and less handling than the other methods considered. However, two major problems were anticipated: (*a*) the life of the shaving tools was expected to be much shorter than that of the other tools in the progressive die (which would have resulted in costly interruption of production to sharpen or replace the shaving tools), and (*b*) it appeared likely that misfeed could occur from jamming of the feeding mechanism by slivers of shaving scrap.

By designing the die and feeding mechanism to eliminate difficulties from these two sources, efficient and economical production was obtained. The tools were of A2 air-hardening tool steel, hardened to Rockwell C 54 to 58 for the forming sections and to Rockwell C 60 to 62 for the cutting sections. The shaving section was made with a replaceable insert to minimize downtime when sharpening was needed. Damage to the progressive die from an accumulation of shaving scrap was prevented by including in the die a stock stop (station 3 in Fig. 34) and misfeed and double-thickness protectors.

The shaving was done in station 4, as shown in Fig. 34. Production rate was 80 pieces per minute in a 60-ton mechanical press having a 2-in. stroke. Tolerance on most sections of the part was ±0.005 in.

The use of shaving to hold the diameter of a hole in a brake-shoe adjusting cam within a total tolerance of 0.003 in. is described in Example 19 in this article. For additional examples of the use of shaving to maintain close tolerances and to improve the quality of hole walls, see the article "Piercing of Low-Carbon Steel" in this volume.

Shaving allowance, or the amount of stock to be removed from the workpiece, depends on the hardness and thickness of the blank. Generally, the smallest amount of stock that will produce the desired result is left for the shaving operation. Shaving allowances recommended by one manufacturer are shown in Table 5.

When shaving only one edge of a blank, shifting of the blank can be reduced by shaving the opposite edge as well, even if not required for function.

Setups for Shaving. Shaving requires that the blank be accurately located over the die or the punch, because only a few thousandths of an inch of metal is removed by the operation (see Table 5). Piloting pins, projecting from the punch, can engage holes in the blank to assure proper location. If the holes are not included in the original design, it may be permissible to add them for locating purposes only.

Table 5. Shaving Allowances Recommended by One Manufacturer

Blank thickness, in.	Allowance per side, in., for steel with Rockwell B hardness of: 50 to 66	75 to 90	90 to 105
First Shave (or a Single Shave)			
3/64 (0.047) ...	0.0025	0.003	0.004
1/16 (0.062) ...	0.003	0.004	0.005
5/64 (0.078) ...	0.0035	0.005	0.006-0.007
3/32 (0.094) ...	0.004	0.006	0.007-0.008
7/64 (0.109) ...	0.005	0.007	0.009-0.011
1/8 (0.125) ...	0.007	0.009	0.012-0.014
Second Shave (Add to First Shave)			
3/64 (0.047) ...	0.00125	0.0015	0.002
1/16 (0.062) ...	0.0015	0.002	0.0025
5/64 (0.078) ...	0.00175	0.0025	0.0030-0.0035
3/32 (0.094) ...	0.002	0.003	0.0035-0.0040
7/64 (0.109) ...	0.0025	0.0035	0.0045-0.0055
1/8 (0.125) ...	0.0035	0.0045	0.006-0.007

One shave
0.482 pierced diam
0.500 shaved diam
0.009 on a side for shaving
Break 25%
Straight 75%
Section A-A

Two shaves
0.473 pierced diam
0.491 first shaved diam
0.500 second shaved diam
0.0135 on a side for shaving
0.009 for first shave
0.0045 for second shave
Break 10%
Straight 90%
Section B-B

Typical shaving of 0.125-in.-thick stock (R_B 75 to 90)

If adding holes is not permitted, a locating device such as that shown in Fig. 35 can be used. The clamping arms engage the blank at suitable nesting points. When the punch descends, the shaved blank falls through the die. The position of the clamping arms is fixed by the two stop pins.

Operation of this die can be improved by the use of a spring-loaded ejector and pressure pad within the die opening. As the punch ascends, the ejector lifts the shaved workpiece above the die face, thereby eliminating the fall through the die block, which may result in dents or other surface defects.

Burr Removal

The shape, height and roughness of burrs must be controlled to some degree in nearly all blanking operations. Complete elimination of burrs is not possible, but their formation can be minimized by the use of proper clearance between punch and die (page 33), and by good maintenance. (See the section on burrs in the article on Blanking and Piercing of Magnetically Soft Materials, page 66.)

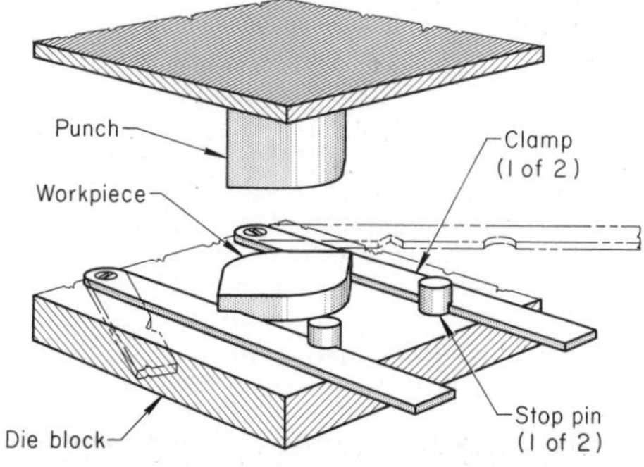

Fig. 35. Shaving die with a device for locating a blank with no holes for piloting

Exposed burrs on the finished part can be unsafe and unsightly. Burrs on some blanked work can cause difficulties in forming and can increase the rate of workpiece breakage and die wear. Burrs can be removed by grinding, which generally removes the burr together with a portion of the work-hardened edge. Tumbling in a barrel is a common method of deburring small parts. Other deburring methods include chemical and electrolytic deburring, belt grinding, polishing and ultrasonic methods, as described in Volume 3 of this Handbook. Hand scrapers can be used to remove burrs from irregular shapes or soft metal parts.

Blanking in Presses vs Alternative Methods

Alternative methods of making blanks include fine-edge blanking, milling, chemical blanking, contour band sawing, and gas cutting.

Fine-edge blanking (see the article that begins on page 56) is used primarily where die break is unacceptable and would require removal by subsequent shaving if conventional blanking were used. In fine-edge blanking there is no die break, and the entire wall surface of the cut is burnished.

Milling is applicable chiefly for cutting stacked parts, for short runs, and for making parts that are subject to frequent design change; it substitutes an inexpensive template for a conventional punch and die.

Chemical blanking may be competitive with blanking in presses for intricate parts that are only a few thousandths of an inch thick. On page 243 in Volume 3 of this Handbook, Table 3 shows a comparison of costs for making a small steel part from 0.008-in.-thick steel by these two methods. Combs for electric shavers, such as illustrated in Example 195 in the present volume, are more frequently made by chemical blanking of stainless steel than by the mechanical blanking method shown.

Contour band sawing and gas cutting may be competitive with blanking for stacked parts and thick material.

Safety

In all blanking operations, as in all press operations, there are hazards to operators, repairmen, and personnel in the vicinity. No press, die, or auxiliary equipment should be considered operable until these hazards are eliminated by installing necessary guards and other safety devices. The operator and all persons working around the blanking operation should be instructed in all precautions for safe operation before work is started. For safety information, see the article that begins on page 1 of this volume and the references listed at the end of that article.

Piercing of Low-Carbon Steel

*By the ASM Committee on Press Forming of Steel**

PIERCING† is the cutting of holes in sheet metal, generally by removing a slug of metal, with a punch and die. Piercing is like blanking, except that in piercing, the work metal that surrounds the piercing punch is the workpiece and the punched-out slug is scrap, whereas in blanking it is the workpiece that is punched out.

Pierced holes can be of almost any size and shape; elongated holes usually are called slots.

Piercing is ordinarily the fastest method of making holes in steel sheet or strip, and is generally the most economical method for medium to high production.

The accuracy of conventional tool steel or carbide dies provides pierced holes with a degree of quality and accuracy that is satisfactory for a wide variety of applications.

For further information on piercing, the reader is referred to the articles in this volume on Blanking of Low-Carbon Steel (page 31), Fine-Edge Blanking and Piercing (page 56), Press Forming of High-Carbon Steel (page 132), and Blanking and Piercing of Magnetically Soft Materials (page 60).

Characteristics of Pierced Holes

Pierced holes are different from through-holes that are produced by drilling or other machining methods. A properly drilled or otherwise machined through-hole has a sidewall that is straight for the full thickness of the work metal, with a high degree of accuracy in size, roundness and straightness. The sidewall of a pierced hole generally is straight and smooth for only a portion of the thickness, beginning near the punch end of the hole; the remainder of the wall is broken out in an irregular cone beyond the straight portion of the hole, producing what is called fracture, breakout, or die break (see Fig. 1).

The operation of hole piercing typically begins as a cut that produces a burnished surface on the hole wall and some rollover (curved surface caused by deformation of the workpiece before cutting commenced) as illustrated in Fig. 1. The punch completes its stroke by breaking and tearing away the metal that was not cut during the initial part of the piercing operation.

*For committee list, see page 112.

†The term "piercing" is used in this article, and in related articles in this volume, to denote the production of a hole by removing a slug of metal with a punch and die. The reader should note, however, that some authorities prefer to use the terms "punching" or "perforating" to denote this method, limiting the term "piercing" to the use of a pointed punch that tears and extrudes a hole without cutting a slug of metal. The term "perforating" is sometimes used also in the special sense of cutting many holes in a sheet metal workpiece by removing slugs with several punches.

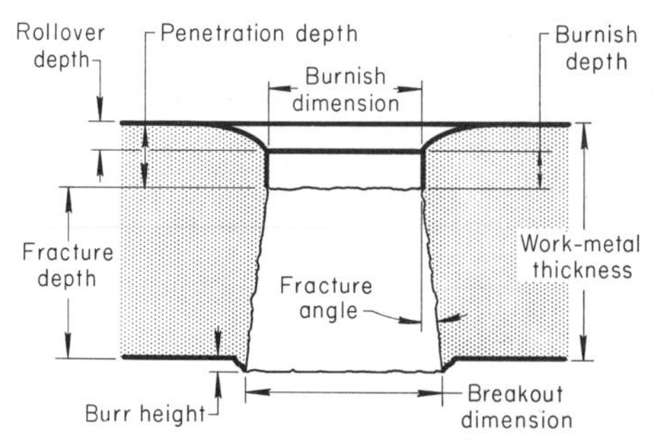

Curvature and angles are exaggerated for emphasis. Compare with Fig. 8 on page 33 in the article "Blanking of Low-Carbon Steel".

Fig. 1. Characteristics of a pierced hole

The combined depth of rollover and burnish is a measure of the penetration depth of the stroke, also shown in Fig. 1. This is the part of the stroke during which the cutting force is exerted, before the metal fractures or breaks away (see Fig. 1).

The amount of penetration before fracture is commonly expressed as a percentage of the stock thickness. In general, the percentage of penetration depends more on the material than on other factors, such as punch-to-die clearance. Table 1 on page 33 in the article "Blanking of Low-Carbon Steel" shows the average percentage of penetration (before fracture) in various metals under typical piercing or blanking conditions. Percentage of penetration affects energy consumption and cutting force in blanking or piercing, as described on page 34 in the article on Blanking.

Quality of Hole Wall

If the sidewall of a pierced hole is not smooth or straight enough for the intended application, it can be improved by shaving in a die, or by reaming. Shaving is the least expensive method of improving the sidewall of a pierced hole, when done in quantity. Shaving in one or two operations generally makes the sidewall of a hole uniform and smooth through 75 to 90% of the stock thickness.

Superior accuracy and smoothness of hole walls can be obtained by fine-edge piercing. With this method, one stroke of a triple-action press pierces holes with smooth and precise edges for the entire thickness of the material. For further information, see the article that begins on page 56.

Burr height is an important element in hole quality, and a maximum burr height is usually specified. For most applications, the limit on burr height is between 5 and 10% of stock thickness. Burr height in piercing a given workpiece is governed primarily by punch-to-die clearance and tool sharpness.

Burr condition and limits usually determine the length of run before the punch and die are resharpened. With good practice, burr height is generally in the range of 0.0005 to 0.003 in., but may be much greater, depending on workpiece material and thickness, clearance, and tool condition. As an alternative to limiting the length of run to control burr condition, unacceptable burrs may be removed by shaving, or by deburring as described on pages 387 to 397 in Volume 2 of this Handbook.

Selection of Die Clearance

Clearance, or space between the punch and the sidewall of the die, affects the reliability of operation of piercing (and blanking) equipment, the characteristics of the cut edges, and the life of the punch and die. Published recommendations for clearances have varied widely, with most suggesting a clearance per side somewhere in the range of 3 to 12.5% of the stock thickness for steel.

Establishment of the clearance to be used for a given piercing or blanking operation is influenced by the required characteristics of the cut edge of the hole or blank, and by the thickness and the properties of the work metal. Larger clearances prolong tool life. An optimum clearance may be defined as the largest clearance that will produce a hole or blank having the required characteristics of the cut edge in a given material and thickness. Because of differences in cut-edge requirements and in the effect of tool life on over-all cost, clearance practices vary among plants and for different applications.

No single table or formula can specify accurately an optimum clearance for all situations encountered in practice. Starting with general guidelines, trial of several different clearances may be needed to establish the most desirable clearance for a specific application. The following general principles are useful in making adjustments:

1. Rollover (plastic deformation) and burnish depth are greater in thick material than in thin material, and are greater in soft material than in hard material.
2. Clearance (in decimal parts of an inch) to produce a given type of edge should vary directly with material thickness and hardness, and inversely with ductility.

All clearance values given in this article are for clearance per side, except where indicated otherwise.

Types of Edges

More specific guidance in selecting die clearances is provided by considering the types of edges produced with different clearances.

The acceptability of a punched hole or a blank generally is based on the

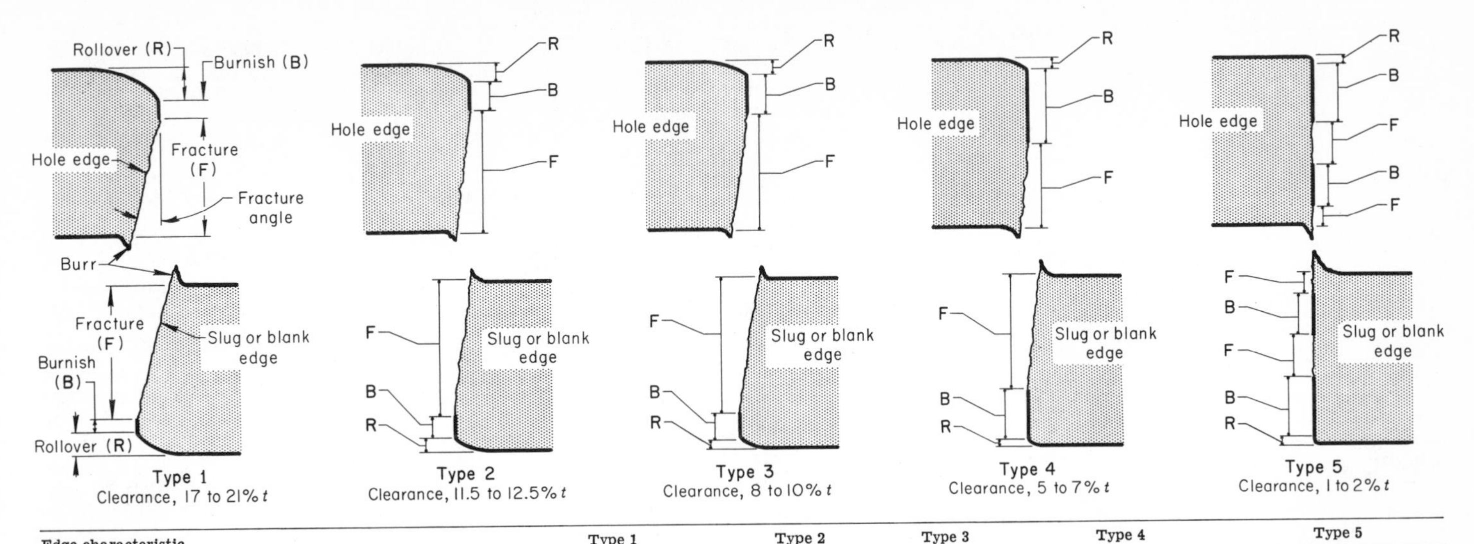

Edge characteristic	Type 1	Type 2	Type 3	Type 4	Type 5
Fracture angle	14° to 16°	8° to 11°	7° to 11°	6° to 11°	....
Rollover(a)	10 to 20% t	8 to 10% t	6 to 8% t	4 to 7% t	2 to 5% t
Burnish(a)	10 to 20% t(b)	15 to 25% t	25 to 40% t	35 to 55% t(c)	50 to 70% t(d)
Fracture	70 to 80% t	60 to 75% t	50 to 60% t	35 to 50% t(e)	25 to 45% t(f)
Burr	Large, tensile plus part distortion	Normal, tensile only	Normal, tensile only	Medium, tensile plus compressive(g)	Large, tensile plus compressive(g)

(a) Rollover plus burnish approximately equals punch penetration before fracture. (b) Burnish on edge of slug or blank may be small and irregular or even absent. (c) With spotty secondary shear. (d) In two separate portions, alternating with fracture. (e) With rough surface. (f) In two separate portions, alternating with burnish. (g) Amount of compressive burr depends on die sharpness.

Fig. 2. Effect of punch-to-die clearance per side (as a percentage of stock thickness, t) on characteristics of edges of holes and slugs (or blanks) produced by piercing or blanking low-carbon steel sheet or strip at a maximum hardness of Rockwell B 75. Table 1 lists clearances for producing the five types of edges in various metals. See text for additional discussion and for applicability of the five types of edges.

condition of the cut edge and its suitability for the application. Usable holes and blanks can be obtained over a broad range of punch-to-die clearances, each resulting in a different edge condition. Five types of edges that result from the use of different clearances in piercing or blanking low-carbon steel at Rockwell B 75 max are shown schematically in Fig. 2. The tabulated data accompanying Fig. 2 include approximate ranges of fracture or breakout angles, rollover, burnish and fracture depths, and burr characteristics for the five edge types. The clearance ranges that will produce these edges when piercing or blanking various metals are given in Table 1.

The characteristics and applicability of these edge types are as follows:

Table 1. Punch-to-Die Clearances for Piercing or Blanking Various Metals to Produce the Five Types of Edges Shown in Fig. 2

(Clearances in this table are based on data published on piercing by Danly Machine Corp., and on blanking in ASTME Paper MF64-151 by L. R. Allingham)

Work metal	Clearance per side, % of stock thickness: Edge type 1	Edge type 2	Edge type 3	Edge type 4	Edge type 5
Low-carbon steel	21 max	11.5 to 12.5	8 to 10	5 to 7	1 to 2
High-carbon steel	25 max	17 to 19	14 to 16	11 to 13	2.5 to 5
Stainless steel	23 max	12.5 to 13.5	9 to 11	3 to 5	1 to 2
Aluminum alloys:					
Up to 33,000-psi TS	17 max	8 to 10	6 to 8	2 to 4	0.5 to 1
Over 33,000-psi TS	20 max	12.5 to 14	9 to 10	5 to 6	0.5 to 1
Brass, annealed	21 max	8 to 10	6 to 8	2 to 3	0.5 to 1
Brass, half hard	24 max	9 to 11	6 to 8	3 to 5	0.5 to 1.5
Phosphor bronze	25 max	12.5 to 13.5	10 to 12	3.5 to 5	1.5 to 2.5
Copper, annealed	25 max	8 to 9	5 to 7	2 to 4	0.5 to 1
Copper, half hard	25 max	9 to 11	6 to 8	3 to 5	1 to 2
Lead	22 max	8 to 10	6.5 to 7.5	4 to 6	1.5 to 2.5
Magnesium alloys	16 max	5 to 7	3.5 to 4.5	1.5 to 2.5	0.5 to 1

NOTE: For clearances that produce edges of types 1, 2 and 3, it is ordinarily necessary to use ejector punches or other devices to prevent the slug from adhering to punch.

Type 1. This type of edge has a large rollover radius and a large burr that consists of a normal tensile burr plus bending or deformation at the edge. Burnish depth is minimal. Fracture depth is about three-fourths of stock thickness, and the fractured surface has a large angle. This edge is satisfactory for noncritical applications where edge quality and part flatness are not important.

Type 2. This edge, which has a moderate rollover radius, normal tensile burr, and a small fracture angle, provides maximum die life and a hole or blank that is acceptable for general work on which a large burnish depth is not required. Burnish depth plus rollover depth is about one-third of stock thickness; fracture depth, about two-thirds.

Type 3. This edge has a small rollover radius, a normal tensile burr and a small fracture angle. It has low residual stress, and therefore is particularly desirable for use in parts made of work-hardenable material that will undergo severe forming. The clean stress-free edge reduces the possibility of edge cracking during forming. Burnish depth plus rollover depth is one-third to one-half of stock thickness.

Type 4. This is a desirable edge for stampings used for mechanisms or parts that must receive edge finishing such as shaving or machining. The edge has a very small rollover radius, a medium tensile and compressive burr, and a small fracture angle. Burnish depth plus rollover depth is about two-thirds of stock thickness. This edge type may be recognized by the spotty showing of secondary shear on the fractured surface.

Type 5. This edge has a minimum rollover radius and a large tensile and compressive burr, and is recognized by the complete secondary shear on the cut surface. It is useful in applications where edges must have a maximum of straight-wall depth without secondary operations. On steel and other hard metals, die life is extremely short. The edge can be useful on some of the softer metals, which allow a reasonable die life.

The exact profile of the edge varies somewhat for different work metals, depending on the properties of the metal. Results may also be affected to a minor degree by:

1. Face shear on punch or die
2. Punch-to-die alignment
3. Proximity to adjacent holes
4. Distance to adjacent blanked edges
5. Orientation of the different portions of the cut edge with respect to the rolling direction of the stock
6. Ratio of hole size to stock thickness
7. Internal construction of the die cavity
8. Lubrication.

The illustrations of edge profiles in Fig. 2, and the estimates of fracture angles and of the relative amounts of rollover, burnish, fracture and burr given in the table accompanying Fig. 2, are intended to represent production conditions, allowing for the normal range of tool sharpness encountered in piercing and blanking of low-carbon steel sheet.

The clearance values given in Table 1 for piercing and blanking various metals to produce the five types of edges were obtained in laboratory tests. The cutting edges of the punches were stoned to a radius of 0.002 to 0.006 in. to simulate an amount of wear corresponding to the approximate midpoint of a production run. No lubricant was used on the work metal.

As clearance is increased from the low values used for type 5 edges to those used for type 1 edges, several effects are evident. The edge profile deviates more and more from straightness and perpendicularity, as rollover,

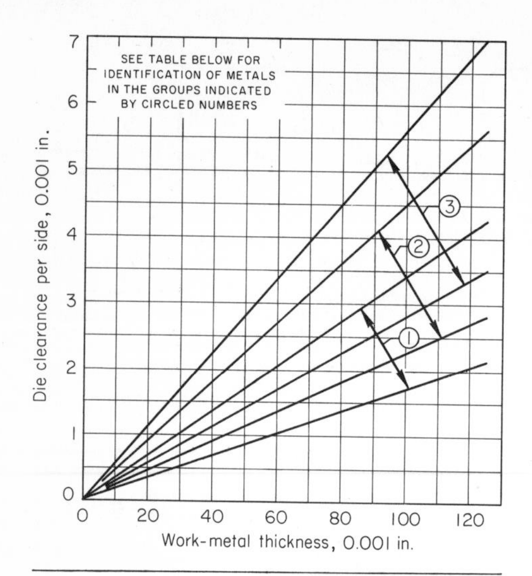

Group	Clearance per side, % of stock thickness(a) Average	Range
1 Aluminum alloys 1100 and 5052, all tempers	2.25	1.7 to 3.4
2 Aluminum alloys 2024 and 6061, T4 and T6 tempers; brass, all tempers; cold rolled steel, dead soft	3.0	2.25 to 4.5
3 Cold rolled steel, half hard	3.75	2.8 to 5.6

NOTE. Incorrect clearance values twice as large as those shown here have appeared with charts of this type in some publications, apparently because of confusion between clearance per side and total clearance. Also, stainless steel has erroneously been included with the metals in groups 2 and 3 in those publications.

(a) Percentages of stock thickness on which the ranges of acceptable clearance in chart are based. See text for clearances used in piercing or blanking of stainless steel. (SOURCE: Sperry Gyroscope Div., Sperry Rand Corp.)

Fig. 3. Ranges of punch-to-die clearance per side recommended by one manufacturer for piercing and blanking of various metals up to 0.125 in. thick

fracture angle and fracture depth increase, while burnish depth decreases proportionately.

Total burr height at first decreases, as its compressive component decreases, leaving only the essentially constant tensile burr on edges of types 3 and 2 (usually in the range of 0.0005 to 0.003 in., depending on the work metal and the tool condition).

With further increase in clearance (edge type 1), bending or deformation at and near the edge adds an additional burr component, increasing the total burr height. This part distortion immediately adjacent to the cut edge is usually accompanied by a more gradual curvature or "dishing" on blanks or slugs; the corresponding curvature is much less pronounced on the stock around a hole, which is usually restrained by a stripper. (Curvature of blanks or stock strip is not shown in Fig. 2.)

At extremely large clearances (substantially above those shown for type 1 edges), double-shear characteristics are sometimes observed on the cut edge.

Effect of Tool Dulling

The sharpness of punch and die edges has an important effect on cut-edge characteristics in piercing and blanking. At the beginning of a run, with punch and die equally sharp, the hole profile is the same as that of the slug or blank. As the run progresses, dulling of the punch increases the rollover and the burnish depth on the hole wall and increases the burr height on the slug or blank. Dulling of the die increases burnish depth and burr height on the hole edge. The punch dulls faster than the die; hence, the changes in hole characteristics related to punch dulling proceed more rapidly than those related to die dulling.

On the average, the following differences between hole edge and blank edge are observed in production work on sheet metal:

1 Rollover is greater on hole edge than on slug or blank edge.
2 Burnish depth is greater on hole edge than on slug or blank edge.

Table 2. Effect of Clearance on Piercing and Stripping Force Required for Piercing 0.257-In.-Diam Holes in Cold Rolled Low-Carbon Steel(a)

Clearance per side, % of stock thickness	Force required: Piercing, 1000 psi(b)	Force required: Stripping, lb (total)	Punch penetration into die, in.(c)
Stock 0.025 In. Thick, Rockwell B 65			
6.0	66.0	158	0.008
12.5	67.0	108	0.008
Stock 0.031 In. Thick, Rockwell B 47			
5.0	50.8	158	0.008
13.0	49.5	113	0.008
Stock 0.034 In. Thick, Rockwell B 87			
4.5	84.5	130	0.008
13.0	82.6	75	0.008
Stock 0.042 In. Thick, Rockwell B 85			
5.0	79.9	282	0.007
12.0	76.5	176	0.007
Stock 0.047 In. Thick, Rockwell B 47			
5.0	49.4	260	0.0185
6.5	51.0	67	0.0185
8.5	49.2	60	0.0185
9.5	51.2	37	0.0185
10.5	50.8	30	0.0185
13.0	48.2	56	0.0185
Stock 0.050 In. Thick, Rockwell B 71			
5.0	58.7	219	0.008
12.5	55.6	97	0.008
5.0	58.6	215	0.020
12.5	57.0	112	0.020
Stock 0.050 In. Thick, Rockwell B 61			
5.0	53.2	260	0.020
12.5	54.2	94	0.020
5.0	53.2	295	0.020
12.5	52.7	158	0.020
Stock 0.059 In. Thick, Rockwell B 74			
5.0	53.5	112	0.0185
6.8	52.0	136	0.0185
7.6	50.8	86	0.0185
8.5	50.6	84	0.0185
9.8	50.2	45	0.0185
13.0	51.5	20	0.0185
Stock 0.062 In. Thick, Rockwell B 50			
5.0	53.8	130	0.0185
6.5	53.8	102	0.0185
7.3	52.6	73	0.0185
8.0	52.8	130	0.0185
9.0	52.4	120	0.0185
12.5	52.6	56	0.0185

(a) Data are results of tests by Day/ton Progress Corp.; no lubricant was used. (b) Pounds per square inch of cross section cut. (c) Penetration required for release of slug.

Table 3. Effect of Punch-to-Die Clearance on Tool Life in Piercing and Blanking of Ferrous and Nonferrous Metals of Various Thicknesses(a)

Stock thickness, in.	Type	Rockwell hardness	Initial clearance: Clearance per side, % of stock thickness	Initial clearance: Tool life per grind, holes	Increased clearance: Clearance per side, % of stock thickness	Increased clearance: Tool life per grind, holes	Tool-life increase with greater clearance, %
Low-Carbon Steels, Cold Rolled							
0.016	Zinc coated	B 79	6.3	30,000	12.5	140,000	366
0.020	1018	C 22	2.5	115,000	5.0	230,000	100
0.036	....	(b)	2.8	67,000	12.5	204,000	205
0.047	1010	...	5.0	10,000	12.5	68,000	580
0.060	....	B 77	4.5	130,000	12.5	400,000	208
0.070	Galvanized	B 32	5.0	100,000	11.0	300,000	200
Low-Carbon Steels, Hot Rolled							
0.053	....	B 72	5.0	80,000	12.5	240,000	230
0.127	....	N 94	5.0	100,000	12.5	250,000	150
High-Carbon Steels							
0.060	1070	...	...	....	15.0	100,000	...
0.078	1090	...	...	....	10.0	835,000	...
0.080	4130	B 73	5.0	....	7.5	70,000	...
0.125	....	C 9	2.5	30,000	8.5	240,000	700
Stainless Steels							
0.005	301	C 45	20.0	15,000	42.0	125,000	900
0.020	410	...	3.8	5,000	12.5	136,000	2600
0.045	304	C 16	6.5	12,000	11.0	30,000	150
0.063	....	B 89	5.0	175,000	9.0	250,000	60
Co-Cr-Ni-Base Heat-Resisting Alloy							
0.036	HS-25 (L-605)	C 22	2.8	1,500	9.5	5,000	230
Aluminum Alloys							
0.018	5086	...	16 to 20(c)	20,000	16 to 20(d)	70,000	250
0.040	3003	(e)	5.0	....	12.5	(f)	...
0.052	....	(g)	5.0	....	8.5	....	50
Copper Alloys							
0.007	Tin-plated brass	B 76	7.0	....	14.0	(h)	50
0.045	Brass	...	3.5	15,000	7.0	110,000	(j)
0.047	Paper-clad brass	B 81	5.0	20,000	10.0	25,000	(j)
0.003	Beryllium copper	B 95(k)	8.5	300,000	25.0	600,000	100

(a) Production data compiled by Day/ton Progress Corp. (b) No. 4 temper. (c) Punch entered die 0.060 in. (d) Punch did not enter die. (e) H12 temper. (f) Higher-quality parts. (g) Soft. (h) Eliminated die breakage. (j) Run completed without regrind. (k) Half hard.

3 Fracture depth is smaller (and fracture angle greater) on hole edge than on slug or blank edge.
4 Burr height on hole edge is less than on slug or blank edge, and varies with tool sharpness.

These differences are shown in Fig. 2.

Use of Small Clearance

Where relatively square edges are required, small clearances can be used to produce holes with edges of type 4. Although tool life is shorter than when larger clearances are used, this may not be an important factor in over-all costs for short or medium production runs.

Figure 3 shows the ranges of die clearance per side used by one electronics manufacturer in piercing and blanking three groups of metals in thicknesses up to 0.125 in. The groups and the percentages of stock thickness on which these ranges of clearance were based are listed with Fig. 3. For stainless steel (not included in Fig. 3), nominal clearance per side was 2.5% of the thickness for stock thicknesses up to 0.187 in., and 4% for thicknesses between 0.187 and 0.250 in.

The data plotted in Fig. 3 were used by the manufacturer to determine whether a given punch and die could be used interchangeably for a metal different in thickness or type from the one for which it had been designed. If the point of intersection of a vertical line for the thickness of the new material with a horizontal line for the existing die clearance was within the range shown for the new material, the punch and die normally were satisfactory for use on the new material.

Use of Large Clearance

Studies of die operation under both laboratory and production conditions have indicated that large clearances can be used to obtain maximum tool life in numerous piercing (and blanking) applications.

Table 2 shows the effect of clearance on force requirements for piercing and stripping, presenting data on test piercing of 0.257-in.-diam holes in cold rolled low-carbon steel of various thicknesses and hardnesses. Although individual results show some inconsistency, as would be expected because of the difficulty in obtaining accurate measurements of this type, the trend toward lower stripping force with an increase in clearance is evident from these data. The amounts of punch penetration into the die needed to release the slug are also listed in Table 2.

Table 3 lists production data on the effect of increased clearance on tool life for piercing and blanking common metals in various thicknesses.

On the basis of these studies and production experience, clearance per side equal to 12.5% of stock thickness has been recommended by some toolmakers and sheet-metal fabricators for general-purpose piercing (and blanking) of cold rolled steel 0.020 to 0.125 in. thick, in all tempers. This practice produces type 2 cut edges (Fig. 2).

Advantages observed when using a clearance of 12.5%, instead of substantially smaller clearances (as for a type 4 edge), include the following:

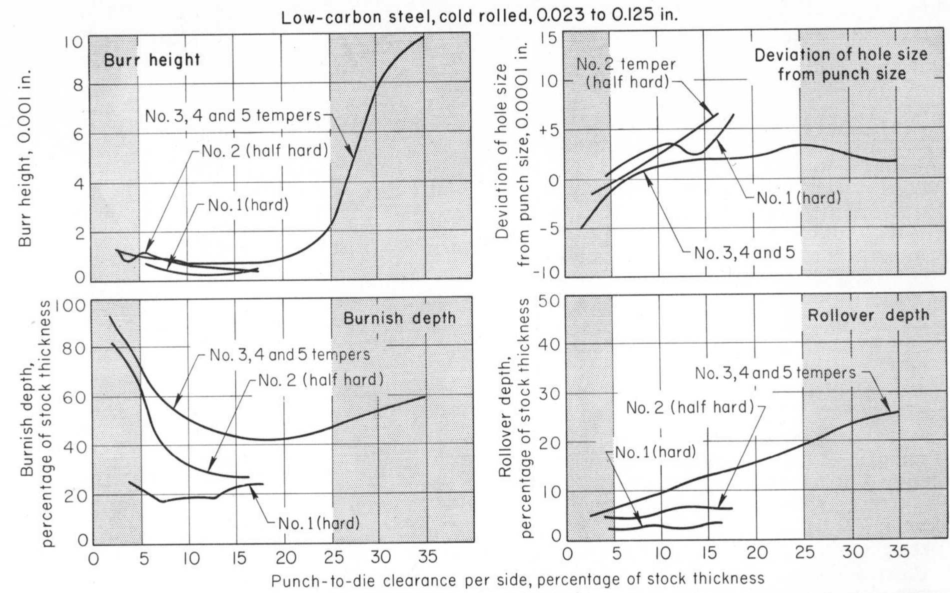

Curves are for the AISI tempers shown, corresponding to the following Rockwell B hardness limits: No. 1, 98 and higher; No. 2, 70 to 85; No. 3, 4 and 5, 75 and lower. Results in shaded areas are not closely reproducible and show trends only. (SOURCE: L. A. Holiga, Day/ton Progress Corp.)

Fig. 4. Edge characteristics (burr height, hole-size deviation, burnish depth and rollover depth) in the piercing of low-carbon steel of different hardnesses with various punch-to-die clearances

1 Total tool life and tool life between regrinds are considerably increased (see Table 3). Punch wear, normally two or three times die wear, is reduced greatly, because the hole is larger than the punch size and because stripping wear is reduced to a minimum.
2 Load on the press may be slightly reduced (see Table 2).
3 Burr height is smaller at the beginning of a run and increases at a slower rate during the run.
4 Distortion or waviness of the work surface is reduced, especially with closely spaced holes.
5 Stripping force is reduced (see Table 2) — which, in part, accounts for reduced punch wear.

Factors that must be considered in applying the 12.5% clearance include:

1 A different clearance may be required for steel outside the thickness range of 0.020 to 0.125 in., or for metals other than steel, or to meet critical edge-quality requirements.
2 A spring-loaded stripper should be used, instead of the positive or fixed type. Also, some means must be provided for preventing the slug or blank from adhering to the end of the punch. These precautions are especially important in transfer dies.
3 Hole size is larger than punch size, particularly with hard or thin materials.
4 With clearance above 15%, slugs of some materials (for example, 0.050-in.-thick type 410 stainless steel at a hardness of Rockwell C 50) may be ejected from the die at high velocity — possibly requiring special safety precautions.

Effect of Work-Metal Hardness

Data on edge characteristics versus punch-to-die clearance in piercing cold rolled low-carbon steel sheet of different hardnesses (tempers) are plotted in Fig. 4. These charts illustrate the basic characteristics of the edges of pierced holes for the standard AISI tempers, at various clearances per side up to 35% of stock thickness.

The data given in Fig. 4 were obtained in laboratory tests on stock 0.023 to 0.125 in. thick in the tempers shown. Cutting edges of the punches used were stoned to a radius of 0.004 in. to simulate midrun wear, and no lubricant was used in the tests.

Similar trends would be expected for the edge characteristics of slugs or blanks, except that rollover and burnish depth would be smaller and burr height would be greater.

Clearance and Tool Size

In blanking, the die opening ordinarily is made to the desired size of the blank, and the punch size then is equal to the die opening minus twice the specified clearance per side. Conversely, in piercing, the punch usually is made to the desired size of the hole, and the die opening then is equal to the punch size plus twice the specified clearance per side.

Clearance per side for blanking dies ordinarily is calculated from the desired percentage of clearance and the nominal thickness of the stock. However, to keep the inventory of piercing tools from becoming too large, a modified practice is employed by some manufacturers for stocking piercing punches and die buttons in commonly used diameters. Punches are ordered to size. Work-metal thickness is classified into several ranges, and die buttons are ordered to the specified clearance per side for the median stock thickness of the range to which the work metal for the given application belongs.

Hole dimensions are affected slightly as the clearance is changed. When using clearances that produce a type 4 edge, the diameter of the pierced hole is about 0.0005 in. less than that of the punch that produced it. By increasing the clearances to those for a type 2 edge, the hole size will be equal to, or approximately 0.0005 in. larger than, the punch diameter.

With tight clearances, the slug is wedged into the die cavity. As the clearance is increased, the wedging action decreases; consequently, the slug may be as much as 0.0005 in. smaller than the die cavity.

Force Requirements

The force needed to pierce a given material depends on shear strength of the work metal, peripheral size of the hole or holes to be pierced, stock thickness, and depth of shear on the punch. The calculation of piercing force is the same as for cutting force in blanking (see page 33 in the article "Blanking of Low-Carbon Steel", in this volume).

Effect of Punch Shear. Shear is the amount of relief ground on the face of a punch (Fig. 5). It is used to reduce the instantaneous total load on the tool and to permit thicker or higher-strength materials to be pierced in the same press. It distributes the total piercing load over a greater portion of the downstroke by introducing the cutting edge in increments rather than instantaneously.

Piercing force (but not contact edge pressure or total work done) varies with the amount of shear on the punch face. With the bottom of the punch flat and parallel to the face of the die, piercing takes place on the entire periphery at once, requiring maximum force. The load on the press and tools rises rapidly after impact to a maximum, and then releases suddenly when piercing is completed. By grinding shear on the punch as shown in Fig. 5, the maximum load is decreased, but the punch travels correspondingly farther to complete the piercing. Load release is also somewhat less sudden.

Shear location is ordinarily selected so as to confine distortion to the scrap metal (slug). Thus in piercing, shear is ground on the punch, because the punched-out metal is to be scrap. Concave shear and double-bevel shear (Fig. 5) provide a balanced load on the punch. Scalloped shear, sometimes ground on round punches, also provides a balanced load on the punch. An unbalanced load may cause deflection and tool breakage or excessive wear.

The amount of shear is determined by trial; however, shear equal to one-third of stock thickness ($t/3$) will reduce piercing force about 25%, and shear equal to stock thickness will reduce piercing force about 50%.

Shear can be applied to punches for large holes but not to small-diameter punches, because they lack column strength.

When a number of small holes are being pierced and the press load must be reduced, the punches can be ground to different lengths. This enables the punches to start cutting at different times and reduces the maximum load.

In selecting a press, it should be noted that the reduction in maximum impact load on the press accomplished by staggering punch length or using shear is not sufficient to enable the use of a press significantly lower in tonnage rating or in strength or rigidity.

Presses

Presses used in piercing are the same as those used in other pressworking operations. Open-back gap-frame presses of the fixed upright, fixed inclined, or inclinable types are common. The stock can be fed from the side with minimum interference from the press frame, and the parts can be removed from the front by the operator or ejected out the back by gravity or air jets.

Fig. 5. Three types of shear on piercing punches. Angle and depth of shear are exaggerated for emphasis.

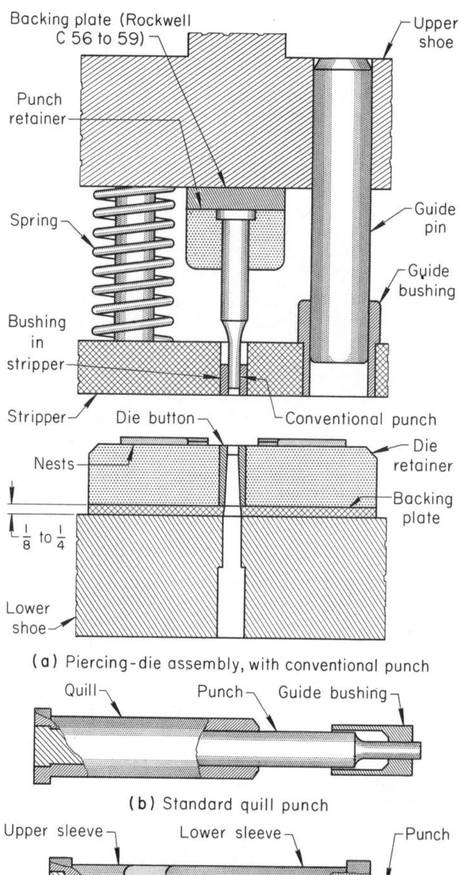

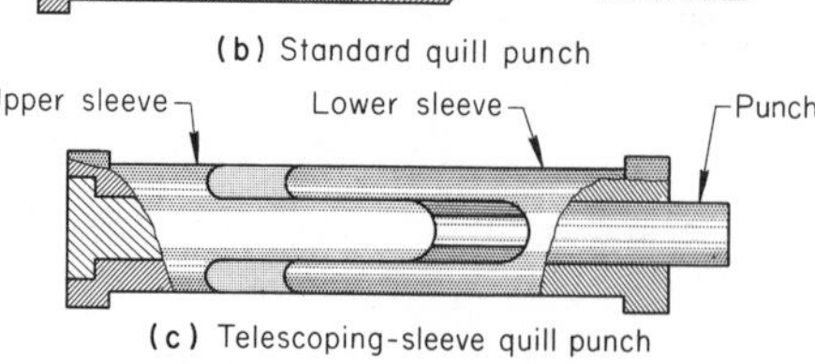

Fig. 6. Layout of a typical piercing die, and three types of punches used. See text for discussion.

Adjustable-bed or horn presses are used for piercing holes in tubing and in the sides of drawn or formed shells and boxes. Adjustable-bed and gap-frame presses generally are rated at capacities of less than 200 tons.

Straight-side presses are commonly used for compound-die and progressive-die operations, for which more accuracy, speed and stability are required.

The turret punch press is a special machine in which the punches and dies are mounted in synchronized indexing tables. Several sets of punches and dies are mounted in the table, which can be manually or automatically indexed into operating position. A flat blank is pierced and notched in a turret punch press by positioning it under the operating punch and tripping the punching mechanism. The blank is secured to a free-floating table on which a template containing the hole pattern is also attached. Each hole size and shape is coded so that all such holes can be pierced before indexing a new punch-and-die set under the press ram. The table is moved so that a pin will drop into a hole in the template; this places the blank in the proper position for piercing a hole. After the holes of one size and shape have been pierced, a new punch and die are indexed into operating position, and piercing continues in this manner until the part is finished. Almost any size or shape of hole can be pierced, within the capacity of the machine. Turret punch presses can also be programed for tape control for increased production.

Tools

A typical piercing die consists of: upper and lower die shoes, to which punch and die retainers are attached; punches and die buttons; and a spring-actuated guided stripper (see Fig. 6).

Small workpieces generally are pierced in compound dies that blank and pierce in the same stroke. Piercing is done also in stations of a progressive die or a transfer die.

Any of these dies can be constructed as multiple dies, in which two or more workpieces are pierced at each stroke of the press. For further information on dies, see the article on Blanking of Low-Carbon Steel, which begins on page 31 in this volume.

Punches. Figure 6 shows three types of punches used for piercing: (*a*) conventional, (*b*) standard quill, and (*c*) telescoping-sleeve quill.

Conventional punches are generally available with a standard maximum shank size of 1 in. in diameter, and can be used to pierce round, square, oblong or rectangular holes that have a size and shape that do not exceed 1 in. in diameter, or of a size and shape that can be machined or ground on the end of the shank as shown in Fig. 6(a). Other sizes and shapes of punch shanks can be ordered. Standard-size punch retainers, backing plates, die buttons and die-button retainers also are generally available.

The head-type punch shown in Fig. 6(a) is held by a carefully positioned and ground punch retainer. This type of punch cannot be replaced without removing the retainer. Headless punches are available with locking devices that permit replacement without removing the retainer.

A spring-loaded and guided stripper is incorporated into the die design. Conventional punches for small-diameter holes and accurately spaced holes are supported and guided by hardened bushings pressed into the guided stripper plate. Piloting punches also may be guided in the same manner. For larger punches that do not need guidance or support, clearance holes are drilled in the stripper plate, and guide bushings for both the punch and the plate are omitted.

In Fig. 6(b) and (c) are shown two types of quill punches that replace conventional punches when piercing conditions are more severe, or when more support is required for the punch when piercing small-diameter and accurately spaced holes to close tolerances. The type shown in Fig. 6(b) was designed to hold and align a small-diameter punch. The quill containing a close-fitting punch is pressed into the punch retainer. The punch can easily be changed and still maintain the original alignment and fit in the retainer. A punch guide bushing is used in the stripper plate, and a hardened backup plate supports the head of the punch. Quills are available for punches with body diameters ranging from 0.040 to 0.375 in. The nib or end can be ground to a smaller diameter if desired.

The telescoping-sleeve quill punch shown in Fig. 6(c), gives complete support to small-diameter punches and eliminates weaknesses encountered in other punch-mounting designs. The upper part of the sleeve is press fitted into the punch retainer; the lower part, into the guided stripper plate. The inside diameter of the sleeve will accommodate punch bodies ranging from 0.015 to 0.375 in. in diameter. However, a punch body at the larger end of the range and with a ground nib is suggested for best results. When piercing holes in printed-circuit boards, a 2° cone-type taper is ground on the bottom surface of the lower sleeve to concentrate the holding and stripping force at the edge of the hole.

Quill punches have been used to pierce holes in low-carbon steel having a thickness up to twice the punch diameter. Supporting sleeves or quills can be used for long, narrow punches of rectangular, oblong or other shape.

Piercing dies can be ground into a hardened die block, or they can be die buttons press fitted into a die retainer, as shown in Fig. 6(a). To coordinate the quill, guide bushing and die button, the punch retainer, stripper plate and die retainer can be clamped together and jig bored and ground at the same time. This is possible because the quill, guide bushing and die button are available with the same body diameters.

Guided Strippers. For all three types of punches, the function of the guided stripper is threefold. On the downstroke, the spring-actuated stripper contacts the work metal ahead of the punches and acts as a hold-down. On the upstroke, the metal is stripped from around the punches. The third function is to guide small punches.

To be sure of having sufficient force at the points of contact and release to accomplish the stripping, stripper springs must exert the calculated force

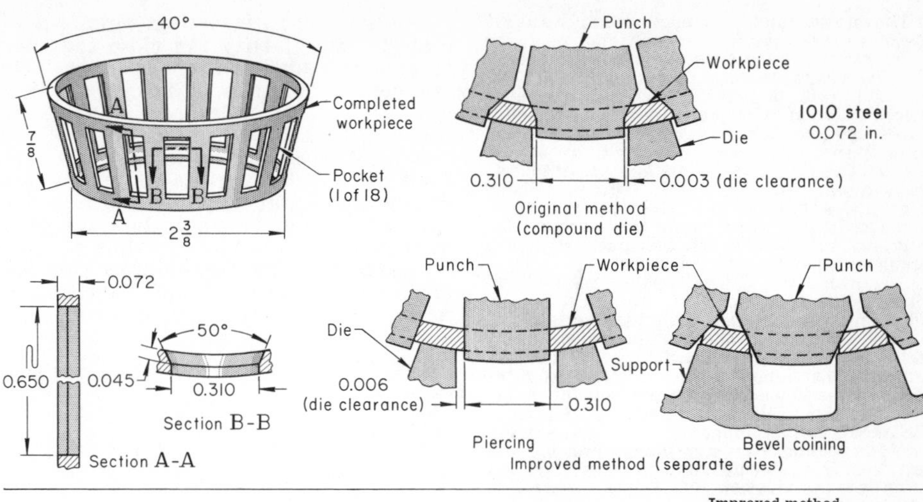

Item	Original method (compound die)	Improved method (separate dies) Piercing	Bevel-coining
Total tool life, pieces(a)	105,000	250,000	350,000
Initial tool cost(b)	$737	$701	$585
Tool cost per 1000 pieces(b)	$7.02	$2.80	$1.67

(a) Includes regrinds. Punches for compound dies were reground after 35,000 to 50,000 pieces; punches for separate dies were reground after 100,000 pieces.
(b) Although dies and punches for piercing and bevel-coining cost $2.55 less per 1000 pieces for the separate-die method, the transfer fingers and die set added $1600 to tool cost. Thus, for the annual maximum production of three million pieces, the saving in tool cost for the separate-die method was realized only after the production of 628,000 pieces.

Fig. 7. Roller-bearing cage (upper left) *for which compound die was replaced by separate dies in a transfer press for piercing and bevel-coining the 18 pockets* (Example 25)

in the open-die position (not just at the closed-die position).

Self-Contained Tools. Piercing tools can also be purchased as individual units consisting of frame, punch, die, and either spring or hydraulic strippers. The self-contained unit is not attached to the press ram, but is located, pinned and bolted to a die plate, template, or T-slot plate mounted on the bed of any type of press having adequate shut height. The units can be reused by relocating, pinning and bolting. They can be used singly or in groups and with notching units of the same construction. Punch and die sizes can be replaced as desired, and standard sizes and shapes are available for piercing thicknesses up to ¾ in. The units are available in various styles for horizontal and vertical piercing of flat or flanged workpieces.

Tool Materials. The materials used for piercing punches and dies are selected to suit the service requirements. In general, the same materials are used as for blanking. (See the article "Blanking of Low-Carbon Steel", page 31 in this volume.)

Piercing involving unusual shock and high impact may require a shock-resisting tool steel such as S7. As in blanking, M2 high speed steel is used for long punch life, particularly in piercing thicker steel, or where high abrasion resistance is required. In Example 36 in this article, a cam-actuated punch made of an air-hardening tool steel was replaced by a punch made of low-carbon steel, carburized and hardened. This change increased tool life tenfold.

Detailed information on selection of tool material and data on tool life are given in the article on Selection of Material for Blanking and Piercing Dies, which begins on page 69.

Use of Single-Operation Dies

Single-operation piercing dies are used: (*a*) when piercing is the only operation to be performed, (*b*) when the holes to be pierced are so close to the edge of the work that the incorporation of a piercing operation into a compound die would weaken the die elements, and (*c*) when the required accuracy or the sequence of operations prevents the inclusion of piercing in compound, progressive or transfer dies.

In large work, such as panels for automobiles, holes often are pierced in a separate operation, for numerous reasons. For example, the holes may distort during forming, accuracy of position may be impaired if holes are pierced before forming, or separate operations may provide a more balanced work load and reduce maintenance.

In the following example, when a hole was pierced and coined to a bevel with the same punch, coining extruded an excessive burr between the punch and the die unless a close punch-to-die clearance was maintained. To reduce die maintenance, separate piercing and coining dies were used.

Example 25. Change From a Compound Die to Single-Operation Dies for Piercing and Bevel-Coining (Fig. 7)

A separator (bearing cage) in a taper roller bearing had 18 pockets with bevel edges (Fig. 7). When the pockets were pierced and beveled by the same punch in a compound die (Fig. 7), the combined operations shortened the life of the punch because of wear and breakage. Beveling was done by a coining action, and the die clearance had to be only 0.003 in. per side (4% of stock thickness) to prevent the extrusion of an excessive burr between the punch and the die. The coining action also crowded the metal around the punch, causing stripping problems. Punches had to be sharpened after piercing and beveling 35,000 to 50,000 pieces, and total punch life averaged 105,000 pieces.

The process was changed so that the 18 pockets were pierced in one die, and the bevel edges were coined in another die (Fig. 7). Die clearance was increased to 0.006 in. per side (8% of stock thickness) for better piercing action. The piercing punch then produced 100,000 pieces before resharpening, and total punch life was increased to 250,000 pieces. The separate-die method provided better support around the hole for the beveling operation and, because of the larger clearance possible, helped to eliminate burrs around the hole on the outside of the part. Stripping problems were also eliminated.

Disadvantages of the revised method included the need for two dies and for an additional operation; but the high annual production (500,000 to three million pieces) permitted the use of a transfer press, in which transfer fingers moved the workpiece from the piercing die in an oriented position for proper beveling and to prevent damage. As shown in the table that accompanies Fig. 7, the added cost for tooling (transfer fingers and die set) for the separate-die method was paid for after the production of 628,000 pieces, at which point tool cost per 1000 pieces was less than for the compound-die method.

Use of Compound Dies

Compound dies are used for most piercing operations in which accuracy of position is important — as in Example 17 in the article on Blanking of Low-Carbon Steel, in which the work was pierced and trimmed in the same stroke of the press.

Except for the production of small lots, the use of a compound die usually is the most economical method for making a pierced and formed part to commercial tolerances. The example that follows describes the use of a compound die to blank and pierce a U-shape bracket before it was formed.

Example 26. Piercing Five Holes With a Compound Blank-and-Pierce Die (Fig. 8)

The mounting bracket shown in Fig. 8 was made of 0.179-in.-thick hot rolled 1010 to 1025 steel strip, 7⅞ in. wide, in two operations: blank and pierce, then U-form.

A compound die was used to blank the outline and pierce three round holes and two slots. The holes were reamed to size in a secondary operation to hold the 0.001-in. tolerance on the diameter. The compound die was made of oil-hardening tool steel (O2) hardened to Rockwell C 58. Punch-to-die clearance was 5% of stock thickness per side.

The blank was located by pins in the 11⁄32-by-9⁄16-in. slots for the forming operation. A spring-loaded pressure pad held the blank firmly against the punch during forming. To overcome springback, the flanges were overbent by 2° to 3°. The forming die was made of air-hardening tool steel (A2).

Total tolerance on location of the in-line holes was 0.010 in. Production lots were 50 to 100 pieces. Expected die life was 15,000 to 20,000 pieces before regrinding.

Use of Progressive Dies

Progressive dies do blanking, piercing and other operations in successive stations of a die. Each station in a progressive die is like a simple die or a compound die. The workpiece in a progressive die remains connected to the strip of work metal until the last station in the die, so that the feeding motion carries the work from station to station.

In a progressive die, piloting holes and notches are pierced in the first station. Other holes may be pierced in any station, provided they are not affected by subsequent cutting or forming. Holes for which the relative position is critical are pierced in the same station; other holes are distributed among several stations if they are close together or near the edge of a die opening. Tolerances on hole shape, size or location dictate whether holes are pierced before or after the part is formed.

It is often advisable to add idle stations or to distribute the work over one or two additional stations, so that holes will not be pierced near the edge of a die block. The die block is thus stronger, and there is less chance of die cracking in operation or fabrication. Adding stations also allows better support for the piercing punches and adds strength to the strip.

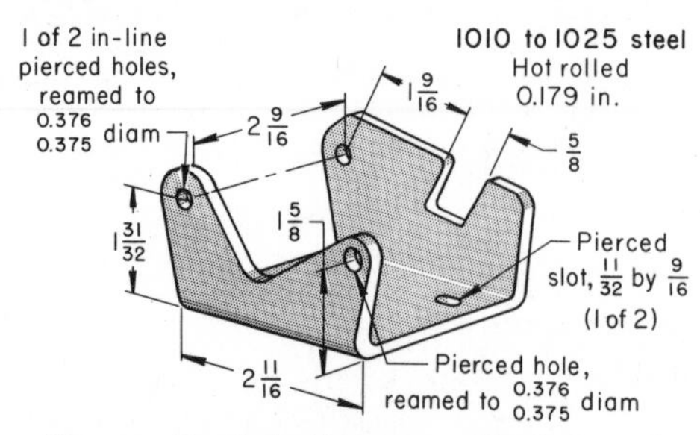

Fig. 8. Bracket that was blanked and pierced in a compound die before being formed (Example 26)

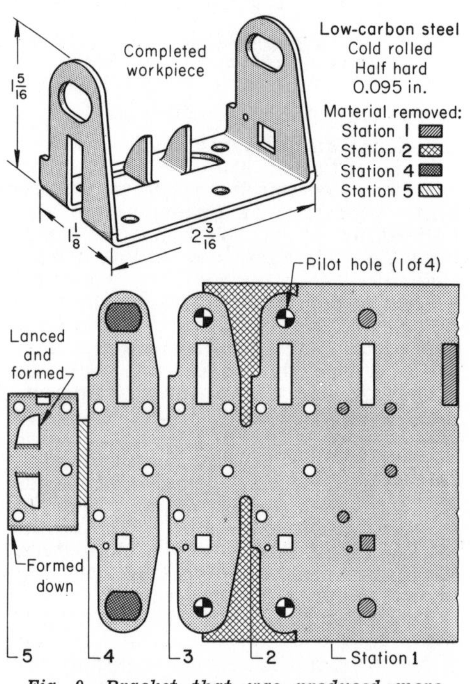

Fig. 9. Bracket that was produced more economically and more accurately in a progressive die (strip layout shown) than by the separate-operation method used for small quantities (Example 27)

Progressive dies cost more than a set of single-operation dies for the same part, and therefore generally are used for high production. However, because one part is made at each press stroke, direct labor costs are greatly reduced; also, one operator often can attend to more than one progressive die. In Example 38 (Fig. 19), manufacturing costs were reduced by making a pierced and formed part in a progressive die, rather than in two separate dies (one compound and one single-operation die).

The amount of scrap produced in progressive dies generally is high, because nesting of parts is somewhat limited and because material must be provided for connecting tabs and carrier strips. A fully automatic press with cutoff, feed, straightener, and coil cradle or reel normally is used with a progressive die, and hence press costs are high.

In the following example, the high-volume production of a bracket in a progressive die is compared with the production of smaller quantities in separate operations in utility tooling.

Example 27. Producing a Bracket in Large Quantities in a Progressive Die and in Small Lots With Utility Tooling (Fig. 9)

Figure 9 shows a bracket and the strip development for producing it in a five-station progressive die in a 75-ton mechanical press that had a 4-in. stroke, an air-actuated stock feeder and an automatic oiler. Material for the bracket was coiled cold rolled low-carbon steel strip 0.095 in. thick by 5¼ in. wide, in the No. 2 (half-hard) temper.

The die was made of D2 tool steel and hardened to Rockwell C 59 to 60. Setup time was 1.5 hr, and the press was stopped for die maintenance at intervals of 15,000 pieces. Production was at the rate of 1200 pieces per hour. A light paraffin oil was the lubricant.

Tolerance on the dimensions of all of the pierced holes was +0.002, −0.001 in., and tolerance on the position of the square hole and the two rounded slots was ±0.005 in.

Small quantities of the brackets were made from coil stock 1⅛ in. wide, in the following operations, using utility tooling:

1. Cut stock into 5-in. lengths (3500 pieces per hour)
2. Trim end in a single-operation die, two strokes per piece (1000 pieces per hour)
3. Pierce two holes 0.398 by 0.523 in. (one at each end) in a single-operation die, two strokes per piece (1000 pieces per hour)
4. Pierce 0.192-in.-wide slot and 0.201-in.-square hole, and lance and form two ears, all in a compound die for accurate relative position (2000 pieces per hour)
5. Bend the ends down, locating on the ears (1000 pieces per hour)
6. Drill four holes 0.193 in. in diameter, in a multiple-spindle drilling machine (500 pieces per hour)
7. Drill small hole next to square hole (500 pieces per hour).

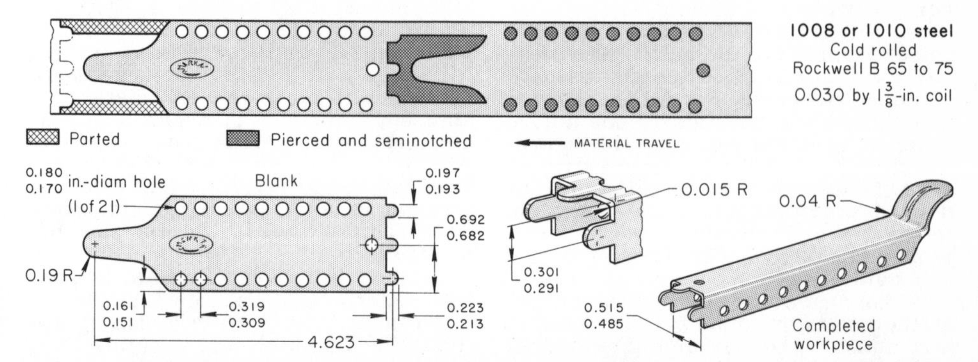

Fig. 10. Strip development in a progressive die to make a pierced and formed part from stock of exact blank width (Example 28)

The short-run method required eight times as many man-hours of labor per 1000 pieces as the progressive-die method, and the brackets produced were less accurate.

Pierced parts sometimes can be made most economically in a progressive die by using coil stock that is the exact width of the developed blank, as in the following example.

Example 28. Piercing, Seminotching and Parting in a Progressive Die (Fig. 10)

An adjustable arm for a shoe tree (Fig. 10) was made in a progressive die from 0.030-in.-thick cold rolled 1008 or 1010 steel coil with a No. 2 finish and a No. 3 edge purchased to the exact developed width of the blank (1⅜ in.). The resultant saving in material, high production rate and low per-piece labor cost were important in marketing this highly competitive, mass-produced item.

The strip development is shown in Fig. 10. The steps in making this part in the progressive die were: pierce 21 holes and seminotch; stamp trademark; part and form.

No deburring, polishing, buffing or barrel finishing operations were needed on the subsequently plated part. The only preparation done before bright nickel plating was solvent cleaning. As a further economy measure, the coil stock was selected to average in the low end of the thickness range.

The production rate was 3500 pieces per hour in a 75-ton mechanical press. Setup time was 3 hr. Yearly production was about five million pieces in lots averaging 400,000 pieces. Typically, regrinding of the dies (D2 tool steel) was required after about 250,000 pieces. A mineral oil lubricant was used.

Use of Transfer Dies

Transfer dies are used for piercing in applications generally similar to those for which progressive dies are used. A number of operations are done in successive stations of the transfer die.

Blanking, cutoff, lancing, notching, forming and drawing (as well as piercing) can be done in transfer dies. The method differs from progressive-die operation in that the workpiece does not remain attached to the strip for feeding, but is fed from station to station by transfer fingers. Production quantities must be large enough to justify the cost of tooling and equipment.

Accuracy

Accuracy in the dimensions between pierced holes is highest for holes that are pierced by the same die in one press stroke. Accuracy in the location of holes relative to an edge or some other feature is highest when the workpiece is blanked and pierced (or pierced and trimmed) in the same stroke in a compound die.

When the above procedures are used, total tolerances of 0.010 in. on hole location and 0.005 in. on hole size are readily met in normal production, and closer tolerances can be met with suitable tools, as shown in Table 4. Usually, both tooling cost and per-piece cost increase in piercing to closer tolerances.

Accuracy ordinarily is somewhat lower for holes pierced by different dies or in different stations of a progressive or transfer die, because of piloting and nesting tolerances.

Tolerances smaller than the lowest shown in Table 4 can be met with the use of special tooling and gaging and close control over the press operations, but only at increased cost and a lower production rate. The use of shaving to produce holes to a tolerance of less than 0.001 in. on size is described in Example 44. The use of fine-edge blanking for improved accuracy and edge quality is discussed in the article beginning on page 56 in this volume.

Table 4. Typical Accuracy in Piercing (a)

Finish on tools	Die retainers used — Typical material	Die retainers used — Locating holes for tools	Total tolerance on pierced holes, in. — Location (b)	Total tolerance on pierced holes, in. — Size (c)
Commercial ground	1020 or 4130 (d)	Drilled in a drill press	0.010	0.005
Commercial ground	1020 or 4130 (d)	Jig bored and jig ground	0.004	0.005
Precision ground	4130 (e)	Jig bored and jig ground	0.002	0.001

(a) For holes that are pierced with a conventional die in the same press stroke. Location will be less accurate for holes that are pierced with different dies, or pierced in different stations of a progressive die or a transfer die. (b) Relation between hole centers, or between hole center and edges or other reference points on the workpiece. (c) Diameter for round holes, or other control dimension for holes of other shapes. (d) May be hardened; other grades of steel also may be used. (e) Hardened and tempered before being jig ground.

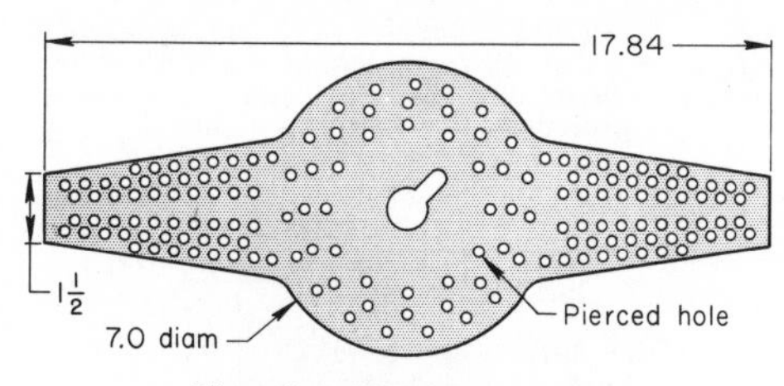

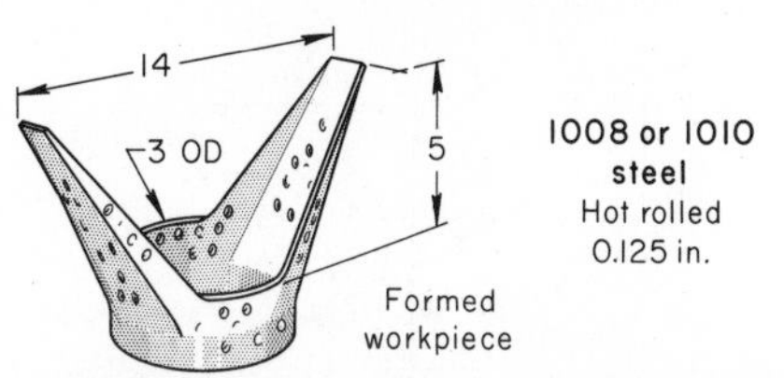

Fig. 11. Wheel spider in which noncritical holes were pierced for deflection under impact and to improve bonding to plastic (Example 29)

Accuracy of hole location is increased by the use of a rigid stripper, precisely aligned on guideposts, to guide the punches. Typical clearance of round punches in the stripper (using drill bushings as guides) is 0.0002 to 0.0005 in. total. Lubrication is important in dies that have such close clearance between punches and stripper. At speeds of 40 strokes and more per minute, the die must be lubricated constantly with a spray of light machine oil to prevent galling of the punches in the guides.

Accuracy often requires that holes be pierced after forming. In Example 38, it was necessary to pierce a hole after forming, to avoid distortion of the hole; in Example 39, holes on opposing flanges were cam-pierced in one stroke after forming, for accurate alignment.

In Example 36, two slots were pierced in flanges after forming, instead of being machined, for accurate alignment and location. In the article on Press Forming, Example 160 describes piercing a slot after forming an offset to hold the location with another hole to a tolerance of ±0.003 in.

Holes in thick stock (0.203 and 0.239 in. thick) were pierced to location tolerances of ±0.010 in. after forming flanges (see Examples 98 and 115 in the article on Press Bending).

Example 164, in the article on Press Forming, cites piercing a hole 6.471 in. in diameter to ±0.002 in., and piercing of six holes on an 8.750 ± 0.004-in.-diam bolt circle in a workpiece that was 0.375 in. thick.

Noncritical holes, for which there are no close tolerances on size or spacing, may be pierced for venting, to provide for free passage of air or other fluids, for lightening, for improved bond with a molded plastic cover, for increased flexibility of a workpiece, and even to provide controlled strength. In the application described in the example that follows, noncritical holes were pierced to weaken a part so it would deflect under impact or shock loading.

Example 29. Piercing Noncritical Holes (Fig. 11)

The workpiece shown in Fig. 11 is a wheel spider that was designed to be enclosed in molded plastic and to deflect under impact load. The spider was made of hot rolled 1008 or 1010 steel, dead soft, pickled and oiled. The steel strip, ⅛ in. thick by 16 in. wide, was hand fed into a two-stage progressive die in a 450-ton mechanical blanking press. In the first stage, noncritical holes were pierced (to make the spider deflect on impact and to provide a better bond with the molded plastic); the piece was blanked in the second stage. The pierced blanks then were fed into a 600-ton mechanical forming press, where the part was formed. The forming die was sprayed with soluble oil.

Hole Size

Pierced holes can be of almost any size, from holes as small across as the thickness of the stock to the largest size that can be adapted to the equipment available. Some holes can be pierced that are smaller across than the stock thickness, but such piercing is not common.

Small holes and slots are pierced much like large holes, except that small holes are more difficult to pierce, because slender punches are comparatively weak. To minimize deflection and breakage, length of punches is limited to that needed for the operation, and punches are specially stiffened and guided (see Fig. 6).

The minimum hole size that can be pierced in a specific application ordinarily is found by trial.

Piercing of Thick Stock

The effects of work-metal thickness on piercing are generally the same as on blanking. Cutting force increases with thickness; consequently, tool design and material, press selection, and operating conditions are influenced by work-metal thickness. The relation of die clearance to work-metal thickness is discussed in the sections on die clearance in this article. The minimum pierced hole size usually is expressed as a function of work-metal thickness, as described in the preceding section.

The two examples that follow illustrate the piercing of unusually thick flat workpieces prior to forming.

Example 30. Use of an Inverted Die for Piercing 0.437-In. Plate (Fig. 12)

The 0.641-in.-diam hole in the 0.437-in.-thick hot rolled 1010 steel bracket shown in Fig. 12 was pierced in the flat blank in a 150-ton mechanical press equipped with a die cushion.

The hole was pierced in an inverted die, which had the punch mounted on the lower shoe and the die on the upper shoe. A pressure pad, actuated by the die cushion, clamped the blank securely against the die during piercing, and stripped the blank from the punch.

The die cushion provided enough force to hold the blank flat during piercing. The same amount of force would have been difficult to obtain with a spring-loaded stripper. Also, the die construction was simpler and less expensive than the usual design. The die produced 300 pieces per hour.

The bracket was first blanked in a 150-ton press at 400 pieces per hour from 4¾-in.-wide strip. This width was needed to provide stock for blanking, and half an inch of stock was left between blanks. There was no nested layout of parts, because angular shear in the blanking die bent the scrap skeleton.

In forming the pierced part, the blank was loaded into a nest in a form die in a 350-ton press. Production rate in forming was 500 pieces per hour.

Dies made of D2 tool steel were used in all three operations, for a yearly production of about 5000 pieces.

Example 31. Piercing a Square Hole in ¾-In. Plate

A hole 1$^{1}/_{16}$ in. square was pierced through high-strength low-alloy steel plate ¾ in. thick, in a die in a 120-ton open-back inclinable press. The die was made to pierce holes one at a time in any of several flat workpieces. A typical workpiece size was ¾ by 12 by 37 in.

Production rate for piercing in D2 tool steel dies was 300 to 360 pieces per hour. Maximum yearly production was 1000 pieces.

After the holes were pierced, the workpiece was heated to 1500 F and formed into a curved shape. The shape was used as a digger bucket, one of many that were bolted to a large wheel (digger rim) of a machine used for digging trenches for sewers and pipelines.

Die design was critical in the following example, in which one piercing operation preceded the forming and a second followed the forming of thick stock in a progressive die.

Example 32. Piercing, Forming and Piercing of 0.179-In. Stock in a Progressive Die of Critical Design (Fig. 13)

The lifting eye shown in Fig. 13 was pierced and formed in a progressive die from cold rolled 1020 steel 0.179 in. thick by 4⅞ in. wide. Thickness of the stock required that piloting punches be used at each of the working stations to hold the strip in place. The two ⅝-in.-diam pilot holes were pierced before forming, and the 1.00-by-1.30-in. slot was pierced after forming, to simplify the pilot punch. During cutoff, a 1-in.-diam pilot punch was used.

The operations used to make the part were:

1 Pierce two ⅝-in.-diam pilot holes, one to be within the 1.00-by-1.30-in. slot.
2 Trim both edges of strip and partial outline of four parts.
3 Pierce four 0.420-in.-diam holes.
4 Form down workpiece 30°, pilot in parts being formed.
5 Pierce 1.00-by-1.30-in. slot.
6 Slug-type punch cutoff to separate the two eyes.

The dies for the holes had a clearance per side of 7% of stock thickness. In the ⅝-in.-diam holes, a burnished band of at least one-half the stock thickness was observed. The small holes and the slots showed evidence of double shearing.

A 250-ton straight-side mechanical press was used, at 40 strokes per minute. The die, made of W1 tool steel and hardened to Rockwell C 52 to 54, had a life of 50,000 pieces between resharpenings. Annual production was about 300,000 pieces. A mineral oil was used as the lubricant.

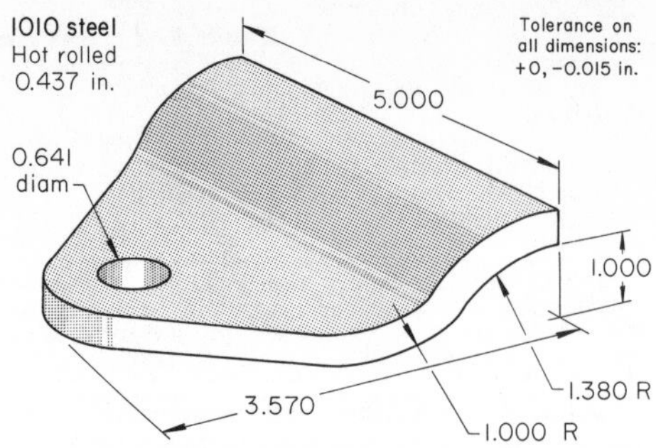

Fig. 12. Thick bracket that was formed from a blank through which the hole was pierced in an inverted die equipped with a pressure pad (Example 30)

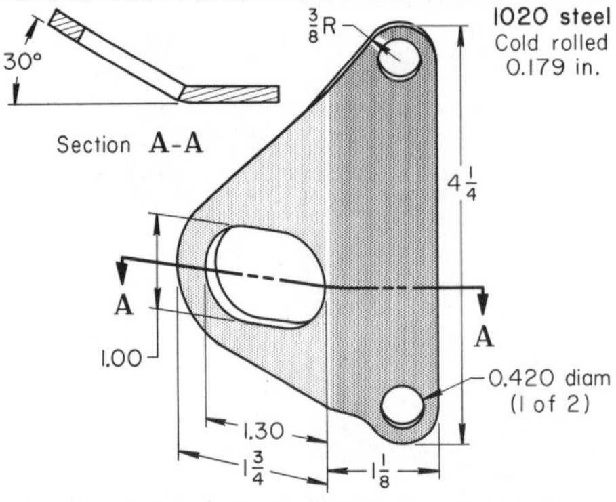

Fig. 13. Lifting eye of thick stock in which the two holes were pierced before forming, and the slot pierced after forming, in a progressive die (Example 32)

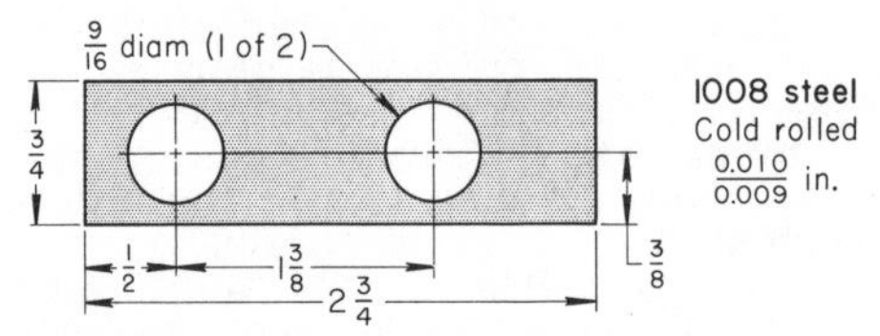

Fig. 14. Shim that was pierced and cut off from thin coiled strip in a compound die (Example 33)

The radial piercing of thick curved workpieces is done in the same way as the piercing of flat workpieces, except that the die must be designed to accommodate the curved parts. Radial piercing of a round hole in steel ⅛ in. thick that had been formed to a ⅝-in. radius is described in Example 38.

The piercing of a hole through round stock, such as a radial hole through a cylinder, is done by using a die with a heavily loaded stripper, both of which fit the round shape of the workpiece. The round hole then is pierced readily with little bulging of the workpiece, even though the hole can be as large as 40% of the diameter of the workpiece. The center of the hole should be at a distance from the end of the workpiece that is at least equal to the work thickness (diameter of the rod).

Piercing of Thin Stock

Because of its strength and rigidity, material thicker than ⅛ in. seldom is blanked or pierced from coil stock or in a progressive die. On the other hand, because of its lack of strength and extreme flexibility, material thinner than 0.020 in. generally requires special handling techniques, as for the blanking and piercing of a perforated comb for an electric shaver from 0.0045-in.-thick steel, which is described in Example 195 in the article on Forming of High-Carbon Steel.

The example that follows describes the blanking of steel shims from thin coil stock in a compound die.

Example 33. Piercing of Shims From 0.010-In. Strip in a Compound Die (Fig. 14)

The shim shown in Fig. 14 was made from coil stock of cold rolled 1008 steel, ¾ in. wide by 0.010 in. thick, in a pierce-and-cutoff compound die. Thickness tolerance was +0, −0.001 in. The coiled strip was fed automatically from a stock reel by an air-operated slide feed into a 25-ton open-back inclinable press that operated at 150 strokes per minute.

The die, which was made of oil-hardening D3 tool steel, produced 230,000 shims before it needed sharpening. Die life was indefinite, because a thickness of 1½ in. had been provided for grinding allowance in repeated sharpenings, to restore the cutting edge.

For a detailed discussion of blanking and piercing of thin stock, see the article on Blanking and Piercing of Magnetically Soft Materials (Electrical Sheet); Example 52 in that article describes the piercing of sheet 0.002 in. thick, and Examples 53 and 54 describe the piercing of sheet 0.004 in. thick.

Hole Spacing

Recommended minimum spacings for pierced holes are given in Table 5. These minimum spacings apply when ordinary pressworking practices are followed, without confinement of the workpiece in the die or other special procedures to prevent distortion.

As noted in Table 5, S_5 (the distance from the edge of a hole to the inside of a flange) may be reduced when the metal is relieved near the pierced hole (as by a slot) to prevent distortion of the hole in forming. Accuracy in the shape and location of pierced holes often demands that the holes be pierced after the workpiece has been formed.

When a round hole must be pierced so as to leave almost no metal between the edge of the hole and the edge of the part, the hole may be cut through the edge in a keyhole shape that minimizes bulging and also does not leave sharp points. In the following example, spacing between the keyhole and the end of the part was only 58% of the recommended spacing in Table 5, and spacing for the round hole and the slot was only 50% of the recommended spacing. Confinement of the blank in the die prevented distortion at the keyhole and the slot.

Example 34. Piercing Holes at Less Than Recommended Minimum Edge Distance (Fig. 15)

The flyweight shown in Fig. 15 was part of a centrifugal device to release pressure. The part was made of hot rolled 1010 steel, pickled and oiled, ¼ in. thick. Preliminary design had a wall thickness of $^{3}/_{32}$ in. between the $^{7}/_{16}$-in.-diam hole and the edge of the part. The original tooling called for a compound die to pierce and blank the part completely in one press stroke. However, with the fragile punch required, it was impossible to hold the 0.315/0.310-in. dimension on the keyhole opening (detail A in Fig. 15).

Production was successful when the part was made in three separate dies, by the sequence of operations shown in the table with Fig. 15. A keyhole punch was used to pierce the $^{7}/_{16}$-in.-diam hole. The hole-to-edge spacing was increased from $^{5}/_{16}$ in. to $^{7}/_{16}$ in.

Distortion was minimized by confining the blank in a nest during piercing. In the compound die, the hole shown in detail A and the edge of the part were connected with a radius tangent to both. When the keyhole punch was used, the punch surface intersected the outer edge at a 45° angle, a change that did not interfere with the function of the part but avoided difficulty in making a transition radius tangent to the outer edge.

The hole to be reamed was pierced with a 0.226-in.-diam punch and a 0.246-in.-diam die. Later the hole was reamed to 0.2475/0.2465-in. diam for nearly its full length, and deburred. This hole was perpendicular to the part surface within +0° 45′.

The special procedures needed to prevent distortion of hole or part when the spacing is less than recommended generally lower the production rate and increase the cost of the part. Accordingly, distortion that does not interfere with part function and is otherwise acceptable sometimes is permitted, as in the next example.

Example 35. Piercing Slots Near the Edge of a Part (Fig. 16)

The male hinge leaf shown in Fig. 16 was made from 0.239 by 2½-in. round-edge strip of hot rolled 1010 steel.

Because the distance from slot to edge was only about ½t, the leaf bulged at each slot (see spacing recommendations in Table 5). However, bulges in this area were not objectionable, and therefore retainers were not used during piercing.

The part was blanked, pierced, curled, and flattened and offset. The curled section was straddle milled, and the 5⁄16-in.-diam hole was reamed, in a subsequent operation. After milling, U-shape grooves were coined in the ends of the curled area to provide lubrication of the hinge pin.

Effect of Forming Requirements

It is simpler to pierce holes in a flat sheet than in a part that has been formed. Holes near a bend radius (see illustration in Table 5) are usually distorted when the part is formed. If distorted holes are unacceptable, or if an accurate relation of holes to other features in a workpiece is specified, piercing must be done after forming.

Dies for piercing after forming are generally more complex and costly, and require more maintenance, than dies for flat blanks. Often these dies have cam-actuated punches.

In Example 41 in this article, when the part was U-formed after piercing, one hole in particular closed in during forming, resulting in an elongated hole. This deformation was taken into consideration during product design.

The following four examples describe applications in which it was necessary to pierce holes after forming.

Example 36. Piercing of Accurately Located Slots After Forming (Fig. 17)

Figure 17 shows a formed part which, because of close tolerances, could not be slotted before forming. The original procedure was to drill the holes and mill the slots to hold the alignment of the slots to the end radii and to the tongue within 0.003 in. Results from machining were unsatisfactory, and it became necessary to pierce the slots after forming, to hold tolerances.

The size and shape of the part and the location of the slots precluded piercing from the outside. Piercing was done from the inside by two punches split on the centerline of the part and moved outward by cam action.

The original punches were made of air-hardening tool steel, hardened to Rockwell C 58 to 60. Because of breakage, the maximum punch life was 10,000 pieces. Changing the punch material to 1025 steel, carburized and hardened, increased the average punch life to 100,000 pieces.

Annual production was about 240,000 pieces in lots of 50,000 to 60,000.

Example 37. Piercing Critical Holes in a Large Frame Member After Forming (Fig. 18)

Figure 18 shows part of a 22-lb side member for an automobile frame that was blanked from 0.089-in.-thick commercial quality 1010 steel. This part could have been made most economically by blanking and piercing, followed by forming, but this would have resulted in out-of-tolerance hole spacing.

The procedure used was: blank and pierce noncritical holes; form; restrike flanges; and then pierce critical holes. Piercing of the critical holes was done by side-acting punches, actuated by 17-ton and 35-ton hydraulic cylinders. Production was at the rate of 200 pieces per hour, in 20,000-piece lots.

Die material was an air-hardening tool steel (A2) hardened to Rockwell C 60 to 61. The dies were expected to last for the production of 225,000 pieces.

Table 5. Recommended Minimum Spacings for Pierced Holes in Flat and Formed Steel and Nonferrous Metal Workpieces

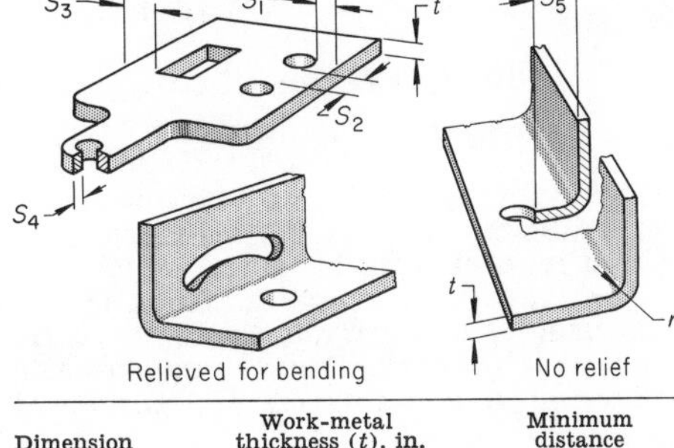

Dimension	Work-metal thickness (t), in.	Minimum distance
S_1 and S_2 ..	Less than 0.062	0.120 in.
	0.062 to 0.380	0.120 in. (but at least 1.5t) (a)
S_3 and S_4 ..	Less than 0.032	0.060 in.
	0.032 to 0.125	2t
	0.125 to 0.380	2.5t
S_5	To 0.380	1.5t + r(b)

(a) For steel. Minimum for nonferrous metals, 2t. (b) For flanges with no relief. Value for S_5 may be reduced when work metal is relieved for bending (as shown at lower left above) to prevent distortion of the pierced hole in forming.

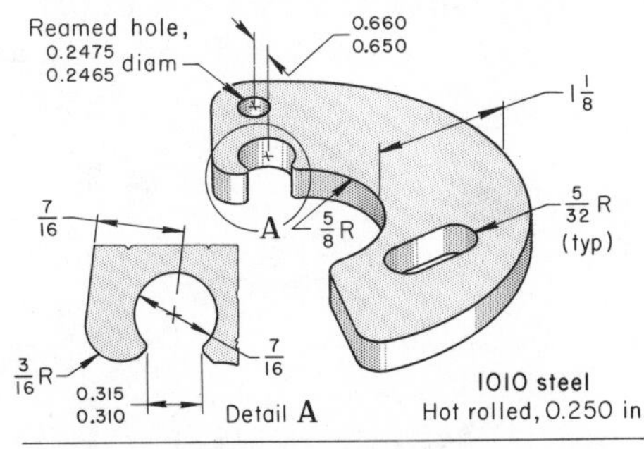

Sequence of Operations

1 Shear 4 to 8 ft long by 3⅞ in. wide
2 Blank outline; pierce round hole (1000 pcs/hr)
3 Ream and deburr round hole (300 pcs/hr)
4 Pierce keyhole and oval slot (770 pcs/hr)

Operating Conditions

Type of press	75-ton mechanical
Press speed	55 strokes per minute
Die material	A2 tool steel at Rc 58 to 60
Lubricant	Sulfur-base, EP type(a)
Production rate(b)	300 pieces per hour
Die life per grind	20,000 pieces
Total die life	1 million pieces

(a) Applied to strip by roller. (b) Lot size was 2500 pieces; annual production, 10,000 pieces.

Fig. 15. Flyweight in which holes were pierced at less than recommended minimum distances from the edge. Over-all length of the flyweight was 3½ in. (Example 34)

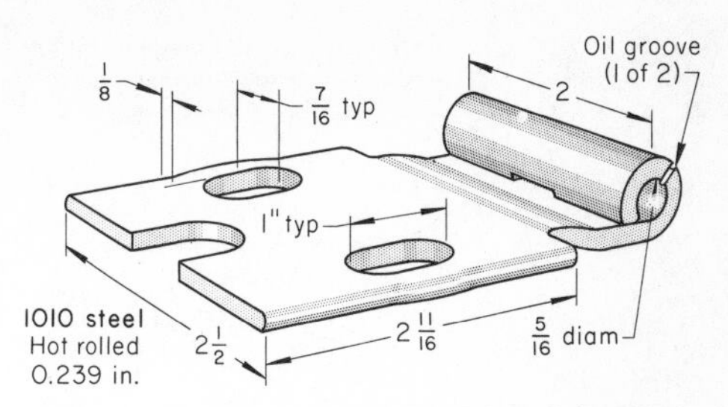

Fig. 16. Male hinge leaf in which slots were pierced near the edges (Example 35)

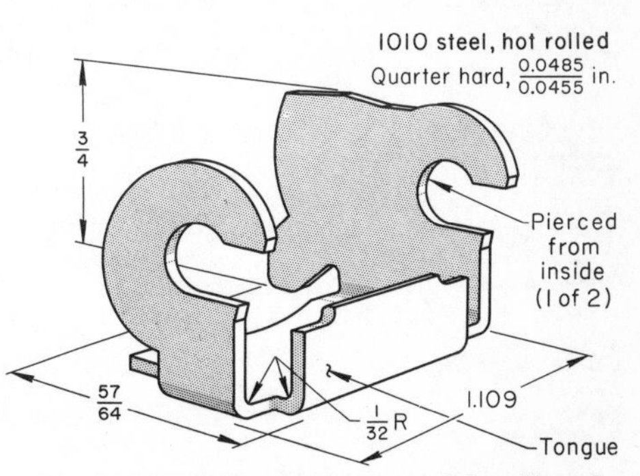

Fig. 17. Part in which accurately aligned slots were pierced (after forming) by two punches cam-operated from the inside (Example 36)

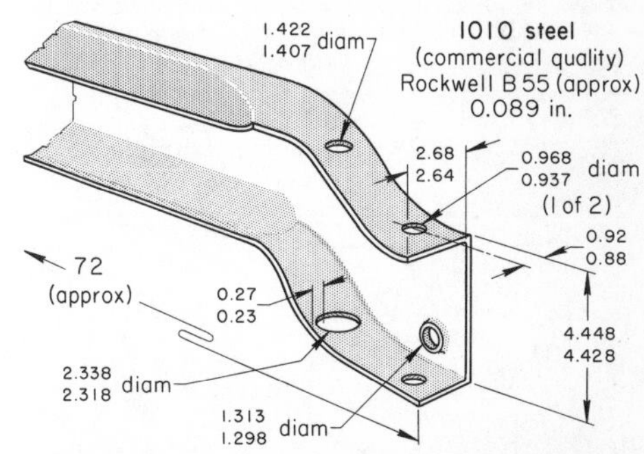

Fig. 18. Portion of an automobile-frame side member that had critical holes pierced in it after forming, to maintain location tolerances (Example 37)

Example 38. Piercing After Forming, to Avoid Distortion of Hole (Fig. 19)

Originally, the bracket shown in Fig. 19 was made by blanking and piercing in a compound die, and then forming, but the round hole was distorted beyond tolerance when the ⅝-in. radius was formed.

The bracket was produced satisfactorily by blanking and forming in a compound die, followed by piercing in a separate die. This two-die method, however, was comparatively costly; therefore, when annual production increased from 80,000 to 300,000 pieces, the part was retooled for complete production in a progressive die. This reduced the cost per piece and relieved tie-up of presses. Costs for making the bracket by the two-die method and the progressive-die method are compared in the table with Fig. 19.

By the improved method, six stations of an eight-station progressive die (two stations idle) were used for the following operations: notch edges and pierce the oval slot; blank outline; completely form the ⅝-in. radius and partly form the other bends; cam-pierce the round hole (see tooling setup in Fig. 19); finish-form bends; and cut off.

An open-back inclinable press, back geared and rated at 100-ton capacity, was used at 40 strokes per minute for the progressive-die method. The dies, which were made of D2 tool steel and hardened to Rockwell C 58 to 60, had a life of 100,000 pieces per grind. Die wear was 0.005 in. per grind.

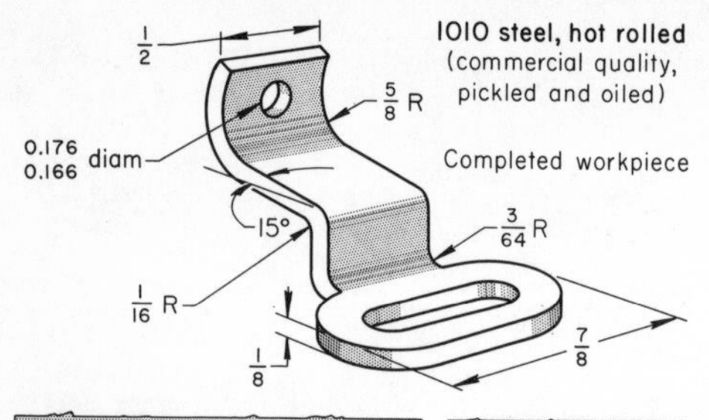

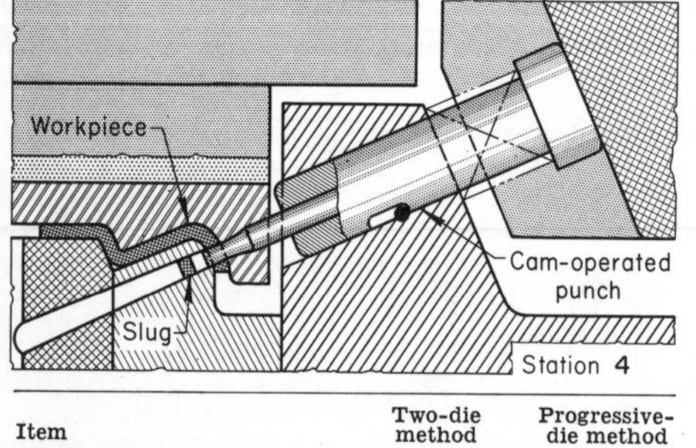

Item	Two-die method	Progressive-die method
Die cost	$2557	$2975
Labor cost per piece(a) .	$0.0134(b)	$0.0033
Total cost, 300,000 pcs(c) .	$6577	$3965

(a) Includes overhead. (b) Blanking and forming, $0.0033; piercing, $0.0101. (c) Annually.

Table compares costs for producing the bracket complete in a progressive die with costs for previous method, blanking and forming in a compound die and piercing in a separate die.

Fig. 19. Bracket in which round hole was cam-pierced (in progressive-die station 4 shown) after ⅝-in. radius had been formed, to avoid distortion of hole (Example 38)

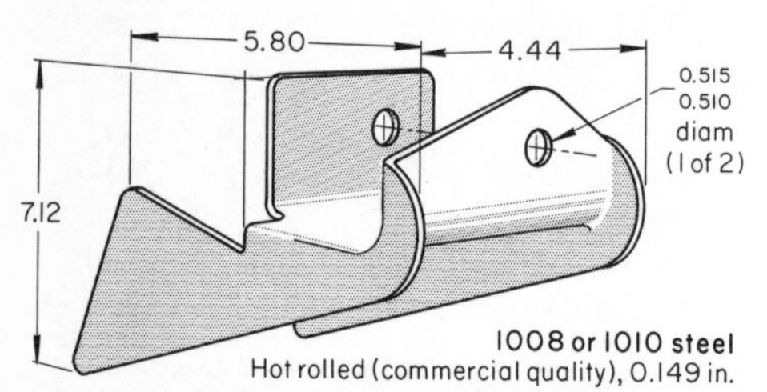

Fig. 20. Bracket in which accurately aligned holes on opposing flanges were cam-pierced in one press stroke after forming (Example 39)

Example 39. Cam-Piercing Holes in Opposing Flanges of a Formed Part for Accurate Alignment (Fig. 20)

To maintain alignment of the two opposing holes in the automobile-frame control-arm bracket shown in Fig. 20, the holes were cam-pierced in one press stroke, after the part was formed. Tolerance on hole alignment was ±0.005 in.

The bracket was made of commercial quality 1008 or 1010 steel, as rolled, 0.149 in. thick, in five operations:

1 Blank two workpieces per stroke
2 Prebend, form and re-form in three separate dies, side by side
3 Form ear
4 Trim in two stages
5 Restrike and cam-pierce.

Blanking was done at 1800 pieces per hour in a 500-ton coil-fed automatic blanking press. The remaining operations were done at 135 pieces per hour in a 300-ton or a 400-ton mechanical press.

The use of high-production equipment, including the cam-operated piercing die, was economical for the annual production of 350,000 pieces in 20,000-piece lots. Drilling would have been used for making the holes if 10,000 or fewer pieces had been needed per year to meet production requirements.

In the following example, timing of the piercing operation was critical in making a central hole in a shallow formed part without fractures or severe distortion of the hole.

Example 40. Significance of Timing in Piercing a Shallow Formed Part (Fig. 21)

The round cover shown in Fig. 21 was made of 0.032-in.-thick, drawing quality, low-carbon steel. An inverted blank-and-draw die was made to form the part. During die tryout the part fractured either partly or all the way around the bottom where indicated in Fig. 21. The ¾-in.-diam hole was pierced in a secondary operation.

Several other forming procedures were tried, also without complete success. When the ¾-in.-diam hole was pierced in the blank, fractures occurred around the hole at about 90° spacing. If the hole was pierced to size 5⁄32 or ¼ in. after forming began, the hole was badly distorted by the remainder of the forming. The hole was 1⁄32 in. oversize, but did not fracture, when pierced 1⁄16 in. above the bottom of the stroke.

To make acceptable parts, the hole piercing elements were made undersize so that the hole would be enlarged to the proper diameter when pierced 1⁄16 in. above the bottom of the stroke.

It was necessary that the hole only appear round and be approximately to size, so that the hole was satisfactory without trimming.

Piercing Holes at an Angle to the Surface

For piercing of holes that are not perpendicular to the surrounding surface, the workpiece is securely clamped to the die with a pressure pad, and the dies usually are ground to fit the contour of the part. The shape of the punch nose depends on the angle of contact with the workpiece and on the stock thickness.

In one application, holes 5⁄16 in. in diameter were pierced in 0.250-in.-thick 1090 steel at an angle of 83° to the surface. The holes were pierced by using sleeved punches and clamping the work tightly to the die with a pressure pad.

In the following example, holes were pierced at an angle of 40° 30′ to the surface of a flat workpiece, which was later formed by bending.

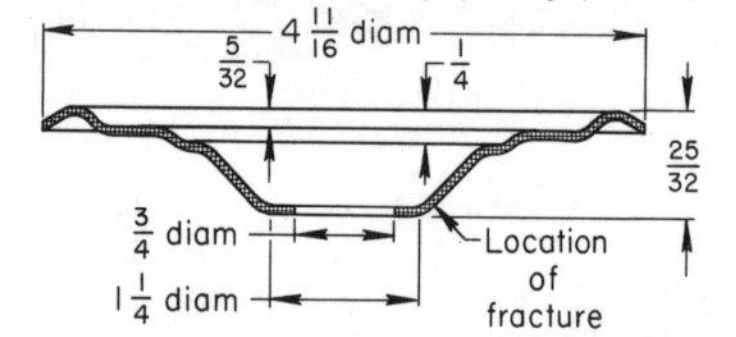

Fig. 21. Drawn and pierced circular cover in which fracture or severe distortion was eliminated when piercing was done at 1⁄16 in. above bottom of stroke (Example 40)

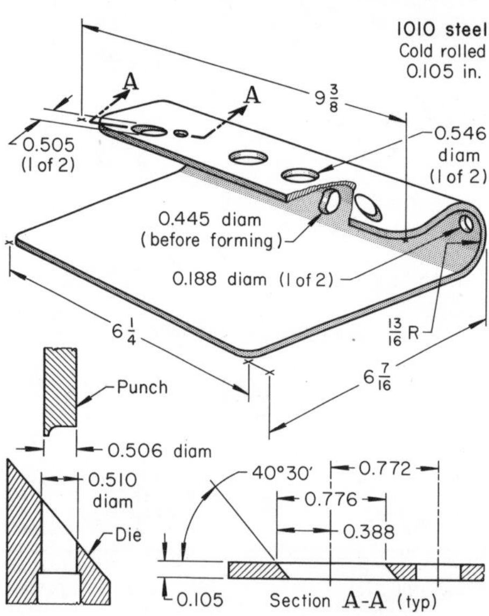

All holes were pierced before the part was formed. The 90° hole in the U-bend zone deformed to an elliptical shape during forming.

Fig. 22. Lamp-bracket base in which two holes were pierced at an angle to the surface, using punch shown at lower left (Example 41)

Example 41. Piercing Holes at an Angle to the Work Surface (Fig. 22)

Two 0.505-in.-diam holes were pierced at an angle of 40° 30′ to the surface in the 0.105-in.-thick cold rolled 1010 steel flat blank for the lamp-bracket base shown in Fig. 22. To pierce the compound-angle holes, the blank was placed in a nest, which held it at the proper angle and position for piercing. By repositioning the blank in a second nest, it was possible to pierce both of these holes with one punch and die.

The face of the die button was ground flush with the surface of the nest. The die had a straight land with a minimum length of ⅜ in. There was a ⅝-in.-diam relief below the land. The punch was ground with a step, as shown in Fig. 22. This step curled the slug, permitting the use of a long straight land in the die. The punch and die were made of M2 high speed steel, hardened to Rockwell C 58 to 59. Punch-to-die clearance was 0.002 in. per side. Die life was 15,000 holes per grind.

The punch was mounted in a heavy quill designed for quick changing, which proved unnecessary. A spring-loaded pressure pad guided and added support to the punch, and also held the blank securely in the nest. The pressure pad was interlocked with the die, so that shifting could not take place after piercing started. The die was run in a 10-ton mechanical press, which produced 300 pieces per hour.

Before the angle holes were pierced as described above, the outline of the part and seven 90° holes had first been produced in a compound blank-and-pierce die. The blanking die and punch, and the punches and die buttons for the 90° holes, were made of O1 tool steel and hardened to Rockwell C 59 to 60. The die was mounted in a 100-ton mechanical press producing 300 pieces per hour. Die life was 40,000 pieces per grind.

When the workpiece was bent through 180° after all the holes had been pierced, the 0.445-in.-diam hole changed in shape, assuming final dimensions of 0.411 by 0.443 in. This deformation did not affect the function of the hole.

Special Piercing Techniques

Piercing operations that require special tooling and techniques include piercing and forming of flanged holes, piercing with a fastener ("self-piercing") and with a pointed punch, and tube piercing.

Flanged holes (sometimes called extruded, countersunk, dimpled or burred holes) are generally used for assembly purposes, such as providing more thread length for a tapped hole, greater bearing surface, or a recess for a flat-head screw or rivet. The flanged hole can be produced by forcing a punch of the desired hole diameter through a smaller prepierced hole, or by using a shouldered or pointed punch that both pierces the hole and flanges it.

The depth of flange that is formed depends on elongation of the metal, and the flange is thinnest at its outer edge. A deeper flange can be made by extruding metal into the flange. Such flanging is done by first piercing a smaller lead hole and then using a punch that extrudes metal around the hole into the die clearance to produce a flange, at the same time coining or forming a slight chamfer (depressed cone) or other shape of recess into the hole. (See also the article on Press Bending of Low-Carbon Steel, page 89 in this volume.) This kind of extruded flange has uniform wall thickness. Such extrusion causes more metal flow and greater work hardening than ordinary piercing of flanged holes.

Flanged holes can be made with accuracy to suit special purposes, as shown in the following example.

Example 42. Flanging and Stepping a Prepierced Hole in One Operation (Fig. 23)

The workpiece shown in Fig. 23 is the upper stalk of a pliers-type can opener, made of cold rolled 1010 to 1015 steel coil, 0.104 in. thick by 3⅞ in. wide, with a maximum hardness of Rockwell B 65, a No. 3 edge and a No. 2 finish. The accurate flanged and stepped hole (Fig. 23) was formed in one operation on a prepierced hole. Coining the step helped to provide enough metal for the flange.

The stalk was produced in seven stations of a progressive die as listed with Fig. 23.

After forming, the stalk was flattened in another press, hardened, and tumbled for deburring. The bright finish of the stock reduced over-all cost by eliminating polishing and buffing before plating with bright nickel. Additional savings were made by buying stock in the lower end of the thickness-tolerance range for this grade of steel.

A 75-ton single-action mechanical press produced 1800 pieces per hour. Setup time was 3 hr. Dies were made of D2 tool steel and had a life of 10,000 pieces per grind. Typical lot size was 15,000 pieces, with an annual production of 60,000 parts. Mineral oil was used as a lubricant.

Piercing with a fastener ("self-piercing") is used chiefly as an assembly technique. A rivet, for example, may be used as a punch to pierce a hole through material that it will join. The following example describes an application in which a square nut with a sharp face served as a piercing tool and then became part of an assembly.

Example 43. Automatic Assembly of Self-Piercing Nut Into a Bracket (Fig. 24)

A square nut was automatically assembled into a body-bolt bracket as shown in Fig. 24. The nut served as the piercing punch to make a 0.687-in.-square hole in the embossed portion of the bracket. The bracket was made of galvanized, hot rolled, 1006 steel, 0.075 in. thick. After being pierced, the metal sprang back into two grooves in the nut, locking the nut into the pierced square hole. The nut was fed from a special installing head that was loaded from a rotary hopper.

Two assemblies were completed (pierced and installed) at each stroke of a 72-ton open-back inclinable press running at 45 strokes per minute. Maximum daily production was 12,000 assemblies. The bracket was fed by a gravity-slide feed at the front of the press, and was unloaded at the rear with the help of a blast of air. [For information on the forming of the bracket, see Example 152 in the article on Press Forming of Low-Carbon Steel.]

The 0.812-in.-diam hole was pierced at the same time the nut was inserted. Commercial punches and die buttons were used.

A standby unit for piercing a square hole was available in case a supply of the square nuts was not on hand when the part was scheduled to run. Later the nuts were inserted and clinched using pneumatic equipment.

Holes made with a pointed punch, such as a cone-point, nail-point, or bullet-nose (ogive) punch, have rough or torn flanges. Such a hole is satisfactory for holding a sheet-metal screw, acting as a spacer, or providing a rough surface (see Example 452 in this volume).

Tube piercing and slotting are done in dies when production lots are large enough to pay for special tooling. Simple dies, and more complex tooling such as cam dies, are designed to hold, locate and pierce tubes, drawn cups, and other round parts.

A mandrel may be used in a horn die for work on tubing and other round

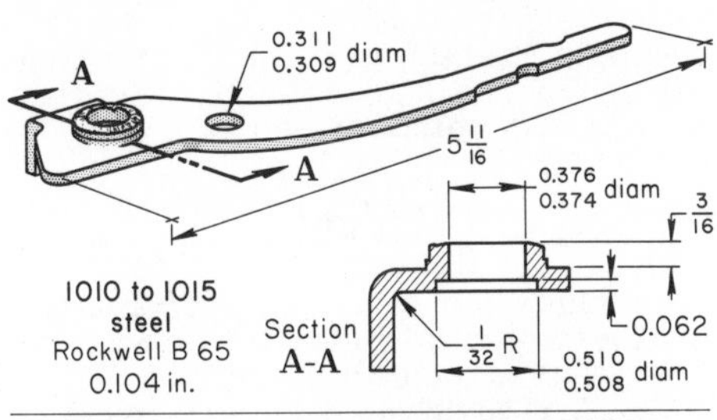

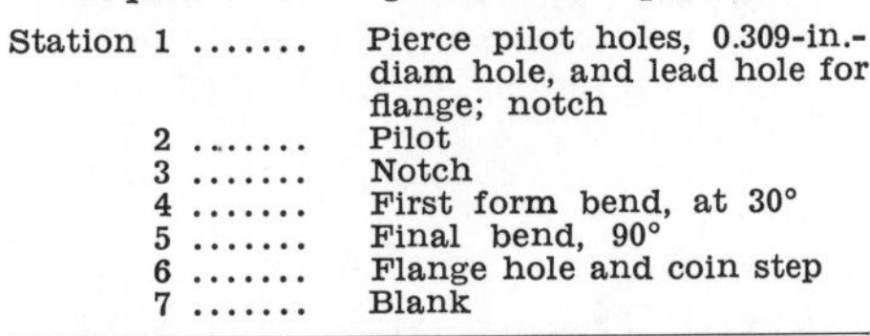

Sequence of Progressive-Die Operations

Station	Operation
Station 1	Pierce pilot holes, 0.309-in.-diam hole, and lead hole for flange; notch
2	Pilot
3	Notch
4	First form bend, at 30°
5	Final bend, 90°
6	Flange hole and coin step
7	Blank

Fig. 23. Can-opener stalk with a hole that was flanged and stepped in one operation in a progressive die (Example 42)

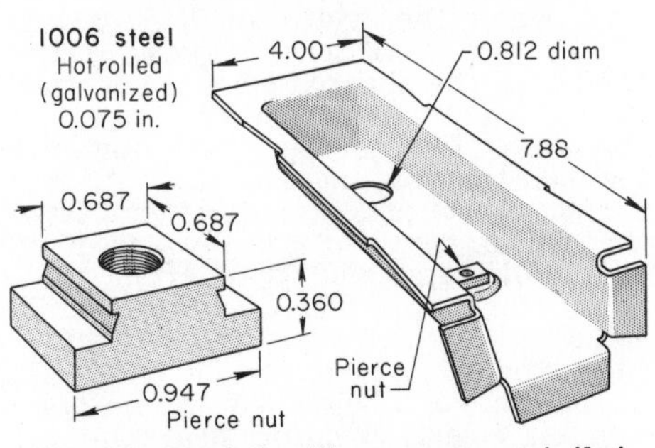

Fig. 24. Bracket with a square nut that pierced a hole for itself (Example 43)

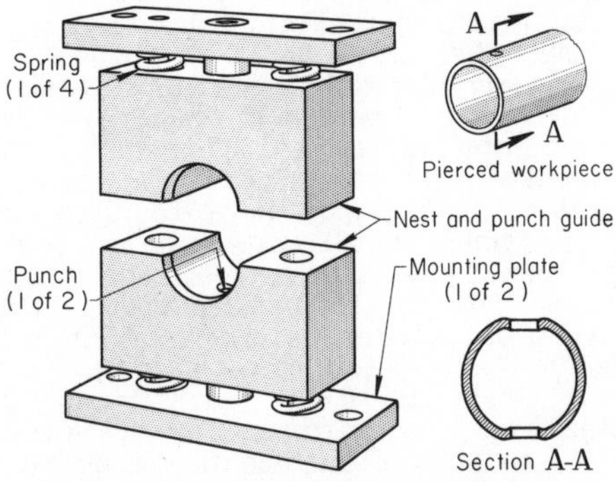

Fig. 25. Tool for tube piercing without a mandrel, and a pierced tube showing indentation around hole

parts, for piercing, slotting and notching. One version of a die that uses a mandrel permits piercing two opposing holes in a tube in one stroke, the slug from one wall going through a hole in the mandrel to act as the punch for the hole in the opposite wall.

Tubes can also be pierced with opposing holes without using a mandrel. The bottom half of the tube is supported by the die, which has a nest with the same diameter as the outside diameter of the tube. A similar nest for the upper half of the tube is in a combined hold-down and punch guide. Thus the tube is completely surrounded during piercing. Because the bottom side of the tube is supported by the die, the lower hole is pierced without any distortion. The tube will collapse slightly around the hole in the top side of the tube. The amount of distortion of the top hole varies with the size of the tube and the hole.

Holes on opposite sides of a tube can be pierced simultaneously, using the tool shown in Fig. 25, which does not require a mandrel. The tool consists of identical upper and lower assemblies, one attached to the press ram and the other to the press bed. Each assembly is made up of a punch and a spring-loaded combined nest, stripper and punch guide. When used for multiple-hole piercing, the assemblies usually are mounted to upper and lower plates having tapped holes or T-slots. There will be a slight indentation around each hole, as shown in Fig. 25.

Shaving

Shaving is done in a separate operation or is included in one station of a progressive die. (See page 42 in the article on Blanking of Low-Carbon Steel, for more information on shaving.) The inclusion of a shaving operation in a progressive die generally increases the need for die maintenance, and the slivers of shaving scrap can jam the feeding mechanism. A replaceable insert may be used in a shaving die, for easier maintenance.

Shaving allowance depends on the workpiece material and on its thickness. See Table 5 on page 43 in the article on Blanking of Low-Carbon Steel.

Shaving plus burnishing is used to produce greater accuracy in a pierced hole than can be obtained by shaving alone, as shown in the next example.

Example 44. Use of Blanking, Piercing, Shaving and Burnishing in Making Gear Blanks to Close Tolerances (Fig. 26)

The small gear blank illustrated in Fig. 26 was produced from 2-in.-wide strip of cold rolled 1010 steel of No. 2 temper in a five-station progressive die, to the following speci-

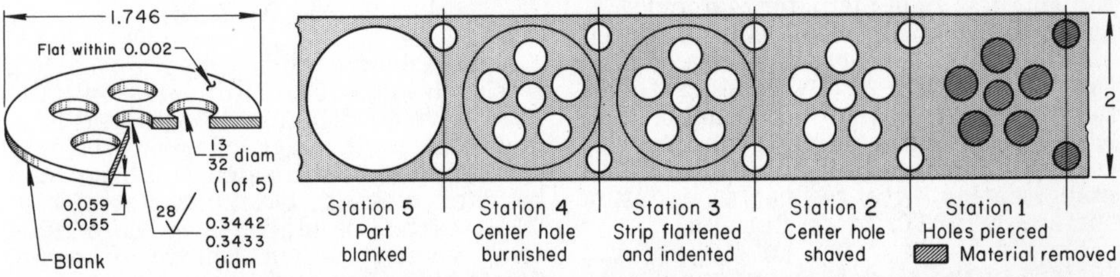

Fig. 26. Gear blank that was produced with an accurate center hole by piercing, shaving and burnishing in a five-station progressive die (Example 44)

fications: a critical tolerance of +0.0005, −0.0004 in. on the center hole; finished blanks flat within 0.002 in.; and a surface finish of 28 micro-in. or smoother for 70% of the center-hole surface. These specifications were met by piercing, shaving and burnishing the center hole, in the sequence of operations indicated by the strip progression.

A sulfurized and chlorinated (EP) lubricant was applied to the coil stock by roller coating.

Annual production was 2 million pieces, in four lots. The gear blanks were made at 150 pieces per minute in a 60-ton press. The dies, made of M2 high speed tool steel, had a life of about 100,000 pieces before regrinding and a total life of about 10 million pieces.

Piercing vs Alternative Methods

Piercing is used chiefly when accurate holes are required and when the production lot is large enough to pay for the tooling. Alternative methods, mostly machining processes, are used instead of piercing for smaller production lots, or for holes that have a diameter less than stock thickness. Such alternative methods include drilling, milling and sawing, and electric-arc and gas cutting, all of which may be done on work that is stacked or nested for greater efficiency.

The fourteen ½-in.-diam holes in the pilot plate illustrated as Example 453 in Fig. 5 on page 238 of Volume 3 could have been pierced in a punch press instead of being drilled by electrochemical machining (ECM). The drilled holes discussed in Examples 757 and 758 on page 384 of Volume 3 also could have been pierced in a punch press.

Safety

Piercing, like other press operations, involves potential hazards to operators, maintenance men and others in the vicinity. The articles on Presses (page 1) and on Blanking of Low-Carbon Steel (page 31) contain information and literature references on safe operation.

Other Examples of Piercing in This Volume

Example	Workpiece
18	Brake-drum back plate
19	Brake-shoe adjusting cam
21	Body-bolt bracket
22	Dished washer
50	Rotor and stator laminations
54	E and I laminations
80	Door-lock mounting plate
96	Pushrod guide
98	Hinge bracket
115	Hinge leaf
117	Mounting bracket
119	Steering-column bracket
125	Flanged panel
138	Automotive control arm
139	Decorative grille
142	Eggbeater wheel
160	Heater control lever
162	Fan blade
164	Truck-wheel disk
170	Lawn-mower yoke bracket
171	Lawn-mower housing
195	Comb for electric shaver
208	Gas-burner body half
235	Thin-wall cup
242	Automotive spring seat
250	Flanged ferrule

Fine-Edge Blanking and Piercing

FINE-EDGE BLANKING (also known as fine blanking, smooth-edge blanking, or fine-flow blanking) produces precise blanks in a single operation without the fractured edges characteristically produced in conventional blanking and piercing. In fine-edge blanking, a V-shape impingement ring (Fig. 1) is forced into the stock to lock it tightly against the die and to force the work metal to flow toward the punch, so that the part can be extruded out of the strip without fracture or die break. Die clearance is extremely small, and punch speed much slower than in conventional blanking.

Fine-edge piercing can be done either separately or at the same time as fine-edge blanking. In piercing small holes, an impingement ring may not be needed.

No further finishing or machining operations are necessary to obtain blank or hole edges comparable to machined edges, or to those that are conventionally blanked or pierced and then shaved. A quick touchup on an abrasive belt or a short treatment in a vibratory finisher may be used to remove the small burr on the blank.

Specially designed single-operation or compound blanking and piercing dies are generally used for the process.

Process Capabilities

Holes can be pierced in low-carbon steel with a diameter as small as 50% of stock thickness. In high-carbon steel, the smallest hole diameter is about 75% of stock thickness. Holes can be spaced as close to each other, or to the edge of the blank, as 50 to 70% of stock thickness. Total tolerances obtainable are: 0.0005 in. on hole diameter and for accuracy of blank outline; 0.001 in. on hole location with respect to a datum surface, and 0.001 in. on flatness.

No die break shows on the sheared surface of the hole. Blank edges may be rough for a few thousandths of an inch of thickness on the burr side of the part when the width of the part is about twice the stock thickness or less. Finish on the sheared edge is governed by the condition of the die edge and the land within the die. Parts fine-edge blanked from stainless steel will have a surface finish of 32 micro-in. or better. Smooth edges also are produced on spheroidize-annealed steel parts.

Burr formation increases rapidly during a run, necessitating frequent grinding of the cutting elements.

Chamfers can be coined around holes and on edges. Forming near the cut edge, or forming offset parts with a bend angle up to 30°, is possible under restricted conditions.

Metals up to 0.125 in. thick having a tensile strength of 85,000 to 115,000 psi are easily blanked. Parts up to ½ in. thick can be blanked if press capacity is available. Material thicker than 0.125 in., especially steel having a carbon content of 0.25% or more, requires an impingement ring on the die so that the corners on the part will not break down. The edges of parts made of 1018 steel work harden as much as 7 to 12 points Rockwell C during blanking.

In tests on 0.60% carbon spring steel with a hardness of Rockwell C 37 to 40, the surface finish on the sheared edges was 32 micro-in. or better, but punch life was only 6000 pieces.

The cutting speed for fine-edge blanking is 0.3 to 0.6 in. per sec.

Work Metals

Low-carbon and medium-carbon steels (1008 to 1035), annealed or half-hard, give good blanked edges and normal tool wear. High-carbon steels in the spheroidize-annealed condition can be blanked easily; blanking of steel with 0.35% carbon or higher is recommended only when it is spheroidize-annealed. Steels quenched and tempered to about Rockwell C 30 are well suited to fine-edge blanking, because they do not require subsequent heat treatment, which could result in deformation.

High-carbon steels and alloy steels such as 4130, 4140, 8620 and 8630 cause considerably higher tool wear than low-carbon plain carbon steels, but surface finish is smoother. Leaded steels are not suitable for fine-edge blanking, because of their low deformability.

Parts made of stainless steels of types 301, 302, 303, 304, 316, 416 and 430, in the form of bright rolled fully annealed strip, have good blanked edges, but cause higher tool wear than steels of low and medium carbon content.

Good results have been experienced with aluminum alloys 1100 (all tempers), 5052-O to 5052-H38, 6061-O to 6061-T6, and others having similar yield strength and elongation. Blanked edges on parts made of aluminum alloy 2024 generally are rougher than edges on other aluminum alloys. Brasses containing more than 64% copper are especially suitable. Nickel alloys, nickel silver, beryllium copper, and gold and silver also are easily fine-edge blanked.

Blank Design

Limitations on blank size depend on stock thickness, tensile strength and hardness of the work metal, and available press capacity. For example, perimeters of approximately 25 in. can be blanked in 0.125-in.-thick low-carbon steel (1008 or 1010). It is possible to blank smaller parts from low-carbon or medium-carbon steel about ½ in. thick.

Sharp corner and fillet radii should be avoided when possible. A radius of 10 to 20% of stock thickness is preferred, particularly on parts over 0.125 in. thick or those made of alloy steel. External angles should be at least 90°. The radius should be increased on sharper corners or on hard materials.

Parts with tiny holes or narrow slots to be pierced, or with narrow teeth or projections to be blanked, may be unsuited to fine-edge blanking. The ratio of hole diameter, slot width, or projection width to metal thickness should be at least 0.7 for reasonably efficient blanking, although a ratio as small as 0.5 has been successful with some parts. The spacing, between holes or between a hole and the edge of the blank should not be less than 0.5 to 0.7 times metal thickness, in order to maintain the quality of hole-wall and blank-edge surfaces, and to avoid distortion.

These limitations have been exceeded. For instance, a ⅝-in.-diam hole was pierced in each end of a 1018 steel link 1 in. wide and 5⁄16 in. thick. Since the part had a ½-in. radius on each end, the wall thickness was 3⁄16 in. The part was offset 0.100 in. in the same die. In a part made of 0.156-in.-thick aluminum alloy 5052-H34, 0.125-in.-diam holes were pierced leaving a wall thickness of 0.040 in. A 0.062-in.-diam hole was pierced in the same part.

The sheared faces of holes pierced during fine-edge blanking are usually vertical, smooth and free from die break, provided the maximum hole dimensions are not more than a few times the stock thickness. As in conventional piercing, there is a slight radius around the punch side of the hole, but there are no torn edges on the die side of the blank. A rough sheared surface on the blank may be caused by too great a punch-to-die clearance, or improper location and height of the impingement ring for the material being blanked. On parts blanked to a small width-to-thickness ratio, a small rough surface may be noticeable, but may not be detrimental (see Example 45).

Presses

A triple-action hydraulic press or a combination hydraulic and mechanical press is used for fine-edge blanking. The action is similar to that of a double-action press working against a die cushion. An outer slide holds the stock firmly against the die ring and forces a V-shape impingement ring into the metal surrounding the outline of the part. The stock is stripped from the punch during the upstroke of the inner and outer slides. An inner slide carries the blanking punch. A lower slide furnishes the counteraction to hold the blank flat and securely against the punch. This slide also ejects the blank.

The stripping and ejection actions are delayed until after the die has opened at least to twice the stock thickness, to prevent the blank from being forced into the strip, or slugs from being forced into the blank. Because loads are high, and clearance between punch and die is extremely small, the clearance between the gibs and press slides must be so close that they are separated by only an oil film.

Force requirements for fine-edge blanking presses are influenced not only by the work metal and the part dimensions, but also by the special design of the dies and pressure pads used for fine-edge blanking. Depending on part size and shape, a 100-ton press can blank stock up to 0.315 in. thick; a 250-ton press, up to 0.470 in. thick; and a 400-ton press, up to 0.500 in. thick.

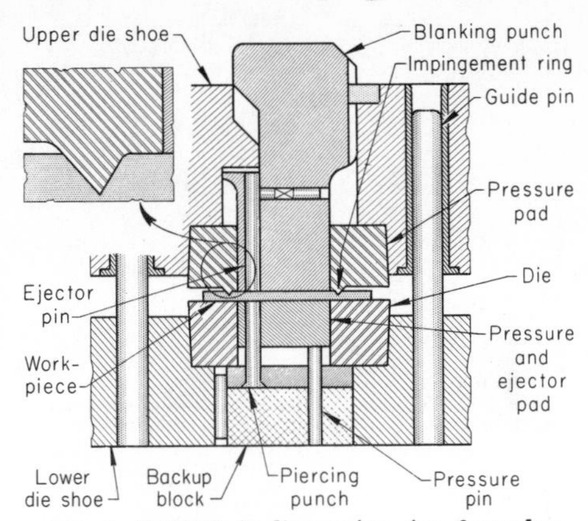

Fig. 1. Typical tooling setup for fine-edge blanking a simple shape

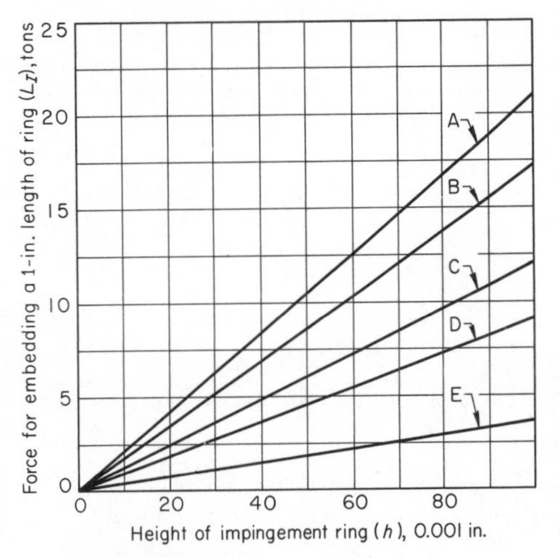

A — Stainless steel
B — Prehardened alloy steel
C — Mild steel; half-hard brass; hard copper; series 6000 aluminum alloys, hard
D — Soft copper; series 6000 aluminum alloys, half hard
E — Commercially pure aluminum, hard

Fig. 2. Force required for embedding impingement rings of various heights into several different work metals

The total load on the press in fine-edge blanking is the sum of three components: the cutting force (L_C); the lower blankholder force (L_{LB}), or counterforce; and the clamping force on the impingement ring (L_{IR}) on the pressure pad. The first two components comprise the total force on the inner slide, and the third component is the force on the outer slide.

The cutting force, in pounds, is calculated from the equation:

$$L_C = 0.8\ S l_B t$$

where 0.8 is an experimentally determined constant; S is the tensile strength of the work metal, psi; l_B is the total length of cut (sum of perimeters of blank and holes pierced in blank), in.; and t is the thickness of the work metal, in.

The counterforce, or lower blankholder force, in pounds, is calculated from the equation:

$$L_{LB} = P_C A$$

where P_C is the counterpressure on the lower side of the blank, psi; and A is the area of the blank, sq in. The counterpressure usually is about 10% of the tensile strength of the work metal.

The clamping force on the impingement ring on the pressure pad, in pounds, can be obtained from:

$$L_{IR} = L_I l_{IR}$$

where L_I is the force to embed a 1-in. length of the impingement ring into the work metal, lb; and l_{IR} is the total length of the impingement ring, in. The force L_I for different work metals, as determined by experience in fine-edge blanking, is given in Fig. 2.

When impingement rings are used on both the pressure pad and the die, the calculation of force is still based only on the pressure-pad impingement ring. The reduced height of impingement rings when used in pairs allows the use of a lower clamping force, and thereby reduces the over-all load on the press. This is because the lower impingement ring is impressed into the workpiece by the reaction force.

If coining, embossing or other forming is done during the blanking, the additional force required for those operations must be added to the force requirements as calculated above.

Tools

The design of tools for fine-edge blanking is based on the shape of the part, the method of making the die, the required load, and the extremely small punch-to-die clearance. The considerable loading and intended accuracy require that the press tools be sturdy and well supported to prevent deflection. The small clearance presupposes precise alignment of the punch and die.

Design. A basic tool comprises three functional components: the die, the punch, and back-pressure components. To produce good-quality blanks, the punch-to-die clearance must be uniform along the entire profile and must be suitable for the thickness and strength of the work metal. The clearance varies between 0.0002 and 0.0004 in.

The components of a typical tooling setup for fine-edge blanking of a part of simple shape are shown in Fig. 1. The profile part of the blanking punch is guided by the pressure pad. A round punch is prevented from rotating by a key fastened to the upper die shoe. The hardened pressure pad is centered by a slightly conical seat in the upper die shoe; this pad contains the V-shape impingement ring.

Some diemakers put a small radius on the cutting edge of the die. This causes a slight bell-mouth condition, which produces a burnishing action as the blank is pushed into the die, improving the edge finish.

If holes are to be pierced in the part, the blanking punch contains the piercing die. The slug is ejected by ejector pins, or through holes in the punch.

The die is centered in the lower die shoe by a slightly conical seat, as is the upper pressure pad. Both the die and the upper pressure pad are preloaded to minimize movement caused by compression. The pressure and ejector pad is guided by the die profile, and is supported by pressure pins and the lower slide. The backup block for the piercing punch also guides the pressure pins.

The die components are mounted in a precision die set with precision guide pins and bushings. Some designers prefer pressing the guide pins into the upper shoe.

Materials and Life. Because of the high loads, close tolerances, and small clearances involved in fine-edge blanking, the die elements are made of high-carbon high-chromium tool steels, such as D2 or D3, or of A2 tool steel, heat treated to about Rockwell C 62.

Punch and die life vary with tool material and hardness, punch-to-die clearance, type of work metal, and workpiece dimensional and surface-finish tolerances.

For most work metals under the usual operating conditions, punch life for fine-edge blanking of ⅛-in.-thick stock is 10,000 to 15,000 blanks between regrinds — assuming that the blanks are of simple shape and that punch wear is such that only 0.002 to 0.005 in. of metal need be removed to restore the punch to its original condition.

The effect of work material on punch and die life can be illustrated by the following data.

In one application, after blanking 33,000 pieces made of 1010 cold rolled steel (No. 2 temper), 0.009 in. was ground from the punch and 0.006 in. from the die. Production rate was 35 pieces per minute. When blanking 8617 and 8620 steel, it was necessary to grind 0.009 in. from the punch after 12,000 pieces and 0.007 in. from the die after 23,000 pieces. The production rate was 27 to 30 pieces per minute.

In another instance, 15,000 to 30,000 pieces per punch grind were produced when blanking annealed 1040 and 1050 steel; and 25,000 to 50,000 pieces for 1010 steel (No. 3 and 4 temper). Punch life for blanking fine-tooth gears made of annealed high-carbon steel was 10,000 to 15,000 pieces, and for steel with a hardness of Rockwell C 32 to 34 was 5,000 to 15,000 pieces. The reason for grinding the punch was to remove the small radius on the edge of the punch, which must be kept sharp and flat to obtain a good edge on the part.

Total die life may be 200,000 to 300,000 blanks per tool. The die is usually sharpened once for each two or three punch sharpenings. It may be necessary to remove from the die an amount of metal up to half the work-metal thickness to restore the die to its original condition.

In some production applications of blanking simple shapes from 0.100-in.-thick 1010 steel, life between regrinds was about 40,000 blanks for punches, and about 80,000 blanks for dies, when punch and die wear of 0.005 to 0.007 in. was allowable and the surface finish of the cut edge was 63 micro-in. or better.

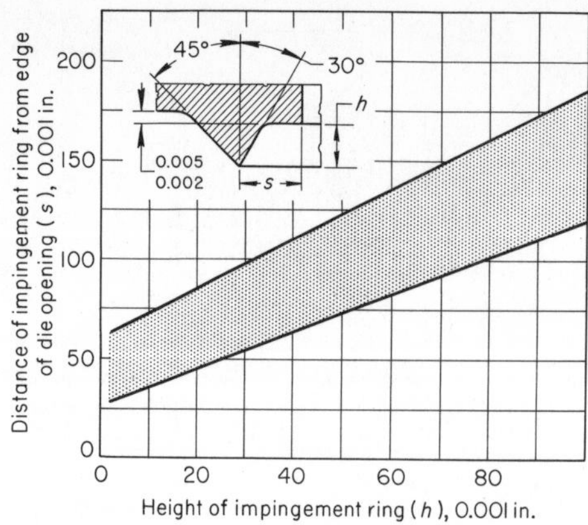

For any ring height (h), distance (s) should be in the shaded area of the graph. Note the 0.005/0.002-in. difference in elevation between the blankholding surfaces inside and outside the impingement ring (inset in graph).

Fig. 3. Relation of height of impingement ring to distance from edge of die opening

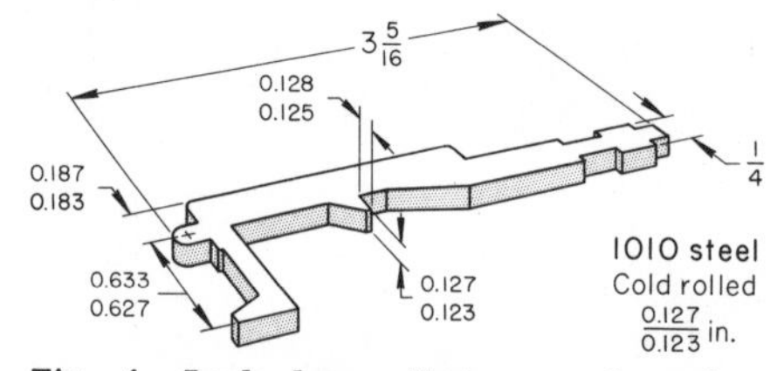

Fig. 4. Lock lever that was fine-edge blanked to close tolerances (Example 45)

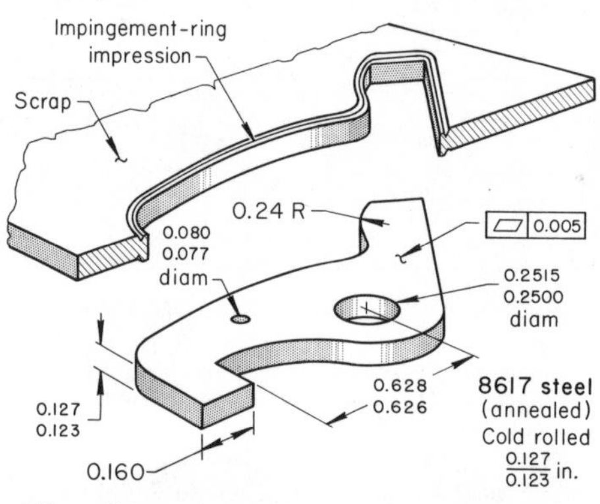

When this part was produced by conventional blanking, the small hole had to be drilled, the large hole pierced undersize and reamed, and the periphery shaved.

Fig. 5. Clutch dog that was fine-edge blanked and pierced with 100% land on edges and in holes (Example 46)

Pressure-Pad Impingement Rings

The most important consideration in the design of a pressure pad for fine-edge blanking is the special construction required to lock the workpiece tightly against the die and force the metal to flow against the punch. A V-shape impingement ring is provided on the pressure pad surrounding the outline of the part (see Fig. 1). The lip of the pressure pad between the ring and the shear line has a difference in elevation of 0.002 to 0.005 in. from the outer surface of the pressure pad (see inset in Fig. 3). The ring (which penetrates to its full depth into the scrap metal outside the shear line) and the lip of the pressure pad hinder metal flow at the shear line during blanking.

The outline of an impingement ring is a closed shape conforming to that of the blank to be produced. Figure 3 shows the minimum and maximum distance of the ring from the edge of the die opening, for rings of various heights. An impingement ring with a 60° angle, instead of the 45° angle shown in Fig. 3, has been used, but more force was required to imbed it into the work metal.

Height of impingement ring depends on the thickness and ductility of the work metal. The height (penetration) of the V-shape is 20% of stock thickness for materials of low ductility. The more ductile materials require a penetration of 32 to 35% of stock thickness.

If rings are used on both sides of the stock, the height of each ring should be half the total penetration required for the metal. Thus, if the penetration required were 0.042 in., the height of each ring would be 0.021 in. The distance to the edge of the die opening (s, in Fig. 3) would be reduced, and so would the length of the impingement ring.

The selection of the ring height and of the exact location within the range defined in Fig. 3 is based on experience. A shallow ring near the shear line has about the same effect as a deeper one farther from the shear line. If the ring is too near the die opening, a large portion of the metal in the zone will flow into the shear or edge radius and impair the efficiency of the ring. When a larger ring is located a greater distance from the die opening, a larger amount of stock is used, and more force is required to impress the ring into the work metal. Improper location and size of the impingement ring can cause rough sheared edges on the blank.

Effect of Stock Thickness. Stock up to 0.156 in. thick usually requires a ring on the pressure pad only. Stock up to 0.188 in. thick may need a partial ring on the die in addition to a full ring on the pressure pad. Full rings on the pressure pad and the die may be necessary for stock over 0.188 in. thick.

Although an impingement ring on the die reduces the edge radius on the blank more than does a similar ring on the pressure pad, its use is avoided when possible, because it makes resharpening of the die difficult.

The need for a full or partial ring on the die, to supplement the ring on the pressure pad, can be reduced by properly orienting the blank design on the strip. More precise and intricate cutting can be done on the side of the blank adjacent to the incoming strip, where ample stock is available to restrain metal flow, than along surfaces near the edges of the strip or along the narrow portion of the web where blanks have already been removed. When a blank cannot be oriented on the strip so that an ample width of stock is adjacent to all critical sections of the shear line, it is usually more economical to use partial rings or straight knife-edge projections on the die than to provide large edge and web widths.

Effect of Part Shape. The impingement ring ordinarily follows the contour of the part at a distance depending on ring height (see Fig. 3), but it cannot follow narrow slots in the part.

Impingement rings are not necessary around holes pierced in blanked parts, particularly holes with dimensions that are only a few times the metal thickness. However, the blank must be securely clamped between the punch and the pressure pad.

In Example 48 a circular ring was used, because it was not feasible to follow the contour of a fine-tooth gear. A gear with larger teeth can be made with a ring having a scalloped outline. An impingement ring can extend into wide notches, but not into narrow ones. In Examples 45, 46 and 47, rings were used that closely paralleled the outline of the workpieces.

Lubrication

The work metal must have a film of oil on both sides to lubricate the punch and die during fine-edge blanking. The lack of a lubricant on either side can reduce punch or die life between sharpenings as much as 50%. Oils used for conventional blanking usually are satisfactory. In severe applications, a wax lubricant may be used. In Examples 46, 47 and 48, a sulfur-free oil was used to lubricate the strip. An extreme-pressure chlorinated oil was used for the part in Example 45.

Examples of Application

The lock lever in the following example was made of low-carbon steel and had a low width-to-thickness ratio. Although a conforming impingement ring was used, a rough surface appeared on the cut surface adjacent to the upper (punch) side of the blank.

Example 45. Blanking of a Long Slender Lock Lever to Close Tolerances (Fig. 4)

A lever for a pushbutton lock (Fig. 4) was fine-edge blanked to a minimum total tolerance of 0.003 in. The maximum total dimensional tolerance was 0.010 in., except on fractional dimensions, which had a tolerance of 1/32 in.

The lever was blanked from cold rolled, commercial quality 1010 steel, 0.127/0.123 in. thick and 2¾ in. wide. The coil stock had a No. 4 temper (soft), No. 3 edge (slit), and a No. 2 finish (bright). The blank design was positioned at an angle on the strip, with a progression of 0.875 in. An impingement ring 0.040 in. high was used on the pressure pad.

The edge of the blank was smooth and perpendicular to the top and bottom surfaces. On the die side of the blank, edge radius (rollover) was noticeable, particularly at the outside corners. (This effect, typical of low-carbon steel in fine-edge blanking, is less pronounced on high-carbon and alloy steels.)

The die was made of D2 tool steel, hardened to Rockwell C 57 to 60, and ground to a fine finish. During blanking, the die was lubricated with an EP chlorinated oil. Die life was 30,000 pieces per grind. The die was mounted in a special 40-ton triple-action hydraulic press operating at 40 to 50 strokes per minute.

The two examples that follow describe applications in which fine-edge blanking replaced conventional blanking, thereby eliminating the need for subsequent drilling, reaming and shaving. In the first example, the smaller of the two holes pierced during fine-edge blanking had a diameter only 62% of stock thickness. In the second example, the distance between the edge of a large hole and the edge of the part was only 50% of stock thickness.

Examples 46 and 47. Fine-Edge Blanking and Piercing to Final Size and Finish, Which Could Not Be Done by Conventional Blanking

Example 46 (Fig. 5). The clutch dog shown in Fig. 5 was fine-edge blanked from annealed, cold rolled, commercial quality 8617 steel, 0.127/0.123 in. thick and 1½ in. wide. The two holes were pierced at the same time the outline was blanked. The periphery of the part and the holes had a 100% land. There was no edge radius on the die side, and the burr on the punch side was small and easy to remove.

The sequence of operations used to make the part by conventional methods was: blank outline and pierce a 3/16-in.-diam hole; drill the 0.080/0.077-in.-diam hole; ream the 3/16-in. hole to 0.2515/0.2500 in.; and shave periphery of part to print requirements.

In fine-edge blanking, impingement rings 0.035 to 0.040 in. high were used on both sides of the blank. On the punch side, the metal between the punch and the ring was deformed, indicating draw-in. The same area on the die side of the stock had a sharp outline, but it was about 0.010 in. below the surface.

The blanking dies were made of D2 tool steel, hardened to Rockwell C 60 to 61, and ground to a finish of 16 micro-in. The life between grinds was 12,000 parts. The die was mounted in a special 110-ton triple-action hydraulic press operating at 20 to 30 strokes per minute. Die setup time was 30 min.

The clutch dog was made in lots of 10,000 pieces; yearly production was 50,000 to 70,000.

Example 47 (Fig. 6). The positive clutch detent shown in Fig. 6 was fine-edge blanked from annealed, cold rolled, commercial quality 8617 steel, 0.127/0.123 in. thick. The two holes were pierced and the blank was severed from the stock in one press stroke. There was no distortion where the edge distance was less than work-metal thickness.

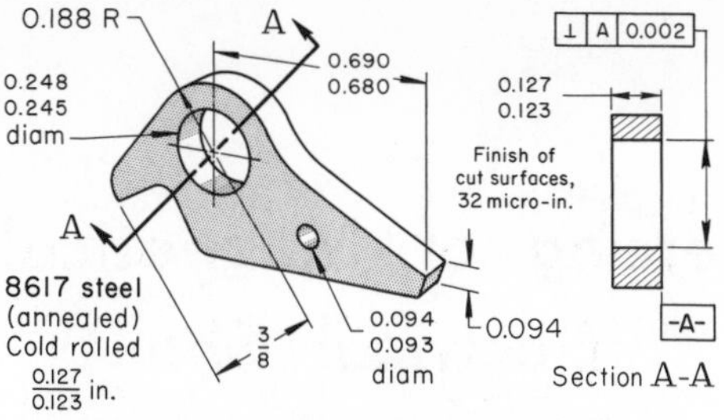

When this part was produced by conventional blanking, holes had to be drilled and reamed, two surfaces shaved, and the part deburred.

Fig. 6. Positive clutch detent that was produced by fine-edge blanking and piercing (Example 47)

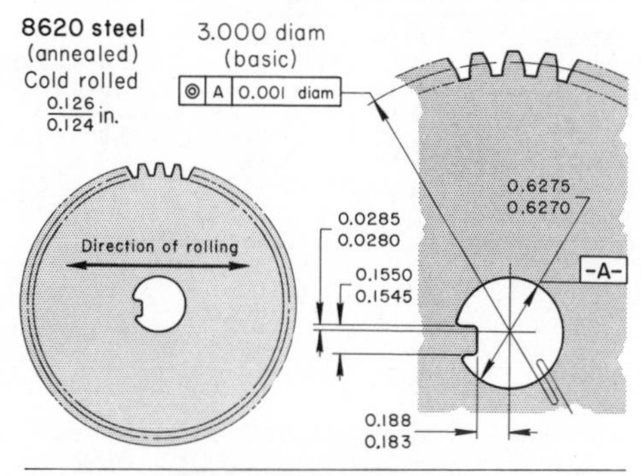

Gear Details

Quality class, precision	I
Number of teeth	48
Diametral pitch	16
Pressure angle	20°
Pitch diameter	3.000 in.
Tooth form	American standard full-depth involute
Circular thickness on pitch circle, max	0.0967 in.
Testing radius (tight mesh with standard master)	1.4995/1.4975 in.
Composite radial variation, max	0.001 in.
Tooth-to-tooth radial variation, max	0.0004 in.
Outside diameter	3.116/3.111 in.
Backlash class	B

Fig. 7. A 48-tooth spur gear that was made in one press stroke by fine-edge blanking (Example 48)

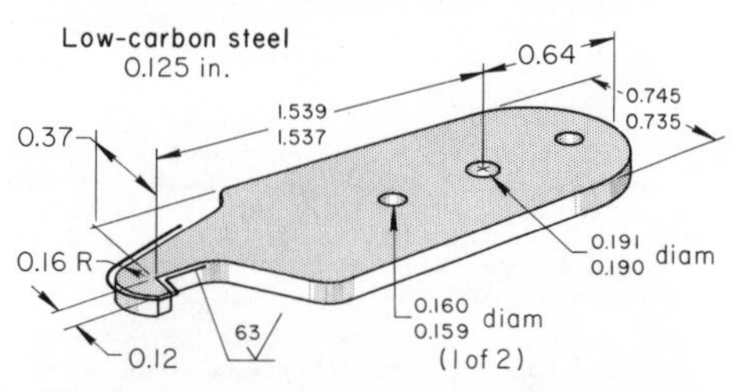

Fig. 8. Latch part that was produced more economically by fine-edge blanking and piercing than by conventional blanking and machining (Example 49)

The conventional method of making this part was: blank, drill and ream the two holes, shave two surfaces, and deburr.

The part had a small edge radius along the die-side surface. This radius was more pronounced at the outside corners. The dimensional tolerances were 0.010 in. total. Surface finish in two areas along the cut edge was 32 micro-in.

The die was made of D2 tool steel, hardened to Rockwell C 60 to 61, and ground to a finish of 16 micro-in. Die life was 12,000 pieces per grind. The impingement ring was 0.035 to 0.040 in. high and in the pressure pad only. The die was set up in a special 110-ton triple-action hydraulic press operating at 20 to 30 strokes per minute.

A sulfur-free oil was used as lubricant for both methods. Production rate for fine-edge blanking was 26 pieces per minute; lot size was 10,000 pieces, for a total production of 50,000 pieces per year.

The blanking of a 16-pitch gear is described in the following example. The impingement ring was circular instead of scalloped because of the small teeth.

Example 48. Blanking a Spur Gear With a Smooth Edge (Fig. 7)

The teeth, center hole, and key of the 16-pitch, 48-tooth spur gear shown in Fig. 7 were fine-edge blanked in one press stroke from annealed, cold rolled, commercial quality 8620 steel strip, 0.126/0.124 in. thick and 3¾ in. wide. The edges of the hole and teeth were smooth, having no fractured area. On the die side of the gear, the corners at the tip of each tooth had a noticeable edge radius, which decreased along the tooth flank until it was zero in the root. On the punch side, the corners were sharp but had a small burr, which was easily removed by vibratory finishing or belt lapping.

The blanking die was made of D2 tool steel, hardened to Rockwell C 60 to 61, and ground to a finish of 16 micro-in. Impingement rings, 0.035 to 0.040 in. high and 3.218 in. in diameter, were used on both the pressure pad and the die. The feed length (strip progression per stroke) was 3.280 in. The die was set up in a special 110-ton hydraulic press with three slides. The press operated at 10 to 15 strokes per minute. Die life was 12,000 pieces per grind. Lubricant was a sulfur-free oil, applied to both sides of the stock.

The gears were made in 15,000-piece lots at a yearly production of 105,000 pieces. Die setup time was 30 min.

The conventional method for making the gear would have required three or four operations: blank and pierce in a compound die, shave hole and outside diameter, and hob the teeth. Two shave operations might have been required, because the tolerance on the hole diameter and key width was 0.0005 in.

In the following example, it was more economical to form the part by fine-edge blanking than by conventional blanking and machining.

Example 49. Fine-Edge Blanking vs Blanking and Machining (Fig. 8)

The latch part shown in Fig. 8 was made of 0.125-in.-thick low-carbon steel having a No. 1 temper and a No. 2 finish.

Originally, the part was made by blanking and shaving, and then was deburred by vibratory finishing. The three holes were drilled and reamed, and the part was disk ground to the required flatness.

The method was changed to fine-edge blanking. The complete part was made in one press stroke, except that a small burr was removed by fine-belt sanding.

Fine-edge blanking resulted in savings of $5000 for annual production of 35,000 pieces.

Safety

Blanking and piercing involve potential hazards. The articles on Presses and Auxiliary Equipment ((page 1) and on Blanking of Low-Carbon Steel (page 31) contain information and literature references on safe operation.

Blanking and Piercing of Magnetically Soft Materials (Electrical Sheet)

*By the ASM Committee on Blanking and Piercing of Magnetically Soft Materials**

MAGNETICALLY SOFT materials are used for various static and rotating electrical devices. The majority of finished parts must be laminated — that is, composed of flat parts of a particular shape that are stacked to a given height and fastened together by riveting, bolting or welding. The stock is flat rolled metal and is usually called "electrical sheet". This sheet is available in coils or cut-to-length. For most applications, stock thickness ranges from 29 gage (0.0135 in.) to 24 gage (0.0239 in.). For some special purposes, sheet less than 0.001 in. thick is used.

Composition of Work Metal. Conventional flat rolled low-carbon steel (1006, 1008 or 1010) is widely used as electrical sheet for noncritical applications. It is not purchased to any specified electrical characteristics. Separate articles on pages 31 to 56 in this volume describe the blanking and piercing of low-carbon steel.

Silicon steels are manufactured to specific magnetic, rather than mechanical, properties and are used in a wide range of applications. Table 1 lists the types most used, and their approximate silicon contents. Note that as the M-number decreases, the silicon content increases, except for the grain-oriented types, which all contain from 2.8 to 3.5% Si. Carbon content is not specified in silicon steels, but is preferably held to less than 0.005%. In most silicon steels, elements other than silicon and iron are present only in residual amounts, although small amounts of aluminum or other elements sometimes are added to obtain specific magnetic characteristics.

Another general type of electrical sheet may be any of several nickel-iron alloys. Like silicon steels, these alloys must meet specified magnetic, rather than composition, requirements. Most of these alloys contain 47 to 81% Ni and much smaller percentages of molybdenum, copper, or other elements; the remainder is iron. Typical compositions and electrical characteristics are tabulated on page 790 in Volume 1 of this Handbook.

Size and Shape. Flat laminations of a wide variety of shapes and sizes are blanked and pierced from electrical sheet. Most, however, have shapes like those in Fig. 1 and 2. Laminations similar to those shown in Fig. 1 can range in diameter from less than 1 in. to 50 in. or more, and laminations similar to those shown in Fig. 2 can range in length from less than 1 in. to 12 in. or more.

Table 1. Designations and Nominal Silicon Contents of Flat Rolled Electrical Steels

AISI type	Nominal silicon, %	AISI type	Nominal silicon, %
M-50	0 to 0.6	M-4(a) ...	2.8 to 3.5
M-45	0 to 0.6	M-5(a) ...	2.8 to 3.5
M-43	0.6 to 1.3	M-6(a) ...	2.8 to 3.5
M-36	1.4 to 2.2	M-7(a) ...	2.8 to 3.5
M-27	1.7 to 3.0	M-8(a) ...	2.8 to 3.5
M-22	2.5 to 3.5	M-15	2.8 to 5.0
M-19	2.5 to 3.8	M-14	4.0 to 5.0

(a) Grain-oriented

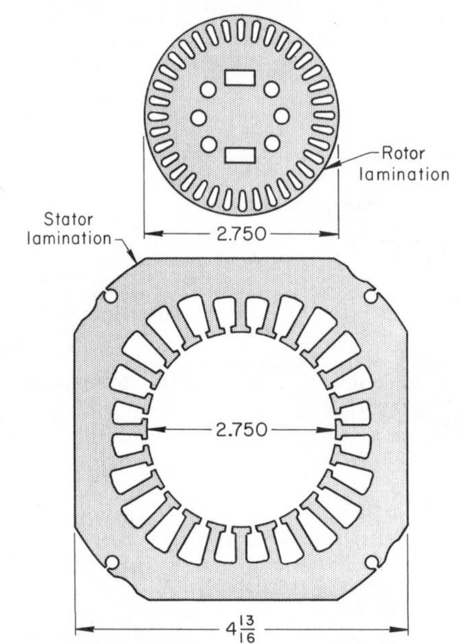

Laminations for rotating electrical machinery are blanked and pierced by single-station dies (sequence shown in Fig. 5), or by progressive dies (strip layouts shown in Fig. 7 and 8), or the slots are made in precut blanks, one at a time, with notching dies (Fig. 6).

Fig. 1. Typical rotor and stator laminations blanked and pierced from electrical sheet

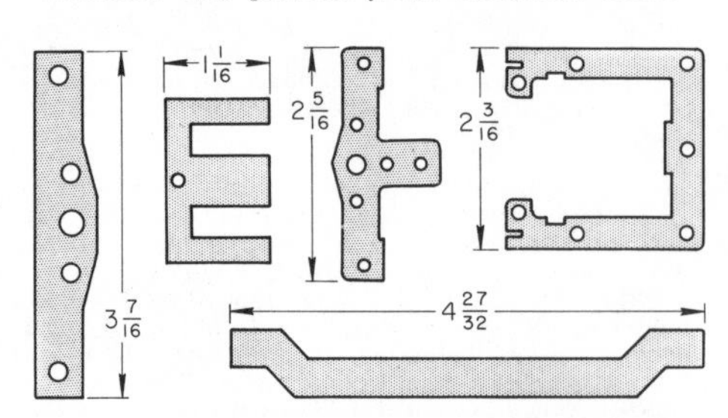

Fig. 2. Typical laminations blanked and pierced from electrical sheet for application in other than rotating machines

Punchability. Materials used for electrical sheet may be classified in the following order with respect to decreasing ease of blanking, piercing and notching: (*a*) conventional flat rolled low-carbon steels, such as 1008; (*b*) nonoriented silicon steels; (*c*) grain-oriented silicon steels; and (*d*) nickel-iron alloys. To a large extent, applications also follow the above classification, as shown in Table 2. Each group has certain distinct characteristics that affect punchability. In addition, differences in composition and hardness within any specific group cause considerable variation in punchability (see the section "Effect of Work-Metal Composition and Condition", on page 65 in this article).

Presses

A general-purpose punch press in good mechanical condition is acceptable for stamping laminations, but large-volume production of laminations by progressive-die methods requires the use of "high-productivity" presses (see the section on page 17 in the article "Presses and Auxiliary Equipment for Forming of Sheet Metal", in this volume). Most high-productivity presses have heavy bed and crown members to minimize deflection and vibration. Bed deflection for lamination presses should be no more than 0.0005 in. per foot of bed length (measured left-to-right between uprights), with a load equal to the rated capacity of the machine distributed over two-thirds of the bed area between tie-rod centers. Deflection of the slide should not exceed 0.0005 in. per foot of the length between the pitman centers, with rated load evenly distributed between those centers. Bending deflection and shear deflection are both considered in these standards. Double-crank presses with two or four points of suspension are preferred for progressive-die applications because of their better resistance to off-center die loads. Parallelism of the bed and slide should be 0.001 in. per foot of bed dimensions, both left-to-right and front-to-back.

Presses designed for producing laminations have heavy connections, large diameters of the mainshaft and con-

*C. H. HANNON (deceased), *Chairman*, Metallurgical Engineer, Power Transformer Dept., Transformer Div., General Electric Co.; DONALD GARRETT, Tool Superintendent, Robbins & Myers, Inc.; J. F. HAMBURG, Senior Development Engineer, Precision Welder & Flexopress Corp.; WALTER S. HAZLETT, Manager of Stamping Operations, Magnetic Metals Co.; JOSEPH I. KARASH, Manufacturing Engineer, Reliance Electric and Engineering Co.; JOHN S. REHRER, Manager of Tool Design and Factory Processes, Franklin Electric Co., Inc.; CLYDE E. SMITH, Director of Engineering, Oberg Manufacturing Co., Inc.; CHARLES E. STROEBEL, Project Engineer, Lamination Stamping Operations, Delco Products Div., General Motors Corp.; H. L. VANDENBERG, Superintendent of Tool Design and Plant Engineering, Norwood Works, Allis-Chalmers Manufacturing Co.

nection bearings, close gib clearances, and thick bolsters. Because of the close gib fits (needed for accurate vertical motion), recirculating oil systems must be used to provide forced-feed lubrication of bearings and slides.

The fact that a die was built with uniform punch-to-die clearance at all cutting edges does not necessarily mean that the clearance is uniform at the instant the punch begins to enter the work metal. The act of applying the load to the work metal can cause lateral deflections in the die and press, which can change the clearances. To minimize these undesirable deflections, the mechanical condition of the press and die must be maintained at a high level. The total tonnage exerted at each stroke must be in proper relation to the tonnage capacity of the press and to the type of press frame (some types of press frames will deflect laterally more than others). Close-fitting gibs and bearings are essential in minimizing lateral deflection. The die should be built with large guideposts and close-fitting bushings.

The following formula has been used in setting gib clearances: $c = ph/w$. Where c is gib clearance; p is total parallelism of slide to bed; h is gib height; and w is width of bed, right-to-left. For example, if gib height is 30 in., width of bed left-to-right is 60 in., and total parallelism maintained is 0.002 in., gib clearance = (0.002 × 30)/60 = 0.001 in.

A preventive maintenance program must be established to insure that all presses are kept in top condition. Special attention should be given to bearing clearances, condition of counterbalance springs or cylinders, and parallelism of slide.

In using the formula $L = S_s tl$ (see page 33 in the article on Blanking of Low-Carbon Steel) for calculating the tonnage required for the blanking of laminations, it is common practice to substitute tensile strength (S_t) for shear strength (S_s). This practice is one way of allowing for the increase in tonnage requirements as the dies become dull.

Auxiliary Equipment

When producing motor laminations in individual dies for each operation, with either upright or inclined presses, blanks can be fed by hand into the die and can be removed by hand for stacking at the front of the press. However, when individual dies are used for simultaneously producing stator and rotor laminations, feeding and stacking equipment is necessary for optimum efficiency. The use of an inclined press is a practical method, because gravity assists in loading the die and removing the laminations. When progressive dies are used, automatic feeding and scrap-cutting equipment is required.

Stock reels, cradles and straighteners are required when coil stock is used. Several types and sizes are available. (See the section beginning on page 13 in the article "Presses and Auxiliary Equipment for Forming of Sheet Metal", in this volume.)

Feed Mechanisms. In progressive-die operations, the common types of feed mechanisms, such as single-roll or double-roll, hitch, grip, and slide, are used to feed strip or coil. Cam feed, which has a fixed feed length, is widely used for large-volume production. This method is accurate at high speeds, because it eliminates slippage that usually occurs in the overriding clutch-and-brake mechanisms of roll feeds.

Table 2. Major Applications for Electrical Sheet Materials

Material(a)	Major applications	Typical shapes
Low-carbon steels (1006, 1008, 1010)	Rotor and stator laminations for low-cost motors	Fig. 1
Nonoriented silicon steels	Rotors and stators for high-efficiency motors	Fig. 1
Grain-oriented silicon steels	Transformers and segmented laminations for large generators	Fig. 2
Nickel-iron alloys	Audio transformers, filters and electronic devices	Fig. 2

(a) Materials are listed according to decreasing ease of blanking, piercing and notching.

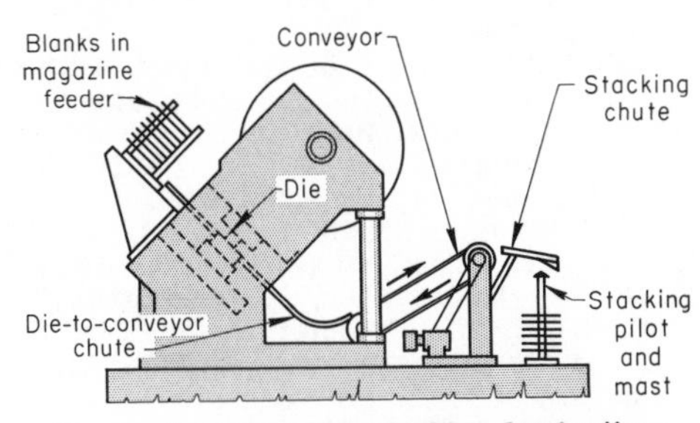

Fig. 3. A method for stacking laminations stamped in individual dies

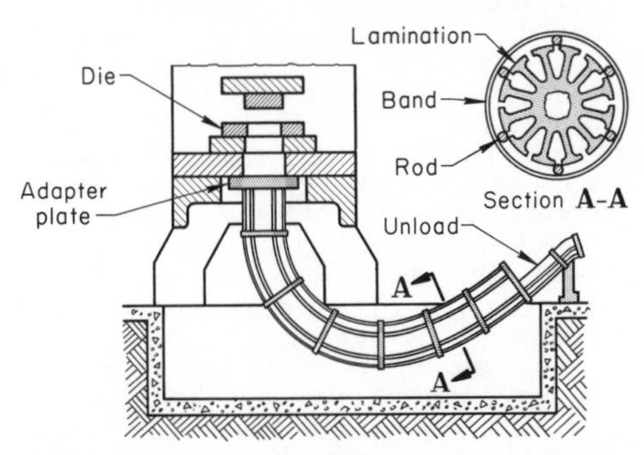

Fig. 4. Chute for stacking rotor laminations produced in a progressive die. See text for a description of the operation of the chute.

Magazine feeds have a mechanism to eject the blank from the bottom of a stack into the die or onto a magnetic belt or chain feed. In inclined presses, the blank may slide by gravity into the die nest after leaving the magazine.

Stacking. Figure 3 shows a method of stacking when each operation is done in an individual die. Blanks are fed to the press (inclined 35° to 45° to the rear) from a magazine feeder. Laminations drop from the press into a chute where they are picked up by a driven elevating belt that conveys them to the stacking chute, from which they fall onto a stacking mast. Stacking masts usually are 15 to 36 in. high. The tops of the masts are either threaded or have tapped holes, to permit their being picked up by handling machines and moved to subsequent operations. Bases of stacking masts are large or weighted, to prevent the masts from tipping or falling when being loaded or moved to the assembly floor.

A simple stacking chute for rotor laminations produced in a progressive die is shown in Fig. 4. When both stator and rotor laminations are made in a progressive die, two stacking chutes are needed. The chute shown in Fig. 4 is made of small-diameter rods held together with steel bands. The chute is secured to the bottom of the press bolster plate by an adapter plate. At the start of the operation, the chute is loaded somewhat beyond the lowest point (on the press side) with wooden plugs, to control the fall of laminations until the chute becomes filled. When loaded, the chute delivers a continuous supply of slot-aligned laminations (aligned by rod guides) from the press to the unloading station, which is above floor level and convenient for unloading. Slot alignment can be maintained by stacking the laminations in fixtures made for the shape being stamped. The laminations must fit the chute, as shown in Fig. 4. For mass production of the same laminations, the expense of a more elaborate and highly automated stacker may be justified.

Scrap disposal is a major consideration in producing laminations. Removal of scrap from a trimming operation or slugs from piercing holes and slots requires consideration during die design. Scrap is discharged through holes in the die shoe onto chutes. The chutes convey the scrap into containers or into automatic scrap conveying systems below the floor. When the die is in the upper shoe, a mechanically operated pan can be used to catch the slugs on the upstroke; slugs are then ejected into a container on the downstroke.

Dies

Single-station dies and progressive dies are used for making laminations.

Single-Station Dies. Each single-station die performs one operation, and a set of dies for a lamination can be mounted in one press or different presses. Simple laminations like those shown in Fig. 2 usually are produced in one operation. More complex parts may

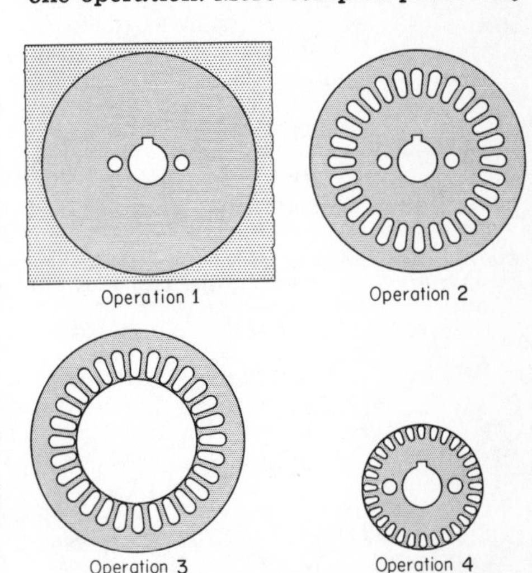

Operation 1: Stock blanked and pierced. **Operation 2:** Stator lamination notched. **Operation 3:** Rotor lamination separated from stator lamination. **Operation 4:** Rotor lamination notched.

Fig. 5. Sequence of operations for producing stator and rotor laminations from one blank using single-station dies

require several operations. Figure 5 shows a typical sequence for the production of stator and rotor laminations in four operations.

Single-station dies can be used for punching any lamination, regardless of size, composition, shape, or quality requirements. However, production with single-station dies is relatively slow, so that the cost per piece is high for mass production. Laminations such as shown in Fig. 1 and 2 can be produced in large quantities at a lower cost in progressive dies.

The size of the workpiece and quantity required influence the degree to which operations can be combined, and the complexity of any one die. For instance, in Fig. 5, slots made in the second and fourth operations can be punched in one stroke in a multiple die for each operation if the die sections are strong enough. An alternative method is to punch the slots in 28 strokes with a single-notch die in a high-speed notching press equipped with an indexing mechanism. This method would use a notching die of the type shown in Fig. 6 for the stator or rotor slots.

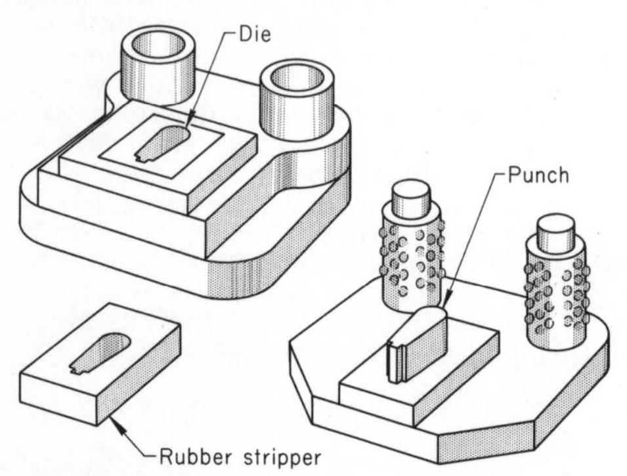

Fig. 6. Single-notch punch and die used for producing rotor or stator slots, one at a time, in a high-speed notching press with an indexing mechanism

Single-notch dies are used in the production of laminations for the following reasons:

1 Tool costs are lower and the single-notch die can be used on several different laminations. (Sometimes the cost is less than 5% of that for a multiple die that can pierce all the holes and slots in one press stroke.)
2 Laminations more than about 15 in. in diameter sometimes are too large to be notched by any other way (because of tool and equipment costs). However, many laminations of larger diameter are multiple-pierced.
3 Limited production does not warrant the cost of a multiple die.
4 Available equipment must be used.

Progressive dies perform a series of operations at two or more die stations during each stroke of the press.

Each working, or active, station in the die performs one or more operations. The work material progresses through succeeding stations until a completed part is produced (see Fig. 7). Idle stations, in which no work is performed, are added to provide strength to the die, to facilitate material travel through the die, to simplify construction, or to increase flexibility for die changes.

The distance the material travels with each press stroke is called feed length, progression, lead, advance, or pitch.

Layout and strip development depend on the size of the part, tolerances, and the amount of work to be done.

One of the common types of progressive die used in the electric-motor field is a five-station die that produces a rotor lamination and a stator lamination with each stroke of the press (Fig. 7). This die can be provided with carbide inserts for the punch and die sections. It has a spring-actuated guided stripper. The die components are mounted on a precision die set with ball bearing guide bushings and hardened guide pins. Slender punches are guided through the stripper by bushings. Usually, such a die has four active stations and one idle station.

The progressive die described above is the blanking or "scrap-all-around" type. For the most efficient use of material, the cutting-off or parting methods of severing the blank from the strip are used where layout permits. For additional information, see the section "Methods of Blanking in Presses", page 31 in the article on Blanking of Low-Carbon Steel.

Processing details for producing specific laminations with cutoff-type dies are given in the two examples that follow. In Example 50, both stator and rotor laminations were made in one progressive die. Sometimes progressive dies are used for blanking and piercing more than one part at a time, as described in Example 51.

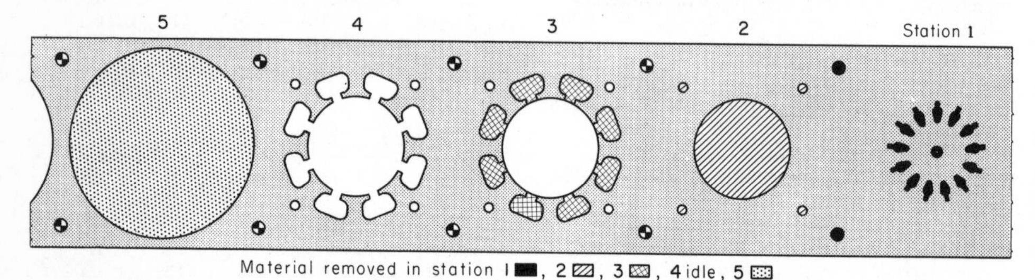

Station 1: Pierce pilot holes, rotor slots, and rotor-shaft hole. **Station 2:** Pierce stator rivet holes and blank rotor. **Station 3:** Pierce stator slots. **Station 4:** Idle. **Station 5:** Blank stator.

Fig. 7. Blanking and piercing sequence for rotor and stator laminations in a five-station progressive die. Two pilot punches were used at each station.

Example 50. Production of Stator and Rotor Laminations in a Progressive Die (Fig. 8)

Stator and rotor laminations shown in Fig. 8 were produced from 0.025-in.-thick M-22 silicon steel in a 60-ton press with 1-in. stroke and 9-in. maximum die space over the bolster. Shut height of the die was 8⅞ in.

The 12-slot rotor was 1.582 in. in outside diameter and had a 0.376-in.-diam center hole. The stator was 2.876 in. long by 2.188 in. wide.

Calculated blanking pressure was 38 tons, and over-all die size was 12¼ by 18 in. The tungsten carbide die averaged 820,000 strokes per sharpening when operated at 200 strokes per minute. The life of the tungsten carbide die was approximately 80 million pairs of laminations.

Example 51. Multiple Blanking of Stator and Rotor Laminations in a Progressive Die, Then Notching in Separate Dies (Fig. 9)

Figure 9 shows stock layout and material-removal sequence for multiple blanking of stator and rotor lamination blanks in a cut-off type of progressive die. Stock, M-36 or M-45 silicon steel 0.025 in. thick, was fed to the press by a roll feed that was accurate to within 0.005 in. per stroke; a lubricant was sprayed on the stock before it entered the die. Both stator and rotor blanks were automatically stacked for piercing in other dies.

Rotor-lamination blanks were received at the piercing press stacked in special bins. The operator removed a stack of blanks about 2 in. high, dipped them in a 1-to-40 mixture of soluble oil and water, and placed them in the hopper of the magazine feeder of the piercing press. The feeder moved a blank from the bottom of the stack and down a chute to a set of gates that were timed mechanically with the press to open and allow the blank to drop into the die.

The press, a 135-ton straight-side eccentric-crank type on a 30° permanently inclined base, operated at 100 strokes per minute. A cam knockout on the press stripped the pierced blank from the punches on the upstroke of the press into an air stream that carried the blank out of the die into a chute that guided the blank onto a stacking rod. Segmented piercing dies were made of tungsten carbide.

Piercing the stator laminations was basically the same as the rotor operation, except that

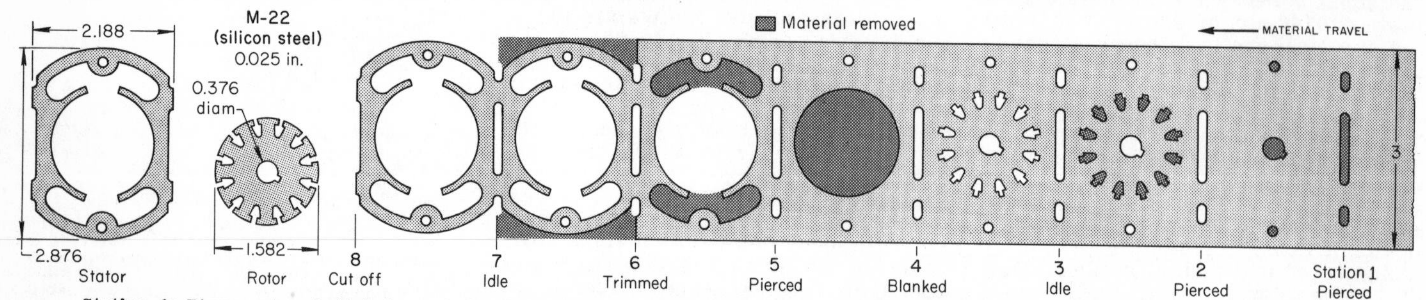

Station 1: Pierce rotor-shaft hole, and five holes in stator. **Station 2:** Pierce slots in rotor. **Station 3:** Idle. **Station 4:** Blank rotor. **Station 5:** Pierce cutouts for stator windings. **Station 6:** Notch end contour of stator. **Station 7:** Idle. **Station 8:** Cut stator from strip.

Fig. 8. Strip layout for producing rotor and stator laminations in a progressive die. Rotor lamination was pierced and blanked, and stator lamination was notched and cut off. (Example 50)

the stator blanks were delivered to the piercing press on rods carrying 1000 blanks, by a monorail conveyor. Equipment (press and feeder) was the same as for the rotor operation.

Principal advantages of progressive dies for blanking laminations are:

1 Handling between operations is eliminated; therefore, cost per piece is lower.
2 Laminations from progressive dies generally are stacked in chutes that allow the press to be operated at uninterrupted maximum capacity (Fig. 4). Stacking chutes fastened to the bottom of the bolster or die shoe keep the laminations oriented in a smooth, uninterrupted flow from the die. Thus, laminations are better controlled as to burr direction and are easier to handle for assembly.

Some disadvantages of progressive dies for blanking laminations are:

1 A progressive die is, to a great extent, a single-purpose die. Even a minor change in part design can necessitate an expensive die alteration or make the die obsolete.
2 Progressive dies are more susceptible to damage from accidents than single-station dies. Progressive dies run at high speed and may make many strokes before the press can be stopped. Misfeed detectors built into the die can help prevent damage. Die damage can halt production in progressive operation. In single-station operations, if there is sufficient inventory of processed material to keep other dies running, a breakdown of a die does not interrupt production.

The minimum size of lamination that can be made depends on the slot size and spacing, work-metal thickness, and tolerances on the slot dimensions. The die must be strong enough to withstand the blanking pressure. Figure 10 shows some very small laminations that were made in progressive dies. The 0.255-in.-diam rotor was made in three stations in order to have the necessary die strength. Part tolerances were such that piercing in three stations produced acceptable parts.

Dies for producing laminations usually are of segmented construction, which provides maximum accuracy; however, electrical discharge or electrochemical machining methods have been used to produce satisfactory dies.

There is no agreement as to the maximum size of lamination that can be produced efficiently in progressive dies. However, progressive dies are seldom used for laminations larger than 15 in. in major dimension. Factors that limit the maximum practical size are:

1 Progressive dies for making laminations more than 15 in. in major dimension represent a large investment (and a significant loss if damaged).
2 Usually, quantity demands are lower for large laminations; thus, the investment is not warranted.
3 Extremely large dies may require an impractically great press capacity.
4 Problems from camber and lack of flatness in the stock are magnified in stamping large laminations in progressive dies.

Selection of Die Material

Almost any hardened tool steel is satisfactory as die material for making a small quantity of laminations, but for production blanking and piercing, either a high-carbon high-chromium cold work tool steel, such as D2, or carbide must be used to resist the abrasiveness of electrical steels.

Shape or size of the lamination seldom affects the choice of die material; dies from the smallest to the largest and from the simplest to the most complex have been made from both high-carbon high-chromium tool steel and carbide. Also, both die materials have been used to blank and pierce all compositions and thicknesses of electrical sheet; composition and thickness of stock rarely affect the choice between carbide and tool steel.

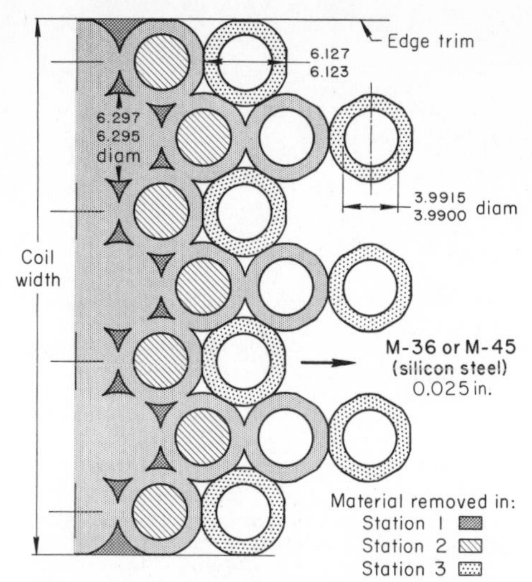

Fig. 9. Stock layout and sequence of material removal in multiple blanking of stator and rotor laminations in a three-station cutoff type of progressive die (Example 51)

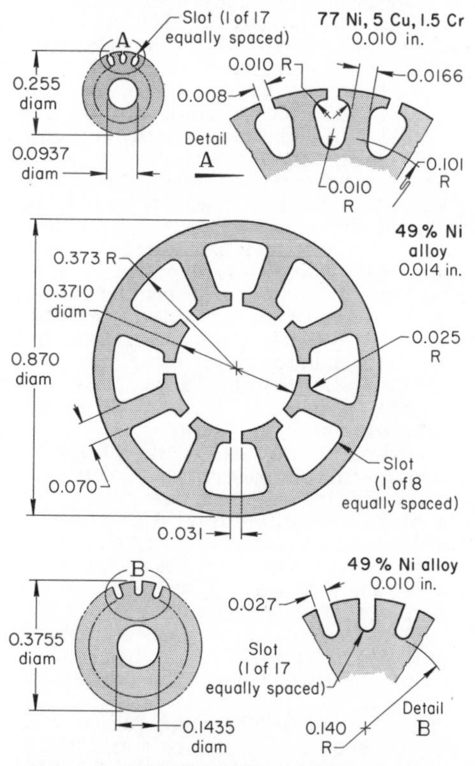

Fig. 10. Small-diameter laminations produced in progressive dies

Production Quantity. If dies are of the same design and construction, total quantity of parts to be produced is the major factor in choosing die material. If the run is so short that it can be made with tool steel dies without sharpening, tool steel is more economical. However, for longer runs, carbide dies have 10 to 20 times as much life per grind as tool steel dies.

Uniform quality of cut edges and minimum burr height will be retained over a much longer run by carbide dies than by tool steel dies. In some instances, edge condition of the lamination is not critical. However, when automatic stacking and core assembly equipment is used after blanking and piercing, burr height is important. Excessive burr height can cause short circuiting of laminations in the core.

Cost. Depending on size and design, a die with carbide cutting edges will cost a minimum of 1½ times as much as a steel die. However, in terms of cost per piece, carbide dies may be more economical. Press downtime and die maintenance affect cost per piece; carbide dies can run about ten times as long per sharpening as tool steel dies.

Press condition is important in the operation of blanking and piercing dies. To achieve the maximum potential usage of carbide dies, press condition must be maintained at a high level. Although tool steel punches and dies can chip and shear because of misalignment, carbide punches and dies are more likely to break. For this reason, presses used for tool steel dies can be in less than top level condition and continue to produce quality laminations. For more information on quality level of equipment, see page 6 in the article "Presses and Auxiliary Equipment for Forming of Sheet Metal", in this volume.

(For further details on die material selection, see the article "Selection of Material for Blanking and Piercing Dies", page 69 in this volume.)

Effect of Stock Thickness

Electrical sheet to be blanked and pierced usually ranges in thickness from 29 gage (0.0135 in.) to 24 gage (0.0239 in.), but for some applications thinner or thicker stock must be used. Blanking and piercing of extremely thin electrical sheet requires close control of equipment and technique. Processing of thick sheet (0.050 in. or more) also can cause difficulty, although press rating in tons is the major factor that determines maximum thickness of sheet that can be blanked and pierced.

Punch-to-die clearance for electrical sheet generally ranges from 3 to 7.5% of stock thickness per side, with clearances as large as 20% reported for grain-oriented stock. These values are similar to those used for low-carbon steel, but the stock thicknesses are thinner than commonly used for the low-carbon steels, which results in close die clearance and requires good die-making practice and accurate press equipment.

Thin Sheet (0.010 In. or Less). Under carefully controlled conditions, laminations can be blanked and pierced from sheet as thin as 0.002 in., but the press must be in the best condition, described on page 6 in the article on Presses and Auxiliary Equipment for Forming, in this volume. In addition, the feeding mechanism must be capable of feeding within ±0.003 in. total error per stroke at a feed rate of 900 in. per minute.

Punches and dies of either hardened tool steel, such as D2, or carbide are satisfactory, although carbide dies and punches will have at least ten times the life of their tool steel counterparts.

Although punch-to-die clearance, in percentage of stock thickness, ranges from 3 to 7.5% per side (see Examples 52 to 58), the value in inches can be as small as 0.0001 to 0.0003 in. for 0.002-in.-thick stock. This requires that the punch and die elements be mounted on a precision die set with large-diameter guideposts and bushings.

The punches must be rigidly supported and guided. The entire tool must be made rugged and accurate enough to maintain alignment. To avoid shearing the punch and die during press setup, it is important that the die be handled carefully to prevent the possibility that some of the components might move out of alignment. The press bed, the bottom of the die shoe, the face of the press slide, and the top of the punch holder must be clean and free of any irregularities that would cause a deviation from parallelism.

The punch and the die as a unit should be aligned square with the centerline of the press. The press slide should then be brought down slowly to meet with the top of the punch holder, and the punch holder should be fastened to the face of the slide. The slide should then be adjusted downward so that the punches enter the die cavities. Finally, the die shoe should be fastened to the bolster or press bed.

Dies with this close clearance often are designed as a unit and the die not fastened to the press ram. Thus, the tool is not subject to the inaccuracies of the press.

A back taper of 0.002 in. per inch per side is commonly used in the die. Because of this angular clearance in the die, total die life is limited by the maximum punch-to-die clearance that can be tolerated. Each time a die having a back taper of 0.002 in. per inch per side is sharpened, the hole diameter will increase 4 micro-in. for each 0.001 in. ground from the top of the die. After grinding 0.100 in. from the die, the punch-to-die clearance will increase 0.0002 in. per side.

If this amount of clearance is too great, the original clearance can be restored by installing new die sections or, if the dimensional tolerance permits, by using an oversize punch. The amount that can be removed from the die depends on the amount of back taper in the die, stock thickness, and maximum punch-to-die clearance permissible. Sometimes dies have a straight land 1/16 to 1/8 in. wide before beginning the back taper.

Lubricant is applied to the stock during blanking and piercing, to keep wear on the cutting edges of the punch and die at an acceptable level. Use of a water-thin lubricant with rapid evaporation and low residue makes it unnecessary to have a burn-off operation before hydrogen annealing.

Difficulties in producing acceptable laminations from thin sheet are magnified as the plan area of the lamination increases.

The five examples that follow deal with procedures for blanking and piercing laminations from sheets 0.002 to 0.010 in. thick.

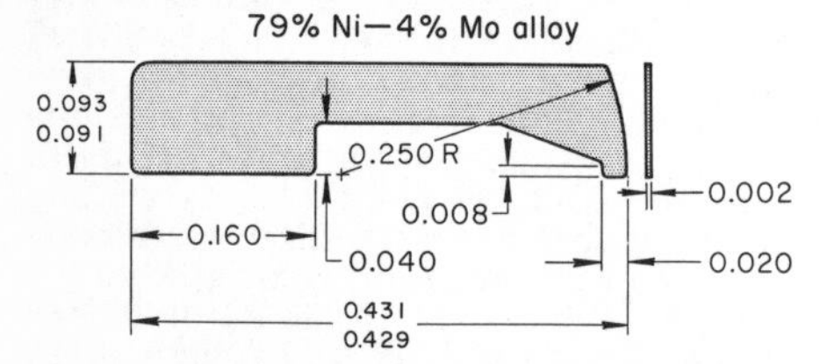

Fig. 11. Pole-piece lamination produced in one stroke from the thinnest stock practical for blanking (Example 52)

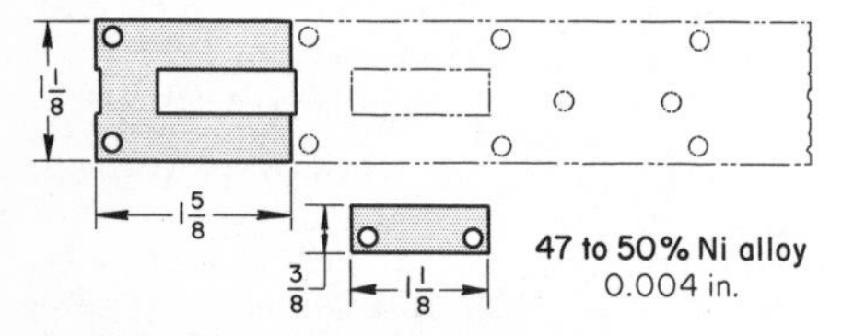

Fig. 12. Two different 0.004-in.-thick laminations that were blanked and pierced simultaneously in a progressive die (Example 53)

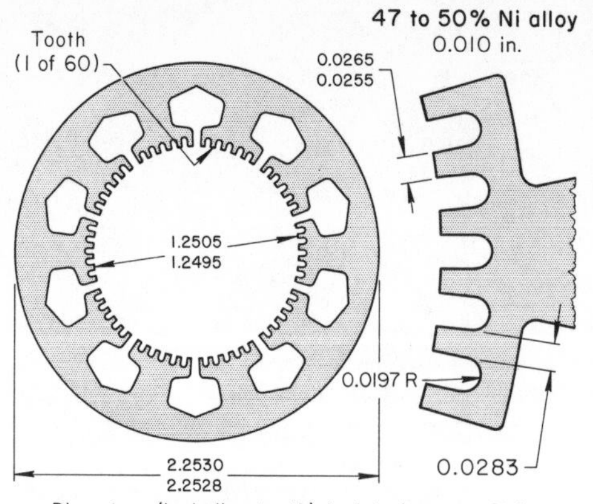

Fig. 14. Stator lamination that was produced to close tolerances in a compound, progressive die (Example 55)

Example 52. Blanking 0.002-In.-Thick Pole Pieces From Nickel-Iron Alloy (Fig. 11)

The pole-piece lamination shown in Fig. 11 was produced in one stroke of a gap-frame press. The 0.002-in.-thick stock was the thinnest that is practical for blanking. Carbide dies with punch-to-die clearance of 0.0001 in. (5% of stock thickness) per side were used. The lamination was made of a nickel-iron alloy, but punch-to-die clearance is critical for punching any thin material, because greater clearances may produce excessive burrs. The die was mounted in a four-post precision die set. The stripper was of the box type (fixed). A bushing in the stripper guided the punch. This type of die operated as fast as the strip could be accurately fed.

Example 53. Blanking and Piercing 0.004-In.-Thick Nickel-Iron Alloy (Fig. 12)

To avoid waste of material, the two laminations shown in Fig. 12 were produced in a three-station progressive die at 250 to 300 strokes per minute. Clearance between punch and die was not allowed to exceed 0.0003 in. (7.5% of stock thickness) per side. A spring-type stripper guided by the die-set guideposts supported the piercing punches and guidepins at the work surface. These laminations were produced in dies made of D2 tool steel (Rockwell C 62 to 63) or of carbide. For 0.001-in. die wear (amount of material that must be removed from faces of punch and die for resharpening), approximately 4000 strokes (two laminations per stroke) could be obtained with steel dies, and approximately 40,000 strokes with carbide dies.

Example 54. Blanking and Piercing Large E and I Laminations From 0.004-In.-Thick M-7 Silicon Steel (Fig. 13)

A punch-to-die clearance of 0.0002 in. per side was maintained in blanking and piercing the relatively large laminations shown in Fig. 13. A 100-ton, 1½-in.-stroke press was used to produce two E-shaped and two I-shaped parts from M-7 (grain-oriented silicon steel) with each press stroke. A cutoff-type progressive carbide die, 20 by 41¼ in. in over-all size, was used, assembled in a custom-made precision die set with a spring-type guided stripper.

The I-laminations were blanked through the die and stacked in a chute. One E-lamination was blanked through the die and stacked while the other slid off the end of the die into a chute.

Example 55. Blanking and Piercing Stator Laminations From 0.010-In.-Thick Nickel-Iron Alloy (Fig. 14)

The stator lamination shown in Fig. 14 was produced from nickel-iron alloy in a compound, progressive carbide die, using a 30-ton gap-frame press with 1½-in. stroke. For greater accuracy, the inside diameter, teeth, and outside diameter were blanked and pierced in the same station and the remaining areas in preceding stations. The 60 teeth had to be equally spaced; maximum dislocation of any one tooth relative to another was held to less than 0.00002 in. Other dimensional tolerances are shown in Fig. 14. Clearance of 0.0004 in. per side was maintained between the punch and die. The die was assembled into a custom-made precision four-post die set with a spring-type guided stripper.

Example 56. Blanking and Piercing Rotor Laminations From 0.010-In.-Thick Nickel-Iron Alloy (Fig. 15)

A punch-to-die clearance of 0.0004 in. per side was maintained in producing a rotor lamination with 64 equally spaced teeth (Fig. 15) from 0.010-in.-thick stock. Maximum dislocation of any one tooth relative to another was held below 0.00002 in. Other dimensional tolerances are shown in Fig. 15. This part was

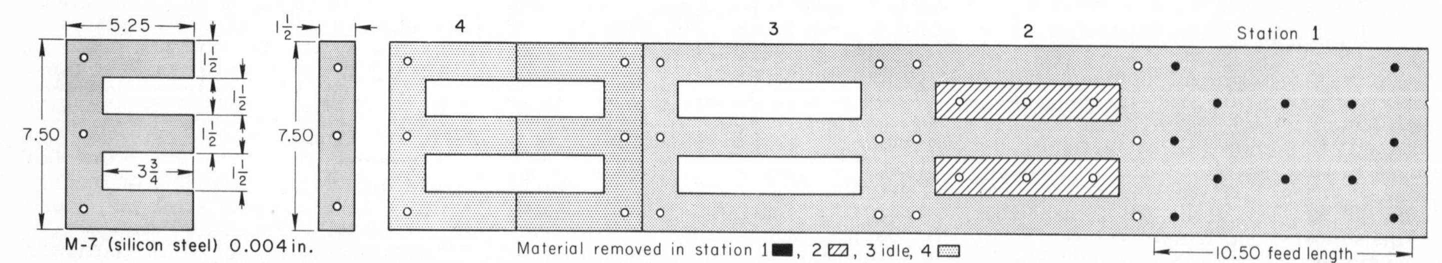

Station 1: Pierce twelve holes. **Station 2:** Blank-through two I-shaped laminations. **Station 3:** Idle. **Station 4:** Blank one E-shaped lamination through the die; the other lamination slides off the end of the die.

Fig. 13. Progressive-die strip layout for laminations difficult to produce from 0.004-in. strip because of their shape and size (Example 54)

produced in a compound carbide die in one stroke of a 30-ton gap-frame press with 1½-in. stroke. The die was assembled into a precision-made four-post die set with a spring-type guided stripper and a mechanical knockout. The part was knocked out of the die at the top of the stroke and was blown free of the die with an air blast.

Thick Sheet (0.050 In. or More). Demand for laminations thicker than about 0.025 in. decreases rapidly with increasing thickness. However, end laminations or laminations for special applications can be as thick as 0.078 in.

In the two examples that follow, a 100-ton press was used, and the work was distributed among several stations of progressive dies.

Example 57. Producing Formed Parts From 0.050-In.-Thick Nickel-Iron Alloy (Fig. 16)

The part shown in Fig. 16 was produced from 0.050-in.-thick nickel-iron alloy in a six-working-station progressive die, using a straight-side 100-ton press with a 1½-in. stroke. The production rate was 250 strokes per minute, making two parts per stroke. Punch-to-die clearance was 0.0002 to 0.0015 in. per side in various stations of the die.

By using a work-metal strip 1.375 in. wide, a right-hand and a left-hand part were made at each press stroke as shown by the strip layout in Fig. 16. As the part was only 0.108/0.112 in. wide, several idle stations provided strength to the working stations.

Producing these parts progressively created a problem because of their small size, the bend, and the shape of the tip. To reduce the tip to the required size and shape, two swaging operations and one trimming operation were used. Punch-to-die clearance for notching and cutoff was 0.0015 in. per side (3%). Clearance at the radiused tip was as close as 0.0002 in. All working stations were made of carbide, and a spring-loaded pressure pad was used to hold the stock and strip the punches. A closely controlled barrel finishing operation produced the tip radius.

Example 58. Blanking, Piercing and Offsetting 0.078-In.-Thick Laminations From M-27 Silicon Steel (Fig. 17)

The lamination shown in Fig. 17 was produced in an eight-station progressive die, using a 100-ton press with 1-in. stroke, operating at 190 strokes per minute. Punch-to-die clearance was 0.0035 to 0.005 in. per side. The die was 17 in. long by 15½ in. wide and had carbide cutting edges. Approximately 250,000 pieces were punched between sharpenings. The laminations were blanked crosswise from a 4³⁄₁₆-in. strip. Feed per stroke was 1.250 in.

The simple contour of this part presented no problem, except that the offset flatness was difficult to maintain because of sheet thickness. A pressure pad held the part against the blanking punch during blanking, which helped maintain flatness.

Effect of Work-Metal Composition and Condition

Each of the four materials most widely used as electrical sheet (low-carbon steels, nonoriented and grain-

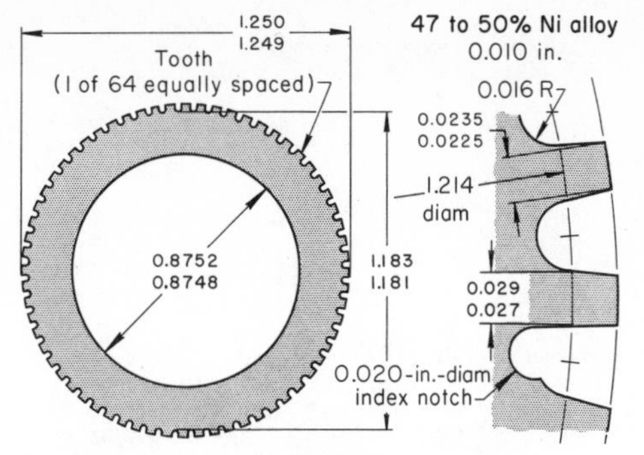

Fig. 15. Rotor lamination that was produced to close tolerances in a compound carbide die in one press stroke (Example 56)

oriented silicon steels, and nickel-iron alloys) has distinctive punching characteristics. These characteristics often necessitate specific procedures to produce laminations of the desired quality at the lowest cost.

Low-carbon steels such as 1008 are used as electrical sheet when their electrical properties can meet requirements, mainly because they cost less than silicon steels, and the cost is lower for blanking and piercing. More pieces per die sharpening are usually obtained in blanking these steels than in blanking silicon steels — with the possible exception of M-50, which has a silicon content (0.6% max) only slightly higher than that of ordinary low-carbon steel. One study of die wear in making stator and rotor laminations similar to those shown in Fig. 1, and ranging in size from 3⅝ to 5⅞ in. in diameter, showed that, with tool steel cutting edges, 120,000 to 150,000 pairs were punched per sharpening when stamping either 1008 or M-50.

Condition of the low-carbon steel stock influences power requirements and punching characteristics. When annealed, this steel has a tensile strength of 55,000 to 60,000 psi, but the strength of full-hard material may be over 100,000 psi. Thus, material condition must be known before tonnage requirements of presses can be determined. Low-carbon, low-silicon steels in the annealed condition are soft, and they are likely to roll at the edges and form excessive burrs. Thus, punch-to-die clearances must be as close for these steels as for electrical sheet of the same thickness (see Examples 52 to 58). Usually, an annealed product is specified, but whether annealed stock is stamped or individual laminations are annealed after stamping is often a matter of convenience, because of press capacity, annealing facilities, or other factors.

Silicon Steels (Nonoriented). As shown in Table 1, there is a marked difference in silicon content from M-50 to M-14. As silicon content increases, the sheet becomes more brittle and more abrasive. As a result, the edges of higher-silicon steel are less likely to roll and make excessive burrs, but die wear is increased because of abrasion.

Die wear increases as silicon content increases, as shown by the following comparison of the number of pairs produced per grind by D2 tool steel dies in blanking and piercing stator and rotor laminations similar to those in Fig. 1 from four types of silicon steel:

M-50 (0-0.6 Si)	120,000-150,000 pairs
M-43 (0.6-1.3 Si)	100,000-120,000
M-36 (1.4-2.2 Si)	80,000-100,000
M-27 (1.7-3.0 Si)	60,000-80,000

The results of this comparison are used for estimating costs. The life per grind is multiplied by ten when carbide dies are used.

Many nonoriented silicon steels are coated with an organic material (core plating) to insulate one lamination from another. This organic core plating also improves the punchability of electrical sheet. In one application, carbide dies produced about 3.5 million laminations from core-plated M-36 between resharpenings. When similar laminations were produced from uncoated M-36, dies required sharpening after each 1.2 million parts. Heating of coated blanks by welding or die casting may destroy the organic coating.

General practice is to use about the same punch-to-die clearances for all silicon steels. Tensile strength of the particular steel must be considered in determining press capacity, because silicon steels may vary in strength, depending on whether they are fully annealed at the time of stamping.

Dies of tool steel and carbide are used for all types; the choice depends on production quantity. Carbide dies are preferable for the high-silicon grades, because high-silicon steels are more abrasive than low-silicon grades.

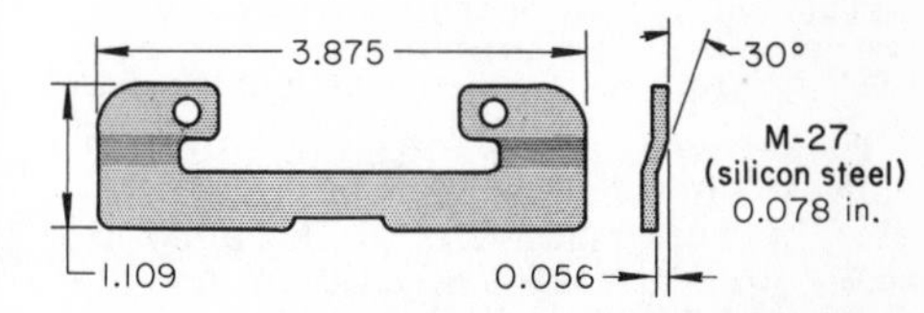

Fig. 17. Lamination that was blanked, pierced and offset from thick electrical sheet in an eight-station progressive die (Example 58)

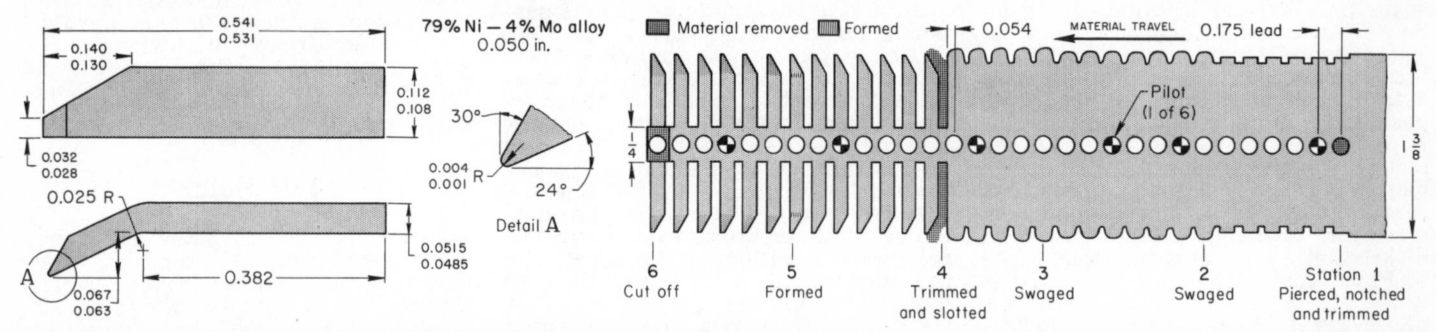

Fig. 16. Formed part (left) that was difficult to produce in a progressive die (strip layout shown at right) because of its small size, abnormal thickness, and tip radius. (Many idle stations separated the various working stations.) (Example 57)

Grain-oriented steels are relatively high-silicon steels (Table 1) that have most of their grains (crystals) oriented with the cube edges parallel with the rolling direction and face diagonals at 90° to the rolling direction. Because of this difference in orientation, these steels have blanking and piercing characteristics different from those of nonoriented steels. Tensile strength will vary as much as 20% between the rolling direction and the transverse direction (strength is greater parallel with the rolling direction).

A magnesium hydroxide coating is applied to grain-oriented steel after normalizing. This coating prevents the coiled strip from welding together during a high-temperature box-anneal. Magnesium hydroxide, in contrast to organic coatings, is highly abrasive and greatly increases die wear; hence, it is not recommended for stamped laminations (see C-2 in Table 5). Tool steel dies wear so rapidly under these conditions, and because of the high silicon content of the steel, that carbide cutting edges are almost always used for blanking and piercing of grain-oriented steel.

Because mechanical properties vary with direction, cutting properties also vary in grain-oriented steels. Cutting across the rolling direction results in a clean break; edges are smeared when cutting is parallel with the rolling direction. Thus, punch-to-die clearance is more critical on the sides parallel with the rolling direction, as shown in the following example.

Example 59. Control of Punch-to-Die Clearance in Blanking and Piercing Grain-Oriented Silicon Steel Sheet (Fig. 18)

Each press stroke produced one U-shaped and one I-shaped lamination (Fig. 18) from 0.014-in.-thick M-7 silicon steel. It was determined that punch-to-die clearance at A (Fig. 18), for cutting across the rolling direction, could be as much as 0.003 in. per side (21% of stock thickness) and provide a good edge condition with minimum burr. However, clearance at B (cutting parallel with the rolling direction) could not exceed 0.0024 in. per side (17% of stock thickness) to produce acceptable results. Initial clearances were established at 0.0016 in. per side at both A and B, but when the clearance increased to 0.0024 in. due to resharpening, new die sections were installed to restore the original clearance.

The punch and die sections were made of carbide and ran about 250,000 strokes between resharpenings. Resharpening removed about 0.007 in. from both punch face and die face.

Nickel-iron alloys often cause difficulties when blanked with tool steel dies, because small bits of the alloy are likely to stick to the side of the die during blanking.

Even with generous lubrication, relatively little lubricant reaches the cut edges of the laminations. As these edges pass through the die, the small bits of metal stick to the cavity walls. This is more common with the higher-nickel grades. As these metal deposits build up, greater force is needed to push the laminations through the die. A point may be reached at which the die members will spread or, with a solid blanking ring, even break. Therefore, carbide cutting edges are commonly used for blanking laminations from nickel-iron alloys. A comparison of D2 tool steel and carbide as die materials in the production of laminations from a nickel-iron alloy is given in the following example.

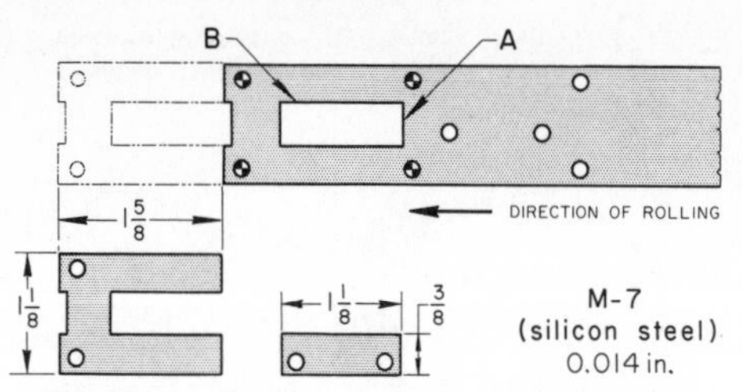

Fig. 18. Laminations that were blanked and pierced from grain-oriented sheet in one press stroke. Die clearances in blanking were determined by relation of direction of cuts (A and B) to direction of rolling. (Example 59)

Table 3. Costs, Setup Times, and Die Life for D2 Tool Steel vs Carbide Dies for Blanking Nickel-Iron Alloy Laminations (Example 60)

Item	D2	Carbide
Cost Data		
Punch and die	$526	$709
Die maintenance, per 1000 pcs	$2.80	$0.24
Operating Conditions		
Setup time per 1000 pcs, hr	0.173	0.030
Pieces per 0.001-in. die wear	1925	11,181

0.014 — 1/4 — 1 1/8 — 80% nickel-iron alloy — 1" — 1/4

Example 60. D2 Tool Steel vs Carbide Dies for Blanking Nickel-Iron Laminations (Table 3)

A D2 die was used for blanking small laminations from an 80% nickel-iron alloy (see sketch in Table 3). Production was low in terms of die life, and die maintenance cost was excessive. Changing the cutting edges to carbide reduced die maintenance cost to less than one-tenth that for the tool steel die (see comparison in Table 3). The height of burr on this part was 0.001 in. max. At each sharpening, 0.005 in. was removed from the punch and die faces.

Camber and Flatness

Camber in electrical sheet is the deviation (parallel to the stock surface) of a side edge from a straight line that extends to both ends of the side, and is customarily limited to ¼ in. for any 96-in. length or fraction thereof. Flatness, or the degree to which a surface of a flat product approaches a plane, is expressed in terms of the deviation from a plane. Flatness tolerances have not been established for electrical sheet; the operations employed to flatten other steel products cannot be used because of their effect on magnetic quality. Flatness requirements for a particular application should be specified.

Camber and flatness are interrelated: The edge of an 8-ft section of sheet may come within the ¼-in. tolerance while lying freely on a flat surface. However, the seemingly flat sheet may have a number of faint waves (sometimes called oil cans). If this sheet is then flattened (as it is in dies), the flattening of these waves causes multidirectional elongation of the sheet, and the edge of the sheet may then be forced into a camber different from that when the sheet is not under flattening pressure. Minimum camber and maximum flatness are desirable for blanking electrical sheet, and are especially important in progressive-die operations.

Effect on Progressive-Die Operation. If there is no camber, it is easy to start the stock through the die correctly by aligning the straight edge of the sheet against a straight-edge starting guide, with the end of the material covering the first die stage. Feed rolls are then engaged and the blanking and piercing can begin.

Even though the edge of the sheet is cambered, it must still be used in the starting alignment. Thus, the material may be misaligned to some degree as it enters the die. A small degree of misalignment is not readily apparent to the press operator.

Minor misalignment in starting the material through a progressive die may not cause immediate difficulties. Operating difficulties result from various misalignments, which have a cumulative effect.

In the first stage of the die, pilot holes are pierced into the sheet, often into a portion that later will be scrap. At subsequent die stations, bullet-nose pilots engage the pilot holes as the die closes. The piloting action may cause the sheet to move slightly into true position before the cutting edges of the die meet the sheet. Powered feed rolls move the sheet between press strokes to an approximate position for the next die station. The feed rolls then open, releasing the sheet so that there is no conflict between the locating action of the pilots and the feed rolls.

When original lineup is not correct or when there are cumulative effects of camber against the stock guides, the sheet may wander from side to side on the die face. Stock guides are provided in progressive dies to limit wandering due to camber and misalignment.

Interference between the pilots and the stock guides may cause the stock to distort and jam in the die, preventing proper flow of the stock. If the stock jams, the press must be stopped at once.

Camber can cause other difficulties. For instance, a change in camber or multidirectional elongation of the sheet as the press flattens the waviness may cause the pilots to distort the piloting holes; thus, misaligned rotor and stator laminations are made. This leads to misalignment of slots in the stacked core. As slots are blanked out, stresses are released that also can change the amount of camber and flatness.

There is no single solution to the problem of camber when producing laminations in progressive dies, because no two shipments of material are exactly alike. Some manufacturers of laminations use less efficient individual dies because of difficulties with camber, even though production volume could justify the use of progressive dies. Others use progressive dies only for laminations below a certain size.

Burr Height

It is impossible to blank and pierce laminations without producing some burr along the cut edges (see Fig. 19). The amount of burr (measured as burr height) depends on the composition and condition of the electrical sheet, thickness of the sheet, clearance between punch and die, and edge condition (sharpness) of the punch and die.

The amount of burr that can be tolerated depends on end use. Burr height influences the stacking factor, which in turn influences magnetic characteristics. Maximum burr height commonly is limited to 0.002 to 0.005 in.

Effect of Variables. Figure 20 shows the results of an investigation to evaluate the effect of two major variables that influence burr height — punch-to-die clearance, and conditions and properties of electrical sheet. All data were obtained from tests made in a special die that was not used in production; press, and punch and die details are given with Fig. 20. Twelve electrical sheets (ranging from low-carbon steel sheet — 1006, 1008 or 1010 — to steel containing more than 3% Si) were used in the evaluation, and all were representative of commercial products. As shown in the table accompanying Fig. 20, sheet thicknesses were restricted to the range most commonly used in practice, and the steels were tested in two conditions — fully processed (annealed) and full hard.

Figure 20(a) shows the effect of punch-to-die clearance on the number of press strokes before a burr height of 0.002 in. was reached. Because of the difference in thickness of the sheets punched, punch-to-die clearance is given as per cent of sheet thickness.

All data shown in Fig. 20(a) were based on measurements of the punched slug, although as far as is known the height of the burr on the punched hole differs little from the height of the burr on the slug, except when factors peculiar to a specific die alter the situation. For example, in a progressive die with a spring-type stripper, the stripper hitting a previously stamped edge of a partly punched lamination is likely to smash down the burr at that edge.

The data in Fig. 20(a) indicate that the rate at which burr height increases is affected by the clearance between punch and die and the properties and conditions of the steels punched. Most of the steels tested showed an optimum clearance. For instance, steel 6, a fully processed high-silicon sheet (see table with Fig. 20) shows an optimum clearance (per side) of about 12% of sheet thickness, or 0.0022 in. Data for steel 9 show that the optimum clearance was not reached during the tests. For more information on punch-to-die clearances, see the discussion on page 44, and Table 1 on page 45, in the article "Piercing of Low-Carbon Steel".

Figure 20(b) relates number of press strokes to burr height for the twelve steels. Punch-to-die clearances used for obtaining the data shown in Fig. 20(b) were not all the same. For each steel, "best" clearances were used: that is, clearances at which burr height increased at the lowest rate in previous tests. Data in Fig. 20(b) show that, for the low-carbon steels (steels 1, 2, 7 and 8), burr height increased most rapidly of all the steels tested, especially in the fully processed condition. For a given grade of steel, burr height increased more rapidly when the sheet was fully processed (ductile) than when it was full hard (brittle).

Data presented in Fig. 20 are typical only for the conditions of the tests (see table with Fig. 20). If the punch and die material were changed to another grade of tool steel or to carbide, the curves in Fig. 20 would probably change. Other factors that could cause variation include size and shape of lamination, lubrication, and type of surface of the electrical sheet. It is believed, however, that the *relative* shape and position of the curves would not change within a wide range of conditions. For instance, core plate would make the burr height increase less rapidly with all steel grades, but would probably not change the performance of one steel grade relative to the others.

Furthermore, different devices and techniques for measuring burr height can result in different readings. All burr-height data given in Fig. 20 were obtained by measuring with a recording air gage, which produced a magnified tracing of the contour of the slug surface, thus differentiating between burr height and distortion of the slug.

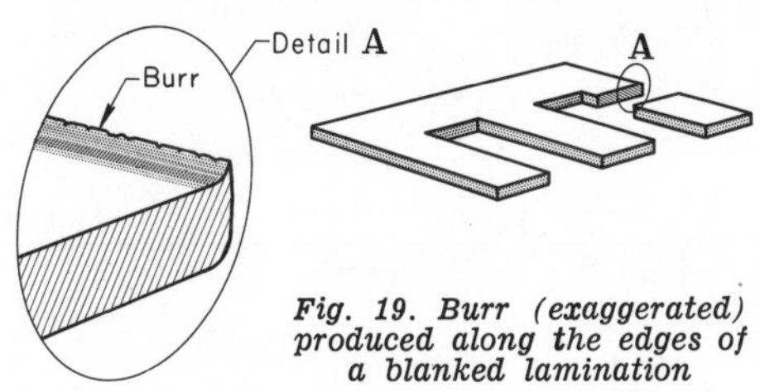
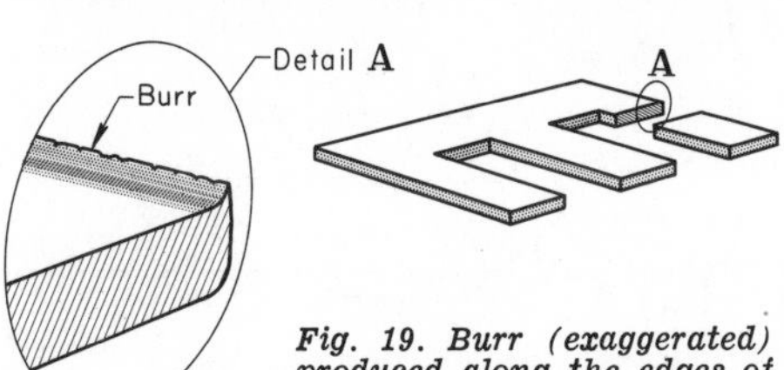
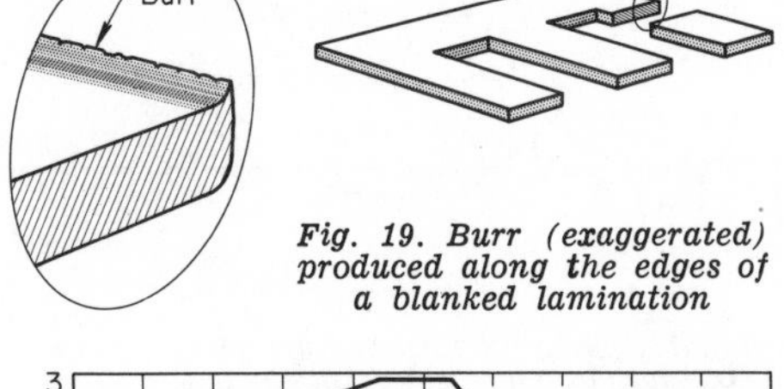

Fig. 19. Burr (exaggerated) produced along the edges of a blanked lamination

Length of Die Run

A die usually is run until the maximum allowable burr height is reached, at which time the punch and die are

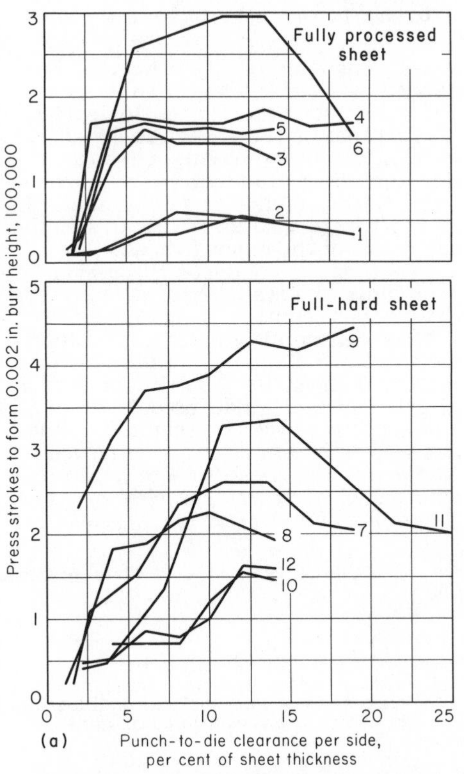

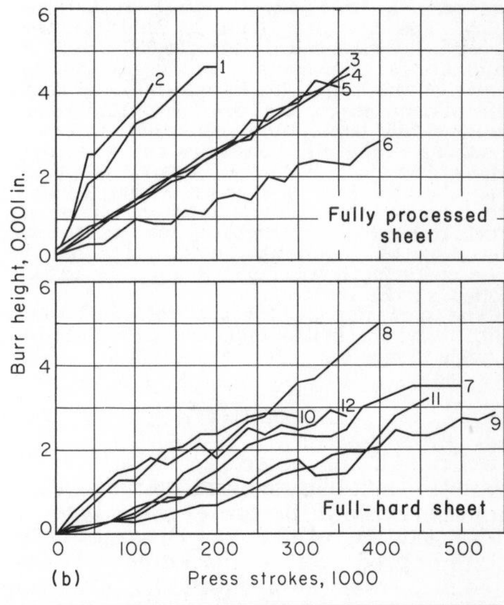

Press Details

Press ......50-ton, 4-post upright; 1-in. stroke
Speed ....112 strokes per minute

Punch and Die Details

Die set ....4-post with sleeve bushings
Stripper ....Spring-type, fully guided(a)
Punch diameter ....⅛ in.
Punch and die material ....A2 tool steel
Punch and die hardness ....Rc 61 to 63
Clearances per side ......0.0003 to 0.0035 in.(b)
Maximum load in blanking ......2 to 5 tons(c)
Lubricant ....None

(a) Clearance of stripper with punches was 0.0003 in. per side. (b) Range represents nine punches with specific clearances as follows: 0.0003, 0.0005, 0.0010, 0.0015, 0.0020, 0.0020, 0.0025, 0.0030, and 0.0035 in. per side. (c) Depending on sheet type and thickness.

Steel No.	Type	Nominal silicon content, %	Sheet thickness, in.	Number of die runs	Yield strength (0.2% offset), psi	Tensile strength, psi	Elongation in 2 in., %	Rockwell hardness
Fully Processed (Annealed) Sheet								
1	Low-carbon	Residual	0.0185	3	47,000	58,000	25	B 68
2	Low-carbon	Residual	0.025	3	49,000	58,000	26	B 68
3	M-36	1.50	0.025	2	37,000	55,000	31	B 71
4	M-27	2.75	0.018	3	54,000	70,000	24	B 80
5	M-27	2.75	0.025	2	58,000	72,000	24	B 82
6	M-22(a)	3.25	0.0185	2	50,000	66,000	21	B 85
Full-Hard Sheet								
7	Low-carbon	Residual	0.0185	3	126,000	132,000	2	C 20
8	Low-carbon	Residual	0.025	2	124,000	131,000	2	C 19
9	M-27	2.75	0.018(b)	3	151,000	154,000	2	C 29
10	M-27(a)	2.75	0.025	2	148,000	152,000	2	C 24
11	M-22(a)	3.25	0.014	2	157,000	158,000	1	C 31
12	M-22(a)	3.25	0.025	4	150,000	154,000	1	C 29

NOTE: Mechanical properties are not necessarily typical of the specific grade, but are average values for coils used in the tests. (a) Contained approximately 0.25% Al. (b) Stock thickness of 0.025 in. was also used for this set of conditions.

Fig. 20. Influence of process variables on burr height, as determined in tests on six low-carbon or silicon steels in two different conditions. (a) Effect of punch-to-die clearance on number of press strokes required for producing a burr height of 0.002 in. (b) Relation of number of press strokes to burr height.

removed for sharpening. Close control is required with this method of determining length of die run.

Optimum Die Run. For greatest economy and convenience of operation, die maintenance requirements and die life (in addition to maximum burr height) are considered in determining the optimum die run.

A die should not be run too long before resharpening; otherwise, excessive stock must be removed from both punch face and die face to restore the cutting edges, and as a result, fewer laminations can be made during the life of a die.

A common method of determining optimum die run is described in the example that follows.

Example 61. Optimum Die Run for Blanking Laminations From Nickel-Iron Alloy (Table 4)

A new carbide die was made for blanking laminations from 0.014-in.-thick nickel-iron alloy. The first run (run 1, Table 4) was arbitrarily established at 200,000 (202,540 laminations were actually produced). At the finish of this run, 0.005 in. was removed from the punch face to restore the cutting edge; thus 40,508 laminations per 0.001 in. were obtained (Table 4). Length of run was then increased (run 2, Table 4). Greatest efficiency was obtained in run 3, when 53,200 laminations per 0.001 in. of die life were obtained. Further increase in length of run resulted in decreased efficiency, as indicated for run 4. The operating level of run 3 was thus established as the optimum.

The part was a 14-slot stator lamination with 0.750-in. inside diameter and 1.400-in. outside diameter.

Lubrication

Although uncoated electrical sheet sometimes is blanked and pierced without lubrication, the use of some type of lubricant is preferred. Organic core plate (used on nonoriented silicon steels) serves as a lubricant, and no further lubrication is needed when blanking and piercing sheet that has core plating.

Tool life will be greatly improved by using a lubricant when blanking and piercing electrical sheet that has no coating or has been coated with magnesium hydroxide, which acts as an abrasive rather than a lubricant.

Oil-type lubricants, such as those used in blanking and forming operations, are not ordinarily used for blanking and piercing electrical sheet, because the cost of removal is too great.

Some plants purchase nonoriented silicon steel sheet without core plate and then subject the punched laminations to an oxidizing anneal, in which the lubricant is burned off; the only requirement is to select a lubricant that will leave the least residue when it is burned off. Water-soluble oils (1 part oil to about 20 parts water) have been used when annealing follows punching. Other low-viscosity, low-residue oils, such as the aliphatic petroleums, also burn off with little residue.

There are several means of applying liquid lubricants. In low-production operations, the work metal can be dipped into the lubricant just before punching. In high-production operations, where the stock is fed continuously, the lubricant can be brushed on just before it enters the press, or it can be dripped onto the sheet a few feet from the press. The top of the sheet is then rubbed with a felt wiper that spreads the lubricant over the entire surface. The bottom of the sheet can be coated with lubricant by having a trough under the sheet that catches the excess drip. A piece of felt or similar material in the trough acts as a wick to wet the underside of the moving sheet.

For a more complete discussion of lubricants, the reader is referred to the article that begins on page 23.

Table 4. Optimum Die Run in Blanking Electrical Sheet as Determined by Relation of Stock Removed From the Punch to Number of Laminations Produced (Example 61)

Run No.	Production: Desired	Production: Actual	Length of punch removed by sharpening, in.	Laminations produced per 0.001 in. of punch
1	200,000	202,540	0.005	40,508
2	300,000	300,300	0.006	50,050
3	400,000	425,600	0.008	53,200
4	500,000	498,300	0.010	49,830

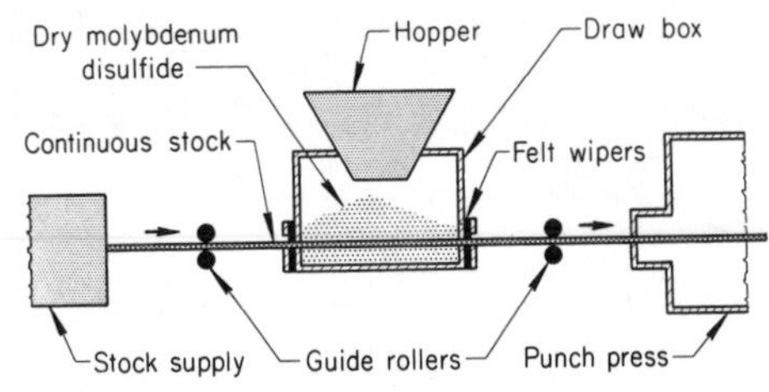

Fig. 21. Setup for applying dry molybdenum disulfide to both sides of electrical sheet

Molybdenum disulfide is a good lubricant for blanking and piercing electrical sheet. Usually, the amount of molybdenum disulfide used is so small that no removal is required. When there is an excess, it can be removed by immersing the sheet for 4 to 5 min in a solution of stripper-type cleaner (4 oz per gallon of water) at 180 F.

Molybdenum disulfide is the basic ingredient of several compounds that are available as dry powder, paste concentrate, and dispersion in liquid.

A common method of applying molybdenum disulfide is shown in Fig. 21. The sheet passes through a box containing the dry powder, and felt wipers remove the excess. A slurry can be used instead of the dry powder. Sheets can also be coated by a spray timed with the stroke of the press; either powder or a liquid suspension can be sprayed.

In low-production operations, a liquid suspension of molybdenum disulfide can be applied to the sheet by brush.

Core Plating

Core plating, or insulation, is a surface coating or treatment applied to electrical steel to reduce interlaminar loss, and sometimes to increase punchability. This treatment does not reduce eddy currents within the laminations. Interlamination resistance is usually improved by annealing the laminations under slightly oxidizing conditions, then core plating them.

The insulating coatings or finishes may be classified as organic or inorganic, and are described in Table 5.

Organic insulation generally consists of enamels or varnishes applied to the steel surfaces. Steels having organic coatings cannot be stress relieved without impairing the insulating value of the coating, but the coating will withstand normal operating temperatures. Coatings are about 0.0001 in. thick.

Inorganic insulation usually includes chemical or thermal treatments, has a high degree of electrical insulation, and can withstand stress relieving. These coatings form a very thin surface layer on the steel and only slightly increase lamination thickness.

Table 5. Types of Core Plate or Insulation for Flat Rolled Electrical Steel (a)

Type	Description
C-0	The natural oxide surface that occurs on flat rolled silicon steel. It is a slight but effective insulating layer sufficient for most small cores and will withstand normal stress-relieving temperatures. This surface condition may be improved by stress relieving of finished cores in a more or less oxidizing atmosphere.
C-1	An enamel or varnish coating for cores not immersed in oil. It is primarily used as a die lubricant to improve punchability rather than for its insulating quality. This organic coating is resistant to normal operating temperatures, but will not withstand stress-relieving temperatures. (b)
C-2	An inorganic insulation consisting of a glasslike film that forms during high-temperature hydrogen annealing of grain-oriented silicon steel as the result of the reaction of a coating of MgO and silicates on the surface of the steel. This insulation is for air-cooled or oil-immersed cores. It will withstand stress-relieving temperatures and has sufficient interlamination resistance for wound cores of narrow-width strip. Because of the abrasiveness of the coating, it is not recommended for blanked and pierced laminations.
C-3	An enamel or varnish coating for air-cooled or oil-immersed cores. The interlamination resistance of this coating is superior to that of the C-1 type of coating. The C-3 coating improves punchability and is resistant to normal operating temperatures, but will not withstand stress-relieving temperatures.
C-4	A chemically treated or phosphated surface for air-cooled or oil-immersed cores. It will withstand stress relieving and improves punchability. It is often applied over a C-2 coating on grain-oriented silicon steel to increase interlamination resistance.
C-5	An inorganic insulation similar to a chemically treated C-4 finish but with ceramic fillers added to improve surface resistance of air-cooled or oil-immersed cores. It is often applied over a C-2 coating on grain-oriented silicon steel and will withstand stress-relieving temperatures.

(a) From "Steel Products Manual, Flat Rolled Electrical Steel", American Iron and Steel Institute, July 1968.

(b) Where organic coatings are used primarily to improve punchability, they may be destroyed in fabricating operations involving heat, such as welding or die casting. The coating should leave as little residue as possible, so as not to interfere with these operations. The producer should be consulted, and the C-1 and C-3 designations of the coatings should be suffixed by the letter A.

Selection of Material for Blanking and Piercing Dies

*By the ASM Committee on Blanking Dies**

THIS ARTICLE deals with the selection of material for punches and dies to blank, pierce and shave metallic and nonmetallic sheet and plate in a punch press, at the lowest over-all production cost. Parts and examples are chosen to cover the ordinary ranges of size, shape, tolerance, work material, thickness, tooling and operations. The examples deal with categories of shapes and sizes that may determine or limit the selection. Recommendations are made on the basis of actual performance of tool materials in similar tooling circumstances.

All of the tool steels discussed in this article are assumed to be conventionally hardened and tempered to their highest usable hardness.

Selection Tables

Recommendations for tool materials are summarized in a series of selection tables herewith. Normal good-quality toolmaking, heat treating, grinding practice, tool design, tool maintenance, press equipment and manufacturing procedures are assumed in all the recommendations. For instance, commonly used clearances are assumed; small clearances used to produce minimum burr would decrease the tool life. Inferior conditions such as off-center punches, erroneous heat treating, or poor lubrication of sheet stock will result in die life shorter than indicated.

Some types of work require more precise toolmaking than others, and this has been allowed for; however, unusually close tolerances have not been. In general, a tolerance of ±0.005 in. (not ±0.005 in. per in.) is assumed for all part dimensions. The tool materials shown in all tables are intended to provide tools of minimum cost per piece for the listed quantities of production. Where more than one tool material is shown for a given application, the one listed first will provide the least expensive dies.

This criterion of least cost has the effect of eliminating high speed steels from the selection tables. However, high speed steel could be selected instead of D2 in many places where D2 is indicated in the tables. The comparability of high speed steel and D2 is demonstrated by the following example.

*Stewart M. DePoy, *Chairman,* W. G. Gaboda, Carl H. Gerlach, D. F. Gerstle, S. P. Karnitz, George E. Keith, V. A. Kortesoja, A. Justus Larson, George J. McLaughlin, M. T. Roberts, Joseph P. Schmidt, Earl E. Swanson, G. A. Warwick and A. S. Wiseman.

[This article is a condensation of the article beginning on page 685 of Volume 1 of this Handbook. Numbering of parts is the same as in the original; some part numbers are missing in this condensed version.]

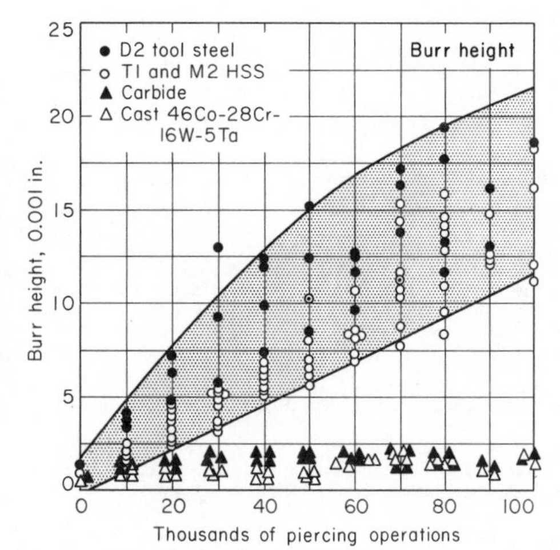

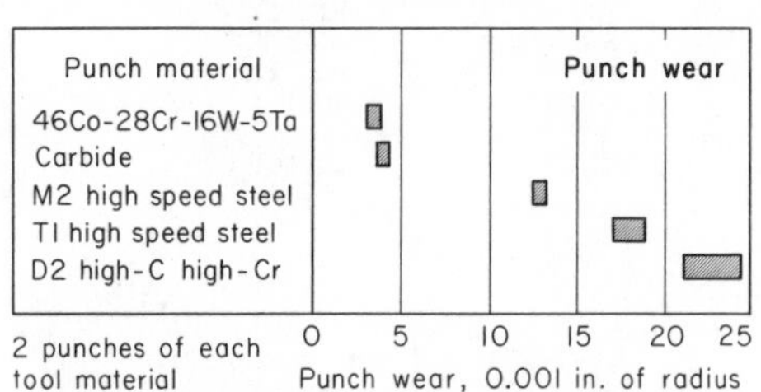

Fig. 1. Comparison of five tool materials for piercing electrical strip (Example 62) (A. T. Hamill, *Am Machinist,* Nov 27, 1950, with additional data from same author)

Example 62. Punch Wear and Burr Height When Piercing Electrical Steel With Five Types of Tool Material (Fig. 1)

A cast alloy tool material, carbide, two grades of high speed steel (M2 and T1), and a high-carbon high-chromium steel (D2) were compared for use as punch materials. These tool materials were used for piercing ¼-in. holes in electrical-grade silicon steel strip (0.052% C, 1.38% Si) that had a bright pickled surface. Tool efficiency was evaluated on the basis of burr height and punch wear (Fig. 1). Two punches of each material were used. Punches were ground after heat treatment. Figure 1 shows that the cast alloy tool material and carbide gave the best results, and that M2 and T1 performed somewhat better in both categories than D2, with some overlapping of burr-height results.

In the selection tables, carbide has been shown at quantities of ten million but not at one million. This is an arbitrary simplification, and, as is pointed out in a later section of this article, carbide should usually be considered for runs of one million pieces.

Tables 1 and 2 deal with the selection of tool material for two sizes of simple blanks, most of them disk-shaped. Size of die, material to be blanked, and total quantity of production are the principal variables affecting selection.

Table 1 recommends tool materials to blank and pierce the ¾-in. part 1 and the other small parts illustrated. The selections apply to dies not ground after hardening except on the top and bottom faces. In this small size, the cost of tool material is such a small fraction of the total die cost that selection of a more expensive material will have little effect on cost. Speed of completing the tooling, total die life, life between grinds, and other considerations will determine the selection.

The recommendations are intended for both punch and die. However, for making up to 100,000 pieces from the first two listed materials, a W1 stock piercing punch can be used, as discussed later.

W1 tool steel is shown in 14 of the 40 places in this table, because the die is so small that size change from hardening is not a serious consideration and there is little danger of cracking.

The case depth of a carburized 5⁄16-in.-diam punch should not exceed 0.020 in.; however, it would probably be as cheap and quicker to make the small punch from W1 drill rod and cyanide it, using an oil quench for hardening.

Table 2 deals with tool material selection for punches and dies to make 12-in. part 3 and similar shapes 16 times as large as part 1. Except where noted, the selections are for both punch and die. For this size tooling, selection of material is predominantly a matter of cost of the tool material, because this may vary from 10% of the total tool cost, for 4140 and zinc tools, to more than 50%, for tool steels such as D2 and D4. The tool steels recommended in this table are all through-hardening forged steel rings, used as fitted inserts in a die holder or punch holder.

Table 3 shows recommended blanking die materials for making part 6 and other 12-in. parts of the shapes illustrated. All tool steels recommended are air-hardening, to minimize distortion and the danger of cracking, except in the few applications where the material is not hardened, or where it is used in simple shapes in a sectional die. A zinc die and A2 punch would be economical for blanking and piercing 1000 pieces from aluminum.

The recommendation of A2 for 1000 pieces may seem extravagant. However, the nondeforming qualities of A2 are necessary in a compound die, and good wear characteristics are desirable in a notching die, because of the additional number of hits necessary.

Part Tolerances

Table 4 shows how selection of tool material is affected by dimensional tolerances for the part. The selections are based on considerations of expected distortion of the dies during heat treating, assuming that only the top and bottom faces would be ground after hardening.

Dimensional tolerance sometimes is the crucial factor in deciding between two possible steels or their exact heat

Table 1. Recommended Punch and Die Materials for Blanking Part 1 and Similar ¾-In. Parts From 0.050-In. Sheet Materials

Material to be cut	Total quantity of parts to be made				
	1,000	10,000	100,000	1,000,000	10,000,000
Aluminum, copper and magnesium alloys	Zn(a), CS(b), W1	W1, O1	O1, A2	D2	Carbide
Carbon and alloy steels, up to 0.70% C, and ferritic stainless steel	CS(b), W1	W1, O1	O1, A2	D2	Carbide
Stainless steel, austenitic, all tempers	W1	W1, A2	A2, D2	D4	Carbide
Spring steel, hardened, Rockwell C 52 max	A2	A2, D2	D2	D4	Carbide
Electrical sheet, 0.025-in., transformer grade	W1, A2	W1, A2	A2, D2	D4	Carbide
Paper, gaskets, and similar soft materials	W1(c)	W1(d)	W1(d), A2(e)	W1(d), A2(e)	D2
Plastic sheet, not reinforced	CS(b), W1	W1, O1	O1, A2	D2	Carbide
Plastic sheet, reinforced	O1(f), A2(g)	A2(g)	A2(g)	D2(g)	Carbide

Part 1 — ¾-in. parts similar to part 1 in severity

NOTE: Although carbide is recommended in this table only for 10 million pieces, it should usually be considered also for runs of 1 to 10 million pieces.

(a) Zn refers to zinc alloy plate for the die, sheared in, using a punch made of hardened tool steel. (b) CS refers to mild steel, such as 1018 or 1020, carburized to a depth of 0.010 to 0.020 in. or cyanided to a depth of 0.004 to 0.008 in.
(c) For punching 1000 parts, the W1 punch and die would be left soft and the punch peened to compensate for wear if necessary.
(d) The W1 punch may be left soft, or a hardened W1 punch and die may be selected for this quantity.
(e) A2 tool steel is preferred if compound tooling is to be used for quantities of 100,000 to 1,000,000. (f) This O1 punch may have to be cyanided to make even 1000 pieces. (g) The punch and die should be gas nitrided for 12 hr at 1000 to 1050 F.

Table 2. Recommended Punch and Die Materials for Blanking Part 3 and Similar 12-In. Parts From 0.050-In. Sheet Materials

Material to be cut	Total quantity of parts to be made				
	1,000	10,000	100,000	1,000,000	10,000,000
Aluminum, copper and magnesium alloys	Zn(a), 4140(b)	4140(c), A2	A2	A2, D2	Carbide
Carbon and alloy steels, up to 0.70% C, and stainless steels up to quarter-hard	4140(c), A2	4140(c), A2	A2	A2, D2	Carbide
Stainless steel, austenitic, over quarter-hard	A2	A2, D2	D2	D2, D4	Carbide
Spring steel, hardened, Rockwell C 52 max	A2	A2, D2	D2	D2, D4	Carbide
Electrical sheet, transformer grade, 0.025 in.	A2	A2, D2	A2, D2	D2, D4	Carbide
Paper, gaskets, and similar soft materials	4140(d)	4140(d)	A2	A2	D2
Plastic sheet, not reinforced	4140(d)	4140(c), A2	A2	D2	Carbide
Plastic sheet, reinforced	A2(e)	A2(e)	D2(e)	D2(e)	Carbide

Part 3 — 12-in. parts similar to part 3 in severity

NOTE: Although carbide is recommended in this table only for 10 million pieces, it should usually be considered also for runs of 1 to 10 million pieces.

(a) Zn refers to zinc alloy plate for the die, sheared in, using a hardened tool steel punch. (b) Soft. (c) Working edges of 4140 are flame hardened in this application. (d) 4140 may be soft or flame hardened. (e) For necessary wear resistance in the application indicated, the punch and die are gas nitrided 12 hr at 1000 to 1050 F.

Table 3. Recommended Punch and Die Materials for Blanking Parts 6, 7 and Similar 12-In. Parts From 0.050-In. Sheet Materials

Material to be cut	Total quantity of parts to be made				
	1,000(a)	10,000	100,000	1,000,000	10,000,000
Aluminum, copper and magnesium alloys	A2	A2	A2, D2	A2, D2	Carbide
Carbon and alloy steels, up to 0.70% C, and ferritic stainless steel	A2	A2	A2, D2	A2, D2	Carbide
Stainless steel, austenitic, up to quarter-hard	A2	A2	A2, D2	D2, D4	Carbide
Stainless steel, austenitic, over quarter-hard	A2	D2	D2	D2, D4	Carbide
Spring steel, hardened, Rockwell C 52 max	A2	A2, D2	D2	D2, D4	Carbide
Electrical sheet, transformer grade, 0.025 in.	A2	A2, D2	D2	D2, D4	Carbide
Paper, gaskets, and other soft materials	W1(b)	W1(b)	W1(c)	W1, A2	D2
Plastic sheet, not reinforced	A2	A2	A2	A2, D2	Carbide
Plastic sheet, reinforced(d)	A2(e)	A2(e)	D2(e)	D2(e)	Carbide

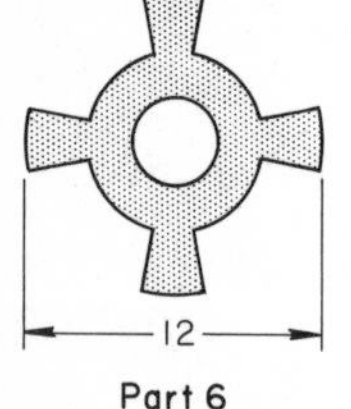

Part 6

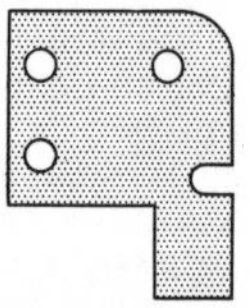
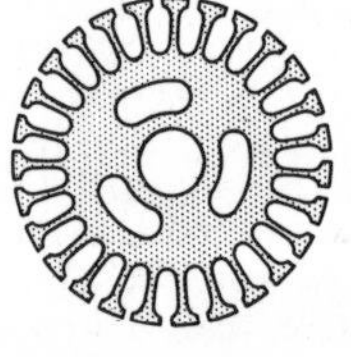
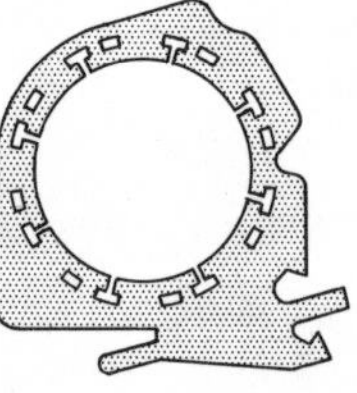
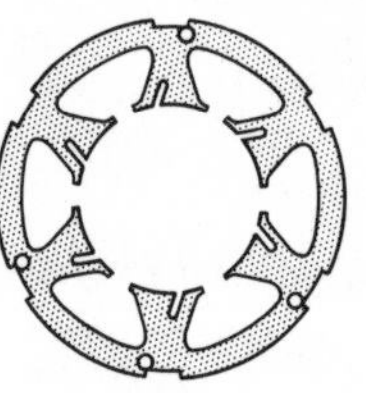
Part 7

12-in. parts similar to part 6 in severity

NOTE: Although carbide is recommended in this table only for 10 million pieces, it should usually be considered also for runs of 1 to 10 million pieces.

(a) Materials in this column are for either notching dies or compound dies. (b) For blanking up to 10,000 pieces, the W1 punch and die would be left soft and the punch peened to compensate for wear if necessary. (c) For blanking 10,000 to 1,000,000 pieces, the W1 die would be hardened and the W1 punch left soft so it can be peened to compensate for wear. (d) Some of the reinforced plastic parts shown might crack during blanking. (e) Punch and die should be gas nitrided 12 hr at 1000 to 1050 F for blanking any quantity of reinforced plastic.

treatment. The bar graph of Fig. 2 indicates relative size change for 18 combinations of steel and quenching temperature. Additional data on distortion in tool steels are given in Volume 1 of this Handbook (on page 645 and pages 654 to 657).

Part Shape

The recommendations in all the selection tables include consideration of quench cracking of the tools during heat treatment. For instance, in part 8 of Table 4, steel O1* is sufficiently resistant to quench cracking and also will meet most of the listed tolerances after heat treatment. However, in part 9, if the 3A/20 dimension (0.075 in. for the ½-in. part) were to become 1A/10 instead, the safety of O1 in hardening would become questionable, and A2 would be the preferred steel. Radii at corners are important; a sharp corner will usually demand an air-hardening die steel, and, regardless of the steel selected, die life for a sharp-cornered part will be only about half that for the same part with a 1/16-in. radius.

Table 4. Recommended Die Steel for Blanking Steel Parts to Different Tolerances
(For 100,000 to 1 million pieces)

Tolerance on dimension A, ±, in.	Recommended die material for: Part 8	Part 9	Part 10
Dimension A, ½ In.; Sheet Thickness, 0.020 In.			
0.008	W1	O1	A2, D2
0.003	W1	O1	A2, D2
0.001	O1	O1	A2, D2
Dimension A, 2 In.; Sheet Thickness, 0.040 In.			
0.008	W1	W1	A2, D2
0.003	O1	O1	A2, D2
0.001	A2	A2	A2, D2
Dimension A, 8 In.; Sheet Thickness, 0.060 In.			
0.015	O1	O1	A2, D2
0.008	A2	O1	A2, D2
0.003	A2	A2	A2, D2
0.001	A2	A2	A2, D2

Part 8 Part 9 Part 10

Where O1 is shown, the recommendation is based on its better machinability and grindability than A2, rather than on the cost advantage of 10¢ per pound.

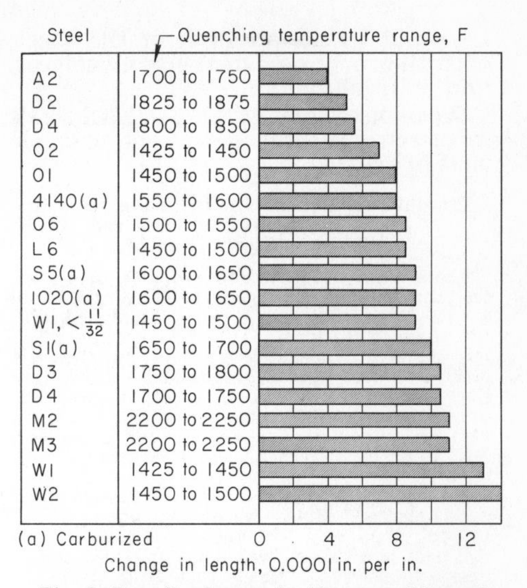

Fig. 2. Length change in the quenching of steels used for blanking dies. These values may be used to estimate differences among steels but not the magnitude of size change of a particular shape of a given steel.

Sheet Thickness

Table 5 shows the change in recommended punch steels as the thickness of the steel being pierced is increased. These changes depend on compromises between chipping resistance and wear resistance of the punch, and the increase in wear with increased thickness. To pierce quantities as low as 10,000 pieces from thick plate (0.250 to 1 in. thick), the shock-resisting steels such as S1 and S5 have adequate resistance to wear and adequate strength to resist breakage; it is improbable that 100,000 piercings could be accomplished in ½-in. plate with one punch. M2 punches (indicated in Table 5) would be borderline. Punches made of M3 or M4 high speed steel, liquid nitrided, would probably perform better.

Punch life in piercing thick plates is unpredictable because punch breakage, rather than wear, is the most common form of failure.

An M2 high speed steel punch, conventionally hardened, would probably fail to survive 100,000 piercings of 1-in. plate. However, liquid nitrided M2 or M3 would have a good chance of achieving this quantity.

*Where O1 or O2 is mentioned in this article, O6 may be substituted, with some increase in wear resistance and slightly more distortion during heat treatment.

Sheet Material

Table 6 lists sheet metals that cause die wear at about equal rates for the same part. Thus, any of the die materials recommended in Tables 1, 2 and 3 for blanking the various types of metals indicated in those tables should also be suitable for blanking similar parts from the sheet materials listed as similar in Table 6.

The least wear on the dies occurs in blanking leaded alpha brasses (1% Pb or more). Unleaded brasses or those with an alpha-beta structure impose more wear on the tools.

Recommendations for blanking part 1 from nonmetallic sheet materials are tabulated on page 690 in Volume 1 of this Handbook.

Tool Wear in Piercing

In a detailed investigation of tool wear in piercing, it has been determined that wear is significantly influenced by the amount of slip between the work material and the faces of the punch and die.† It was found that the amount of slip varied with the rough-

†O. and W. Kienzle, Tool Wear in the Cutting of Thin-Gage Steel Sheets, *Stahl und Eisen*, June 12, 1958

Table 5. Recommended Punch Steel for Piercing 3-In. Holes in Steel Sheet and Plate (Rockwell B 75 to 85) of Seven Different Thicknesses

Thickness of steel, in.	Total quantity of parts to be pierced: 1,000	10,000	100,000	1,000,000
0.010	W1	W1	W1	W1, A2
0.031	W1	W1	W1	D2
0.062	W1	W1	W1	D2
0.125	W2	W2	W2, A2	D2
0.250	S5(a)	S5(a)	A2, S1(a)	D2, M2
0.500	S5(a), S1(a)	S5(a), M2	M2	D2(b), M2(b)
1.000	S1(a)	S1(b), M2	M2(b)	....

(a) Carburized to obtain 0.70 to 0.75% C to a depth of 0.010 to 0.020 in. (b) It is doubtful whether this quantity can be made with one punch, even with successive regrindings.

Table 6. Classification of Sheet Metals That Require Similar Die Materials

Sheet metals for which blanking-die materials are shown in Tables 1, 2 and 3	Other sheet metals for which the same blanking-die materials are recommended
Aluminum, copper and magnesium; ferritic steels to 0.30% C; ferritic stainless steel	Zinc, tin, lead and noble metal alloys; 5050 alloy steel; beryllium copper, annealed
Carbon and alloy steel, up to 0.70% C	2024-T4; 10 and 18% nickel silver, alloys A and B, hard and spring tempers; phosphor bronze, grades A and C, spring and extra-spring tempers; type 420 stainless steel, annealed; Monel, hard tempers; K-Monel, annealed
Stainless steel, austenitic, up to quarter-hard	Mumetal, annealed; 4750 alloy (50% Ni); 45% Permalloy; beryllium copper, condition A; nickel-palladium bimetal; 17-7 PH stainless steel, annealed
Stainless steel, austenitic, over quarter-hard	Beryllium copper B194, all tempers (acid cleaned); type 410 stainless steel, heat treated; 4-79 Moly Permalloy
Spring steel, Rockwell C 52 max	Beryllium copper, half-hard and harder; vanadium Permendur; 17-7 PH stainless steel, hardened
Electrical sheet, transformer grades(a)	M-22 dynamo grades, HR and CR; AISI transformer grades as follows: M-6, grade 66, CR; M-7, grade 73, CR; M-8, grade 80, CR; M-17, grade 65, HR, PQ, and grades 58 and 65, HR; and M-19, grade 72, HR and CR, and grade 58 HR, PQ

(a) Other AISI types give up to ten times the die life, depending approximately on silicon content and hardness. These include field grade, CR, 0.25% Si; M-27 motor grade, HR and CR, 2.80% Si; M-36 electrical grade, HR, 1.30% Si, and CR, 1.60% Si; and M-43 armature grade, HR, 0.70% Si. CR means cold rolled; HR, hot rolled; and PQ, punching quality.

ness and tensile strength of the sheet, with the roughness of the tool surfaces, and with lubrication.

Wear of tools of O2 and D3 tool steels in piercing is discussed in the example that follows.

Example 63. Punch and Die Face Wear in Piercing Carbon, Electrical and Stainless Steels (Fig. 3)

Tests were conducted to evaluate face wear on punches and dies made of O2 and D3 tool steels. Both tool steels were hardened and tempered to Rockwell C 61 and were run without lubricant. Clearance angle on punches, die clearance, and surface roughness of the tools were the same for all tests. Press speed (60 strokes per minute), stroke setting, striking velocity, punch and die design, and automatic feed apparatus were also standardized for all tests.

Thirteen different grades of steel sheet were pierced. Holes were approximately ¼ in. in diameter. Thickness of carbon and stainless steel sheet was 0.039 in., and thickness of electrical sheet was from 0.014 to 0.020 in.

With O2 tool steel, the wear on the dies was from 9 to 46% greater than the wear on the punches (Fig. 3). With D3 tool steel, the wear on the dies and punches was almost equal, but punch wear sometimes slightly exceeded die wear. On D3 tool steel punches and dies, carbon steel sheet produced the least face wear, stainless steel sheet the most, and electrical sheet an intermediate amount.

In another series of tests connected with the same program, the influence of tool hardness on face wear was evaluated for O2 tool steel at hardness levels of Rockwell C 59 to 61. It was shown that face wear depends markedly on tool hardness and that an increase in hardness can result in a 25% decrease in face wear. An increase in impact speed from 0.26 to 0.65 ft per second *decreased* tool wear by about 8%. This is a significant indication that the wear of tool steel piercing tools does not increase with higher impact speeds.

Burr Measurements. Depending on quality requirements, burr height is normally limited to a predetermined maximum. A correlation between burr height and face wear is shown in the example that follows.

Example 64. Burr Height and Face Wear in Piercing Carbon Steel Sheet (Fig. 4)

A punch and die of D3 tool steel were used to pierce holes ¼ in. in diameter in carbon steel sheet 0.039 in. thick. Maximum burr height was measured on five slugs and five holes after every 5000 cuts. Figure 4 summarizes the results. Burr height increased proportionately with the number of cuts up to 50,000. From 50,000 to 75,000 cuts, burr growth proceeded at a slower rate. From 75,000 to 85,000 cuts, the rate of burr growth increased until the initial rate was reached. Beyond 85,000 cuts, the rate of burr growth increased rapidly. The height of the burr on the slug was always a few microns greater than that on the pierced sheet.

Face wear on the die and punch during this test is shown in the lower chart of Fig. 4. Wear on the die proceeded at a slightly faster rate than wear on the punch, but both punch wear and die wear were nearly parallel to burr-height increases.

Because burr size is more dependent on die clearance than on tool wear, it was concluded that measurement of tool wear was a more accurate indicator of both tool life and pierceability. Although face, side, and longitudinal edge wear are all available for measurement, the investigators determined that measurements of face wear provided the most dependable reference, because the cross section of the volume worn away is directly related to the number of cuts. In addition, measurements of worn cross section are independent of the length of the cutting line and the diameter of the punch. A test

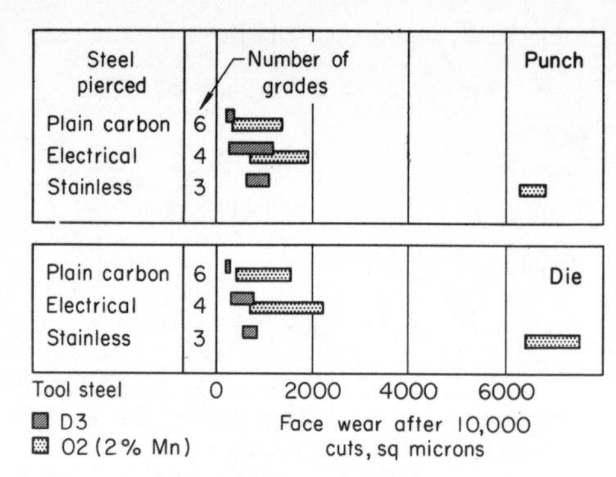

Fig. 3. Face wear on punches and dies made of O2 and D3 tool steels (Example 63) (O. and W. Kienzle, *Stahl und Eisen*, June 12, 1958)

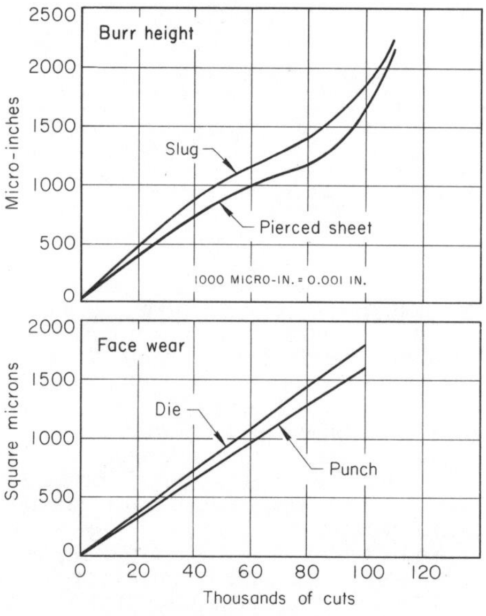

Fig. 4. Burr height and face wear in piercing carbon steel sheet with D3 tools (Example 64) (O. and W. Kienzle, *Stahl und Eisen*, June 12, 1958)

procedure based on face-wear measurements of punch and die was subsequently proposed.

Die-Life Data

In general, a life of about 50,000 parts per grind would be expected from W1 (1% C) or O1 dies used on 0.062-in. steel parts and about 100,000 per grind for brass parts where burr height is held between 0.003 and 0.006 in. On the steel parts, A2 dies will run 100,000 parts per grind, D2 dies double that, and carbide from 8 to 12 times as many as D2.

Die life between grinds where 0.015-in. cold rolled steel was blanked with a 0.002-in. permissible burr, in an actual case, was about 200,000 pieces with D2 dies and 700,000 with carbide dies. In another case, 100,000 steel parts 0.125 in. thick were blanked between grinds on a D2 die when the burr height was over 0.005 in.

In blanking smoothly contoured parts from 0.110 to 0.120-in. cold rolled steel with an A2 die that gives a burr height of 0.002 in. at the start, production between grinds has averaged:

Burr height	Press strokes
0.003 in.	5,000 to 10,000
0.005	20,000 to 25,000

Cold rolled spring steel parts 0.010 in. thick which produce a 0.001-in. burr at the beginning of production on D4 dies have developed average burr heights as shown below:

Burr height	Press strokes
0.002 in.	10,000 to 15,000
0.003	65,000 to 85,000

Brass parts approximately 0.080 in. thick were blanked and pierced on a D2 die and produced the following results:

Burr height	Press strokes
0.001 in.	40,000 to 60,000
0.002	80,000 to 120,000

Type 302, quarter-hard stainless steel parts 0.060 in. thick that begin production on high speed steel dies with a 0.001-in. burr have averaged the following production between grinds:

Burr height	Press strokes
0.002 in.	1,000 to 3,000
0.003	4,000 to 6,000
0.005	8,000 to 12,000

Parts with a burr limit of 0.002 in. made from annealed 301 stainless steel 0.080 in. thick in an actual application ran an average of 20,000 pieces between grinds on dies made of D2 and 110,000 on carbide dies.

Production of one million pieces from low-silicon electrical sheet blanked with burr heights from 0.003 to 0.005 in. would require a thickness allowance on dies of about 3/16 in. for regrinding, for dies made of D2 or D3.

Life between grinds in blanking and piercing 0.025-in. electrical laminations from steel having a silicon content between 2 and 4½% may be estimated as follows:

Burr height	Press strokes: D2 steel	Press strokes: Carbide
0.001 in.	25,000	200,000
0.002	60,000	500,000

In another set of data, the total life of eight D2 dies blanking and piercing motor-grade electrical sheet (2.80% Si) averaged 5.5 million and of twenty D3 dies blanking and piercing armature-grade (0.70% Si) averaged 6.99 million, both based on an allowance of 1⅜ in. to be ground off the dies during their life. In a similar application, and confirmed by results obtained in other, unrelated tests, T1 dies gave an average total production of 5.8 million pieces under the same operating conditions.

In controlled tests blanking and piercing electrical-grade lamination stock, dies made of D4 and M2 had about equal life, and at the same burr height exceeded dies of D3 by about 23% and dies of D2 by about 28%. Dies made of carburized M2 had about 35% longer life at the same burr height than both D4 and M2 with standard treatments.

Quantity

In small dies, particularly those smaller than 6 in., the cost of even D2 tool steel is only about 10% of the die cost, and avoidance of the risk of wearing out and the necessity for rebuilding the tools is more important than savings in the cost of tool steel.

In dies larger than about 12 in., the cost of tool steel is often more than 50% of the total die cost. Material selection is important, whether the quantity is large or small. If the quantity is small, flame-hardened 4140 or a

Table 7. Recommended Material for Piercing Punches

Material to be pierced	Total quantity of parts to be pierced: 10,000	100,000	1,000,000	Punch shape
Punch Diameters up to ¼ In.				
Aluminum, brass, carbon steel, paper and plastics	M2	M2	M2	
Spring steel, stainless, electrical sheet and reinforced plastics	M2	M2	M2	
Punch Diameters Over ¼ In.				
Aluminum, brass, carbon steel, paper and plastics	W1	W1	D2	
Spring steel, stainless, electrical sheet and reinforced plastics	M2	M2	M2	

Table 8. Recommended Material for Piercing-Punch Bushings

Material to be pierced	Total quantity of parts to be made: 10,000	100,000	1,000,000
Aluminum, brass, carbon steel, paper and plastics	W1(a)	W1(a)	D2
Spring steel, stainless, electrical sheet and reinforced plastics ...	D2	D2	D2 or carbide

(a) When bushings are of a shape that cannot be ground after hardening, an oil-hardening or air-hardening steel is recommended.

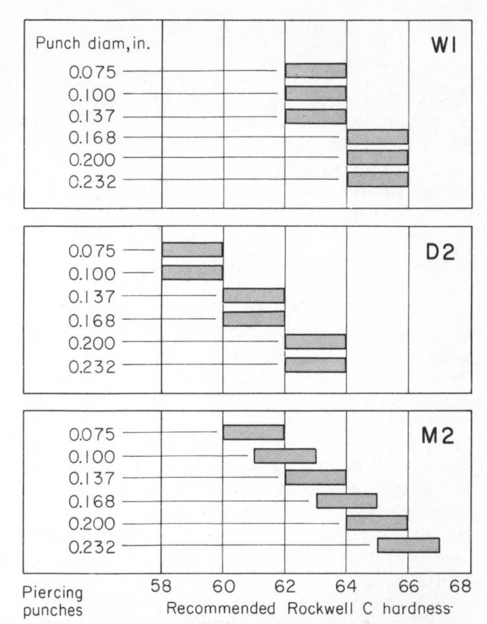

Fig. 5. Recommended hardness for tool steel piercing punches. Punches should be tempered to Rockwell C 56 to 60 when they are subjected to heavy shock or used to pierce thick material.

die of zinc alloy and a punch of W1, O1 or A2 may be selected, as indicated in the tables. Frequently, a die can be built up from a combination of specially made sections and standard purchased punches and bushings, in order to economize on the cost of material and fabrication.

Kind of Tooling

In general, short-run or single-operation dies are used for small-volume production where the cost of tooling must be kept low because it is the major cost factor, and the cheapest tool materials are used. Compound dies are used for medium to large-volume production where intricacy is not the dominant problem and where accuracy often is. Progressive dies are used for medium-volume, and particularly for large-volume, production where the die is preferably not made as intricate as the part.

In adjacent and simultaneous blanking operations where the die sections are thin or intricate, type A2 tool steel is preferred for runs up to 100,000 parts of most materials. M2, D2, D3 or carbide is preferred for longer runs.

Die Components

Piercing punches of the type illustrated in Table 7 may be made of the materials listed in that table.

The usual limiting slenderness ratio of punch diameter to sheet thickness for aluminum, brass and steel is 2.5-to-1 for unguided punches and 1-to-1 for guided punches. The limiting slenderness ratio of punch diameter to sheet thickness for piercing spring steel and stainless steel is from 3-to-1 to 1.5-to-1 for unguided punches, and from 1-to-1 to 0.5-to-1 for accurately guided punches.

Where these usual limits are exceeded, and breakage cannot be eliminated by stepping the punches, tool steels such as O1, A2 and M2 are used. W1 is used if the diameter is greater than ⅜ in. but less than ¾ or 1 in. The recommended hardnesses for W1, D2 and M2 piercing punches are given in Fig. 5.

Piercing-Punch Bushings. Table 8 shows recommended materials for piercing-punch bushings of all three types (quill retainer, guide or stripper, and die button), particularly for bushings of the precision type — for instance, where the outside diameter is ground to −0, +0.0003 in., concentric with the inside diameter within 0.0002 in. TIR. The hardness of the W1 bushing should be Rockwell C 62 to 64; that of the D2 bushing, Rockwell C 61 to 63.

Die plates and die parts that hold inserts are made of class 50 gray iron, alloy steel, or (for heavy work) tool steel, and of cast iron or low-carbon wrought steel for blanking and piercing soft and thin materials.

For blanking or piercing thick sheets or hard materials, either gray iron of 40,000 to 60,000 psi tensile strength or 4140 treated to Rockwell C 30 to 40 should be used. Particularly on heavy-gage or hard material and on long runs for which inserts are pressed in, steels like 4340 or H11 are used; when inserts are screwed into the die plate, 4340 is nearly always used.

Die plates for blanking or piercing thin or soft sheets may be made of gray iron of 20,000 to 40,000 psi tensile strength, or mild steel.

Punch holders and die shoes for carbide dies are of high-strength gray iron or mild steel plate. Yokes retaining carbide sections are usually made of O1, hardened to Rockwell C 55 to 60.

Backup plates for carbide tools are preferably made of O1, hardened to Rockwell C 48 to 52.

Stripper plates can ordinarily be made of some low-carbon or medium-carbon steel like 1020 or 1035. Where a hardened plate is used for medium-production work, the preferred steels are flame-hardened 4140, conventionally hardened W1, or, for intricate shapes, cyanided and oil-quenched W1. For carbide dies and high-production D2 or D4 dies, hardened strippers are of O1 or A2 at Rockwell C 50 to 54.

Guides and locator pins can be made from W1 or W2 for most dies, or from alloy steels such as 4140 for short-run low-cost dies. Many commercial guide pins are made from 1117, carburized, hardened, and finished to 15 micro-in.

Combined operations like blank-and-draw or pierce-and-extrude give rise to selection problems best solved by determining which of the operations is the more severe, and selecting for that operation. The article on page 194 may be referred to in selecting steel of the required wear resistance for blank-and-draw operations. Selection of material for pierce-and-extrude sections of dies should follow the recommendations of this article.

Wear of extrusion or embossing dies can be offset by nitriding A2 and D2 materials. However, nitriding may shorten the life of blanking tools because edges are likely to chip, unless the dies are used for thin or soft sheet.

Table 9 lists the recommended punch and die materials for shaving 0.050-in.-thick material of various kinds, including nonferrous alloys, carbon and alloy steels, and stainless steels. For thicker sheets, either the next best material should be selected or shorter life should be accepted.

Table 9. Recommended Punch and Die Materials for Shaving 0.050-In. Sheet

Material to be shaved	Total quantity of parts to be made: 1,000	10,000	100,000	1,000,000
Aluminum, copper and magnesium alloys	O1(a)	A2	A2	D4(b)
Carbon and alloy steels, to 0.30 C; ferritic stainless	A2	A2	D2	D4(b)
Carbon and alloy steels, 0.30 to 0.70 C	A2	D2	D2	D4(b)
Stainless steel, austenitic, to quarter-hard	A2	D2	D4(b)	D4(b)
Stainless steel, austenitic, over quarter-hard; spring steel hardened to Rockwell C 52 max	A2	D2	D4(b)	M2(b)

(a) It is preferable to use O2 for dies that must be made by broaching. (b) On frail or intricate sections, D2 should be used. Carbide shaving punches may also be practical for this quantity.

Cost

Figure 6 compares the relative cost of tools to make part 3 when using the types of tooling shown in Fig. 7. Factors that are not affected by the selection of tool material are not included in these cost figures. All punches in Fig. 7 are included in the punch costs of Fig. 6.

Tool Materials

Table 10 shows nominal compositions of the tool steels recommended in the selection tables. All of these steels serve best when used at maximum tempered hardness, particularly in blanking thin material and when shock will be absent. For conditions of shock, the hardness is lowered to produce a tolerable level of breakage. Whether longer die life can be achieved by tempering to a lower hardness or by using a tougher steel at full hardness cannot be readily predicted.

W1 and W2 are readily available, readily machinable, wear-resistant and highly versatile water-hardening grades, furnished with various carbon contents in 0.10% ranges. W1 and W2 are interchangeable in performance, but W2 is of little advantage except that coarse grain is less likely to develop in the steel as a result of overheating.

The depth of hardness of the water-hardening grades is shallow (from about 0.125 to 0.150 in. in a 1-in.-diam bar), and for this reason such steels should not be used where grinding of the hard case will be needed to correct for distortion due to heat treating, except for short-run dies. W1 may make a brittle, easily broken punch if less than ⅜ in. in diameter, but a tough one if the diameter is about ¾ in. Hardness should be the highest obtainable at a tempering temperature of 325 to 375 F — usually Rockwell C 62 to 66.

Shock-resisting tool steels S1 and S5 are used for punches only where the probability of breakage is high. With normal heat treatment they have unacceptable levels of wear resistance, and they are economical only if they are carburized to obtain 0.010 to 0.020-in. case containing 0.70 to 0.75% C. S1 should be used at Rockwell C 57 to 60, and S5 at Rockwell C 59 to 62.

Oil-hardening steel O1 is safer to harden and distorts less than W1 steel. O2 is preferred to O1 for dies that are to be made by broaching. It distorts less in hardening. Steel O6 is easier to weld, has consistently better life in blanking and piercing dies than O1, and has reduced regrinding and maintenance by about one-half in blanking 1040 and other steels up to ⅜ in. thick. Although less widely available than O1, the usage of O6 steel has increased greatly during recent years. Advantages derived from the use of O6 in die applications relate to its greater resistance to sliding wear and its better machinability, as compared with other O grades; however, it may distort more during heat treatment.

A2 air-hardening medium-alloy (5% Cr) tool steel has wear resistance about halfway between that of oil-hardening steels and that of D2. A2 presents the least hazard of size change and cracking in heat treatment of all the tool steels, followed closely by D2, air-hardened D4, and then by oil-hardened O and oil-hardened S types. Like D2, the A2 steel can be nitrided for dies for thin or soft materials or reinforced plastics, to resist wear and heat.

D2 high-carbon high-chromium air-hardening tool steel is probably the most commonly used and may be the most satisfactory and most widely available tool steel for large-volume production of blanks. It is about the second-best steel for high accuracy and for safety in heat treatment, and it through-hardens in 3-in. sections. Its highest usable hardness of Rockwell C 62 to 63 is recommended for punches and dies where breakage is not a problem, as in dies blanking steel less than 0.062 in. thick and softer than Rockwell B 90. Maximum resistance to breakage may be developed by tempering back to Rockwell C 58 to 60, but only at a sacrifice in wear resistance. For lamination dies, the hardness should not be less than Rockwell C 61 or 62.

D4 high-carbon high-chromium air-hardening tool steel is somewhat more wear resistant than D2 and D3, particularly in blanking and piercing electrical sheet, where, at Rockwell C 63 to 65, it often wears about 20% less than D2 and D3 and about the same as M2 high speed steel. All of the high-carbon high-chromium steels should be nitrided to extend die life only for blanking reinforced plastics or for soft or thin materials.

D5 high-carbon high-chromium tool steel has replaced D2, D3, M2 and M3 in some plants for the piercing, trimming and blanking of austenitic stainless steel. Metal pickup and scoring have been minimized in such applications by the use of D5, with an increase of 100 to 200% in die life for some stainless steel parts.

M2 high speed steel is the least costly, most used, and most readily available high speed steel for blanking dies and punches. It is equal to, or better than, D4 in wear resistance. For blanking and piercing electrical sheet, the conventionally hardened M2 is surpassed only by carbide, cast alloys, and carburized M2.

When carburized, M2 is about 30% more resistant to punch wear in making laminations than it is with standard heat treatment. It is equaled only by D4 and three less widely used high speed steels: M4 carburized, T1 carburized, and T15 carburized. It is

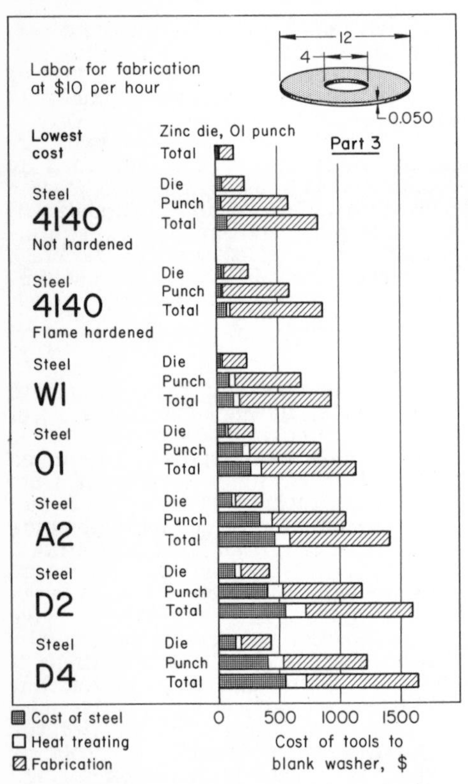

Fig. 6. Relative cost of tooling to make the part illustrated. Schematic representations of the tool setups are shown in Fig. 7.

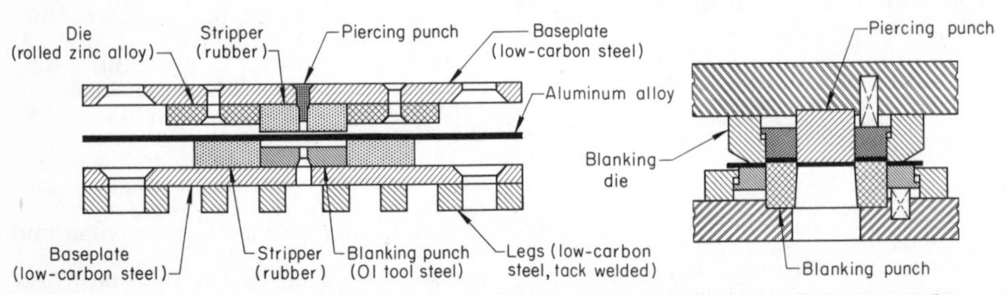

Fig. 7. Tooling for making part 3 (shown in Fig. 6). Tools at left are for short-run production with zinc alloy die and O1 steel punch; all components of tools at right are of steel.

Table 10. Nominal Composition of Tool Steels Recommended in the Selection Tables

Steel	C	Mn	Cr	Mo	Other
W1	1.00(a)	...	...	...	...
W2	1.00(a)	...	...	...	0.25 V
S1	0.50	...	1.50	...	2.50 W
S5	0.55	0.80	...	0.40	2.00 Si
O1	0.90	1.00	0.50	...	0.50 W
A2	1.00	...	5.00	1.00	...
D2	1.50	...	12.00	1.00	...
D4	2.25	...	12.00	1.00	...
M2	0.80	...	4.00	5.00	(b)

(a) Carbon is 0.60 to 1.40%, in 0.10% ranges in available steels. (b) 6.00 W, 2.00 V.

Table 11. Survey of Operating Conditions for 40 Carbide Dies in Various Plants

Condition	Value
Press condition(a):	
Excellent	17%
Good	48%
Fair	35%
Press tonnage utilized, % of rated capacity (avg)	47%
Feed, in. per min (avg)	474
Carbide removed per grind, in. (avg):	
Punch	0.006
Die	0.006
Depth of carbide chipping, in. (avg)	0.012
Stripper construction preferred:	
Spring	45%
Solid	41%
Combination	14%
Hits per grind (avg) (silicon steels only)	976,000

(a) See "Condition of Press", page 76, for definitions of "excellent", "good" and "fair".

recommended in Table 5 with standard heat treatment because it is less likely to break than other steels of equal wear resistance and has much better wear resistance than the shock-resisting steels S1 or S5. In blanking dies, it should be used at the hardness given in Fig. 5.

M3 high speed steel, with its 1% carbon and high vanadium content, is more wear-resistant than M2 and the D grades. Its wear resistance can be improved by liquid nitriding. Selection of M3 depends on whether the dies can be ground economically; to reduce the amount of grinding, M3 is generally used only for inserts. M3 is more difficult to grind than M2; caution must be used to avoid "burning" and the formation of surface cracks.

Hot rolled mild steel plate with carbon content from 0.10 to 0.20% may be used for short runs of small parts after it has been surface hardened, either by carburizing to a depth of 0.010 to 0.020 in. or by cyaniding to 0.004 to 0.008 in. Because it distorts in heat treatment, its use is limited to small, symmetrical shapes.

4140 alloy steel is generally available in various sizes of plate of aircraft quality. It is flame hardened to about Rockwell C 50 for long blanking runs on soft materials. However, flame-hardened tools that have either inside or outside corners are likely to have soft spots that will wear rapidly. For large dies, flame hardening the working edge only, instead of hardening the entire die, has the advantage of minimizing the changes in size and the warpage that occur as a result of heat treatment.

Rolled zinc alloy or tooling plate is available in the form of ¼-in. plate from the principal suppliers of zinc-base die-casting alloys and lead-free zinc at about the same cost as W1. Dies of this material are sheared-in with a flame-hardened O1 punch. Zinc dies cost about one-fifth as much as tool steel dies and are in major use for blanking fewer than 2000 parts from aluminum sheet as thick as 0.064 in.

Carbide tooling is usually considered where production is four or more times the life of a D4 tool steel die, especially where close tolerances and minimum burr are required and a heavier press is available. Partial or complete inserts of carbide in tool steel may be considered for lower quantities or where the tool life between grinds needs to be extended. However, brazed sections are hazardous, and dovetailed or mechanically held sections will approach the cost of a complete carbide die.

Composition and hardness of carbide grades frequently used in blanking and piercing dies are as follows:

Nominal composition: Tungsten	Carbon	Cobalt	Rockwell A hardness
75.1	4.9	20.0	86
78.9	5.1	16.0	86
81.7	5.3	13.0	88
88.3	5.7	6.0	91

The first material should be used where shock is appreciable. The second of the above combines toughness and wear resistance, and is preferred for heavy-duty service, such as piercing silicon steel. Where close tolerances must be held in piercing silicon steel laminations, the third material is useful. The last of the carbides listed will be best for guides and guide rolls, or for applications involving very light shock.

Comparison of Tool Steel and Carbide*

Although the cost of carbide has been reduced considerably in recent years, it is estimated that the average carbide die will cost from 2¼ to 3 times as much as its tool steel counterpart. Therefore, justification for the use of a carbide die is normally based on its greater productive capacity. It can be expected to produce from 8 to 12 times as many pieces per grind as a high-carbon high-chromium tool steel die.

Initial Costs. The higher initial cost of carbide dies reflects several factors. The cost of raw material in rough carbide sections is approximately 15 times that of tool steel on a pound-for-pound basis. Grinding time is increased by 25% on carbide sections.

The cost of supporting sections is higher, because these sections must be stronger to accommodate carbide dies. Many carbide die designs require more elaborate sectioning to avoid losing an entire complicated contour in case of accident. As a result, more die pieces must be fitted together. These costs, along with the cost of a diamond grinding wheel, are the major additional costs involved in converting from tool steel to carbide.

Whether or not the initial cost of a carbide die is a determining factor in die material selection will depend primarily on the production quantities required. At some quantity level, there is a break-even point at which either carbide or tool steel dies could be used with equal justification. As quantity of parts is increased above this break-even point, the probability of 8 to 12 times greater production per grind can justify the cost of carbide dies.

*Based on an article, How Do Steel Dies Compare With Carbide Dies, by Joseph P. Schmidt (*Carbide Engineering,* Dec 1958). This discussion has been considerably extended to include previously unpublished data provided by the author and others.

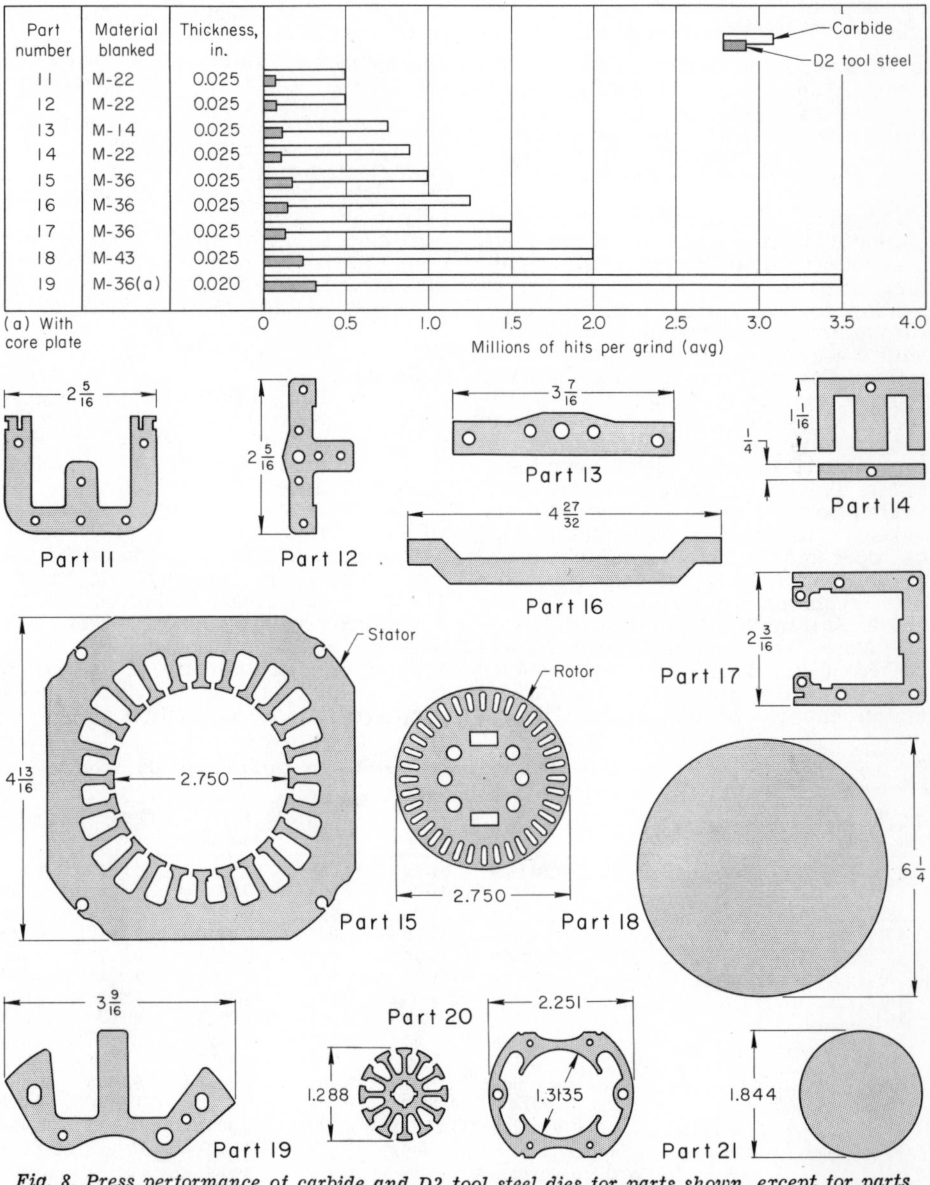

Part number	Material blanked	Thickness, in.
11	M-22	0.025
12	M-22	0.025
13	M-14	0.025
14	M-22	0.025
15	M-36	0.025
16	M-36	0.025
17	M-36	0.025
18	M-43	0.025
19	M-36(a)	0.020

(a) With core plate

Fig. 8. Press performance of carbide and D2 tool steel dies for parts shown, except for parts 20 and 21, for which data are given in Fig. 9 and 10 and in Tables 12 and 13 (Example 65)

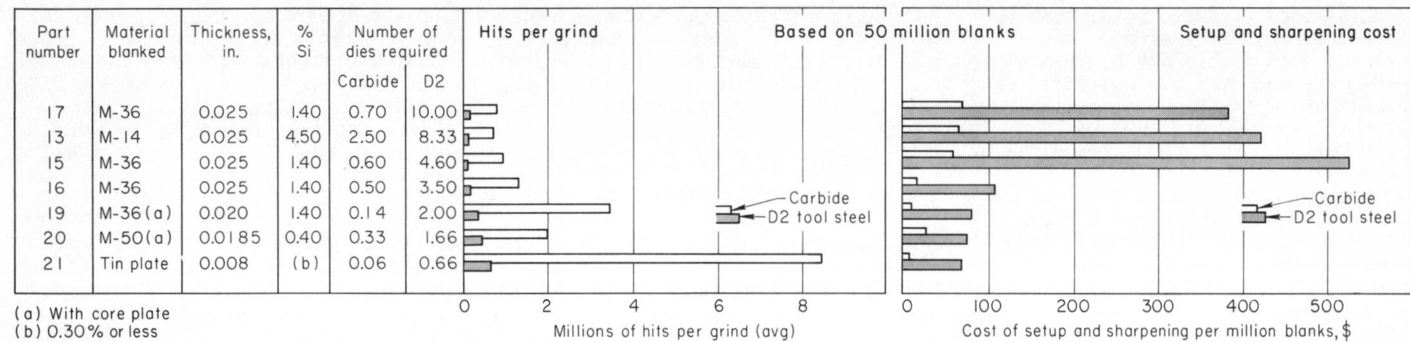

Setup and sharpening costs are derived from data in Table 13, comparing the number of dies required to produce 50 million blanks. All of the carbide dies were resharpened before the maximum allowable burr height was reached. Had they been run until they produced a burr comparable to that from their tool steel counterparts, the ratio of hits per grind would have been higher.

Fig. 9. Production results and operating costs for carbide dies and D2 tool steel dies used to make seven different parts. Parts (shown in Fig. 8) and operating conditions were similar for both carbide and tool steel dies. (Example 65)

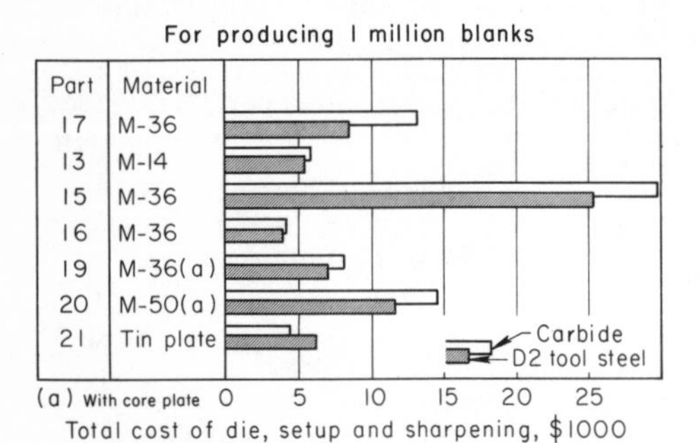

Fig. 10. Comparison of total cost of die, setup and sharpening for blanking one million each of seven parts shown in Fig. 8 with carbide and D2 tool steel dies

Chipping and Breakage. Occasional chipping of carbide dies in normal usage is not uncommon. However, the metallurgical nature of carbide lends itself to shallow flaking, rather than deep fracturing. Proper and careful handling will assure a minimum of chipping.

Condition of Press. During the early years of carbide die building, it was assumed that such dies would operate properly only on new presses or on those with extremely close press tolerances. This is an extreme and unwarranted point of view, although it is obviously true that carbide dies cannot be operated in any available press, regardless of its condition. Normally, press requirements for carbide dies include: (*a*) sufficient tonnage, (*b*) average close-fitting slides, (*c*) good ram-to-bed parallelism, (*d*) an accurate feeding device, and (*e*) a satisfactory clutch capable of fast stops. The die should have a misfeed detector, to actuate the fast stop.

In general, a press that functions accurately with tool steel dies without chipping them, and with no excess deflection or abnormal wear of pins and bushings, should be suitable for carbide dies. An exception to this rule is dies for blanking and piercing thin material (under 0.025 in. thick) with minimum punch-to-die clearance.

Suggested minimum press tolerances for carbide operation are as follows: (*a*) ram-to-bed parallelism should be within 0.001 in. per foot; (*b*) roll feed accuracy should be within 0.005 in., and even closer for materials less than 0.025 in. thick; and (*c*) slide fit should be held within 0.0015 in.

In blanking, a complete break should occur when the punch penetrates the die opening for a distance equivalent to the stock thickness. Failure of the stock to break with this amount of penetration indicates excessive play or press deflection.

A press that conforms to these standards of accuracy may be classified as being in "good" condition. A press whose accuracy is such as to halve these tolerances may be considered to be in "excellent" condition. A press whose accuracy deviates slightly below the minimum standards described as "good" may be classified as "fair". These classifications of press condition are referred to in the survey data presented in Table 11, page 74.

Table 11 is a summary of operating, design, and performance factors encountered in an examination of 40 carbide dies operating successfully under varying conditions. Only 17% reported their press equipment in "excellent" condition. No reports of "poor" presses were received. Reports on press tonnage show that the average user holds press load at about 50% of capacity. Figures on stripper construction indicate the users of spring and of box strippers are about even. In terms of performance, no appreciable difference was noted because of stripper type.

Sharpening Equipment. Assuming the availability of a surface grinder of sufficient capacity to sharpen steel dies, additional equipment needed for carbide is a diamond wheel of adequate size, a wheel mount, and a simple diamond dresser. It is important that operators be properly trained in procedures of sharpening with a diamond wheel. Figures on the cost of such training are not available.

Costs of Design Changes. Most changes in high-production parts develop as minor modifications over a period of time, requiring simple die revisions. Drastic changes in part design are fairly uncommon. The cost of resectioning or modifying a carbide die follows about the same ratio as the initial steel-carbide die cost (carbide 2¼ to 3 times as much as steel). Electrical discharge machining makes possible various die revisions with a minimum of original section replacement.

Cost and Production Data. Based on information supplied by carbide users, considerable data on both die costs and the performance of dies in production have been made available.

Table 12. Production Results on Carbide and D2 Tool Steel Dies (Example 65)

Part No. (Fig. 8)	Material: Die	Material: Blank	Maximum burr allowed, in.	Clearance: Punch to die, in. per side	Clearance: Angular, in./in. per side	Average grind, in., on: Punch	Average grind, in., on: Die	Average grinding time, hr	Average hits per grind	Estimated total hits per die	Usable die life, in.
17	Carbide	M-14	0.003	0.001	0.002	0.002	0.002	5	750,000	70,000,000	3/16
17	D2	M-14	0.003	0.001	0.002	0.010	0.005	5	125,000	5,000,000	3/16
13	Carbide	M-36	0.003	0.0012	0.0017	0.009	0.007	4	750,000	20,000,000	5/16
13	D2	M-36	0.003	0.0012	0.0013	0.013	0.010	3	100,000	6,000,000	½
15	Carbide	M-36	0.003	0.0009	0.0015	0.005	0.005	6	900,000	80,000,000	¾
15	D2	M-36	0.003	0.0009	0.0015	0.008	0.008	5	80,000	11,000,000	1¼
16	Carbide	M-50(a)	0.0025	0.0007	0.002	0.004	0.004	5	2,000,000	150,000,000	⅝
16	D2	M-50(a)	0.004	0.0007	0.002	0.010	0.010	2	400,000	30,000,000	¾
19	Carbide	M-36	0.001	0.001	Cutoff	0.005	0.005	2½	1,250,000	140,000,000	½
19	D2	M-36	0.002	0.001	Cutoff	0.009	0.009	2	140,000	14,000,000	1¼
20	Carbide	M-36(a)	0.003	0.0008	0.0025	0.006	0.006	4	3,500,000	350,000,000	⅝
20	D2	M-36(a)	0.003	0.0008	0.0025	0.010	0.010	3	300,000	25,000,000	¾
21	Carbide	Tin plate	0.0007	0.0004	0.0015	0.004	0.004	8	8,500,000	875,000,000	¾
21	D2	Tin plate	0.0007	Sheared in	0.0015	0.007	0.007	5	600,000	72,000,000	¾

(a) With core plate. See Table 5, page 68, for designations and descriptions of core-plate materials.

Example 65. Carbide vs D2 Tool Steel Dies (Fig. 8 and 9, and Tables 12 and 13)

Similar parts were blanked from four grades of electrical sheet and from tin plate, using carbide and D2 tool steel dies. The parts are shown in Fig. 8. Thickness of the sheet varied from 0.008 in. for the tin plate to 0.0185 to 0.025 in. for the electrical sheet. Table 12 gives maximum burr height on all parts and clearances for all blanking operations. The amount of material removed from dies and punches per grind was 0.002 to 0.009 in. for carbide and 0.005 to 0.013 in. for D2. Average grinding time was usually less for tool steel than for carbide dies, and costs for setup and sharpening were less (Fig. 9 and Table 13). Both average hits per grind (Fig. 9 and Table 12) and estimated total hits per die (Table 12) favored carbide. Operating costs using the carbide and D2 dies are given in Table 13. The savings realized by the use of carbide dies were based on sharpening and setup costs only. Total savings were considerably higher, because they included such factors as reduction in press downtime and initial die costs.

In the preceding example, the setup and sharpening costs (Fig. 9 and Table 13) are based on the production of 50 million blanks. Because only a relatively few operations are likely to require quantities this large, estimated data are presented in Fig. 10 for the production of one million each of seven of the parts shown in Fig. 8. These data, which combine the setup and sharpening costs in Fig. 9 and Table 13 with initial die costs for carbide and D2, indicate that, for one million pieces, the use of D2 offers the greatest over-all economy, for all seven parts.

Despite certain operational advantages provided by carbide dies, it cannot be assumed that the conversion of any steel die to carbide will automatically increase production to the level of a million hits per grind. On the average, however, a carbide die can be expected to provide from 10 to 12 times the production normally achieved by its tool steel counterpart.

Lamination Dies

As shown in Fig. 8 and 9, die life can be significantly increased by the use of core plate on electrical sheet. This is further borne out by the data in Fig. 11, which show that, although a gradual increase in die life occurs with decreasing silicon content of electrical sheet, core plate markedly increases die life. (Some types of core plate, however, *decrease* die life, because of their abrasiveness; see Example 68.) Factors such as steel deoxidation method, annealing procedure, and punch-to-die clearance also have a considerable effect on die life and productivity.

Lamination dies are extensively discussed in the article "Blanking and Piercing of Magnetically Soft Materials", pages 60 to 68.

Die life is influenced by a number of variables, most of which pertain to the die material, die design, or the nature and condition of the material being blanked. In the example that follows, tool material was varied and work metal and design were the same.

Example 66. Die Life for Blanking Silicon Steel (Fig. 12)

In blanking 0.014-in.-thick 3.25% silicon steel, the measure of die life was set at the number of strokes before a 0.005-in. burr was developed on the stamped material. Dies were made of D2 and M2 (at Rockwell C 61) and carbide. The difference between the high-carbon high-chromium tool steel and the high speed steel was negligible when compared with the carbide (Fig. 12). [C. S. Wukusick and R. S. Zeno, Improving Punchability of Silicon Steel, *The Tool Engineer,* Dec 1958.]

In addition to the factors discussed in the preceding section, consistency of production experience is sometimes an important consideration in the choice between tool steel and carbide. One company producing many millions of laminations discontinued the use of tool steel dies because of the wide variation in die life, as shown in the example that follows.

Example 67. Carbide vs Tool Steel Dies for Reliability of Behavior (Fig. 13)

Five different parts of M-22 electrical sheet were blanked on lamination dies made of D2 tool steel. All dies were run on either a 60-ton or a 100-ton dieing machine with a high degree of press accuracy. Dies were reground when burr height on parts was 0.004

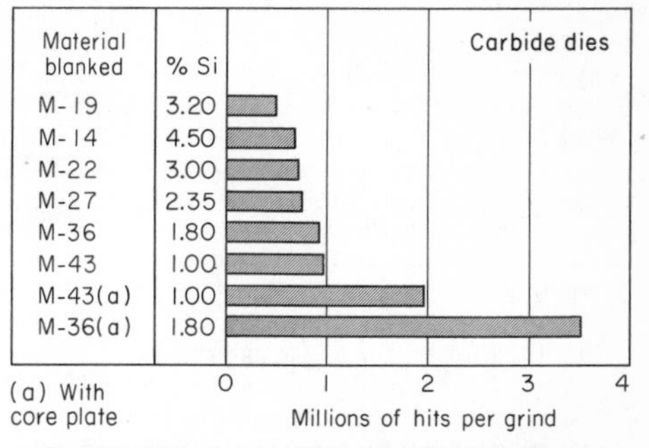

Fig. 11. Effect of silicon content and core plate of electrical sheet steel on the service life of carbide dies

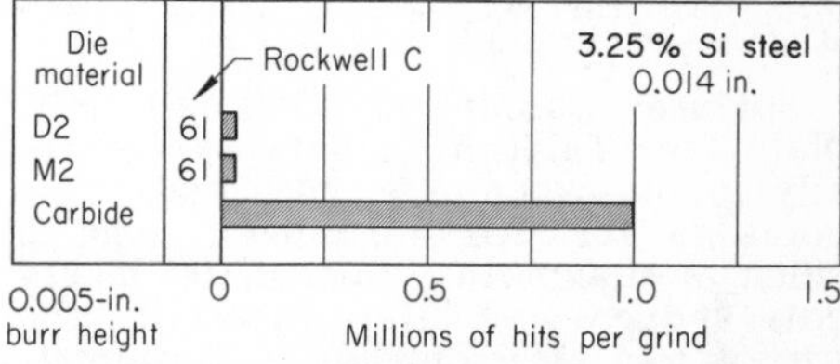

Fig. 12. Life of three blanking-die materials under the same operating conditions (Example 66)

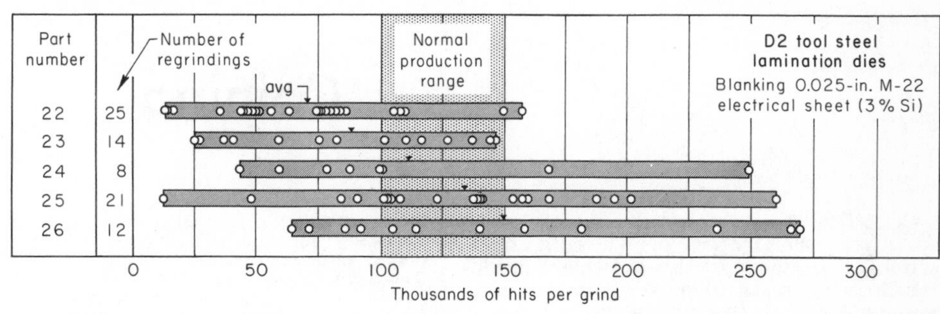

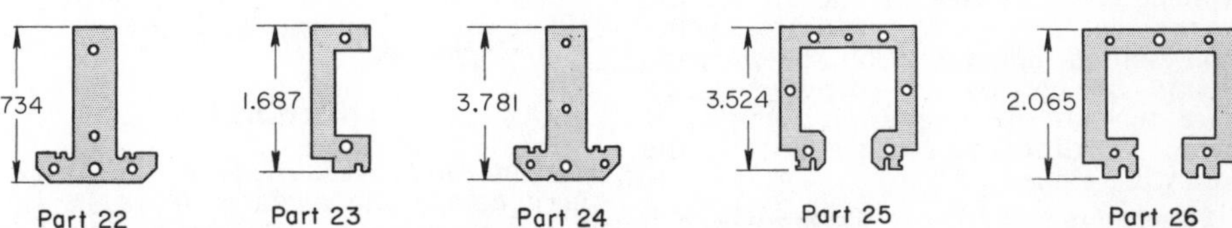

Fig. 13. Experience with D2 tool steel lamination dies blanking five parts (Example 67)

Table 13. Operating Costs of Carbide Versus D2 Tool Steel Dies Producing 50 Million Identical Parts (Example 65)

Part No. (Fig. 8)	Die material	No. of dies needed	Die cost differential(a), %	Setup time, hr	Sharpening time, hr	Cost: Setup (b)	Cost: Sharpening (b)	Cost: Total (b)	Cost: Per 1,000,000 blanks	Cost: Per 1,000 blanks	Savings per 50 million blanks(c)
17	Carbide	0.7	....	200	333	$ 1,200.00	$ 2,331.00	$ 3,531.00	$ 70.62	$ 0.0706	$ 15,669.00
17	D2	10	+700	1200	2000	7,200.00	12,000.00	19,200.00	380.40	0.3804	....
13	Carbide	2½	....	264	264	1,584.00	1,848.00	3,432.00	68.64	0.0686	17,568.00
13	D2	8⅓	+166	2000	1500	12,000.00	9,000.00	21,000.00	420.00	0.4200	....
15	Carbide	0.6	....	111	333	666.00	2,331.00	2,997.00	59.94	0.0599	23,253.00
15	D2	4.6	+383	1250	3125	7,500.00	18,750.00	26,250.00	525.00	0.5250	....
16	Carbide	⅓	....	75	125	450.00	875.00	1,325.00	26.50	0.0265	2,425.00
16	D2	1⅔	+250	375	250	2,250.00	1,500.00	3,750.00	75.00	0.0750	....
19	Carbide	½	....	20	100	120.00	700.00	820.00	16.40	0.0164	4,532.00
19	D2	3½	+350	178	714	1,068.00	4,284.00	5,352.00	107.04	0.1070	....
20	Carbide	1/7	....	14	59	84.00	413.00	497.00	9.94	0.0099	3,487.00
20	D2	2	+700	166	498	996.00	2,988.00	3,984.00	79.68	0.0797	....
21	Carbide	1/17	....	12	48	72.00	336.00	408.00	8.16	0.0082	3,078.00
21	D2	⅔	+560	166	415	996.00	2,490.00	3,486.00	69.72	0.0697	....

(a) Assuming carbide die cost at twice that of D2 steel (high-carbon high-chromium) dies. (b) Based on an average setup cost of $6.00 per hour for either type of die; sharpening cost of $6.00 per hour on steel dies, $7.00 per hour on carbide dies. ($7.00 includes $1.00 per hour diamond wheel wear.) (c) Savings in setup and sharpening costs through the use of carbide.

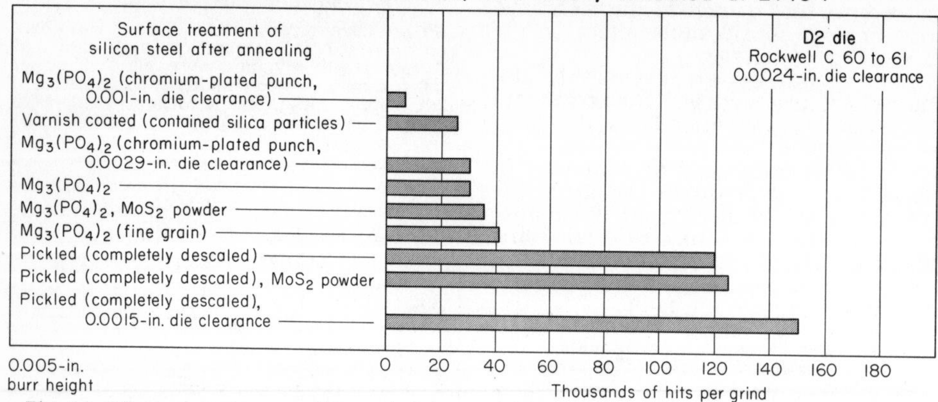

Fig. 14. Effect of surface condition of strip on the life of D2 tool steel dies blanking 3.25% silicon steel sheet (Example 68)

in. Average die life for parts 22 and 23 was below the normal range, and life of dies was inconsistent among the five parts (Fig. 13). When carbide dies were used to make the same parts, die life was increased to 750,000 pieces per grind with a high degree of consistency in performance.

Surface Condition. Although core plate (see Table 5 on page 68) generally increases die life, core plate that contains abrasive substances, such as silica or magnesium phosphate, markedly reduces die life — especially the life of tool steel dies, as in the application described in the next example.

Example 68. Effect of Surface Condition of Electrical Sheet on Die Wear in Blanking (Fig. 14)

Magnesium phosphate (AISI C-4 finish), varnish, and pickled finishes were compared for abrasiveness to D2 dies in blanking 3.25% silicon steel 0.014 in. thick. Those treatments that increased the abrasiveness of the surface of the blank material (high-temperature annealing in the presence of magnesium phosphate, and the use of a silica-containing varnish) affected die life adversely (Fig. 14). Pickling of the electrical sheet removed abrasive surface materials and increased die life. Die lubricants also extended die life. Other data concerning the finishes, lubricants, and dies are given in Fig. 14.

Examples in This Volume That Evaluate Die Materials

Three examples in other articles in this volume compare the life of carbide and D2 tool steel dies:

Example 53. Two laminations were produced in a three-stage progressive die. The life of D2 dies for 0.001-in. die wear was 4000 strokes. The same wear was produced in the carbide die with 40,000 strokes.

Example 60. Small laminations were blanked from an 80% nickel-iron alloy, first with D2 dies and then with carbide-edged dies. Results were as follows:

Item	D2	Carbide
Cost		
Punch and die	$526	$709
Die maintenance per 1000 pieces	$2.80	$0.24
Operation		
Setup time per 1000 pieces, hr	0.173	0.030
Production per 0.001 in. of die wear, pieces	1925	11,181

Example 190. A small part was blanked and pierced from bright finished 1045 steel with a hardness of Rockwell 15-N 70 to 75. With D2 tool steel hardened to Rockwell C 62 to 63, life between regrinds was 25,000 pieces. The total die life was 1,950,000 pieces. With carbide tools, life between grinds was increased to 350,000 pieces.

In Example 61, optimum grinding interval for a carbide die was established at 400,000 pieces between regrinds.

Coining

*By the ASM Committee on Coining**

COINING is a closed-die squeezing operation, usually performed cold, in which all surfaces of the workpiece are confined or restrained, resulting in a well-defined imprint of the die on the workpiece. It is also a restriking operation (called, depending on the purpose, sizing, or bottom or corner setting) used to sharpen or change a radius or profile. Ordinarily, coining entails the following steps:

1 **Preliminary Workpiece Preparation.** Full contact between the blank and die surfaces, which is necessary for coining, usually requires some preliminary metal redistribution by other processes, such as forging or extrusion, because only a small amount of metal redistribution can take place in the coining dies in single-station coining. In progressive-die operations, coining is done as in single-station dies, but it is preceded by other operations such as blanking, drawing, piercing and bending. Coining often is the final operation in a progressive-die sequence, although blanking or trimming, or both, frequently follow coining.

2 **Development of Detail in the Workpiece.** In coining dies, the prepared blank is loaded above the compressive yield strength and is held in this condition during coining. Dwell time under load is important for the development of dimensions in sizing and embossing; it is also necessary for the reproduction of fine detail, as in engraving.

3 **Trimming.** Flash that developed during coining and any hangers used to carry the blank through coining, especially in progressive-die coining, must be trimmed from the piece.

Applicability

In coining, the surface of the workpiece copies the surface detail in the dies with dimensional accuracy that is seldom obtained by any other process. (It is because of this that the process is used for the minting of metallic coins.)

Decorative items, such as patterned tableware, medallions, and metal buttons, as well as coins, are produced by coining. When articles with a design and a polished surface are required, coining is the only practical production method to use. Also, coining is well suited to the manufacture of extremely small items, such as interlocking-fastener elements.

Dimensional accuracy equal to that available only with the very best machining practice can often be obtained in coining. Many automotive components are sized by coining. Sizing is usually done on semifinished products and provides accuracy equal to that obtained with good machining practice, often with significant savings in material and labor costs.

Corner setting and bottom setting (restriking), although coining operations, are closely related to sizing in forming and deep-drawing operations, and are discussed in the articles in this volume that deal with these processes.

Workpiece Size. In principle, any workpiece that can be loaded above the compressive yield strength can be coined. Practical limits on workpiece size are imposed mainly by available press capacities and properties of the die material. For example, work metal with a compressive yield strength of 100,000 psi loaded in a press of 2500-ton

Table 1. Ram Weights Required for Coining Tableware With Pneumatic Drop Hammers

Thickness of blank, in.	Area of blank, sq in.	Ram weight required, lb
0.050 to 0.080	Up to 4	900
0.080 to 0.150	4 to 5	1200
0.150 and over	Over 5	2000

*L. R. MAITLAND, *Chairman,* Chief Project Engineer, Slider Section, Engineering Div., Talon, Inc.; A. E. CARLILE, Senior Project Engineer, Development and New Products Engineering, Talon, Inc.; WILLIAM J. GILMORE, Chief Development Engineer, Wire Products Group, American Chain and Cable Co., Inc.; P. J. HOGAN, Project Engineer, Automotive Div., Budd Co.; WALTER E. MOULTON, Chief Metallurgist, Oneida Ltd.; FRED ROY, Chief Manufacturing Engineer, Gorham Corp.; J. R. SCHETTIG, Metallurgical Engineer, Vasco, a Teledyne Co.

capacity can be coined in a maximum surface area of 50 sq in. As the yield strength increases, the area that can be coined using the same pressure will decrease in proportion. However, increase in strength of the workpiece must be limited so that plastic failure of the die does not take place.

Hammers and Presses

In coining, the workpiece is squeezed between the dies so that the entire surface area is simultaneously loaded above the yield strength. To achieve the desired deformation of metal, the load determined from the compressive yield strength must be increased three to five times. Because of the area loading requirement and the great stress needed to insure metal movement, press loading for coining is very severe, frequently approaching the capacity of the equipment used, with consequent danger of overloading.

Some coining equipment, such as drop hammers, cannot be readily overloaded, but presses (especially mechanical presses) can be severely overloaded. This is most likely to happen if more than one blank is fed to the coining dies at a time. Such overloading can lead to breakage of the press and of the dies, and it will certainly shorten the life of the dies.

Overloading may be prevented by the use of overload-release devices, and many presses are equipped with such devices. However, the usual means for preventing overloading in presses is careful control of workpiece thickness, which must be sufficient to allow acceptable coining, but which should not lead to press overloading. Such thickness control, combined with blank-feeding procedures designed to minimize double blanking, is normally adequate to prevent overloading.

Coining may be satisfactorily undertaken in any type of press that has the needed capacity. Metal movement, however, is accomplished during a relatively short portion of the stroke, so that a coining load is required only during a small portion of the press cycle. Drop hammers, and knuckle-type and eccentric-driven mechanical presses are extensively used in coining. High-speed hydraulic presses also are well adapted for coining, especially when progressive dies are used. Large-capacity hydraulic presses are ideal for coining and sizing operations on large workpieces.

When it is feasible to coin large numbers of small connected parts, as in a continuous strip of work metal, roll coining is the most economical method.

Drop Hammers. Gravity drop hammers in the size range of 900 to 2000 lb (weight of the ram) are used extensively in the tableware industry. Board hammers can be used, although pneumatic-lift hammers predominate for this type of coining. In producing tableware, reproduction of detail and finish are more important than dimensional control.

Capacities of drop hammers are determined by ram weight and drop height, and coining pressures are stated in terms of these two quantities. Ram weight is usually selected in relation to the thickness and area of the blank, as shown in Table 1 for pneumatic drop hammers. The drop height and number of blows are determined by the complexity of the detail that is to be developed in the workpiece.

Mechanical presses with capacities of a few tons to several hundred tons are widely used in coining. The larger presses are usually of the knuckle type with production rates up to about 7500 pieces per hour. Small, specially built eccentric-driven presses are used for coining tiny parts at a rate of 2000 per minute.

Mechanical presses are well adapted for controlling size. Also, one-stroke sizing is generally preferred to a process requiring multiple blows, because there is less likelihood of fracturing the work metal.

Crank-driven mechanical presses have been used successfully in progressive-die coining. For these processes, coining usually follows combinations of piercing, forming and blanking.

Hydraulic presses are used extensively for sizing operations, especially for workpieces with large surfaces to be coined. Spacers ("kissing blocks") are required for maintaining close tolerances on the final dimensions of the part being sized. Hydraulic presses are sometimes favored, because they are readily equipped with limiting devices that prevent overloading and possible breaking of the dies.

Smaller hydraulic presses, of about 8-ton capacity, can be operated at speeds up to 250 strokes per minute. These small high-speed presses are used extensively with progressive dies.

Capacity determination for a coining operation, for open-die forming or for sizing, can be accomplished (*a*) by measuring in a compression machine the forces necessary to cause metal movement, or (*b*) by measuring the compressive yield strength and multiplying three to five times this value by the coined area of the part.

Strip of closely controlled thickness used in high-speed coining machines frequently is produced by rolling from round wire. The strain history and consequent strain-hardening behavior of progressively flattened round wire usually is not known. Also, since interaction between die and workpiece changes continuously with deformation, the loads required to flatten round wire are difficult to calculate and should be measured. Suitable measurements of load and dimensional changes for two grades and sizes of steel wire are given in Table 2.

To obtain the data in Table 2, lengths of round wire of two different diameters were flattened in a carefully aligned flat compression die 2.250 in. wide, by application of the loads given in the first column in Table 2. Each flattened specimen was removed and measured for final dimensions. These measurements, oriented according to the left-hand sketch in Table 2 and listed in the table, were used to calculate the nominal pressures required for coining these metals at the respective deformation levels. The percentage

Table 2. Effect of Press Load on Dimensional Changes in Round Steel Wire Loaded in Flat Dies

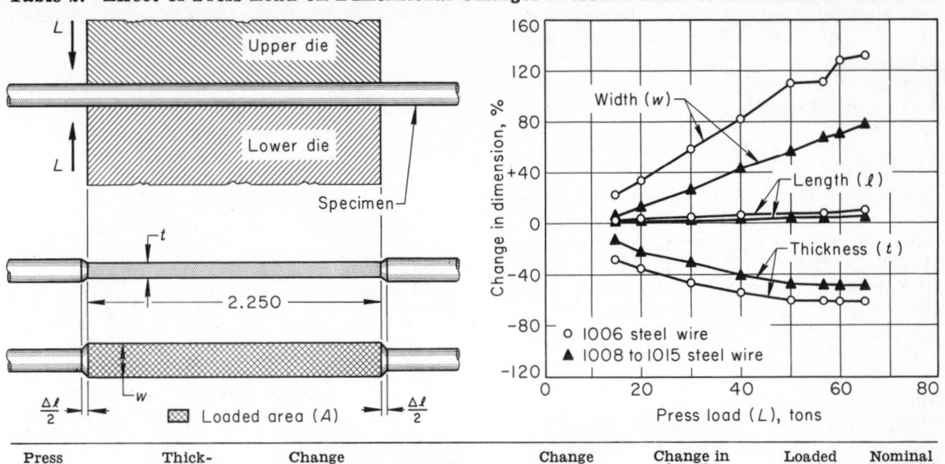

Press load (L), tons	Thickness (t), in.	Change in thickness, in.	Width (w), in.	Change in width, in.	Change in length (Δl), in.	Loaded area (A), sq in.	Nominal stress, tsi of area
0.177-In.-Diam Wire of 1008 to 1015 Steel, Zinc Coated (Tensile strength, 90,000 to 100,000 psi)							
15	0.152	—0.025	0.187	0.010	0.006	0.42	36
20	0.136	—0.041	0.198	0.021	0.010	0.45	44
30	0.120	—0.057	0.223	0.046	0.019	0.50	60
40	0.104	—0.073	0.251	0.074	0.034	0.56	71
50	0.091	—0.086	0.276	0.099	0.050	0.62	81
57	0.088	—0.089	0.293	0.116	0.053	0.66	86
60	0.083	—0.094	0.300	0.123	0.058	0.68	88
65	0.082	—0.095	0.3125	0.1355	0.060	0.70	93
0.196-In.-Diam Wire of 1006 Steel, Uncoated (Tensile strength, 50,000 psi)							
15	0.139	—0.057	0.240	0.044	0.028	0.54	28
20	0.125	—0.071	0.261	0.065	0.051	0.59	34
30	0.103	—0.093	0.310	0.114	0.091	0.70	43
40	0.089	—0.107	0.355	0.159	0.120	0.80	50
50	0.076	—0.120	0.410	0.214	...	0.92	54.5
57	0.075	—0.121	0.414	0.218	0.150	0.93	61
60	0.070	—0.126	0.446	0.250	...	1.00	60
65	0.069	—0.127	0.453	0.257	0.195	1.02	64

change in the major dimensions of the specimens is plotted in the right-hand sketch in Table 2. The stress values given in the last column of Table 2 are directly usable for coining of different cross-sectional areas.

Lubricants

Whenever possible, coining without a lubricant is preferred. If entrapped in the coining dies, lubricants can cause flaws in the workpieces. For example, under conditions of constrained plastic flow, an entrapped lubricant will be loaded in hydrostatic compression and will interfere with transfer of die detail to the workpiece. In many coining operations, however, because of work-metal composition or severity of coining, or both, the use of some lubricant is mandatory to prevent galling or seizing of the dies and the work metal.

For coining teaspoons, medallions or similar items from sterling silver, no lubricant is used. Some type of lubricant is ordinarily used for coining copper and aluminum and their alloys, and for coining stainless, alloy and carbon steels. When coining intricate designs, such as the design on the handles of stainless steel teaspoons, the lubricant must be used sparingly. A film of soap solution is usually sufficient. Excessive amounts of lubricant adversely affect workpiece finish and interfere with transfer of the design.

When coining items that do not require transfer of intricate detail, the type and amount of lubricant are less critical. A mixture of 50% oleum spirits and 50% medium-viscosity machine oil has been successful for prevention of galling and seizing for a large variety of coining operations. When coining involves maximum metal movement and high pressure, a commercial deep-drawing compound is sometimes used.

Dies

Dies for coining may be either single-station or progressive and usually are made from W1, O1, A2 or D2 tool steels. The use of these steels is indicated in Tables 3 and 4, which give tool steel recommendations for coining specific shapes. Recommended working hardnesses of coining dies made of the tool steels listed in Tables 3 and 4 are:

W1	Rockwell C 59 to 62
O1	Rockwell C 58 to 60
A2 and D2	Rockwell C 56 to 58

Tool steels L6, S1 and S2 have also been used for coining dies of various designs. However, tool steels other than those mentioned above are sometimes more suitable, because of the small size of the dies. For instance, the cup illustrated in Table 4 is typical of the coining stage in the production of a part in a press from strip material by progressive forming operations with die and punch inserts for each stage. Frequently, the dimensions of the inserts are below or near the minimum amount of die stock required by good practice, because of the over-all space available. In such dies, the hot work tool steels have been found to give better life than W1, O1, A2 or S2. For instance, the separate pieces of the punch body and the insert shown in

Table 3. Recommended Tool Steels for Dies to Coin a ½-In.-Diam Emblem or Similar Part

Use of die	Punch and die material for coining a total quantity of(a): 1000	10,000	100,000
Machined Dies			
Drop hammers	W1	W1	O1(b), A2
Presses	O1	O1, A2	O1, A2
Hubbed Dies			
Drop hammers	W1	W1	W1(c)
Presses	O1	O1, A2	A2, D2(d)

(a) For coining the emblem from aluminum, copper, gold or silver alloys, or from low-carbon, alloy or stainless steel. (b) O1 is recommended only for coining low-carbon steel, and copper, gold or silver alloys. (c) The average life of W1 dies in coining copper, gold and silver alloys softer than Rockwell B 60 would be about 40,000 ± 10,000 pieces. The life of W1 dies coining harder metals would be about half as great; thus, more than one set of dies would be needed for 100,000 parts. (d) Hot hubbed.

Table 4. Recommended Tool Steels for Coining a Preformed Cup to Final Size on a Press

Metal to be coined	Die material for coining a total quantity of (a): 1000	10,000	100,000
Low-carbon steel	W1	O1	D2
Alloy steel, stainless steel, heat-resisting alloys	O1	A2	D2
Al and Cu alloys	W1	W1	D2

1.34 diam
Coined surface
Cup
Punch body
Insert
Die
Ejector

(a) For quantities over 10,000, the die material refers to insert material. The materials shown are for dies made by machining. The punch material would be the same except that where heat treating of W1 would be hazardous, O1 would be safer in hardening.

Table 4 might be made of H12 at Rockwell C 49 to 52, to give a compromise between softer material that would score badly and harder material that would be likely to fracture. Scoring of the punch insert is best prevented by a hard chromium plate, 0.0003 to 0.0005 in. in thickness and baked at 300 to 400 F for at least 3 hr to minimize hydrogen embrittlement.

In the coining die, type H12 hot work tool steel at Rockwell C 45 to 48 would probably show better resistance to splitting than any of the cold coining die steels. For the ejector, an L6 tool steel at a hardness of Rockwell C 40 to 45 is recommended.

Compared with higher-carbon steels, H11, H12, H20 and H21 at or near their full hardness of Rockwell C 50 to 54 often perform well in coining dies with circular grooves, beads, thin sections, or any configuration that demands improved resistance to breakage at the sacrifice of wear resistance.

For more complete details on materials for coining dies, see the article that begins on page 717 in Volume 1 of this Handbook.

Tableware is generally manufactured in single-station dies mounted in a drop hammer. The obverse and reverse configurations are usually hubbed into the matching surfaces of contoured die halves that are massive compared to the item to be coined (see Fig. 1). The coining surfaces of the dies are polished to give the necessary bright finish on the tableware.

The coining dies are usually mounted in a drop hammer with the upper half keyed or dovetailed to the hammer ram and the lower half dovetailed to an adjustable anvil that allows it to be aligned (mitered) to the upper half. Contoured surfaces of the dies must match within 0.003 in. when the dies are closed. Adjustment is checked by ink or feeler gages.

In the coining operation, the hammer ram is raised to the required height, and the blank is placed by tongs over the bottom die and is aligned by means of a locating gage attached to the die. The ram is released and the upper die strikes the blank. For stainless steel tableware, drop height and size of blank are controlled so that no flash will develop, because flash leads to excessive tool breakage. For sterling silver tableware, on the other hand, a flash will usually form. Coining dies for sterling silver are designed to confine flash thickness to 0.012 to 0.018 in. to avoid premature failure of trimming tools.

Coining die life will vary widely depending on sharp lines, corner contours, depth of pattern and relationship between front and back design. A pair of dies may produce only a few thousand pieces in some designs, whereas a more simple die design may produce 100,000 pieces. Some dies crack in use; others wear out.

Details of the dies and manufacturing practice for coining a stainless steel teaspoon handle are given in the following example.

Example 69. Dies and Procedure for Coining Teaspoon Handles of Stainless Steel (Fig. 1)

The dies and the semifinished blank for a stainless steel teaspoon are shown in Fig. 1. The spoon handle was coined by means of single-station tooling in a 900-lb drop hammer. The dovetail sections of the dies were used to secure them in the drop hammer.

Type 301 stainless steel was used for the spoon. The blank was of graded thickness and cut to an outline to fit the die outline, producing very little or no flash. Additional manufacturing details are given with Fig. 1.

Stainless steel spoons are frequently coined in two stages; first the handle is coined and then the bowl. This method of manufacture allows selection of die material that will give optimum life in the dies for the handle and bowl segments of the spoon. It also provides a convenient grip area for tong feeding. Two-stage coining is permissible if the two coined segments can be faired together without objectionable die marks. Tableware can also be coined in progressive dies.

Sizing dies are usually flat-surfaced with kissing or stop blocks to control the shut height of the die. Frequently, they are made of D3 or S2 tool steels hardened to Rockwell C 58 to 60 for maximum toughness. Die surfaces often are polished so as to refine the coined surface of the workpiece.

Single-Station Dies. Depending mainly on workpiece configuration and product form of the work metal, either single-station or progressive-die tooling may be used for mass production of small workpieces. In the example that follows, single-station tooling was used for producing small parts by coining.

Example 70. Use of Single-Station Tooling for Coining a Small Fastener Component From Wire (Fig. 2)

A small fastener component with projections of different shapes on two sides (Fig. 2) was coined in a single station from copper alloy 226 (jewelry bronze; 87.5 Cu – 12.5 Zn) wire fed continuously into a 250-ton mechanical press. The dies, shown in position in Fig. 2, were finished to 1.5 by 1 by 1 in. The contour was worked into the upper die by hubbing and into the lower die by broaching. Both dies were lapped to a fine finish. Because of the height of the coined area in the lower die, an ejector was required. Additional manufacturing details are tabulated with Fig. 2.

Progressive Dies. Small steel headers, as described in Example 71, are coined in progressive dies. These items are produced by pressworking competitively with automatic machining. Piercing and trimming operations precede coining to develop a freely suspended blank at the coining station. This is good practice, because it allows free expansion of the workpiece at the coining station. Following coining, the headers are trimmed to the specified size (at the blanking station) and removed from the die. Generally, a final trimming operation is needed in a progressive-die coining operation to remove the hangers that carry the blank through the coining station. It is important that the coined blank be removed from the coining station by a failproof procedure, to prevent double blanking that might otherwise occur. It is also good practice to install an air blast at the coining station to remove oil or dirt, which, if allowed to accumulate in the die, interferes with die fill.

Example 71. Progressive-Die Tooling for Coining of Small Headers (Fig. 3)

Small headers as illustrated in Fig. 3 were coined from 1010 steel strip having a tolerance of ±0.002 in., No. 3 temper, No. 2 bright finish and ASTM grain size of 7 to 8. Coining was done in a progressive die using a sequence of piercing, trimming, coining and blanking, as shown in Fig. 3. The coining station consisted of a punch, a die, and a lower plunger for ejecting the coined header (see details of the die station in Fig. 3).

The die was operated by a 30-ton mechanical crank press having a 2-in. stroke. Additional manufacturing details are given in the table with Fig. 3.

Coinability of Metals

Limits to coining are established mainly by the unit loads in compression that the coining dies will withstand before deforming. Deformation of the dies results in dimensions that are out of tolerance in the workpiece and premature failure of the dies through the action of low-frequency fatigue.

In coining, deformation of the work metal is accomplished largely in a compression strain cycle, which leads to a progressive increase in compression flow strength as deformation progresses. This deformation cycle results in a product that has good bearing properties and wear resistance in service, but in the coining operation it can raise the yield strength to a level that approaches the permissible maximum die load, and the coining action stops.

Deformation strengthens the workpiece, and it also increases the area of contact between the die and workpiece. As this contact area increases, radial displacement of the metal becomes increasingly difficult. Significant radial displacement is practical only for relatively soft metals, like sterling silver.

In general, if significant metal movement is required, this should be effected before coining by processes such as rolling or by machining. To allow preliminary deformation to take place readily, the metal being coined should be soft, and it should have a low rate of strain hardening. If a metal lacks these characteristics, it can still be coined if first softened by annealing.

Steels and Irons. Steels that are most easily coined include carbon and alloy grades with carbon content up to about 0.30%. Coinability decreases as carbon or alloy content increases. Steels with carbon content higher than about 0.30% are infrequently coined, because they are likely to crack. Leaded steels usually coin as well as their nonleaded counterparts. However, other free-machining grades, such as those containing substantial amounts of sulfur, are not recommended for coining, because they are susceptible to cracking. When steels are annealed for coining, full annealing is recommended. Process annealing is not recommended, because it is likely to result in excessive grain growth, which will impair the coined finish. A grain size no coarser than ASTM 6 is recommended.

Malleable iron castings are frequently sized by coining. The amount of coining that is practical depends mainly on the hardness.

Stainless steels of types 301, 302, 304, 305, 410 and 430 are those generally preferred for coining. Free-machining type 303 is sometimes coined, the selenium-bearing rather than the sulfur-bearing grade being preferred.

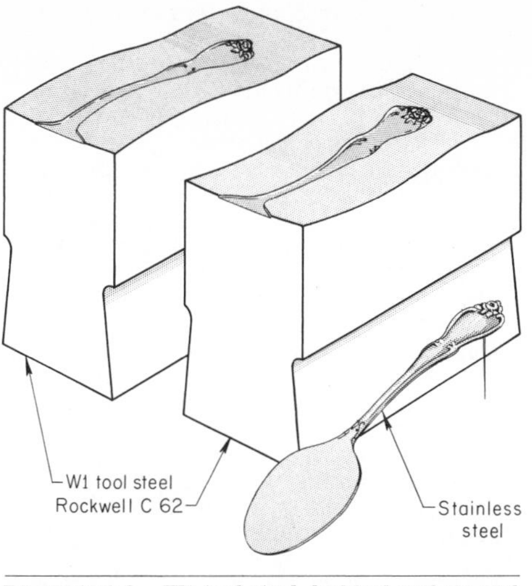

Die material	W1 tool steel, hubbed and ground
Die hardness	Rockwell C 62
Die size	2 by 3½ by 5¼ in.
Die finish	2 micro-in.
Coining pressure	250,000 psi(a)
Finish on blank	4 to 6 micro-in.
Finish on spoon	4 micro-in.
Setup time	1 hr
Die life	5000 to 100,000 pieces
Tool cost	$60 per set
Production rate	1400 pieces per hour

(a) 900-lb ram, 12-in. drop height

Fig. 1. Dies for coining a stainless steel teaspoon handle (Example 69)

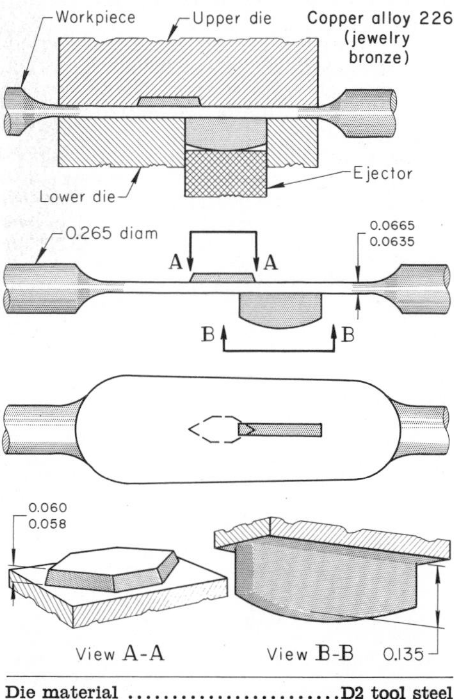

Die material	D2 tool steel
Die hardness	Rockwell C 59 to 61
Coining pressure	100 tons
Lubricant	Emulsion of natural fat and petroleum (pH, 7.3 to 7.8)
Setup time	½ hr
Die life per grind	200,000 pieces
Tool cost	$85
Production rate	7500 pieces per hour

Fig. 2. Coining a fastener component from wire in a single-station die (Example 70)

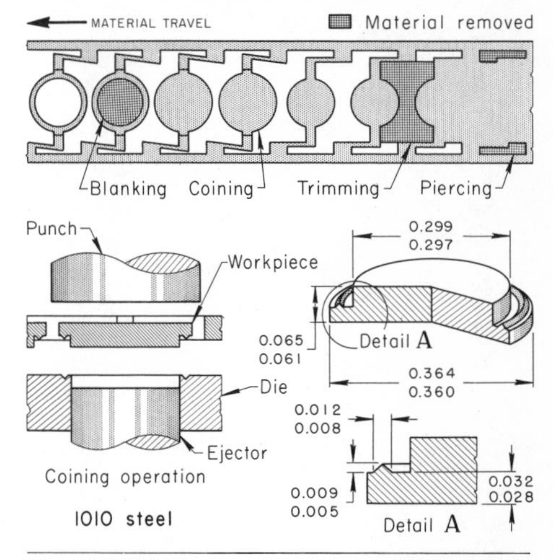

Die material(a)	D2 tool steel
Die hardness	Rockwell C 59 to 61
Coining pressure	17 tons
Lubricant, coining	None
Lubricant, blanking	Soluble oil
Die life per recut(b)	10,000 pieces
Production rate	15,000 pieces per hour(c)
Tool cost	$0.75 per 1000 pieces
Setup and die-maintenance cost	$0.35 per 1000 pieces

(a) Die was made by turning, hardening, grinding and polishing. (b) Die was recut with carbide form tool when worn. (c) Constant operation using 250 strokes per min.

Fig. 3. Production of small headers by piercing, trimming, coining and blanking in a progressive die (Example 71)

For tableware, types 301 and 430 have been used extensively in coining of spoons and forks. Type 302 has also been used for such items. Type 305 coins well, but is not widely used, because the stock costs more than types 301 and 302.

Stainless steels are relatively hard to coin and are consequently preferred in the soft annealed condition, in the range of Rockwell B 75 to 85.

For 301 or similar types of austenitic stainless steel, the variation in nickel content permitted by the composition specifications will significantly influence the strain-hardening characteristics of the steel. The low-nickel compositions will work harden more than the high-nickel compositions. For example, in low-nickel and high-nickel lots of type 301 stainless steel, the hardnesses after graded rolling to form a teaspoon bowl were, respectively, Rockwell C 45 and 40. Harder metal leads to shortened life of the blanking die.

The surface of a well-finished piece of coined stainless steel will be about 1 to 4 micro-in.; this must be developed in the coining operation, because no major finishing can be done after coining without damage to design details. For functional parts, where the item is coined only for sizing, the finish may be less important. In general, however, the surface of the blank must be free from seams, pits or scratches.

Copper, silver, gold and their alloys have excellent coinability and are widely used in coin and medallion manufacture. These metals were the first to be minted, and the process of coining developed in working them.

The pure metals are sufficiently soft and coinable to allow extreme deformation in coining, but even after such deformation, they are too soft to wear well. As a consequence, important coining metals are prepared by alloying. In the alloyed condition, a relatively wide range of hardness is obtainable, as illustrated by the data in Table 5 for a sterling silver (92.5 Ag – 7.5 Cu) teaspoon blank. In Table 5, the hardness of this alloy is given for four standards (temper, Brown & Sharpe, Rockwell 15-T, and Rockwell 30-T), each showing a progressive increase starting from the annealed or soft condition. One of the uses of this alloy is for tableware, so the last column in Table 5 shows the relative position on the hardness scales of a teaspoon blank — annealed, after coining once, and after coining twice. As shown in Table 5, the hardness increases rapidly with the initial blow, but only slightly with the second blow. The hardness increase from each succeeding blow is also slight.

Table 5. Hardness of a Sterling Silver Teaspoon Blank as Influenced by Coining

Temper	Change in B & S No.	Rockwell hardness 15-T	Rockwell hardness 30-T	Blank condition
Soft	..	70 max	35	Annealed
1/8 hard ..	1/2	..	..	....
1/4 hard ..	1	79	51	Coined once
1/2 hard ..	2	81	57	Coined twice
Hard	4	84	63	....
Extra hard	6	86	68	....
Spring ...	8	87	70	....

Table 6. Grain Size and Surface Appearance After Coining of Annealed Sterling Silver

Annealing temperature, F(a)	Grain size, mm	Appearance of coined surface
1200	0.011	Excellent
1300	0.020	Excellent
1400	0.035	Rough; difficult to polish

(a) Samples annealed 15 min at temperature

Grain size of sterling silver coined workpieces must be controlled, if a polished surface is to be readily obtained (see Table 6).

Composite metals are being coined, principally in the minting of coins. Pressures for coining composites are slightly modified, according to the bulk properties of the metal laminates used, but otherwise the coining operation is unaffected.

Coinability ratings of metals and alloys are difficult to establish on a quantitative basis, although the conditions under which a ductile metal will not coin can be stated in terms of the compressive loads that the die system can exert on the workpiece.

For simple die contours, coining loads can be determined readily, but for complex, incised die contours, coining behavior is a function of both the strength and deformation characteristics of the metal. The relations are so complex that stress calculations alone are not meaningful, and decorative items are coined in sequences that are established largely by experience. In addition, the coinability of a metal is frequently established by the difficulty encountered in preparing the blank for coining. Therefore, it is evident that a number of somewhat arbitrary factors enter into a determination of the coinability of a possible series of metals for a given item. This is especially true for tableware, which is required to be both decorative and useful.

Sterling Silver Compared With Stainless Steel. Because of its low yield strength, sterling silver is more readily deformed in the coining dies than is stainless steel. The deep ornate handle pattern of the sterling silver spoon and fork in Examples 72 and 73 (Fig. 4) would normally be considered beyond the capabilities of stainless steel. The handle for the stainless steel fork in Example 74 (Fig. 4) by comparison is in low relief. The pattern for the sterling silver spoon and fork could be developed in a stainless steel handle by multiple processing, but this would be very expensive.

The silver handle must be trimmed of flash, whereas the stainless steel blanks are of a size that will form no flash. If flash is allowed to develop in coining stainless steel, the life of coining dies will be markedly reduced. It is clear that the silver alloy possesses the combination of strength, ductility, and low rate of work hardening that results in excellent coinability. The stainless steel, although adequate for the coining operations to which it is subjected, is a less coinable alloy.

Item	Example 72	Example 73	Example 74
Die material	S1 tool steel	S1 tool steel	W1 tool steel
Die hardness	R_C 58 to 60	R_C 58 to 60	R_C 60 to 61
Coining pressure:			
Ram weight, lb	1200	2000	1200
Drop height, in.	24	24	24
Lubricant	None	None	None
Production rate, pieces per hour	500	500	500
Setup time, hr	1/2	1/2	1/2
Total die life, pieces	10,000 to 15,000	10,000 to 15,000	72,000 to 100,000
Cost of dies:			
Initial	$2200	$2400	$900
Replacement	$ 450	$ 500	$450

Fig. 4. Sterling silver and stainless steel tableware items that were produced by coining (Examples 72, 73 and 74)

Examples 72, 73 and 74. Coining of Tableware From Sterling Silver and Stainless Steel

Example 72 — Deep Ornate Sterling Silver Teaspoons (Fig. 4). Blanks for the sterling silver (92.5 Ag – 7.5 Cu) teaspoons with the ornate handle pattern shown in Fig. 4 weighed 1.25 troy oz (±1%) each. They were flat graded and outlined before coining by being rolled between dimensionally prepared segment rolls that were ground or machined to radii that elongated and graded the blank. The thickness-graded outline blanks were contracted 0.015 in. along the periphery outline to allow for metal spread and to avoid pinching that would occur with a blank overlap.

After grading, blanks were annealed at 1250 F, and air cooled. After the first striking operation, the ornately designed area of the handle was annealed at 1250 to 1300 F for 5 min, and water quenched. (Partial annealing was used to maintain maximum hardness in the shanks of the flatware.) The blanks were then dipped in a 5% sulfuric acid solution to remove any black oxide caused by annealing.

Restriking in the coining dies and trimming followed the second annealing treatment. The spoons were coined in a single-station die in a gravity drop hammer using manual feed. Additional manufacturing details are given in the table with Fig. 4.

Example 73 — Deep Ornate Sterling Silver Forks (Fig. 4). The blanks for the sterling silver fork shown in Fig. 4 weighed 1.66 troy oz (±1%) each. Blank preparation, coining and annealing procedures were the same as for the teaspoons described in Example 72. Manufacturing details for coining these forks are given in the table accompanying Fig. 4.

Example 74 — Stainless Steel Forks (Fig. 4). The fork at the far right in Fig. 4 was coined from a 3-oz blank of type 302 stainless steel. Blanks were prepared by automatically rolling between segment rolls that were ground to radii that elongated and graded the blanks to specifications. The thickness-graded blanks then were outline blanked to coincide with the outline contour of the dies. Coining was done in a gravity drop hammer. The upper half of the coining die was keyed or dovetailed to the hammer ram; the lower half was dovetailed and held to the hammer anvil by square-head set screws that allowed dies to be mitered or aligned. Contour surfaces of the die when closed were required to match within 0.003 in. A high-polish surface was obtained.

Stainless steel blanks were annealed at 1975 F in an oxygen-free atmosphere, and then belt fed into a cooling chamber. Annealing and cooling time was 15 min, total. Additional manufacturing details are given with Fig. 4.

If flatware is to be coined in the thickness of the coil or strip material from which it is made, coining will immediately follow the outline-blanking operation. However, good-quality tableware requires graded-thickness control to coin satisfactorily; this is included in the following steps:

1. Interlocking blanks are cut.
2. The blank is rolled lengthwise in segmented rolls to produce a graded thickness at each point for later coining.
3. The item is outline blanked.
4. The blank is annealed.
5. In one or more sets of dies, the blank is coined to the desired contour, pattern, and surface finish.
6. Flash is removed by trimming.
7. The workpiece is annealed.
8. A second coining operation (restrike) completes the pattern.
9. Flash is removed by trimming.

A stainless steel fork or spoon will usually be finished after operation 5 and will pass to inspection. Sterling silver tableware will be processed through operation 6.

Sometimes, however, for a deep ornate handle pattern (as in Fig. 4), the pattern detail is incomplete after the first coining operation. Under these conditions, the item is further processed by omitting operation 6 and proceeding with operations 7, 8 and 9.

Production Practice

Although coining operations are done as a part of many metalworking processes, by convention the operations narrowly designated as coining processes are of fairly limited scope. The range of coining processes is illustrated by the several examples that follow. In these examples, coining processes fall into two broad categories. In the first category, the objective is the reproduction of ornate detail with a prescribed surface finish. In the second category, the objective is the close size control of an element, again with a prescribed surface finish.

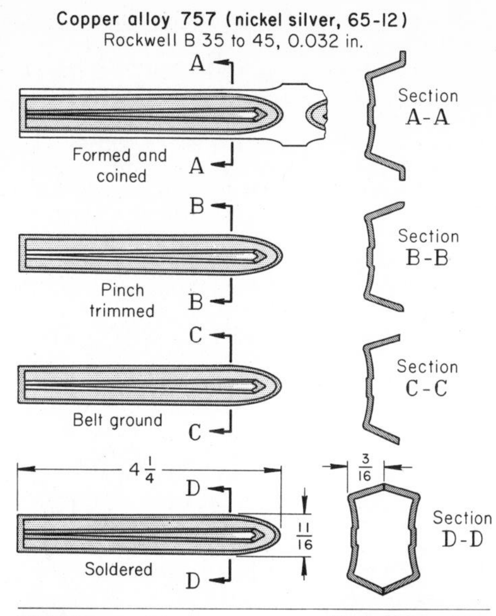

Operation	Production per hour
Blank	(Purchased)
Form and coin (two blows)	1000 assemblies
Slit	2100 halves
Pinch trim	1000 halves
Belt grind	1100 halves
Solder flux	1000 assemblies
Fixture	1000 assemblies
Furnace solder	1500 assemblies

Fig. 5. Production of a hollow knife handle by forming and coining (Example 75)

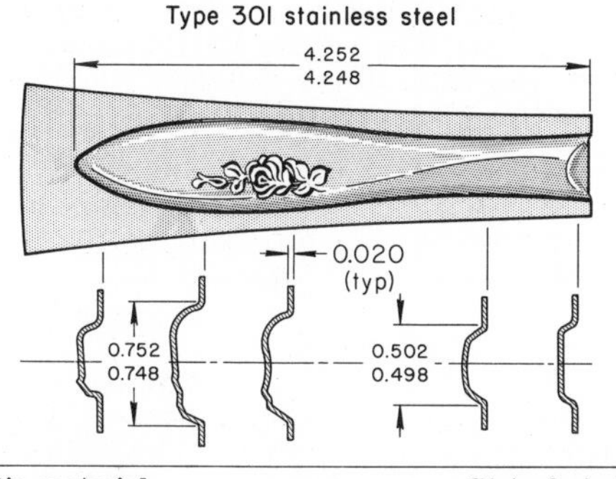

Die material	S1 tool steel
Die hardness	Rockwell C 58
Coining pressure	40 tons
Lubricant	None
Setup time	¾ hr
Production rate	5400 half-handles per hour
Die life, total	1 million half-handles
Cost of progressive die	$2400

Fig. 6. Knife-handle half produced in a four-station progressive die in production lots of 50,000 or more (Example 76)

Tableware. Most tableware is coined in single-station dies after extensive preparation of blanks (see Examples 69, 72, 73 and 74). Each coined item must bear a reproduced ornate design and a polished finish.

Table knives may be made with flat or graded-thickness blades and solid or hollow handles. Flat blades are made by contour blanking followed by coining to develop the cutting edge and a desired surface finish. These blades are then soldered into handles. A stainless steel blade will be blanked, rolled to a graded thickness, outline blanked in one or more stages, and then coined. Type 410 stainless steel hardens to a point that it will not move in the coining operation. Therefore, blades made from type 410 stainless steel are usually heated (to 1400 F in Example 87) to permit successful coining.

Sheet metal blanks for hollow handle are manually fed to a coining die mounted in a drop hammer. The blank is coined into an ornamented and polished knife half-handle, and then trimmed. Matched half-handles are soldered together, and the blade is soldered or cemented to the handle, as in the following example.

Example 75. Production of a Nickel Silver Knife Handle by Forming and Coining in a Drop Hammer (Fig. 5)

Figure 5 shows the sequence of shapes in the production of a hollow handle for a table knife formed and coined in a 900-lb pneumatic drop hammer. The work metal was a 0.032-in.-thick strip of copper alloy 757 (nickel silver; 65 Cu – 12 Ni), annealed to a hardness of Rockwell B 35 to 45; blank size was 1 by 9 in.

Two workpieces were formed and coined simultaneously (see Fig. 5) from one blank, in two blows of the drop hammer. The two-cavity die permitted easy loading and unloading of parts and also provided symmetry to prevent shifting of the punch. A volatile, fatty oil-base lubricant was applied to the blank by rollers.

The formed and coined halves were separated by slitting with a rotating cutter made of T1 tool steel, and the flange was removed in a pinch-trim operation. After belt grinding to deburr and provide a smooth flat surface, the half handles were fluxed along the edges and soldered together. The soldered handles were then pickled, washed, and finished by a light emery on the soldered seams, and were silver plated. The handle and blade were assembled and finish buffed. Production rates for the various operations are given in the table that accompanies Fig. 5.

An alternative process for manufacturing half-handles is progressive-die coining, as discussed in the following example. The strip, after piercing and blank preparation, is used to carry the blank to the coining and trimming stations. The half-handles after trimming to a close miter are ejected from the die. Soldering of half-handles and blades is done simultaneously.

Example 76. Low-Volume and High-Volume Methods for Coining of Knife-Handle Halves (Fig. 6)

Flat skived blanks, of uniform 0.020-in. thickness, were used in producing hollow stainless steel knife handles to the design and dimensions shown in Fig. 6. Each handle was coined in two halves, which were then trimmed of flash and soldered together at mitered seams. Finished handles had a highly polished surface.

For producing quantities of 100 to 50,000 pieces, tooling consisted of an interlocking blanker, a female die, a male forcer, and a trimming tool. Blanks were hand fed, one at a time. Each blank was positioned to a gage on the die, and was struck one blow by a 600-lb pneumatic hammer with 12-in. drop height.

For steady high production in quantities over 50,000 pieces, a 100-ton mechanical press equipped with automatic roll feed was used, in conjunction with a progressive die that incorporated all the forming, coining and trimming operations in four stations automatically fed by coil stock. Soldering the two halves together was a separate operation. Details of the high-volume method of production are given in the table with Fig. 6.

Coins and medallions are produced by closed-die coining, in which a prepared blank is compressed between the coining dies while it is retained and positioned between the dies by a ring or collar. The volume of metal in the workpiece is equal to the volume of the die space when the die is closed. The volume of metal cannot exceed the closed-die space without developing excessive loads that may break the die and press. The simplest means of ensuring volume control in a coin blank is by carefully controlling the weight, which is easily measured and converted to volume.

In general, coins are needed in large quantities (about 300,000 before die dressing). To facilitate production and minimize die wear, the detail incorporated into the coin design is in low relief. The coin should have good wear resistance, and this is achieved by the compressive working of the metal during coining. Wear of the coin face is prevented by raising the edge of the coin, which is usually serrated to have a so-called milled edge. This edge detail is machined into the retaining ring and is transferred to the expanding workpiece during coining.

A typical procedure for coin manufacture is as follows:

1 Coin disks are blanked from sheet of prescribed thickness and surface finish.
2 The disks are barrel tumbled to deburr, to develop a suitable surface finish, and to control weight.
3 The disks are edge rolled.

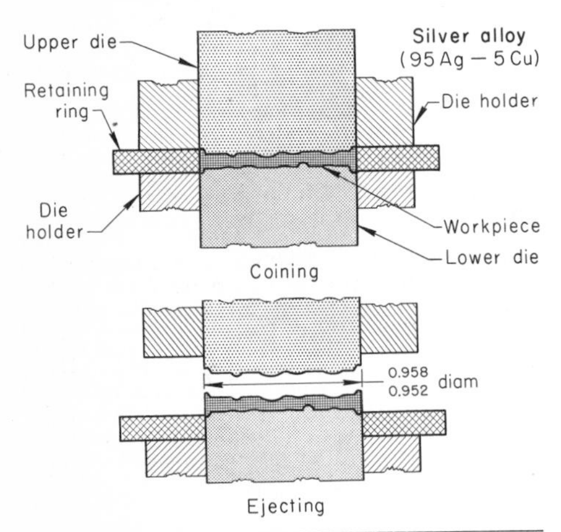

Die material	W1 tool steel
Retaining-ring material	O1 tool steel
Hardness of die and ring	Rockwell C 60
Coining pressure	60 to 90 tons
Lubricant	None
Production rate	180 pieces per minute
Die life, total	300,000 pieces

Fig. 7. Setup for production of silver alloy coins (Example 77)

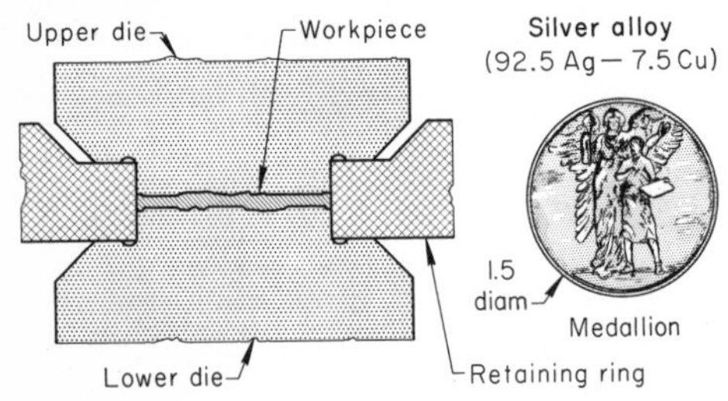

Die material	O1 tool steel
Die hardness	Rockwell C 60
Coining pressure	150 tons
Lubricant	None
Setup time	0.25 hr
Die life, total	1000 to 10,000 pieces
Tool cost	$600
Production rate	48 pieces per hour

Fig. 8. Die setup used to produce silver alloy medallions by coining and restriking (Example 78)

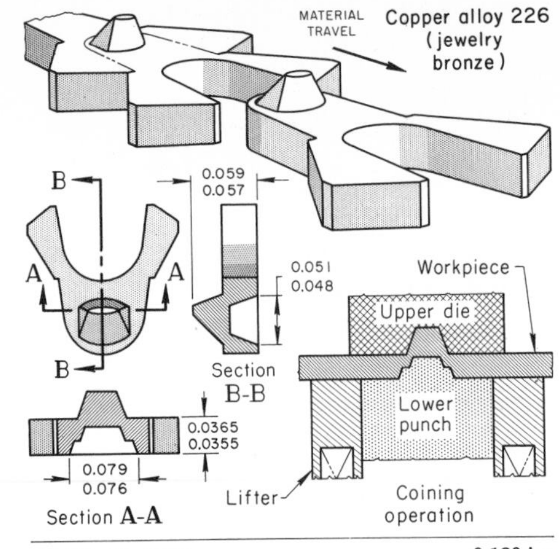

Width of stock	0.180 in.
Die and notching-tool material	D2 tool steel(a)
Coining pressure	500 lb
Lubricant	High-viscosity oil
Setup time	½ hr
Die life, total	2 million pieces
Tool cost	$65
Production rate	120,000 pieces per hour

(a) Hubbed, ground and hardened (Rockwell C 59 to 61)

Fig. 9. Interlocking-fastener element produced by coining and notching in a progressive die (Example 79)

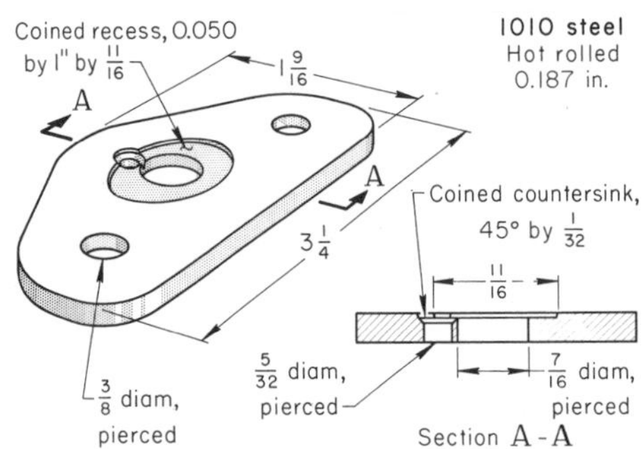

Fig. 10. Mounting plate with assembly and mounting features coined into its face (Example 80)

4 The disks are fed, one at a time, to the coining station and are coined.
5 The coins are ejected from the retaining ring. This may be done by movement of the upper or lower die rather than using a conventional ejector.

Presses or hammers used for producing coins usually vary in capacity from about 35 tons for coining dimes to 160 tons or more for coining silver dollars. A procedure used for making specific silver alloy coins is described in the following example.

Example 77. Production of Silver Alloy Coins (Fig. 7)

Principal components of a single-station die setup used for producing coins weighing 0.804 gram (±1.5 grains) from a silver alloy (95 Ag – 5 Cu) are shown in Fig. 7. Blanking, deburring and edge rolling preceded coining, which was done in a 140-ton hydraulic press. The coins were required to have a satin-smooth finish when examined with binoculars at 3× magnification. Other details of this coining process are given in the table that accompanies Fig. 7.

The steps employed to manufacture coins may be used also for medallions. Usually the processing of medallions does not require edging operations, but if the design details are in high relief, the full development of details may require restriking. Coined blanks are usually annealed before restriking. The blank must be reinserted into the coining dies in its initial position and then restruck. The use of this method for the manufacture of a medallion is described in the example that follows.

Example 78. Coining of Silver Alloy Medallions (Fig. 8)

Medallions made from a silver alloy (92.5 Ag – 7.5 Cu) and weighing 1 oz. (±1%) were made by coining, using the die setup illustrated in Fig. 8. Disks were blanked from strip and barrel finished. Following the first coining operation, the workpiece was annealed at 1275 F, repositioned in the die and restruck. The single-station tooling consisted of the upper and lower incised dies and a retaining ring. After coining, the medallion was manually removed from the retaining ring, because of the low production requirements. Coining was done in a 400-ton knuckle-type mechanical press. Additional manufacturing details are given in the table with Fig. 8.

Minute parts are frequently produced in volume by coining in high-speed presses. For such operations, it is difficult to obtain commercial flat stock to the tolerances required, so it is common practice to prepare strip by rolling wire of the required material on precision rolls. The strip so prepared is coiled and fed to the coining die as needed.

Also, in the manufacture of small precise parts, the transfer of the workpiece into and out of the coining station is an important operation. For this purpose, progressive-die tooling is used. For the manufacture of a metal interlocking-fastener element, this can be done as described in the following example. In this example, strip was of a copper alloy; however, aluminum alloy has also been used for the same application.

Example 79. Coining Interlocking-Fastener Elements in a Progressive Die (Fig. 9)

The interlocking-fastener element shown in Fig. 9 was manufactured from a precision-rolled, lubricated, flat strip of copper alloy 226 (jewelry bronze; 87.5 Cu – 12.5 Zn), 0.180 in. wide.

A special high-speed eccentric-shaft mechanical press with a 3/16-in. stroke was used. Tooling consisted of a progressive die that had edge-notching and coining stations. A ratchet-type roll feed was used. The coining portion of the die consisted of an upper die and a lower punch, with a spring-loaded stock lifter. The element was made by notching, coining and blanking, and then was attached to a tape. Manufacturing details are given in the table with Fig. 9.

Recesses or mounting and locating features are coined into high-production parts in a variety of products. Countersinks for screw heads, and offsets for mating parts, are regularly produced by coining. Often, one piece will have several mounting or assembly details coined into its face, as in the following example.

Example 80. Assembly and Mounting Details Coined into a Mounting Plate (Fig. 10)

The mounting recess for an oval post and the countersink for locating the end of a spring were coined into a mounting plate that was part of an automobile door lock (Fig. 10). The oval was coined to a depth of 0.050 in. in the third station of a six-station progressive die.

The plate, as shown in Fig. 10, was made of 1010 hot rolled steel 0.187 in. thick. The first station of the progressive die pierced the two end holes, which were then used as pilot holes for the other stations.

The location of these two holes took into consideration the growth in length of the part during coining. The second station pierced the center hole and the hole for the spring. The recess and the countersink were coined in the third station; the fourth station re-pierced the center hole. The plate was flattened in the fifth station and blanked in the sixth station. Later the two end holes were countersunk and the oval post was assembled to the oval recess. Production rate was 125 plates per minute; annual production was five million pieces

The dies were made of air-hardening and oil-hardening tool steels and had a life of 250,000 pieces before reconditioning. The piercing punch for the small hole had a life of about 50,000 pieces and could be changed without removing the die from the press.

Roll coining may be used when large numbers of very small items are to be produced and where the coining die is a repetitive single-station die that can be placed on a small roll. This method of coining is an advantage when coining parts in a strip, because the roll serves as both the feed control mechanism and the coining station. This procedure eliminates problems that develop in handling a continuous strip in a press. In press coining, the strip must be brought to a full stop during a prescribed portion of the press stroke.

Roll coining has been used for producing small parts to close dimensional tolerances. In the following example, multiple dies on rolls, together with the method of stock feeding used with roll coining dies, gave rates of production that were unattainable in presses.

Example 81. Roll Coining of Small Interlocking-Fastener Elements From Round Wire (Fig. 11)

Copper alloy 226 (jewelry bronze; 87.5 Cu – 12.5 Zn) wire was fed into coining rolls to form elements of an interlocking-fastener strip (Fig. 11).

The rolls illustrated in Fig. 11 were geared together so that the male and female forms hubbed into the roll peripheries were accurately matched. Roll peripheries were a whole-number multiple of the lengths of the article coined. Diameters were kept as small as possible, to minimize the expense of replacement of the rolls if there were premature failure. The rolls enclosed a coining space nominally equal in cross section to that of the wire fed into them. This wire was forged and coined to fill the section presented in the roll space, to give the configuration shown in Fig. 11.

Sizing to close dimensional tolerances on several nonparallel surfaces can be achieved readily in the manufacture of small parts, such as the interlocking-fastener elements discussed in Examples 79 and 81. For large workpieces, ingenuity may be required to develop a coining process for sizing — ingenuity in the design of tooling to minimize the effect of distortion in the press, and ingenuity in the preparation of the workpiece to make necessary a minimum of metal flow during coining.

For the flange of the automobile front-wheel hub discussed in Example 82 (Fig. 12), the sizing operation required redistribution of the metal in the workpiece; this is possible in coining only over relatively short distances (a few multiples of the section thickness). If the surface of an article to be coined is large compared with the thickness, as in Example 82, the coining loads may be such that the required metal movement does not take place and the sizing operation fails. If the upper and lower surfaces of the workpiece to be coined are excessively out-of-parallel, this deviation cannot be corrected by coining.

In the forging step before coining the flange in Example 82, the stock was alternately gathered and thinned into concentric rings. With this metal distribution, contact was established between the die and the gathered flange before the die was fully closed. The regions of gathered metal, as the dies closed, were then squeezed into the regions that were initially thinned, and the thinning and leveling required in the flange took place. Because the die was not filled evenly, there were surfaces of the flange that showed highly coined areas adjacent to areas that were compressed a lesser amount. All measurements of dimensions under such circumstances were referenced to the highly coined surfaces.

For the flange-sizing operation, no surface-finish requirement was specified, because of the conditions under which the surfaces of the workpiece and the dies made contact. However, the finish of the surfaces coined was refined to 40 to 45 micro-in. from the typical shot-blast finish of 350 to 400 micro-in.

The coining die setup described in Example 82 was designed to insure control of thickness and parallelism (see also Examples 86 and 88).

Upper roll $1\frac{1}{2}$ diam
0.036
Workpiece
Upper roll
Lower roll
Copper alloy 226 (jewelry bronze)
Lower roll $1\frac{1}{2}$ diam

Roll material ....3312 steel, carburized to $\frac{1}{32}$-in. depth
Coining pressure ....1 ton (approx)
Lubricant ....Thin soluble oil
Setup time ....2 hr
Tool cost ....$4000 per roll
Roll life, total ....10 million pieces

Fig. 11. Interlocking-fastener element produced on coining rolls (Example 81)

1030 or 1130 steel forging, shot blasted
$\frac{5}{8}$ R
Detail A
0.285
0.275
$2\frac{1}{4}$ diam

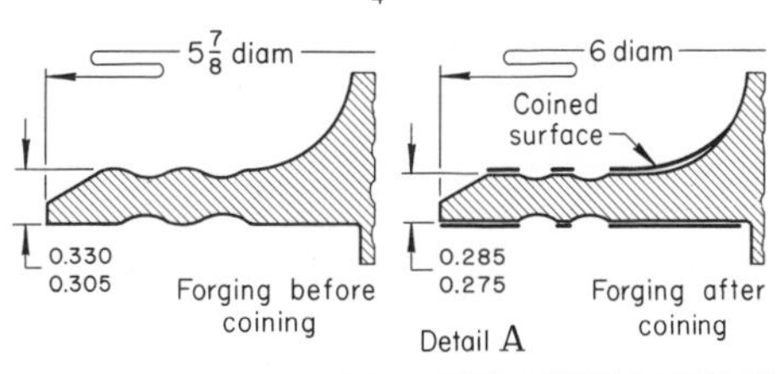

Coining Conditions

Die material ....S2 tool steel
Die hardness ....Rockwell C 58 to 60
Coining pressure ....1200 tons
Lubricant ....None
Workpiece finish:
Before coining(a) ....350 to 400 micro-in.
After coining ....40 micro-in.
Setup time ....4 hr
Die life per rework ....20,000 hubs
Total die life (20 reworks) ....400,000 hubs
Production rate ....1200 hubs per hour

Cost Comparison, Machining vs Coining

	Machining	Coining
Material saving	...	$0.051(b)
Machining cost per hub ..	$0.050(c)	$0.040(d)
Cost of coining per hub ..	...	$0.003
Total saving per hub by coining		$0.058(e)

(a) Shot blasted. (b) Saved 12 oz of steel at $0.075 per lb. (c) Labor cost only, based on machining 80 hubs per hour at $4 per hour. (d) Labor cost only, based on machining 100 hubs per hour at $4 per hour. (e) Sum of metal saving and labor saving ($0.051 + $0.010) less labor cost for coining ($0.003).

Fig. 12. Coining the flange on a forged wheel hub to final size, which cost less than sizing the flange by machining (Example 82)

Example 82. Sizing an Automobile Front-Wheel Hub by Coining in Preference to Machining (Fig. 12)

The die setup illustrated in Fig. 12 was used to coin flanges of forged front-wheel hubs using single-station tooling in a 2000-ton knuckle-type mechanical press with a six-station feed table. Tolerances on the coined flange were: thickness within ±0.005 in. and parallelism within 0.004 in. To maintain these tolerances, the flange thickness as-forged could be no more than 0.055 in. greater than the coined dimension and had to be parallel within 0.017 in. The flange was coined to tolerances by centering the forged hub on the lower ring-shaped die. The top die, with a cavity of depth equal to the specified flange thickness, was positioned over the wheel hub, and the coining load was applied. The top die was brought into contact with the lower die and, since the bearing surfaces of the upper and lower dies were parallel, the required parallelism was developed in the flange surfaces as the thickness was brought to that specified. Coining conditions are given with Fig. 12.

Originally, the hub flanges were machined at the same time as the other surfaces were machined, at a total machining labor cost of $0.05 for each hub. By coining the hub to size, the total machining labor cost was $0.04 for each hub, a saving of $0.01 per hub. (These cost figures deal exclusively with material saving and labor cost — no equipment amortization or overhead costs were included. However, it was determined that tool costs for turning and for coining were essentially the same; thus, the saving of $0.058 shown in the table with Fig. 12 represents a net figure.)

In general, sizing by coining may be desirable when parallel surfaces are required in a workpiece, even though the workpiece is so large that maximum press capacities are required. However, sizing operations on nonparallel surfaces are feasible only if the work metal can be moved by the sizing-die surface without distorting the dies. Such metal movement is possible if the width of the metal being coined is about the same as the thickness. (For very soft metals, this movement is usually possible to a pronounced degree, but a sizing operation is of little significance for such materials.) In general, gross movement of the metal should not be required, and machining or forging should be used to bring the

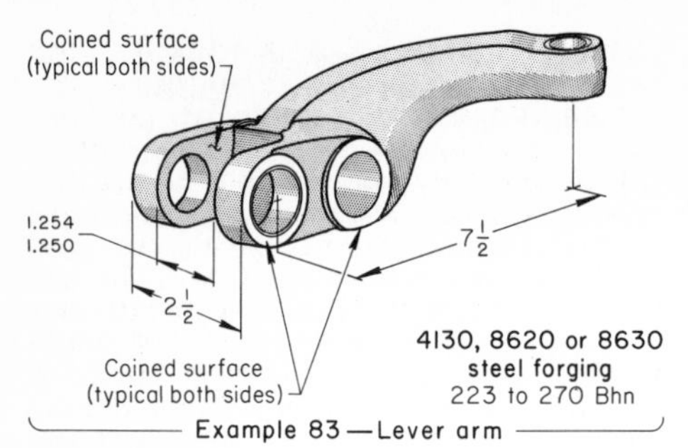

Example 83 — Lever arm

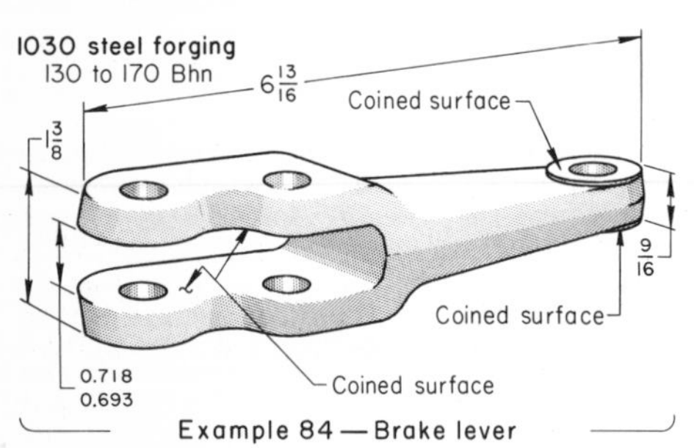

Example 84 — Brake lever

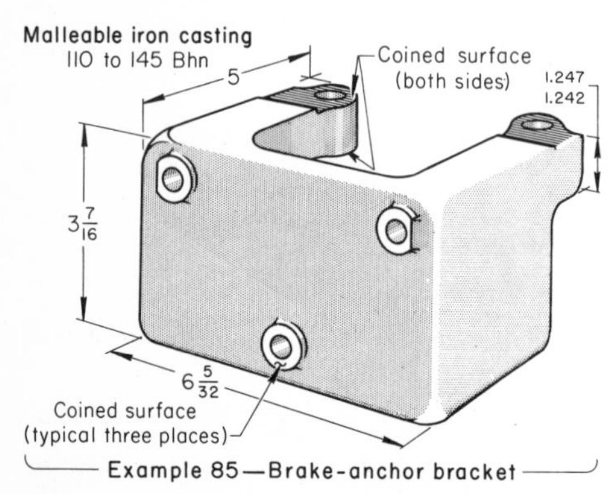

Example 85—Brake-anchor bracket

Item	Example No. 83	84	85
Production, pcs/hr	250	500	200
Labor saved by coining ..	74%	93%	77%

All three parts were coined in a 1500-ton mechanical press using dies made of D3 tool steel and a lubricant consisting of viscous non-pigmented drawing oil thinned with SAE 20 lubricating oil.

Fig. 13. Surfaces on three parts that were coined at less labor cost than by machining (Examples 83, 84 and 85)

workpiece to approximate dimensions before sizing is attempted. When this is done, sizing by coining can produce workpieces having dimensional tolerances that are acceptable in good machining practice, often with significant savings in material and labor costs.

The three examples that follow describe applications in which coin sizing eliminated the need for other operations, including spotfacing, slot milling, straddle milling, and deburring.

Examples 83, 84 and 85. Savings in Labor by Coining Instead of Machining

Example 83 — Lever Arm (Fig. 13). By coining the six surfaces on the lever arm illustrated in Fig. 13, it was possible to eliminate the following operations: spotfacing, slot milling, and deburring. Labor, expressed as units, was 138 for the original procedure and 36 after changing to coining, or a labor saving of 74%.

Inside surfaces were coined simultaneously with outside surfaces by inserting a floating paddle made of hardened tool steel. Other coining conditions are given with Fig. 13.

Example 84 — Brake Lever (Fig. 13). By coining two inside and two outside surfaces of the brake lever illustrated in Fig. 13, slot milling and deburring were eliminated. The number of labor units required for the original method was 181, compared with 13.5 for coining; thus, labor saving was 93%.

The two inside surfaces were coined by inserting a floating paddle made of hardened tool steel. Other coining conditions are given in the table with Fig. 13.

Example 85 — Brake-Anchor Bracket (Fig. 13). Originally, the three bosses on the malleable iron bracket shown in Fig. 13 were finished to dimensions by spotfacing and deburring. The four other surfaces (1.247/1.242-in. dimension) were finished by straddle milling and deburring. By changing to coining, acceptable dimensions were obtained on all seven surfaces. Coining reduced the amount of labor from 399 units, for the original method, to 93 units — a saving of 77%. Coining conditions are given in the table with Fig. 13.

Processing Problems and Solutions

Establishment of a suitable blank-preparation sequence is required to give the desired results from coining operations. Blank preparation may consist simply of annealing the blanks before or after coining, or both, followed by restriking to permit transfer of die detail to the workpiece. In Examples 72, 73 and 78, this technique was used to coin the design to full depth.

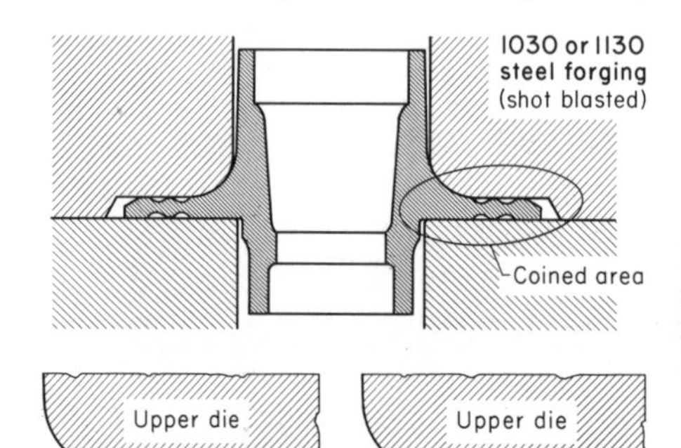

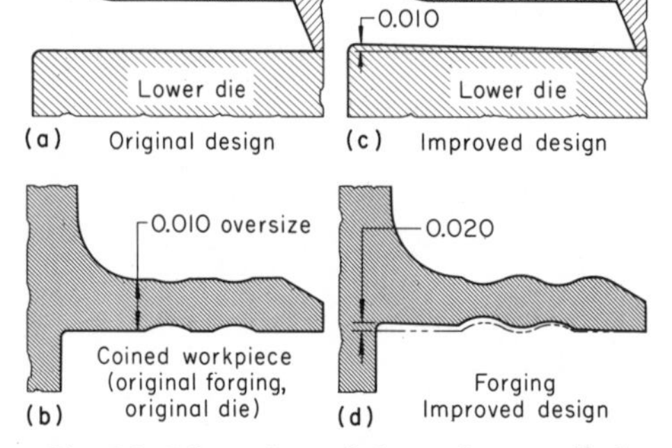

Fig. 14. Die and workpiece changes that eliminated cracking of dies in coining the flange on a wheel hub (Example 86)

Type 410 stainless steel (annealed)
Flash
Coined from original blank
Coined from improved blank

Die material	W1 tool steel
Die hardness	Rockwell C 59 to 61
Lubricant	None
Setup time	0.25 hr
Die life, total	500,000 pieces
Tool cost	$180
Production rate	1500 pieces per hour

Fig. 15. Knife blade that was coined from a smaller blank size (lower blade) to eliminate flash in the bolster and tang, as shown in upper blade (Example 87)

Faulty coining may occur because die surfaces are not clean. Directing a jet of air across the die to remove loose dirt can eliminate some causes of incomplete detail in coined parts. Regular and frequent inspection of finished parts and dies is necessary to insure that dies have not picked up stock or lubricant that can damage the surfaces of following pieces.

Another frequent source of trouble in coining is faulty die alignment. Coining dies must be aligned to the degree of precision expected in the coined item.

Excessive tool breakage from die overloading is a common problem in coining, and it is difficult to suggest steps to eliminate it. In the manufacture of tableware, tool breakage is accepted, because replacement of tools is inexpensive and inspection procedures are adequate to prevent the buildup of large numbers of rejected items. When this approach to the problem is undesirable, the alternative is to establish the nature and magnitude of the overload and to relieve it, as was done in the following two examples.

Example 86. Process Modification That Eliminated Die Failure (Fig. 14)

The initial die design (Fig. 14a) for sizing the wheel-hub flange discussed in Example 82 (Fig. 12) produced flanges that were 0.010 in. oversize at the junction with the barrels, as illustrated in Fig. 14(b). The lower die was redesigned to take up the excess 0.010-in. thickness, as illustrated in Fig. 14(c). This die effected the desired sizing but failed prematurely by cracking. Die hardness was reduced, but this did not suppress the cracking. Solution of the die-failure problem was achieved by forging the flange 0.020 in. thinner at the point of die failure (Fig. 14d).

Example 87. Change of Blank Size That Eliminated Die Failure (Fig. 15)

Originally, a type 410 stainless steel knife blade was manufactured in the following sequence of operations: cut blank, roll forge, trim outline, coin, and trim bolster and tang. Flash developed in the bolster and tang areas, as illustrated in the upper sketch in Fig 15, and led to premature failure of the coining and trimming dies.

Failures in the coining dies were reduced by modifications in the roll-forging operation to reduce the volume of metal in the bolster and tang portions of the blank and to hold metal distribution to closer thickness tolerances (±0.005 in.) before coining. The metal remaining after outline trimming was just sufficient to fill the coining dies, which then lasted five times as long as for the initial condition. At the same time, since no flash was formed (see lower sketch in Fig. 15), the final trimming stage was completely eliminated.

The outline-graded blanks were annealed at 1400 F prior to coining in a 1200-lb drop hammer using a 12-in. drop height. Further details of the coining process are given in the table that accompanies Fig. 15.

Control of Dimensions, Finish and Weight

The quality of coined items is judged by various criteria, depending on end use. For decorative items, surface finish and transfer of detail are usually the primary objectives; for functional items, such as machinery components, dimensional accuracy and consistency are usually the most important factors.

Weight is important in coining sterling silver or other precious metals and must be controlled, mainly for economic reasons. Also, controlling the weight of a blank is a convenient way to control the volume of metal in a blank (see Example 93).

Dimensional Tolerances. Sizing is used to maintain dimensions to close tolerances and to refine the surface finish. In the following example coining was used to hold the flange thickness to a total variation of 0.010 in. The same coining operation also controlled parallelism between the same two surfaces (see Example 82 and Fig. 12).

Example 88. Accuracy in Sizing of Steel Forgings by Coining (Fig. 16)

The variation in thickness of the flange of a forged wheel hub that had been sized by coining is given in Fig. 16. The flange thickness of 60 hubs that were selected from a run of 300 was measured. These dimensions were not influenced by die wear or die setup variations. The dies were set to kiss empty (close without a part in the die) and show a 1200-ton force on a strain gage.

A maximum force of 900 tons was used to coin the part, the additional 300 tons assured that the kissing surfaces were in contact.

None of the parts measured exceeded the ±0.005-in. tolerance. Most of the parts varied −0.003 to +0.002 in. from the mean dimension.

Coining was used to form the steel cam described in the following example. To hold the dimensions to the specified tolerance, the part was annealed and coined again.

Example 89. Intermediate Annealing Before Coining to Dimension (Fig. 17)

The breaker cam shown in Fig. 17 was made of 0.128/0.125-in.-thick 1010 cold rolled, special-killed steel. Strips 3⅜ in. wide and 96 in. long were purchased with a No. 4 temper (Rockwell B 65 max) and a No. 2 bright finish.

Cold working the cam surface by coining made it necessary for the parts to be annealed before flattening and restriking. The part contour and dimensions were extremely difficult to maintain. The surface finish was 15 micro-in. A pack anneal was used to minimize distortion and scale. The sequence of operations to make the part was:

1 Shear strips to 48-in. lengths.
2 Coin cam contour, pierce and blank in a progressive die. High point on the cam was 0.123/0.124 in. thick.
3 Pack anneal at 1650 to 1700 F. The part had to be free of heat checks and scale.
4 Restrike to flatten and coin to 0.122 ± 0.003 in. at the high point. Gage point (at 20.5° on open side) was 0.0115 ± 0.0005 in. below the high point on the cam.
5 Ream holes to 0.1895/0.1905-in. diam.
6 Case harden 0.0008 in. deep for a wear-resistant surface (Rockwell 15-N 73 to 77).
7 Wash and clean after case hardening.
8 Inspect dimensions and flatness.

The cam was made in four lots of 2500 for a total of 10,000 per year. A 200-ton mechanical press operating at 18 strokes per minute was used for operations 2 and 4. Lubricant was an equal-part mixture of mineral oil and an extreme-pressure chlorinated oil.

The die was made of D2 tool steel, and had a life of 50,000 pieces between sharpenings for the cutting elements. The coining dies required more frequent attention because of the tolerance and finish requirements.

Other methods of making the part were machining and powder metallurgy. Parts machined to the required tolerances cost four times as much as coined parts. A powder metallurgy part did not meet the wear-resistance requirements.

Dimensional control of blank thickness, as well as contour, is important in coining flatware. Common practice is to hold the blank thickness to ±0.001 in. This is done by grading (preforming) the blank in a die or by roll forming. This operation also distributes the metal so that the blank can be coined with a minimum of metal movement.

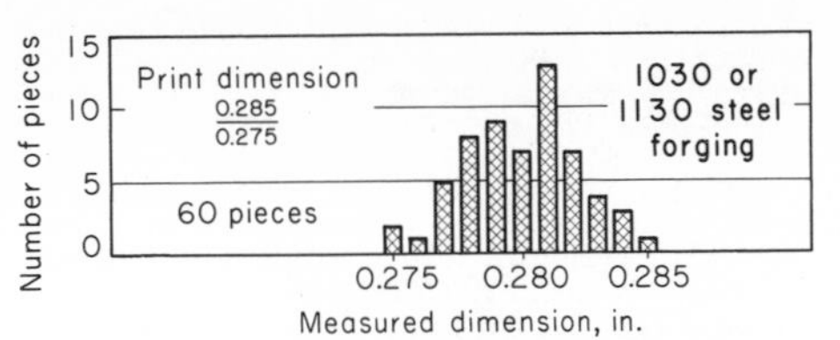

Fig. 16. Variation in thickness of coined flanges on forged wheel hubs discussed in Example 82 and shown in Fig. 12 (Example 88)

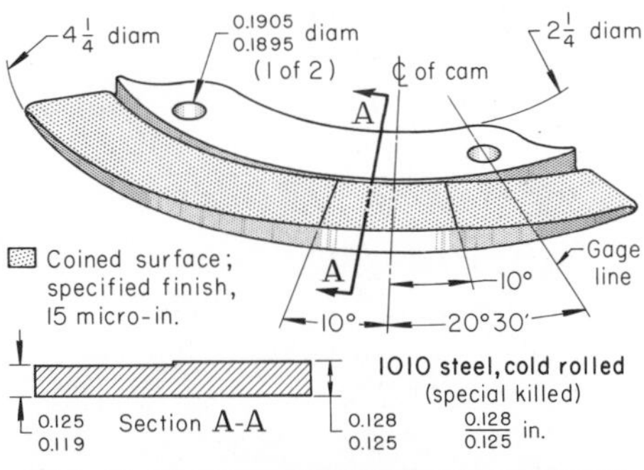

Fig. 17. Breaker cam that was given an intermediate anneal before being coined to final dimensions (Example 89)

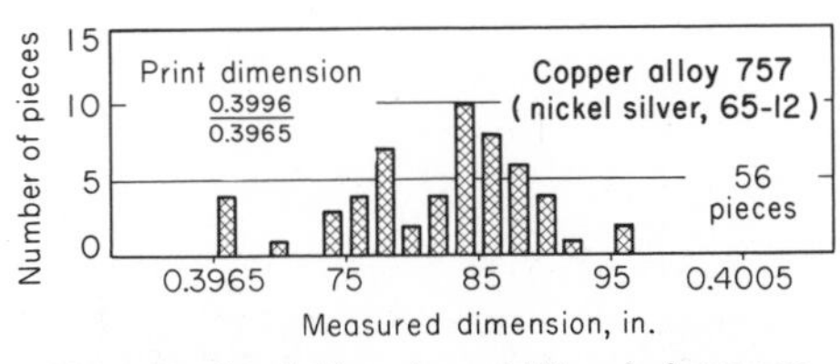

Fig. 18. Variation in width of teaspoon handles selected at random intervals from an order of 54,000 pieces (Example 90)

The commercial thickness tolerance of strip stock results in variations greater than desired for coined flatware. When the thickness is on the high side, the load on the dies and press is greatly increased. When the stock thickness is on the low side, the detail may not be completely filled and flats will appear on the high points. Because the dies are normally loaded near their ultimate strength, thick blanks would result in early failure of the dies. Thus, it is essential for the preliminary steps leading to coining to be closely controlled.

To obtain uniform coining and edge condition, the blanks in the following example were grade rolled to a thickness tolerance of ±0.001 in., and then blanked to contour.

Example 90. Dimensional Control in the Coining of Nickel Silver Teaspoons (Fig. 18)

Teaspoon blanks of copper alloy 757 (nickel silver; 65 Cu − 12 Ni) were grade rolled to a thickness tolerance of ±0.001 in. and were made to a size to fill a coining die without flash. To insure control of the process, on an order of 54,000 spoons, handles of 56 spoons, selected at random intervals of about 1000, were measured at the widest point. Here, thickness was 0.075 ± 0.001 in., and widths were as plotted in Fig. 18. Variations in spoon width were approximately ±0.0015 in. at the point measured. It might appear that the final measurements should have been on the thickness, but because of design detail, this varied irregularly across the handle and consistent results could not be expected from such measurements. The spoon handle was almost entirely coined at the edges. A thickness of about 0.02 in. showed evidence of the blanking cut.

Metal is displaced during coining and, if the blank is not confined, the coined detail will not be of uniform depth. The flow of metal also can affect the location of holes pierced before the coining operation and the dimensions of the finished workpiece, unless precautionary measures are taken. In the following example, two heeled punches were used to confine the metal while coining near the edge of the strip. A positive stop in the cutting station controlled the length of the part and the location of a pierced hole.

Example 91. Coining a Small Brass Part (Fig. 19)

The rectangular flat part shown in Fig. 19 was made from annealed copper alloy 268 (yellow brass, 65%) strip 1$\frac{5}{16}$ in. wide. As indicated in Fig. 19, the coiled strip was fed by automatic roll feed to a progressive die, where it was notched, coined, pierced, cut off, and ejected.

The width of the part was confined by the heels on the coining punch, and the displacement of material in coining resulted in increased thickness and length. Because the increase in length varied with the thickness and hardness of the stock, special provisions had to be made to maintain the hole location and the ±0.005-in. tolerance on finished length. As shown in Fig. 19, this was done by allowing about 30% additional length of stock between the parts and by feeding the stock against a positive stop that served as a reference point for piercing and cutting off. Notching before coining avoided distortion of the grooves, which were only about 0.024 in. from the edge of the part.

The work metal had a grain size of 0.005 to 0.025 mm, and a hardness of Rockwell F 73 to 91. Light mineral oil, applied to the strip by dripping, was used as a lubricant. Additional processing details are given with Fig. 19.

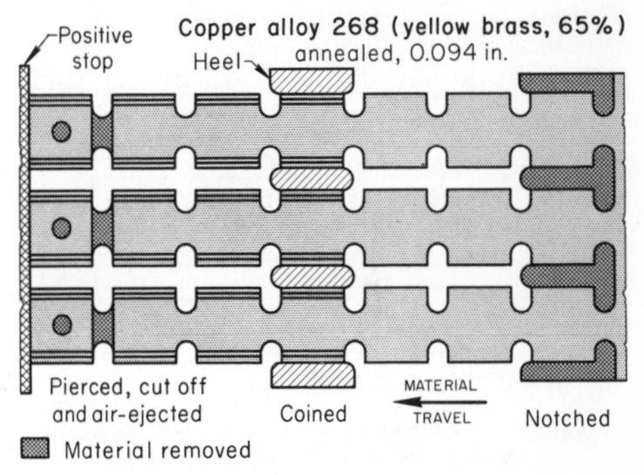

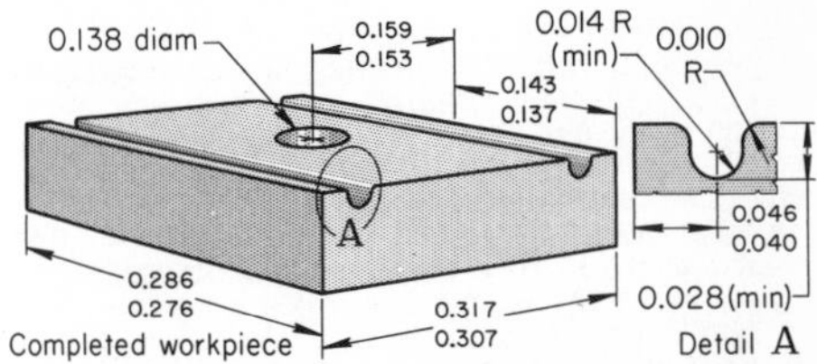

Press and Die Details

Press type	Mechanical, straight-side with automatic roll feed
Press capacity	35 tons
Press stroke	2 in.
Die material	T1 tool steel
Die hardness	Rockwell C 60 to 63

Operating Conditions

Setup time	30 min
Lubricant	Light mineral oil
Tool life	300,000 pieces per grind
Production rate	18,000 pieces per hour

Cost per 1000 Pieces

Material	$2.40
Labor	0.15
Total	$2.55

Fig. 19. Controlling dimensions in the production of a small brass part from coiled strip in a progressive die (Example 91)

Surface Finish. Tableware, coins, medallions and many other coined items require a high surface finish. To achieve this, the dies must have an excellent surface, and the finish on the blank also must be good. Dies are carefully matched, tooled, stoned and polished by hand. Stoning is usually done by using diemakers' polishing stones soaked in lard oil. Polishing is done by using wood sticks, lard oil, and various grits of emery. Typical surface finish before and after coining of sterling silver, when using the above practice, is illustrated in the following example.

Example 92. Effect of Die Finish on Finish of Coined Sterling Silver Fork (Fig. 20)

Seven surface-finish readings taken in the fork portion of uncoined sterling silver blanks showed an average of 11 micro-in. (upper sketch of Fig. 20). When coining with dies that were not hand polished, the average finish in the fork section was reduced to 9 micro-in.

Dies were hand-stoned and polished prior to a production run of 4000 forks. Workpiece finish improved to an average of 5 micro-in., as shown in Fig. 20 (lower sketch). To maintain this finish, hand polishing of the dies after each 1000-piece run was required. Coining was done in a 1200-lb air-lift gravity drop hammer using a drop height of 24 in. Other processing details are given in the table that accompanies Fig. 20.

Weight of the blanks for items coined from precious metals often is specified to close tolerances. These metals are soft and can be coined to intricate detail. However, the volume of metal placed in the die must be carefully controlled so that the metal can completely fill the design but not overload the die and press. A convenient method of controlling the volume of metal in a blank is by specifying the weight of the blank to close tolerances as well as the thickness, width and length.

Sterling silver flatware not only is inspected for perfection of design detail and surface finish, but the blank is periodically checked for weight, which usually is held to ±1%. Typical inspection procedures and results are given in the following example.

Example 93. Weight Control of Blanks in Coining Sterling Silver Teaspoons

Inspection procedures for control of the weight of blanks for sterling silver teaspoons were as follows: Blanks for coining were graded and held to a thickness tolerance of ±0.002 in. During grading operations, the blanks were also checked for weight. Tolerance for this weight was ±1% of the specified weight of 12.00 troy oz per dozen blanks. During a run, 12 teaspoon blanks were weighed at the beginning and at every 1000 pieces thereafter. Results of five of these weight checks, tabulated below, showed all samples to be within tolerance:

1st check (pieces 1 to 12)	12.10 troy oz
2nd check (pieces 1001 to 1012) ..	12.00
3rd check (pieces 2001 to 2012) ...	12.05
4th check (pieces 3001 to 3012) ...	11.90
5th check (pieces 4001 to 4012) ...	12.00

When weights were found out of tolerance, production was stopped and required adjustments were made in the equipment used for preparing blanks.

Costs

Equipment requirements for coining may be modest for small articles. As the size of the coined article increases, the basic equipment requirements increase rapidly, and the cost of the equipment increases correspondingly.

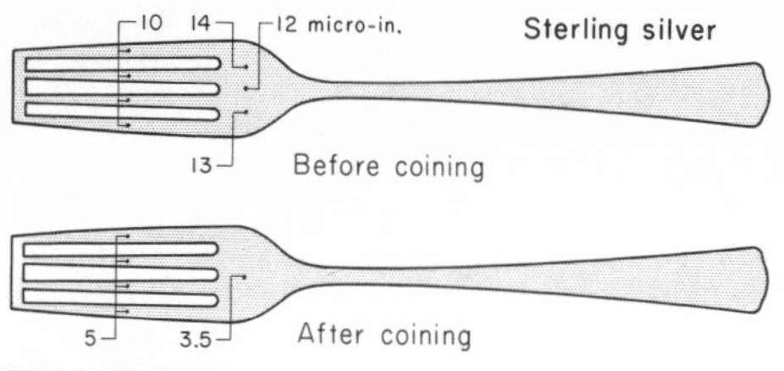

Die material .... S1 tool steel
Die hardness .... Rockwell C 58 to 60
Setup time .... ½ hr
Die life, total .... 10,000 to 15,000 pieces
Production rate .... 500 pieces per hour

Fig. 20. Surface finish of a sterling silver fork before and after coining with hand-stoned and polished dies (Example 92)

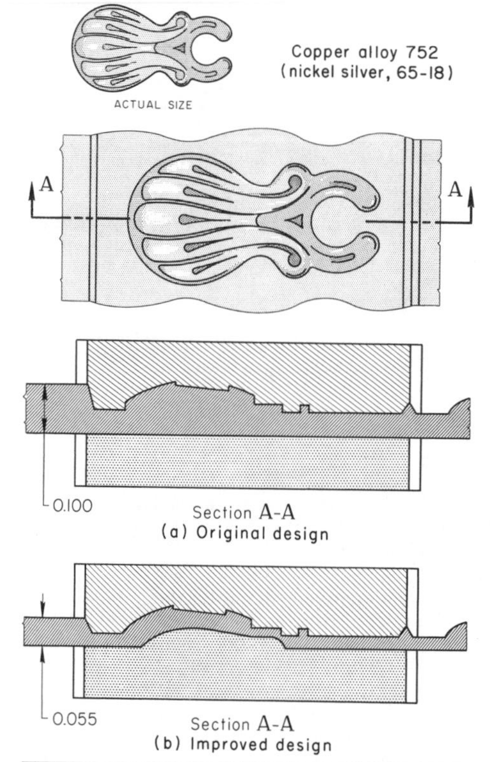

Die material .... D2 tool steel
Die hardness .... Rockwell C 58 to 59
Coining pressure .... 100 tons
Lubricant .... Soluble oil (very light coat)
Setup time .... ½ hr
Die life, total .... 200,000 pieces
Tool cost (excluding hob) $150
Production rate .... 7500 pieces per hour

Fig. 21. Change in die design that saved metal in coining an emblem (Example 95)

In general, however, hammers, presses or other basic equipment expenses do not enter directly, and the cost of coined items will be determined by die cost and cost of labor and material.

Production quantity is a major factor in the cost of coining, as is true for almost any manufacturing process. Although labor cost for any given method of production is usually proportional to the number of items produced, cost of dies and setup are major variables influenced by quantity. The effect of quantity and setup cost is illustrated in the following example.

Example 94. Effect of Quantity and Setup Cost on Manufacturing Cost (Table 7)

The effect of setup cost on per-piece cost of sterling silver flatware coined in five different quantities is shown in Table 7. Because the labor cost per piece is constant, the only per-piece cost variable is the setup charge, which is amortized over the production lot. The costs for material, dies and overhead must be added to obtain the total cost per piece. Because the dies have a life longer than 4000 pieces, their cost would be amortized over the total die life.

Table 7. Effect of Quantity and Setup Cost on Operating Cost in Manufacturing Sterling Silver Teaspoons (Example 94)

Quantity produced	Cost per piece: Setup	Labor	Total, setup and labor
1	$6.50	$0.0210	$6.521
10	0.65	0.0210	0.671
100	0.065	0.0210	0.086
1000	0.0065	0.0210	0.0275
4000	0.0016	0.0210	0.0226

Costs are for all operations from preparation through trimming. Costs of dies, material and overhead are not included.

Die costs and material costs per item depend on the material and shape coined. These costs can vary widely, as in the manufacture of the sterling silver and stainless steel forks in Examples 73 and 74 (Fig. 4). The silver fork was highly ornate, compared with the stainless steel fork, and this is reflected in the costs of the initial dies, $2400 and $900, respectively. Because of the detail in the silver-coining dies, failure may be expected after 10,000 to 15,000 pieces, whereas the dies for coining the stainless steel forks will produce 72,000 to 100,000 pieces. If 72,000 silver forks of the illustrated design were manufactured, the initial dies (at $2400) and probably five sets of replacement dies (at $500 each) would be required. The die costs for the silver forks would be $4900, compared with $900 for the less-ornate stainless steel forks. To this should be added setup costs, which would be in about the same ratio. The unit material costs would be the comparative prices of 1.66 troy oz of sterling silver and 3 oz of type 302 stainless steel. Thus, an ornate sterling silver fork is significantly more expensive to manufacture than is a less-ornate stainless steel fork, despite the greater coinability of silver.

If the sterling silver fork had been of the same pattern as the one made of stainless steel, the die life would have been much greater, thus reducing die cost and, in turn, the total manufacturing cost per piece.

Die changes may frequently be used to effect savings, either by reducing the weight of work metal per item (as in the following example) or by improving the die life, or both.

Example 95. Change in Die Design That Resulted in Saving in Metal (Fig. 21)

The emblem illustrated in Fig. 21 was originally coined from 0.100-in.-thick strips of copper alloy 752 (nickel silver; 65 Cu – 18 Ni – 17 Zn), using a flat lower die (Fig. 21a). Because neither thickness nor design was specified for the reverse side of the emblem, the lower die was changed to the contour shown in Fig. 21(b). This change allowed the use of 0.055-in.-thick strip and still provided acceptable stiffness in the emblem. By using the thinner strip, 230 emblems per pound of metal were obtained, compared with 170 per pound when using the 0.100-in.-thick strip.

For both methods, single-station tooling was used in a 150-ton knuckle-type mechanical press. Dies were made by hubbing. Additional manufacturing details are given in the table with Fig. 21.

Press Bending of Low-Carbon Steel

*By the ASM Committee on Press Forming of Steel**

PUNCH PRESSES are used for bending, flanging and hemming of low-carbon steel when production quantities are large, when close tolerances must be met, or when the parts are relatively small. Press brakes ordinarily are used for small lots, uncritical work, and long parts.

To estimate the press capacity needed for bending in V-dies, the bending load in tons can be computed from:

$$L = \frac{lt^2kS}{s}$$

where L is press load, in tons; l is length of bend (parallel to bend axis), in inches; t is work-metal thickness, in inches; k is a die-opening factor (varying from 1.2 for a die opening of $16t$ to 1.33 for a die opening of $8t$); S is tensile strength of the work metal, in tons per square inch; and s is width of die opening, in inches.

For U-dies, the constant k should be twice the values shown above; for the bending of flanges with wiping dies, see the section on Straight Flanging in this article (page 98).

The characteristics of the various presses commonly used for forming sheet metal are summarized in the article on Presses and Auxiliary Equipment, which begins on page 1.

Bendability and Selection of Steels

Figure 1 shows the types of bends for which the standard AISI tempers of cold rolled carbon steel strip are suited. Stock of No. 1 temper is not recommended for bending, except to large radii. Stock of No. 2 temper can be bent 90° over a radius equal to strip thickness, perpendicular to the rolling direction. Stock of No. 3 temper can be bent 90° over a radius equal to strip thickness, parallel to the rolling direction; it can also be bent 180° around a strip of the same thickness when the bend is perpendicular to the rolling direction. Stock of No. 4 or No. 5 temper can be bent 180° flat on itself in any direction. The No. 5 temper stock may develop stretcher strains and should not be used if these markings are objectionable.

Table 1 shows the effect of carbon content of some grades of carbon steel strip and sheet on bend radius in standard bend tests; Table 2 shows the effect of quality or temper on minimum bend radius of 1008 or 1010 steel sheet; and Table 1 on page 135 in the article on Press Forming of High-Carbon Steel shows the effect of composition on minimum bend radius, by comparing minimum radii for common grades of carbon and low-alloy steels.

*For committee list, see page 112.

Table 1. Bending Limits for Hot Rolled, Commercial Quality Carbon Steel Strip and Cold or Hot Rolled Carbon Steel Sheet (a)

Carbon, %	Bending limit
0.15 or less	180° bend flat on itself, in any direction
0.15 to 0.25	180° bend around one thickness of the material, in any direction

(a) If greater ductility is needed, drawing quality or physical quality steel can be used.

Minimum Bend Radius

Minimum bend radii are limited by angle of bend, length of bend, material properties, condition of the cut edge perpendicular to the bend line, and orientation of bend with respect to direction of rolling. Minimum bend radii are larger for a larger angle of bend.

Parts in which the length of the bend (direction parallel with the bend axis) exceeds eight times metal thickness have a fairly constant minimum bend radius. When the bend length is less than eight times metal thickness, the bend radius generally is greater.

Temper of the metal affects minimum bend radius (see Fig. 1). Steel in the higher tempers (low hardness and high ductility) can be bent 180° to a sharp radius without cracks or tears. Bend radii usually can be smaller for bends made across the rolling direction than for bends made parallel to it. However, examples in this article demonstrate that sharp bends often are made parallel to the rolling direction.

Effect of Edge Condition. When bending low-carbon steel, the condition of the edge perpendicular to the bend axis has little effect on the minimum bend radius. But steels that are susceptible to work hardening or hardening by heating during gas or electric-arc cutting may crack during bending because of edge condition. For these steels, it is often necessary to remove burrs and hardened edge metal in the bend area to prevent fracture. Edges can be prepared for bending by grinding parallel with the surface of the sheet and removing sharp corners in the bend area by radiusing or chamfering, as in Example 133 in the article on Press-Brake Forming.

If the burr side is on the inside of the bend, cracking is less likely to occur during bending. This is important on parts with small bend radii in comparison with the metal thickness, and also on parts with metal thickness greater than 1/16 in., because fractures are likely to start from stress-raising irregularities in the burr edge if it is on the outside of the bend.

Effect of Metal Thickness. Minimum bend radii generally are expressed in multiples or fractions of the thickness of the work metal.

On parts that require a minimum flange width or a minimum width of flat on the flange, stock thickness will limit both of these dimensions. If thickness is not critical in the design, the use of thinner stock, as in the following example, can make bending small radii and narrow flanges feasible.

DIRECTION OF ROLLING
No. 1 temper (hard) Rockwell B 84 min
No. 2 temper (half hard) Rockwell B 70 to 85
R = t
No. 3 temper (quarter hard) Rockwell B 60 to 75
No. 4 temper (skin rolled) Rockwell B 65 max
Stretcher strains
No. 5 temper (dead soft) Rockwell B 55 max

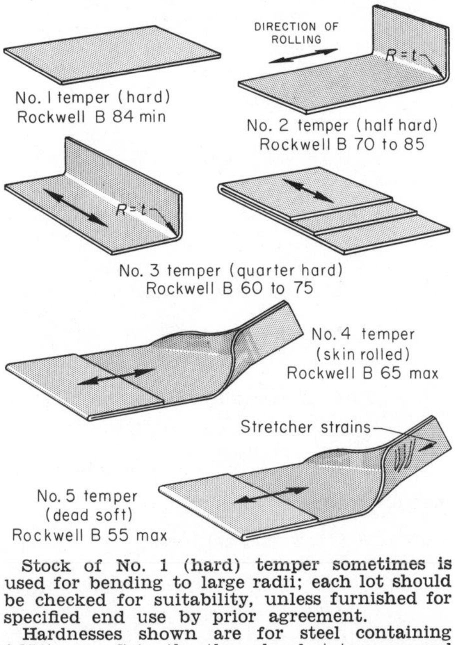

Stock of No. 1 (hard) temper sometimes is used for bending to large radii; each lot should be checked for suitability, unless furnished for specified end use by prior agreement.

Hardnesses shown are for steel containing 0.25% max C in the three hardest tempers and 0.15% max C in the No. 4 and 5 tempers. Hardness for No. 1 temper applies to thicknesses of 0.070 in. and greater; for thinner sheet, hardness would be Rockwell B 90 min.

Fig. 1. The most severe bend that can be tolerated by each of the standard tempers of cold rolled carbon steel strip (AISI Steel Products Manual on Carbon Steel Strip)

Example 96. Use of Thinner Stock to Enable Bending of Narrow Flanges to Small Radii (Fig. 2)

Originally, the pushrod guide shown in Fig. 2 was made of 0.148-in.-thick hot rolled 1008 steel. Because of difficulties in forming the offset and flanges to the radii and widths shown in Fig. 2, the stock thickness was reduced to 0.089 in.

The part was made in a progressive die in nine operations:

1 Pierce pilot hole, and notch sides to start outline of part.
2 Seminotch center of strip to finish outline of part.
3 Form offset.
4 Form four flanges.
5 Notch two of the flanges, pierce second hole, and enlarge pilot hole.
6 Cut off the two unnotched flanges.
7 Coin burr side of holes.
8 Restrike flanges to square up.
9 Cut off.

Stock was provided for two extra flanges opposite the finished flanges to balance forces and prevent shifting during forming. The two extra flanges were trimmed off in operation 6 after they had served their purpose.

Carbon Steels. Table 2 gives minimum bend radii for 1008 or 1010 hot and cold rolled steel sheet in each of the available qualities. Bend radii for higher-carbon steels and two low-alloy steels are given in Table 1 in the article on Press Forming of High-Carbon Steel.

As suggested by Table 2, the quality of steel has a major influence on the minimum bend radius that can be made in it. This is especially true of hot rolled steel, for which, according to Table 2, a change from commercial quality to drawing quality reduces minimum bend radius by 33 to 50%.

Low-carbon steels of commercial quality differ in bendability, as indicated by Table 3, which is for typical commercial quality steels suitable for 90° and 180° bends.

High-strength low-alloy steels, because of their higher yield strength and lower ductility, are more difficult to bend than plain carbon steels — requiring more power, greater bend radii, more die clearance, and greater allowance for springback. It may be necessary to remove shear burrs, and to smooth corners, in the area of the bend. Whenever possible, the axis of the bend should be across the direction of rolling. If the bend axis must be parallel with the rolling direction, it may be necessary to use cross-rolled material, depending on the severity of the bend.

All high-strength low-alloy steels are not equal in formability; however, for the more readily formable grades and the quenched-and-tempered grades, the minimum bend radii in the following table are recommended:

Steel thickness (t), in.	Minimum bend radius for steel with minimum yield strength (psi) of: 45,000	50,000
Up to 1/16	½t	1t
1/16 to ¼	1t	2t
¼ to ½	2t	3t

These minimum bend radii are for bending with the bend axis across the rolling direction. The use of smaller bend radii increases the probability of cracking. Hot bending is recommended for thicknesses greater than ½ in.

Hot bending is necessary when the product shapes are too complex or bend radii are too small for cold forming. The high-strength low-alloy steels can be successfully hot bent at temperatures as low as 1200 F; however, when maximum bendability is needed, temperatures of 1550 to 1650 F are recommended. Cooling in still air from these temperatures returns the material nearly to the as-rolled mechanical properties.

The following example describes the use of a columbium-bearing steel that provided the necessary high yield strength at low cost.

Example 97. Change in Steel Grade That Reduced Cost (Fig. 3)

The use of columbium-bearing steel in place of the original high-strength low-alloy steel for the 65.5-lb Z-section truck-trailer frame member shown in Fig. 3 brought about a 17% saving in cost of the product. The steel used had to have a minimum yield strength of 50,000 psi. However, not all of the corrosion resistance of a high-strength low-alloy steel was needed, so a lower-cost columbium-bearing steel could be used. It had the added advantage of greater ductility than the previously used steel at the same yield strength, and therefore bend radii could be smaller.

Table 2. Minimum Bend Radii for 1008 or 1010 Steel Sheet

Quality or temper	Minimum bend radius — Parallel to rolling direction	Across rolling direction
Cold Rolled		
Commercial	0.01 in.	0.01 in.
Drawing, rimmed	0.01 in.	0.01 in.
Drawing, killed	0.01 in.	0.01 in.
Enameling	0.01 in.	0.01 in.
Cold Rolled, Special Properties		
Quarter hard(a)	1t	½t
Half hard(b)	NR	1t
Full hard(c)	NR	NR
Hot Rolled		
Commercial:		
Up to 0.090 in.	¾t	½t
Over 0.090 in.	1½t	1t
Drawing:		
Up to 0.090 in.	½t	¼t
Over 0.090 in.	¾t	½t

t = sheet thickness; NR = Not recommended

(a) Rockwell B 60 to 75. (b) Rockwell B 70 to 85. (c) Rockwell B 84 minimum.

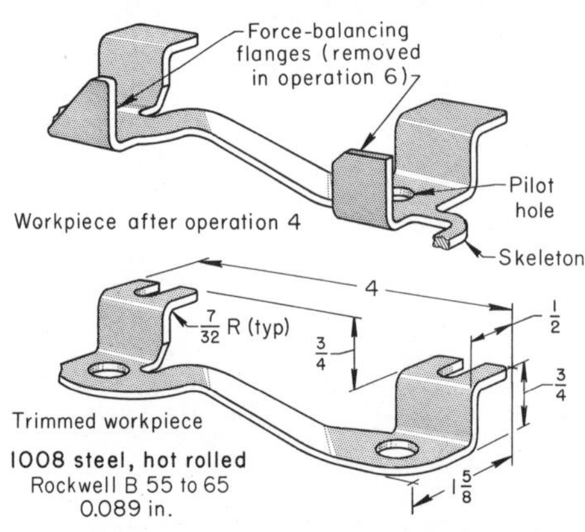

The stock from which this pushrod guide originally was made was 0.148 in. thick.

Fig. 2. Pushrod guide for which stock thickness was reduced to facilitate bending of narrow flanges to small radii (Example 96)

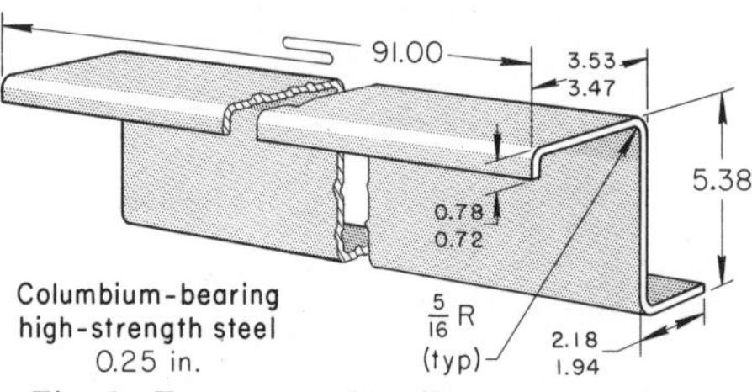

Fig. 3. Frame member that was produced at lower cost by changing to a less expensive steel with equivalent strength (Example 97)

To provide the corrosion resistance that was needed in this application, a small amount of copper was added to the columbium-bearing steel.

The frame member was produced in four operations: blank; form lip; form large flange; form bottom flange. All bends were parallel with the direction of rolling in a plate 0.25 in. thick and 10 1/16 in. wide. Fracturing along the bends was not a problem with either material; however, incidence of fracturing was reduced when the material was changed.

Production lots were about 1000 pieces, and tool life was 20,000 pieces.

Orientation of Bend

Ordinarily it is better to orient a part on the stock so that bends are made across the rolling direction. Sharper bends can be made across than can be made parallel with the rolling direction, without increasing the probability of cracking the work metal (see Fig. 1 and Table 2).

Sometimes, when bends are to be made in two or more directions, the piece can be oriented in the layout in such a way that none of the bends is parallel with the rolling direction. In some applications, however, as in those described in the two examples that follow, there is no practical way to avoid making bends parallel with the rolling direction. These examples demonstrate approximate limits for bending parallel with the rolling direction.

Example 98. Bending Hot Rolled Steel Parallel With and Across the Direction of Rolling (Fig. 4)

The steel hinge bracket shown in Fig. 4 was made with sharp corners on the ¾-in.-wide tabs, which were bent across the rolling direction. In the other direction (parallel with the direction of rolling), the flange bend radius was 3/16 in. for most of the length, but sharpened to 3/64 in. at the 3/32-in. offset on each side. The severity of forming and the sharpness of the bends required the selection of hot rolled 1010 steel. Thickness of the work metal was 0.203 in.

A sleeved punch guided by the stripper was used for the ¼-in.-diam hole. Hole locations and over-all dimensions were held to ±0.010 in. The bracket was produced in an eight-station progressive die. Punch and die were of air-hardening tool steel. Punch-to-die clearance per side was held to 10% of stock thickness. A 300-ton straight-side double-crank mechanical press that operated at 60 strokes per minute was used.

Sometimes a choice has to be made in orientation to favor one or another consideration. For instance, a blank can be oriented in a strip for economy and the least possible scrap. It can be oriented so that the grain direction will reinforce the metal that receives maxi-

Table 3. Suitability of Commercial Quality Low-Carbon Steel Sheet for Bending

Class and hardness of steel, and bending conditions	90° bends		180° bends	
Cold Rolled Steel up to 0.062 In. Thick				
Suitable commercial quality steels	1008 or 1010, rimmed, temper passed		1008 or 1010, rimmed, annealed	
Maximum Rockwell B hardness	80(a)		65	
Minimum bend radius	1t		0.01 in.	
Hot Rolled Steel up to 0.250 In. Thick				
Suitable commercial quality steels(b)	1008, 1010	Up to 1030	1008, 1010	Up to 1015
Maximum Rockwell B hardness(c)	68	80	68	72
Minimum bend radius:				
Sheet up to 0.090 in. thick	¾t	1½t	1t	1½t
Sheet 0.090 to 0.250 in. thick	1t	2t	1½t	2t

(a) For 90° bends made across the direction of rolling. The acceptable maximum hardness for 90° bends parallel with the direction of rolling is Rockwell B 70. (b) Rimmed or capped. (c) Can be met on hot rolled unpickled steel or steel pickled in sheet form. Hardness values will be higher on mill pickled hot rolled coil. With higher hardness values somewhat larger bend radii will sometimes be required.

mum stress in service. Or it can be oriented, as in the following example, so there is no end-grain runout on a wear surface. In any of these cases, orientation may not be optimum for bending.

Example 99. Bending Parallel With Rolling Direction (Fig. 5)

Conflicting demands called for a choice in the orientation of the blank for the can-opener blade shown in Fig. 5. Because an orientation that would favor the bends would have meant a cross-grain surface on the cutting edge, with consequent poor wearing quality, the blank was oriented so that the grain favored the cutting edge, and the bends were made nearly parallel with the direction of rolling.

To make sure that the stock would withstand the three sharp-radius 90° bends, the steel specification called for stock that would withstand a 180° bend both parallel with and across the direction of rolling. In order to limit distortion during subsequent heat treatment, steel that could be oil hardened was specified. A modified 1023 steel (with 0.85 to 1.15% manganese) met all of the requirements. The stock was 2-in.-wide cold rolled strip 0.045 in. thick. A No. 2 finish was specified, to minimize the amount of polishing or burnishing before plating.

The blade was made in a 12-station progressive die, run in a 75-ton mechanical press. Operations performed in the die included: pierce four holes (one in the scrap area served as a pilot hole), notch outline of part, coin cutting edge, emboss center hole, form bends, and cut off.

The die was made of D2 tool steel, except at station 12 (bending and cutoff), for which the die material was C-5 carbide at Rockwell C 71. Die life per grind was 300,000 pieces. Mineral oil was the lubricant.

Production rate was 4500 pieces per hour; annual production was eight million pieces, in 700,000-piece lots.

After forming, the part was oil hardened, barrel finished in oil and sawdust, and bright nickel plated.

Orientation of bends with respect to the grain affects not only the severity of bend that can be made, but also the service life of that bend, as shown in the following example:

Example 100. Bending Across the Rolling Direction (Fig. 6)

Vibration of an internal-combustion engine frequently caused failure of the fuel-tank bracket shown in Fig. 6. The bracket broke at the upper bend, where a comparatively narrow tab attached the tank to the engine head. To eliminate premature failure at this bend, a reinforcing strip 0.109 in. thick was welded to the back of the upper bend at the narrowest section of stock, where the bracket overhung the engine head (see section A-A in Fig. 6). To reinforce the bracket and reduce vibration, the front leg, which was flattened back (bent 180°), was spot welded to the tank cradle in two spots, as shown in section B-B in Fig. 6.

The bend at the ¾-in.-wide tab, the 180° bend at the front, and the bend on the reinforcing strip were all made perpendicular to the rolling direction.

Because of offsets in the developed blanks, they could be nested slightly by reversing every other one in stock layout. Production procedure was as follows:

1 Shear blank to 10½ by 17¾ in.
2 Blank and pierce two parts from sheared blank.
3 Form 3¼-in. radius and 1-in. flange.
4 Bend 3-in. leg down 90°.
5 Flatten 3-in. leg.
6 Spot weld 3-in. leg.
7 Arc weld reinforcing strip.

A 100-ton single-action mechanical press was used for operations 2, 3 and 4; operation 5 was done in a press brake. Single-operation dies were used for all operations. Blanking tools were of D2 tool steel; bending tools were of O1 tool steel with a ground finish. Life of the tools before regrind was 50,000 pieces. Mineral oil was the lubricant. Production lots were about 2500 pieces, and annual production was approximately 10,000 pieces.

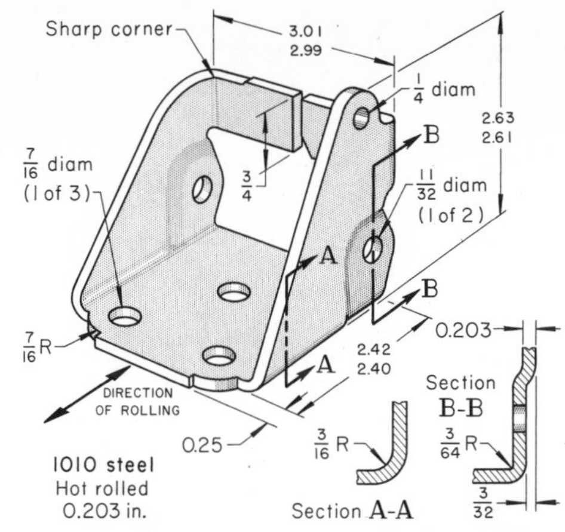

Fig. 4. Hinge bracket on which small-radius bends were made parallel with and across the rolling direction (Example 98)

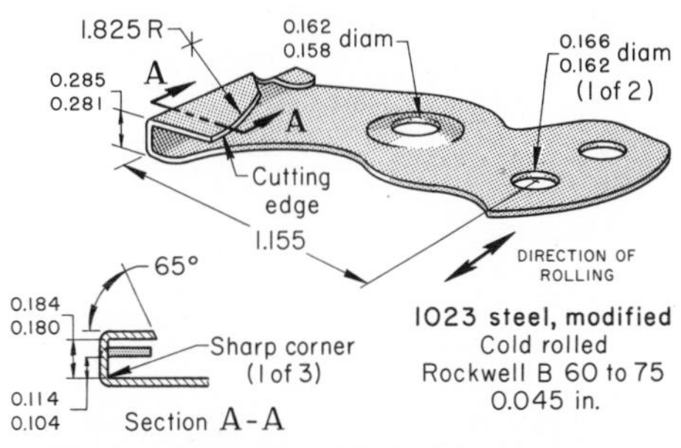

Fig. 5. Can-opener blade that was bent parallel with the direction of rolling, to promote long service life of the cutting edge (Example 99)

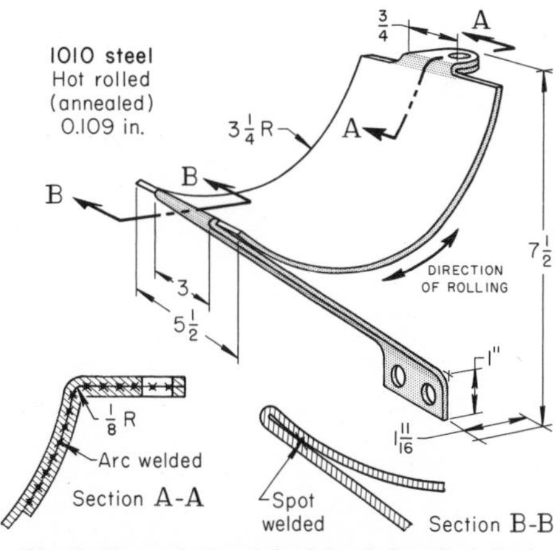

Fig. 6. Severely bent fuel-tank bracket that was protected against fatigue failure by bending across the grain and by local reinforcement (Example 100)

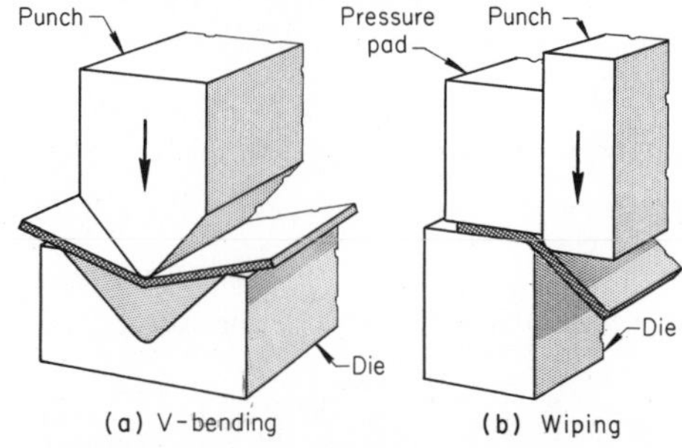

The wiping-type die can be of inverted design. The workpiece would move downward by the action of the punch against the pressure pad, and the flange would bend upward.

Fig. 7. Bending in a V-die and a wiping die

Die Construction

Although the same types of bending dies as those used in press brakes generally can be used in presses, there are major differences, as indicated below:

1 Because presses ordinarily are not long and narrow like press brakes, more consideration has to be given to clearance for removing the finished workpiece when the press is open, as well as clearance for the legs of the bend when the piece is being formed. The bed dimensions of a press also limit the size of workpiece that can be bent.
2 Presses cycle rapidly, and shut height is not as easy to change; therefore, fewer pieces are bent in air, as described in the article on Press-Brake Forming in this volume. More frequently, pieces are formed by bottoming the dies. This has the advantage of decreasing springback.
3 Usually (but not always), presses are used for workpieces less than 2 ft long, and press brakes for pieces longer than 2 ft. However, the automotive industry bends very large sheet-metal structural members on large presses by mass-production methods.

V-dies are composed of a V-block for a die and a wedge-shaped punch (see Fig. 7a). The width of the opening in the V is ordinarily at least eight times stock thickness. In bending, the workpiece is laid over the V in the die, and the punch descends to press the workpiece into the V to form the bend.

The included angle of a V-bend can be changed by adjusting the distance that the punch forces the sheet metal into the V-die. When the piece must be overbent (to allow for springback), the angle of the punch is smaller than the included angle on the part. Bottoming the punch and striking the metal severely at the bend is a means of reducing springback.

In V-die bending a flange along the edge of a wide sheet, distortion is likely to occur. Most of the sheet overhangs the die and lifts up as bending takes place. If the punch strikes too fast, the workpiece will distort and will have irregular break lines. However, if the press ram is slowed down just before the punch hits the work, distortion is minimized.

For this type of V-die work, presses are available in which the ram advances rapidly, slows down just above the work, proceeds slowly through the bottom of the stroke, and returns rapidly. Also, there are presses in which the rate of ram advance can be controlled somewhat by the operator.

Wiping Dies. Another type of bending die is the wiping die (Fig. 7b). A pressure pad that is either spring loaded or attached to a fluid cylinder clamps the workpiece to the die before the punch makes contact. The punch descends and wipes one side of the workpiece over the edge of the die. The bend radius is on the edge of the die. To prevent the wiping action from being too severe, there may be a radius or chamfer on the mating face of the punch. When compensation for springback is necessary, the die is undercut to permit overbending. The flange metal can be put in slight tension by ironing it between the punch and the die. Sharp bends generally cannot be made in one operation in a wiping die without cracking the metal, because a punch or die with a sharp edge will cut the metal rather than bend it.

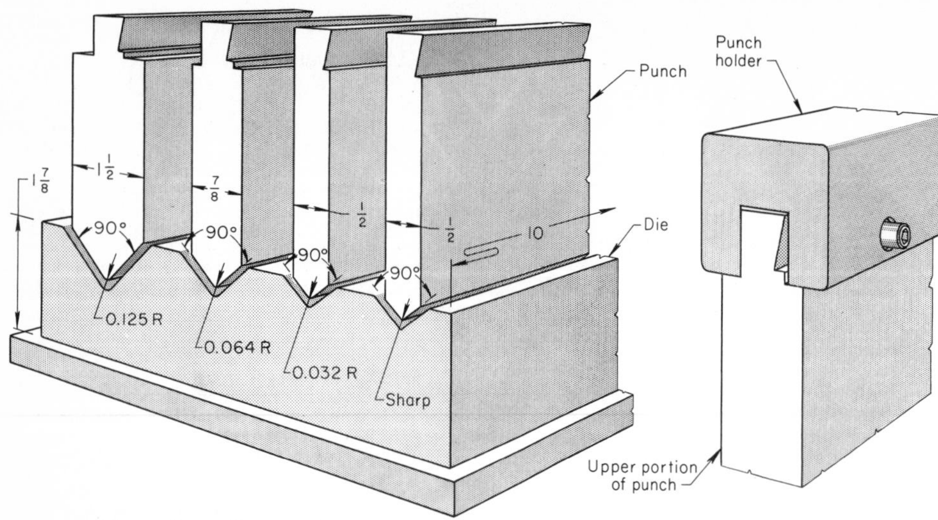

Fig. 8. V-bending punch and die for making a variety of bends in a punch press

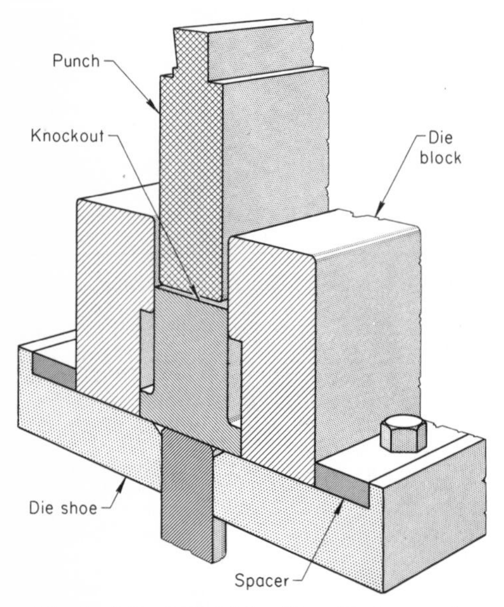

Fig. 9. Adjustable U-bending die for use in a punch press

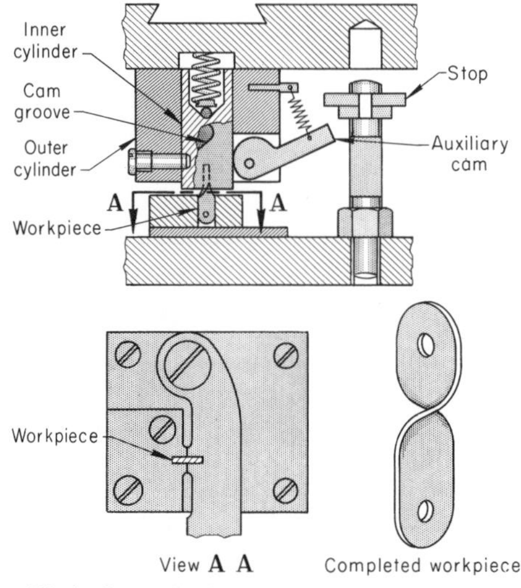

Die is shown in closed position; inner cylinder has rotated to give workpiece a 90° twist. The auxiliary cam prevents rotation of the inner cylinder until it is free of workpiece.

Fig. 10. Rotary bending die used for 90° twisting of strip metal

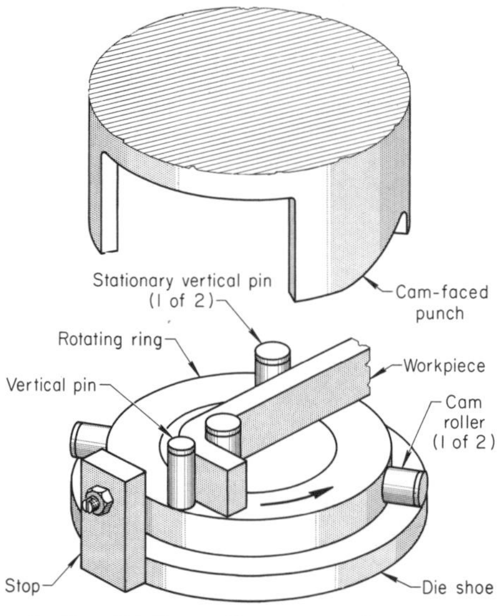

As the die closes, the cam surfaces on the punch contact the cam rollers, causing the outer die ring to rotate and bend the workpiece.

Fig. 11. Rotary die used for bending

Interchangeable V-Dies. Figure 8 shows equipment for making various sizes of V-bends in a punch press. Four different sizes of punches can be mounted into the punch holder, which is attached to the press slide. In operation, the groove in the die that gives the needed bend is aligned with the punch, and then the die is fastened to the bolster plate on the press bed. Adjustable side and end stops can be used to position the blanks for bending.

Using equipment like that in Fig. 8, rectangular boxes in a range of shapes and sizes often are produced more economically by bending flat blanks into folded-end shapes than by deep drawing. Making folded-end pans by bending in adjustable wing dies and cam dies with interchangeable punches is described in Example 210 in the article on Press Forming of Coated Steel.

U-Bending Dies. U-shape pieces can be bent in a die like the one shown in Fig. 9. Width of the U is adjustable by means of spacers and by changing the width of the knockout. Punches can be mounted in the press with a holder similar to that shown in Fig. 8, and can be provided to the proper width and shape to make either a U or a channel shape, whichever is needed. Side clearance should be 10% more than stock thickness.

Rotary bending dies (Fig. 10 and 11) are used to make bends or twists in bars or strip. These dies use cam action to rotate the workpiece.

In Fig. 10, a 90° twist is being given to strip metal to make a connecting link. The punch is made in two major parts: a hollow cylinder that is solidly mounted to the ram, and inside it a solid cylinder that is free to rotate. The inner cylinder has a 90° helical cam groove in its cylindrical surface that engages a hardened pin in the outer cylinder.

When the ram descends, a slot in the face of the inner cylinder engages the end of the workpiece. After the inner cylinder bottoms, as the ram continues to move down, the spring compresses, letting the outer cylinder move down over the inner cylinder. The action of the pin in the groove makes the inner cylinder rotate, giving the workpiece a 90° twist.

An auxiliary cam keeps the inner cylinder from rotating back in the return stroke, until it has cleared the workpiece. Near the top of the stroke, the auxiliary cam is released by a stop, allowing the inner cylinder to return to its starting position.

In Fig. 11, the punch is a large hollow cylinder, the bottom face of which is a two-slope cam. The die, or more properly, the workholder, is made in rings, one of which rotates. The rotating ring has rollers to engage the two slopes of the cam, and a vertical pin to engage the workpiece. Another vertical pin and a forming pin are in the stationary part of the workholder.

The workpiece is placed between the pins. Usually, there is an end stop to locate the blank. Cam action rotates the ring as the punch descends, and the bend is formed between the two vertical pins. The third pin holds the workpiece.

Cam-Actuated Flanging Dies. Horizontal motion is often needed to form, or partly form, a flange on a workpiece. One of the most common methods of producing this motion at right angles to the motion of the main press ram is with an inclined surface, or cam, in the die mechanism. Three such cam-actuated dies, of progressively increasing complexity, are shown in Fig. 12, 13 and 14. In each of the three, a blankholder contacts the work first and holds it in position. Resiliency, either in the form of pressure pins leading to a die cushion or in the form of a spring, allows the ram to continue to descend. A cam actuates the sliding punch, which either forms or completes the forming of the flange and is then retracted.

In Fig. 12, the blank is placed on the pressure pad, where it is held by punch A and wiped past the cam-actuated sliding punch to form the flange. Near the bottom of the stroke, punch B contacts the cam head, which moves the sliding punch to set the flange to the 0.406-in. dimension and a 90° angle.

Cam-actuated sliding punches on each side of the forming punch can be used for setting flanges on channel and U-shape parts.

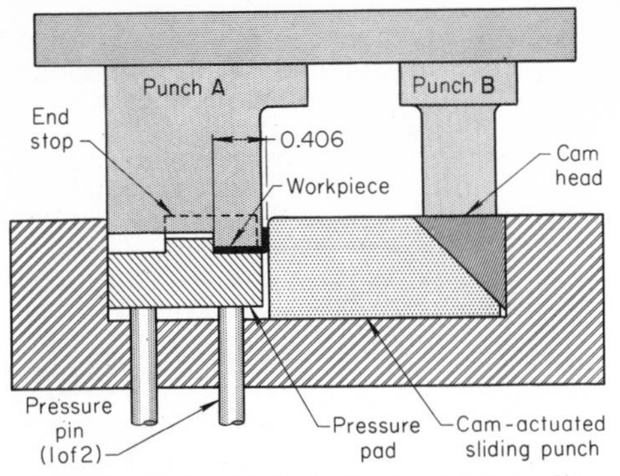

Fig. 12. Cam-actuated single flanging die used for producing a multiflanged part. See text for description of operation.

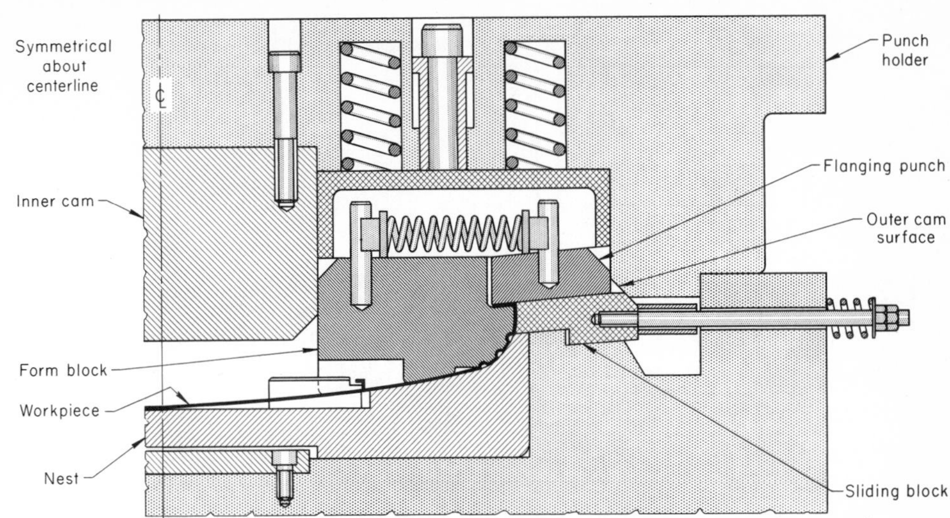

Fig. 13. Cam-actuated flanging die for producing a reverse flange on a door panel

A die for bending a reverse flange is shown in Fig. 13. In operation, the preformed part is placed in the nest of the lower die. As the die closes, the form block contacts the workpiece, causing the spring-loaded plate to remain stationary while the punch holder continues downward. The inner cam then moves the form block outward to support the workpiece firmly in the nest. As the inner cam surface passes the cam on the form block, the outer cam moves the flanging punch inward, bending the flange over the form block. To assist in setting the bend radius, the sliding block on the lower shoe is pushed against the panel by the same cam surface that actuates the flanging punch. All sliding members are spring-returned to their neutral positions.

In Fig. 14, a hemming die is shown finishing the edge of an automobile fender. The workpiece entering the die has a 90° flange, which the cam-actuated sliding punch bends before the hemming punch descends to flatten it. The spring-loaded blankholder holds the workpiece firmly during the operation. The actuating cam on the cam punch advances the sliding punch to form the 135° bend. The second cam surface returns the slide before the hemming punch strikes.

Cam-actuated dies are often used in combination with other tooling to produce complicated parts. In the following example, a cam-actuated die and a progressive die were used to reduce the cost of a piece that previously had been formed in nine separate steps in a press brake.

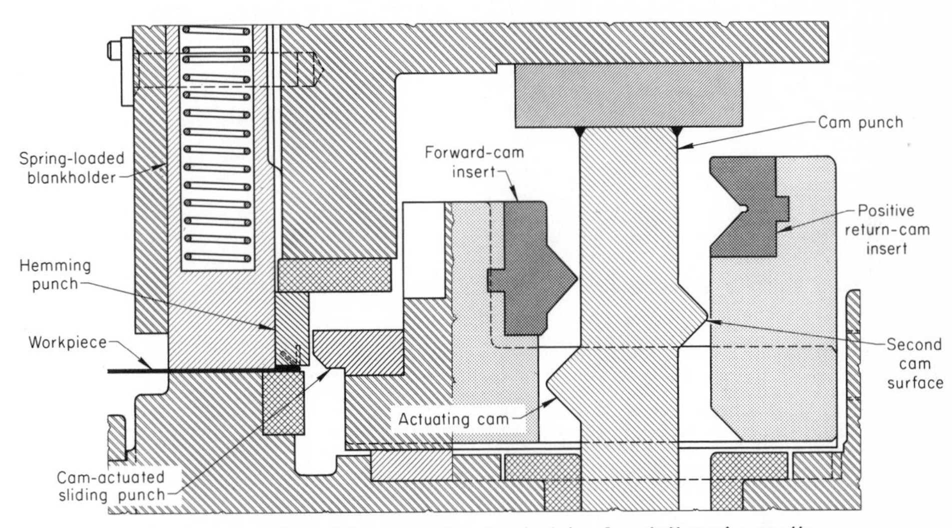

Fig. 14. Cam-actuated hemming die. See text for description of operation.

Example 101. Use of a Cam-Actuated Die and a Progressive Die to Reduce Cost (Fig. 15)

The drawer front shown in Fig. 15 was produced originally in nine operations: two shearing, two notching, one piercing, one box-forming, and three flanging. The box-forming and flanging operations were done in a press brake. The blank was 0.030-in.-thick 1010 steel with a hardness of Rockwell B 40 to 60.

A study proved that cost per piece, even for relatively small production quantities, could be reduced by slitting coil to width; notching, piercing and cutting off in a progressive die; box-forming the four sides in a second die; and flanging the sides, top and bottom in a cam-actuated flanging die.

Figure 15 compares the labor and tool costs per piece for various quantities of the drawer fronts produced by the two methods. Cost of tooling was nearly the same for both methods; most of the saving for the four-operation method was from reduced labor cost.

To make the four-operation method the more economical, production had to be high enough to amortize the cost of coil-handling and slitting equipment and a large press for use with the cam-actuated die.

Dies were made of D2 tool steel, and the progressive die had a life of 50,000 to 75,000 parts between resharpenings. The box-forming die for the improved method was a conventional wipe-down type with a spring pressure pad. Box forming was done in a 90-ton gap-frame press and cam flanging in a 100-ton gap-frame press. Sometimes, both dies were set up and run at the same time in a 225-ton press brake.

The wipe-down die formed the box sides to an inside radius of 0.015 in.; the cam-formed flanges had an inside radius of 0.030 in.

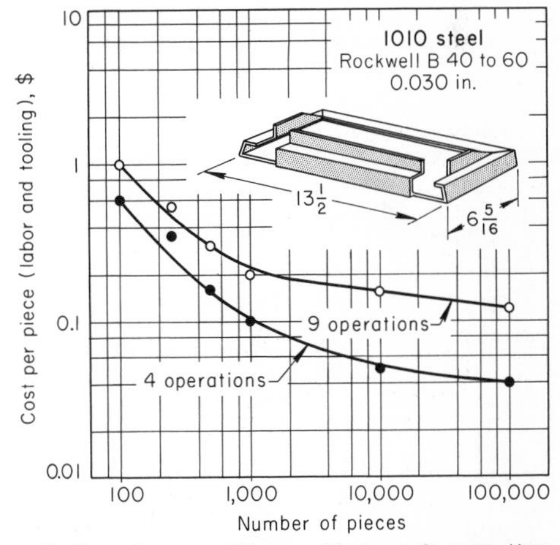

In the nine-operation method, each operation was performed separately; box forming and flanging were done in a press brake. In the four-operation method, several operations were combined by the use of a progressive die and a cam-actuated flanging die.

Fig. 15. Relation of cost to quantity for forming drawer fronts by two different methods (Example 101)

Cam-actuated dies have an advantage over simple wiping dies in bending flanges to acute angles, as demonstrated in the following example.

Example 102. Bending of Two Flanges to an Acute Angle in a Cam-Actuated Compound Die (Fig. 16)

Figure 16 shows a compound die in which a retaining clip (shown in the lower right corner of the illustration) was formed with three punch motions. Strip stock the width of the clip was fed into the press. Material was cold rolled 1010 steel, 0.010 in. thick, one side of which was painted or nickel or chromium plated.

The cutoff-blade holder and the first forming punch were spring loaded with enough force to perform their function yet deflect with continued ram travel. As the ram descended, the cutoff punch engaged the stock first and sheared the blank.

The cutoff blade stopped moving after shearing the blank, but the first forming punch continued down, forming the strip into a shallow U-shape. The forming punch stopped moving while cam-driven horizontal

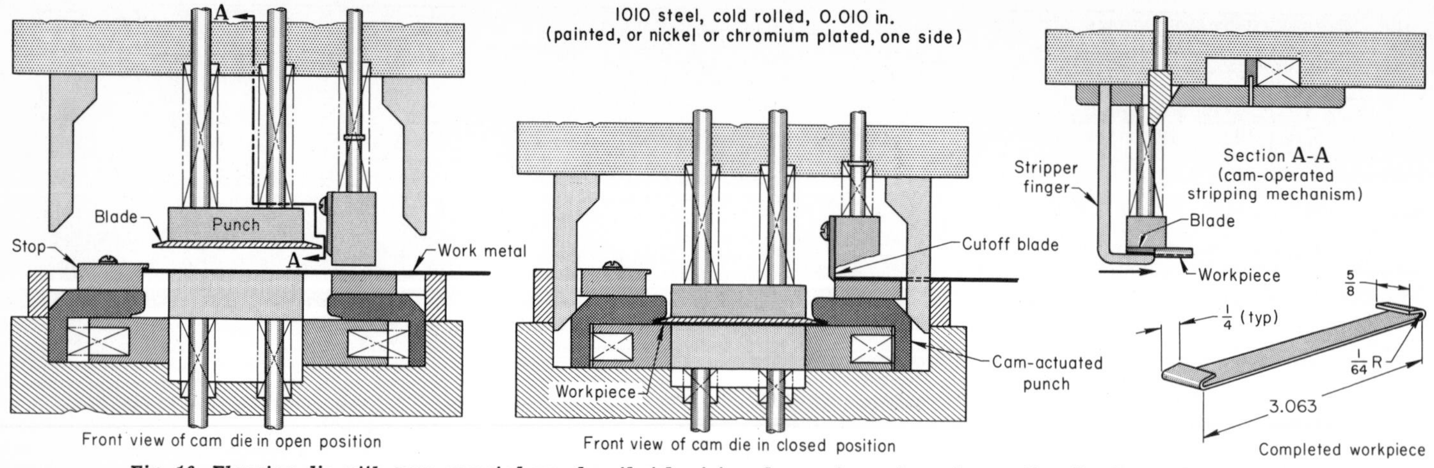

Fig. 16. Flanging die with cam-operated punches that bent two flanges to acute angles on the clip shown (Example 102)

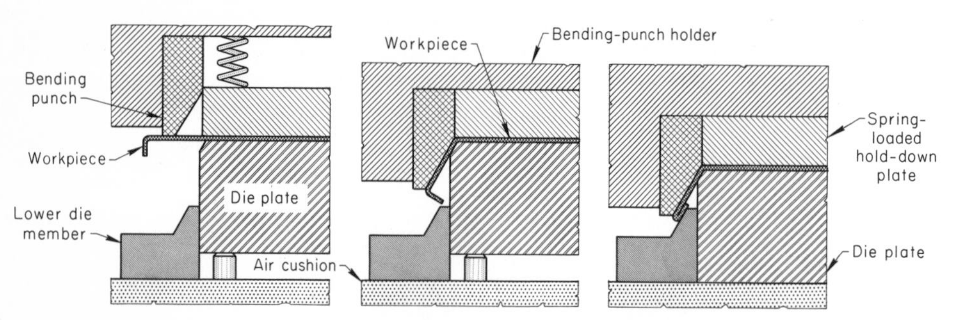

Fig. 17. Compound flanging and hemming die without horizontal motion. See text.

punches turned the flanges over replaceable forming blades on the sides of the first forming punch, to complete the forming of the acute-angle flanges.

When the flanges were wrapped over the forming blades, the workpiece could not be stripped vertically from the punch. Instead, spring-loaded fingers were cammed horizontally against the clip by a stationary stripping mechanism (section A-A in Fig. 16) on the return stroke, which pushed the clip off the blades. When the clip was clear of the punch, an air stream blasted it into a delivery chute. On the downstroke, when the punch cleared the cam that actuated the stripping mechanism, heavy springs retracted the fingers to the starting position for the next cycle.

The die was made of O1 tool steel hardened to Rockwell C 58 to 60. Production rate was 1200 pieces per hour, and die life was about 20 hr. Lot size was 25,000 to 50,000 pieces.

Compound Flanging and Hemming Die. The compound flanging and hemming die shown in Fig. 17 is unusual in having no horizontal motion of punches or dies. There are two cushions: a spring-loaded hold-down plate and an air cushion for the die plate. As the ram descends, the hold-down makes first contact, clamping the piece securely to the die. As the ram continues to descend, the springs compress and the angled flange is formed between the angled face of the bending punch and the die plate.

The angle of bend is set and slightly coined between the chamfer on the edge of the die plate and the angled face of the punch. At this point, the hold-down plate bottoms against the bending-punch holder, then the air cushion begins to yield, lowering the die plate. The edge of the workpiece bumps the corner of the lower die member and folds up into a hem that is completed between the angled face of the bending punch and the mating face of the lower die member.

Fig. 18. Blower blade blanked and formed from strip stock in a compound die (Example 103)

Wing Dies. Special dies for making U-shape bends have "wings" that turn up on each side as the punch descends. They are described in the article on Bending and Forming of Tubing, and are illustrated in Fig. 5 in that article (page 311). Wing dies were used in making the folded-end baking pans described in Example 210 in the article on Press Forming of Coated Steel.

Die Materials. Simple bending dies are ordinarily subjected to less shock than other press-working tools; therefore, they can often be made of low-carbon steel, heat treated low-alloy steel such as 4140, or cast iron for low production of low-carbon steel pieces. For moderately high production, they should be made of flame-hardening grades of carbon steel, such as 1045, or flame-hardening cast iron, such as class 40 gray iron. Cam-operated dies, wiping dies, and dies used to make curved flanges (shrink or stretch) must be made of a higher grade of material. Tool steels such as O1 or A2 are used for moderately long production runs. For a total tool life of a million or more pieces, D2 tool steel is used.

Single-Operation Dies

Single-operation dies are used for low production or on pieces that are so difficult to bend that only one operation at a time is feasible. Some single-operation dies are general-purpose dies that can make bends in simple workpieces of many different designs. Others are single-purpose dies for a particular piece. Examples 453 and 455 in "Forming of Stainless Steel" show the use of single-operation dies for bending one flange and for making a U-shape part.

Use of Compound Dies

In a compound die, two or more operations are combined at a single work station without relocating the workpiece in the die, so that a finished piece is produced with each stroke of the press. One or more of the operations done in the die can be bending.

Inasmuch as the press speed (strokes per minute) for compound dies is generally only slightly lower than for single-operation dies, production time and labor cost per piece are decreased almost in proportion to the number of operations done in the compound die.

In most applications, the cost of a compound die does not differ greatly from the combined cost for equivalent separate dies, and sometimes is less. Operations must be judiciously combined in making a compound die in order not to have die sections that are too thin to be heat treated without distortion, or that will break down under the cyclic loading of ordinary die operation. If these precautions are observed, die life and die-maintenance costs should be nearly the same as for equivalent simple dies.

Compound dies can be fed individual blanks, or they can be fed strip stock, as in the following example:

Example 103. Use of a Compound Die for Production of Blower Blades From Strip Stock (Fig. 18)

Blower blades, shaped as shown in Fig. 18, were cut off from strip stock and bent in a compound die, in a 60-ton mechanical press. The blades were made of 0.030-in.-thick cold rolled, commercial quality 1008 or 1010 steel, either plain or galvanized. Some aluminum blades were also made in the same die.

As shown in Fig. 18, the leading edge of one blade was made with the same cut as the trailing edge of the next; the bend axis of the flanges was parallel with the rolling direction of the metal, and the curvature on the surface of the blade behind the flanges was formed across the rolling direction.

Die material was W2 or A5 tool steel. For both materials, die life between regrinds was one million pieces. A 1-to-5 mixture of soluble oil and water was used as a lubricant, because a wiping action was used in bending the flanges. Production rate was 1600 pieces per hour; annual production was 150,000 pieces.

The flanges at the ends of each blade were used for attaching the blades at assembly, as described in Example 276, on page 208.

Use of Progressive Dies

Progressive dies are similar in function to compound dies in that they combine in one die several operations that are performed with one stroke of the press. In a progressive die, however, the operations are separated and distributed among a number of stations. The stock progresses through these stations in strip form until the finished workpiece is cut from the strip at the last station. Consequently, at the start of a strip there are several press strokes before a piece is produced. Thereafter, a finished workpiece is produced with each stroke of the press, up to the end of the strip.

If the strips are short, sheared from sheets, they can be fed into the die so that each strip is butted against the end of the preceding strip for continuous production. Otherwise, starting stops are used for each new strip.

Coil stock is fed into the die at one end. Usually, a hole or notch is made in the strip at the first station, and subsequent stations use this as a pilot to keep the strip properly aligned and positioned while the operations are performed. When the workpiece is complete, it is cut from the strip, which has acted as a holder to carry the piece from station to station. Intricate pieces, often needing no further work, can be made in one press.

The following example describes the use of a simple progressive die for bending of flanges.

Example 104. Forming a Channel-Shape Clip in a Progressive Die (Fig. 19)

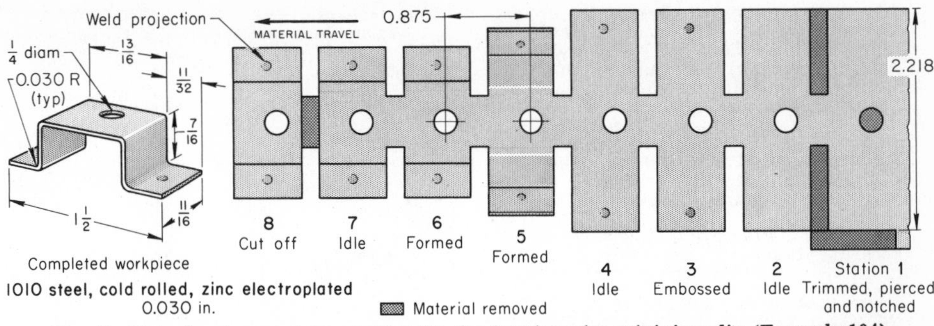

Fig. 19. Strip development for progressive-die forming of a retaining clip (Example 104)

The strip development for production of a retaining clip in a simple, eight-station progressive die is shown in Fig. 19. The part was mass produced from 2⁷⁄₁₆-in.-wide by 0.030-in.-thick cold rolled 1010 steel, zinc electroplated.

In the first station, the strip was held firmly against a rear stock guide and trimmed along the front edge to a developed width of 2.218 in. In addition to trimming in the first station, a ¼-in.-diam hole was pierced and two notches, ³⁄₁₆ by ⁵⁵⁄₆₄ in., were cut, leaving a center carrier tab ½ in. wide.

In the next working station (No. 3), two weld projections were embossed. Then, in station 5, the two bottom flanges were bent 90° and the upper bends were partly completed. Final bending was done in station 6, and the part was cut off in station 8 by a slug-type punch. Stations 2, 4, and 7 were idle to make room for mounting the punch and die elements.

The die was run in a 75-ton open-back inclinable press at the rate of 80 strokes per minute. Die material was W1 tool steel hardened to Rockwell C 58 to 60. Die life was about 300,000 pieces per grind. When the die was resharpened, a deposit of zinc flash or particles was cleaned from it. Mineral oil was used as the forming lubricant.

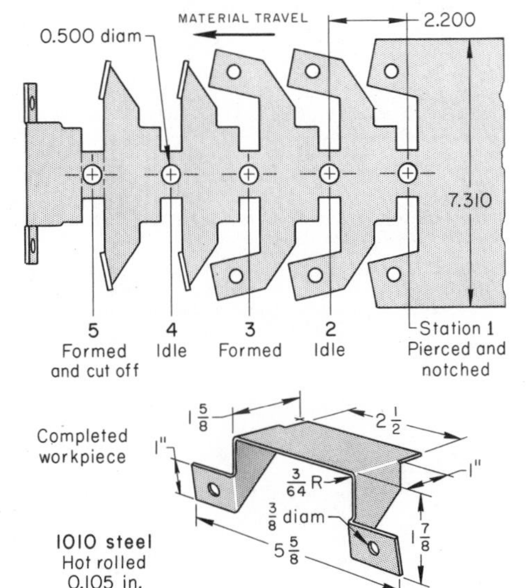

Fig. 20. Layout for progressive-die production of a bracket, with blanks nested to save stock (Example 105)

In Example 104, above, press capacity could have been utilized more effectively by running two parts at a time. To do this, the strip width would have to be increased to 4⅝ in. In station 1, two holes would be pierced and a center slot ³⁄₁₆ in. wide by 1²³⁄₃₂ in. long would be punched, in addition to the two side notches and edge trim. A working station between stations 2 and 3 would be added to emboss one of the adjacent weld projections. Two additional stations would be needed between stations 4 and 5; the first would separate the two parts by lancing the metal, and the other would be idle. The additional die elements would not double die cost; however, the production rate would double, because both dies could be operated at the same number of strokes per minute. A lower cost per piece would result, but the die cost would have to be justified by the annual production and the reduced press time.

In planning the strip layout for progressive-die operations, consideration must be given to development of the part outline, to provision for piloting, to distribution of press load and strength of die elements, and to assuring minimum waste of metal. Some compromise among these factors is usually necessary in developing a sequence of operations and designing a progressive die to do these operations.

The strip layout in the following example used the metal efficiently by having the developed flanges surround the body of the preceding part.

Example 105. Nesting of Workpieces to Minimize Stock Waste (Fig. 20)

The bracket shown in the lower part of Fig. 20 was formed from hot rolled 1010 steel strip in a progressive die with three working and two idle stations. As shown in the upper part of Fig. 20, pieces were nested on the strip to minimize scrap. The operations in the three working stations were: pierce one pilot hole and two flange holes and notch the contour; bend two tabs upward; and flange and cut off from the center connecting tab.

The die was used in a 150-ton mechanical press that could make 50 strokes per minute. Allowing for setup and downtime, production was 2800 pieces per hour. A light mineral oil was the lubricant.

The die was made of W1 tool steel hardened to Rockwell C 58 to 60. The punch-to-die clearance for cutting elements was 6% of stock thickness per side. Annual production was 100,000 brackets.

Use of Progressive Dies vs Separate Dies

The choice between a progressive die and two or more separate dies (single-operation or compound) is not always clear-cut. Various considerations can influence the decision, perhaps the most important being the size of the production order. Other considerations are the rate of obsolescence of the product, and the rate at which tool cost must be amortized.

The next three examples show how these considerations can affect choice of type of die. In each of these examples, increased annual production requirements justified the use of a progressive die. In Example 107, reduction in handling costs made the use of a progressive die economical for even a relatively small production lot.

Example 106. Change From Three Separate Dies to a Progressive Die (Fig. 21)

The part shown in Fig. 21(b) was produced from 0.062-in.-thick cold rolled 1010 steel that had a hardness of Rockwell B 58 max. A progressive die, which made a finished part at each press stroke, replaced three dies in which 12 press strokes were required for producing one piece. The separate dies were a standard piercing and notching die, an embossing die, and a conventional V-die. Setup time for each die was ½ hr.

The progressive die cost $7000 and produced parts at a cost of 41¢ each, compared with 62¢ each by the original method. The cost of the progressive die was justified for the annual production of 60,000 parts (break-even point was 34,000 parts). Both methods made parts that were within the maximum dimensional tolerance of ±¹⁄₆₄ in., and to the maximum bend radius of ¹⁄₃₂ in.

The original dies had been used in a 100-ton press brake that operated at 600 strokes per hour on sheared blanks 8¹¹⁄₁₆ in. wide by 18¼ in. long. The press-brake operation consisted of piercing five holes in the flange and one in the center and notching one corner, as shown in Fig. 21(a). The other holes and the three other corner notches were produced with three more strokes, with the workpiece being turned after each stroke. Four more strokes were needed for embossing four holes (see Fig. 21b). Bending required four strokes, bringing the total to 12 strokes.

The progressive die, made of O1 tool steel, pierced, embossed, notched and cut off the strut from 8$\frac{11}{16}$-in.-wide coil stock at a rate of 225 per hour. The die was set up in a 300-ton mechanical press. Mineral oil was used as the lubricant for both methods.

Example 107. Progressive Die vs Separate Dies for Producing File-Drawer Parts (Fig. 22)

Straps, such as shown in Fig. 22, used in file-drawer suspension cradles, were originally produced by shearing blanks from sheet, notching and piercing in one die, and forming to shape in a second die. Both dies were set up in a press brake. Because of increased demand, production was changed to the use of a progressive die that was fed by a coil, the width of which equaled the length of the workpiece before forming.

The straps were used in pairs. The individual straps differed only in height — ⅛ and ½ in. A five-station progressive die produced a pair of straps at each stroke of a 300-ton straight-side mechanical press. The die was made of D2 tool steel and had a life of 20,000 to 30,000 parts between resharpenings. Strip width for the progressive die was 15⅞ in. Stock hardness was Rockwell B 50 to 70. All bend radii were about twice stock thickness.

The relation of tool and labor cost to quantity for producing the pairs of straps by the two methods is shown in Fig. 22. Cost per piece for producing 250 pieces with a progressive die was 22 times that with separate dies. Costs for producing 1000 pieces by both methods were the same, but for larger quantities the progressive die was more economical.

Example 108. Four Separate Dies vs a Progressive Die (Table 4)

Table 4 compares the direct-labor costs of production, setup, and die maintenance for the use of four separate dies versus a progressive die in the production of a small 1010 steel bracket (also shown in Table 4) in a 20,000-piece run. Acceptable pieces were produced by both methods, but the 20,000 pieces were produced in a progressive die for about one-fourth the labor cost of producing them in four separate dies. The saving resulted from the reduced production time per piece; setup and die-maintenance costs were nearly the same for the two methods.

Transfer Dies

Transfer dies are similar in operation to progressive dies. The important difference is in the method of transferring workpieces from station to station. Whereas the workpieces remain fastened to the stock strip in a progressive die, they are separate in a transfer die and are transferred from station to station within the die between press strokes by mechanical fingers, levers or cams. Transfer dies are particularly suited to the making of parts that would be difficult to connect to the stock skeleton with carrier tabs. Bends that cannot be made in a single step often are made in several stages in transfer dies, and bending is often combined with cutting or other forming operations in transfer dies.

Advantages of transfer dies for bending include high production rate, greater versatility than progressive dies, and more efficient use of stock. The last advantage ordinarily is achieved by blanking in a separate press, which permits close nesting of parts. Disadvantages include high equipment cost (for dies, press attachments, and feeding devices), high setup and tool-maintenance cost, difficulty in handling thin work metal, and poor applicability to

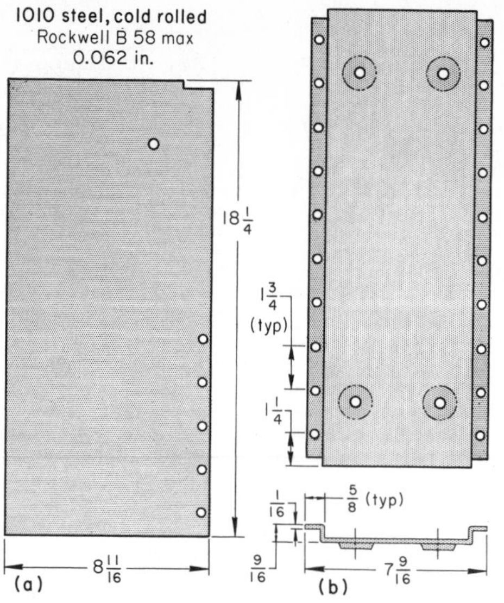

(a) Blank after first stroke with standard tooling. (b) Finished part.

Fig. 21. Strut that was produced in fewer press strokes with a progressive die than with standard press-brake tooling (Example 106)

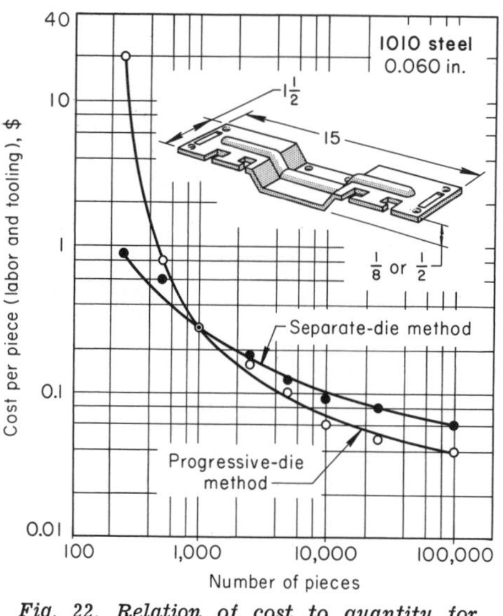

Fig. 22. Relation of cost to quantity for making straps for file-drawer suspension cradles in a progressive die or in two separate dies (Example 107)

Table 4. Labor Costs for Producing 20,000 Brackets in Four Separate Dies vs a Progressive Die (Example 108)

Item	Separate dies	Progressive die
Production	$116.00(a)	$19.40
Setup ($2.50/hr)	10.00	5.00
Die maintenance ($3/hr)	6.00(b)	9.00
Total direct-labor cost	$132.00	$33.40

(a) Includes $4.80 for blanking and piercing, $34.60 for forming the tabs, $34.60 for bending, and $42.00 for notching. (b) For grinding the blanking die and the notching die, 1 hr each.

large or odd-shape parts that need variations in blankholder pressure and contour.

Transfer dies are well suited to the bending of small rings, cups and cylinders. Transfer dies are used to make rings with one joint. (The making of a ring with one joint in a four-station die incorporating a transfer mechanism is described in Example 110.)

Use of Multiple-Slide Machines

Multiple-slide machines combine many operations, including bending, to make small products from strip up to 3/32 in. thick and 3 in. wide. The article that begins on page 154 in this volume describes the construction and operation of these machines.

The use of a multiple-slide machine for bending a sheet-metal part is described in the following example.

Example 109. Producing a Bearing Retainer in a Multiple-Slide Machine (Fig. 23)

The roller-bearing retainer (cage) shown in Fig. 23 was made from coil stock in a 60-ton multiple-slide machine equipped with a double-ram toggle press and a welding attachment. (Previously, the part had been made in a transfer press.) The coiled strip was cold rolled, commercial quality 1010 steel, 0.050 in. thick by 0.625 in. wide, with a No. 2 finish and a No. 5 edge. One ram of the toggle press was used to pierce the pockets; the second ram was used to offset the dividers between pockets by 0.050 in.

Tooling for the multiple-slide machine is also shown in Fig. 23. The sequence of operations was as follows: after the stock clamp gripped the work, the top tool moved down and the cutoff blade attached to its side cut the piece from the incoming strip. The top tool then moved on down and formed the piece into an inverted U over the center post, which was stationary.

The top tool and the cutoff blade retracted to clear the cutoff die, which withdrew into the tool plate. Then the top tool returned to hold the top of the workpiece while the side tools advanced to complete the circle. After the side tools retracted, the bottom tool moved up to set the bend.

Magnetic transfer rods picked up the formed retainer and carried it to the welding station. The welding cycle was actuated by a cam on the multiple-slide machine. Production was continuous, at 120 strokes per minute.

Light oil was the lubricant. Die material was D2 tool steel hardened to Rockwell C 61 to 62. Die life per grind was 150,000 pieces.

The pocket width was held to ±0.0015 in. after forming. This included the pocket in which welding was done. The maximum hardness of the work metal was Rockwell B 65; however, the desired (but not specified) hardness was Rockwell B 52 to 57. Production was about six million pieces per year.

As shown in Fig. 23, the stock was fed through the press and forming stations horizontally instead of vertically. This required a multiple-slide machine with a vertical press station and with forming slides mounted in a vertical plane. [Vertical stock feed with horizontal press and forming stations is described in "Forming of Steel Strip in Multiple-Slide Machines", which begins on page 154.]

Lubrication

Lubrication is less important for most bending operations than it is for other types of forming. In many bending operations, no lubricant is used; in others, mill oil remaining on the stock or a light mineral oil applied before forming is sufficient to prevent galling.

Exceptions to this practice are hole flanging, compression and stretch flanging, and severe bending in which wiping, ironing or drawing of the work metal may call for more effective lubrication. For more information and recommendations on lubrication, see the article "Selection and Use of Lubricants in Forming of Sheet Metal", which begins on page 23.

Five examples in this article describe applications in which lubricants were used because of the nature of the bending operations performed. In Example 99, where accuracy was important and sharp-radius bends were made parallel with the direction of rolling, the workpiece was lubricated with mineral oil before bending. In Example 100, mineral oil was applied to the workpiece before flattening a bend to 180°. In Example 103, a soluble oil – water mixture was used with a compound die that had a wiping component. In Example 109, light oil was applied at the start of a multiple-slide operation because of the severity of the bending to be performed. In Example 113, a drawing compound with a graphite-base additive diluted with paraffin oil was applied to the strip with rolls before forming a curved, flanged part.

Bending Cylindrical Parts

Generally, as the bend radius becomes larger, the allowance for springback must be more generous, because less of the bent metal has been stressed beyond its yield strength. Very large radii cannot easily be formed by ordinary bending, but must be stretch formed (see the article "Stretch Forming", beginning on page 239).

On large-radius bends, where the workpiece is formed to half a circle or more, the bend is often made in several stages, as in the two examples that follow (see also Example 109).

Example 110. Making a Ring in Three Bends in a Transfer Die (Fig. 24)

The 1.5-in.-OD ring illustrated in Fig. 24 was made in a four-station transfer die from coiled cold rolled 1008 steel strip, 3⁄16 in. thick by 1 in. wide. The strip was fed at right angles to its motion through the die. The first station sheared a 4.10-in. blank from the strip. Levers pushed the blank to the second station, where the ends were bent down.

The following blank pushed the workpiece onto a horizontal mandrel, or center post, at the third station, where it was bent down into an inverted U with turned-in ends. Succeeding pieces pushed the U to the fourth station, where a bottom punch completed the ring. The following workpieces pushed the completed ring off the end of the mandrel.

These rings were made in a 160-ton straight-side mechanical press that was operated at 60 strokes per minute.

Example 111. Bending a Cylindrical Part in a Progressive Die (Fig. 25)

The part shown in Fig. 25 was made in a six-station progressive die, from 0.048-in.-thick cold rolled 1010 or 1020 steel having a hardness of Rockwell B 65 to 75. The part was a valve to adjust the size of the air intake in a gas burner.

The operations for making the part included piercing the 0.112/0.109-in.-diam hole, blanking the rectangular cutout, notching the outside of the blank (leaving a ½-in.-wide center carrier tab), bending the circle in three steps starting at the outside edge, and cutoff. The 0.112/0.109-in.-diam hole was tapped with 6–32 UNC threads in an automatic tapper at 12 pieces per minute. The two 1⁄16-in.-deep circular notches were to assure that the air intake could not be closed completely.

Cutting and forming elements of the die were made of O1 tool steel. hardened to Rockwell C 58 to 60. Die life was 80,000 pieces per regrind. The die was run in a 45-ton press at the rate of 40 pieces per minute to produce lots averaging 10,000 pieces. The part later was zinc plated and bright dipped.

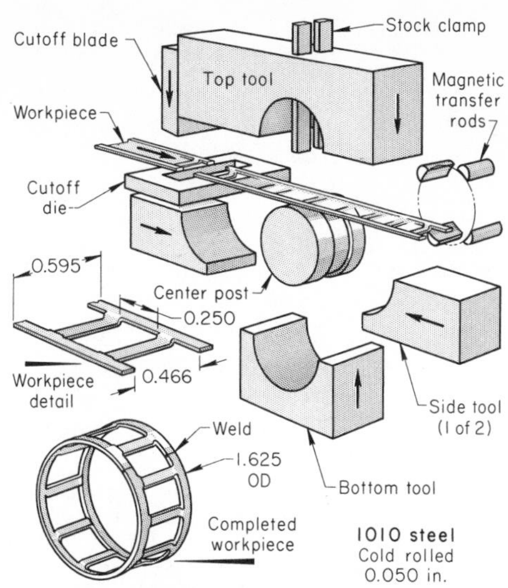

Fig. 23. Tooling setup for forming of a roller-bearing retainer in a multiple-slide machine (Example 109)

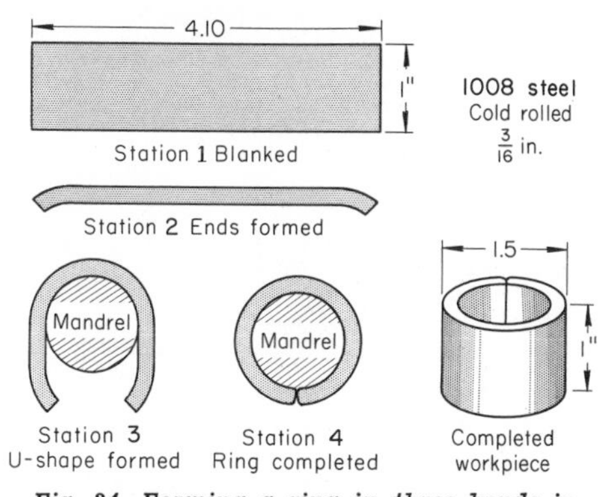

Fig. 24. Forming a ring in three bends in a four-station transfer die (Example 110)

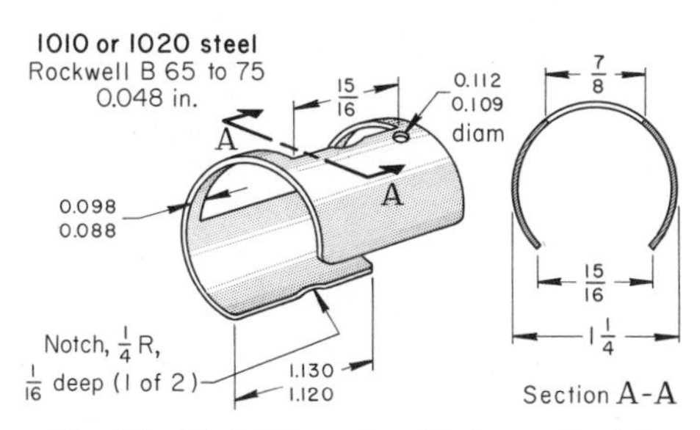

Fig. 25. Air-intake valve that was bent to circular form in three stages in a six-station progressive die (Example 111)

Edge Bending

Bending of parts with the bend radius perpendicular to the width rather than to the thickness, as is the usual practice, is called edge bending.

It is sometimes possible to save material by producing fairly large blanks in simple rectangular form (square-sheared) and then edge bending them into shape. Finish blanking (trimming) is frequently done after edge bending.

Before choosing edge bending in preference to blanking from sheet, it is necessary to consider the effect of cold work from the bending operation on subsequent forming. High breakage during edge bending can wipe out the cost advantage of the saving in material. Another consideration is the higher cost of labor and tooling for edge bending, which also can offset the saving in material.

The following example describes edge bending that was done both to save material and to strengthen the part. (For another application of edge bending, see Example 161 in the article "Press Forming of Low-Carbon Steel".)

Example 112. Edge Bending (Fig. 26)

Figure 26 shows a curved-end automotive foot-pedal lever that was produced by edge bending a blank sheared from a bar of hot rolled 1010 steel. The bar, ¼ in. thick, 2⅜ in. wide, and 14½ in. long, was sheared lengthwise to produce two blanks 1⅝ in. wide at one end and ¾ in. wide at the other. Edge bending resulted in substantial material savings over blanking and also a stronger part.

Each blank was edge bent to a 2-in. radius at the narrow end. Other operations included bending the offset and making the two other bends, piercing the ½-in.-diam hole, extruding four weld projections (see section A-A in Fig. 26), and trimming the radius on the small end. The cutting and forming sections of the dies were made of air-hardening tool steel.

The stock was cut to length in a 120-ton end-wheel press (mainshaft extending front-to-back) operating at 60 strokes per minute. Edge bending, forming, trimming and piercing were done by separate dies in a 190-ton open-back inclinable press at 30 pieces per minute.

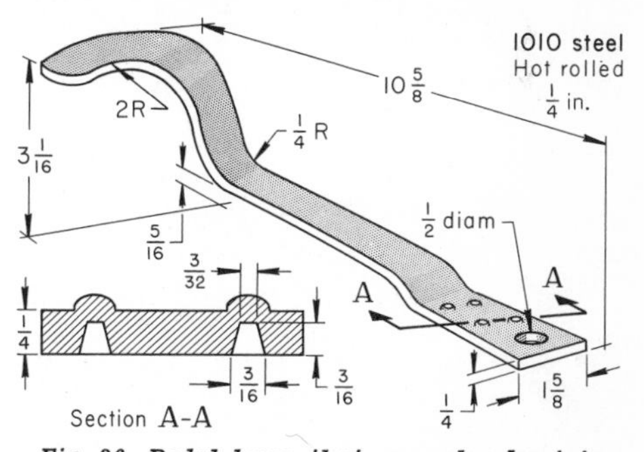

Fig. 26. Pedal lever that was edge bent to save metal and increase strength of the part (Example 112)

The size of the offset radii, the length and depth of the offset, and the location of the offset with respect to the flanges, precluded edge bending a rectangular blank in the following example. The potential cracking and thinning of the outer edge and wrinkling of the inner edge made the use of a blanked shape more practical.

Example 113. Blanking Instead of Edge Bending (Fig. 27)

The folding-cot leg splice shown in Fig. 27 was provided with the S-curve by blanking, rather than by edge bending, because of the abrupt change in shape, and because there

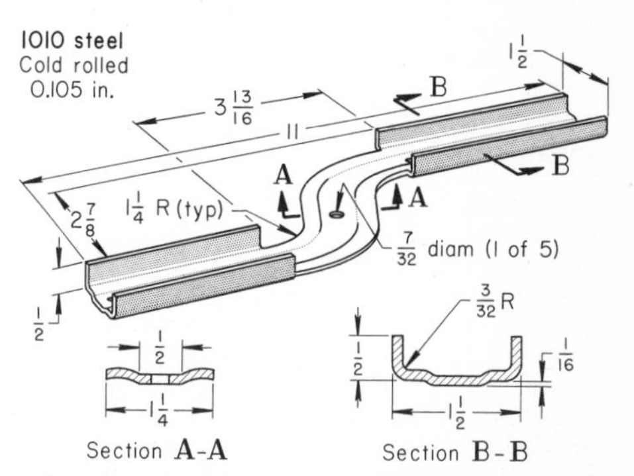

Fig. 27. Folding-cot leg splice that was made by blanking instead of by edge bending (Example 113)

were no stretch and shrink flanges around the bend to offset metal stress. An offset extending the full length of the part and flanges on each end served as stiffeners. The legs of the cot were riveted to these splices, which also acted as hinges.

The part was made in a five-station progressive die, from cold rolled 1010 steel strip, 0.105 in. thick and 11¾ in. wide. The edges in the area without flanges were bent downward slightly (see section A-A in Fig. 27) so that contact with the mating hardware was on curved surfaces and not along the edges. The ends of the flanges were blended into the center section without a bend-relief cutout — which would have weakened the part.

A 150-ton press operating at 45 strokes per minute and equipped with a single roll feed was used. Misfeed detectors assured that the part was ejected, and that not more than one blank was in the forming station.

A drawing compound containing a graphite-base additive plus a paraffin oil was applied to the strip with rolls. One set of dies made over 900,000 parts, justifying the cost of a progressive die. Also, the labor cost saved by the progressive die was greater than the cost of the metal that would have been saved by using individual dies, which would have been necessary if the blank had been edge bent.

Straight Flanging

Flange bending (flanging) in a wiping die is like cantilever loading of a beam. To prevent movement during bending, the workpiece is clamped to the die by a pressure pad before the punch contacts the workpiece. The bend axis is parallel with the edge of the die.

Flanging dies are often cam-actuated, with attendant loss of efficiency. Hold-down pads must be used, adding further to the press capacity requirement. Considering all factors, the press capacity for flanging in a wiping die may be up to ten times that for forming a similar length of bend in a V-die with a spacing of at least eight times the thickness of the work metal.

In some operations, only single flanges are bent. More often, more than one flange is bent at a time, as in Examples 96, 98, 101, 102, 103, 116, 121 and 122. Dies can be simple V-dies, U-dies, wiping dies, or complex flanging dies like those shown in Fig. 12 and 13.

Even when fairly close tolerances must be held, simple V-dies can be used to make a complex part if production is low, as in Example 207 in the article on Press Forming of Coated Steel.

Flanging dies cost more than ordinary press-brake dies, but considering the time and labor saved in making simple flanged pieces in flanging dies, they often pay for themselves quickly. The following example shows that even for low production, special dies would have been paid for in two years.

Example 114. Utility Tooling vs Special Tooling (Including a Flanging Die) (Table 5)

The stationery tray shown in Table 5 was produced in quantities of 40,000 per year. The trays had been made by a method (see footnote a in Table 5) in which only simple, utility tooling was used, with most of the work being done in press brakes and power shears.

Another method was proposed, to make production more efficient. The proposed method (see footnote b in Table 5) would have combined all of the operations into five dies.

Costs for the two methods, projected over two years' production (80,000 pieces), are compared in Table 5. As this comparison shows, the proposed special-tooling method, because of the saving in cost of labor and overhead, would have saved about 7% in total cost per piece over the two-year period, in spite of the much higher tooling cost.

Table 5. Costs for Producing 80,000 Stationery Trays by Utility Tooling vs Special Tooling (Example 114)

Cost item, per piece	Utility tooling(a)	Special tooling(b)
Labor and overhead	$0.154	$0.07
Setup(c)	0.0234	0.0162
Tools(d)	0.0019	0.0812
Total	$0.1793	$0.1674
Saving per piece		$0.0119
Saving for 80,000 pieces		$952

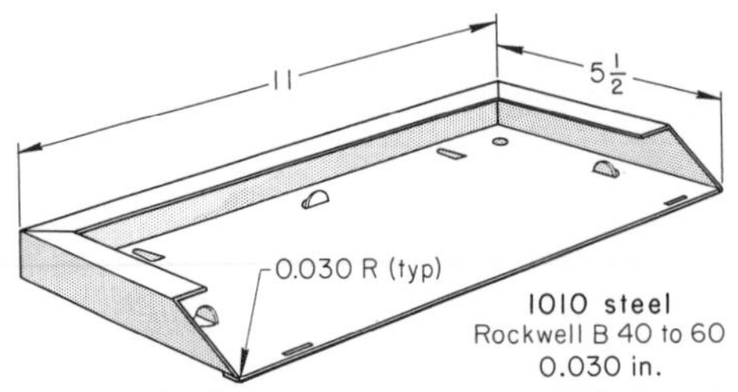

(a) Operations: slit to width; cut off blanks; notch four corners and pierce two holes; hem front edge (two strokes); pierce two slots; brake form sides and back (six strokes); pierce and lance. (b) Operations: slit to width; blank and pierce two holes; hem front edge (in hemming die); box form three sides; finish form three sides (in flanging die); pierce and lance. (c) Twelve setups: $156 each for utility tooling and $108 for special tooling. (d) Total cost of $150 for utility tooling and $6500 for special.

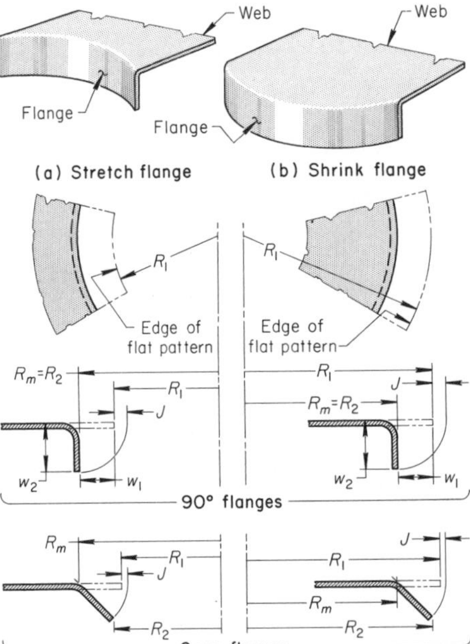

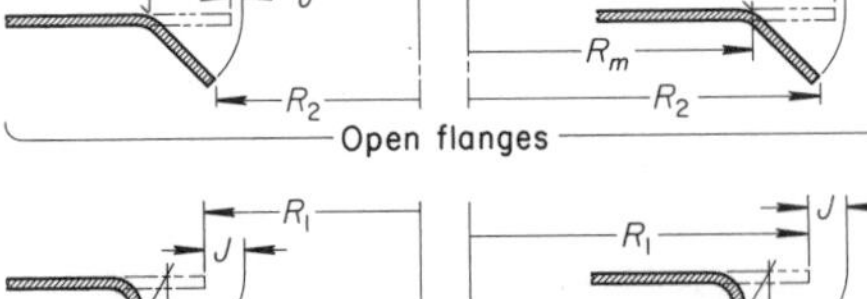

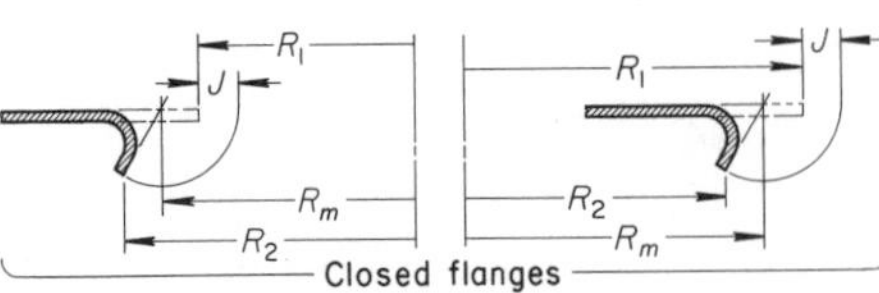

R_1 = edge radius before forming.
R_2 = edge radius after forming.
R_m = mold-line radius.
W_1 = width of flange before forming.
W_2 = width of formed flange.
J = bend allowance (difference between flange width measured from the mold line after bending and the length of the neutral axis of the metal before bending).

Fig. 28. Dimensional relationships for three types of stretch and shrink flanges

Hemming is an operation in which flanges are flattened against the workpiece in 180° bends to make a finished or reinforced edge. If the flange to be hemmed has been bent somewhat more than 90° the hemming die can be a simple flat bed or anvil and a simple flat punch. Both flanging and hemming can be done in one press in a compound die, as shown in Fig. 17.

Bending of Curved Flanges

When a flange has concave curvature, the metal in the flange is in tension, and the flange is called a stretch flange (see Fig. 28a). When the curvature is convex, the metal in the flange is in compression, and the flange is called a shrink flange (see Fig. 28b). The amount of tension or compression in either type of flange increases from the bend radius to the edge of the flange. Excessive tension in a concave (stretch) flange causes cracks and tears; excessive compression in the convex (shrink) flange causes wrinkles.

Stretch and shrink flanges are commonly formed adjacent to each other, producing a reverse flange (as shown in Fig. 30, for Example 116).

Bend allowances for use in development of a flat blank are given in Table 2 in "Press-Brake Forming", page 110.

Flanging Limits. Flange radii, flange width and angle of bend for curved flanges are limited chiefly by the amount of deformation that can be tolerated by the flange edges — which depends on the type, thickness and hardness of the metal and the method of forming. Greater fineness of detail can be achieved in conventional dies than by rubber-pad forming, because of the limited pressures in rubber-pad forming. However, rubber pads provide a uniform pressure over the entire surface of the workpiece, and they can be used to advantage where conventional dies would shear or tear the material.

The approximate percentage of deformation of the free edge is equal to $100[(R_2/R_1) - 1]$, where R_1 is the edge radius before forming (flat-pattern radius) and R_2 is the edge radius after forming, as shown in Fig. 28. For 90° flanges, R_2 is the same as R_m. Positive values of percentage of deformation indicate elongation (stretch); negative values indicate compression (shrink).

The permissible limits for conventional die forming of curved flanges in three common steels, 0.040 in. thick or more, are as follows:

Steel	Stretch, %	Shrink, %
1010	38	10
1020	22	10
8630	17	8

These limits should be reduced slightly for thin stock, particularly for shrink flanges. The limits for stretch flanges can be increased if there is an adjoining shrink flange. The compression in the shrink flange helps to relieve the stress in the stretch flange (and vice versa). Also, limits of permissible stretch may be increased by filing or grinding the edges of the blank lengthwise; with this procedure, flanges having a calculated stretch of about 100% can be formed, as in Example 116. Shrink flanges are more easily formed if the motion of the die causes some ironing of the metal in the direction of the edge of the flange.

Severe Contour Flanging. In small pieces, when enough press force is available, shrink flanges can be formed with sufficient metal flow that the flanges resemble drawn shapes, without using bend reliefs. Such severe flanging is shown in the following example.

Example 115. Severe Contour Flanging of Thick Stock (Fig. 29)

The hinge half shown in Fig. 29 was formed in one stroke of a 900-ton press. By close control of clearances, it was possible to produce the contour, the sharp inside corner on the bend of the flange, and close matching of the outside planes of the flanges and the edges of the part. The metal was drawing quality hot rolled 1010 steel, 0.239 in. thick.

A slight puckering of the metal at the corners between the flanges and the back indicated the severity of the forming. Relief cutouts were not used in this piece, but because of the severity of the forming, the five holes were pierced after forming, to hold the location of the two in-line holes in the flanges within ±0.010 in. of the three other holes. [Compare this practice with that described in Example 121, in which holes were pierced before the part was flanged, and yet hole locations were held within ±0.010 in.]

The forming die was made of W1 tool steel and was hardened to Rockwell C 58 to 60. The die was reconditioned after each production lot of 20,000 to 25,000 pieces. Production rate was 600 hinge halves per hour.

Edge Grinding. If they are rough, the edges of stretch flanges may crack or tear at critical points. In the following example, a severe bend was made in a difficult-to-form flange, without cracking, after the rough edges had been ground to smooth the surface.

Example 116. Use of an Edge-Ground Blank to Minimize Cracking of a Severe Stretch Flange (Fig. 30)

The crossmember of a truck chassis was made from hot rolled low-carbon steel, pickled and oiled. It was bent from a developed blank into the channel shape shown in Fig. 30. In bending the blank, the edges of the stretch flanges cracked and tore. This problem was solved by filing the edges smooth in the portion of the blank where the stretch and shrink flanges would be formed. Bends were made parallel to the rolling direction.

Because hand filing of the rough edges was costly, grinding was tried, with good results so long as the direction of grinding was along the edge rather than across it. Cross grinding left grooves that increased stress to the same degree as did the original roughness.

Forming was done in a 425-ton hydraulic press. The die was a single-action pressure-pad type made of tool steel and had an estimated life of 300,000 pieces. Production rate was two or three channels per minute, in 800-piece production lots.

Hole Flanging. A flange formed around a pierced hole is a continuous stretch flange. One manufacturer has standardized flange dimensions for holes to be tapped in low-carbon steel. These dimensions, as related to work-metal thickness, are shown in Fig. 31.

In thick stock, the length of the flange around a hole can be greater than shown in Fig. 31, but the flange thickness will taper rather than be relatively uniform. In the following example, the design of the flanging punch was changed to produce a flange that would have a wall thickness at the bottom adequate for tapping.

Example 117. Redesign of Punch for Acceptable Wall Thickness of Flanged Hole (Fig. 32)

Piercing and flanging a hole, followed by tapping a minimum of four full threads, was the most economical method of making a bracket (Fig. 32a) used in pairs for mounting unit heaters that weighed 100 to 600 lb. The material was 0.105-in.-thick low-carbon rimmed steel, cold rolled, drawing quality.

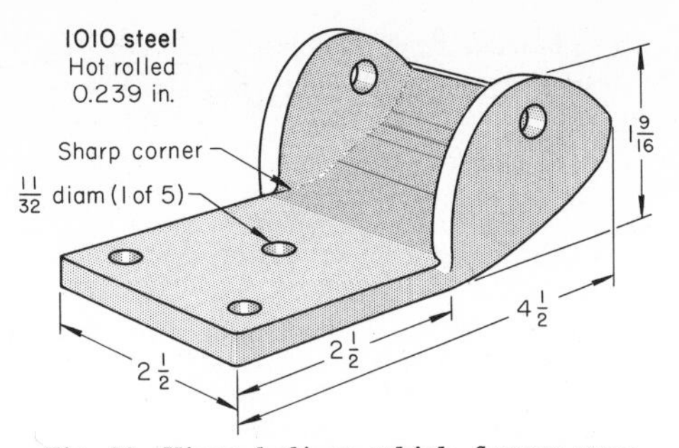

Fig. 29. Hinge half on which flanges were formed flush with adjacent surfaces (Example 115)

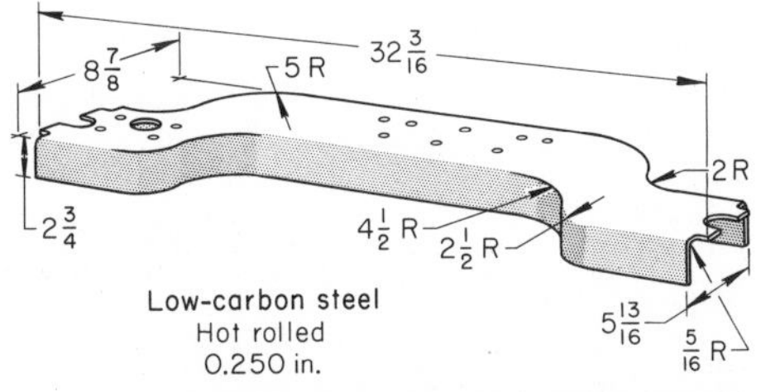

Over the length of the two stretch flanges, the 5/16-in. inside bend radius was increased, being blended to and from a maximum of 1 in.

Fig. 30. Truck-frame crossmember that was bent from edge-ground blanks to prevent cracking and tearing of the stretch flanges (Example 116)

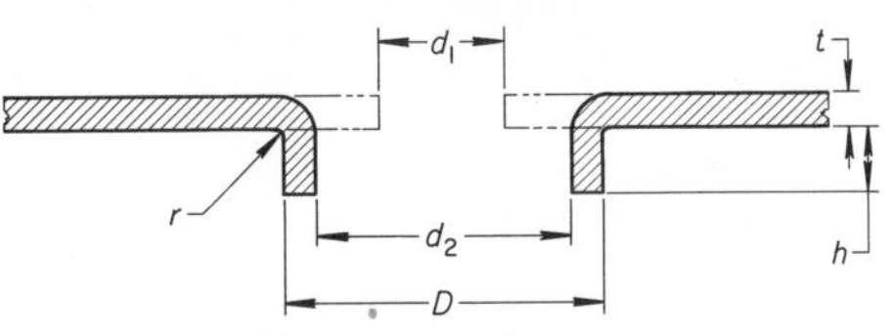

$D = d_2 + 5t/4$ when t is 0.045 in. or less.
$D = d_2 + t$ when t is greater than 0.045 in.
$h = t$ when t is less than 0.035 in.
$h = 4t/5$ when t is 0.035 to 0.050 in.
$h = 3t/5$ when t is greater than 0.050 in.
$r = t/4$ when t is 0.045 in. or less.
$r = t/3$ when t is greater than 0.045 in.

$$d_1 = \sqrt{\frac{tD^2 + 4td_2^2 + 4hd_2^2 - 4hD^2}{9t}}$$

Fig. 31. Dimensions of flanged holes to be tapped, as a function of thickness, for low-carbon steel

Originally, a flanging punch having a 0.125-in. corner radius, as shown in Fig. 32(b), was used. With this punch (O1 tool steel, Rockwell C 62), the flange wall was thinned so much that at the start of the third thread, wall thickness was only 0.013 in. and did not provide sufficient strength.

A punch having a pilot and a spherical end, as shown in Fig. 32(c), produced a flange with a wall thickness of 0.036 in. at the start of the third thread. Although the flange height was 1/32 in. less than that produced by the original punch, the threads withstood a 40,000-lb pull test and performed satisfactorily in service.

Strips 1¼ in. wide were sheared from sheets 120 in. long by 24⅞ in. wide. The strips were hand fed into a progressive die, which produced the brackets by piercing, flanging and cutoff. Production rates and costs for all operations entailed in making these parts are given in the table with Fig. 32.

Control of Springback

Springback has little effect in bending of low-carbon steel, and is considered only when close dimensional control is needed. It ordinarily ranges from ½° to 1½° and can be controlled by overbending or by restriking the bend area. Factors that affect springback include ratio of bend radius to stock thickness, angle of bend (degrees of bend from flat), method of bending (V-bending or wiping), and amount of compression in the bend zone.

When the bend radius is several times the stock thickness, the metal will need more overbending to stress it beyond the yield point than when the radius is $2t$ or less. A greater amount of overbending is needed to correct for springback on small bend angles than on large bend angles.

In curved flanges, the radius of curvature and flange length have an effect on the tension or compression in the flange metal, which in turn affects springback.

Springback can vary in a production run of a given part because of variation in stock thickness, variation in stock hardness or temper, tool wear, variation in tool adjustment, and variation in power input (line surges).

Multiple Bends. When more than one bend is made in a part, the effect of springback is ordinarily cumulative and may necessitate closer control of the operation than would be needed for just one bend. The following example shows the variation in springback in a part with more than one bend:

Example 118. Variation in Springback in a Part With Eight Bends (Fig. 33)

The part shown in Fig. 33 was produced from 1008 steel in three operations: blank, bend, and trim. In three of the eight bends, springback reduced the 2.155-in. dimension, and in five, it increased that dimension.

To find the net magnitude of the springback and how much variation could be expected, 100 random samples were measured from a production lot of 10,000 pieces. The net effect of the springback (as expected) was to enlarge the 2.155-in. dimension, by amounts

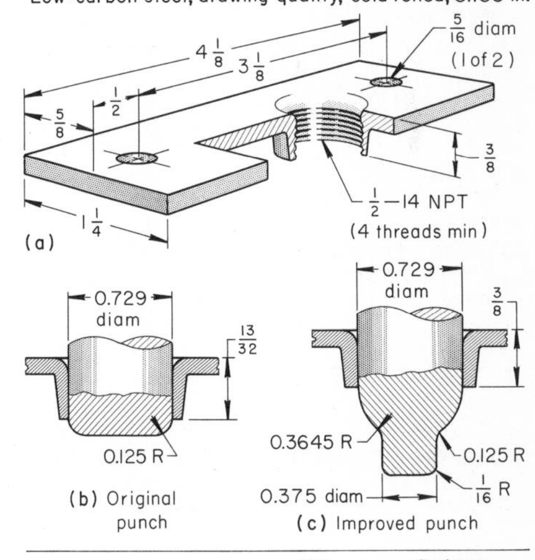

Operation	Production, pcs/hr	Cost per piece for: Labor	Cost per piece for: Burden
Pierce 3 holes; flange; cut off	470	$0.01	$0.02
Spotface	90	0.03	0.06
Tap ½–14 NPT thread	205	0.01	0.03
Total cost(a)		$0.05	$0.11

(a) Progressive die for piercing, flanging and cutting off cost $485; with amortization over 60,000 pieces (annual production), tool cost was $0.008 per piece. Steel cost was $0.03 per piece. Thus, total cost per piece was: $0.05 + $0.11 + $0.008 + $0.03 = $0.198.

Fig. 32. Bracket with threaded flanged hole for which the design of the flanging punch was changed to provide adequate wall thickness for threads in the flange (Example 117)

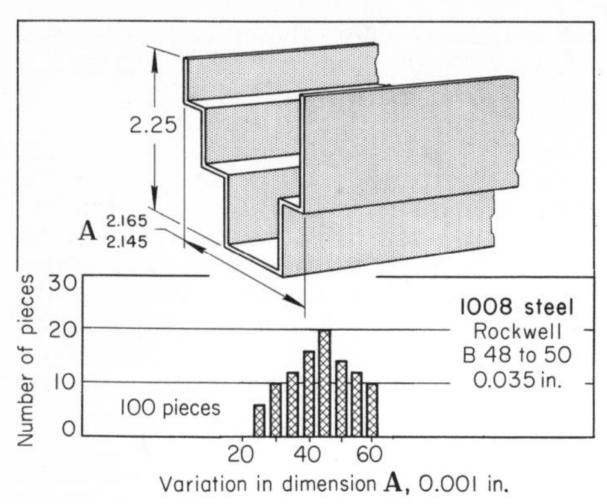

Fig. 33. Variation in flange spacing caused by springback in a part with eight bends (Example 118)

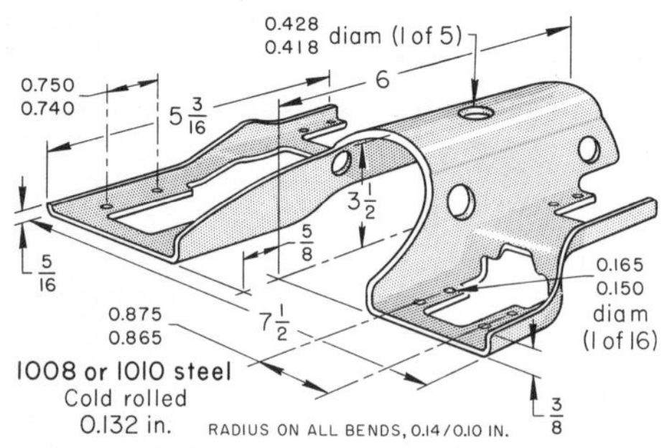

Fig. 34. Bracket with unbalanced shape that was held within bending tolerances by restriking and by extra-close clearances on some parts of bending dies (Example 119)

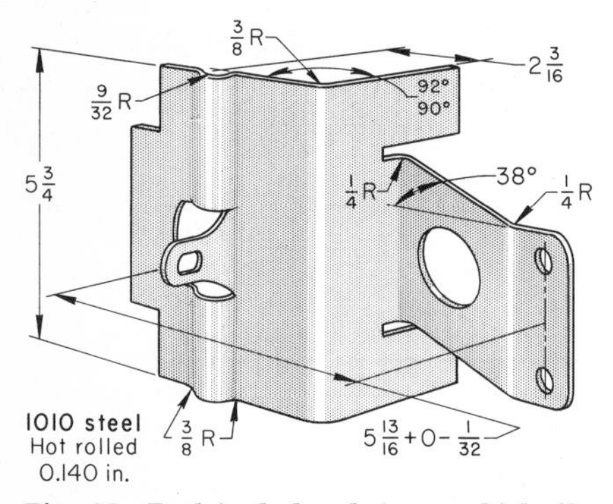

Fig. 35. Fuel-tank bracket on which the critical dimension (5¹³⁄₁₆ in.) was maintained by overbending to control springback (Example 120)

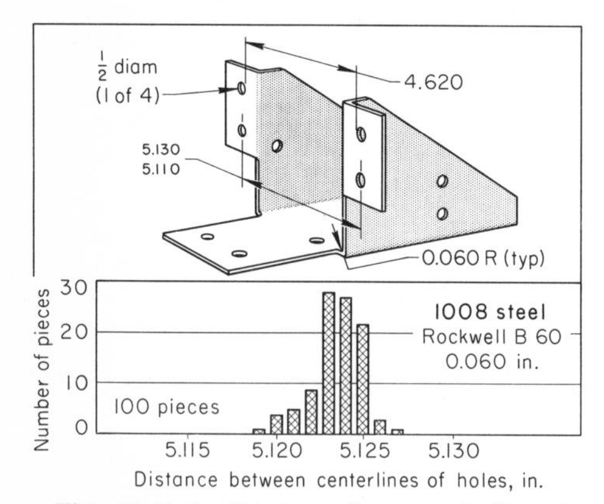

The plotted distances from centerline to centerline were determined by adding 0.500 in. to the gage readings of distances between the inner edges of the holes.

Fig. 36. Variation in distance between centerlines of holes prepierced in opposite flanges of press-bent workpieces (Example 121)

ranging from 0.025 to 0.060 in., as shown in Fig. 33.

The variation in stock thickness was ±0.002 in. The inside radius on all bends was equal to stock thickness.

Restriking and overbending can be used to set flanges and offset the effects of springback, as in the following two examples.

Example 119. Use of Restriking and Close-Fitting Tools to Control Springback in a Flanged Part (Fig. 34)

The column-support bracket shown in Fig. 34 was made of 0.132-in.-thick drawing quality, cold rolled 1008 or 1010 steel having a hardness of Rockwell B 48 to 51. The use of close-fitting punches and dies for certain areas and restriking other areas made it possible to obtain the dimensional accuracy necessary for hole positions, cutouts and flanges.

All the round holes were pierced in the flat strip before notching, trimming, punching and forming. The positions of the small holes with respect to the center were important. The spacing of each set of four small holes was also critical. The flanges along the outer edges had to be uniform in height and set square with the adjacent surface. The open center design and the unbalanced form made it difficult to hold the hole distances and the uniform flange heights.

The forming was done in a progressive die, which was made of O2 tool steel. The cutting punch-to-die clearance was 10% of stock thickness per side. To hold the burr to a minimum height, the die was resharpened after each 50,000 strokes.

The die operated at 400 to 500 strokes per hour. The die was expected to produce parts at this rate for two years, and then it would be used for making replacement parts, for which the tolerances were less critical.

Example 120. Control of Springback by Overbending (Fig. 35)

The fuel-tank bracket shown in Fig. 35 superseded an assembly in which the mounting tab was welded on. Cutting out and bending back the tab made a stronger part. It was necessary to control springback in the 90° bend by overbending and by careful adjustment of bending dies to maintain the 5¹³⁄₁₆-in. mounting dimension.

The part was formed in a 150-ton open-back inclinable mechanical press with a pneumatic die cushion. To keep the work from shifting in the die, a blankholding force of about 45 tons was applied by the die cushion.

The bracket was made from hot rolled, commercial quality 1010 steel. The procedure was as follows:

1 Shear strips to 10¹³⁄₁₆ in. wide.
2 Blank the developed form (blanking die was made of D2 tool steel).
3 Bend in single-operation dies (bending dies were made of O1 tool steel).

Die life between regrinds was 50,000 pieces. The pieces were lubricated with mineral oil. About four production runs of 2500 pieces each were made per year.

Accurate Location and Form of Holes

Hole position sometimes cannot be held to tolerance when a workpiece is pierced before bending. When this is so, holes must be pierced after bending—which may require the use of cam-actuated punches, or specially shaped dies to support overhanging formed flanges, or punches and dies that are shaped to pierce at an angle.

Holes made before bending are likely to be displaced during bending. Whether or not this displacement can be tolerated must be carefully considered in planning the sequence of operations.

The following example typifies the kind of variation in hole location that can be expected in formed pieces. In this example, had the tolerance on spacing of the holes been ±0.001 in. instead of ±0.010 in., the holes would have been pierced after forming, as they were in Example 115.

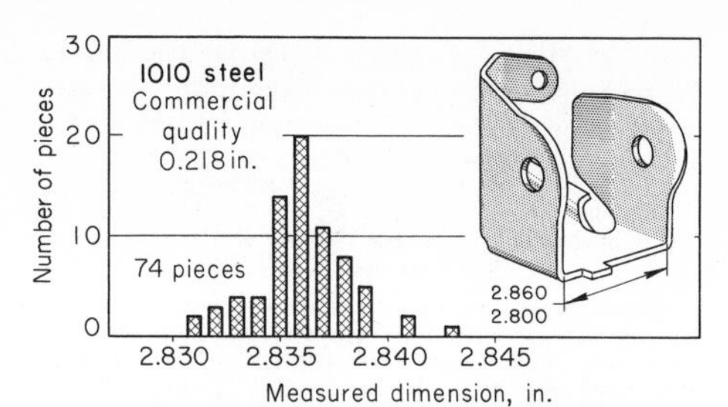

Fig. 37. Accuracy of flange spacing obtained by maintenance of small gib clearance and close ram-to-bolster parallelism in press bending of control-arm brackets for passenger-car frames (Example 122)

Example 121. Variation in Distance Between Prepierced Holes in a Formed Part (Fig. 36)

The bracket shown in Fig. 36 was formed in three operations: blanking and piercing; bending the two small flanges; and bending the two large flanges. The 5.120-in. spacing between hole centerlines in opposite flanges had to be held within ±0.010 in.

A reference dimension of 4.620 in. between the inner edges of the holes was computed for the purpose of checking hole spacing with vernier calipers. Caliper measurements of that dimension on 100 randomly selected pieces (from a run of 10,000 pieces) showed variations of −0.001 to +0.007 in. (see Fig. 36).

Free bending of a workpiece is likely to displace holes from true position and also to distort and elongate them. In many press-bent workpieces, this deformation is slight enough to be negligible, but sometimes it causes serious difficulties in assembly or fitting. The likelihood of distortion is minimized when holes are located at least one stock thickness away from the beginning curve of a bend. Other precautions include trapping the hole with a hold-down pad that is heavily loaded, or relieving the area around the hole with a crescent-shape cutout. For more information on design and protection of pierced holes during subsequent bending, see the section "Effect of Forming Requirements" on page 53 in the article "Piercing of Low-Carbon Steel", in this volume. Examples 36, 37, 38 and 39 in that article describe applications in which holes were pierced after bending, to avoid hole distortion and displacement during the bending operation.

An instance of acceptable distortion of pierced holes by subsequent bending is described in Example 41 in the article "Piercing of Low-Carbon Steel".

Other examples on piercing holes before bending are Examples 26 and 27 in the article on Piercing of Low-Carbon Steel. Example 43 in that article describes an application in which holes were pierced after bending.

Accurate Spacing of Flanges

The distance between flanges is another dimension that depends on accuracy of bending. For assembly purposes, this distance may need to be held very closely. Ordinarily, the dimensions at the bases of the flanges are fairly uniform and variation in the distance between flanges is greater near the free edges.

If a flanged part is to fit over a mating piece, oversize dimensions may be preferable to undersize dimensions, as in the following example.

Example 122. Flange Spacing That Was Obtained by Maintaining Tight Gibs and a True Ram (Fig. 37)

The bracket shown in Fig. 37 was produced from 0.218-in.-thick commercial quality 1010 steel by shearing, blanking, forming, and piercing. The flanges and other bends in the bracket were produced in a five-station transfer die mounted in a 400-ton mechanical press. The opposing holes in the flanges were either 0.630/0.626 or 0.505/0.501 in. in diameter, and were pierced after forming. Bend radii were 0.22 in. Work-metal hardness was Rockwell B 55 max.

For proper fit of the bracket with its mating part, the dimension between the two opposing flanges had to be held between 2.800 and 2.860 in.; the basic dimension was 2.800 in. Figure 37 plots the distance between flanges as measured on 74 pieces during a total production run of 6345 brackets. As these data show, all samples were well within tolerance.

To obtain this degree of accuracy on the heavy-gage bracket, gib clearance in the press was kept between 0.006 and 0.008 in., and parallelism of the face of the ram with the top of the bolster was maintained within 0.020 in. Also, before forming, the blanks were checked for thickness, and the forming tool was adjusted to compensate for variations.

The dies were made of A2 tool steel and were hardened to Rockwell C 60 to 62.

Safety

Press bending, like all other press operations, involves potential hazards to operators, maintenance men, and other personnel in the vicinity. The articles on Presses and Auxiliary Equipment and on Blanking of Low-Carbon Steel contain information and literature references on safe operation.

Press-Brake Forming

*By the ASM Committee on Press-Brake Forming and Three-Roll Forming of Steel**

PRESS-BRAKE FORMING is a process in which the workpiece is placed over an open die and is pressed down into the die by a punch that is actuated by the ram portion of a machine called a press brake. The process is most widely used for forming of relatively long, narrow parts that are not adaptable to press forming, and for applications in which production quantities are too small to warrant the tooling cost for contour roll forming.

Simple V-bends or more intricate shapes can be formed in a press brake. Operations such as blanking, piercing, lancing, shearing, straightening, embossing, beading, wiring, flattening, corrugating and flanging can also be performed in a press brake.

Principles

In press-brake forming, as in other forming processes, when a bend is made, the metal on the inside of the bend is compressed or shrunk, and that on the outside of the bend is stretched. The applied forces create a strain gradient across the thickness of the work metal in the area of die contact. Tensile strain occurs in the outer fiber, and compressive strain in the inner fiber; both decrease in magnitude toward the neutral axis.

The setup and tooling for press-brake forming (Fig. 1) are relatively simple. The distance the punch enters the die determines the bend angle and is controlled by the shut height of the machine. The span width of the die, or the width of the die opening, affects the force needed to bend the workpiece. The minimum width is determined by the thickness of the work and sometimes by the punch-nose radius. (Acceptable criteria for press-brake forming dies are shown as the shaded area between the upper and lower limit lines in Fig. 2 in the article on Forming of Titanium, page 440). After the tools have been set up and the shut height has been adjusted, the press brake is cycled and the work metal is bent to the desired angle around the nose radius of the punch.

Applicability

Press-brake forming is most widely used for producing shapes from ferrous and nonferrous metal sheet and plate. Although sheet or plate 0.250 in. thick or less is most commonly formed in a press brake, metals up to 1 in. thick have often been used, as in the following example (see also Example 133):

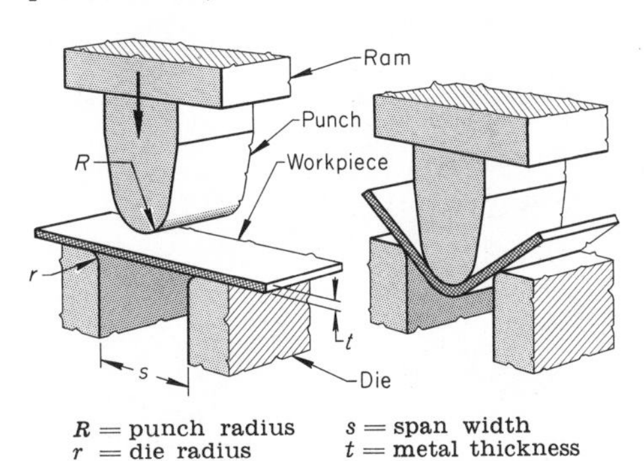

R = punch radius s = span width
r = die radius t = metal thickness

Fig. 1. Typical setup for press-brake forming in a die with a vertical opening

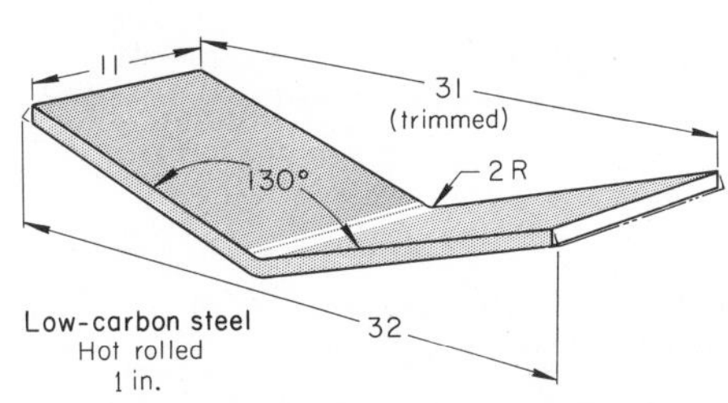

Fig. 2. Frame brace that was air bent from thick plate in a V-die in a 300-ton press brake (Example 123)

Example 123. Bending 1-In.-Thick Steel Plate (Fig. 2)

An 11-in.-long bend was made in a 1-in.-thick low-carbon steel plate in a 300-ton press brake to make the part shown in Fig. 2. The bend radius was 2 in.; the included angle was 130°. The plate was air bent in a V-die with a punch that was made from a steel tube 4 in. in diameter.

After bending, the edges of the part were machined parallel, as shown in Fig. 2. The workpiece became part of a welded assembly — a frame brace on an industrial lift truck.

The length of plate or sheet that can be bent is limited only by the size of the press brake. For instance, a 600-ton press brake can bend a 10-ft length of ¾-in.-thick low-carbon steel plate to a 90° angle, with an inside radius of the bend equal to stock thickness. If the included angle of the bend is greater than 90°, or if the bend radius is larger than stock thickness, or if the length of bend is less than the bed length, a press of correspondingly lower capacity can be used.

Forming can be done at room or elevated temperature. For elevated-temperature forming in which the punch bottoms, the punch and die should be heated as well as the blank. In air bending, the blank is heated, and sometimes the punch is heated, depending on the area of contact between punch and blank, and the metal thickness.

Work Metals. Press-brake forming is applicable to any metal that can be formed by other methods, such as press forming and roll forming. Low-carbon steels, high-strength low-alloy steels, stainless steels, aluminum alloys, and copper alloys are commonly formed in press brakes. High-carbon steels and titanium alloys are less frequently formed in a press brake, because they are more difficult to form.

*K. J. HUMBERSTONE, *Chairman,* Vice President, American Tank and Fabricating Co.; F. R. CERVARICH, Vice President, Capital City Iron Works, Inc.; JOHN E. CHOATE, Plant Manager, Vulcan Manufacturing Co.; EDWARD J. CLARKIN, Manufacturing Superintendent, Nooter Corp.

JAMES DURKIN, Assistant Foreman – Boiler Shop, Sun Shipbuilding & Dry Dock Co.; FRANK G. FLOCKE, Thornton Co.; ROBERT L. HALEY, Mechanical Engineer, Farm Equipment Div., Memphis Works, International Harvester Co.; RAYMOND J. IMARS, General Foreman of Fabrication, Steel Processing and Fabrication Dept., E. F. Hauserman Co.; J. J. LYNCH, Metallurgist, American Tank and Fabricating Co.; EUGENE F. PAUL, Supervisor of Special Equipment Projects, Emerson Electric Co.

LAWRENCE G. SCHREINER, Chief Industrial Engineer, American Hoist & Derrick Co.; R. F. SLOVICK, Planning Engineer, Hawthorne Works, Western Electric Co., Inc.; J. H. WORL, Mechanical Engineer, Bertsch & Co., Inc.; H. H. WORTHINGTON, Tool Engineer, Power Systems Div., McGraw-Edison Co.

Table 1. Capacities, Sizes, Speeds and Ratings for Mechanical and Hydraulic Press Brakes

Capacity, tons: Mid-stroke	Capacity, tons: Near bottom of stroke	Bed length, ft	Stroke length, in.	Speed, strokes per min	Bending capacity (ft) with standard stroke, for low-carbon steel with thickness of: 1/16 in.	3/16 in.	1/4 in.	1/2 in.	3/4 in.	1 in.	Motor, hp
Mechanical Press Brakes											
...	15	4 to 10	2	20 to 50	4	¾	...	...	...	...	¾ to 1
...	25	6 to 12	2	20 to 50	6½	1½	...	...	...	...	1½
36	55	6 to 12	2½	40	12	3	...	...	...	...	3
60	90	6 to 14	3	40	...	6	...	...	...	...	5
90	135	6 to 14	3	36, 12	...	11	6	...	...	...	7½
115	175	6 to 14	3	36, 12	...	...	10	...	...	...	10
150	225	6 to 16	3	33, 11	...	...	13	...	...	...	15
200	300	8 to 18	4	30, 10	...	...	18	6	...	...	20
260	400	8⅔ to 18⅔	4	30, 10	...	...	...	8	...	...	20
335	500	8⅔ to 18⅔	4	30, 10	...	...	...	10	5	...	25
400	600	10 to 24	4	30, 10	...	...	...	12	5	...	30
520	750	10 to 24	4	23, 7	...	...	...	18	10	...	40
650	1000	10 to 24	5	23, 7	...	...	...	24	12	6	40
825	1250	14 to 22	6	20, 6	...	...	...	...	17	10	50
1000	1500	14 to 24	6	20, 6	...	...	...	...	21	12	50
Hydraulic Press Brakes											
...	200	8⅔ to 18⅔	12	21, 34(a,b)	...	14	12	...	...	...	25
...	300	8⅔ to 18⅔	12	25(a,c)	...	...	16	8	...	...	30
...	400	8⅔ to 18⅔	12	26(a,d)	...	...	...	12	6	...	40
...	500	8⅔ to 18⅔	12	25(a,e)	...	...	...	14	9	...	40
...	600	10 to 24	12	25(a,f)	...	...	...	16	10	...	50
...	750	14 to 24	12	21(a,g)	...	...	...	22	14	10	60
...	1000	14 to 24	18	21(a,h)	...	...	...	...	18	14	75

(a) Normal press speed gives rated capacity. High press speeds, in inches per minute (ipm), together with press tonnage ratings, are as follows: (b) 57 and 65 ipm at 70 tons; (c) 44 and 62 ipm at 120 tons; (d) 51 and 62 ipm at 160 tons; (e) 54 and 58 ipm at 200 tons; (f) 56 and 51 ipm at 240 tons; (g) 48 and 47 ipm at 300 tons; (h) 58 and 44 ipm at 400 tons.

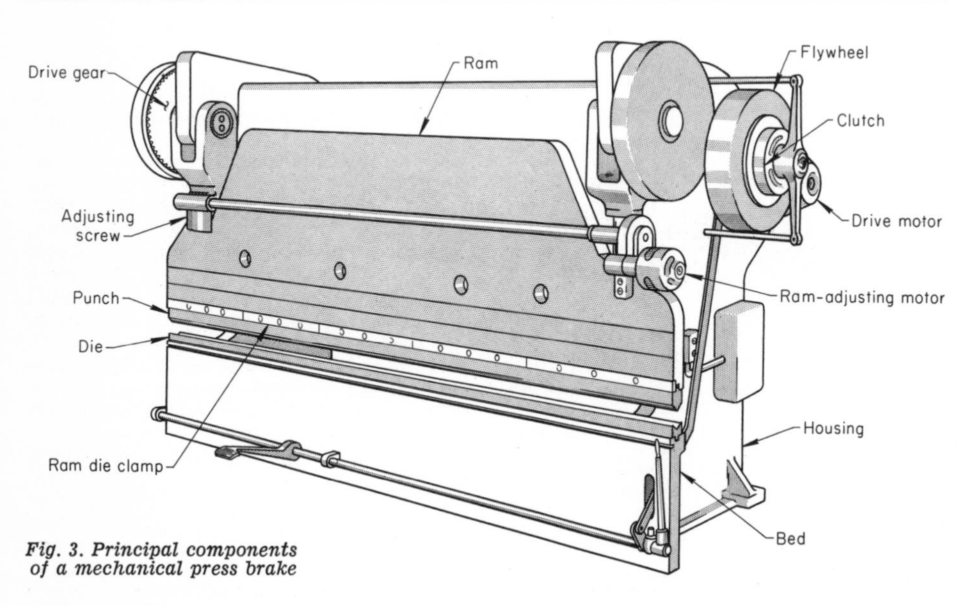

Fig. 3. Principal components of a mechanical press brake

The formability of all metals decreases as the yield strength increases. Hence, in press-brake forming, power requirements and springback problems increase, and the degree of bending that is practical decreases, as the yield strength of the work metal increases.

Press Brakes

The main advantages of press brakes are versatility, the ease and speed with which they can be changed over to a new setup, and low tooling costs. A press brake is basically a slow-speed punch press that has a long, relatively narrow bed and a ram mounted between end housings (Fig. 3). Rams are actuated mechanically or hydraulically.

Mechanical Press Brakes. The ram of a mechanical press brake is actuated by a crank or an eccentric through a gear train in which there is a clutch and a flywheel. The gear train is usually designed to provide fast movement of the ram. Shut height (the distance between ram and bed at the bottom of the stroke) is adjustable by means of a screw (usually powered) in the pitman, or link, at each end of the ram. Length of ram stroke, however, is constant.

One advantage of a mechanical over a hydraulic press brake is that the mechanical type can develop greater-than-rated tonnage, because of the inertia of the flywheel moving the ram and the mechanical advantage of the crank near the bottom of the stroke. As a result, most mechanical press brakes have extra-strong frames to allow for occasional overloading. However, overloading should not be encouraged, because serious damage to the press brake may occur from improper setup.

Another advantage is that operating speeds are greater than in hydraulic press brakes. The greater speed is especially useful for long-run production of workpieces that are easily handled. Greater speed also permits instantaneous high tonnage when the punch contacts the work metal. This impact force is useful in some operations, although it can damage the machine if the setup lacks rigidity.

A disadvantage of a mechanical press brake is that the stroke cannot be adjusted or controlled to the same degree as is possible with the hydraulic type. However, at extra cost, mechanical press brakes are available with devices that permit a rapid advance to work, then a slower speed during forming.

Hydraulic Press Brakes. The ram of a hydraulic press brake is actuated by two double-acting cylinders, one at each end of the ram. Force supplied by the hydraulic mechanism will not exceed the press rating; therefore, it is almost impossible to overload a hydraulic press brake. (When thicker metal is inadvertently used, the ram stalls.) For this reason, frames can be lighter and less costly than those for mechanical press brakes, which are subject to overloading.

In hydraulic press brakes, length of stroke and location of the top and bottom of the stroke (within limits of the cylinder length) are adjustable. Also, the point of rapid advance and return of the ram and its speed during contact with the workpiece are adjustable; this adjustment makes possible a dwell period, often helpful in controlling springback. Cycles established by means of the various adjustments are reproduced by switches in the control circuit.

Even though devices are available that permit some control of the stroke of a mechanical press brake, the degree of control that is possible for a hydraulic press brake is considerably greater. For instance, the ram on a hydraulic press brake can be reversed, or its speed can be changed, at any point on the stroke. Because of these features, a hydraulic press brake is often preferred for the segmental forming of stock longer than the dies, for forming of large sheets that would be likely to whip in a mechanical press brake, and for forming difficult-to-form metals.

Selection of Machine

A mechanical press brake is usually preferred for quantity production, because its speed is greater than that of a hydraulic press brake. Conversely, a hydraulic press brake is generally preferred for varied short-run production because it is more versatile.

Apart from the method of actuating the ram, major factors that must be considered in the selection of a press brake for a given application are the size, length of stroke, and tonnage capacity of the press brake. Table 1 gives capacities and other details for press brakes from one manufacturer.

Size is determined by length of bed and length of stroke (maximum stroke, in a hydraulic press brake). The bed length must be able to accommodate the longest bend required. Bed length may also be dictated by the need to mount more than one die in the press to permit a sequence of related operations in the machine at the same time. Under these conditions it may be necessary to shim the dies so the punches will bottom simultaneously. For example, if the parts are 12 in. long and six dies are required, the parts could be mounted on a press brake with a bed length of 72 in. plus allowance for space between dies.

Standard press brakes are available with a maximum bed length of 24 ft. Still larger press brakes are available on special order. The longer the bed, however, the more massive it must be to provide enough rigidity for holding product dimensions, until a length is finally reached where cost is prohibitive. Likewise, for a given capacity, the maximum stock thickness that can be accommodated decreases as bed length increases.

Length of stroke is an important consideration in any operation in which the height of the sides of the member after bending (such as a deep channel or box) causes interference between the top edge of the formed section and the ram. Also, the greater the leg height after forming, the longer the stroke must be to allow the finished part to be withdrawn (unless it can be withdrawn from the end, under which conditions length of stroke is not important). Press brakes having a stroke length as great as 6 in. (mechanical) and 18 in. (hydraulic) are available as standard equipment. Modifications for providing increased stroke length are available at extra cost.

Capacity is stated in tons of force developed by the ram at the midpoint of the stroke. Capacities of commercial press brakes range from 8 to 2500 tons. Required capacity is governed by the size and bending characteristics of the work metal, and by the type of bend to be made. A formula for determining the capacity required for 90° bends using V-dies without bottoming is:

$$L = \frac{lt^2kS}{s}$$

where L is press load, in tons; l is length of bend (parallel to bend axis), in inches; t is work-metal thickness, in inches; k is a die-opening factor (varying from 1.2 for a die opening of $16t$ to 1.33 for a die opening of $8t$); S is tensile strength of the work metal, in tons per square inch; and s is width of die opening, in inches. (See Fig. 1.)

Sample Calculation. Assume a constant of 1.33, a V-die opening of $8t$, and a bend 12 in. long made in 0.250-in.-thick plate having a tensile strength of 30 tons per sq in. After substituting these numerical values in the equation, it becomes:

$$L = \frac{12 \times 0.250^2 \times 1.33 \times 30}{2}$$

or approximately a 15-ton capacity requirement for this 90° bend.

For simple bending, the force required increases proportionately with the length of the workpiece or with the square of the work-metal thickness. For instance, in the preceding calculation, if the workpiece were 48 in. long, 60-ton capacity would be needed.

For producing offset bends (see Fig. 4b), about four times as much pressure is required as for simple V-bends.

Dies and Punches

V-bending dies and their corresponding punches (Fig. 4a and d) are the tools most commonly used in press-brake forming. The width of the die opening (s in Fig. 4a) is usually a minimum of $8t$ (eight times the thickness of the work metal).

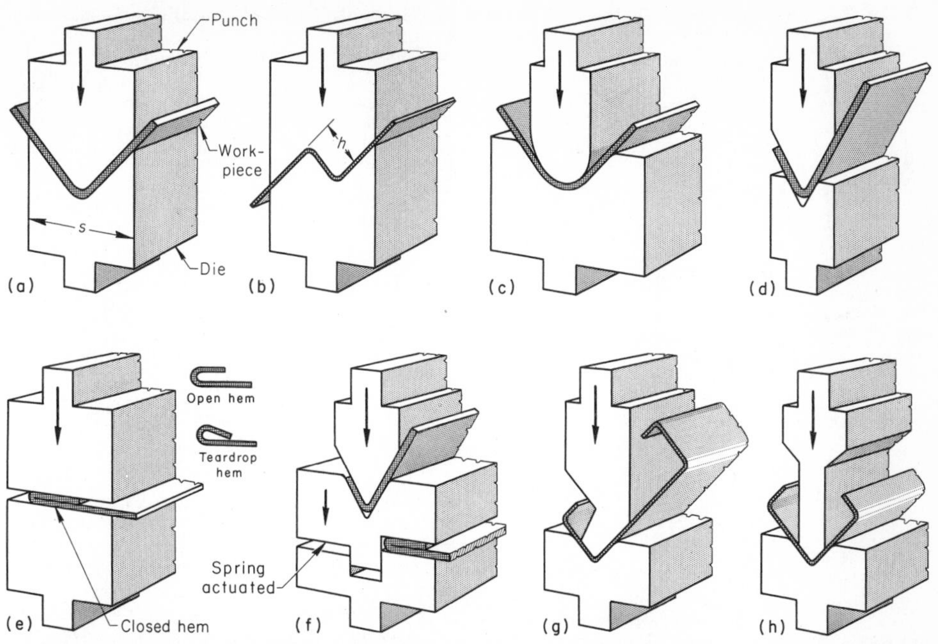

(a) 90° V-bending. (b) Offset bending. (c) Radiused 90° bending. (d) Acute-angle bending. (e) Flattening, for three types of hems. (f) Combination bending and flattening. (g) Gooseneck punch for multiple bends. (h) Special clearance punch for multiple bends.

Fig. 4. Dies and punches most commonly used in press-brake forming

The nose radius of the punch should not be less than $1t$ for bending low-carbon steel, and it must be increased as the formability of the work metal decreases. The radius of the V-bending die must be greater than the nose radius of the punch by an amount equal to or somewhat greater than the stock thickness, to allow the punch to bottom. Best dimensional control is obtained by bottoming the punch to set the bend.

For producing 90° bends in a bottoming die, the V-die is ordinarily provided with an included angle of 85° to 87°. Often, several trials are necessary and various adjustments must be made on the punch setting before the required 90° bend can be obtained.

Offset Dies. Punch-and-die combinations like the one shown in Fig. 4(b) are often used to produce offset bends. Because an offset bend requires about four times as much force as a 90° V-bend, offset bending is usually restricted to relatively light-gage metal (0.125 in. or less). The depth of offset (h in Fig. 4b) should be a minimum of six times work-metal thickness, to provide stability at the bends.

Radius forming is done with a 90° die and a punch, each having a large radius (Fig. 4c). When the punch is bottomed, the inside radius of bend in the workpiece conforms to the radius of the punch over a part of the curve. The harder the punch bottoms, the more closely the work metal wraps around the punch nose, resulting in a smaller radius of bend and less springback. Uniformity of bend angle depends greatly on uniformity of the work-metal thickness.

Acute angles are formed by the die and punch shown in Fig. 4(d). The air-bending technique (see page 104) is often used for producing acute angles. Acute angles are formed as the first step in making a hem. For this purpose the die is often bottomed, to make the bend angle as acute as possible. A disadvantage of bottoming is that the metal becomes work hardened, so that the hem is likely to crack when formed.

Flattening dies, shown in Fig. 4(e), are used to produce three types of hems (also shown in Fig. 4e) after the metal has been formed into an acute angle. The combination die shown in Fig. 4(f) produces an acute angle on one workpiece and a hem on another, so that a piece is begun and a piece completed with each stroke of the press brake.

Gooseneck punches (Fig. 4g) and narrow-body or special clearance punches (Fig. 4h) are used to form workpieces to shapes that prevent the use of punches having conventional width (two such workpiece shapes also are shown in Fig. 4g and h).

Tongue Design. The punches shown in Fig. 4 as well as in several other illustrations in this article are provided with a simple, straight tongue for securing the punch to the ram. Although this design of tongue is generally accepted, in some shops punches with a hook type of tongue (see Fig. 8, and the punch for operation 4 in Fig. 18) are used exclusively as a safety precaution. A punch mounted with a hooked tongue cannot fall out.

In one shop it was estimated that hooked tongues increased punch cost by about 10% over the cost of straight-tongue punches.

Special Dies and Punches

Dies that combine two or more operations to increase productivity in press-brake forming are generally more complicated than those illustrated in Fig. 4 and are therefore more costly. Before special dies are designed for a specific application, the increased tooling cost must be balanced against decreased

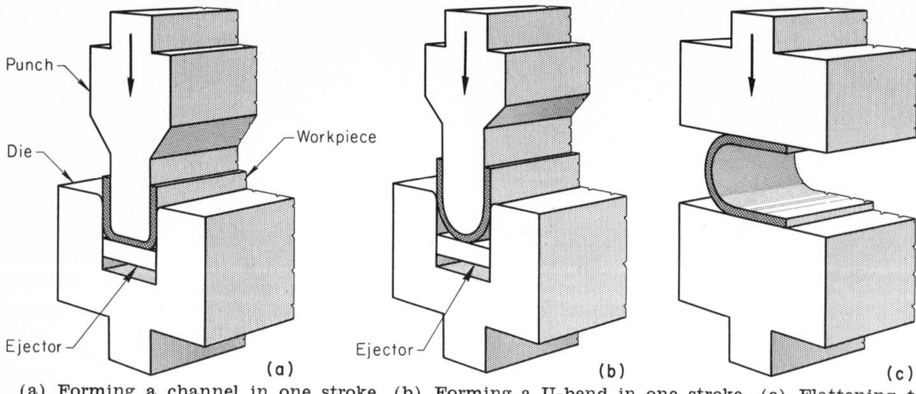

(a) Forming a channel in one stroke. (b) Forming a U-bend in one stroke. (c) Flattening to remove springback after U-bending.

Fig. 5. Three types of special punches and dies for press-brake forming

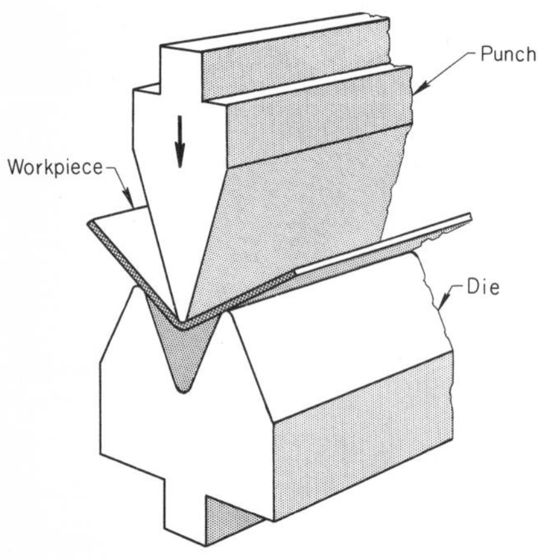

Fig. 6. Setup for air bending with an acute-angle punch and die in a press brake

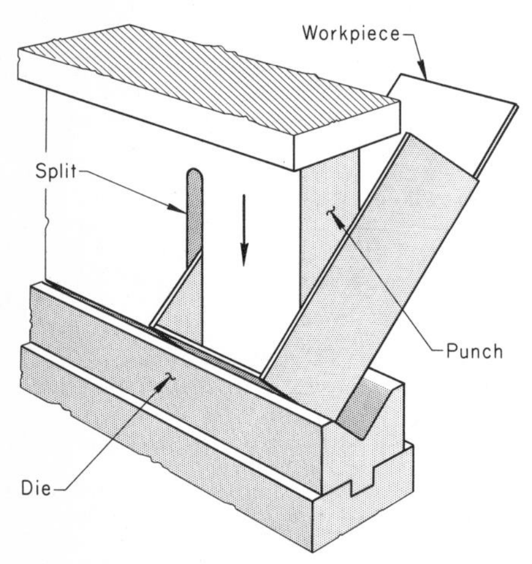

Fig. 7. Setup for forming a rectangular box, using a punch split vertically to clear the long sides during forming of the short sides

time on the press brake. As a rule, quantity of identical parts to be produced is the major factor in selecting special dies.

Channel Dies. A channel die (Fig. 5a) can form a channel in one stroke of the press brake, whereas two strokes would be required using a conventional V-die. Because it is necessary to have an ejector in the die to extract the workpiece, channel dies cost more than conventional dies. This higher cost can be justified only on the basis of large-quantity production. Ordinarily, it is not necessary to have a stripper on the punch, because springback usually causes the part to release. The ejector in the die may be of the spring, hydraulic or air-return type. The stripper for the punch (if needed) is a release-wedge device or a knockout piece.

The use of a channel die, regardless of production quantities, is limited by work-metal thickness, corner radii, and required flatness of the web.

A modification of the channel die is the U-bend die (Fig. 5b). Springback is a common problem with this type of die; one means of overcoming it is to perform a secondary operation on flat dies, as shown in Fig. 5(c).

Air Bending. In air bending, the die is deep enough that "setting" does not take place at the bottom of the stroke. The die can have a V shape as shown in Fig. 6, or the sides can be vertical as shown in Fig. 1 and 23. The shape and nose radius of the punch are varied to suit the workpiece. The required angle is produced on the workpiece by adjusting the depth to which the punch enters the die opening. This permits the operator to overbend the metal sufficiently to produce the required angle after springback.

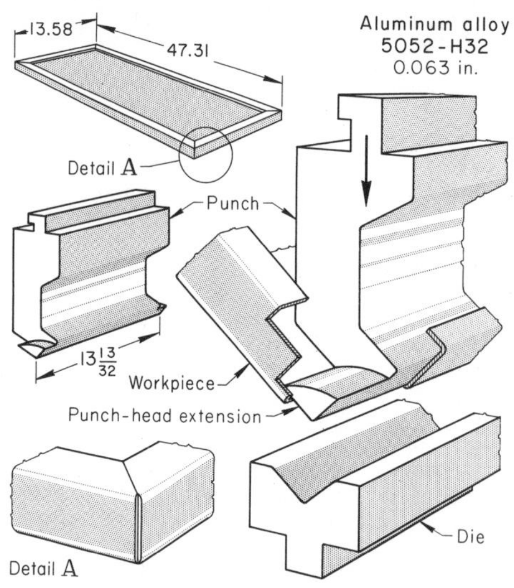

Fig. 8. Folding over sides of a boxlike workpiece, using an arbor-type punch for forming beneath reverse flanges

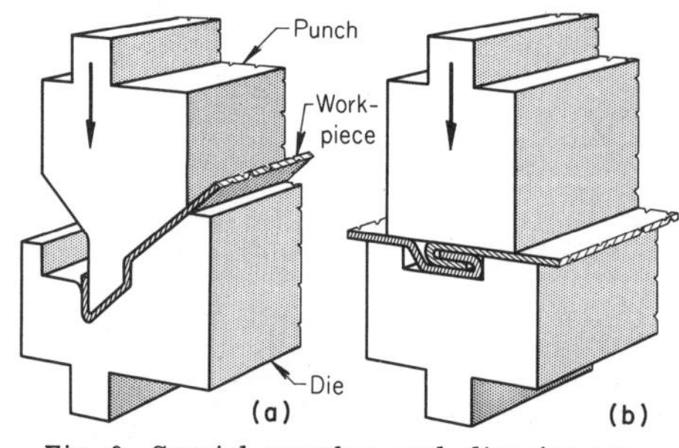

Fig. 9. Special punches and dies for producing lock seams in a press brake

When metal is bent beyond its yield strength, the radius formed bears a definite relation to the opening in the die. A small die opening produces a small radius; the use of a large die opening increases the radius, but also the amount of springback. Springback must be compensated for by overbending. Changing the size of the die opening also changes the amount of force needed to make the bend. As the die opening is increased, less force is required; as the die opening decreases, the bending leverage is less, and thus more force is required.

For air bending of metal up to ½ in. thick, the die opening usually is equal to eight times the work-metal thickness. This keeps the bend radius approximately equal to the metal thickness. For metal thicker than ½ in., and for some high-tensile-strength metals, the die opening should be at least ten times the work-metal thickness, to increase the bend radius and thus reduce the possibility of fracture at the bend.

The principal advantage of the air-bend method is the variety of forming that can be done with a minimum number of punches and dies. Air bending also requires less force for a given bend, thus preventing excessive strain on the press brake.

The main disadvantage of air bending is the possible inconsistency in the bends. Because of variations in dimensions and temper of the work metal as it is received from the mill, springback varies throughout a production run. However, the operator can adjust the ram to compensate for these irregularities. When air bending in a hydraulic press brake, the operator can use a preset pressure, check each part with a gage, and restrike if necessary. With a mechanical press brake, the shut height can be easily adjusted for a restrike, then reset for the next part.

Box-forming dies are similar to standard V-dies, except that the punch is sometimes specially made to clear the sides of the box being formed. For square boxes, the punch length can be the inside length, and the sides of the box can be formed in any sequence. However, for forming of rectangular boxes, different tools or techniques are required. One approach is the use of a punch that is split vertically (Fig. 7) so that the punch can clear the sides on the long dimension while forming the sides of the short dimension. In most instances, however, a punch long enough for forming the long sides can be used without splitting, by forming the short sides first.

When bottoming dies are used in box forming (to overform and coin the metal to overcome springback), the metal can be work hardened excessively if the same force is used for forming the short sides as is used for the long sides. In some shops, when the short sides are less than two-thirds as long as the long sides, force is reduced for forming the short sides.

Arbor-type punches can be used when the sides of a boxlike workpiece must be folded over (see detail A in Fig. 8). As shown in Fig. 8, the head of the punch extends beyond the punch body, so that the formed-over sides can fit over the punch extensions while the remaining folds are made. The extensions on the punch are approximately triangular in cross section so that the punch can be withdrawn after opposite sides of the workpiece are closed.

Lock-Seam Dies. Lock seams are made in a press brake when quantities are too small to warrant more elaborate equipment. The usual procedure is to form one component with a special punch and die as shown in Fig. 9(a). The second component of the assembly is formed in a simple V-die. The two components are then locked together in a single stroke of the press brake using another special die (Fig. 9b).

Curling Dies. Curling in a press brake is usually done in two steps using special dies like those shown in Fig. 10(a).

Rocker-Type Dies. Dies that operate with spring-actuated rocker punches can produce bends that would be impossible with the punch operating in a vertical direction only. A typical rocker-type die for U-bending is illustrated in Fig. 10(b).

One-Stroke Hemming Dies. With specially designed spring-actuated dies, it is possible to hem a length of metal sheet in a single stroke. A typical die used for this operation and the movement of die components required for completing the hem are illustrated in Fig. 11. When provided with an adjustable stop, the die shown in Fig. 11 can produce hems of different widths (over a narrow range).

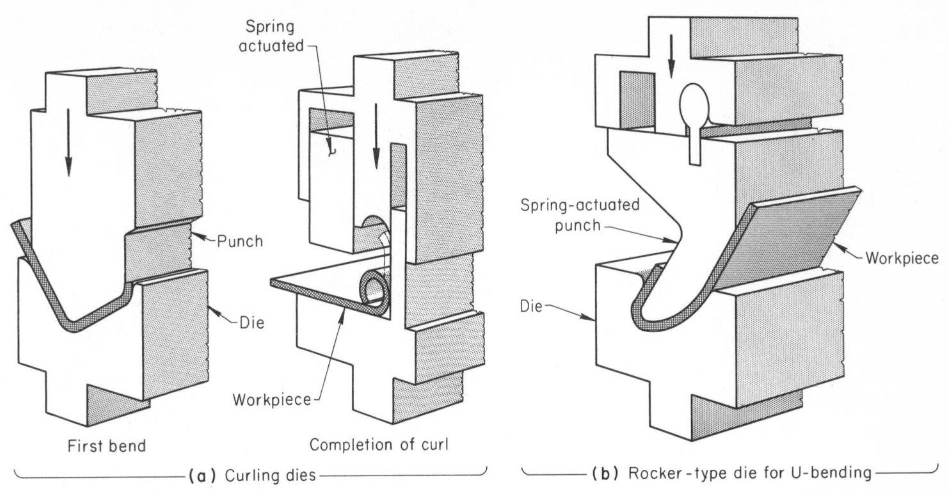

Fig. 10. Special punches and dies for curling and U-bending in a press brake

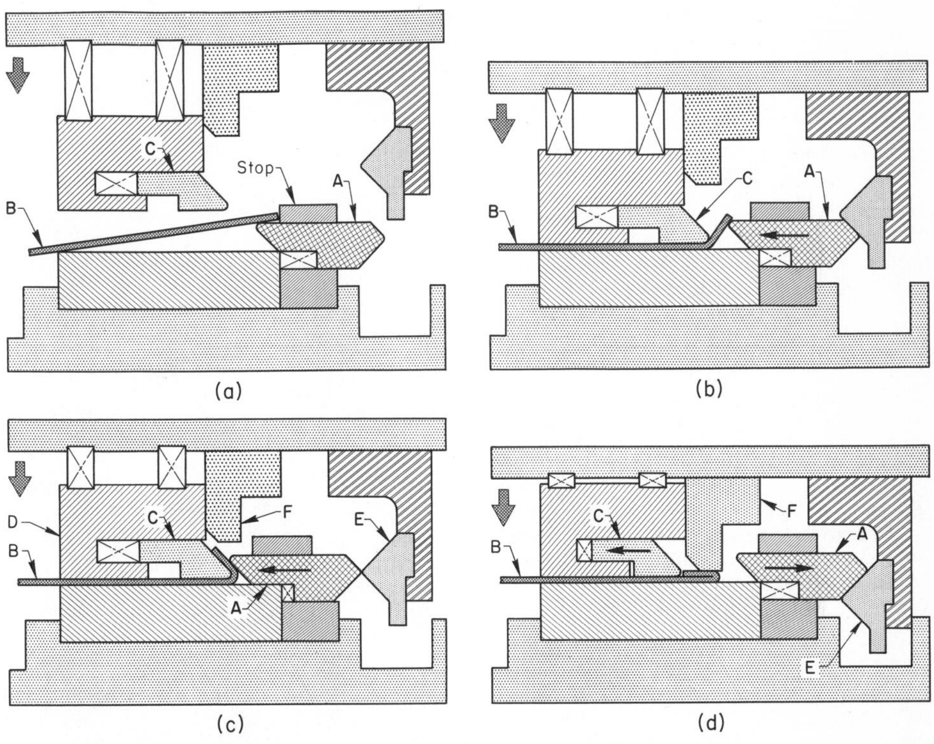

(a) Workpiece, B, is placed over slide A, using a component of the die as a stop, and the entire upper die section begins to move down.
(b) Slide C contacts the workpiece and makes the first bend for the hem.
(c) With slide D holding the workpiece rigidly in place, die component E forces slide A to the left, forming the bent section of the workpiece into an acute angle.
(d) As the die continues to move down, die component E permits slide A to retract, providing clearance for F to contact and flatten the workpiece as it forces slide C to the left, thus completing the hem. On the upstroke of the press brake, die components return to original positions.

Fig. 11. One-stroke hemming die, and movement of die components during hemming

Dies for Shearing, Lancing, Blanking, Piercing and Notching

Shearing can be done in a press brake, but hold-downs and knife supports must be used to obtain reasonable accuracy. For best results, a shearing machine should be used (see the article on Shearing of Plate and Sheet, which begins on page 265 in this volume). There are, however, applications in which shearing in a press brake is convenient because it can be combined with another operation.

Lancing is often done in a press brake. An example is in the production of louvers, such as those used in cabinet or locker doors. The punch, die and die pad used for simultaneous lancing and forming of sheet metal into louvers are shown in Fig. 12.

Blanking. When long, narrow dies are required for a given application, metal can be blanked in a press brake if adequate support can be provided by the dies or the press brake. Removal of long, narrow workpieces is sometimes a problem. If excessive adherence to the punches is encountered, spring-type or rubber strippers can be added.

Piercing and Notching. Press brakes are used extensively for piercing (punching) and notching. A press brake is more practical than a punch press for piercing or notching of long, narrow workpieces — flats, channels or other cross-sectional shapes. Press brakes are especially well adapted to piercing holes close to the edge of long panels (see Example 125), or to notching of the edges. Quick-change punching units (available from several suppliers) help to extend the versatility of a press brake for piercing and notching. These punching units can be quickly changed to accommodate different workpieces by use of setup templates.

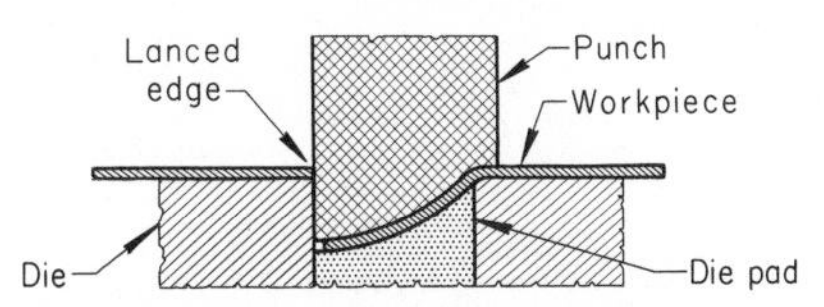

Fig. 12. Punch, die and die pad used for simultaneously lancing and forming louvers in a press brake

Selection of Tool Material

Selection of tool material for punches and dies used in press brakes depends on composition of the work metal, shape of the workpiece (severity of forming), and quantity to be produced.

Tool material used for press-brake bending and forming ranges from hardwood to carbide, although the use of carbide has usually been confined to inserts at high-wear areas. Hardwood

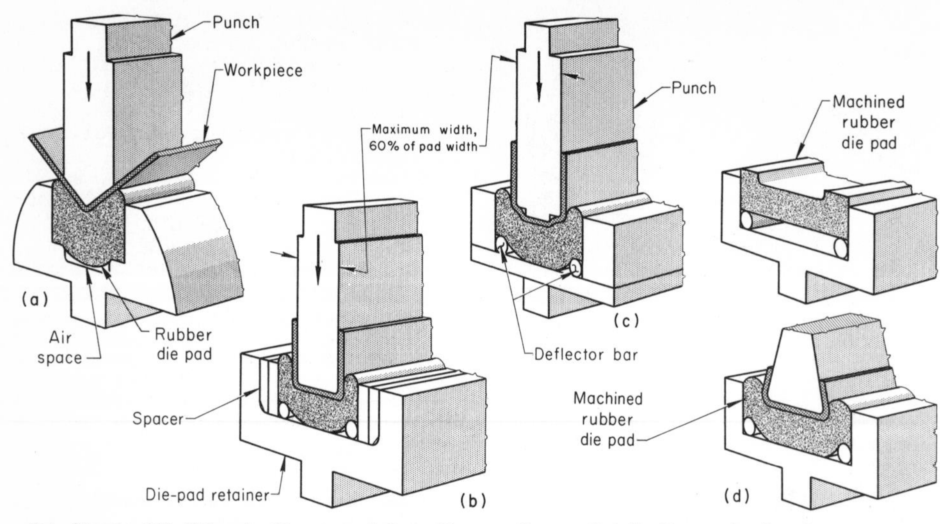

(a) Simple 90° V-bend. Air space below die pad permits deep penetration. (b) Simple U-bend or channel. Spacers enable channels of varying widths to be formed in the same die-pad retainer. Deflector bars help to provide uniform distribution of forming pressure. (c) Modified channel, with partial air bending. (d) Acute-angle channel. High side pressures are obtained by using a conforming rubber die pad and deflector bars.

Fig. 13. Setups for rubber-pad forming of various shapes in a press brake

and carbide represent the rare extremes; hardwood is suitable only for making a few simple bends in the most formable work metal, and carbide would be considered only for making severe bends in a less-formable work metal (such as high-strength low-alloy steel) in high production.

Simple Bending. Most dies and punches used for simple V-bending operations are made from low-carbon steel (such as 1020) or gray iron. Both of these materials are inexpensive and give acceptable tool life in mild service.

If production runs are long or the work metal is less formable, some upgrading of the tool material may be desired to retain accuracy over a longer period. Gray iron can be upgraded without adding greatly to tool cost by making both punch and die from a hardenable grade (such as ASTM class 40), and then flame hardening the nose of the punch and the upper edges (high-wear areas) of the V-die to 450 to 550 Bhn. Low-carbon steel tools can be upgraded by changing to a hardenable grade of steel (such as 1045). High-wear portions of the tools can be flame hardened (usually to Rockwell C 50 to 55) in the same manner as the gray iron tools.

Severe Bending. As the severity of bending and forming increases, such as in producing channels in a single stroke (see Fig. 5a), tool materials should be upgraded when more than low-production quantities are needed. For operations that require severe bending, tool-material requirements for press-brake operations parallel those for punch-press operations (see page 148 in the article "Selection of Material for Press Forming Dies", in this volume).

Blanking and piercing are done in a press brake with tools of the same materials as are used in punch presses (see the article "Selection of Material for Blanking and Piercing Dies", which begins on page 69 in this volume).

Rubber Pads. The use of rubber pads in press-brake dies (see Fig. 13) enables the forming of shapes difficult or impossible to form without the pads. The pads also minimize damage to work-metal surfaces and decrease die cost. (For additional information on rubber-pad forming, see the article that begins on page 209.)

Urethane rubber is the type most widely used. Pads inserted into the bottom of the die can be used for forming V and channel sections in various metals ranging from soft aluminum to low-carbon steel up to 12 gage (0.1046 in.) in thickness. When using the urethane-pad technique, the urethane is, in effect, the die. It is almost impossible to compress urethane — its shape changes but not its volume. With minimum penetration of the punch, the pad begins to deflect, exerting continuous forming pressure around the punch. At the bottom of the stroke, the urethane has assumed the shape of the punch. When the pressure is released, the pad returns to its original shape.

Urethane pads are generally used for short-run production, although in one plant 14,000 boiler-casing channels were formed from 16-gage (0.0598-in.) low-carbon steel in 16-ft lengths on the same urethane pad before replacement.

Urethane rubber is made in several different grades ranging in tensile strength from 2600 to 11,000 psi, and in hardness from Durometer 80A to 79D. Selection of grade depends on work-metal hardness and thickness, and on severity of forming. Experimentation is often needed to determine the optimum grade of urethane for the application.

Work-Metal Finish. When preservation of work-metal finish is a primary objective, the dies or punches, or both, are sometimes chromium plated. Other means of preserving work-metal finish include the use of oil-impregnated paper between the tools and the work metal, or spraying the tools with a plastic of the type used to coat metal sheets for deep drawing.

Procedures for Specific Shapes

Procedures and tooling for press-brake operations vary widely, influenced mainly by workpiece shape. The six examples that follow describe the procedures used for producing several different shapes, including simple boxlike parts, panels, flanged parts, architectural columns, fully closed parts, and semicircular parts.

Example 124. Four-Stroke Forming of Closed-Bottom Boxes From Notched Blanks (Fig. 14)

Closed-bottom boxes were produced from 1010 steel blanks sheared to 20 by 24 in. in a press brake. The four corners were notched to a depth of 4 in. in a standard notching die in the same press brake as used for making the blanks. The box was then formed in four strokes of the press brake, using a standard 90° V-die, but with a deeper-than-normal punch (Fig. 14). By bending the 12-in. sides first, all four bends could be made with a die 16 in. long. Hourly production rates for the four operations were:

Shear blanks	55 pieces
Notch corners (four strokes)	57
Bend four sides (four strokes)	44

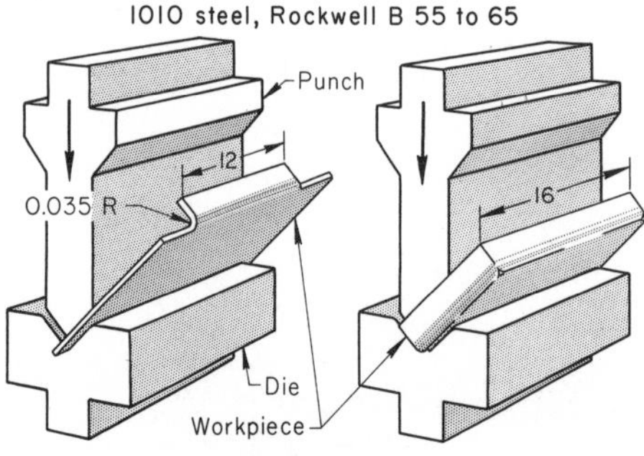

Fig. 14. Die and punch setup for bending sides in the production of a closed-bottom box (Example 124)

Example 125. Use of a Press Brake for Piercing and Bending (Fig. 15)

Flanged panels requiring 25 holes and eight bends (Fig. 15) were made in a 400-ton hydraulic press brake measuring 10 ft between housings. Setup and production details are given in the table with Fig. 15.

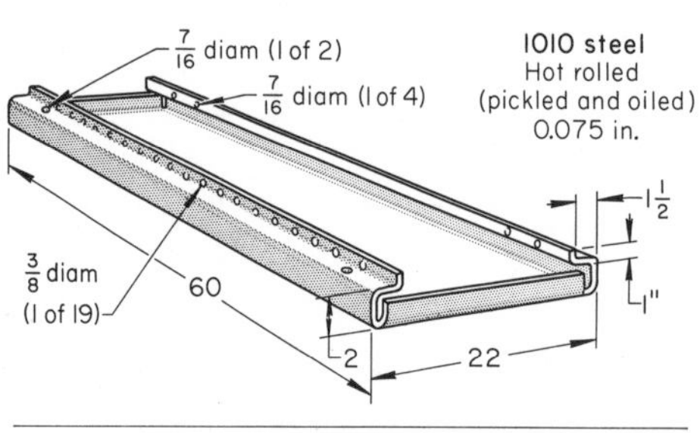

Setup Times, Hr	
Setup and dismantle:	
Base for piercing	0.242
Template for piercing(a)	0.068
25 piercing units	0.575
Two end gages	0.046
V-die	0.621
Change back gage three times	0.111
Total	1.663
Production Times per 100 Pieces, Machine-Hr(b)	
Pierce two 7/16-in.-diam holes	0.62
Pierce four 7/16-in. and nineteen 3/8-in.-diam holes	0.62
Bend two ends	0.96
Bend first flange (two bends)	0.96
Bend second flange (two bends)	0.96
Bend third flange (two bends)	0.96
Total	5.08

(a) Template contained all locating holes for piercing units, but units were relocated between the first and second piercing operations.
(b) Man-hours are double these machine-hours, because two men operated the machine.

Fig. 15. Flanged panel that was produced by piercing and bending in a press brake (Example 125)

Example 126. Forming Radii in a Housing After Forming Flange (Fig. 16)

The housing shown in Fig. 16(a) was produced from a blank cut in a shearing machine. Piercing, notching and bending operations were done in a 400-ton press brake measuring 10 ft between housings. The main problem in producing this shape was to form the two 90° bends, each having a 2⅝-in. radius, after forming the flange. To prevent distortion of the flange, a disk was bolted to the end of the punch, as shown in Fig. 16(b). As the punch traveled downward, the flange was confined between the face of the die and the disk, thus preventing the flange from distorting as the radius was formed. The sequence of operations, and setup and production times, are given in the table with Fig. 16. Because of part size, an operator and a helper were used at the machine.

Example 127. Six-Operation Forming of an Architectural Column (Fig. 17)

An architectural column 10 ft long was produced in six operations in a press brake. Figure 17 shows the sequence of shapes produced. Channel dies were used for operations 1 and 2. Operation 3 required a special punch and die for producing the large-radius bends. A simple channel die was used for operation 4, and a V-die for operation 5. Operation 6 was performed with a gooseneck punch, necked-in sufficiently to clear the edge flanges as the part closed in.

The major problem in forming this shape was to obtain sharp 90° bends at all corners and to keep the flanges in the same plane. Because the part was 10 ft long, considerable shimming of the tools was required to produce satisfactory parts.

Correct shimming is a major factor in maintaining accuracy when producing shapes like that in Fig. 17 in a press brake. Shims are required to adjust for the discrepancies between bed plate and bolster. Also, deflections produced by the punch bottoming on all hits will be greater in the center of the die than at the edges, and shimming is required to equalize the pressure along the entire length of the bend. Optimum shimming is accomplished mainly by trial and error, because of the variations among machines, tools and workpieces.

Example 128. Producing a Completely Closed Triangular Shape (Fig. 18)

Figure 18 shows the four separate setups that were used for producing a 34-in.-long completely closed triangular part in a press brake. The blanks, 21⁹⁄₃₂ by 34 in., were prepared by shearing on separate equipment. As shown in Fig. 18, the first press-brake operation produced a 90° bend, and the second operation produced a 68° bend; simple straight-sided punches were used for both bends. In the third operation, a special punch 1⅛ in. thick and having an offset nose was used to produce a 32° bend. By bending only to 32°, sufficient space was allowed for withdrawal of the punch. The punch had an offset nose because of the off-center seam location (a design requirement); had the seam been centered, the punch would have been symmetrical. In the fourth operation the part was closed. The part just before the fourth operation is shown at the upper right in Fig. 18. Time to complete the four operations was 0.9916 min. Total time per part was 1.0412 min (production rate, 57.7 parts per hour).

Semicircular Shapes and U-Bends. Flat stock can be formed into semicircular shapes and U-bends in a press brake. If the press capacity is adequate for the work-metal thickness and dimensions required, forming can be done in one operation as in 90° V-bending. As shown in Fig. 5(b), the radius of the punch nose forms the inside radius of the workpiece.

Air bending is used to form semicircular shapes and U-bends when the work-metal thickness and dimensions exceed press capacity. A typical setup is shown in Fig. 19. Starting from the end of the workpiece at the right, at a distance of half the span of the die opening, pairs of equally spaced center-punch marks are made near each side of the workpiece, progressing to the left in two straight lines at 90° to the bend axis. These two rows of punch marks guide the operator in maintaining the alignment of the bend.

To form the part, the blank is placed across the die opening with the center-punch marks facing up, so that the punch will contact the blank at the first pair of punch marks. A bend is made at each pair of punch marks progressively toward the center of the blank (Fig. 19). When the center is reached, a quarter circle will have been formed. The blank is rotated 180°, and the procedure is repeated until a semicircle is formed. The radius of the semicircle will depend on the amount of bending done with each blow of the press, and the distance between the punch marks.

Bending should always proceed from the end of the blank toward the center, to avoid interference between the ram and the formed workpiece. After forming, the straight section at each end of the workpiece is sheared off. The following example describes an application of this procedure for producing semicircular parts by air bending.

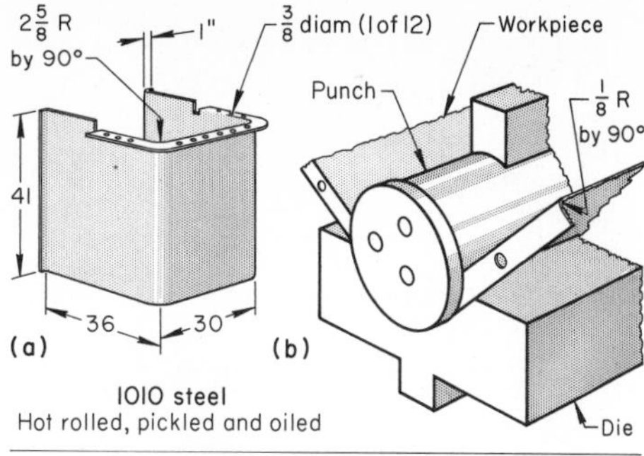

Setup Times, Hr

Item	Hr
Setup and dismantle:	
Base for piercing	0.242
Template for piercing	0.068
Piercing units	0.320
Side gages	0.046
V-die	0.621
Radius-forming die	0.370
Change back gage	0.037
Total	1.704

Production Times per 100 Pieces, Machine-Hr(a)

Operation	Machine-Hr
Pierce twelve ⅜-in.-diam holes and two notches	0.62
Bend two ends	2.10
Bend pierced portion for flange	0.93
Bend to form two radii	1.30
Total	4.95

(a) Man-hours are double these machine-hours, because two men operated the machine.

Fig. 16. (a) Flanged housing produced by piercing and bending in a press brake. (b) Setup used to prevent distortion of flange when forming radii. (Example 126)

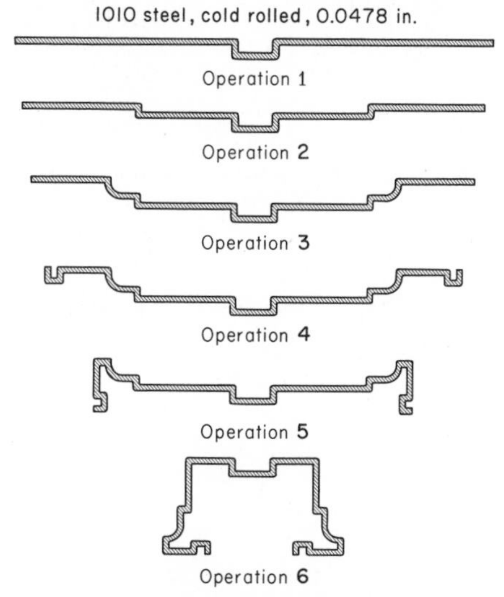

Fig. 17. Shapes progressively produced in six-operation forming of an architectural column in a press brake (Example 127)

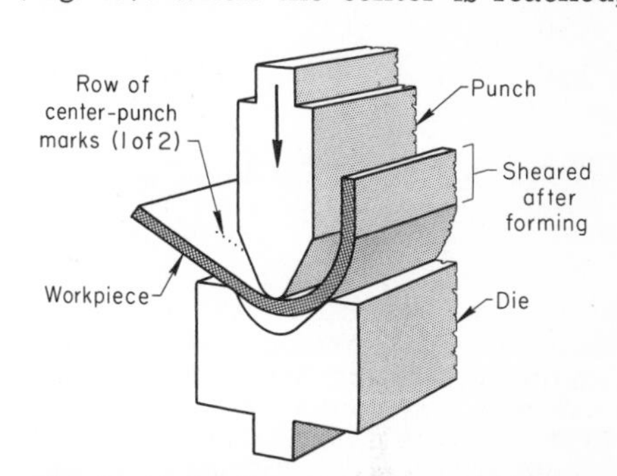

Fig. 19. Air bending to form a semicircular part by progressive strokes of the punch

Example 129. Forming Semicircular Parts by Air Bending

Two semicircular parts were formed from ¾-in.-thick low-carbon steel plate, and welded together to produce a 10-in.-OD hollow cylinder 10 in. long. Blank size for each semicircular part was 10 by 18½ in. The bend length required for each part was 14½ in., but the blanks were cut to 18½ in. to allow for trimming after forming (see Fig. 19).

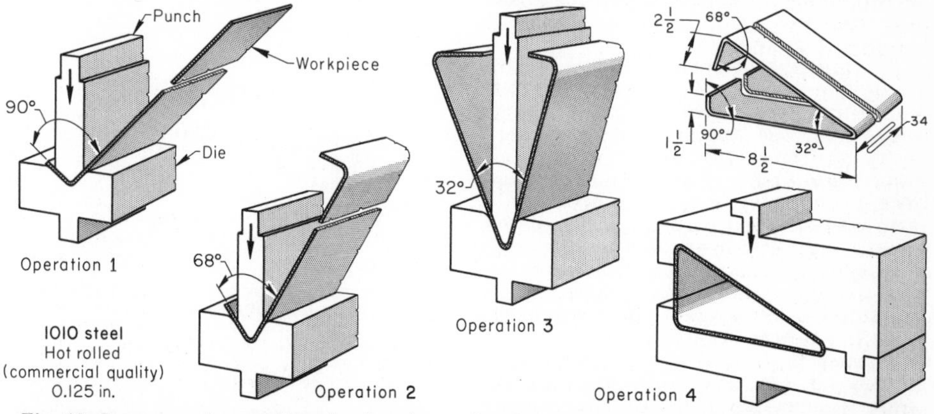

Fig. 18. Sequence of operations for forming a closed triangle in a press brake (Example 128)

Before forming, two rows of center-punch marks were made on the blanks (see Fig. 19). The first mark was 2 in. from the blank edge, with subsequent marks every ½ in. of the 14½-in. bend length.

The parts were formed in a 200-ton mechanical press brake using a standard V-die and round-nose punch. Thirty bends were required to form each semicircular part. After several bends, the curve was checked with a template to determine accuracy of the bend. After forming a quarter of the circle, the workpiece was rotated 180° and the operation was repeated to complete the half circle. The final bend was made at the center of the workpiece. The 2-in. allowance at each end of the workpiece was then sheared off.

Corrugated Sheet. By special procedures it is possible to make bends in corrugated metal that are perpendicular to the corrugations, without flattening the corrugations. The use of cast-on plastic blankets is one means of achieving this (see Example 515 in the article on Forming of Aluminum Alloys).

Effect of Work-Metal Variables on Results

Thickness variations, yield strength, and grain direction are the work-metal variables that have the greatest effect on results in press-brake operations.

Whenever possible, any metal to be formed should be purchased only to commercial tolerances; special tolerances increase cost. However, when workpiece tolerances are close, it is sometimes necessary to purchase metal with special thickness tolerances, because in forming, normal variations can use up a substantial amount of the assigned final tolerance (see the subsequent section on Dimensional Accuracy).

Yield Strength. As yield strength of the work metal increases, so does difficulty in bending. This difficulty occurs as cracking at the bends, increased power requirements, or an increase in springback.

For instance, bending of stainless steel requires about 50 to 60% more power than bending a comparable thickness of low-carbon steel. Because of its resistance to bending, stainless steel often causes difficulty in obtaining acceptable results. (For additional information, refer to page 355 in the article on Forming of Stainless Steel.)

Springback. In a wiping type of bending operation, in which the metal is bent to position but the corner is not coined to set the bend, the metal attempts to return to its original position. This movement, known as springback, is evident to some extent in all metals, and increases as the yield strength of the metal increases.

The amount of springback is usually negligible for a soft metal like 1100 aluminum alloy. However, for aluminum alloys like 2024 the amount of springback can be significant. In general, low-carbon steels exhibit more springback than do aluminum or copper alloys, and still more springback can be expected for stainless steel.

A usual technique to overcome springback is to overbend by approximately the number of degrees of springback. Several trials in tool development may be needed to obtain the proper angle, because of variations in mechanical properties, work-hardening rate, metal thickness, and die clearances. Tables for springback have been developed for specific metals (see Table 3 on page 382 in the article on Forming of Aluminum Alloys; also, tables in other forming articles in this volume).

Sometimes springback from one bend can be used to offset that from another, as in the example that follows.

Example 130. Use of a Bowed Web to Offset Springback in Flanges (Fig. 20)

Springback of the flanges of the crossmember shown in Fig. 20 was more than could be tolerated when the flanges were bent in standard press-brake V-dies. A special bottoming die could have been built that would set the bends, but it was more economical to build a die that bowed the web (see section A-A in Fig. 20). Springback of the web bow brought the flanges into tolerance. In use, two of these parts were bolted back to back, and any residual bow in the web was pulled out by the bolts.

The crossmember was formed from high-strength low-alloy steel in a 425-ton hydraulic press brake capable of operating at eight strokes per minute. All forming was done with the direction of rolling perpendicular to the axis of the bends.

Another technique for overcoming springback is the use of specially designed bottoming dies that strike the workpiece severely at the radius of the bend. This action stresses the metal in the bend area beyond the yield point through almost the entire thickness and thus eliminates springback. Bottoming must be carefully controlled, particularly if done in a mechanical press brake, because of the very high force that can be developed by this machine.

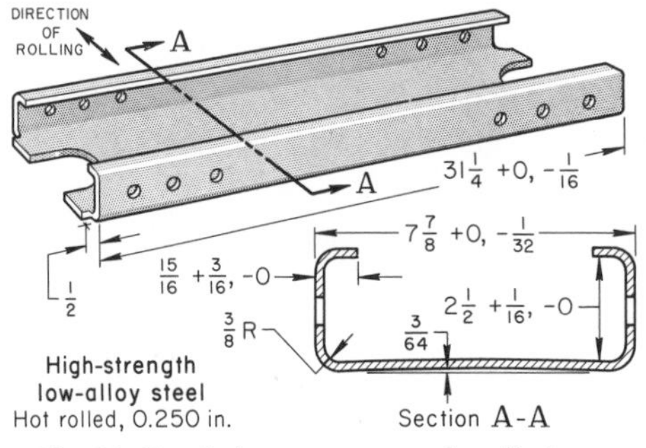

Fig. 20. Truck-frame crossmember that was formed with a 3/64-in. bow in the web to offset springback in flanges (Example 130)

Restriking in the original dies or special fixtures will reduce springback to a low level. It requires an extra operation, but may entail little or no additional equipment. In the example that follows, a second stroke was used.

Example 131. Correcting Springback in the Forming of a Complex Shape (Fig. 21)

The shape shown at the lower right in Fig. 21 was produced from 0.036-in.-thick 1010 steel in lengths ranging from 3 to 8 ft. The five operations used in producing the part are shown in Fig. 21(a) to (e). The box section was formed by a wiping action (Fig. 21d) with no force on the outermost portion of the box. Consequently, springback occurred and required another step to correct by overforming (Fig. 21e). The shut height of the die was adjusted to provide the correction.

Grain Direction. In press-brake forming of steel, the effect of grain direction is often a greater problem than in other methods, because long members are usually bent in a press brake and bends are made with axes parallel to the rolling direction, which is the least favorable orientation. Sometimes, however, it is possible to take advantage of directionality. The most severe bends can be made perpendicular to the direction of rolling, or if several bends are required along axes that are not parallel with each other, the layout can be planned so that all bends run diagonally to the direction of rolling.

The difference in behavior of the same steel bent in both directions in a press brake is demonstrated in the following example:

Example 132. Effect of Grain Direction on Bending (Fig. 22)

An axle bearing support was produced in four bends (Fig. 22) in a press brake using standard 90° V-dies. Cracks could not be tolerated. No cracks appeared on the flanges formed on the short dimensions, which were bent 90° to the direction of rolling to a ¼-in.

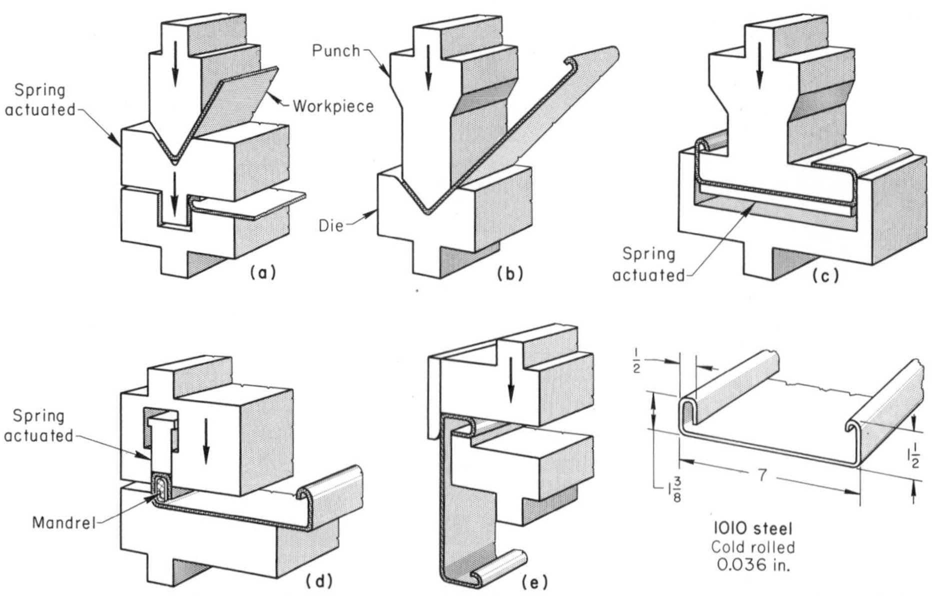

(a) Forming hem in two strokes. (b) Forming of first 90° angle for box section. (c) Forming channel. (d) Closing of box section over a mandrel. Part was moved by sliding it off mandrel. (e) Restriking of box section to eliminate springback.

Fig. 21. Setups and sequence of operations for forming a complex shape in a press brake, showing use of a restriking operation to eliminate springback (Example 131)

radius. However, in bending the flanges on the long dimensions, parallel with the direction of rolling, open breaks appeared along the length of the bend. To prevent this cracking, it was necessary to increase the bend radius on the long dimensions to ½ in., and to prepare the blanks so that the long flanges were formed at a slight angle to the direction of rolling.

As thickness and yield strength of the work metal increase, the relation between bend angle and grain direction becomes more important. For instance, when stock thickness reaches about 1 in. and the yield strength is relatively high, as in high-strength low-alloy steels, the bend radius should be at least twice (and preferably three times) the stock thickness, even for bends of no more than 45°, when the bend axis is parallel with the direction of rolling:

Example 133. Bending of Thick High-Strength Low-Alloy Steel Parallel With Rolling Direction (Fig. 23)

Boom spreaders for earthmovers were constructed by welding together two bent plates, one of which is illustrated in Fig. 23. The angle of each bend was 45° and the radius was 3 in., which is nearly the maximum severity of bend that can be made without cracking for this grade and thickness of work metal (1-in.-thick high-strength low-alloy steel having a yield strength of 50,000 to 60,000 psi) when the axis of bend is parallel with the direction of rolling. The blanks for these parts, 59½ by 27$^{5}/_{16}$ in., were gas cut from plate stock. Before bending, the edges of the blanks were snag ground in four places (see Fig. 23) to remove decarburized metal and round the sharp corners to approximately $^{1}/_{16}$-in. radius. It was necessary to do this grinding thoroughly, to prevent cracks from developing in service.

The spreader sections were air bent using the tools shown in Fig. 23. Each bend demanded 350 to 400 tons of force. Less force would have been needed if the die span could have been wider, but one leg of the part was barely long enough to bridge the 12-in. span that was used. The edges of the die were lubricated with heavy oil. The hydraulic press brake used had a capacity of 1250 tons.

In press-brake forming of long narrow workpieces, bending at an angle to the direction of rolling is seldom practical. For such work, the use of steel sheet that has been cross rolled or subjected to a pinch pass is usually the simplest means of minimizing adverse effects from grain direction. Other effective but less desirable procedures are: (*a*) obtaining steel sheet that has been spheroidized; (*b*) using special killed sheet; (*c*) heating steel blanks above their transformation temperature, water quenching, reheating to 1250 F and cooling slowly; or (*d*) cycle annealing.

Dimensional Accuracy

The generally accepted tolerance for dimensions resulting from bending is ±0.016 in. for metals up to and including 0.125-in. thickness. For thicker metals, the tolerance is increased proportionately. As in many other mechanical operations, obtainable tolerances are influenced by design, stock tolerances, blank preparation, and condition of the machine and tooling. In some instances, close control of variables can provide closer dimensions at no additional cost; in others, cost will be increased.

Design. Bends or holes too close to the workpiece edges make it difficult to maintain an accurate bend line. Notches

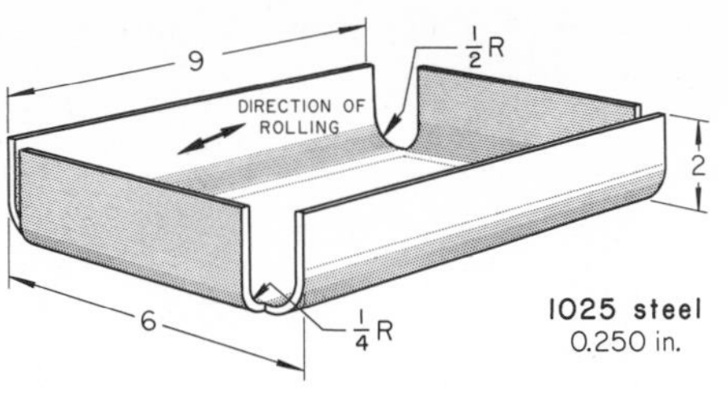

Fig. 22. Axle bearing support for which blank was prepared so that long flanges were formed at a slight angle to direction of rolling, to prevent cracking (Example 132)

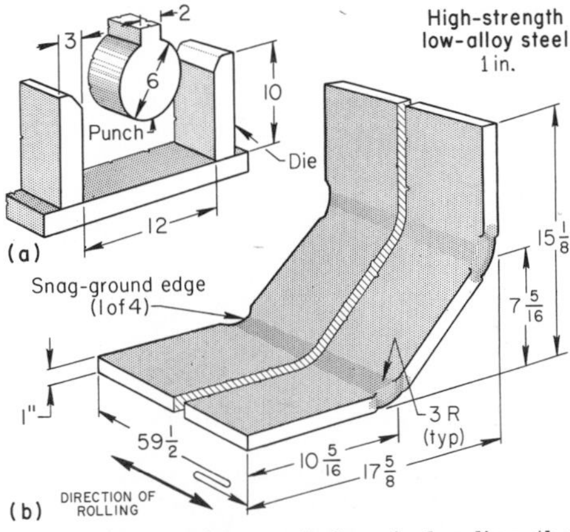

(a) Tooling setup used for air bending the part in a press brake. (b) Part, one of two that were welded together to make a boom spreader for an earthmover, was formed to large radii (3*t*), and from a blank that was snag ground at edges of bends, to avoid cracking of the thick, high-yield-strength (50,000 to 60,000 psi) stock.

Fig. 23. Heavy-gage part that was bent parallel with direction of rolling (Example 133)

and cutouts on the bend line make it difficult to hold accurate bend location. Offset bends will shift unless the distance between bends in the offset is at least six times the thickness of the work metal.

Stock tolerances affect dimensional accuracy of the finished part because they use up a portion of the assigned final tolerance. Commercial tolerances, particularly on thickness to which the specified metal is furnished, should be ascertained. For aluminum, there are minor differences in thickness limits between clad and unclad alloys. For steels, there are significant differences both in thickness tolerances and in cost among hot rolled sheet, hot rolled strip, cold rolled sheet, and cold rolled strip.

Cold rolled steel sheet is produced to closer tolerances than hot rolled sheet, but its cost is higher. Tolerances on steel strip, either hot rolled or cold rolled, are closer than those for corresponding sheet. Established tolerances are closer as the product becomes narrower or thinner.

Thickness tolerances for steel plate are considerably wider than those for hot rolled steel sheet and strip. When ordered to thickness, the allowable minimum is 0.010 in. less than that specified, regardless of thickness, and the allowable maximum for an individual plate is 1⅓ times the values that are published by the mills and expressed as a percentage of the nominal weight. Therefore, when tolerance requirements are stringent, it should be determined whether the metal can be obtained as strip or sheet rather than as plate.

Blank preparation can have an important effect on tolerances and cost of the finished part. If a blank is prepared by merely cutting to length from purchased stock, it will be low in cost, but the width tolerance will be that of the mill product. This may be greater than the tolerance obtainable by shearing. If it is necessary to shear all sides of a blank, the cost will increase, but good shearing can result in greater accuracy.

The stock from which blanks are cut must be flat enough for the blanks to be properly inserted into tooling and to remain in position during forming. Stretcher-leveled and resquared sheet costs a little more, but it usually is necessary when tolerances are close.

Blank Size. To determine the size of blank needed to produce a specified bent part, the blank dimension (usually, the blank width) at 90° to the bend axis can be developed on the basis of the dimension along the neutral axis.

For 90° bends, as shown in Table 2, the developed blank width can be obtained by deducting bend allowances from the theoretical distance along the outside mold line. These allowances take into account the type and thickness of the work metal and the bend radius — each of which can affect the location of the neutral axis, and hence the developed width. The application of these allowances, which are based on shop practice with low-carbon steel and aluminum alloy 5052, is shown in the illustration in Table 2, for parts having one, two, three or four bends.

For setting the stock stops from the centerline of the punch and die, the distance from the edge of the workpiece to the bend line at the neutral axis (see Table 2) must be determined. To establish this value for 90° bends, subtract one-half the bend allowance from the outside flange width.

For bend angles other than 90° or radii other than those listed in Table 2, the width of a strip needed to produce a given shape can be calculated by dividing the shape into its component straight and curved segments and totaling the developed width along the neutral axis. The following formula can be used to determine the developed width (w) of a curved segment:

$$w = 0.01745\,\alpha\,(r + kt)$$

where 0.01745 is a factor to convert degrees to radians; α is the included angle to which the metal is bent, in degrees; r is the inside radius of the bend, in inches; and k is the distance of neutral plane or axis from the inside surface at the bend, expressed as the fraction of the metal thickness (t) at the bend. Empirically determined values of k are: ⅓, for bends of radius less than $2t$; and ½, for bends of greater radius. (Sample calculations showing the use of the above formula are presented on page 228 in the article "Contour Roll Forming".)

Permissible bend radii depend mainly on the properties of the work metal and on tool design. For most metals, the ratio of minimum bend radius to thickness is approximately constant,

Table 2. Bend Allowances for 90° Bends in Low-Carbon Steel and Aluminum Alloy 5052

Metal thickness (t), in.	Bend allowance, in., for bends with inside radius (r) of: 1/32 in. Steel	1/32 in. Al	1/16 in. Steel	1/16 in. Al	3/32 in. Steel	3/32 in. Al	1/8 in. Steel	1/8 in. Al	1/4 in. (steel)	1/2 in. (steel)
0.032 ...	0.059	0.057	0.066	0.068	0.079	0.082	0.093	0.095	0.146	0.254
0.050 ...	0.087	0.078	0.101	0.091	0.114	0.105	0.129	0.118	0.168	0.276
0.062 ...	0.105	0.095	0.118	0.108	0.132	0.120	0.145	0.133	0.183	0.290
0.078 ...	0.128	0.116	0.142	0.131	0.155	0.144	0.169	0.157	0.202	0.310
0.090 ...	0.146	0.130	0.160	0.144	0.173	0.157	0.187	0.170	0.217	0.324
0.125 ...	0.198	0.175	0.211	0.189	0.224	0.203	0.243	0.216	0.260	0.367
0.188 ...	0.289	0.256	0.302	0.217	0.316	0.283	0.329	0.297	0.383	0.443
0.250 ...	0.382	0.338	0.395	0.351	0.409	0.365	0.424	0.378	0.476	0.519
0.313 ...	0.474	...	0.488	...	0.501	...	0.515	...	0.569	0.676
0.375 ...	0.566	...	0.580	...	0.593	...	0.607	...	0.661	0.768
0.437 ...	0.658	...	0.672	...	0.685	...	0.699	...	0.752	0.860
0.500 ...	0.750	...	0.764	...	0.777	...	0.791	...	0.845	0.952

Bend line (typ)

$w = a + b -$ bend allowance

$w = a + b + c -$ (2 × bend allowance)

$w = a + b + c + d -$ (3 × bend allowance)

$w = a + b + c + d + e -$ (4 × bend allowance)

NOTE: w = developed width of blank, t = metal thickness, r = inside radius of bend.

Table 3. Time and Cost for Press-Brake vs Punch-Press Forming of V-Bends (Example 134)

Item	Press brake(a)	Punch press(b)
Lot size (monthly), pieces	100	100
Production, pieces per hour	491	812
Setup time per lot, minutes	24	45
Time per Piece, Minutes		
Transport, position and remove workpiece	0.0461	0.0400(c)
Work handling(d)	0.0219	0.0219
Machine action (forming)	0.0484	0.0098
Net total	0.1164	0.0717
Plus allowance	0.0058	0.0022
Total production time	0.1222	0.0739
Tool and Setup Costs		
Punch and die cost	$57	$800
Setup cost per 100-piece lot	$7.61	$14.27

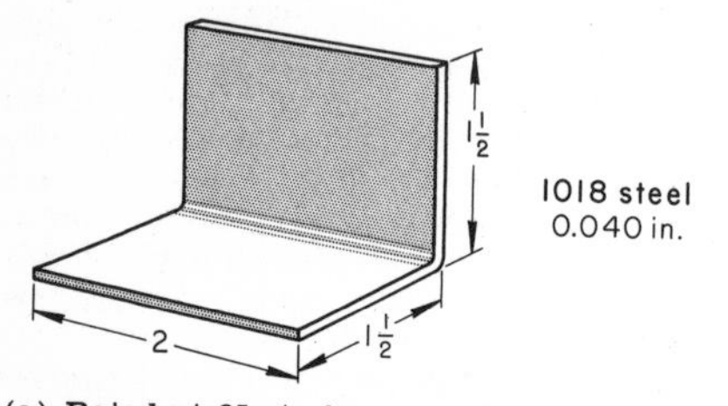

(a) Rated at 25 strokes per minute. (b) Rated at 100 strokes per minute. (c) Formed parts were removed by air ejection. (d) Soft-metal pliers (usually aluminum) were used to insert and remove workpieces from unguarded tools; no part of operator's body was allowed within 4 in. of the "pinch point" of any tool.

because ductility is the primary limitation on minimum bend radius.

Another complicating factor is the effect of work hardening during bending, which will vary with metal and heat treatment.

Condition of Machines and Tools. Machines and tools must be kept in the best possible condition for maintaining close dimensions in the finished product. General-purpose tooling is seldom built for precision work and frequently is given hard usage, which contributes further to inaccuracy through wear. Uneven wear aggravates the condition. If the press brake has been allowed to become loose and out-of-square, and ram guides and pitman bearings are worn, it cannot produce accurate work. Good maintenance is as essential to successful press-brake operation as to any other mechanical process.

Press-Brake Forming vs Alternative Processes

For many applications, press-brake forming is the only practical method for producing a given shape — such as, for example, a massive workpiece 10 to 12 ft long that required several bends spaced at least 6 in. apart.

Under certain conditions, either a punch press or a contour roll former will compete with a press brake in performance and economy. When a workpiece can be produced by two or all of these methods, the choice will depend mainly on quantity to be produced and availability of equipment.

Press Brake vs Punch Press. When a given workpiece can be made to an equal degree of acceptability in either a press brake or a punch press, the punch press usually is more economical, and is more efficient than the press brake in terms of power requirements for a given force on the ram and number of strokes per unit of time. In addition, air ejection is more readily adapted to a punch press than to a press brake, and this is a factor when air is required for ejecting either the workpiece or scrap.

Advantages of a punch press over a press brake are generally greater when production quantities are large and workpieces are relatively small. As workpiece size increases, the advantages of a punch press diminish.

Tooling for a press brake is usually simpler and less costly than counterpart tooling for a punch press — an important consideration for small production quantities. One disadvantage of punch presses is that they are more sensitive to thickness variations of the work metal, because they operate faster.

The advantage in productivity of the punch press for producing a small part requiring a simple V-bend is demonstrated in the example that follows. (If this part had been 2 ft instead of 2 in. long, however, the production rate might easily have been reversed in favor of the press brake.)

Example 134. Press Brake vs Punch Press for Making Single V-Bends (Table 3)

A small part that required a single V-bend (sketch in Table 3) was first produced in a press brake operating at 25 strokes per minute. When production requirements increased to 1200 pieces per year (in monthly lots of 100 pieces), the operation was transferred to a punch press that was operated at 100 strokes per minute. Air ejection was used in the punch-press operation to remove the formed workpiece.

With the press brake, bending took 0.1222 min per piece, or 491 pieces per hour. By changing to the punch press, time per piece was reduced to 0.0739 min, or 812 pieces per hour. A detailed breakdown of the time required for each method is given in Table 3, together with tool costs, setup costs, and rates of production.

The following formula was applied to determine the break-even point (x number of pieces) between press brake and punch press:

$$x = \frac{S_B - S_A}{P_A - P_B}$$

where P_A is production time per piece for the press brake, S_A is setup time per 100-piece lot for the press brake, P_B is production time per piece for the punch press, and S_B is setup time per 100-piece lot for the punch press.

Substituting the numerical values from Table 3 in the above formula, the following is obtained:

$$x = \frac{45 - 24}{0.1222 - 0.0739} = 437$$

Therefore, a lot size of fewer than 437 pieces was producible more economically in a press brake. (Tool costs as shown in Table 3 are not considered in this calculation, because available punches and dies were used for both the press-brake and the punch-press methods.)

In the example that follows, the situation was reversed; the quantity of parts considered was produced in a press brake for approximately one third of the cost of production in a punch press using a progressive die.

Example 135. Effect of Tool Cost on Cost per Piece — Press Brake vs Punch Press (Table 4)

The corner bracket illustrated in Table 4 was produced in two press brakes, in a series of separate operations: shearing, blanking, notching and piercing, in a 35-ton press brake; and forming in three strokes and embossing, in a 45-ton press brake. A low-viscosity machine oil was used as a lubricant. Acceptable parts were produced, and tool life was considered satisfactory.

Because the brackets were of complex design, a study was made for producing them in a punch press using a progressive die. By this method, the brackets would have been made from coiled strip, slit to width; thus, all operations would have been done in the progressive die. However, tooling cost had to be amortized in one year, and the annual requirement was only 12,000 brackets. As shown in Table 4, this quantity was too small to justify the cost of the progressive die. Although cost per piece for setup, labor and overhead was 25 times greater for the press-brake method than for the punch-press method, the high per-piece cost for the progressive die made its use uneconomical.

Press-Brake vs Contour Roll Forming. For many parts usually formed in a press brake, contour roll forming is an acceptable alternative method of production, and the choice between the two processes depends mainly on the quantity to be formed. Press-brake forming is adaptable for quantities ranging from a single piece to a medium-size production run, whereas contour roll forming is usually restricted to large-quantity production, because of higher tooling costs. Examples 320 and 321 in the article "Contour Roll Forming" compare costs for both forming methods. An advantage of contour roll forming is that coil stock can be used, whereas cut-to-length stock must be used in a press brake. The next two examples compare efficiency of press-brake forming and contour roll forming.

Examples 136 and 137. Press-Brake Forming vs Contour Roll Forming

Example 136 (Fig. 24). Parts were produced to the shape shown in Fig. 24 in lengths up to 12 ft and widths varying from 12 to 60 in. The six bends were originally made in a press brake, in three operations. When quantity requirements increased, production was changed to contour roll forming in a ten-station machine, from sheared-to-size sheets. Contour roll forming not only decreased the production time (see table with Fig. 24), but also resulted in improved surface finish, because less handling of the work metal was required.

Example 137 (Table 5). Parts requiring two offset bends and one V-bend (see illustration in Table 5) were originally produced in a press brake from stock sheared to length and width. To reduce costs, contour roll forming was used when production requirements were increased. Five separate operations, including shearing (0.21 min) and turning the part 180° once (0.04 min), were needed to produce the part in a press brake. Production time for each piece was 0.7037 min, or 85 pieces per hour. By changing to contour roll forming, the 80-in.-long pieces were rolled at 400 in. per min. Production time per piece was 0.21 min, or 286 pieces per hour.

Table 4. Comparison of Costs for Press Brake vs Punch Press in the Forming of Corner Brackets (Example 135)

Item	Press brake (utility tooling)	Punch press (progressive die)
Total tool cost	$3000	$9000
Setup, labor and overhead costs per piece(a)	$0.135	$0.0053
Tool cost per piece(b)	0.25	0.75
Total cost per piece	$0.385	$0.7553

1010 steel
Hot rolled
Rockwell
B 50 to 70
0.089 in.
ALL BENDS MADE TO 3/64-IN. INSIDE RADIUS
5/16 diam

(a) Material cost not included. (b) Based on production of 12,000 brackets in one year.

Table 5. Comparison of Production Rates and Tool Costs for Press-Brake vs Contour Roll Forming (Example 137)

Item	Time per piece, min: Press brake	Time per piece, min: Contour roll
Shear to width and length	0.2100	(a)
Position and remove work	0.2088(b)	(c)
Form bends(d)	0.1452	...
Work handling(e)	0.0657	...
Turn part 180° once	0.0405	...
Roll form 80 in. at 400 ipm	...	0.2000
Net total	0.6702	0.2000
Plus allowance	0.0335	0.0100
Total time per piece	0.7037	0.2100
Production rate, pcs/hr	85	286
Tool cost	$608	$3625

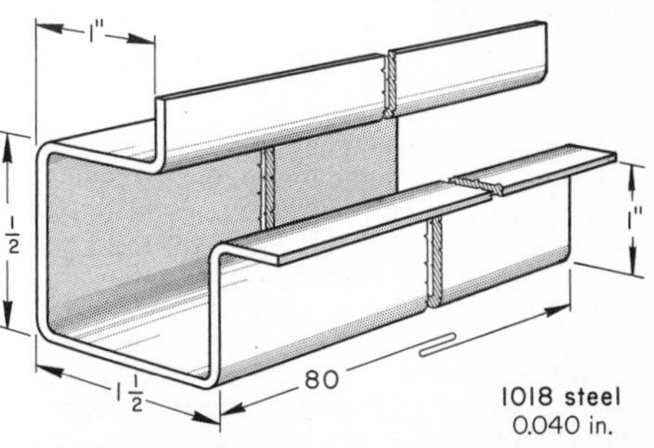

(a) Shearing not required for coil stock used in contour roll forming. (b) Done twice; 0.1044 min for each operation. (c) Coil positioning was included in setup time, and formed part was removed while machine was forming next part. (d) Two offset bends; one straight bend. (e) Soft-metal pliers were used to load and unload die.

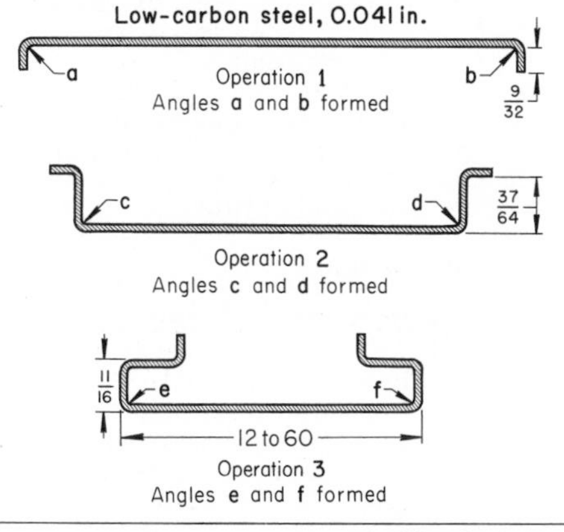

Item	Time, hr: Press brake	Time, hr: Roll former
Setup	2.1(a)	9.2(b)
Production of 100 pieces(c)	6.8	0.8

(a) Total for all operations, including dies and gages. (b) Includes dismantling. (c) Pieces 100 in. long and 48 in. wide.

Fig. 24. Workpiece formed in six bends in either a press brake or a ten-station contour roll former (Example 136)

Combination Processes. A combination of two methods is sometimes the most economical means of producing a shape. Example 303 in the article "Contour Roll Forming" describes an application in which preliminary forming was done in a contour roll former and then the workpieces were completed in a press brake.

Safety

Press-brake operations involve the hazards of other press operations. The work-handling method noted in Tables 3 and 5 in this article points out the need for proper feeding devices. Because more than one operator is often needed, added precautions are necessary to prevent the operation of a press brake without the direct consent of each man.

The article on Presses and Auxiliary Equipment, which begins on page 1, contains information and literature references on safe operation. Three other references on the subject are:

Frank E. McElroy (editor), "Accident Prevention Manual for Industrial Operations", Fifth Edition, National Safety Council, 1964, Chapters 22 and 23.

"Press Brakes", National Safety Council, Data Sheet 419, Revision A, 1968.

"Safety Code for Power Presses", U.S.A. Standards Institute, Bulletin B11.1, 1960.

Following are some of the precautions noted in these publications.

Barrier guards should be used wherever possible. Hand feeding devices such as vacuum lifters, special pliers, or magnetic pickups should always be used to keep operators' hands clear of dies.

When a large workpiece extends in front of the die, the operator often must use his hands to support the workpiece during forming. If a barrier guard cannot be used, because of the arc of travel of the front leg during forming, or because the workpiece is of such shape that a guard would prevent loading or unloading of the workpiece, the sheet should be inserted against back gages. These gages, or stops, are adjusted so that the workpiece cannot slide over them.

The workpiece is supported by hand only if there is no other way to support it, and even then only if the operator's hands are not within reach of the die or any pinch point. A die apron or table should be provided to aid in loading large sheets into the die and to act as a support for sheets that do not require hand support. The formed sheet should be removed from the front of the press; parts that cannot be unloaded from the front of the press are moved to the end for removal. End supports may be required to prevent the workpieces from falling.

For versatility, a press brake is provided with a foot pedal to operate the machine. The foot pedal must have a cover guard so the press cannot be tripped accidentally. A foot-operated press brake should incorporate a single-stroke mechanism and be used as a single-operator machine.

When a press brake is used as a power press for stamping, shearing and notching operations, the foot pedal should not be used. Instead, the press brake should be equipped with electropneumatic clutch and brake controls and should be provided with a single-stroke device. The foot pedal is replaced with "two-hand" palm switches, which are spaced so that the operator must use both hands to hold the switches until the die is closed. If a press brake is used exclusively for press work, the foot pedal should be permanently removed.

Other Examples of Press-Brake Forming in This Volume

Example	Workpiece
101	Drawer front (carbon steel)
106	Strut (carbon steel)
114	Stationery tray (carbon steel)
213	Lighting fixture (plastic-coated steel)
214	Drawer front (plastic-coated steel)
215	Lighting fixture (prepainted steel)
303	Architectural section (carbon steel)
320	Structural shape (carbon steel)
321	Structural shape (carbon steel)
453	Flanged bracket (stainless steel)
454	Corrugated sheet (stainless steel)
455	Handrails (stainless steel)
456	Mounting channel (stainless steel)
514	Curtain-wall panel (aluminum)
515	Corrugated sheet (aluminum)
516	Mounting bracket (aluminum)
517	Reinforcing member (aluminum)
518	Housing (aluminum)
519	Cabinet top (aluminum)

Press Forming of Low-Carbon Steel

*By the ASM Committee on Press Forming of Steel**

PRESS FORMING is a metalworking process in which the workpiece takes the shape imposed by the punch and die. The applied forces may be tensile, compressive, bending or shearing, or various combinations of these. In some applications, the metal requires appreciable stretching in order to retain the shape of the formed part.

Although some of the applications described in examples in this article include cutting operations such as blanking, trimming and piercing, these operations are treated more specifically in the articles in this volume on Blanking (page 31) and on Piercing (page 44). Production of hollow shells from flat blanks is dealt with in the article on Deep Drawing (page 162). Forming that involves only bending is treated in the article on Press Bending (page 89). Selection of low-carbon steel sheet for formability is discussed in Volume 1 of this Handbook, pages 319 to 330. Steels 1008 to 1020 were used for the parts described in most of the examples in the present article.

Presses

The characteristics of the various types of presses used in forming sheet-metal parts are discussed in the article on Presses and Auxiliary Equipment, page 1 in this volume.

Restriking, coining and embossing are usually done in presses with more available tonnage than is needed for simple forming of similarly sized areas, because in those operations the metal is confined while being forced into plastic flow. Progressive dies are used in presses with enough tonnage to meet the total demands of the various stations, and with enough dimensional capacity for the long multiple-station dies. Although some progressive dies are hand fed, most have auxiliary equipment such as stock feeders, scrap choppers, coil reels, and chutes to carry the finished parts to containers.

Whether or not a press has a die cushion has some effect on die design and construction costs. Single-action and double-action presses are available in about the same ranges of bed size and tonnage. Shallow forming can be done in single-action presses using die cushions or springs to provide the blankholder pressure. Deeper forming and the forming of large irregular shapes generally must be done in double-action presses with die cushions.

Springs, cams, fluid pressure, or press knockouts are used for piece ejection. The use of blank feeders and piece ejectors or extractors depends on production rate and safety requirements.

Example 2 in the article on Selection of Presses describes an application in which forming was done in a 1000-ton press because of stock thickness.

Transfer Presses. In transfer machines (eyelet machines) the mechanism for moving the workpiece from station to station is a part of the machine to which suitable transfer fingers are attached. Transfer presses are generally long-bed straight-side presses. The transfer mechanism as a part of the press is actuated by the main press drive or powered separately.

A dial feed is a type of transfer mechanism that moves the workpiece from die to die in a circular path rather than in a straight line.

The following example describes an application in which the size and shape of the workpiece made it suitable for forming in a transfer press.

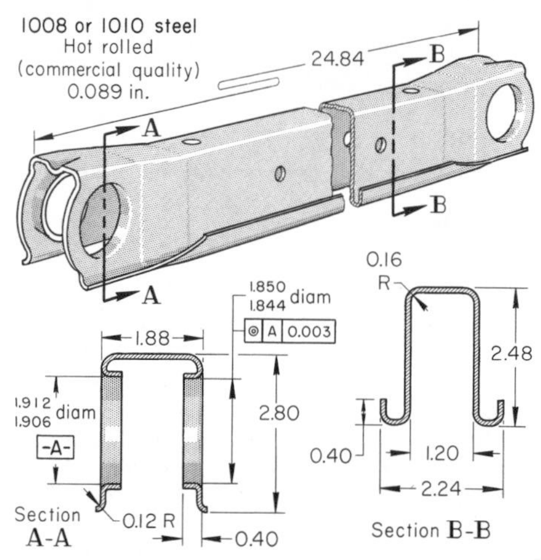

The two holes in the top of the control arm are 0.500-in.-diam tooling holes that were pierced during the blanking operation. (See Example 21 in the article on Blanking of Low-Carbon Steel.)

Fig. 1. Automotive control arm that was formed and pierced in a transfer press in five operations (Example 138)

Example 138. Forming a Channel-Shape Workpiece in a Transfer Press (Fig. 1)

The control arm shown in Fig. 1 was formed in five operations in a transfer press from a precut blank (see Example 21 in the article on Blanking of Low-Carbon Steel). The stock was hot rolled, commercial quality 1008 or 1010 steel, 0.089 in. thick, pickled and oiled.

The blanks were delivered to the transfer press in stacks. A vacuum-cup lifter attached to the transfer mechanism lifted each blank to a position from which it was gripped by the transfer fingers to be fed sideways.

The first station formed the general shape of the workpiece, leaving the flanges straight. The second station set the workpiece shape and radii, formed the conical recess in the top at each end, and curled the flanges.

The four large side holes were pierced in the third station. These holes were pierced after forming because they had to be concentric within 0.003 in. The four small side holes were pierced in the fourth station. (These holes could have been pierced along with the four large holes in the third station, but the four small holes had been added to the design of the part after dies had been built and put into operation, so a separate station was added for piercing them.) In the fifth station, the four large holes were flanged and ironed to size with cam-actuated punches.

Because of variations in the steel, occasional difficulties were encountered in forming the flanges around the holes. Bends parallel with the direction of rolling had generous radii; thus, forming was not severe. A chlorinated drawing oil with a viscosity of 55 to 65 SUS at 210 F, which was easy to remove, was applied to each blank.

The forming dies were made of A2 tool steel, hardened to Rockwell C 57 to 60. The hole punches had a clearance of 0.012 in. per side. Tool life was expected to be at least one year's production (approximately three million pieces). A 1600-ton straight-side open-end mechanical press with a bed 210 in. long and 54 in. wide was used. The press ran at 18.5 strokes per minute. The distance between the dies was 16 in.

The application described in the preceding example demonstrates the greater versatility of transfer-press forming as compared with forming in a progressive die.

Although the control arm could have been formed in a progressive die, the conical recesses in each end would have made attaching the part to a carrier strip difficult. The incorporation of cam-piercing and flanging punches operating parallel with the direction of feed is more complicated in a progressive die than in a die for a transfer press. The adding of the four small holes in the side of the part caused little trouble in the transfer press. A progressive die would have needed six

*PAUL G. NELSON, *Chairman,* Manager of Production Laboratory, Budd Co.; JOHN T. ARMSTRONG, Process Planning Supervisor, New Departure – Hyatt Bearings Div., General Motors Corp.; DONALD BASSLER, Supervisor of Tool Design, Textile Machine Works; H. T. BURKE, Vice President and Director of Engineering, Ingersoll Products Div., Borg-Warner Corp.

A. J. COOK, Supervisor of Tools and Equipment, Standard Control Div., Westinghouse Electric Corp.; D. G. FARNSWORTH, Appliance Div., Philco-Ford Corp.; ERIC E. FERDA, Tool Superintendent, Arnold, Schwinn & Co.; J. H. GOLATA, Director of Engineering, Motor Wheel Corp.; GORTON M. GOODWIN, Metallurgical Supervisor, Stamping Group, Materials and Processes Laboratory, Chrysler Corp.; ROBERT W. HOHL, Manager of Manufacturing Services, Columbia-Hallowell Div., Standard Pressed Steel Co.; JOSEPH KLAVON, Chief Tool Engineer, Jackson Div., Kelsey-Hayes Co.

ROY PEARSON, Chief Tool Engineer, Bryant Manufacturing Div., Carrier Corp.; ARTHUR PETERSON, Link, Inc.; JEROME RUDAT, Tool Room Supervisor, Modine Manufacturing Co.; A. E. SWEET, Manager of Tooling and Equipment, Maytag Co.; ROBERT WAWROUSEK, Chief Metallurgist, Parish Pressed Steel Div., Dana Corp.

or seven working stations with at least one idle station between the working stations. Had the workpiece been run through the press lengthwise instead of sideways, a much longer press bed would have been required.

Multiple-slide machines are designed for automatic, complete production of a variety of small formed parts. Flat stock is fed into a straightener, then to a feed mechanism and through one or more presses incorporated in the multiple-slide machine, for operations such as piercing, notching and bending — often in a progressive die. The feed mechanism then moves the metal into the multiple-slide forming area, where it is first severed by a cutoff mechanism to predetermined lengths. The piece is usually formed around a center post by four sets of tools mounted 90° apart around the forming post. Finally, the part is stripped off the center post and dropped through a hole in the bed.

Examples of parts made in multiple-slide machines are presented in the following articles in this volume: "Forming of Steel Strip in Multiple-Slide Machines" (page 154), "Press Forming of High-Carbon Steel" (page 136), "Forming of Stainless Steel" (page 360), and "Forming of Copper and Copper Alloys" (page 417).

Speed of Forming

Speed of forming has little effect on formability of steels used for simple bending or flanging, or moderate stretching. The maximum velocity of the punch when it contacts the blank in such conventional press forming is not usually greater than about 200 ft per min. However, the steels used for most parts that involve local stretching of more than 20% in forming move considerably over the face of the punch or flow appreciably over the blankholder. The flow of the metal in such operations is controlled by frictional forces so sensitive to speed that the steel often stretches to failure before moving against the frictional forces, provided the punch velocity exceeds a critical value, which differs for each steel and die combination. Maximum punch velocity of 40 ft per min is recommended.

High speed shortens tool life. Example 3 in the article on Selection of Presses shows how a 9% decrease in flywheel speed increased tool life by a factor of six or more.

Reselection of the steel may sometimes be avoided when speed of forming becomes a problem. Frictional forces may be decreased by the use of lubricants at the punch face and in certain blankholder areas. If lubrication does not solve the problem, and the die and press program has already been designed for reduced friction at the beginning of the forming operation, then either the speed of the punch will have to be reduced as it contacts the blank or a change in the quality of steel must be made.

Lubrication

The type of lubricant usually has little effect on the grade of steel selected to form a given part. The main effects of a lubricant are to prevent die galling and die wear and to reduce the friction over critical areas, thus allowing proper flow of metal and possibly a reduction in severity class. The thicker gages and higher forming speeds require increasingly effective lubricants. Types of lubricants employed for different severities of forming are dealt with in the article on Lubricants, on page 23.

In progressive dies, a light oil sprayed on the strip as it enters the die often is enough to keep the stock lubricated through all stages. Generally, the oil is applied to the stock between the feeding device and the die. Applying oil to the stock ahead of the feeder may cause variation in the feed length, depending on the type of feeder.

For some applications, residual mill oil or the residue from emulsion cleaning provides enough lubrication for forming (see Example 156). When this is not adequate, a spray or mist lubricant can be applied to the work metal as it enters the die.

Dies

Dies for press forming of low-carbon steel are made from a wide range of materials, including plastics, cast iron, tool steel and sintered carbide. Severity of forming, number of parts to be produced, workpiece shape, work-metal hardness, specified surface condition, and tolerances affect selection of the die material. These factors are discussed in the article on Selection of Materials for Press Forming Dies, page 145 in this volume.

Low-carbon steel can be formed by any of the several types of dies described in the following paragraphs. Workpiece size and shape, production volume, tolerances, and available presses are the major factors that determine the most suitable type of die for a specific application. A summary of the characteristics that determine the application of the four principal types of dies is given in Table 1.

Table 1. Characteristics of Four Types of Dies That Determine Their Suitability

Single-Operation Dies

1 Production in a single die doing one operation at a time requires more dies to complete a part.
2 More severe forming can be done in one operation.
3 Smaller-capacity presses can be used, because less total work is done in each press stroke.
4 Individual die cost is low, but total cost of a set of dies may be medium to high.
5 Labor cost is high, because of the number of times a part is handled.
6 Setup cost may be high, because of the number of dies in a set. But simplicity of setup may reduce setup time.
7 Utilization of work metal is good when time permits development of blank layout, because parts can be closely spaced, and can be nested, in the blank.
8 Production rate is low for manual feed, and higher for automatic feed.

Compound Dies

1 Several compatible operations can be done in a single stage.
2 Severity of an operation can be reduced by dividing it and combining it with other operations.
3 Larger-capacity presses are required than for single-operation dies, because more total work is being done.
4 Cost is higher for each die than for single-operation dies, because of the combined operations. Cost for the set, however, may be competitive with the cost for single-operation dies.
5 Labor cost is lower than with single-operation dies, because fewer dies mean less handling.
6 Die-setup costs are lower than for single-operation dies, although more complex adjustments are required per die.
7 Utilization of work metal is good, because parts can be closely spaced, and can be nested, in the blank layout.
8 Production rate is low for manual feed, higher for automatic feed. Over-all production is higher than with single-operation dies, because of fewer setups.

Progressive Dies

1 Die cost is very high, because the die consists of many compact and precisely made die components. Extra die parts are needed to locate the strip.
2 Severe forming can be done by dividing the operations into several setups. Work done in each station is limited by the adjoining stations; press operations must be done on the parts attached to the strip skeleton without distorting the parts or disturbing the position of adjacent parts.
3 Presses must be of larger tonnage and bed size than are required for single-operation dies or for compound dies.

Progressive Dies (continued)

4 Use is limited to making small and medium-size parts that do not need to be turned over or around to complete.
5 Coil stock generally is used, requiring feeds, cradles, reels and other coil-handling equipment.
6 Die-setting and die-maintenance costs are high, because of necessary adjustments.
7 Utilization of work metal is only fair; optimum nesting is not always practical, and allowances must be made for piloting.
8 Both thin and heavy sheet metal can be formed, but with thin and soft metal, pilots are likely to distort holes rather than shift strip into location.
9 Production rate is very high. Coil stock is fed automatically and part is ejected into a container. Press is run continuously and not paced by operator's loading and unloading of parts.
10 Labor costs per piece are low, because production rate is high, and because one operator may run more than one press.

Transfer Dies

1 Die cost is very high. The number of dies or stations compares with a progressive die for the same part.
2 Severe forming can be done by dividing into several steps. Transfer dies have greater versatility than progressive dies, because parts are not fastened together or to a skeleton, and each station is independent of the others.
3 Larger presses may be required than for progressive dies, because the stations are not as compact, and parts may be larger. Special attachments are required for operating parts-feeding equipment.
4 Part size ranges from tiny to large, depending on type of equipment. Plunger machines (eyelet presses) make tiny to small or medium-size parts. Transfer presses make medium-size and large parts.
5 Feeding equipment must be compatible with stock. Both coil stock and precut blanks are used.
6 Utilization of work metal is good, because blanks are moved mechanically from station to station and no strip skeleton is used.
7 Die-setting and die-maintenance costs are high, because of necessary adjustments.
8 Thickness of work metal depends on part size. Fragile or weak parts can be distorted when gripped by the feed fingers.
9 Production rate is very high. Blanks or coil stock is fed automatically, and parts are ejected into a container.
10 Labor cost per piece is low, because production rate is high, and because one operator may run more than one press. (Although sometimes operators are needed to put parts on conveyors as they come from the press.)

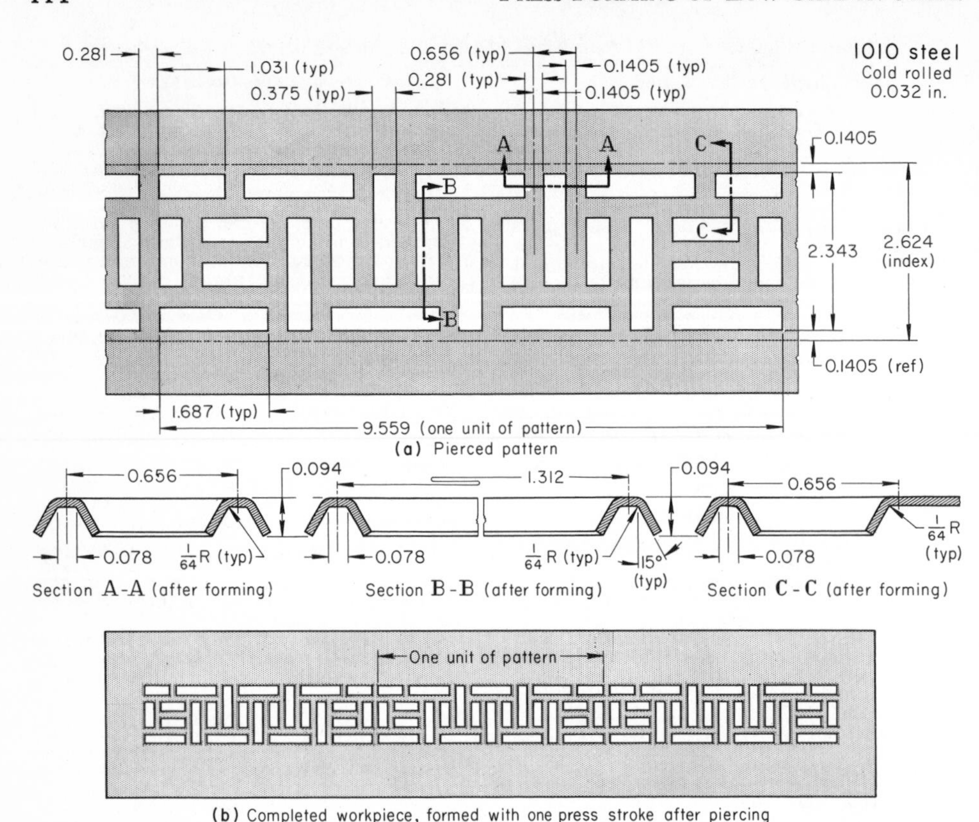

Fig. 2. Decorative grill with a repetitive pattern, pierced and formed in single-operation dies (Example 139)

Single-operation dies perform one operation at a time and are individually loaded and unloaded. They are usually set up in a press, and the operation is performed on a specific lot size. The die is then removed from the press, and the next die in the sequence is set up. For continuous production, a line of presses, each operating a single die, can produce finished pieces from raw stock without interruption for change in setup. Occasionally, more than one die is set up in a press at a time, and the parts are moved manually from one die to the next, as was done in Example 140. With this type of tooling, more than one operation is done in each stroke of the press.

Single-operation dies are used when:

1. The operations are so interrelated that they cannot be done in a compound die.
2. The amount of work done on a part is approaching press capacity, and more work would overload the press.
3. Production quantity is low, and two or more single-operation dies would be less costly than a die combining operations.

Single-operation dies do not necessarily have a low production rate. Coil stock can be fed automatically into blanking dies at a high rate. Blanks can be fed into, and workpieces ejected from, forming dies either manually or mechanically. Presses with inclined beds permit high-speed loading and unloading.

Single-operation dies often can be run at high speed. When a higher rate of production is needed, it sometimes is more practical to increase the speed of the press than to use an additional die, provided the flywheel, bearings, gibs and gears can withstand the additional speed.

In the following example, two single-operation dies were used to pierce and form repetitive designs in grills. Grill sizes were varied in increments of the repetitive pattern.

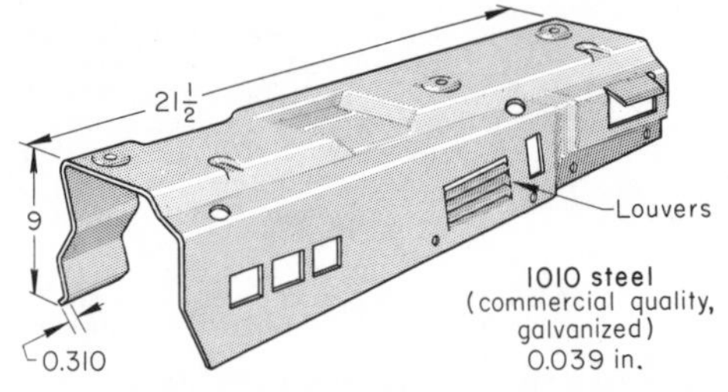

Several hooded rectangular openings like the one shown at the right end of the wrapper were made on the blind side of the piece by lancing and forming tabs.

Fig. 3. Housing wrapper that was formed in one press in six stages in compound and single-operation dies (Example 140)

Example 139. Piercing and Forming a Panel With a Repetitive Grill Pattern in Single-Operation Dies (Fig. 2)

The grill pattern shown in Fig. 2(a) was designed to cover the intake and outlet ducts of a room heating and cooling unit. The pattern was used in a single row, or in several rows repeating at 2.624-in. intervals, depending on design requirements. The sheet-metal grill replaced one made of cast iron.

The panel was made of 0.032-in.-thick cold rolled 1010 steel. The grill was made in small quantities in four operations: shear blank to size, pierce cutouts, form ribs, and paint.

Single-operation piercing and forming dies, 31 in. wide, were built to produce the pattern in a row three units long (Fig. 2b) in one stroke of the press. After the cutouts were pierced, the metal separating the cutouts was formed to a U-shape (with sections as shown in Fig. 2), to give stiffness to the panel and depth to the design.

The piercing and forming dies were made of D2 tool steel, hardened to Rockwell C 58 to 60. The grill was pierced in a 250-ton mechanical press, and formed in a 150-ton press to the contour shown in Fig. 2.

Compound dies are one-station dies in which more than one operation is done on a workpiece in one press stroke without relocating the workpiece in the die. The operations done must be such that their inclusion does not weaken the die elements or restrict other operations. Generally the operations are done successively in the course of the press stroke, rather than simultaneously.

Typical combinations of operations are: cutting a blank from a strip, then forming; lancing and forming a tab or louver; or forming a flange and embossing a stiffening bead. When a die is used for blanking and forming a part, holes often can be pierced in the bottom with the same die. When pierced holes are required in a flange, piercing should be done after the flange has been formed; otherwise, the hole (and perhaps the edge of the flange) can be distorted. The combination of lancing and forming is common. Continued travel of the lancing punch does the forming. Flanging can be combined with forming or embossing, provided that no metal flow is necessary after the flange has been formed.

A compound die may or may not cost more than a set of single-operation dies. Loading and unloading can be automated or manual. In the automotive industry, both single-operation and compound dies are set up in a press line. Coil stock or blanks are automatically fed into the first press, and the workpiece is automatically removed and transferred to the next press, where the cycle is repeated until the workpiece is completed. Typical parts are front grills, hoods, roof panels and deck lids.

Compound dies generally are operated at slower speed than single-operation dies.

Several operations can be performed successively on a workpiece in a press, using two or more compound or single-operation dies. The parts can be manually transferred from die to die, eliminating storage and transfer between presses. The capacity of a large-bed press may be more fully utilized by performing several operations during each press stroke.

In the following example, four operators manually transferred parts to and from six different dies, some of which were compound dies. All six of the dies were mounted in one press.

Example 140. Forming a Housing Wrapper in Six Dies Mounted in One Press (Fig. 3)

After some preliminary forming in a 150-ton mechanical press, a wrapper for an automotive air-conditioner/heater housing (Fig. 3) was formed in six stages in compound and single-operation dies in a 250-ton mechanical press. The material was 0.039-in.-thick galvanized, commercial quality 1010 steel, sheared into rectangular blanks 22¾ by 21½ in.

Preliminary piercing and forming operations were done on the flat sheet in the 150-ton mechanical press. These included dimpling, piercing of locating holes, notching part of a side opening, forming an angled recess, and forming one flange.

The workpiece was moved to the 250-ton press, where four operators transferred it to and from six different dies at each press stroke. Three dies were along the front of the press and three along the back. The first die trimmed the outer contour and pierced holes. The second lanced and formed tabs, and used a cam to pierce a hole horizontally. The third die formed one side. The fourth die finished the form of the housing and provided a restrike for surfaces already formed. The fifth die notched out the side opening. The sixth die lanced and formed the side louvers, and formed a tab. A lubricant was not used; the zinc coating provided sufficient lubrication for the job.

Production was on a round-the-clock schedule, and 2400 pieces per day were produced.

Progressive dies perform a series of operations at two or more die stations during each press stroke as the stock is moved through the die. One or more operations are done on the workpiece at each die station. As the outline of the workpiece is developed in the trimming or forming stations, connecting tabs link the workpiece to the strip until the workpiece reaches the last station, where it is cut off and ejected from the die. Pilot holes that are engaged by pilot pins in the die keep the workpieces aligned and properly spaced as they progress through the die.

Initial cost of a progressive die generally is greater than that of a series of individual dies for the same workpiece. However, unless the production quantity is low, the lower setup, maintenance, and direct-labor costs for the progressive die will often outweigh its higher initial cost.

A set of individual dies is sometimes used for making a complex part prior to the designing and building of a progressive die. This is done for two reasons: (*a*) a set of individual dies usually can be made in less time than a progressive die, thus permitting earlier production startup; and (*b*) the experience gained in producing the parts in individual dies can be used in designing the progressive die. From this experience, it can be determined (*a*) how the metal flows and reacts in the die, (*b*) how much work can be done in each operation, (*c*) what is the best sequence of operations, and (*d*) what the size and shape of the developed blank should be.

Although a progressive die runs more slowly than a single-operation or a compound die for similar work, over-all production is usually higher, because the die is operated more continuously.

Progressive dies are used to perform an almost endless variety of operations on one piece. Operations that can be combined in a progressive die include notching, piercing, coining, embossing, lancing, forming, cupping, drawing and trimming. The next two examples illustrate the variety of forms these operations can take.

Example 141. Use of a Progressive Die to Bend, Pierce, Emboss, Draw and Cut Off (Fig. 4)

A spring end for a paper-towel holder (Fig. 4) was blanked and formed from coiled strip in an 11-stage progressive die in a 100-ton single-action mechanical press at a rate of 2800 pieces per hour. Typical production-lot size was 120,000 pieces, and annual production was 1½ million pieces.

The work metal was a modified 1022 steel that differed from the standard composition by containing 0.20 to 0.25% carbon, and 0.15 to 0.30% silicon. This variation in composition made it possible to use an oil quench in hardening and thus to limit distortion of the finished product. The coil stock was 6 in. wide and 0.026 in. thick, with a No. 3 (slit) edge. Cold rolled steel with a No. 2 finish was used to eliminate polishing and buffing before plating. Hardness before forming was Rockwell B 60 to 75.

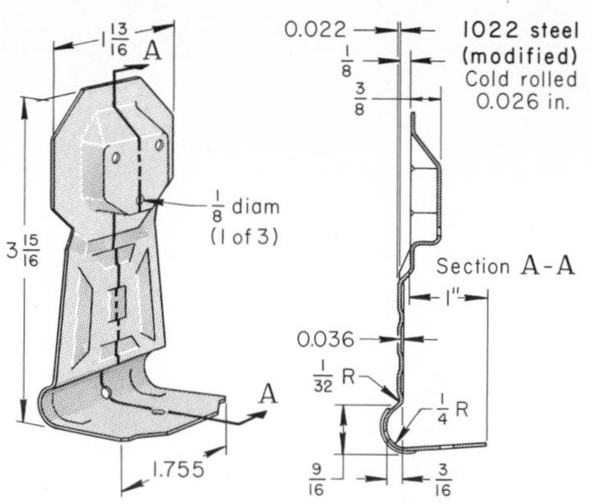

Fig. 4. Spring end of a paper-towel holder that was bent, pierced, embossed, drawn and cut off in a progressive die (Example 141)

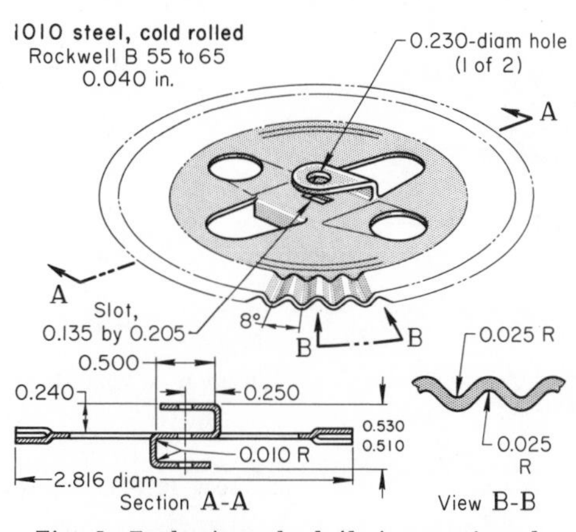

Fig. 5. Eggbeater wheel that was pierced, coined, lanced and blanked in a progressive die, prior to forming of hub tabs and integral gear teeth in separate dies (Example 142)

Die material was D2 tool steel, hardened to Rockwell C 60 to 62. Die life between regrinds was about 400,000 pieces.

Embossing added to the rigidity of the piece and provided a decorative appearance. The ¼-in. bend radius and the offset gave the part the flexibility needed for spring action in use.

After it was formed, the piece was hardened to Rockwell C 39 to 45 by quenching in oil. It was then burnished, and plated with bright nickel and chromium.

Example 142. Use of a Progressive Die for High-Volume Production of an Eggbeater Wheel (Fig. 5)

An annual production of about 600,000 pieces justified the design and construction of a progressive die for the first four operations in making the eggbeater wheel shown in Fig. 5.

For economy, this part was designed to be produced in one piece. Rigid shaft mounting, for which a separate hub is ordinarily required, was provided by bent-over tabs that gave adequate spread for assembly to the shaft. A flattened section of the shaft fit in the 0.135-in. by 0.205-in. slot to drive the gear wheel.

In the progressive die, the holes were pierced, the trademark was coined, the hub was lanced and partly bent, and the wheel was blanked. In subsequent operations in separate dies, drive teeth were formed by rippling the wheel edge, and the hub tabs were bent over to working position.

The dies, made of D2 tool steel, had a life of about 85,000 pieces before regrind. Production rate was 1100 pieces per hour in a 100-ton mechanical press. Lot size averaged about 50,000 pieces.

Because the workpiece was to be bright plated with nickel and chromium after forming, work metal was used that needed minimum polishing and buffing before the plating process. The stock was cold rolled 1010 steel in 3-in.-wide coils, 0.040 in. thick, with a No. 2 finish and a No. 3 edge. Hardness was Rockwell B 55 to 65. Stock was ordered in the low end of the thickness tolerance, to reduce material cost.

Transfer dies are similar to progressive dies except that the workpieces being processed are not attached to a strip but are mechanically moved from station to station. A blank is automatically fed into the first station and moved to the next at each press stroke. The first station can be a blanking die, which cuts a blank from manually or automatically fed stock during each press stroke. Ring forming in a transfer die is illustrated in Example 110 in the article on Press Bending.

Selection of Steel for Forming

Selection of low-carbon steel sheet for formability is discussed in detail on pages 319 to 330 in Volume 1 of this Handbook. The severity classifications in Tables 1 and 2 on page 320 in Volume 1 provide a basis for selection of class (cold or hot rolled), quality (commercial or drawing), deoxidation practice (rimmed, capped, semikilled or killed), or special treatment (temper passed or annealed).

Hot rolled, commercial quality, rimmed steel is suitable for many forming applications, and has the advantage of minimum cost. Cold rolled, drawing quality, special killed and temper passed steel has maximum formability and yields parts with the best appearance and finishing characteristics, but is premium-priced.

In selecting steel for forming, attention must be paid to deoxidation practice. Killed steel is preferred where sheets must be free of significant changes in mechanical properties (strain aging) for a long time; where neither stretcher strains nor roller leveling is permitted; or where better mechanical properties are desired for severe forming applications.

Generally, killed steel has mechanical properties superior to rimmed steel of drawing quality (particularly, it has low yield point and elastic ratio) and has better formability and performance, less tendency to form buckles, and is usually free from aging. However, inferior surface properties and more surface defects can be expected from killed steel than from rimmed steel, with consequent higher scrap or repair loss because of these defects. Also, panels produced from killed steel are usually less resistant to handling damage and "oil can", because of the lower yield strength of this steel.

Most major producers of stampings restrict the use of killed steel to the most severe draws, to low-volume parts when the steel inventory cannot be used before aging begins in rimmed steel, and to small or irregularly shaped parts for which sheet cannot be roller leveled successfully.

To assure optimum performance, killed steel should have a fine, flat, elongated grain; ASTM grain size 7 to 8 is preferred. Stretcher strains may often be removed by roller leveling if the size and shape of the blank permit. However, this is the supplier's responsibility, since killed steel is expected to be usable without roller leveling.

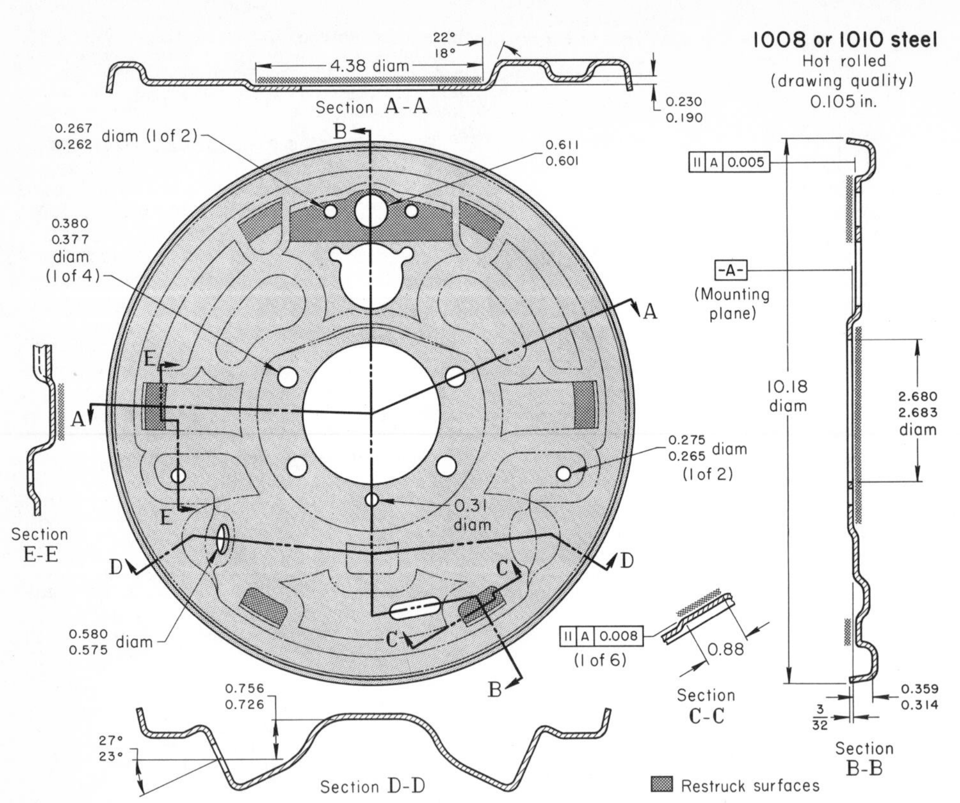

Fig. 6. Brake backing plate that was formed from drawing quality steel because of severity of forming (Example 144)

Adding a die operation may reduce the severity of forming enough so that a rimmed steel can be used instead of a killed steel.

The over-all cost of producing a part ordinarily is the criterion for determining whether to use a more expensive grade of steel or a more expensive die system. If production is high (over 200,000 pieces), the saving in material may offset the additional die costs. Blank size and die complexity may reduce or raise this break-even quantity; in the example that follows, 150,000 pieces were necessary for break-even operation.

Example 143. Change to Lower-Cost Steel and Higher-Cost Die System

For a shallow-drawn part, the cost for a blank of drawing quality killed steel was $2.41, and for a blank of drawing quality rimmed steel, $2.25. The cost for labor and burden to operate the additional tooling, including roller leveling, required for the less expensive blank was $0.06 per blank, which brought the cost for the rimmed steel blanks to $2.31 each, or $0.10 less than the killed steel blank. Additional dies needed to produce acceptable parts from the rimmed steel cost $15,000, and therefore production of 150,000 pieces was necessary to amortize the additional die cost.

In the example that follows, severe forming dictated the use of drawing quality steel for a relatively thick part.

Example 144. Use of Drawing Quality Steel for Severe Forming (Fig. 6)

The automobile-brake backing plate shown in Fig. 6 was produced in large quantities from 0.105-in.-thick hot rolled, drawing quality 1008 or 1010 steel, pickled and oiled. Drawing quality steel was used because of severe forming in two areas of the part.

Total tolerances were 0.045 in max on formed surfaces, and ranged from 0.002 to 0.030 in. on hole location. Maximum tolerance on angles was ±2°. The forming radii ranged from minimum stock thickness to 0.090 in. over maximum stock thickness.

Inserts for the forming and cutting dies were made of D2 tool steel, ground and polished.

The first operation consisted of blanking and rough forming the recessed and elevated surfaces, except the deeper pockets, in a 350-ton press at 600 pieces per hour. The stock had been sheared to a strip width of 11.75 in. and to length in multiples of 11.75 in.

The second operation rough formed the pockets with generous radii to reduce the severity of forming. A 350-ton press made 600 pieces per hour. The third operation formed the pockets to size and shape and established the level of all flat surfaces. A 500-ton press formed 600 parts per hour. This same 500-ton press was used for the fourth operation, in which the outside diameter was trimmed, the flange was curled, and all the critical flats were restruck (see Fig. 6).

All the holes except the 0.580/0.575-in.-diam hole at 25° ± 2° (see section D-D in Fig. 6) were pierced in a 100-ton press, processing 700 pieces per hour. The 25°-angle hole was pierced in a 30-ton horn press at 700 pieces per hour.

The pieces were straightened, if necessary, in a 60-ton press. The amount of straightening depended on the amount of springback.

An oil lubricant was used for the third forming operation.

Stretcher Strains

Stretcher strains, or Lüders lines, and the Piobert effect or (in shop parlance) "worms" are characteristic markings that appear on the surface of low-carbon steel that has been annealed as a final mill operation. These lines appear during the early stages of stretching and almost disappear as the stretch exceeds 5 to 10%. In tension the lines are depressions in the surface, in compression they are raised, and in bending the same phenomenon causes flutes or kinks. Stretcher strains have no harmful effect on strength. In stampings that are visible in service, stretcher strains are generally unacceptable because they show clearly through paint.

Stretcher strains can be avoided by a temper pass of about 1% cold reduction after the final anneal. The correction is normally permanent in killed steel, but in rimmed steel, stretcher strains frequently recur unless it is formed in a week or less, depending on the amount of temper pass, the temperature, variables such as high nitrogen because of steel-making practice, and the amount of forming in the stamping.

The probability of stretcher straining can be eliminated from temper-passed rimmed steel and from insufficiently temper-passed killed steel by roller leveling through a machine that flexes the sheet in bending enough to remove the sharp yield point and the yield point elongation that cause stretcher strains. This amount of cold work does not reduce drawing quality (in some steels the quality may be improved by reducing the yield point), but additional strain aging is induced, which reduces formability if the steel is stored after roller leveling. Roller-leveled steel should be used within 24 to 72 hr after leveling. The sheet should be passed through the roller leveler once in each direction, because about 18 in. of the entering end of the sheet is not flexed.

Occasionally a lift, or even a shipment, of steel does not respond to roller leveling. If such material is unsatisfactory after two passes through the roller leveler, it should not be used for parts that will be exposed in service.

The performance of annealed steel used for a very difficult unexposed part may be improved by a single pass through the roller leveler.

Annealed sheet cannot be roller leveled for an exposed part because the flex roll kinks the sheet so severely that, after forming, the deformation will not disappear and, in addition, small stretcher strains will occur between the kinks.

Coil breaks and stickers have the appearance of stretcher strains, but both are distinctively different. Coil breaks are regularly spaced, and stickers are spotty. Roller leveling has no effect on these defects.

Strain Aging

The effect of aging of rimmed steel on formability is variable and may be unpredictable on the basis of tests. One rimmed steel may not age at all, while another may make the most difficult draws when received, and, after aging 30 days, may not make minimum draws.

After an operation such as blanking, forming or finishing, strain aging is more pronounced than for unworked steel. It is therefore advisable to complete the sequence of operations on a part without intervening storage unless artificial aging tests positively indicate the absence of aging.

Artificial aging tests give an approximate measure of the strain aging characteristics of the steel but do not predict the time at which definite changes in mechanical properties will occur. Artificial aging does not change the tensile strength appreciably, but yield strength and hardness will always increase while the elongation, uniform elongation, and Olsen cup height will always decrease.

Surface Finish

Surface roughness of sheet steel has an effect on the finishing cost and the appearance of the formed product as well as on processing in dies and on other operations. Dull or slightly roughened surfaces are used especially in parts with the deepest draws, to retain lubricant through the operations for minimum scoring of the dies and for better flow of metal over pressure pads. Sheet with a surface roughness of about 30 to 50 micro-in. draws well and is smooth enough for most painted parts, such as hood tops and fenders, requiring average paint finish.

Single-dip or painted parts intended for trim and interior moldings require a smoother surface of about 10 to 20 micro-in. Sheet for average decorative chromium-plated parts should have surface roughness no greater than 10 micro-in. where the surface is to have no preparation except a light polishing to remove die marks. Parts with surface roughness as high as 15 micro-in. require extra surface preparation — for example, buffed copper plate applied before another plating.

Applicability of the standard AISI finishes for cold rolled steel sheet and strip is described in Table 2.

The selection of fine-grained steel (ASTM 9) with minimum surface roughness for forming usually sacrifices some ductility and latitude in die design. With fine grain the steel will be somewhat harder, higher in yield point and elastic ratio, lower in elongation and uniform elongation, and will be more likely to strain age.

Surface defects in parts not exposed to view may be acceptable if the function or the strength of the part is unaffected. The example that follows describes the use of two different grades of steel for forming a concealed panel on which surface defects were acceptable and for forming a panel that required a smooth surface for painting.

Example 145. Effect of Grade of Steel on Surface Finish of Severely Formed Parts (Fig. 7)

Figure 7 shows an inner panel for a glove-compartment door that was made of 0.032-in.-thick cold rolled, drawing quality rimmed 1008 steel.

On some parts, stretcher strains appeared in the severely stretched flat surface, as shown in Fig. 7. When the stock strained, the parts were used for a part number where the surface was covered by another detail. (Parts that had severe stretcher strains also cracked in the areas shown in Fig. 7 and were not acceptable.)

The outer panel for the same door, however, was visible and had to have a maximum surface roughness of 45 micro-in. before it was painted. Titanium-killed or flex rolled steel strip was used for the outer panel, to minimize the stretcher strains.

The transfer die for the door panel was set up in an 800-ton straight-side mechanical press operating at 500 strokes per hour. The die was cleaned after each shift, and resharpened after making 40,000 pieces. Lubrication was a chlorinated oil applied to the stock by rollers.

Process Development

Users should control the type of tryout steel furnished for process and tool development and tryout runs. Steels that are below the average quality expected in regular production shipments should be selected. For tentative severity classification of a part, a steel near maximum in hardness and near minimum in formability (as indicated by Olsen cup value) should be used.

Tools developed with steel of below-average quality are seldom troublesome and run with minimum tool breakage and steel rejection when the production run begins. They are also less sensitive to pressure adjustments and to variations in sheet thickness or to normal variations in steel properties, and maintenance costs are usually less. Conversely, tools developed with steel of above-average quality often are unsatisfactory when forming regular production shipments of steel. In the example that follows, rimmed steel was replaced by killed steel after initial forming experience.

Example 146. Use of Killed Steel to Avoid Annealing (Fig. 8)

A time lapse of up to several days between blanking and forming made it necessary to purchase killed steel, to avoid annealing before forming the cross-suspension member shown in Fig. 8. The steel originally used was 0.096-in.-thick hot rolled, drawing quality, rimmed 1010 steel, and the blank edges strain hardened sufficiently during the elapsed time to cause the edge in the hump area (see Fig. 8) to fracture during forming.

The part was produced in the following sequence of operations: blank; coat with dry soap film lubricant; preform to start the center hump; form; pierce holes in the side of the channel section (not shown in Fig. 8). In the hump area, the stretch along the edge was 25 to 33%. The blanking operation was separate from the forming operation, and usually one or more days elapsed between blanking and forming. It was during this period that the strain aging occurred. The lapse of time between blanking and forming included application of the lubricant, which involved heating the blanks to 212 F to dry the film. The strain aging occurred as a combined result of the baking temperature and time lapse.

Table 2. Suitability of Standard AISI Finishes on Cold Rolled Carbon Steel Sheet and Strip for Press-Formed Parts Requiring Subsequent Plating or Painting

Applications	Suitable AISI finishes: Strip	Suitable AISI finishes: Sheet
Decorative (bright) electroplating of highest quality, with little or no polishing or buffing	No. 3 (Best Bright Finish), produced on ground and polished rolls	Bright (or Plating) Finish, produced on ground and polished rolls
Decorative (bright) electroplating of intermediate quality, after polishing or buffing; decorative or functional painting	No. 2 (Regular Bright Finish), produced on rolls having a moderately smooth finish	Luster Finish, produced on ground rolls
Paint adhesion; retention of forming lubricants; functional or noncritical plating or painting. (Barrel finishing or other pretreatment may be required.)	No. 1 (Dull Finish), produced on rolls that have been roughened by mechanical methods or by chemical means.	Matte Finish, produced on blasted rolls to specified degree of roughness for end use of product

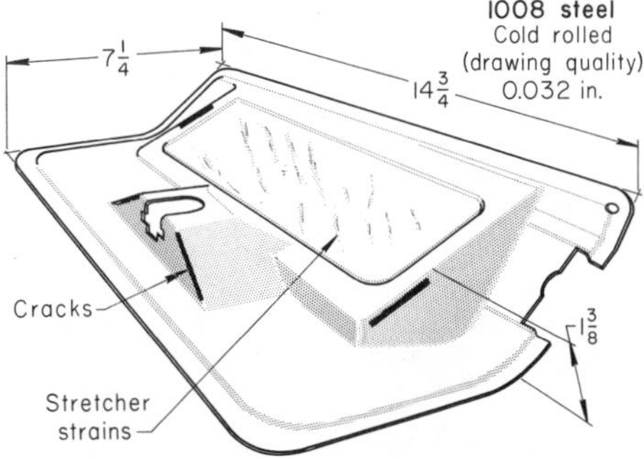

Fig. 7. Formed panel on which stretcher strains and cracks sometimes occurred. Some of the strained parts could be used in applications where they were concealed in service; cracked parts were unacceptable. (Example 145)

In the first effort to correct this condition, the rimmed steel blanks were annealed before forming. Cost of annealing was $10 per ton plus the cost of handling. The use of special killed 1010 steel (also hot rolled and drawing quality) was then considered. The killed steel cost $8 per ton more than the rimmed steel, but the elimination of annealing and handling costs yielded a saving of at least $2 per ton.

The parts were run in a 500-ton double-action toggle press at 12 strokes per minute. Annual production was 300,000 pieces.

It is sometimes necessary to change the design of a part in order to reduce the forming severity, as well as to change the steel. This is illustrated in the following example, in which the grade of steel was changed from hot rolled to cold rolled, drawing quality, and a troublesome flange was eliminated, to avoid splitting.

Example 147. Change in Steel and in Design to Avoid Cracking During Severe Forming (Fig. 9)

An automobile-bumper support bracket (Fig. 9) was produced from cold rolled, drawing quality 1008 or 1010 steel, 0.079 in. thick. Because of the limitations of the equipment and the strip width, the long dimension of the blank was positioned about 30° to the

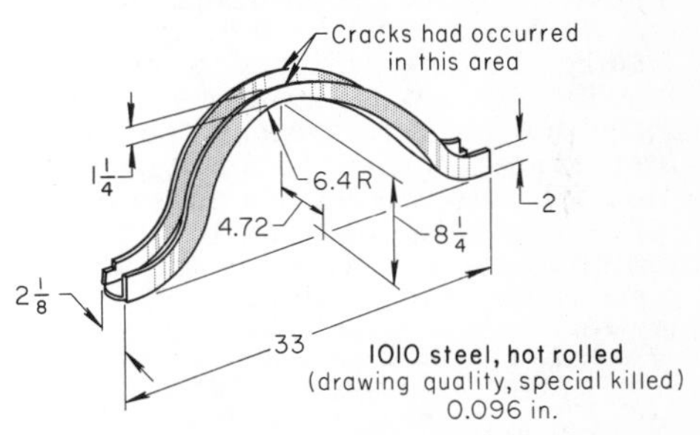

Fig. 8. Cross-suspension member that was made of killed steel rather than rimmed steel to avoid strain hardening that caused cracking during forming (Example 146)

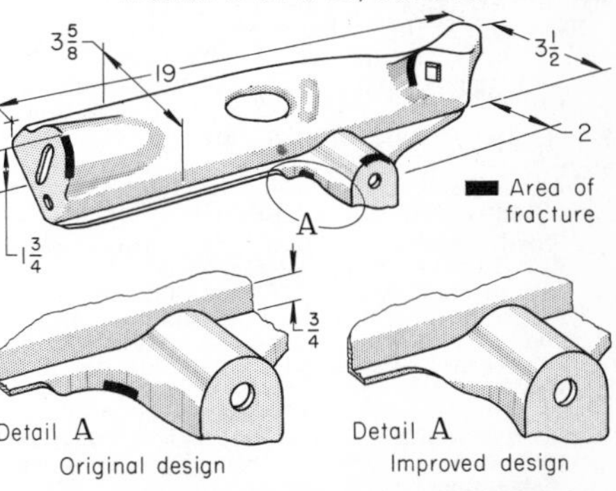

Fig. 9. Support bracket that cracked in areas indicated when it was made of hot rolled steel and before redesign of flange as shown in detail A (Example 147)

rolling direction. This proved advantageous, because of severe forming at the ends.

Originally, the bracket was made of hot rolled steel, but scrap loss was high because of splitting in the four regions indicated by black bars in Fig. 9. A short flange formerly surrounded the semicircular extension (see detail A in Fig. 9, original design), but it was omitted because severe stretching of the metal at the corner radius caused splitting.

The operations used to make the part included: blanking, forming, restriking, piercing of the large oval hole, piercing four holes, and forming a flange around the large oval hole. Right-hand and left-hand parts were made from right-hand and left-hand blanks. The blanking punch and die were sharpened after 10,000 to 15,000 pieces to keep the burr height to a maximum of 0.003 in. The pieces were formed with the burr side down. Direction of the burr affected the forming operation, so that unsatisfactory parts were made if this procedure was not followed.

The steel had a hardness of Rockwell B 54 to 55, which was the maximum for forming this part without adding extra stock for blankholding. Harder steel cracked.

The forming and piercing operations were done in three compound dies made of D2 tool steel that was hardened to Rockwell C 63 to 65. The dies were reconditioned after making 40,000 pieces. Two 300-ton and one 500-ton straight-side presses were used to make 700 to 800 parts per hour. The dies were manually loaded and unloaded.

The blanks were coated with a pigmented drawing compound.

Annealing

Descriptions of procedures for full annealing, in-process annealing, spheroidizing and normalizing are given on pages 1 to 14 in Volume 2 of this Handbook. Pieces formed from fully annealed sheet have a tendency toward stretcher straining and fluting, and fully annealed sheet is therefore used most often for unexposed parts, where these conditions are not objectionable.

Where only a spot or local anneal is needed for further forming, the area can be heated with torches to 1600 to 1700 F. The disadvantages of torch annealing are lack of close control and formation of scale. Areas that have been heated must be cleaned by pickling, abrasive blasting, or polishing.

The application described in the following example is typical of the advantageous use of torch annealing.

Example 148. Local Annealing of Severely Stretched Areas of a Formed Cabinet Top (Fig. 10)

The corners of the cabinet top shown in Fig. 10 required annealing before return flanging in operation 4 (see below), because of a time lapse before trimming the sides and reforming the flanges. Annealing was necessary to prevent splitting of the corners, which had been severely formed in operation 1 and had strain aged rapidly after forming.

To anneal the corners, the workpiece was placed in a fixture with torches at all four corners (Fig. 10), and heated to about 1700 F. After removal from the fixture, the workpiece was cooled in air and mechanically cleaned to remove scale.

The sequence of operations used to form the cabinet top was as follows:

1 Trim corners of blank, draw inner recess and flange around outside. When the punch was within 0.25 in. of the bottom of the stroke, a 10-in.-diam hole was blanked in the recess allowing metal to be drawn from the center. No additional metal could be drawn from the outside, because forming of the 2¾-in.-deep sides had already started. Forming the recess around the edge and embossing in the control panel area were also done.
2 Trim and pierce sides in a trimming machine.
3 Trim and flange center hole and pierce all holes in top (not shown in Fig. 10).

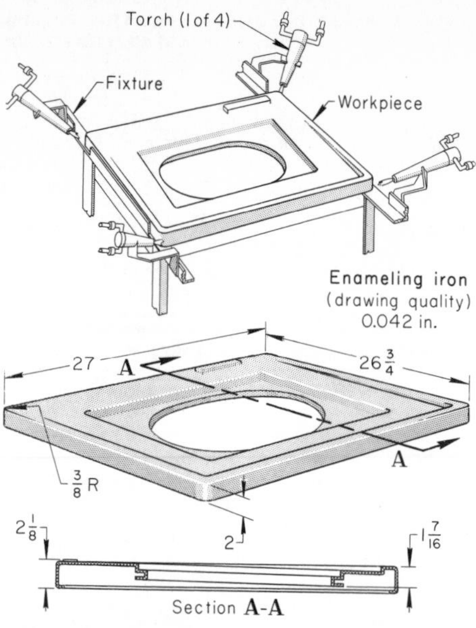

Fig. 10. Cabinet top that was torch annealed after severe forming, to prevent splitting at corners (Example 148)

4 In cam-actuated die, return bend all outer flanges and cam pierce flume opening (not shown in Fig. 10) in flange around center hole.
5 Curl flange around center opening.

The part was made from ASTM A424 grade B (drawing quality) enameling iron, 0.042 in. thick. The basic tools were designed with interchangeable elements so that more than one style of top could be made with minor tooling changeover.

Workpieces that must have a specified hardness after forming are made of annealed, spheroidize annealed, or pretempered stock, depending on the severity of the forming operation. Examples 196 and 198 in the article on Press Forming of High-Carbon Steel describe applications in which annealing or pretempering was required.

In-process annealing is done after some press-forming operations to remove the effects of cold work and to increase formability for subsequent operations. To prevent the formation of scale, a protective atmosphere is used during heating and cooling the workpiece. A low-cost exothermic atmosphere is sufficient for low-carbon steel. If a protective atmosphere is not available, the annealed work usually must be pickled or abrasive blasted to remove scale.

Process annealing frequently causes excessive grain growth. If the pieces have been subjected to a considerable amount of cold work before annealing, they may crack during subsequent forming, and may have a rough surface appearance in the formed area. (In Example 89 in the article "Coining", the workpiece was severely coined over much of its area. The necessary intermediate anneal was done at a temperature that assured a full anneal and a minimum of grain growth.)

Cleaning

The procedure for cleaning steel sheet before forming depends on the type and amount of soil present, and on the finish specified for the formed surface. Removing soil before forming improves the surface finish, prevents marking of the formed piece and prolongs die life. Large particles can be removed by wiping, which allows oil to remain and act as a lubricant. Coil stock can be cleaned by feeding it between wiping pads at the press. Another method is to feed the coil through a vat of emulsion cleaner or a light-duty drawing lubricant before it passes between the wiper pads. This procedure is an economical means of simultaneously removing foreign material and providing lubrication.

Normally, cleaning the steel in this manner does not completely remove the smudge from the surface. This condition is generally desirable, because the smudge acts as a filler in the lubricant. Many parts are formed using only mill oil with its smudge for lubrication. If smudge must be removed, a rotating brush can be used between the emulsion cleaner and the press to scrub the work-metal surfaces.

Scale is often removed by abrasive blasting or pickling before the hot rolled sheet is formed. Both methods remove the residual lubricant. Workpieces that have been in-process annealed without a protective atmosphere usually are cleaned by abrasive blasting before final forming. The need to clean parts after forming is determined by the operations that follow and the necessary finish. By choosing lubricants that are compatible with welding, painting, plating cycles, and handling, the necessity for cleaning immediately after forming can be minimized. Cleaning of parts is discussed in the section on Metal Cleaning, pages 307 to 370 in Volume 2 of this Handbook.

Deburring of Blanks

Deburring of blanks prior to forming depends on the operations performed on a blank, and on the end use of the formed part. Burrs on blanks that will be severely formed can reduce formability and increase breakage. On the exposed portion of consumer products, burrs are unsafe and unsightly.

Burrs on blanked or pierced parts cannot be avoided, but their formation can be minimized by the use of proper clearance between punch and die, and by keeping tools sharp. (See Fig. 2 in the article on Piercing of Low-Carbon Steel, page 45.)

In Example 147 in the present article, burr height was minimized by keeping the blanking die sharp; also, the blank was placed in the die with the burr side down, so that it would be on the inside of the finished part.

Work-Metal Thickness

Thickness variations in sheet steel can cause parts made on the same tooling to be of different shapes, because of springback or because the pressure applied is either insufficient or excessive at sharp corners or at sides that are to be held at a predetermined angle.

If the sheet is too thick, a die or roll adjusted to a certain thickness may pinch the steel and may localize the stretching, thus causing fracturing; or it may work harden the steel and cause excessive springback in a succeeding operation. Thickness greater than the die clearance may cause undesirable marring of the surface of the part or galling and scoring on the surface of the tools, and in some instances may be the reason for breakage of tools.

In the following example, two thicknesses of stock were used for the same part design.

Example 149. Forming of Backing Plate From Stock of Two Different Thicknesses (Fig. 11)

The backing plate (Fig. 11) for an automotive brake drum was made from hot rolled 1008 low-carbon steel, pickled and oiled, in either of two thicknesses — 0.218 or 0.250 in. Some dies were used without change (except for press adjustment) to work both thicknesses of stock; one die needed only a simple change; and some operations were done in a different die for each thickness. The stock was marked in different colors for the two thicknesses, so that the operator would not use a blank of the wrong thickness.

Five operations were used to form and trim the backing plate, all at the rate of 300 pieces per hour. Four more operations, all at the rate of 500 pieces per hour in a 120-ton or a 140-ton press, pierced and embossed the backing plate.

The first three operations did all of the forming, except the outer flange, in the same dies, regardless of stock thickness. Prior to flanging, the outside diameter was trimmed in a different die for each stock thickness. The same die could have been used, except that in the heavier plate the extra stock thickness made the flange width narrower when formed from the same diameter, because more stock was absorbed in the bend.

The flange was curled and critical surfaces were restruck (see Fig. 11) using the same punch. However, the flanging-die ring was changed by turning it upside down to accommodate the difference in stock thickness, and the press stroke was adjusted accordingly.

The holes were pierced in the same dies regardless of stock thickness, one die for left-hand and one for right-hand parts.

The six pads (see section C-C in Fig. 11) were embossed in two groups of three in a separate operation in the same die for both stock thicknesses.

The dies were made of D2 tool steel and lasted for one year's production. No lubricant other than the mill oil was needed.

Workpiece Shape

The shape of the workpiece and the number of operations needed to make it must be considered in determining press capacity (both tonnage and bed size) and the type of tooling used.

Open-end parts, or parts with one or more open edges, can be formed two or more at a time from a single blank. Sheet-metal elbows that cannot be made from tubing are formed four halves at a time, then separated and assembled into two elbows. Small flanged parts with a low ratio of flange width to stock thickness frequently are difficult to form, because of slippage and unbalanced forces. Forming two at a time can balance the forces and reduce scrap, as in the following example.

Example 150. Two-at-a-Time Forming to Balance Forces and Increase Production (Fig. 12)

Originally, the chain-guard anchor shown in Fig. 12 was produced one at a time in two compound dies, in the following operations: (*a*) blank, and pierce the round hole; and (*b*) extrude the oval projection, and form the 1$\frac{1}{16}$-in. radius and the 90° bend. Because of the shortness of the leg bent to 90°, the heavy gage of the work metal (0.125 in.), and the sharpness of the 90° bend ($\frac{1}{32}$-in. radius), it was difficult to prevent the blank from slipping during forming, and consequently the rejection rate was high. Also, because the compound dies were hand fed, production rate

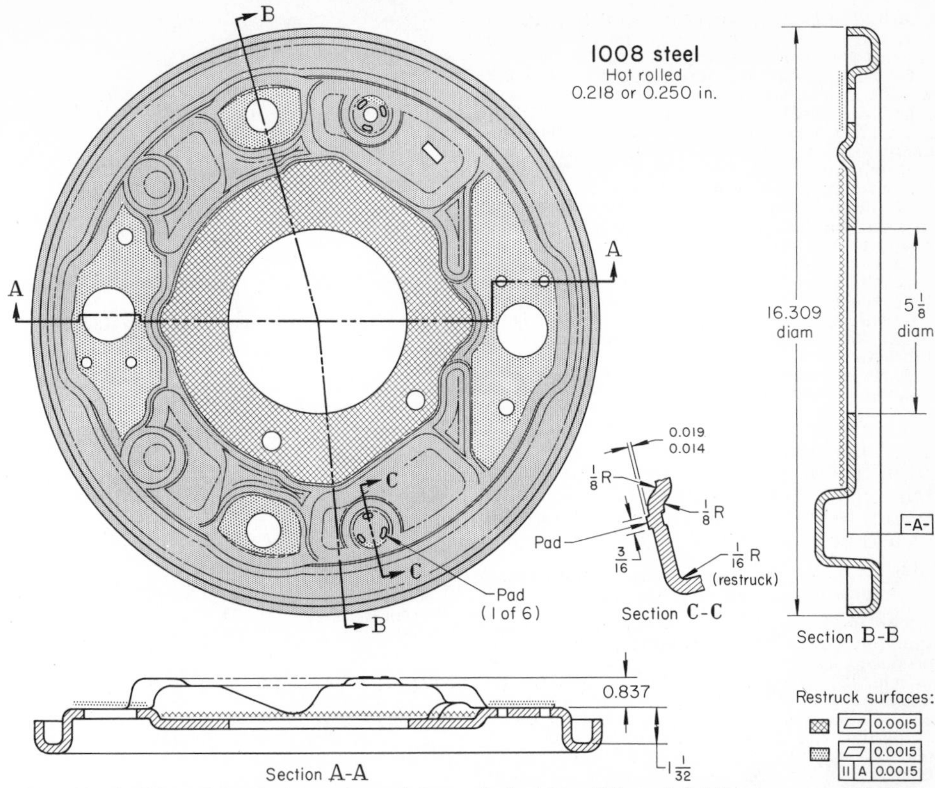

Fig. 11. Backing plate that was formed from steel of two different thicknesses, necessitating process modifications as described in Example 149

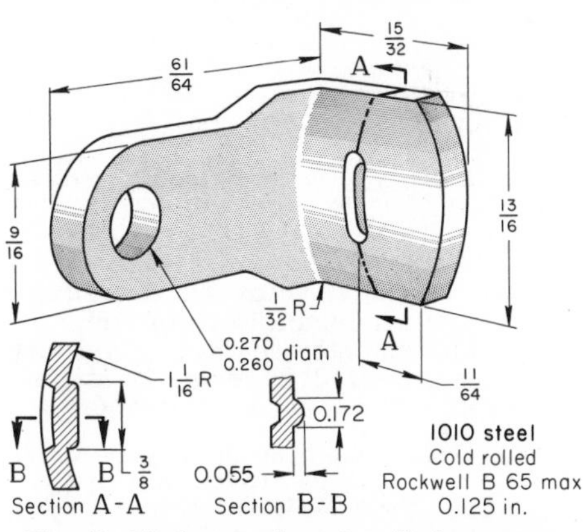

Fig. 12. Chain-guard anchor that was produced two at a time in a progressive die at lower rejection rate and labor cost than when made one at a time in two compound dies (Example 150)

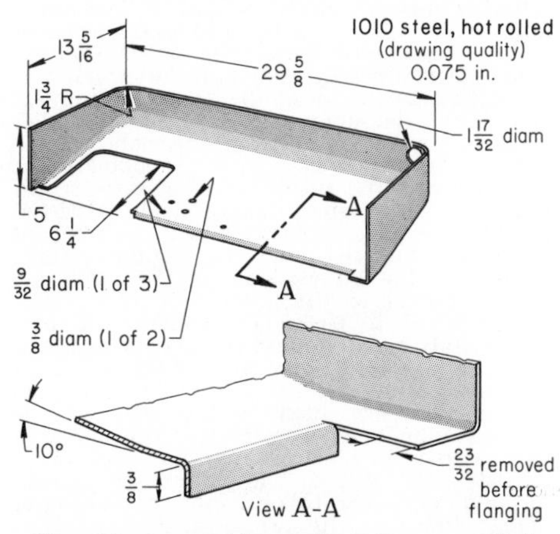

Fig. 13. Open-side rectangular pan that was formed two in one piece, and then parted, in order to balance the forming forces (Example 151)

was low (1050 pieces per hour, including rejects) and labor and overhead cost was high ($0.021 per piece).

Production was moved to an eight-station progressive die, in which two of the anchors were made simultaneously, joined until cutoff in the last station. Thus, forming was done on a U-shaped piece, with an ample holding surface provided and with two equal lengths being bent at 90°, so that the forces applied to the blank were equalized and slippage was eliminated. The sequence of operations in the die stations was as follows:

1 Pierce two round holes (one in each part)
2 Pilot
3 Blank contour
4 Pilot
5 Idle
6 Bend 90°, extrude the projections, and form the 1$\frac{1}{16}$-in. radius
7 Idle (reserved for restriking, if required)
8 Cut off.

In addition to preventing the slippage that had caused the high rejection rate, the progressive-die method also increased production rate to 5760 pieces per hour (at 80% efficiency), and decreased labor and overhead cost per piece to $0.004. At an annual production quantity of 600,000 pieces, the reduction in per-piece cost amounted to a saving of $10,200 per year.

Both types of dies were used in a 75-ton mechanical press with a 4-in. stroke, operated at 60 strokes per minute. The compound dies were of O1 tool steel, at a hardness of Rockwell C 55 to 57; die life between sharpenings was 50,000 pieces. The progressive-die material was D2 tool steel, at a hardness of Rockwell C 58 to 60, and produced 100,000 pieces between sharpenings.

The need for balance of forming forces and for the economical use of press capacity led to the production of a truck body part two at a time, as described in the following example.

Example 151. Forming an Open-Side Rectangular Pan Two Pieces at a Time (Fig. 13)

The shop-truck front wrapper shown in Fig. 13 was formed as a rectangular pan large enough to make two pieces, and then parted before being pierced and flanged. The stock was 0.075-in.-thick hot rolled, drawing quality 1010 steel, pickled and oiled. The blank, large enough for two pieces, was 37 by 41½ in.

Drawing, to a maximum depth of 5¼ in., was done in a 350-ton mechanical press having a die cushion. The draw die consisted of a punch, a draw ring and a blankholder. The drawn shape then was cut into two pieces and trimmed to height. The 6¼-in. and 23/32-in. cutouts, three 9/32-in.-diam holes and two ⅜-in.-diam holes were pierced simultaneously in a mechanical press. After lancing (see view A-A in Fig. 13), the ⅜-in.-wide flange was bent in a press brake with a standard flanging die. The 1 17/32-in.-diam hole was pierced in a press brake with a horn die. The draw die was still in good condition after 20,000 draws. A water-soluble oil was used for a lubricant.

Parts were made in lots of 200 pieces; annual production was 1200 to 1500 pieces.

The shape of the open-end part in the following example was such that forming one part at a time from a pretrimmed blank was more efficient than trying to balance forces by forming two at a time.

Example 152. Forming an Open-End Part With Flanges on One End (Fig. 14)

The body-bolt bracket shown in Fig. 14(a) was formed in two operations from a blank produced as described in Example 6 in the article "Blanking of Low-Carbon Steel". The material was hot rolled, galvanized, commercial quality 1006 steel strip, 0.075 in. thick.

Because the bracket had flanges at the open end, it was not practical to form two parts from one blank. Two blanks were placed in the first forming die to stretch form the pocket as shown in Fig. 14(b).

The second operation finished flanging the sides, formed the three flanges on the end, formed a boss for a nut to be later assembled to the bracket by self-piercing (see Example 43 in the article on Piercing), and stamped the identification.

Both operations were done in a 100-ton open-back inclinable press with a die cushion and a maximum speed of 40 strokes per minute. Production requirements were about 12,000 pieces per day. Dies for both operations were made of W5 tool steel, hardened to Rockwell C 60 to 64. They were expected to last for one year's production (approximately three million pieces). No lubricant was required for the galvanized steel.

Recessed parts require special precautions in forming, to avoid wrinkling in the flat area surrounding the recesses, and to prevent cracking the corners of the recess. In the application described in Example 163, adjustment of the blankholder pressure was necessary to prevent such failures. In that same application, the deep recess was formed first, with the material being drawn into the recess from the end and two sides of the blank; stretching done in the final forming removed wrinkles.

When the cross section of the recess is a circular arc, acceptable percentages of stretch for recesses with various height-to-diameter (h/d) ratios are:

h/d ratio	0.10	0.15	0.20	0.25	0.30
Stretch, %	3	6	10	15	22

Dish-shape parts having only one recess, of regular or irregular shape, are commonly formed by stretching the metal over a punch rather than by combined stretch and plastic flow. The punch nose should be smoothly contoured so as not to trap the metal, and should have as large a radius as possible. Parts with a straight sloping surface can be free-formed by stretching between a clamp ring and a small-diameter punch. On large parts, stretch is most severe near the punch, and the work metal elongates and drapes from its own weight, forming an undesirable concavity in the wall. Both of these defects, uneven stretch and concavity, can be minimized by using a stepped punch, as in the following example.

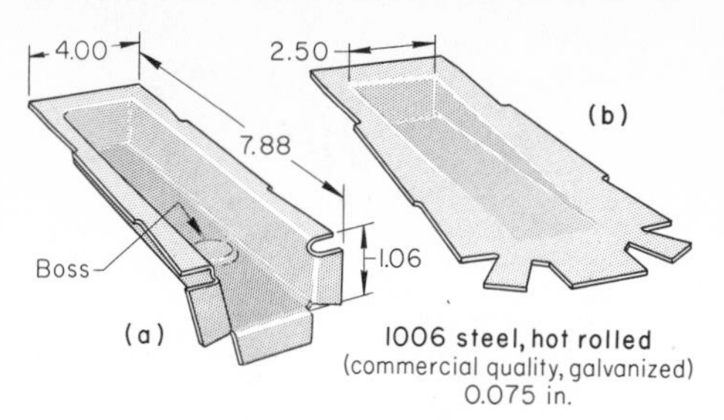

Fig. 14. Contoured bracket with a flanged open end, that was formed one at a time, in two operations (Example 152)

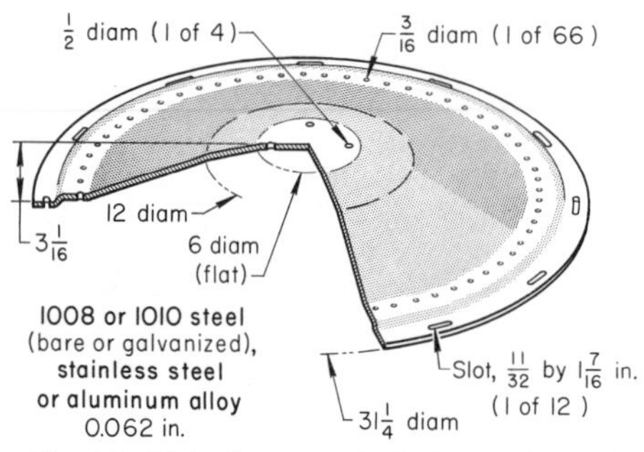

Fig. 15. Dish-shape part that was formed more accurately and with less center thin-out by stretching the work metal over a two-step punch (Example 153)

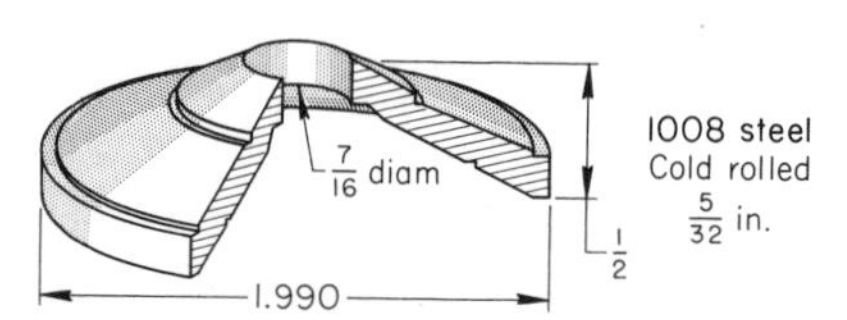

Fig. 16. Cone-shape part produced in a three-station progressive die. Three pieces, across width of strip, were formed, pierced, and blanked in one stroke at each of the stations. (Example 154)

Example 153. Addition of a Step to a Punch, to Equalize Stretch in a Dish-Shape Part (Fig. 15)

The disk shown in Fig. 15 was one of a pair that were riveted together to form the center support of a centrifugal blower. The disks, which were 31¼ in. in diameter, were formed from 0.062-in.-thick sheet in a 145-ton press with a pneumatic die cushion. Several different work metals were used interchangeably: cold rolled 1008 or 1010 steel (some of which was formed bare, then hot dip galvanized after assembly, and some of which was galvanized before forming), type 409 stainless steel and aluminum alloy 3003-O. Smaller disks were made by the same method.

When the draw ring and the blankholder closed to grip the sheet, an offset was formed near the outer edge. This offset restricted metal movement during stretch forming of the cone surface over the center punch. Originally, the punch was of the same diameter (6 in.) as the flat center area where the hub was to be attached. When formed, the metal hung somewhat loosely between punch and blankholder; also, there was considerable thinning of metal near the punch.

A more stable shape in the cone surface and a minimum of stretch near the flat area were produced by adding a second and larger diameter (12 in.) to the punch. In stretch forming, when the blank contacted the outer punch diameter, the metal inside this point was locked in, confining further metal stretch to the outer part of the blank.

After forming, twelve 1 7/16-in.-long by 11/32-in.-wide slots equally spaced on a 30⅝-in.-diam circle were pierced in the flat offset area. In the same setup, four ½-in.-diam holes were pierced on a 4¾-in.-diam circle in the flat center area. The workpiece was then placed in a 30-ton mechanical press with air-actuated indexing, where the outer diameter was nibbled to size and 66 rivet holes 3/16 in. in diameter were pierced on a 29¼-in.-diam circle. The blank was 32½ in. square.

The forming punch was made of medium-carbon steel and flame hardened, and produced 60,000 to 100,000 pieces between reworkings. The lubricant consisted of soluble oil and water, in a 1-to-5 mixture. Cost of the tooling for all four operations (blank; stretch form; pierce 12 slots and 4 holes; trim outer diameter and pierce 66 rivet holes) was $70,000. The disks were produced in runs of 30,000 to 40,000 pieces at 79 pieces per hour.

Cone-shape parts that are formed by a combined stretch-and-draw operation can be made in a progressive die without first cutting the contour. This reduces the number of die stations that are required, and often more than one part can be formed at a time, as in the following example.

Example 154. Forming of Three Cone-Shape Cover Plates per Stroke in a Progressive Die (Fig. 16)

The cone-shape cover plate illustrated in Fig. 16 was made in a three-station progressive die in a 250-ton press. The stock was 5/32-in.-thick cold rolled 1008 steel strip, in coils. Three pieces, staggered across the 5-in. width of the strip, were made by the die in each press stroke. The first station formed the cups; the second station pierced the center holes; and the third station blanked the parts from the strip. A scrap cutter at the end of the die cut up the scrap skeleton into small pieces.

Shapes With Locked-in Metal. In the forming of some shapes, metal may become locked-in (formed so that metal flow is stopped) before enough of it has been drawn into the cavity to form the part completely, and the metal sometimes fractures before the punch has reached the bottom of the stroke. In some instances the strain that causes the fracturing can be relieved by piercing a hole or lancing the metal in a noncritical area:

Example 155. Lancing During Forming, to Relieve Stress and Release Locked-in Metal (Fig. 17)

The lanced corners on the formed tail-lamp housing shown in Fig. 17 relieved stress and let metal flow into the previously locked-in vertical sides of the recess, so that the four projections on the sidewalls could be formed without tearing the metal.

Initially, the part had been made from a solid blank and formed without lancing the corners of the cutout. This was tried because tooling was simple and inexpensive, and because close tolerances on the dimensions of the cutout were easier to hold when the cutout was produced after forming.

Commercial quality 1008 steel was first used, but it tore badly around the sidewall projections. Cold rolled, drawing quality 1008 steel was better, but it also fractured around the projections. A blank with a cut-out center was tried, but the center cutout was out of tolerance after forming and promoted buckling on the corners. Finally, lancing cutters were added to the forming punch. The cutters acted during the last ⅛ in. of punch travel, thus allowing some controlled metal flow—enough to prevent splits. With the lanced corners, the final metal thickness around the previously fractured zones was 30% greater.

The die was made of alloy cast iron with the wear surfaces flame hardened to Rockwell C 50. The die was still in good condition after making 160,000 pieces. A 200-ton double-action toggle press with a maximum speed of 35 strokes per minute produced 256 pieces per hour in lots of 8000. A light-duty emulsion was used as lubricant.

Severely Formed Shapes. Developed blanks are sometimes used to provide sufficient metal in critical areas of severely formed parts. Preforming helps to distribute the metal before final forming and restriking operations, thus reducing the severity of these operations. Edge condition and ductility have great influence on the success of severe forming.

Decreased ductility as a result of strain aging led to cracking at a severely formed shoulder in ¼-in.-thick stock, in the application described in the following example.

Example 156. Severely Formed Part That Was Susceptible to Strain-Age Cracking (Fig. 18)

The only problem experienced in the production of the severely formed bicycle-fork-stem wedge illustrated in Fig. 18 was caused by strain age hardening of the ¼-in.-thick stock if it was kept in warehouse too long. Parts made of aged stock had slight cracks at the shoulders after being formed. Although the cracks were not cause for rejection, the stock was used as soon as possible after it came from the mill, because aged stock also caused dies to break in a subsequent pierce-and-flange operation. The material was ¼-in.-thick hot rolled, rimmed 1010 or 1020 steel that had been pickled and oiled.

The blanks were made with punches of high speed steel and a die of D2 tool steel at five blanks per stroke, 36 strokes per minute. The blanking tools were reground after 65,000 strokes while they were still fairly sharp. Clearance per side on the blanking dies was 8% of stock thickness.

The blanks were hand fed one at a time into a D2 tool steel die in a 200-ton knuckle press that formed the wedge to final shape in one stroke. No lubrication was used in forming, other than the mill oil that remained on the workpiece after blanking. Production rate in forming was 26 pieces per minute.

After forming, the adjusting-screw hole was pierced and flanged. It was in this operation that punches broke when used on stock that had age hardened. The pierced and flanged hole was then tapped with a 5⁄16–24 UNF thread, for completion of the part. Annual production quantity was one million pieces.

In the following example, metal was moved into the severe forming regions before final forming and restriking:

Example 157. Severe Forming of an Automobile-Frame Side Rail (Fig. 19)

A one-piece side rail (Fig. 19) for an automobile frame was formed from hot rolled, rimmed 1008 steel, 0.089 in. thick, pickled, and coated with dried soap. The complex form of the part caused extreme stretch in the sumps and on the flange edges and also high compression in the flanges.

Three lanced and formed detents in each flange were used to position the mating parts during welding.

The side rail was produced in the following operations:

1 Blank to developed size and shape, leaving trim stock in some regions
2 Crimp and preform, gathering material in zones that would be severely stretched in finish forming
3 Pierce web holes
4 Finish form, including master gage hole and flanged slots
5 Restrike top flange and trim top flange at center bulge and at rear splay
6 Trim bottom flange at center bulge
7 Restrike bottom flange, form turned-up flange at center bulge and trim bottom flange at rear splay.

Cracking of the flange edges was experienced, the most troublesome region being in the bottom flange to the rear of the center bulge. A blank was etched with 0.2-in.-diam circles in this region and then formed. Along the apex of the curvature the circles were elongated, and at the outer edge of the flange stretch was so severe that the circles elongated to 0.35 in. parallel to the edge and contracted to 0.15 in. in the opposite direction.

Cracking was caused by edge condition and by insufficient ductility in the material. Although costly, furnace annealing of the large blank corrected both conditions.

The lack of ductility was traced to the supplier, who, when furnishing pickled and

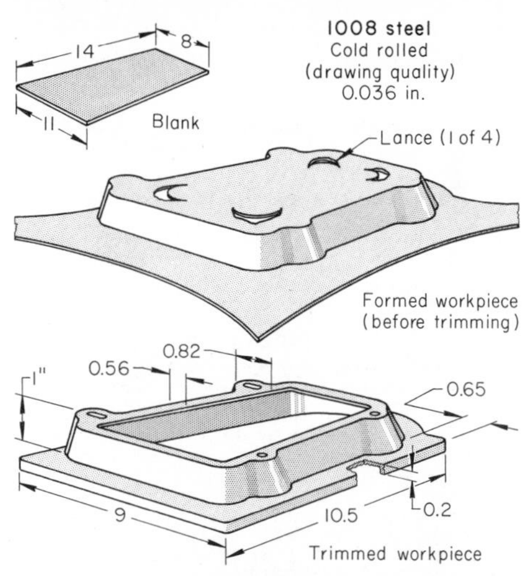

Fig. 17. Tail-lamp housing in which stress caused by locked-in metal was eliminated by lancing during forming (Example 155)

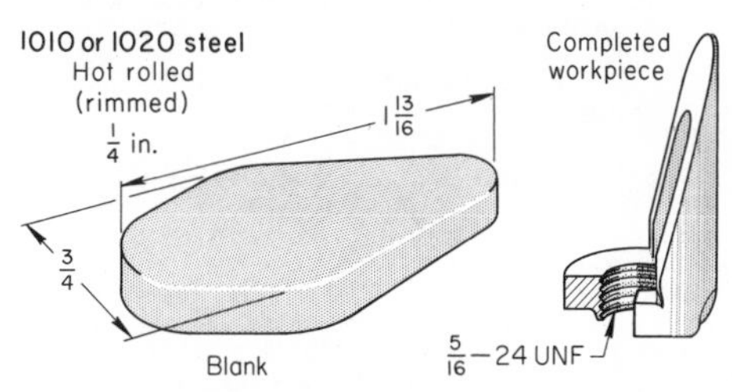

Fig. 18. Formed wedge that was susceptible to strain-age cracking at the severely formed shoulder (Example 156)

oiled material, was reprocessing coils. This entailed re-coiling, which apparently increased hardness. The use of material not processed in this manner was more successful. The edge in the critical region was ground to overcome the edge hardness. These two precautions made the furnace anneal unnecessary.

The dies were made of cast iron with D2 tool steel inserts, hardened to Rockwell C 61 to 64. The punches were made of alloy tool steel with L6 tool steel inserts at wear points. Except for minor repairs, tools were in good condition after making 1½ million pieces. An 800-ton column press was used to make 575 to 600 pieces per hour, in 10,000-piece production lots.

The amount of work done in a compound die is usually greater than that done in one station of a progressive die or a transfer die. In Example 150, two compound dies were replaced by an eight-station progressive die having four working stations, with provisions for at least two more if too much work was being done in one station.

The variety of contours, the sharp radii and the alignment of surfaces required for the part in the following example make it necessary that the forming be carefully distributed in a progressive die.

Example 158. Forming a Complex Hasp in a Progressive Die (Fig. 20)

Because of its complex shape and small bend radii, and the flatness required on three surfaces, the ammunition-box hasp shown in Fig. 20 was well suited for progressive-die forming. In an eight-station progressive die, the hasp was notched, blanked, formed and cut off from cold rolled 1010 or 1020 steel strip 0.075 in. thick and 6.58 in. wide.

The forming was done with the bend axes parallel to the direction of rolling. Some cracks appeared along the 1⁄32-in. radii, because of the severe bending in that area. The three surfaces indicated as A, B and C in Fig. 20 were held flat and in a common plane, so that the part could be spot welded to a metal box.

The die was made of D2 tool steel and had a life between grinds of 250,000 pieces. Total die life was 1¼ million pieces. Improvements in die design increased the life of a second die to over two million pieces. The die was run in a 150-ton straight-side mechanical press with a single roll feed at a rate of 45 strokes per minute.

The part in the following example had some design features that could not be made in one die or die station. These features included a stretch-formed dish, a bead, and lanced and curled edges.

Example 159. Lancing and Forming a Center Disk for Press Fit With Blades at Assembly (Fig. 21)

The center disk for a 9-in.-diam by 9-in.-long blower was designed for assembly with blades by inserting the blades into slashes

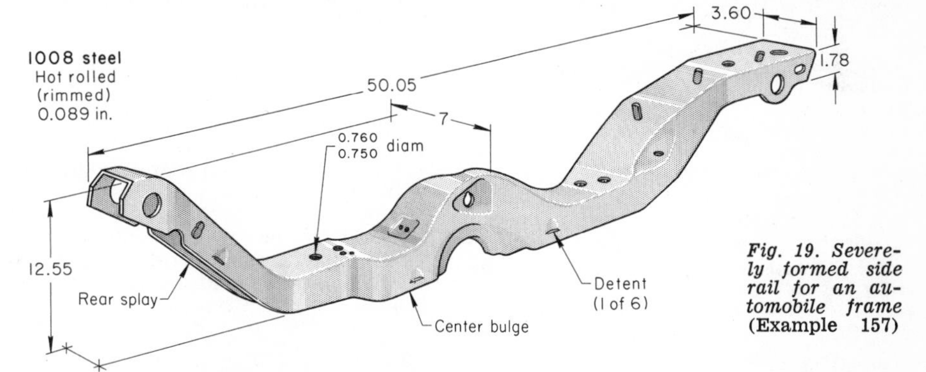

Fig. 19. Severely formed side rail for an automobile frame (Example 157)

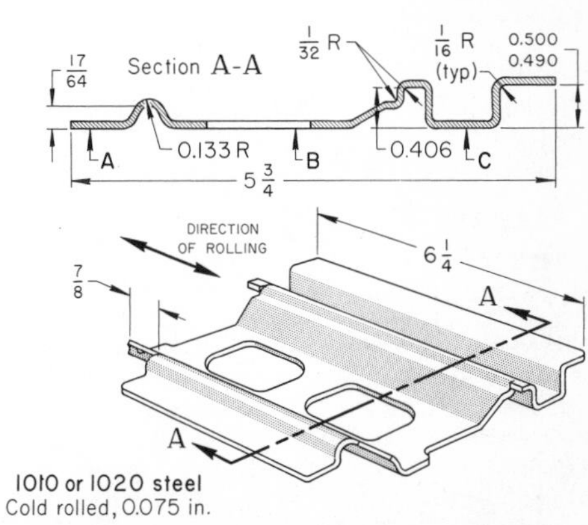

Fig. 20. Complex hasp that was formed to small bend radii in a progressive die (Example 158)

at the edge of the disk and flattening the disk for an interference fit. Slashes were made in the disk by lancing and partial curling. The disk, shown in Fig. 21, was made of 0.028-in.-thick cold rolled 1008 or 1010 steel in four press operations:

1 Blank outside diameter, pierce center hole, pierce sixteen 3⁄16-in.-diam holes, and form bead
2 Form cone shape, using the bead to help hold the metal
3 Lance 16 slots and curl one side of slots
4 Curl second side of slots.

All operations were done in a 60-ton open-back inclinable press using a 1-to-5 mixture of soluble oil and water as a lubricant. Shedder-type punches were used in the compound die for the first operation, to prevent slugs from sticking to the end of the punches. The total punch-to-die clearance for the 3⁄16-in.-diam piercing punches was 30% of stock thickness.

The four dies were made of A5 tool steel hardened to Rockwell C 60 to 62 and cost $18,000. Tool life was 250,000 pieces, or nearly one year's production. The production rate was 500 disks per hour.

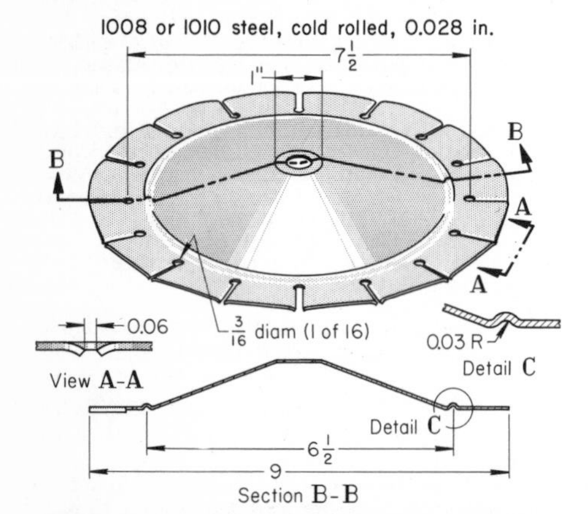

Fig. 21. Center disk that was lanced and formed for press fit with blades for a blower (Example 159)

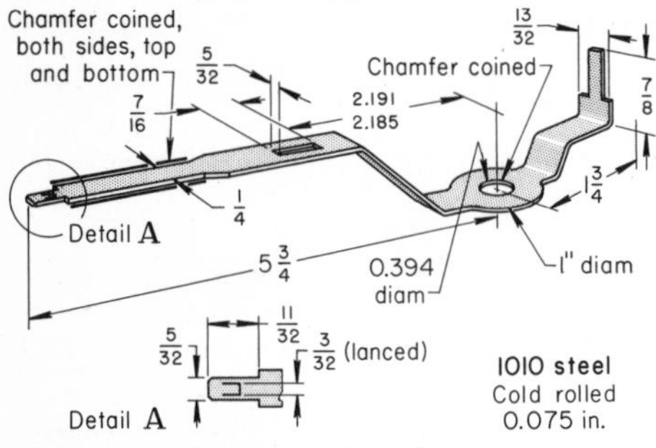

Fig. 22. Heater control lever that was formed in a progressive die because of its complex shape (Example 160)

The lever described in the next example was so complex in design that it required ten progressive-die operations. The lever could have been blanked and formed with fewer individual dies, but production rate would have been lower.

Example 160. Forming a Long Narrow Lever in Ten Progressive-Die Operations (Fig. 22)

The lever shown in Fig. 22 was used for the air regulator of a heater. It was made in ten operations in a progressive die, from 0.075-in.-thick cold rolled 1010 steel, 7⅛ in. wide. The slenderness of the part made it necessary to hold the strip securely while the outline was trimmed. Tolerance on the location of the rectangular slot was close; therefore, it was pierced after the lever was formed. The operations in the progressive die were:

1 Pierce three 0.394-in.-diam holes and 3⁄32-in.-wide lance. (Two of the holes were in the scrap area of the strip, and were used for piloting at the next station, which was idle.)
2 Trim adjacent outlines of two neighboring pieces. Remove pilot holes, but leave part connected to strip at ends and at the hub.
3 Complete trimming short end
4 Complete trimming long end
5 Coin a chamfer on both sides of 0.394-in.-diam hole
6 Coin a chamfer on four edges on the ¼-in.-wide step on long leg (see Fig. 22)
7 Form joggles in legs
8 Form flange on short leg; restrike joggles
9 Pierce 5⁄32-by-7⁄16-in. slot
10 Cut off.

A combination stock lifter and guide was used in early stations of the die. Spring-loaded lifters contacting the stock in the hub area were used in three later stations.

The die elements were made of W1 tool steel and hardened to Rockwell C 58 to 60. Commercial die buttons, piercing punches and pilot punches were used. Die life was 75,000 pieces between resharpenings. Mineral oil was used as lubricant.

The part was made in a 150-ton straight-side mechanical press operating at 2400 strokes per hour. Annual production was 600,000 levers.

Offset Parts (Edge Bending). Scrap loss can sometimes be reduced when blanks can be produced in simple rectangular form and subsequently edge bent into the final shape. Whether the severity of the edge-bending operation will adversely affect subsequent forming operations must be considered. Potential savings of work metal can be quickly lost if edge bending work hardens the pieces so much that many are broken in forming. In some applications, as in Example 161, which follows, the tensile and compressive stresses set up in edge-bent blanks can be counteracted by forming stretch flanges around the inner contours of the bends, and compression flanges on the outer contours. The same flanges made on a cut blank instead of an edge-bent blank could fracture during flanging. On the other hand, reverse flanges made on an edge-bent blank may cause more severe stress than they would on a cut blank, and might possibly lead to a high scrap rate.

The edge-bending operation and its tooling are an added expense in making the part. This expense must be compared with the saving of work metal when one method is to be selected over the other.

Edge bending was economical in the preparation of blanks for automobile and truck-frame side rails in the following example. Here the quantities were large and the cost of edge-bending tooling was amortized by the saving in material. (Edge bending was also used in the forming of brake-pedal levers in Example 112 in the article on Press Bending of Low-Carbon Steel.)

Example 161. Edge Bending and Forming An Automobile-Frame Side Rail (Fig. 23)

A one-piece side rail for an automobile frame (see Fig. 23) was made of 0.093-in.-thick hot rolled, rimmed 1008 steel, pickled and oiled. The blank was 8 in. wide and 194 in. long, with a hardness of Rockwell B 55 to 60. The following operations were done automatically up to a rate of 900 pieces per hour: slit and shear to width and length; edge bend to form offsets on each end; pierce and notch; blank to contour; and form.

The severity of the edge bending and forming sometimes necessitated edge annealing or grinding to avoid cracking. The compressive and tensile stresses built up by edge bending were counteracted by forming the flanges.

The blank could have been cut from a large sheet and then formed. However, this method would have used up to 10 lb more metal per side rail, and the advantage of counteracting stresses by edge bending and forming would not have been possible.

Lot sizes ranged from 2000 to 10,000 pieces for an annual production of 200,000 to one million rails.

The blanks were edge bent in a specially designed 500-ton press capable of offsetting blanks up to 0.156 in. thick and 17 ft long. After offsetting and trimming, the blanks were formed into a channel shape having a typical section of 5½-in. web and 2½-in. flanges.

Side rails up to 0.250 in. thick and 20 ft long for trucks were made in a similar manner in an 800-ton edge-bending press. Edge bending the truck side rails saved up to 17 lb of material per rail. The truck rails were made of hot rolled rimmed steel, pickled and oiled, 0.156 to 0.375 in. thick. A 4000-ton open-side press was used to form the top and bottom flanges simultaneously.

The automobile side rails were made in individual dies set up in presses arranged in line with automatic transfer equipment between the presses. The presses ran at 14 strokes per minute. The pierce-and-notch and blank-to-contour operations were done in 400-ton mechanical presses. Forming was done in a 1000-ton mechanical press, which formed both right-hand and left-hand rails.

The offsetting dies were made of aluminum bronze and W2 tool steel, hardened to Rockwell C 57 to 60. The forming dies were made of cast iron with W2 tool steel inserts, hardened to Rockwell C 61 to 64. The punches were made of 1045 steel and flame hardened, and had inserts of W2 tool steel, hardened to Rockwell C 57 to 60.

A dry film of soap plus borax applied to the blanks generally provided adequate lubrication, but sometimes it was necessary to apply an oil-base lubricant over the dry film.

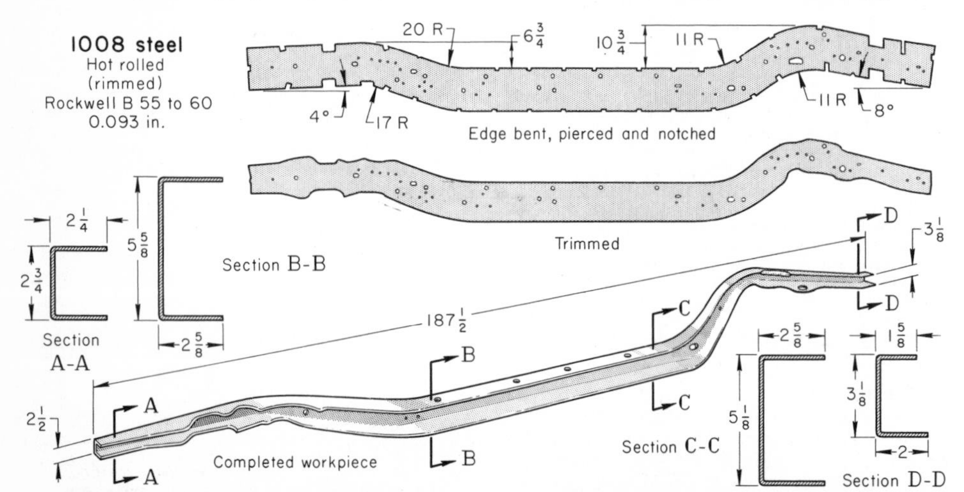

Fig. 23. Automobile-frame side rail made by edge bending and forming (Example 161)

Large Irregular Shapes

Large parts usually are formed in single-operation or compound dies mounted in large-bed presses. If the part is irregular in shape, care must be taken in shaping the blankholder surfaces, in planning the orientation of the workpiece in the die, and in planning the die operation to get approximately even stressing of all areas of the workpiece and to form the piece in the fewest possible operations.

To make shallow draws, sometimes the metal must be locked in place by the blankholder, in order to stretch the sheet metal over the punch enough to set the contours, as was done when forming the blower disk described in Example 153. Draw beads or selective local applications of drawing compound are used to restrict and control metal flow.

Large irregular-shape parts are often made by preshaping blanks before forming. The automobile-frame side rail described in Example 161 was made by using a blank that was edge-bent before flanges were formed. This method reduced scrap when making the blank and neutralized the tensile and compressive stresses in the flanges. The blanks for automobile fenders and other parts have been preshaped by bending and tack welding them into a cone shape.

Use of Shaped Blankholders. Some parts that are made from preformed blanks are formed with the aid of shaped blankholders to avoid distortion of the previously formed contours. Also, parts that are not completely formed in one operation may have to be clamped in a shaped blankholder in a second-operation die.

The part in the following example had a peripheral offset that served as a locating surface in the second-operation die, but the part had to be clamped to prevent distortion during final forming.

Example 162. Holding a Previously Formed Workpiece in a Shaped Blankholder to Prevent Distortion During Subsequent Forming (Fig. 24)

After the first forming operation, the blank for the fan shown in Fig. 24 had a 0.188-in. offset outer rim and a ⅞-in.-deep recessed inner web. These surfaces were used as locators in a shaped blankholder for the subsequent trimming and forming operations.

Spring-loaded pressure pads held the rim and the web while the blades were twisted. The pressure pads bottomed at the end of the stroke, so that any deformation in the rim or the web could be flattened. The 0.188-in. offset was placed over a close-fitting plug to prevent radial distortion of the rim.

Three operations were needed for producing the part. In the first operation, the 0.188-in. offset was formed to 18.550-in. diam, and the ⅞-in.-deep recess was formed at the same time. In the second operation, the 19.121-in. OD was trimmed, and the 1.755-in.-diam hole and 24 T-shape cutouts at 15° spacing were pierced. The T-slots gave shape to the fan blades and necked the ends of the blades prior to twisting at 45°, which was done in the third operation.

The cutting elements in the dies were made of A2 tool steel. The forming dies for the offset rim and recessed web were of low-carbon, high-strength alloy cast iron. The blade formers were made of prehardened low-alloy tool steel. The workpiece was made of a 0.035-in.-thick cold rolled 1010 steel blank, 20$\frac{1}{16}$ in. square.

Recesses in Large Panels. Forming of recesses in large panels at some distance from the edge can be difficult. Because the sheet is large, the recesses appear to be shallow, but forming may actually be severe in terms of localized deformation.

If the recess is fairly small and far enough from the edges of the blank so that there is a large resistance to metal flow, the metal can be overstressed at the punch nose and fracture or tear.

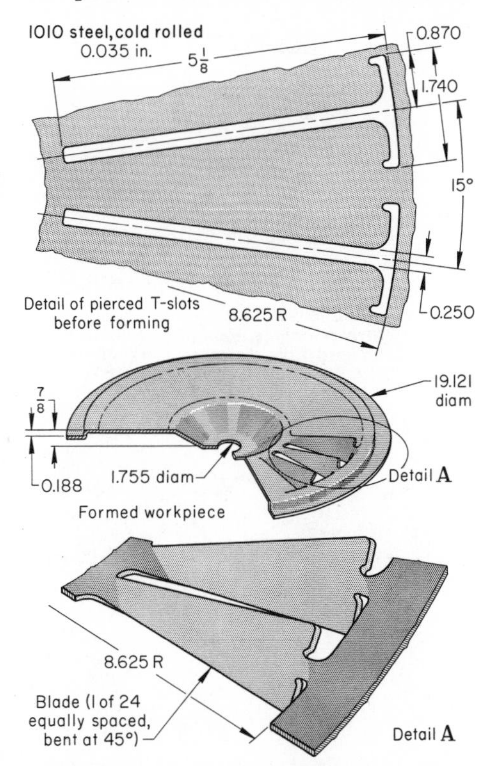

Fig. 24. Large sheet-metal fan that was clamped in a shaped blankholder during the second forming operation (Example 162)

To prevent tearing, blankholder pressure is kept as low as possible to allow almost unrestricted metal flow. This, however, may produce wrinkles radiating from the lip of the recess. These can be removed by stretching the sidewalls of the recess in a second forming operation, as in the following example.

Example 163. Forming a Deep Recess in a Large Panel (Fig. 25)

The 1.906-in.-deep recess in the heater-drum head shown in Fig. 25 was located 10$\frac{1}{16}$ in. from one side and 7$\frac{13}{16}$ in. from the edges of an enameling iron blank 0.027 in. thick, 32¾ in. wide and 40⅝ in. long. To allow the most unrestricted metal flow across this large area, the blankholder pressure was kept to a minimum, thus preventing large compression wrinkles from being formed around the ends of the recess. The large punch-nose and die radii required by the part design promoted the necessary flow of metal along the sides of the recess, but did not provide good control of metal flow at the ends of the recess.

The first operation, forming the 2-in.-wide, 25-in.-long recess to a depth of 1.608 in., was the most severe. Using a ⅜-in. die radius along one side, as shown in Fig. 25, helped to control metal flow. Embossing the top surface and forming the sidewalls in the second operation (during which the recess was finish formed) stretched the metal enough to remove small wrinkles. In the final operation, the flange was trimmed, and bolt holes were pierced.

The punches for forming the recess were made of prehardened alloy tool steel; the blankholders and draw dies were made of low-carbon, high-strength alloy cast iron. The embossing punch and die were made of 1045 steel. The replaceable inserts for identification lettering were made from flat-ground oil-hardening tool steel.

Large cup-shape parts that must be stronger in the bottom surface than in the wall are often designed with tapered wall sections. A tapered section can be made by machining the part either before or after drawing.

High-strength low-carbon steels of thinner gage than conventional low-carbon steels can be used without tapering, but they are more difficult to draw, and they cost more. The use of a tapered blank for a cup-shape part is described in the following example.

Example 164. Forming a Large Disk From a Tapered Circular Blank (Fig. 26)

The truck-wheel disk illustrated in Fig. 26 was formed from a blank 24 in. in diameter that had been roller tapered from a 19$\frac{11}{16}$-in.-diam blank with a 3$\frac{9}{16}$-in.-diam center hole. Taper was about 0.040 in. per inch of radius. The material was dead-soft hot rolled 1012 or 1015 steel, 0.375 in. thick, abrasive blasted to remove scale and oxide.

The blanks were tapered back to back, two at a time, giving each disk only one rolled surface. The tapering rolls were stopped before reaching the edge of the blank, in order to maintain an even taper. Otherwise, lack of resisting stock at the edge would have caused

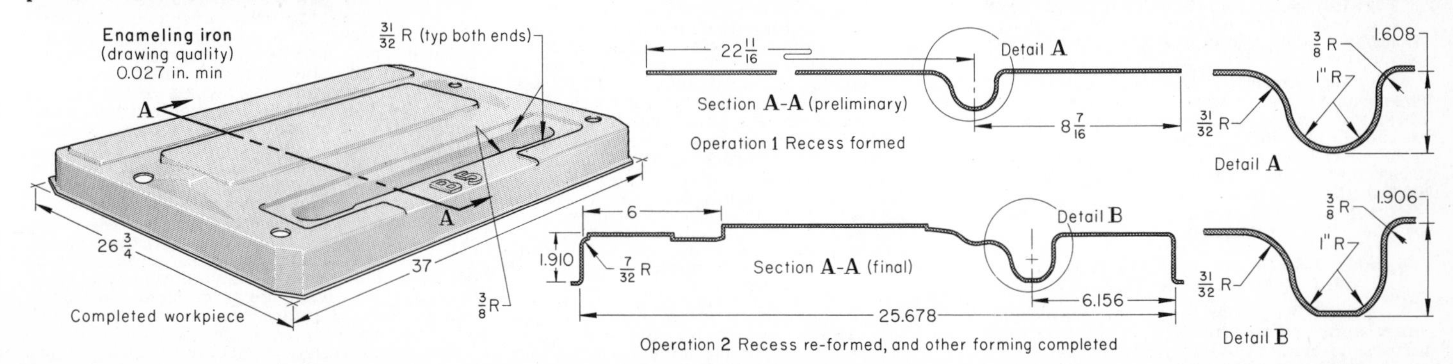

Fig. 25. Heater-drum head with a recess that needed carefully controlled metal flow and stretch in forming (Example 163)

a torn edge. Tapering started at 10¼-in. diameter (just beyond the circle describing the outer edges of the six round holes), which gave a stock thickness of 0.330 in. at the 0.69/0.50-in. radius.

The combined forming and trimming operation was done in a 1500-ton hydraulic press with the rolled surface of the work face down in the die. The blank was trimmed to 23 in. in diameter in a compound blank-and-draw die at a rate of 375 per hour. The die was made of O1 tool steel and was reworked after making 40,000 pieces.

A second operation sized the 19.616-in. OD, enlarged the center hole to 6.471±0.002-in. diam, and pierced six 1.28-in.-diam holes, using an 800-ton mechanical press. In the third operation, six hand holes were punched, one at a time. To attach a rim to a disk, 16 rivet holes evenly spaced around the circumference of the flange were pierced in both the disk and rim at the same time.

The optional 1015 steel had the highest carbon content that could be used in this part. Work hardening increased its strength and hardness. If hardness of the workpieces exceeded Rockwell B 91, hairline cracks radiated from the rivet holes, causing rejection, as observed when 1020 steel was used.

Localized severe forming is encountered in making many large irregular shapes by press forming. This imposes stringent demands on process planning, quality of work metal, and lubrication, and on the design, material and maintenance of dies — as is demonstrated in the two examples that follow.

Example 165. Severe Embossing and Hole Flanging in Press Forming a Control Arm (Fig. 27)

The severe embossing and hole flanging demanded on the automobile control arm shown in Fig. 27 required the use of drawing quality steel for the workpiece and high-quality tool steel for the dies, close attention to tool maintenance, and the use of a heavy-duty lubricant.

The stock was hot rolled, drawing quality, rimmed 1008 or 1010 steel, pickled and oiled, with a hardness of Rockwell B 55. Commercial quality steel had been tried but was unsatisfactory for the severe forming. Stock thickness was 0.156 or 0.164 in. Wall thickness of the hole flanges had to be at least 0.105 in. and flange width, 0.30 in. The parts were formed with dies of hardened W2 tool steel. A developed blank was used, making a final trimming operation unnecessary.

Operations were as follows:

1 Blank to developed outline; pierce two locating holes; form center boss — done in a 200-ton mechanical press with die inserts of W2 tool steel, hardened to Rockwell C 57 to 60.
2 Form in a 600-ton mechanical press using dies made of W2 tool steel, hardened to Rockwell C 61 to 64.
3 Pierce two holes in flanges; enlarge one locating hole; pierce oval hole in center boss — done in a 70-ton, inclined-bed mechanical press.
4 Restrike to size and sharpen radii, form dimple, and flange round hole and oval hole in a 600-ton mechanical press.
5 Pierce remaining holes in a 70-ton inclined-bed mechanical press.
6 Outward flange two side holes to 1.398/1.394-in. diam, 0.105-in. minimum wall thickness, and 0.30-in. minimum flange height, using hydraulic equipment designed for this part.

A dry-film lubricant consisting of soap and borax was applied to the blank. Where further lubrication was needed, an oil-base compound was added. Production rate ranged from 200 to 325 pieces per hour; production-lot size was 10,000 pieces; and annual demand was over 200,000 pieces.

Except for minor repairs, the dies were good for one year's production.

Example 166. Severe Flanging That Provided Reinforcement (Fig. 28)

A flanged design provided the automobile control arm shown in Fig. 28 with enough stiffness to enable production of the part from relatively thin stock, and deep hole flanges made to a tolerance of 0.004 in. TIR on diameter and alignment eliminated the need for use of bushings to reinforce the holes.

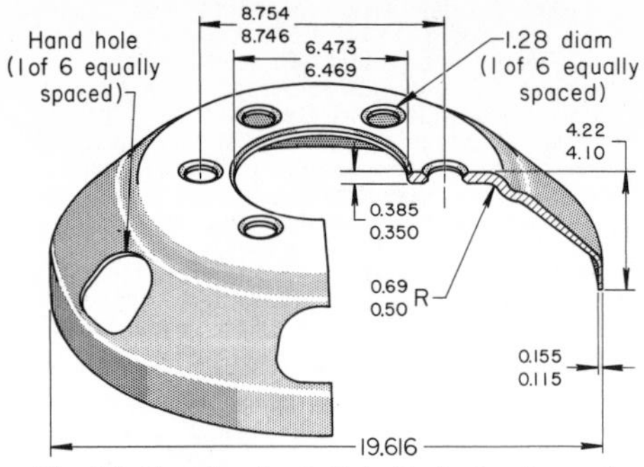

Fig. 26. Truck-wheel disk that was formed from a tapered blank (Example 164)

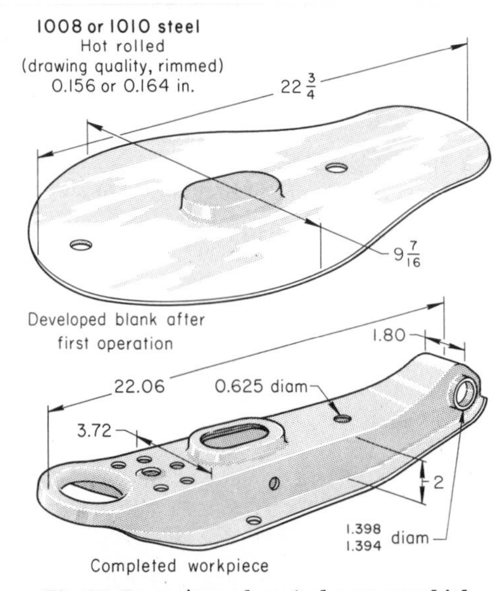

Fig. 27. Press-formed control arm on which embossing and hole flanging were of near-maximum severity (Example 165)

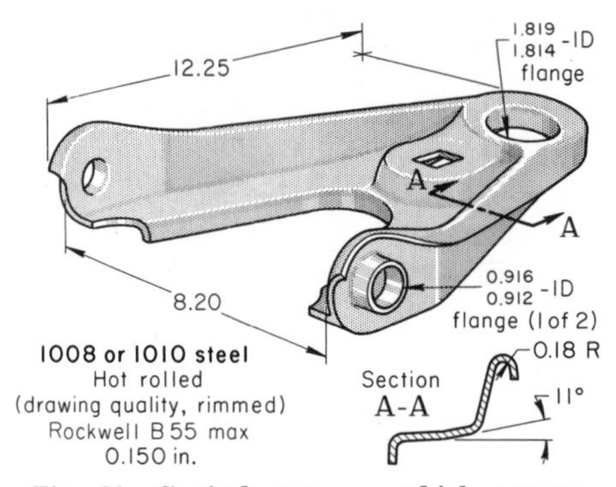

Fig. 28. Control arm on which reverse flanging and hole flanging of near-maximum severity were done in presses (Example 166)

The material was 0.150-in.-thick hot rolled, drawing quality, rimmed 1008 or 1010 steel with a maximum hardness of Rockwell B 55. The control arm was produced from a triangular blank (14⅛-in. base, 14¹³⁄₁₆-in. height) in the following sequence of operations:

1 Blank to developed outline, and pierce a 0.656-in.-diam locating hole, in a 300-ton open-back inclinable mechanical press operating at 15 to 20 strokes per minute
2 Preform center area, and inside and outside flanges, in a 100-ton mechanical press at 400 to 575 pieces per hour
3 Restrike to finish form, in a 300-ton mechanical press at 400 to 575 pieces per hour
4 Pierce three round holes and one square hole, and trim outside flanges around side holes, in a 70-ton inclined-bed mechanical press
5 Flange three holes in two stages, holding diameters of two side holes to 0.916/0.912 in., and the third hole to 1.819/1.814 in., in a hydraulically actuated machine at the rate of 350 to 425 pieces per hour.

The forming dies were made with W2 tool steel inserts, hardened to Rockwell C 61 to 64. Punches were of 4340 steel (Rockwell C 50 to 55) with W2 tool steel inserts like those on the die at wear points. A dry-film lubricant of soap and borax was applied to the blank. An oil-base compound was added to critical areas during forming and flanging. More than 200,000 pieces were produced annually, in lots of about 10,000 pieces. Except for minor repairs, such as replacing small punches, the dies were good for one year's production.

Blanks That Cannot Be Nested. Irregularly shaped parts frequently must be made from developed blanks with a contour that makes close nesting of the blanks impossible. Channel-shape parts with flanges or web of varying width use blanks that are cut with more scrap than parts with flanges or web of unvarying width, and an excessive amount of scrap may be generated in producing them.

In some applications, material that otherwise would be wasted can be moved into a useful location after notching or lancing. This was done in the following example, in which the web was notched at the end and then spread into a V-shape, to increase flange height at the ends and reduce blanking scrap.

Example 167. Use of a Notched Blank to Increase Flange Width and Reduce Scrap in Forming an Irregular Channel-Shape Part (Fig. 29)

A flange of varying width was needed on the channel-shape truck-frame member shown in Fig. 29. Instead of using a contoured blank, which would have meant considerable waste in blanking, the extra flange width was gained by notching each end of a nearly rectangular blank and spreading the notch into a V-shape during the forming operation. The end of each notch was radiused to minimize cracking during forming. The stock saved by notching the blank was 3 lb per piece.

The workpiece was made of 0.179-in.-thick hot rolled, rimmed 1008 steel, pickled and oiled. Each of the two notches in the blank was 0.36 in. wide by 7⅛ in. long. The notches were spread to make V-shape openings 2.24 in. wide at the ends. Flange widths varied from 2 in. at the center of the part to 5 in. at each end of the channel. The operations were:

1 Cut blank to developed outline, and pierce large center hole (see Fig. 29). A 350-ton mechanical press with a mechanical unloader produced 300 to 400 blanks per hour.
2 Form completely, including flange around center hole, in an 1800-ton hydraulic press.
3 Pierce all holes in the web, and trim 0.74-in. radius at two places on each end, in a 325-ton mechanical press.
4 Pierce holes in top and bottom flanges, and restrike flange ends, in a 325-ton mechanical press.

Presses for operations 2, 3 and 4, operating at 250 to 310 strokes per hour, were set up in a line with transfer equipment between them. In operation 2, a spreader was incorporated in the die to assist in opening the notch to a V-shape. The 7⅛-in. length of the notch had been carefully developed so that the notch would spread to the required maximum width without causing the work metal to split. After forming, a 0.625-in.-diam hole was pierced at the end of each notch to remove any fractured material or other stress raisers aggravated by the severe edge forming.

Forming punches were made of 1045 steel. Wear surfaces on the punch and die were of W2 tool steel, hardened to Rockwell C 61 to 64. As a lubricant, a soap solution was dried on the stock. Some heats of steel were difficult to form; for these, an oil-base compound was used as additional lubricant.

The truck-frame member was made in lots of 27,000 pieces for an annual production of 270,000 pieces.

Except for minor repairs, such as replacing small punches, the dies were good for one year's production.

Use of Draw Beads. A draw bead in a blankholder controls the movement of metal into the cavity by providing additional resistance to metal flow. The location of the beads is usually determined in die tryout; dies for producing similar parts can be used as a guide.

A single bead is generally placed around the cavity, and additional beads are placed in areas where more control is needed. Conditions may indicate that the bead size should be reduced, or the whole bead omitted, in some places. Short beads may be placed at an angle to deflect metal into or away from local areas.

Whether the bead is placed in the draw ring or in the blankholder is determined by the die construction. Placing the groove in the upper member has the advantage that it will not catch dirt. However, the groove should be put in the member that is to be altered during spotting for mating of opposing surfaces. For convenience in making alterations, this usually is the lower member.

Unless part of the product design (see Example 159), draw beads are placed outside the trim line, as shown in Fig. 30(a). The trim line can be on either the punch or the blankholder. A locking draw bead, such as shown in Fig. 30(b), is used to provide maximum restriction to metal flow. Locking beads are used when forming to shape is done primarily by stretching the metal under the punch, rather than by moving metal into the cavity.

Figure 30(c) shows the use of both conventional and locking beads. Here, conventional beads control metal flow into the die cavity until the last portion of the punch movement, when the locking bead gradually engages the metal to restrict its flow. The last fraction of an inch of punch travel causes stretch in the metal under the punch.

Beads in concave surfaces of a blankholder are usually 0.12 in. deeper than beads on the top or straight surfaces. This eliminates locking on the top surfaces during preforming of the blank to the shape of the concave blankholder surface.

Sometimes draw beads need not be used for the full depth of draw, or need to be used only in certain locations like corners of regular or irregular polygon-shape parts. In such cases, some of the material may be allowed to slip through the draw bead, to be retained at the end of the stroke only by blankholder pressure.

Additional discussion of the design and construction of draw beads, and an example of their use, are given on pages 174 and 175 in this volume.

Forming of Ribs, Beads and Bosses

Otherwise unsupported sheet metal surfaces that might buckle or "oil can" are often stiffened by the addition of long thin bosses called beads or ribs. Round or nearly round bosses are sometimes called buttons. Dimples are sometimes used as a recess for a rivet or screw head. The forming of ribs, beads and bosses is a combination of bending, stretching and drawing, and involves high shear forces.

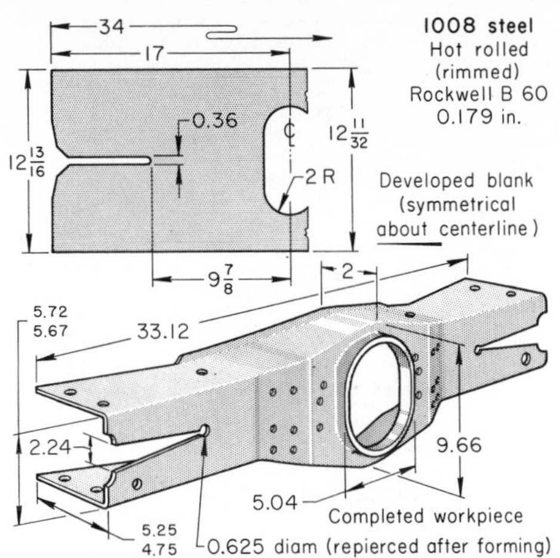

Fig. 29. Press-formed truck-frame member that was notched and spread to increase flange width locally and thus save material in blanking (Example 167)

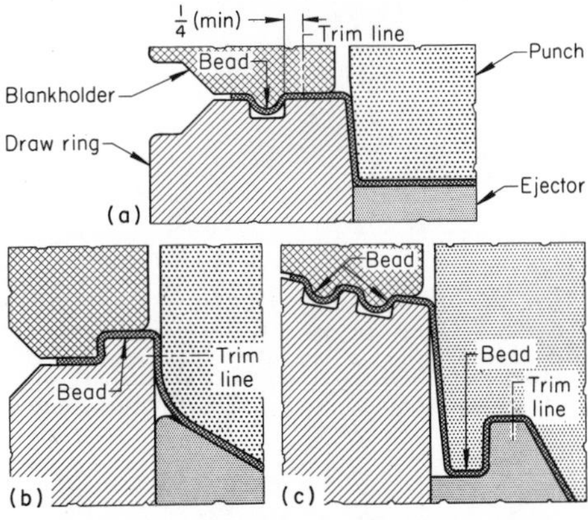

Fig. 30. Use of draw beads: (a) *conventional,* (b) *locking,* (c) *combined conventional and locking*

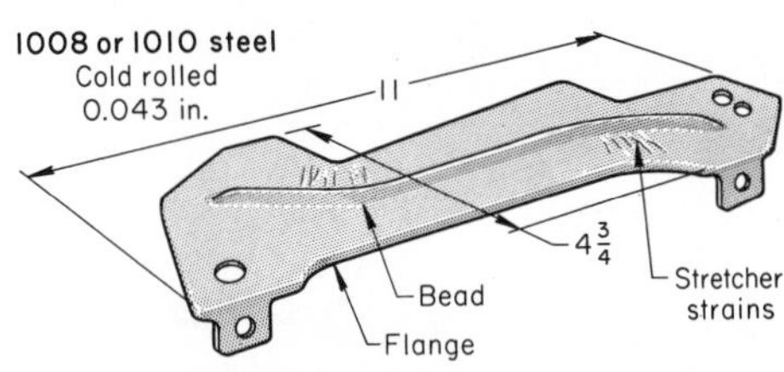

Fig. 31. Corner bracket that was stiffened by beading and flanging (Example 168)

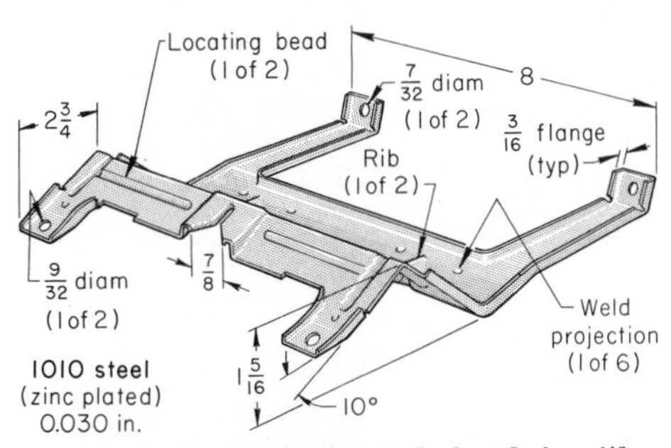

Fig. 32. Instrument-panel bracket with beads used as locators, ribs used as reinforcements, and bosses used as weld projections (Example 169)

Design of Bosses. Ordinarily, bosses are about one stock thickness in depth. The radius of curvature on the inside of bends is about one stock thickness. A typical bead appears to be about four stock thicknesses wide on the convex side, and about three stock thicknesses wide on the concave side.

Some recesses for screw heads have sloping sides with very little curvature.

Usually, bosses are produced at the same time that other forming operations are done and in the same dies, although they may be formed at separate stations in a progressive die. Die clearances can be critical in the forming of decorative bosses and embossed lettering, especially when definition must be sharp and detail must be accurate. On the other hand, reinforcing beads usually do not require great accuracy, and can be produced in dies with the clearances typical of ordinary forming.

Use of Bosses. In Example 152, a boss was used to stiffen the area around a nut as well as to provide a flat mounting surface. In Examples 153 and 159, cone-shape bosses served to stiffen disks, as well as to separate bearing surfaces. The part in Example 176 was embossed to maintain flatness.

Reinforcing and stiffening beads were formed in Examples 168, 169 and 170. In Example 171, the contoured raised surface between the sidewall and the center hole of a lawn-mower housing acted as a boss in helping to support the motor and the cutting blade. In Example 165, an oval boss was used as a hole-locating surface and as the hole flange. The most frequent use of embossed beads is to lighten the weight of products by making it possible to use thinner metal than would be feasible without bosses, as described in the following example.

Example 168. Use of a Bead for Stiffening a Corner Bracket (Fig. 31)

The corner bracket shown in Fig. 31 had a bead on the flat surface to produce stiffness. The work material was 0.043-in.-thick cold rolled 1008 or 1010 steel. The bead made the use of heavier stock unnecessary. A short flange around the periphery of the bracket also added to the stiffness.

The bracket was produced in a progressive die in the following operations: trim to shape, pierce, form bead, form flange, and pinch trim from the carrier strip. The die was run in a 500-ton press operating at 600 strokes per hour. Forming of the bead caused some distortion of the pilot holes, and resulted in stretcher strains that extended from the inside radius of the bead to the part edge.

The progressive die was made of D2 tool steel and hardened to Rockwell C 62 to 64. One hour per week was needed to clean the die and make minor repairs. Die lubricant was chlorinated oil.

Embossed features can serve as locators for subsequent operations, as welding projections, or as stiffeners. Three different types of bosses were produced on the formed part described in the following example, each type serving one of the above functions.

Example 169. Forming a Bracket on Which Bosses Served Three Functions (Fig. 32)

The T-shape beads on the instrument-panel bracket shown in Fig. 32 were used as locators, and to prevent slippage, during subsequent forming. Six weld projections and two stiffening ribs were also embossed on the bracket, as shown in Fig. 32. The beads were made in a progressive-die sequence that comprised the following operations: trim the blank outline, pierce four holes, emboss six weld projections, and form the two T-shape beads. The die was run in a 450-ton press, which operated at 60 strokes per minute. Alloy cast iron was used for the punch and the die shoes. Forming and wear surfaces were of W1 tool steel, hardened to Rockwell C 58 to 60.

After beading, the bracket was formed in a 100-ton press equipped with a hydraulic system that had a patented pressure-control valve and a pneumatic die cushion. A predetermined pressure, up to 3000 psi, was maintained in the hydraulic cylinders supporting a moving punch in the upper die shoe. Thus, the workpiece was clamped at a constant pressure against the die-cushion-actuated blankholder during the forming stroke.

When it was loaded into the die, the blank was located by the two locating beads and by ¼-in.-diam pins in the two 9⁄32-in.-diam holes. As the die closed, the hydraulically controlled punch clamped on the 2¾-in. length of the workpiece and formed the 10° bend against die-cushion pressure. As the die continued to close, the 1 5⁄16-in. offset and the bends in the legs were formed by first contact of the fixed punch in the upper die shoe, and flanges were formed around the workpiece and in the slot between the locating beads. The punches and blankholder bottomed to set the bend radii, form two stiffening ribs, and re-form the two T-shape beads.

In some areas, bend-relief cutouts were used at the flanges to minimize fracture. In other areas, both stretch and shrink flanges were formed around corners without difficulty.

A pigmented mineral oil was used as lubricant. Die life was 250,000 pieces before reconditioning. Annual production was 1½ million brackets.

Orientation of the part with respect to the direction of rolling is an important consideration in the forming of beads. When several features are sensitive to orientation on the strip, a compromise layout may be advisable, as in the following example.

Example 170. Orientation of Rolling Direction When Forming Beads and an Offset (Fig. 33)

The long straight edge of the lawn-mower yoke bracket shown in Fig. 33 was oriented at 40° from the edge of the strip, so that neither the offset nor the beads were formed parallel to the direction of rolling. The bracket was made of 0.120-in.-thick hot rolled 1010 steel that had been pickled and oiled. A strip 8 in. wide by 46¼ in. long was sheared from a sheet. Six blanks were made from this strip. The developed outline was blanked and pierced in a 75-ton mechanical press. To make left-hand yoke brackets, blanks were turned over. On the left-hand pieces, burrs on the holes to be flanged would have been on the wrong side had the holes been pierced; hence, on left-hand pieces, the holes were drilled, with a No. 23 drill (0.154-in. diam). Holes were flanged in a 40-ton press prior to being tapped with ⅜–16 UNC threads. Another 40-ton press formed the beads, and a 75-ton press with a die cushion was used to form the offset.

The strip was covered with an oil compound before shearing, and enough lubricant remained on the surface for forming. Production rate was 600 pieces per hour.

Embossing is a severe forming operation and may need a special quality of work metal for successful completion, as in Example 165 and the following example.

Example 171. Change From Commercial Quality to Drawing Quality Steel to Avoid Cracking at Sharp Corners of a Large Boss (Fig. 34)

Figure 34 shows a lawn-mower housing on which cracking occurred on the corners of the sharp step at the inside of the large boss when the part was formed from commercial quality steel. To avoid this cracking, the housing was made from cold rolled, drawing quality 1010 steel, 0.075 in. thick.

The boss, which surrounded the motor mount on the housing of the mower, served three functions: it added stiffness to the top (which was to support a vibrating motor); it made a natural wind tunnel to guide air and cuttings from the whirling blade to the 3¼ by 9-in. exit hole in the side of the housing; and it contained a ¼-in.-deep locating step for mounting the motor.

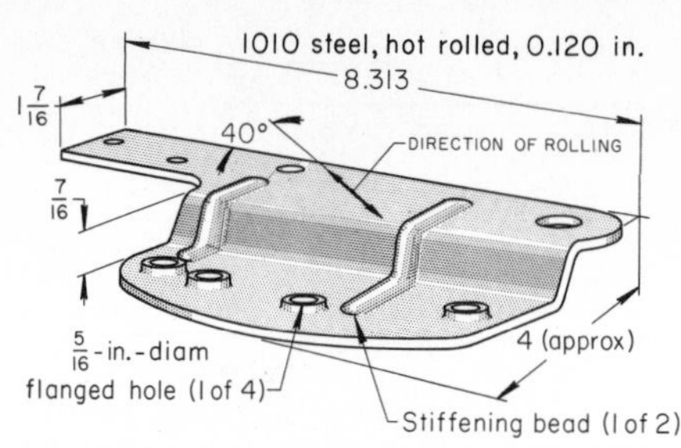

Fig. 33. Yoke bracket on which offset and stiffening beads were formed at an angle to the direction of rolling (Example 170)

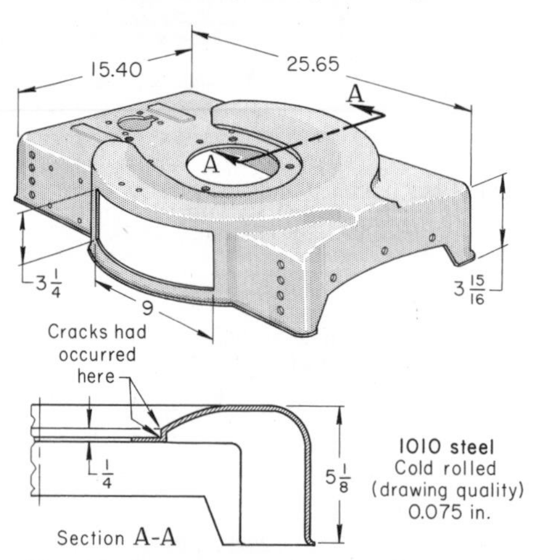

Fig. 34. Lawn-mower housing for which drawing quality steel was substituted for commercial quality steel, to avoid cracking at sharp step of the large formed boss (Example 171)

A 150-ton press cut three developed blanks from each sheet of stock. The sheets were 33⅞ by 86½ in. The blanks were formed to the shape shown in Fig. 34 in a 1000-ton single-action mechanical press with a die cushion. For this operation, the blanks were lubricated with an oil-base drawing compound.

Two piercing dies were set up in a 350-ton mechanical press, and the workpieces were transferred manually from one die to the other. In the first die, the flange was trimmed and all top holes were pierced. In the second die, the rectangular side opening and all side holes were cam-pierced. A 40-ton adjustable-bed press was used to notch and pierce three holes in the front. Production rate was 200 housings per hour.

Accuracy

Tolerances that can be maintained in press forming of steel depend on press condition, accuracy of the tools, workpiece shape, and hardness and variation in thickness of the work metal.

Flange Width. In forming 90° flanges, if the break lines in the plan view and side elevation are straight or nearly straight, there should be no difficulty in holding a tolerance of ±0.030 in. on flange width. When flange break lines are curved significantly, tolerance usually must be increased to ±0.060 in.

Over-all length and width of large formed parts, such as automobile hoods and deck lids, usually can be held to a tolerance of ±0.030 in. For small formed parts, closer tolerances can be met in production.

Bend Angle. Tolerances that can be held on bend angles depend greatly on the thickness and hardness of the work metal and on the flange height, because these factors affect springback.

A 90° bend in low-carbon steel will spring back about 3°; for this reason either dies are built to overform by this amount, or the bend region is compressed to set the corner. To provide enough metal for gripping in the die, the minimum inside flange height should be 2½ times the stock thickness, plus the bend radius.

Distance Between Holes. Distances between centerlines of pierced holes that lie in a common surface of a formed part commonly are held within a total tolerance of 0.010 in. or less. (See page 52 in the article on Piercing of Low-Carbon Steel, in this volume.) The relation of hole positions in parallel or in-line surfaces of formed parts can be held to ±0.015 in.; holes with a smaller tolerance on the centerline distance should be pierced after forming (see Fig. 36).

Distance Between Offset Surfaces. In ordinary commercial practice, the distance between two offset flat surfaces in parallel planes can be maintained within ±0.015 in. For closer tolerances, extreme accuracy must be built into the tools, and the stock thickness must be held closer than normal mill tolerances. The following example describes the techniques used to maintain a tolerance of ±0.010 in. on the distance between surfaces.

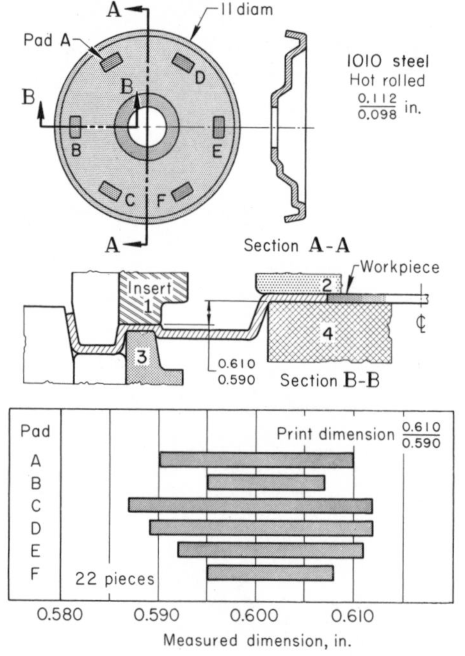

Fig. 35. Variation of offset distance in a formed and coined backing plate for a brake assembly (Example 172)

Example 172. Variation of a Critical Distance Between Offset Parallel Planes (Fig. 35)

On the brake-assembly backing plate shown in Fig. 35, the distance between the tops of the six pads (A to F in Fig. 35) and the bottom of the center mounting face had to be within ±0.010 in. (0.610/0.590 in.).

The ranges of dimensions for all six pads as measured on 22 pieces are plotted in the graph in Fig. 35. Of the 132 individual measurements, only seven exceeded the limits. The spread in dimensions was the result of a combination of variables, including stock thickness (±0.007 in.), springback after forming and coining, and condition of the press.

Springback was unpredictable, and varied among different lots of steel. For this reason,

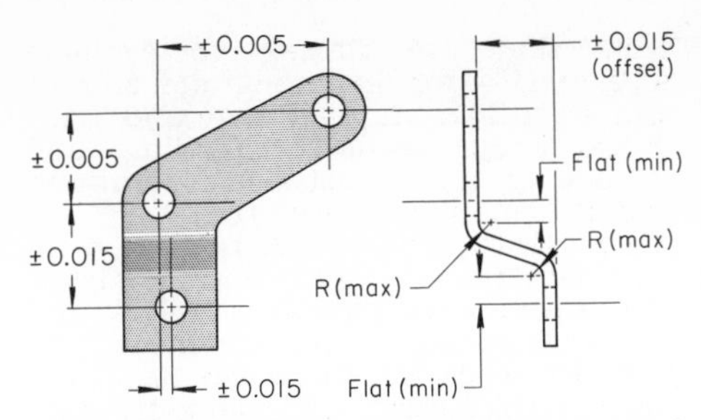

The tolerances shown apply to holes pierced before forming; holes in offset parallel surfaces with position tolerances less than ±0.015 in. should be pierced after forming.

Fig. 36. Tolerances on hole position and distance between offset parallel surfaces on formed parts, and recommended dimensions to be specified for formed offsets

the die was made extra rigid and the inserts for coining the pads (inserts 1 and 3 in section B-B in Fig. 35) were made adjustable to compensate for variations in stock thickness. Coining reduced stock thickness at the 2.5-sq-in. pads to 0.080 to 0.090 in. — a 15% reduction.

The backing plate was made in two operations, both in an 800-ton mechanical knuckle press with a 5-in. stroke, which was operated at 20 strokes per minute. In the first operation, coil stock was fed into a progressive die, where the inner portions of the part were formed, the six pads were partly completed, the center hole was pierced, and the outside diameter was blanked. The outside flange was formed and the six pads were coined to height and parallelism in a second die (see section B-B in Fig. 35).

The press slide was parallel to the bolster within 0.003 in. per foot. The slide and the press bed were large enough to keep the die set centered, thus minimizing the possibility of error. The die set had four heavy guideposts in long bushings. The main parts of the punch and die were made of 6145 steel, hardened to Rockwell C 45 to 50 and ground after hardening, and the inserts for coining (inserts 1 through 4 in Section B-B in Fig. 35) were made of O1 tool steel, hardened to Rockwell C 60 to 61, and ground.

Holes Close to a Bend. Whether a hole that is close to a bend is pierced before or after forming depends on the function of the hole, its closeness to the bend, the bend radius and the stock thickness. When the distance from the edge of the hole to the inside surface of the other leg of the bend is less than 1½ times the stock thickness, plus the bend radius, the outer portion of the hole is likely to deform as a result of stretching of the metal. If the deformation is acceptable, the hole can be pierced before forming; otherwise, it must be pierced after forming.

When the offset angle on formed parts is unimportant, stating the minimum flat and maximum radius dimensions as in Fig. 36 allows the maximum practical leeway in producing acceptable parts.

For additional discussion of accuracy of hole shape and location, see pages 53, 54 and 100 in this volume.

Trimmed edges can be held to close tolerances when they are trimmed by one punch and when trimming is done after any forming that would cause distortion, as in the following example.

Example 173. Forming and Accurate Trimming in a Progressive Die (Fig. 37)

Figure 37 shows an eggbeater side frame that was produced in a four-station progressive die from 0.040-in.-thick cold rolled 1008 or 1010 steel strip ¾ in. wide. For accurate fit in assembly, the end of the part was trimmed to the close tolerances indicated in Fig. 37 after the U-shape bead flanked by the vertical tabs had been formed. The bead was formed by drawing metal from the surrounding area, as well as by stretching.

The stock had a No. 6 edge, a No. 3 finish and a hardness of Rockwell B 55 to 65. The No. 6 edge (a square edge produced by edge rolling the natural edge of hot rolled strip or slit-edge strip) was relatively burr-free. Since the edges of the strip were also the edges of the completed part, the use of a No. 6 edge eliminated a deburring operation. The No. 3 finish was suited particularly for bright nickel plating without prior polishing or buffing. Stock was purchased to average in the lower part of the standard thickness range of ±0.002 in. and within the standard width tolerance of ±0.015 in.

The sequence of operations in the four die stations was as follows:

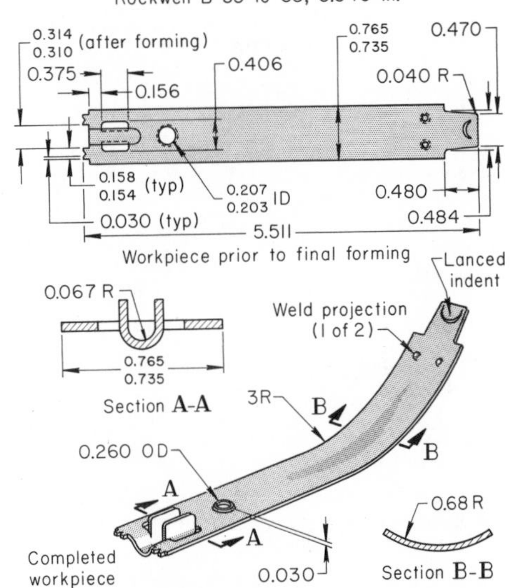

Fig. 37. Eggbeater side frame that was formed and accurately trimmed in a progressive die (Example 173)

1 Lance and form semicircular indent, and notch-trim
2 Pierce rectangular slot at one end, pierce round hole, and emboss weld projections
3 Lance tabs, form bead and form flange around round hole
4 Cut off (trim) and form contour.

The die, which was made of D2 tool steel, was used in a 75-ton press; die life between regrinds was 65,000 pieces. Mineral oil was used as the lubricant. Production rate was 360 pieces per hour; annual production quantity was 600,000 pieces.

Close Tolerances. Closer than conventional accuracy can be attained in sheet metal parts with accurate dies, precise location of the parts in the dies, and handling equipment designed to avoid damage to semifinished or finished workpieces. Press condition is also an important factor.

The two examples that follow describe the techniques used for close-tolerance forming in progressive dies.

Example 174. Blanking, Shaving and Forming to Close Tolerances (Fig. 38)

The part illustrated in Fig. 38 (a comb support for an electric shaver) was blanked and shaved to tolerances of ±0.002 in., and was formed to straightness within 0.001 in. TIR, and to flatness and parallelism within 0.003 in. TIR.

The part was made from 2½-in.-wide coiled, cold rolled 1010 steel strip 0.042/0.041 in. thick. The steel had a No. 2 temper (Rockwell B 70 to 85), a No. 3 edge (approximately square, produced by slitting) and a No. 2 regular bright finish. After forming, the part was given a black oxide finish.

The flat blank for the part was developed in a six-station progressive die, by piercing, shaving, forming of the twenty-three 0.041/0.040-in.-diam projections (see detail C in Fig. 38), and cutoff. The die was used in a 100-ton mechanical press operating at 120 strokes per minute.

In a 45-ton mechanical press, individual dies, hand-fed, were used to shave the cutouts and periphery a second and a third time, and to form and restrike the part to the radii

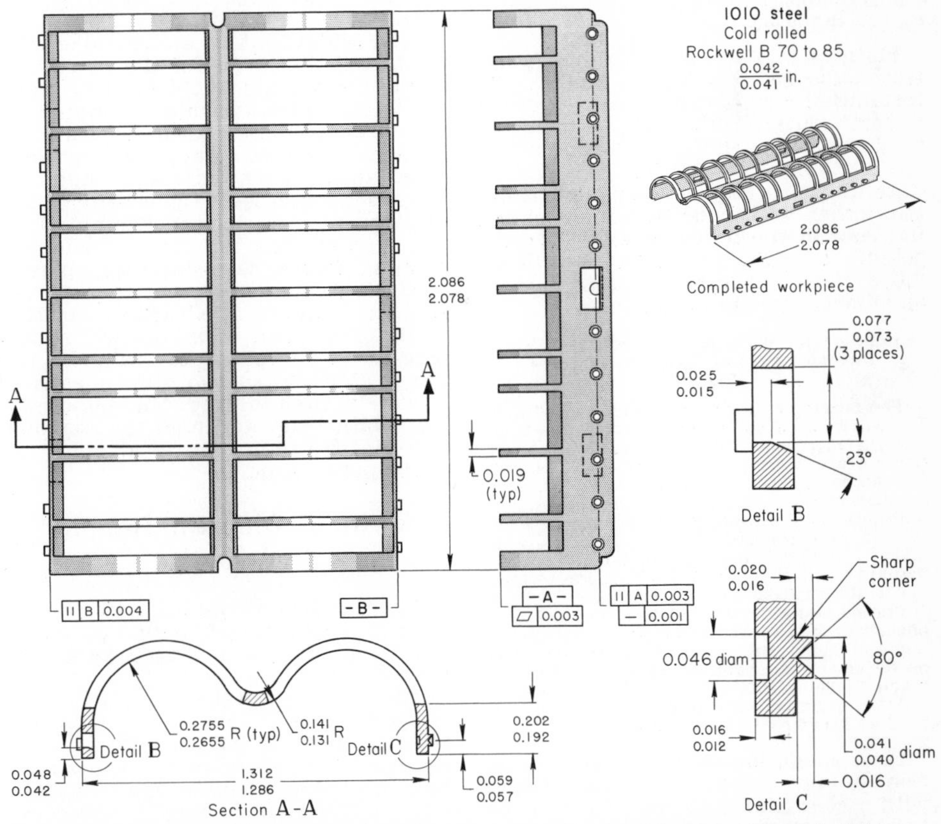

Fig. 38. Comb support blanked, shaved and formed to close tolerances (Example 174)

shown in detail A in Fig. 38. Production rate was five or six pieces per minute.

The dies were made of D2 tool steel. All die elements, except those for shaving, had a life between regrinds of about 50,000 pieces. Die life between regrinds for the shaving tools was 5000 to 10,000 pieces. The progressive die had replaceable shaving dies that could be changed in one hour. Mineral oil was used as a lubricant.

Special handling trays with dividers were used to avoid piece-to-piece contact or any load on the workpieces. This was done because of the fragile nature of the part and the need for accuracy and freedom from defects. Annual production was 500,000 pieces.

Example 175. Use of a Progressive Die to Meet Close Tolerances on a Lamp Bracket (Fig. 39)

The lamp bracket shown in Fig. 39 had several tolerances that were closer than normal. Three holes had to be pierced to a tolerance of +0.005, −0 in. on diameter, and two of the holes had to be in line within 0.010 in. after forming. Also, when the 104° bend was made with the preformed flanges out, the radius of bend on the flanges had to be held within 0.015 in. TIR, and the 10° angle of the flanges had to be held within ±5°. The bracket was produced in a seven-station progressive die with two piloting stations that could have been used for auxiliary operations such as shaving or restriking if necessary. Operations were as follows:

1 Notch for stop; pierce one 0.395-in. hole; pierce two 0.265-in. holes
2 Blank the contour of the ears
3 Pilot
4 Blank the partial contour
5 Form the two long flanges
6 Pilot
7 Form the 104° angle and cut off.

The material was cold rolled 1010 steel strip in No. 4 temper. The strip was 0.095 in. thick by 3⅜ in. wide. The progressive die was mounted in a 75-ton straight-side mechanical press with a flywheel drive, a 6-in. stroke and a maximum rate of 60 strokes per minute. The press was equipped with an air clutch. Ball-lock punches, die bushings, and easily reproducible die sections were used throughout.

The die was made of D2 tool steel and hardened to Rockwell C 58 to 60, and had a life of 55,000 pieces per regrind. Production was discontinued after 2½ million lamp brackets had been made.

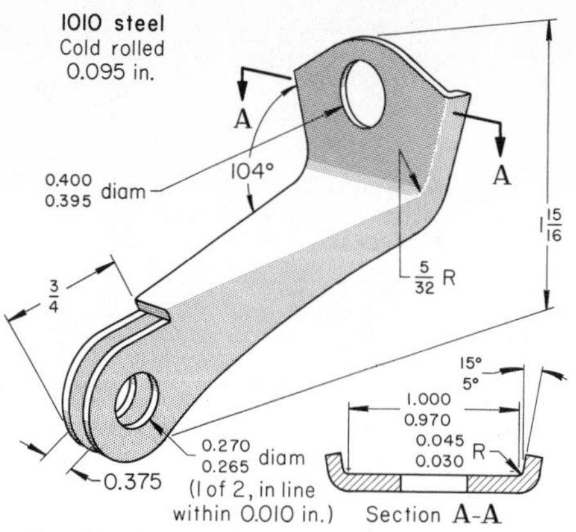

Fig. 39. Lamp bracket that was press formed to close tolerances in a progressive die (Example 175)

Flatness. The longitudinal and transverse stresses set up during the forming of a part can cause it to warp — particularly if the part is made of steel that is not uniform. Depending on the size and shape of the part, smooth flattening dies can be used. Embossing is another technique for maintaining flatness. In the following example, embossing a waffle pattern over a large flat surface helped to maintain flatness on adjacent functional surfaces.

Example 176. Waffling (Embossing) a Surface of a Part to Maintain Flatness (Fig. 40)

The bearing race shown in Fig. 40 had to be flat within 0.030 in. To keep within this tolerance, it was necessary to emboss the adjacent flat surface with a waffle pattern. The part was made of 0.042-in.-thick cold rolled, commercial quality 1010 steel with a maximum hardness of Rockwell B 60. Sheets 10 to 12 ft long were sheared to strips 10.09 in. wide, which were fed into a compound die for blanking and piercing. A combination forming and embossing die finished the part.

The blanking die was made of D2 tool steel, hardened to Rockwell C 60 to 62. The forming and embossing die was of S5 tool steel, hardened to Rockwell C 58 to 60. The die made 75,000 pieces without showing wear.

A 100-ton mechanical press was used and produced four parts per minute.

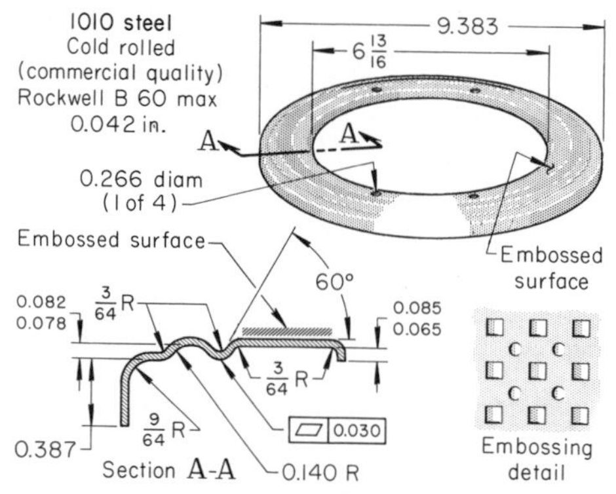

Fig. 40. Bearing race that was embossed in a waffle pattern to meet tolerance on flatness (Example 176)

Press Condition. Accuracy and condition of presses must be maintained within close limits when tolerances on formed parts are critical, regardless of the type of operation. For normal workpiece tolerances, presses should be maintained as discussed under "Press Accuracy", on page 6 in the article on Presses, in this volume.

Press slides that are not parallel with the bed at the bottom of the stroke can cause uneven stock thicknesses when the punch bottoms against the die surface. The gradual loss of accuracy on formed parts as parallelism between slide and bolster decreases and gib clearance increases with continued use of a press is described in Example 1, in the article on Presses. Unbalanced forming forces can shift the punch, producing out-of-tolerance workpieces. In some forming applications, shifting of the punch can be minimized by tipping the workpiece to balance the forces. Heel blocks and other means of positively maintaining the punch-to-die relationship are used to overcome unbalanced forming forces and shifting of the punch slide.

Costs of Different Forming Methods

Cost per piece is the ultimate consideration in selecting tooling and methods for producing a formed part. The process that produces the greatest number of acceptable pieces in the shortest time is not necessarily the most economical for a given run. The following factors affect the cost of the final workpiece: tooling, labor, material, tolerances and overhead. Overhead costs include indirect and intangible costs that are difficult to evaluate separately — for example, die storage and handling, stock storage and handling, scrap handling, handling and storage of pieces between operations, and, in some shops, setup time.

Amortization of tooling is the central consideration in most cost analyses. The seven examples that follow describe applications in which over-all cost per piece was the basis for selection, or reselection, of tooling for various methods of forming.

Example 177. Compound Dies vs a Progressive Die for Various Quantities (Table 3)

Change from the use of four compound dies to the use of a progressive die was justified for producing the motor cradle shown in Table 3 when annual production reached 16,000 pieces. In the compound dies, the part was produced from 0.120-in.-thick sheet, 76⅛ in. long by 39 in. wide. The sequence of operations, and standard times per piece, were as follows: shear to 15⅛-in. length (0.0007 hr); shear to 3½-in. width (0.00053 hr); form ribs (0.00235 hr); trim and pierce (0.00235 hr); finish pierce and notch (0.00235 hr); form flanges and tabs (0.00235 hr). Total time per piece for these operations was 0.01063 hr. The dies were run in a 60-ton open-back inclinable press.

Time per piece was reduced by almost 92%, to 0.00087 hr, by making the part in a progressive die using a 150-ton mechanical press. In addition, a 6½% saving was realized in the cost of material, because the steel was purchased in basic coil widths and slit to the necessary 15⅛-in. width. Standard times per piece were as follows: slit coil to width, 0.0002 hr; notch, trim, cut off, and form complete in progressive die, 0.00055 hr; coil-change allowance, 0.00012 hr.

A comparison of costs for the two methods of production is given in Table 3. For an annual production of 50,000 pieces, the use of the progressive die is shown to have resulted in a saving of $1986; for 100,000 pieces annually, the saving was $4860.

Table 3 also shows the cost of using a set of compound dies suitable only for making a small run of 5000 pieces. Although it was the least expensive of any of the die systems for making 5000 pieces, its simpler die design and less expensive tool materials would not have withstood a much longer production run, and total replacement would have made the system much more expensive than either of the others for the production of more than 5000 pieces.

The compound die for making 5000 pieces per year was made of flame-hardened 6145 steel. The compound and progressive dies suitable for 50,000 pieces were made of water-hardening and air-hardening tool steels. The dies suitable for 100,000 pieces per year were made of air-hardening tool steel. The dies could be maintained in usable condition economically for 10 years.

The residual mill oil was used as lubricant.

Example 178. Changes in Die Systems to Meet Increases in Annual Production Quantity (Fig. 41)

Originally, flanges for locking-nut assemblies were produced on a contract that called for 250,000 pieces annually for two years. With such a relatively small order, only a minimum of die cost was justified. Production was done in four stages and was a combination of simple die work and machining. As shown in the upper half of Fig. 41, the sequence of operations was as follows: blank; form; pierce; turn outside diameter, face, and countersink.

In the first operation, 1700 pieces per hour were blanked from manually fed 1025 to 1030 steel strip, 0.187 in. thick by $2\frac{7}{16}$ in. wide, in a 30-ton gap-frame press. This consumed 0.3 lb of steel per piece. Forming was done in a 135-ton straight-side double-action mechanical press that was manually loaded and unloaded; production rate was 495 pieces per hour. The piece was pierced in a 7-ton single-station gap-frame inclinable press at a rate of 1700 pieces per hour. Turning, facing and countersinking were done in a special machine at a rate of 480 pieces per hour. Production cost by this method, including material, labor, burden and amortization, was $0.0982 per piece.

Before the end of the two-year period, a revised contract was received for an annual production of one million pieces, and the time was extended for two more years. This 300% increase in production rate and the extended production period justified the cost of more efficient tooling. A slight redesign of the part, shown at the extreme right in the lower half of Fig. 41, improved the function of the part, and also made it possible to eliminate the previous machining operations and produce the countersink by coining. A new die, used in a 30-ton gap-frame press, blanked and pierced 1700 pieces per hour, in one operation. The forming and coining die was a transfer die operated in an 800-ton straight-side mechanical coining press at a rate of 990 pieces per hour. The die had two stations and was manually loaded and unloaded. Final piercing was done in a 7-ton gap-frame press at 1700 pieces per hour. With the new process, the blank diameter was reduced from 2.187 to 2.000 in. and strip width to 2.250 in., reducing the stock consumption per piece to 0.255 lb. Cost per piece by this method was $0.0522.

Shortly, demand rose to two million pieces per year, and more-automatic tooling was developed for producing the part in the same three operations as for the first improved method. The blanking and piercing die for the third tooling system was a two-stage (center-pierce and push-through) die that produced three blanks per stroke from a 6-in.-wide blank with a staggered pattern that used 0.237 lb of raw material per blank. This die was operated in a 150-ton inclinable gap-frame press that produced 8022 blanks per hour, compared to 1700 for previous blanking equipment. The forming and coining die and the die for final piercing were the same as those used in the second die system, and were run in the same types of presses, but both were now equipped with automatic blank-feeding magazines, which increased their production rate from 1700 to 2400 pieces per hour. The cost per piece by this system was $0.0328.

Table 3. Cost of Producing Motor Cradles in Various Quantities Using Four Compound Dies vs a Progressive Die (Example 177)

Cost item	Cost for producing annual quantity of: 5000	50,000	100,000
Compound Dies			
Material	$ 668	$ 6,680	$13,360
Setup(a)	200	200	200
Labor(b)	266	2,658	5,315
Tooling(c)	3,500	6,000(d)	6,000(d)
Total	$4,634	$15,538	$24,875
Cost per piece	$0.927	$ 0.311	$ 0.249
Progressive Die			
Material		$ 6,245	$12,490
Setup(a)		90	90
Labor(b)		217	435
Tooling(c)		7,000	7,000
Total		$13,552	$20,015
Cost per piece		$ 0.271	$ 0.200

1010 steel
Hot rolled
Rockwell B 55 to 60
0.120 in.

(a) At $5 per hour, for ten setups of 4 hr each for compound dies and of 1.8 hr each for the progressive die. (b) At $5 per hour. (c) Amortized over one year for quantity shown. (d) Rib-forming die, $1100; trimming and piercing die, $1800; finish-piercing and notching die, $1100; die for forming flanges and tabs, $2000.

Example 179. Change to Progressive Dies to Meet Increased Demand (Table 4)

The air deflector illustrated in Table 4 was formerly made in two dies. Parts were pierced, notched and cut off in the first die and formed in the second die. These deflectors, for forced-air space heaters, were all 1½ in. wide, but were of various lengths, ranging from 11⁹⁄₃₂ to 25³¹⁄₃₂ in. One die with an adjustable stop was used for all workpiece lengths for the first operation, but three different forming dies were needed to accommodate the range of lengths.

When demand rose, from 78,200 to 279,500 pieces per year, production was moved from the separate dies to three progressive dies (three were needed to produce the full range of sizes). As the comparison of labor and tooling costs in Table 4 shows, the progressive dies produced the 279,500 pieces at a saving of $2895 in comparison to what it would have cost for using the separate dies for this increased annual quantity. (Actually, the break-even point for the two methods was 183,000 pieces per year.) An added advantage of the progressive dies was that they were built so that coil feed could be used if production demands were further increased.

By the separate-die method, the first die produced 340 pieces per hour, and the second die produced 500 pieces per hour. Each of the progressive dies produced 500 pieces per hour. By either method, tool life between regrinds was 150,000 pieces. Residual mill oil was the only lubricant used with the separate dies, but a light oil was added with the progressive dies.

The pierce, notch and cutoff die for the original method was of O1 tool steel hardened to Rockwell C 60 to 62. It was set up in a 50-ton open-back inclinable press, which operated at 55 strokes per minute. The forming die was of O2 tool steel hardened to Rockwell C 60 to 62. The die was run in a 90-ton mechanical press at 42 strokes per minute.

The three progressive dies that replaced the original dies had four stations. An O1 tool steel was used for all details except the cutting elements, which were made of D3 tool steel. The progressive die was run at 35 strokes per minute in a 150-ton straight-side mechanical press equipped with an air slide feed and coil-handling equipment.

Example 180. Costs for Forming Fenders by Medium-Production and High-Production Tooling (Fig. 42)

Two die systems for making automobile fenders are compared in Fig. 42. The medium-production system proposed consisted mainly of simple dies and a few compound dies—all of them hand fed. Sheet stock would have had to be used. Presses would have been smaller and lower in capacity than those used in the high-production system, but more presses would have been needed. Furthermore, since the medium-production system was capable of producing only 18,000 pairs of fenders per week on a two-shift basis, a high weekly production (25,000 pairs) would have demanded two complete sets of dies. Continuous three-shift production might have met the demand, but the time of the third shift would have been needed for maintenance of the press and dies.

In contrast, the high-production system in use produced 34,000 pairs per week in two shifts. It used fewer presses than the medium-production system, although the presses were larger and of higher capacity. The shut height of the presses used in the high-production system had to be greater than in the medium-production system to accommodate the automatic feeding mechanisms. A double blanking die cut blanks from coil stock to keep the system operating at capacity.

The chart in Fig. 42 shows that the medium-production system would have been more economical for small production quotas (below 125,000 pairs). But above that quantity the high-production system was the more economical.

The stock used for the fenders was cold rolled, drawing quality, rimmed 1008 steel with a hardness of Rockwell B 40 to 50. The maximum stretch in the metal was 20%.

The die material for both the medium-production and the high-production forming dies would be alloy cast iron. Trimming dies for medium production would be W1 tool steel and would have a life of 10,000 pieces between regrinds. The high-production trimming dies were made of D2 tool steel and had a life of 20,000 pieces between regrinds.

Table 4. Costs for Producing Air Deflectors in Separate Dies vs Progressive Dies (Example 179) (a)

Cost item	Cost for 279,500 pieces: Separate dies	Progressive dies
Labor and burden	$16,770(b)	$ 8,385(c)
Tooling	3,800(d)	9,290(e)
Total	$20,570	$17,675
Saving		$ 2,895

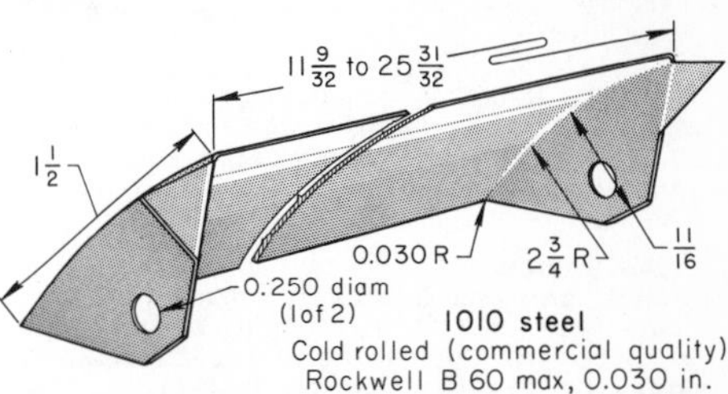

(a) Air deflector, illustrated above, was produced in several different lengths, thus requiring the use of three different forming dies in the separate-die method and three different progressive dies. Cost of material (not included here) was approximately the same for both methods, varying from $0.014 to $0.030 per piece, depending on deflector length.

(b) At $0.02 per piece for labor and $0.04 per piece for burden. (c) At $0.01 per piece for labor and $0.02 per piece for burden. (d) One die for piercing, notching and cutting off at $800; and three dies for forming at $800, $1000 and $1200. (e) Three dies cost $2940, $2975 and $3375.

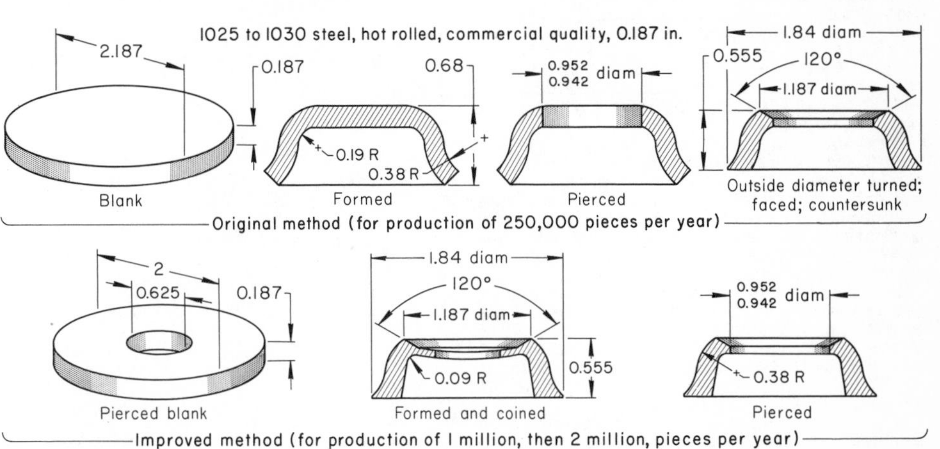

Fig. 41. Original method of producing a flange for a locking-nut assembly, and improved method used with two different die systems when two increases in annual production quantity justified higher costs for more efficient tooling (Example 178)

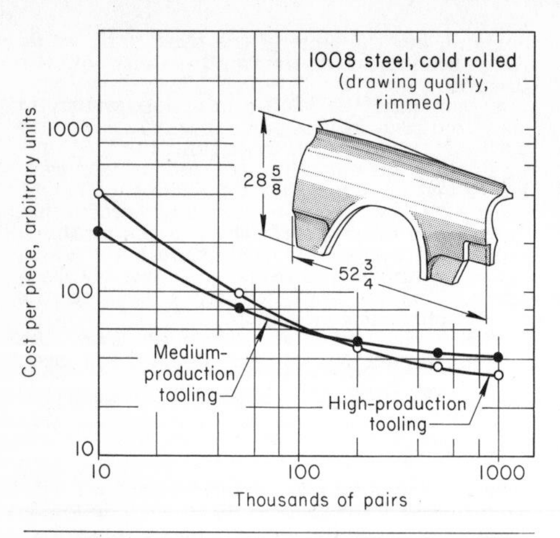

Operations in Medium-Production Tooling(a)

1 - Blank. 2 - Draw. 3 - Final trim, except front; rough trim front. 4 - Re-form and final form; wrap out. 5 - Flange wheelhouse. 6 - Pierce holes at wheelarch; form offset, front and rear. 7 - Flange top of doorway. 8 - Flange extension. 9 - Pierce extension flange and flange wheelarch. 10 - Restrike doorway flange. 11 - Trim bottom front. 12 - Form hood ledge and flange cowl; form bottom return flange at front. 13 - Trim and pierce front. 14 - Pierce hood ledge and restrike.

Operations in High-Production Tooling(b)

1 - Blank (two pieces per stroke). 2 - Draw. 3 - Final trim, direct, except front; trim front by cam. 4 - Re-form and final form. 5 - Wrap out. 6 - Flange, partly direct and partly by cam. 7 - Pierce and flange. 8 - Flange, partly direct and partly by cam. 9 - Trim and pierce, direct and by cam.

(a) Total tool cost, $415,000. (b) Total tool cost, $700,000.

Fig. 42. Relation of cost (including tool amortization) to quantity for forming pairs of fenders by medium-production and high-production tooling (Example 180)

The production rate for the medium-production dies was estimated at 240 pieces per hour, while the high-production line made 480 pieces per hour using automatic handling equipment. For the high-production line, 600-ton double-action mechanical presses were employed.

The lubricant was a filled compound or paste, which usually consisted of lithopone, whiting or other fillers in a soap - animal-fat base.

The medium-production line could make about 200,000 fenders per year; the high-production line about 750,000 per year.

Example 181. Addition of Stations to a Progressive Die (Fig. 43)

The cable bracket shown in Fig. 43 was originally made in a five-station progressive die. Since too much work (namely, forming the 7⁄16-in. radius, forming the tab and cutting off) was done in the last station, the formed part had to be restruck (particularly to correct severe deformation of the 0.280-in. hole), and die breakdowns were frequent and repair was costly.

The die was redesigned, distributing the operations among seven stations, including cam-punching the 0.280-in.-diam hole after the tab was formed. The new die eliminated the need for restriking and, as shown in the comparison of costs accompanying Fig. 43, reduced the labor cost $0.011 per piece — or $1650 for the annual production of 150,000 parts. This saving paid for the new die in less than two years, and the frequency of die repair was reduced.

The work metal was 0.093-in.-thick and 1.375-in.-wide cold rolled 1010 steel with No. 3 (mill) edge and No. 5 temper, Rockwell B 55 max.

The die was of D2 tool steel hardened to Rockwell C 58 to 60 and produced 50,000 pieces between regrinds. Estimated die life was 2½ to 3 million brackets. A 75-ton gap-frame mechanical press was used at 120 strokes per minute, max.

Example 182. Influence of Labor Cost per Hour on Savings Possible With a Progressive Die (Table 5)

Annual requirement for the small frame illustrated in Table 5 was 120,000 pieces. Total time for producing this quantity in separate dies was 788.40 hr; this compared with an estimate of only 174 hr for production in a progressive die — or a difference of 614.40 hr. However, the progressive die would cost $5000 more than the separate dies. Thus, by dividing $5000 by 614.40 hr it was found that if labor and overhead were $8.15 per hour, the progressive die would be amortized in one year. For a lower cost of labor and overhead, more than one year would be required for amortization. Conversely, for a higher labor and overhead rate, the progressive die would amortize itself in less than a year.

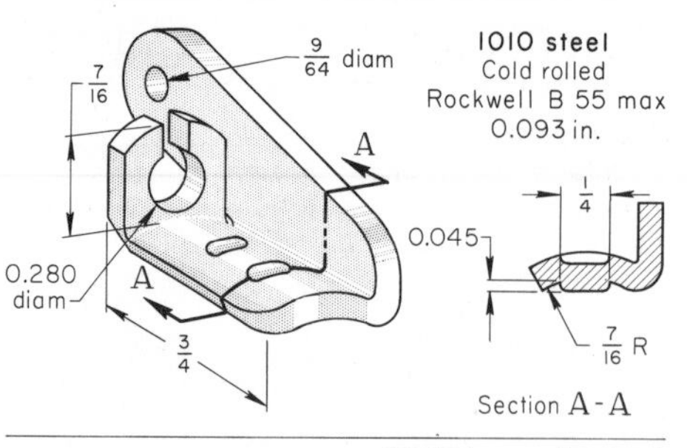

Item	Original method	Improved method
Cost of Dies		
Progressive die	$1500	$3175
Restrike-and-size die	450	(a)
Total	$1950	$3175
Cost of Labor and Burden, per Piece		
First operation	$0.004	$0.003
Second operation	0.010	...
Total	$0.014	$0.003

(a) Restriking not required

Fig. 43. Bracket for which die-repair frequency and production cost were reduced by redesign of a progressive die (Example 181)

Table 5. Time Comparison for Producing 120,000 Small Frames per Year in Separate Dies vs a Progressive Die (Example 182) (a)

Operation	Production: Rate, pcs/hr	Production: Time for 120,000 pcs, hr
Seven Separate Dies(b)		
Emboss, pierce, blank	2362	50.76
Pierce, extrude, trim, scribe	732	163.92
Pierce, lance, emboss	1200	99.96
Pierce, trim	1091	109.92
Lance, form, emboss	1053	113.88
First form, trim, emboss	1200	99.96
Final form	800	150.00
Total		788.40
Progressive Die(c)		
Combine first six operations of separate-die method	5000	24.0
Final form	800	150.0
Total		174.0

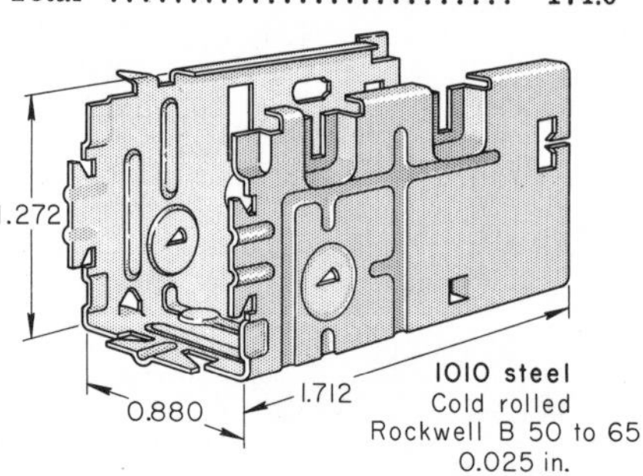

(a) Data for the separate-die method are based on actual production. Data for the progressive-die method are estimated. (b) Operated in a 30-ton press; tooling cost, $10,000. (c) Operated in a 100-ton press; tooling cost, $15,000.

It should be noted, however, that the separate dies were operated in a 30-ton press, whereas a 100-ton press would have been required for the progressive die.

Example 183. Material Costs vs Labor Costs in Selection of a Transfer Die Over a Progressive Die

Small tapered separators for roller bearings were produced from 0.072-in.-thick cold rolled, commercial quality, rimmed steel strip at lower labor cost (89¢ less per thousand) in a progressive die than in a cam-operated transfer die. However, a strip 3.150 in. wide was needed for the progressive die, whereas a 3.000-in.-wide strip was enough for the transfer die. The savings in using the narrower strip amounted to $1.24 per thousand pieces. Thus, the net saving per thousand pieces using the transfer die was 35¢. At an annual production of three million pieces, the net saving per year was $1050.

The sequence of operations in the progressive die was as follows: blank, form cup, blank the bottom, pierce holes for pockets, form pockets, and spread the cage. A double-roll mechanism fed strip to the die. Because a portion of the carrying strip was drawn into the die in forming of the cup, lifting the cup from the die and clipping it from the strip presented problems. When the transfer die was used, the strip was fed across a blanking die, then through a scrap chopper. The blank was then passed through subsequent operations by fingers mounted on transfer arms and actuated by cams. Workpieces were held by cam-operated slides until the fingers were in position to hold them while the punch was withdrawn.

Because of construction, the progressive die required stock with a thickness tolerance of ±0.002 in., whereas the transfer die could use stock with a thickness tolerance of ±0.006 in.

For both sets of tools, the draw-die elements were made of A2 tool steel, the forming die elements of L6 tool steel, and the cutting die elements of D2 tool steel. Die life was 80,000 to 100,000 parts.

The lubricant was a drawing compound mixed 1-to-1 with mineral seal oil.

Hot Forming

In hot forming, the work metal is heated above the transformation temperature. Less press capacity is needed to hot form a given shape than to cold form it. The press, dies, and related equipment, however, must be designed to withstand high temperature. Sometimes, meeting this requirement is more difficult than the procurement of a higher-capacity press for cold forming.

In some applications a steel workpiece can be quenched directly from the forming temperature. In the following example, 1-in.-thick high-strength low-alloy steel blanks heated to 1500 F were press formed and then allowed to cool in air.

Example 184. Hot Forming High-Strength Low-Alloy Steel (Fig. 44)

A 1-in.-thick blank of high-strength low-alloy steel was hot formed into a bucket blade for earthmoving equipment (Fig. 44). The blank was cut by oxy-fuel gas to 12 by 67 in. from a flat plate, then furnace heated to 1500 F. The hot workpiece was formed with one stroke of a 200-ton hydraulic press. No lubricant was used, because production quantities were small and surface condition of the part was not critical. After being formed, the part was quickly removed from the die and allowed to cool on the floor. Time from furnace to press to floor was 4 min per piece.

Heating the blank to 1500 F permitted forming in a much smaller press and with greater accuracy than could have been done had the blank been formed at room temperature. Tolerances of ±1⁄16 in. were maintained on the over-all dimensions of the formed part.

The forming die was a weldment made of hot rolled 1045 steel, flame hardened at the critical wear points. Production was 400 buckets per year in lots of 60. Die life was 2400 pieces before reworking.

Auxiliary Operations in Presses

Presses are used to fasten parts together by rivets, or by plastically deforming mating areas in either or both of the parts. In operations such as staking, folding, crimping, curling or press assembly, projections of various sizes and shapes are deformed so that the assembly is reasonably strong.

In the following example, a press was used to curl the lip of a hub over a disk for a tight torque-resistant joint.

Example 185. Assembly of Hub to Center Disk by Curling in a Hydraulic Press (Fig. 45)

Center disks of large blower wheels were assembled to hubs by curling as shown in Fig. 45. The hub was an automatic bar machine product made of cold drawn 1018 steel tubing. The length of the hub was 1⅛ in. before curling, and the curled lip was ⅛ in. high. The disks were similar to those described in Example 153 in this article.

The work was done in a 55-ton hydraulic press with no lubricant. Because the disks and hubs were assembled and positioned manually, production rate was only 30 pieces per hour. The joint could have been made much faster by spinning, but spinning equipment that could accommodate the large disks was not readily available.

The curling tool was made of A5 tool steel, cost $300, and had a life of several years. The blower-disk assemblies were made in quantities of 20,000 per year.

The flattening and crimping of preformed tabs was used for assembly of sheet-metal parts in a mechanical press operation, in the next example.

Example 186. Assembly of Blower Wheels by Press Forming (Fig. 46)

A blower wheel 9 in. in diameter by 9 in. long was assembled using the fixture shown in Fig. 46. Two disks, formed as described in Example 159, were fastened to 16 steel blades 0.028 in. thick.

The fixture held the blades and disks in correct relationship while the curved edges of the slots were flattened against the blades by a pressing punch. A 60-ton mechanical press was used to crimp 120 assemblies per hour. The fixture and the pressing punch, slotted like the fixture to accommodate the blades, were made of flame-hardened medium-carbon tool steel at a cost of $13,000.

Production was 150,000 blower wheels per year. A soluble oil mixed with water in a 1-to-5 ratio was used as lubricant.

The example that follows describes an application in which the production of three small triangular projections for holding a phenolic seat was incorporated into one station of a progressive die.

Example 187. Progressive-Die Forming of Projections for Holding a Phenolic Seat (Fig. 47)

A ball socket had to have three sharp projections on the inner surface of the wall, as shown in Fig. 47, to retain a phenolic seat. A staking operation to form the projections was incorporated in the progressive die that made the part.

The socket was made of hot rolled 1008 or 1010 steel strip, pickled and oiled, 4¼ in. wide and ⅛ in. thick. A water-soluble oil was sprayed on the strip as it entered the die.

The progressive die, made of D2 or D5 tool steel, was mounted in a 100-ton press that had a maximum speed of 60 strokes per minute. However, since the strip was hand fed, the production rate was only 15 to 20 pieces per minute.

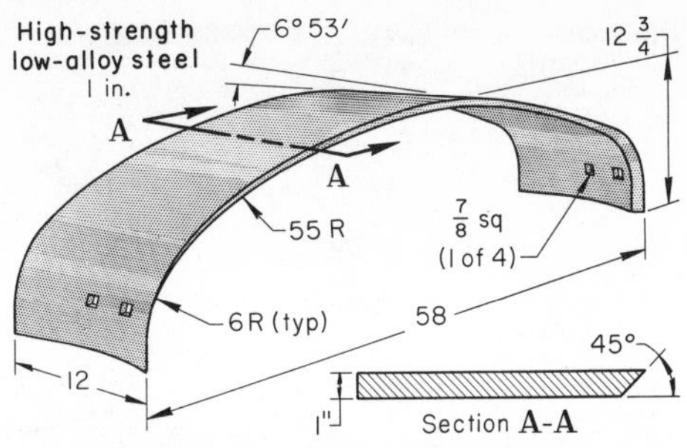

Fig. 44. Digger-bucket blade that was hot formed in a hydraulic press (Example 184)

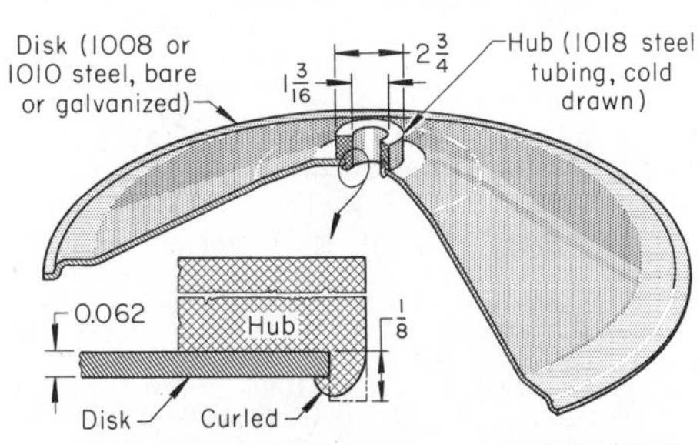

Fig. 45. Hub and disk that were assembled by curling in a press (Example 185)

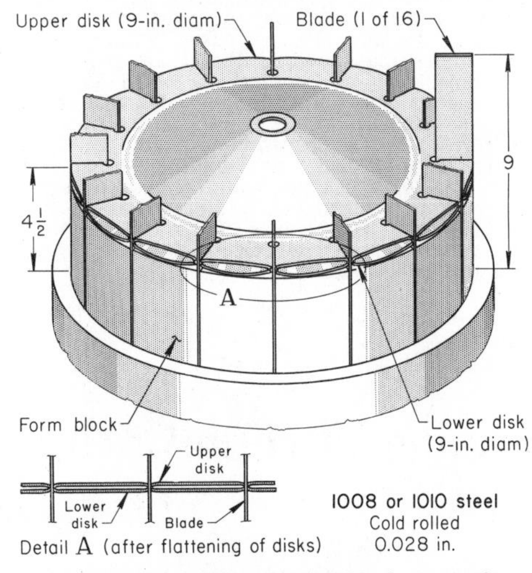

Fig. 46. Blower-wheel assembly in press fixture for flattening of disks against blades (Example 186)

Press Forming vs Alternative Methods

If a part can be made by forming sheet metal in a press, this ordinarily is the least expensive method of manufacture, except when only a few pieces are needed. The low cost per piece results from the high production rates and the efficient use of metal ordinarily obtainable in press forming of sheet metal.

The accuracy inherent in press forming is satisfactory for most requirements, and greater accuracy can be achieved by the use of precision tooling and by maintaining close control over press conditions.

The disadvantages of relatively high tool cost and long tooling time often can be offset, except for the production of very small quantities, by the use of short-run tooling. Sometimes, the design of a part can be modified to permit the use of press forming instead of alternative methods.

Example 139 in this article discusses the forming from sheet metal of a grill that formerly had been produced as a casting. An application in which cost was reduced when forming replaced forging is described in the example that follows.

Example 188. Press Forming vs Forging (Fig. 48)

The bicycle-fork stem shown in Fig. 48 was formed from hot rolled, commercial quality 1008 or 1010 steel sheet 0.164 in. thick, pickled and oiled. The formed part cost much less than the machined forging it replaced. More than a year was required to perfect the forming process.

The pieces were blanked two at a time in a 250-ton press operating at 40 strokes per minute. They were formed in a nine-station transfer die that ran at 20 to 26 strokes per minute in a 300-ton press loaded at 50% of its tonnage rating, as shown by a meter. The blanks were fed into the first station from a magazine feeder by a slide. After forming, one hole was reamed and another was drilled and tapped, in a rotary indexing machine.

The severity of forming required the use of a drawing compound. Production of a million pieces per year caused no unusual problems except those that resulted from aging of the stock. If the stock was not used shortly after receipt from the mill, there was some splitting at the most severely formed areas, such as the shoulders of the fork stem, and some surfaces showed an orange-peel effect.

After forming, the part was plated for appearance and to resist rust.

The blanking die was of D2 tool steel, hardened to Rockwell C 56 to 58. After runs of 50,000 parts, the die was resharpened by removing 0.012 in. from the punch and die. The forming punches were of O1 and A2 tool steels, hardened to Rockwell C 52 to 54. The forming-die sections were of D2 tool steel hardened to Rockwell C 54 to 56. The high-wear areas were coated with a deposit of tungsten carbide. The dies made over 300,000 acceptable parts.

Sometimes workpieces that are closely similar can be made equally well, and at about the same cost, by two or more different methods. Under these

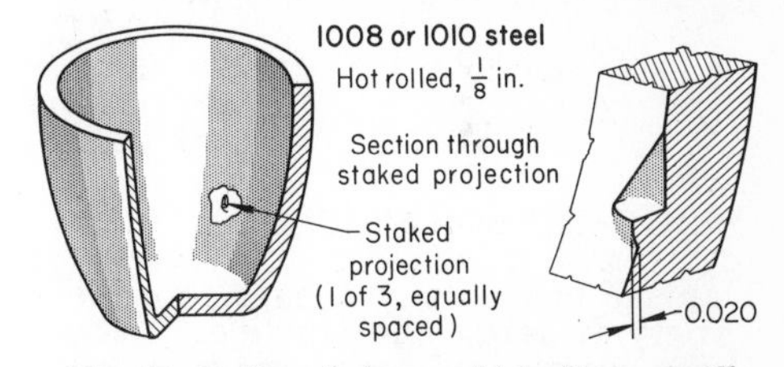

Fig. 47. Ball socket on which three small projections, for holding a phenolic seat, were staked in one station of the progressive die in which the part was produced (Example 187)

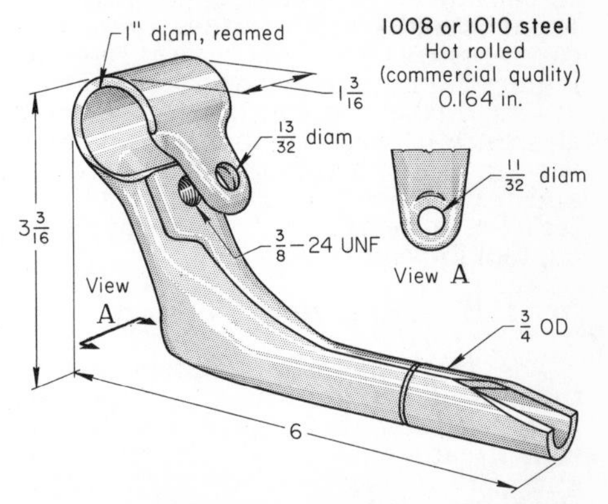

Fig. 48. Bicycle-fork stem that cost less when formed from sheet steel than when produced as a machined forging (Example 188)

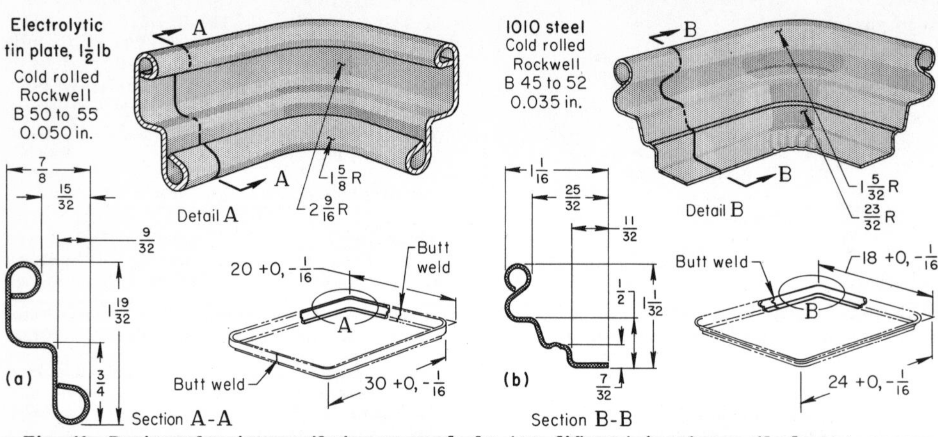

Fig. 49. Rectangular frames that were made by two different forming methods: (a) *press forming in a V-die, and* (b) *bending in a rotary draw bender* (Example 189)

conditions, the choice of method may depend on availability of equipment, as in the example that follows.

Example 189. Press Forming in V-Dies vs Rotary Draw Bending (Fig. 49)

The two types of rectangular frames shown in Fig. 49 were made by two different forming methods. Each type of frame could have been made by either method, but, because of the kind of equipment that was available, the corners of the frame shown in Fig. 49(a) were press formed in a V-die, and those shown in Fig. 49(b) were made by rotary draw bending. Each type of frame was made in a number of sizes by making individual bends in succession on precut lengths of contour rolled or press-brake-formed steel strip and welding the ends together.

The corners for frames made from 0.050-in.-thick electrolytic tin plate (Fig. 49a) were formed one at a time in a 6-in.-stroke, 56-ton mechanical press, using a developed V-die made of D2 tool steel. Each corner was restruck twice for accuracy of bend angle and contour. Because of the tin coating, no lubricant was needed. The production rate was 420 corners per hour. Die life was indefinite. Lot size averaged about 1000 frames, for a yearly production of about 25,000 frames of various sizes.

The corners for a second line of frames (Fig. 49b) were bent from contour roll formed 2⁵⁄₃₂-by-0.035-in. 1010 steel strip in a rotary draw bending machine equipped with conforming die and clamp blocks. [This type of bending is illustrated in Fig. 1, on page 305, in the article on Bending of Bars.] The die and clamp blocks were made of D2 tool steel; residual mineral oil from the preceding contour roll forming operation provided sufficient lubrication for the draw bending. Production rate was 600 bends per hour for a total yearly production of about one million frames in lots of 1000 to 10,000 frames. These frames were phosphate coated and electrostatically spray painted after welding.

Safety

Press forming, like other press operations, involves potential hazards to operators, maintenance men, and other persons in the work area. No press, die, or auxiliary equipment can be considered ready for operation until hazards are eliminated by the installation of necessary safety devices. Operators and all persons working around the operation should be properly instructed in safe operation of the equipment. The article "Presses and Auxiliary Equipment for Forming of Sheet Metal", which begins on page 1 in this volume, contains information and literature references on safe operation.

Examples in This Volume That Describe Press Forming of Metals Other Than Carbon Steels

Example	Workpiece
457	Muffler header (321 stainless steel)
458	Dome (302 stainless steel)
459	Wheel cover (302 stainless steel)
462	Piston ring (301 stainless steel)
463	Bracket (302 stainless steel)
464	Bellows lever (430 stainless steel)
465	Frame (430 stainless steel)
496	End caps (A-286 alloy)
499	Fluted piece (Hastelloy X)
569	Joggle (Beryllium sheet)
576	Diaphragm (Beryllium copper)
579	Spring clip (Beryllium copper)
581	Mirror back (Copper alloy 260)
582	Socket contact (Copper alloy 510)
583	Copper alloy 172 part
584	Copper alloy 757 part
585	Flanged washer (Copper alloy 260)
602	Corner plate (AZ31B-O magnesium)
611	Titanium alloy part

Press Forming of High-Carbon Steel

*By the ASM Committee on Press Forming of Steel**

HIGH-CARBON STEEL strip (including spring steel and tool steel) is blanked, pierced and formed to make a variety of parts. The practices, precautions, presses and tools used in making high-carbon steel parts are like those used to produce similar parts of low-carbon steel (see the preceding articles in this volume). Differences that must be considered in blanking, piercing and forming high-carbon rather than low-carbon steel are: (*a*) more force is required for high-carbon steel because of its higher strength; (*b*) greater clearance between the punch and die is necessary in blanking and piercing; and (*c*) a more wear-resistant tool material may be required before acceptable tool life can be obtained.

Blanking and Piercing

The most important difference between blanking and piercing of high-carbon and of low-carbon steels is that greater clearance between punch and die is required for high-carbon steels. The clearances needed for producing each of the five edge types in blanking and piercing high-carbon and low-carbon steels are compared in Table 1 on page 45 in the article "Piercing of Low-Carbon Steel". As shown in that table (and the accompanying Fig. 2 on the same page), at equal clearance rollover depth will be smaller and burnish depth greater for high-carbon than for low-carbon steel. (For example, 12% clearance per side will produce a type 4 edge on high-carbon steel, and a type 2 edge on low-carbon steel.)

This relation of cut-edge characteristics to carbon content is different from the relation of cut-edge characteristics to temper or hardness of low-carbon steel. Figure 4 on page 47 in the article "Piercing of Low-Carbon Steel" shows that both rollover depth and burnish depth are smaller for harder tempers of low-carbon steel than for softer tempers.

Tool materials recommended for blanking and piercing high-carbon steel are listed in the article on Selection of Material for Blanking and Piercing Dies, page 69 in this volume. Selection tables in that article show that while complexity of the workpiece and total quantity to be blanked are more significant factors in selection of tool material than is work-metal composition, nevertheless work-metal hardness is significant. Carbide dies are often used for large quantities (see Example 190, below).

Die life in the blanking and piercing of high-carbon steel varies with different applications, depending greatly on the dimensional accuracy that must be maintained and the burr height that can be tolerated on the blanked parts. The example that follows describes an application in which a change in tool material increased die life by a factor of about 28.

Example 190. Change From Tool Steel to Carbide Punches and Dies (Fig. 1)

The part shown in Fig. 1 was blanked and pierced from 1⅞-in.-wide coils of bright-finish 1045 steel having a hardness of Rockwell 15-N 70 to 75 (equivalent to Rockwell C 20 to 30). Thickness ranged from 0.019 to 0.0388 in.; tolerance for all thicknesses was +0.000, −0.001 in.

Originally, both the punch and the die were made of D2 tool steel at Rockwell C 62 to 63. To keep burr height on the parts at or below the maximum of 0.003 in., it was necessary to grind the die after each 25,000 pieces. The steel die had a usable depth of ⅝ in., and 0.008 in. was removed with each grinding. Therefore, with 78 grindings the total die life was 1,950,000 pieces.

*For committee list, see page 112.

To improve die life, tool material for both the punch and the die was changed to carbide. The carbide tools cost three times as much as the steel punch and die, but production between grinds increased to 350,000 pieces and only 0.004 in. of stock was removed per grind. Thus, with the same amount of usable die, the total die life would be 54,600,000 pieces.

The die was a compound type and was operated in a 50-ton open-back inclinable mechanical press having a 3-in. stroke and mechanical feed.

Tooling for Greatest Efficiency. Along with the increase in punch-to-die clearance, other tool changes are required for efficiency in blanking and piercing high-carbon steel. For instance, with high-carbon steel more than with low-carbon steel, the scrap skeleton from blanking and piercing operations is likely, in springing back, to adhere to the punch, sometimes causing spalling of the punch edges. To strip this scrap from the punch it is common practice to include in the punch mechanism a second, chisel-pointed punch placed as close as possible to the blanking edge. This second punch serves to spread the scrap skeleton, minimizing its adherence to the blanking punch (see Example 191).

The next three examples deal with changes in tooling that reduced cost. In the first of the three examples, blanking replaced machining. In the two other examples, alterations in the tools used for blanking and piercing decreased cost per piece.

Example 191. Cost Reduction When Blanking Replaced Milling (Fig. 2)

The blanked workpiece shown in Fig. 2 replaced a machined part of slightly different dimensions. For the machined part, starting blanks 3 in. long by $^{11}/_{16}$ in. wide by $^{5}/_{32}$ in. thick were sawed from ground flat stock of A2 tool steel spheroidize-annealed to Rockwell C 14 to 18. The long edges of the blanks were ground to reduce the width of the blank from $^{11}/_{16}$ in. to 0.625 in. Grinding was followed by four separate milling operations. Cost of tools for the machining operations was \$1000; time for producing 100 pieces was 28 hr; and the machined parts cost \$0.84 each.

Even though production demand for this part was low (300 per month), a change in production method — from milling to blanking — was tried with success: Tools for blanking cost only \$375; time per 100 pieces was reduced to 0.23 hr; and cost per piece was reduced to \$0.0069.

The blanking was done in a 32-ton open-back inclinable mechanical press with a punch and die made from A2 tool steel at Rockwell C 60 to 62. To obtain acceptable edges on the workpiece, a punch-to-die clearance of 8 to 10% of stock thickness per side was used. Because of the force required for stripping, it was necessary to add a chisel-edge punch adjacent to the blanking punch to spread the scrap skeleton and prevent damage to the blanking punch. Also, a minimum corner radius of 0.062 in. was necessary for efficient stripping, and the over-all width of the part was increased to 0.696 in.

Example 192. Change in Tooling That Eliminated a Separate Slotting Operation (Fig. 3)

The springlike part shown in Fig. 3 was originally blanked in two operations; the 0.020-in.-wide by 0.2654-in.-long slot was cut in a second operation. Tools for the blanking operation cost \$1800. Tools for piercing the slot cost \$300 per set, but the life of the slotting punch and die was such that 20 sets were required to equal the life of the blanking tools. Thus, tools for both operations cost \$7800. Cost of labor for the blanked and slotted parts was \$3.06 per 1000 pieces.

In an improved method, a die blanked and slotted the part in one press stroke. Tools for this method cost \$3000, and labor cost per 1000 pieces was reduced to \$0.30.

Fig. 1. Blanked and pierced textile-machine part for which carbide compound dies had 28 times the total life of those made of D2 tool steel (Example 190)

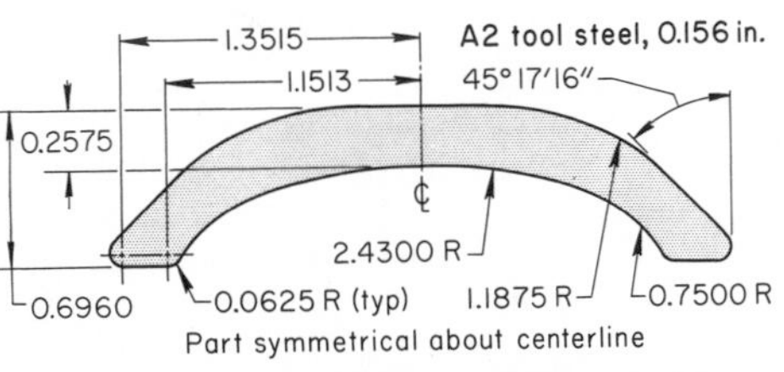

Fig. 2. Part produced by blanking for less than 1% of the per-piece cost of producing it by milling. The punch was modified to solve a stripping problem. (Example 191)

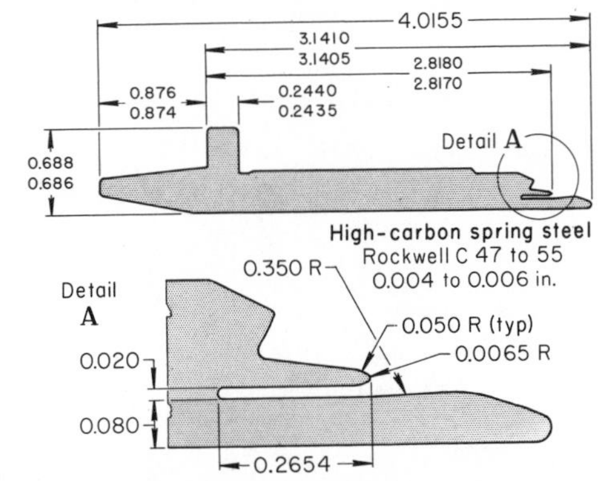

Fig. 3. Part that was blanked complete in one operation at a saving of 90% of the per-piece cost by a previous method, in which slot was cut in a separate operation (Example 192)

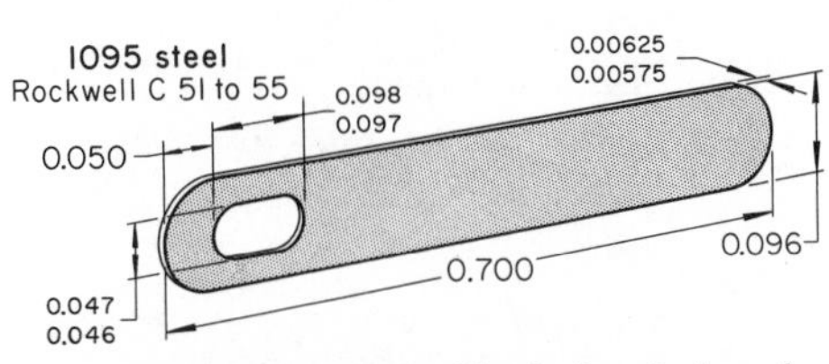

Fig. 4. Spring that was blanked and pierced in a redesigned progressive die, without misfeed (Example 193)

By the original method, the blanking was done at a rate of 10,000 pieces per hour. By the improved method only 8500 pieces per hour were blanked and slotted: Even though the press ran at the same speed for both methods, more time was required for reconditioning the tools that blanked and slotted simultaneously. However, this reduction in speed was offset by the elimination of the second operation, formerly needed for slotting — in which production rate had been only 900 pieces per hour — and by the reduced tool cost.

The work metal was bright-finish, pretempered (Rockwell C 47 to 55) high-carbon spring steel in 1-in.-wide coils at thicknesses of 0.004 to 0.006 in. ±0.0002 in. The press used was a 30-ton open-back inclinable mechanical type having a 1½ in. stroke, and stock feed. Dies and punches were made of T1 high speed steel with a hardness of Rockwell C 64 to 65.

Surface finish on the blanked edges was specified as 15 to 30 micro-in.; some dimensions had a total tolerance of 0.0005 in. These specifications called for a very accurate die and an extremely smooth finish on the surfaces of the punch and die.

Example 193. Redesign of Progressive Die to Prevent Misfeed in Simultaneous Blanking and Piercing (Fig. 4)

The spring shown in Fig. 4 was produced from 1-in.-wide coils of bright-finish, pretempered (Rockwell C 51 to 55) 1095 steel by blanking and piercing in a progressive die. Accurate feeding was necessary, because the pierced hole had to be within 0.001 in. of the center of the part. The hole was too small to be used for piloting. Misfeed occurred, either breaking the punch or distorting the hole.

The immediate remedy was to blank and pierce in separate operations, but the cost — \$0.219 per 100 pieces — was not acceptable.

It was determined that to provide an accurate means of feeding, the blanking and piercing die had to be redesigned. A trim stop was added, whereby the edge of a portion of the stock was notched for a length equal to the lead of the die. The resulting shoulder was pushed against a solid block mounted on top of the die block. The feed-roll pressure was set to allow slight slippage and over-feeding a few thousandths of an inch. The press ran continuously at 140 strokes per minute. By this procedure, satisfactory parts were produced, and cost was reduced to \$0.036 per 100 pieces.

Dies and punches were made from D2 tool steel and hardened to Rockwell C 62 to 63, and were used in a 5-ton mechanical bench press having a 1-in. stroke and a roll feed.

Dimensional accuracy in blanking and piercing of high-carbon steel depends largely on the accuracy of the tooling. Initially, the practical accuracy is the same as for blanking and piercing of other metals. However, because rate of tool wear usually is higher in blanking and piercing of high-carbon steel (especially if pretempered) than it is for many other work metals, maintenance of tolerances can be more difficult and may require more frequent reconditioning of the tools.

The following example describes a spring for which it was impossible to attain the specified tolerance on one dimension without subsequently grinding. Variations in two dimensions, measured on 124 pieces during the production run, are shown in bar graphs.

Example 194. Variations in Dimensions of Blanked Springs (Fig. 5)

The data in Fig. 5 show variations in two dimensions measured on 124 blanked springs randomly selected from a production run of

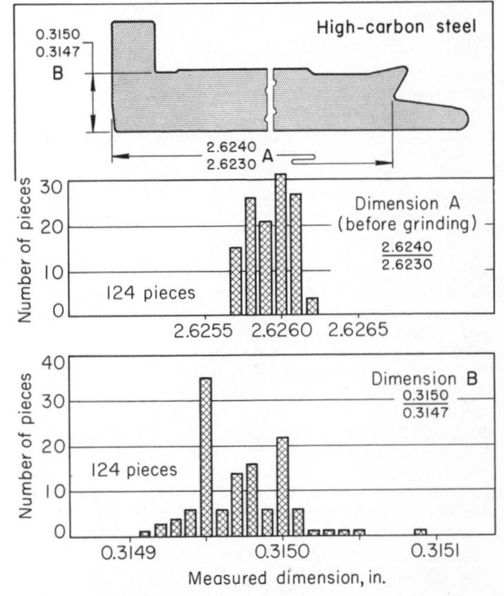

Fig. 5. Variations in two dimensions of blanked springs (Example 194)

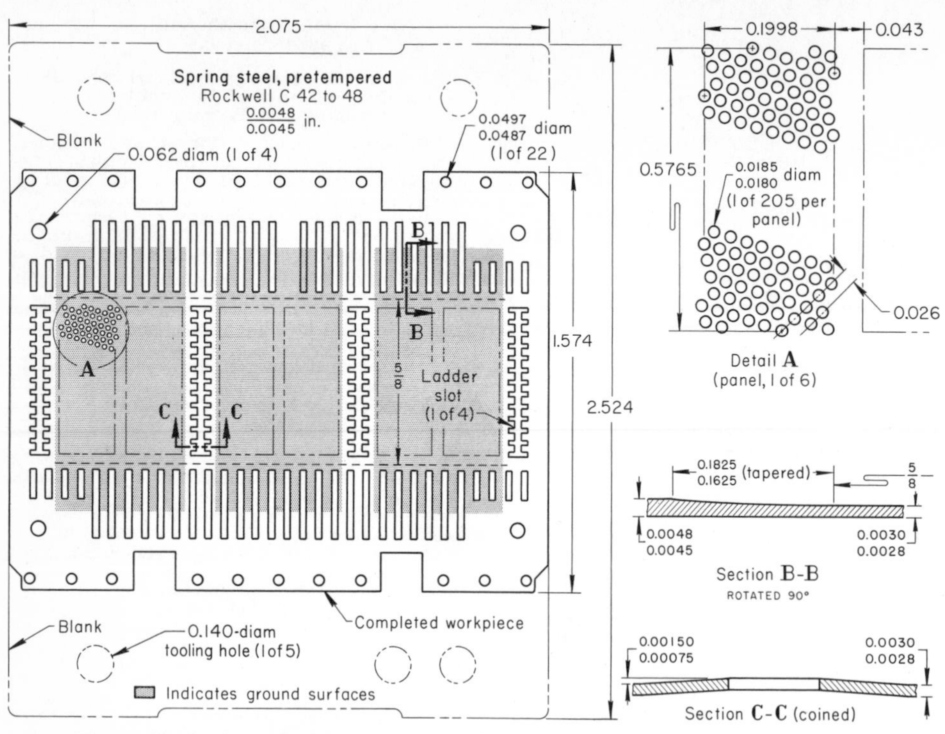

Fig. 6. Comb of an electric shaver made by blanking and piercing (Example 195)

50,000 pieces. The total tolerance on the length (dimension A) was 0.001 in., which was not practical for blanking. Therefore, the springs were blanked slightly oversize, and about 0.002 in. was removed by grinding the square end. The total tolerance on dimension B was 0.0003 in. As shown in Fig. 5, all but 11 of the springs conformed to this tolerance.

The springs were blanked from 1-in.-wide, bright-finish, pretempered high-carbon steel (1.15 to 1.35% C, Rockwell 15-N 84 to 87.5). Thicknesses ranged, in steps of 0.0005 in., from 0.004 to 0.0065 in., ±0.0002 in. The die was made of T1 high speed steel at Rockwell C 64 to 65, and operated in a 30-ton open-back inclinable mechanical press having a 1½-in. stroke and an automatic feed.

The tolerances that can be held and the size and spacing of holes and slots that are practical in press dies are illustrated in the following example.

Example 195. Blanking and Piercing an Intricate Pattern (Fig. 6)

The comb of an electric shaver (Fig. 6), made of pretempered spring steel, had an intricate pattern of slots and holes. Because more than 7 million of these combs were produced yearly, it was economical to construct the dies needed to make them by blanking and piercing. Most of the dimensions on the part were held to a tolerance of ±0.001 in. (Similar parts of stainless steel were made by chemical machining.)

The stock was 2³⁄₁₆-in.-wide high-carbon spring steel, pretempered to Rockwell C 42 to 48. Thickness was 0.0045/0.0048 in. Blanks sheared from the stock were 2.075 in. wide by 2.524 in. long and included, at each end, 0.475 in. that was later trimmed. This trimmed stock contained five tooling holes, one of which was a foolproof hole that prevented incorrect placement of the blank in the die.

In the first piercing operation, the rectangular slots at each end of the cutting areas were pierced, along with the five 0.140-in.-diam tooling holes in the trim area and four ladder slots that bordered the three cutting areas. After this operation, the three cutting areas were ground to 0.0028/0.0030 in. thick. This ground surface, 0.625 by 0.495 in., tapered to the original stock surface in 0.162/0.182 in.

In the third operation, 0.018-in.-diam holes were pierced in the cutting areas at a centerline spacing of 0.0225 in. in one direction and 0.026 in. in the other direction. Each of the three cutting areas had 410 holes arranged in two panels of 205 holes each.

After the third operation, workpieces were deburred and the area around each of the four ladder slots was coined to a depth of 0.00075/0.0015 in. The surface was buffed before plating, removing 0.0003 in. of stock. Finally the comb was trimmed from the rough blank, and four 0.062-in.-diam holes for locating studs and 22 rivet holes 0.0487/0.0497 in. in diameter were pierced. The piece was plated after assembly with the comb support.

Dies were made of D2 tool steel and hardened to Rockwell C 58 to 60. Some additional wear resistance that could have been attained by hardening to Rockwell C 60 to 62 was sacrificed in order to make the delicate punches more resistant to shock. The presses were 70 and 75-ton mechanical presses operated at 5 or 6 strokes per minute to accommodate meticulous hand feeding of workpieces. Production lots consisted of 50,000 pieces each.

Forming Pretempered Steel

Mild forming of high-carbon steel in the quenched and tempered ("pretempered") condition (usually Rockwell C 47 to 55) is common practice. The severity of forming that can be done without cracking of the work metal depends mainly on thickness. When metal thickness is no more than about 0.015 in. it is possible to make relatively severe bends without fracturing the work metal. However, as metal thickness increases, the amount of forming that can be done on pretempered steel decreases rapidly.

The three examples that follow describe the production of parts by blanking, piercing and forming in progressive dies. The hardness and abrasiveness of the work metal reduced die life well below that experienced with low-carbon steel or annealed high-carbon steel, as shown in the second and third of these three examples.

Example 196. Clutch Springs From 1074 Steel (Fig. 7)

The clutch spring shown in Fig. 7 was blanked, pierced and formed from 0.010/0.011-in.-thick 1074 steel in an eight-station progressive die. The stock was pretempered to Rockwell C 48. The sequence of operations in the eight die stations was:

1 Trim edge of stock to provide a trim stop
2 Pierce pilot hole and center hole
3 Pierce 0.025-in.-wide slot
4 Idle
5 Notch profile
6 Idle
7 Form helix and turn down tab
8 Cut part from strip.

After the eighth station, the scrap skeleton was cut into small pieces and pushed through the die. The completed spring remained on top of the die and was removed by air. Idle stations 4 and 6 were provided to give strength and rigidity to the die.

The die was operated in a 30-ton mechanical press with an automatic feed.

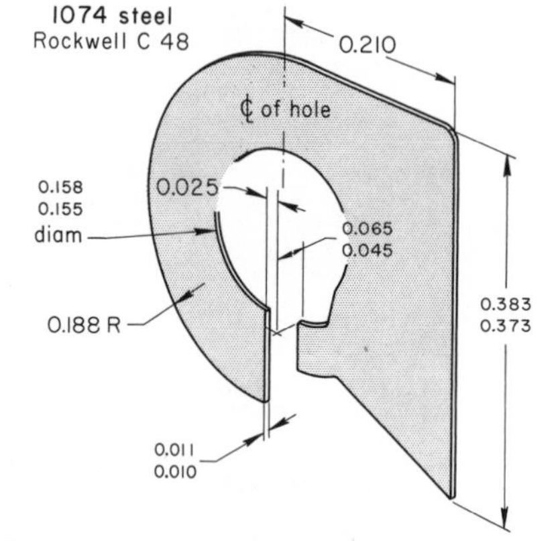

Pretempered stock eliminated the need for heat treating after forming.

Fig. 7. Clutch spring that was blanked, pierced and formed in an eight-station progressive die (Example 196)

Example 197. Ratchet Springs From 1064 Steel (Fig. 8)

The ratchet spring shown in Fig. 8 was made from 0.032-in.-thick 1064 blue spring steel in three operations in a progressive die. The die was used in a 65-ton mechanical press operated at 110 strokes per minute.

Press operations included punching a 1.281-in.-diam hole, lancing and forming five equally spaced tabs, and blanking the spring from the strip. Strip width was 2¼ in. The angle for the lancing-and-forming punch was determined before the progressive die was made.

The punches and dies were of D2 tool steel hardened to Rockwell C 58 to 60. Tools were reconditioned after making 25,000 pieces.

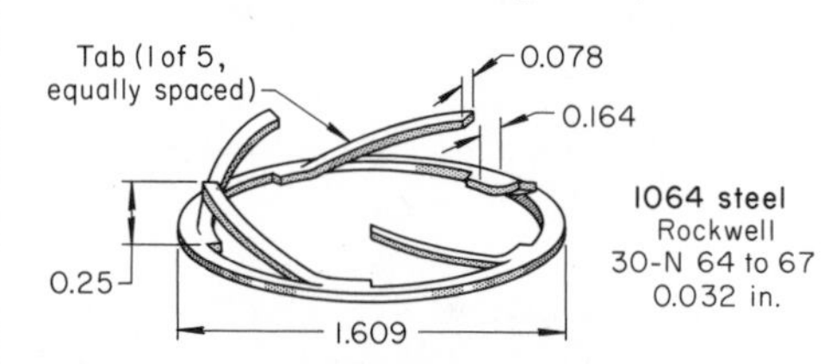

Fig. 8. Ratchet spring produced in three operations (punching, lancing-and-forming, and blanking) in a progressive die (Example 197)

In the following example, tabs were coined to a spherical radius after being bent to a 45° angle. This required resetting the die to overcome variations in each coil of stock.

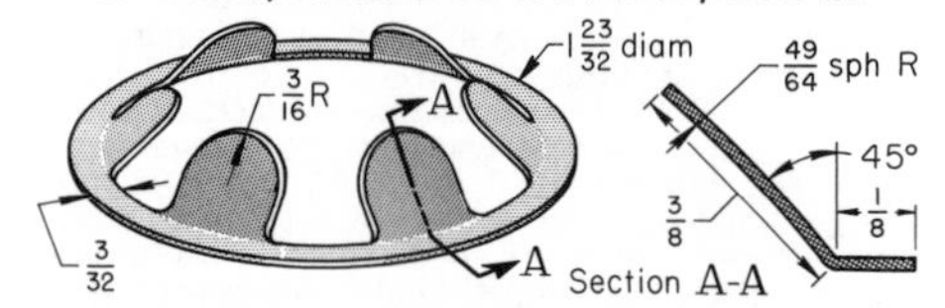

Three progressive-die stations cut tabs to shape and coined them to spherical radius.

Fig. 9. Lockwasher blanked and formed of pretempered steel. To control tab dimensions, dies had to be reset for each new coil of stock. (Example 198)

Example 198. Lockwashers From 1074 Steel (Fig. 9)

The lockwasher shown in Fig. 9 was made from 1074 pretempered steel with a hardness of Rockwell 30-N 64 to 67. Coil stock was 2½ in. wide and 0.015 in. thick. A progressive die with three working stations was used to cut the tabs to shape, bend and coin the tabs to a spherical radius, and blank the part from the strip. Idle stations were placed between the working stations for added die strength. D2 tool steel was used for the cutting and forming die elements. Die life between sharpenings was about 25,000 pieces.

Adjustment of the die setting was necessary for each coil of stock, so that the tabs would be coined and bent to the proper angle. A 65-ton mechanical press operating at 110 strokes per minute was used.

Forming Annealed Steel

Moderately severe forming can be done on cold rolled stock that has not been quenched and tempered, and on high-carbon steel that has been spheroidize-annealed. Such materials are usually hardened and tempered after forming, for better spring properties.

Table 1 shows the effect of the carbon content of steel on bendability, and demonstrates the major importance of sheet thickness.

The next four examples describe the forming of parts from annealed stock, or from cold rolled stock that had not been hardened. The first two examples deal with parts redesigned to improve producibility in the press; the other two, with parts for which the forming severity required annealed or unhardened stock. (Annealed stock was used also in Example 203.)

Example 199. Bracket That Was Redesigned to Prevent Punch Breakage (Fig. 10)

The bracket shown in Fig. 10 was made of 0.042-in.-thick spheroidize-annealed 1070 spring steel at Rockwell B 70 to 82. It was blanked, pierced and formed by a progressive die in a 60-ton double-eccentric straight-side press, at the rate of 210 pieces per minute.

The bracket was used to attach electric conduit and other building components to the flanges of beams and other structural members. In the original design of the bracket, the lanced barbs (Fig. 10) caused frequent breaking of a punch. Redesign as shown in Fig. 10 produced a barb with better holding power, and permitted the use of a stronger punch, reducing the cost of die maintenance and press downtime.

After forming, the parts were heat treated to Rockwell C 44 to 48 and phosphate coated.

Example 200. Conduit Clip That Was Redesigned for Increased Production Rate and Reduced Die Maintenance Cost (Fig. 11)

The conduit clip shown in Fig. 11 was made of 0.037-in.-thick spheroidize-annealed 1070 spring steel. It was blanked, pierced and formed by a progressive die in a 60-ton double-eccentric straight-side press.

The clip was used to fasten electrical conduit to rods or flanges of structural members. In the original clip design (Fig. 11), gripping was done by two sharp corners embedded into the structural members at two places. The sharp corners were cut by one punch; therefore, corner sharpness depended on the condition of the punch.

Product redesign simplified the part and improved its gripping ability. In the new die, two intersecting cuts produced the sharp corners, so that sharpness no longer depended on punch condition. The improved design (Fig. 11) also permitted two pieces, instead of one, to be made in each stroke of the press, thus increasing the production rate and reducing die maintenance costs. Production increased from 150 pieces per minute to 250 (2 pieces per stroke; 125 strokes per minute). After forming, the parts were quenched and

Table 1. Typical Effects of Carbon Content and Sheet Thickness on Minimum Bend Radius of Annealed Steels

Thickness of sheet, in.	Minimum bend radius, in. — Steels 1020 to 1025	Steels 4130 and 8630	Steels 1070 and 1095
0.016	0.03	0.03	0.06
0.020	0.03	0.03	0.06
0.025	0.03	0.03	0.06
0.030	0.03	0.06	0.09
0.035	0.06	0.06	0.09
0.042	0.06	0.06	0.13
0.050	0.06	0.09	0.13
0.062	0.06	0.09	0.16
0.078	0.09	0.13	0.19
0.093	0.09	0.16	0.25
0.109	0.13	0.16	0.31
0.125	0.13	0.19	0.31
0.156	0.16	0.25	0.38
0.187	0.19	0.31	0.50

SOURCE: Die Design Handbook, 2nd edition, ASTME, McGraw-Hill, New York, 1964.

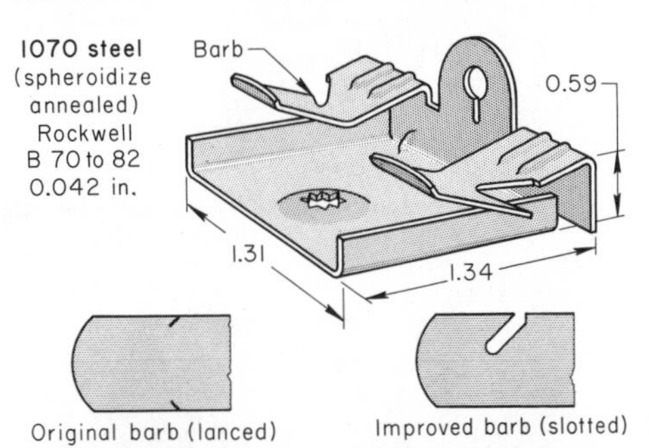

Improved design of barb reduced die-maintenance cost and press downtime, and also gave the barb more holding power in service.

Fig. 10. Bracket produced by blanking, piercing and forming in a progressive die (Example 199)

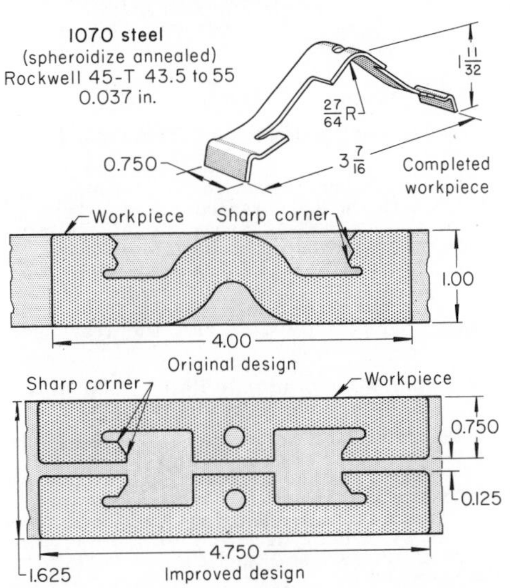

Improved design increased the producibility of sharp corners, decreased die maintenance, and increased production rate.

Fig. 11. Conduit clip produced by blanking, piercing and forming in a progressive die (Example 200)

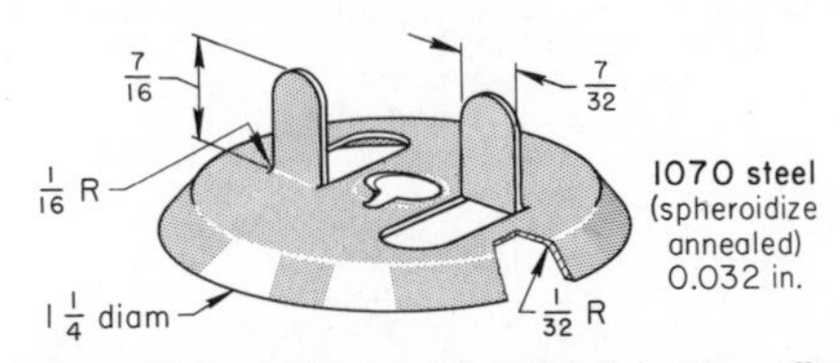

The edges of the center-hole slot were offset to the pitch of the screw thread, so the part could serve as both a nut and a washer.

Fig. 12. Washer-wingnut that was made in a progressive die (Example 201)

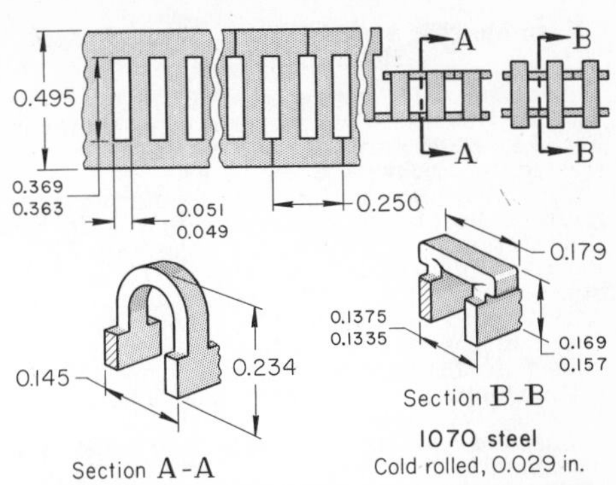

Fig. 13. Strip development, and details of sequentially formed shapes, for a piston-ring expander made from unhardened stock in a progressive die (Example 202)

tempered to a hardness of Rockwell 45-N 45 to 50, and a rust-preventive coating was applied. Hardness was governed by a requirement that the ends be able to return to their original shape without cracking, after being bent together.

Example 201. Use of a Progressive Die to Outline, Pierce, Form and Blank (Fig. 12)

The washer-wingnut shown in Fig. 12 replaced two parts, a washer and a wingnut. To produce the unit as one piece, spheroidize-annealed 1070 steel was used. The part was quenched and tempered after forming.

A progressive die was used to outline, pierce, form, and blank the part from coil stock. The metal around the center hole was slotted and spiral formed, as in making a speed nut, to engage threads. A 60-ton double-eccentric straight-side press operating at 180 strokes per minute produced three wingnuts per stroke, or 540 per minute.

The progressive die was made of D2 tool steel and hardened to Rockwell C 58 to 60. Die life was 200,000 strokes between regrinds. An EP lubricant was used on the strip. Annual production was 3.4 million pieces.

Example 202. Use of a Progressive Die to Perforate, Lance, U-Form and Cam-Form (Fig. 13)

The 1070 steel used for the piston-ring expander shown in Fig. 13 would have been too hard to form at the required production rate after hardening, so the ring expanders were formed from cold rolled stock before heat treatment. The steel was coil stock 0.028 to 0.030 in. thick and 0.495 in. wide.

Four-station progressive-die carbide tooling was used to perforate the 0.049/0.051 by 0.363/0.369-in. slots, lance the sides at 0.250-in. staggered spacing, U-form, then cam-form and flatten the stock for the piston-ring expander shown in Fig. 13. After forming, the stock was induction heated and air cooled while being continuously wound onto a tube with a pin-type coiler similar to that used for coiling springs. When the tube was full, the coils were tempered to Rockwell C 48 to 52 and then cut off.

The carbide punches and dies were reconditioned after one million strokes. A 30-ton press operating at 300 strokes per minute was used. Feed length was 2¼ in., giving a feed rate of 675 in. per minute. Presses operated two or three shifts per day. Lubrication was avoided because it would have caused smoke during the induction heating operation.

Hole Flanging

Flanges are formed around holes to increase bearing surface or to increase the number of threads that will fit in a tapped hole. The relation of stock thickness, hole size and flange height is discussed in the article "Press Bending of Low-Carbon Steel", page 89 in this volume. In the following example, flanges were formed around holes that were large compared with the flange width, to provide a bearing surface.

Example 203. Swivel Washer With Flanged Holes (Fig. 14)

Annealed 1070 spring steel 0.010 in. thick was used to make the swivel washer shown in Fig. 14. After forming, the parts were heat treated to Rockwell C 46 to 48.

The strip layout for the six-station progressive die also is shown in Fig. 14. In the first station, two rectangular holes, one 0.250-in.-diam pilot hole, and two 0.710-in.-diam holes were pierced. The larger round holes were flanged to 0.798 in. in diameter by 1⁄16-in. depth in the second station. The washer was lanced in the third station and formed in the fifth. The part was cut off in the sixth station. Station 4 was idle.

The die was made of A2 tool steel and hardened to Rockwell C 60 to 61. It ran in a 15-ton open-back inclinable press at 2000 strokes per hour. To maintain a minimum burr height, the die was sharpened after making 60,000 pieces. Total die life was more than 3 million pieces.

Multiple-Slide Forming

Small parts that are used in large quantities and require considerable forming often are produced on multiple-slide machines. Generally, more severe forming can be done in the forming station of a multiple-slide machine than in a progressive die. (For a discussion of multiple-slide forming, see the article beginning on page 154 in this volume. Examples 225 and 227 in that article deal with high-carbon steel.)

The three examples that follow illustrate high-carbon steel parts produced in multiple-slide forming machines.

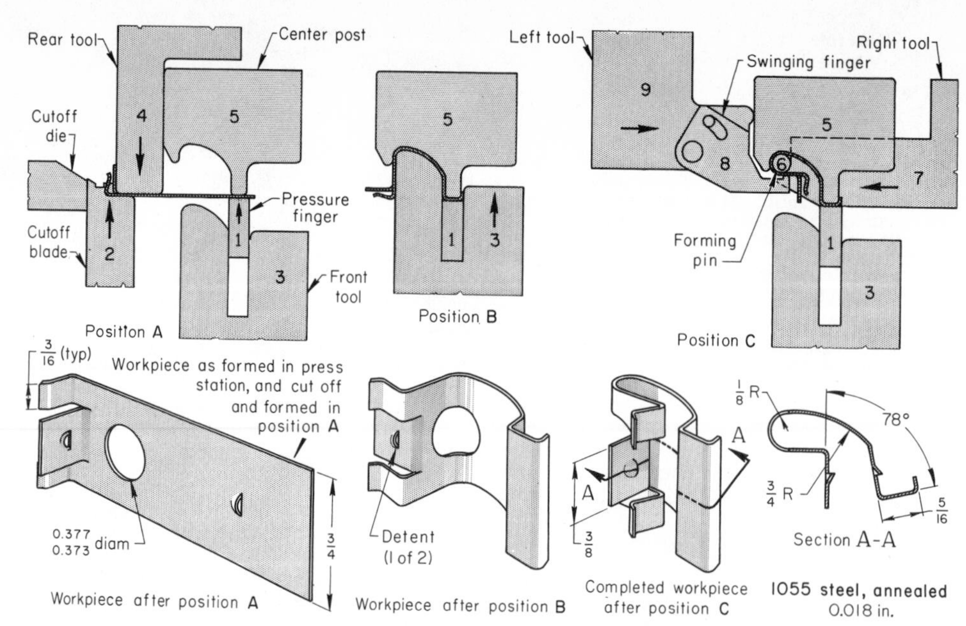

Fig. 16. Sequence in the forming of a spring clip in a multiple-slide machine, and layouts of the forming operation (Example 205)

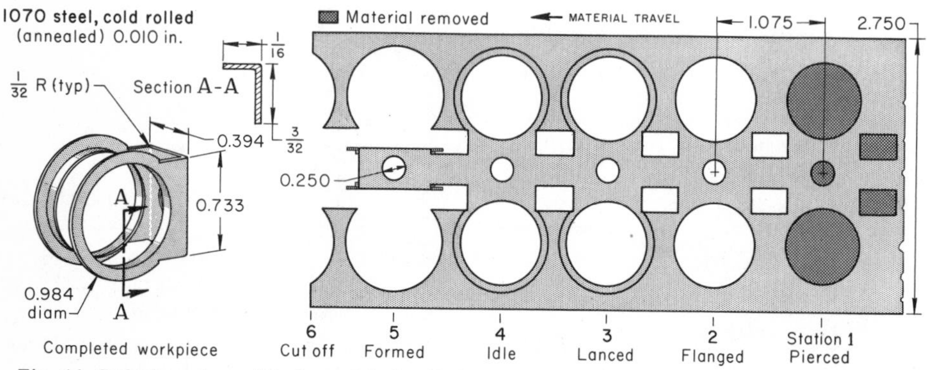

Fig. 14. Swivel washer with flanged holes that was made in a progressive die (Example 203)

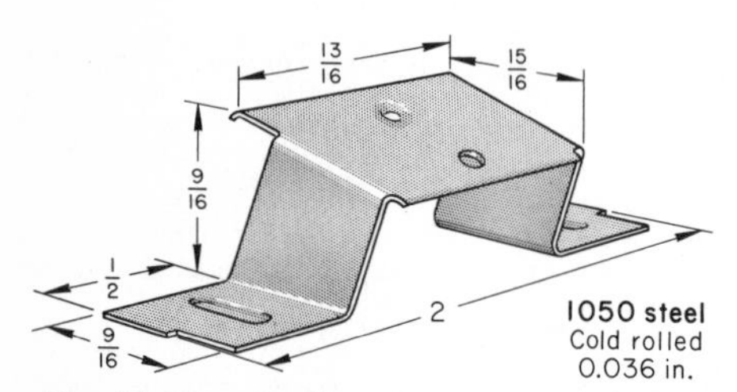

Fig. 15. Mounting bracket that was blanked and bent in a multiple-slide machine (Example 204)

Example 204. Blanking and Bending a Bracket in a Multiple-Slide Machine (Fig. 15)

The mounting bracket shown in Fig. 15 was embossed, pierced and notched in a progressive die in the press station of a multiple-slide machine. It was then cut off and bent. Production was at the rate of 100 pieces per minute. The work metal was coiled cold rolled 1050 steel strip, 0.036 in. thick by 1¼ in. wide.

In the press station, two holes were pierced, two weld projections were embossed, one hole was flanged, the outline was notched, and the top surface was flanged to improve stiffness. The strip then moved to the forming station, where the part was cut off and bent to the final form shown in Fig. 15. All slides in this station moved in a horizontal plane. A front slide tool held the part against the center post and preformed the flanges. A cam action on the right and left slides formed the flanges against the post and the rear slide tool.

Example 205. Forming a Spring Clip in a Multiple-Slide Machine (Fig. 16)

The spring clip shown in Fig. 16 was made of annealed 1055 steel 0.018 in. thick by ¾ in. wide. After forming, the part was heat treated to Rockwell C 43 to 47 and hot dip galvanized. The shape of the forming tools and the amount of bending necessary to maintain the shape of the part and hold the 78° angle were developed by trial.

A four-station progressive die (not shown in Fig. 16) was used to lance, curl, prebend and form the two 3⁄16-in.-wide spring fingers; pierce the 0.373/0.377-in.-diam hole; and lance and form the two half-moon-shape detents. Feed length was 2.600 in.

The two spring fingers were formed over a sliding form block, which was moved into position by a cam mounted on the punch-holder shoe of the progressive die. In the open position, the form blocks had slots that permitted the formed fingers to move with the strip to the next die station. Also, there were slots in the die to clear the fingers as the strip moved to the forming station.

The half-moon-shape detent in the ⅜-in.-wide flange was formed toward the punch holder by a lancing and forming punch actuated by a cam on the backshaft.

The sequence of work done in the forming station of the machine is shown in Fig. 16.

In forming position A, the blank was cut off from the strip with cutoff blade 2 mounted on the cutoff slide. The cutoff die was mounted on the cutoff-unit body. The cutoff slide advanced tool 2 far enough to form the ⅜-in.-wide flange around rear tool 4. The pressure finger 1, actuated by the positive blankholder, held the blank against center post 5 during cutoff and all forming operations.

Next (position B in Fig. 16), the cutoff slide and rear slide retracted. The front slide advanced tool 3 to form the large radius at the center of the clip and the small flange along the right-hand end. The form on center post 5 and front tool 3 was developed to shape the part properly and control springback.

To finish forming the part (position C in Fig. 16), the front slide retracted enough to clear the side tools while the pressure finger held the part against the center post. A special stripper cam having a stroke-dwell-stroke motion moved the ¼-in.-diam pin 6 into position. Right-hand tool 7 advanced to give this pin support while the swinging finger 8, on left-hand tool 9, finished forming the clip by making a 90° bend.

The progressive die and the cutoff blade and die were made of D7 tool steel and hardened to Rockwell C 62 to 64. The center post, final forming pin, and swinging finger were made of S1 tool steel. Tool life per grind was 200,000 pieces. Total life of the dies and forming tools was 8 million pieces.

The press station had a capacity of 20 tons; the forming station, 12 tons. The machine operated at 110 strokes per minute. A chlorinated oil was used for lubrication.

Example 206. Forming an Electrical Cover in Both the Press and the Forming Stations of a Multiple-Slide Machine (Fig. 17)

The side flanges on the part shown in Fig. 17 were formed in the press station, and the ends in the forming station, of a multiple-slide machine. The work metal was annealed cold rolled 1070 steel, 0.020 in. thick and 1.868 in. wide, in coils. After forming, the cover was heat treated to Rockwell C 43 to 47 and hot dip galvanized.

The progressive die, mounted in the press station, had four working stations and one idle station. Operations were: emboss four stiffening beads, pierce slot, trim outline, and bend flanges. The slot was used for piloting in idle station 4 and forming station 5. The flanges were overbent 3° by pivoting form blocks. Clearances between the piercing punch and die, and the trimming punch and die, were 0.0008 in. per side. Feed length per stroke was 2.595 in. The major parts of the die were made of D7 tool steel and hardened to Rockwell C 62 to 64. Heel blocks and die retainers were made of O1 tool steel. Life between grinds was 200,000 pieces; total tool life was 8 million pieces.

The sequence of work done in the forming station of the machine is shown in Fig. 17.

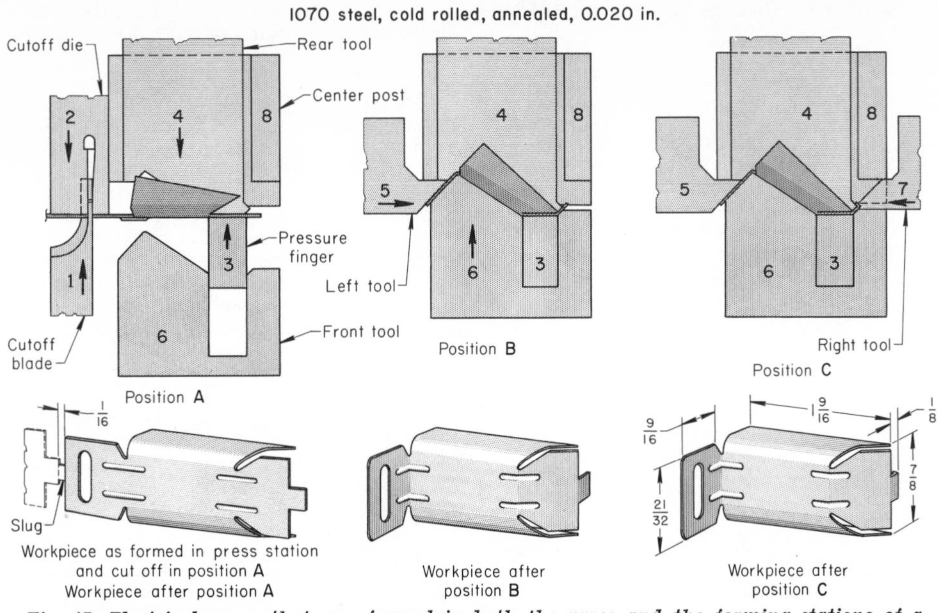

Fig. 17. Electrical cover that was formed in both the press and the forming stations of a multiple-slide machine (Example 206)

The rear slide was in two parts, each actuated by a separate cam on the backshaft.

In forming position A, the 1/16-in.-wide slug connecting the blanks was removed by cutoff blade 1 on the cutoff slide and cutoff die 2 on the left-hand portion of the rear slide. The pressure finger 3, in front tool 6, held the blank against rear tool 4, mounted on the right-hand portion of the rear slide. Center post 8 was a support for, and stripped the finished part from, rear tool 4.

In position B, left-hand tool 5 advanced to form, in conjunction with rear tool 4, the V-die for bending the 90° flange. Front tool 6 formed the three bends in the top of the cover.

In position C, right-hand tool 7 bent the short flange on the anchor tab over rear tool 4.

The cutoff tools were made of D7 tool steel and hardened to Rockwell C 62 to 64. The forming tools were made of O1 tool steel and hardened to Rockwell C 58 to 60.

Capacity of the press station was 20 tons, and that of the forming station 18 tons. The machine ran at 100 strokes per minute. A chlorinated oil was used as lubricant.

The machines that formed the parts described in the preceding examples have slides that operate in the horizontal plane. There are also machines in which the center post is horizontal and the slides operate in a vertical plane normal to the center post.

Press Forming of Coated Steel

COATED STEEL sheet or strip is formed in the same presses as are used for forming uncoated steel. Forming procedures, however, must sometimes be modified, depending on the type of coating. During processing, scratching or breaking the coating (sometimes, only marring the surface) must be avoided, because these defects could cause rejection of the finished part.

Resistance to forming forces varies directly with the thickness and hardness of the steel base, so that the coating on thicker or harder steel is subjected to greater abrasion, surface shear, and die pressure. The coating can be sheared off the steel sheet or the action of die forces can cause scratches, gouge marks or increased gloss in pressure areas on the coated product.

In many applications, special handling and processing techniques in forming are needed. Formability may be less than for the same metal uncoated. Further restrictions are imposed on severity of forming by the need to avoid fracture or excessive porosity in corrosion-resistant surfaces, to avoid roughening or "orange peel" on decorative surfaces, or to avoid flaking of hot dip zinc or aluminum coatings. However, soft, ductile metallic coatings generally increase die life and reduce lubrication requirements, and in some applications may improve formability. Matte coatings can improve the retention of forming lubricants.

Zinc-Coated Steel

Most of the zinc-coated steel used in forming applications is hot dip galvanized low-carbon steel sheet and strip. A layer of metallic zinc on the surface of the work metal prevents galling during forming by eliminating direct contact of the steel against the die, and generally increases die life, because of the softness and lubricity of the zinc. The need for lubrication during forming is reduced by the presence of the zinc coating.

Formability is reduced to some extent by the brittle layer of iron-zinc alloy that is produced between the metallic zinc and the steel base during hot dip galvanizing. The thickness of the alloy layer depends on the temperature-time cycle in galvanizing, but it also is affected by the percentage of other metals in the molten-zinc bath (see the article "Hot Dip Galvanizing", pages 498 to 503 in Volume 2 of this Handbook). The decrease in formability usually is in direct proportion to the thickness of the iron-zinc alloy layer.

Processing conditions for continuous galvanizing of coil stock that is intended for forming are regulated to keep the thickness of brittle alloy to a minimum, thus making the loss of formability negligible in many mild to moderately severe forming applications. In deep drawing, the beneficial effects of the metallic zinc outweigh the adverse effect of the alloy layer, often permitting greater reductions and greater draw depths than with similar uncoated steel.

Table 1. Weights and Approximate Thicknesses of AISI Classes of Zinc Coating for Galvanized Steel Sheet(a)

AISI coating class, oz per sq ft(b)	Minimum check limit, oz per sq ft(c)		Nominal coating thickness per side, mils
	Triple-spot test	Single-spot test	
2.75	2.35	2.00	2.15
2.50	2.10	1.80	1.95
2.25	1.85	1.60	1.75
2.00	1.65	1.40	1.55
1.75	1.40	1.20	1.35
1.50	1.15	1.00	1.15
1.25 (commercial)	0.90	0.80	0.90
Light commercial	0.60	0.50	0.65

(a) Includes iron-zinc alloy. (b) Total for both sides; nominal weight of zinc used in processing, including bottom dross and surface skimming losses. (c) As noted in ASTM A525.

Formability is influenced by other factors as well — principally, by the initial properties of the steel base, by the amount of mechanical work before or after galvanizing, and by the response of the steel to the heating cycle for galvanizing, to supplementary heat treatments, and to aging. These factors often have a greater effect on the formability of galvanized steel than does the coating of zinc metal and the iron-zinc alloy.

Mill Products. Galvanized steel sheet for use in forming is generally purchased in one of four AISI grades: commercial quality, drawing quality, drawing quality special killed, and lock forming quality. These grades are available in either the dead soft or the temper rolled condition. Physical quality steel, which is less frequently formed, is usually specified on the basis of strength or hardness, and is generally suitable for corrugating and for making 90° bends.

The thickness of the zinc coating per side, including the iron-zinc alloy layer, ranges from about 2.15 mils for the heaviest coating to 0.65 mils (light commercial), in eight coating classes. Table 1 lists the standard AISI coating classes, and gives the minimum check limits on coating weight and the nominal coating thickness per side for each class.

Although improvements have been made in the formability of hot dip galvanized mill products (particularly, of drawing quality and of drawing quality

Table 2. Formability Limits for Parts Made From Galvanized Steel up to 0.060 In. Thick

Type of operation	Maximum severity of forming	Grade of steel(a) Unexposed parts	Exposed parts
90° bend	1t radius, minimum	CQ, CA or BA	CQ(b), CA or BA
Up to 180° bend	0.01-in. radius(c)	CQ, CA or BA	CQ(b), CA or BA
Drawing	10 to 20% elongation	DQ, CA(d) or BA	DQ(b), CA(d) or BA
Drawing	20 to 30% elongation	DQ, CA(d) or BA(e)	DQSK(b), CA(d) or BA
Drawing(f)	30 to 35% elongation	DQSK, CA(d) or BA(e)	DQSK(b), BA(e)

Source: P. G. Nelson, *Metal Progress*, 82, 104 to 108 (Oct 1962)

(a) CQ = commercial quality; DQ = drawing quality; DQSK = drawing quality, special killed; CA = continuous annealed; BA = box annealed. (b) Must be temper rolled after galvanizing. (c) For 10% maximum elongation. (d) Heat treated after galvanizing. (e) Dead soft or annealed before galvanizing. (f) With possible buckling during drawing.

special-killed steels), their average formability does not equal that of uncoated steel except in some deep drawing operations.

Steel in the dead soft condition usually has better formability, but it is suitable only for unexposed parts because of susceptibility to stretcher strains. Steel that is temper rolled after hot dip galvanizing is less formable, but it has a more suitable surface for exposed parts, because stretcher strains are eliminated and large zinc crystals on the surface are smoothed out.

Table 2 gives formability limits of galvanized steel for exposed and unexposed parts, and Table 3 shows the effect of coating thickness on the diameter at which no flaking of the coating occurs at the outside of the bend in a bend test.

Deep Drawing. Greater reductions and greater draw depths can be obtained on hot dip galvanized steel (in spite of its generally lower formability) than on uncoated steel of similar mechanical properties. The zinc coating reduces galling and pickup; therefore, drawing compounds are seldom necessary — straight mineral oils of various viscosities are satisfactory. Flaking of particles from the surface of the coating may occur where forming is moderate to severe. In one application, zinc-electroplated steel was used alternately with hot dip galvanized steel, because the hot dip galvanizing caused a buildup on the forming die, and the electrolytic zinc plate caused enough wear to remove the buildup.

Tool Design. Tools for forming zinc-coated steel parts are of conventional design, and are made of cast iron and standard tool steels. However, parts formed of commercial quality continuous-annealed steel, and of steel over 0.060 in. thick, require more compensation for springback than conventional box-annealed steel and uncoated steel (which have lower yield strength and hardness). Post-heat-treated continuous-annealed and box-annealed drawing quality galvanized steels require the same tooling as uncoated steels in most forming operations.

Forming Applications. Galvanized steel is used for parts that differ widely in forming severity; typical formed parts include automobile frame and body parts, roofing, siding, gutters and downspouts, ductwork, signs, awnings, outdoor hardware, highway guardrails, and culverts. Parts formed of hot dip galvanized steel sheet are described in Examples 140, 152, 153 and 185 in the article on Press Forming of Low-Carbon Steel in this volume.

Electroplated Zinc. Because the intermediate layer of iron-zinc alloy is either

Table 3. Bend Test Diameters for Galvanized Steel With Various Coating Thicknesses (a)

AISI coating class, oz per sq ft(b)	Bend test diameter(c) for sheet thickness, in., of: 0.168 to 0.078	0.071 to 0.040	0.037 to 0.016
2.75	3t	3t	2t
2.50	2t	2t	2t
2.25	2t	2t	2t
2.00	2t	2t	2t
1.75	2t	1t	1t
1.50	1t	0t	0t
1.25 (commercial)	1t	0t	0t
Light commercial	0t	0t	0t

(a) According to ASTM A525. (b) Total for both sides; nominal weight of zinc used in processing, including bottom dross and surface skimming losses. (c) Specimen shall stand bending through 180° in any direction without flaking of the coating on the outside surface of the bend only; t = thickness of sheet.

absent or very thin on zinc-plated steel, presence of the zinc coating does not reduce the formability of the steel, as may occur with hot dip galvanized steel. There is no measurable thickness of iron-zinc alloy on the plated coil stock even after long storage at room temperature; the amount of alloy produced in heat treating the plated stock before forming is usually too small to affect formability. The plating (about 0.1 to 0.3 mil thick) is tightly adherent, even under the most severe deformation; there is no flaking or peeling during severe forming, as sometimes occurs on hot dip galvanized steel. The forming of typical parts from zinc-plated steel is described in Example 104 in the article on Press Bending, and Example 169 in the article on Press Forming of Low-Carbon Steel.

Hot Dip Aluminum-Coated Steel

Moderately severe forming is done on hot dip aluminum-coated steel ("aluminized" steel). The same dies and pressworking practices are applicable to aluminum-coated stock as for similar uncoated stock. Drawing compounds are recommended for forming and drawing operations.

Aluminum-coated steel is produced in a coil by a continuous hot dip process in a bath of molten aluminum. The coating process and the effect of process variables (composition of the steel base and of the aluminum bath, and the time-temperature cycle) on the properties of hot dip aluminum-coated steel are discussed in the article "Aluminum Coating of Steel", pages 489 to 497 in Volume 2 of this Handbook.

The aluminum coating influences the formability of the steel base in the same way as does the zinc coating on galvanized steel, with opposing effects from the relatively ductile surface layer of metallic aluminum and an underlying brittle layer of iron-aluminum alloy. Although silicon additions to the coating bath substantially reduce the thickness of the alloy layer, they also lower the ductility of the outer coating layer. The thicker the outer coating layer, the greater the reduction in ductility for a given addition of silicon.

Inasmuch as an increase in coating weight for greater protective value is accomplished principally by an increase in the thickness of the outer layer, there is a corresponding decrease in adherence of the coating. Thickness of heavy coatings must be reduced in proportion to the severity of forming if satisfactory adherence is to be maintained during forming.

In heat treating steel that has been hot dip coated with aluminum, temperature-time cycles that substantially increase the thickness of the brittle alloy layer are avoided if the material is to be formed.

Mill products are referred to as aluminum-coated sheets, and are generally produced with two types of coatings, type 1 and type 2 (AISI designations).

Type 1, which is used principally for heat resistance, and where adherence is a prime factor (as in forming and drawing), is produced in two coating weights, regular and light, as described in Table 4. Type 1 coatings are generally applied to commercial quality, drawing quality, or drawing quality special-killed steels. The coating contains about 5 to 10% silicon to reduce the rate of diffusion alloying with the steel base at elevated temperature during the coating process and in service (see Table 4 on page 491 in Volume 2 of this Handbook). The thickness of the alloy layer in type 1 coatings is about 0.3 mil per surface.

Type 2 coating, used mainly for atmospheric corrosion resistance, has a nominal weight of 1 oz per sq ft (thickness of about 2 mils per surface). The steel base usually is of commercial quality. The coating may be produced in a commercially pure aluminum bath (for an alloy thickness of about 0.9 mil per surface) or in a silicon-containing bath (alloy thickness of 0.3 mil per surface, as for type 1).

Formability of Mill Products. Forming operations of moderate severity can be done on commercial quality steel with a type 1 or 2 coating. Sheet stock withstands bending 180° flat on itself in any direction, without fracture of the steel base, and bending 180° over two thicknesses of the material without flaking or peeling on the outside of the bend. When greater ductility is needed, drawing quality or drawing quality special-killed steels with type 1 coating are used, and are supplied in a quality suitable for forming a specific part. Physical quality sheet is sometimes used for applications that require higher strength or hardness than is found in commercial quality sheet.

Requirements for resistance to corrosion in service often limit the permissible severity of forming to less than that described in the preceding paragraph. Hairline cracks that develop in the aluminum coating lead to lower service life at high temperature or in atmospheric exposure. Table 5 gives minimum diameters for 180° bends for

25 cycles of exposure for 30 min at 1100 F and cooling for 30 min (type 1 coating), or for a service life of one year in a mild industrial atmosphere (type 2 commercially pure aluminum coating).

Adherence testing by reverse bending has shown good correlation in predicting the suitability for forming and drawing of steel sheet with aluminum hot dip coatings of different composition, structure, and thickness or coating weight.

Compressive forces are more destructive than tensile forces to the adherence of the coating. In a 180° bend test, the coating always fails first on the compression side of the bend, if it fails at all. Similarly, in a coating failure occurring during a drawing operation, peeling always develops first on the compression side.

In applications involving tension only, as in an elongated tensile specimen, the alloy layer is fractured, but the fractures do not show at the outer surface of the coating. Microscopic examination has verified the ability of the more ductile outer layer to elongate and provide continuous coverage of the cracked alloy particles.

Examples of Application. In the two examples that follow, steel with a type 1 hot dip aluminum coating was used for parts subject to heat and a corrosive environment in service. The parts originally were made of uncoated steel and covered with aluminum paint after assembly. The dies were not altered when the work metal was changed.

Examples 207 and 208. Forming of Two Clothes-Dryer Burner Parts From Type 1 Aluminum-Coated Steel

Example 207 — Flame-Spreader Flange (Fig. 1). Figure 1 shows a flame-spreader flange for the burner of a gas-fired clothes dryer. This part was formed in five bends from 0.036-in.-thick aluminum-coated (type 1) 0.10% carbon steel, drawing quality, aluminum killed, and non-age-hardening. This material was selected to resist corrosion caused by the gas flame and by condensation from the high humidity in many basements.

The blank was pierced, notched and cut off, and the first bend was made, in a progressive die. The remaining bends were made in pairs in single-operation V-dies, in the order indicated by the circled numbers in Fig. 1. The cutting and forming dies were made of O1 tool steel and hardened to Rockwell C 59 to 60. Die life was 80,000 pieces per grind.

Careful adjustment of the press stroke and gages in the single-operation bending dies was needed, to hold the ±0.005-in. tolerance on the location and spacing of the holes. The same operations were used for aluminum-coated steel as had been used for uncoated steel. Production rate was 2000 pieces per hour for lots of 10,000 pieces.

Example 208 — Body Half (Fig. 2). The burner body half (Fig. 2) for a gas-fired clothes dryer was made from hot dip aluminum-coated steel strip for resistance to corrosion in use. The aluminum coating also acted as a lubricant carrier for an oil-base drawing compound that was applied to the strip by a roller coater.

The part was formed from a 3-by-7¹⁄₁₆-in. blank of 0.037-in.-thick 0.10% carbon steel, aluminum killed and non-age-hardening. Originally, the part had been made of 1010 steel and then coated with aluminum paint.

Forming was done in a compound cutoff-and-form die mounted in a 50-ton mechanical press and operating at 30 strokes per minute. A die cushion was used to apply force to the blankholder. Slight thinning of the coating in the sidewalls of the 1.250-in.-diam form (see Fig. 2) did not affect the corrosion resistance of the part.

Other operations included trimming to width and length in one die and then punching the

Table 4. Weights and Approximate Thicknesses of AISI Type 1 Hot Dip Aluminum Coatings on Steel(a)

AISI type 1 coating description	Nominal coating weight, oz per sq ft of sheet	Minimum check limit, oz per sq ft(b): Triple-spot test	Single-spot test	Nominal coating thickness per side, mil
Regular	0.50	0.40	0.30	1.0
Light	0.35	0.25	0.20	0.7

(a) Includes iron-aluminum alloy. (b) Total on both sides of sheet, as set forth in ASTM specification A428.

Table 5. Minimum Diameters for Corrosion-Resistant 180° Bends in Various Thicknesses of Steel Sheet With AISI Types 1 and 2 Hot Dip Aluminum Coating

Sheet thickness (t), in.	Minimum bend diameter: Type 1 coating(a)	Type 2 coating(b)
0.0635	$3t$	$5t$
0.0516	$3t$	$4t$
0.0396	$3t$	$3t$
0.0336	..	$2t$
0.0276, 0.0217 and 0.0187	$1t$	$1t$

(a) Coating containing about 9% silicon and weighing 0.5 oz per sq ft. Minimum diameters are for no rusting at outside of bend after exposure in air to 25 cycles consisting of 30 min at 1100 F and 30 min of cooling.

(b) Coating of commercially pure aluminum and weighing 1.15 oz per sq ft. Minimum bend diameters for a type 2 coating are for no rusting at the outside of the bend after one year of exposure to a mild industrial atmosphere.

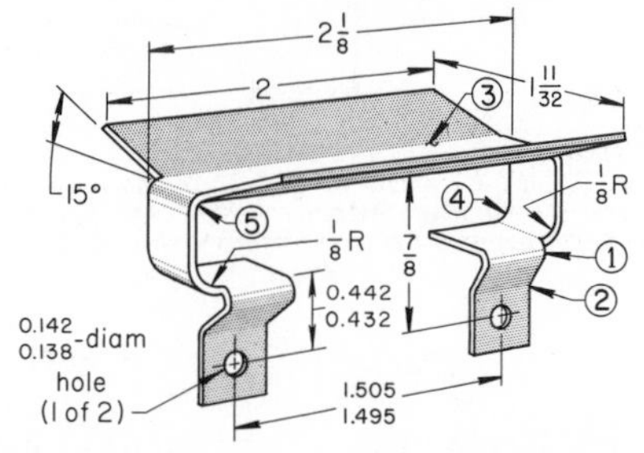

Bends were made (in pairs, simultaneously) in the sequence indicated by the circled numbers in the illustration. Inside radius of bends was ¹⁄₃₂ in., except for the ⅛-in. radii shown.

Fig. 1. Gas-burner flange that was formed from aluminum-coated steel to close tolerance on the location and spacing of holes (Example 207)

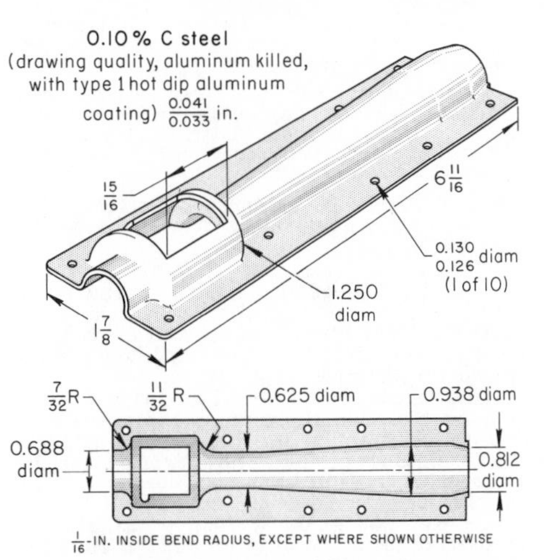

Fig. 2. Gas-burner body half that was produced from aluminum-coated steel for corrosion resistance. The aluminum coating served also as a carrier for the forming lubricant. (Example 208)

rectangular slot and ten 0.128-in.-diam holes in another die.

The forming and trimming punches and dies were made of O1 tool steel hardened to Rockwell C 59 to 60. Commercial punches and die buttons of high speed tool steel were used for the 0.128-in.-diam holes. Die life was 80,000 pieces per grind of the cutoff edge of the trimming punch, and the forming punch and die were used for 120,000 pieces before being reconditioned.

Less work was needed to recondition the forming tools than had been required when the part had been made from uncoated steel. Also, less difficulty was encountered in making the draws than with uncoated steel.

The production rate was 1800 pieces per hour for lots of 20,000 pieces.

Tin-Coated and Terne-Coated Steel

Nearly all of the common forming methods are used on tin-coated and terne-coated low-carbon steel. Spinning is not ordinarily done on these materials, because of the likelihood of excessively thinning the coatings or of fusing the coatings.

More than 95% of the steel sheet and strip that is coated with tin at the mill has an electroplated coating of tin; the remainder has a hot dip coating. The properties of these products are determined by the requirements for their use in the canning industry, and are described in Volume 1 of this Handbook, pages 1133 to 1141.

The amount of tin on electroplated mill products ordinarily ranges from 0.25 to 1.5 lb per base box (31,360 sq in. of sheet), corresponding to a coating thickness per surface of 15 to 90 micro-in. Hot dip products have coating weights of 1.10 to about 2.5 lb per base box (66 to 150 micro-in. of thickness per surface).

Terne-coated steel products are hot dip coated with a lead-tin alloy that contains 10 to 25% by weight of tin. Terne coatings range from the thinnest coating that gives complete coverage of the steel to about 8 lb per double base box (about 40 to 170 micro-in. of thickness per surface).

The steel to which tin and terne coatings are applied varies in composition for different products and among different manufacturers, but is generally similar to 1008 or 1010.

Effect of Coating on Formability. The thin, ductile layer of pure tin (or lead-tin alloy) increases die life and reduces lubrication requirements in forming, as do zinc and aluminum coatings. However, in contrast to hot dip zinc and aluminum coatings, the tin and lead-tin coatings have too thin an alloy layer to reduce the formability of the steel base noticeably. Thus, in general, the formability of steel with a tin or terne coating is the same as that of the base steel.

The formability of electrolytic tin-coated sheets and long terne sheets is related to the quality designation of the steel. Commercial quality sheets are suitable for moderate deformation and can be bent flat on themselves in any direction without fracture of the base steel or the coating. Drawing quality, drawing quality special-killed, and, less frequently, physical quality sheets are used to meet specific deep drawing and severe forming requirements.

Tin mill products (electrolytic and hot dip tin plate and short terneplate), which are not produced to the above quality designations, are rated for formability on the basis of temper designation and hardness, as summarized in Table 6. The temper designations in the table apply only to box-annealed material, but the relation of forming characteristics to hardness is generally applicable.

Deep Drawing. A tin coating on steel produces a substantial improvement in drawability of the base material. Data on effect of thickness of tin coating are given in the Appendix to this article.

Applications. Tin plate containers for various items are made at high speed by blanking, forming, rolling, lockseaming and crimping. Other applications for which tin plate is formed include household utensils and appliances, commercial baking pans, automotive parts, toys, and hardware.

The behavior of terneplate in forming is generally the same as that of tin plate. Although terneplate, because of its high lead content, is toxic and not suitable for food containers, it is formed into containers for gasoline and paint. Because of its excellent resistance to atmospheric corrosion and its low cost, terneplate is used in formed products such as roofing, door frames and automotive parts.

The forming of tin plate is described in the following two examples. In the first example, the use of material on which the matte as-plated coating had not been "flow brightened" at the mill (see "Surface Effects" on page 1134 in Volume 1 of this Handbook) assisted in the deep drawing of an automotive part. In the second example, selection of base steel to permit sharp corners and tight 180° bends was critical, and no forming lubricant was needed.

Example 209. Deep Drawing a Rocker-Arm Cover From Tin Plate (Fig. 3)

The rocker-arm cover shown in Fig. 3 was made from coiled tin-coated steel strip.

The tin coating, which had not been flow brightened, served as a carrier for a dry drawing lubricant containing a borax compound. Also, it helped to prevent corrosion when baffles were spot welded to the inside of the cover during a secondary piercing operation, and while the cover was transported to another plant for painting.

Localized buildup of lubricant in the die or on the strip stock caused some minor problems. However, the lubricant was easily removed with a minimum of delay.

The part was drawn in an 800-ton press operating at 600 strokes per hour. Stock feed was from a coil at the right side of the press. The sequence of operations was as follows:

1 Crimp strip to provide stock for drawing.
2 Draw.
3 Redraw to form contour of top and indentations on sides.
4 Pierce five holes.
5 Form flange around hole and recess for gasket.
6 Cut off and drop through to a chute out the front of the press.

An average of 80,000 pieces was produced between resharpenings of the cutting and forming tools. Annual production was about two million pieces.

Making this part from uncoated steel instead of tin plate would have required the use of a heavy pigmented drawing compound.

Example 210. Forming of Folded-End Commercial Baking Pans From Electrolytic Tin Plate (Fig. 4)

Material and forming requirements were critical for the commercial baking pan shown in Fig. 4(a).

The 180° bends and sharp corners had to be made without cracking the material, while maintaining adequate hardness and wall strength. The work metal was 0.022-in.-thick (195-lb) electrolytic tin plate with a 1.5-lb tin coating; the steel base for the closely controlled tin plate was type MC-T4 (see Table 6 in this article, and Table 1 on page 1133 in Volume 1 of this Handbook), and was specified to be suitable for the end-use requirements. Because of the natural lubricity of the tin coating, no lubricant was needed for the forming operation.

The pan was made by folding rather than by deep drawing, because production runs included pans of different dimensions and construction details. These variations could be handled quickly and economically with adjustable dies and interchangeable wood punches capped with ¼-in.-thick D2 tool steel.

Table 6. Suitability of Tin Mill Products (Electrolytic and Hot Dip Tin Plate and Short Terneplate) for Forming

Temper designation(a)	Approximate Rockwell 30-T hardness(b)	Suitable forming operations
T1	46 to 52	Deep drawing
T2	50 to 56	Moderate drawing where some stiffness is required
T3	54 to 60	Shallow drawing, with fair degree of stiffness to minimize fluting
T4	58 to 64	Noncritical shallow drawing; bending to radius of ½t min
T5	62 to 68	Mild forming; bending to radius of 1t to 2t
T6	67 to 73	Very mild forming, and bending to large radii

(a) Applies only to box-annealed material. (b) Material thinner than about 0.008 in. or 75 lb per base box is normally tested using the Rockwell 15-T scale and the results are converted to the Rockwell 30-T scale.

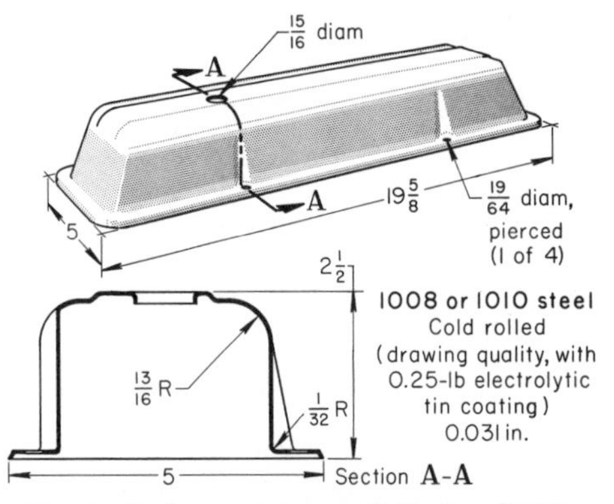

Fig. 3. Rocker-arm cover that was drawn from tin-coated steel. The tin coating served also as a carrier for the drawing lubricant. (Example 209)

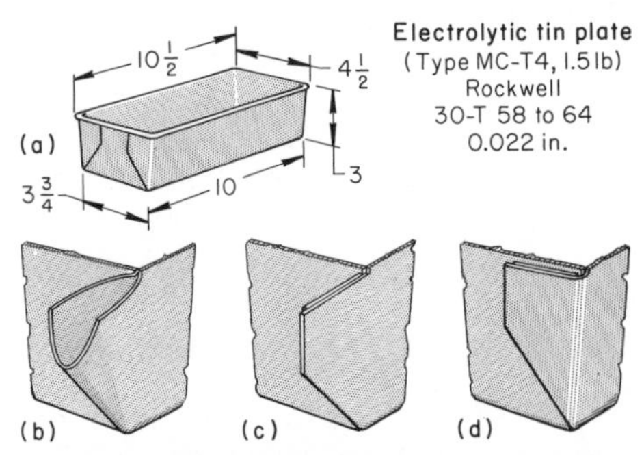

(a) Completed pan. (b) Pan corner after flaps were loosely folded in a wing die. (c) Pan corner after folds were flattened in a cam-actuated die. (d) Pan corner after flaps were folded tight against end.

Fig. 4. Stages in production of a folded-end pan from tin plate (Example 210)

Producing the same variety of pans by deep drawing would have required a large inventory of costly draw dies.

Notched flat blanks first were folded in a wing die to the form shown in Fig. 4(b). The loops of metal at the corners then were flattened into end flaps (Fig. 4c) by a cam die. Maximum permissible thickness of the flaps was twice the metal thickness plus 0.010 in. In another cam die, the flaps were folded tightly against the ends of the pan (Fig. 4d). The resulting pan end had to be folded tightly enough to allow projection welding of support strapping to the three layers of the folded end.

The inside radius around the bottom of the pans typically was 3⁄16 in. In a final cornering restrike, the space between ends and sidewalls inside the pans was reduced to 0.010 in. or less. The partly formed curl at the top of the pan was wrapped around a 5⁄32-in. wire to complete the pan.

Production rate was 600 to 800 pans per hour, and yearly quantities ranged from 200 to 10,000 pans of any one type.

Example 189 in the article "Press Forming of Low-Carbon Steel" describes a method for forming rectangular frames from electrolytic tin plate.

Nickel-Plated and Chromium-Plated Steel

Press forming and roll forming are done on steel that has been electroplated in the coil with decorative copper-nickel or copper-nickel-chromium.

Conventional lubricants may be used in press forming of this material, particularly in high-volume production. Sometimes, however, no lubricant is used in making decorative parts. Instead, surface contact between the work metal and tools is prevented by the use of strippable plastic coatings or adhesive-backed paper on the work metal, or of loose paper between the work metal and the punch or the die. These materials protect the decorative finish on the preplated steel, prevent galling, and provide a controlled amount of friction for forming; and they can be removed from the completed parts without harming the finish.

Polished die surfaces, or dies or die inserts made of rubber or plastic, also protect parts during forming. Coated blanks or parts may be interleaved with paper, cardboard or plastic sheet material, or may be placed in containers with separate compartments made of wood, to protect the decorative surfaces from damage during storage or handling between forming operations.

Conventional lubricants are used in roll forming. Volatile materials that evaporate completely may be used where cleaning after forming presents problems. Mineral seal oil is preferred in some applications, because it leaves only a light residue that may not require removal.

Standard Products. The steel base for these decorative preplated materials usually is 1008 or 1010 cold rolled steel. For forming applications in which there is only mild or moderate deformation, rimmed steel is used. In applications where strain lines or aging presents a problem, aluminum-killed steel is used. Where the utmost in severity of deformation is encountered, drawing quality steel may be needed, although its use entails some sacrifice in surface finish in the formed areas.

Stock thickness usually is from 0.008 to 0.050 in. for coils, and up to 0.062

in. for cut sheets. Number 4 temper is used most frequently. One manufacturer of preplated strip specifies a hardness of Rockwell 30-T 50 to 60 on the raw material. Harder tempers, up to No. 1 (hard), can be used to meet special requirements. (See the description of bendability of AISI standard strip tempers in Fig. 1 of the article "Press Bending of Low-Carbon Steel", on page 89 in this volume.)

Finish requirements on the steel base vary with the application. Strip usually has a No. 3 or No. 2 finish; sheet, a bright or luster finish (see Table 2 in the article "Press Forming of Low-Carbon Steel", page 117).

Ordinarily, copper plating thickness and nickel plating thickness are 0.1 to 0.3 mil each, and the chromium plating is 3 to 10 micro-in. thick. A nickel deposit thicker than 0.3 mil gives greater corrosion resistance, but usually cannot be produced on coil stock.

Plating conditions are controlled to give a ductile deposit with minimum stress. The copper is buffed, and the nickel is buffed or given a satin finish.

Formability. The ductility of the plated steel may be different from that of the unplated coil stock, depending on the metal or metals deposited, plating bath and plating conditions, and the effects of aging or buffing. It may also be affected to some extent by work hardening from the extra coiling and uncoiling of stock during plating.

Ordinarily, the plating procedure is selected and controlled to yield ductile electrodeposits and a plated product that (after buffing or aging for several days) has formability at least as good as the unplated raw material. Formability of this quality is obtained with buffed, ductile electrodeposits of copper or nickel, or a composite of the two, up to a total plating thickness of 0.0025 in., with the normal bright chromium plate over these. Ductility is reduced by the use of nonductile electrodeposits from bright or contaminated plating baths, or by the use of unfavorable plating conditions in depositing a heavier-than-normal chromium coating.

Dynamic ductility measurements (ASTM B69) have been used by one manufacturer in studying the formability of plated low-carbon steel and in routine control of production of decorative preplated coil stock. This is a cupping test, done with a ⅞-in.-diam ball at 85 to 90 strokes per minute to simulate the speed of deformation of press operations.

The severity of forming permitted usually is limited, not by ability to deform the preplated stock without cracking or rupturing, but by the need to avoid objectionable visible roughening of the plating or lowering of corrosion resistance in the regions of severe deformation.

Average bend radii for nickel-plated or chromium-plated steel (No. 4 temper) recommended by one manufacturer of preplated coiled steel strip are given below, for various thicknesses of steel (t = stock thickness):

Steel	Bend radius
Steel up to 0.018 in. thick	2t
0.019 to 0.024 in.	3t
0.025 to 0.031 in.	4t
0.032 to 0.044 in.	5t
0.045 to 0.062 in.	6t

Bends to smaller radii are acceptable in some applications, depending on requirements for corrosion resistance and appearance. If a bend is not satisfactory on a given part, the local corrosion resistance can sometimes be improved by increasing the thickness of the nickel plating, thus avoiding the need to modify tools. The use of thinner stock sometimes has the same effect.

Examples of Application. The forming operations described in the following two examples illustrate the use of paper and plastic coatings in forming decorative chromium-plated steel. For both applications, aluminum-killed steel was selected, to prevent the formation of stretcher strains. The workpiece in the first example was formed with a sharp bend radius; the bend radii on the workpiece in the second example were larger than the recommended radii. The exceptionally close tolerances needed in the blanking and piercing operations in these two examples caused lower die life.

Example 211. Forming a Broiler Top From Decorative Chromium-Preplated Steel, Using Plastic and Paper for Surface Protection (Fig. 5)

The broiler top shown in Fig. 5 was made in three separate mechanical-press operations from preplated steel. The base metal was cold rolled, No. 4 temper, aluminum-killed 1008 or 1010 steel strip, 0.025 in. thick and 12.75 in. wide, in coils. The steel had a satin-finish copper-nickel-chromium plate on the face side and a buffed copper-nickel plate on the reverse side. The face side of the stock was protected against damage by a 0.0005-in.-thick strippable plastic film, which was blown off with compressed air after the part was made. The reverse side was protected with a loose sheet of 40-lb kraft paper, which was removed after the first operation. The flange, which was bent with a sharp radius around the outer edges (see Fig. 5), was therefore protected only by the thin layer of strippable plastic film. The sequence of operations in producing the broiler top was:

1 Cut off from coil and draw recess.
2 Blank, and pierce seven 0.156-in.-diam holes.
3 Form 90° flange.

Annual production was about 100,000 pieces, in 10 to 15 runs.

The first operation was done with a compound die in a 125-ton single-action press equipped with a spring-loaded die cushion. Production rate was 150 to 200 pieces per hour, using D2 tool steel dies that had an average life of about 25,000 pieces between sharpenings.

Instead of using a lubricant, 40-lb kraft paper was placed between the part and the punch, and was removed after the first operation. Various drawing lubricants, including compounds based on molybdenum disulfide, had been tried in this drawing operation, but none consistently prevented galling on the nickel-plated side of the stock (paraffin wax came closest to being acceptable). An additional drawback to the use of lubricants was the need to remove them after forming.

The second operation, blanking and piercing, was done with a compound die in a 30-ton (or 75-ton) single-action press. Production rate was 300 to 400 pieces per hour, using D5 tool steel dies that made 4000 to 6000 pieces per sharpening. (The D2 dies had needed resharpening after 1500 to 2500 pieces.)

Total clearance on the blank-and-pierce dies was held at 0.001 to 0.002 in. to prevent the formation of burrs, which are usually larger for nickel or nickel-chromium plated steel than for bare steel. Burrs would lead to galling or to elongation of pierced holes during flanging; also, burrs were unacceptable on exposed edges of the part.

In the final operation, a 5/16-in.-wide 90° flange was formed (sharp bend) around the outside of the part, using a 30-ton single-action press. Production rate was 300 to 400 pieces per hour, using O1 or A2 tool steel dies, which had an indefinite life. (At a slower press speed, control of the operation would be less critical and the rejection rate lower, but production rate would then be lower and the cost per piece higher.)

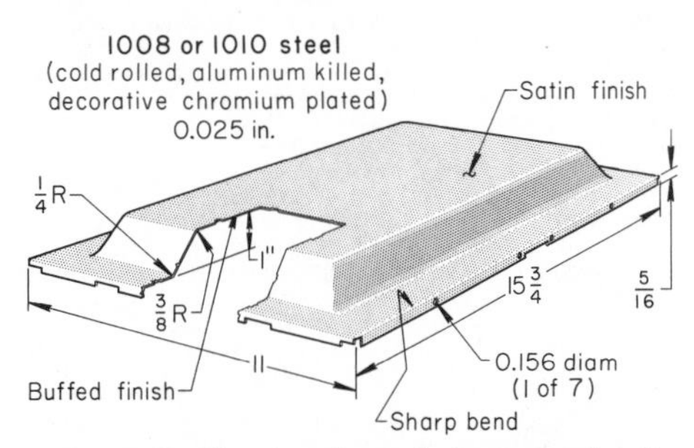

Fig. 5. Broiler top formed from preplated steel, with the use of a thin strippable plastic film and a loose sheet of paper for protection of plated surfaces (Example 211)

Example 212. Forming a Hotplate Top From Decorative Chromium-Preplated Steel Coated on the Face Side With Low-Tack Adhesive Paper (Fig. 6)

The hotplate top shown in Fig. 6 was made in five separate mechanical-press operations from preplated 0.030-by-16-in. cold rolled, aluminum-killed, No. 4 temper, 1008 or 1010 steel strip. The steel had copper-nickel-chromium plating on both sides, with a satin finish on the face side only. The face side was coated with low-tack adhesive paper to protect it against damage to the finish and to aid in drawing; the paper was peeled off after the part was completed. The forming radii were larger than the 4t recommended for material 0.030 in. thick (see the table above, under "Formability").

The sequence of operations is given in the table with Fig. 6, together with press and production-rate data. Annual production was about 100,000 pieces, in 10 to 15 runs. Dies were made of D2 tool steel, with the cavities in the draw dies hard chromium plated. Expected die life before sharpening was in

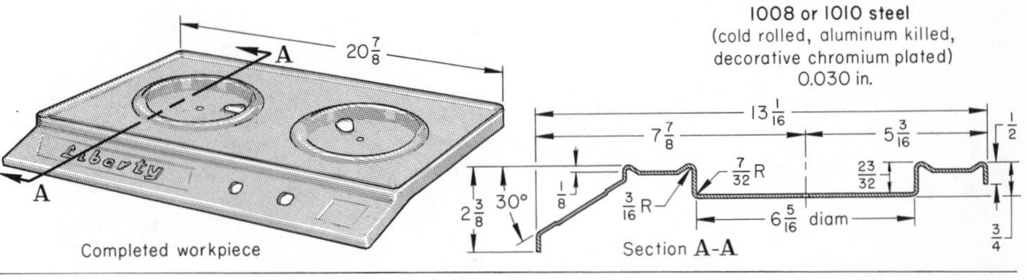

Operation	Press cap'y, tons(a)	Air-cushion pressure, psi	Production, pcs/hr
1 Cutoff; first draw	125	65	200
2 Second draw; flange	150	65-75	250
3 Trim	100	None	300
4 Wipe down	150	55	300
5 Pierce	100	None	300

(a) Mechanical single-action press

Fig. 6. Hotplate top that was formed from decorative chromium-plated steel coated on the face side with low-tack adhesive paper (Example 212)

excess of 200,000 pieces, except for the blanking (trimming) and the piercing dies, which produced only 1500 to 2500 pieces between sharpenings. Because of the increased die life obtainable with D5 tool steel (see Example 211), replacement dies were to be made of D5.

In the first operation, two 6 5/16-in.-diam recesses near the center of the part were drawn to a 23/32-in. depth, with punch and draw radii of about 3/8 in., and the front edge was formed down at a 30° angle to a depth of 2 3/8 in. In the second operation, the radii of the drawn recesses were reduced to 7/32 in., a rounded 1/2-in. flange was formed all around the part, and the upper flat portion was recessed, leaving a 1/8-in.-high lip on all sides and around the 6 5/16-in.-diam recesses. After trimming and piercing the rounded triangular openings in the recesses (third operation), the rounded flange was wiped down to make it vertical and reduce the radius to 3/16 in. (fourth operation). In the final operation, the rounded triangular holes were flanged, the angled front panel was embossed, and the holes in the front panel were pierced.

A number of problems were encountered in the drawing operations. Stretcher strains, which were observed when using rimmed steel, were eliminated by changing to aluminum-killed steel. Adjustment of air-cushion pressure kept the incidence of wrinkling down to an acceptable level. Galling, however, was never eliminated, because any lubricant that performed satisfactorily attacked the adhesive on the paper. The adhesiveness of the paper had to be closely controlled, as wrinkles were produced when the adhesion was low.

Example 102 in "Press Bending of Low-Carbon Steel" describes a bending operation (0.010-in. strip, 1/64-in. bend radius) in making a retaining clip from steel plated with decorative chromium.

Painted and Plastic-Coated Steel

Steel that is painted or plastic coated in the coil is formed by the commonly used press and roll methods, using the same equipment as for uncoated stock. The thickness of the steel base usually is 0.010 to 0.062 in., but it may be 0.008 in. (or less) to 0.075 in.

The same tools as are used on uncoated steel usually can be used for painted or plastic-coated steel. However, die materials lower in strength, shock resistance, and wear resistance than those generally used in forming uncoated steel are satisfactory in many applications. Dies may have inserts of rubber or plastic to help protect the coating during forming.

Because organic coatings generally provide a less abrasive surface than bare steel, they promote long tool life. This effect varies with the composition of the coating. The abrasiveness of an organic coating increases with decreasing gloss, varying in direct proportion to the amount of flatting agents present in the coating. Reducing gloss 5% in the low-gloss range (as from 20 to 15%) by increasing the content of flatting agent causes an observable shortening of tool life. In the high-gloss range, a much larger addition of flatting agent is needed to shorten tool life.

To avoid scoring or marring the organic coatings, die surfaces must be highly polished and workpieces must be handled with care. For forming metals that have coatings only a few tenths of a mil thick, little or no increase in clearance is needed. However, the resilience and compressibility of the thicker dispersion coatings and vinyl-film laminates must be taken into consideration in the design of tooling, to insure that dimensional tolerances are maintained during forming.

Table 7. Forming Characteristics of Sheet Steel Precoated With Organic Coatings(a)
(E = Excellent; G = Good; F = Fair)

Type of coating (and thickness, mils)	Adhesion of coating	Minimum radius of 180° bend(b)	Suitability for severe forming or drawing
Paints, Solution			
Alkyd-amino (0.1 to 1.2)	G	3t	F
Vinyl-alkyd (0.1 to 1.2)	G	2t	F
Silicone-polyester (0.7 to 1.2)	G	2t to 3t	F
Acrylic, thermoset (0.9 to 1.2)	E	1t to 3t	F-G(c) (d)
Epoxy, solution (0.1 to 1.0)	E	0t	E
Epoxy, ester (0.1 to 1.0)	E	0t	E
Polyester (0.1 to 1.2)	G	2t	G
Vinyl, solution (0.1 to 1.2)	E	0t	E
Paints, Dispersion			
Vinyl, organosol (0.7 to 4.0)	E	0t	E
Vinyl, plastisol (4.0 to 20.0)	E	0t	E(e)
Polyvinyl fluoride (0.5 to 2.0)	G	0t	G
Polyvinylidene fluoride (0.5 to 2.0)	G	0t	G
Plastics, Laminated			
Polyvinyl fluoride (1.5 to 2.0)	G	1/8 in.	G(f)
Polyvinyl chloride (4.0 to 25.0)	E	0t	E(g)
Polyester (0.5 to 14.0)	F	0t	F(c) (h)
Fluorocarbon, TFE (1.0 to 20.0)	G	0t	E(j)
Acrylic (3.0 to 6.0)	G	0t	G

(a) For coil stock of steel, hot dip or electrolytic zinc-coated or tin-coated steel, and hot dip aluminum-coated steel. Applies also to aluminum, copper and brass. For tin-coated steel, the ratings apply only for epoxy coatings; other coatings have lower ratings. For copper and brass, the ratings apply only when primers based on epoxy or phenolic resins are used. Data are based on the use of suitable chemical conversion treatments and suitable primers; results may vary for different base metals. Chemical conversion treatment and primer improve results with most coating-metal combinations. (b) t = thickness of sheet. (c) Results are greatly affected by coating thickness.
(d) Coating of medium thickness is good for deep drawing. (e) Coating can bridge cracks produced in the metal by severe forming; compressibility of the coating must be considered in forming to close tolerances. (f) Results are greatly affected by type and thickness of basis metal. (g) Bond may be destroyed in extreme draws or sharp bends. (h) Bond strength may be seriously reduced after slight deformation. (j) Particularly susceptible to damage by scoring of coating during forming.
(Data are adapted from information compiled by the Technical Committee on the National Coil Coaters Association.)

Lubricants and Handling. Lubricants must be selected so as to avoid affecting the appearance or properties of the coating, and so that they can be removed readily without damaging the coating. Adhesive-backed paper or strippable plastic films sometimes are used in place of or in conjunction with a lubricant.

Coated stock may be interleaved with paper, cardboard or plastic sheet material or placed in containers with separate compartments made of wood, to protect the coating from damage during storage or handling.

Formability of organic-coated metals generally is limited to a severity that will not mar or damage the appearance of the coating, reduce its protective value, or impair its adhesion (although some coatings are flexible enough to withstand deformation that fractures the underlying metal). The effect of the coating on formability, tooling and forming procedure depends primarily on the type and thickness of the coating and the pretreatment of the base metal.

Table 7 lists a number of types of organic coatings and gives the normal thickness range and adhesion rating for each coating, plus the minimum bend radius and formability rating for the coated sheet metal.

The ranges of coating thickness shown in Table 7 represent the extreme limits that are technically feasible; most production coatings have much narrower limits of thickness. Primer thickness is not included in the values for coating thickness.

Surface condition of the metal base can influence the permissible severity of forming, particularly with thin (about 1 mil) coatings. Highly polished metal surfaces give a more uniform distribution of the surface stresses induced by tools during forming. This more effectively preserves the appearance and texture of the coating and would allow greater severity of deformation if it were not counteracted by the generation of heat over the entire surface of the coating that is in contact with the forming die.

A metal base with a relatively coarse surface finish subjects the high points of the coating (which for thin coatings are a reproduction of those of the metal beneath) to higher stresses and greater wear during forming. However, the smaller area of contact results in generation of less heat from friction.

Adhesion and Flexibility. The adhesion of commonly used coatings is rated in Table 7. The minimum bend radii and formability ratings in Table 7 are a measure of the combined effect of coating adhesion and flexibility. Vinyl plastisol coatings have such outstanding flexibility that they can bridge cracks produced in the metal base by severe forming.

To provide the adhesion generally required for forming, chemical conversion coatings, selected for the metal surface to be painted or plastic coated, are applied to coil stock or blanks by spray or immersion treatment, and this treatment is usually followed by the application of a prime coat compatible with the final coating material. Bare steel is given an iron phosphate coating, 35 to 45 mg per sq ft (specification TT-C-490, type II). Zinc-coated steel receives a zinc phosphate coating, 150 to 250 mg per sq ft on hot dip coatings and 100 to 175 mg per sq ft on electroplated coatings (specification TT-C-490, type I). Aluminum-coated steel is treated with a chromate coating, 20 to 25 mg per sq ft (specification MIL-C-5541-A). (These coating weights refer to area of stock and must be doubled when treatment of both sides of the stock is considered.) Conversion coating processes are discussed in Volume 2 of this Handbook, on pages 531 to 547.

Organic coatings applied to untreated and unprimed metal surfaces have better flexibility than those applied to pretreated surfaces. However, without pretreatment or use of a suitable primer, the degree of adhesion necessary to withstand forming forces or to have adequate service life and corrosion resistance usually cannot be assured. As stated in footnote (a) to Table 7, forming characteristics are generally improved by the use of a primer. An exception is tin-coated steel.

The thicker films of organosols, plastisols, and vinyl-film laminates have better flexibility than films of solution coatings in the 1-mil dry-film range. Because of their greater thickness, the reduction in thickness from elongation in bending is a smaller percentage than for the thinner films of solution coatings. The stress of forming is absorbed within the thicker films, and is not transferred to the interface with the metal, at which adhesion is established.

Solution coatings, because of increasing film strength, have less flexibility and adhesion near the upper thickness limit. The most severe forming can be done near the lower thickness limit, but such thin coatings may not fulfill service requirements. Although solution coatings of silicone-polyesters and thermosetting acrylics can be applied as thin as 0.1 mil, as exterior coatings they are used almost exclusively in the heavier thicknesses shown in Table 7. Laminated plastic coatings may show excessive film strength and hence less flexibility and adhesion at the upper end of the thickness range, and low tensile strength at the lower end.

The color and gloss of an organic coating also affect coating flexibility, which decreases with increased pigment loading.

Hardness of coatings is in the range of HB to 3H pencil hardness for most of the commonly used paints and about Durometer A 85 to 90 for plastisol coatings and laminated plastics. Softer coatings are more likely to be damaged by scoring in the forming die. Die pressure transmitted through an organic coating to the interface can destroy adhesion. In heavy films and vinyl-film laminates, the elastic, compressible finish coating normally yields under die pressure, but the relatively brittle adhesive primer layer may be damaged by localized high die pressure.

Shearing, Blanking and Piercing. Sharpness of cutting tools and direction and speed of cut affect the performance of coatings in the cut area. Dull cutting tools or high impact speeds cause high-energy impact on the coating surface and may shatter the bond in the surrounding areas, particularly in coatings of borderline adhesion strength. Flaking or lifting of the coating may result. In cutting operations, the cut edge is bent in the direction of the blade motion, and coatings with "memory" (tendency to return to original shape) may return to the flattened position, separating from the steel base. When the metal is cut so that the finish coat is on the burr side of the blank, the "memory" effect is eliminated, and the burr protects the adhesion of the coating at the cut edge by reducing access to the interface.

Bending. Minimum bend radii for organic-coated metals are given in Table 7. Slow bending will prevent breakage of the coating more effectively than rapid bending. When bending with contour forming rolls, the finish of the organic coating will be preserved, and less stress will be imposed on the steel base if the radii are bent over several rolls instead of one or two rolls.

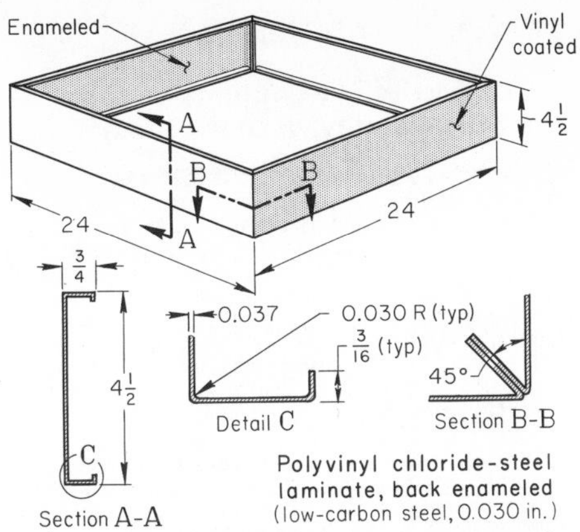

Fig. 7. Lighting fixture that was formed from a polyvinyl chloride – steel laminate (Example 213)

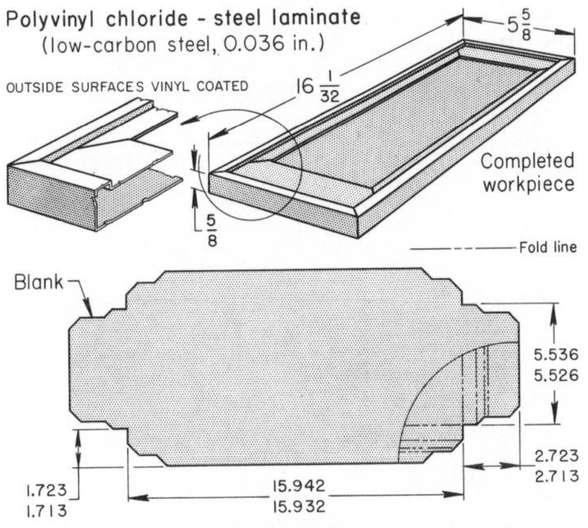

Fig. 8. Blank development, and completed drawer front that was press-brake formed from a polyvinyl chloride – steel laminate (Example 214)

Bending short flanges close to a cut edge or where the coating is scored by the bending tool at the peak of the bend can cause the coating to lift off the steel base. In both cases, the cohesive strength of the film has been weakened and coatings with high film strength will attempt to return to the shape in which they were applied.

Deep Drawing. Suitability of the organic-coated metals for deep drawing (or severe forming) is rated in Table 7. The effect of speed of drawing or forming is generally the same as that described for bending.

The more steps used, the more severely a part can be drawn or formed without damaging the organic coating. However, the ductility and work-hardening behavior of the steel, as well as the flexibility of the coating system, must be considered in the design of a forming or drawing die.

Forming Temperature. Depending on the effect of temperature on the properties of the organic coating, heating up to 120 F before forming will reduce the likelihood of coating fracture. Some coatings, such as silicone-polyester coatings with a high silicone content, can be formed at a temperature as high as 150 F.

Overheating must be avoided. Organic coatings, especially the thermosetting types, can be softened enough to make them subject to surface damage from die action and handling.

Heating can be done with infrared radiant heaters, hot air, or an open gas flame, or by storing the coiled stock in a heated room until fabrication.

Examples of Application. Of the three examples that follow, the first two deal with the forming of plastic-steel laminate, and the third deals with the forming of prepainted steel. In the first example, the use of unhardened carbon steel dies fitted with plastic inserts is described, and insert materials are compared. Precision location in bending an accurately cut developed blank was needed in making the more complex shape of the drawer front described in the second example.

Example 213. Forming a Lighting Fixture From a Polyvinyl Chloride – Steel Laminate (Fig. 7)

The four-piece fluorescent lighting fixture shown in Fig. 7 was formed from a polyvinyl chloride – steel laminate. The work metal was 0.030-in.-thick low-carbon steel with a 0.005-in.-thick walnut-grain vinyl coating on the face, and a 0.002-in.-thick coat of synthetic enamel on the back, making a total thickness of 0.037 in. The laminate was purchased in a coil slit to the prescribed width.

The stock was uncoiled and passed through straightening rolls, and then blanks were sheared to length. Forming was done in a press brake with an 8-ft-long bed.

In the first operation, the corners were notched and holes (not shown in Fig. 7) were pierced, using universal tools. In subsequent press-brake operations, the part was bent into a shallow channel with narrow inside flanges, and the ends of the channel were bent at right angles. Then the ends were bent to make 45° bends (see section B-B in Fig. 7), in a 30 or 40-ton open-back inclinable press. The inside bend radius was equal to stock thickness. No lubricant was used.

The square frame was assembled by bending metal tabs to lock the four pieces together, the tabs being concealed in the assembly.

Production rates for the various operations were as high as 200 pieces per hour, in lots of 2000 assemblies. Extreme care was used to prevent scratches and other defects.

The forming tools were made of 1045 carbon steel and were not heat treated. Since the steel tools would scratch the painted surface and cause some damage to the vinyl coating, nylon inserts were added to the tools. Some defects were caused by the nylon, and a hard rubber was substituted. The rubber outlasted nylon in resisting fatigue, and did less damage to the surfaces of the workpiece. The rubber inserts had a life of 50,000 or more pieces.

Example 214. Press-Brake Forming of Polyvinyl Chloride – Steel Laminate (Fig. 8)

The drawer front shown in Fig. 8 was formed from plastic-coated low-carbon steel 0.036 in. thick. The 10-mil-thick polyvinyl chloride coating on the outside surface of the part was either white or wood grained. Corners and joints could not be welded to correct any misfits, so the pattern for the blank was developed with extra care, and the blank dimensions were held to ±0.005 in. (Fig. 8).

The same care was used in locating the workpiece for bending in the press brake. The more accurately it was positioned, the better the corner joints closed. The slightly recessed return surface on the back of the panel was designed to receive a plain backing panel, which was fastened into the recess with sheet-metal screws (the pierced holes for which are not shown in Fig. 8).

Inside bend radii for the 16 bends on the drawer front were held at 0.015 in. to assure close-fitting corners. No loss of adhesion occurred, even in the inside bends along the sides, where the flanges were very narrow. At 10 strokes per minute, the production rate was 33 pieces per hour, making a lot of about 400 pieces every six months.

No lubricant was used in forming the drawer front from the vinyl-coated steel, but a water-base wax-type lubricant was applied to piercing and notching dies. [No forming lubricant would be needed in making similar parts from such alternative materials as uncoated steel (to be painted later) or uncoated stainless steel. Uncoated steel would require the same lubrication of the piercing and notching dies, whereas a heavy-duty sulfurized oil would be used in piercing and notching stainless.]

The design and surface finish of tools and the selection of handling procedures and equipment are important in forming organic-coated metals. Depending on the accuracy requirements and the coating thickness, allowance may have to be made for the coating thickness in dimensioning the forming tools. When accuracy requirements and coating thicknesses permit, the same dies can often be used for painted and plated metals.

The small clip in Example 102 in the article "Press Bending of Low-Carbon Steel" was made of nickel-plated and chromium-plated steel, and of prepainted steel, using the same dies.

To prevent scratching and scoring of prepainted surfaces, the die surfaces must be polished and sharp corners rounded off. Also, damage during ejection and subsequent handling of the parts must be prevented. In the following example, marring of prepainted workpiece surfaces was avoided both during and after forming operations.

Example 215. Preventing Damage to Painted Surfaces in Forming Prepainted Steel

Three prepainted steel parts were used in the assembly of a fluorescent lighting fixture. All the parts were made of low-carbon steel that had a finish coat of white enamel on one side and a thin (wash) coat on the other. Preventing scratching of parts during ejection from the press and in handling between operations was the greatest problem. Special containers were used to separate the parts.

The 4-ft-long by 2¾-in.-wide by 0.036-in.-thick channel that was the base of the fixture was formed with standard tools in a press brake to a depth of 1⅞ in., with an inside bend radius of 0.080 in. The tools were polished to prevent damage to the paint coatings.

In press forming the other two parts of the fixture, the dies, originally made to form uncoated steel, were used without change, except for honing and polishing the surfaces and rounding and polishing the sharp corners.

The first of the two press-formed parts, the bracket for the fluorescent-tube receptacle, was a shallow box with an open end and a half-round closed end. Bend radii were 0.060 in. There were holes in the back for mounting to the channel base. This bracket was made in a five-station progressive die in a small open-back inclinable press. The dies were made of W1, W2, and air-hardening tool steel. The parts, made two at a time, were produced at the rate of 2000 per hour for a 500,000-piece lot, with no marring of the painted surfaces. No lubrication was used.

The canopy (which fits against the ceiling) was a shallow cup of uniform curvature, 5 in. in diameter and 1⅛ in. deep, drawn from prepainted steel 0.024 in. thick. It was drawn in one operation in a small press at the rate of 600 pieces per hour, in 50,000-piece lots, using tool steel dies without a lubricant. The trimming tools (shear and pinch trim) had to be sharp to minimize formation of burrs and thus prevent scratching the painted surface when the completed parts were nested.

Costs for the prepainted parts were much less than for bare steel parts painted after forming. Also, the paint acted as a lubricant and increased tool life substantially.

APPENDIX

Effect of Tin Coatings on the Drawability of Steel Sheet*

Mild steel sheet 0.028 in. thick was obtained in three grades: general-purpose, deep drawing, and extra deep drawing. Most of the experimental work was done on the latter two grades. The deep drawing steel had a hardness of Rockwell 30-T 56 with tensile strength of 47,000 psi and 40% elongation. The extra deep drawing steel had a hardness of Rockwell 30-T 53 with tensile strength of 43,000 psi and 40% elongation. Samples of the steels were tin plated, on either one or both faces, by electroplating in an alkaline sodium stannate bath after electrolytic degreasing and pickling in hydrochloric acid. The thicknesses of tin coating and weight per base box (total weight, both faces) were as follows:

3 micro-in. (0.05 lb per base box)
6 micro-in. (0.1 lb per base box)
16 micro-in. (0.25 lb per base box)
59 micro-in. (1.0 lb per base box).

Tension tests were repeated after plating, and it was found that the values for the deep drawing and extra deep drawing steels were not changed by the plating process.

*Digest of an article by R. Duckett, B. T. K. Barry and D. A. Robins (Tin Research Institute), *Sheet Metal Industries*, Sept 1968.

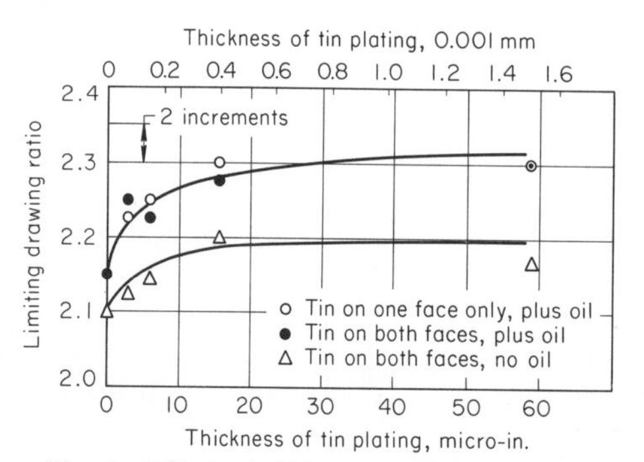

Fig. 9. Effect of thickness of tin coating on limiting drawing ratio (LDR) of steel sheet with and without lubrication

In addition to the electroplated samples, others were hot tinned by wiping. This produced a thicker but more variable coating with considerable iron-tin compound at the interface of the metals.

The effect of tin coating on drawability was determined by the Swift cupping test and an ironing test. Both tests were carried out on a Roell and Korthaus sheet-metal testing machine. The punch for the cupping test was 1.260 in. in diameter with a flat face and a corner radius of 0.177 in. The die was 1.361 in. in diameter with a corner radius of 0.358 in. The blankholder load was 900 lb, and the drawing speed was 5⁄16 in. per sec — the maximum speed available. The blank diameters were increased in increments of 1⁄32 in. for each series of tests.

Six tests were run for each diameter, and the limiting drawing ratio (LDR) was calculated for the largest disk diameter for which at least three of the six specimens passed the cupping test. The ironing tests used the same punch as the cupping test, but used a series of five dies with decreasing diameters. Each die reduced the wall thickness 10%, giving an over-all reduction in thickness of 50%. Three factors determined the drawability: scoring of the surface, failure of the metal, and the force required for the drawing operation.

Samples were tested with and without a lubricant. All disks were vapor degreased after machining. The lubricant used in all tests, unless otherwise stated, was that for the standard Swift test (TSD 996), which contains an extreme-pressure (EP) additive. (See the article "Assessment of the Drawing and Forming Qualities of Sheet Metal by the Swift Cup-Forming Test", by O. H. Kemmis, *Sheet Metal Industries*, **34**, 1957, p 203.) The lubricants that were tested in addition to the standard Swift lubricant were liquid paraffin, light machinery oil, and a viscous high-pressure oil.

To determine the distribution of tin on the surface of the cups after ironing 50%, a cup was machined into a series of rings, which were analyzed for tin.

The results of Swift cupping tests on lubricated deep drawing steel showed that the thinnest tin coating, 3 micro-in., produced a considerable increase in the limiting drawing ratio, and the increase was greater for the heavier coating thicknesses (Fig. 9). The thinner tin coatings gave improvements of 3 to 4 Swift increments (increments of

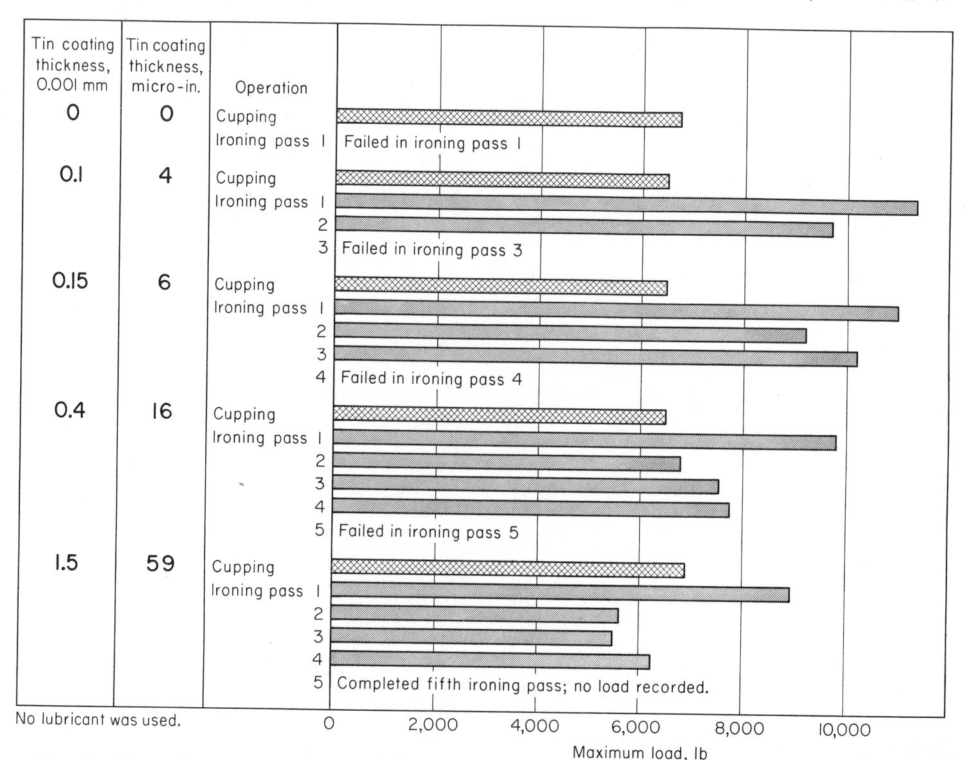

Fig. 10. Effect of thickness of tin coating on maximum load required for cupping and ironing of unlubricated steel sheet

LDR) over unplated steel, and this increased to 6 Swift increments for the heaviest coating (59 micro-in.).

Tests of unlubricated tin-coated sheet showed the same result, except to a lesser degree (Fig. 9). The LDR of unlubricated unplated steel was 2 Swift increments lower than for lubricated steel, and the increase for thin tin coatings was only 1 to 2 increments and 3 to 4 for the thicker coatings.

To determine whether the increase in drawability was dependent on the steel base, lubricated Swift tests were made for all three grades of steel. The general-purpose steel was variable, but similar in drawing quality to the deep drawing steel. With no tin coating, the drawability of the extra deep drawing steel was 2 Swift increments above that of the deep drawing grade. The presence of a tin coating on all three grades of steel produced a substantial improvement in drawability, provided the plated face was the face away from the punch.

The effect of tin coating on the two grades of steel was similar, and, for a given thickness of tin, the improved drawability of the extra deep drawing steel was maintained. The thinnest tin coating applied to deep drawing steel produced a higher LDR (2.225) than was obtained with extra deep drawing steel without a tin coating (which had a limiting drawing ratio of 2.20).

The limiting drawing ratio was determined also for deep drawing steel that had been hot tinned by wiping. The ratio was 2.325, compared to 2.15 for uncoated steel — an increase of 7 Swift increments. This increase was greater than that of the thickest electrodeposited coating. This is inconsistent, because the coating produced by hot tinning had an average thickness greater than the thickest electrolytic coating.

During hot tinning, a layer of intermetallic compound ($FeSn_2$) is formed at the iron-tin interface. To expose this compound layer, the unalloyed tin was selectively dissolved in a sodium plumbite solution and the limiting drawing ratio was determined. A value of 2.25 was obtained — 3 Swift increments lower than before removal of the free tin, but 4 increments higher than was obtained on uncoated deep drawing steel.

Swift tests of sheet lubricated with liquid paraffin, light machinery oil, or a viscous high-pressure oil did not produce differences in drawability for either plated or unplated steel when compared with tests in which the sheet was lubricated with the standard Swift oil.

To determine the effect of surface finish of the steel on the drawability, tests were made on the deep drawing steel after abrading the surface with emery paper. Even a relatively coarse surface produced by 180-grit paper had no measurable effect on the limiting drawing ratio for the uncoated steel.

Ironing of drawn cups of uncoated deep drawing steel, using the standard lubricant, produced scoring of the die and roughness on the ironed surface during the third step (30% reduction). This became progressively worse in the remaining dies. The steel coated with 16 micro-in. of tin did not score the dies, and the cup retained a good surface for all five steps. This was true also for the steel with a 59-micro-in. coating.

Since the test was not sufficiently severe, it was repeated without a lubricant (Fig. 10). Without tin or oil, the deep drawing steel fractured during the first ironing operation. With 4 micro-in. of tin, two ironing passes were completed, and fracture occurred on the third pass. Failure occurred in the fourth and fifth ironing passes for tin thicknesses of 6 and 16 micro-in., respectively. The thickest tin coating (59 micro-in.) completed all five ironing steps without failure. The forces required during the various stages were also progressively reduced with increasing tin thickness. After 50% total reduction in ironing, the tin coating had been reduced uniformly in thickness by 50%.

The severity of the ironing tests without a lubricant emphasized the beneficial effect of the tin coating, which made possible an operation that was otherwise impossible. The force required during the sequence of ironing passes showed a dependence on the thickness of tin coating (Fig. 10). For example, during the second ironing operation, the maximum load decreased from 9700 lb for the thinnest coating to 5600 lb for the thickest. Thus, in the absence of oil, tin coating acted as a lubricant. Whereas a tin coating acts as a lubricant on steel in the absence of oil, a tin coating with an oil film has an even more pronounced beneficial effect.

With the experimental arrangement used in these tests, it was not possible to carry out a detailed study of tool wear, but the ability of tin coatings to prevent scoring of dies during the ironing tests suggests that they may provide an increase in tool life.

Selection of Material for Press Forming Dies

*By the ASM Committee on Press Forming Dies**

THE USEFUL PERFORMANCE of a forming die is measured in terms of its wear. For a given tool material, total wear is affected primarily by length of production run and by severity of the forming operation. Hence, quantity is the principal variable in the accompanying selection tables, and the importance of severity is recognized by the inclusion of a separate table for each of six parts of different size or shape.

The metal being formed, its thickness, and the finish and dimensional tolerances required in the part are also important factors and are included as additional variables in the tables.

The amount of wear on a given die material during forming is proportional to the distance the sheet metal slides over the die at a given pressure between the surfaces in contact. Thin, soft or weak sheet metals exert the least pressure and thus cause the least wear; strong and thick metals cause the most rapid wear. However, the rate of wear for each combination of metals may be considerably different, depending on their surface characteristics, the speed of forming, and the type of lubrication. In the forming of parts with dies that produce wrinkles, high localized pressures are developed on the tools, and attempts to iron out such wrinkles almost always produce prohibitively high rates of wear and galling.

The recommendations made in this article are based on observed performance of a wide range of die materials in producing a great variety of parts. These recommendations are listed in the selection tables for the six parts shown in Fig. 1, ranging from the simplest, such as parts 1 and 2, to moderately severe, such as parts 5 and 6.

Recommended die materials include the range from plastics for low production of simple to moderate parts, up to the most wear-resistant tool steels, surface hardened by nitriding, for making severely formed parts. Parts that are even more difficult to form, or those that are produced in quantities larger than one million, may require dies or inserts of sintered carbide.

Where the tables show more than one material for the same conditions of tooling, the materials are listed in the order of preference with regard to the expected cost per piece; the ultimate choice will often depend on availability, rather than on the small differences in performance or cost of the materials for a given set of conditions.

The tools for parts 1 and 2 consist of a punch and an upper and lower die. None of these die components would wear much, because there is little deformation of the sheet metal during forming of such extremely simple parts, and therefore there is little or no sliding of the sheet over the lower die and little movement over the punch. Thus, large quantities of such parts can be formed by tools made of any die material available in a convenient size.

Tooling for part 3 consists of a punch and die. In operation, the punch pushes the blank through the die, which re-

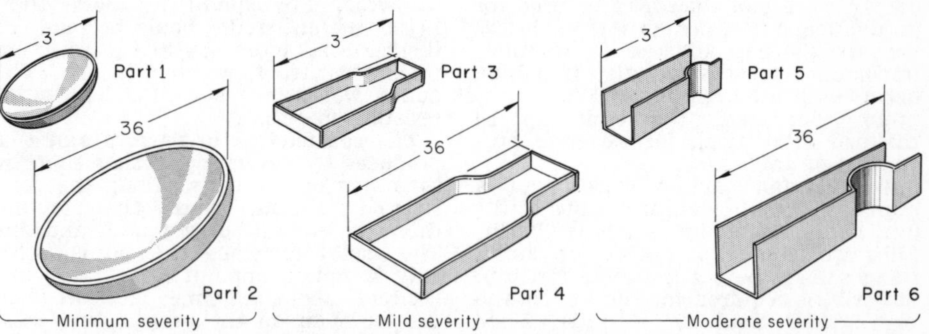

Fig. 1. Parts for which die materials are recommended in the selection tables

*PAUL G. NELSON, *Chairman*, WILLIAM T. COX, CARL H. GERLACH, ROBERT W. HOHL, H. A. HOLBERSON, JOSEPH KLAVON, A. JUSTUS LARSON, RAYMOND L. MCGAUGHEY, WILHELM OLSON, J. H. ROBINSON, R. WAWROUSEK, THOMAS L. WHITE, J. N. WOOLRICH.

[This article is a condensation of the article beginning on page 699 of Volume 1 of this Handbook.]

Selection Table for Part 1. Recommended Punch Material for Forming a Small Part of Minimum Severity

Part (made of 0.050-in. sheet)	Requirements			Recommended punch material(a) — Total quantity of parts to be formed				
Metal being formed	Finish	Tolerance, in.	Lubrication(b)	100	1,000	10,000	100,000	1,000,000
1100 aluminum, brass, copper(c)	None	None	Yes	Epoxy-metal, mild steel	Epoxy-metal, polyester-metal, mild steel	Epoxy(d), polyester (d), mild steel	Polyester-glass (d), mild steel	O1
1100 aluminum, brass, copper(c)	Best	None	No	Epoxy-metal, mild steel	Epoxy-metal, polyester-metal, mild steel	Epoxy(d), mild steel	Polyester-glass (d), mild steel	O1
Magnesium or titanium(e)	Best	None	Yes	Mild steel	Mild steel	Mild steel	Mild steel	A2
Low-carbon steel, to ¼ hard	None	None	Yes	Epoxy-metal, polyester-metal, mild steel	Epoxy-glass-metal, polyester-glass-metal, mild steel	Polyester-glass(d), mild steel	Mild steel	O1, A2
Type 300 stainless, to ¼ hard	None	None	Yes	Epoxy-metal, polyester-metal, mild steel	Epoxy-glass-metal, polyester-glass-metal, mild steel	Polyester-glass(d), mild steel	Mild steel	O1, A2
Low-carbon steel, to ¼ hard	Best	None	Yes	Epoxy-metal, polyester-metal, mild steel	Epoxy-glass-metal, polyester-glass-metal, mild steel	Mild steel	Mild steel	O1, A2
High-strength aluminum or copper alloys	Best	None	No	Epoxy-metal, polyester-metal, mild steel	Epoxy-glass-metal, polyester-glass-metal, mild steel	Mild steel	Mild steel	O1, A2
Heat-resisting alloys	Best	None	No	Epoxy-metal, polyester-metal, mild steel	Polyester-glass-metal, mild steel	Mild steel	Mild steel	O1, A2
Type 300 stainless, to ¼ hard	Best	None	No	Epoxy-metal, polyester-metal, mild steel	Epoxy-glass-metal, polyester-glass-metal, mild steel	Mild steel	Mild steel	O1, A2

Part 1

Selection Table for Part 2. Recommended Punch Material for Forming a Large Part of Minimum Severity

Metal being formed	Finish	Tolerance, in.	Lubrication(b)	100	1,000	10,000	100,000	1,000,000
1100 aluminum, brass, copper(c)	None	None	Yes	Epoxy-metal, zinc alloy	Epoxy-metal, polyester-metal, zinc alloy	Epoxy(d), polyester (d), zinc alloy	Polyester-glass (d), zinc alloy	Gray cast iron
1100 aluminum, brass, copper(c)	Best	None	No	Epoxy-metal, zinc alloy	Epoxy-metal, polyester-metal, zinc alloy	Epoxy(d), polyester (d), zinc alloy	Zinc alloy	Gray cast iron
Magnesium or titanium(e)	Best	None	Yes	Zinc alloy	Gray cast iron	Gray cast iron	Gray cast iron	Alloy cast iron
Low-carbon steel, to ¼ hard	None	None	Yes	Epoxy-metal, polyester-metal, zinc alloy	Epoxy-glass-metal, polyester-glass-metal, zinc alloy	Polyester-glass(d), zinc alloy	Gray cast iron	Alloy cast iron
Type 300 stainless, to ¼ hard	None	None	Yes	Epoxy-metal, polyester-metal, zinc alloy	Epoxy-glass-metal, polyester-glass-metal, zinc alloy	Polyester-glass(d), zinc alloy	Gray cast iron	Alloy cast iron
Low-carbon steel, to ¼ hard	Best	None	Yes	Epoxy-metal, polyester-metal, zinc alloy	Epoxy-glass-metal, polyester-glass-metal, zinc alloy	Polyester-glass(d), zinc alloy	Gray cast iron	Alloy cast iron
High-strength aluminum or copper alloys	Best	None	No	Epoxy-metal, polyester-metal, zinc alloy	Epoxy-glass-metal, polyester-glass-metal, zinc alloy	Polyester-glass(d), zinc alloy	Gray cast iron	Gray cast iron
Heat-resisting alloys	Best	None	No	Epoxy-metal, polyester-metal, zinc alloy	Epoxy-glass-metal, polyester-glass-metal, zinc alloy	Gray cast iron	Alloy cast iron	Alloy cast iron
Type 300 stainless, to ¼ hard	Best	None	No	Epoxy-metal, polyester-metal, zinc alloy	Epoxy-glass-metal, polyester-glass-metal, zinc alloy	Gray cast iron	Alloy cast iron	Alloy cast iron

NOTE: Where mild steel is recommended for forming fewer than 10,000 pieces, the dies are not heat treated. For forming 10,000 pieces and more, such dies should be carburized and hardened. For information on the effect of sheet thickness on selection of die materials, see Table 1. For information on the cost of tooling, see Table 3.

(a) Description of materials is given in Table 2. When more than one material for the same conditions of tooling is given, the materials are listed in order of cost preference with the least expensive being first; however, final choice often depends on availability rather than on small differences in cost or performance of the materials. (b) Refers to specially applied lubrication rather than mill oil. (c) Soft. (d) With inserts. (e) Heated sheet.

Part 2

sults in wear on the die. The metal closely envelops the punch, with little sliding. Thus, the punch generally will produce ten times as many parts with the same wear as the die made of the same material. However, wear and possibly galling will occur at the areas of moderate shrinkage of this part, particularly when the part is formed on these single-action dies. For this small die, type D2 tool steel may be used for production quantities as low as 10,000, because the cost of steel is of minor importance for a small die. If galling occurs with the high-carbon high-chromium tool steel, the tool can be nitrided after trial, for effective prevention of galling.

Tooling for part 4 consists of a punch, a blankholder, and a die. Without the blankholder, excessive wrinkling would be expected at the shrink flanges. As in part 3, less wear-resistant material is required for the punch and blankholder than for the die. When tool steel is recommended for making part 4, the tool steel should be in the form of inserts in a gray cast iron die, and the punch should be made of a cast tool steel such as D2. For example, for 10,000 to 100,000 pieces, a gray cast iron die might be used with A2 or D2 inserts at points of most wear. For quantities greater than 100,000 pieces, or when this part must have close tolerances, the die would have inserts of type D2 tool steel at all surfaces subject to wear. For quantities less than 10,000, the entire die would be made of the material indicated in the selection table for part 4, without inserts. The punch would be made of a less wear-resistant material.

The constriction in parts 5 and 6 is produced by stretching, rather than by shrinking of the metal along the constricted region, and the tooling therefore consists of a punch and die. The metal envelops the punch with only a minor amount of sliding, but produces about ten times more wear on the die than on the punch. Gray cast iron dies with inserts of type A2 or D2 tool steel are needed for production of 10,000 parts or more. However, the same material is indicated for both the punch and die for part 5 in the selection table, because of the small size and minor tool material cost.

In the selection table for part 6, the recommendations refer to the material to be used for the wearing edges of the die. The body of the die would be made of gray cast iron with wearing edges of tool steel in those instances where tool steel is recommended in the table. The punch for making part 6 could be of a material about one tenth as wear resistant as tool steel — for example, alloy cast iron. For a quantity large enough to require a punch material of greater wear resistance than alloy cast iron or cast steel, a tool steel insert should be used at the constriction.

Sheet Thickness

Thick sheets of any metal will exert greater pressure on the dies than thin sheets of the same metal. The selection tables list recommendations only for

Selection Table for Part 3. Recommended Lower-Die Material for Forming a Small Part of Mild Severity

Part (made of 0.050-in. sheet): Metal being formed	Requirements: Finish	Requirements: Tolerance, in.	Lubrication(b)	Recommended lower-die material(a), Total quantity of parts to be formed: 100	1,000	10,000	100,000	1,000,000
1100 aluminum, brass, copper(c)	None	None	Yes	Epoxy-metal, mild steel	Polyester-metal, mild and 4140 steel	Polyester-glass(d), mild and 4140 steel	O1, 4140	A2, D2
1100 aluminum, brass, copper(c)	None	±0.005 R	Yes	Epoxy-metal, mild and 4140 steel	Polyester-metal, mild and 4140 steel	Polyester-glass(d), mild and 4140 steel	4140, O1, A2, D2	A2, D2
1100 aluminum, brass, copper(c)	Best	±0.005 R	Yes	Epoxy-metal, mild steel	Polyester-metal, mild and 4140 steel	Polyester-glass(d), mild and 4140 steel	4140, O1, A2	A2, D2
Magnesium or titanium(e)	Best	±0.005 R	Yes	Mild steel	Mild and 4140 steel	A2	A2	A2, D2
Low-carbon steel, to ¼ hard	None	None	Yes	Mild and 4140 steel	Mild and 4140 steel	4140, mild steel chromium plated, D2	A2	D2
Type 300 stainless, to ¼ hard	None	None	Yes	Mild and 4140 steel	Mild and 4140 steel	Mild and 4140 steel	A2, D2	D2
Low-carbon steel	Best	±0.005 R	Yes	Mild and 4140 steel	Mild and 4140 steel	Mild and 4140 steel	A2, D2 nitrided D2	D2, nitrided D2
High-strength aluminum or copper alloys	Best	±0.005 R	No(f)	Mild and 4140 steel	Mild and 4140 steel	Mild steel chromium plated and 4140	Cr-plated O1; A2	D2, nitrided D2
Type 300 stainless, to ¼ hard	None	±0.005 R	Yes	Mild and 4140 steel	Mild and 4140 steel	Mild and 4140 steel	Cr-plated O1; A2	D2
Type 300 stainless, to ¼ hard	Best	±0.005 R	Yes	Mild and 4140 steel	Mild and 4140 steel	Mild steel chromium plated, D2	D2, nitrided D2	D2, nitrided D2
Heat-resisting alloys	Best	±0.005 R	Yes	Mild and 4140 steel	Mild and 4140 steel	Mild steel chromium plated, D2	D2, nitrided D2	D2, nitrided D2
Low-carbon steel	Good	±0.005 R	No(f)	Mild and 4140 steel	Mild and 4140 steel	Mild steel chromium plated	D2, nitrided D2	D2, nitrided D2

Part 3

Selection Table for Part 4. Recommended Lower-Die Material for Forming a Large Part of Mild Severity

Metal being formed	Finish	Tolerance, in.	Lubrication(b)	100	1,000	10,000	100,000	1,000,000
1100 aluminum, brass, copper(c)	None	None	Yes	Epoxy-metal, polyester-metal, zinc alloy	Polyester-metal, zinc alloy	Epoxy or polyester-glass(d), zinc alloy	Alloy cast iron	Gray cast iron or A2(g)
1100 aluminum, brass, copper(c)	None	±0.005 R	Yes	Epoxy-metal, polyester-metal, zinc alloy	Polyester-metal, zinc alloy	Alloy cast iron	Alloy cast iron	Alloy cast iron
1100 aluminum, brass, copper(c)	Best	±0.005 R	Yes	Epoxy-metal, polyester-metal, zinc alloy	Polyester-metal, zinc alloy	Alloy cast iron	Alloy cast iron	Alloy cast iron, A2(g)
Magnesium or titanium(e)	Best	±0.005 R	Yes	Gray cast iron, zinc alloy	Gray cast iron, zinc alloy	Gray cast iron	Alloy cast iron	Alloy cast iron, A2(g)
Low-carbon steel, to ¼ hard	None	None	Yes	Epoxy-metal, polyester-metal, zinc alloy	Epoxy-glass, polyester-glass, zinc alloy	Epoxy or polyester-glass(d), gray cast iron	Alloy cast iron	.....
Type 300 stainless, to ¼ hard	None	None	Yes	Epoxy-metal, polyester-metal, zinc alloy	Epoxy-glass, polyester-glass, zinc alloy	Epoxy or polyester-glass(d), alloy cast iron	A2(g)	D2(g)
Low-carbon steel	Best	±0.005 R	Yes	Zinc alloy	Epoxy-glass, polyester-glass, zinc alloy	Alloy cast iron	D2; nitrided A2(g)	D2, nitrided D2(g)
High-strength aluminum or copper alloys	Best	±0.005 R	No(f)	Zinc alloy	Polyester-glass, zinc alloy	Alloy cast iron	Alloy cast iron	Nitrided A2(g), nitrided D2(g)
Type 300 stainless, to ¼ hard	None	±0.005 R	Yes	Zinc alloy	Zinc alloy	Alloy cast iron	D2; nitrided A2(g)	D2(g), nitrided D2(g)
Type 300 stainless, to ¼ hard	Best	±0.005 R	Yes	Zinc alloy	Zinc alloy	Alloy cast iron	Nitrided D2	Nitrided D2(g)
Heat-resisting alloys	Best	±0.005 R	Yes	Zinc alloy	Zinc alloy	Alloy cast iron	Nitrided D2	Nitrided D2(g)
Low-carbon steel	Good	±0.005 R	No(f)	Zinc alloy	Zinc alloy	Alloy cast iron	Nitrided D2	Nitrided D2(g)

NOTE: Where mild steel is recommended for forming fewer than 10,000 pieces, the dies are not heat treated. For forming 10,000 pieces and more, such dies should be carburized and hardened. Where 4140 is recommended for fewer than 10,000 pieces, it should be pretreated to a hardness of Rockwell C 28 to 32. Flame hardening of high wear areas is recommended for quantities greater than 10,000 pieces. For the effect of sheet thickness on selection of die materials for making parts 3 and 4, see Table 1. For relative cost of tooling to make these parts, see Table 3.

(a) Description of materials is given in Table 2. When more than one material for the same conditions of tooling is given, the materials are listed in order of increasing cost; however, the final choice often will depend on availability rather than on small differences in cost or performance. Under conditions for which tool steel is recommended for making part 4, the lower die should be of gray cast iron with wrought tool steel inserts and the punch of a cast tool steel such as D2. For example, for 10,000 to 100,000 pieces, a gray cast iron die might be used with A2 or D2 inserts at the shrink flanges; over 100,000 pieces, dies would have D2 inserts at all wear surfaces. (b) Specially applied lubrication, rather than mill oil. (c) Soft. (d) With inserts. (e) Heated sheet. (f) Except for 10,000 or more parts, or with soft steel dies. (g) Use as inserts in gray cast iron body.

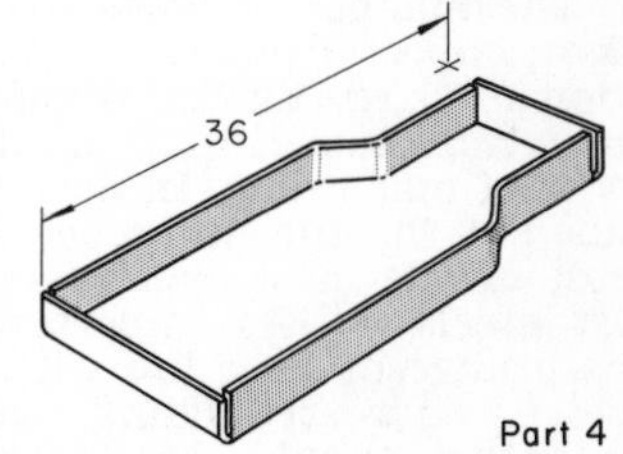

Part 4

sheets 0.050 in. thick. Table 1 recommends materials for dies to make parts 3 and 4 in three sizes, from sheet of four different thicknesses. The selections in Table 1 (page 149) illustrate the increasing effect of galling and wear as parts are made from thicker sheets — especially on the smaller parts with shrink flanges, which need more sturdy dies for medium production quantities.

Table 1 deals only with die materials for forming steel parts. The forming pressure depends not only on the thickness but also on the strength of the sheet being formed. Wear and galling are less severe with any thickness of soft metal, such as aluminum and copper alloys, than with low-carbon steel, but more severe with high-strength metals such as stainless steels and heat-resisting alloys.

Size of Part

For small stampings, such as parts 1, 3 and 5, cast or plastic dies are uneconomical unless they are made from a model already available and with only minor finishing operations required on the dies. When the cost of patternmaking is included, cast or plastic dies will usually be more expensive than dies machined from other materials. The cost of the die material is usually a small fraction of the total cost of dies for a small part, and the availability of material in a size that will minimize machining on the dies will usually be a greater factor in cost than any other.

As the size of the part increases, cost savings resulting from minimizing machining by the use of a casting close to final size will more than offset the cost of a pattern. However, inserts of tool steel or carbide must be used on high-production dies subject to severe wear and galling. The selection of both the material and the locations of the inserts should be conservative when production must not be interrupted for alteration of the tooling. If tools can be taken out of production, gray cast iron dies may be used, with the wear surface flame hardened and inserts added later if needed because of wear on the critical surfaces.

Selection Table for Part 5. Recommended Lower-Die Material for Forming a Small Part of Moderate Severity

Part (made of 0.050-in. sheet)	Requirements			Recommended lower-die material(a)				
				Total quantity of parts to be formed				
Metal being formed	Finish	Toler-ance, in.	Lubrica-tion(b)	100	1,000	10,000	100,000	1,000,000
1100 aluminum, brass, copper(c)	None	None	Yes	Mild steel	Mild steel	Mild steel	O1, A2	A2
1100 aluminum, brass, copper(c)	Best	±0.020 R	Yes	Mild steel	Mild steel	Mild steel	O1, A2	A2
Magnesium or titanium(d)	Best	±0.020 R	Yes	Mild steel	Mild steel	A2	D2	D2
Low-carbon steel, to ¼ hard	Best	None	Yes	Mild steel, O1	Mild steel, O1	Mild steel, A2	Mild steel chromium plated, A2	D2
Type 300 stainless, to ¼ hard	None	None	Yes	Mild steel, O1	Mild steel, O1, A2 tool steel	Mild steel chromium plated, A2	Mild steel chromium plated, D2	D2
Low-carbon steel	Best	±0.020 R	Yes	Mild steel, O1 or nitrided A2	Mild steel, O1 or nitrided A2	Mild steel chromium plated, D2	Mild steel chromium plated, nitrided D2	Nitrided D2
High-strength aluminum or copper alloys	Best	±0.020 R	(e)	Mild steel, O1	Mild steel, O1	Mild steel chromium plated	A2	D2
Type 300 stainless, to ¼ hard	None	±0.020 R	Yes	Mild steel, O1	Mild steel	Mild steel chromium plated, A2	D2	D2
Type 300 stainless, to ¼ hard	Best	±0.020 R	Yes	Mild steel, O1	Mild steel, O1	Mild steel chromium plated	Nitrided D2, nitrided A2	Nitrided D2
Low-carbon steel	Good	±0.020 R	(e)	Mild steel, O1	Mild steel, O1	Mild steel, A2	A2	D2

Selection Table for Part 6. Recommended Lower-Die Material for Forming a Large Part of Moderate Severity

Metal being formed	Finish	Toler-ance, in.	Lubrica-tion(b)	100	1,000	10,000	100,000	1,000,000
1100 aluminum, brass, copper(c)	None	None	Yes	Zinc alloy	Zinc alloy	Gray cast iron	Alloy cast iron	D2, A2
1100 aluminum, brass, copper(c)	Best	±0.031 R	Yes	Zinc alloy	Zinc alloy	Gray cast iron	Alloy cast iron	A2, D2
Magnesium or titanium(d)	Best	±0.031 R	Yes	Gray cast iron	Gray cast iron	Alloy cast iron	A2	D2
Low-carbon steel, to ¼ hard	None	None	Yes	Zinc alloy	Gray cast iron	Gray cast iron	Alloy cast iron	D2, A2
Type 300 stainless, to ¼ hard	None	None	Yes	Zinc alloy	Gray cast iron	Alloy cast iron	D2, A2	D2, nitrided D2
Low-carbon steel	Best	±0.031 R	Yes	Zinc alloy	Gray cast iron	Alloy cast iron	Alloy cast iron	Nitrided D2
High-strength aluminum or copper alloys	Best	±0.031 R	Yes	Zinc alloy	Zinc alloy	Alloy cast iron	Alloy cast iron	D2, A2
Type 300 stainless, to ¼ hard	None	±0.031 R	Yes	Zinc alloy	Zinc alloy	A2	A2	D2
Type 300 stainless, to ¼ hard	Best	±0.031 R	Yes	Zinc alloy	Alloy cast iron	D2, nitrided A2	Nitrided D2	Nitrided D2

NOTE: Where mild steel is recommended for forming fewer than 10,000 pieces, the dies are not heat treated. For forming 10,000 pieces and more, such dies should be carburized and hardened. For information concerning the effect of sheet thickness on selection of die materials, see Table 1. For information on the cost of tooling to make parts of different sizes, see Table 3.

(a) Description of material is given in Table 2. When more than one material for the same conditions of tooling is given, the materials are listed in order of increasing cost; however, the final choice often will depend on availability rather than on the small differences in cost or performance. Gray cast iron dies with inserts of type A2 or D2 tool steel would be needed for making 10,000 parts; however, the same material is recommended for punch and lower die for part 5 because of the small size and minor cost of material. Recommendations for making part 6 are the materials for the wearing edges of the lower die; body of the lower die would be of gray cast iron with wearing edges of the tool steel recommended; the punch could be of a material about one tenth as wear-resistant as tool steel.
(b) Refers to specially applied lubrication rather than mill oil. (c) Soft. (d) Heated sheet. (e) Special lubrication may be needed with soft steel tools.

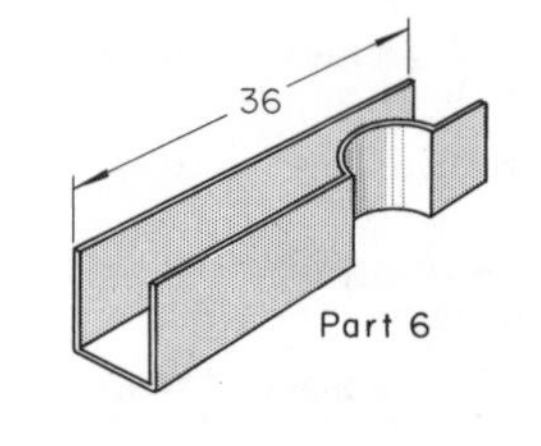

Quantity

The number of parts to be produced is an important factor in material selection for large dies in which the cost of material is equal to or greater than the cost of machining. In dies smaller than about 6 in., the difference between the cost of the most expensive and cheapest steels is less important than the assurance of long life without the necessity for rebuilding tools if the quantity should be increased above original expectations, or if the die material should prove to have been underspecified. However, for large dies, both the choice of tool material and the design of the dies depend on the number of parts to be produced, particularly for more than 1000 parts.

On parts such as part 6, in which there is considerable movement of the sheet over die surfaces, greatly increased die wear is likely. With such parts, die inserts can be shimmed to allow for wear of the die, whereas a solid die cannot be adjusted readily for wear. Therefore, risks may be taken in the selection of steel for inserts on jobs where production can be interrupted for this operation. However, if the insert is small, the cost of material may be of much less consequence than the cost of diemaking and shimming, which may run from $10 to $100 per hour for lost press time, plus labor. Thus, cheap steel inserts may be uneconomical.

Adjustable inserts are often impractical for small dies. Therefore, for high-production dies working under severe wear conditions and producing parts to close tolerances, it is often desirable to use a complete insert or to make the die of wear-resistant material such as carbide or nitrided D2 tool steel.

Tolerance Requirements

Tolerance requirements of the part may have an important effect on the choice of tool material when the part is to be finished without restriking. If the part is to be restruck, the material used in the restriking die is of less importance, because it usually will be subjected to less wear than the die that performs the primary operation. A major factor in the choice between a wear-resistant material and a less costly and less wear-resistant material is the necessity for maintenance during the production run.

Work Metal

The sheet metals of higher hardness usually will wear dies more rapidly, but other factors, such as the presence of scale on the surface of hot rolled, unpickled steels, will cause two to five times more wear. However, scaled surfaces cause less galling, which, on tool materials, may be an even more serious condition than wear, because galling or "pickup" on a die will cause frequent interruptions of production forming for reconditioning the die.

Soft brass and aluminum cause less wear and galling than carbon steel; stainless steels and heat-resisting alloys cause more wear and galling. Where galling is anticipated, it is desirable to use materials such as D2 tool steel that can be treated subsequently, if necessary, to eliminate the difficulty. Possible treatments include chromium plating of any hardened steel, the hardening of alloy cast iron, and the nitriding of tool steels such as A2 and D2, which are preferred for nitriding because of the presence of nitride formers such as chromium and molybdenum.

Lubrication

In making parts at low and medium production (up to 10,000 pieces), it is often economical to use lubricants. With zinc dies, it is necessary. However, the most effective lubricants are difficult to apply and remove, and they add significantly to the cost. Efficient application of lubricants is particularly difficult in high-production operations where presses are fed automatically. In such operations, it is usually economical to use die metals that are more costly but more resistant to galling in combination with the usually less-effective lubricants that can be applied automatically. Examples of these materials are aluminum bronze, nitrided D2 tool steel, and carbide, which often can be used for forming low-carbon steel with only mill-oil lubrication.

Prevention of Galling

Attempting to stretch sheet metal beyond practical limits, poor tool fit, and rough finish on the surface of tools are common causes of galling. For short and medium runs, surface-hardened hot rolled steel dies will produce parts equal to those produced from most tool steel dies. Exceptions may be encountered in severe reductions or in forming metals that show a greater tendency to gall, such as austenitic stainless steel. However, tool steel dies may also gall under these conditions.

When galling occurs, the tool fit and the thickness of the metal being formed should be checked first, to determine whether clearance is adequate. Attempts to iron out wrinkles will often cause galling. Whenever possible, wrinkles should be prevented by the design of the tools.

Nitriding minimizes or prevents the galling of dies made from alloy steel or alloy tool steel such as A2 or D2. It is not recommended for steels that contain no nitride-forming elements such as chromium or molybdenum. Nitrided surfaces on such steels may spall from radii smaller than about ⅛ in., and plated surfaces may spall from radii less than ¼ in., thus increasing the risk of failure in these locations.

Hard chromium plating will usually eliminate galling of mild steel, alloy steel, and tool steel dies, and it is often used for severe duty. For operations involving high local pressures, hardened steels such as alloy or tool steels will be less likely to yield plastically and to cause cracking of hard chromium plate.

Dirt, grit and shot fragments on the sheet cause greater damage to nitrided and chromium-plated tools than to hardened tool steels; hard particles may cause minute spalling and small pits, especially at radii in areas of high forming pressure. When these pits in the die cause scratches on the formed sheet, the pits must be stoned out if high finish is required on the part. After such repairs have been made several times in the same area, the soft underlying metal will be exposed and renewal of the nitrided case or the chromium plate will be necessary.

Galling is less likely if the die materials and the metal being formed are dissimilar in hardness, chemical composition, and surface characteristics. For instance, effective combinations are: (*a*) aluminum bronze tools for forming carbon steel and stainless steel; (*b*) tool steel for forming aluminum and copper alloys; and (*c*) carbide tools for forming carbon steel, stainless steel, and aluminum.

Die Finish. Although usually galling can be minimized or eliminated by careful selection of die materials, die finish is an important factor affecting susceptibility to galling. The probability of galling increases as the severity of forming increases.

The influence of die finish, with other factors constant, is illustrated in the following example.

Table 1. Recommended Materials for Lower Die for Forming Steel Parts of Three Sizes, Each in Four Thicknesses
(Assuming no finish or tolerance requirements)

Sheet thickness, in.	Recommended lower-die material(a) — Total quantity to be produced: 100	1,000	10,000	100,000(b)	1,000,000(b)
For Part 3, Maximum Dimension of 3 In.					
0.031	Mild steel and 4140	Mild steel and 4140	Mild steel and 4140	4140; Cr-plated mild steel; D2	D2
0.062	Mild steel and 4140	Mild steel and 4140	Mild steel and 4140	4140; Cr-plated mild steel; D2	D2
0.125	Mild steel and 4140	Mild steel and 4140	Mild steel, 4140 and A2	D2	D2
0.250	Mild steel and 4140	Mild steel and 4140	A2 and D2	D2	D2
For a 12-In. Part Similar to Parts 3 and 4					
0.031	Mild steel, 4140 and zinc alloy	Mild steel, 4140 and zinc alloy	Mild steel, 4140, zinc alloy and alloy cast iron	Alloy cast iron(c); Cr-plated mild steel; 4140	D2
0.062	Mild steel, 4140 and zinc alloy	Mild steel, 4140 and zinc alloy	Mild steel, 4140, zinc alloy and alloy cast iron	Alloy cast iron(c) and A2	D2
0.125	Mild steel, 4140 and zinc alloy	Mild steel, 4140 and gray cast iron	Mild(c) and A2 steels	A2 and D2	D2
0.250	Mild steel, 4140 and gray cast iron	Mild steel and alloy cast iron	Mild(c) and A2 steels	A2 and D2	D2
For Part 4, Maximum Dimension of 36 In.					
0.031	Epoxy-metal, polyester-metal, zinc alloy	Epoxy-glass, polyester-glass, zinc alloy	Epoxy or polyester-glass(d), alloy cast iron, zinc alloy(d)	Alloy cast iron(c)	D2
0.062	Epoxy-metal, polyester-metal, zinc alloy	Epoxy-glass, polyester-glass, zinc alloy	Epoxy or polyester-glass(d), alloy cast iron, zinc alloy(d)	A2	D2
0.125	Zinc alloy	Zinc alloy, gray cast iron	Alloy cast iron(c)	A2 and D2	D2
0.250	Zinc alloy, gray cast iron	Alloy cast iron	Alloy cast iron(c)	A2 and D2	D2

Part 3. For a sketch of the die for this part, see Fig. 4.

A 12-in. part similar to parts 3 and 4. For a sketch of the die for this part, see Fig. 4. The cost of tooling is given in Table 4.

Part 4. Tooling for this part is shown in the sketch of Fig. 5.

(a) See Table 2 for description of materials. Materials recommended in above table are for forming parts from low-carbon steel; wear and galling will be less with aluminum and copper alloys, and more with stainless steel and heat-resisting alloys, than with low-carbon steel.
(b) All A2 or D2 tool steels are nitrided after tryout if required. (c) Inserts of A2 tool steel are recommended for wear edges for the shrink flange. (d) At the quantity level indicated, use of inserts with these materials is required.

Example 216. Effect of Die Finish on Galling

A hat section with walls that were nearly perpendicular to the original blank (fairly drastic severity) was formed of annealed 1010 steel. The punch portion of the die was made from A6 tool steel at Rockwell C 60 with a finish of 30 to 35 micro-in. The die ring was made of nitrided medium-carbon alloy steel having a hardness of Rockwell C 63, and was also finished to 30 to 35 micro-in. Both components were copiously lubricated, but after ten hits there were indications of metal pickup, and after 30 hits the tools were removed because of excessive galling. Both die components were refinished to about 30 micro-in., after which 300 parts were produced before galling was excessive. The tools were then refinished to 8 to 10 micro-in., after which 3000 parts were made with no sign of galling.

Producing the high finish reported in Example 216 over the entire working surface of the dies is costly and is not always warranted, but it should be considered when galling occurs in severe forming. Sometimes the use of lubricants can be minimized by improving the die finish.

Die Wear and Die Life

Composition and hardness of die material and part, and thickness, shape and quantity of the parts being formed are of primary importance in die wear and life (the total useful life of the die). Effects of these factors are described in seven examples that follow.

Examples 217 to 223. Examples of Die Wear and Die Life (Fig. 2)

Example 217 — Effect of Hardness of Die Material. The chart at the top in Fig. 2 shows the effect of die hardness on die life in forming a bench-leg top. Nitrided 4140 mod steel at Rockwell C 60 outperformed unnitrided 4140 mod at Rockwell C 25 by 800%.

Examples 218, 219 and 220 — Effect of Composition and Hardness of Die Material. The middle charts in Fig. 2 show the effect of composition and hardness of die material on die life in forming a label holder (1008 steel), a bushing (1008 steel), and a garbage-shredder ring (17-7 PH stainless steel). For forming the

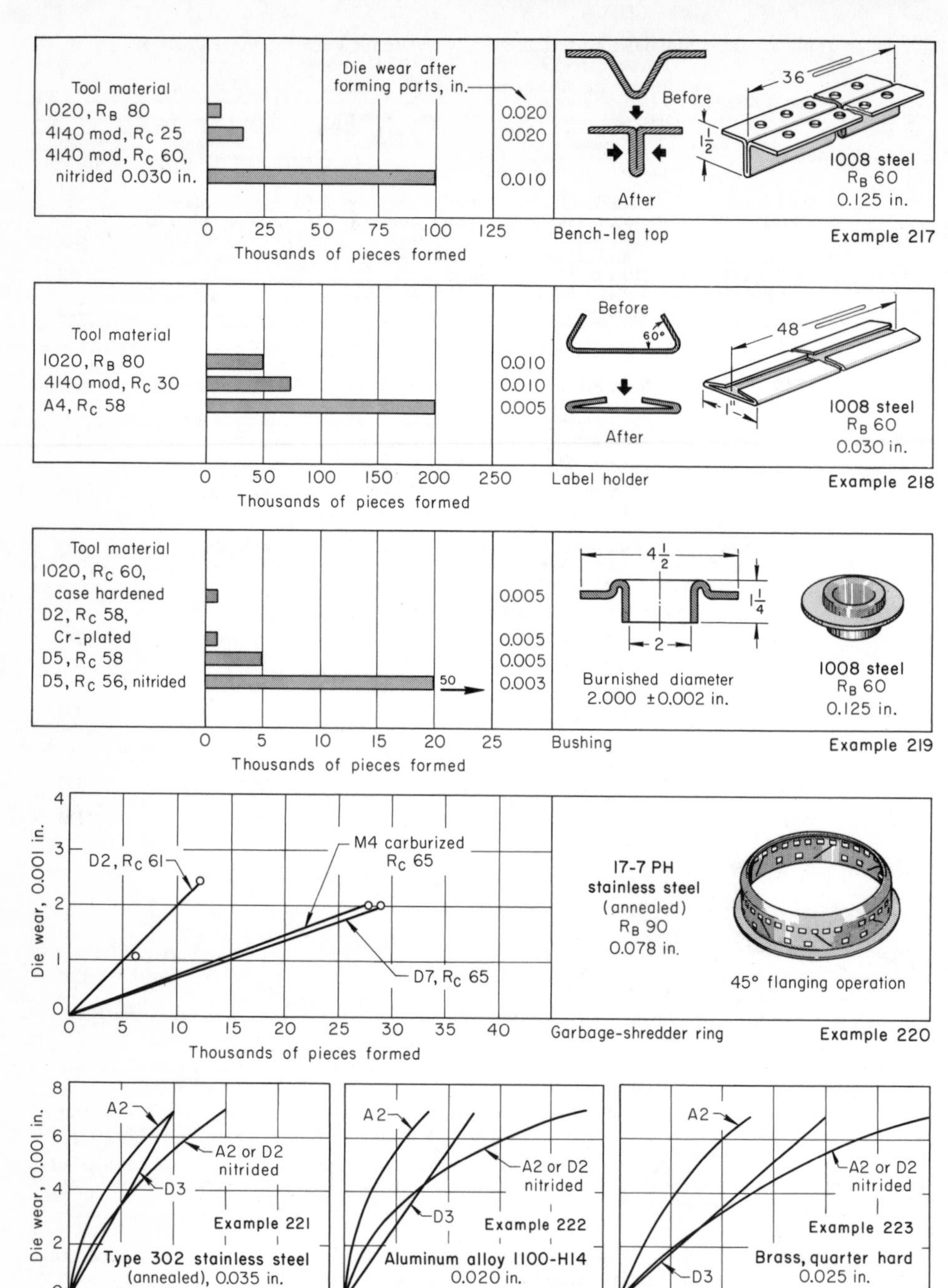

Fig. 2. Die wear and die life for various types of parts and work metals. The three graphs in the bottom row relate to small instrument parts having a maximum area of 3 sq in. (Examples 217 to 223)

label holder, A4 dies at Rockwell C 58 had less wear and produced more parts than dies of 1020 steel at Rockwell B 80 or than dies of 4140 mod at Rockwell C 30. For forming the bushing, dies of nitrided D5 at Rockwell C 56 had much superior wear properties to the other materials tried and to unnitrided D5 at Rockwell C 58. For forming the flange on the garbage-shredder ring, M4 and D7 at Rockwell C 65 gave more than twice the die life of D2 at Rockwell C 61.

Examples 221, 222 and 223 — Effect of Material Being Formed. Wear of dies of A2, D3 and nitrided A2 and D2 was compared in forming small instrument parts of type 302 stainless steel, 1100-H14 aluminum, and quarter-hard brass. The curves for die wear (lowest row of charts in Fig. 2) are similar for all of the materials, and nitrided A2 or D2 outperformed the other tool steels in all instances. Almost twice as many parts could be formed of 0.025-in.-thick brass as of 0.035-in.-thick type 302 for the same amount of die wear, but only a few more than of aluminum.

Effect on die life of composition and increased resistance to deformation by the metal being formed is shown in Fig. 3. Also shown in Fig. 3 are comparisons of different tool materials forming the same work metal.

Tool Steels

Table 2 lists nominal compositions of tool steels for which recommendations or performance data are given.

Water-hardening tool steels are the least costly and the best in machinability and weldability, but distort more readily during heat treatment. They have better resistance to galling and wear than O1, but not as good as A2 or D2. They may be used for such operations as forming aluminum with dies that will not distort much during heat treatment, or for dies that can be selectively hardened, as for the dies for making part 1 of aluminum. Carbon tool steel can be used in the annealed condition, hard faced with bronze or other materials that have greater resistance to galling and wear.

Steel O1 overcomes most of the heat treating problems of water-hardening tool steel, and has almost as good machinability. However, it is only slightly less costly than a more wear-resistant steel such as A2, has poor weldability, and is less resistant to galling and wear than the water-hardening steels. Steel O1 is suitable for moderate conditions and where distortion in heat treatment precludes water-hardening steels.

A2, only slightly more costly than O1, is superior to O1 in resistance to wear and galling, and this resistance can be improved still further by nitriding. However, A2 has poor weldability. A2 can be used for inserts or cast to shape.

D2 is more costly and less easily machined and welded than A2 but deforms very little in heat treatment. Its excellent resistance to galling and wear can be improved by nitriding.

D3, D5 and D7 are similar to D2, and can be used as solid dies, castings, or inserts for forming materials such as stainless steel in severe applications. D3 must be quenched in oil. D5 contains an addition of cobalt, costs more, is more difficult to machine and quench, and can be nitrided to increase its useful life (Fig. 2). D7 contains additions of molybdenum and vanadium. It is hardened in air and is the most costly and most difficult of all the high-carbon high-chromium tool steels to machine and grind. For these reasons, it is rarely used except for extremely small solid dies, and for inserts in areas where larger dies have excessive wear.

The high-vanadium high speed steels such as M4 can be used for forming dies and may be desirable in specific applications — for instance, carburized M4 was used in making the shredder ring in Example 220 (Fig. 2). However, these high speed steels cost more and are less readily available than the high-carbon high-chromium types. Carburized high speed steels have been used successfully.

Shock-resisting tool steels such as S1 are used primarily for die components that are fragile or subject to impact in service. S1 tool steel has good machinability, distorts little in heat treatment, and when carburized has good resistance to galling and wear.

Cast Iron

Cast iron is a useful die material for forming parts larger than about 12 in. (Table 1). Its performance makes it suitable for use in medium-production runs or in short runs of large parts. When cast iron is used with inserts, it will produce greater quantities, as shown in the tables.

Both types of cast iron listed in Table 2 should have predominantly fine pearlite with no massive carbides and a minimum of ferrite. Graphite should be of AFS-ASTM type A distribution with a preferred flake size of 4 to 5.

Alloy cast iron should be flame hardenable to the equivalent of 450 Bhn

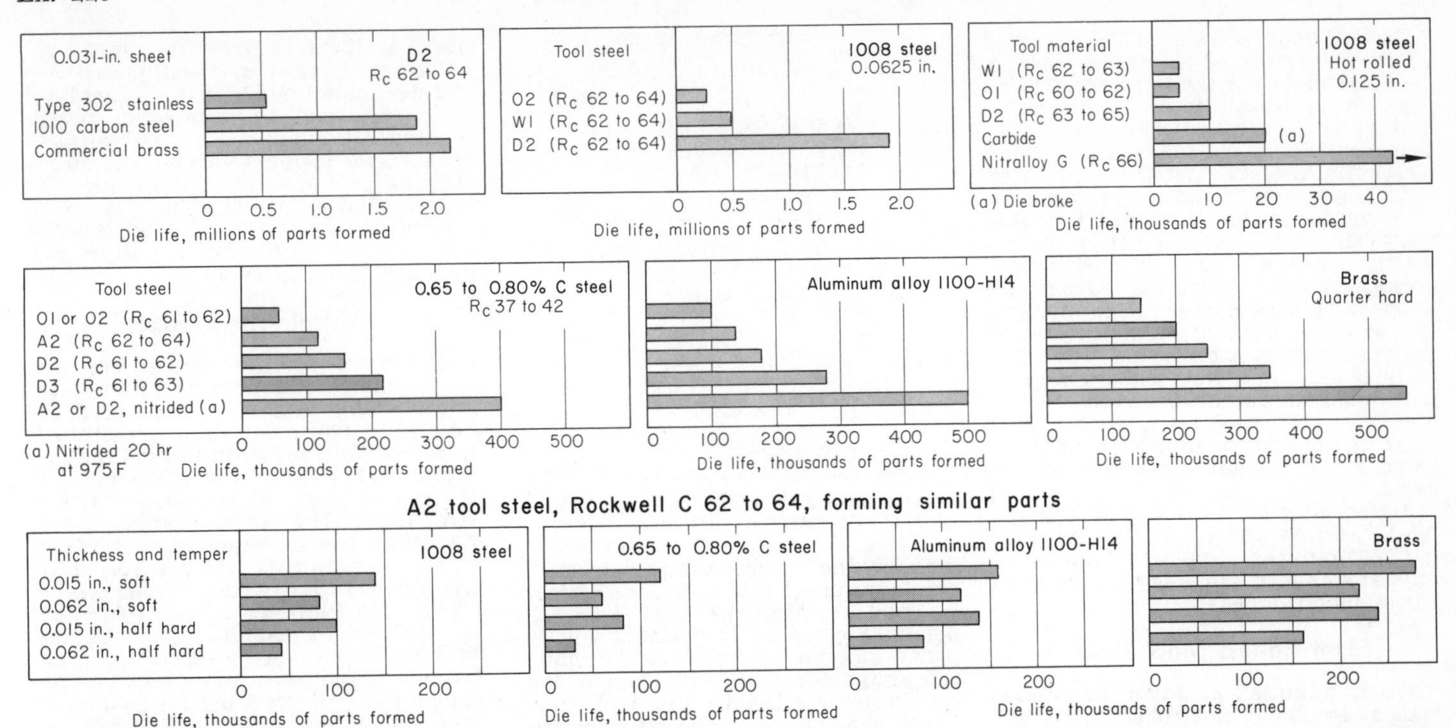

Upper Left and Center. Effect of material being formed on life of D2 dies, and comparison of die life for O2, W1 and D2. These parts have a maximum area of approximately 4 sq in., and the forming is largely medium severity (upper left) and simple 90° bend (upper center).
Upper Right. Severe forming of drawing quality 1008 hot rolled strip. The blank is curled to form a full round bushing.
Center Three Graphs. Comparison of different die materials and effect on die life of the material being formed. Charts indicate summary results for dies forming a variety of small instrument parts having a maximum area of 3 sq in. and thickness of 0.062 in.
Lower Four Graphs. Effect of temper, thickness and composition of material being formed on the life of A2 dies. The formed parts to which these data refer are closely similar in shape to those parts dealt with in the center graphs above.

Fig. 3. Die-life data for various press forming operations

Table 2. Nominal Compositions of Tool Materials for Press Forming Dies

Material	Composition
Tool Steels	
W1, water-hardening	0.60 to 1.40 C
S1, oil-hardening, shock-resisting	0.50 C; 1.50 Cr; 2.50 W
O1, oil-hardening	0.50 C; 1.50 Cr; 2.50 W
A2, air-hardening, medium-alloy	1.00 C; 5.00 Cr; 1.00 Mo
A4, low-temperature air-hardening	1.00 C; 2.00 Mn; 1.00 Cr; 1.00 Mo
D2, high-carbon high-chromium	1.50 C; 12.00 Cr; 1.00 Mo
D3, high-carbon high-chromium	2.25 C; 12.00 Cr
D5, high-carbon high-chromium	1.50 C; 12.00 Cr; 1.00 Mo; 3.00 Co
D7, high-carbon high-chromium	2.35 C; 12.00 Cr; 1.00 Mo; 4.00 V
M2, molybdenum high speed	0.80 C; 4.00 Cr; 5.00 Mo; 6.00 W; 2.00 V
M4, molybdenum high speed	1.30 C; 4.00 Cr; 4.50 Mo; 5.50 W; 4.00 V
Other Ferrous Alloys	
Hot rolled mild steel	Steels 1010 to 1018
Gray cast iron, 185 to 225 Bhn	3% total C; 1.6 Si; 0.7 Mn (or equivalent)
Alloy cast iron, 200 to 250 Bhn	3% total C; 0.7% combined C; 1.6 Si; 0.4 Cr; 0.4 Mo (or equivalent)
Cast carbon steel, 185 to 225 Bhn	0.75 C
Cast alloy steel, 200 to 235 Bhn	0.45 C; 1.10 Cr; 0.40 Mo
4140 alloy steel	0.40 C; 0.60 Mn; 0.30 Si; 1 Cr; 0.20 Mo
Nitralloy	0.35 C; 1.20 Cr; 0.20 Mo; 1.00 Al
Nonferrous Alloys	
Zinc alloy	4 Al; 3 Cu; 0.03 Mg; rem, Zn
Aluminum bronze, 270 to 300 Bhn	13 Al; 4 Fe; rem, Cu
Plastics	
Polyester-glass	50% polyester plastic, 50% glass in the form of cloth, strand or chopped fibers
Epoxy-glass	50% epoxy plastic, 50% glass as above
Polyester-metal	Polyester plastic reinforced with metal powder
Epoxy-metal	Epoxy plastic reinforced with metal powder
Nylon-metal	Polyamide plastic reinforced with metal powder
Polyester or epoxy-glass-metal	Polyester or epoxy plastic with both glass and metal as above

with air cooling. The alloy iron listed in Table 2 is sufficiently hardenable for oil quenching of small dies and local flame hardening with air cooling for dies too large to be quenched. When no heat treating is anticipated, the unalloyed gray iron is usually preferred, because of lower cost and better machinability. However, alloy iron will usually wear less, even without flame hardening or other heat treatment.

Zinc Alloy

Zinc alloy has high pattern fidelity when cast, but requires accurate shrink patterns to minimize hand labor in finishing. Zinc alloy is economical for die components that are 12 in. long, and it is most economical in dies about 36 in. long, as is evident in the selection tables. One of the principal values of zinc alloy is for complicated dies that would require intricate machining and hand tooling if made of gray cast iron, but which can be cast more closely to shape in zinc alloy. In tensile strength, compressive strength, and hardness, zinc tool alloys are inferior to other metals used in die construction.

If compound curves on the face of a stamping have no sharp creases or embossments with sharp corners, it is not unusual for zinc alloy dies to give the length of service indicated in the selection table for part 2. Zinc alloy tools are particularly sensitive to surface roughness and to the thickness and hardness of the sheet metal being formed. The increase of any one of these multiplies unit pressures over a small area of the die face.

Contrary to conventional diemaking practice, zinc alloy dies, cast to shape, are made of as few components as possible. This not only results in a lower cost because fasteners are largely eliminated, but also adds to die simplicity and durability. Otherwise, zinc alloy tools for conventional press production are designed according to usual practice.

Virtually all the zinc alloy in a tool can be salvaged for reuse simply by melting. For greatest economy, the user must have melting and molding facilities available; the commercial scrap value of the alloy is about 65% of the original cost, but remelting costs the user about as much as melting purchased metal. These facilities, plus the necessary auxiliaries, cost a minimum of $50,000 to install.

Cycle time or press speed has a great effect on the life of zinc alloy tools. A die component moving more than 25 in. per minute during its working cycle is highly destructive to zinc alloy. The best results have been obtained on double-action presses that average three strokes per minute and involve drawing to a depth of more than 6 in. For this work, zinc dies perform better in hydraulic presses than in mechanical presses. Therefore, tools made from zinc alloys have a minimum size limit. Even the slowest speed of small presses is greater than is permissible with zinc alloy tooling, and the cost is excessive if a small die is run on a large press merely to suit speed requirements. Zinc alloy dies cannot be used with unlubricated stock because wear will be too rapid.

A zinc alloy containing 4 Al, 3.25 Cu, 0.1 Mg, 0.7 Ni and 0.2 Ti has provided die life up to three times that indicated for the standard zinc alloy (Table 2) in the selection tables.

Hot Rolled Mild Steel

Where a limited variety of tool materials is available, hot rolled mild steel plate with carbon content from 0.10 to 0.20% is in major use as a die material. It is also widely used for backup tools for short-run forming of small parts. This type of steel is not recommended without surface hardening, except for quantities of less than 10,000 parts. Dies are made by torch cutting, then normalizing and grinding. The dies are easily machined and generally are carburized, quenched and tempered after finish machining. No grinding should be done after carburizing. For a production quantity of 100,000 parts such as part 5, the die is chromium plated after hardening.

Hot rolled mild steel can be used for dies only where straightening facilities are available for correcting distortion induced by heat treatment. Straightening is necessary for all except symmetrical and thick shapes, such as a large round punch.

Medium-Carbon Alloy Steels

Several medium-carbon alloy steels such as 4140 are available in plate form and are useful for some types of forming dies. For example, 4140 (or a slightly modified composition sold as a proprietary steel) is available prehardened to about Rockwell C 30. Dies machined from this material are used without heat treatment for moderate forming or short runs — for example, the label-holder die of Example 218 (Fig. 2). For longer runs or more severe forming, dies made from this prehardened steel can be nitrided — for instance, the die for a bench-leg top, Example 217 (Fig. 2). These steels are also suitable for flame hardening. They can be flame hardened by a hand torch for smoothly contoured parts similar to part 3, where the flame-hardening operation could progress continuously along the wearing surfaces.

The 4140 steel die to form part 3 is a simple five-element tool consisting of a punch, a die mounted to a pair of die shoes, and a spring or rubber-backed

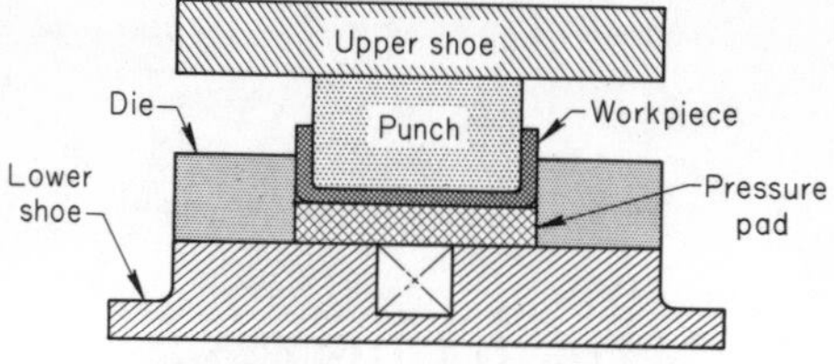

Fig. 4. Die for Tables 1 and 3, to make 3-in. and 12-in. parts

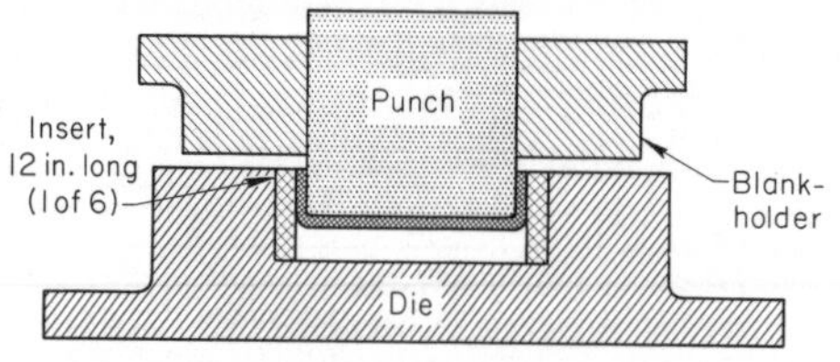

Fig. 5. Die for Tables 1 and 3, to make part with maximum dimension of 36 in.

pressure pad to eject the part from the die. A spring or rubber-backed stripper is used to strip the part from the punch. Steel 4140 is selected for the punch and die because a component of this shape and size lends itself to low-cost design and toolmaking techniques. The punch and die can be cut from plate with a band saw so that only a small amount of filing and fitting is necessary. The edges of both the punch and the die are then flame hardened, which eliminates furnace heat treatment. After grinding and polishing out the edges as necessary, the punch and die are fitted to mating die shoes, and the pressure pad and stripper are added, along with the necessary gages for locating the blanks.

When properly hardened and finished, such a die can produce 100,000 pieces or more. Some tools of this kind have produced more than 200,000 pieces from 0.060-in. cold rolled 1010 steel.

Steels 8640 and 5140 are suitable alternatives for 4140 and cost about the same.

Several medium-carbon free-cutting grades sold as proprietary steels are also used for flame-hardened dies. Typical compositions are: 0.45 C, 1.10 Mn, 0.25 S; and 0.50 C, 1.10 Mn, 0.08 S, and 0.15 Mo. These steels, which are not recommended for nitriding, cost less than 4140 but usually require water quenching to develop full hardness after flame heating, whereas 4140, with its higher hardenability, does not.

Cast Steel

Cast steel is used for forming parts larger than 12 in. long where the shape of the part makes a casting more practical than wrought stock. Plain carbon steel (0.65 to 0.85 C) and alloy cast steel (0.40 to 0.50 C, 0.90 to 1.25 Mn, 0.90 to 1.25 Cr, 0.35 to 0.50 Mo) are two commonly used compositions. Cast steel is more costly and more difficult to machine than gray cast iron and is more likely to gall. However, it is tougher and more resistant to abrasive wear than cast iron. Both the alloy and plain carbon grades of cast steel can be flame hardened; the plain carbon grade must be water quenched, whereas the alloy grade will harden in air.

One important advantage of cast steel, particularly the plain carbon grade, is its weldability. It can be rewelded with steel or hard faced with tool steel, aluminum bronze or other hard facing material. Because of its poorer resistance to galling, it is less desirable for dies for forming carbon and stainless steels than for aluminum and copper alloys. Cast steel is also useful for restrike, flanging and other types of dies that are less likely to gall or pick up metal from the sheet.

Aluminum Bronze

Aluminum bronzes, which are primarily alloys of copper and aluminum, are available in a wide range of hardness from 120 to 340 Bhn. These alloys have excellent resistance to galling and are desirable for dies where best finish is required on carbon and stainless steel parts. The softer grades (120 to 270 Bhn) wear rapidly, particularly where wrinkling is likely to occur on the formed part. The harder grades (270 to 340 Bhn) wear less rapidly, but are difficult to machine, drill and tap. Where elimination of scratches is extremely important, aluminum bronze should be considered, but for medium to high production (10,000 to 100,000), replacement inserts should be available to permit reconditioning of worn tools.

Plastics

The raw materials used in plastics formulations are readily available, as are the prepared tool plastics. Although satisfactory dies may be produced from plastics even in initial experiments, quality and economy improve with experience.

Plastic tooling requires no outlay for special equipment, but may be produced on the usual toolmaking facilities. Patterns, prototype parts, or models must be available for casting the resin (if no reinforcement is to be used) or for placing resin-impregnated glass reinforcement on the face of dies that are built with reinforcement throughout. When a pattern of some kind is not available, there will be little or no cost advantage in using plastic dies rather than metal dies.

Such terms as nylon-metal, epoxy-metal, polyester-metal, which appear in the selection tables, refer to plastics reinforced by the addition of metal powder to the uncured resin. The reference to inserts in footnote (d) of the selection tables for parts 1, 2, 3 and 4 indicates that plastic dies selected to produce the quantities shown are reinforced at the areas of highest pressure and wear with inserts of tool steel, gray cast iron, or alloy steel bolted or doweled in place in the die component.

The strength (10,000 to 40,000 psi) and, in particular, the hardness of plastics are inferior to those of metallic die materials. In some applications, the problem of obtaining the required strength in a plastic die must be solved by extra care in designing or developing; but in many dies the regions of high pressure are confined to local areas, which, if anticipated, are strengthened with metallic inserts.

When plastic tooling is selected for a part that is subsequently changed in design, the necessary alterations of the tooling will be costly. In addition, if maintenance is required on a plastic die, the bonding of repair plastic to worn areas of the die may be inadequate because of previous absorption of oil by the plastic.

Except for very short runs, plastics should not be selected for blankholder material where burred edges of the blank slide over the plastic surface. Because plastics cannot withstand such abrasion, these areas will wear severely on plastic dies.

Cost of Tooling

Table 3 shows the relative cost of dies for forming parts such as parts 3 and 4 in sizes of 3, 12 and 36 in. The cost covers only the basic die components indicated; accessories, such as gages, knockouts, wipers, guards, blankholder plates, and the like, have been omitted because they do not affect the comparison of cost. For the 3-in. and 12-in. parts, the tooling consists of a punch, a die, and a pressure pad only, as shown in Fig. 4; for the 36-in. part, the tooling consists of a punch, a blankholder, and a die, as shown in Fig. 5.

As shown in Table 3, in one set of dies the gray cast iron die had inserts of A2 tool steel; in another, D2 tool steel inserts were used; in both sets of dies, the punch was made of cast steel without inserts.

Cost of a pattern was included for the 3-in. plastic die. If this pattern were already available from some other operation and could be used without additional expense for making the die, the cost would be reduced from $360 to $278.

For the 36-in. part, costs are not shown for hot rolled mild steel, because distortion in heat treatment makes this size impractical.

Machinability of Tool Steel

The high carbon and alloy content of tool steel promotes the formation of large alloy carbides and makes it difficult to obtain a low hardness in the annealed steels; both conditions affect machining characteristics adversely. The alloying elements chromium, tungsten, molybdenum and vanadium readily form carbides. Therefore, tool steels are more difficult to machine than low-carbon steel.

With a percentage rating of 100 for group W tool steels, group S steels have a machinability rating of 60 to 70%; groups A and O steels, 45 to 60%; and group D steels, 30 to 40%.

Although there is considerable variation in grindability among the steels in the W, S and O groups, all are classified as high-grindability steels. Except for D7, the tool steels in the A and D groups listed in Table 2 and M2 are classified as medium in grindability. D7 and high speed steel M4 have a low grindability rating. These steels are used where abrasion resistance is needed, and thus are expected to have low grindability.

All tool steels are to some degree susceptible to tempering from overheating during grinding, but the W, S and O steels are more susceptible than the more highly alloyed steels.

Table 3. Relative Cost of Tooling to Form Parts 3 and 4 (See Fig. 4 and 5, Page 152, for Tools)

Item	Cost of die components(a), $ — Upper and lower shoes	Punch	Die	Pressure pad	All others	Template	Pattern	Totals
Tooling for Part 3, Maximum Dimension of 3 In. (See Fig. 4)								
Solid D2 tool steel								
Material	$ 34	$ 4	$ 18	$ 3	$ 2	...	....	$ 61
Labor	60	120	200	50	20	...	....	450
Total	94	124	218	53	22	...	....	511
Solid A2 tool steel								
Material	34	2	12	2	2	...	....	52
Labor	60	100	160	50	20	...	....	390
Total	94	102	172	52	22	...	....	442
Unalloyed gray cast iron								
Material	34	1	3	1	1	...	....	40
Labor	60	70	100	50	20	...	....	300
Total	94	71	103	51	21	...	....	340
Hot rolled mild steel, carburized								
Material	34	1	1	1	1	...	....	38
Labor	60	80	120	50	20	...	....	330
Total	94	81	121	51	21	...	....	368
4140 alloy steel								
Material	34	1	2	1	1	...	....	39
Labor	60	80	120	50	20	...	....	330
Total	94	81	122	51	21	...	....	369
Epoxy-metal(b)								
Material	34	3	....	....	1	...	$ 2	40
Labor	60	160	....	....	20	...	80	320
Total	94	163	....	....	21	...	82	360
Tooling for a 12-In. Part Similar to Parts 3 and 4 (See Fig. 4)								
Cast iron with inserts of D2 tool steel								
Material	$ 127	$ 9	$107	$ 7	$ 5	...	....	$ 255
Labor	80	200	620(c)	100	40	...	....	1040
Total	207	209	727	107	45	...	....	1295
Cast iron with inserts of A2 tool steel								
Material	127	5	72	7	5	...	....	216
Labor	80	160	580(d)	100	40	...	....	960
Total	207	165	652	107	45	...	....	1176
Unalloyed gray cast iron								
Material	127	9	18	7	2	...	....	163
Labor	80	130	240	100	40	...	....	590
Total	207	139	258	107	42	...	....	753
Hot rolled mild steel, carburized								
Material	127	6	13	5	2	...	....	153
Labor	80	140	260	100	40	...	....	620
Total	207	146	273	105	42	...	....	773
4140 alloy steel								
Material	127	18	32	14	2	...	....	193
Labor	80	140	260	100	40	...	....	620
Total	207	158	292	114	42	...	....	813
Alloy die iron, 225 Bhn								
Material	127	9	18	7	2	...	....	163
Labor	80	130	240	100	40	...	....	590
Total	207	139	258	107	42	...	....	753
Alloy die iron with inserts of aluminum bronze, 285 Bhn								
Material	127	9	53	7	2	...	....	198
Labor	80	130	800	100	40	...	....	1150
Total	207	139	853	107	42	...	....	1348
Plastic cast (epoxy, iron-filled)								
Material	127	20	15	6	....	...	....	168
Labor	80	240	120	100	....	...	....	540
Total	207	260	135	106	....	...	....	708
Epoxy-metal(b)								
Material	50	15	....	....	2	...	$ 5	72
Labor	40	120	....	....	15	...	60	235
Total	90	135	....	....	17	...	65	307

Item	Cost of die components(a), $ — Punch	Blankholder	Lower die — Die	Lower die — Inserts	All others	Template	Pattern	Totals
Tooling for Part 4, Maximum Dimension of 36 In. (See Fig. 5)								
Cast iron with inserts of D2 tool steel								
Material	$ 224	$ 88	$172	$233	$ 8	...	$ 12	$ 737
Labor	480	460	480	680	160	$80	560	2900
Total	704	548	652	913	168	80	572	3637
Cast iron with inserts of A2 tool steel								
Material	224	88	172	151	8	...	12	655
Labor	480	460	480	560	160	80	560	2780
Total	704	548	652	711	168	80	572	3435
Unalloyed gray cast iron, 210 Bhn								
Material	100	51	110	....	5	...	12	278
Labor	400	440	620	....	160	80	560	2260
Total	500	491	730	....	165	80	572	2538
Zinc alloy (Zn-Al-Cu-Mg)								
Material	Pattern, $325; metal (3450 lb at $0.2525 per pound), $871							1196(e)
Labor	Foundry, $660; machining, $400; spotting and fitting, $800							1860
Total	....				....			3056(e)
Alloy die iron, 225 Bhn								
Material	120	61	131	....	5	...	12	329
Labor	400	440	620	....	160	80	560	2260
Total	520	501	751	....	165	80	572	2589
Alloy die iron with inserts of aluminum bronze, 285 Bhn								
Material	120	61	131	100	5	...	12	429
Labor	400	440	670	620	160	80	560	2930
Total	520	501	801	720	165	80	572	3359
Combination of cast and laminated construction (epoxy, iron-filled)								
Material	157	146	240	....	....	...	....	543
Labor	1010	480	640	....	....	...	....	2130
Total	1167	626	880	....	....	...	....	2673

(a) The cost of labor includes overhead and was computed at $10 per hr. (b) Costs listed under punch for epoxy-metal include die and pressure pad also. (c) The labor cost for making the inserts is $360. (d) The labor cost for making the inserts is $320. (e) Allowing 65% scrap value for the metal reduces total cost from $3056 to $2490.

Forming of Steel Strip in Multiple-Slide Machines

MULTIPLE-SLIDE FORMING is a process in which the workpiece is progressively formed in a combination of units that can be used in various ways to make automatically a large variety of simple and intricately shaped parts from coil stock or wire.

Operations such as straightening, feeding, trimming, blanking, embossing, coining, lettering, forming to shape, and ejecting can all be done in one cycle of a multiple-slide machine. Forming generally is limited to bending operations, but the four slides and center post permit making some very complex parts. Deep drawing is not generally done in the forming or press stations of a multiple-slide machine.

Applicability

Multiple-slide forming is used to produce shapes from coiled strip or wire. The maximum size of workpiece that can be formed from strip metal in a multiple-slide machine is 3 in. wide by 14 in. long. Parts made from wire to 24-in. lengths (or longer if a special machine is used) and up to ⅜ in. in diameter can be formed automatically from coil stock.

This article has been prepared from "The Multiform Manual" (T. Hanson, published by Heenan & Froude Limited, Worcester, England), by permission.

This article deals with forming of strip stock; the making of wire forms is discussed in the article on Forming of Wire, pages 349 to 351. Additional examples on the forming of strip stock are included in the articles in this volume on Press Forming of High-Carbon Steel (page 136), Forming of Stainless Steel (page 360), and Forming of Copper and Copper Alloys (page 416).

If the work metal is comparatively thin and the bending is not severe, tempered strip material can be formed. Plated or otherwise coated materials can be formed, but it is usually better to coat after forming, because it is difficult to avoid marring coated surfaces during forming. However, nonmetallic inserts at appropriate points in the straightener, feeder and forming tools can be used to reduce tool marks.

In bending materials such as stainless steel, phosphor bronze, certain grades of brass and beryllium copper, or high-carbon steel, springback must be considered. Adjustments can be made in the forming tools to provide the amount of overbending required for the accuracy of the finished work.

More than one piece can be made in each cycle of a multiple-slide machine. For instance, a part that had previously been made in seven conventional press operations was replanned for multiple-slide production of four pieces per cycle at 200 cycles per minute.

Multiple-Slide Machines

Multiple-slide machines are made in a range of sizes, all similar in construction and principle. The larger machines have a longer die space, which enables more die stations to be used for the manufacture of complicated components. Generally, the number of strokes per minute decreases and the horsepower increases as the machine size increases.

The combination of a stock straightener, feed unit, horizontal press station, and cutoff head, and a forming station that includes a center post and four forming slides (see Fig. 1), provides an efficient machine for producing automatically workpieces that would require a number of dies or die stations in conventional single-action or double-action mechanical presses.

The four forming slides of a multiple-slide machine are generally sufficient for ordinary part-forming needs. However, complex parts can be formed at two or three levels around the center post, thereby doubling or tripling the number of forming positions available.

Figure 1 shows a plan view of the main units of a medium-size multiple-slide machine that uses a floor space of 12 by 5 ft, including the stock reel. Four shafts (A, B, C and D), mounted to a flat-top bedplate, are driven at equal speed through spur gearing E by an

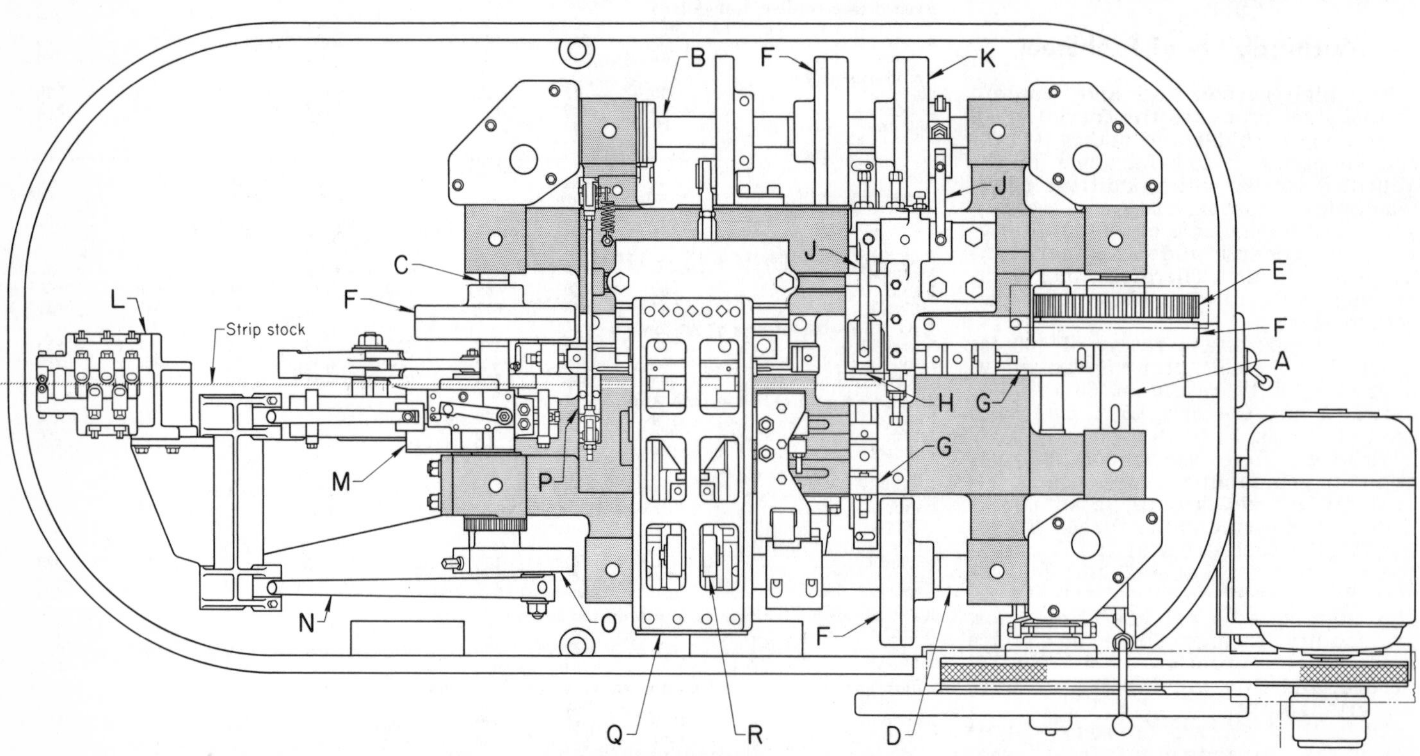

A, B, C and D – Integrated shafts. E – Spur gearing. F – Positive-action cam. G – Slide. H – Vertical post. J – Bell crank. K and R – Cams. L – Stock straightener. M – Automatic gripper in a feed slide. N – Links. O – Adjustable crank. P – Stationary gripper with cam-operated jaws. Q – Horizontal press containing dies. R – Cam.

Fig. 1. Plan view of a multiple-slide machine, showing major components. See text for description of operation.

electric motor. Each of the four shafts is fitted with a positive-action cam F that drives a slide G (only 2 of 4 identified) on which the forming tools may be secured. In the center of the machine is a vertical post H into which the center post or former is fixed, and around which the work material is bent. The formed workpiece is removed from the center post by a stripper mechanism, which usually consists of hardened steel plate embracing the center post and secured to a vertical rod connected to a bell crank J operated by a cam K on the rear shaft to give up-and-down motion to the stripper. All these parts comprise the "forming station" of the machine.

To the left of the machine proper is a stock straightener L, shown in working position with strip stock passing through it. Intermittent feeding of the work metal is accomplished by an automatic gripper in feed slide M actuated by link N and adjustable crank O, which is attached to shaft C. A separate gripper P is provided with cam-operated jaws, which grip the strip on the return stroke of the feed slide to prevent backward motion of the strip.

The work-metal strip, fed through the machine in a vertical plane ("on edge"), passes horizontally through dies in a horizontal press Q. A short, powerful stroke is given to the horizontal press slide by a cam R on the front shaft D. (See also Fig. 2.)

Stock straighteners used on multiple-slide machines are similar to those described in the article on Presses that begins on page 1 in this volume. The main difference is that in a multiple-slide machine the rolls are mounted vertically to straighten the work metal as it passes through the machine on edge, instead of horizontally as in a conventional press.

Stock-feed mechanism of a multiple-slide machine is made of two separate units comprising the forward gripping and transporting device (M in Fig. 1) and a stationary gripping unit P to hold the strip when it is released on the return stroke of the feed. Similar units are described in the article that begins on page 1 of this volume. The stock-feed slide is reciprocated through a system of links from a crank disk keyed to the left-hand camshaft of the machine (see M, N, O and C in Fig. 1).

Press Station. The die used for piercing, trimming, embossing and minor forming of the stock is mounted in the press station, which consists essentially of a horizontal press operated by a cam on the front shaft (Q, R and D in Fig. 1). It may consist of a single unit, as shown in Fig. 2, or extra units can be placed side by side, especially in the larger machines.

Cams provide a positive movement to the press slide in both directions, so that the tools are withdrawn from the strip at the end of the working stroke. Means are provided for adjusting the shut height of the die; also, the entire unit can be moved longitudinally along the bedplate to the desired position established by the feed length.

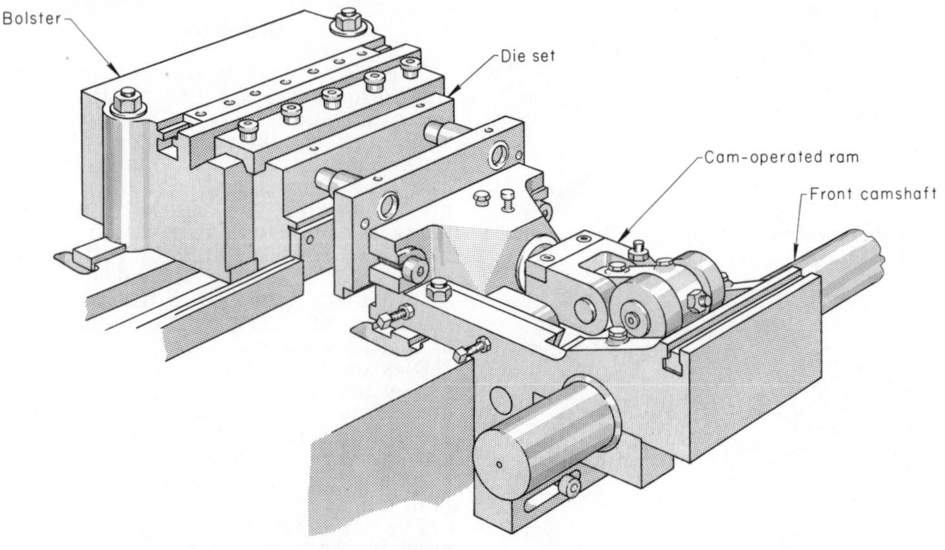

Fig. 2. Press station of a multiple-slide machine. See text for discussion.

A bolster provides support for the die shoe, and a cam-actuated ram provides support and motion for the punch holder.

The cutoff unit, placed between the press and the front forming slide, is used for cutting the work metal into blanks before they are bent to shape. The ends may be cut off straight, or the cut may be curved.

The cutoff unit consists basically of a horizontal slide that is operated through a lever from a cam on the front shaft. The unit can be adjusted along the bedplate in order to cut off the blank at the required distance from the center post. A positive cam action returns the slide so that the cutoff tool will not interfere with forming.

Generally, the cutting die and stripper, through which the work metal is fed, are stationary, while the punch moves to cut off the blank.

Occasionally, it is desirable to install a second cutoff unit on the right-hand side of the center post. The two units trim the two ends of the blank to an accurate length. Because both ends of the blank are trimmed, slightly more stock is required when this method is used, but the inaccuracies of a long feed length are corrected.

The forming station consists of four slides, a center post, and a stripper mechanism. Shaped tools in the four slides progressively bend the workpiece around the center post. In most applications, the center post controls the shape of the workpiece. The first forming tool, usually on the front slide, holds the blank against the center post during cutoff.

Each of the four forming slides runs in its own slideway machined in the bedplate, and each slide is operated positively in both directions by cams. The front, rear and right-hand slides are all similar in design; the left-hand slide is different, because it must pass underneath the press unit.

The tool holder and slide have a mating key and keyway machined parallel to the slide motion, so that the forming tool can be adjusted in this direction. A keyway in the top of the tool holder at right angles to the slide movement and a mating key on the end of the forming tool allow sidewise adjustment.

The cam that operates each forming slide is made in two halves and has radially disposed slots so it can be easily exchanged or timing can be adjusted.

The unit shown in Fig. 3 holds the center post rigidly in position for the forming tools to operate around and also provides the means for stripping the completed parts off the center post.

The center post is fitted and rigidly secured to a king post, which generally consists of a square or rectangular steel bar. The king post fits into a recess in an overhead horizontal slide and is clamped in position by a steel plate and screws. This arrangement holds the king post and center tool rigid and allows for easy adjustment of the vertical position of the center post. The center tool is held square with the forming tools at all times.

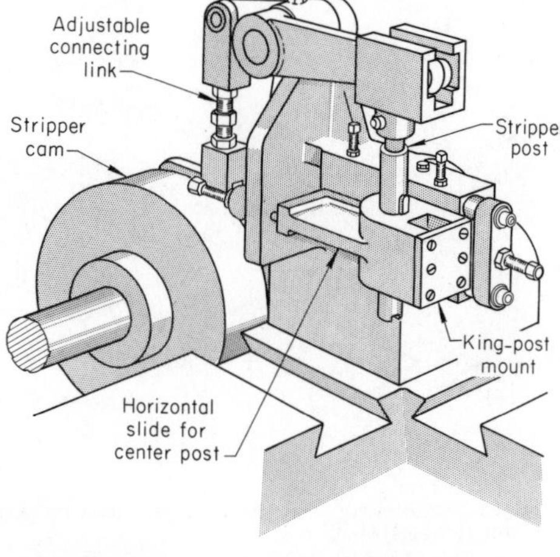

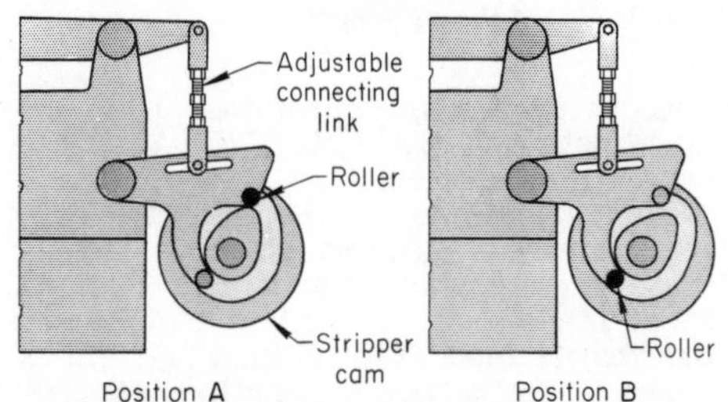

Fig. 3. Unit that contains the cam-operated stripping mechanism and horizontal slide for mounting of the center-post assembly. See text for discussion.

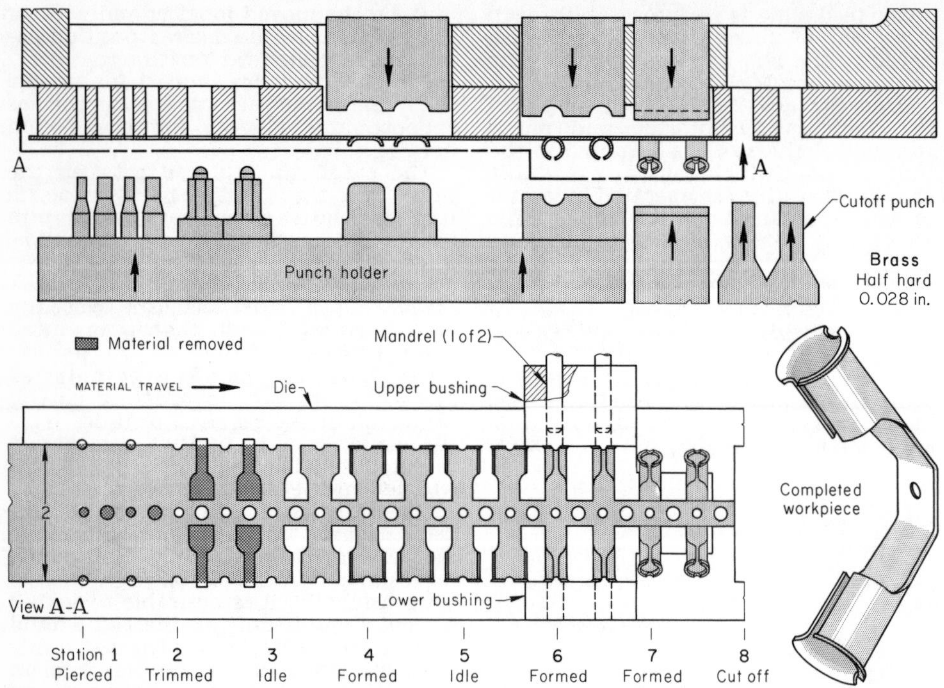

Fig. 4. Extended die that was used to form two double-socket contacts per cycle in eight die stations (Example 224)

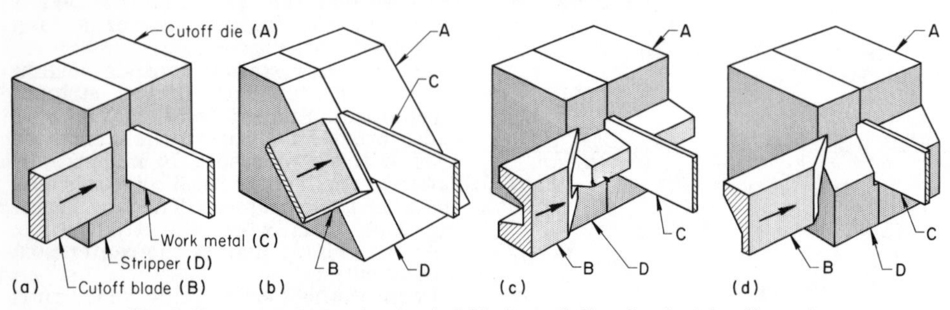

Fig. 5. Four arrangements of cutoff blades and dies. See text for discussion.

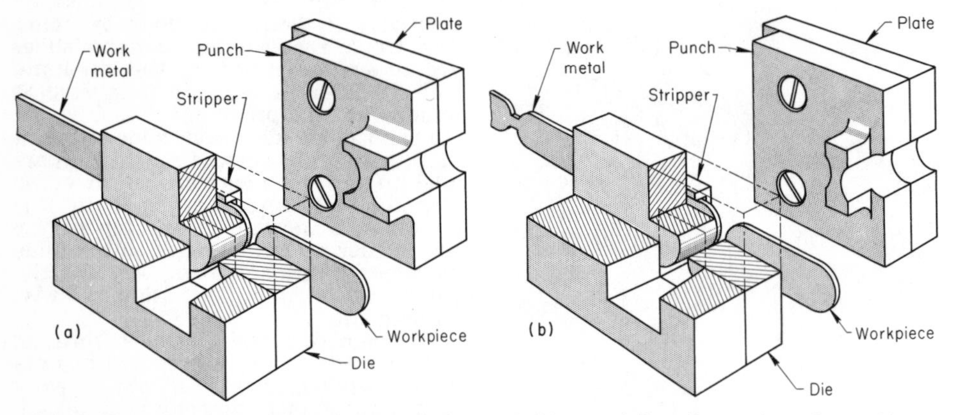

(a) Cutting the full contour in one stroke, and (b) completing the contour by parting a partly developed blank from the strip by severing the connecting tab.

Fig. 6. Two types of parting dies that shape the ends of blanks in preparation for forming

The overhead slide, carrying the center post, moves parallel with the front and rear slides and is pushed backward by the action of the front tool holding the strip against the center post until the slide reaches a stop, when the metal is bent to shape.

When the front tool retracts, the slide containing the center post is returned by spring pressure until a stop is reached. If desired, the slide may be held in a fixed position by adjustment of the two stops. The sliding center post arrangement minimizes interference between the cutoff die and the left-hand slide tools.

Workpieces are ejected from the center post by a suitably shaped stripper plate moving downward; the stripper plate is held on a vertical rod, which derives its motion through a system of levers from a positive-action cam on the rear shaft. During forming, the stripper plate is positioned above the forming tools. The vertical rod is guided by a bushing in the overhead slide.

The stripper-cam lever has provision for the roller to be in one of two positions. With the roller as shown in position A, Fig. 3, the cam acts as a normal ejector, moving quickly down and returning the stripper rod almost immediately. With the roller in position B, the rod is held down for a longer period and remains in the upward position for a short time only. This arrangement is used when a retractable mandrel is attached to the mechanism in place of a stripper plate. The mandrel can be held down for a long time while the forming takes place and then be quickly retracted, as may be required in a further forming or closing operation. (The use of two mandrels attached to the stripper mechanism is shown in Fig. 4 and discussed in Example 224.)

Blanking

The blank that is bent to shape in the forming station has all the prior operations done in the press station. Trimming the blank outline, piercing holes, embossing ribs, weld projections and hole flanges, and stamping letters and numerals are done before the blank is cut off and formed. The blank is severed from the strip by cutting off, parting or blanking methods. These methods are described in the article on Blanking of Low-Carbon Steel, page 31 in this volume.

Dies used in multiple-slide machines are either single-stage or progressive, depending on the complexity of the part being formed. Generally a progressive die is used, even though it may be only a simple two-station pierce-and-pilot die, as in Example 225.

The dies for producing the blank must be made as accurately for a multiple-slide machine as they are for a conventional press. However, the multiple-slide dies are of a simpler design and less expensive than conventional press dies, because most of the forming is done in a separate station and around the center post.

The strip layout and die construction are similar to those for progressive dies used in conventional presses. However, as noted in previous sections, the bending operations are usually done in the forming station and cutting off by the cutoff unit, unless a transfer unit is used to transport the blank from the press station to the forming station. Air jets are used where possible to eject the pierced slugs from the die.

Forming lanced detents and flanged holes toward the punch side of the blank can be done by actuating the punches with cams on the rear camshaft. Additional movements of die units can be obtained from any of the three other camshafts.

Extended dies are progressive dies that are mounted in the press station and extend into the forming station. After the usual piercing, notching and piloting operations, bending or forming is done by a combination of elements in the progressive die and those actuated by the front and rear camshafts. The stripper mechanism can be used to advance and retract a mandrel around which the part is bent. The moving or positioning of punches and dies by the camshafts can make it possible to use tools that are much simpler in design than those made for operations in conventional presses.

Parts made in extended dies generally are those that can be retained on the strip until all operations are complete before the part is cut off.

The application of an extended die for making two parts at a time is described in the following example.

Example 224. Use of an Extended Die for Forming Socket Contacts Two at a Time (Fig. 4)

The layout of an extended die for forming a double-socket contact is shown in Fig. 4. The stock was half-hard brass, 2 in. wide and 0.028 in. thick. Production rate was 200 parts (100 cycles) per minute.

The progressive die mounted in the press station extended into the forming station, where the parts were formed and then cut off.

In the first die station, the edges were notched and four holes were pierced along the center of the strip. The two large holes in the center of the connecting tabs were used for piloting the strip in subsequent stations.

The shape of the two blanks was cut in station 2 by four identical punches, leaving the center connecting tabs for piloting and carrying the stock through the die. The edges of the cylindrical portion were curled in station 4. These were bent against anvils on the punch holder by a tool at the rear of the die, operated by a cam on the rear shaft of the machine. Stations 3 and 5 were idle, to add strength to the die.

Next, two vertical mandrels, actuated by the stripper mechanism, descended in front of the work metal. The mandrels were supported above and below the stock by guide bushings. A second rear tool moved in and bent the edge-curled metal around each mandrel. The cylinders were completed by mating tools on the punch holder. (To obtain the proper dwell for the mandrels, the stripper mechanism used the position B shown in Fig. 3 for the cam follower.)

When the tools and mandrels retracted, the strip was moved to station 7, where the cylindrical portions of the sockets were bent to the specified angle by the combined action of the front and rear forming tools. Finally, at station 8, two punches cut the finished sockets from the connecting tabs and ejected them through the die to a container.

The ability to time the movement of the forming tools simplified the dies and kept the parts under control until completely formed.

Cutting off the blank is usually done with a blade and die mounted in the cutoff unit. The die is fixed to the housing across which the strip of work metal passes; the blade is secured to the slide so that when it is given a forward movement, the blank is sheared from the strip.

Basically, the cutoff tool is comprised of two flat pieces of metal (see Fig. 5a): the cutoff die A and the blade B. A fixed stripper D holds the work metal C against the die, and when the blade moves across the face of the die, the metal is severed. Most of the parts shown in this article were cut from the strip by this method.

The die and blade can be modified to give a shaped cut, as shown in Fig. 5(b), (c) and (d). The shapes shown can be used when forming ringlike parts that have a smooth-fitting joint.

Shaped ends on a workpiece can be formed by cutting the full contour of the ends of two adjacent parts in one machine stroke, as shown in Fig. 6(a), or by partly developing the contour in the press station and then using the cutoff station to complete the contour by parting the blank from the strip by shearing the connecting tab, as shown in Fig. 6(b).

Parting of blanks by removing connecting tabs is also used when the ends are not of the same shape. This practice is illustrated in progressive-die layouts included in several articles in this volume.

Blending the parting punch with the previously cut contour may necessitate the use of a punch with sharp corners, which could cause short punch life. If not properly blended, flats or other evidence of mismatch will appear on the severed workpiece.

As shown in Fig. 6, the parting punch is mounted on the plate at the rear of the strip. The die is fitted with a stripper into which the metal is guided across the front of the die. Both the die and stripper are mounted on the slide of the cutoff unit and move horizontally toward the punch, carrying the strip metal with them. On contact of the work metal with the punch, the ends are sheared. The scrap is ejected through the die.

Normal press practice is for the die to remain stationary and the punch to move. This is reversed when parting in the cutoff unit, so that the end of the metal can swing clear, which would not be possible if the die were at the back of the strip.

Another way in which shaped ends can be produced is to provide a cutoff unit at each side of the front forming tool, each unit being fitted with a die to cut one end. When pilots cannot be used in the die or when a long blank is being cut, the second unit helps in solving tooling problems.

Short Blanks. When the length of the blank is short and the end very close to the forming slides, the cutoff blade can be fastened to the front tool. The blade is fitted and secured to the front tool; an adjustment screw provides for positioning the blade. The cutoff die is positioned to mate with the blade.

Transfer of blanks from the cutoff unit to the forming station generally is unnecessary, since the blank can be moved into the forming station before it is cut from the strip. However, it is sometimes desirable to cut the blank from the strip at the last station in the progressive die, as in ordinary press blanking. In such a cycle, a transfer unit like that shown in Fig. 7(a) is used, which transfers the blank to the forming station. The transfer head is actuated by a stub shaft located below the left-hand camshaft (C in Fig. 1).

After the blanking punch has retracted, the blank is held in the die cavity. Then the blank is pushed out of the die cavity with a plunger moved forward by a cam fixed to the rear shaft and into the waiting pickup finger. The blank is transported horizontally to the forming station, where the first forming tool pushes the blank out of the pickup finger and against the center post. While the forming tools are bending the blank around the center post, the transfer head moves back to the press station for another blank.

A blank can be picked up in the blanking station in one position and indexed to the forming position during the transfer motion (see Fig. 7b). This permits the strip layout to be designed for best stock utilization; also, bends can be positioned favorably with respect to the rolling direction.

The transfer of blanks from the blanking position to the forming position without reorientation is shown in Fig. 7(c). The pickup finger is mounted in the transfer head so that no swiveling or indexing takes place.

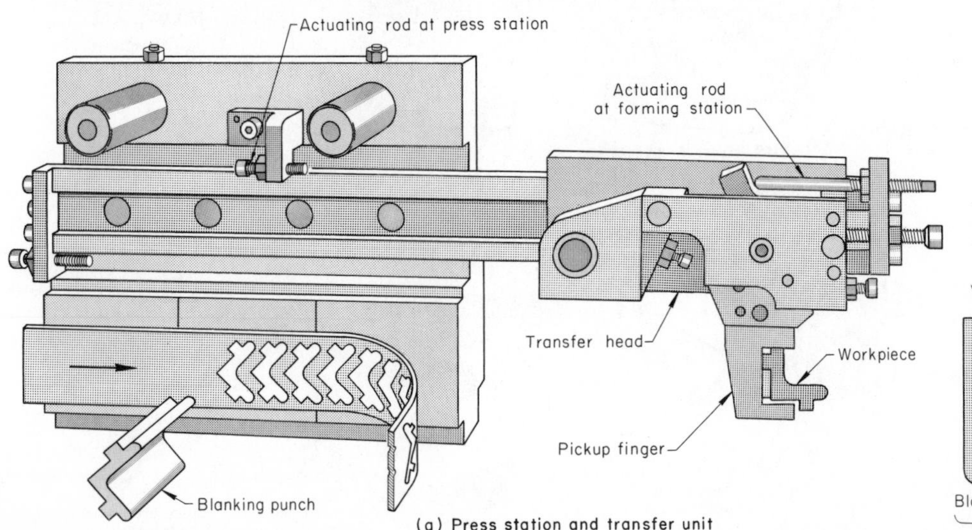

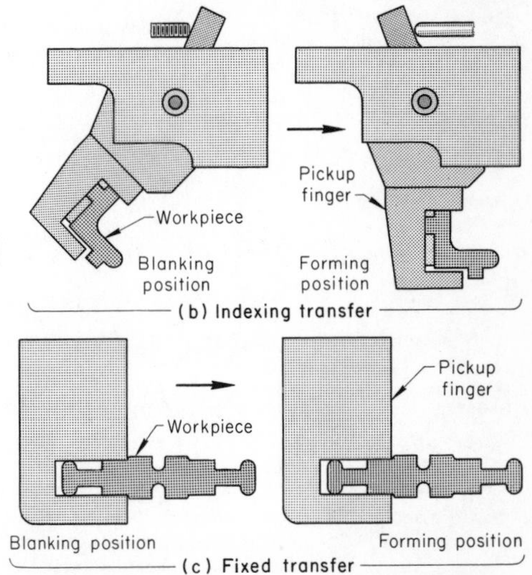

Fig. 7. Mechanism for indexing and fixed transfer of blanks from the press station to the forming station of a multiple-slide machine

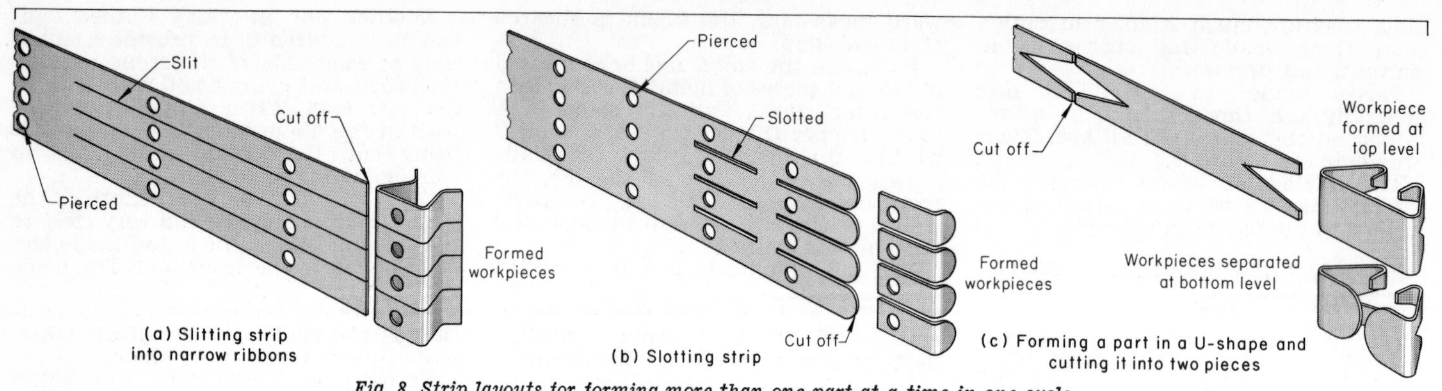

Fig. 8. Strip layouts for forming more than one part at a time in one cycle

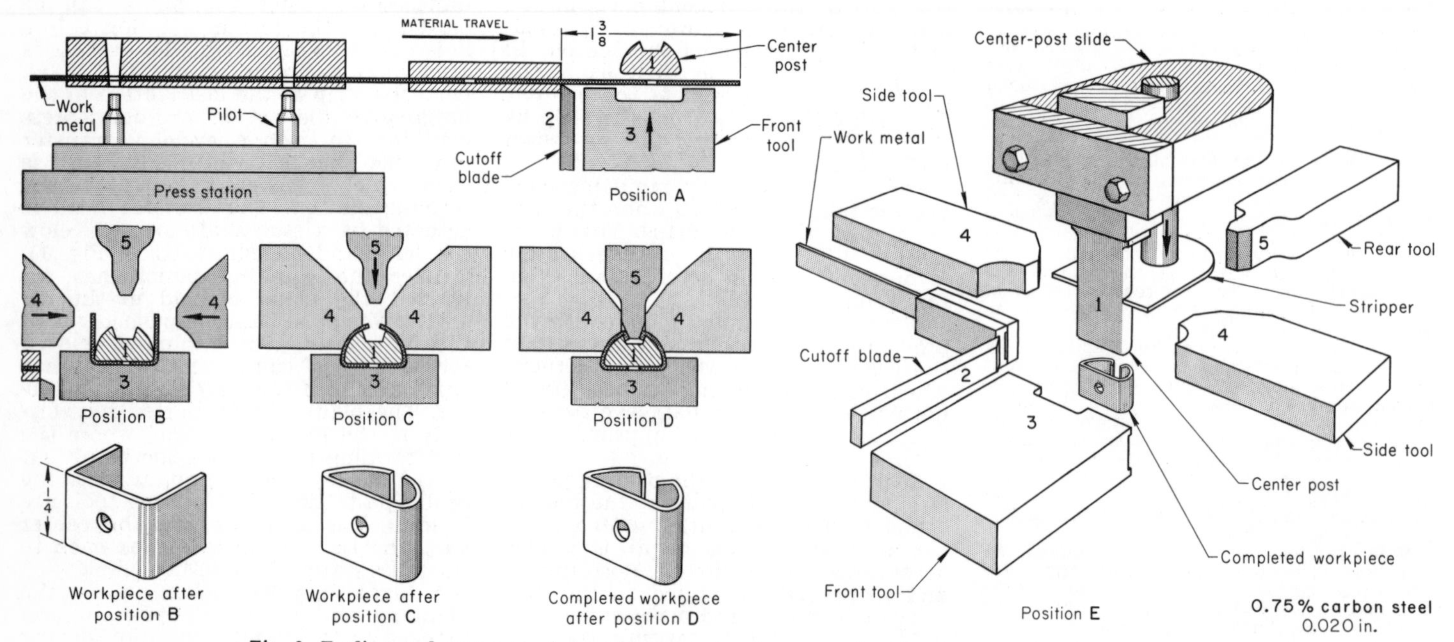

Fig. 9. Tooling and sequence of operations for forming a simple clip at one level (Example 225)

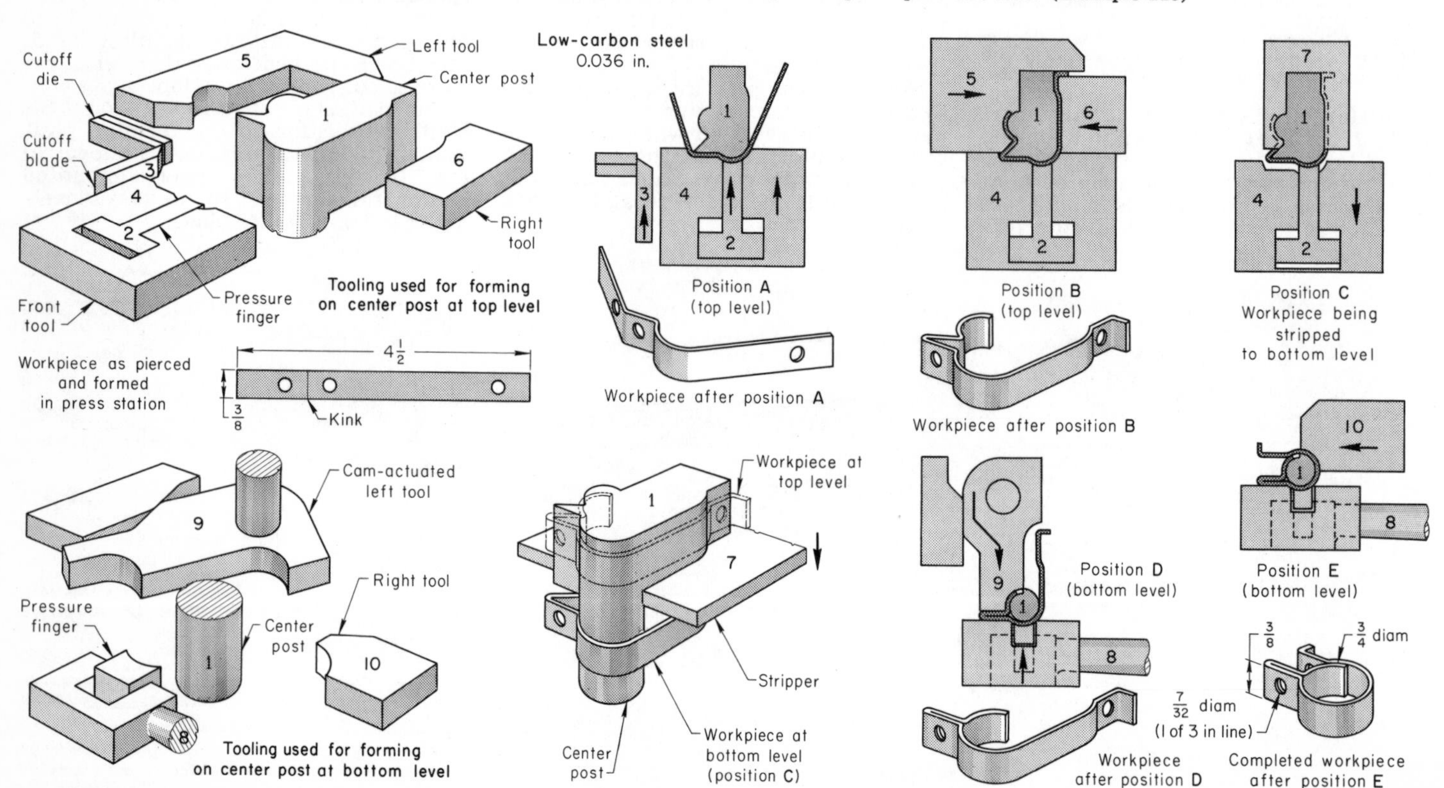

Fig. 10. Forming tools and sequence of operations in the two-level forming of a hose clamp (Example 226)

Timing of the transfer-head motion is important; the finger must be in position for loading or unloading but must not interfere with the blanking punch or the forming slides.

Forming

As the work-metal strip leaves the press station it passes through the cutoff unit and between the center post and the first forming tool (usually the front tool). Simultaneously with the cutting off of the blank, the front forming tool moves forward and holds the blank firmly against the center post. By continued movement of the front tool, the blank is bent around the center post. Tools on the two side slides move in to make further bends, and these can be followed by a fourth tool on the rear slide to complete the forming. The sequence in which the slides move is not fixed, nor is it always necessary to use all four slides when forming a part.

Holding blanks firmly in position against the center post is necessary while they are being severed from the stock and also during the initial forming operation, to prevent slipping and to insure against premature bending or kinking across a weak section. The work metal is likely to bulge when a U-shape part is being formed, such as that shown in Fig. 12. Such a bulge is not removed when the tools are fully closed, because the surplus metal cannot flow while the blank is held firmly by the two corners of the bending tool. In some applications, a spring-loaded plunger in the first forming tool is positioned slightly in advance of the bending portions and prevents the blank from bulging when the bends are started. A positive blankholder is essential to hold forms having a weak section between the bends or to prevent slipping or dragging of a blank around the corner when bending takes place.

A partly formed blank also must be held while being moved to the lower level and until a form tool can grip it.

There are two general types of mechanically operated blankholders. One makes use of the standard stripping mechanism; the other is operated by a cam and lever from one of the shafts.

Part Ejection. After all tools are retracted, the formed part is ready for ejection by the stripper plate. During forming, the stripper plate is positioned at the top and clear of the forming tools. After forming, the stripper plate moves down and ejects the part from the center post.

The stripper also can move a partly formed component into a second, or even a third, forming level on the center post.

Multiple-Part Forming. Forming of more than one part per cycle of the machine should be considered when planning the tools for production, but the increased loading must be within the capacity of the equipment. How the outline of the part is developed depends largely on its finished shape. If a part can be made of strip stock by piercing, cutting off and forming, more than one part can be made in each cycle by slitting the strip into two or more ribbons, as shown in Fig. 8(a). For parts having shaped ends (for example, semicircular), the strip can be slotted and the blank then cut off as shown in Fig. 8(b). Slotting the strip may eliminate the need for sharp corners on the punch and die, thus increasing their life. Parts with more complex outlines require more complex trimming punches. The blank is severed from the strip by either cutoff or parting methods.

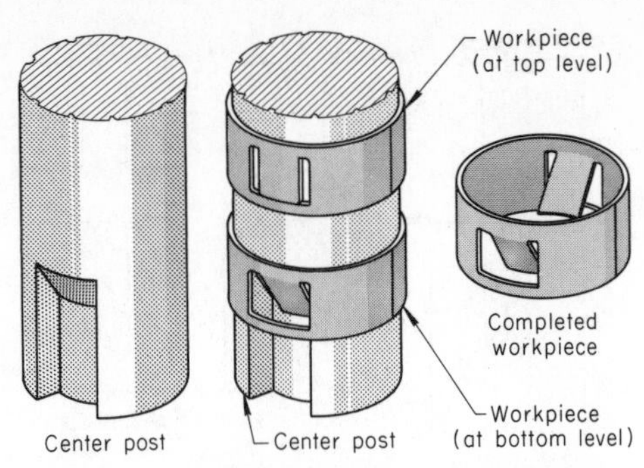

Fig. 11. Two-level forming of parts with internally bent tabs, showing lower portion of center post slotted

Some parts, such as those having the basic shape of an L, are easier to form into a U-shape and then part after forming. The bottom forming level of a multiple-slide machine can be used for parting, as shown in Fig. 8(c). The parting punch is positioned on the rear tool slide, and the die on the front tool. The center post has a clearance hole for the punch.

Parts similar to the one shown in Fig. 4 (Example 224) are also made in multiples, by using extended dies.

Forming Level. Forming can be done around the center post at the same level at which the blank enters the forming station (single-level forming) or at one or two positions below that level (two-level or three-level forming). Parts can be finish formed at the lower level, resistance welded into ringlike parts, or finish formed and then cut into two or more pieces (see Fig. 8c). The partly completed workpieces usually are moved to the lower level by the stripper mechanism.

Single-level forming is used when all the bends can be made with one set of forming tools, usually with one forward stroke per machine cycle. Sometimes a bend can be made by partly forming, retracting the tool, doing some work by another tool, and then advancing the first tool to finish the bend. Auxiliary forming tools actuated by separate cams or lever arrangements can be used to do more work on a piece.

Wide blanks are usually formed at one level, because of the length of center post needed to support more than one part, and because of the limited space available for mounting tools.

The forming of a simple clip at one level is described in the next example.

Example 225. Making a Small Clip (Fig. 9)

The small clip shown in Fig. 9 was made in a multiple-slide machine from spring steel strip ¼ in. wide that was cut into blanks by a cutoff blade mounted in the cutoff unit. A two-station progressive die mounted in the press station pierced the center hole and piloted the strip to control the accuracy of feed length and cutoff.

At position A, the strip is shown just before cutoff. The cutoff blade moved to shear the stock at the same time the front tool moved to grip the blank and then bend it around the center post.

At position B, the front tool has formed the part around the center post, the cutoff blade has retracted, and the two side tools are moving toward the center post. At position C, the side tools have performed their function and the rear tool is moving inward.

Position D shows all the forming tools at the end of their strokes holding the completed workpiece against the center post. At position E, all the forming tools are shown in their starting positions, and the stripper has ejected the clip from the center post so that a new cycle can begin.

During two-level forming, two components are on the center post — one at the top level, the other at the bottom level. Work is done simultaneously on each piece by the forming tools. Frequently, forming is done at both levels simultaneously, by providing each slide with a tool shaped to perform an operation on each piece. The workpiece at the lower level is pushed off the center post by the partly completed piece being moved downward from the top level.

One of the simplest applications of two-level forming is the manufacture of bushings and ferrules by forming the center and the ends of the blank at the top level and finish forming to final diameter at the bottom level.

A more complicated application of two-level forming is described in the example that follows.

Example 226. Two-Level Forming of a Hose Clamp (Fig. 10)

The hose clamp shown in Fig. 10 was made from cadmium-plated steel ⅜ in. wide at two levels on the center post in a multiple-slide machine. At the press station, the three holes were pierced and a score mark or slight kink was formed between two holes to insure that the two holes would coincide after the metal had been folded back on itself. Pilots in the press station assured accurate location of the strip for cutoff and forming.

Forming tools for the two levels are shown at the left in Fig. 10.

At position A, the cutoff blade 3 sheared the blank from the strip while it was held against the center post 1 by the pressure finger 2. The front tool 4 formed the blank as shown. Side tools 5 and 6 are shown pressing the stock around the center post in position B. With the front and side tools retracted in position C, the pressure finger held the formed part against the center post while the stripper 7 moved the part to the lower level, where the spring-loaded lever arm and pressure finger 8 held the part.

In position D at the bottom level, the pivoting rear tool 9 formed the part around the center post (circular in shape at this level). The rear tool also set the folded-over metal against an extension of the front tool 4. The final forming operation by the right tool 10 was as shown in position E.

In the next cycle the stripper pushed a new workpiece down to the bottom level, as the completed hose clamp was pushed off the center post. Cycle time was about 60 components per minute.

Tabs or projections bent internally in workpieces cause difficulty in forming, because the center post must be relieved (slotted vertically) to clear the tabs in stripping. In such applications, it is usual to form the workpiece at the top level and then to move it down to a lower level where the center post can be slotted so that tools can form the internal tab and not impede stripping (see Fig. 11).

Two-level forming can be used to relieve severe forming loads on center posts of small diameter. The heavier

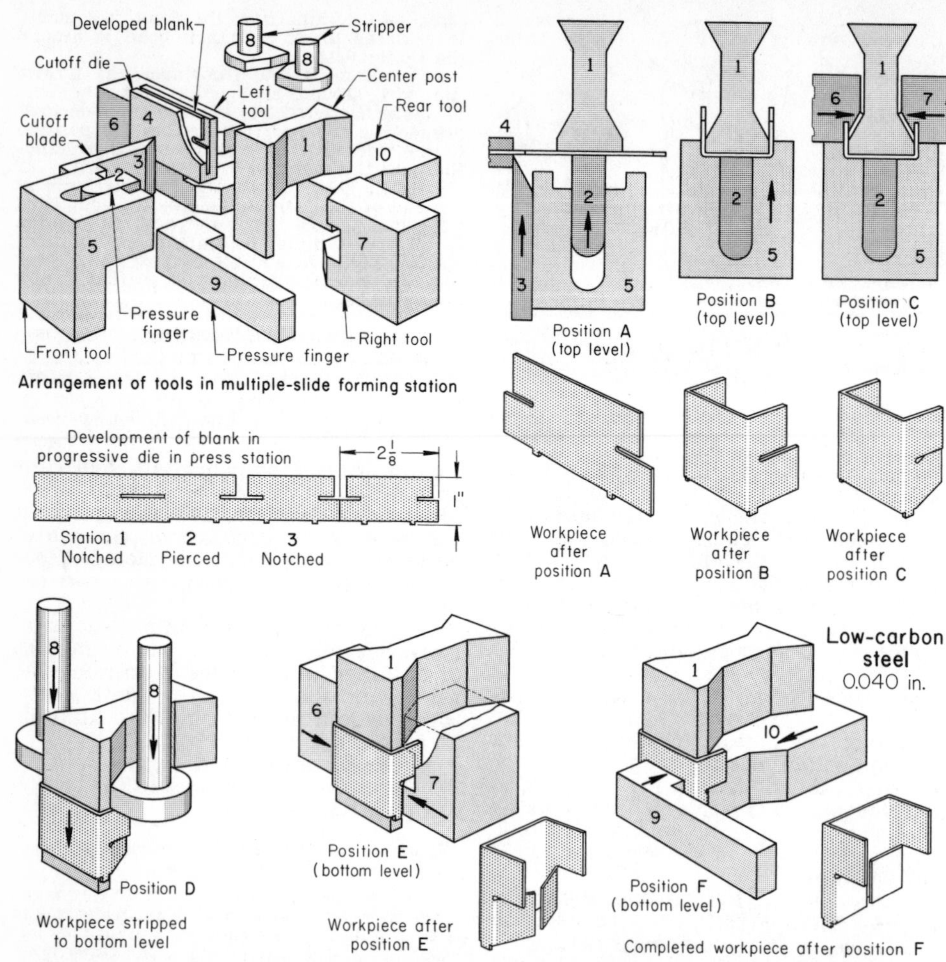

Fig. 12. Two-level forming of a strapping seal. Note narrow lower portion of center post.

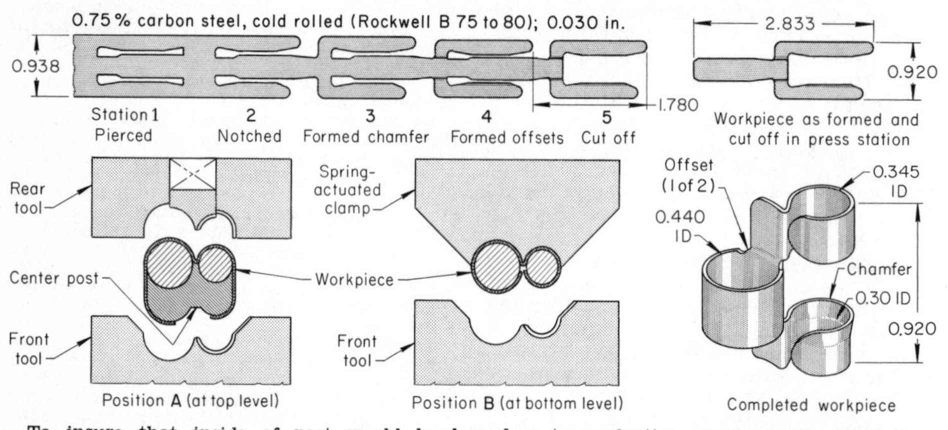

To insure that inside of part would be burr-free (a production requirement), blank was positioned between rear tool and center post for the first forming operation at the top level.

Fig. 13. Two-level forming of a cartridge-belt link (Example 227)

forming operations are done at the top level around a rugged center post. The lower end of the post is of smaller section, shaped to suit the shape of the finished part. When forming tubular shapes, the lower surface of the first forming tool can hold the workpiece against the center post at the second level and, at the same time, counteract the forces of the finish forming tools.

The closed portion of the strapping seal shown in Fig. 12 had to be formed on a thin center post of rectangular section. Two-level forming permitted a post with a heavy section at the top for forming the blank to a U-shape and partial bending of the lower half. A thinner section was used at the lower level for finish forming. The partly completed form was held in position at the lower level by a spring-loaded pressure finger (9 in Fig. 12). The forces exerted by the lower-level tools 6, 7 and 10 against the narrow section of the center post were counteracted by the lower surface of the front tool backing up the pressure finger 9.

The arrangement of tools at the forming station, strip development, and forming steps at both levels are shown in Fig. 12. The part was made of low-carbon steel strip 1 in. wide and 0.040 in. thick at a production rate of 120 pieces per minute.

In multiple-slide forming, general practice is to pass the blank in front of the center post for subsequent forming. However, where it is important that the internal edges of a part be free of burrs, the sequence can be changed to use the rear tool as the first forming tool by feeding the blank behind the center post, as in the following example of two-level forming that used a center post and forming tools shaped to suit the needs of each level.

Example 227. Use of Rear Tool as First Forming Tool in Top Level to Insure Burr-Free Internal Edges (Fig. 13)

The internal edges of the loops on the cartridge-belt link shown in Fig. 13 had to be free of burrs and sharp edges. This was accomplished in multiple-slide forming by feeding the blank behind the center post and using the rear tool as the first forming tool at the top level. This procedure was simpler than positioning the die on the movable platen in the press station so that the burrs would be on the top side of the blank.

Scrap was reduced by cutting the stock for the large single loop from between the two smaller loops. Thus, a blank 2.833 in. long was produced from a feed length of only 1.780 in. The stock was cold rolled steel (0.75% carbon) 0.030 in. thick and 0.938 in. wide. Production rate was 120 links per minute.

Forming was done at two levels around the center post with front and rear tools only. Position A (Fig. 13) shows the forming done at the top level; position B shows the finish forming, at the bottom level. The lower surface of the rear tool held the part against the center post during final forming and counteracted the force of the finish-forming tool on the center post.

Because the left-hand tool was not used in forming the link, the press unit was placed close enough to the center post so that cutoff was done in the die instead of with the cutoff unit.

Lockseaming. Metal strip is used to make large quantities and varieties of small open-end boxes, tubes and cylinders to be used as ferrules for paint brushes, radio shields, and many other common products. All of these are made with some locking method to join the ends of the metal.

In lockseaming or can seaming, one end of the metal is formed over the other and flattened into a tight joint. Other methods of locking two ends of metal together in a multiple-slide machine include: interlocking dovetails, raised tabs inserted through slots and then flattened or twisted, a tongue inserted into a lanced slot and then swaged, and lancing and forming through two stock thicknesses.

Lockseaming can be done at either one or two levels around the center post. Single-level forming is used where the tubes are long or where projecting lugs would be too weak to push the finished part off the center post. This method requires that the rear and side tools be advanced two or three times during each cycle of the machine.

Two-level forming with an attachment that gives a positive movement to the seaming tools is a more efficient method of making lockseams. The sliding head containing the center post can be used to make several sizes of lockseam tubes by setting the rear and side tools a fixed distance from the strip line, and then changing only the front tool and the center post. The following example describes a two-level forming operation for external lockseaming to make a short cylindrical tube.

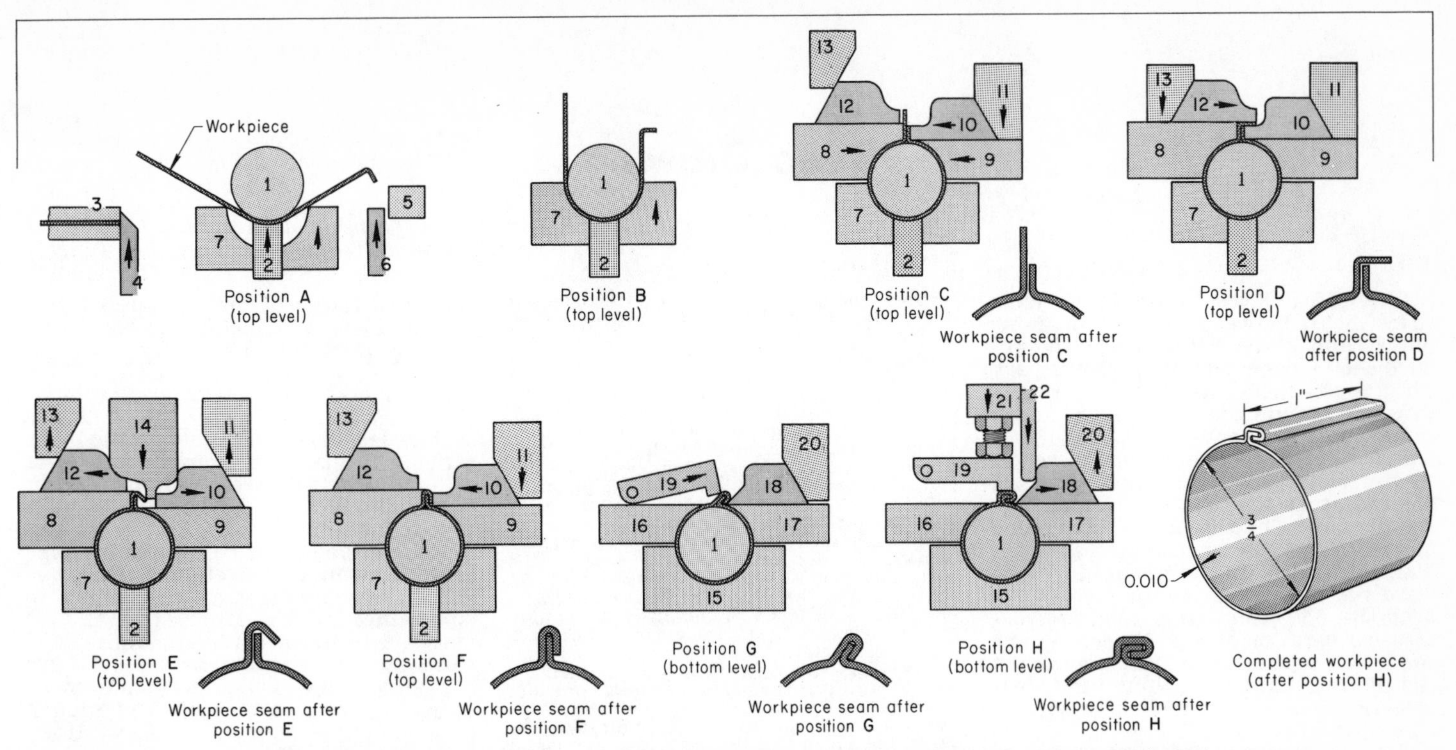

Fig. 14. Two-level forming of an external lockseam to produce a cylindrical part (Example 228)

Example 228. Two-Level External Lockseaming to Produce a Round Tube (Fig. 14)

The external lockseam of the tube shown in Fig. 14 was formed at two levels in a multiple-slide machine. At position A, the strip had been fed between the center post 1 and the pressure finger 2 and sheared by the cutoff die 3 and blade 4. At the same time, the right-hand end of the blank had a small flange formed by fixed tool 5 and blade 6. Position B shows the blank formed into a U-shape by front tool 7. Forming of the cylinder by side tools 8 and 9 is shown in position C. The two ends extend at right angles to the surface, one end being longer than the other. Right tool 10, moved by cam 11, supported the previously bent flange as left tool 8 formed the longer end. At position D, left tool 12, actuated by cam 13, bent the long end over the shorter end.

At position E, cams 11 and 13 retracted, allowing side tools 10 and 12 to be pushed aside by the advancing rear tool 14, thus permitting the end of the seam to be bent. Rear tool 14 retracted, and cam 11 advanced to move side tool 10 to flatten the seam against left tool 8, as shown in position F. The part then was transferred to the lower level by the stripper (not shown).

At the bottom level, front tool 15 and side tools 16 and 17 held the cylinder on the center post. Front tool 15 also backed up the center post during the final forming operations. As shown in position G, anvil 18 supported the seam while swinging tool 19 moved forward to bend the seam at an angle. Anvil 18 is moved by cam 20. Final flattening of the seam is shown in position H. As rear tool 21 advanced, cam projection 22 contacted anvil 18, pushing it clear as swinging tool 19 closed the seam.

Two workpieces were on the center post at this stage, and both were formed at the same time. One, formed through position F, was at the top level; the other was at the bottom level. Both were held tightly on the center post. The completed piece was pushed off the center post and into a container.

Internal lockseams can be made by forming an external seam, such as shown in Fig. 14, and then re-forming the part to make the seam flush with the outer surface. The part is moved to the lower level, where a vertical slot in the center post provides space for the seam as it is pushed inward.

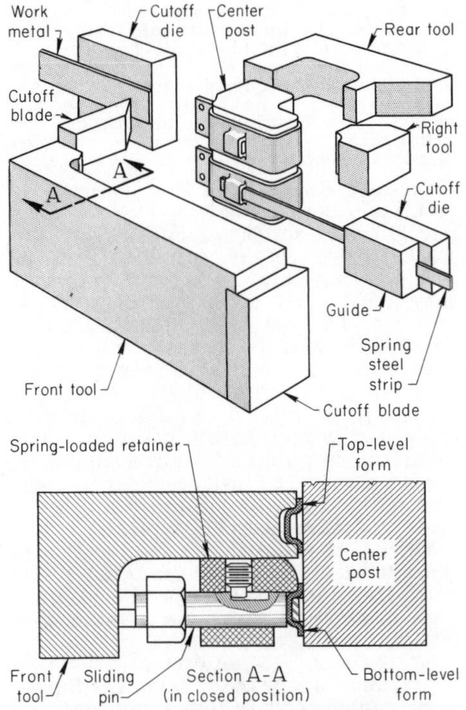

Fig. 15. Assembly of spring steel strip into a bracket at the bottom level of a two-level multiple-slide forming operation

Assembly Operations

By means of auxiliary feeding attachments, one or more components can be assembled to a part being formed during the same machine cycle. Hopper feeding units can sort and orient machined or previously formed parts for feeding into the part being formed in the multiple-slide machine. These devices can be arranged to feed horizontally adjacent to any forming slide, or be operated vertically.

Hopper feeding involves the automatic sorting and transfer of components placed randomly in a hopper of suitable design and shape for delivery by gravity to a track, correctly positioned and in ordered sequence to a machine.

Production Practice. Figure 15 shows the assembly of a flat steel spring into a small steel bracket at the lower level of a two-level multiple-slide machine operation. The bracket was made from ½-in.-wide stock, 0.030 in. thick. The two holes were pierced, and the lug slit and raised, in the press station. The bracket was bent to shape around the center post at the top level by the action of the front, rear and right forming tools. Next it was moved to the bottom forming level by the stripper and held in position against the center post by a spring-loaded retainer. A sliding pin mounted in the retainer was used to flatten the lug against the spring steel strip.

The spring steel strip was fed into the recess formed by the lug; then the front tool moved in, contacted the sliding pin, flattened the lug, and secured the strip to the bracket, and at the same time severed the spring steel strip by a blade mounted to the front tool.

On the next cycle, the assembly was ejected from the center post by the downward movement of the succeeding component. The lower part of the spring-loaded retainer was cut away to clear the strip as it was fed into the lug, and also to permit ejection.

Other Examples of Forming in Multiple-Slide Machines in This Volume

Example	Workpiece
204	Mounting bracket (high-carbon steel)
205	Spring clip (high-carbon steel)
206	Electrical cover (high-carbon steel)
466	Wristband link (stainless steel)
586	Terminal plug (copper alloy)
587	Circuit-breaker terminal (copper alloy)

Deep Drawing

*By the ASM Committee on Forming of Sheet Metal in Presses and the ASM Committee on Press Forming of Steel**

DRAWING is a process for forming sheet metal between an edge-opposing punch and a die (draw ring) to produce a cup, cone, box or shell-like part. The work metal is bent over and wrapped around the punch nose. At the same time, the outer portions of the blank move radially toward the center of the blank until they flow over the die radius as the blank is drawn into the die cavity by the punch. The radial movement of the metal increases the blank thickness as the metal moves toward the die radius; as the metal flows over the die radius, this thickness decreases, because of the tension in the shell wall between the punch nose and the die radius, and (in some instances) because of the clearance between the punch and the die.

The distinction between shallow drawing and deep drawing is arbitrary, although shallow drawing generally refers to the forming of a cup no deeper than half its diameter, with little thinning of the metal. In deep drawing, the cup is deeper than half its diameter, and wall thinning, although not necessarily intentional, may be more than in shallow drawing. Wall thinning is more pronounced in stainless steel parts than in those made of low-carbon steel. One or more redraws, with or without intermediate annealing, are often required in order to complete a deep drawn part.

The fundamentals of drawing discussed in this article are generally applicable to all ductile metals, although drawing practice varies for different work metals. Most of the examples of practice presented here are concerned with the processing of flat rolled low-carbon steels such as 1006, 1008 and 1010. For drawing other metals, the reader may consult the articles in this volume that deal with forming of specific metals.

Mild drawing of low-carbon steel, as one stage of a forming sequence, is dealt with in the article "Press Forming of Low-Carbon Steel", which begins on page 112. Many of the practices discussed in that article can be applied also to the forming of other ductile metals.

Additional press operations performed on drawn workpieces are redrawing, reducing, expanding, bulging, sizing and ironing.

Redrawing is used to reduce the diameter and increase the height of a previously drawn cup, either for the full length or for a specified distance from the bottom. A punch pulls the cup into the die and reduces the diameter by either direct or reverse redrawing.

Reducing differs from redrawing in that the diameter is reduced at the mouth of the shell rather than at the bottom or for the full length. The top of the shell is pushed or compressed into the die rather than pulled through the die by the punch. Reducing is often referred to as necking, tapering, nosing or closing.

Expanding or bulging is the forming of irregular contours or surfaces of revolution on shells or rings by expanding or reducing the diameter for a portion of its cylindrical length. Such shapes cannot be removed from a regular punch or die. The change in shape is produced by a wedge-action punch or die, or by the use of a fluid or a rubber punch.

Sizing is used for forming workpieces to specific dimensions. The final forming of sharp radii should be combined with a small reduction in the cross-sectional area of the part. The metal should be crowded and not stretched into sharp corners. When the sizing operation is designed to eliminate oil-canning in the sidewall of a box or to establish a depth, the metal is stretched.

Ironing is the intentional thinning of the wall of a drawn shell. The operation provides uniform wall thickness or produces a thin-wall, thick-bottom part. The clearance between the punch and the die is less than metal thickness; this reduces wall thickness and increases the height as the shell is drawn through the die by the punch. Some slight redrawing takes place as the wall is thinned by ironing. The small reduction in diameter is employed mainly to permit free entry of the punch into the shell. Because the ironed shell clings to the punch, the stresses in the metal are compressive. A part with an ironed sidewall is less susceptible to cracking and distortion in machining than is a drawn part that has not been ironed.

Product Shape. Drawing is used to produce both shallow and deep straight-wall shells (or cups) from flat stock. These shells can be used as formed, like some pots and pans, or they may need attachments such as handles and pouring spouts. Drawn shells can also be thread rolled and edge curled to form a variety of products (such as screw caps). Drawing is used to develop shell walls that slope in or out, or to produce simple or complex square or rectangular boxlike shapes. It is also possible to produce drawn shells that have walls of nonuniform thickness; cartridge cases are typical.

When shell-derived products are small and are required in large numbers, they are usually produced in a high-production press, such as an eyelet-type transfer machine.

By reducing, expanding and bulging operations, shells can have contoured walls, which may be noncylindrical and embossed for decorative purposes (typical products are metal tumblers and cooking utensils). The screw ends on electric light bulbs are drawn, as are many metal slip cases and tubular products (shells with the bottoms trimmed). Seamless tubular products, ranging in diameter from a fraction of an inch to several feet, with a closed or partly closed end, may be made from drawn shells.

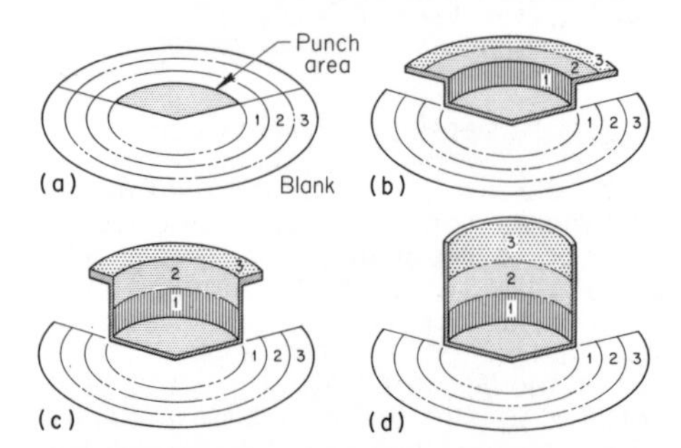

Fig. 1. Progression of metal flow in drawing a cup from a flat blank

Shallow shells can be formed by combined drawing and stretching. For some shells, the process may be similar to embossing, which requires that the metal being formed remain under tensile load. For a panel that must have compound curvatures, this requirement frequently cannot be met, and such a panel may be difficult to draw. However, by use of a process such as stretch forming, the required curvatures can be developed with minimum wrinkling; wrinkles in the scrap area can be removed by trimming.

Sheet-metal shapes such as used in aerospace structures are usually assembled from drawn and stretch formed components. An automobile body is assembled from shallow drawn, deep drawn, and stretch formed components. Smaller structural shapes, such as home-appliance components, are also made from drawn shells.

Fundamentals of Drawing

A flat blank is formed into a cup by forcing a punch against the center portion of a blank that rests on the die ring. Progressive stages of metal flow in drawing a cup from a flat blank are shown schematically in Fig. 1. During the first stage, the punch contacts the blank (Fig. 1a), and the metal section denoted as 1 in Fig. 1 is bent and wrapped around the punch nose (Fig. 1b). Simultaneously and in sequence, the outer sections of the blank, denoted as 2 and 3 in Fig. 1, move radially toward the center of the blank until the remainder of the blank has bent around the punch nose and a straight-wall cup is formed (Fig. 1c and d). During drawing, the center of the blank (denoted as punch area in Fig. 1a) is essentially unchanged as it forms the bottom of the drawn cup. The areas that become the sidewall of the cup (1, 2 and 3 in Fig. 1) change from the shape of annular segments to longer parallel-side cylindrical elements as they are drawn over the die radius. Metal flow occurs until all the metal has been drawn over the die radius.

A blankholder is used in a draw die to prevent the formation of wrinkles as compressive action rearranges the metal from flange to sidewall. Wrinkling starts because of some lack of uniformity in the movement or the resistance

*For committee lists, see pages 1 and 112.

to movement in the cross section of the metal. A blankholder force sufficient to resist or compensate for this nonuniform movement prevents wrinkling. Once a wrinkle starts, the blankholder is raised from the surface of the metal so that others can form easily. The force to hold the blank flat during drawing of cylindrical shells varies from practically zero for relatively thick blanks to about one-third of the drawing load for a blank 0.030 in. thick. Thinner blanks often require proportionally greater blankholder force.

Conditions for drawing without a blankholder depend on the ratio of the supported length of the blank to its thickness (see page 173 and Fig. 20), the amount of reduction from blank diameter to cup diameter, and the ratio of blank diameter to stock thickness. For thick sheets, the maximum reduction of blank diameter to cup diameter in drawing without a blankholder is about 25%. This ratio approaches zero for thin foil-like sheet. If a blankholder is employed, the maximum reduction is increased to about 50% for metals of maximum drawability and 25 to 30% for metals of marginal drawability in the same equipment.

Draw Ratios

The reduction in drawing cylindrical shells is generally expressed in terms of the diameters of the blank and the cup. Strain depends only slightly on the blank thickness. (See Appendix 2 at the end of this article.) The drawability of a metal is expressed either as the ratio of the blank diameter to the punch diameter, D/d, or as the percentage reduction from the blank diameter to the cup diameter, $100(1 - d/D)$.

The ratio of the height of the cup to the diameter of the cup sometimes is used as an expression of drawing ratio. However, this ratio varies with the drawability of the metal and the amount of thickening or thinning of the sidewall. Draw-reduction values for cupping and redrawing cylindrical shells in a double-action press or a die provided with a blankholder are given in Table 1.

It is emphasized that the values in Table 1 are approximate; they vary with work-metal composition, thickness and hardness, and with shell contour. For instance, a metal with maximum drawability, such as copper, can be reduced initially as much as 55%, but a refractory metal may allow an initial reduction of only 25%.

In drawing a shell with enough punch-to-die clearance to prevent ironing, the sidewall is thicker than the original blank for a short distance from the top; near the bottom, the wall is a little thinner than blank thickness. The amount of thickening or thinning depends on the metal, the percentage reduction, and the tensile stress in the sidewall.

The first, or cupping, reduction percentage is given in Table 1 as 40%. In general, flaws introduced into the cup during the first draw cannot be removed in subsequent processing. Rather, they are aggravated, especially if they have resulted from strain instability, which can lead to wrinkles, puckers or metal

Table 1. Typical Relations of Shell Depth to Draw Reduction for Ductile Metal(a)

Depth of shell, in diameters	Number of draws	Reduction, %(b) Cupping	First redraw	Second redraw	Third redraw
½	1	40	..	..	..
1	2	40	25	..	..
1½	3	40	25	15	..
2	4	40	25	15	11

(a) Values are based on deep drawing of steel in a double-action press or a die provided with a blankholder. These values can serve as a guide for drawing of most ductile metals. Values are based on annealing between operations. (b) Percentage reduction = $100(1 - d/D)$.

Table 2. Nominal Height of Cup Calculated From Blank Diameter, Cup Diameter, and Percentage Reduction

Reduction, %(a)	Cup diam (d), in.	Cup height (h), in.(b)	Ratio h/d
Blank Diameter, 2 In.			
20	1.6	0.23	0.14
30	1.4	0.37	0.26
40	1.2	0.54	0.45
50	1.0	0.75	0.75
Blank Diameter, 5 In.			
20	4.0	0.55	0.14
30	3.5	0.92	0.26
40	3.0	1.35	0.45
50	2.5	1.87	0.75
Blank Diameter, 10 In.			
20	8	1.15	0.14
30	7	1.87	0.26
40	6	2.7	0.45
50	5	3.75	0.75
Blank Diameter, 20 In.			
20	16	2.2	0.14
30	14	3.6	0.26
40	12	5.3	0.44
50	10	7.4	0.74

(a) Reduction = $100(1 - d/D)$.
(b) $h = (D^2 - d^2)/4d$.

Developed from Charts IV and V, "Computations for Metal Working Presses", published by the E. W. Bliss Co.

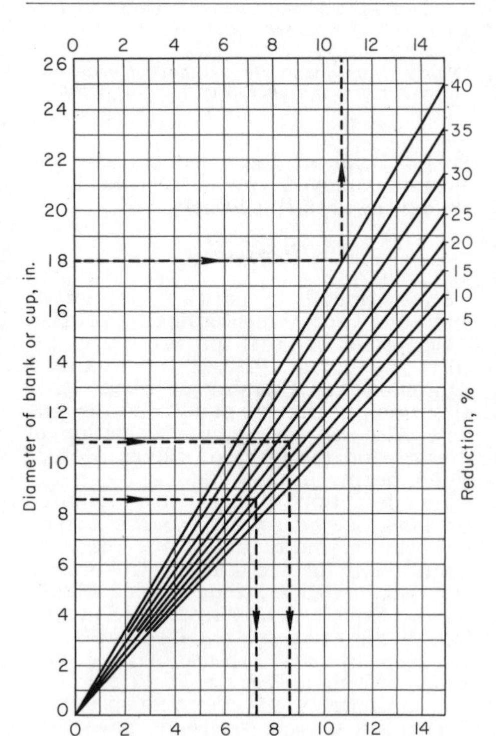

Fig. 2. Chart for checking percentage reduction in the drawing of cups. See text for sample calculation. The inside diameter is ordinarily used for the cup diameter.

thinning. Intermediate annealing is frequently not needed, and may be undesirable. For example, metal processed in an eyelet machine, a transfer die, or a progressive die cannot be annealed during forming, yet the shells processed in such equipment frequently undergo several redraws. Metal fed into these machines must be selected to allow redrawing without annealing.

Some metals cannot be redrawn without first being annealed. This is especially true of metals (such as stainless steels) that initially possess high strength or that cold work or strain harden rapidly to high strength levels. High work-metal strength causes excessive force on the drawing tools, which can cause tool breakage. In addition, excessive force can cause lubrication difficulties. Breakdown of lubricant causes galling of the workpiece on the tools and leads to shell breakage.

Annealing for redrawing, if not closely controlled, can impair drawability. This is especially true if grain coarsening results from the annealing. This characteristic varies widely among different work metals.

Blank Size vs Cup Diameter. Reduction of drawn cups is usually expressed as the percentage reduction from the diameter of the blank to the inside diameter of the cup, or from the inside diameter of one shell to that of the next. Percentage reduction is calculated using the formula $100(1 - d/D)$. Thus, the drawing of a 6-in.-diam cup from a 10-in.-diam blank results in a reduction of 40%. Nominal cup heights resulting from diameter reductions of 20, 30, 40 and 50% for blanks 2, 5, 10 and 20 in. in diameter are given in Table 2.

A chart that can be used to estimate cup size from blank size or cup size from an earlier draw is shown in Fig. 2.

Sample Calculation Using Fig. 2. To illustrate the use of Fig. 2, assume the problem of determining whether a cup of 7½-in. ID can be made in three draws of 40, 20, and 15% reduction, respectively, from an 18-in.-diam blank. To find the diameter of the cup after the first draw, trace the line for 18-in. blank diameter horizontally to its intersection with the diagonal for 40% reduction. From this intersection, draw a vertical line to the top of the chart and read 10.8 in. for the inside diameter of the cup after the first draw. Next, trace a horizontal line from 10.8 on the vertical axis until it intersects the diagonal for 20% reduction. From this point draw a vertical line to the bottom of the chart and read 8.6 in., which is the inside diameter of the cup after the second draw. The inside diameter of the cup after the third draw, assumed to be 15% reduction, is found using the same procedure, by drawing a line horizontally from 8.6 to its intersection with the diagonal for 15% reduction and from there to the bottom of the chart, which gives a reading of 7¼ in. Accordingly, it is concluded that a 7½-in.-ID cup can be drawn from an 18-in.-diam blank in the three assumed reductions.

Rectangular Shells. The drawing of oval, square or rectangular shells involves true drawing at the corners only; at the sides and ends, metal movement is more accurately described as bending. The stresses at the corner of the shell are compressive in the metal moving toward the die radius and are tensile in the metal that has already moved over the die radius. The metal between the corners is in tension only, in both the sidewall and flange areas. Stresses in the metal in the corner areas are severe, compared with the sidewall areas where only bending occurs. A portion of the surplus metal in the corner areas tends to move into the sidewall areas. If the punch-to-die clearance at the corners or in the sidewalls adjacent to the corners is too great, the metal may wrinkle rather than shrink or be compressed.

For square and rectangular boxes, except those with a width slightly more than twice the corner radius, the depth that the box can be drawn in one operation depends more on the size of the corner radius and on the stock thickness than on the width of the box.

When the ratio of the depth to the corner radius is 6 or less, the shell can usually be drawn in one operation. The basic ratio is 12 for two draws, 17 for three draws, and 22 for four draws. Square, or nearly square, cups and nearly cylindrical oval cups can be drawn in one operation if the area of the blank does not exceed the cross-sectional area of the punch by four times. This ratio is 4½ for boxes with a length-to-width ratio of 3, and decreases as the length-to-width ratio increases. Square boxes with a small corner radius (about 3% of box width) can be drawn to a maximum depth of about 80% of the width from low-carbon steel or some stainless steels, and to 70 to 75% of the width from aluminum alloys 3003-O and 5052-O.

Other factors that influence the producibility of a rectangular shell are work-metal composition, hardness and thickness, and radius at the bottom of the shell. Soft brass can easily be drawn to a depth of six times the corner radius in one operation, but some stainless steels can be drawn to a depth of only three times the corner radius. Likewise, thin material and small corner radii at the bottom of the shell reduce the maximum depth of draw. Shells that have a depth of more than six times the corner radius must be drawn in two or more operations. If two or more draws are necessary, the first-draw die contour can be determined from Fig. 3 as follows:

Dimension a is half the length or width of the finished box; b is the decrease in box size on a side; c is the thickness of an internal blankholder at the corner; r is the finished-shell radius; and R is the first-draw radius.

A rectangular shell can be reduced on a side by an amount b that depends on corner radius r and is determined by multiplying r by 1½. If the corner radius is greater than ½ in., the reduction should remain the same as for a ½-in. radius. The first-draw radius R should be four or five times larger than r when laid out, so that c is not less than ⅛ in. The R/r ratio will vary according to other dimensions.

If more than one redraw is necessary, the proportions of additional redraws can be determined by the above method, unless the end of the cup is semicircular after the first draw, under which condition reductions for round cups apply.

Defects in Drawn Parts

Most drawing problems can be averted by precautionary measures based on a knowledge of their causes. Table 3 contains some frequently encountered evidences of trouble, with the possible

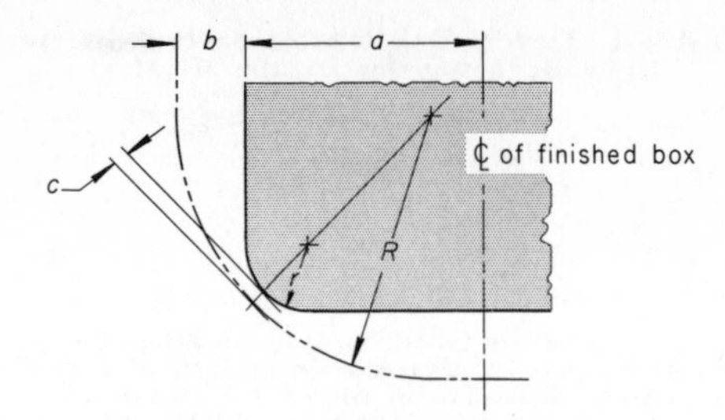

Fig. 3. Relation of draw and redraw dies for drawing a rectangular box. See text for explanation.

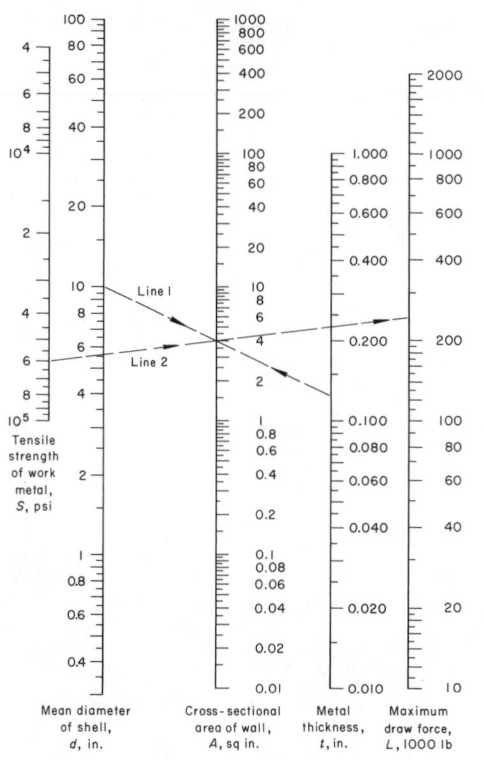

Fig. 4. Nomograph for estimating drawing force for a round shell. See text for sample calculation.

causes. Some of these defects and the means employed for correcting them are discussed in this article.

Presses

Sheet metal is drawn in either hydraulic or mechanical presses. Descriptions of these machines are given in the article "Presses and Auxiliary Equipment for Forming of Sheet Metal", which begins on page 1 in this volume. Also see the article "Selection of Presses for Forming of Sheet Metal", which begins on page 18.

Double-action presses are required for most deep drawing, because a more uniform blankholding force can be maintained for the entire stroke than is possible with a spring-loaded blankholder. Double-action hydraulic presses with a die cushion are often preferred for deep drawing, because of their constant drawing speed, stroke adjustment, and uniformity of clamping pressure. Regardless of the source of power for the slides, double-action straight-side presses with die cushions are best for deep drawing. Straight-side presses provide a wide choice of tonnage capacity, bed size, stroke and shut height.

Factors in Selection. Tonnage requirements, die space, and the length of stroke are the most important considerations in selecting a press for deep drawing. The condition of the crankshaft and connection bearings and gibs is also a factor in press selection.

Tonnage required for producing round cups is equal to the product of the cross-sectional area and the tensile strength of the work metal.

The force (load) required for drawing a round cup is expressed by the following empirical equation:

$$L = \pi dtS\left(\frac{D}{d} - k\right)$$

where L is press load, in pounds; d is cup diameter, in inches; D is blank diameter, in inches; t is work-metal thickness, in inches; S is tensile strength, in pounds per square inch; and k, a constant that takes into account frictional and bending forces, is usually 0.6 to 0.7.

The force (load) required for drawing a rectangular cup can be calculated from the following equation:

$$L = tS(2\pi Rk_A + lk_B)$$

where L is press load, in pounds; t is work-metal thickness, in inches; S is tensile strength, in pounds per square inch; R is corner radius of the cup, in inches; l is the sum of the lengths of straight sections of the sides, in inches; and k_A and k_B are constants. Values for k_A range from 0.5 (for a shallow cup) to 2.0 (for a cup of depth five to six times the corner radius). Values for k_B range from 0.2 (for easy draw radius, ample clearance, and no blankholding force) and 0.3 (for similar free flow and normal blankholding force of about $L/3$) to a maximum of 1.0 (for metal clamped too tightly to flow).

Figure 4 can be used as a general guide for computing maximum drawing load for a round shell. These relations are based on a free draw with sufficient clearance so that there is no ironing, using a maximum reduction of 50%. The nomograph gives the load required to fracture the cup. A typical example of its use is as follows:

Sample Calculation Using Fig. 4. Assuming that 0.125-in.-thick metal with a tensile strength of 60,000 psi will be drawn into a 10-in.-diam cup, the maximum drawing load L is determined from Fig. 4 as follows: Draw line 1 to connect point 10 on the d scale to point 0.125 on the t scale. Line 1 intersects the A scale at 4.0, which is the approximate cross-sectional area of the wall. Then draw line 2 to connect point 4.0 on the A scale to 60,000 on the S scale. When line 2 is extended to the right, it intersects the L scale at 240,000 lb, or approximately the maximum drawing load for this cup.

When blankholder cylinders are mounted on the main slide of the press, the blankholder tonnage must be added to the calculated main-slide or drawing tonnage. When a die cushion is used to eject workpieces, the main slide works against this force; therefore, tonnage is required in addition to the tonnage calculated for the deep drawing load.

In toggle draw presses, the blankholding force is taken on the rocker shaft bearings in the press frame, so that the crankshaft bearings sustain only the drawing load. In other types

Table 3. Causes of Common Problems in Deep Drawing

Metal Fracture During Cupping

1 Blank thickness wrong or out-of-tolerance
2 Metal hardness, grain size or quality not suitable for part being drawn. Correct by proper annealing or upgrading quality of work metal.
3 Scratches, blemishes, dirt, etched-in stains or other defects on surface of blank, with cupping causing additional stress in the metal at surface defects
4 Draw radii, draw beads, die ring and blankholder surfaces not smooth. These surfaces should be smooth, sometimes highly polished, with no radial lines, scratches, galling or welding.
5 Draw radius too small, creating resistance to metal flow sufficient to cause undue thinning or fracture. Correct by increasing die radius or by changing die entrance to conical or elliptical shape.
6 Clearance between punch and die too little, too great, or uneven
7 Blankholding pressure too great
8 Percentage reduction of blank diameter to cup diameter too great
9 Punch nose radius too small. Correct by drawing cup with a larger bottom radius and restriking to smaller radius.
10 Lubrication inadequate or unsuitable

Wrinkles on Top Edge or Flange of Cup

1 Blankholding pressure too light
2 Draw radius too large
3 Punch nose radius too large. Dome-shape cups frequently have this defect because of the amount of free metal between the punch and draw radius.
4 Wrinkles on one side of cup or flange, caused by burr on blank or by an unbalanced blankholding pressure

Uneven Top Rim or Flange in Drawn Cup

1 Earing or formation of scallops around the edge, caused by differences in directional properties of the sheet metal
2 Nicks or burrs along the periphery of the blank
3 Punch, die or blank locators not concentric. Too much material pulled into the die by off-center forming punch or from off-center blank prevents forming of an even cup depth or flange width.
4 Scratches, blemishes, dirt, etched-in stains, or other types of defects present on the surface of the blank
5 Blankholder exerting an unbalanced force on the blank, permitting metal to be drawn unevenly into the die

Flange Wrinkled, Puckered or Split During Redrawing

1 Blank thickness wrong or out-of-tolerance
2 Draw radius too large
3 Depth of previously drawn cup too short or redraw operation too deep. Flange of previously drawn cup is drawn into the die, or sidewall of shell is thinned.
4 Clearance between punch and die too great for the stock thickness

Severe or Localized Wall Thinning Near Shell Bottom

1 Quality of steel unsuitable for redrawing
2 Nose radii of redraw punch not properly blended to bottom and side of punch
3 Draw radii too small, thus increasing tension in sidewall and stretching the metal
4 Diameter reductions too severe
5 Lubricant inadequate or unsuitable

Fracture at Bottom of Redrawn Shell

1 Surface defects that were present in original blank but that did not cause rejection after cupping
2 Draw radius and blankholding surfaces scratched, nicked or galled, restricting metal flow into the die
3 Punch nose and draw radii too small to permit proper metal flow
4 Diameter reduction too great or previously drawn shell too short for redrawing operation
5 Metal in previously drawn shell wall adjacent to bottom radius too thin to withstand redrawing
6 Lubrication inadequate or unsuitable

Fracture in or at Flange of Redrawn Cup

1 Surface defects or improper grain size in original blank that did not cause rejection after cupping
2 Punch and die clearance too small, and excess metal crowded into flange

Excess Material at Top of Redrawn Shell

1 Metal thickness too great or punch-to-die clearance too small or uneven. Shell wall is ironed and excess metal is crowded into flange or shell-mouth radius.
2 Punch nose radius larger than cup-bottom radius, causing excess metal to flow up sidewall
3 Draw radius in preceding operation too large, permitting wrinkles to start that enlarge during redrawing of cup
4 Cup is too long for the redrawing operation, which causes the redraw punch to bottom before the sidewall of the cup is drawn into the die. The same thing happens if the redraw punch is too short.

SEE NOTES BELOW FOR DISCUSSION OF ILLUSTRATIONS.

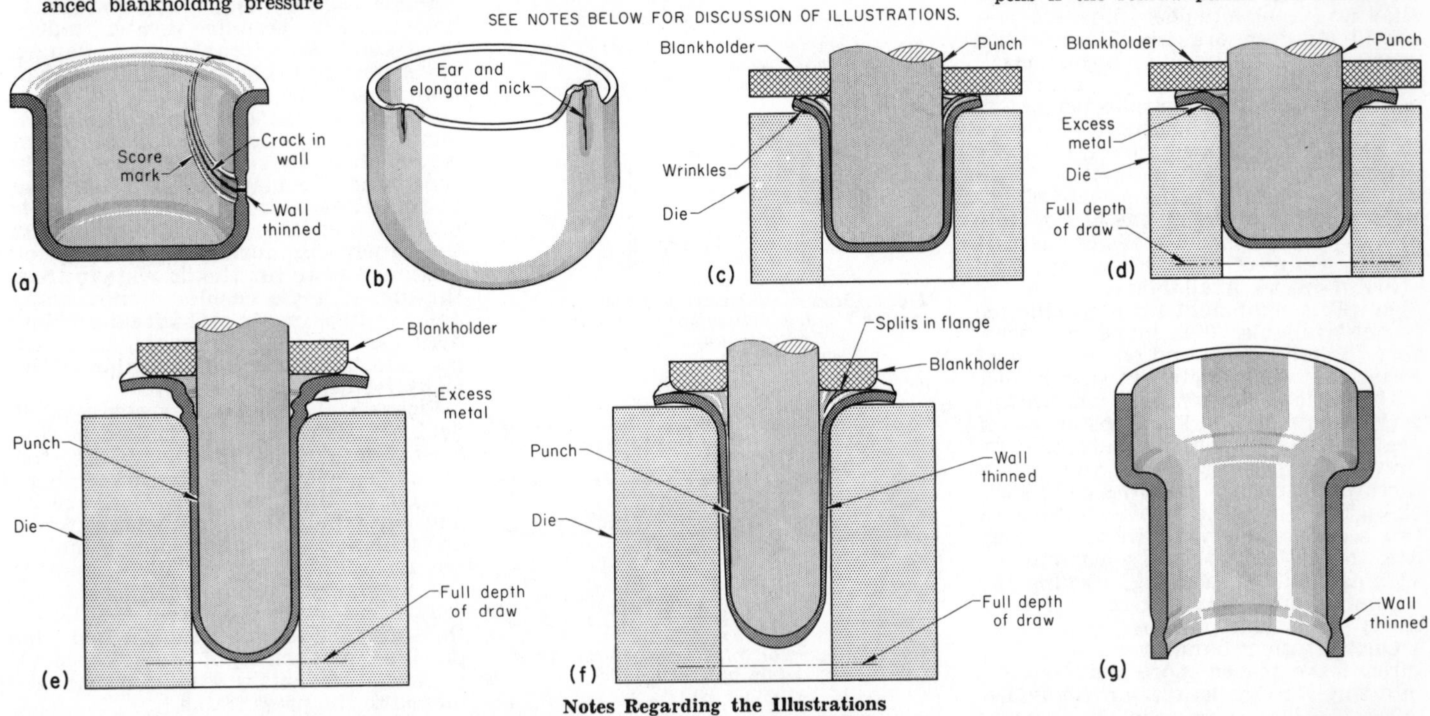

Notes Regarding the Illustrations

(a) Material flaw affects cupping. Original flaw widens near bottom of cup, reducing wall thickness. Marked cracking appears along the flaw and in the flange. (b) Earing, and elongation of nicks during cupping. Nicks were in periphery of blank before cupping.
(c) Wrinkles in flange from insufficient blankholding pressure or thin metal. (d) Excess metal in shell-mouth radius from thick metal or insufficient punch-to-die clearance. (e) Cup too long for redraw operation. Excess metal is forced up under flange, distorting shell-mouth radius. (f) Cup too short for redraw operation. Shell wall thinned, possible fracture at shell bottom, or flange splitting. (g) Localized wall thinning resulting from punch nose radius that is too small or not well blended with side or end of punch.

of presses, both the drawing and blankholding loads are on the crankshaft, and allowances are made when computing press capacity. For round work, the allowance for blankholding should be 30 to 40% of the drawing force. For large rectangular work, the drawing force is relatively lower than for round work, but the blankholding force may be equal to the drawing force. Where stretching is involved and the blank must be gripped tightly around the edge (and a draw bead is not permissible), the blankholding force may be two or three times the drawing force.

Blank size governs the size of the blankholder surfaces. Some presses with sufficient force cannot be considered for deep drawing because the bed size and shut height are inadequate.

Depth of Draw. Both length of stroke and the force required at the beginning of the working portion of the stroke are important considerations. When drawing parts that have straight walls, often the part can be drawn through the die cavity, and then stripped from the punch and ejected from the bottom of the press. Even under these ideal conditions, the minimum stroke will be equal to the sum of the length of the drawn part, the radius of the draw die, the stock thickness, and the depth of the die to the stripping point, plus some clearance for placing the blank in the die.

Workpieces with flanges or tapered walls must be removed from the top of the die. In drawing these workpieces, the minimum press stroke is twice the length of the drawn workpiece, plus clearance for loading the die. In an automatic operation using progressive dies or transfer mechanisms, at least half the stroke must be reserved for stock feed, because the tooling must clear the part before feeding starts for the next stroke. For automatic operation, it is common practice to allow a press stroke of four times the length of the drawn workpiece. For this reason, some equipment is not suited to automatic operation, or it is necessary to use manual feed with an automatic unloader, or vice versa, because of shortage of suitable presses.

Slide Velocity. When selecting a press, it is also necessary to check slide velocity through the working portion of the stroke (see the section in this article on Effect of Press Speed, page 175).

Means of Holding the Blank. Double-action presses with a punch slide and a blankholder slide are preferred for deep drawing. Single-action presses with die cushions (pneumatic or hydraulic) can be used, but are less suitable for drawing complex parts.

Draw beads are incorporated in the blankholder for drawing parts requiring greater restraint of metal flow than can be obtained by using a plain blankholder or for diverting metal flow into or away from specific areas of the part (see Restraint of Metal Flow, page 172).

Selection vs Availability. Often the ideal press equipment for a specific job is not available. This makes it necessary to design tools and choose product forms of work metal in accordance with available presses and supplementary equipment. For instance, if available presses are not adequate for drawing large workpieces, the manufacturing sequence must be completely changed. It may be necessary to draw two sections and weld them together. Also, operations otherwise combinable, such as blanking, piercing, drawing and trimming, may have to be performed singly in separate presses.

On the other hand, some manufacturers have placed more than one die in a single press, because of the availability of a large press and the shortage of smaller presses. Usually this procedure causes lower production, because all blanks must be positioned before the press can be operated. However, storage of partly formed workpieces and additional handling between press operations are eliminated. Where several small dies are used to reduce over-all tool cost, there is economic justification for the use of small-capacity presses. If small presses are not available, frequently it is more economical to use compound dies. This is particularly true if over-all part production is likely to exceed original estimates.

Nest
Punch
Workpiece
Die
(a) Single-action die

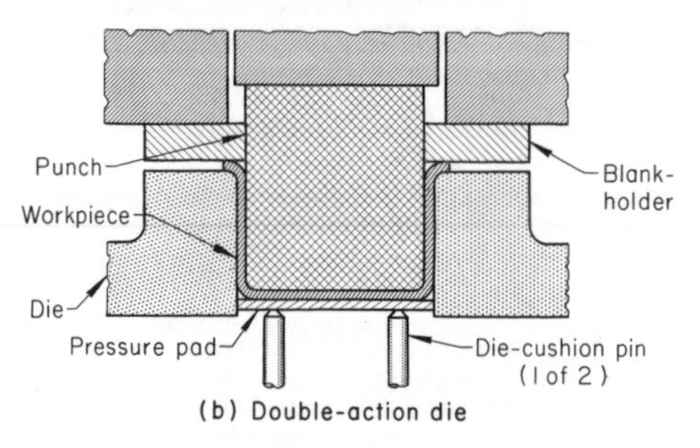

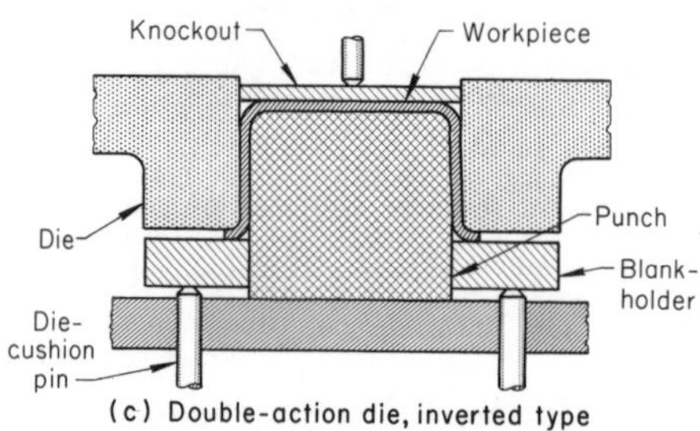

Fig. 5. Components of three types of simple dies, shown in setup for drawing a round cup. See text for discussion.

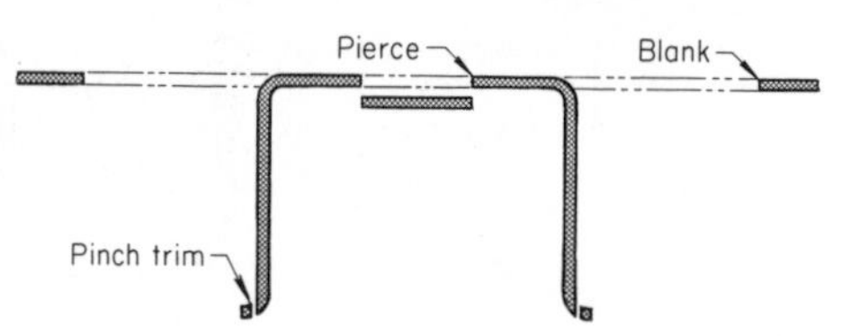

Fig. 6. Progressive blanking, drawing, piercing and pinch trimming of a cup in a compound die

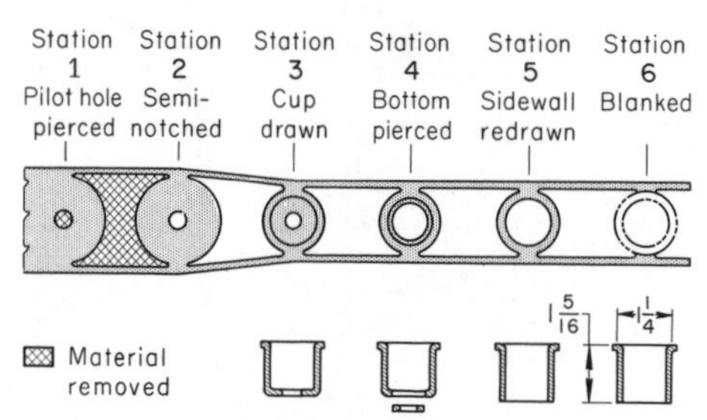

Fig. 7. Production of a small ferrule in a six-station progressive die

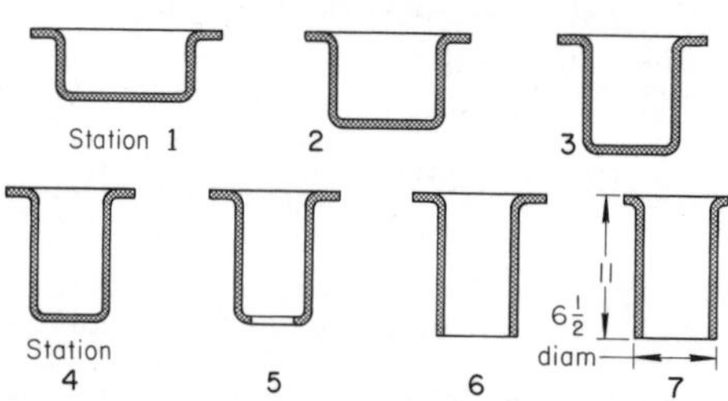

Sequence of operations: 1 – Cup. 2 – Redraw. 3 – Redraw. 4 – Redraw. 5 – Pierce bottom. 6 – Extrude bottom. 7 – Trim flange.

Fig. 8. Seven-station drawing and piercing of a cylinder in a multiple die and transfer mechanism

Availability of auxiliary equipment may also influence the type of press and tooling used. For instance, if equipment is available for handling coils, plans will be made accordingly. However, if coil-handling equipment is not available and straight lengths of sheet or strip are to be processed, a compatible tooling procedure must be used, even though it might not be the most economical procedure.

Dies

Dies used for drawing sheet metal are usually one of the following basic types or some modification thereof: (*a*) single-action dies; (*b*) double-action dies; (*c*) compound dies; (*d*) progressive dies; or (*e*) multiple dies with transfer mechanism. Selection of type depends largely on part size, severity of draw, and quantity of parts to be produced.

Single-action dies (Fig. 5a) are the simplest of all drawing dies and have only a punch and a die. A nest or locator is provided to position the blank. The drawn part is pushed through the die and is stripped from the punch by the counterbore in the bottom of the die. The rim of the cup expands slightly to make this possible. Single-action dies can be used only when the forming limit permits cupping without the use of a blankholder.

Double-action dies have a blankholder. This permits greater reductions and the drawing of flanged parts. Figure 5(b) shows a double-action die of the type used in a double-action press. In this design, the die is mounted on the lower shoe; the punch is attached to the inner, or punch, slide; and the blankholder is attached to the outer slide. The pressure pad is used to hold the blank firmly against the punch nose during the drawing operation, and to lift the drawn cup from the die. If a die cushion is not available, springs or air or hydraulic cylinders can be used; however, they are less effective than a die cushion, especially for deep draws.

Figure 5(c) shows an inverted type of double-action die, which is used in single-action presses. In this design, the punch is mounted on the lower shoe; the die on the upper shoe. A die cushion can supply the blankholding force, or springs or air or hydraulic cylinders are incorporated in the die to supply the necessary blankholding force. The drawn cup is removed from the die on the upstroke of the ram, when the pin-like extension of the knockout strikes a stationary knockout bar attached to the press frame.

Compound Dies. When the initial cost is warranted by production demands, it is practical to combine several operations in a single die. Blanking and drawing are two operations commonly placed in compound dies. Figure 6 shows how a cup is blanked, drawn, pierced and pinch trimmed in a single operation using a compound die. By this means, workpieces can be produced up to four times as fast as by the simple dies shown in Fig. 5.

Progressive Dies. The initial cost and length of bed needed for progressive dies usually limit their application to relatively small workpieces. Figure 7 shows a typical six-station progression for making small shell-like workpieces on a mass-production basis (see also Examples 229 and 230). However, larger parts, such as liners for automobile headlights, have been drawn in progressive dies.

Total number of parts to be produced and production rate often determine whether or not a progressive die will be used when two or more operations are required. There are, however, some practical considerations that may rule against a progressive die, regardless of quantity. These considerations are: (*a*) the workpiece must remain attached to the scrap skeleton until the final station, without hindering the drawing operations; (*b*) drawing operations must be completed before the final station is reached; (*c*) sometimes in deep drawing it is difficult to move the workpiece to the next station; (*d*) if the draw is relatively deep, stripping is often a problem; and (*e*) the length of press stroke must be more than twice the depth of draw.

Assuming that a progressive die can be used to make acceptable drawn parts, cost per piece usually is the final consideration. Progressive-die drawing is usually considered economical if saving in material and labor can pay for the die in one year. Ordinarily, the saving effected by the use of a progressive die results from decreased labor.

Multiple dies, in conjunction with transfer mechanisms, are often used instead of progressive dies for mass production of larger parts. Multiple dies and transfer mechanisms are practical for a wider range of workpiece sizes than are progressive dies. Although the eyelet-type transfer method is most widely used for making parts less than 1 in. in diameter, transfer dies are practical for much larger workpieces. The seven-station operation for making a 6½-in.-OD cylindrical shell shown in Fig. 8 represents a typical sequence for the transfer-die method. The workpiece is mechanically transferred from one die to the next. One advantage of the transfer-die method, as opposed to the progressive-die method, is the greater flexibility permitted in processing procedure, mainly because in transfer dies the workpiece does not remain attached to the scrap skeleton during forming. Because of this, precut blanks can be drawn by the transfer method.

Preforms can also be used as blanks. For instance, oil pans for automobiles are blanked and partly drawn in a compound die, then finish formed, pierced and trimmed by the transfer method.

Dies for producing a given part usually cost more for the transfer-die method than for a separate-die operation, but about the same as for a progressive-die operation. The cost of adapting the transfer unit to the part is not included in the die cost. Likewise, the production rate for the transfer method is usually greater than for single-die operation, but 10 to 25% less than for drawing in a progressive die. Many parts can be produced equally well by all these methods. Under these conditions, tool cost, rate of production, and total quantity of parts to be drawn determine the choice of procedure.

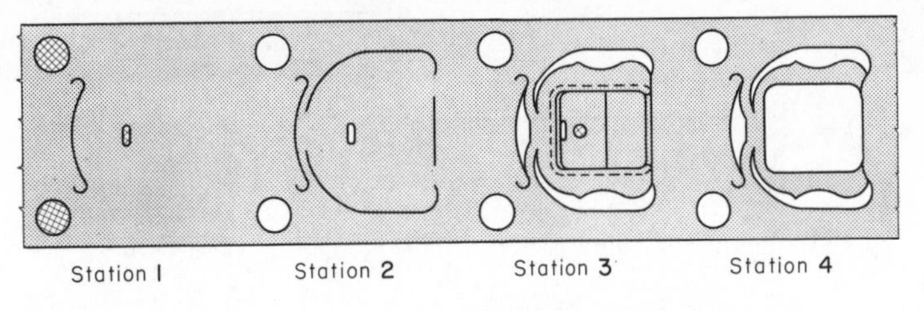

Station 1: Pilot holes and oval hole are pierced; arc is lanced. **Station 2:** Outline of blank is lanced preparatory to drawing. **Station 3:** Cup is drawn; as punch bottoms, mounting hole is pierced upward. **Station 4:** Part is pinched off; scrap skeleton is trimmed off.

Fig. 9. Producing a small drawn part in a four-station progressive die (Example 229)

Table 4. Comparison of Costs for Drawing Ball Races in Separate vs Progressive Dies (Example 230)

Item	Separate dies	Progressive die
Tool cost (total)	$3190	$4575
Cost of labor and burden:		
Per piece	$0.0173	$0.0039
For 750,000 pcs/year..	$12,975	$2925
First-year saving(a) ...	...	$8665

1.572 / 1.568 — 1.286 — 0.651 — 1010 steel, Cold rolled, 0.095 in.

(a) $10,050 saving in cost of labor and burden, minus $1385 additional tool cost. Tools were amortized over one year.

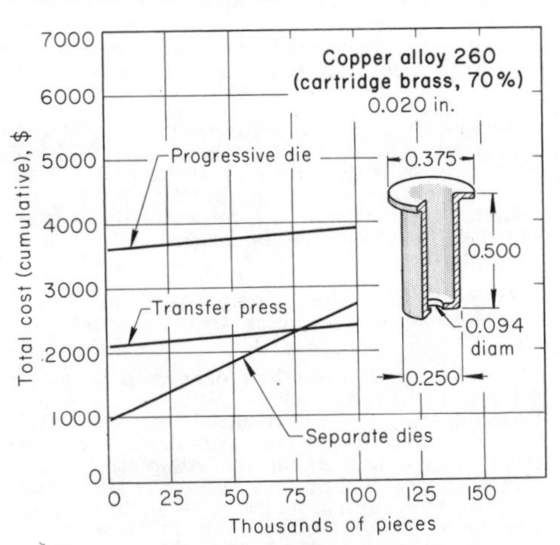

Item	Separate dies	Transfer press	Progressive die
Production, pcs/hr ...	1200(a)	5400(b)	7800(b)
Tool cost	$960	$2100	$3600
Cost per 1000 Pieces			
Labor, production(c) ..	$15.71	$0.56	$0.38
Labor, maintenance(d)	...	0.48	0.48
Material	2.16	1.76	2.16
Total	$17.87	$2.80	$3.02

(a) Number of pieces drawn (four draws), pierced and trimmed; blanks were produced in an automatic press at the rate of 4200 per hour. (b) Rate for all operations, including blanking. (c) Direct labor, at $3 per hour. Cost for separate-die method represents $2.50 (5⁄6 hr, for 1000 pieces, times $3 hourly rate) for each of the six operations (four draws, pierce and trim) plus $0.71 for blanking (5⁄21 hr, for 1000 pieces at 4200 pieces per hour, times $3). (d) At $6 per hour.

Fig. 10. Effect of quantity on cost of producing a flanged cup by three different methods (Example 231)

Effect of Tooling Procedure on Cost

Parts made from blanks less than about 3½ in. across can be drawn by various methods, ranging from a hand press for making a few pieces to a progressive die for continuous high production. For these parts, quantity is usually the major influence on choice of procedure. Usually, the initial cost for individual dies is less than for a progressive die, and so individual dies are used for producing small quantities. However, when several operations must be performed, the initial cost of a single progressive die is often less for small parts than the cost of several individual dies, and so a progressive die is used regardless of production quantity.

As workpiece size increases, the cost of a progressive die is likely to become prohibitive or its use impractical. Thus, for larger workpieces, the choice of tooling is more often a choice between separate dies and multiple dies with a transfer mechanism, based principally on the quantity of workpieces to be drawn. The four examples that follow compare costs for producing the same parts by two or more types of tooling. The first two of these examples compare production by separate versus progressive dies; the third example compares the cost of production by three types of tooling; the fourth example compares the cost of tooling for two different die setups. (See also Examples 233 and 234, which show the effect of production quantity on cost.)

Example 229. Saving of 37% in Die Cost by Use of a Progressive Die Instead of Four Individual Dies (Fig. 9)

The small cup-shape part shown in Fig. 9 was produced from low-carbon steel in a four-station progressive die, in the steps shown. The only critical dimension was the location of the mounting hole, which had a tolerance of ±0.005 in.; this was held without difficulty. The progressive die cost $1975, compared to an estimated $3150 total for four individual dies to make the same part.

The progressive die was made from an air-hardening tool steel (Rockwell C 60 to 62) and operated in a 50-ton dieing machine at 75 strokes per minute. Lubricant was die oil. Average production run was 75,000 pieces.

Example 230. Cost Savings by Change From Separate-Die to Progressive-Die Production (Table 4)

Ring-shape ball races with two diameters (see drawing in Table 4) were originally produced in three operations by separate dies. In the first operation, the workpiece was blanked and the center hole was pierced. Drawing, partly done in the second die, was completed in the third die, where the inside radius was coined.

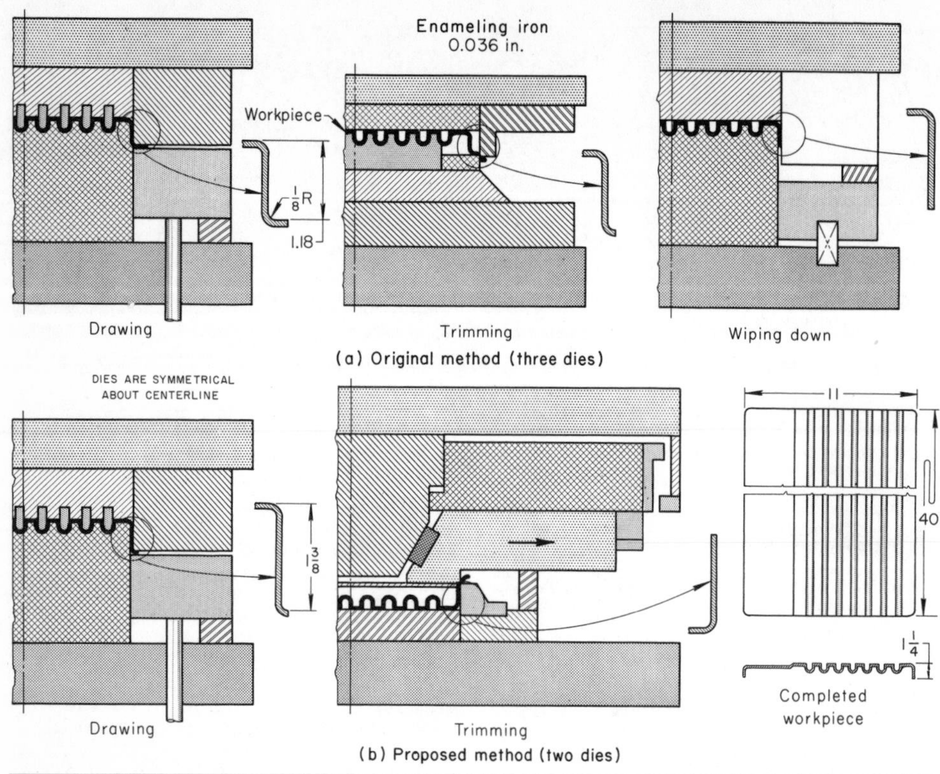

Operation	Tool cost	Setup cost(a)	Labor cost(a)
Original Method (Three Dies)			
Draw	$ 4,400	$200	$298.50
Trim	2,800	150	298.50
Wipe down	3,200	150	298.50
Total	$10,400	$500	$895.50

Operation	Tool cost	Setup cost(a)	Labor cost(a)
Proposed Method (Two Dies)			
Draw	$ 4,400	$200	$298.50
Trim	9,000	150	298.50
Total	$13,400	$350	$597.00

(a) Based on $5 per hour, and on ten setups of 1000 pieces per run (total of 10,000 pieces)

Fig. 11. Two-die and three-die methods for producing range-drawer panels. Higher tool cost for the two-die method made it impractical for 10,000 pieces per year. (Example 232)

When annual production increased to 750,000 parts, use of a progressive die became advisable. A six-station (two idle stations) progressive die produced the parts from strip by piercing a center hole in station 1, shaving the center hole in station 3, blanking out and pushing back into strip (as a means of feeding the blank to the next station) in station 4, and extruding (flanging) and drawing in station 6. The last operation (at station 6) produced a smooth surface on the inside radius without coining.

As shown by the cost comparison in Table 4, 750,000 parts were produced in a progressive die for about one-fourth the cost of producing the same quantity in separate dies, although the die itself was more costly.

Example 231. Relation of Quantity to Cost of Producing Flanged Cups in Separate Dies, a Transfer Press, or a Progressive Die (Fig. 10)

The cost of producing a flanged cup in various quantities by three different methods is shown graphically in Fig. 10. At zero production, tool costs only are shown: $960 for separate dies, $2100 for dies used in a transfer press, and $3600 for a progressive die.

As shown in the table that accompanies Fig. 10, production rate was lowest for separate dies and highest for the progressive die. Although labor cost for production was highest for separate-die operation and lowest for processing in a progressive die, cost per piece for labor and material was lowest for the transfer method, because blanks for both the separate and the progressive dies were taken from a single-width strip, whereas the transfer method permitted use of wider strip. By staggering the blank layout, it was possible to obtain twice the number of workpieces using a strip less than twice the width required for a single blank. The wider strip was then run through the dies twice. This technique resulted in a material saving of 18%.

Figure 10 shows that for fewer than 77,000 pieces the separate-die method was the least costly (considering initial cost of tools), and that for quantities of more than 77,000 the transfer method was the least costly. A progressive die would not be economical for any quantity of this part.

Example 232. Cost Comparison for Two Methods of Producing Drawer Panels (Fig. 11)

In the original method of drawing panels for electric-range drawers (Fig. 11a), a wipe-down operation was required because, with the trim line beyond the ⅛-in. draw radius, a recoil line remained on the completed workpiece. The recoil line was caused by the metal at the draw radius taking a set; thinning of the metal usually occurred in this area.

In a proposed method (Fig. 11b), the depth of draw was 1⅜ in. (slightly deeper than in the original method), to allow for relocation of the trim line ahead of the radius, and a cam trimming die eliminated the recoil line and hence the need for wiping down. Tool cost for the proposed method, however, was $3000 more than for the original method (see cost comparison with Fig. 11), and although there was a saving of $298.50 in labor and $150 in setup, the proposed method could not be justified for an annual production of only 10,000 panels since the break-even point was 67,000 pieces per year. Each operation produced 335 pieces per hour, at a press speed of 22 strokes per minute. A dry-coat lubricant was applied with heat and an over-and-under roller coater.

Material for Dies and Punches

The selection of material for dies and punches for drawing sheet metal depends on work-metal composition, workpiece size, severity of the draw, quantity of parts to be drawn, and tolerances and surface finish specified for the drawn workpieces.

To meet the wide range of requirements, punch and die materials ranging from epoxy resin to highly alloyed tool steels with nitrided surfaces, and even carbide, are used. On rare occasions, for drawing only a few pieces, masonite or hard wood has been used as a tool material.

For detailed information on tool materials, see the articles "Selection of Material for Press Forming Dies" (which begins on page 145) and "Selection of Material for Deep Drawing Dies" (which begins on page 194). Selection tables in those articles consider the variables enumerated above.

Tooling for Low, Medium and High Production

The term "short run" may refer to quantities ranging from prototype manufacturing up to 10,000 pieces, depending on the type of product being considered.

In addition to low demand for a specific drawn shape, the possibility of a change in part design is often a reason for minimizing the tooling investment.

For producing any given shape, data such as shown in Fig. 10 should be obtained; that is, manufacturing costs should be calculated, or at least estimated, on the basis of quantity requirements. Usually, short-run tooling is relatively low in cost, but production labor costs for using it are high. Conversely, more elaborate tooling is initially expensive, but labor and other manufacturing costs are invariably less than when using short-run tooling. Therefore, when comparative costs are plotted graphically as in Fig. 10, there is usually a break-even point at some specific quantity. For quantities lower than the break-even point, short-run tooling is cheaper on a cost-per-piece basis, whereas greater quantities justify the cost of more elaborate tooling.

Total quantity to be drawn is not always the most practical basis for a choice between short-run and long-run tooling. Production demands may be such that the quantity of parts to be produced within a given time must be considered, and this can rule out short-run tooling because of low productivity. On the other hand, short-run tooling is sometimes used because of an anticipated change in workpiece design, even though total quantity would warrant the cost and use of long-run tooling.

Short-run tooling differs from long-run in one or more of three ways: (*a*) lower-cost materials are used for short-run tools; (*b*) short-run tools are made for individual operations, which often are performed in different presses; and (*c*) short-run tooling may need handwork to finish the part and involves a minimum of automation.

On the basis of material and processing costs alone, a large die or punch often can be made at much less cost by using a low-cost material instead of a high-cost tool steel that is difficult to machine and heat treat (for example, zinc alloy versus hardened D2 tool steel). However, factors other than tool materials are usually more influential in determining the cost of tooling.

One means of minimizing tool cost is to produce the workpiece in a series of simple operations (like blanking, drawing and piercing) without attempting to combine them. In this way, it is often possible to use standard tools already on hand.

In short-run tooling, the accuracy of the contour of the finished part edge determines the need for, and means of, trimming. A hand-cut developed blank is often used to eliminate the need for a trimming die. Numerous manual operations can be substituted for machine operations, often eliminating the need for a die or at least simplifying the construction of a die. Individual die sets are often eliminated for short runs, the punch and die being installed directly into a master die set, which is then mounted in the press. Standardization of tools can result in low-cost short-run tooling, because required tooling components are more likely to be on hand.

One approach to low-cost tools for short runs is the use of interchangeable inserts. Figure 12 shows how three different inserts can be used in the same draw ring, so that the ring can produce parts of different radii. The use of inserts is especially appropriate when a design change or a change in work-metal composition is expected. Insert practice can also be an important element in a standardization program.

Medium-production tooling usually has the following features:

1. Punches and dies with adjustable holders for use after regrinding
2. Jig-ground locating holes
3. Carbide or high-alloy die steel on wearing surfaces
4. Ejector pins
5. Engineered mechanisms for stripping and lifting out formed workpieces
6. Heeled trim punches
7. Mechanized equipment for either loading or unloading of the dies.

High-production tooling would include the above items, but would be built so as to reduce the downtime needed for maintenance. Holes in the die shoes would provide accessibility to lifters and air cylinders, and for the removal of drawing compound that has accumulated beneath the pressure pad.

Automatic equipment would be used to load the blank and to unload finished workpieces. The upper surface of the lifters would be covered with soft brass to prevent marking the panel. Steel guides would control movement of the incoming blank and the outgoing part.

The two examples that follow show cost-quantity relations for different tooling setups.

Example 233. Comparative Costs for Three Methods of Producing Bearing Separators (Fig. 13)

Separators for tapered roller bearings were made by three different tooling methods. Relations of cost to quantity for the three methods are shown in Fig. 13. Costs of tools, setup and labor are itemized in the table with Fig. 13.

The higher tooling cost for the intermediate-volume method balanced the higher labor cost for the low-volume method at approximately 37,000 pieces, where cost per piece was 19¢. The break-even point for the high-volume method occurred at 345,000 pieces, where cost per piece was 5¢. Each 1000 parts required 230 lb of steel, which was purchased as auto-body sheet and slit to width.

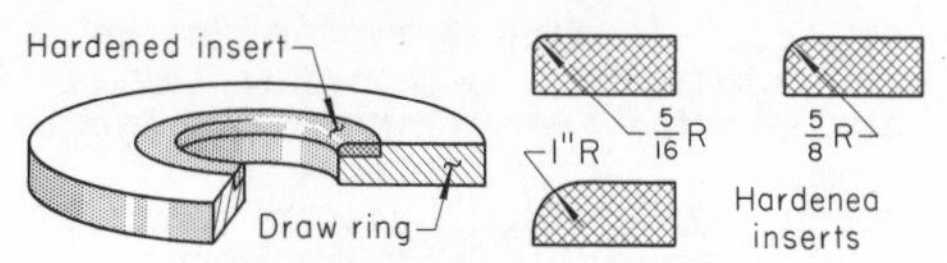

Fig. 12. Interchangeable inserts for use in a gray cast iron draw ring

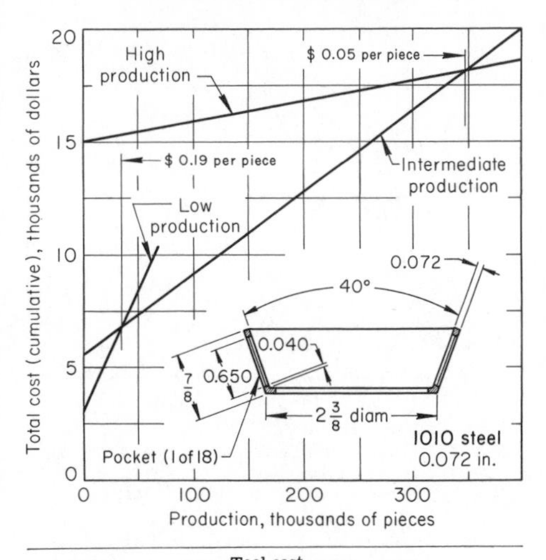

Operation or tool	Tool cost: Fixed	Tool cost: Maintenance(a)	Setup cost(b)	Labor cost(c)
Low-Volume Production				
Blank; draw	$2200	$1.80	$15.63	$ 1.76
Index; pierce	300	2.60	18.75	35.20
Index; form	175	1.48	18.75	35.20
Bottom blank	300	0.60	9.37	8.80
Spread	70	0.30	9.37	8.80
Total	$3045	$6.78	$71.87(d)	$89.76
Intermediate-Volume Production				
Blank; draw	$2200	$1.80	$15.62	$ 1.76
Bottom blank	300	0.60	9.37	8.80
Pierce; form	2800	7.02	12.50	8.80
Spread	140	0.40	12.50	5.28
Total	$5440	$9.82	$49.99(e)	$24.64
High-Volume Production (One operation in a transfer press)				
Dies	$13,333	$7.27	$0.25(f)	$2.31
Transfer fingers and cams	1,600	...	...	...
Total	$14,933	$7.27	$0.25	$2.31

(a) Cost per 1000 pieces. (b) At $6.25 per hour. (c) Per 1000 pieces; at $5.50 per hour. (d) Setup cost per 1000 pieces was $4.10. (e) Setup cost per 1000 pieces was $1.18. (f) Setup cost per 1000 pieces.

Fig. 13. Effect of quantity on cost of producing bearing separators by three different tooling methods (Example 233)

Example 234. Use of High-Production Tooling to Increase Output of Wheel Housings (Fig. 14)

Wheel housings (Fig. 14) were produced in pairs to reduce scrap losses and to minimize the number of dies required. At first, these housings were made with medium-production tooling. Tool cost was $88,000, and production rate was 3200 pairs of housings per week (two 8-hr shifts for five days).

Changing to high-production tooling, at a cost of $120,000, increased production from 3200 to 18,000 pairs of housings for the same time. Relation of cost per pair (in arbitrary units) to total production by the two different tooling methods is shown in Fig. 14. The break-even point occurred at approximately 45,000 pairs. Operations involved in the two methods are listed in the table with Fig. 14. Automation in the high-production procedure was the major difference. Medium-production tools were designed for a total production of 50,000 to 200,000 pairs, whereas high-production tooling was designed for a total production of 500,000 to 2 million pairs.

The work metal was commercial quality, cold rolled low-carbon steel that was roller coated with a water-soluble drawing oil before being drawn.

Effect of Punch and Die Radii

As the blank is struck by the punch at the start of drawing, it is wrapped around the punch and die radii; the stress and strain that develop in the workpiece are similar to those in bending, with an added stretching component. The bends, once formed, have the radii of the punch and die corners. The bend over the punch is stationary with reference to both punch and shell wall. The bend over the die radius, however, is continuously displaced with reference to both the punch radius and the blank, and it also undergoes a gradual thickening as the shell is drawn. The force required to draw the shell at the intermediate position has a minimum of three components: (*a*) the force required for bending and unbending the metal flowing from the flange into the sidewall; (*b*) the force required for overcoming frictional resistance of the metal passing under the blankholder and over the die radius; and (*c*) the force required for circumferential compression and radial stretching of the metal in the flange.

Because of the variation in metal volume and in resistance to metal flow, the punch force increases rapidly, passes through a maximum, and gradually decreases to zero as the edges of the flange approach and enter the die opening and pass into the shell wall. With the cup diameter remaining constant, the maximum press load and the length of stroke required to draw the cup depend on the size of the blank.

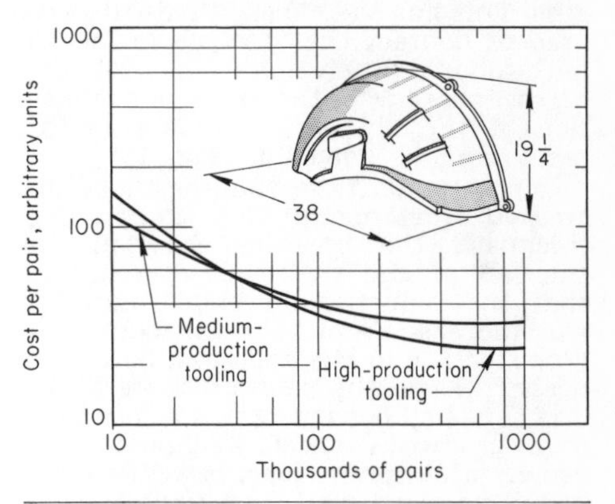

Sequence of Operations
(For producing a pair of parts)

Medium-Production Tooling	High-Production Tooling
First Set of Operations: Pair of Wheel Housings Handled Together	
Draw and cut off corners; lift up	Draw and cut off corners; scrap drops through; lift up
Trim	Trim; lift up and eject to conveyor; scrap drops through
Pierce and part	Pierce and part; lift up and eject to conveyor; scrap drops through
Second Set of Operations: Housings Formed Separately, but in Two Dies on Same Press	
Flange and restrike	Flange and restrike; lift up and eject to conveyor
Final form	Final form; lift and eject to conveyor

Fig. 14. Relation of quantity and cost for deep drawing of pairs of wheel housings by medium-production vs high-production tooling. Cost units include amortization of tools. (Example 234)

The punch force-stroke relations for drawing blanks of various diameters from brass sheet 0.060 in. thick, using a 2-in.-diam punch, are shown in Fig. 15.

Under the conditions shown in Fig. 15, during cupping, the shell bottom is subjected to tensile stress in all directions, while the lower portions of the shell wall, particularly the radiused portion connecting the bottom with the wall, are subjected primarily to longitudinal tension. The stress in the metal being drawn into the shell wall consists of combined compressive and tensile stresses. Separation of the shell bottom from the wall is likely if a reduction is made that requires a force greater than the strength of the shell wall near the bottom (see curve for 4.40-in.-diam blank in Fig. 15).

The punch and die radii and percentage of reduction determine the load at which the bottom of the shell is torn out. Drawing is promoted by increasing punch and die radii. For a given drawing condition, the punch force needed to move the metal into the die decreases as the die radius increases, as shown in Fig. 16.

The reduction of drawing force in a double-action die by modification of the effective die radius can be accomplished in two convenient ways, which are shown in Fig. 17 and 18. In the conic lead-in die (Fig. 17), the cutout is effective in reducing frictional loads by removal of the portions of the die surface that are usually heavily loaded and increase friction. In Fig. 18, the sheet metal is formed into a conic shape before appreciable drawing begins. This has the effect of reducing the area of contact over the die radius by an amount proportional to $\alpha/90$ degrees (where α is the angle to declination of the hold-down surface to the horizontal, as shown in Fig. 18).

If the punch nose radius can be increased from one to five times metal thickness, the breaking load in the sidewall of the shell will decrease so that the reduction in blank diameter will increase from 35% to about 50% (for steel), and the shell can be drawn deeper before the sidewall tears.

If the shell bottom radius is less than four times the sheet thickness, it is usually desirable to form it with a larger-radius punch and then to restrike to develop the specified radius. This will minimize bottom failures. However, the bottom corner radius usually cannot be increased beyond ten times the sheet thickness without likelihood of wrinkling. The metal in dome-shape parts is likely to pucker in the unconfined area between the punch nose and die radius. Frequently, high blankholding forces or draw beads are used to induce combined stretching and drawing of the metal when forming dome shapes (see Example 255).

Deep drawing of boxes in stainless steel and other high-strength alloys with sides longer than fifty times stock thickness may result in a stability problem called "oil canning". The deflection of the sides by snap action can be eliminated by drawing the part in two operations with slightly different punches and an intermediate anneal. The first draw punch will have a larger nose radius than the second so that in the second drawing operation the metal can be stretched to eliminate the oil-canning effect. Stretching of the metal in parts with long sidewalls can be improved by gradually increasing the punch nose radius from the corner toward the center. A constant nose radius is used on the second-draw punch.

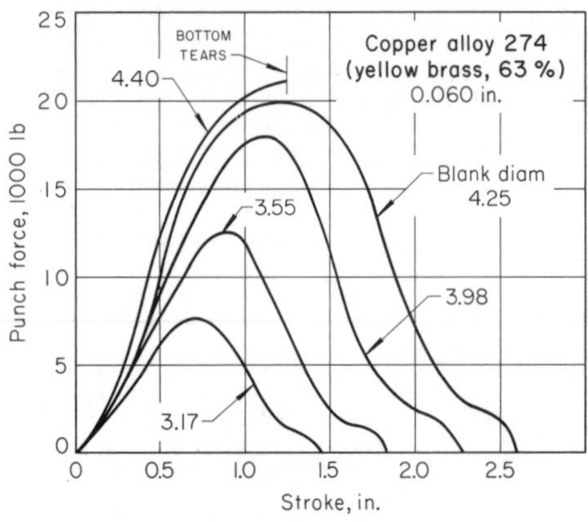

Fig. 15. Force-stroke relations for drawing blanks of various diameters from 0.060-in. brass sheet, using a 2-in.-diam punch

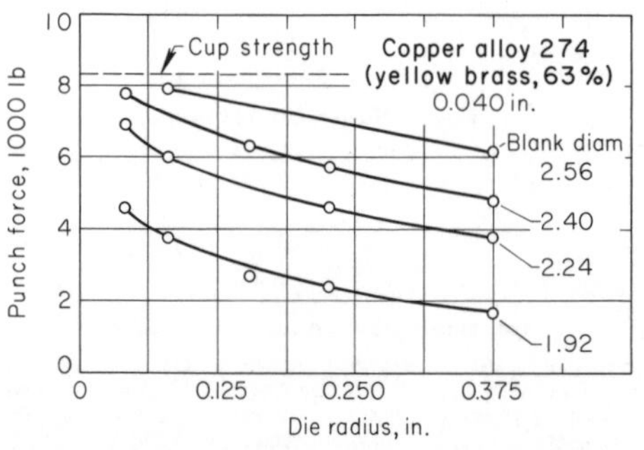

Fig. 16. Effect of die radius on punch force required for cupping various diameters of 0.040-in.-thick brass blanks, using a 1.2-in.-diam punch with a nose radius of 0.24 in.

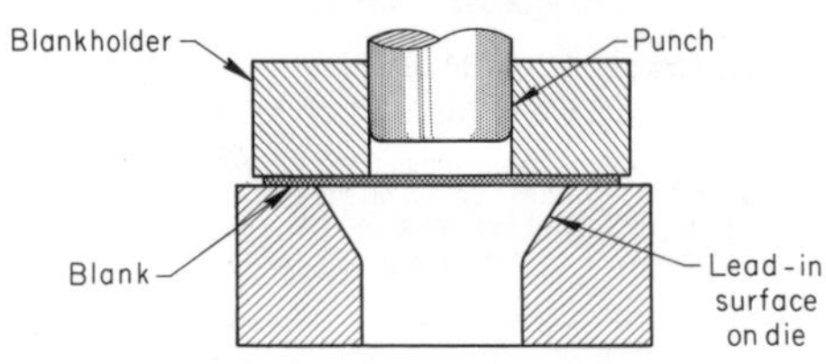

Fig. 17. Conic lead-in on die, which reduces drawing load

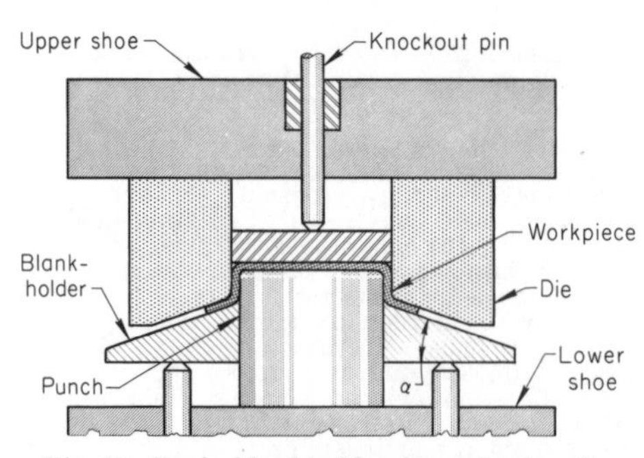

Fig. 18. Conic blankholder for reducing the severity of draw

Effect of Punch-to-Die Clearance

The selection of punch-to-die clearance depends on the requirements of the drawn part and on the work metal. Because there is a decrease, then a gradual increase, in the thickness of the metal as it is drawn over the die radius, clearance per side of 7 to 15% greater than stock thickness (1.07 to 1.15*t*) helps prevent burnishing the sidewall and punching out the bottom of the cup.

The drawing force is minimum when the clearance per side is 15 to 20% greater than stock thickness (1.15 to 1.20*t*) and the cupped portions of the part are not in contact with the walls of the punch and die. The force increases as the clearance decreases, and a secondary peak occurs on the force-stroke curve where the metal thickness is slightly greater than the clearance and ironing starts.

Redrawing operations require greater clearance, in relation to blank thickness, than the first draw, to compensate for the increase in metal thickness during cupping. A sizing redraw is used where the diameter or wall thickness is important or where it is necessary to improve surface finish to reduce finishing costs. The clearance used is less than that for the first draw.

Table 5 lists clearances for cupping, redrawing, and sizing draws of cylindrical parts from metal of various thicknesses. As the tensile strength of the stock decreases, the clearance must be increased.

Clearance between the punch and die for a rectangular shell, at the sidewalls and ends, is about the same as, or a little less than, for a circular shell. Clearance at the corners may be as much as 50% greater than stock thickness, to avoid ironing in these areas and to increase drawability.

Sheet Steel for Drawing

The principal factors affecting the selection of grade and quality of low-carbon steel sheet for deep drawing are (*a*) severity of draw (as determined by the amount of reduction and the punch nose radius), (*b*) thickness of sheet, (*c*) shape of the part (round, rectangular or conical), (*d*) flange requirements, (*e*) ironing requirements, (*f*) desired finish, (*g*) grain size, (*h*) press speed, (*i*) availability of material, and (*j*) cost.

The three principal classes of available low-carbon sheet steel are commercial quality, drawing quality, and aluminum killed ("special killed"), in order of increasing drawability.

For hot rolled sheets, the mill oxide on the surface is detrimental for deep drawing, because it impairs the flow of

Table 5. Punch-to-Die Clearance for Drawing Operations

Metal thickness(*t*), in.	Clearance-to-metal-thickness relationship for: Cupping	Redrawing	Sizing draws
Up to 0.015	1.07 to 1.09*t*	1.08 to 1.10*t*	1.04 to 1.05*t*
0.016 to 0.050	1.08 to 1.10*t*	1.09 to 1.12*t*	1.05 to 1.06*t*
0.051 to 0.125	1.10 to 1.12*t*	1.12 to 1.14*t*	1.07 to 1.09*t*
0.126 and up	1.12 to 1.14*t*	1.15 to 1.20*t*	1.08 to 1.10*t*

Table 6. Selection Table for Low-Carbon Steel Sheet for Deep Drawing of Cylindrical Cups

Punch nose radius	Reduction in drawing(a) — 0.036 in. thick (20 gage) 20%	30%	40%	50%	0.105 in. thick (12 gage) 20%	30%	40%	50%	0.250 in. thick 20%	30%	40%	50%
No Flange, No Ironing												
2t	CR,DQ	....	....	....	....	....	....	....	....	....	....	....
4t	CR,DQ	CR,DQ	CR,DQ,SK	....	HR,DQ	HR,DQ CR,CQ	HR,DQ CR,DQ	....	HR,CQ	HR,CQ	HR,DQ	....
8t	CR,CQ	CR,CQ	CR,DQ	CR,DQ,SK	HR,CQ	HR,CQ	HR,DQ CR,CQ	HR,DQ CR,DQ	HR,CQ	HR,CQ	HR,DQ	HR,DQ
16t	CR,CQ	CR,CQ	CR,CQ	CR,DQ	HR,CQ	HR,CQ	HR,CQ	HR,DQ CR,CQ	HR,CQ	HR,CQ	HR,CQ	HR,DQ
32t	CR,CQ	CR,CQ	CR,CQ	CR,DQ	HR,CQ	HR,CQ	HR,CQ	HR,CQ CR,CQ	HR,CQ	HR,CQ	HR,CQ	HR,DQ
No Flange, Ironed(b)												
2t	CR,DQ,SK	....	....	....	....	....	....	....	....	....	....	....
4t	CR,DQ	CR,DQ,SK	....	....	HR,DQ	HR,DQ	HR,DQ CR,DQ	....	HR,DQ	HR,DQ	....	....
8t	CR,DQ	CR,DQ,SK	CR,DQ,SK	....	HR,CQ	HR,CQ	HR,DQ	HR,DQ CR,DQ	HR,CQ	HR,DQ	HR,DQ	....
16t	CR,DQ	CR,DQ	CR,DQ,SK	CR,DQ,SK	HR,CQ	HR,CQ	HR,DQ	HR,DQ	HR,CQ	HR,CQ	HR,DQ	HR,DQ
32t	CR,DQ	CR,DQ	CR,DQ	CR,DQ,SK	HR,CQ	HR,CQ	HR,CQ	HR,DQ	HR,CQ	HR,CQ	HR,CQ	HR,DQ
With Flange, No Ironing												
2t	....	....	....	....	....	....	....	....	....	....	....	....
4t	CR,DQ	CR,DQ,SK	CR,DQ,SK	....	CR,DQ	CR,DQ,SK	CR,DQ,SK	....	HR,DQ	HR,DQ	....	....
8t	CR,DQ	CR,DQ	CR,DQ,SK	CR,DQ,SK	HR,DQ	CR,DQ	CR,DQ	CR,DQ,SK	HR,DQ	HR,DQ	HR,DQ	HR,DQ
16t	CR,CQ	CR,CQ	CR,DQ	CR,DQ	HR,CQ	HR,CQ CR,CQ	HR,DQ CR,DQ	CR,DQ	HR,DQ	HR,DQ	HR,DQ	HR,DQ
32t	CR,CQ	CR,CQ	CR,CQ	CR,DQ	HR,CQ	HR,CQ	HR,DQ CR,CQ	CR,CQ	HR,CQ	HR,DQ	HR,DQ	HR,DQ
With Flange, Ironed(b)												
2t	....	....	....	....	....	....	....	....	....	....	....	....
4t	CR,DQ,SK	CR,DQ,SK	....	....	CR,DQ,SK	CR,DQ,SK	CR,DQ,SK	....	HR,DQ	....	....	....
8t	CR,DQ,SK	CR,DQ	....	....	HR,DQ	CR,DQ	CR,DQ,SK	....	HR,DQ	HR,DQ	....	....
16t	CR,DQ	CR,DQ	CR,DQ,SK	CR,DQ,SK	HR,DQ	HR,DQ CR,DQ	HR,DQ CR,DQ	CR,DQ,SK	HR,DQ	HR,DQ	HR,DQ	HR,DQ
32t	CR,CQ	CR,CQ	CR,DQ	CR,DQ,SK	HR,DQ	HR,DQ	HR,DQ	HR,DQ CR,DQ	HR,DQ	HR,DQ	HR,DQ	HR,DQ

CR = cold rolled; CQ = commercial quality; DQ = drawing quality; HR = hot rolled; SK = special killed.

NOTES: (1) Two entries in one space indicate that the choice is borderline and will be influenced by uniformity, price, quantity, and availability. (2) Omission of an entry (....) in this table

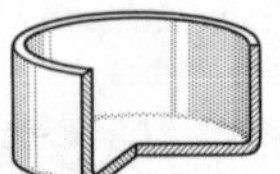

indicates that the draw is usually too severe to be completed successfully.

(a) In terms of reduction from blank diameter to cup diameter. (b) Operation that will bring the sidewall to a uniform thickness with the minimum amount of reduction.

metal and increases tool wear. "Special surface" can be obtained for any of the three qualities at extra cost, or oxide can be removed by pickling, which also adds to the cost. Hot rolled sheets for deep drawing are usually purchased pickled and oiled.

The primary consideration in selection between hot and cold rolled steel for deep drawing is availability of the required sheet thickness. Where superior surface finish is required, cold rolled sheet or strip is specified. The choice between commercial or drawing quality in either the hot or cold rolled sheets depends on the severity of draw.

Drawing quality is generally specified for severe draws because, with a nominal cost extra, required drawability is guaranteed. The problem is to recognize when it is expedient to pay the extra price for drawing performance guaranteed by the supplier.

Rimmed steels are satisfactory for most draws of mild to moderate severity. The use of special killed steels is usually limited to cold rolled steel for draws requiring freedom from strain aging, maximum uniformity within a shipment and among successive shipments, and maximum drawability.

The first approach to selection can be made as follows: (*a*) When surface conditions of the finished piece are most important, a cold rolled, rimmed steel will be specified; (*b*) when drawability requires freedom from aging or if the design specifies severe forming, such as flanges, ironing, sharp corner radii, extreme cup depth, or lack of symmetry, special killed quality is indicated. Assuming correct tooling and normal reductions, any scrap losses with special killed steel will probably result from the opening of small surface disturbances during drawing. This occurs more often in coil stock than in sheet.

"Special soundness" refers to the internal condition and is not a prerequisite for deep drawing. It is specified only when subsequent operations such as bright plating, highly critical welding, or restrictive carburizing require maximum uniformity and homogeneity.

Severity Classification. Table 6 shows the grades of low-carbon steel recommended for drawing round cups. Severity is based on cup reduction and punch nose radius for specific sheet thicknesses. Optimum tooling and lubrication are assumed for the most difficult draws. Within the four sections of Table 6, the effects of flanges and ironing are also considered. Similarly, Table 7 shows grades recommended for drawing rectangular cups or boxes having corner radii equal to the punch nose radius. In both tables, severity of drawing increases toward the upper right corner of each of the subdivisions that define the various conditions. The sequence of steels recommended to meet the increasing severity conditions is: commercial quality, drawing quality, and drawing quality special killed.

Availability is considered in Tables 6 and 7 as follows: Steel recommendations in the 20-gage thickness column (0.036 in.) are confined to cold rolled. Recommendations for the 12-gage thickness (0.105 in.) are predominantly hot rolled, although some cold rolled steels are included for extreme severities. Only hot rolled grades are available for the 0.250-in. thickness (borderline between sheet and plate).

The portions of Tables 6 and 7 relating to 0.105-in. sheet include both cold and hot finished grades; this sheet thickness is within the range where a cold rolled sheet is competitive with the hot rolled material. When all the requirements of one particular part are considered, the price differential between the two grades for surface finish only is often a negligible fraction of the cost of either. When the usually specified extra for pickling and oiling is added to the base price of hot rolled sheet, the price of hot finished steel is approximately the same as the cold finished grade of the same quality level.

The cold finished grade provides the advantage of greater uniformity of properties throughout the shipment, a result of the closer process control of annealing temperature, compared with finishing temperature in hot rolling. Another influential factor is that the cold rolled sheet has a more nearly uniform thickness extending to the edges of the sheet. Roll wear on the hot mill sometimes makes close thickness tolerances at the edges difficult to maintain. In some applications, this "feathered" edge is unusable, and the outside portion of the sheet must be discarded; thus, in blanking, the blank must be confined within the area of more uniform thickness. The alternative is to specify the hot rolled sheet with a cut edge at extra cost.

Table 7. Selection Table for Low-Carbon Steel Sheet for Deep Drawing of Rectangular Box-Shape Cups Without a Flange

Punch nose radius	Reduction in drawing(a) — 0.036 in. thick (20 gage)				0.105 in. thick (12 gage)				0.250 in. thick			
	20%	30%	40%	50%	20%	30%	40%	50%	20%	30%	40%	50%
No Flange, No Ironing												
4t	....	....	....	....	....	....	....	....	....	....	....	....
8t	CR,DQ,SK	....	....	....	HR,DQ	HR,DQ CR,DQ	....	....	HR,CQ	HR,DQ	....	....
16t	CR,DQ,SK	CR,DQ,SK	CR,DQ,SK	....	HR,DQ	HR,DQ	HR,DQ CR,DQ	....	HR,CQ	HR,DQ	HR,DQ	....
32t	CR,DQ	CR,DQ,SK	CR,DQ,SK	....	HR,DQ	HR,DQ	HR,DQ CR,DQ	CR,DQ,SK	HR,CQ	HR,CQ	HR,CQ	HR,DQ
No Flange, Ironed(b)												
4t	....	....	....	....	....	....	....	....	....	....	....	....
8t	CR,DQ,SK	....	....	....	HR,DQ	CR,DQ	....	....	HR,DQ	....	....	....
16t	CR,DQ,SK	CR,DQ,SK	....	....	HR,DQ	HR,DQ	CR,DQ,SK	....	HR,CQ	HR,DQ	HR,DQ	....
32t	CR,DQ	CR,DQ,SK	CR,DQ,SK	....	HR,DQ	HR,DQ	HR,DQ CR,DQ	CR,DQ,SK	HR,CQ	HR,CQ	HR,DQ	HR,DQ

CR = cold rolled; CQ = commercial quality; DQ = drawing quality; HR = hot rolled; SK = special killed.

NOTES: (1) Two entries in one space indicate that the choice will be influenced by uniformity, price, quantity, and availability. (2) Omission of an entry (....) in this table indicates that the draw is too severe to be completed successfully.

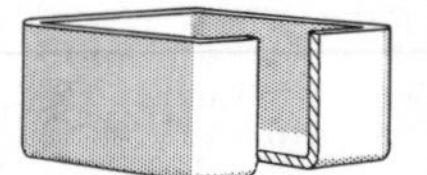

(a) In terms of reduction from blank width to cup width. Corner radii are the same as punch nose radius. (b) Operation that will bring the sidewall to a uniform thickness with the minimum amount of reduction.

Between 12 and 18 gage (0.105 and 0.048 in.), both hot and cold rolled grades are widely available and offer a greater range of selection. The hot and cold rolled steels become most closely competitive at about 16 gage (0.060 in.). Finish requirements on the parts will usually determine the final choice between the two grades indicated for each specific severity.

Either normalizing or annealing may be necessary for the most severe drawing requirements of Tables 6 and 7 — for instance, in Table 7, for the 0.250-in. thickness. In such borderline applications, quality of tooling and the experience of operators will often determine whether even the highest grade of sheet will make the part.

Grain size and surface finish affect drawability and may influence the selection of a grade. Grain sizes of 5 and coarser may result in objectionable surface roughness as well as reduced drawability. The dull finish normally supplied on drawing sheets is designed to hold lubricants and improve drawability. Brighter finishes are required if parts are to be electroplated.

Higher-Strength Grades. Higher strength can be obtained in drawn steel products at some sacrifice in drawability by using "physical quality" carbon steel (available with tensile strength as high as 80,000 psi min), high-manganese steel (up to about 0.20% C and 1.60% Mn), high-strength low-alloy steel conforming to ASTM A242 or SAE 950, or higher-carbon steels such as 1020 to 1060.

An example of a deep drawn part where high strength is required and heat treatment is impractical is a pressure tank for propane gas, which is being made from a 1.5% manganese steel by deep drawing the two halves and joining them by welding. For additional discussion and examples of deep drawing higher-strength grades, see the section on Deep Drawing of Pressure Vessels, on page 188.

Ironing. In cup drawing, the lip of the cup is usually thicker than the sidewall adjacent to the base. When uniformity of both wall thickness and strength is required in the drawn article and the steel is not subsequently heat treated, a certain maximum amount of ironing is allowable during the drawing operation. Permissible sidewall reductions for maintaining uniform strength in steels of various carbon contents are given in Table 8. The allowable reduction decreases as the carbon content and the amount of work hardening increase.

Table 8. Comparative Allowable Ironing to Maintain Uniform Strength of Cold Rolled Carbon Steel During Cup Drawing

Steel	Permissible reduction in wall, %
1008	
Drawing quality, special killed	12
Drawing quality	8
Commercial quality	7
1020	
Drawing quality, special killed, electric furnace	10
Drawing quality, annealed	8
Commercial quality, annealed	6
1030	
Special killed, electric furnace, annealed	8
Commercial quality, annealed	5
1040	
Special killed, electric furnace, annealed	7
Commercial quality, annealed	4

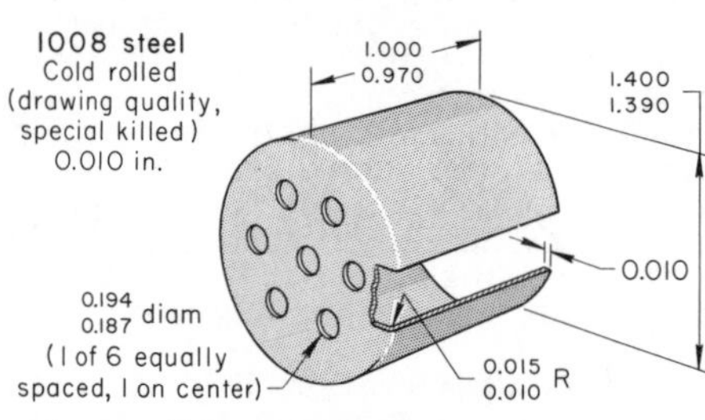

Fig. 19. Thin-wall cup that was made in a compound die, using a special lubricant containing graphite (Example 235)

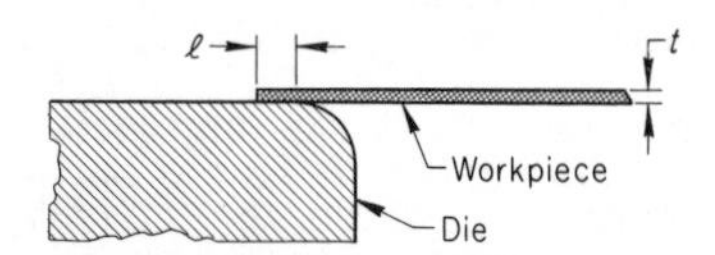

Fig. 20. Ratio of sheet thickness(t) *to supported length*(l) *determines need for use of a blankholder when drawing.*

Effect of Sheet Thickness

The development of wrinkles in drawing is caused by mechanical instability in the plane of the blank. This instability accompanies the circumferential compression to which the blank is subjected as it is drawn to the die radius. When dome shapes are drawn, the same compressive stress can develop in the shell wall or bottom, and a pucker will result.

The probability of wrinkling increases as the sheet thickness decreases to 0.032 in. or less. For a given drawing application, the sheet should be as thick as possible to suppress wrinkle formation. However, as thickness increases, press load rises, thereby increasing the probability of scoring, and production rate decreases.

Parts made of thin metal may be difficult to remove from the punch because the lubricant fills the space between the part and the punch, causing a vacuum. An air vent in the punch eliminates this problem.

In the following example, the thin-wall cup and the narrow scrap ring had to be removed from the drawing die carefully to prevent damage to the die and the cup.

Example 235. Thin-Wall Cup That Was Susceptible to Damage During Removal From the Die (Fig. 19)

The thin-wall cup shown in Fig. 19 had to be carefully removed from the drawing die to prevent denting the sides and distorting the bottom. Also, the narrow pinch-trimmed scrap ring had to be removed by the operator to prevent damage to the strip during feeding and damage to the die because of more than one stock thickness.

The cup was drawn from 0.010-in.-thick strip 3 in. wide (1008 steel, cold rolled, drawing quality, special killed). The steel was pickled, had a No. 4 or 5 temper (Rockwell B 65 max), and a No. 2 surface finish. A specially compounded lubricant containing graphite was used to blank, draw, pinch trim, and pierce seven 0.194/0.187-in.-diam holes, in a compound die. The die was made of D5 tool steel.

A 45-ton mechanical press with a die cushion, operating at 50 strokes per minute, was used. An air-operated hitch-type stock feeder moved the strip through the die.

Restraint of Metal Flow

Even in the simplest drawing operation, as shown in Fig. 5(a), the thickness of the work metal and the die radius offer some restraint to the flow of metal into the die. For drawing all but the simplest of shapes, some added restraint is usually required to control the flow of metal. This additional restraint is usually obtained by the use of a blankholder, as illustrated in Fig. (5b) and (c). The purpose of the blankholder is to suppress wrinkling and puckering, and to control the flow of the work metal into the die.

Drawing Without a Blankholder. A blank is not susceptible to wrinkling, and a blankholder need not be used, if the ratio of supported width to sheet thickness is within certain limits. In Fig. 20, the supported length (l) is the length from the edge of the blank to the die cavity (point of tangency). The sheet thickness is denoted as t. The l/t ratio is influenced little by other geometrical conditions, and differs little for the various metals commonly drawn. When the l/t ratio does not exceed 3 to 1, a cup can be drawn from annealed brass, aluminum (to half-hard), and low-carbon steel without a blankholder. For slightly harder work metals, such as hard copper or half-hard brass, this ratio should not exceed 2.5 to 1.

An elliptical or conical die opening, such as in Fig. 17, can be used where the die radius required to draw the part reduces the length of the blank-supporting surface to less than three times stock thickness. The distance between the die opening and the punch should not exceed ten times stock thickness.

A 30° elliptical radius derived from a circle created by a given draw radius increases the strain on the metal being drawn by 4.2%, but it decreases the metal out of control by 47% of the length of the original draw radius. This shape has been helpful in the drawing of tapered shells from a flat blank. For these draws, it is desirable to increase the strain slightly to prevent puckers and to reduce the metal out of control for the same reason.

A 45° elliptical radius derived as above reduces the strain on the metal being drawn by 1.03% and also reduces the metal out of control by 33% of the length of the original draw radius. The 45° ellipse is useful only when a large radius will draw the part, but produces wrinkles, and a smaller radius will not permit the draw.

A 60° elliptical radius does not measurably reduce drawing strain and accounts for only a 9% reduction of metal out of control. Its use on draw dies is not economically feasible when the small gains derived are considered in relation to the cost of producing the contour.

Drawing thick metal without a blankholder is frequently done when the blank diameter is no greater than 20 times stock thickness.

The part described in the following example was drawn in a die having a conical opening and a ratio of blank diameter to thickness of 19 to 1.

Example 236. Drawing a Thick Blank Without Use of a Blankholder (Fig. 21)

The cup (Fig. 21) for a disk-brake piston was drawn and sized in four operations from a drawing quality, hot rolled 1008 steel blank 0.250 in. thick and 4¾ in. in diameter without the use of a blankholder to prevent wrinkles. The workpieces were carried from station to station in a hydraulic-actuated dial feed. Spring-loaded fingers stripped the workpiece from the punch on the upstroke and held it in an indexing table to carry it to the next station. A die cushion provided the force for a pressure pad during the first three forming operations and also ejected the parts from the die cavities.

Blanks were stacked in a magazine with the cut (burnished) edge up and were fed into the first station of the die by an air-actuated slide. As the blank moved forward, it was roller coated with molybdenum disulfide lubricant.

In the first operation, the cup was drawn to 3-in. OD, 2⅓₂ in. high, with a ½-in. inside radius. The top inside corner of the cup was chamfered by the draw punch. A blankholder was not necessary, because of the stock thickness and the relatively low ratio of blank diameter to stock thickness (19 to 1). The die opening was conical (30° from top of die), and a 1-in. radius blended the entry angle with the sidewall.

In the second operation, the cup was reduced to 2.800-in. OD, 2⅛ in. deep, with a ¼-in. inside radius. The third station compressed the flange to a height of 2 in. to form sharp inside and outside corners.

The last station sized the cup to 2.770-in. OD, formed the concave end, and provided the elliptical form on the outside corner and the flat on the bottom. The cup height was 2⅓₂ in. The sizing ring was originally made of tungsten carbide, which required considerable maintenance to produce the required surface finish on the sidewalls. Changing to an aluminum bronze ring increased ring life and reduced maintenance.

Clearances per side between the punch and die for each of the operations performed in the dial index setup were: first operation, 0.305 in.; second operation, 0.239 in.; third operation, 0.253 in.; and fourth operation, 0.250 in.

The die operated in an 800-ton mechanical press at 14 strokes per minute. Yearly production was over 3 million pieces.

In subsequent operations, the part was machined to 2.753/2.751-in. OD, and height to 1.937 in. The groove was machined in and the bottom corner was burnished to 15-micro-in. finish.

Another method of making the same part competitively was by cold extrusion from a steel slug.

A similar setup was used to make a cup 2.376 in. in diameter from a 4½-in.-diam blank.

Blankholders. The purpose of a blankholder is to prevent wrinkles from forming in the flange of a part during drawing. The formation of wrinkles interferes with, or prevents, the compressive action that rearranges the metal from flange to sidewall. Much greater reductions are possible when a blankholder is used.

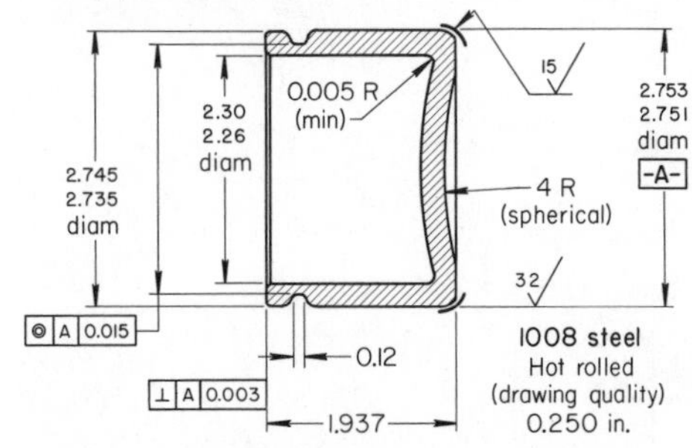

Fig. 21. Thick-wall cup that was drawn without a blankholder, then machined to size and shape shown (Example 236)

Blankholders can be used in both double-action and single-action presses. In a double-action press, the blankholder advances slightly ahead of the punch, and dwells at the bottom of its stroke throughout the drawing phase of the punch cycle. The blankholder dwell usually extends to a point on the punch upstroke at which positive stripping of the shell is assured. By using a die cushion and an inverted die, similar action can be obtained in a single-action press. A die cushion in a double-action press supports the blank and holds it against the punch during the drawing operation; it then lifts the finished part out of the die.

A blankholder must allow the work metal to thicken as the edge of the blank moves inward toward the working edge of the die. The amount of thickening is expressed by:

$$t_1/t = \sqrt{D/D_1}$$

where t is the thickness of the blank; t_1 is the thickness of the flange at any instant during the drawing operation; D is the diameter of the blank; and D_1 is the diameter of the flange at any instant during the drawing operation, or the mean diameter of the workpiece without the flange. As the metal flows, paths of least resistance are taken; therefore, the actual value of t_1 will be less than that calculated from the formula.

Types of Blankholders. The simplest type of blankholder is fixed to the die block and has a flat hold-down surface, as shown in Fig. 22(a). A disadvantage of this type is that maintenance of the optimum gap between the die surface and the flat hold-down surface requires careful adjustment. As shown in the illustration, the blankholder does not quite touch the work metal as drawing begins; restraint begins and increases as the flange portion thickens. A gap that is either too small or too large increases force and reduces drawability. For best results, the gap should be slightly smaller than the flange thickness, allowing 50 to 75% of the final thickening before the work metal touches the blankholder.

Some of the difficulty in maintaining adjustment of a fixed flat blankholder can be avoided by tapering the hold-down surface, as shown in Fig. 22(b). A tapered fixed blankholder can tightly clamp the blank edge at the beginning of the operation. The amount of taper is not critical and is usually ½ to 1½ times the theoretical taper (thickness of the blank to maximum thickness of the flange).

The flat controlled-pressure blankholder shown in Fig. 22(c) is generally preferred in production operations, because it can be adjusted to a predeter-

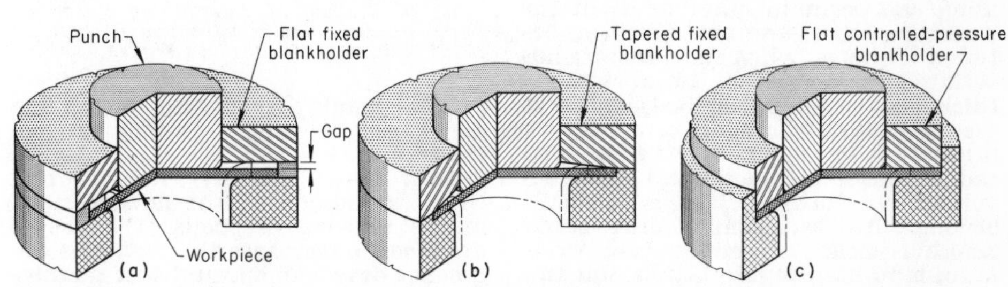

Fig. 22. Setups showing use of three types of blankholders. See text for discussion.

mined and closely controlled value by hydraulic or pneumatic pressure. Springs, unless extremely long, are not suitable for supplying pressure to a blankholder during deep drawing, because the force exerted by a spring increases rapidly as it is compressed. The force on hydraulic or pneumatic die cushions will increase about 20% when compressed the full stroke length. Some hydraulic systems have pressure control valves that supply a more nearly constant pressure during the entire stroke.

The fixed-type blankholder (Fig. 22a and b) draws a cup without a flange and ejects it through the bottom of the die. The blankholder shown in Fig. 5(b) and (c) and Fig. 22(c) can be used for drawing a cup with or without a flange. The cup is stripped from the punch by the blankholder and ejected from the die by a knockout or pressure pad. Cups without a flange can be pushed through the die if a pressure pad is not needed to support the blank.

Thin-face shimmed blankholders, like the one shown in Fig. 23, are used when the flange must be restrained with a minimum of marking or damage to the material, and where draw beads normally would be needed. (Draw beads are used to restrain metal flow at points found by trial or by experience to give the needed control.) The shim is not continuous, but exerts pressure at selected points to restrict flow. This kind of blankholder is inexpensively produced and maintained. Costs for setup and production are about the same as for a conventional blankholder.

Blankholder Pressure. The restraint needed in drawing varies during the press stroke as the draw progresses. Ideally, the pressure of the blankholder should be light at first, increasing as the draw progresses, and then should become lighter again as the flange thickens. However, it is not practical to vary the blankholder pressure, and an average value is used.

Optimum blankholder pressure depends largely on the amount of reduction and the die contour. However, assuming a generous radius on the die, hold-down force varies little for a wide range of work-metal thicknesses, and is approximately proportional to the area of the portion of the blank initially held by the blankholder.

Approximate blankholder pressures, based on mechanical properties of the metal, are given for several different metals in Table 9. Blankholder forces for drawing a wide range of thicknesses of low-carbon steel, as a percentage of drawing forces, are given in Table 10.

The pressures in Tables 9 and 10 are used only to prevent wrinkling at the edges of the blank and flange. Wrinkling can occur in other areas of the workpiece that are not confined between the tools. When the punch radius is large in proportion to work-metal thickness, wrinkling is likely to occur (see Fig. 49). Wrinkling can often be prevented by superimposing a high radial tension on the normal stress developed in drawing. This is normally accomplished by means of draw beads. Another means of eliminating wrinkling is to use oversize blanks, but this is wasteful of work metal. Also, an

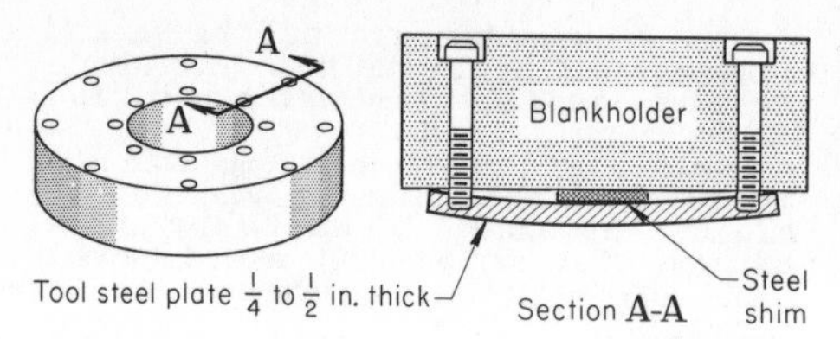

Fig. 23. Thin-face shimmed blankholder

Table 9. Blankholder Pressures for Several Annealed Metals

Metal	Pressure, psi(a)
Low-carbon steel	500
Austenitic stainless steel	1000
Aluminum	100
Aluminum alloys	200 to 500
Copper	200
Alpha brasses	250 to 300
Phosphor bronze	400

(a) Values are approximately 1/150 to 1/200 of the sum of the yield strength and tensile strength of the specific metal.

Table 10. Blankholder Forces for Deep Drawing of Low-Carbon Steel(a)

Work-metal thickness, in.	Blankholder force, % of drawing force	Work-metal thickness, in.	Blankholder force, % of drawing force
0.005	85	0.050	23
0.010	67	0.070	14
0.015	57	0.100	9
0.020	50	0.125	8½
0.025	44	0.187	8¼
0.030	39	0.250	8

(a) Values given should not be used for shallow drawing, particularly of elliptical or hemispherical shapes.

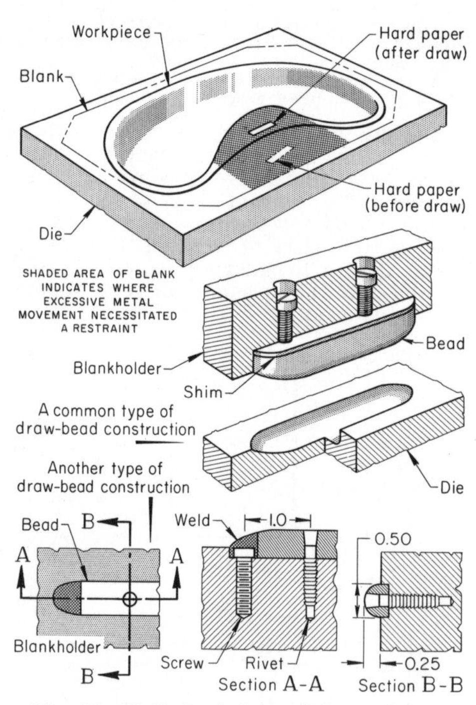

Fig. 24. Method of determining optimum bead location, and construction of typical draw beads. See also Fig. 49.

oversize blank may restrict metal flow and cause excessive thinning or even fracture.

Draw beads (Fig. 24) help prevent wrinkles and control the flow of metal in the drawing of shells. The use of draw beads increases the cost of tools, product development, and tool maintenance. However, they often are the only means of controlling metal flow in drawing odd shapes. Draw beads are ordinarily used for the first draw only; thus, production rates are the same as when conventional blankholders are used.

Optimum location of the draw bead can be determined by placing a piece of hard paper on the flange of the workpiece, as shown in Fig. 24. The paper will move as the workpiece is drawn, indicating where restraint is needed.

Two methods of constructing draw beads are illustrated in Fig. 24 (lower views). Beads are usually made from water-hardening tool steel, such as SAE W108, to resist wear from the sliding work metal. The height of a bead fastened with screws from the top can be adjusted by shimming.

The second bead design shown in Fig. 24 uses a drive rivet that has hardened serrations and a soft tapered head. Rivets are driven into holes in the blankholder, and the heads are peened and ground flush with the bead. Additional anchorage is provided by welding the ends of the bead to a low-carbon steel screw after the bead is flame hardened. The weld is ground to blend with the bead and blankholder surface. The bead is seated in a close-fitting groove to prevent tipping during the draw operation.

For low production, draw beads often are made by laying a weld bead on the die after the optimum location has been determined.

Restraint of the metal flow, to the extreme of locking the flange of the blank to prevent motion, is needed for some draws. A deep shell with sloping walls may be made by drawing followed by several redraws. This results in a stepped workpiece. The final sizing draw is a stretching operation, made with the flange secured by a locking bead in the blankholder, as shown in Fig. 25. This kind of blankholder is also used in making shallow drawn panels.

For additional information on the design and use of draw beads, see page 125 of "Press Forming of Low-Carbon Steel", in this volume.

Sometimes draw beads need not be used for the full depth of draw, or need be used only in certain locations, such as corners of regular or irregular polygon-shape parts. In such applications, some of the work metal may be allowed to slip through the draw bead, to be retained at the end of the stroke only by blankholder pressure, as in the following example.

Example 237. Forming a Large Irregular Shape With the Aid of Draw Beads (Fig. 26)

When parted, the drawn shape shown in Fig. 26 made a right-hand and left-hand wheel housing for an automobile. Forming the two housings together reduced scrap loss and minimized the number of dies required. A 1010 steel blank 48 in. wide by 54 in. long and 0.042 in. thick was used. Operations were:

1. Shear blank to size and trim corners 4 in. by 45°.
2. Draw in a toggle press with 400-ton outer slide and 440-ton inner slide.
3. Separate shell into two pieces in a 300-ton mechanical press.
4. Restrike to sharpen radii and flare bottom edge in a 300-ton mechanical press.
5. Trim periphery of part in a 300-ton mechanical press.

Draw beads similar to those shown in Fig. 24 were placed in the blankholder about 6 in.

from the cavity, surrounding it. This arrangement provided additional control of the blank during the initial drawing stage.

After drawing to about half the full depth, the edge of the blank had moved inside the draw bead at certain places along the sides and ends, and it was held only by the blankholder surfaces. The amount of metal controlled by the draw beads decreased as the depth of draw increased. At the end of the operation, four to eight points of the blank were still confined by the bead. The amount of metal still outside the draw bead depended on the earing characteristics of the metal, the centering of the blank under the punch, and the uniformity of metal movement between blankholder faces.

A pigmented emulsified drawing compound slightly thinned with water was used during drawing.

The drawing die for operation 2 was made of ductile iron. The dies for operations 3 and 5 were gray iron faced with O1 tool steel cutting edges. The restrike die for operation 4 was ductile iron.

Production rate was 150 draws per hour. Die life was three model years.

Effect of Press Speed

Drawing speed is usually expressed in linear feet per minute. Under ideal conditions, press speeds as high as 75 ft per min are used for deep drawing of low-carbon steel. However, 20 to 55 ft per min is the usual range — up to 55 ft per min for single-action presses and 35 to 50 ft per min for double-action presses (Table 11). Ideal conditions include: (*a*) use of a drawing quality of work metal; (*b*) symmetrical workpieces of relatively mild severity; (*c*) adequate lubrication; (*d*) precision carbide tools; (*e*) carefully controlled blankholding pressure; and (*f*) presses that are maintained to a high level of accuracy. When one or more of the above conditions is less than ideal, some reduction in press speed is required. If all, or nearly all, are substantially less than ideal, press speed may have to be reduced to 20 ft per min. When the operation includes ironing, the drawing speed is usually reduced to about 25 ft per min, regardless of other factors.

The punch speed in hydraulic presses is relatively constant throughout the stroke. In mechanical presses, "punch speed" is that at mid-stroke, since the velocity changes in a characteristic manner throughout the drawing stroke, from maximum velocity to zero. The only adjustment in speed that can be made is to decrease flywheel speed or to use a press with a shorter stroke that operates at the same number of strokes per minute. This proportionately decreases maximum punch speed.

Speed is of greater significance in drawing stainless steels and heat-resisting alloys than in drawing softer, more ductile metals. Excessive press speeds have caused cracking and excessive wall thinning in drawing these stronger, less ductile metals. Nominal speeds for drawing various metals are given in Table 11. Effect of speed on drawability of low-carbon steel is shown in Table 12.

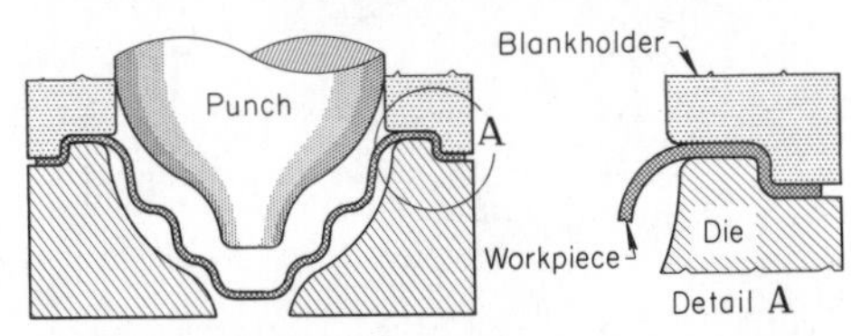

Fig. 25. Locking blankholder used for final sizing draw

1010 steel, cold rolled, drawing quality, 0.042 in.

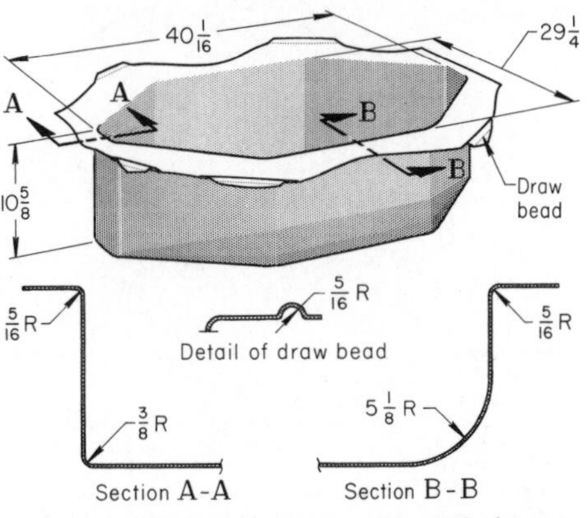

Fig. 26. Large irregular shape that was drawn with the aid of draw beads. The shell was later parted to make two wheel housings. (Example 237)

Table 11. Nominal Speeds for Drawing of Various Metals

Metal	Speed, ft per min: Single-action press	Double-action press
Aluminum	175	100
High-strength aluminum	...	30 to 40
Brass	200	100
Copper	150	85
Steel	55	35 to 50
Steel (with carbide dies)	...	60
Stainless steel	...	20 to 30
Zinc	150	40

Effect of Lubrication

When two metals are in sliding contact under pressure, as with the dies and the work metal in drawing, galling (pressure welding) of the tools and the work metal is likely. When extreme galling occurs, drawing force increases and becomes unevenly distributed, causing fracture of the workpiece.

The likelihood of pressure welding depends on the amount of force and the work-metal composition. Some work metals are more "sticky" than others. For instance, austenitic stainless steel is more likely to adhere to steel tools than is low-carbon steel.

Lubricants are used in most drawing operations. They range from ordinary machine oil to pigmented compounds.

Selection of lubricant is based primarily on ability to prevent galling, wrinkling or tearing during deep drawing. It is also influenced by ease of application and removal, corrosivity and other factors, as described on page 25 in the article on Lubrication.

If a lubricant cannot be applied uniformly by ordinary shop methods, its purpose is defeated, regardless of its ability to prevent pressure welding. In general, as the effectiveness of a lubricant increases, the difficulty of removing it also increases. For example, grease or oil can be easily removed, whereas special procedures (frequently including some hand scrubbing) are required for removing lubricants that contain zinc oxide, lithopone, white lead, molybdenum disulfide, or graphite.

Sometimes a lubricant is too corrosive for use on certain metals. For example, copper alloys are susceptible to staining by lubricants that contain large amounts of sulfur or chlorine compounds. Lubricants containing lead or zinc compounds are not recommended for drawing stainless steel or heat-resisting alloys, because if not thoroughly removed, the compounds can cause intergranular attack when the workpieces are heat treated or placed in high-temperature service.

Table 12. Effect of Press Speed on Drawability of Low-Carbon Steel Sheet, Cold Rolled, Drawing Quality, Aluminum Killed

Punch nose radius	Reduction in blank diameter: 20%	30%	40%	50%
10 Strokes per Minute				
2*t*	Satisfactory	Some thinning at radius	Fracture at radius	Complete fracture at radius
4*t*	Satisfactory	Satisfactory	Some thinning at radius	Slight fracture at radius
8*t*	Satisfactory	Satisfactory	Satisfactory	Excessive thinning at radius
16*t*	Satisfactory	Satisfactory	Satisfactory	Satisfactory
32*t*	Satisfactory	Satisfactory	Satisfactory	Satisfactory
60 Strokes per Minute				
2*t*	Some thinning at radius	Some thinning at radius	Fracture at radius	....
4*t*	Satisfactory	Satisfactory	Some thinning at radius	Fracture at bottom
8*t*	Satisfactory	Satisfactory	Satisfactory	Excessive thinning at radius
16*t*	Satisfactory	Satisfactory	Satisfactory	Excessive thinning at radius
32*t*	Satisfactory	Satisfactory	Satisfactory	Satisfactory
150 Strokes per Minute				
2*t*	Excessive thinning at radius	Fracture at radius	....	....
4*t*	Some thinning at radius	Some thinning at radius	Fractured at radius	....
8*t*	Satisfactory	Some thinning at radius	Excessive thinning at radius	....
16*t*	Satisfactory	Satisfactory	Satisfactory	Almost complete fracture at radius
32*t*	Satisfactory	Satisfactory	Satisfactory	Partial fracture at radius

Simple round cups, no flange, not ironed, 20-gage sheet, 0.036 in. thick. Blank spaces indicate bottom pushed out.

Suitable safety precautions are necessary with toxic or flammable lubricants.

Some metals, such as magnesium and titanium, are drawn at elevated temperature, which complicates selection of the lubricant. Most oil-base and soap-base lubricants can be used successfully up to 250 F, but above this temperature the choice narrows rapidly. Some special soap-base lubricants can be used on work metals up to 450 F. Molybdenum disulfide and graphite can be used at higher temperatures.

Any lubricant must remain stable, without becoming rancid, when stored for a period of several months at various temperatures.

The cost of application and removal of the lubricant, as well as its initial cost, must be considered, because all these items can add substantially to the cost of the drawn workpieces.

In some plants, when a new application is started, a heavily pigmented drawing lubricant is used, regardless of the difficulty of applying and removing it. Lubricant is then downgraded as much as possible, to simplify the operation and reduce cost. In other plants, the reverse of this practice is used — that is, a simple lubricant, such as machine oil, is used at first, and lubricant is then upgraded when necessary.

In the following example, two similar parts were drawn from heavy stock, using extreme-pressure lubricants. However, a higher-grade lubricant was needed for one part because of embossing in the bottom.

Example 238. Variations in Lubrication for Two Similar Caps (Fig. 27)

Figure 27 shows the top and bottom caps for a tubular part that were made in similar production lines. The top cap, of cold rolled 1008 or 1010 steel 0.125 in. thick, had a 9⁄16-in. hole pierced in its center. The bottom cap also was made of cold rolled 1008 or 1010 steel, but 0.140 in. thick. It had a stud welded to the base and three locating lugs embossed into the bottom. The top cap was lubricated with water-soluble oil-base drawing compound, and the bottom cap with a mixture of wax and a drawing compound.

For each cap, the sequence of operations was about the same:

1. Blank in a 200-ton mechanical press. (Strip for the top cap was lubricated with water-soluble oil-base drawing compound.)
2. Lubricate with drawing compound (dripped on while blanks were moving on a conveyor).
3. Draw in a 190-ton inclined, straight-side press.
4. Pierce hole in top cap (dial index table mounted in a 75-ton press).
5. Coin chamfer.
6. Size in a 75-ton press by pushing through a sizing die.

The example that follows describes an application in which the lubricant was changed from a pigmented drawing compound to a water-soluble chlorinated oil to prevent excessive rise in workpiece temperature during three-stage drawing:

Example 239. Change of Lubricant to Facilitate Handling of Workpiece (Fig. 28)

The oil-filter shell shown in Fig. 28 was drawn in three stages from a cold rolled rimmed steel blank 0.089 in. thick and 13.19-in. diam. The three dies were installed in a single 550-ton mechanical press. Between strokes, the shells were transferred from die to die by hand. Direct redrawing was used for the last two stages, and the bottom was embossed in the last stage. The shell was trimmed to height in a separate operation by a trimming machine.

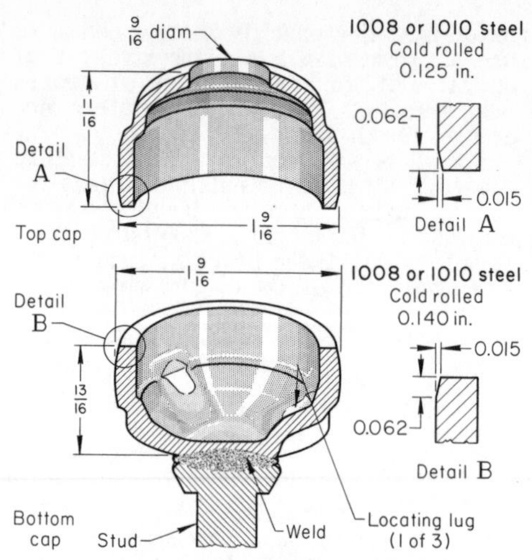

Fig. 27. Caps that required different lubricants for forming (Example 238)

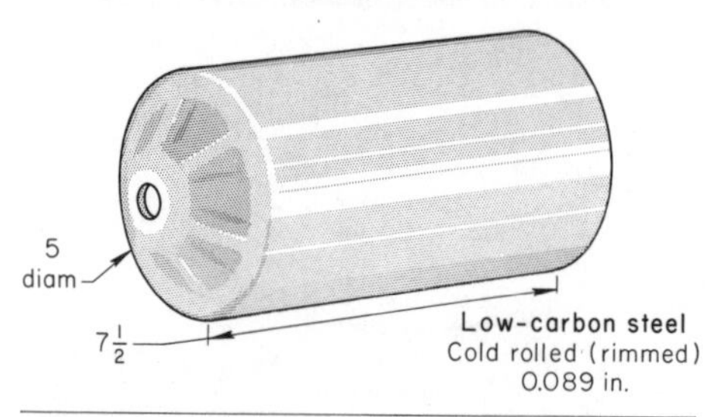

Stock size ....0.0885 ± 0.0035 in. by 39⅝ by 68 in.
Sequence of operations:
Cup to 7½-in. diam by 4 in. deep
First redraw to 6-in. diam by 6 in. deep
Final redraw to 5-in. diam by 7½ in. deep
Tool material:
Draw dies ....7140 alloy steel
Draw punches ....O2 tool steel
Lubricant finally selected ....Water-soluble chlorinated drawing oil
Production lot (average) ....2500 pieces
Production rate ....120 pieces per hour

Fig. 28. Oil-filter shell for which lubricant was changed to reduce workpiece temperature during drawing (Example 239)

Table 13. Typical Lubricants Used in Drawing Steel
(See page 25 for more complete list.)

Mild Severity (10% or Less)(a)

1. Mineral oil, at a viscosity of 250 to 350 SUS
2. 5% soap solutions

Average Severity (About 25%)(a)

1. Heavy-duty emulsions
2. Dissimilar metals deposited on steel, using heavy-duty emulsions

Maximum Severity (50% or More)(a)

1. Phosphate or dissimilar metal coatings, with dried soap or wax film
2. Phosphate or dissimilar metal coatings, with compounds containing one or more of materials such as whiting, lithopone, mica, white lead, talc, china clay, or molybdenum disulfide.

(a) Percentage reduction from blank diameter to cup diameter

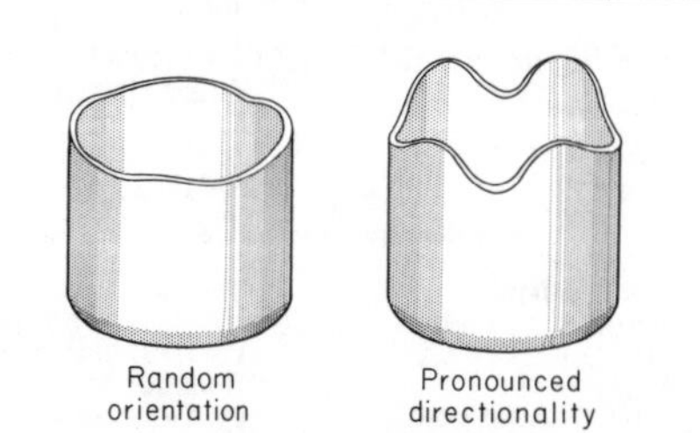

Fig. 29. Effect of grain orientation on earing of drawn 80 Cu – 20 Ni sheet

Two lubricants were tried. With a pigmented drawing compound, results were satisfactory but the temperature of the workpieces rose to 400 F during drawing — hot enough so that the operator had to use asbestos gloves for handling the workpieces. The lubricant was then changed to a water-soluble chlorinated oil, which would keep the parts cool enough so they could be transferred without the use of special gloves. This lubricant was also easier to remove; workpieces were cleaned in a warm alkaline solution before the next operation (brazing).

Tools lasted for three years (about 200,000 pieces). Draw dies were of nitrided 7140 alloy steel and punches of O2 tool steel. The dies did not have to be reground, but occasionally buildup of work metal on the die radius had to be stoned away.

Radii and clearance on the die elements were as follows:

Item	Cupping	First redraw	Second redraw
Die radius, in.	11/32	1/4	1/4
Punch radius, in. ..	3/8	15/32	1/4
Punch-to-die clearance per side, in. ..	0.090	0.122	0.114
Pressure-pad radius, in.	Flat	13/32	1/4

The difficulty of removing drawing lubricants is an important consideration in production operations. In a number of applications, changes in drawing techniques (such as increasing the number of draws) or in workpiece design (larger radii, for example) have been made solely to permit use of an easier-to-remove drawing lubricant. (Cleaning methods are discussed in the section of this article on Cleaning of Workpieces, page 187.)

Typical lubricants used in drawing steel are given in Table 13, according to severity of draw, or the percentage reduction from blank to cup diameter. The entries in Table 13 are arranged in the order of increasing effectiveness, but there are exceptions. For example, in some applications, dried soap and wax perform better than pigmented compounds for more severe drawing operations.

For more detailed information on lubricants for drawing of steel and other metals, see the article on page 23 of this volume, and articles dealing with the forming of specific metals.

Zinc phosphate coating of the steel to be drawn is helpful for any drawing operation, and the importance of phosphate coating increases as severity of draw increases. Although the phosphate coating alone has some value as a lubricant, its principal function is to serve as a wick to retain lubricant in the areas where the need is greatest. For methods of application and other details on the use of phosphate coating, see the article that begins on page 531 in Volume 2 of this Handbook.

Effect of Rolling Direction

The mechanical properties and drawability of a sheet or plate depend considerably on its processing history and to a certain extent on the quality of the ingot from which it was rolled. Elongation of the metal during rolling introduces a phenomenon called directionality, anisotropy or, sometimes, fibering. Any wrought product exhibits different properties in different directions. The directionality may be significant for certain applications and immaterial for others.

Gross mechanical directionality seldom hampers the forming of sheet and strip. However, if it is associated with an agglomeration of hard constituents or segregations, mechanical directionality may make thick sheet and plate susceptible to separation along a plane parallel to the surfaces. Such laminations occasionally occur in drawing and heading of cartridge cases.

Crystallographic directionality is common in both annealed and cold worked sheet and strip. The best-known result from directionality is "earing" — the development of ears, or scallops, on a deep drawn cup or tubular part (Fig. 29).

Abnormal earing requires additional trimming, causes scrap loss, and may require special stripping procedures to remove the workpiece from the punch. Sheet with pronounced directionality is also more susceptible to cracking during drawing than sheet with random orientation.

The drawing of a small cylindrical cup is a common test method for evaluating the directionality of sheet metal. Another method is the tear-length test. Slots are cut in various directions on the edges of a piece of sheet to be tested, forming short tabs. Each of these tabs is gripped with pliers or a slotted key, and the metal is torn until a triangular tongue is separated from it. Variation in length of the tongues indicates varying directionality.

The directionality of grain orientation produced by rolling is sometimes a factor in the selection of low-carbon steel sheet for deep drawing. Although it can affect the deep drawing characteristics of heavier-gage material, it is particularly important in deep drawing sheet 0.062 in. thick or less.

Direct Redrawing

Shells that are too deep to be drawn in a single operation are completed by one or more redraws.

In direct redrawing in a single-action die, the drawn cup is slipped over the punch and is loaded in the die, as shown in Fig. 30. At first, the bottom of the cup is wrapped around the punch nose without reducing the diameter of the cylindrical section. Then the sidewall section enters the die and is gradually reduced to its final diameter. Metal flow takes place as the cup is drawn into the die, so that the wall of the redrawn shell is parallel to and deeper than the wall of the cup at the start of the redraw. At the beginning of redrawing, the cup must be supported and guided by a recess in the die, or by a blankholder, to prevent it from tipping, because tipping would result in an uneven shell.

In a single-action redraw, the metal must be thick enough to withstand the compressive forces set up in reducing the cup diameter without wrinkling. Wrinkling can be prevented by the use of an internal blankholder and a double-action press (upper right view in Fig. 30), which usually permits a shell to be formed in fewer operations than by single-action drawing without the use of a blankholder.

Internal blankholders (Fig. 31) are slip-fitted into drawn shells to provide support and prevent wrinkling during direct redrawing. The blankholder presses on the drawn shell at the working edge of the die before the punch contacts the bottom of the shell and begins the redraw. It dwells against the shell as the metal is drawn into the die by the punch, preventing wrinkles.

The bottom of the cup to be redrawn can be tapered (Fig. 31a) or radiused (Fig. 31b), with the tip of the blankholder and the mouth of the die designed accordingly. An angle of 30° is used for metal thinner than 1/32 in. and 45° for thicker work metal. A modification of the above is a blankholder fitted against an S-curve die (Fig. 31b). The main disadvantage of an S-curve die is that it is more expensive to make and maintain.

Near the bottom of a redrawn shell, there is usually a narrow ring, caused by the bottom radius of the preceding shell, that is thinner and harder than the adjacent metal. (See Example 290 in the article on Rubber-Pad Forming.)

Redrawing may be required for reasons other than the severity of the drawn shape. The two examples that follow describe redrawing that was necessary to prevent thinning and bulging.

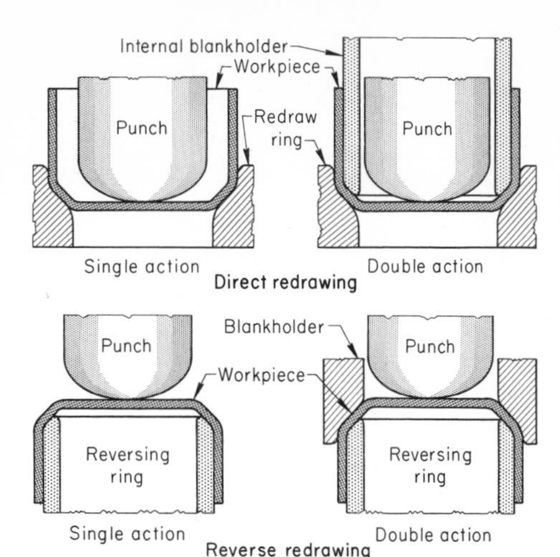

Fig. 30. Direct and reverse redrawing in single-action and double-action dies

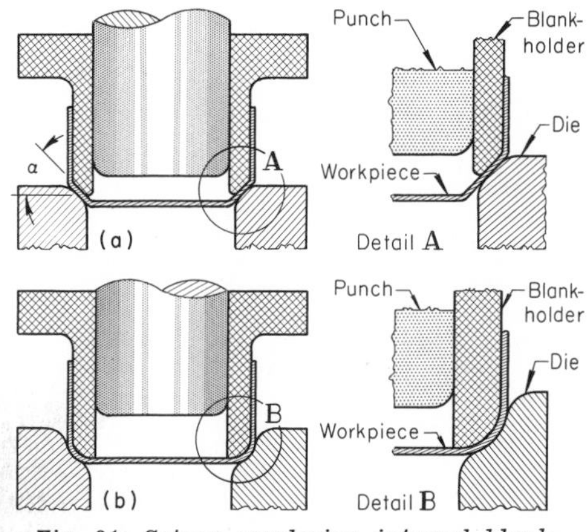

Fig. 31. Setups employing internal blankholders for restraint of metal in redrawing shells. See text for discussion.

Example 240. Use of Redrawing to Prevent Wall Thinning (Fig. 32)

Figure 32 shows a ferrule and the setups for drawing it in two operations from coiled special-killed steel 2¾ in. wide by 0.035 in. thick. After being drawn, the ferrules were pierced, finish formed, and trimmed in two additional operations.

The ferrules could have been produced in a single draw, but excessive thinning of the walls would have resulted. The additional operation permitted larger radii on tools used for the first draw. The first operation (blanking and drawing) was done in a 50-ton, hand-fed mechanical press with a 3-in. stroke. A 35-ton press with a 3-in. stroke was used for subsequent operations. Forming components of the punch and die were made of O1 tool steel and were hardened to Rockwell C 58, and cutting components were made from the same tool steel and were hardened to Rockwell C 61. Each operation produced 2000 pieces per hour. The lubricant applied to the strip stock was a commercial nonpigmented drawing compound.

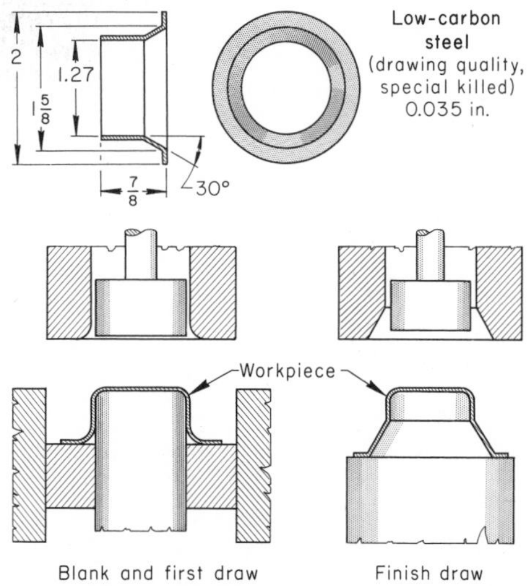

Fig. 32. Ferrule drawn in two operations to minimize wall thinning (Example 240)

Example 241. Change From One to Two Draws to Prevent Bulging (Fig. 33)

A 36-in.-diam cup was originally made in one draw from a circular blank in a double-action mechanical press with a capacity of 700 tons on the ram and 500 tons on the blankholder. Ram stroke was 42 in. and blankholder stroke was 27 in. The cup was produced successfully, but with bulged sides (see "Original method" in Fig. 33).

Bulging was prevented by first drawing to the shape shown in operation 1 of the improved method in Fig. 33, and then restriking to the final shape (operation 2). Punches and dies were made from gray iron with tool steel inserts; average life was 100,000 pieces. Production rate was about 150 pieces per hour. Lubricant was dry soap.

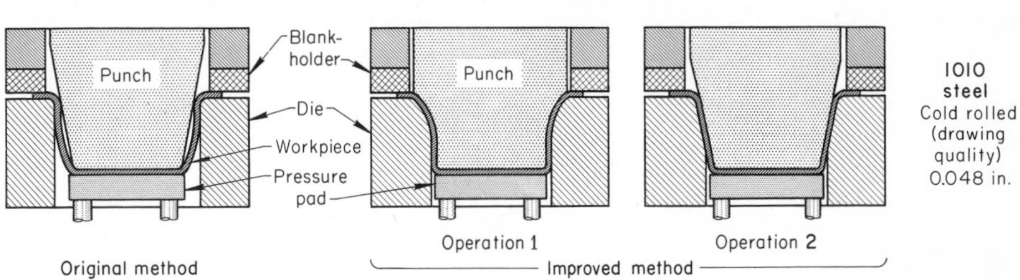

Fig. 33. Change from single draw to two-operation draw that prevented bulging of the sidewalls of a cup (Example 241)

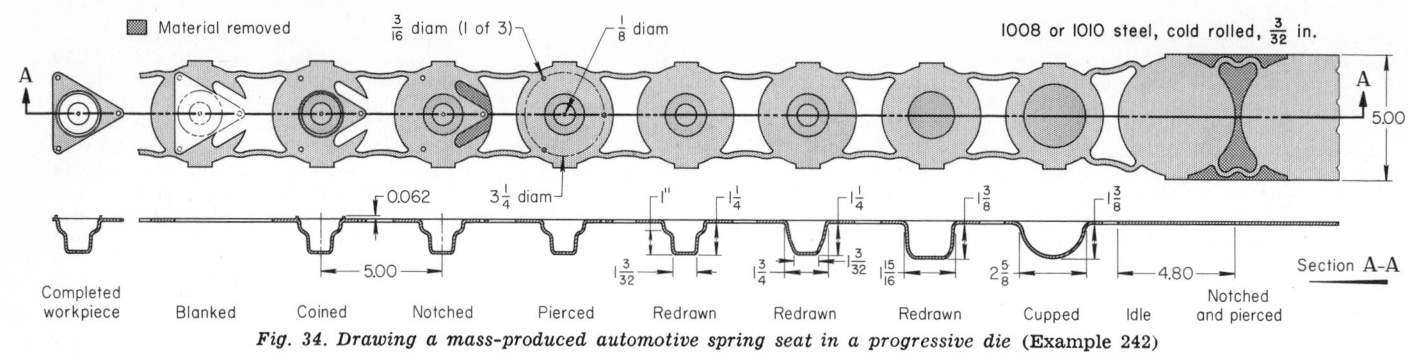

Fig. 34. Drawing a mass-produced automotive spring seat in a progressive die (Example 242)

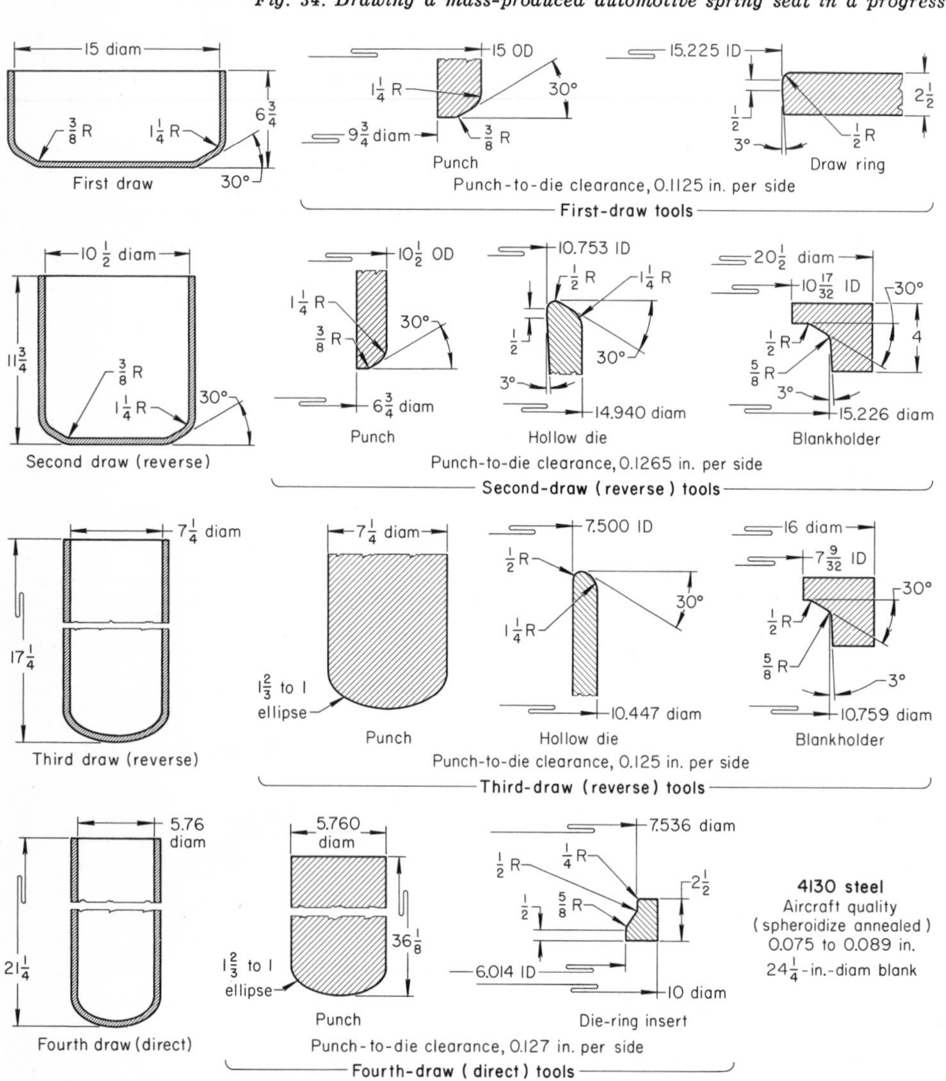

Fig. 35. Progression of shapes produced, and details of tooling used, in forming a deep shell in four draws, including reverse and direct redrawing (Example 243)

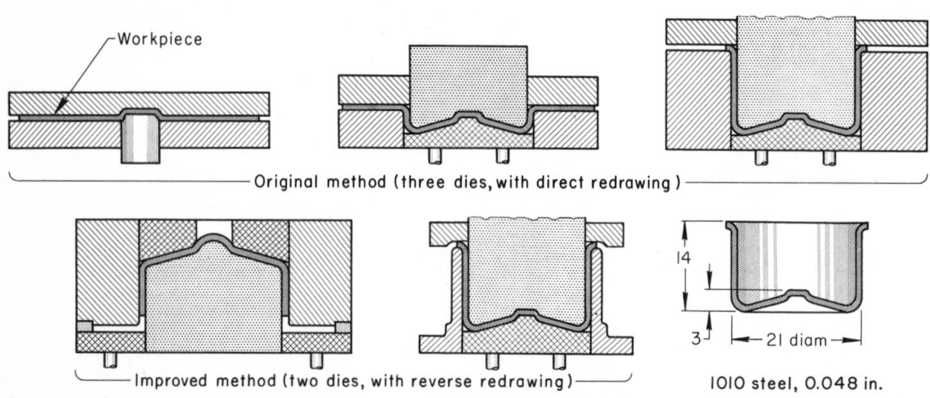

Fig. 36. Original and improved methods of drawing a washing-machine tub (Example 244)

The draw radius for operation 1 of the improved method was 2 in., with a 10-in. radius blending with the draw radius and the straight sides. The depth of draw was 11.43 in. For operation 2, the draw radius was 0.125 in., and the depth of draw was 11.50 in. The punches for both operations 1 and 2 had a nose radius of 1.195 in.

Redrawing can be done in a progressive die while the part is still attached to the strip. Where space permits the extra stations, the amount of work done in each station will be less than that done in a single die. This reduces the severity of draw and promotes high-speed operation. In the following example, parts were direct redrawn without using an internal blankholder to assist in forming the cup, although a flat blankholder was used to control the metal in the surrounding flange.

Example 242. Redrawing a Spring Seat in a Progressive Die (Fig. 34)

The spring seat shown in Fig. 34 was drawn in a progressive die in quantities of more than a million pieces per year. After cupping, three redraws were used to form the cup to shape, depth and diameter. The die was operated in a 100-ton mechanical press at 60 strokes per minute.

Stock was cold rolled 1008 or 1010 steel 5 in. wide by 3/32 in. thick. A sulfurized oil was originally used as the lubricant, but it was found that a water-soluble oil did the job and was easier to remove. The lubricant was applied by intermittent spraying.

The sequence of operations in the progressive die was as follows:

1 Pierce and notch blank outline, leaving two narrow deformable carrier strips.
2 Cup.
3 Redraw to reduce diameter.
4 Redraw to reduce diameter and form taper.
5 Redraw to reduce diameter for part of depth only.
6 Pierce four holes (one in bottom of cup).
7 Partially trim outline.
8 Coin ridge around cup.
9 Cut off.

Tool material was D2 tool steel. Tool life was three years or more, but design changes made the tool obsolete before it wore out.

Reverse Redrawing

In reverse redrawing, the cupped workpiece is placed over a reversing ring and redrawn in the direction opposite to that used for drawing the initial cup. As shown in the two lower views in Fig. 30, reverse redrawing can be done with or without a blankholder. The blankholder serves the same purposes as in direct redrawing.

Advantages of reverse redrawing as compared with direct redrawing include: (*a*) drawing and redrawing can be accomplished in one stroke of a triple-action hydraulic press, or of a double-action mechanical press with a die cushion, which can eliminate the need for a second press (Example 246); (*b*) greater reductions per redraw are possible with reverse redrawing (Examples 243 and 244); (c) one or more intermediate annealing operations can often be eliminated by using the reverse technique; and (d) better distribution of metal can be obtained in a complex shape (Example 245).

In borderline applications, annealing is required between redraws in direct redrawing, but is not needed in reverse redrawing.

Disadvantages of reverse redrawing are: (a) the technique is not practical for work metal thicker than ¼ in., and (b) reverse redrawing requires a longer stroke than does direct redrawing.

Usually, metals that can be direct redrawn can be reverse redrawn. All of the carbon and low-alloy steels, austenitic and ferritic stainless steels, aluminum alloys, and copper alloys can be reverse redrawn.

Reverse redrawing requires more closely controlled processing than does direct redrawing. This control must begin with the blanks, which should be free from nicks and scratches, especially at the edges.

The restraint in reverse redrawing must be uniform and low. For low friction, polished dies and effective lubrication of the work are needed. Friction is also affected by hold-down pressure and by the shape of the reversing ring. Radii of tools should be as large as practical—ten times the thickness of the work metal if possible.

The examples that follow describe specific conditions where it was advantageous to use reverse redrawing.

Example 243. Use of Reverse Redrawing to Obtain Greater Reduction Than Possible by Direct Redrawing (Fig. 35)

The 5.76-in.-ID by 21¼-in.-deep shell shown in Fig. 35 was drawn from an aircraft-quality spheroidize-annealed 4130 steel blank, 0.075 to 0.089 in. thick by 24¼ in. in diameter, in four drawing operations. The shells were annealed after the first and second redraws. The total reduction in diameter of 76% would have needed six direct redrawing operations for a part four diameters deep. By using the reverse redrawing technique for two operations, acceptable workpieces were made in four operations, as illustrated in Fig. 35. The reduction in diameter for each operation was 38, 30, 31 and 21%, respectively.

The first three operations were done in a double-action hydraulic press at a drawing speed of 200 in. per min, using a blankholder. The direct redraw (operation 4) was done in a single-action press at the same speed but without a blankholder. The forces used for the operations were as follows:

	Force, tons, for operation: 1	2	3	4
Drawing	150	100	100	50
Die cushion	6	25	20	..
Blankholder	60	56	32	..

A phosphate coating was applied to the steel strip, and then the stock was immersion coated with a soap solution and dried before being fed into the blanking die. The shells were relubricated after each anneal.

The shapes of the die elements for the various operations and of the shells after each operation are shown in Fig. 35.

Example 244. Direct vs Reverse Redrawing of Tubs (Fig. 36)

A 21-in.-diam tub for a washing machine was originally produced in three direct draws, as shown in the sequence at the top of Fig. 36. This procedure required three presses, three dies, and three operators. Changing to reverse redrawing permitted the tub to be produced in two draws (sequence shown at the bottom of Fig. 36). By this procedure, cost was reduced, because one press, one die, and one operator were eliminated. Reverse redrawing also eliminated thinning and rings on the diameter, which had occurred in the radiused area at the junction of the flange and the sidewall (formed in the second draw), as the flange was drawn into the sidewall during the third draw.

The material was cold rolled, drawing quality 1010 steel, coated with a dry soap lubricant. Production rate was 130 parts per hour.

The first drawing operation was done in a single-action press. The punch-nose radius was 1.75 in., the die radius was 0.187 in., and punch-to-die clearance was 0.053 in. per side. Depth of draw was 10 in.

Reverse redrawing was done in a double-action press. The punch-nose radius was 2 in., die radius 0.250 in., and punch-to-die clearance 0.085 in. per side.

Tubs having depths of 14 and 16 in. were drawn in the same dies.

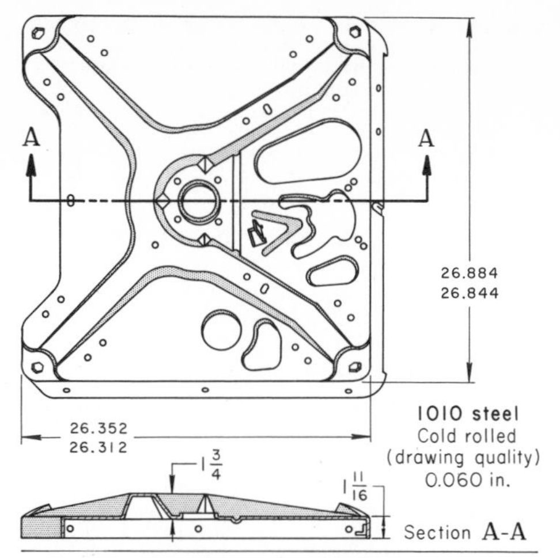

Sequence of Operations

1 Draw to form the center area in a 400-ton hydraulic press.
2 Reverse redraw to form spider in a 700-ton hydraulic press.
3 Wipe down sides and restrike in a 250-ton mechanical press.
4 Trim and pierce sides in a 175-ton trimming machine.
5 Pierce top holes and cam-form front.
6 Form flanges around openings in top.

Operations 5 and 6 were done simultaneously in separate dies in a 200-ton mechanical press.

Fig. 37. Washing-machine base that was produced by drawing and reverse redrawing to provide better distribution of metal (Example 245)

Example 245. Reverse Redrawing for Better Distribution of Metal in a Complex Shape (Fig. 37)

The base of an automatic washer (Fig. 37) required drawing and reverse redrawing for adequate distribution of the metal. Bases were produced from 0.060-in.-thick cold rolled, drawing quality 1010 steel. The first drawing operation provided sufficient metal to form the center of the base before metal was trapped by the spider (leg) sections. The workpiece was then reverse redrawn, which allowed the metal needed for forming the spiders to be drawn from the outside. Drawing was followed by restriking, trimming and piercing the sides, piercing holes in the top and cam-forming the front edge, and flanging the holes in the top.

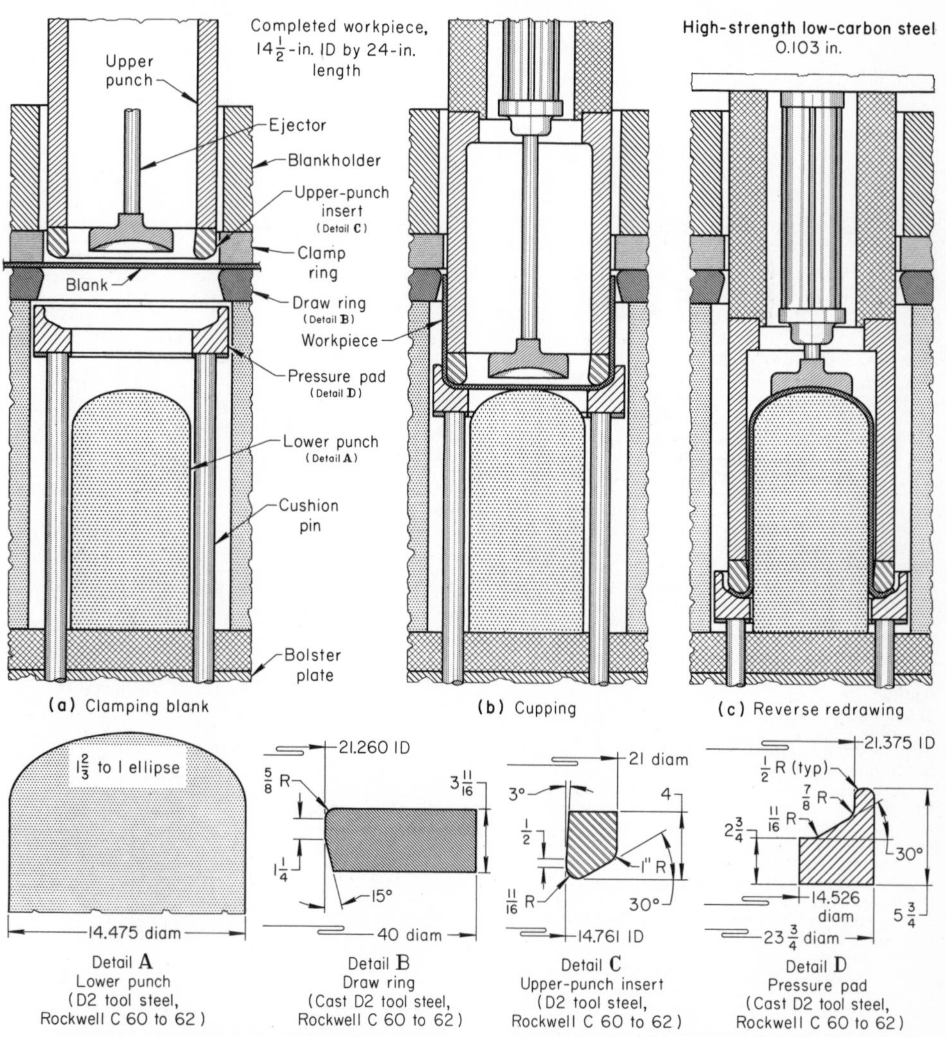

Fig. 38. Drawing a shell in a double-action press with a die cushion (Example 246)

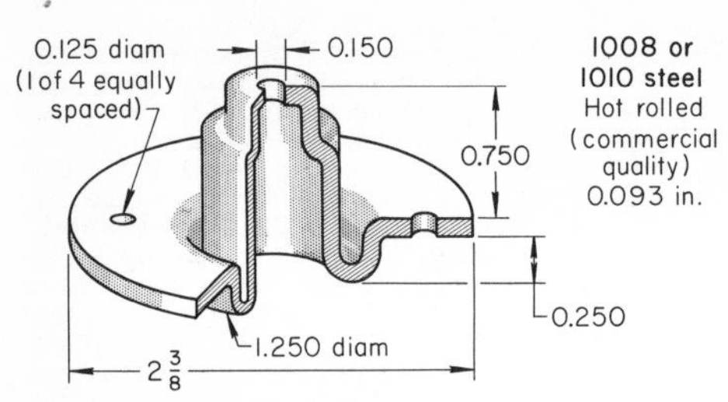

Sequence of operations: 1 – Pierce and notch to outline blank. 2 – Draw. 3 – Redraw. 4 to 8 – Reverse redraw (five stages). 9 – Pierce center hole. 10 – Blank. 11 – Cut scrap.

Fig. 39. Retainer cap that was made using five reverse redraws in an 11-station progressive die (Example 247)

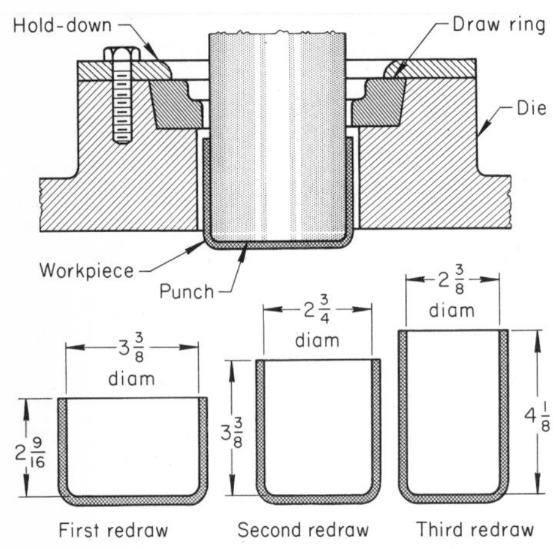

Fig. 40. Die in which draw rings and punches can be replaced for producing three successive redraws

The dies were made of cast iron with tool steel inserts. A dry soap lubricant was used on the blanks. Production rate was 220 bases per hour.

In the following example, reverse redrawing followed cupping to produce a deep drawn shell in one stroke of a hydraulic press. A description of a similar setup is given in Example 4, on page 22 in the article on Selection of Presses. Drawing of a similar part in two operations is described in Example 264 in the present article.

Example 246. Reverse Redrawing in a Double-Action Press for One-Stroke Forming of a Flanged Shell (Fig. 38)

By using a double-action hydraulic press with a die cushion and reverse redrawing, it was possible to produce flanged shells with a 14½-in. ID and a length of 24 in. from 38½-in.-diam flat blanks.

As shown in Fig. 38(a), the lubricated blank was first clamped by the downward stroke of the blankholder slide against the draw ring. The hollow upper punch then advanced to draw the cup, as shown in Fig. 38(b). A pressure pad, supported by die-cushion pins, held the shell against the upper punch during the final stages of cupping and during reverse redrawing.

In a third action, as the upper punch continued its downward motion, the cup was turned inside out over the lower punch by reverse redrawing to produce the flanged part, as shown in Fig. 38(c). Finally, after the upper slides had returned to their starting position, the pressure pad lifted the workpiece from the lower punch. A cylinder on the punch slide pushed the part out of the hollow upper punch.

The material was commercial quality, box-annealed, high-strength low-carbon steel. A dry soap coating was used as a lubricant.

The shapes of the draw ring, pressure pad, and upper punch nose are shown in Fig. 38. Clearance per side between the draw punch and die for the first operation was 130% of stock thickness, and for the redraw operation, 143% of stock thickness. The force on the upper punch was 350 tons, and on the blankholder and die cushion, 100 tons.

The die surfaces subject to wear were made of D2 tool steel and hardened to Rockwell C 60 to 62.

Reverse redrawing can be done in a progressive die as well as in single-stage dies, provided the operations are divided to distribute the work and reduce the severity of each stage, as in the following example.

Example 247. Progressive-Die Forming of Retainer Cap, Using Reverse Redrawing (Fig. 39)

Reverse redrawing was used in five of the 11 stations of a progressive die used to form the part shown in Fig. 39. Although the completed workpiece shows severe forming, the work was divided among stations so that at no station did the forming present a serious problem. A water-soluble oil-base drawing compound was sprayed on the strip as it entered the die.

The work material was 3¼-in.-wide by 0.093-in.-thick commercial quality hot rolled 1008 or 1010 steel that had been pickled and oiled. The blank was outlined by a combined pierce-and-notch stage, but carrier tabs kept the blank attached to the skeleton until the last stage of the die. A scrap cutter broke up the skeleton.

The drawing tools were mounted in a 100-ton mechanical press that operated at 60 strokes per minute. Considering setup time, coil-loading time, and maintenance, production efficiency was estimated at 75%.

The dies were made of D2 or D5 tool steel. Total tool life was about 8 million pieces.

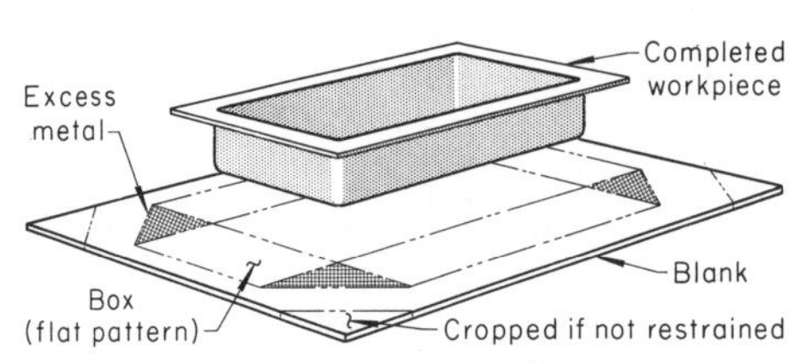

Fig. 41. Flanged rectangular box drawn from a blank with restraint at the corners. See text for discussion.

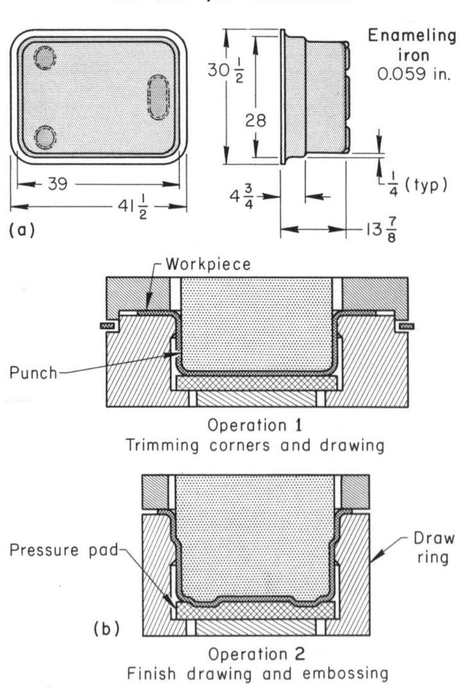

Fig. 42. Large rectangular container produced by two drawing operations in the setups shown (Example 248)

Tooling for Redrawing

Tooling for redrawing depends mainly on the number of parts to be redrawn and on available equipment. In continuous high production, a complete die is used for each redraw; the workpieces are conveyed from press to press until completed. In low or medium production, it is common practice to use a die with replaceable draw rings and punches. A die of this type used for three redrawing operations is shown in Fig. 40; the three redraws were made by changing to successively smaller draw rings and punches. The cup was drawn in a compound blank-and-draw die from a blank 0.067 in. thick and 6¾ in. in diameter.

Boxlike Shells

Square or rectangular shells can be formed by redrawing circular shells when there is no flange. When flanges are required, the difficulty of producing acceptable boxlike shapes by drawing is increased. For deep drawn square or rectangular shells (for example, where the depth is greater than either length or width), the best approach for forming a narrow flange is to allow sufficient stock, and to form the flange after redrawing from a cylindrical shell.

Shallower boxlike shapes (for instance, with proportions similar to the box illustrated in Fig. 41) can be drawn with a flange, which is then trimmed to the desired width. Calculations for the area of a blank used for a circular workpiece cannot be used for a square or rectangular box. These require metal in the bottom, ends, sides and flange, as shown when a box is unfolded ("flat pattern" in Fig. 41). The excess metal at the corners (shaded areas in Fig. 41) is a problem.

A seamless square or rectangular shell is made by drawing metal into the corners. The metal not needed for the corners is pushed into the walls adjacent to the corner radius, and into earlike extensions of the corners. The compressive stresses set up when the metal in the corners is rearranged cause the metal to be thicker in the corners than in the sidewall, or in the original blank. Drawing limits and blank development for square or rectangular shells are given in Appendix 2 at the end of this article.

The more difficult draws are made more easily by using a blank that is carefully developed. There are methods of developing the shape at the corners of a blank for a square or rectangular shell so that there is a minimum of excess metal. However, by cropping the corners as shown in Fig. 41 and by using a blankholder, satisfactory parts generally can be made. Draw beads in the blankholding surface surrounding the die, as in Example 237, are frequently used.

In the following example, the corners of the blank were trimmed and a blankholder was used to draw a large rectangular shell.

Example 248. Stepped Container Produced by Two Drawing Operations (Fig. 42)

The part shown in Fig. 42(a) was drawn in two operations from an enameling iron blank 60 by 70 in. by 0.059 in. thick. The shape after each drawing operation is shown in Fig. 42(b). A double-action press was used to trim the corners and make the first draw. The same press was used for drawing the 4¾-in.-deep step and embossing the bottom. The end of the second-operation punch fitted the previously drawn shell and drew metal from the flange to finish the part. A pressure pad held the part against the punch during the second operation and ejected the finished part from the die. It also served as a die to emboss three pads in the bottom of the part. Embossing the bottom eliminated an oil-canning condition. After the two drawing operations, workpieces were inverted for piercing 24 holes in the flange and trimming excess metal from the flange.

The double-action mechanical presses used had 700-ton capacity and a 42-in. stroke on the ram, and 500-ton capacity and a 27-in. stroke on the blankholder. Dies were made from gray iron, and drawing surfaces were flame hardened. Setup time was 4 hr. Dies produced approximately 100,000 parts before reconditioning (not including polishing of radii). Production rate was 80 to 100 parts per hour.

The draw radius for operation 1 was 0.62 in. along the sides, but increased to 0.75 in. at the corners. Punch-to-die clearance was 0.090 in. per side. For operation 2, the draw radius was 0.50 in. and the punch-to-die clearance 0.075 in. per side. The punch nose radius for both operations was 1 in., and the corner radius 3.25 in.

Workpieces With Flanges

Regardless of whether the drawn workpiece is circular, rectangular or unsymmetrical, producing acceptable small-width flanges on workpieces is seldom a problem. Flanged workpieces are usually drawn in two or more operations, frequently with restriking as a final operation. The two examples that follow demonstrate procedures for producing small parts with flanges.

Example 249. Separate Dies for Drawing a Small Flanged Cup (Fig. 43)

The flanged cup shown in Fig. 43 was produced from 3½-in.-wide enameling iron sheet in three consecutive operations: blanking and drawing; redrawing; and restriking. The changes in shape from blank to restrike are shown in Fig. 43. Three open-back inclinable mechanical presses with capacities of 90 to 100 tons and 5-in. strokes were used. A die cushion was used for the first operation. Each operation could produce approximately 1500 pieces per hour. using conventional hardened tool steel dies. Lubricant was a compound of zinc phosphate and dry soap.

Example 250. Use of a Progressive Die for Drawing a Small Flanged Ferrule (Fig. 44)

The production of a small flanged ferrule in a five-station progressive die is shown in Fig. 44. The cost per piece by this method was 40% of that estimated for producing the part in separate dies. three of which would have been required. This did not include the cost of setup, which would be greater for three separate dies.

The progressive die was made of D2 tool steel and was hardened to Rockwell C 60 to 61. A 35-ton press with a 1-in. stroke and hand feed produced 1500 pieces per hour from 1½-in.-wide coil stock. The die produced 10,000 parts before reconditioning was required. Commercial drawing lubricant was supplied by an automatic oiler.

Cylindrical workpieces with wide flanges are troublesome to draw because of excessive wrinkling or fracturing in the sidewall due to lack of metal flow. Even though the metal is restrained by a blankholder, it is difficult to obtain acceptable flatness without special procedures.

Wide flanges on relatively large workpieces can be made flat by coining after drawing. Another means of dealing with wrinkling, when design permits, is to provide ribs in the flange. (This controls the wrinkling by allowing space for the excess metal.) Ribs are usually spaced radially around the flange (as in the example that follows), although circular, concentric ribs also are effective.

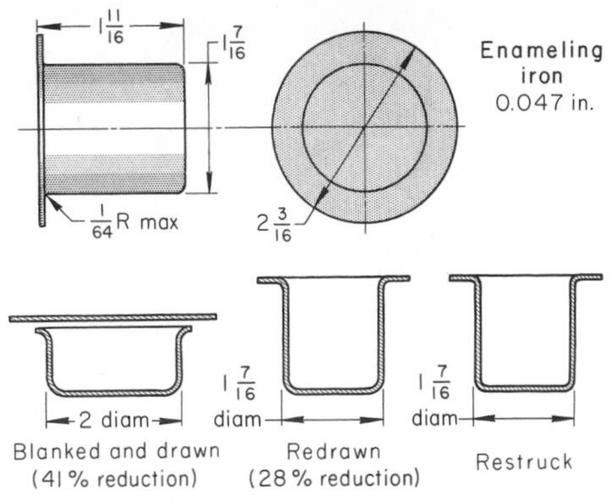

Fig. 43. Flanged cup drawn in three operations in separate dies (Example 249)

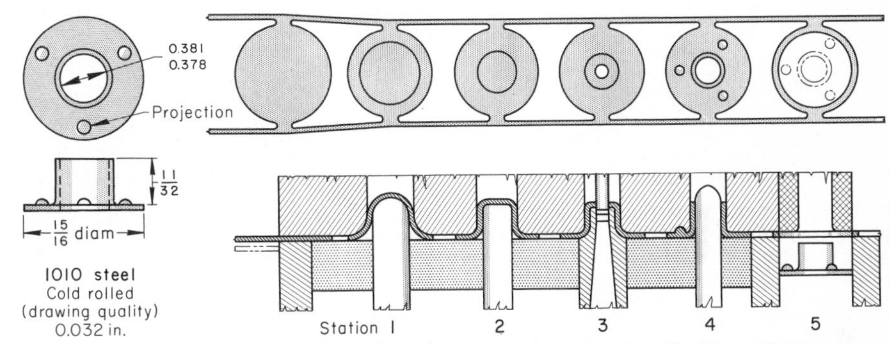

Fig. 44. Production of a small flanged ferrule in a progressive die (Example 250)

Example 251. Addition of Ribs to a Wide Flange for Attaining Specified Flatness (Fig. 45)

The wide-flange workpiece shown in Fig. 45 was originally designed with a flat flange and was drawn using a conventional blankholder. By this method, flatness of the flange could not be held within 0.030 in. TIR as specified. However, by adding the eight ribs shown in Fig. 45, which were formed by the die, it was possible to obtain acceptable flatness. Twenty-five ribbed workpieces were measured for flange flatness; the pieces were supported on three equally spaced points, and measurements were taken on a 7.75-in.-diam circle. Twenty-four had flatness within 0.026 in.; the twenty-fifth was only slightly out of the specified range (0.034 in.).

Rectangular, boxlike workpieces that have flanges are difficult to redraw in such a manner that the flange is unaffected in redrawing operations. For this reason, it is common practice to draw the part first to a shallower depth and with larger bottom radii than needed for shaping the final contour. The part is then re-formed in a final operation. The following example demonstrates one procedure for maintaining flatness in a flanged workpiece.

Example 252. Maintaining Flatness Within 0.010 In. on a Flanged Rectangular Box (Fig. 46)

One of the requirements for the workpiece shown in Fig. 46 was that the bottom and end should be flat within 0.010 in. The depth of draw was established by trial, and was assured in each setup by the position of the knockout pad that formed the bottom of the die. The cavity usually was about 1/32 in. deeper than the workpiece. The shape of the blank used was determined by trial. The blank size and shape, in conjunction with the mating of the blankholder surfaces, were important in minimizing wrinkling. After the blank size and its location on the blankholder surface were determined, four spring-loaded locating pins were placed in the die. The blankholder surfaces were spotted-in from a drawn part.

Along three sides, the bottom radius of the finished part was 3/64 in., or equal to stock thickness; therefore, two draw punches were used. The first punch had a nose radius four times stock thickness (3/16 in.). The box was drawn to approximately 3/64 in. from the bottom, and was then annealed and restruck with the second punch, which had a nose radius to suit the finished-part dimensions. The flange was trimmed as shown in the view at the lower left of Fig. 46.

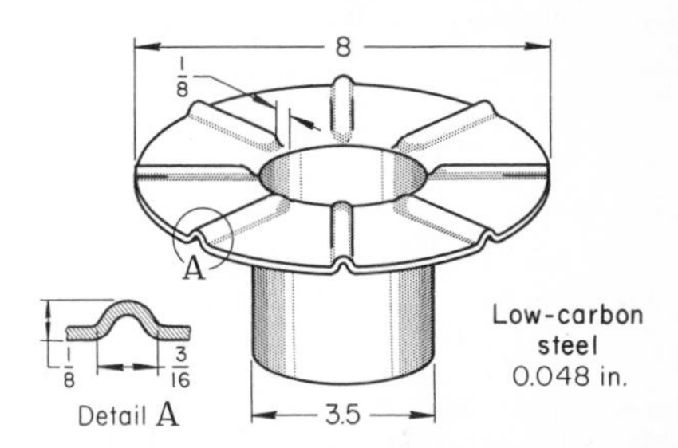

Fig. 45. Part on which addition of ribs to the wide flange enabled it to be drawn to specified flatness (Example 251)

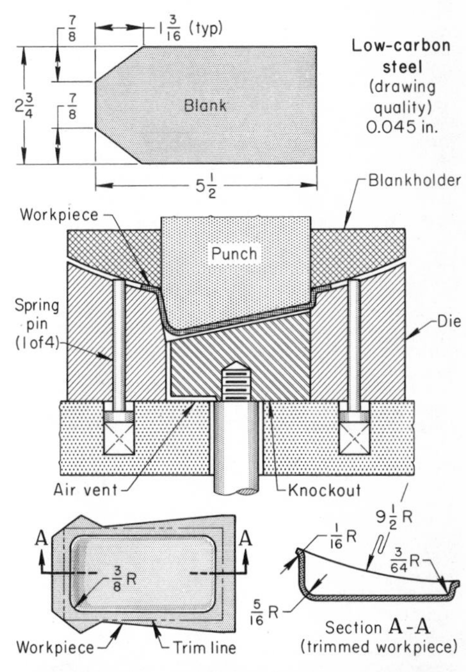

Fig. 46. Setup used for drawing a flanged rectangular box to flatness within 0.010 in. for bottom and end (Example 252)

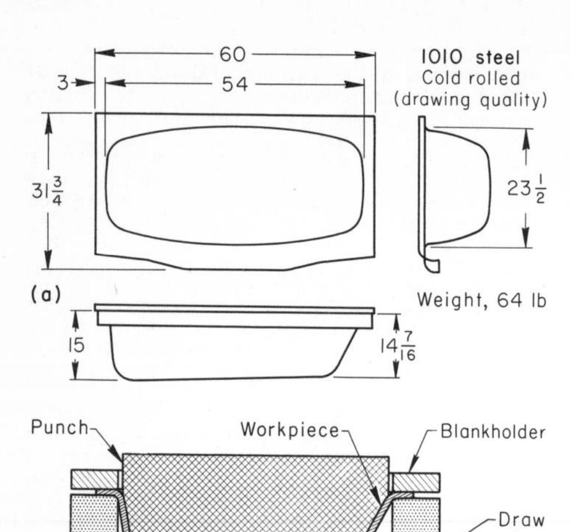

Fig. 47. Bathtub completed in one draw except for forming flange and trimming (Example 253)

The part was drawn in a double-action press. Hardened tool steels were used for the punch, die, blankholder and knockout.

Unsymmetrical workpieces that have flanges are often difficult to draw, particularly when neither draw beads in the die nor ribs in the workpiece can be permitted. Under these conditions, considerable development is usually required to determine the blankholder pressure that will result in the desired metal flow without using a larger blank than necessary. Drawing of bathtubs, for example, requires careful control of the die surfaces and blankholding pressure, even though the tubs can be drawn in one operation, as in the following example.

Example 253. Forming a Bathtub in One Operation (Fig. 47)

The bathtub shown in Fig. 47(a) was made from cold rolled, drawing quality 1010 steel in a single drawing operation. The flange was formed and trimmed in a subsequent operation. Because the bathtub was unsymmetrical and neither draw beads in the die nor ribs in the workpiece were permitted, metal flow had to be controlled otherwise. Design of the tub permitted no straight lines or flat surfaces, and constantly changing curves kept the metal stretching, so that no "loose" areas or oil canning would develop. In addition, extreme care was used in spotting-in the draw ring and the blankholder, and in balancing them with blankholder pressure. Blanks were no larger than necessary, and corners were trimmed before drawing. Bathtubs were produced in quantities of 100,000 to one million at a rate of 100 per hour.

Complex Shapes

Several operations are usually required in drawing complex shapes. However, for mass production, it is usually feasible to combine press operations, so that extremely complex shapes can be produced in no more than six or seven separate operations. For small complex parts, progressive dies are generally used, but for parts as large as the automobile wheel disk described in the following example, progressive dies would not be practical.

Example 254. Drawing a Complex Shape From 0.136-In. Steel (Fig. 48)

Automobile wheels were produced by welding a drawn outer disk to a roll formed inner rim (Fig. 48). Outer disks for 15-in. wheels were completed in six operations (including one reverse redraw), as shown in Fig. 48.

The first operation (blanking and drawing) was done in a 1200-ton press with a 20-in. stroke. The center portion of the disk was reverse redrawn in an 800-ton press with a 14-in. stroke. A 500-ton press with a 14-in. stroke was used for the first reduction, and an 800-ton press with a 16-in. stroke for the second reduction. A 1500-ton press with a 30-in. stroke was used for the fifth operation; then the disks were transferred to a 500-ton, 14-in.-stroke press for piercing and coining.

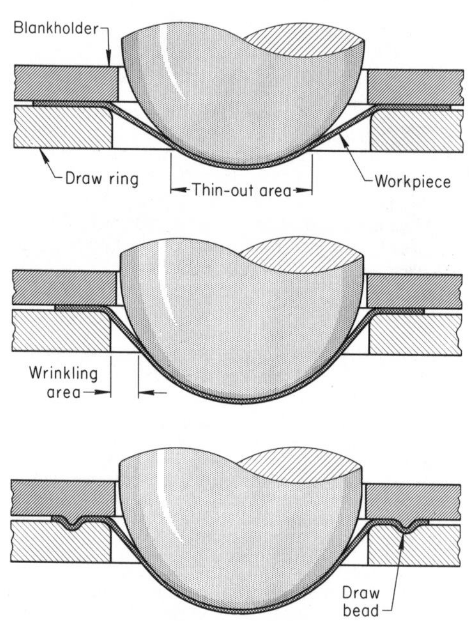

Fig. 49. Drawing a hemisphere with and without a draw bead. Text discusses effect of restraint on thin-out and wrinkling.

Hemispheres

In the drawing of a hemisphere, metal flow must be closely controlled for balance between excessive thinning in one area and wrinkling in another. In the upper sketch of Fig. 49, the punch has begun to stretch the round blank, which is restrained by the blankholder, and the crown section of the hemisphere is being formed. At this stage, the crown section is subjected to biaxial tension, which results in metal thinning. With correct pressure on the blankholder, thinning is in the range of 10 to 15%. More than 15% thinning is likely to result in fracture of the crown section. In the upper sketch of Fig. 49, the portion of the blank under the blankholder has not begun to move.

As the drawing operation continues, the metal begins to move from the blankholder and a different problem develops (center sketch of Fig. 49). Here the metal has been drawn into a partial hemisphere with unsupported metal in a tangential slope between the punch and the clamped surface. Unlike the drawing of straight-sided shapes, having the wide gap (indicated in Fig. 49 as wrinkling area) prevents the use of the draw-ring bore as a means of forcing the metal against the punch surface, and thus the probability of wrinkling increases. Because the metal cannot be confined between the punch and die, wrinkling is likely to occur in this area. To prevent wrinkles, the metal must flow from the flange area and, at the same time, must be securely held in tension. This requires an additional stretching force, derived from the portion of the blank that remains clamped. The area of metal between the clamping surfaces is gradually reduced as the punch advances, but the draw radius offers some resistance because the metal must follow a sharper bend as it moves into the die. One means of controlling wrinkling is by the use of draw beads, as shown in the lower sketch of Fig. 49, and another means is by a sharp draw radius. Small radii are susceptible to metal pickup and, depending on sharpness, can produce undesirable circumferential grooves in the hemisphere if the punch does not move at a steady rate.

In the following example, metal flow was controlled by a draw bead that was outside the trim line.

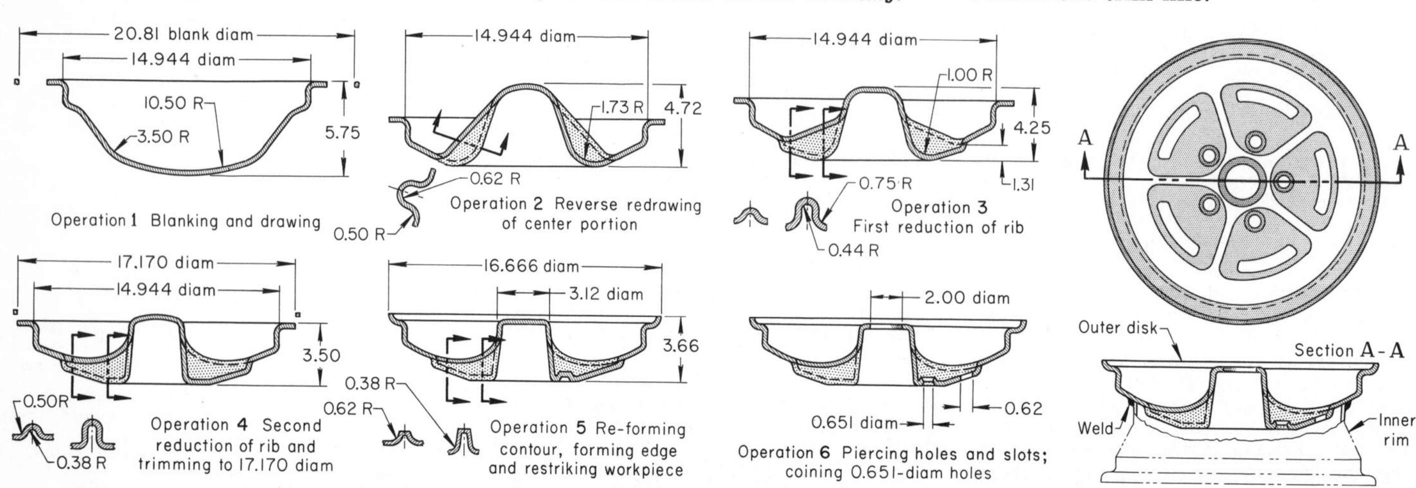

Fig. 48. Production of the outer disk of an automobile wheel in six operations (Example 254)

Example 255. Maximum Thinning of 13% Maintained by a Draw Bead (Fig. 50)

The 37-in.-ID hemisphere shown in Fig. 50 was originally drawn by simply clamping the blank between the blankholder and the draw ring. By this procedure, it was impossible to produce hemispheres free of wrinkles without having areas that were thinner than 0.211 in. (the minimum allowable thickness).

By using a draw bead in the draw ring and blankholder like that illustrated in the bottom view in Fig. 49, it was possible to produce hemispheres that were free of wrinkles and thicker in all areas than the allowable minimum. Figure 50 shows 31 thickness measurements on a typical hemisphere produced with a draw bead. Note that the minimum thickness reading (0.221 in.) was only about 13% less than the 0.255-in. nominal thickness of the blank.

The material was ASTM A285, grade C steel (hot rolled, flange quality). The lubricant used was a mixture of equal parts of chlorinated and sulfurized oils.

The press had a maximum blankholder pressure of 600 tons. Although hemispheres free of wrinkles could not be produced with flat draw rings, with draw beads the parts were successfully produced free of wrinkles or draw-ring marks using 500 to 600 tons of blankholding force.

The blankholder and draw ring were made of an abrasion-resistant cast steel and were hardened to Rockwell C 58 to 63. Figure 50 shows the draw bead and draw radius that were machined into the die.

In the following example, special killed, drawing quality steel was used to minimize thinning in a dome-shape deep drawn housing.

Example 256. Drawing a Compressor Housing in a Compound Die (Fig. 51)

The lower compressor housing for a refrigeration unit shown in Fig. 51 was made in a compound blank-and-draw die. The part was deep drawn from 1008 steel (hot rolled, drawing quality, special killed), 0.120 in. thick. Coil stock 15⅞ in. wide was fed into a 300-ton press, which produced 350 parts per hour. The special killed steel permitted drawing the part to a depth of 7¼ in. in one operation, while also forming several embossments (not shown) on the bottom of the housing without excessive loss because of cracking or thinning. The amount of thinning was important because the operating pressure for the housing assembly was 650 psi. Tests on the assembly were conducted at 1300 psi.

The blanking and drawing components of the die were made of A2 tool steel and were hardened to Rockwell C 56 to 58. Clearance between the blanking punch and die was 0.008 in. (about 7% of stock thickness) per side.

Clearance between the draw punch and draw ring was 0.125 in. per side, and the punch had a back taper of 0.001 in. per inch to compensate for thickening of the metal in the sidewalls. Draw radius was 0.50 in. A pigmented drawing compound was used as the lubricant.

After drawing, the shell was trimmed to a height of 6⅝ in. in a trimming machine. Annual production was one million housings.

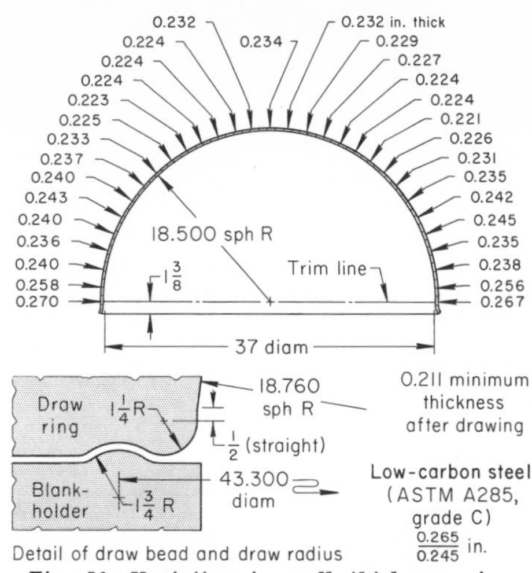

Fig. 50. Variation in wall thickness of a hemisphere drawn with the use of a draw bead (Example 255)

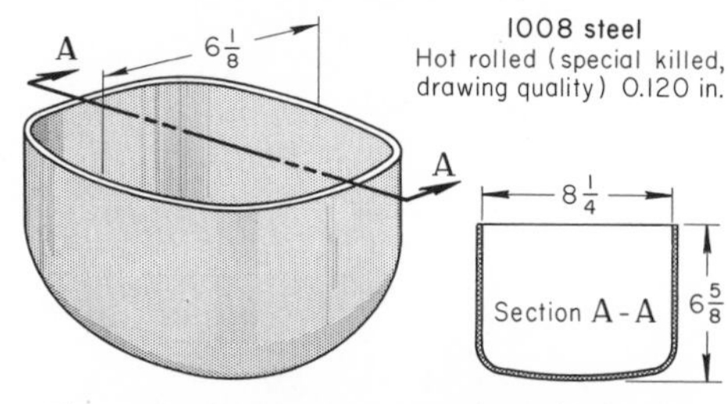

Fig. 51. Compressor housing that was blanked and drawn in a compound die in one operation (Example 256)

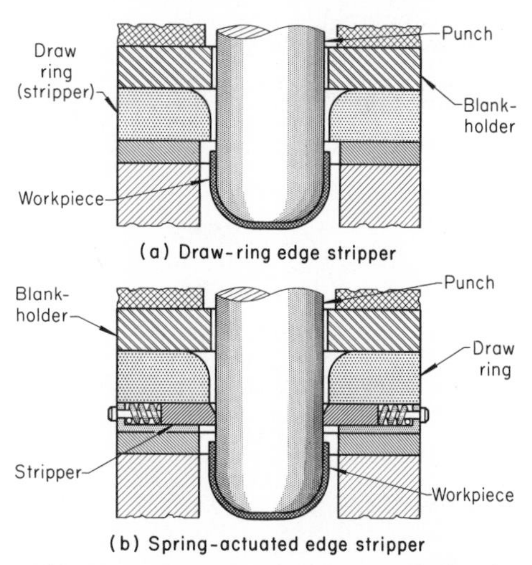

Fig. 52. Setups showing two methods of ejecting a drawn workpiece through the bottom of the press by edge stripping

Ejection of Workpieces

In drawing operations, the drawn workpiece may adhere to either the punch or the die. Adherence is increased by depth of draw, straightness of workpiece walls, and viscosity of lubricant.

The simplest means of ejecting a small workpiece is by compressed air through jets in the punch or the die. Timed air blast is widely used for ejecting relatively small workpieces — for example, where cup diameter is no greater than 4 or 5 in. In some production drawing operations, not only is the workpiece ejected by compressed air, but another timed blast of air from the side removes the piece by sending it down a chute or into a container. However, for larger workpieces or for those that are deep, some other means of ejection is required.

Mechanical methods of ejection include: edge stripping by means of a lip on the draw ring (Fig. 52a) or by a spring-actuated stripper (Fig. 52b); the use of a blankholder in combination with an upper ejector (Fig. 53); and the use of a lower ejector in combination with an upper stripper ring (Fig. 54).

Numerous other mechanical methods using cams or links have been devised to meet specific requirements. These methods are usually modifications of those described above. For instance, thin shells are sometimes stripped from punches near the top of the press stroke by a cam-actuated rod that extends through the punch. This method often is used to avoid damage to the open end of the shell, which can occur when the piece is ejected by other methods.

Major factors influencing the method of ejection are workpiece design (especially the presence or absence of a flange), work-metal composition and thickness, and the type of equipment available.

Ejection by Edge Stripping. The simplest means of mechanical ejection is illustrated in Fig. 52(a). Here, the cup is drawn in a double-action press using a blankholder, and with relief between the bore of the draw ring and its support. As the edge of the workpiece passes below this relief, slight springback is sufficient for the workpiece to catch on the lower edge of the draw ring and be stripped from the punch on its return stroke. The workpiece is removed from the bottom of the press. However, there are four requirements for success with this method: (*a*) there must be an opening in the press bed and the bolster plate, or the die must be raised above the bolster plate; (*b*) the workpiece must permit straight-through ejection (no flange); (*c*) the work metal must have some springback; and (*d*) work metal must be sufficiently thick.

Minimum work-metal thickness that permits use of the above procedure depends on work-metal characteristics and on punch-to-draw-ring clearance. There must be enough springback and sufficient work-metal thickness to catch the lower edge of the draw ring. In the drawing of steel, which always has some springback, the minimum shell wall thickness that allows simple edge stripping is usually about 18 gage (0.0478 in.). For the drawing of soft nonferrous metals, the thickness should be greater than 18 gage.

A modification of the draw-ring-edge method is shown in Fig. 52(b). The principle is the same, except that a spring-loaded stripper is used. This refinement in method allows stripping of thin-wall workpieces. However, requirements for workpiece design and type of press are the same as for the simple edge stripper. When this procedure is used, two strippers mounted 180° apart are usually sufficient; for stripping large workpieces, three or four strippers equally spaced around the draw-ring periphery are ordinarily used.

Ejection From Inverted Dies. The edge-stripping principle can also be used as an aid in ejecting from an inverted die if the workpiece does not have a flange. The top view in Fig. 53 shows how the sheet metal is drawn over a stationary lower punch. In the reverse stroke (bottom view in Fig. 53), the blankholder moves upward, lifting the workpiece off the punch. Movement of the blankholder is usually delayed to avoid pushing the part into the draw ring. If the part remains inside the draw ring, an ejector actuated by a cam or by a knockout bar ejects the workpiece from the draw ring (middle view in Fig. 53). This design functions equally well on parts with a flange.

Upward Ejection. Presses with a die cushion or without an opening in the bed do not permit ejection through the press bed even though the workpiece shape permits straight-through ejection. Also, a flange on the workpiece precludes straight-through ejection, regardless of the press design. Under these conditions, the workpiece can be ejected by the method shown in Fig. 54. Here, the workpiece is drawn downward through the draw ring, as indicated in the upper view in Fig. 54. On the return stroke (Fig. 54, lower view), the workpiece is forced upward by the ejector; if the workpiece adheres to the punch, it is stripped off the punch by the stripper ring, as shown. The stripper ring is held in position by three or four support legs. The procedure illustrated in Fig. 54 is adaptable only to single-action drawing or redrawing. The support legs must be positioned so that the die can be loaded and unloaded.

Developed Blanks vs Final Trimming

The most important factor that influences a choice between using a developed blank or a final trimming operation is whether or not the shape of the drawn edge is acceptable. Sometimes a semideveloped blank is necessary to draw an acceptable part, and the edge must be trimmed to meet dimensional tolerances.

The next consideration is the cost of blanking versus final trimming. This would include the adaptability of the process to the available equipment, based on expected production requirements. The principal advantage of a developed blank is that strip or coiled work metal can be used. The use of strip eliminates the need for shearing the work metal to a rough-blank shape, as is sometimes required when final trimming is used. The developed-blank approach is usually more economical than final trimming, because a blanking die is frequently less expensive than a final-trimming die.

When using developed blanks, the draw dies are made and several blanks are drawn to select the optimum developed shape before the blanking die is made. This delays putting the draw die into production. However, with proper planning and scheduling, this should not be a problem.

Another disadvantage of developed blanks occurs when variations in work-metal properties and thickness are sufficient to affect the uniformity of the drawn workpiece. Under these conditions, closer tolerances are obtained by final trimming.

It is possible to develop blank contours accurately enough so that the outline of the drawn part is within tolerance, thus avoiding a final-trimming operation, as in this example:

Example 257. Developed Blank vs Final Trimming for Table Bases (Fig. 55)

The table base shown in Fig. 55 was producible either from a developed blank or by final trimming; a study was made to determine the more economical procedure. Because of work-metal thickness (3/16 in.) and part shape, both roll and pinch trimming were ruled out. Therefore, the study was made on the basis of trimming a partly formed workpiece, followed by a wipe-down operation in the die.

For either method, three separate sets of dies were required: dies for blanking, drawing and piercing for the developed-blank method; and dies for partial drawing, combination trimming and piercing, and final drawing (wiping down) for the final-trimming method. For both methods, available space and equipment permitted the use of dies in progression, so that a completed workpiece was obtained with each stroke of the press. It was estimated that the three dies used for the trimming method would cost 30% more than those for the developed-blank method. In addition, shearing would increase production cost of the workpiece by 500% over the cost of the developed-blank method. This large difference was caused by the necessity of preparing rectangular blanks with trimmed corners for the trimming method, whereas strip metal was used for the developed-blank method. To minimize cost, it was decided to use the developed-blank method, despite a delay in the start of production. Workpieces were less accurate than if they had been finally trimmed, but the variations obtained were acceptable.

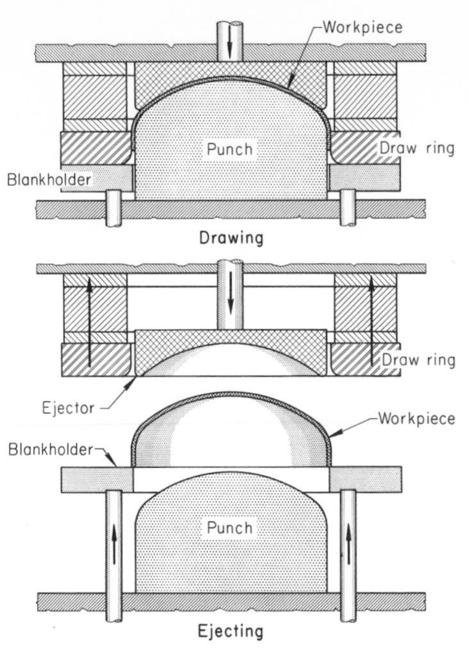

Fig. 53. Use of a blankholder and ejector for stripping of a drawn workpiece from inverted dies

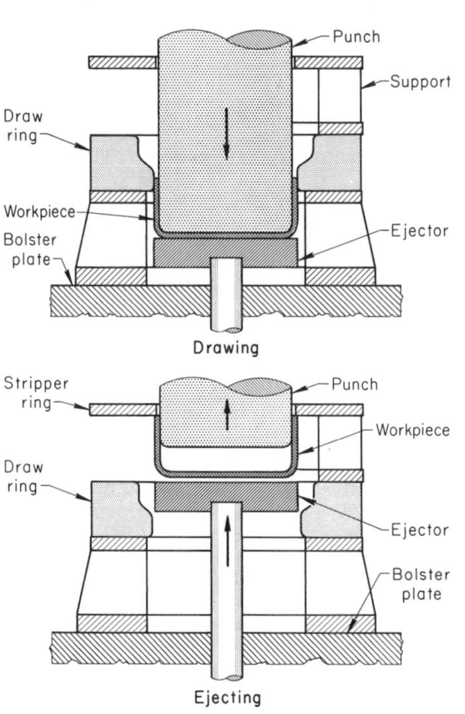

Fig. 54. Setup in which a drawn workpiece is lifted from the die by an ejector and is stripped off punch by a fixed stripper ring

Trimming

Trimming in a lathe (using a cutting tool), roll trimming in a lathe, rotary shearing, die trimming (regular and pinch), and trimming on special machines are the methods most commonly used for trimming drawn workpieces. In one plant, the costs of trimming methods (not including tool cost) are rated according to the following scale of percentages:

Lathe trimming (cutting tool)	100%
Lathe trimming (roll)	30
Rotary shearing	30
Die trimming	5 to 20
Special-machine trimming	10

Methods for Specific Shapes. Cylindrical workpieces like the one in Fig. 56(a) can be trimmed by at least four different methods:

1. In a lathe, with a cutting tool, but production cost is high.
2. By roll trimming in a lathe or in a rotary shear. Production cost is lower than for trimming with a cutting tool, but the finish of a rolled edge is poor and maintenance cost of the rolls is high.
3. By pinch trimming in the press at the bottom of the drawing stroke. This entails almost no increase in production cost, but requires a more expensive die. This method produces a thinned edge at the trim line, which may be unacceptable.
4. In a shimmy die or trimming machine, but production quantities must be high to warrant the investment.

Cylindrical workpieces with flanges, like the one in Fig. 56(b), can also be trimmed in a lathe, although shapes like this are ideal for trimming in a die and can be die trimmed for about 5% of the cost of trimming in a lathe. Rotary shearing can also be used for trimming circular drawn parts with flanges, provided the dimensional tolerance is 0.030 in. or more.

Drawn workpieces with an irregular trim line, as in Fig. 56(c), can be trimmed in a die, for low-production requirements, or with a shimmy die or trimming machine, for high-production requirements. The cost of a trimming die is about half that for a special trimmer (excluding the cost of the original machine). However, the trimming cost per piece with the special trimmer will be only about half the per-piece cost with multiple dies, and the trimmed edges will be better.

Flanged workpieces like the one in Fig. 56(d) can be trimmed in a die for 5% of the cost of trimming in a rotary shear. In low production, drawn workpieces of such a shape are frequently trimmed in a nibbler and filed to conform to a template. This means of trimming costs up to 60 times as much as die trimming.

Reducing Drawn Shells

Necking and nosing are used for reducing the diameter of a drawn cup or shell for a part of its height.

Necking. By the die-reduction method, the work metal is forced into compression, resulting in an increase in length and wall thickness.

The thicknesses of a shell before and after necking are related by the following formula:

$$t_2 = t_1 \sqrt{d_1/d_2}$$

and heights before and after necking, by the formula:

$$h_2 = h_1 \sqrt{d_1/d_2}$$

where t_1 is shell thickness before necking, t_2 is shell thickness in the necked area after necking, d_1 is mean diameter of the shell before necking, d_2 is mean diameter after necking, h_1 is unit of height before necking, and h_2 is unit of height after necking.

Figure 57 shows the flow of metal in a necking operation. As the metal flows, paths of least resistance are taken; therefore, the actual values for t_2 will be less, and for h_2 greater, than those calculated from the formulas.

Necking results are uniformly better if the workpiece has been slightly cold worked. This provides added strength to resist bulging in the column section and buckling in the section being reduced. The entry angle on the necking die is important, because the probability that the metal will collapse is decreased as the angle with the vertical becomes smaller. This angle should be less than 45° (Fig. 57). If the angle is greater than 45°, a series of reductions may be necessary with localized annealing between reducing operations. With a die entry angle less than 45°, thin-wall tubes can be reduced as much as 15% in diameter; thick-wall tubes can be reduced as much as 20%.

The following example describes how a missile component was produced by reducing a drawn shell.

Example 258. Necking a Shell for a Missile Case (Fig. 58)

The drawn shell shown at the left in Fig. 58 had been slightly cold worked by previous ironing of the wall. The setup for necking the shell is illustrated in the center sketch of Fig. 58. The split bottom die, which had a hinged door with a cam latch, supported the shell during necking, and also provided the holding friction needed when the workpiece was stripped from the necking die. The necking die, by use of the entry configuration, wedged the compressed metal into the desired shape and size. The sizing plug controlled the inside diameter and kept it within tolerance, preventing bellmouthing.

The drawn shell was necked as follows:

1 Shell was loaded into the split bottom die, which was closed by locking with a cam.
2 Downstroke of the press formed the neck.
3 Return stroke of the press lifted the necking die and sizing plug.
4 Split bottom die was unclamped and the workpiece was removed.

The necking die and sizing plug were made of D2 tool steel and were hardened to Rockwell C 58 to 60. Tallow was applied to the shell for lubrication.

A 750-ton hydraulic press was used (because of availability, not tonnage requirements).

Nosing reduces the open end of a shell by tapering or rounding the end (usually by cold reduction), and is used chiefly in making ammunition. Shells often are machined before, instead of after, nosing. Shells often are cold reduced as much as 30% of their original diameter by nosing. Typical nosing practice is described in Example 401, in the article "Bending and Forming of Tubing", in this volume.

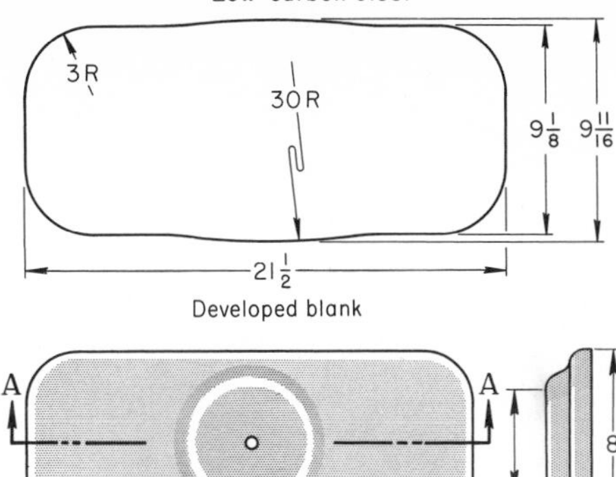

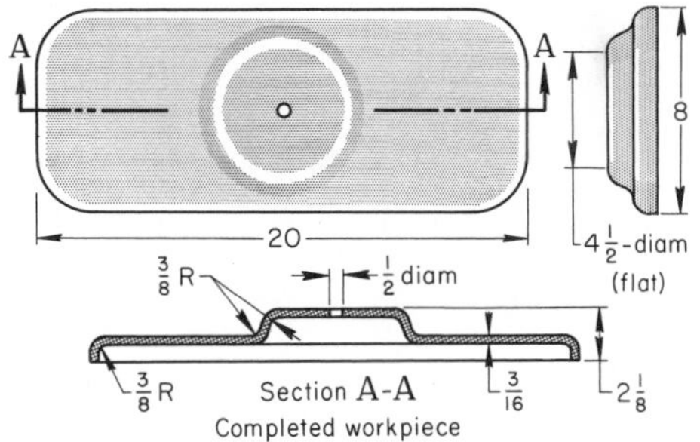

Fig. 55. Table base drawn from a developed blank (Example 257)

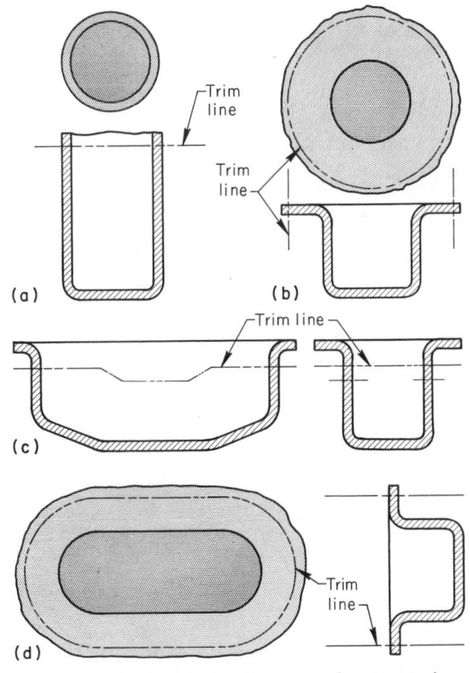

Fig. 56. Typical trim lines on drawn parts. (Text discusses trimming methods applicable to these representative shapes.)

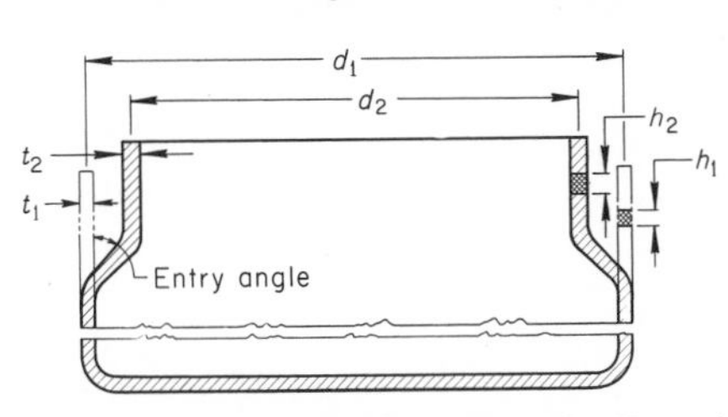

Fig. 57. Flow of metal in the reduction of a drawn shell by necking. See text for formulas and discussion.

Ironing is the intentional reduction in wall thickness of a shell by confining the metal between the punch and the die wall. When ironing occurs, the force to displace the punch often increases to a secondary maximum in the force-displacement curve. The second force maximum can be of such magnitude that the shell will break. However, after ironing has started and metal has been wrapped around the punch, the force is uniform and frequently less than that for redrawing operations.

Ironing is seldom used with redrawing operations unless the amount of wall thinning is relatively small, because it results in excessive die wear, causes workpiece breakage, and increases press tonnage requirements. If a shell with constant wall thickness is needed, however, it can be obtained only by ironing.

In the following example, the wall thickness was reduced during the cupping operation, as well as in two ironing operations.

Example 259. Ironing Used to Make a Thin-Wall, Thick-Bottom Shell (Fig. 59)

The part shown in Fig. 59 was produced by reducing the sidewalls during the cupping operation and two ironing operations. The 12-in.-diam blanks were cut on a 400-ton press from hot rolled, drawing quality 1008 steel 0.188 in. thick. The blanks were phosphate coated, and a pigmented drawing compound was applied before cupping.

A 400-ton press was used to draw a 9-in.-diam cup 1.50 in. deep. The wall was ironed during cupping by using a punch-to-die clearance of 0.150 in. per side. The punch nose radius was 0.25 in. and draw radius was 0.50 in. for this operation. The punch, draw ring and blankholder were made of A2 tool steel and hardened to Rockwell C 56 to 58.

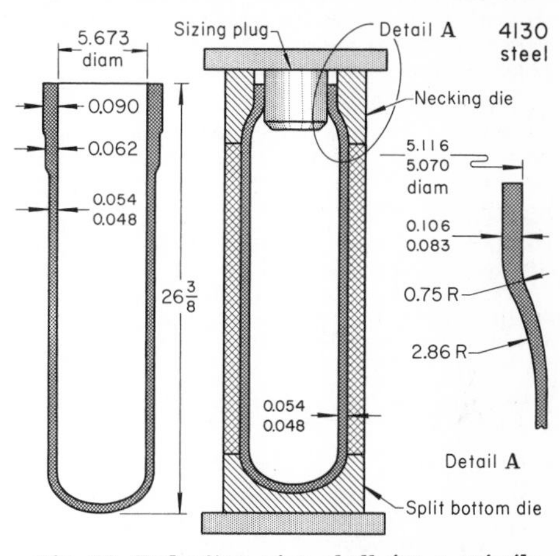

Fig. 58. Reduction of a shell for a missile case by necking (Example 258)

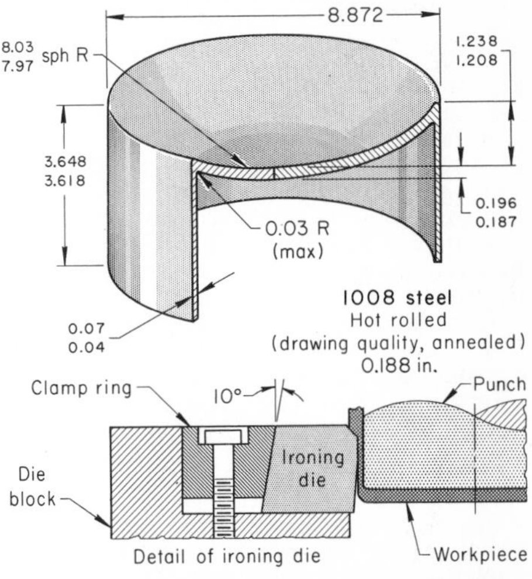

Fig. 59. Cup with a reversed spherical bottom, which was drawn in a 400-ton press, using phosphate-carried drawing compound (Example 259)

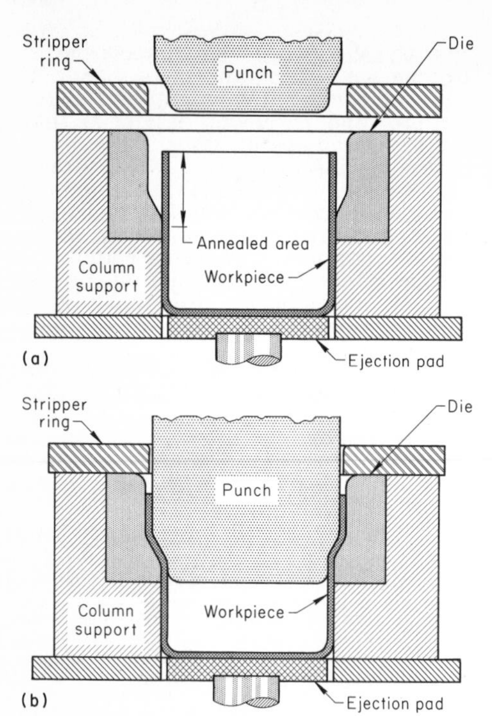

Fig. 60. Expanding the mouth of a drawn shell with a punch

The first ironing operation reduced the outside diameter of the shell to 8.952 in., and the wall thickness to 0.110 in. The bottom radius was 0.125 in. The bottom radius after the second ironing operation was 0.06 in.; the final diameter and wall thickness were as shown in Fig. 59. Figure 59 also shows a detail of the ironing die.

The ironing dies were made of tungsten carbide. They were held in a low-carbon steel die block with an O1 tool steel clamp ring. The ironing punches were made from A2 tool steel. Ironing was done in a 350-ton press at 300 pieces per hour. Annual production quantity was 750,000 pieces.

After a rotary shear trimmed the part to height, the spherical bottom was reverse redrawn and the corner radius reduced to 0.030 in. in a 350-ton press.

Expanding Drawn Workpieces

There are several methods for expanding portions of drawn workpieces in a press. Because the wall thickness is reduced during expansion, it is not advisable to increase the diameter for ductile metal shells (such as low-carbon steel or copper) more than 30%. If a diameter increase of more than 30% is required, the operation should be done in two or more stages, with annealing between stages.

Expanding With a Punch. In expanding with a punch, as in Fig. 60, the portion to be expanded is first annealed. Localized annealing, instead of annealing the entire cup, helps retain strength in the remainder of the cup. Regardless of whether or not the strength is required in the finished part, maximum column strength is desirable to prevent buckling as the punch enters the cup.

After the cup has been placed in the die (Fig. 60a), the punch moves downward and expands the top of the cup (Fig. 60b). During the return stroke, the workpiece is stripped from the punch by the stripper ring and is ejected from the die by the ejection pad.

In an expanding operation of this kind, die dimensions are predetermined within reasonably close limits during the design stage. However, the possibility of later design changes must always be considered. Depending on the shape and location of the expanded section, a height reduction of the cup may occur that will require some modification of the die and punch after tryout.

Expanding with segmented dies is often used for forming sidewalls of drawn shells or sections of tubing. The forming segments are contracted by compression springs and expanded radially by a tapered punch. The die is made of two or more segments held apart by compression springs. As the press ram descends, cams move the die segments together. The punch then moves the inner segments outward, thus forming the contours in the sidewall. This method is illustrated by Fig. 16 in the article "Bending and Forming of Tubing", in this volume. The presence of gaps between the forming segments is one of the drawbacks of this method and is the reason that an alternative method, such as rubber-pad forming, is sometimes selected.

Edge Curling

Curling the edge of a curved sheet, tube or shell is essentially a stretch or shrink flanging operation.

A spring-loaded segmented punch can support a drawn workpiece during edge-curling operations in which the punch must contract to free the workpiece, as in the following example.

Example 260. Supporting a Dome-Shape Workpiece During Edge Curling (Fig. 61)

The workpiece shown in Fig. 61 required support by a spring-loaded segmented punch during curling of the flange section. Without this support, the work-hardened dome wall would have resisted curling, so that the flange section would have pulled in and sections of the head would have buckled.

The design and sequential operation of the tooling used for this edge-curling operation are also shown in Fig. 61. Eight expanding segments moved radially in and out on the taper of the punch. A garter spring held the segments tightly against the punch, and compression springs moved the segments to their contracted position. Stop pins were used to control the up position of the segments. The punch was supported by a die cushion that had greater force than the springs, thus assuring that the punch would expand before curling took place.

In operation, the drawn workpiece was positioned on the contracted segments of the punch, as shown in Fig. 61. As the press ram moved downward with the blankholder, the workpiece was contacted and in turn pushed the segments downward and into an expanded position, as shown. Continued movement of the ram forced the die cushion downward, carrying the part into the curling die. On the return stroke of the press ram, the die-cushion pressure stripped the part from the curling die, and the springs returned the segments to their original (contracted) position. With the segments contracted, the workpiece was removed without difficulty.

Dimensional Accuracy

Dimensional accuracy in deep drawing is affected by the variation in work-metal thickness, variation in work-metal condition (chiefly hardness), drawing technique (particularly the number of operations), accuracy of the tools, rate of tool wear, and press condition.

Control of dimensions begins with the purchase of sheet to closer-than-commercial thickness tolerance, which adds substantially to the cost. Close control of sheet hardness also costs more. In-process annealing may be required to minimize springback or warpage; it will not be needed if tolerances are more liberal. Annealing, handling and cleaning operations are costly.

As tolerances become closer, it is often necessary to add more die stations to minimize the amount of drawing in any one station. Close tolerances may demand restriking operations that would not be necessary for parts with more liberal tolerances. Additional operations increase tool costs and decrease productivity, thereby increasing the cost per piece.

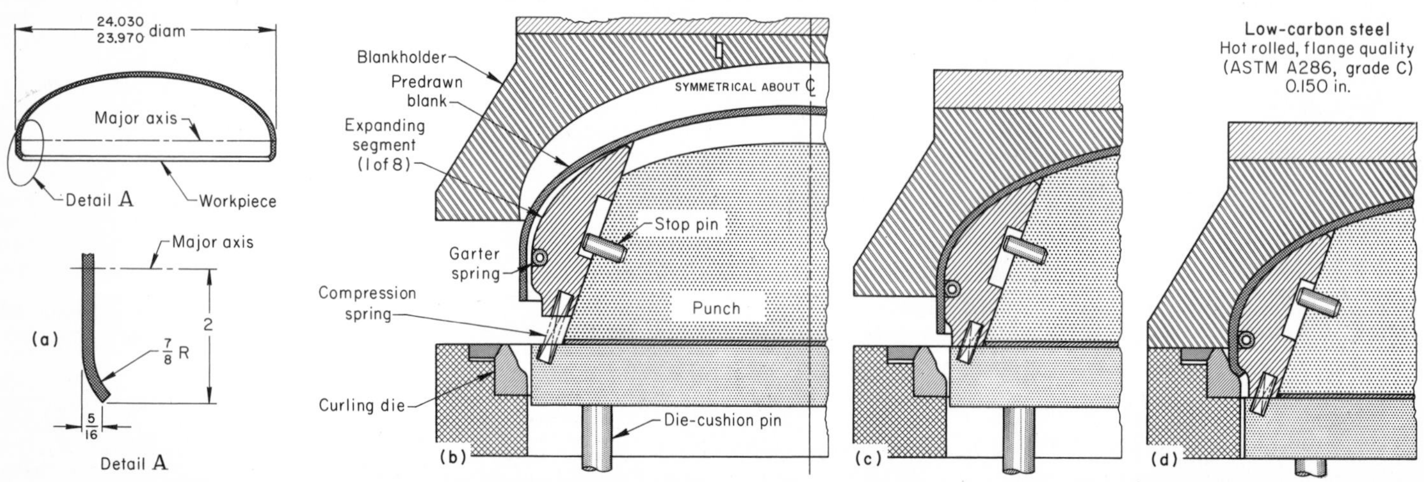

Fig. 61. Use of a spring-loaded segmented punch for support of a dome-shape workpiece during edge curling (Example 260)

The initial cost of tools increases as tolerances become closer, because of greater cost for precision machining and grinding, or more costly tool materials. In addition, tool life before reconditioning and total tool life decrease as tolerances become closer. Maintenance costs and downtime of presses are also greater.

When required, extremely close tolerances can be maintained on some parts by precise control, as shown in the following example:

Example 261. Inside Diameter of Cups Maintained Within 0.0005 In. (Fig. 62)

The needle-bearing cup shown in cross section in the upper part of Fig. 62 had to be produced to a tolerance of 0.0005 in. on the smallest inside diameter (bearing pathway), and had to be free from scratches, nicks or pits, both inside and outside. Originally, a high speed steel die was used, but about 45 pieces were under the specified diameter until the die warmed up, after which tolerances could be maintained. Changing to a carbide die eliminated this problem.

For cups produced by both types of die material, the bearing-pathway diameter was measured on every fifth piece for the first 100 pieces, and then at intervals of 2000 pieces for the cups produced in the high speed steel die and 5000 pieces for the cups produced in the carbide die. Results, plotted in the graph in Fig. 62, show that (after warm-up of the tool steel die) all pieces measured were within the 0.0005-in. tolerance.

To obtain this high degree of accuracy, process variables were closely controlled: cups were drawn from a special grade of steel strip (copper washed); the press was in first-class condition (plungers were square with the bed within 0.001 in. and were carried in a slide that was guided on 3½-in.-diam posts with 0.0015-in. maximum clearance in the bushings); and only nine stations of an 11-station transfer press were used. The 60-ton multiple-pillar press operated at 55 strokes per minute. A flowing water-soluble die lubricant was used.

Cups were gaged before curling to allow the entire pathway to be engaged by an air spindle. Cups had to pass through a 1.1911-in.-diam gage, and then were pressed into confinement rings with an inside diameter of 1.1875 ± 0.0001 in. — at which time all three inside diameters were measured.

In most deep drawing, the accuracy shown in Fig. 62 is either impossible or impractical. The more usual practice when dimensional accuracy is important is to check critical dimensions at specified intervals during a production run and plot the variation. Data from this method of quality control show the capabilities of the process under shop conditions and the magnitude of drift during a production run. When results (either initially or during a run) are unacceptable, one or more of the controls discussed at the beginning of this section can be applied.

Typical variation in diameter of deep drawn parts during a production run is shown in the following example:

Example 262. Variation in Diameter of Deep Drawn Parts (Fig. 63)

Figure 63 shows the variation in the inside diameter of 25 washer tubs produced by deep drawing. The 25 tubs were selected at random, and dimensions were obtained by measuring the circumference with a tape and calculating diameter from circumference. As shown in Fig. 63, diameters of only two of the 25 tubs were out-of-tolerance. Out-of-roundness, measured by inside micrometers, averaged 0.105 in. for the 25 pieces. Height of the 25 tubs varied from 13.303 to 13.326 in.

The press in which the tubs were drawn was in good condition; gib clearance was 0.005 to 0.008 in., and bolster and ram faces were parallel within 0.005 to 0.010 in.

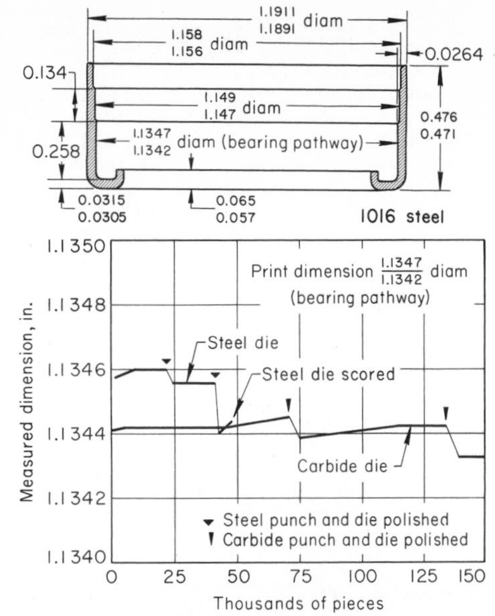

Fig. 62. Variation in bearing-pathway diameter of a needle-bearing cup drawn with high speed steel and carbide dies (Example 261)

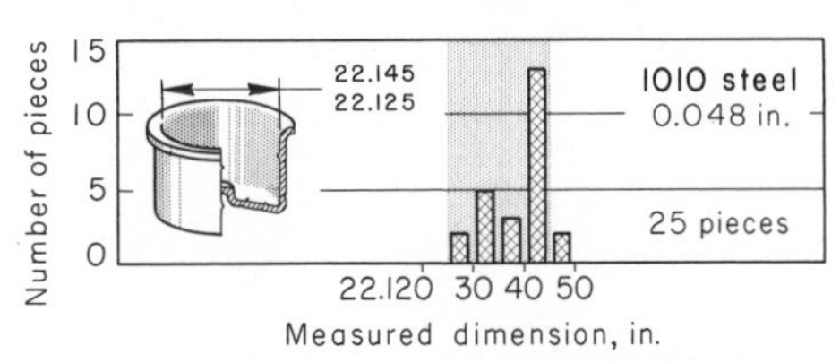

Fig. 63. Variation in inside diameter of 25 deep drawn washer tubs (Example 262)

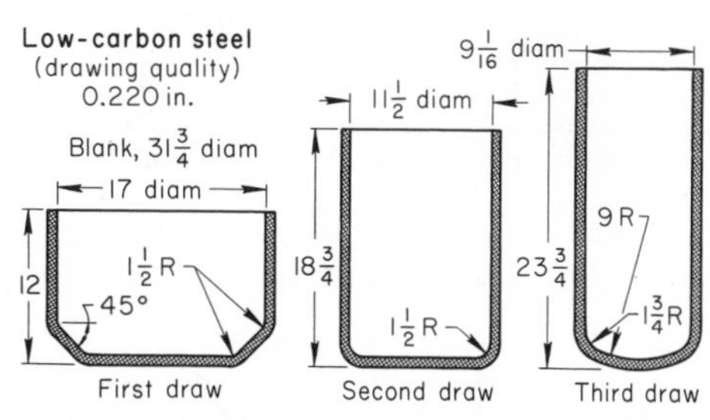

Fig. 64. Progression of shapes in the production of a shell in three drawing operations with intermediate annealing (Example 263)

In-Process Annealing

For severe drawing (more than 50% reduction), it is often helpful, and sometimes necessary, to anneal the workpiece one or more times. Although annealing between draws greatly extends the total amount of reduction that can be done, it is expensive. Handling and cleaning (before annealing and sometimes after annealing) are usually major factors in the total cost of in-process annealing. The following discussion and the production example relate strictly to processing of low-carbon steel. For in-process annealing of other metals, see the articles in this volume that deal with forming of specific metals.

Practice for Steel. Pack annealing requires the workpieces to be packed in an inert material, heated above the upper critical temperature (usually 1700 F for low-carbon steel), and then cooled slowly. This procedure is effective, but it is harmful if the packing material is not absolutely inert, because low-carbon steels carburize readily if heated in a carbonaceous atmosphere. In addition, some cleaning is usually required after annealing.

A preferred method of annealing is to heat the workpiece to 1700 F in an exothermic atmosphere, and then to cool it in a water-jacketed controlled-atmosphere chamber; in this way, scaling of the workpiece is prevented during the entire annealing cycle. Exothermic atmospheres are decarburizing (not harmful and sometimes helpful to deep drawing steels) rather than carburizing. Exothermic atmospheres are relatively low in cost, and if the furnace has been properly purged, cleaning of the workpiece after annealing is not necessary.

Sometimes, subcritical annealing at 1250 to 1300 F (process annealing) is used between draws, but this treatment is seldom recommended, because: (*a*) grain growth may occur, which will impair rather than enhance further drawing, even though the steel is softer; and (*b*) low-cost atmospheres are not suited to the temperature range involved, and therefore scaling will occur and cleaning after annealing will probably be required.

Although in-process annealing is costly, it often makes deeper draws possible and so eliminates some redrawing operations, and its cost is often justified. The benefits of annealing are more often realized when drawing thick-wall parts, as in this example:

Example 263. Number of Draws Reduced by Annealing (Fig. 64)

Figure 64 shows the evolution of a deep shell that was made in three drawing operations from a blank 31¾ in. in diameter by 0.220 in. thick. The shells were annealed in a controlled atmosphere at 1700 F after the first and second operations. Without annealing, at least four redrawing operations would have been needed. For this part, annealing cost less than two more redraws.

Cleaning of Workpieces

In general, the more effective the lubricant, the more difficult it is to remove. For this reason, an overly effective drawing lubricant should be avoided.

The cleaning method depends on the work-metal composition, the lubricant, the degree of cleanness required, workpiece shape, and sometimes on the length of time between application of lubricant and its removal.

Some metals will be attacked by cleaners that are not harmful to others. For example, strong alkaline cleaners are suitable for cleaning steel and many other metals, whereas they are likely to attack aluminum alloys. For detailed information, refer to articles on the cleaning and finishing of the specific metals in Volume 2 of this Handbook.

Unpigmented oils and greases can be removed from steel workpieces by several simple shop methods, which include alkaline dipping, emulsion cleaning, and cold solvent dipping. These methods are usually sufficient for in-process cleaning. However, if the workpieces are to be painted, a more thorough cleaning by emulsion spray or

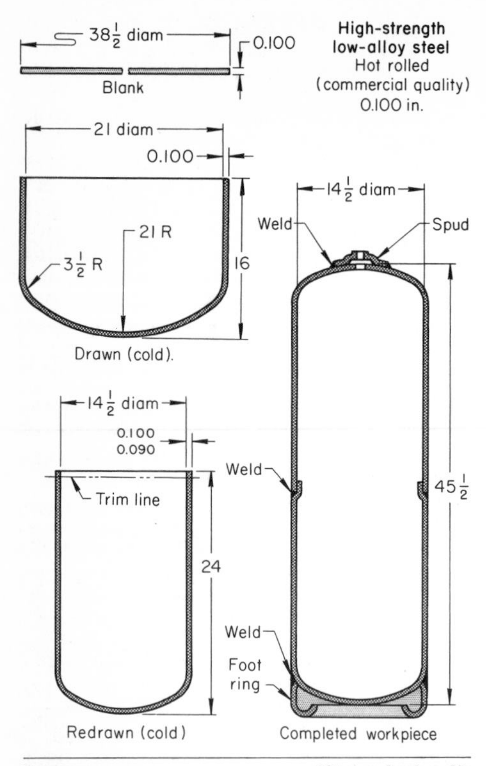

Draw press	500-ton hydraulic
Redraw press	300-ton hydraulic
Lubricant	Dry soap
Die materials:	
Draw	Graphitic tungsten tool steel(a)
Redraw	D2 tool steel
Die hardness	Rockwell C 60
Tool life, pieces per grind	1000
Lot size, pieces	10,000
Annual production, pieces	60,000

(a) 1.50% C, 0.40% Mn, 0.65% Si, 2.80% W

Fig. 65. Cylinder (for liquefied petroleum gas, LPG) that was made of two shells, each of which was deep drawn in two draws, as shown at left (Example 264)

vapor degreasing is required. For plating, electrolytic cleaning plus etching in acid (immediately prior to plating) is required. These latter methods usually follow a rough cleaning operation.

Pigmented drawing lubricants and waxes greatly increase cleaning problems. At a minimum, in-process cleaning usually requires slushing in a hot emulsion or vapor degreasing. If the lubricant is not removed for several days after application, soaking in a hot alkaline cleaner or an emulsion cleaner may be required. Particularly for complex workpiece shapes, some hand or power brush scrubbing may be needed. If the workpieces are to be painted or plated, additional cleaning will be required, as described above.

For detailed information on choice of method, see the article "Selection of Cleaning Process", pages 307 to 316 in Volume 2 of this Handbook.

Deep Drawing of Pressure Vessels

Various grades of steel — many of them high-strength alloys — are deep drawn to make cylinders for compressed gases. Joints (when they are made) are around the girth of the vessel, rather than longitudinal. Integrity of the vessel and enough strength to hold pressure are important features and are regulated by Interstate Commerce Commission (ICC) specifications. Specification number and other important information are coined on each cylinder head after a test that proves that the cylinder is able to meet the specification. Commercial quality, hot rolled steels in the as-rolled condition are generally used. Work metal is usually induction heated or induction annealed, because this results in a minimum of scale. The following three examples indicate the range of practice in producing low, medium and high-strength compressed gas cylinders.

Example 264. Deep Drawing Two Pieces for a 100-Lb LPG Cylinder (Fig. 65)

The cylinder shown in Fig. 65 was drawn in two parts from commercial quality, hot rolled, low-alloy high-strength steel with a minimum yield strength of 50,000 psi. The 38½-in.-diam blank, 0.100 in. thick, was lubricated with dry soap and drawn to a 21-in.-ID cup in a 500-ton, double-action hydraulic press. After drawing, the cup was induction annealed and relubricated with dry soap. It was redrawn to 14½ in. in diameter in a 300-ton, double-action hydraulic press. The shell was trimmed to length with a cutoff wheel. One shell of each pair had an offset formed so that it would fit inside the other shell for a strong joggle-butt weld. The top shell was pierced and fitted with a spud for later insertion of a valve. Before welding, the shells were washed.

After welding, the cylinder (for LPG) was heat treated to relieve welding and drawing stresses, and to develop strength sufficient to meet ICC specification 4BA240. It was pressure tested, stamped with its rating, and painted with a prime coat.

In blanking, clearance between the punch and die was 6% of stock thickness per side. The radius for the draw die was 0.800 in., or eight times stock thickness. Clearance between the draw die and punch was 0.125 in. The redraw die had a 40°-per-side conical entrance that was 3 in. deep, and a ⅝-in.-wide land connected to the conical entrance by a 1¾-in. radius. There was a 10° relief below the land. The clearance between the punch and redraw die was 0.110 in. The sidewall thickened enough to be slightly ironed for a distance of about 2 in. at the top of the shell.

The drawing of a similar shell is described in Example 246 in this article.

Example 265. Deep Drawing a Single Shell for a 100-Lb Chlorine Cylinder (Fig. 66)

The chlorine-gas cylinder shown in Fig. 66 was made in one piece from a 39-in.-diam blank, 0.220 in. thick, by drawing, redrawing and ironing. The end was reduced by spinning to produce the spherical top and spud for tapping.

The blank was lubricated with sulfonated oil, and cold drawn to a 20-in.-diam cup in a 1500-ton, double-action hydraulic press. To withstand a draw of this severity (almost 50% reduction), the material selected was commercial quality, hot rolled 1020 steel.

The cup was next heated to 1700 F, and three redraws were made while it was still hot. In these operations, the cup was redrawn successively to inside diameters of 14 in., 10½ in., and 8¼ in. Redrawing was done in 500-ton presses — one double-action press and two single-action presses.

The 8¼-in.-diam cup was annealed to relieve stresses left by hot redrawing, pickled, and lubricated with dry soap. Then it was reduced to 8¹⁄₁₆ in. in inside diameter, while the sidewalls were ironed to an average thickness of 0.210 in. After another anneal, pickle and dry-soap lubrication, ironing was repeated, reducing the inside diameter to 8 in. and wall thickness to 0.150 in. Ironing gave the sidewalls an excellent finish, both inside and outside.

The shell was cut to length. Part of the scrap was used for a foot ring. Sidewalls were inspected for thickness and finish. Then the open end of the shell was heated and spun down to a small neck. The cylinder was heat treated to the strength required by ICC specification 3A480. Finishing the cylinder included drilling and tapping threads in the neck for a valve, proof testing, stamping, painting and baking.

In blanking, punch-to-die clearance was 0.012 in. per side, or about 6% of stock thickness. For the drawing and redrawing operations, punch-to-die clearance was 0.270 in. per side. The ironing operation (6) used a punch-to-die clearance of 0.148 to 0.150 in.

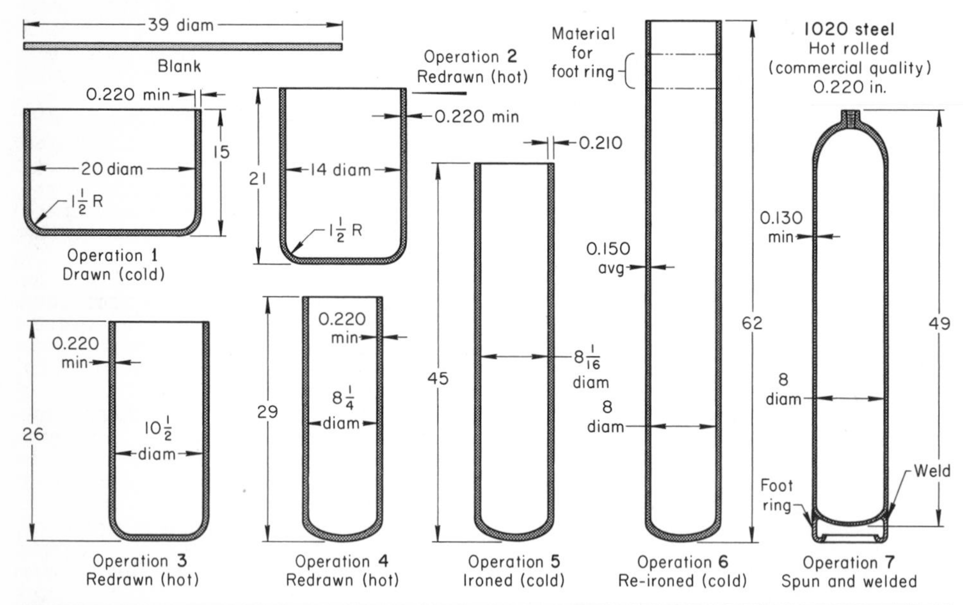

Presses:	
Draw	1500-ton double-action hydraulic
First redraw	500-ton double-action hydraulic
Other redraws	500-ton single-action hydraulic
Lubricants:	
Draw	Sulfonated oil
Fourth and fifth redraws(a)	Dry soap

Die materials:	
Hot operations	Graphitic tungsten tool steel(b)
Cold operations	D2 tool steel
Die hardness	Rockwell C 60
Tool life, pieces per grind(c)	1000
Lot size, pieces	1000
Annual production, pieces	1000

(a) Including ironing operations, which needed additional lubrication. (b) 1.50% C, 0.40% Mn, 0.65% Si, 2.80% W. (c) Tools were reconditioned after annual run.

Fig. 66. Cylinder (for chlorine gas) that was produced from one blank (Example 265)

In the example that follows, a different procedure was used, because the cylinders were much heavier than those described in Examples 264 and 265, and the service pressure rating was much higher — 2015 psi, compared to 240 psi and 480 psi for the LPG and chlorine-gas cylinders, respectively.

Example 266. Drawing a Compressed-Oxygen Cylinder From an Extruded Shell (Fig. 67)

The first step in the production of the compressed-oxygen cylinder shown in Fig. 67 was the hot extrusion of a shell from a slug. The slug was cut from a billet of hot rolled 4130 steel, induction heated to 2300 ± 50 F, and backward extruded into a shell with an 8.7-in. inside diameter and an 0.83-in.-thick wall in a double-action, 1750-ton hydraulic press. While still hot, the shell was reduced to 8.56 in. in inside diameter and 0.230 in. in wall thickness in a draw bench by pressing it through seven dies. The force on the hydraulic ram was 250 tons. Closing the end and tapping threads for the valve were done in much the same manner as described in the previous example. The cylinder was heat treated to ICC specification 3AA2015.

The dies were made of nickel-molybdenum-silicon gray iron and were heat treated to Rockwell C 40. Tool life was 1200 pieces per grind. Lubricant was graphite in oil. Annual production was 150,000 cylinders, made in lots of 5000.

For propane gas, pressure tanks must have high strength at minimum weight. In one application, the weight of such a tank was reduced from 130 to 70 lb by changing from 1025 steel to a high-manganese, deep drawing steel (0.20% C, 1.60% Mn, 0.025% P and 0.030% S — all percentages maximums). Before drawing, the high-manganese steel had a minimum yield strength of 50,000 psi and a minimum tensile strength of 70,000 psi.

Bottles for dispensing small quantities of liquefied gases or gases under high pressure are commonly made of drawing quality low-carbon steel to take advantage of the improved mechanical properties produced by deep drawing. The bottles range in size from ½-in. diameter by 1¼ in. long to 1½-in. diameter by 6 in. long. The following example describes the drawing of a medium-size bottle.

Example 267. Deep Drawing of a Carbon Dioxide Bottle (Fig. 68)

The bottle shown in Fig. 68(a) was drawn and necked from aluminum-killed, acid-etched 1008 steel 0.037 to 0.039 in. thick. The permissible hardness range was Rockwell B 38 to 52, but the lower part of the range was preferred. The strip stock was 5½ in. wide and had a No. 2 finish, with a rolled edge.

In the first operation (Fig. 68b), two pieces per press stroke were blanked and cupped, using a compound die in a 70-ton mechanical press operating at 45 strokes per minute. Blank diameter was 2.825 in. and cup diameter was 1.590 in., for a reduction of 43.7%. The progression was 4.375 in. and the blank center distance across the strip was 2.500 in.

The cup was direct redrawn in five operations to the dimensions and shape shown in Fig. 68(c), pinch trimmed to 2½ in. long, and sized to 0.735/0.730 in. in diameter in a transfer die. The first redraw reduced the shell diameter 20%. The percentage reduction was reduced with each redraw, the last being 11%. The die operated in a 75-ton straight-side mechanical press at 44 strokes per minute. Draw rings were tungsten carbide with highly polished working surfaces. Punches and blankholders were D3 tool steel, hardened to Rockwell C 61 to 63.

The open end of the shell was annealed to permit necking in five steps to the dimensions shown in Fig. 68(d). The bottle was moved to each of the five tungsten carbide necking dies by a rotary-feed table. Necking was done in a 50-ton mechanical press at 3200 pieces per hour.

An automatic lathe was used to counterbore the neck, form internal serrations that retained the seal, chamfer the end, and face the bottle to length. A caution notice and date were imprinted by a roll-type stamping device. Some bottles had a circumferential indentation, which was roll formed. This indentation was used as a locator in the application and, because it was a depressed surface, provided a safe place for a color band indicating the type of gas in the container.

A water-soluble mineral oil was used as a lubricant for drawing, reducing and necking.

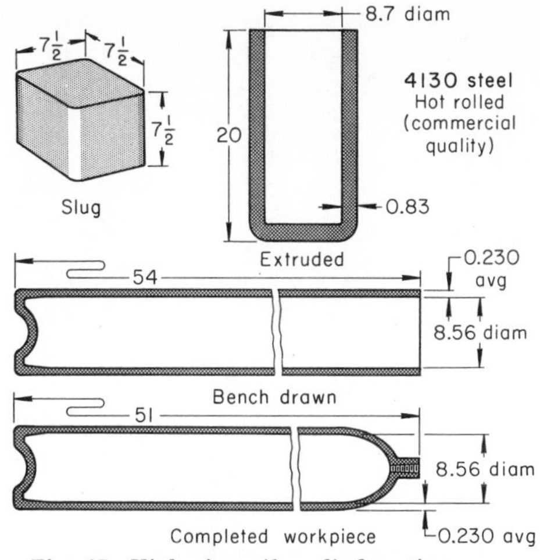

Fig. 67. High-strength cylinder (for compressed oxygen) that was drawn from a hot extruded shell (Example 266)

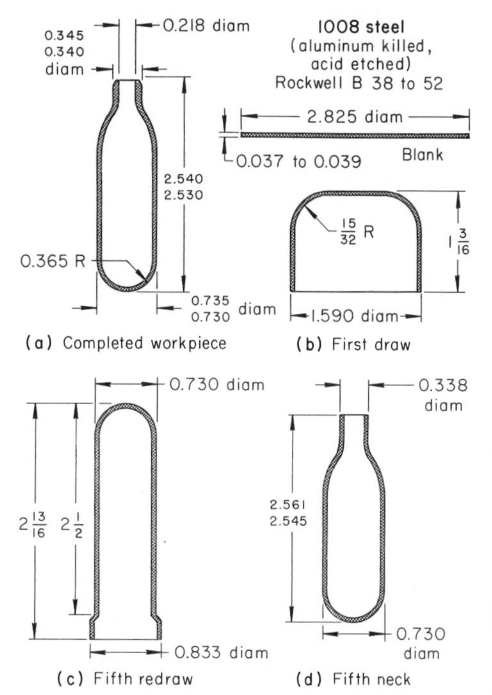

Fig. 68. Drawing and necking a bottle for carbon dioxide gas (Example 267)

Safety

Deep drawing, like other press operations, involves potential hazards to operators, maintenance men and other personnel in the work area. No press, die, or auxiliary equipment can be considered ready for operation until these hazards are eliminated by the installation of necessary safety devices. Operators should be properly instructed in safe operation of equipment. The article that begins on page 1 in this volume contains information and literature references on safe operation.

APPENDIX 1

Deep Drawing With Ultra-High Pressure

By F. J. Fuchs and J. W. Archer*

In conventional deep drawing, the maximum depth to which a shell can be drawn in a single operation is limited by the tensile strength and ductility of the work metal and by friction between workpiece and tooling. Expressed as the ratio of blank diameter to shell diameter, the accepted limit of depth of draw for the most drawable metals is only slightly greater than 2 to 1. The high-pressure techniques described here make possible a blank-to-shell diameter ratio of at least 3.3 to 1, or a reduction of nearly 70% in a single draw.

The important differences between high-pressure drawing and conventional drawing are that the ductility of the work metal is actually increased during high-pressure drawing and stress patterns are controlled so that the tensile strength of the work metal is supplemented by applied compressive stress, which effectively cancels out the strength limitation. The high pressure, properly controlled, can be applied to the surface of the blank either by a fluid or by mechanical means.

Fluid Techniques

The high-pressure-fluid technique is the most efficient way of overcoming work-metal strength limitations, low ductility, and friction. In conventional drawing, forces to overcome friction on the surfaces of the blank and to compress the blank circumferentially to reduce its size can come only from the force generated by the punch pressing on the bottom of the cup. This force creates tensile stress in the cup wall and will pull the cup into two parts when the tensile strength of the work metal is exceeded. Also, in the conventional operation, ductility is constant or decreases as the work metal deforms during drawing. Because of the high blankholding force needed to prevent flange wrinkling, friction is high and is distributed over the top and bottom surfaces of the blank in contact with the draw ring.

In the high-pressure-fluid method, the fluid pressure acting on the edge of the blank produces radial compressive forces through the blank and the radial stress terminates as an axial compressive force in the cup, partially or completely balancing the tensile force normally found. The balance can be controlled by altering the pressure of the fluid.

Improved ductility arises from the effect demonstrated by P. W. Bridgman that metals under high hydrostatic pressure become more ductile. In the high-pressure-fluid method of drawing, the portion of the blank that extends beyond the die radius is completely enveloped in a high-pressure fluid; therefore, it has increased ductility, and is the portion of the metal un-

*Engineering Research Center, Western Electric Co. This Appendix is condensed from ASM Technical Report C7-13.2 (October 1967).

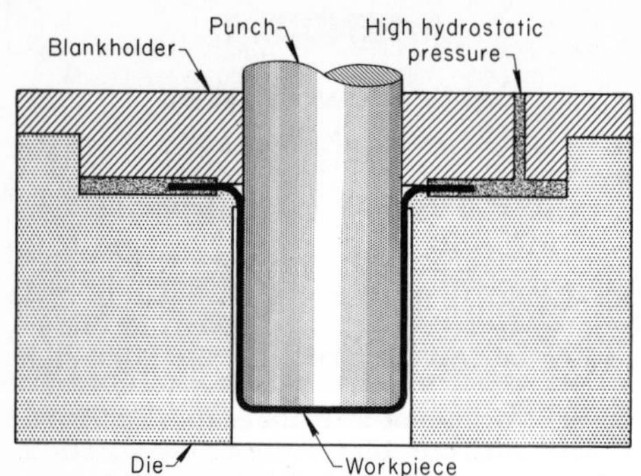

Fig. 69. Elements of deep drawing by the high-pressure-fluid technique

dergoing the most deformation. The remaining metal under deformation is a small annular section at the die radius. The compressive forces between punch and die wall in conjunction with the radial compressive force contributed by the fluid pressure mechanically subject this small annular section to high environmental compression so it, too, has increased ductility. Referring to Fig. 69, it is evident that since the only mechanical clamping force on the blank is a small seal area outside the die radius, friction forces are minimized. The fluid will flow inward in a restricted way both above and below the blank to create positive lubrication, further decreasing friction.

Fluid-Pressure Equipment. The equipment shown in Fig. 70 is designed for use in a hydraulic press having a 1000-ton upper ram and a 150-ton lower ram. The die is made to draw 3/32-in.-thick blanks having a maximum diameter of 3.5 in. The blanks are placed on the lower half of the die, which is secured to the bottom platen of the press. A locating ring centers the blank. The assembly mounted to the upper ram of the press consists of three telescopically related parts. As the upper ram is lowered, the high-pressure chamber seats on the lower die assembly. As the ram continues down, the upper die moves within the chamber to seat on the lower die and to clamp the blank. The ram continues down to pressurize the fluid (castor oil), which is above the die.

The pressurized fluid flows through the channels in the die to surround the blank, except for the circular areas on the blank described by the punch and the throat of the die. The fluid is prevented from entering the punch and die areas by annular protrusions on both halves of the tool. The protrusions pinch the blank, and effect a metal-to-metal seal. The punch and die are vented to prevent any buildup of back pressure caused by leakage past the blank. To form the shell, the punch actuation is coordinated with the generation of high pressure.

The two die halves are made of modified H11 tool steel. The contact surfaces of the die halves are polished to a mirror finish and hard chromium plated. The punch is of high speed steel, polished and hard chromium plated. The chamber is a pressed-ring vessel with a 4-in.-diam bore, fabricated of maraging steel. The chamber is designed for use to fluid pressures of 125,000 psi. The maximum working pressure is gen-

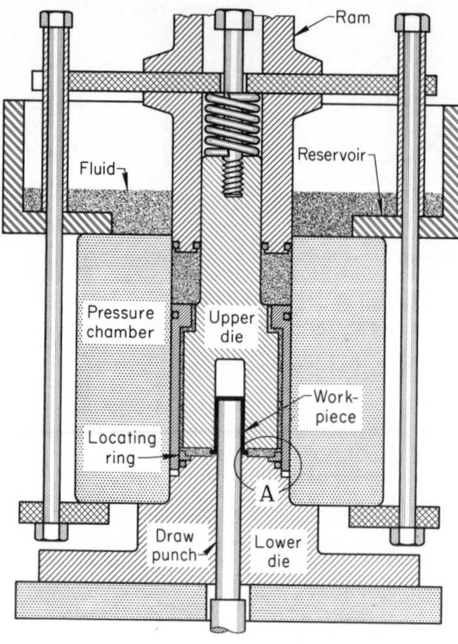

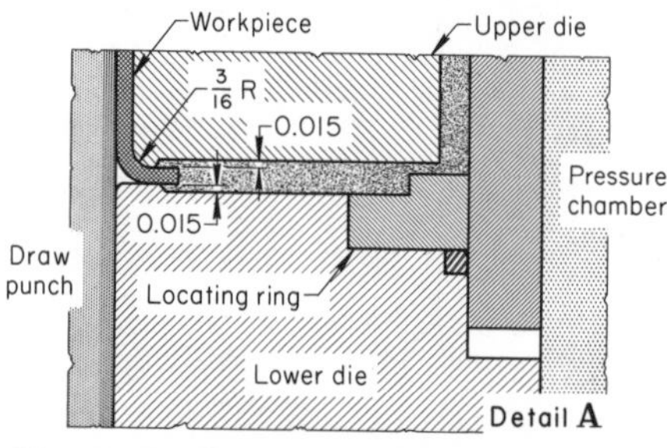

Fig. 70. Equipment for fluid-pressure deep drawing in a hydraulic press

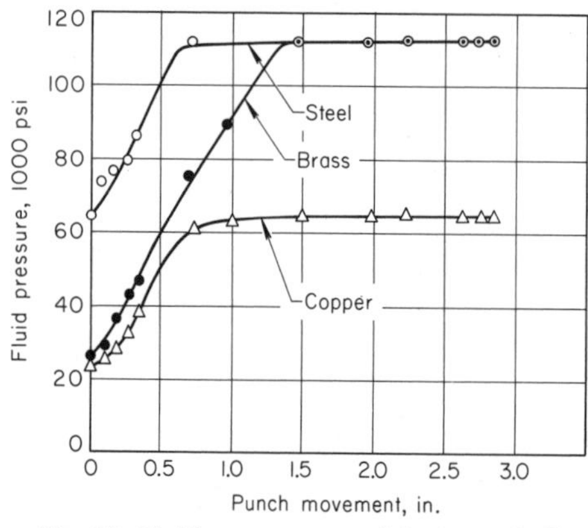

Fig. 71. Fluid pressures used to form shells by high-pressure drawing from copper, brass and steel blanks

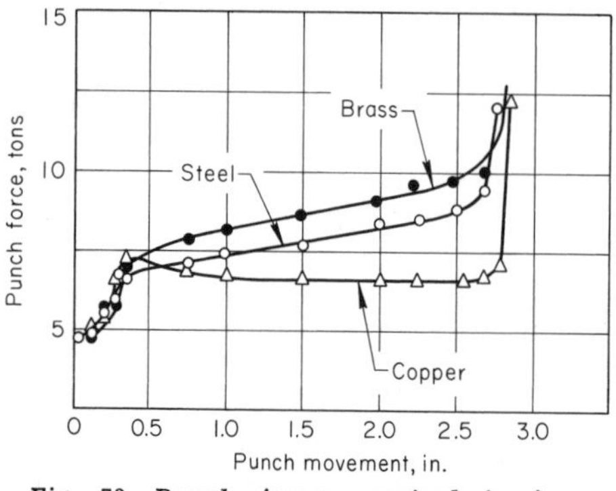

Fig. 72. Punch forces required to form shells by high-pressure drawing from copper, brass and steel blanks

erated by using approximately 640 tons of the available capacity of the press.

From the 3.5-in. blank, a flanged shell is formed having a depth of 2.78 in., an outside diameter of 1.054 in., and an inside diameter of 0.875 in. The blank-to-cup diameter ratio is approximately 3.3 to 1, or a reduction of nearly 70%. The die has a 3/16-in. radius, and the punch a 1/16-in. radius. These radii are considerably less than those that could be used in conventional deep drawing of a 3/32-in.-thick blank. Punch-to-die clearance is 0.0035 in. less than nominal stock thickness so that the sidewall of the shell is slightly ironed to give a uniform wall thickness and improved surface finish.

The sealing surface on the upper die extends 0.015 in. beyond the surrounding surface. The 3/16-in. die radius blends into the surrounding die surface without a flat at the tangent point to make a 0.015-in.-high sealing ring. The sealing surface on the lower die also is 0.015 in. high, but it has a short flat beyond the tangent point of the upper die radius before blending into the surrounding die surface. The size and shape of the sealing surfaces assure a good metal-to-metal seal. The space between the upper and lower die surfaces is greater than the amount of stock thickening that occurs in the blank; thus, the blank is always surrounded by the pressurized fluid and is in a state of increased ductility.

The high-pressure tool operation is completely automatic. When the cycle is started, the tool closes and the high pressure is generated. The bottom ram or draw punch is then actuated by a pressure switch mounted on the input port to the upper ram, which generates the high pressure. At the end of the punch movement, the punch is hydraulically locked in position and the upper ram is retracted. After the upper ram pulls the die off the shell, the punch retracts. The higher friction force between shell and punch, and the opening sequence used, prevent the shell from remaining in the die. Unloading the shell and loading the next blank are done manually before the next cycle is initiated.

Results. A series of tests was conducted on each of three commercial sheet metals: (*a*) 1010 steel (commercial quality, annealed, Rockwell B 51 to 53); (*b*) oxygen-free copper (annealed); and (*c*) cartridge brass (annealed 1½ hr at 1000 F from the half-hard condition).

The steel blanks were phosphate coated and lubricated with soap. The copper and brass were lubricated with a drawing wax. Some blanks of each material were lightly sand blasted and coated with 0.002-in.-thick Teflon. The steel and brass blanks had a nominal thickness of 0.089 in.; copper blanks of 0.089 and 0.093-in. thicknesses were used to establish semiquantitatively the effect of ironing on the forces required to form a shell.

The first phase of testing each material consisted of establishing the maximum fluid pressure to be used in the tool and the pressure at which the punch should be actuated. The pressure curve was purely a function of time and took 4 to 5 sec to reach its maximum value, because of the slow speed of the upper ram. It was found that the punch must move during buildup of the high pressure. If the punch started to move when the pressure was too low, a hole was pierced in the blank. If the hydrostatic pressure was too high, extrusion of the blank occurred without the aid of the punch, and a shell that had a bulged end was produced.

Each material tested was formed to the full depth of the die. Figures 71 and 72 show the converted values for the fluid pressure and the punch force required, as a function of punch movement. These curves were obtained while forming acceptable shells.

All shells showed some earing, but the anisotropy was not severe for shells of this wall thickness. All shells were structurally sound with no shear cracks in the walls. For very deep draws, beyond the limits of the present tools, it is conceivable that anisotropy of the sheet metal may be the limiting factor. Cross-rolled or drawing quality materials may be required.

The quality of the parts made by the high-pressure single-draw method was far better than obtainable by conventional multiple-draw techniques. The results show that expensive redrawing and annealing operations can be eliminated, significantly decreasing the cost of making shells. Because of ironing in the high-pressure process, the shells had smooth surfaces, approaching the mirror finish of the punch and die. The ironing also resulted in uniform shell thicknesses. The axial variation found for copper and steel shells was never more than 0.0007 in. on the outside diameter. The inside diameters varied no more than the axial tolerance of the punch and were about 0.0005 in. smaller than the punch. The variation between outside diameters of copper shells was less than 0.0007 in., for steel shells less than 0.0012 in., and for brass shells less than 0.0006 in.

The equipment shown in Fig. 70 can be used for production cycles of less than 1 min. However, the high-pressure piston has to be the same in area as the blank being formed, and therefore when a sizable blank is used, the press requirement can be very large. For instance, if a 6-in.-diam blank is to be formed with a pressure of 300,000 psi, a 4500-ton press would be needed. Again referring to Fig. 70, large radial forces are created in the chamber because the fluid under pressure operates over a considerable height in the chamber. So a massive chamber would be required for large work.

In order to improve the mechanical relations, a new type of deep drawing equipment has been evolved, as shown in Fig. 73. Here the vertical forces due to pressure are contained by a quick-opening breech mechanism that mounts into the walls of the pressure vessel. The breech can be closed and opened by direct in-and-out motion of a small ram. The pressurizing fluid occupies a space only slightly larger than the blank itself, and therefore exerts a low radial force. The high-pressure fluid is supplied by small built-in intensifiers mounted in the base block of the tool. These are powered by a relatively small lower ram on the press. With this type of equipment, a 6-in.-diam blank in fluid at 300,000-psi pressure can be formed with a 100-ton press.

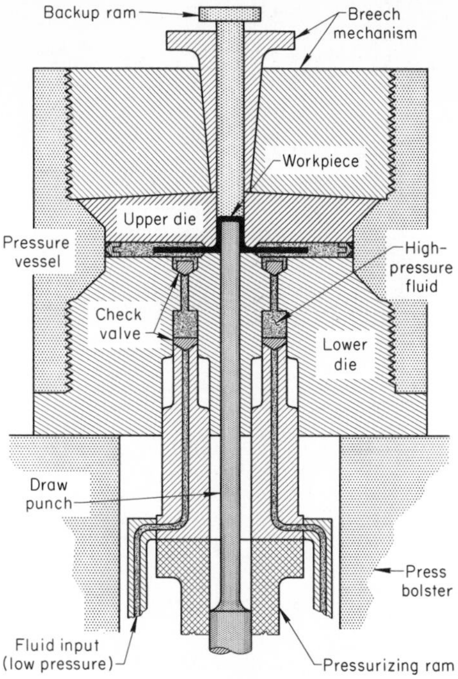

Fig. 73. Improved equipment for fluid-pressure deep drawing

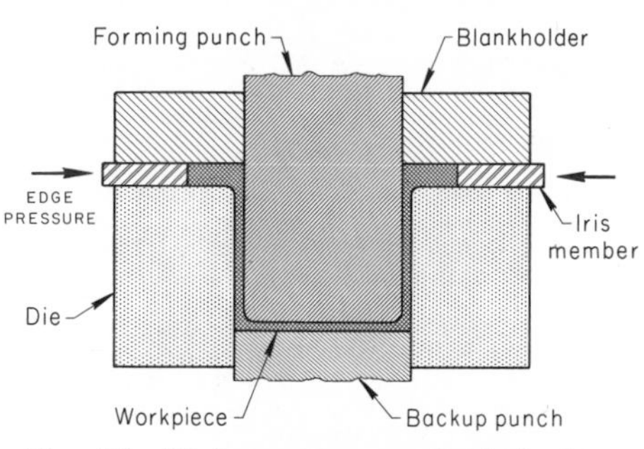

Fig. 74. High-pressure mechanical deep drawing process

Mechanical Edge-Pressure Technique

Another approach to high-pressure drawing involves the use of mechanical members to apply the high compressive forces to attain high work-metal ductility. Figures 74 and 75 show the process and the equipment. The pressure on the edge of the blank is created by an iris assembly that closes radially. The iris members are driven by high-intensity hydraulic rams. The vertical forces applied to the blank result from the top and bottom plate closure activated by the press ram. In this respect, the mechanical technique suffers the same limitation of press capacity as the fluid technique, although the press stroke is much shorter because it is a simple clamping action. Another disadvantage of the mechanical technique is the considerably higher friction on the surfaces of the blank, making excellent lubrication desirable.

In spite of these problems, the mechanical tool has desirable capabilities. The ease of operation and decreased stress on tools afforded by not using the high-pressure fluid are helpful. The mechanical iris members make possible shells without the anisotropic distortion of flange edges. Because of this, parts can be made with finished flanges or scrap-free ends. The pressures that can be generated in this type of tool are limited only by the compressive strength of the tool steels used.

The dies and punches are made of 18% nickel maraged steel. The iris members are driven by high-intensity rams of 150 tons capacity, each fed by 35,000-psi intensifiers. The backup ram

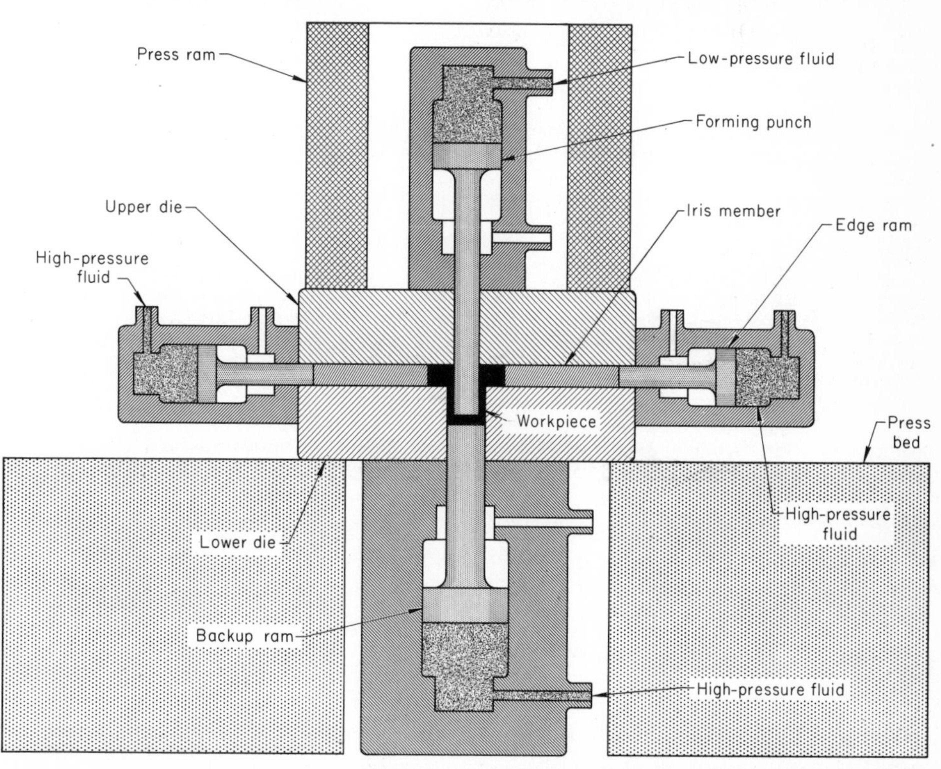

Fig. 75. Tools for deep drawing by the high-pressure mechanical process

is also a 150-ton subpress. The draw punch is actuated by a 150-ton ram built into the 1000-ton press, which itself does the clamping. The equipment is designed to make a rectangular shell of 1/16-in. wall up to 5 in. long from a blank 1/4 in. thick.

In an example of the application of this equipment, a fully annealed 4¼-by-3⅛-by-¼-in. blank of oxygen-free copper was used. Blanks were coated with either wax or 0.002-in.-thick Teflon. During initial punch movement, the mechanical pressure acting on the edge of the blank built up to about 140,000 psi. This pressure extruded the ¼-in. blank into the 1/16-in. walls of the rectangular shell. Metal flow was satisfactory, even with the small punch and die radii used. The shell walls were uniform as a result of the compressive forces being applied in all directions.

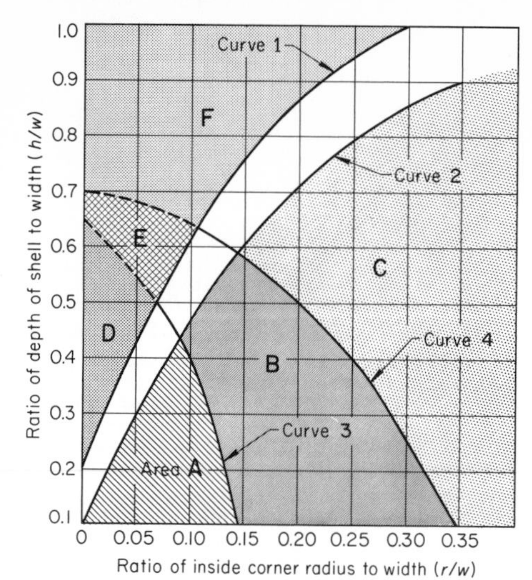

Fig. 76. Dimensional relations defining six areas of formability of square or rectangular drawn shells of 1010 steel. See text.

APPENDIX 2

Effect of Metal Thickness on Deep Drawing

By H. E. IHLE

The stock thickness and its relation to the diameter or width of the blank affects the formability of round, square and rectangular shells. Stock thickness also affects the depth of shell that can be drawn in one operation.

Table 14. Formability Factors (d/D Ratios) for Drawing Round Shells Without Flanges From 1010 Steel(a)

Stock thickness, % of blank diameter	Formability factor (d/D ratio): First draw	Second draw	Third draw	Fourth draw	Fifth draw
2.0	0.48	0.73	0.76	0.78	0.80
1.5	0.50	0.75	0.78	0.80	0.82
1.0	0.53	0.76	0.79	0.81	0.84
0.6	0.55	0.78	0.80	0.82	0.85
0.3	0.58	0.79	0.81	0.83	0.86
0.15	0.60	0.80	0.82	0.85	0.87
0.08	0.63	0.82	0.84	0.86	0.88

(a) For draw-die radii of $8t$ to $15t$ (t = stock thickness); factors may increase about 2% for draw-die radii of $4t$ to $8t$.

Round Shells

The number of drawing operations needed to produce a finished round shell depends on blank diameter, depth and diameter of the shell, properties and thickness of the work metal, and draw-die and punch-nose radii.

The ratio of the punch diameter to the blank diameter (d/D) is a simple and practical measure for use in determining formability. The maximum d/D ratio depends markedly on the metal thickness and the draw-die radius. The ratio of metal thickness to blank diameter (t/D) reflects the principle of volume constancy between the blank and the shell and, as shown in Tables 14 and 17, affects the formability factor d/D. The formability factors in Table 14 are multiplied by the blank diameter, or by the previous shell diameter, to obtain the shell diameter. For each redraw, the factors increase, indicating a decrease in formability. The size of the draw-die radius also has an effect on the formability factors, as footnoted in Table 14. When the factors given in Table 14 are not exceeded, three or four draws can be made in 1010 steel without annealing if the punch-nose radius is at least 75% of the draw-die radius.

The ratio of draw depth to shell diameter, and the size of the draw-die radius, depend on the t/D ratio, as shown in Table 15.

Table 15. Maximum Depth-to-Diameter (h/d) Ratios for Drawing Round Shells Without Flanges From 1010 Steel(a)

Drawing operation	Maximum h/d ratio for steel with thickness of the following percentages of blank diameter: 2.0 to 1.5%	1.5 to 1.0%	1.0 to 0.6%	0.6 to 0.3%	0.3 to 0.15%	0.15 to 0.08%
First	0.94 to 0.77	0.84 to 0.65	0.70 to 0.57	0.62 to 0.50	0.52 to 0.45	0.46 to 0.38
Second ..	1.88 to 1.54	1.60 to 1.32	1.36 to 1.1	1.13 to 0.94	0.96 to 0.83	0.90 to 0.70
Third ...	3.5 to 2.7	2.8 to 2.2	2.3 to 1.8	1.9 to 1.5	1.6 to 1.3	1.3 to 1.1
Fourth ..	5.6 to 4.3	4.3 to 3.5	3.6 to 2.9	2.9 to 2.4	2.4 to 2.0	2.0 to 1.5
Fifth	8.9 to 6.6	6.6 to 5.1	5.2 to 4.1	4.1 to 3.3	3.3 to 2.7	2.7 to 2.0

(a) The larger h/d ratios in each range are for draw-die radii of $4t$ to $8t$ (t = stock thickness); the smaller ratios are for draw-die radii of $8t$ to $15t$. Also, draw-die radii increase as ratios of stock thickness to blank diameter (t/D ratios) decrease.

Table 16. Maximum Depth-to-Diameter (h/d) Ratios for Drawing Round Shells With Flanges in One Operation From 1010 Steel(a)

D_f/d ratio(b)	Maximum h/d ratio for steel with thickness of the following percentages of blank diameter: 2.0 to 1.5%	1.5 to 1.0%	1.0 to 0.6%	0.6 to 0.3%	0.3 to 0.15%
1.1	0.90 to 0.75	0.82 to 0.65	0.70 to 0.57	0.62 to 0.50	0.52 to 0.45
1.3	0.80 to 0.65	0.72 to 0.56	0.60 to 0.50	0.53 to 0.45	0.47 to 0.40
1.5	0.70 to 0.58	0.63 to 0.50	0.53 to 0.45	0.48 to 0.40	0.42 to 0.35
1.8	0.58 to 0.48	0.53 to 0.42	0.44 to 0.37	0.39 to 0.34	0.35 to 0.29
2.0	0.51 to 0.42	0.46 to 0.36	0.38 to 0.32	0.34 to 0.29	0.30 to 0.25
2.2	0.45 to 0.35	0.40 to 0.31	0.33 to 0.27	0.29 to 0.25	0.26 to 0.22
2.5	0.35 to 0.28	0.32 to 0.25	0.27 to 0.22	0.23 to 0.20	0.21 to 0.17
2.8	0.27 to 0.22	0.24 to 0.19	0.21 to 0.17	0.18 to 0.15	0.16 to 0.13
3.0	0.22 to 0.18	0.20 to 0.16	0.17 to 0.14	0.15 to 0.12	0.13 to 0.10

(a) The larger h/d ratios in each range are for draw-die radii of $4t$ to $8t$ (t = stock thickness); the smaller ratios are for draw-die radii of $8t$ to $15t$. Also, draw-die radii increase as t/D ratios decrease. (b) Ratio of flange diameter (D_f) to shell diameter (d).

When drawing flanged round shells, the ratio of the flange diameter to the shell diameter (D_f/d) and the t/D ratio both affect the maximum depth-to-diameter ratio of the shell (see Table 16). The formability factors d/D shown in Table 17 should not be exceeded during the first drawing operation for a flanged round shell.

Square or Rectangular Shells

Drawing of square or rectangular shells subjects the metal in the corners to compressive stresses. Metal in the sidewalls is subject to tensile stresses after the metal has been drawn over the die radius. Compressive stresses in the sidewalls are caused by the flow of metal from the corner areas.

Compression of the metal from the corner areas into the sidewalls depends on the ratio of the inside vertical corner radius of the shell to the width of the shell (r/w). Resistance of the metal to bending and wrinkling depends on the ratio of metal thickness to blank width (t/W). Formability factors ($0.71\sqrt{r/h}$) for square or rectangular shells drawn in one operation from 1010 steel are listed in Table 18; formability factors for less ductile metals are up to 10% larger.

Maximum ratios of depth to width for square or rectangular shells drawn in one operation are given in Table 19; these values are based on the ratio of shell corner radius to shell width (r/w), and on the ratio of metal thickness to blank width (t/W).

The number of drawing operations needed is influenced by the ratio of shell depth to shell width (h/w), and the ratio of the inside vertical corner radius of the shell to the width of the shell (r/w), as shown in Fig. 76. Areas A, B and C below curve 2 in Fig. 76 represent the limits for drawing square or rectangular shells in one operation. Shells in areas D, E and F above curve 1 need two or more operations. The space between the curves 1 and 2 represents shells that are borderline for drawing in one operation. Shells in areas A, B and C have a stock thickness of no more than 0.6% of the blank width; in areas D, E and F, the stock thickness is not less than 2% of blank width.

Each area in Fig. 76 represents shells with certain characteristics. Area A represents shallow shells with small inside corner radii and an $r/(w-h)$ ratio of no more than 0.17. With these shells, only a small amount of metal moves into the sidewalls from the corner areas; thus, the sidewall height is constant. Typical blank development for area-A shells is shown in Fig. 77.

Area B in Fig. 76 represents shallow shells with medium-size corner radii and an $r/(w-h)$ ratio of 0.17 to 0.4. The movement of metal into the sidewalls from the corner areas causes some earing in this type of shell. Figures 77(c) and 78 show a typical corner of a blank for an area-B shell.

Area C in Fig. 76 represents shells with medium to large corner radii and with an $r/(w-h)$ ratio of more than 0.4. The compression of metal into the sidewalls of these shells causes considerable earing. One method of developing the corner of the blank for wide or shallow area-C shells is illustrated in Fig. 78.

Workpieces in area D in Fig. 76 have an h/w ratio no greater than 0.65, and a blank shaped as shown in Fig. 77(d). Area F represents shells with an h/w ratio greater than 0.7. The ranges of areas D and F overlap into area E.

The procedure for laying out the corners of blanks for shells in areas A, B and D in Fig. 76 is described below, with reference to Fig. 77(a):

1 Lay out a square or rectangle by drawing lines through the loci of the workpiece corner radii. These lines are the primary datum lines.
2 The width of metal needed for the sidewall and bottom radius is $h + 0.57r_b$, where h is the shell depth, in inches, and r_b is the bottom inside radius, in inches. This width is added to each side of the layout of step 1, from the primary datum lines.
3 The corner radius R of the blank, which provides the metal needed for each corner of the shell, is:

$$R = \sqrt{r^2 + 2hr - 0.86r_b(r + 0.16r_b)}$$

where r is the inside corner radius of the

workpiece, in inches. For parts in area D, radius R is increased by 10 to 20%.

4 Lay out corner radius R, using the loci of the workpiece corner radii as center points, so as to intersect the lines drawn in step 1 at points b and c.

5 Bisect ab and cd. Through the dividing points e and f, draw gh and ij tangent to arc of corner radius R drawn in step 4. [These tangents may coincide (Fig. 77b), they may cross each other outwardly (Fig. 77c), or they may cross each other inwardly (Fig. 77d).]

6 Blend the intersections of the tangents and the edges of the blank with an arc of radius R. When the tangents intersect inwardly, blend the intersections with an outward arc of radius R (detail A in Fig. 77a).

Shells in area B in Fig. 76 and shallow or wide shells in area C have a larger amount of metal compressed into the sidewalls than in area A. The blank is adjusted for this by increasing the metal for the corners and decreasing the metal for the sidewalls, as described below, with reference to Fig. 78:

1 Start the blank layout using steps 1, 2, 3 and 4 in the procedure detailed above. If the corner radius is not the same as the bottom radius, the loci of the bottom radii establish secondary datum lines from which the metal for the sidewalls found in step 2 in the six-step procedure previously listed is projected.

2 The corrected corner radius R_c is calculated by the formula:

$$R_c = R[0.074(R/2r)^2 + 0.982]$$

3 The width of metal for the sidewalls is reduced by h_w and h_l, calculated by the formulas:

$$h_w = yR^2/(w - 2r) \text{ and } h_l = yR^2/(l - 2r)$$

Values for factor y are given in Table 20.

4 Blend the intersections of the width, length and corner radii of the blank by making R_w tangent to R_c and the blank width; and R_l tangent to R_c and the blank length.

Square shells in area F, and in area C with a large h/w ratio, can be drawn from round blanks. The blank diameter is determined according to the following formula:

$$D = 1.13\sqrt{w^2 + 4w(h - 0.43r) - 1.72r(h + 0.33r)}$$

Rectangular shells in areas C and F with large h/w ratios usually are drawn from blanks with semicircular ends connected by two parallel sides; their length is the difference between the length and width of the shell.

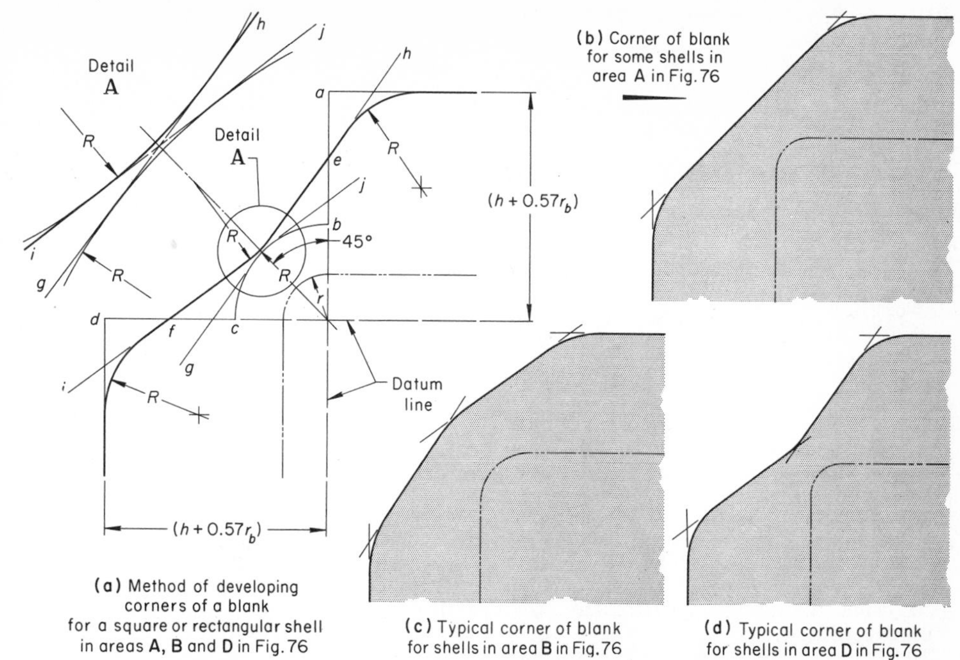

(a) Method of developing corners of a blank for a square or rectangular shell in areas A, B and D in Fig. 76
(c) Typical corner of blank for shells in area B in Fig. 76
(d) Typical corner of blank for shells in area D in Fig. 76

Fig. 77. Corner-layout method, and typical corners, for blanks for square or rectangular shells in areas A, B and D in Fig. 76. Corner shape varies with shell dimensions, and the shape typical of area B and that typical of area D extend into adjacent areas.

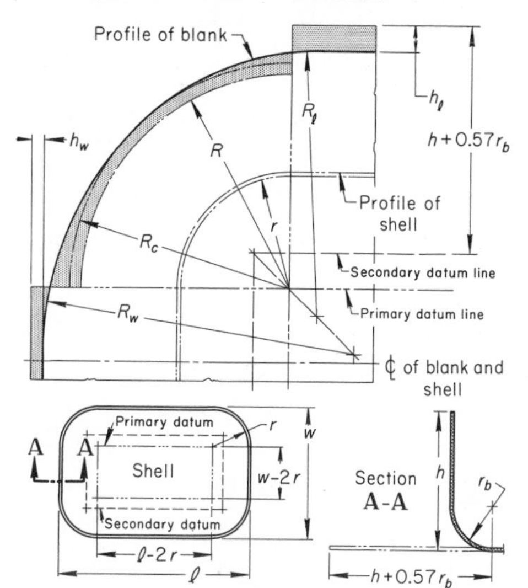

Fig. 78. Corner-layout method for wide shells with large corner radii in areas B and C in Fig. 76

Table 17. Formability Factors (d/D Ratios) for Drawing Round Shells With Flanges in One Operation From 1010 Steel

D_f/d ratio(a)	Formability factor (d/D ratio) for steel with thickness of the following percentages of blank diameter: 2.0 to 1.5%	1.5 to 1.0%	1.0 to 0.6%	0.6 to 0.3%	0.3 to 0.15%
1.1	0.51	0.53	0.55	0.57	0.59
1.3	0.49	0.51	0.53	0.54	0.55
1.5	0.47	0.49	0.50	0.51	0.52
1.8	0.45	0.46	0.47	0.48	0.48
2.0	0.42	0.43	0.44	0.45	0.45
2.2	0.40	0.41	0.42	0.42	0.42
2.5	0.37	0.38	0.38	0.38	0.38
2.8	0.34	0.35	0.35	0.35	0.35
3.0	0.32	0.33	0.33	0.33	0.33

(a) Ratio of flange diameter to shell diameter

Table 18. Formability Factors for Square or Rectangular Shells Drawn in One Operation From 1010 Steel

r/w ratio(a)	Formability factor ($0.71\sqrt{r/h}$) for steel with thickness of the following percentages of blank width: 2.0%	1.0%	0.6%	0.3%
0.4	0.40	0.42	0.44	0.48
0.3	0.36	0.38	0.40	0.42
0.2	0.33	0.34	0.36	0.38
0.1	0.25	0.25	0.25	0.25
0.05	0.15	0.15	0.15	0.15

(a) Ratio of inside vertical corner radius of shell to width of shell

Table 19. Maximum Depth-to-Width (h/w) Ratios for Square or Rectangular Shells Drawn in One Operation From 1010 Steel

r/w ratio(a)	Maximum h/w ratio for steel with thickness of the following percentages of blank width: 2.0 to 1.5%	1.5 to 1.0%	1.0 to 0.6%	0.6 to 0.3%
0.3	1.0	0.95	0.90	0.85
0.2	0.90	0.82	0.76	0.70
0.15	0.75	0.70	0.65	0.60
0.10	0.60	0.55	0.50	0.45
0.05	0.40	0.35	0.30	0.25

(a) Ratio of inside vertical corner radius of shell to width of shell

Table 20. Factor y for Corner Radius of Blank for a Square or Rectangular Shell in Area C in Fig. 76

r/w ratio(a)	Factor y for shell with h/w ratio(b) of: 0.3	0.4	0.5	0.6
0.10	...	0.15	0.20	0.27
0.15	0.08	0.11	0.17	0.20
0.20	0.06	0.10	0.12	0.17
0.25	0.05	0.08	0.10	0.12
0.30	0.04	0.06	0.08	...

(a) Ratio of inside vertical corner radius of shell to width of shell. (b) Ratio of shell depth to shell width.

Selected References

George Sachs, "Principles and Methods of Sheet Metal Fabricating", revised and enlarged by Henry E. Voegeli, Second Edition, Reinhold Publishing Co., New York, 1966. [A textbook on theory and practice. Chapters 11 through 15 (109 p) in particular analyze the processes of drawing thin-wall and thick-wall cylindrical cups and box-shape parts, and the redrawing and ironing of tubular parts. Extensive bibliographies are included.]

J. Dudley Jevons, "The Metallurgy of Deep Drawing and Pressing", Second Edition, Chapman and Hall, Ltd., London (England), 1941; 735 p. [A fundamental textbook. Comprehensive up to the date of its publication.]

"Die Design Handbook", prepared for the American Society of Tool and Manufacturing Engineers, Second Edition, McGraw-Hill Book Co., New York, 1965. [Section 10 (28 p), by Anton E. Mohrnheim, examines the mode of displacement of metal in drawing, and details algebraic and graphic methods for developing the blanks for cylindrical and rectangular draws. Section 11 (37 p) gives examples of the draw reductions used in forming many typical parts and illustrates the dies employed.]

Gerhard Oehler, "Schnitt-, Stanz- und Ziehwerkzeuge", Fifth Edition, Springer-Verlag, Berlin (West Germany), 1966; 643 p. [A standard textbook on cutting, stamping and deep drawing of metals. In German.]

J. M. Alexander, An Appraisal of the Theory of Deep Drawing, *Metallurgical Reviews*, 5(19), 1960, 349-411. [A critical review of the mathematical approach to the determination of the stresses in a material during deep drawing. The theory can assist in specifying punch and die profile radii and clearances. 38 references.]

W. P. Romanowski, "Handbuch der Stanzereitechnik", Veb Verlag Technik, Berlin (East Germany), 1959; 569 p. [A comprehensive textbook. 232 references. In German.]

C. W. Hinman, "Press Working of Metals", Second Edition, McGraw-Hill Book Co., New York, 1950; 551 p. [Chapter 16 (46 p) illustrates the die sequences used in some typical deep drawing operations, and Chapter 18 (57 p) contains formulas and reference tables for developing shell blanks.]

John A. Grainger, The Deep Drawing and Spinning of Sheet Metal, with Particular Reference to Non-Ferrous Materials, *Journal of the Institute of Metals*, 84, 1955-1956, 133-146. [Discusses deep drawing techniques, with special reference to the choice of lubricant.]

G. S. A. Shawki, Assessing Deep Drawing Qualities of Sheet, *Sheet Metal Industries*, 42, May, June and July 1965, 363-368, 417-424, 524-532. [A critical review, concluding that no single test is adequate. 124 references.]

J. C. Wright, Phenomenon of "Earing" in Deep Drawing, *Sheet Metal Industries*, 42, Nov 1965, 814-831. [Reviews the causes and control of earing. 32 references.]

Selection of Material for Deep Drawing Dies

*By the ASM Committee on Deep Drawing Dies**

THE PERFORMANCE of a drawing die is determined by the amount of wear or galling during a production run. Wear of a given die material is determined largely by the kind and thickness of the sheet metal being drawn, sharpness of die radii, lubrication, die construction and die finish. The amount of wear on die radii can vary by a factor of 20 between the sharpest and most liberal radii. Use of the most liberal radii is the best practice, and this practice is assumed in the accompanying selection tables. Types of dies and other tooling components are illustrated in Fig. 1.

In drawing square cups, the formation of wrinkles at the corners, accompanied by high localized pressure, may produce prohibitively high rates of wear. The square cups dealt with in this article have liberal corner radii consistent with favorable die life. Small radii will produce greater wear and shorter life of the dies.

Quantity is the principal variable in the selection tables. The kind of material to be drawn is also recognized as a variable because it determines the amount of wear and galling.

High localized pressure caused by inaccurate fitting of dies during tryout, rough surface on the drawn sheet or on the working surfaces of the die, inadequate lubrication, and poor maintenance (stoning) of dies are typical of uneconomical practice. This article makes no attempt to deal with improvement of die life under poor production practices, because such mistakes should never be alleviated by selection of die material.

Selection Tables

In the many instances where the tables list more than one recommended material for the same conditions of tooling, the materials are listed in order of increasing cost per piece, but the ultimate choice will usually depend on availability, rather than on the small differences in either the performance or the cost of the tool materials.

Drawing-quality sheets of aluminum and copper alloys, steel and stainless steel are considered in the tables. The maximum hardness for aluminum and copper alloys is 58 Bhn, Rockwell F 61, and Rockwell 30-T 28. Maximum hardness of steel sheets dealt with is Rockwell B 70, and for stainless steel the maximum is Rockwell B 95, with Rockwell B 85 preferred.

Each part shown in Tables 1 to 9 (and in Fig. 4) involves multiple-operation drawing, with a maximum reduction of about 35%, and ironing of the walls to a uniform thickness. Shallow draws of 15 to 20% would approximately double the die life for the indicated materials.

Table 1 shows the selection of draw-ring or draw-die material for cups up to about 3 in. in diameter or square. For such mild service, selection of a low-cost die material might be expected. However, the ratio of the cost of tool material to total tool cost is so small in small dies that negligible savings would result. In fact, the selection problem for such dies is easy because there is such a slight difference in cost in using even the most expensive tool steels.

If only 50 or 100 small cups were to be made of aluminum and if there were no ironing involved, materials such as zinc, plastics, hot rolled soft steel, or masonite might be economical, provided experience in constructing dies from such lower-cost materials was sufficient to accelerate toolmaking.

The materials recommended for making the square cup (part 3) involve conservative radii at punch nose, punch nose corners, and punch and die corners where the sheet material gathers and may wrinkle in proportion to the sharpness of the radius. More liberal radii than those shown would not greatly increase die life nor influence die material selection. Sharper radii would increase the scrap rate in drawing and might increase die wear as much as 20 times unless tool material selection was upgraded.

This square cup (part 3) is more difficult to draw and, for equal die life, requires better draw-ring material at the corners than is needed in the draw ring for part 2. The fact that the recommended materials are the same for all parts in Table 1 indicates that the recommendations for the two cylindrical cups are conservative.

Table 2 recommends materials for the wearing edge of the die for drawing large cups, like parts 4 and 5, 12 and 24 in. in diameter, respectively, and 18 in. deep. Where tool steel or aluminum bronze is indicated in the table, the material is used as an inserted ring, preferably made from a forging but otherwise, with slightly less die life, from a casting. A sectional ring could be used, but this is an inferior alternative and would not perform with the die life indicated in the tables, because die surfaces and corners would deteriorate along the joints between sections. As noted in footnote b of Table 2, inserts are usually pressed into a die made of flame-hardened alloy cast iron. However, the alloy iron could be left unhardened, or soft gray iron could be used, to make 1000 cups from any sheet metal shown in Table 2.

Although the recommendations in Table 2 apply particularly to parts 12 to 24 in. in diameter, there is no suitable material of less cost than alloy cast iron into which inserts can be placed satisfactorily. Larger dies, therefore, would be made of the same materials as in Table 2. However, for deeper draws, the life of the indicated drawing materials would be less.

Table 3 deals with the materials for corner inserts at the point of greatest wear of the draw die for a large square cup such as part 6, or for any similar part more than 8 in. square of equal depth and with equally conservative corner radii. For drawing aluminum and steel, the inserts extend 2 in. beyond the radius at the corner and are fitted to blend into the adjoining flame-hardened

*S. R. Prance, *Chairman*, Emil C. Blocks, Victor J. Boll, John J. Carroll, George L. Chase, Carl H. Gerlach, L. L. Jaffe, Ervin M. Sylvester, J. H. Wolfhart.

[This article is a condensation of the article beginning on page 709 of Volume 1 of this Handbook.]

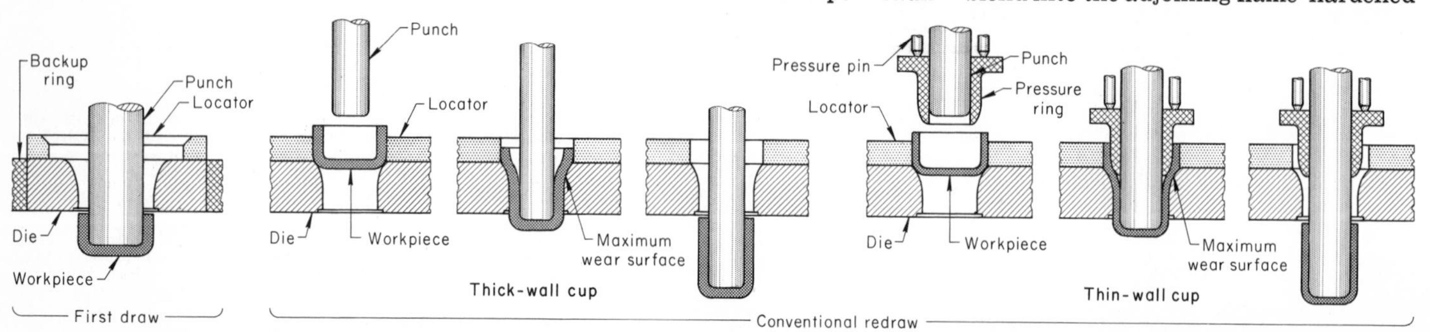

Fig. 1. Types of dies and other tooling components used in the first draw and in conventional redrawing operations

draw die of alloy cast iron. Drawing this part from series 300 stainless steel requires inserts completely around the wearing surfaces of the flame-hardened alloy cast iron die if the best finish is to be maintained. If galling is a more serious problem than wear, nitridable tool steels or an aluminum bronze should be selected for drawing stainless steel. The nitrided steels are superior in wear resistance also.

Short-run quantities of 1000 pieces made of aluminum or copper alloys or of carbon steel can be made satisfactorily from dies of flame-hardened alloy cast iron without corner inserts. One thousand pieces of stainless steel can be drawn in a die of flame-hardened alloy cast iron (preferably not over 400 Bhn) or with aluminum bronze corner inserts, where the best and most uniform surface appearance is necessary.

Table 4 gives the recommended tool materials for the wearing edge to draw a shallow 54 by 36-in. pan shaped like part 7. This part is shallower and of thinner sheet (0.031-in.) than part 6 and requires less wear-resistant die materials. About 1000 of these parts could be drawn from aluminum or steel sheet with an unhardened alloy iron die, but for a stainless steel part of good finish, aluminum bronze inserts would be needed in the corners. When cost is a minor consideration, aluminum bronze inserts can be used for all wear surfaces, to obtain the best finish.

Thickness of Sheet Metal

In drawing thick sheets of a given metal, the pressure on the dies increases in proportion to the square of the sheet thickness. The pressure involved is concentrated on the draw radius, and increasing sheet thickness will localize the wear in this high-pressure area without a similar effect on other surfaces of the die.

Thick stock will wrinkle less than thin stock. As a result, the pressures required to prevent wrinkling are no greater, and may even be less, than those required for thin stock. In fact, heavy sheets are often drawn without a pressure pad. Wear-resistance requirements for pressure pads used on heavy stock are usually no greater than for thin material.

Table 5 recommends tool materials for drawing and ironing sheet steel and plate ranging in thickness from 0.015 to 0.500 in. Where alloy cast iron is recommended, for long runs and thick sheets, it is intended to be flame hardened; for small quantities and thin sheets, it may be used as cast; for the mildest applications, even unalloyed gray iron at 200 to 250 Bhn can be used.

The O1, A2 and D2 tool steels recommended in the tables are preferably forged rings, but may be cast rings inserted into flame-hardened dies.

Punches, Blankholders and Other Components

Table 6 lists materials for punches and blankholder pressure pads or sleeves for drawing and ironing steel parts 2, 4 and 5. The same die materials are satisfactory for all operations in

Table 1. Recommended Draw-Ring Materials for Drawing and Ironing Cups up to About 3 In. in Diameter or Square From 0.062-In. Sheet (Parts 1, 2 and 3)

Metal to be drawn	Total quantity of parts to be drawn: 10,000	100,000	1,000,000
Drawing-quality aluminum and copper alloys	W1, O1	O1, A2	A2, D2
Drawing-quality steel	W1, O1	O1, A2	A2, D2
Series 300 stainless steel	W1 chromium plated, aluminum bronze	Nitrided A2, aluminum bronze	Nitrided D2 or D3, sintered carbide

Table 2. Recommended Draw-Ring Material for Drawing and Ironing Large Round Cups 12 In. or More in Diameter From 0.062-In. Sheet (Parts 4 and 5)

Metal to be drawn	Total quantity of parts to be drawn: 10,000	100,000	1,000,000
Drawing-quality aluminum and copper alloys	Alloy cast iron(a)	Alloy cast iron(a) or A2 inserts(b)	A2 or D2 inserts(b)
Drawing-quality steel	Alloy cast iron(a)	Alloy cast iron(c) or A2 inserts(b)	A2 or D2 inserts(b)
Series 300 stainless steel	Alloy cast iron(d) or aluminum bronze inserts(b)	A2 or aluminum bronze inserts(b)	A2 or D2 nitrided inserts(b)

(a) Wearing surfaces are flame hardened. (b) In flame-hardened alloy cast iron. (c) Quenched and tempered for drawing part 4; flame hardened for drawing part 5. (d) Flame hardened on wearing surfaces to not over 420 Bhn.

Table 3. Recommended Insert Materials for Draw Rings for Drawing and Ironing Large Square Cups Similar to Part 6 From 0.062-In. Sheet

Metal to be drawn	Total quantity of parts to be drawn: 10,000	100,000	1,000,000
Drawing-quality aluminum and copper alloys	W1	O1, A2	A2, D2
Drawing-quality steel	W1	O1, A2	A2, D2, nitrided A2 or D2
Series 300 stainless steel	W1 or aluminum bronze	Nitrided A2, aluminum bronze	Nitrided A2 or D2

For drawing aluminum alloys, copper alloys, and steel, the tool material would be used as corner inserts. For drawing stainless steel, the inserts would be used for all wear surfaces. Recommended selections in this table are applicable to both the push-through and the inverted-draw methods of tooling.

Table 4. Recommended Draw-Ring Material for Drawing and Ironing a Large Pan Similar to Part 7 From 0.031-In. Sheet

Metal to be drawn	Total quantity of parts to be drawn: 10,000	100,000	1,000,000
Drawing-quality aluminum and copper alloys	Alloy cast iron(a)	Alloy cast iron(a) or A2 corner inserts(b)	Nitrided A2 or D2 inserts(b)
Drawing-quality steel	Alloy cast iron(a)	Alloy cast iron(a) or A2 corner inserts(b)	Nitrided A2 or D2 inserts(b)
Series 300 stainless steel	Alloy cast iron(c) or aluminum bronze inserts(b)	Nitrided A2 or aluminum bronze inserts(b)	Nitrided A2 or D2 inserts(b)

(a) Wearing surfaces are flame hardened.
(b) In flame-hardened alloy cast iron.
(c) Flame hardened on wearing surfaces to not over 420 Bhn.

Table 5. Recommended Draw-Ring Material for Drawing and Ironing Part 4 From Flat Rolled Steel of Six Different Thicknesses

Thickness of steel, in.	Total quantity of parts to be drawn: 1,000	10,000	100,000	1,000,000
0.015	Alloy cast iron(a)	Alloy cast iron(a)	Alloy cast iron(a)	Alloy cast iron(b), O1, A2
0.031	Alloy cast iron(a)	Alloy cast iron(a)	Alloy cast iron(b)	A2, D2
0.062	Alloy cast iron(a)	Alloy cast iron(b)	Alloy cast iron(b), A2	A2, D2
0.125	Alloy cast iron(b)	Alloy cast iron(b)	A2, D2	D2
0.250	A2	A2	D2	D2
0.500	A2	A2	D2	D2

(a) Flame hardening is not necessary.
(b) Wearing surfaces are flame hardened.

Tool steels are inserted into flame-hardened alloy cast iron. In drawing the 0.500-in. plate with A2 or D2 inserts, press speed would be slower than for the thinner stock and the plate would be phosphate coated.

Table 6. Recommended Materials for Punch and Blankholder Pressure Pad or Sleeve for Drawing and Ironing Round Steel Cups Like Parts 2, 4 and 5

Die component	Total quantity of parts to be drawn: 10,000	100,000	1,000,000
Part 2			
Punch(a)	4140 carburized, W1	W1, S1 carburized	A2, D2
Blankholder pressure pad or sleeve	W1, O1	W1, O1	W1, O1
Parts 4 and 5			
Punch(a)	Alloy cast iron(b)	O1(c)	A2(b), D2(b)
Blankholder pressure pad or sleeve	Alloy cast iron(b)	Alloy cast iron(d)	O1, A2

(a) Chromium plating is optional on these punches, to reduce friction between the part and the punch for removal of the part. Cast iron, however, should not be plated. (b) Flame hardening not necessary. (c) Punch holder is flame-hardened alloy cast iron with a nose insert of the indicated tool steel. (d) For part 4, blankholder is quenched and tempered; for part 5, it is flame hardened.

Table 7. Recommended Materials for Punch and Blankholder Pressure Pad or Sleeve for Drawing and Ironing Square Steel Cups Like Parts 3, 6 and 7

Die component	Total quantity of parts to be drawn: 10,000	100,000	1,000,000
Part 3			
Punch(a)	4140 carburized, W1	W1, S1 carburized	A2, D2
Blankholder pressure pad or sleeve	W1, O1	W1, O1	W1, O1
Parts 6 and 7			
Punch(a)	4140 carburized(b)	W1, O1(c)	Nitrided A2, D2(c)
Blankholder pressure pad or sleeve	Alloy cast iron(d)	W1, O1	O1, A2

(a) Chromium plating is optional on these punches, to reduce friction between the part and the punch for removal of the part. (b) The punch holder is alloy cast iron with a nose insert of 4140 carburized steel. (c) The punch holder is flame-hardened alloy cast iron with a nose insert of the indicated tool steel. (d) Flame hardening is unnecessary.

the sequence that makes the part, provided no reduction is greater than 35%.

Punches, except those of cast iron, can be chromium plated to facilitate removal of the part. As indicated in the table, large punches to produce more than 10,000 parts have a nose insert of tool steel.

Punch steel selection depends on the size of punch and the drawing pressure required to make the cup. Increases in sheet thickness produce a disproportionate increase in drawing pressure for a specific punch diameter. As the resulting punch pressure increases from low to maximum values, the selection of punch material for short runs changes in the following order: alloy cast iron, 4140, W1, W2, O1, and carburized S1. For long runs, the selection as pressure increases is as follows: W1, W2, O1, S1 (slightly carburized), A2, D2 and M2.

Usually, in drawing without ironing, there is slight metal movement over the punch, which is subjected to relatively little wear regardless of the thickness of the metal drawn. When the piece is ironed while being drawn, the pressure and movement of metal over the punch become considerable, and a tool material of better wear resistance is required.

The selection of a punch material to resist wear is the same regardless of the alloy being drawn. For example, in a cup like part 2, if the last diameter reduction is 35% and if reduction is combined with ironing, the punch material would be the same to make identical quantities, whether the sheet being drawn is aluminum, steel or stainless steel, without a finish requirement. The selection, therefore, would be based on Table 6. Frequently, tool steel ironing punches are chromium plated 0.0002 to 0.0008 in., to facilitate removal of the part from the punch. Plating also improves punch life but usually is less effective than selecting the next better tool steel.

The materials shown in the column headed "10,000" are the lowest in cost that can be recommended for punches where ironing is combined with drawing, even for quantities considerably less than 10,000.

The blankholder pressure pad or sleeve to make part 2 is subject to little wear, as indicated by the recommendation of W1 or O1 as the tool material for 1,000,000 parts in Table 6. In fact, unhardened mild steel may be used for making 10,000 such parts whenever galling on the inside of the part is not objectionable. Table 7 is a continuation of Table 6, showing recommended materials for drawing square cups.

Inserts are not used in blankholder pressure pads except possibly on the first operation for square parts, or for maintaining finish inside the cup.

Pressure sleeves (also called pressure pads) are used where minimum pressure is required close to the punch. The contact area is generally less than for the pressure pads used where greater blank hold-down surface is required. An example would be a pressure pad for part 7 (Table 4) and a pressure sleeve for the operation illustrated in Fig. 4.

Materials recommended for either pad or sleeve depend on the size of the blank and the number of parts to be drawn. As the blank size increases or the number of parts decreases, softer and less expensive materials are used.

Holding, shrink or backup rings for holding the pressed-in draw-ring insert, usually about three times the radial width of the draw ring, are made of heat treated medium-carbon steel and, for assembly, are heated to about 1000 F to obtain expansion and to allow pressing-in of the inserts.

Draw beads, frequently needed to control the flow of metal in irregular drawn shapes, are made of a material the same or nearly the same as the draw die. Beads applied by rivets or other fasteners are made of hardened W1 bead stock for medium-size dies or of hardened W2 bead stock for large dies. Inserted locking beads are usually made of hardened W1 or W2.

Ironing Tools

Table 8 shows the effect of various sidewall reductions on the selection of punches and dies for ironing. Blank-holder pressure-pad material is independent of ironing reduction and can be selected from Tables 6 and 7. Cast iron is not used for ironing punches, because it sinks and breaks. Sidewall reduction is measured at the top, at a point where the drawn cup is to be trimmed to a specific length.

Reverse-Redrawing Tools

Occasionally, specifications for redrawn shells may require a wrinkle-free sidewall of uniform thickness, or may require a section in the bottom of the cup to be sharply raised and formed in two operations. Such operations are difficult, impossible or uneconomical in conventional single-action drawing but are easy in reverse drawing. Figure 2 shows tooling for reverse redrawing of thin-wall shells.

Table 9 recommends punch and die materials for the reverse redrawing of steel cups of various sizes and wall thicknesses. Pressure-ring materials may be the same as die materials.

The draw ring to produce quantities of about 100 small, thick-wall parts can be made of 1018, 4140, 8620, 6150 or any similar steel, either soft, or carburized and hardened, provided distortion in heat treating is not a problem. In large parts, where die material cost is an important factor, steels such as 4140 or 6150, when carburized and finely polished, can be expected to make 10,000 parts; any carbon or alloy steel will make 1000 parts when heat treated but only a few hundred when left soft.

To redraw 1000 small, thick-wall parts, recommended punch material is a hardened alloy steel such as 4140 or 6150. For all types of parts, in quantities less than 100, the punch may be made of the same steel, not hardened.

Combined Operations

Combined operations, including a combination of drawing and coining in one operation and a combination of successive or tandem operations called double drawing or double ironing, can increase production by doubling reductions and decreasing the number of operations; however, for combined operations, a larger press is needed.

For instance, in deep cold drawing, a blank of 0.30% carbon steel ½ in. thick and 4 in. in diameter can be cupped with a 35% sidewall reduction in a 250-ton press. A blank of the same structure and composition but with a thickness of 7⁄16 in. and approximate diameter of 3⅞ in., when cupped by the combined process, can be given a 50% coining reduction and an average sidewall reduction of 60% with a press of 1500 tons. The combined deep cold drawing operation saves raw material and time, and produces a more accurate cup that aids in obtaining closer tolerances in a subsequent operation.

Selection of tool steels for combined drawing and coining with reductions over 40% has little or no relation to the quantity to be produced, up to 500,000 pieces. The minimum steel to be used for both punches and dies is undecarburized D2. However, D2 should not be used for long, small-diameter punches because misalignment or accidents may cause shattering. Instead, such punches should be made of honed, slightly carburized, chromium-plated S1. A reduction in punch life should be expected in such applications.

Sidewall reductions of 60% or more, combined with quantities of 500,000 to 1,000,000 pieces, require carbide draw rings with a 0.010-in. shrink fit into the backup ring. Several S1 tool steel punches will be required to produce these larger quantities.

Double-drawing or double-ironing operations are successive operations in one tooling setup, with two dies placed in tandem so that a punch forces the cup through one die and then directly through the second die while the cup is still hot. Punches are longer, and because of their slenderness, S1 tool steel is preferred. Die materials are much the same as in single operations, except that when temperatures are high in the second operation, selection is confined to tool steels such as A2 and D2. These more temper-resistant steels can better withstand the higher temperatures.

Table 8. Recommended Steels for Punches and Dies to Iron Various Reductions of Steel Sheet up to Rockwell B 75, or Softer Metals

Ironing reduction, %	Total quantity of shells to be ironed: 1,000	10,000	100,000	1,000,000
Ironing Punches(a)				
Up to 25	W1	O1	A2	A2, S1 carburized
25 to 35	W1	A2	A2, S1 carburized	D2
35 to 50	A2	A2, S1 carburized	D2	D2
Over 50	D2	D2	D2	D2
Ironing Dies				
Up to 25	W1(b)	O1	O1	D2
25 to 35(c)	W1(b)	O1	D2	D2
35 to 50(c)	O1	D2	D2	D2
Over 50(c)	D2	D2	D2	D2

(a) All tool steel punches should be chromium plated 0.0002 to 0.0004 in., for easier removal of the part from the punch. (b) W1 is quenched on the inside and tempered to Rockwell C 60 min for these applications. (c) Draw rings must be inserted in shrink rings to iron reductions greater than 25% and for quantities of more than 10,000.

Table 9. Recommended Punch and Die Materials for Reverse Redrawing Steel Cups of Various Sizes and Wall Thicknesses

(For parts having no specific finish or tolerance requirements)

Die component	Total quantity of parts to be redrawn: 1,000	10,000	100,000	1,000,000
Small Thick-Wall Cups				
Die and pressure ring	O1	O1(a)	A2(b)	D2(b)
Punch(c)	4140, 6150	O1, A2	D2	D3
Medium and Large Thin-Wall Cups				
Die and pressure ring	1018(d), 4140	4140(e), O1	A2(b)	D2(b)
Punch(c)	W1	A2	D2	D2, D3

(a) The die is polished and chromium plated. (b) A2 and D2 should be nitrided. (c) All punches to make more than 1000 pieces should be heat treated to Rockwell C 60 to 62, polished and chromium plated. (d) Carburized, hardened, and polished to a fine finish. (e) 4140 or 6150 may be used when carburized and highly polished.

Table 10. Classification of Sheet Metals That Require Similar Drawing Die Materials

Sheet metals listed in Tables 1 to 9	Maximum hardness	Metals that require similar drawing die materials
Drawing-quality aluminum and copper alloys	58 Bhn (500 kg) Rockwell F 61 Rockwell 30-T 28	All aluminum and clad aluminum alloy sheet, copper and alloys, zinc and alloys, silver, pewter and Monel
Drawing-quality steel	Rockwell B 70	1008 to 1020
	Rockwell B 75	1021 to 1030
Stainless steel	Rockwell B 95	301, 302, 304, 305, 308, 310, 316, 317, 410 and 430; PH stainless steels; carbon steels clad with stainless steel; copper clad with stainless steel

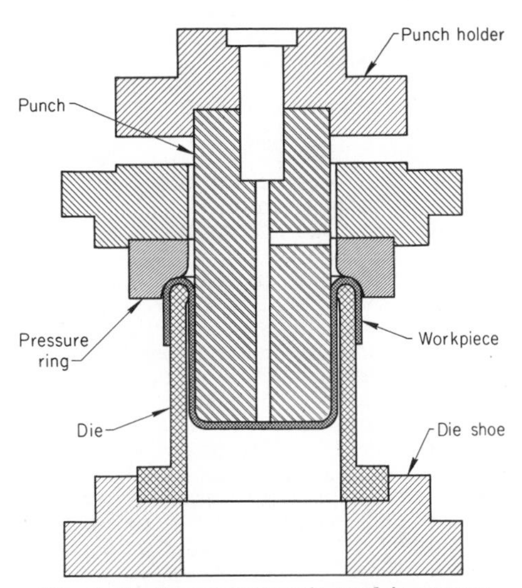

Fig. 2. Tooling components used in reverse redrawing of thin-wall shells

Work-Metal Classification

Table 10 classifies various sheet metals into groups requiring the same die materials for equivalent tooling circumstances. Although aluminum and copper are listed separately from steel in Table 10, nonferrous alloys to quarter hard or even half hard cause almost as much die wear as drawing-quality steel, as shown in the various selection tables. Ferritic stainless steels are similar to carbon and alloy steels of the same hardness in rate of wear of dies.

Tool Life

The example that follows shows differences in life of punches and dies made of various tool and constructional steels. The effect of chromium plating of punches is evident from Table 11.

Example 268. Punch and Die Life in Drawing Cups From 1020 Steel (Table 11)

A comparison of nine tool materials for producing cups 1⁵⁄₁₆ in. wide by 2⅝ in. deep from hot rolled and annealed 1020 steel are shown in Table 11. The blank was at a hardness of Rockwell B 65 to 70 before drawing. Lubricant was zinc phosphate and soap. Reductions were 40% of the wall and 7% of the diameter at 20 strokes per minute in a 100-ton mechanical press with a 10-in. stroke.

The life, or end point, of the punch or die was taken as the production quantity where the tool no longer was capable of maintaining dimensional tolerances of ±0.003 in. for the 0.062 and 1⁵⁄₁₆-in. dimensions and ±0.015 in. for the 2⅝-in. dimension.

Table 11. Service Life of Nine Tool Materials in Drawing a Steel Cup (Example 268)

Punch and die material	Service life, pieces — Punches — Honed and not plated	Honed and chromium plated(a)	Dies smoothly polished
1040(b)	34,000	42,000	....
2340(b)	45,000	55,000	....
W2	46,000	59,000	52,000
3140(b)	50,000	66,000	....
4140(b)	62,000	87,000	....
O1	67,000	79,000	78,000
O6	68,000	....	78,000
A2	83,000	104,000	82,000
D5	107,000	125,000	87,000

(a) Chromium plate was 0.0002 to 0.0005 in. thick. (b) Punch material with carburized case of 0.010 in. min after grinding.

Production Quantity

The runs shown in the selection tables should be achieved with one set of dies under the conditions outlined in this article. For small dies, in which material cost is a small percentage of total cost, whenever the quantities are likely to be increased above the original order, overspecification of die material is justified, or a nitridable tool steel, such as A2 or D2, should be selected.

Large dies that cannot be removed from the production line obviously must be made of material certain to last for the required production period, as given in the selection tables. In drawing rectangular shells such as part 6, there is considerable crowding of the sheet in the corners, with a moderate probability that wrinkles will form there, and greatly increased die wear is possible. Where inserts are used and the dies may be shimmed to allow for wear, risks may be taken in selecting tool material. However, if the insert is small, the cost of material may be inconsequential, compared with the cost of diemaking and shimming, which may run from $10 to $100 per hour for lost time of the press, plus labor. Thus, it is usually uneconomical to underspecify the steel for inserts.

Short-Run Tooling

Where a cup is to be ironed, selection of draw-ring material for production quantities of 10,000 pieces is the same as for quantities smaller than 10,000 pieces. Lower-cost die materials can be recommended only in a few instances where less than 10,000 pieces of small parts are to be drawn and ironed. For production quantities of 1000 of parts 1 and 2, any carburized steel will make the run, but with a lower-quality finish. However, the difference in tooling cost compared with W1 is insignificant, and distortion in heat treating the carburized steel would be expected to exceed that of W1.

If 1000 pieces were to be run of parts 4 and 5 made of aluminum or copper alloy or carbon steel, a draw-ring material of cast iron, either alloyed or unalloyed, with a hardness of 200 to 250 Bhn would be recommended. Dies made of flame-hardened alloy cast iron without corner inserts will satisfactorily produce 1000 of parts 6 and 7 made of carbon steel or aluminum.

When low production quantities of 10 to 100 cups such as parts 4 and 5 are to be made without finish requirements and without ironing, the selection of tooling material is not critical. The draw ring may be made of either hardenable or unhardenable steel. If the die is not designed to iron the cup, plastic, masonite and zinc alloys are used to produce up to 1000 cups like those shown in Fig. 3 from thin sheets of easily drawn alloys. Such materials are especially well adapted to fast tooling-up, particularly when the user can make his own dies.

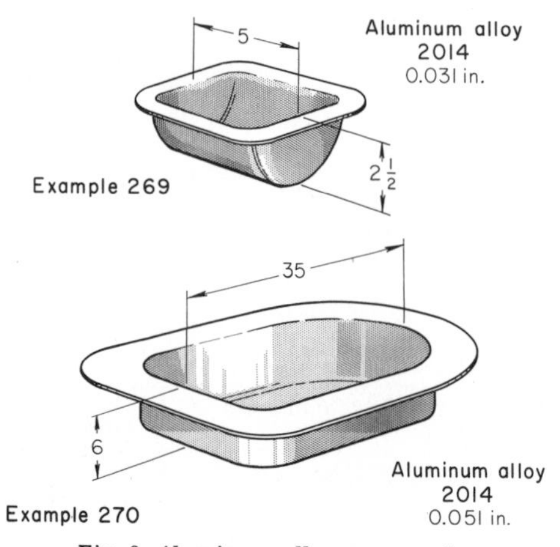

Fig. 3. Aluminum alloy pans made on low-production tooling (Examples 269 and 270)

Examples 269 and 270. Tooling for Low-Production Drawing of Aluminum Pans

Example 269 — 5-by-4-by-2½-In. Pan (Fig. 3). Masonite and plastic tooling were used to produce 1000 parts from 0.031-in.-thick 2014 aluminum alloy sheet, without reworking the tools. The 5-by-4-in. parts were drawn 2½ in. deep over a ³⁄₁₆-in. radius, using a masonite punch with a 1-in. nose radius, a masonite blankholder pressure pad, and a phenolic die held in a masonite backup.

Example 270 — 35-by-25-by-6-In. Pan (Fig. 3.) The lower pan in Fig. 3 was drawn on a double-action press from 2014 aluminum alloy sheet, 0.051 in. thick. Five hundred pieces were made with tooling consisting of a punch nose insert of epoxy resin impregnated with fiber glass, with ½-in. punch nose radius, and a zinc alloy punch holder. The die was cast phenolic resin, and the blankholder pressure pad was cast iron. The punch nose insert was reworked once to run the 500 parts.

Galling

Common causes of galling are: attempting to stretch sheet metal beyond practical limits, poor tool fitting with poor alignment or insufficient die clearance for the sheet thickness, wrinkles, the use of galling-susceptible tool steel without improving the lubricants, and rough finish on the surface of tools. For short runs, carburized hot rolled steel or hardened alloy steel dies will, in many instances, produce parts equal to those made from most tool steel dies. Exceptions may be encountered in severe reductions or in drawing metals that show a greater tendency to gall, such as austenitic stainless steel. However, tool steel dies also may gall under these conditions. The longest life can be expected if die surfaces are finished to the least roughness, with final surface scratches parallel to the direction of drawing.

Die materials to resist galling can be selected on the following basis: For parts drawn of carbon steel or nonferrous alloy sheet, the die material can be selected without regard to galling and then, as a finishing operation, the punch and die should be either nitrided or chromium plated. If tool steels such as A2, D2, D3 or D4, which contain chromium and molybdenum, have been selected, the smoothly ground tools should be nitrided, and polished or buffed after nitriding. Otherwise, the tools should be hardened to at least Rockwell C 60, smoothly finished on the wearing surfaces, hard chromium plated, and the plating polished or buffed. Punches should receive 0.0002 to 0.0004 in. of hard chromium plate. However, to prevent spalling and flaking, dies should receive a plate that is no more than 0.0002 in. thick.

When the parts are drawn from stainless steel or from high-nickel alloy steel, the draw-ring material with best resistance to galling is aluminum bronze. The second choice is D2, D3 or D4, smoothly ground, nitrided and polished. The third choice is alloy cast iron, quenched and tempered to 400 to 420 Bhn. Punch material is selected without regard to galling and is then chromium plated, unless it is a cast iron.

Sintered carbide, which is only as efficient as the lubricants used, has proved economical for nonferrous alloys, carbon steel, and stainless steel in many long, continuous runs, but galling will occur if lubrication is faulty.

Lubrication

Correct lubrication of the parts being drawn is essential to reduce friction, wear and galling. In fact, deep drawing is impossible without lubrication. In actual practice, die materials are selected after trials employing the production lubricants. If excessive wear or galling occurs, a better lubricant is usually applied. For extremely difficult draws, the best lubricants are usually applied at the outset.

Tool material recommendations given in Tables 1 to 9 are predicated on the concurrent selection of suitable lubricants. Recommendations for lubricants, based on severity of deformation, are presented in the article on Selection and Use of Lubricants, which begins on page 23 in this volume. A tin coating on sheet steel acts as a lubricant in drawing and ironing. The effect of such a coating on drawability and ironability is described on pages 144 and 145.

Chromium Plating

Chromium plating is used on tool steel draw rings to improve life. On punches, its primary function is to reduce the frictional forces and facilitate removal of the parts from the punch after the sidewalls have been ironed tight to the punch. Chromium plating usually improves punch life somewhat less than would selection of the next better tool steel.

For successful performance of tools, chromium plate must always be deposited on a surface harder than Rockwell C 50, and the thickness of the coating should preferably be 0.0002 to 0.0004 in., and never less than 0.0001 in. This gives the required hardness and reduction of friction without excessive spalling or chipping at corners. Chromium-plated tools should be heated to 300 to 400 F for a minimum of 3 hr immediately after plating to minimize the possibility of hydrogen embrittlement.

Tool Steels

Table 12 lists the nominal chemical compositions of the die materials recommended in the selection tables.

W1 water-hardening tool steel has the advantage of low cost and good machinability. Wear resistance is fair to good, increasing with carbon content. W1 is usually limited to dies having balanced sections that are least likely to distort or crack during quenching. The success of the water-hardening grade W1 recommended in the tables for draw rings is attributed to hole hardening or inside-diameter hardening in a brine quench, followed by shrink fitting into heated (1000 F) medium-carbon steel backup rings approximately three times the width of the draw ring. When through hardened instead of hole hardened, W1 may fail by cracking after a short service life. Rockwell C 60 to 62 is the usual working hardness for W1 punches and dies.

W2 can be used where shallow hardening and an increase in toughness are desirable. W6 can be used where deeper hardening is required.

O1 oil-hardening tool steel costs almost twice as much as the lowest-cost water-hardening grade but only a little more than the most expensive grades. However, with oil-hardening steels, distortion from heat treatment is much less. Wear resistance is slightly better than for the water-hardening grades, and machinability is good to fair.

Among the oil-hardening grades, O1 is the most readily available in almost

Table 12. Nominal Chemical Compositions of Tool Materials Recommended in Tables 1 to 9

Material	Compositions
Tool Steels	
W1	0.95 to 1.10 C
O1	0.90 C, 1.00 Mn, 0.50 Cr, 0.50 W
A2	1.00 C, 5.00 Cr, 1.00 Mo
S1	0.50 C, 1.50 Cr, 2.50 W
D2	1.50 C, 12.00 Cr, 1.00 Mo
D3	2.25 C, 12.00 Cr
Other Ferrous Alloys	
Alloy cast iron	3.0 total C, 0.7 combined C, 1.6 Si, 0.4 Cr, 0.4 Mo (or equivalent)
4140	0.40 C, 0.85 Mn, 0.30 Si, 1 Cr, 0.20 Mo
6150	0.50 C, 0.80 Mn, 0.30 Si, 0.95 Cr, 0.20 V
Nonferrous Alloy and Sintered Carbide	
Aluminum bronze	10-12 Al, 3-4 Fe, rem Cu
Sintered carbide(a)	5.6 C, 85.4 W, 9.0 Co

(a) The sintered carbide referred to has a hardness of Rockwell A 90, a density of 14.60 g per cu cm, and a grain size of 1 micron.

every warehousing district in the United States. Where it is available, O2 is equivalent to O1, and the graphitic tool steel O6 has greater wear resistance than O1. For deep drawing applications, O1 is commonly hardened to Rockwell C 57 to 62.

A2 air-hardening tool steel is only slightly more costly than the oil-hardening grades O1, O2 and O6, but it is more difficult to machine. Its advantages include the best nondeforming properties and much greater resistance to wear and galling than O1. It can be nitrided to greatly improve resistance to wear and galling. A2 is machined more easily than D2; both steels can be obtained as castings, as well as in wrought form. Punches made from A2 are usually hardened to Rockwell C 58 to 60, and dies are hardened to Rockwell C 60 to 62.

D2 high-carbon high-chromium air-hardening tool steel is the most readily available of its type. D3 is at least equal to D2 in resistance to wear and galling, especially for drawing stainless steel; however, it distorts more in hardening. D4 and D5 are equal to, or better than, D2 and D3 in wear resistance and may have longer life in drawing cups like part 2 from sheet steel ⅛ in. or more thick. Resistance to wear and galling is greatly improved by nitriding. Long slender punches made of the D steels may fail by shattering. The recommended hardness of D2 and other D steels for both punches and dies is Rockwell C 57 to 59.

S1 shock-resisting steel, often used where susceptibility to breakage of punches is high, does not wear well unless the surface is slightly carburized during heat treatment, to obtain 0.70 to 0.75% carbon to a depth of 0.010 to 0.020 in. S2 is tougher, less costly, and less wear resistant than S1. S1 at Rockwell C 53 to 58 has excellent resistance to breaking under high compressive loads when used as long slender punches for either short or medium runs, except where much heat is generated.

Standard Alloy Steels

Alloy steel 4140 is suitable for short runs, and die life can be prolonged by carburizing or other surface-hardening treatments. Steels of this type are seldom selected for long production runs. Other alloy steels that will give comparable results are 6150 and 8640. For small dies, material costs are a small part of the total cost. Therefore, a tool steel punch and die is usually justified even for short runs, especially when future production requirements have not been established.

Alloy Cast Iron

One of the commonly used die materials for large deep drawing dies is alloy cast iron. In designing dies for parts 8 in. in diameter or larger, alloy cast iron should be considered as a die material.

If properly made, alloy iron has reasonably good wear resistance in the as-cast condition and can be used for short to moderate runs, depending on the severity of the draw. If it is of the proper composition and microstructure, it will respond to flame hardening, and this will increase its wear resistance. For long runs and heavy pressures, it becomes necessary to use hardened tool steel inserts at wear areas in the die sections. The hardened tool steel inserts must be large enough to cover the entire area of heavy wear; otherwise, because of the different rates of wear of the insert and die materials, a difference in tool dimension will develop where they meet, resulting in broken parts or unsatisfactory shapes.

Alloy cast iron flame hardened to the maximum value (above Rockwell C 50) is not recommended for dies used for stainless steel, because of the high probability of galling. Unhardened cast iron is compatible with stainless steel but wears rapidly so that it is unsuitable for long runs. Alloy iron heat treated to about 400 Bhn will give longer die life without the high probability of galling when drawing stainless steel. This hardness level can be obtained by oil quenching the dies from between 1500 and 1600 F and then tempering them at 600 F.

In selecting an alloy cast iron for deep drawing dies, the two most important properties required are a suitable microstructure and sufficient hardenability; composition is secondary, provided these two requirements are met. Good foundry practice is imperative in obtaining these properties.

A typical composition of a cast iron suitable for die sections 3 to 12 in. thick is as follows:

Total carbon	2.80 to 3.50%
Combined carbon	0.60 min
Manganese	0.60 to 0.90
Phosphorus	0.12 max
Sulfur	0.12 max
Silicon	1.50 to 2.25
Molybdenum	0.35 to 0.50
Chromium	0.35 to 0.50

The silicon content should be adjusted to produce the hardness specified.

Although the composition given above has been found suitable for die sections, it is not the only satisfactory iron (Table 12). Other compositions that will produce the properties listed below are equally satisfactory:

Hardness (after stress relieving at 1000 F): 207 to 255 Bhn
Microstructure: Predominantly fine pearlite; minimum ferrite; no massive carbides
Preferred graphite flake size (AFS-ASTM): 3 to 5
Graphite distribution: Type A

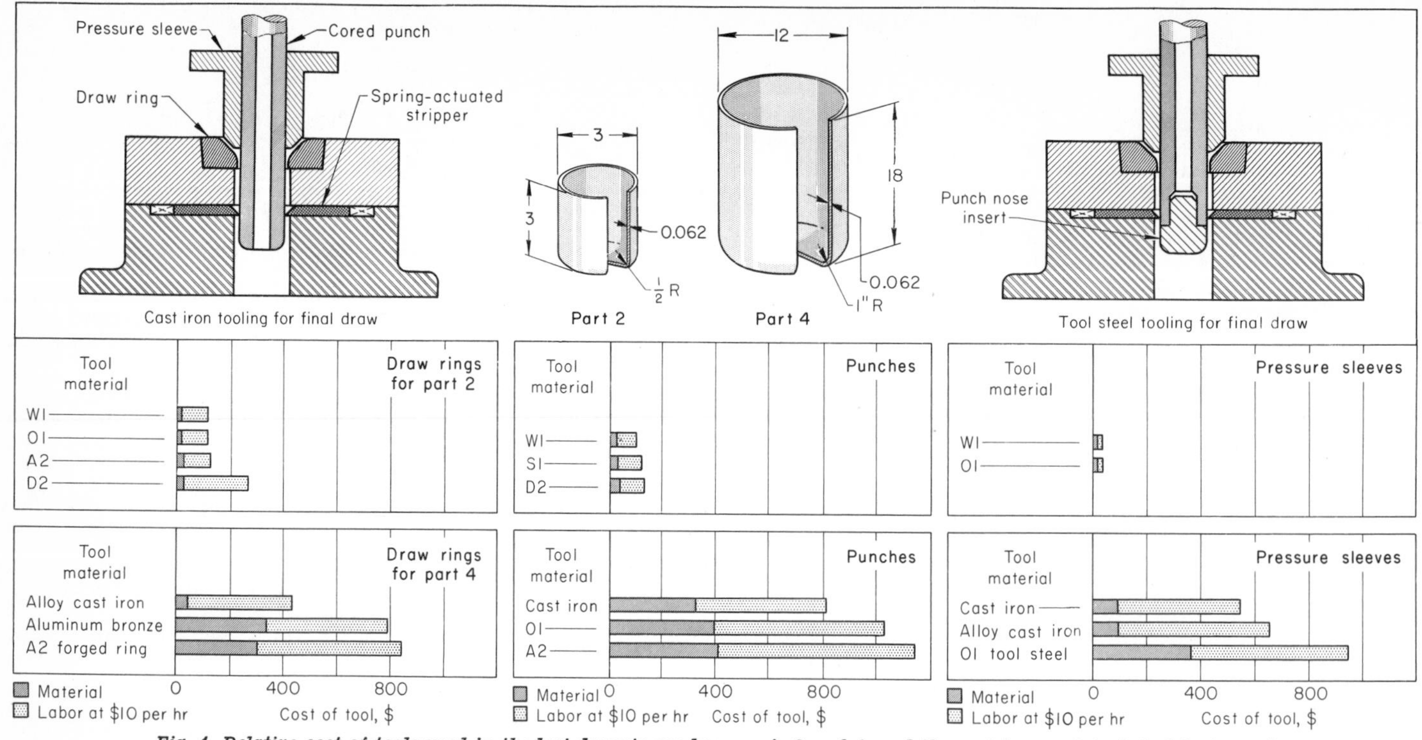

Fig. 4. Relative cost of tools used in the last draw to produce parts 2 and 4, and the cast iron and tool steel tools used

Hardness after hardening: Rockwell C 50, minimum. (A test coupon 3 by 3 by 6 in. is cast with the die. One 6-in. and one 3-in. side at right angles to each other are machined to remove 0.250 in. of metal. These sides are flame heated above the transformation temperature, and air cooled.)

Aluminum Bronze

Aluminum bronzes are available in a wide range of hardness from 120 to 340 Bhn. These alloys have excellent resistance to galling and are recommended for dies where best finish is mandatory on carbon steel and stainless steel parts, and sometimes to avoid iron pickup on the surface of stainless steel parts, which might later give the parts a rusty appearance. The softer grades (120 to 270 Bhn) wear rapidly, particularly where wrinkling is likely to occur. The harder grades (270 to 340 Bhn) wear less rapidly but are difficult to mill, drill and tap. Where elimination of scratches on the part is extremely important, aluminum bronzes should be considered, but for medium to high production (10,000 to 100,000 parts), replacement inserts should be available to permit reconditioning of worn tools.

Sintered Carbide

For long runs, inserts of sintered carbide are widely used in deep drawing dies. In dies of about 8 in. or less for continuous production of over 1,000,000 pieces, carbide has in many instances proved to be the most economical die material. Such dies have maintained size in drawing 60% reductions of more than 500,000 pieces and have made as many as 1,000,000 parts with reductions greater than 40% when the steel to be drawn was surface treated with zinc phosphate and soap. However, carbide is not superior to tool steels such as D2 in complex deep drawing operations, such as those with reductions greater than 40% in which drawing is combined with coining operations.

Plastics

Even more than with other tooling materials, the quality and economy of plastic tooling improves with shop experience and volume. Polyester, epoxy, phenolic resin, and nylon are used.

The plastic dies of longest life are constructed so that the wearing surface is faced with glass cloth that has had most of the plastic material forced out under pressure before and during curing. Plastics are most economical when a model is available as a pattern for the lay-up of the plastic-impregnated glass-cloth facing, which is backed up with chopped glass fibers impregnated with 50% resin.

Except for very short runs, plastics should not be selected for blankholder material where burred edges of the blank slide over the plastic surface. Such areas will wear severely on plastic dies. Examples 269 and 270 in this article illustrate the use of plastic tooling for short-run production.

Zinc Alloy

Zinc alloy is economical only for die components 12 in. or more in size, and it is most economical in dies for short-run quantities of cups such as parts 4 and 5. In tensile strength, compressive strength and hardness, zinc tool alloys are inferior to other metals used in die construction. For this reason, dies that both draw and iron the part should not be made of zinc.

Zinc alloy tools have application only in drawing small quantities of thin-wall parts where no wrinkling is likely to occur during the drawing cycle, and where lubricated stock only is being drawn. For additional information on cost and processing with zinc alloy dies, see pages 151 and 152 in the article on Material for Press Forming Dies.

Cost of Tooling

Figure 4 gives the cost of tools to make parts 2 and 4; the tooling also is illustrated in Fig. 4. The costs are computed for a single set of tools, excluding overhead charges, profit allowance, tool design, die tryout, and development, none of which influence relative tooling cost. Costs are given for a flame-hardened alloy cast iron draw ring. An unhardened ring would cost $60 less and would not be recommended for making more than 1000 parts.

Dies requiring section sizes of 8 in. or larger are most economically made as castings with inserts, because rolled sections of this size are not available. Therefore, dies 8 in. and larger require patterns and castings for the holding or backup ring and, if the draw-ring insert is cast rather than forged, also require a pattern for the insert. Figure 4 includes the cost of backup-ring casting but not the pattern cost. Insert costs are for forged rings.

The costs given in Fig. 4 are for die components used in the final draw of parts 2 and 4, which requires the smallest die of the three operations to make this part. Dies for prior operations would be larger and more costly. For example, the flame-hardened alloy cast iron draw ring for part 4 costs $422 for the final (third) operation and $476 for the first operation. Moreover, a flame-hardened alloy cast iron pressure sleeve costs $660 for the third operation, and the pressure pad for the first operation costs $1000, using the same material.

Analysis of Fig. 4 with respect to cost of large and small dies shows that material cost in small dies is a minor percentage of die cost. In large dies, however, material cost rises appreciably and may approach half the total cost.

Spinning

*By the ASM Committee on Spinning**

SPINNING is a method of forming sheet metal or tubing into seamless hollow cylinders, cones, hemispheres or other circular shapes by a combination of rotation and force. On the basis of techniques used, applications, and results obtainable, the method may be divided into two categories: manual spinning (with or without mechanical assistance to increase the force) and power spinning. This article describes spinning of sheet; spinning of tube is dealt with in the article beginning on page 317.

Manual spinning entails no appreciable thinning of metal. The operation, ordinarily done in a lathe, consists of pressing a tool against a circular metal blank that is rotated by the headstock. The blank is ordinarily forced over a mandrel of pre-established shape, but simple shapes can be spun without a mandrel. By using various mechanical devices for applying force, the range of applications for manual spinning is broadened, because thicker blanks can be spun than by manual force alone.

Power spinning is also known as shear spinning, because in this method metal is intentionally thinned, by shear forces. In power spinning, forces as great as 400 tons are used.

Power spinning is used for two broad fields of application: cone spinning and tube spinning. In cone spinning, the deformation or displacement of the metal from the flat blank into the spun shape conforms to the sine law (see page 203). In tube spinning, the sine law does not apply, and metal displacement follows a purely volumetric rule.

Manual Spinning

Any metal ductile enough to be cold formed by other methods can be spun. Most spinning is done without applying heat to the work metal, although sometimes the metal is preheated to achieve one of two objectives: (*a*) to increase the ductility of hard-to-form metals such as beryllium, refractory metals, or magnesium; or (*b*) to reduce the strength of work metals, thus permitting greater thicknesses to be spun.

Applicability. Manual spinning is used for forming flanges, rolled rims, cups, cones and double-curved surfaces of revolution such as bells. Several typical shapes formed by manual spinning are shown in Fig. 1. Products regularly produced by manual spinning include light reflectors, tank ends, covers, housings, shields, and components for musical instruments. Manual spinning is also extensively used for the production of aircraft and aerospace components, often with mechanical assistance for increased force, because of large blank size (see Example 274, which describes hot spinning of an alloy steel blank into a hemisphere in three stages).

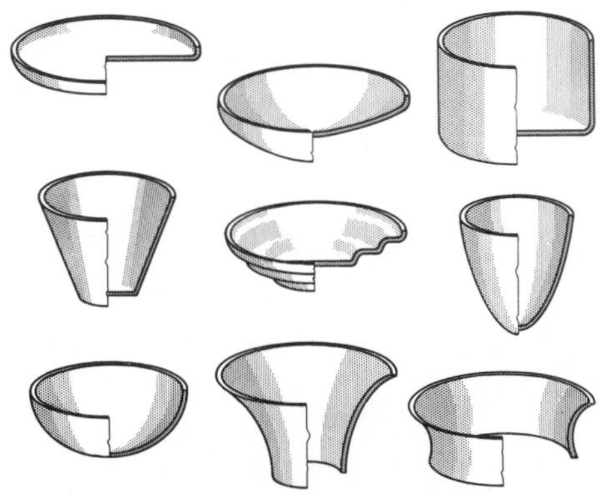

Fig. 1. Typical conical, cylindrical and dome shapes formed by manual spinning

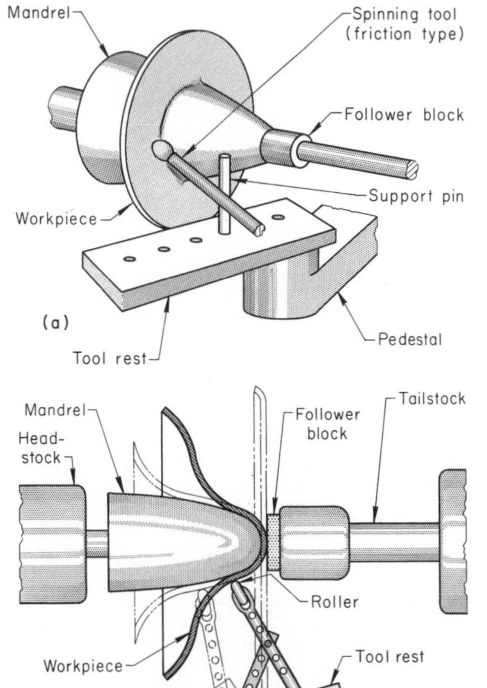

(a) Setup using a simple hand tool, applied like a pry bar. (b) Setup using scissorlike levers and a roller spinning tool.

Fig. 2. Manual spinning in a lathe

The practical maximum thickness of low-carbon steel that can be spun without mechanical assistance is ⅛ in. In this thickness, the diameter can be as great as 72 in. Diameters can be greater when the sheet steel is thinner, but the maximum practical diameter is often limited by the availability of equipment. The upper limit of thickness increases as work-metal ductility increases or strength decreases. For instance, manual spinning of aluminum as thick as ¼ in. is feasible.

Advantages and Disadvantages. Manual spinning has the following advantages over a competitive process such as press forming: (*a*) tooling costs less, and investment in capital equipment is relatively small; (*b*) setup time is shorter; (*c*) design changes in the workpiece can be made at minimum expense; and (*d*) changes in work-metal composition or thickness require a minimum of tool changes.

Disadvantages of manual spinning include the following: (*a*) skilled operators are required, because uniformity of results depends greatly on operator skill; (*b*) manual spinning is usually slower than press forming; and (*c*) available force is more likely to be inadequate in manual spinning than in press forming. The last disadvantage is overcome to some extent by the use of mechanical assistance for increasing force in manual spinning.

Equipment for Manual Spinning

A typical tool and workpiece setup for manual spinning is shown in Fig. 2(a). The mandrel is mounted on the headstock of a lathe. The circular blank (workpiece) is clamped to the mandrel by the follower block. An antifriction center is used between the follower and the tailstock spindle, and pressure is applied at the tailstock by

*M. Eugene Merchant, *Chairman,* Director of Scientific Research, Cincinnati Milling Machine Co.; F. L. Banta, Engineering Specialist – Materials and Fabrication, Propulsion Div., Aerojet-General Corp.; Othmar C. Besch, Manufacturing Research Engineer, Research Laboratories, Lockheed Missiles & Space Co.

Richard M. Cogan, Senior Engineer, Metalworking Research, Thomson Engineering Laboratory, General Electric Co.; Frank J. Covelli, Manager – Pressed Steel Engineering, Commercial Shearing & Stamping Co.; Joseph Fekete, Process Engineer Group Leader, Lycoming Div., Avco Corp.; Serope Kalpakjian, Associate Professor, Department of Mechanical and Aerospace Engineering, Illinois Institute of Technology; J. D. Stewart, Product Line Manager, Standard Pressed Steel Co.

George A. Storch, Engineering Supervisor, Forming Div., Cincinnati Milling and Grinding Machines, Inc.; E. G. Thomsen, Professor of Metal Processing, Department of Industrial Engineering, College of Engineering, University of California; G. L. Vonnegut, Section Chief, Materials Laboratories, Allison Div., General Motors Corp.; William A. Wenman, Vice President, Metal Spinning Div., Phoenix Products Co., Inc.

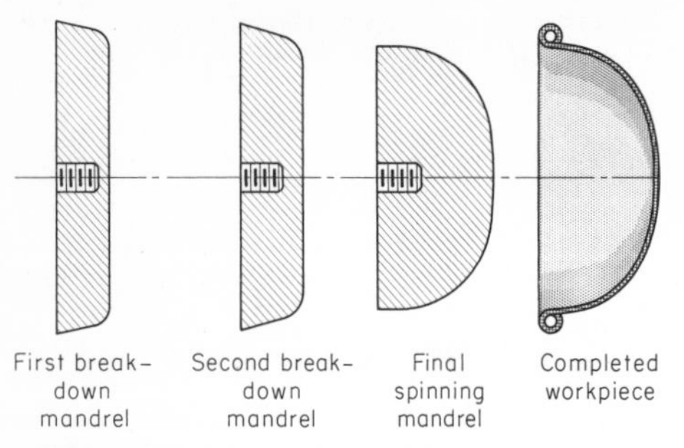

Fig. 3. Breakdown and final mandrels used in three-stage manual spinning of a cup

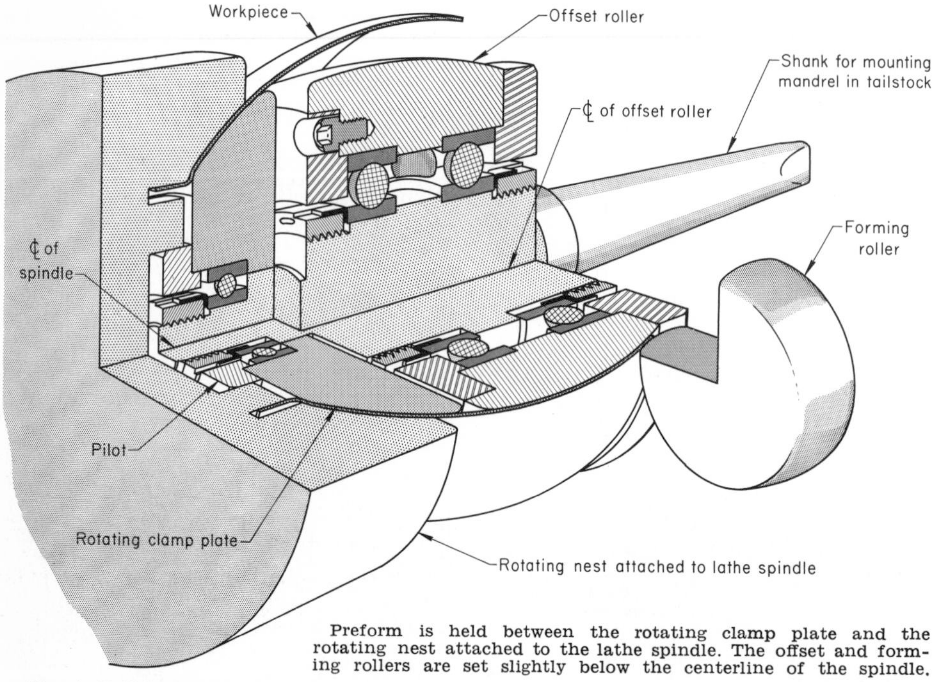

Preform is held between the rotating clamp plate and the rotating nest attached to the lathe spindle. The offset and forming rollers are set slightly below the centerline of the spindle.

Fig. 4. Tailstock-mounted mandrel with offset roller used for spinning of re-entrant shapes

means of a screw, or by air or hydraulic pressure, depending on the size and type of lathe. The tool rest and pedestal permit the support pin (fulcrum) to be moved to various positions by swinging the tool rest and moving the support pin from one hole to another as needed. Spinning is done by manually applying the friction-type spinning tool like a pry bar.

Figure 2(b) shows a more complex setup for manual spinning. Here, the spinning tools (rollers) are mounted in the fork sections of long levers, and the tool support has a series of holes for rapid changing of tool position. The tool is manipulated by pulling, pushing or pivoting the two scissorlike handles, with the roller against the workpiece.

Lathes. Several sizes of standard horizontal spinning lathes are available that can spin blanks ranging from ¼ in. to 72 in. in diameter. Special pit lathes permit the spinning of blanks as large as 192 in. in diameter. Standard lathes can be fitted with special chucks for making oval parts. Lathes should be equipped with variable-speed drives to permit quick changes of speed as judged necessary by the operator.

Mandrels, also known as form blocks or spin blocks, are usually made of seasoned hard-maple wood. Most hardwood mandrels are constructed by gluing strips of maple 1 to 2 in. thick into the main block to create a cross-laminated structure, and then turning the glued structure to the desired shape. Such mandrels are stronger and more durable than mandrels turned from a solid block. Some wooden mandrels are steel-reinforced at the ends and at small radii to ensure maintenance of radii in the spun workpieces. Sharp corners can be produced in workpieces by spinning them over mandrels cornered with steel, but minimum inside radii of $^{1}/_{16}$ in. are more common than sharp corners, and ⅛-in. minimum radii are preferred where possible.

Some mandrels are made up of alternating wood and steel plates or rings, to obtain a more economical yet durable mandrel. Other materials include fiber compositions, steel, cast iron, aluminum, magnesium, and plastic-coated wood. Few mandrels are made entirely of heavy metals like steel and cast iron, except for close-tolerance work. Cored castings of these metals are then preferred, because of the saving in weight. Solid steel or cast iron mandrels must be statically balanced, and for use at high speed they should also be dynamically balanced.

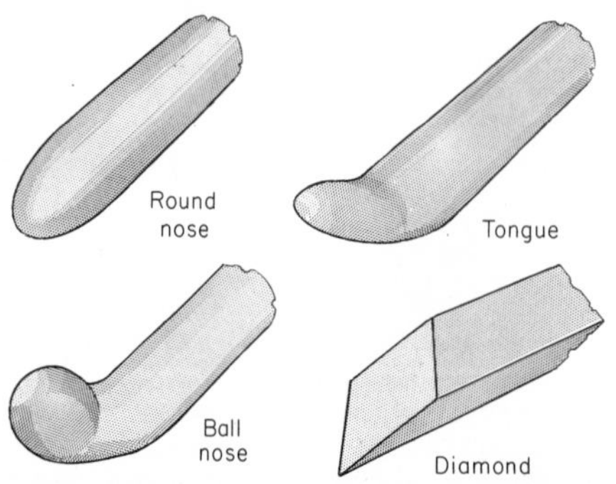

Round-nose, tongue and ball-nose tools are used for spinning; diamond tool, for trimming.

Fig. 5. Typical shapes of working ends of tools used in manual spinning

Mandrels are usually made to the shape of the completed workpiece. When the workpiece is to have a shape more complex than can be spun in one setup, or when it needs intermediate heat treatment, a series of mandrels can be used. Mandrels for earlier stages of the workpiece are called preform or breakdown mandrels (see Fig. 3).

Mandrels can be made collapsible, for use in spinning workpieces that have a turn-in or re-entrant shape smaller than the largest diameter of the workpiece. A collapsible mandrel is an assembly of sections held in place by one key section. When the key section is removed, the mandrel collapses and the remaining sections can be removed from the spun workpiece one at a time.

Another method of spinning workpieces having re-entrant sections is to make the mandrel from a low-melting alloy (some have melting temperatures as low as 117 F). After spinning, the mandrel and workpiece are heated and the mandrel is melted. This method, however, is seldom used except for prototype work.

For production quantities of re-entrant shapes, the use of off-center setups and internal rollers is the most practical approach. Usually, the main shape of the workpiece is preformed by spinning in the conventional manner. To form the re-entrant shape, the mandrel is mounted in the tailstock, and the follower block is mounted on the spindle. The mandrel consists of a rotating clamp plate and an offset roller. A pilot, used to support the end of the mandrel, is fastened to the rotating clamp plate. A nest attached to the spindle serves as a follower block to hold the preformed shell against the clamp plate. The nest also has a recess to receive the mandrel pilot. In operation, the preform is placed on the mandrel, and the tailstock is moved forward to clamp the work in the nest. The preformed shell is then worked down to the offset roller by the forming roller set slightly below the center of the spindle (see Fig. 4).

(Example 598, on page 422, describes the spinning of a workpiece with a re-entrant curve from a drawn shell, using a mandrel that was split radially at the minor diameter.)

Spinning Tools. Simple spinning tools are usually made by forging carbon or low-alloy tool steels (such as W1 or O1) to the desired shape, and then hardening the working ends to about Rockwell C 60 and polishing them. Several typical shapes are illustrated in Fig. 5. Tools of shaped aluminum bronze are also satisfactory, especially for the spinning of steel. Tools made of hardwood have performed satisfactorily in spinning thin-gage ductile metals.

With the lever arrangement (Fig. 2b), the tools usually consist of rollers (sometimes called tool rings) mounted in forks. Most rollers are made of hardened tool steel or of aluminum bronze.

Manual Spinning Practice

Because of the low tooling cost, manual spinning is used extensively for prototypes and for production runs of 1000 pieces or less. Larger lots can usually be produced at lower cost by power spinning or press forming.

For instance, the part in the middle of the second row in Fig. 1 is a stainless steel cover for a food-processing machine, produced in one plant at the rate of 100 per year. The parts were produced satisfactorily by manual spinning, using only two hardwood mandrels, the cost of which was only a fraction of the tooling cost for press forming the same shape.

The relation of quantity and cost for producing a flanged cylinder by manual spinning versus drawing in a press is described in the following example.

Example 271. Cost of Steel Shells: Spinning vs Drawing (Fig. 6)

Figure 6 shows a part that was producible by either spinning or drawing, and plots graphically the per-piece costs, in arbitrary units, for producing various quantities of the part by the two methods. As shown, the breakeven point for the two methods was 700 pieces — spinning being the lower-cost method for quantities of less than 700 pieces, and drawing in a press for larger quantities.

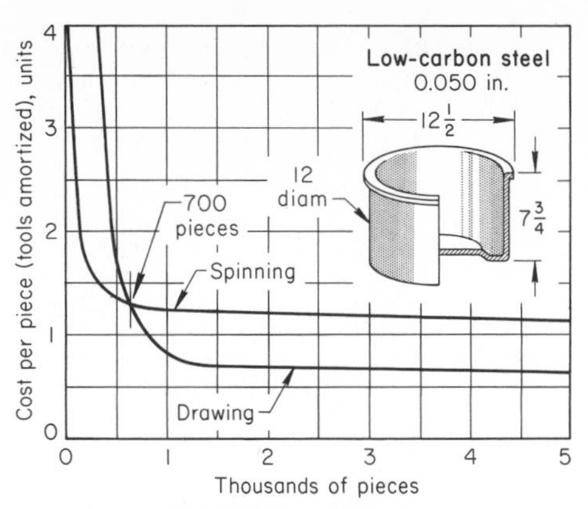

Fig. 6. Relation of quantity and cost for producing a flanged cylindrical part by manual spinning vs drawing in a press (Example 271)

Conical parts (like the shape on the left in the middle row in Fig. 1) are ideal for spinning, because only one tool is required whereas drawing in dies would require four or five operations. Many such cones, depending on their included angle, can be spun in one operation at a moderate production rate. For this reason, manual spinning is often used for quantities up to medium production (less than 1000 units). For large-quantity production, power spinning (shear spinning) is generally cheaper than manual spinning.

Control of quality, including freedom from wrinkles and scratches, and maintenance of dimensional accuracy, is largely a function of operator skill in manual and power-assist spinning. Dimensional tolerances that are practical to maintain in manual spinning increase as the diameter of the blank increases, as shown in Table 1. These tolerances are typical of demands for commercial products and parts for aerospace applications.

Speeds (in surface feet per minute) best suited for manual spinning depend mainly on work-metal composition and thickness. For instance, a given blank of stainless steel is successfully spun at 200 sfm (based on the diameter of the starting blank), and it is determined by "operator feel" that this is maximum for the conditions. Under otherwise identical conditions, changing to a blank of aluminum will permit speeds of 400 to 600 sfm. Similarly, if the thickness of the stainless steel blank were decreased to half the original thickness (no other changes), speed could be safely doubled or tripled.

Selection of optimum speed depends largely on "operator feel". In many spinning operations, speed is changed (usually increased) during the operation by means of a variable-speed drive on the headstock.

Lubricants should be used in all room-temperature spinning operations regardless of work-metal composition, workpiece shape, or type of spinning tools used. The usual practice is to apply the lubricant to the blank with a swab or brush before loading the blank into the machine. In some instances, additional lubricant is added during operation as judged necessary by the operator. The need for additional lubricant depends on the tenacity of the lubricant used and blank-rotation speed.

The most important property of a lubricant used for spinning is its ability to adhere to the rotating blank. Ordinary cup grease is often used. It can be heated to reduce its viscosity, thus making it easier to apply to the blank. Upon application to the cold blank, viscosity of the grease increases. Also, cup grease can be easily removed.

Other lubricants used for spinning include soaps, waxes and tallows (and proprietary mixtures of two or more of these materials), and pigmented drawing compounds. All of these, however, are more difficult to remove than simple grease. For this reason, the more tenacious lubricants are not used if an easier-to-remove lubricant will provide acceptable results. Methods of cleaning formed metal parts are described in the articles that begin on page 307 of Volume 2 of this Handbook.

Power Spinning

Virtually all ductile metals are processed by power spinning. Products range from small hardware items made in large quantities (metal tumblers, for instance) to large components for aerospace applications in unit or low-volume production.

Blanks as large as 240 in. in diameter have been successfully power spun. Plate stock up to 1 in. thick can be power spun without applying heat; when heated, blanks as thick as 5½ in. have been successfully spun.

Conical and curvilinear shapes are those most commonly produced from flat (or preformed) blanks by power spinning. The mechanics of the process should be known, and the rules followed, when planning manufacturing processes that include power spinning.

Mechanics of Cone Spinning

The application of shear spinning to conical shapes is shown schematically in Fig. 7. The metal deformation is such that forming is in accordance with the sine law, which states that the wall thickness of the starting blank and that of the finished workpiece are related as follows:

$$t_2 = t_1(\sin \alpha)$$

Where t_1 is the thickness of the starting blank, t_2 is the thickness of the spun workpiece, and α is one-half the apex angle of the cone.

Table 1. Typical Dimensional Tolerances for Manual Spinning

Diameter of blank, in.	Tolerance, in. Commercial	Tolerance, in. Aerospace
Up to 12	±1/64	±0.008
13 to 36	±1/32	±0.015
37 to 54	±1/16	±0.020
55 to 96	±1/8	±0.030
97 to 144	±1/4	±0.040

Reducing wall thickness by 50% in accordance with the sine law is illustrated in Fig. 7, where:

D = diameter (the same in starting blank and cone)
t_1 = flat plate thickness
t_2 = wall thickness of side of spun cone
α = 30° (which is half the included angle).

Using the sine law for Fig. 7,

$$t_2 = t_1(\sin \alpha) = 0.500 \times 0.5 = 0.250 \text{ in.}$$

When spinning in accordance with the sine law, the axial thickness is the same as the thickness of the starting blank (Fig. 7).

When spinning cones to small angles (less than 35° included angle), the best practice is to use more than one spinning pass with a different cone angle for each pass, as illustrated in Fig. 8. When using this technique, the workpiece is annealed or stress relieved between passes.

This practice permits a high total reduction while maintaining a practical limit of 50 to 75% between process anneals. The reduction between successive annealing operations is determined by the maximum acceptable limits of deformation for the metal being spun (see Table 2 on the next page), obtained by multiplying t_1 by a factor (0.5 for 50%, 0.25 for 75%, and so on) and then dividing the result by t_1 to obtain the sine of the required half angle.

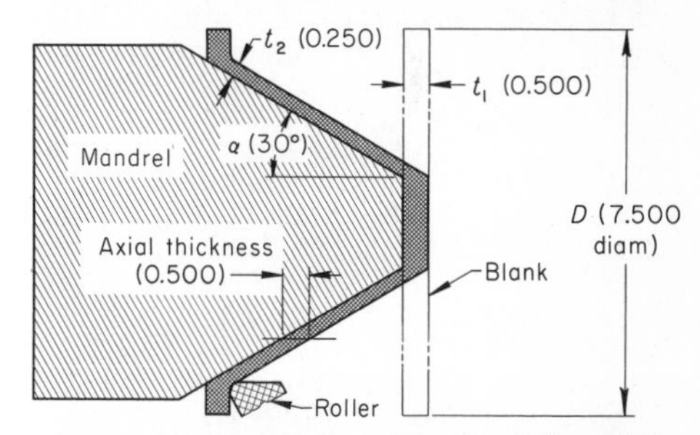

Fig. 7. Setup and dimensional relations for one-operation power spinning of a cone. See text for application of sine law in relation to this illustration.

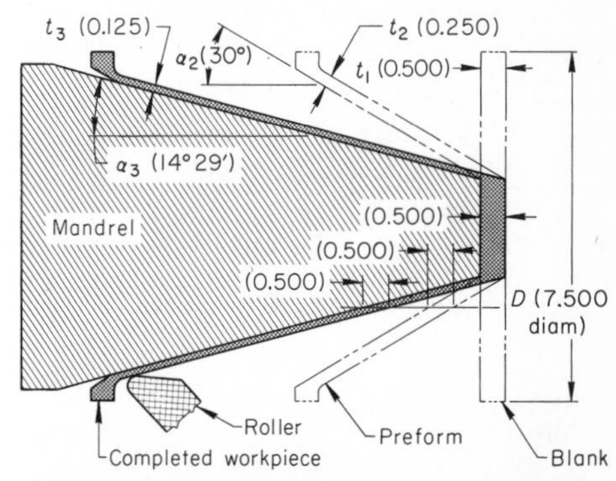

Fig. 8. Setup and dimensional relations for two-operation spinning of a cone to a small angle (less than 35° included angle)

Table 2. Maximum Reductions for Power Spinning of Various Metals Without Intermediate Annealing

Work metal	Maximum reduction, % — Cone	Hemisphere	Tube
Alloy Steels			
4130	75	50	75
4340	65	50	75
6434	70	50	75
D-6ac	70	50	75
H11	50	35	60
Maraging steel (18% Ni)	65	50	82
Stainless Steels			
321	75	50	75
347	75	50	75
410	60	50	65
17-7 PH	65	45	65
Heat-Resisting Alloys			
A-286	70	55	70
René 41	40	35	60
Waspaloy	40	35	60
Aluminum Alloys			
1100	75	50	75
2014	50	40	70
2024	50	..	70
2219	50	40	70
3003, 3004	75	50	75
5052, 5056	50	35	75
5086	65	50	60
5154	65	50	75
6061	75	50	75
7075	65	50	75
Titanium Alloys (Spun Hot)			
Commercially pure	45	..	65
Ti-6Al-4V	55	..	75
Ti-6Al-6V-2Sn	50	..	70
Ti-3Al-13V-11Cr	30	..	30
Other Metals (Spun Hot)			
Beryllium	35	..	..
Molybdenum	60	45	60
Tungsten	50	..	..

Even in multiple-pass spinning, the original blank diameter is retained and the exact volume of material is used in the final part. At any diameter of either the preform or the completed workpiece, the axial thickness equals the thickness of the original blank. For instance, if a flat plate has a diameter of 7½ in. and a thickness of ½-in., the spun preform has this same ½-in. axial thickness but the wall thickness is only ¼ in. (t_1 in Fig. 8), thus satisfying the sine law. Likewise, the final workpiece has an axial thickness of ½ in., but in accordance with the sine law has a wall thickness of only ⅛ in. (t_3 in Fig. 8).

The sine law applies to multiple-operation spinning as follows, wherein a total reduction of wall thickness of 75% is obtained without exceeding 50% in any one operation:

t_1 = flat-plate thickness
t_2 = preform wall thickness
t_3 = final-part wall thickness = 0.125 in.
α_2 = half angle of preform
α_3 = half angle of final part = 14° 29′

$$t_3 = t_1(\sin \alpha_3)$$

To find the flat-plate thickness and the preform cone angle and thickness, the following procedure is used:

$$t_1 = \frac{t_3}{\sin \alpha_3} = \frac{0.125}{0.250} = 0.500 \text{ in.}$$

To satisfy the requirement for a 50% maximum reduction:

$$t_2 = t_1 \times 0.5 = 0.500 \times 0.5 = 0.250 \text{ in.}$$

The half angle required to achieve this reduction is found by:

$$\sin \alpha_2 = t_2/t_1 = \frac{0.250}{0.500} = 0.500 \text{ or } \alpha_2 = 30°$$

Effects of Deviation From the Sine Law. Deviation from the sine law is usually expressed in terms of overreduction or underreduction. In overreduction, the final thickness of the workpiece is less than that dictated by the sine law; in underreduction, the thickness is greater. In overreduction, the flange will lean forward; in underreduction, the flange will lean backward. If a thin blank is spun with severe underreduction, the flange will wrinkle. This phenomenon corresponds to a deep-drawing operation in which the blankholder pressure is insufficient.

In power spinning, overreduction has an additional effect on the shape of the workpiece. As the workpiece is overreduced, back extrusion (Fig. 9) can occur. For a given amount of reduction, the likelihood of back extrusion increases with increasing mandrel angle (Fig. 9).

The phenomenon of back extrusion in spinning is explained in terms of compressive stress in the spun workpiece that pushes the spun section backward. If the tailstock of the machine is removed, it is possible to obtain curvilinear shapes on a conical mandrel by varying the amount of overreduction during spinning.

Machines for Power Spinning

Most power spinning is done in machines specially built for the purpose. Significant components of such a machine are shown in Fig. 10. Although Fig. 10 illustrates power spinning of a conical shape, similar machines are used for spinning of tubes (see the article on Tube Spinning, which begins on page 317 in this volume).

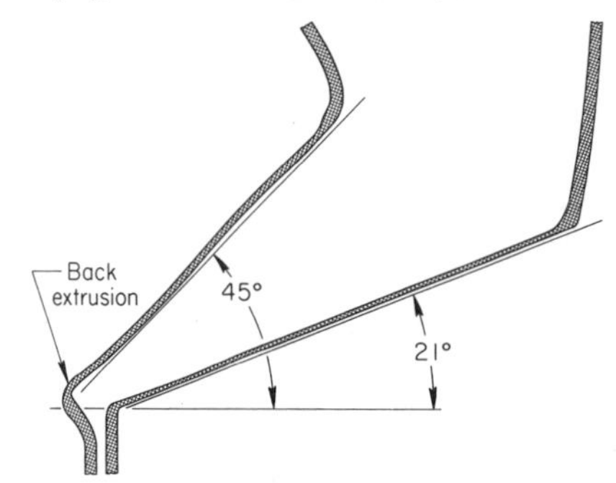

Fig. 9. Back extrusion as a result of overreduction in power spinning of low-carbon steel

Machines for power spinning are usually described by specifying the diameter and the length, in inches, of the largest workpiece that can be spun, and also the amount of force that can be applied to the work. For instance, a 45 by 70-in. by 75,000-lb spinning machine can spin a workpiece measuring 45 in. in diameter by 70 in. long, and the greatest force that can be applied by each tool is 75,000 lb. It is also common practice to specify that the machine can spin a given thickness of metal at a 50% reduction in thickness in one pass.

The capacity of spinning machines ranges from 18 by 15 in. by 4000 lb to machines capable of spinning workpieces as large as 240 in. in diameter by 240 in. long. Force on the work can be as great as 800,000 lb. Machines have been built that spin steel 5½ in. thick.

Spinning machines can be vertical or horizontal. Machines used for spinning workpieces 70 in. or more in diameter are usually vertical because they are better suited for handling large work.

Machines for power spinning can be automated to various degrees. The majority of spinning machines utilize template guides that control the shape and accuracy of the workpiece. Most machines used for production spinning are semiautomatic; that is, they are loaded and unloaded by the operator, but the entire spinning cycle is controlled automatically. Machines can also be equipped with automatic loading and unloading devices, thus making them fully automatic.

Tools for Power Spinning of Cones

Mandrels, rollers and other tools are subjected to more rigorous service in power spinning than in manual spinning; thus, more careful consideration must be given to design and materials of construction.

Mandrels. A typical mandrel profile is illustrated in Fig. 11. Dimensions A and B and angle α can vary as required. Usual practice is to have an integral flange to permit bolting the mandrel to the headstock and a boss of suitable diameter and at least ⅝ in. thick that fits into the headstock of the machine (Fig. 11). Radius R can vary from a minimum of $\frac{1}{32}$ in. to a round nose.

Mandrel wear or failure is frequently a problem in power spinning of conical shapes. Mandrels used in production spinning must be hard, to resist wear, and must also be resistant to fatigue resulting from normal eccentric loading.

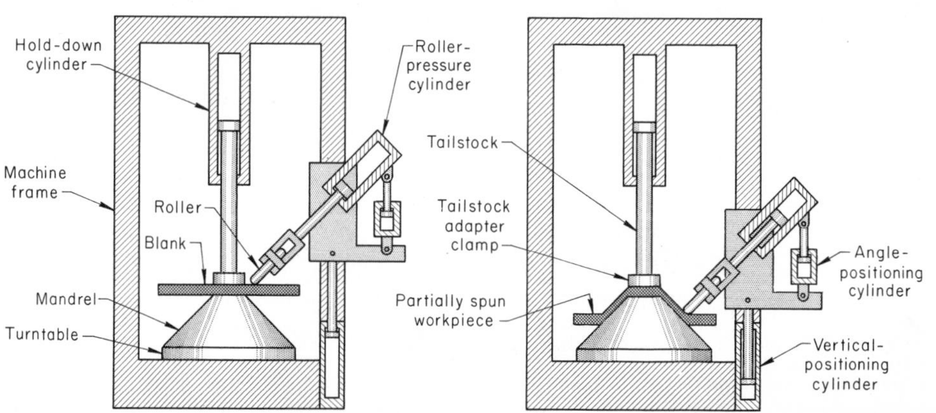

Fig. 10. Schematic illustration of power spinning in a vertical machine

Failure is often caused by spalling (flaking off). Mandrels can also be damaged by the rollers plunging into the workpiece at the start of metal flow. The need for plunging can sometimes be eliminated by machining a ring on the preform to a depth equal to the depth the rollers would otherwise be plunged. This technique permits the rollers to enter the machined space before they start moving along the mandrel, thus eliminating the severe stress on the mandrel as spinning is begun.

Materials for mandrels used in cone spinning depend mainly on the number of identical workpieces to be spun. Based on quantity, the most commonly used materials are:

1 Gray iron (as cast), for low-production spinning of soft metals (10 to 100 pieces)
2 Alloy cast iron (sometimes flame hardened in areas susceptible to high wear), for spinning 100 to 250 pieces
3 Steel — 4150 or 52100 hardened to about Rockwell C 60, for spinning 250 to 750 pieces
4 Tool steels such as O6, A2, D2 or D4 hardened to Rockwell C 60 or slightly higher, for high production.

Finish of mandrels should be no rougher than 60 micro-in. The various diameters should be within ±0.001 in. and concentric with each other within approximately 0.002 in. TIR.

Rollers. Three types of rollers are shown in Fig. 12. Rollers usually are 12 to 20 in. in outside diameter, depending on the type and size of the spinning machine. Roller widths are usually 2 to 3 in., and inside diameters range from 10 to 15 in. The shape of the rollers depends largely on the shape of the workpiece to be spun. Full-radius rollers (Fig. 12a) are usually used for producing curvilinear shapes, whereas those illustrated in Fig. 12(b) and (c) are preferred for the spinning of cones.

Angle α shown in Fig. 12(b) and (c) is necessarily varied to suit the work being spun (particularly the angle of the cone). This angle is intended for clearance and should be such that the work metal does not touch face A (Fig. 12b), or either face A or face B (Fig. 12c). The radius R should not be less than the final wall thickness.

The type of roller illustrated in Fig. 12(b) is widely used in cone spinning. A typical setup, using two of these rollers opposed, is illustrated in Fig. 13. When two rollers are used to spin a part from flat plate, the rollers are set the same. However, when spinning is done from a preformed shape, common practice is to make one the lead roller and to set it ahead of the other by 1/16 to 1/8 in. If more than two rollers are used, this increment is continued between successive rollers. The angle between the axis around which the rollers revolve and the workpiece (angle α in Fig. 13) is usually about 10°, whereas the angle between the same roller axis and the peripheral face of the roller (angle β in Fig. 13) may vary, and is shown in Fig. 13 as approximately 30°.

Rollers are made from a variety of hard materials. The five materials most widely used for power spinning of conical shapes, in order of ascending wearability and cost, are W2 tool steel, O6 tool steel, D2 tool steel, D4 tool steel, and carbide. Choosing among these materials is usually done on the basis

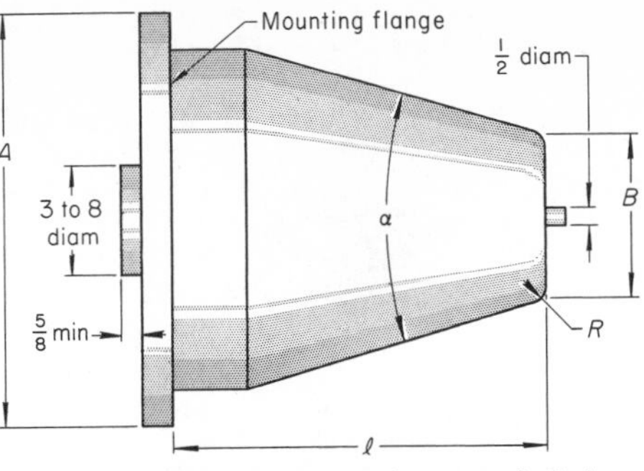

Fig. 11. Typical profile of a mandrel for power spinning of cones

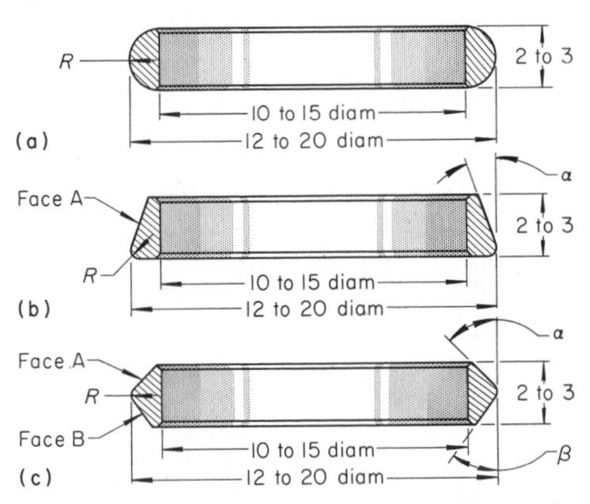

Fig. 12. Typical rollers used in spinning of cones and hemispheres

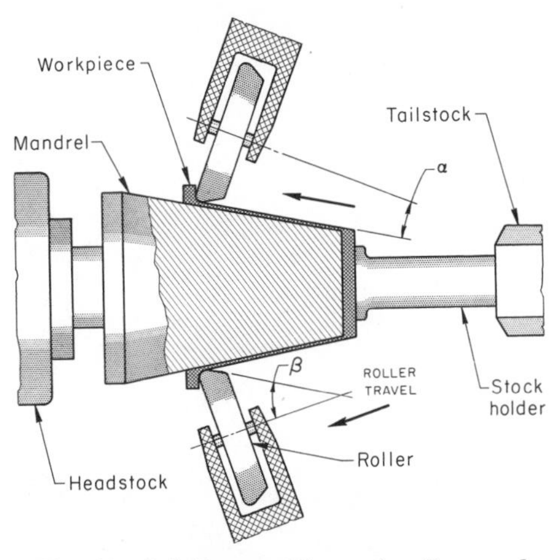

Fig. 13. Relative positions of rollers and workpiece in spinning a cone

of quantity of workpieces to be spun. The less costly W2 and O6 are generally suitable for low to medium production quantities. Tool steels D2 and D4 are preferred for high production quantities. Carbide is seldom used except for specialized applications in which the need has been proved and the high cost can be justified.

Rollers made from any of the above tool steels should be hardened to Rockwell C 60 to 65. All rollers should be polished to a maximum surface roughness of 10 micro-in.

Auxiliary tools for cone spinning include tailstock adapters, tracer templates, tracer followers, and stripping devices. A tailstock adapter clamps the work to the mandrel (Fig. 10) and is made of carbon or alloy steels such as 1045 or 4150, or of tool steel. The clamping face of the tailstock adapter must be ground square to the spindle axis.

Tracers are used for spinning workpieces that vary in wall thickness or shape. Tracer templates are made of low-carbon steel such as 1020, 1/8 to 3/16 in. thick. Large templates have lightening holes for easier handling. Tracer templates are made to the same standards of accuracy as are dies and similar tools. Tracer followers can be ball bearings or hardened tool steel fingers, depending on cone shape.

Stripping devices may be full rings or fork-type fingers, attached to the roller carrier. The need for stripping devices depends on the size and the shape of the workpiece.

Preforms for Spinning Cones

The use of preforms is common in cone spinning when the included angle of the cone is less than 35° or when the percentage of wall reduction is high.

Preforms are usually prepared by cold forming in a die, although hot forging or machining or a combination of both can be used. Some preforms are made by spinning.

The following example describes a procedure for producing a narrow cone from a preform.

Example 272. Power Spinning a Narrow Cone From a Preform (Fig. 14)

The final workpiece shown in Fig. 14 represents the near-maximum reduction that can be obtained without intermediate annealing.

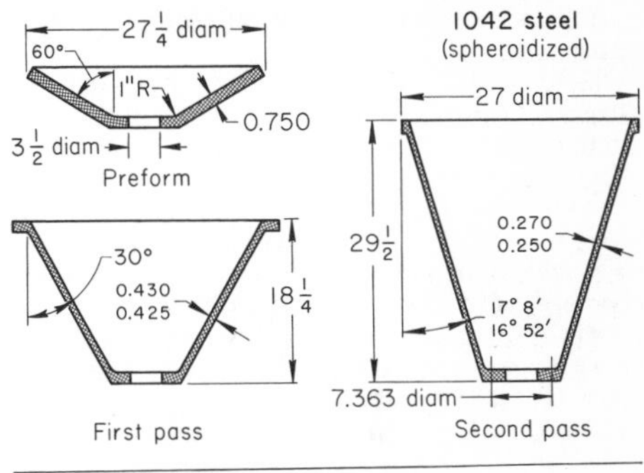

Spinning Conditions

Speed, first pass	400 to 1450 sfm(a)
Speed, second pass	400 to 1600 sfm(b)
Feed, first pass	1.5 to 4 ipm(c)
Feed, second pass	6 ipm
Lubricant and coolant	(d)

Tool Costs

Die for preforming	$1500
Mandrels (2 required)	4000
Tailstock pieces (2 required)	300
Rollers (4 required)	1000
Checking fixture (after second pass)	300
Total tool cost	$7100(e)

Operation	Production rate, pieces per hour	Cost per piece(f)
Production Rates and Costs		
Gas cutting	5	$1.50
Drilling	5	1.70
Grinding	15	0.70
Forming	80	0.40
First spinning pass	4	7.50
Second spinning pass	6	5.00
Total production cost		$16.80

(a) At 200 to 210 rpm. (b) At 230 rpm. (c) Continuously varied by electronic control. (d) Workpieces were initially coated with proprietary spinning oil, and a chemical emulsion was used as coolant. (e) Amortized over 500 pieces. (f) Total production cost (not including material and overhead) was $17.32 per piece in lots of 500 ($16.80 + 1/500 of setup cost). Setup cost for forming and spinning was $260.

Fig. 14. Steps in production of narrow cones by two-pass spinning of a preform (Example 272)

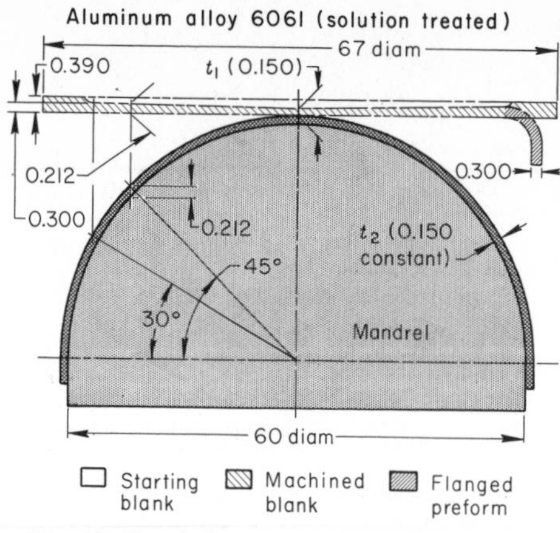

Fig. 15. Hemisphere spun from a machined and preformed blank (Example 273)

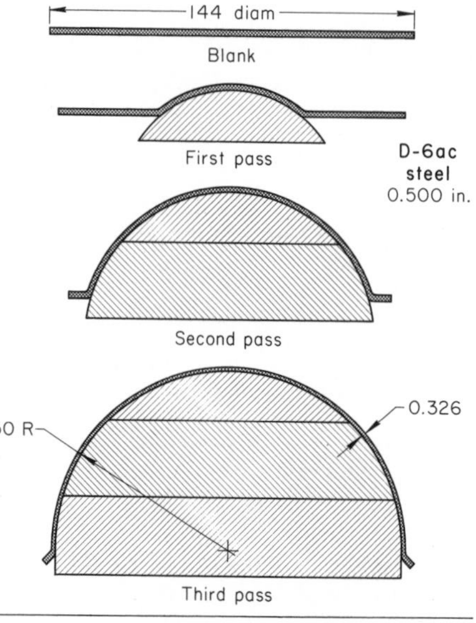

Processing Details

Type of machine .... Power-assisted conventional manual spinning machine
Speed .... 800 to 1200 sfm
Lubricant .... Molybdenum disulfide in oil
Time per piece .... 20 min per pass(a)

Tool Details

Spinning tool .. Full-radius roller; H11 tool steel
Mandrel material .... Gray iron

(a) Plus setup time

Fig. 16. Breakdown sequence used for forming a large hemisphere by power-assisted hot spinning (Example 274)

The cones were produced by gas cutting 30-in.-diam blanks, drilling the 3½-in.-diam center hole, grinding the edges to remove burrs and slag, and then making the 120° preforms (Fig. 14) in a 2000-ton press. The preforms were then spun to an included angle of 60° (denoted as "First pass" in Fig. 14) in a 100-hp spinning machine. The workpiece was completed in a second spinning pass. Total wall reduction was:

$$\frac{0.750\text{ in.} - 0.250\text{ in.}}{0.750\text{ in.}} = \frac{0.500\text{ in.}}{0.750\text{ in.}} = 66\tfrac{2}{3}\%$$

Processing and cost details are given in the table with Fig. 14.

Speeds and Feeds for Cone Spinning

Most metals spin best at high speeds. The minimum speed considered practical is about 400 sfm, but speeds this low are seldom used except for spinning small-diameter workpieces. Sometimes for such workpieces machine spindles cannot rotate fast enough to achieve the desired surface speed. Speeds of 1000 to 2000 sfm are most widely used, regardless of work-metal composition, workpiece shape, or reduction per pass.

Feed. Most cone spinning operations are done at feeds of 0.010 to 0.080 ipr. In practice, however, feeds are usually calculated in inches per minute (ipm). Most machines used in cone spinning are equipped with electronic or hydraulic devices that steplessly change the rate of feed as the diameter on which the rollers are working changes continuously. The rate of feed usually ranges from 1½ to 15 ipm.

Feed rate is important, because it controls the workpiece finish and the fit of the workpiece to the mandrel. With all other factors constant, an increase in feed rate will make the workpiece fit tighter on the mandrel, and the finish of the workpiece will coarsen. On the other hand, a decrease in feed rate will cause a loose fit, and workpiece finish will improve. The diameter of the mandrel should be the same as the inside diameter required on the workpiece (no allowance for springback), and the workpiece should be spun to fit the mandrel. The fit may be loose, snug or tight. For example, a feed rate of 0.005 to 0.010 in. per revolution per roll will result in a loose fit, because this approaches a ring-rolling operation, in which the workpiece is caused to increase in diameter rather than in length. A feed rate of 0.015 to 0.020 in. per revolution per roll will result in a snug fit, and a feed rate of 0.025 to 0.030 in. per revolution per roll will result in a tight fit on the mandrel. Closest tolerances are obtained by a snug-to-tight fit between the workpiece and the mandrel.

To find the optimum combination of speed, feed and pressure, a few pieces should be spun experimentally when a new job is set up. During continuous operation, the temperature of the mandrels and spinning tools changes; therefore, after the first hour or so, it is often necessary to adjust the pressure, speed and feed for uniform results.

Power Spinning of Hemispheres

The use of preforms to control percentage of reduction has enabled power spinning to be applied to the forming of hemispheres, ellipses, ogives and, in general, any curvilinear surface of revolution. However, design of the preform for curvilinear shapes is more complicated than for conical shapes. In spinning of conical shapes, it is possible to find an axial thickness of the spun part that corresponds to the thickness of the blank (see Fig. 8 and the discussion of this figure). No such relationship exists for a curvilinear surface. In the path from the pole to the equator, the axial thickness of the metal on a hemisphere changes from stock thickness at the pole to infinity at the equator (the inverse of sin 90° being infinity). The blank thickness must be back-tapered to compensate for the change in thickness that will take place during spinning. This is shown in Fig. 15, where the machined taper started at 0.150-in. thickness (in the center of the blank) and ended at 0.300-in. thickness at the circle where the 30° radial line of the sphere was projected to the blank. At the corresponding 45° line, the blank thickness was 0.212 in., and at the 15° line 0.580 in. Below the 30° line, however, reduction was greater than permissible for the material, and the operation was planned as if spinning a cylinder. The blank for this portion had a flange with a thickness proportional to the percentage reduction. A usable blank can be designed thus:

Find in Table 2 the allowable reduction for the work metal to be used. Select a beginning stock thickness that, with this amount of reduction, will give the thickness desired on the sphere. Use the ratio of finished stock thickness to original stock thickness as the sine of an angle. This will be the angle of the surface at the latitude where preforming must start, because beyond this point the reduction required to make the hemisphere will be greater than is permissible for the work metal. There will be no reduction at the pole because there blank thickness and final thickness will be the same. At 45° from the pole, final part thickness will be 0.707 times blank thickness. At a corresponding circle on the blank, therefore, the stock must be 1.414 times final part thickness. Other latitudes can be similarly chosen and necessary stock thickness at a corresponding circle on the blank determined. At the circle corresponding to the limiting latitude (maximum permissible reduction has taken place), preforming must start.

In a cross-sectional view, the circles will appear as points and the thickness of the stock at these points can be determined. Fairing between the known points will give a smooth curve that can be machined to produce a blank of the correct thickness. When the points are laid out, a dozen or more points are connected to give the final shape. Trigonometric calculations can replace layouts; then as many as 180 to 360 points can be used, resulting in a more accurate curve. Calculations are now being replaced in many plants by the use of computers, with which it is common practice to use 1200 to 1500 points on a shape such as a large hemisphere.

The starting-blank thickness can be obtained by multiplying the known thickness of the finished part by an appropriate factor. Likewise, by dividing the starting-blank thickness by the appropriate factor, the thickness of the finished part is obtained. The factors are related to the percentage reduction and are the reciprocal of the difference between the percentage reduction (expressed as a decimal) and one, as follows:

For 50% reduction, use a factor of 2.
For 66⅔% reduction, use a factor of 3.
For 75% reduction, use a factor of 4.
For 82½% reduction, use a factor of 5.

Use of this system is illustrated in the example that follows.

Example 273. Forming a 60-In.-Diam Hemisphere by Power Spinning (Fig. 15)

Large hemispheres (Fig. 15) were power spun from solution treated 6061 aluminum alloy, using the following calculations.

From Table 2, it was determined that a 50% reduction could be made with this alloy. Preliminary calculations for thickness of the starting blank were as follows:

t = final wall thickness × factor for percentage reduction
= 0.150 × 2 = 0.300 in.

In calculating the blank thickness at various points on the sphere, it was found that at the pole, or 90° point, the thickness had to be reduced to 0.150 in., and that some reduction was required out to a point directly above the 30° tangency on the hemisphere, where the thickness of the starting blank had to be 0.300 in. Beyond this point, a flange would be preformed by spinning and an additional thickness would be required. It was estimated that an increase in blank thickness of 30% would be enough, and initial blank thickness was established at 0.390 in.

Machining of the blank to graded thickness was done in a tracer-controlled vertical boring mill, with the blank held on a vacuum chuck. Following machining, the flange was preformed to the desired contour by conventional power spinning, accomplishing a reduction in wall thickness that provided a uniform 0.300-in. wall.

Final spinning was accomplished in one pass of the rollers after the alloy was given a controlled amount of room-temperature aging (usually 13 to 18 hr). During final spinning, one roller led the other by a vertical offset of 1/16 to 1/8 in., using 3/4-in.-radius tool rings at a feed of about 0.090 in. per revolution. Speed varied from 300 rpm max down to 40 rpm at the flange.

The procedure described in Example 273 has also been successfully applied to the forming of hemispheres and ellipses 6 to 70 in. in diameter from 17-7 PH and type 410 stainless steels, from alloy steels such as 4130 and 4140, and from aluminum alloys 5086, 2014 and 2024 (as well as 6061). In one instance, the procedure was used for hot spinning an ogive 30 in. in diameter and length from molybdenum.

An application involving hot manual spinning of a hemisphere by the use of three breakdown operations is described in Example 274.

Hot Spinning of Hemispheres

The use of heat for decreasing the strength and increasing the ductility of the work metal is sometimes required either because the machine capacity is insufficient for cold forming the thickness to be spun or because the room-temperature ductility of the work metal is too low.

Hot spinning is done only when necessary, because heating, subsequent cleaning, and increased tool deterioration all contribute to increased cost. A specific application where high-strength steel was heated for spinning is described in the example that follows.

Example 274. Hot Spinning of 144-In.-Diam Alloy Steel Blanks (Fig. 16)

A manually operated machine with hydraulic power assist was used to spin 100-in.-diam hemispherical heads from 0.500-in.-thick by 144-in.-diam circular blanks of D-6ac alloy steel. Spinning to final shape was accomplished in a series of three breakdowns (Fig. 16) by heating to 1550 F with oxyacetylene torches. Temperature was determined with an optical pyrometer. After spinning, the workpiece was stress relieved, sand blasted, and inspected by the magnetic particle method. A minimum wall thickness of 0.272 in. was specified. However, measurements taken after spinning indicated an actual minimum thickness of 0.326 in. To guarantee a uniform wall thickness after spinning, it was necessary to machine both the inside and the outside surfaces. Machining also removed decarburization resulting from elevated temperatures.

Lubricants and Coolants for Power Spinning

Power spinning requires the use of a fluid that serves as both a lubricant and a coolant. Because of the large amount of heat generated, a water-base fluid is most commonly used. Usually, a colloidal suspension of zinc in lithium soap or molybdenum disulfide paste is mixed with water to function as the lubricant. These lubricant-

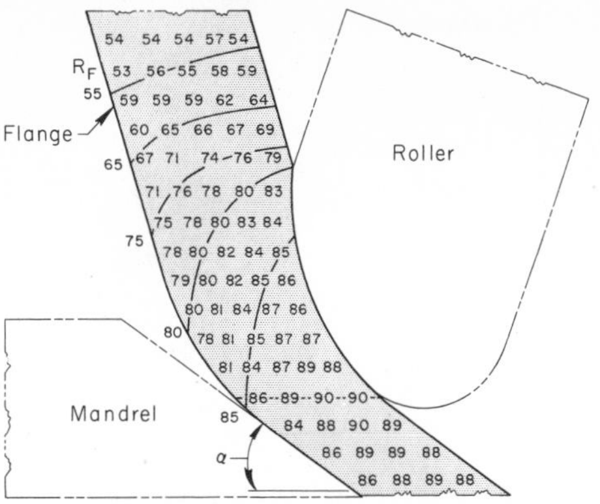

Fig. 17. Distribution of hardness (Rockwell F) in a copper workpiece reduced 43% by spinning

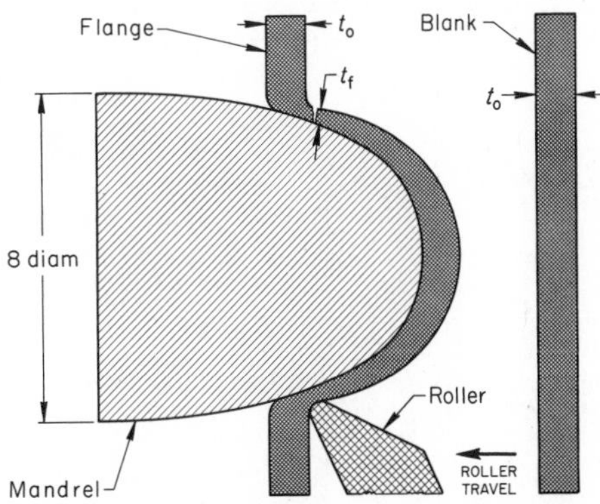

Fig. 18. Setup for testing shear spinnability

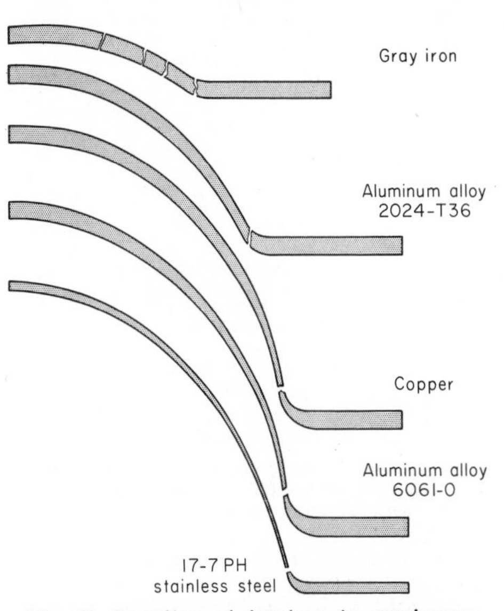

Fig. 19. Location of fracture in specimens of five different metals that were tested for shear spinnability

coolant combinations are satisfactory for most metals, although zinc-free lubricants and coolants should be used for spinning stainless steel to avoid surface contamination.

Various oils and oil mixtures, such as 10% lard oil in kerosine, have also been used successfully for power spinning. Regardless of composition, the fluid must be free flowing and applied by pumps in copious amounts or both workpieces and tools will be damaged from heat.

When spinning aluminum or stainless steel, the workpieces or mandrels, or both, are sometimes coated with the lubricant before spinning. During spinning, workpieces and tools are flooded with a coolant such as an emulsion of soluble oil in water.

Effects of Spinning on Work-Metal Properties

Power spinning is a severe cold working operation and therefore has a marked effect on mechanical properties of the work metal. Grain size is refined and made directional by power spinning. Surface finish of a spun workpiece is usually good enough so that no additional machining is required after spinning. Spun finishes are commonly about 60 micro-in., although finishes as smooth as 20 micro-in. have been produced by power spinning.

Strength and Hardness. In spinning, tensile and yield strengths increase and ductility decreases. The magnitude of effect depends on the amount of wall reduction and the susceptibility of the metal to work hardening (see Tables 2 and 3 in the article on Tube Spinning, pages 321 and 322).

In many applications, the increase in strength caused by spinning is highly desirable because it eliminates the need for heat treating. In other applications, the change in mechanical properties is not desired and the workpieces must be annealed after spinning.

To measure the work hardening in the deformation zone, Rockwell F readings were taken on the cross section of a spun copper workpiece that was reduced 43%. The results are shown in Fig. 17. It is evident that the area near the roller contact has higher hardness than at the mandrel side.

Shear Spinnability of Metals

Spinnability is defined as the maximum reduction a metal can withstand before failure during spinning.

The setup for testing shear spinnability shown in Fig. 18 consists of a half-ellipsoid mandrel 8 in. at its lesser diameter. According to the sine law, when a flat blank is shear spun on this shape of mandrel, the thickness of the spun part will vary gradually from its original to zero. All metals will fail somewhere between these two limits. Shear spinnability is defined as the maximum percentage reduction in thickness a metal can undergo before failure. Thus, maximum spinning reduction percentage is:

$$\frac{t_0 - t_f}{t_0} \times 100$$

Several specimens tested by this method (Fig. 19) show that gray iron and 2024-T36 aluminum alloy fractured in a brittle manner under the roller. In contrast to this type of fracture, copper, 6061-O aluminum alloy, and 17-7 PH stainless steel all failed in tension behind the roller.

Experiments on the influence of roller corner radius, roller swivel, roller axial velocity, and speed of mandrel rotation have indicated that none of these process variables has a significant effect on maximum reduction. Nor was any appreciable difference in spinnability observed between results with dry

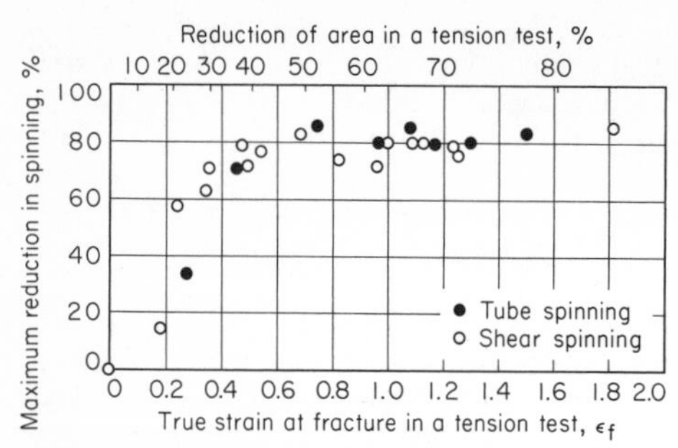

Fig. 20. Correlation of maximum reduction in spinning with reduction of area in a tension test

and lubricated mandrels. The variable that influenced maximum reduction the most was deviation from sine-law thickness. Thus, if the spun section was thicker than that dictated by the sine law, the maximum reduction was less than when the thickness was less than the sine-law thickness. The difference in spinnability, however, was only a few per cent for a deviation from sine-law thickness of ±30%.

In comparing the values of maximum reduction in shear spinning with conventional mechanical properties of the metals used in the spinnability tests, it was found that the best correlation is with reduction of area in a tension-test specimen. Figure 20 shows such data and indicates a transition in the type of failure of spun parts (metals included those shown in Fig. 19). For metals with a true necking strain, ϵ_f, of 0.6 (corresponding to about 45% reduction of area) or greater in a tension-test specimen, the maximum shear-spinning reduction for one pass is about 80%. Further increase in the ductility of the metal does not appreciably increase this maximum spinning reduction. For metals with a true necking strain below 0.6, spinnability depends on ductility. In production spinning and in spinnability tests, the minimum included cone angle to which a metal can be shear spun from a flat blank in one pass is approximately 30°.

Spinnability of tubes is described on page 322. A setup for testing the spinnability of tubes is also shown.

Tube Spinning

Tube spinning, one of the major applications of the power spinning process, is described in the article beginning on page 317 in this volume.

Combination Processes

In some applications, two types of spinning can be used in combination with each other or in combination with other fabricating methods to produce a required shape. The following example describes a procedure for producing tank halves by using two types of spinning and machining.

Example 275. Aluminum Alloy Tank Halves Produced by Manual Spinning, Machining and Tube Spinning (Fig. 21)

Storage-tank halves were produced by first manually spinning a flat blank to the shape shown in Fig. 21(a), and then machining the workpiece as shown in Fig. 21(b). Next the workpiece (aluminum alloy 6061) was solution treated by heating to 970 F, water quenching, and aging at 70 F for 17 hr. It was then tube

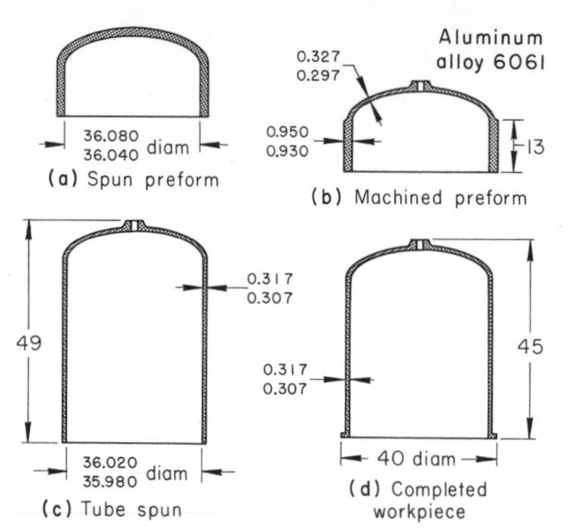

Fig. 21. Sequence of shapes in production of a tank half by manual spinning, machining and tube spinning (Example 275)

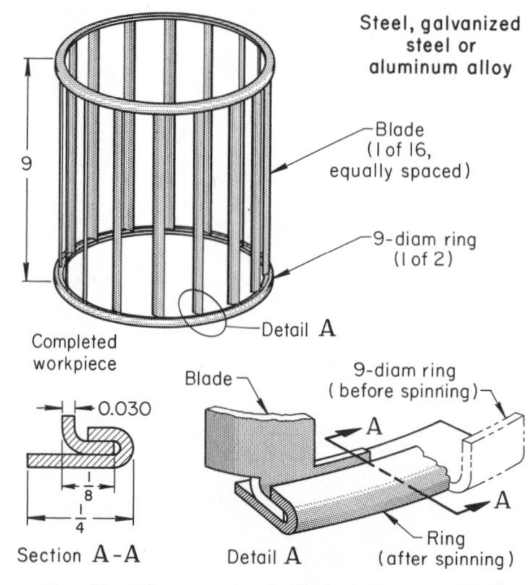

Fig. 22. Blower wheel that was assembled by spinning (Example 276)

spun in two passes to reduce the wall thickness by approximately 66% (Fig. 21c). The end portion was heated to 600 F, and the flange was manually spun (Fig. 21d).

Assembly by Spinning

Spinning is frequently employed for less conventional applications than those described earlier in this article and in the article on Tube Spinning, page 317. It is often the cheapest means of joining two or more parts to form an assembly. For instance, a tube can be inserted through a hole in a plate, and then the protruding end of the tube can be spun to secure it to the plate. Small parts are assembled by this technique with a special tool rotated by a drill press.

Assembly of components by spinning is not, however, restricted to small parts, as illustrated by the example that follows.

Example 276. Use of Spinning to Assemble a Blower Wheel (Fig. 22)

Spinning was used to assemble the blower wheel shown in Fig. 22. The 16 blades were picked up in order by a template, which held them in position for assembly into the end rings. The assembly was placed in a special spinning machine that had a 3-hp motor. As the assembly rotated, the flange on the end rings was spun over and flattened on the tabs of the blades (Fig. 22) by a guide-rail shoe. After both flanges were spun, the template was removed and used to collect blades for the next assembly. Assemblies were produced at a rate of 91 per hour.

Production of the blower-wheel blades is described in Example 103 in the article on Press Bending of Low-Carbon Steel.

Selected References

J. P. Vidosic, "Metal Forming and Forming Technology", Ronald Press Co., New York, 1964, 558 p. Chapter 10 (19 p) is an illustrated account of spin forming, written for students.

Erich G. Thomsen, Charles T. Yang, and Shiro Kobayashi, "Plastic Deformation in Metal Processing", Macmillan Co., New York; Collier-Macmillan Ltd., London (England); 1965; 486 p. Chapter 19 (23 p) analyzes mathematically the force components and the movements of material in spin forging, a form of spinning with high forces in which each element of sheet is substantially reduced in thickness by a squeezing operation, which avoids radial displacement. Tubes may be made by spin forging.

Richard L. Kegg, A New Method for Determination of Spinnability of Metals, *Journal of Engineering for Industry (Transactions ASME), Series B*, 83, 119 to 124 (May 1961). Maximum spinning reduction possible is determined by tests in a shear-spinning machine, using an ellipsoidal mandrel.

Serope Kalpakcioglu, On the Mechanics of Shear Spinning, *Journal of Engineering for Industry (Transactions ASME), Series B*, 83, 125 to 130 (May 1961). Flow of metal was studied by the grid-line technique.

Serope Kalpakcioglu, A Study of Shear-Spinnability of Metals, *Journal of Engineering for Industry (Transactions ASME), Series B*, 93, 478 to 484 (Nov 1961). An analysis of the flow of metal in shear spinning explains how overreduction may cause fracture and how back extrusion takes place. The minimum angle to which a metal may be shear-spun from a flat blank is about 15°.

S. Kobayashi, I. K. Hall, and E. G. Thomsen, A Theory of Shear Spinning of Cones, *Journal of Engineering for Industry (Transactions ASME), Series B*, 83, 485 to 495 (Nov 1961). Power-spinning forces as predicted by theory agree with those for aluminum and lead.

Other Examples of Spinning Applications in This Volume(a)

Type of spinning	Number of passes	Type of alloy	Example number
Stainless Steel			
Manual	4	305	476
Power	1	430	477
Heat-Resisting Alloys			
Power(b)	...	A-286	496
Tube(c)	3	A-286	497
Tube(d)	...	N-155	503
Refractory Metals			
Power	1	C-103	506
Power	3	Ta-10W	507
Power	1	Tungsten	508
Aluminum Alloy			
Power(e)	Multiple	6061-O	531
Beryllium			
Power(f)	...	Powder sheet(g)	572
Manual	2	Powder sheet(g)	573
Manual	9	Powder sheet(g)	574
Copper and Copper Alloys			
Manual(h)	...	Alloy 110	597
Manual(j)	...	Alloy 220	598
Magnesium Alloy			
Manual(k)	1	HK31-H24	608
Titanium Alloys			
Power(m)	1	Ti-6Al-4V	614
Power	1	Ti-13V-11Cr-3Al	615
Tube	2	Ti-13V-11Cr-3Al	616

(a) See also the section on Spinning, page 434, in the article "Forming of Nickel Alloys" in this volume. (b) Operation was changed from spinning to deep drawing. (c) Starting groove was machined. Flange was left on each end to avoid distortion. (d) Direction of grain circumferential to resist hoop stress.

(e) Hemisphere produced. (f) Sheet was sandwiched between two steel sheets. (g) Cross rolled. (h) Partly formed on mandrel; partly free formed. (j) Hourglass shape spun on a split mandrel. (k) Sizing operation on a welded preform. (m) Spun at room temperature. The same alloy, twice as thick, was spun at 800 F.

Rubber-Pad Forming

RUBBER-PAD FORMING employs a rubber pad on the ram of the press and a form block on the platen. The form block usually is similar to the punch in a conventional die, but it can be the die cavity. The rubber acts somewhat like hydraulic fluid in exerting nearly equal pressure on all workpiece surfaces as it is pressed around the form block.

The advantages of the rubber-pad forming processes are:

1 One rubber pad takes the place of many different die shapes, returning to its original shape when the pressure is released.
2 Tools have fewer components and are made of easier-to-machine materials than conventional tools.
3 The forming radius decreases progressively during the forming stroke, unlike the fixed radius on conventional dies.
4 Thinning of the work metal (such as occurs in conventional deep drawing) is almost completely eliminated.

The disadvantages are:

1 Rubber wears out quickly, or tears on sharp projections. The average life of a rubber pad is about 20,000 pieces.
2 Without special or accessory equipment, rubber pads exert less pressure, and definition may be less sharp, than with conventional dies.
3 Shrink flanges may have wrinkles that need hand work.

Equipment. The hydraulic presses used in most rubber-pad forming are similar to those described in the article on Presses, beginning on page 1 in this volume. Some rubber-pad processes use special machines, which are described in the discussion of the specific process. In most applications, only the form block is specially made. Form blocks can be made of epoxy resin, cast iron, hardwood or other low-cost material.

Equipment is available with cycling rates as high as 1500 per hour. Rubber-pad forming has been applied to high-volume production, such as the forming of deeply recessed taillight reflectors for automobiles, and the deep drawing of toaster shells (Example 286).

The application of rubber pads in press-brake dies is discussed in the article "Press-Brake Forming", beginning on page 101 in this volume. The four most widely used rubber-pad forming processes (discussed here) are the Guerin process, the Verson-Wheelon process, the Marform process, and rubber-diaphragm forming.

Guerin Process

The Guerin process is the oldest and most basic of the production rubber-pad forming processes. Its advantages are simplicity of equipment, adaptation to small-lot production, and ease of changeover.

Some metals commonly formed by the Guerin process are listed in Table 1. Titanium can be formed only if both the workpiece and the form block are heated. Often, the resulting deterioration of the rubber pad makes the process too costly compared with forming by conventional dies.

Table 1. Metals Commonly Formed by the Guerin Rubber-Pad Process

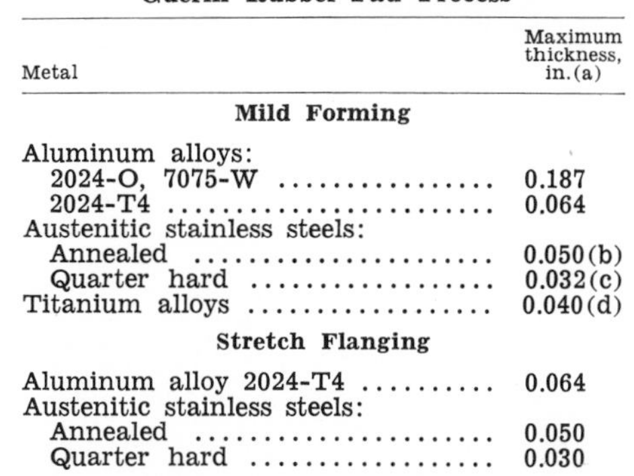

Metal	Maximum thickness, in.(a)
Mild Forming	
Aluminum alloys:	
2024-O, 7075-W	0.187
2024-T4	0.064
Austenitic stainless steels:	
Annealed	0.050(b)
Quarter hard	0.032(c)
Titanium alloys	0.040(d)
Stretch Flanging	
Aluminum alloy 2024-T4	0.064
Austenitic stainless steels:	
Annealed	0.050
Quarter hard	0.030

(a) Typical; varies with type of equipment and part design. (b) Up to 0.078 in. when compression dams (see "Accessory Equipment", on this page, and Fig. 5, 6 and 7) are used. (c) Only very mild forming. (d) When heated to 600 F.

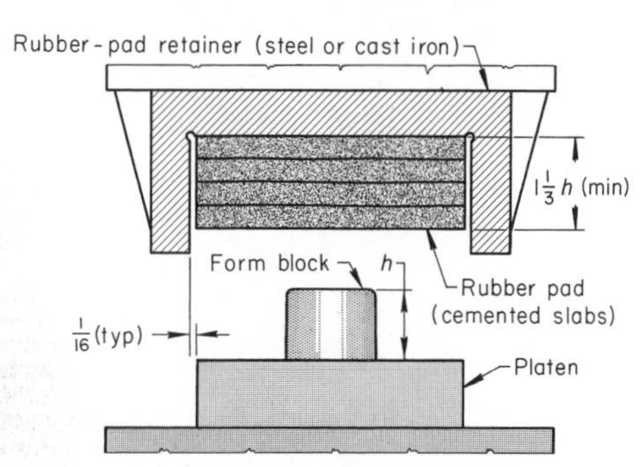

Fig. 1. Tooling and setup for rubber-pad forming by the Guerin process

Presses. Almost any hydraulic press can be used in the Guerin process. For maximum forming capability, the press tonnage and area of the rubber pad must be suitable for the operation under consideration. Generally, the rubber pad is about the same size as the press ram; however, it can be smaller. (See Example 280.)

Tools. The main tools are the rubber pad and the form block (Fig. 1). The rubber pad is fairly soft (about Durometer A 60 to 75) and is usually three times as deep as the part to be formed. The pad can consist of a solid block of rubber, or of laminated slabs cemented together and held in a retainer, as shown in Fig. 1. The slabs can also be held loose in a flanged retainer. The retainer is generally made of steel or cast iron, and is an inch or so deeper than the rubber pad. It is also strong enough to withstand the forming pressures that are generated (up to 20,000 psi in some applications, although an upper limit of 2000 psi is more common).

The minimum pad thickness is 1⅓ times the height of the form block, as shown in Fig. 1. However, pad thicknesses generally vary from 6 to 12 in., and the most commonly used thickness is 8 or 9 in.

Form blocks (punches) are made of wood, plastic, masonite, cast iron, steel, or alloys of aluminum, magnesium, zinc or bismuth. The softer materials are used in making prototypes or experimental models or in small production runs. The life of a wood, plastic or soft metal form block can be extended by facing it with steel. Form blocks are fitted with locating pins to hold the blanks in position while they are being formed.

The form block is loosely mounted on a platen, or pressing block (see Fig. 1), which fits closely into the rubber-pad retainer to avoid extrusion of the rubber during the forming process. Often, several form blocks are mounted on one platen, so that several parts can be formed simultaneously with one stroke of the press. Two or three platens can be used with each press; they can be slid or rotated from under the press ram for loading and unloading.

Accessory Equipment. Draw clips, cover plates, wiping plates, forming rings and forming bars, and dams and wedge blocks are used to increase the pressure on the workpiece in specific locations and to aid in the forming of difficult shapes.

Draw clips are fastened to the edge of a blank to equalize the drawing force on a flange and to keep it from wrinkling. Wiping plates, usually hinged to the pressing block, mechanically transfer the pressure of the rubber pad to hard-to-form flanges. Forming rings and forming bars work in the same way, except that they encircle the part and therefore are not hinged. Dams are shaped and positioned so that with the sidewall of the form block they form a trap. The dam has a face sloping toward this trap so that as the rubber pad moves down, rubber is cammed against the sidewall, thus increasing the pressure in that area. Wedge blocks use the same kind of camming action to apply mechanical pressure to the side of a workpiece. Examples 280, 281, 282 and 285 in this article illustrate the use of dams.

Cover plates are used to hold blanks flat during forming, or to protect previously formed areas from distortion (see Example 278).

Procedure. The rubber-pad retainer is fixed to the upper ram of the press, and the platen, containing the form block, is placed on the bed of the press; a blank is placed on the form block and held in position by two or more locating pins. The pins must be rigidly mounted in the form block so that the rubber will not drive them down into the pinhole or push them out of position, and they must be no higher than necessary to hold the blank, or they will puncture the rubber pad. (In some applications, nests can be used to locate the blank during forming.)

As the ram descends, the rubber presses the blank around the form block, thus forming the workpiece. The rubber-pad retainer fits closely around the platen, forming an enclosure that traps the rubber as pressure is applied. Ordinarily, the pressure produced in the Guerin process is between 1000 and 7000 psi. Pressure can be increased by reducing the size of the platen; pressures as high as 20,000 psi have been developed by the use of small platens in high-capacity presses (see Examples 280, 281 and 282).

The pressure is not a function of the number of parts being formed, but of the platen area. To obtain maximum production with each stroke of the press, therefore, as many form blocks as possible are mounted on a single platen. The depth of finished parts formed by this process seldom exceeds 1½ in. However, deeper parts can be formed by using a large-tonnage press and a rubber pad with a small surface area. In one application, such a setup produced 20,000-psi pressure, and was able to form a flange 2¾ in. deep.

Straight flanges can be bent easily by the Guerin process, if they are wide enough to develop adequate forming force; if they are not, accessory tools must be used.

Minimum widths for flanges of stainless steel and aluminum alloys that can be bent by rubber-pad forming are listed in Table 2. Generally, angles on flanges in soft metal can be held to a maximum variation of ±1°. In hard metals, such as half-hard stainless steels, which have more springback than annealed stainless steels, a ±5° tolerance can be met only with special care. An envelope (all-around) tolerance of ±0.015 in. is possible on the contour of soft-metal pieces, but on hard metal, the tolerance must be increased to ±0.020 in.

Stretch flanges and shrink flanges can be formed around curves and holes if the deformation is slight to moderate. If forming is severe, auxiliary tools must be used to support the work and prevent wrinkling.

The following example describes the forming of a workpiece with stretch flanges, by the Guerin process.

Example 277. Forming a Fuselage Stiffener by the Guerin Process (Fig. 2)

The fuselage stiffener shown in Fig. 2 was formed from a blank of alclad aluminum alloy 7075-O, 19 in. wide by 26.50 in. long and 0.040 in. thick.

Tooling holes were drilled, and the blank was routed and deburred before forming. This was done to prevent the soft rubber pads from tearing on the burrs, and also to avoid splitting the edges of the stretch flanges.

The forming was done in a 2500-ton hydraulic press with a 44 by 112-in. bed. The joggle was set to depth by hand tools after the forming operation.

After forming, the masonite form block was used as a checking block to inspect and straighten the piece. The piece was then aged to the T6 temper.

Processing time (forming, joggle setting, inspecting and straightening) was 5 min per piece. A typical lot size was 20 pieces.

Cover plates are often used to hold webs flat while flanges are being formed, as in the following example:

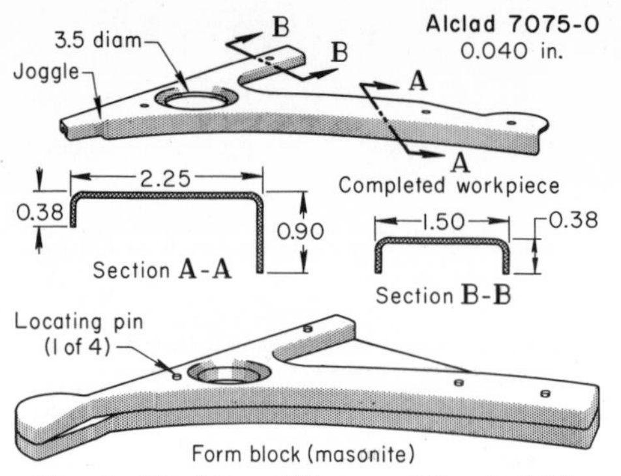

Fig. 2. Fuselage stiffener with straight, stretch and shrink flanges that was formed by the Guerin process (Example 277)

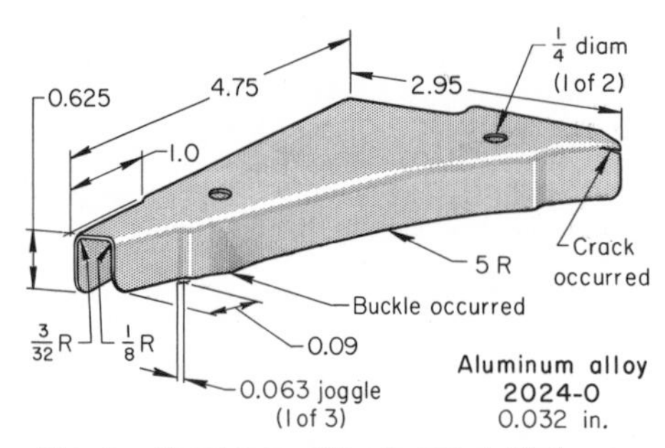

Fig. 3. Aluminum alloy bracket that was formed by the Guerin process with the use of an aluminum cover plate (Example 278)

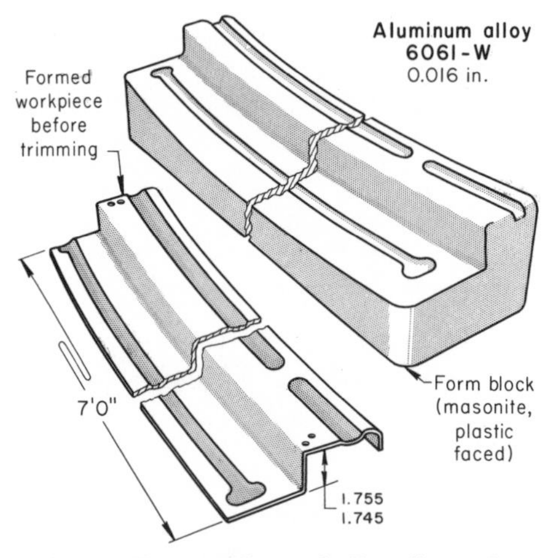

Fig. 4. Honeycomb-panel Z-section edge member that was formed by the Guerin process and also in a Verson-Wheelon press (Example 279)

Example 278. Use of a Cover Plate in Forming an Aluminum Bracket by the Guerin Process (Fig. 3)

A ¼-in.-thick aluminum cover plate was used to keep the web flat while the flanges were being formed on the bracket shown in Fig. 3. The edges of the cover plate were beveled at 30° and rounded to improve flow of the rubber pad around the form block. The form block was made from a 1¼-in.-thick aluminum plate to form the ⅝-in.-wide flanges.

The rubber pad was 9 in. thick and was protected by a ½-in.-thick throw sheet; both had a hardness of Durometer A 70. The pad was mounted in a 1000-ton hydraulic press. Cycle time was 1½ min. A small buckle appeared in the flange adjacent to the joggle at the narrow end of the part. It was removed when the joggles were restruck by hand to sharpen the offset. There were occasional cracks in the radius of the stretch flange at the wide end, possibly caused by metal trapped under the cover plate or along the surface of the rubber. By the use of powdered talc on the blank, loss from this cause was limited to 1 or 2%.

Table 2. Minimum Formable Flange Widths for Rubber-Pad Forming of Stainless Steels and Aluminum Alloys

Alloy and/or temper	Minimum flange width, in.(a)
Stainless Steels	
Annealed	3/16 + 4.5t(b)
Quarter hard	⅝
Aluminum Alloys	
2024-O, 7075-O	1/16 + 2.5t(b)
2024-T3, 2024-T4	⅛ + 4t(b)

(a) Using minimum permissible bend radius; a larger bend radius requires a wider flange. (b) t = sheet thickness.

Developed blanks were cut by a high-speed router from 0.032-in.-thick aluminum alloy 2024-O, and were hand deburred. A typical lot was 150 pieces.

The following example describes the forming of a Z-section edge member by the Guerin process and by the Verson-Wheelon process (see page 212).

Example 279. Drawing vs Rubber-Pad Forming of a Z-Section Edge Member (Fig. 4)

Both drawing and rubber-pad forming were considered for the production of the Z-section shown in Fig. 4 (a honeycomb-panel edge member). The drawing tool would have taken 200 hr to make but would have produced two pieces at a time. Also, drawing would have needed press setup time that could be amortized only on long production runs. Because of the slight curvature required on the part, it could not have been formed in a press brake. Rubber-pad forming, therefore, was the method used.

A blank 10 in. wide by 7 ft long was cut from 0.016-in.-thick aluminum alloy 6061-O and solution heat treated to the unstable W temper, rolled flat, and lubricated with drawing wax before forming.

The form block, made of masonite and faced with plastic to conform to the contour of the part, contained bead cavities outside the trim lines of the part, to control flow of the metal during forming. The form block took 32 man-hr to make.

Minimum forming pressure needed was 2400 psi. This pressure was available in the press adapted to the Guerin process and in the Verson-Wheelon press. Both types of presses were used; 12 pieces per hour were produced by the Guerin process, and 4 pieces per hour in the Verson-Wheelon press.

After forming, the part was re-pressed with a pusher to keep the 1.750-in. height within the ±0.005-in. tolerance.

In the three examples that follow, a pressure of 20,000 psi was used to form parts so well that a minimum of hand reworking was required. To obtain the 20,000-psi pressure, a rubber pad 20 in. in diameter (surface area of about 300 sq in.) was mounted in a 3000-ton hydraulic press. The bed size of the press was 60 in. front-to-back and 62 in. left-to-right. Stroke length was 18 in., and shut height 50 in. The press had a turntable that held two form blocks; thus, one block could be unloaded and loaded while the other was under the press ram. The rubber pad was 8 in. thick and made in two pieces. One piece was 7 in. thick and had a hardness of Durometer A 80 to 85. The second piece, which was replaceable, was 1 in. thick and had a hardness of Durometer A 70 to 75.

Example 280. Shallow Drawing of a Fuselage Tail Cap by the Guerin Process (Fig. 5)

The fuselage tail cap shown in Fig. 5 was rubber-pad formed at 20,000 psi using the 3000-ton hydraulic press and the 20-in.-diam pad described above. Originally, the cap was made by spinning, but at a rate of only one piece per hour. Changing to high-pressure rubber-pad forming by the Guerin process increased the production rate to 12 pieces per hour.

A blank of aluminum alloy 2014-O, 0.032 in. thick, was solution heat treated to the W temper, and lubricated with heavy-duty floor wax. The part was formed before age hardening was complete. A compression dam surrounded the form block (see Fig. 5) and was used to concentrate pressure on the flange.

Time for producing the form block for both spinning and rubber-pad forming was approximately 24 man-hr.

Example 281. Forming a Shrink Flange and Joggles in One Operation by the Guerin Process (Fig. 6)

The 20,000-psi rubber-pad forming setup described above was used to form the aircraft control-surface rib shown in Fig. 6, without wrinkling the severe shrink flanges. Because of the high pressure used, only one operation was needed to form the 45° flanges on the lightening hole and the shrink flanges with the joggles. A removable compression dam (see Fig. 6) was used to concentrate the forming pressure on the flange around the end of the part.

A developed blank, 0.020 in. thick, was cut from aluminum alloy 2014-O and lubricated with heavy-duty floor wax before forming.

The form block was made of aluminum alloy 2014-T6, 2024-T4, or 7075-T6 and the removable dam of masonite. Production rate was 20 pieces per hour. The fine detail and the severe shrink flange could not have been produced with ordinarily available Guerin-process equipment without considerable hand work or subsequent forming.

Example 282. Forming a Combination Stretch-and-Shrink Flange by the Guerin Process (Fig. 7)

The aircraft-frame tail section shown in Fig. 7 was formed by the high-pressure (20,000 psi) Guerin-process setup used for the two preceding examples. During forming, a smooth transition was made from stretch to shrink flanging on the workpiece. The blank used was 0.050-in.-thick aluminum alloy 2024-O. The part was restruck after solution heat treatment. A heavy-duty floor wax was used as lubricant.

An aluminum alloy form block and a removable dam (see Fig. 7) made of masonite, took 20 man-hr to make. The blank was located between bolted-on end plates on the form block. The ripples in the contour of the larger locating plate (see Fig. 7) kept the workpiece from sliding during forming. The metal dimpled into previously used locating-pin holes to further stabilize the workpiece. The 1.75-in.-diam lightening hole was not flanged. Production rate was 20 pieces per hour.

The tail section could have been formed in tool steel dies in a press, but this would have been practical only for long production runs (2000 pieces or more), because of the high tooling cost (130 man-hr was estimated to be the time required for producing the dies) and long press-setup time.

In the following example, accurately matched laminations were made by forming one over the other on a form block by the Guerin process. This exact part match could not have been produced by any production method except the Guerin process or the Verson-Wheelon process.

Example 283. Forming a Two-Piece Cockpit Rail on a Single Form Block (Fig. 8)

By using a rubber pad instead of a conventional die, it was possible to form the two mating parts of a cockpit rail section on a single form block. One of the two parts is shown in Fig. 8. The second part was formed over the first after it had been formed.

A fully developed blank, 0.100 in. thick, was cut from aluminum alloy 2014-O and solution heat treated. Forming was done by the Guerin process with a minimum pressure of 7500 psi. No lubricant was used. The form block (Fig. 8) was made of masonite and was plastic faced. Total time for making the tooling was 40 man-hr. Production rate was 20 pieces per hour.

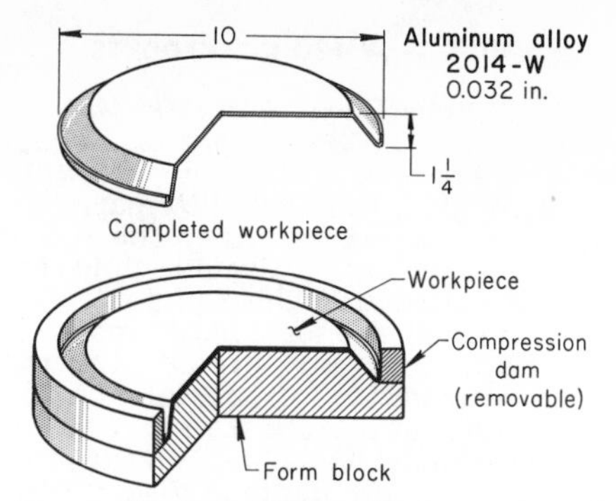

Fig. 5. Fuselage tail cap that was formed by the Guerin process in a high-pressure setup (Example 280)

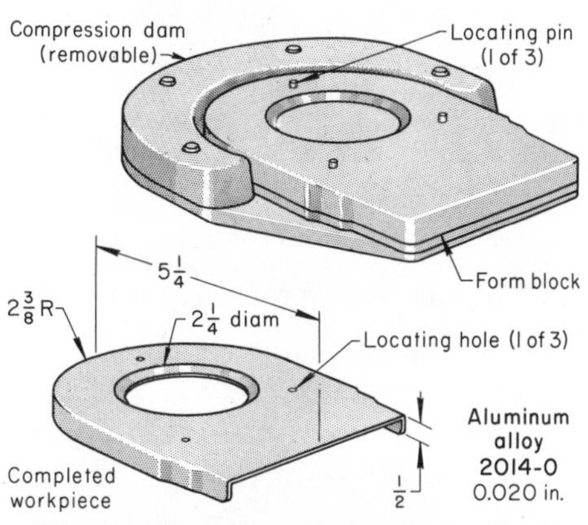

Fig. 6. Aircraft control-surface rib in which compression flange and joggles were formed in one operation by the Guerin process in a high-pressure setup (Example 281)

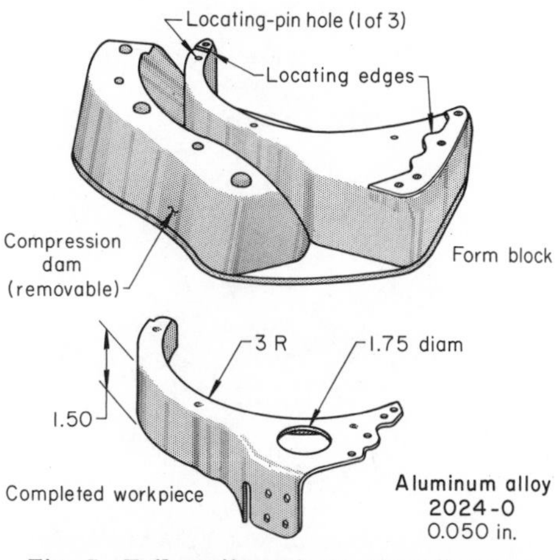

Fig. 7. Tail section of an aircraft frame that was flanged by combination stretch and shrink forming by the Guerin process using a high-pressure setup (Example 282)

Blanking. With the Guerin process, rubber pads can be used for blanking and piercing as well as for forming. Rubber pads produce better edges on the workpiece than band sawing, and almost as good as those made by routing. An edge radius up to the thickness of the metal can be produced on some heavy-gage metals. The rubber-pad method can blank aluminum alloy 2024-O up to 0.032 in. thick and, for some shapes, up to 0.040 in. thick. Minimum hole diameter or width of cutout is 2 in. A minimum of 1½-in. trim is needed for external cuts.

The form block is provided with a sharp cutting edge where the blank is to be sheared. In hard metal blocks, this edge can be cut into the form block, as shown in Fig. 9(a) and (b). Form blocks of soft metal, plastic, or wood need a steel shear plate for the cutting edge (Fig. 9c); the shearing edge should be undercut 3° to 6°.

The trim metal beyond the line of shear must be clamped firmly, so that the work metal will break over the sharp edge instead of forming around it. This clamping is done by a lock ring (Fig. 9a), by a grip plate (Fig. 9b), or by a raised extension of the form block (Fig. 9c).

These clamping devices also localize pressure at or near the cutting line. A rounded edge on the finished blank can be produced by locating the lock ring or grip plate a small distance from the shear edge (see Fig. 9a and b). The metal droops in the unsupported area and forms around the sharp corner before it shears. The result is a smooth, rounded edge.

Drawing of shallow parts is often done by a modification of the Guerin process in which the contour is recessed into the form block rather than being raised on it. The blank is securely clamped between the rubber pad and the surface around the recess before forming begins.

Clamping the work metal before drawing and the amount of pressure used are both important for successful drawing. The work metal must be

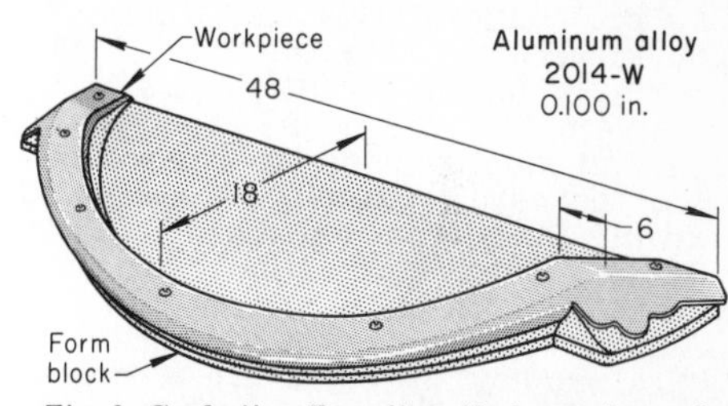

Fig. 8. Cockpit rail section that was formed on a single form block by the Guerin process (Example 283)

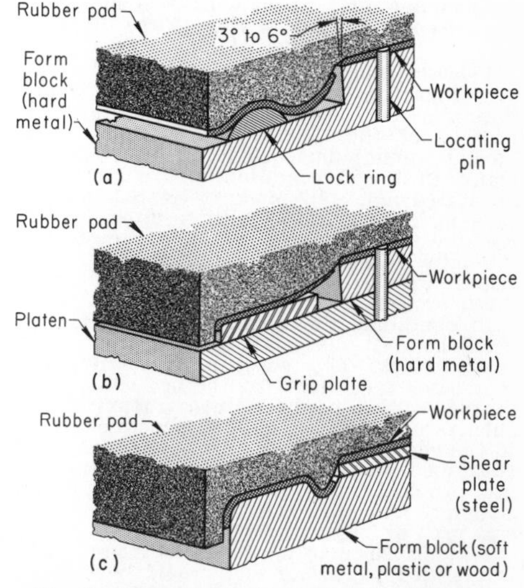

Fig. 9. Three techniques for blanking by the Guerin process. See text for discussion.

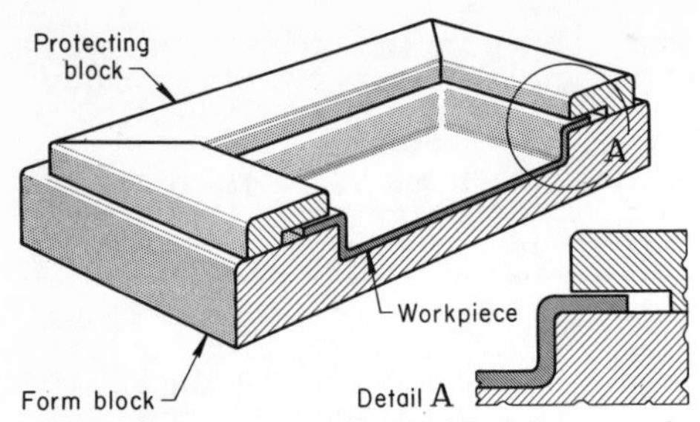

Fig. 10. Use of a protecting block to prevent work-metal irregularities in shallow drawing by the Guerin process

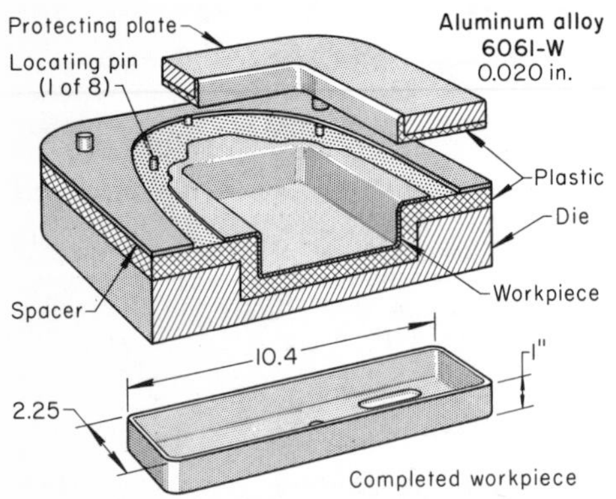

Fig. 11. Three-piece die and workpiece setup for a shallow draw with a rubber pad using a modification of the Guerin process (Example 284)

clamped securely to prevent it from flowing irregularly and subsequently forming wrinkles, but not so tightly that the metal cannot flow at all, which will cause thinning, or even tearing, of the work metal. To avoid this, either the edges can be lubricated or a protecting block with an undercut slot to accommodate the flange (Fig. 10) can be placed over the edges of the workpiece. The width of the block and undercut must provide the correct balance between clamping force and drawing force. The undercut should be 0.003 to 0.006 in. higher than the thickness of the work metal.

The following example describes a typical shallow draw using a modification of the Guerin process where a die cavity was used instead of a form block.

Example 284. Shallow Draw Using a Rubber Pad and a Three-Piece Die (Fig. 11)

The stiffener panel for an engine access door shown in Fig. 11 was made from aluminum alloy 6061, 0.020 in. thick, using a modification of the Guerin process in a press having a minimum capacity of 1600 psi. The blank, in the O condition, was cut oversize, lubricated and solution heat treated. Instead of a male form block, a three-piece die was used, which consisted of a die cavity of masonite faced with plastic, a sheet-metal spacer with an oval cutout, and a plastic-faced protecting plate.

In operation, the aluminum blank was located between the small locating pins in the cavity block. The sheet-metal spacer surrounded it and supported the protecting plate so that only a predetermined amount of the rubber-pad pressure applied clamping force to the edge of the blank. Thus, the blank was restrained when pressure from the rubber pad was applied, and entered the die cavity smoothly and evenly. A heavy-duty floor wax was used as lubricant.

It took 60 man-hr to make these tools. Conventional drawing tools would have taken three times as long to make. Production rate was 10 pieces per hour.

Verson-Wheelon Process

The Verson-Wheelon process was developed from the Guerin process. It uses higher pressure and is designed primarily for forming shallow parts, using a rubber pad as either the die or punch. A flexible hydraulic fluid cell forces an auxiliary rubber pad to follow the contour of the form block and exert a nearly uniform pressure at all points.

The distribution of pressure on the sides of the form block permits forming of wider flanges than the Guerin process. Also, shrink flanges, joggles, and beads and ribs in flanges and web surfaces can be formed in one operation to rather sharp detail in aluminum, low-carbon steel, stainless steel, heat-resisting alloys, and titanium.

Presses. The Verson-Wheelon press has a horizontal cylindrical steel housing, the roof of which contains a hydraulic fluid cell (Fig. 12). Hydraulic fluid is pumped into the cell, causing it to inflate or expand. The expansion creates the force needed to flow the rubber of the work pad downward, over and around the form block and the metal to be formed.

Below the chamber containing the rubber pad and the hydraulic fluid cell is a passage, extending the length of the press, that is wide and high enough to accommodate a sliding table containing form blocks. At each end of the passage is a sliding table that alternately can be moved into position for forming.

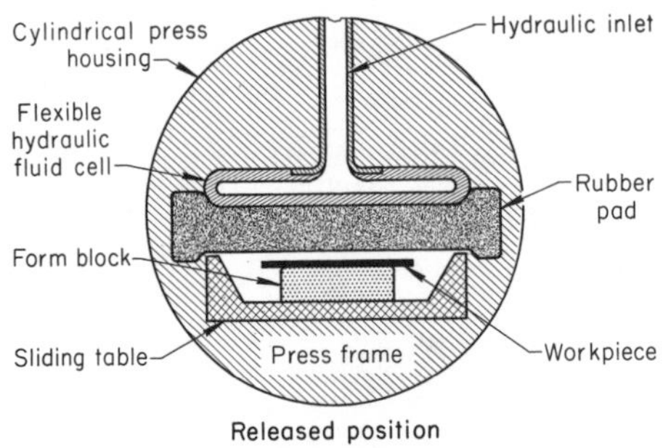

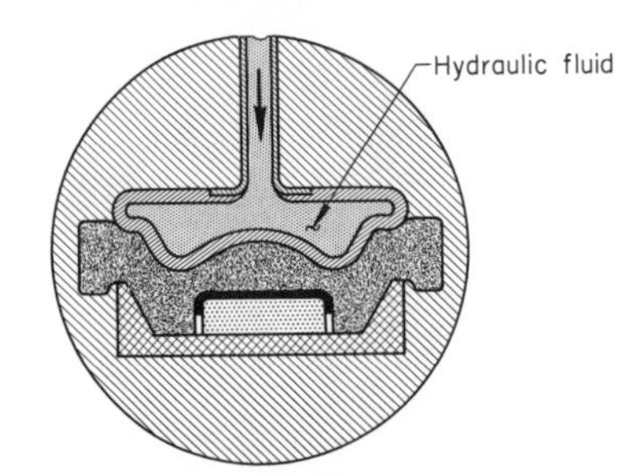

Fig. 12. Principles of the Verson-Wheelon process. See text for discussion.

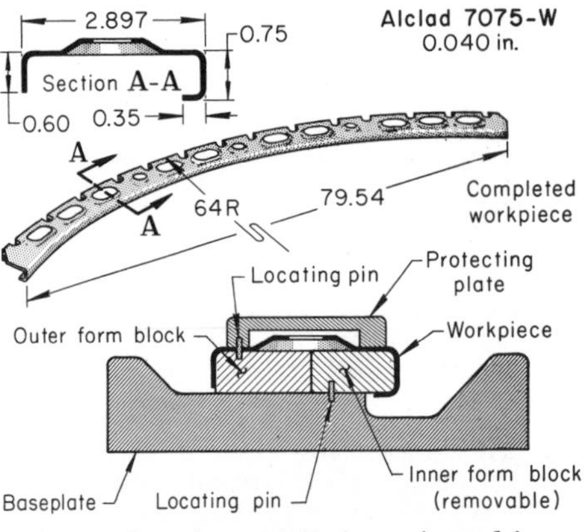

Fig. 13. Complex part that was formed in a Verson-Wheelon press (Example 285)

The rubber pad used in the Verson-Wheelon process has a hardness of about Durometer A 35. It is usually protected from sharp corners on the form block and blank by a throw sheet or work pad that is harder and tougher than the pad itself. The throw sheet is much less costly to replace than the rubber pad below the fluid cell.

The maximum pressures exerted by the machine are 5000, 7500 or 10,000 psi. Sliding tables range in size from 20 by 50 in. to 50 by 164 in. The larger machine can form parts having a flange width up to 9⅜ in.

Heating elements can be used with the sliding tables for producing parts made of magnesium. The maximum temperature is 800 F, and special heat-resisting throw pads are used to protect the hydraulic fluid cell.

Tools. The form blocks are made in much the same way as are the form blocks for the Guerin process. Compression dams or deflector bars can be used to direct pressure into local areas for forming shrink flanges or return bends, as described in Example 285.

Aluminum alloy or zinc alloy form blocks are recommended. Because of the high pressures, masonite or wood form blocks may break down from repeated use. More than one form block can be used at a time, the number depending on their size and shape.

Damage to the rubber pad can be reduced by removing all burrs and sharp edges from the blank. Form blocks should be smooth; all sharp corners and projecting edges should be well rounded; high tooling pins should be eliminated; deep narrow crevices or gaps between parts of form blocks should be eliminated; holes in blocks should be plugged during forming.

Procedure. The sliding table containing the form blocks is loaded and slid into the press. Hydraulic fluid is pumped into the cell, expanding it and driving the rubber pad down against the workpiece and around the form blocks. The pressure is released, and the table of formed pieces is slid out, unloaded and reloaded for another cycle.

Repositioning the form blocks after a few cycles will distribute the wear on the rubber pad and lengthen its life. The use of a hard rubber (or occasionally leather) pad a little larger than the blank assists in the uniform forming of flanges and prevents wrinkles.

The cycle time for the Verson-Wheelon process is longer than that of conventional presses such as are used with the Guerin process. To reduce cell filling and draining time, it is good practice to load the table to capacity or to have dummy blocks on the sliding table when only one part is being formed.

In the following example, the time to form a part in a Verson-Wheelon press was less than when the part was made by the Guerin process. The higher forming pressure completely formed the part in one operation (whereas the

Guerin process had required two operations) and reduced hand work after machine forming.

Example 285. Verson-Wheelon vs Guerin Process for Forming a Complex Part (Fig. 13)

The complex part shown in Fig. 13 was originally formed by the Guerin process in a 4500-ton hydraulic press from 0.040-in.-thick alclad aluminum alloy 7075-W. The improved method used a Verson-Wheelon press that could exert a pressure of 10,000 psi and had a capacity of 41,000 tons. A pressure of 7000 psi was needed to form the part. The same tool was used for both processes.

In the Guerin process, forming was done in two operations. Joggles and stringer tabs were set by hand after forming. In the first press operation, the outer flange was formed and the inner and return flanges were partly formed. In the second operation, the forming was completed with rubber strips confined by the dams. The two press operations took 8 man-min per piece, and the additional hand work took 3 man-min per piece.

In the Verson-Wheelon process, the outer, inner and return flanges and the joggles were formed in one operation. Press forming time per piece was only 6 man-min; hand work, which was limited to setting the tabs, required 1.5 man-min. Thus, total time per piece saved by the Verson-Wheelon process was 3.5 man-min, or 31.8%.

The heat treated aluminum alloy 6061 form block was mounted to a baseplate with inner and outer rims acting as dams. Because of the return flange on the inside radius of the part, the aluminum alloy form block was split lengthwise and the outer half was fastened to the baseplate (see tooling setup in Fig. 13). The inner half, bushed and located on pins projecting from the baseplate, was removed from the base with the finished part. Locating holes in the blank and outer form block matched locating pins in the cover plate.

The 5-by-88-in. blank was routed, and lightening holes were individually pierced and flanged, in a punch press in both processes before rubber-pad forming. After forming, the part was aged to the T6 temper. The production lot was 20 pieces. Several thousand pieces were produced on the form blocks.

Even though higher forming pressures are used, many pieces made by the Verson-Wheelon process (as well as by the Guerin process) need hand work to remove wrinkles and add definition to details, as in Example 541 in the article on Forming of Aluminum Alloys.

A further refinement in the use of throw pads is a shaped rubber pad. Pad laminations are built up around a cavity that approximates the shape of the part, so that flow of the rubber is less severe and forming pressure is more evenly distributed than with the conventional flat rubber pad. The shape of the cavity is only approximate and can be used for similar parts.

Marform Process

The Marform process was developed to apply the inexpensive tooling of the Guerin and Verson-Wheelon processes to deep drawing and forming of wrinkle-free shrink flanges.

A blankholder plate and a hydraulic cylinder with a pressure-regulating valve are used with a thick rubber pad and a form block similar to those used in the Guerin process. The blank is gripped between the blankholder and the rubber pad. The pressure-regulating valve controls the pressure applied to the blank while it is being drawn over the form block.

While forming a soft aluminum alloy blank, the diameter normally can be reduced 57%, and reductions as high as

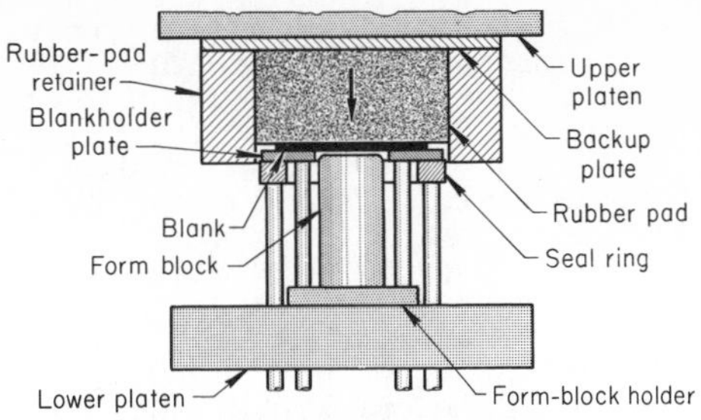

Fig. 14. Tooling and setup for rubber-pad forming by the Marform process

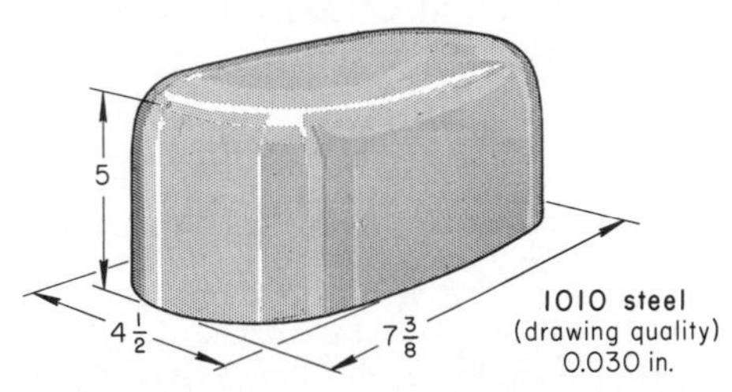

Fig. 15. Toaster shell that was deep drawn by the Marform process (Example 286)

72% have been obtained. A shell depth equal to the shell diameter is normal when the minimum stock thickness is 1% of the cup diameter. Depths up to three times shell diameter have been reached with multiple-operation forming. Minimum cup diameter is 1½ in.

Foil as thin as 0.0015 in. can be formed by placing the blank between two aluminum blanks about 0.030 in. thick and forming the three pieces as a unit, the inner and outer shells being discarded.

Presses. The Marform process is best suited to a single-action hydraulic press where pressure and speed of operation can be varied and controlled. A Marforming unit can be installed in a hydraulic press having ample stroke length and shut height. However, a press that incorporates a hydraulic cushion system in its bed has been designed specifically for Marforming.

Rubber pressures used depend on the press tonnage and surface area of the rubber pad. Present installations range from 5000 to 10,000 psi.

Tools. The rubber pad is similar to that used in the Guerin process. It normally is 1½ to 2 times as thick as the total depth of the part, including trim allowance. The rubber pad can be protected from scoring by the use of a throw sheet, which is either cemented to the pad or thrown over the blank.

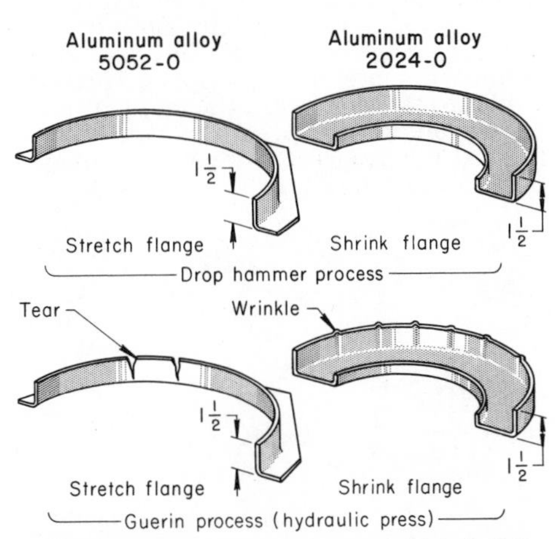

Fig. 16. Effect of impact in forming stretch and shrink flanges by the drop hammer (or trapped-rubber) and Guerin processes

Well polished steel form blocks are used for long runs and deep draws. Aluminum alloy form blocks must be hard coated to prevent galling for draws deeper than 1½ in. Masonite form blocks can be used if they can withstand the abuse and wear of forming a particular part in a given quantity. When a cast shape is more economical, aluminum or zinc alloy form blocks may be used.

Blankholder plates are usually made of low-carbon steel. The contact surface is ground flat and polished to avoid scratching of the blank. Clearance between the form block and the mating hole in the blankholder is 0.030 to 0.060 in. per side. The edge should have a 1/16-in. radius.

A radius plate is necessary when the machine pressure is insufficient for forming the flange radius within tolerance. The part is drawn first without the plate, then redrawn using the plate to form the exact radius. The radius plate usually is ½ in. thick, and 1 in. wider than the workpiece. A sealing ring is used to prevent the rubber pad from extruding out of the container.

Procedure. The blank rests on the blankholder plate above the form block. The rods supporting the seal ring and blankholder plate (see Fig. 14) are supported on a variable-pressure hydraulic cushion. As the press ram is lowered, the blank is clamped between the rubber pad and the blankholder before forming begins. As the rubber pad continues to descend, the blank is drawn over the form block while the pressure-control valve in the hydraulic cushion releases fluid at a controlled rate. The pressure in the hydraulic cushion must be adjusted so as to prevent wrinkles forming in the flange but to permit the blank to be drawn into a smooth shell. The part is stripped from the form block by the blankholder.

The following example describes an application of the process.

Example 286. Deep Drawing of Toaster Shells by the Marform Process (Fig. 15)

The toaster shell shown in Fig. 15 was deep drawn in large quantities (80,000 pieces) from 0.030-in.-thick, deep drawing quality 1010 steel. The blanks were lubricated by brushing with a soap compound. Available pressure was 6000 psi. Depth of the trimmed shell was 5 in. Production time per piece was 22 sec.

Drop Hammer Forming With Trapped Rubber

A process similar to the Guerin process, for forming shallow workpieces, is a trapped-rubber process, which uses a drop hammer in place of the hydraulic press; the main difference is the faster forming speed and the impact force of the hammer. The use of rubber pads in drop hammer forming is illustrated by Fig. 2 on page 246, and the accompanying discussion in the article "Drop Hammer Forming".

In Fig. 16, the effects of forming flanges on aluminum alloys 5052-O and 2024-O by the drop hammer (trapped-rubber) and Guerin processes are shown.

When flanges deeper than 1¼ in. are made by the Guerin process, stretch flanges can tear and shrink flanges can wrinkle. However, when the drop hammer process is used, fewer deformities occur (see Fig. 16).

Rubber-Diaphragm Forming

This process differs from those previously described in that the die cavity is not completely filled with rubber, but with hydraulic fluid retained by a 2½-in.-thick cup-shape rubber diaphragm. This cavity is called the pressure dome (see Fig. 17). A replaceable wear sheet is cemented to the lower surface of the diaphragm (Fig. 17).

More severe draws can be made by this method than in conventional draw dies because the oil pressure against the diaphragm causes the metal to be held tightly against the sides as well as against the top of the punch.

Reductions in blank diameter of 60 to 70% are common for a first draw.

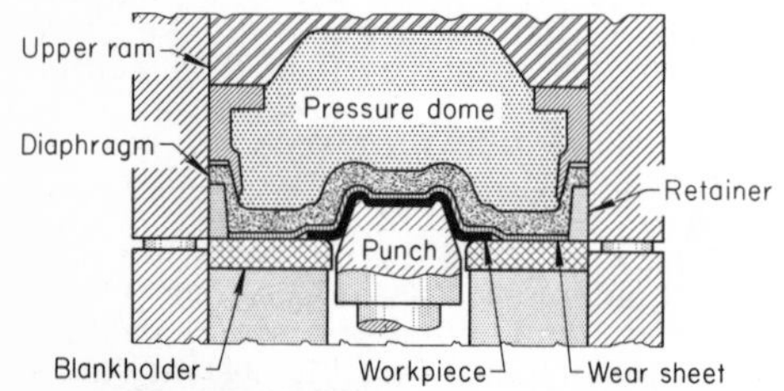

Fig. 17. Rubber-diaphragm forming in a Hydroform press

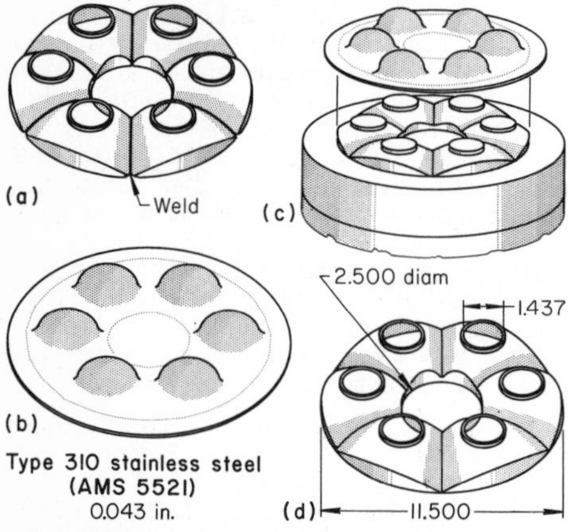

(a) Part formed by original method; six press-formed sections welded together. (b) Partly drawn blank ready for rubber-diaphragm forming. (c) Punch of six similar wedge-shape segments doweled into bottom plate, used for rubber-diaphragm forming. (d) Swirl cup as formed by the rubber-diaphragm method and subsequently pierced and trimmed.

Fig. 18. Original and improved methods of forming a fuel nozzle swirl cup for a turbojet engine (Example 287)

When redrawing is necessary, reductions can reach 40%. Low-carbon steel, stainless steel, and aluminum in thicknesses from 0.010 to 0.065 in. are commonly formed. Parts made of heat-resisting alloys and copper alloys are also formed by the process.

Presses. A special press, called a Hydroform press, is used for this process. A lower hydraulic ram drives the punch upward; the upper ram is basically a positioning device. A hydraulic pump delivers fluid under pressure to the pressure dome. The blankholder is supported by a solid bolster, and does not move during the operation.

The largest press of this type can draw a blank 25 in. in diameter to a maximum depth of 12 in. Punch diameter can range up to 19 in. Maximum dome pressure is 15,000 psi. Maximum rating is 1500 cycles per hour. Practical production rate in cycles per hour is usually about two-thirds the machine rating. However, the operation often takes the place of two or three conventional press operations.

(A variation of this process has the punch stationary and the blankholder actuated by the die cushion of a single-action hydraulic press, as shown in Fig. 22.)

Tools. Punches can be made of tool steel, cold rolled steel, cast iron, zinc alloy, plastic, brass, aluminum, or hardwood. Choice of material depends largely on the work metal to be formed, number of parts to be made, shape of the part, and severity of the draw.

Blankholders are usually made of cast iron or steel, and are hardened if necessary. Clearance between punch and blankholder is not critical — it may be 50% or more of the thickness of the metal being drawn.

For short runs, an auxiliary blankholding plate can be placed on a blankholder that is already in place. The auxiliary blankholder plate should not overhang in the punch clearance more than its thickness, and it should not be larger than the blankholder.

Rubber strips are placed on the blank to break the vacuum caused by dome action during drawing. Blankholders can be contoured to match the shape of a preformed blank, or to preform the blank as an aid in forming.

Procedure. The blank to be formed is placed on the blankholder. The pressure dome, filled with the hydraulic fluid and covered by the rubber diaphragm, is lowered over the blank, and preliminary pressure is applied through a pump in the hydraulic supply line. The preliminary pressure can range from 200 to 10,000 psi, depending on the part to be formed.

The punch is raised and pushed into the blank from underneath. As the form in the blank rises into the hydraulic chamber, the pressure in the chamber increases sharply, reaching as high as 15,000 psi. A pressure-control valve keeps the pressure within programmed limits. When parts are formed of thin metal, a vacuum release valve can be built into the punch to aid stripping after forming.

Three cams on the machine are programmed to control the machine's operation; the first controls the height of rise of the punch, the second controls "edging" or sharpening of the corner radii, and the third returns the punch at the end of the stroke while the blankholder strips the finished part from the punch.

Forming a complex part by the rubber-diaphragm process is described in the following example.

Example 287. Rubber-Diaphragm Forming of a Complex Jet-Engine Part (Fig. 18)

Fuel nozzle swirl cups for high-performance turbojet engines were originally produced by welding six press-formed sections of type 310 stainless steel, AMS 5521 (Fig. 18a). Forming the six sections was difficult, and finished parts were expensive. Rejection rate was also high.

Rubber-diaphragm forming in a Hydroform press was tried. This press formed the part from one blank 0.043 in. thick by 12¾ in. in diameter. Less press force was used, and costs were reduced 50%.

Before forming, the blank was rough drawn (Fig. 18b) in a 150-ton hydraulic press to a depth of 1.40 in., and its thickness was reduced to 0.039 in.

After degreasing and annealing, the partly formed blank was drawn in a 12-in. Hydroform press, using the punch shown in Fig. 18(c). The blank rested on a blankholder mounted on a sub-bolster. Diametral clearance between punch and blankholder was a minimum of 50% of the work-metal thickness. Production rate was 30 pieces per hour.

After forming, six equally spaced 1.437-in.-diam holes and a 2.500-in.-diam center hole were pierced in a 55-ton mechanical press. The outside diameter was trimmed in a lathe after the part had been pierced, annealed and restruck. The completed workpiece is shown in Fig. 18(d).

The two examples that follow show the importance of lubricant and its application when the depth of draw is near the limit for the rubber-diaphragm process.

Example 288. Deep Drawing by the Rubber-Diaphragm Process (Fig. 19)

The steering-column cover shown in Fig. 19 was made from a cup-shape workpiece 3¾ in. in diameter and 5⅝ in. deep that was drawn in one operation in a Hydroform press from a 10-in.-diam blank of 0.032-in.-thick, pickled, cold rolled, aluminum-killed 1010 steel.

A light mineral oil was applied to the flat blank with a roller coater. Before drawing was started, a ¼-in.-wide (minimum) surface around the outer edge of the blank was wiped clean of oil to provide a gripping surface for the blankholder. When too much oil was on the blank, or when the cleaned edge was too narrow, three or four folds, caused by wrinkling, appeared in the flange. Parts with folds were not scrapped, because the depth of draw was such that the defects could be trimmed away, but the wear sheet was damaged if wrinkling occurred frequently. Burrs on the blank also damaged the wear sheet.

Operations subsequent to rubber-diaphragm forming were: reduce diameter of closed end and taper remaining length, trim top and bottom in a shimmy die, anneal part of small diameter with gas torch, form small end, and punch slot. Annealing the small diameter of the tube was necessary because the metal work hardened during the two previous operations.

1010 steel, aluminum killed
Cold rolled, 0.032 in.

Drawn — Reduced and tapered — Completed workpiece

Fig. 19. Steering-column cover that was drawn from a circular blank in one operation by rubber-diaphragm forming in a Hydroform press. Operations that followed drawing were done with conventional tooling. (Example 288)

Parts not annealed cracked during forming of the small end.

The rubber-diaphragm process not only eliminated one or two redraws, but also produced the part without scratches or draw marks on the outer surface (later painted), which might have been produced by a conventional drawing operation.

The 10,000-psi machine used was larger than necessary, but permitted a production rate of 180 to 190 pieces per hour.

Example 289. Use of Lubricant to Eliminate Tearing and Wrinkling in Severe Rubber-Diaphragm Drawing (Fig. 20)

The stepped cover shown in Fig. 20 represented the limit of forming severity for the rubber-diaphragm equipment that was available. Material was 0.040-in.-thick cold rolled drawing quality 1008 steel. The shell was 4 in. deep and had a step in its outer contour. Attempts to draw the stepped shell in one operation in a Hydroform press were not successful. Subsequently, two Hydroforming operations were developed in which the larger width of the cover was drawn first, and then the narrower portion above the step was produced in a redrawing operation to complete the part.

In the first operation, the blankholding pressure had to be carefully adjusted. When the pressure was too low, the metal moved freely and wrinkles appeared at the corners. Too high a blankholding pressure caused tears along the narrow end. Tears and wrinkles damaged the wear sheet and, in extreme cases, the diaphragm itself. Each wear sheet cost $3; each diaphragm, $30.

A lubrication program was developed that prevented wrinkling or tearing. After the first draw, the workpiece was cleaned, annealed, and phosphate coated. The phosphate made it possible to use a lighter oil, and also to apply it more effectively, with heavy applications in some areas and little or none in others. With experience, operators became expert at judging location and thickness of lubricant. Mechanical application of lubricant could not be made selective enough or controlled closely enough for consistent results.

Because the part was nearly impossible to produce by conventional deep drawing techniques, rubber-diaphragm forming was used. The tools, consisting of two punches and a blankholder, cost considerably less than the several sets of draw dies that would otherwise have been needed, and with the lubricating technique that was developed, there was less danger of tearing or wrinkling than by other processes.

A major reason for using any rubber-pad process is to preserve the surface finish of the work metal, which would be scuffed or marked by ordinary press forming tools. In the following example, appearance was an important consideration. The part was to be plated with copper-nickel-chromium. Forming by the rubber-diaphragm method prevented marks that would have been difficult to buff out before plating.

Example 290. Use of the Rubber-Diaphragm Process to Preserve Surface Finish on a Flatiron Shell (Fig. 21)

Because a mechanical draw press caused an impact line on the workpiece that was difficult to remove by buffing, production of the flatiron shell shown in Fig. 21 was changed to a rubber-diaphragm process, using a 400-ton Hydroform press. A rubber draw ring of Durometer A 92 hardness helped adjust hold-down pressure so that wrinkles were avoided in the finished product. Two rubber pads were used on the rubber diaphragm. One covered the diaphragm as a reinforcement and protector; the other was a ⅜-in.-thick ring molded to the shell outline. The blank was located in a nest on the blankholder.

Previously the part had been drawn on a single-action mechanical press of 100-ton capacity. In this press, the tools had been made of D2 tool steel. The stock was treated with soap and wiped with hydraulic oil near the point of the shell to minimize tearing.

The Hydroform press cycled at 450 strokes per minute. Production-lot size was 50,000 pieces, and yearly production was 850,000 pieces. Life of the rubber pads was as high as 20,000 pieces, and the finish of the part was good enough for subsequent plating with a minimum of buffing.

Sequence of operations was as follows: cut off blank, draw in Hydroform press, trim, pierce, copper plate, buff, nickel-chromium plate. The stock was 0.033 ± 0.003-in.-thick cold rolled low-carbon steel sheet slit to width. Two different qualities were used, as follows: (*a*) aluminum-killed, drawing quality, special-surface steel with a commercial finish, dry, maximum hardness Rockwell B 60; and (*b*) cold rolled aluminum-killed steel strip with a No. 2 finish, dry, dead soft, maximum hardness Rockwell B 55.

Tolerance on important dimensions was ±0.003 in.; on angles, ±½°.

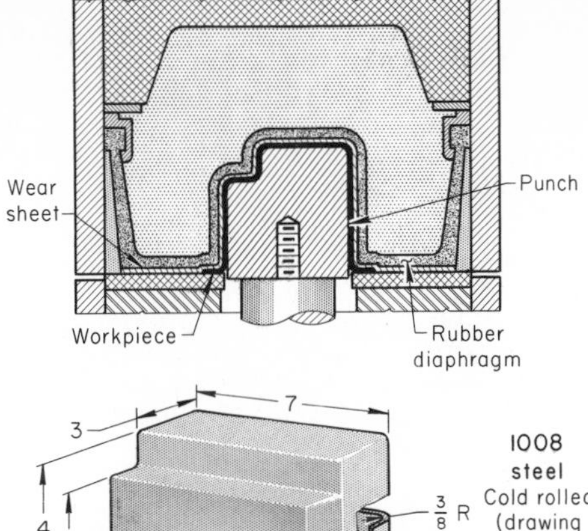

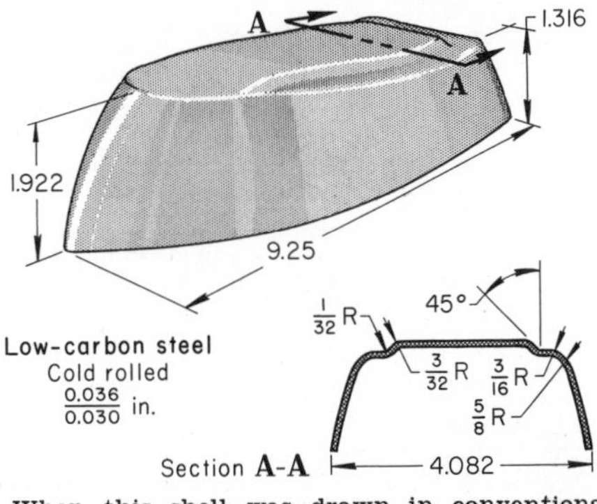

Fig. 20. Drawing a stepped cover by the rubber-diaphragm process (Example 289)

When this shell was drawn in conventional dies, an impact line was caused below the radius that was difficult to remove in buffing.

Fig. 21. Flatiron shell that was formed by the rubber-diaphragm process in a Hydroform press to preserve the surface finish (Example 290)

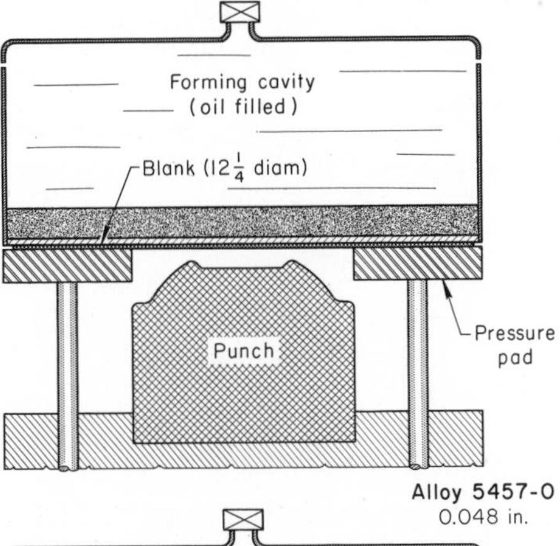

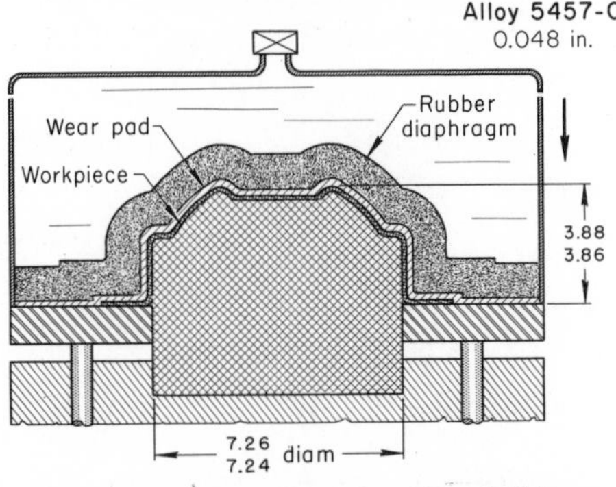

Fig. 22. Forming an automotive tail-lamp housing in one draw in a rubber-diaphragm press (Example 291)

In the following example, a pressure dome was mounted on the ram of a single-action hydraulic press. The punch was fixed to a shoe mounted on the bolster plate. A die cushion provided the blankholding force. This setup functioned much like a conventional draw die except that the oil-filled pressure dome and rubber diaphragm replaced the draw ring and die cavity.

Example 291. Forming an Automotive Tail-Lamp Housing in One Drawing Operation in a Rubber-Diaphragm Press (Fig. 22)

An automotive tail-lamp housing was drawn in one operation from an aluminum alloy 5457-O blank, 0.048 in. thick and 12¼ in. in diameter, in a rubber-diaphragm press rated at 10,000 psi, as shown in Fig. 22. A water-soluble low-foaming lubricant was used. Production rate was 425 to 450 pieces per hour.

To produce this part with conventional tooling, two drawing operations would have been needed to form the sharp radii at the top and bottom of the part.

Tooling costs for the rubber-diaphragm press were less than one-third the cost for conventional press tooling.

The blanks were moved from a stack adjacent to the press to an automatic feeder by a pneumatic suction transfer device. A photoelectric cell prevented more than one blank being transferred. The blank passed between lubricating rollers before being fed automatically into the die.

In subsequent operations, the housing was trimmed, flanged and pierced in a mechanical press, using two conventional dies.

Rubber Punches

For some applications, the male member of a die set is made of rubber, and the female member is made of a hard material. In the Guerin process, shallow draws are made by recessing the form block and using the rubber pad as a punch to form the part (see "Drawing of Shallow Parts", page 211). The advantage of this method is that the flange is clamped before drawing, thus preventing wrinkling.

In the SAAB rubber-diaphragm method, hydraulic fluid is used behind a comparatively thin rubber pad or diaphragm. A hydraulic piston compresses the fluid against the rubber and forces the blank into the die, as shown in Fig. 23 on the next page.

In all rubber-punch forming processes, air vents are provided in the die, to allow the air trapped between workpiece and die to escape (Fig. 23). Without air vents, the trapped air would prevent the workpiece from reaching the full contours of the die and the workpiece would have to be removed after partial forming to release the compressed air, and then replaced in the same die to complete the forming.

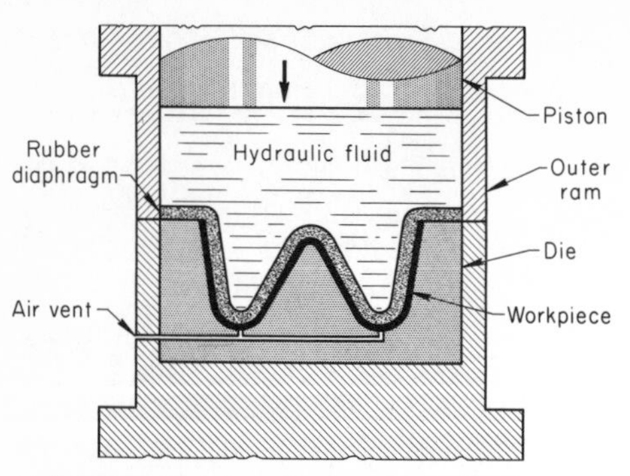

Fig. 23. Principles of SAAB *rubber-diaphragm forming. The air vents keep trapped air from making blisters on the workpiece.*

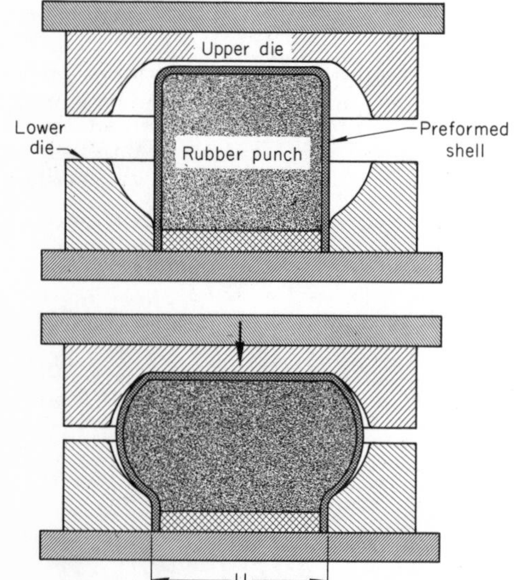

Fig. 24. Bulging a mushroom shape from a preformed shell in a two-piece die with a rubber punch (Example 292)

Bulging Punches. Rubber punches can be used to make tubular parts that must be expanded or beaded somewhere along their lengths. If such parts were made with solid punches, the punches would have to be collapsible so that they could be withdrawn.

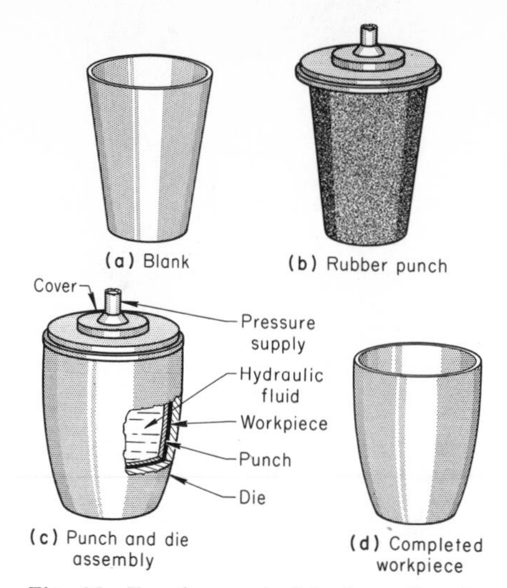

Fig. 25. Forming a fuel-tank section by the Demarest process (Example 293)

Hollow shapes can be bulged into suitable mating dies by applying a vertical force to the punch. The dies must be segmented so that the resulting bulged product can be removed, as shown in the following example.

Example 292. Forming a Mushroom Shape in a Segmented Bulging Die (Fig. 24)

Figure 24 shows the process used in forming a mushroom-shape frying-pan cover. The workpiece was a rectangular drawn shell of stainless steel, which was placed over a rubber punch of the same shape.

The two dies, which contained between them a cavity of the shape required, were closed until the rubber punch bulged the workpiece. Amount of bulge was determined by the depth of stroke. When the dies were opened, the punch returned to its original shape and was easily extracted from the finished part.

Demarest Process. Cylindrical and conical parts can also be formed by a modified rubber bulging punch. The punch, equipped with a hydraulic cell, is placed inside the workpiece, which in turn is placed inside the die. Hydraulic pressure expands the punch.

Forming with an expanding punch using the Demarest process is described in the following example.

Example 293. Use of Expanding Punches to Form Aircraft Fuel-Tank Sections (Fig. 25)

Aluminum alloy workpieces, rolled and welded into cones (Fig. 25a), were formed into aircraft fuel-tank sections with expanding rubber punches (Fig. 25b). The cones were lowered into cast iron dies, which weighed 3500 lb each and were designed to withstand 1500-psi forming pressure.

The rubber punch was lowered into the workpiece and a steel cover clamped over the whole assembly (Fig. 25c). The punch was expanded under 400-psi hydraulic pressure, which formed the work metal into the curved shape of the die (Fig. 25d).

The time taken for the whole process, including dismantling of the die and unloading of the workpiece, was 3 min, as against 15 to 20 min for spinning.

Other Examples

Details of other production applications of rubber-pad forming are given in five examples in articles in this volume that deal with the forming of specific metals. These examples are:

Example	Application
479	Use of cover plate and curved die to protect the web of a stainless steel workpiece and compensate for springback.
541	Hand setting of joggles to sharpen contours after forming an aluminum workpiece by the Verson-Wheelon process.
542	Forming of beads in an aluminum workpiece with a concave die, by a modification of the Guerin process.
600	Forming a coffee urn of copper alloy 110 (ETP copper) in one operation by the rubber-diaphragm process.
617	Forming of shrink and stretch flanges on a titanium workpiece, with an undercut form block to allow for springback.

Failures in Rubber-Pad Flanging

Rubber-pad forming of flanges can be performed within certain limits. The flange must be wide enough to develop sufficient bending force (see Table 2), but not so wide as to exceed the permissible depth of the part. Figure 26 shows some typical flanging failures.

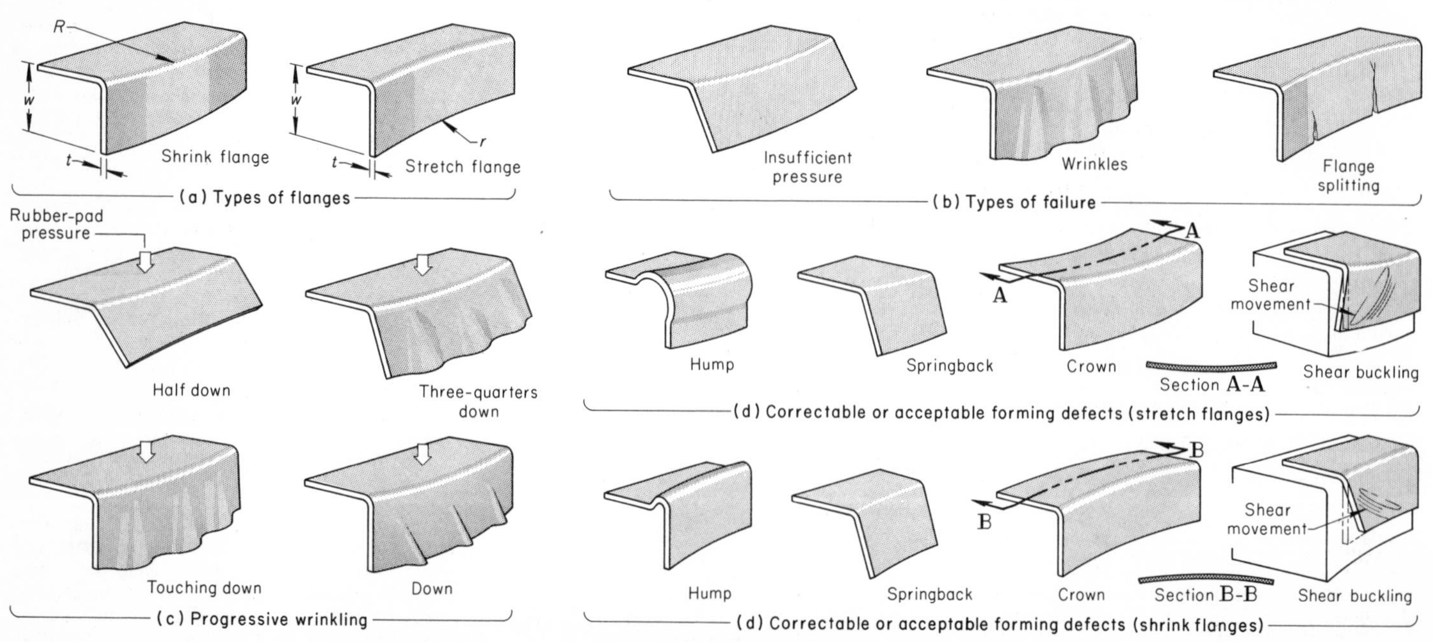

Fig. 26. Principal types of failure in curved flanges made by rubber-pad forming

Three-Roll Forming

*By the ASM Committee on Press-Brake Forming and Three-Roll Forming of Steel**

THREE-ROLL FORMING is a process for forming plate, sheet, bars, beams, angles, or pipe into various shapes by passing the work metal between three properly spaced rolls. Sheet and plate are the mill products most often formed by the three-roll process.

Shapes Produced. Some of the shapes commonly produced by three-roll forming from flat stock are illustrated in Fig. 1.

The plain round cylinder in Fig. 1 is used for pressure tanks, boilers and related containers, and comprises a large portion of the shapes produced. The corrugated cylinder is produced in quantity for culvert pipe, and is formed from flat stock corrugated at the mill. To retain the corrugations in the workpiece, the forming rolls also must be corrugated.

The flattened cylinder (obround) is used mainly for oil-supply tanks for heating systems and transformer cases. The elliptical cylinder is used for tank trucks hauling liquid food products, petroleum products and chemicals.

Both symmetrical and unsymmetrical cones are used in a wide variety of hoppers, bins, vertical storage tanks, concrete mixers, and vessels for chemical and food processing, as well as in piping and ductwork.

In addition to the shapes produced for commercial use, three-roll forming is used also for producing various regular and irregular shapes for structural sections of submarines, aircraft, and nuclear reactors.

Metals Formed. Any metal ductile enough to be cold formed by other processes can be formed in a three-roll machine. Steels having a maximum carbon content of 0.25% comprise a major portion of the total tonnage used in three-roll forming. Steel sheet or plate in the 1010 to 1020 category sometimes is used, but most of the steels formed by this process conform to one of the plate specifications: either plain carbon or low-alloy steels, such as ASTM A515 grade 60, A515 grade 70, A516 grade 70, A285, A441, A283, A306 and A36. For the most successful three-roll forming, steels having a minimum elongation of 18% are preferred.

Stainless steels, heat-resisting alloys, and aluminum and copper alloys also can be successfully formed by the three-roll process.

Metal thicknesses commonly used range from 0.0598-in. sheet (16 gage) to 10-in. plate. In a few applications, 12-in. plate has been formed successfully. The principal factors limiting maximum thickness are size and power of the rolling machine. Minimum thickness is usually limited only by handling equipment. Usually, any sheet that can be handled without damage can be rolled.

It is not practical to roll thicknesses ranging from 0.0598 to 10 in. on the same machine, although any machine can handle a relatively wide range of work-metal thicknesses. For example, a machine capable of rolling ⅜-in. plate (maximum or near maximum) generally can roll sheet as thin as 0.0598 in., whereas a machine having a maximum capability for rolling 6-in. plate can successfully roll plate as thin as ½ in. (even less on some machines).

Diameter and Width. The minimum diameter of a workpiece that can be formed successfully in a given machine is governed by the diameter of the top roll on either of the two types of machines used in three-roll forming (pinch type or pyramid type). In general, the smallest cylinder that can be rolled under optimum conditions is 2 in. larger in diameter than the top roll of a pinch-type machine. On a pyramid-type machine the minimum workpiece diameter is rarely less than 6 in. greater than the top roll. However, more power is required to form sheet or plate into cylinders of minimum diameter than to form cylinders substantially larger than the top roll.

The maximum workpiece diameter that can be rolled is limited primarily by the space available above the machine to accommodate extremely large circles. Thin-gage metal rolled to a large diameter on horizontal rolls becomes less self-supporting as the workpiece diameter increases, and out-of-round cylinders will result if supports are not used. However, by use of supports, almost any diameter can be rolled from thin metal. As a general guide, 0.0598-in.-thick low-carbon steel sheet can be formed into cylinders as large as 48 in. in diameter without support, whereas ¼-in.-thick low-carbon steel can be formed into cylinders as large as 84-in. diam without support.

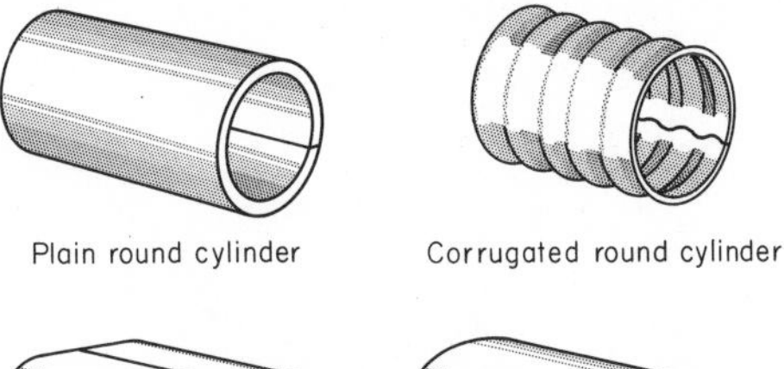

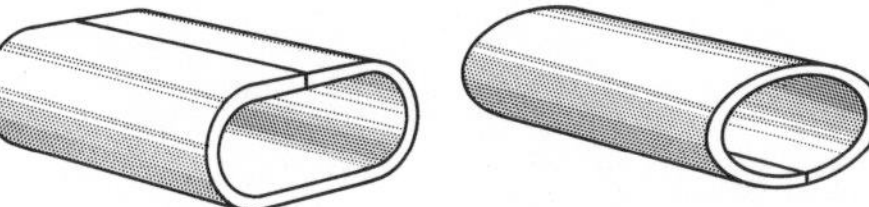

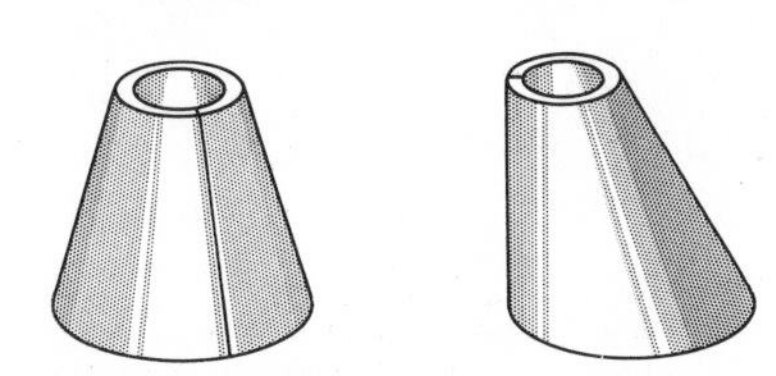

Fig. 1. Typical shapes produced from flat stock by three-roll forming

The width (dimension of the work metal parallel with the axes of the rolls, designated as length in the formed cylinder) of sheet or plate that can be rolled is limited by the size of the equipment; machines with rolls as long as 41 ft have been built. The width-to-diameter relation for workpieces extremely large in both directions is limited by problems in handling.

Machines

There are two basic types of three-roll forming machines: the pinch-roll type and the pyramid-roll type. The rolls on most three-roll machines are positioned horizontally; a few vertical machines are used, mainly in shipyards. Vertical machines have one advantage in forming scaly plate: loose scale is less likely to become embedded in the work metal than when bending is done in horizontal rolls (especially, pinch-type rolls). With vertical rolls, however, it is difficult to handle wide sections that require careful support to avoid skewness in rolling. Most vertical machines have short rolls for fast unloading, and are used for bending of narrow plate, bars, and structural sections.

Conventional pinch-type machines have the roll arrangement shown in Fig. 2. For rolling flat stock up to about 1 in. thick, each roll is of the same diameter. However, on larger machines, the top rolls sometimes are smaller in diameter to maintain approximately the same surface speed on both the inside and outside surfaces of the plate being formed. These heavier machines are supplied also with a slip-friction drive on the front roll to permit slip, because of the differential in surface speed of the rolls. Thus, as work-metal thickness increases, the diameter of the top roll is decreased in relation to the diameter of the lower rolls.

The position of the top roll is fixed, whereas the lower front roll is adjustable vertically to suit the thickness of the blank. Optimum adjustment of the lower roll is important, not only for gripping the stock but also for minimizing the length of the flat areas on the workpiece. The rear or bending roll is adjustable angularly (usually 30° off vertical), as shown in Fig. 2. Angular movement of this roll determines the diameter of the cylinder to be formed.

On most pinch-type machines, all rolls are powered. On some machines, however, only the two front rolls are powered and the bending roll is rotated

*For committee list, see page 101.

by friction between the roll and the work metal, as shown in Fig. 2. This arrangement is usually satisfactory in forming medium-to-heavy stock to large diameters. However, when forming sheet or plate that is thin or soft, or both, or when the diameter is large, the amount of friction is sometimes insufficient to rotate the bending roll. This condition can result in a marred surface if the work metal is soft or has a bright mill finish (aluminum sheet, for example).

A pinch-type machine can produce a more nearly true cylindrical shape than a pyramid-type machine, because the work metal is held more firmly, resulting in smaller flat areas on the leading and trailing ends of the workpiece.

As shown in Fig. 2, the work metal is fed to the powered pinch rolls (front), which grip the plate and move it through the machine. Forming begins when the work metal contacts the bending roll (rear) and is forced upward. As the forward motion of the workpiece continues, a cylindrical shape is produced, except for the unformed flat area along the leading end and a small flat area at the trailing end of the workpiece, as shown in Fig. 2. The width of the flat area on the trailing end usually ranges from $\frac{1}{2}t$ to $2t$ (t = work-metal thickness), depending on the design of the machine.

In most pinch-roll forming, one of two procedures is used to minimize flat areas. The most common method is to preform both ends of the work metal in the machine. This is done by reversing the rotation of the rolls and feeding a short section of the work metal from the rear, thus preforming one end. The work metal then is removed from the machine and the formed section can be fed into the machine from the front, or it can be turned to the opposite unformed end and fed through from the rear of the machine. This procedure eliminates most of the flat areas.

Another method is to preform the leading and trailing ends of the work metal in a press brake, hydraulic press, or joggling press. However, this technique is not often used, because it is usually more convenient to preform in the pinch-roll machine.

On the other hand, preforming in a press brake, or in hydraulic or joggling presses, can sometimes save time in the rolling machine, thus increasing the productivity of the machine.

Additional advantages of a pinch-roll machine, compared to a pyramid-roll machine, are:

1 When all rolls are power driven, thinner sheets can be rolled, and cylinders can be formed to within about 2 in. of the diameter of the top roll.
2 A given size of a pinch-type machine can roll a greater range of metal thicknesses, because of the method of feed.
3 Greater dimensional accuracy can be obtained in one pass in a pinch-type machine than in a pyramid-type machine.

The principal disadvantage of a pinch-roll machine is its unsuitability for rolling workpieces from angles, channels and other structural forms.

Shoe-Type Pinch-Roll Machines. One important modification of the conventional three-roll pinch-type machine is the shoe-type machine, which uses the pinch principle but in addition incorporates a forming shoe, as shown in Fig. 3. Because of the relation of the two front rolls and the forming shoe to the workpiece, the flat area becomes barely discernible compared with the length of flat area obtained when rolling in a conventional machine (without preforming).

The shoe-type machine is often used for manufacture of transformer cases and small tanks, such as jackets for hot-water tanks. This type of machine can be completely automated, so that the work metal can be positioned on the table and fed into the machine automatically. During the work cycle, the cylinder is formed and ejected by means of an ejector mechanism and an automatically controlled drop end. Thus, a shoe-type machine is primarily a production machine used where large quantities of identical workpieces are to be rolled. For this reason and because of the limitations listed in the following, shoe-type machines seldom compete directly with conventional pinch-type machines.

1 Thickness of work metal is limited to 12 gage (0.1046 in.).
2 Width of sheet is limited to 72 in.
3 Shoe-type machines are best adapted to rolling of round cylinders; rolling of ovals or obrounds is not practical.
4 Shoe-type machines are applicable only to cold forming.

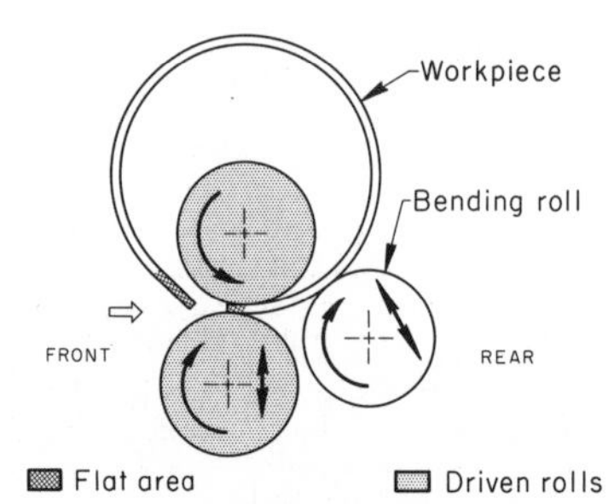

Fig. 2. End view of a cylindrical workpiece being rolled in a conventional pinch-type machine. Note large flat area on leading end, and smaller flat area on trailing end.

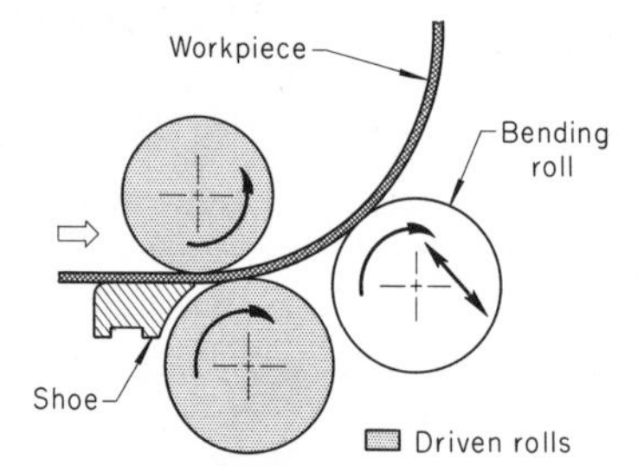

Fig. 3. End view of a cylindrical workpiece being rolled in a shoe-type machine with two powered rolls

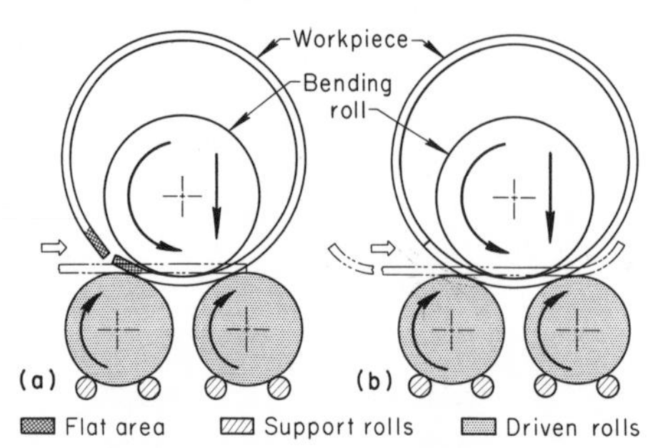

(a) Entrance of flat workpiece and shape of a nearly finished workpiece, including the flat areas on the leading and trailing ends. (b) Similar, except that the workpiece was prebent to minimize the flat areas on the ends.

Fig. 4. Arrangement of rolls in a pyramid-type machine

Within their range of applicability, however, shoe-type machines can produce a rolled cylinder in about half the time required in a conventional machine, mainly because preforming is not required with a shoe-type machine.

Pyramid-Type Machines. Figure 4 illustrates the arrangement of the rolls in a pyramid-type machine. The bottom rolls are of equal diameter, but are about 50% smaller in diameter than the top roll. The bottom rolls are gear-driven and (normally) fixed; each roll is supported by two smaller rolls (Fig. 4). The top roll is adjustable vertically to control the diameter of the cylinder formed. The top roll, which rotates freely, depends on friction with the work metal for rotation. Backup rolls are not used on the top roll.

As shown in Fig. 4, the work metal is placed on the bottom rolls while the top roll is in a raised position. The top roll is then lowered to contact and bend the work metal a predetermined amount, depending on the diameter of the workpiece to be formed. Machines are usually equipped with a device that indicates the amount of initial bend. Some machines use an ammeter, which shows the amount of current used in forcing the roll downward. However, this device measures force only; variables in the work metal can cause differences in the amount of bend for a given force.

As required bending force increases, machines are designed with rolls of larger diameter, and the distance between centers of the bottom rolls increases. Because bending forces are applied midway between the bottom rolls, less force is needed for a given deflection, but less curvature is produced.

Because the top roll is adjustable, pyramid rolls can be used for forming irregular shapes by bolting dies to the top roll — a technique that is not adaptable to pinch-type machines. In addition, plate, beams, angles and other structural forms can be straightened with greater ease, because the bottom rolls are on the same elevation.

Because the top roll is an idler, there are definite limitations on minimum thickness of work metal that can be rolled (especially when forming large diameters). Adequate stiffness in the work metal is essential to provide enough friction to rotate the top roll. The minimum thickness that can be rolled varies, depending on the specific machine and the work-metal composition.

Another disadvantage of the pyramid machine is the large flat areas that remain on both the leading and the trailing ends of the work metal. Because the workpiece must remain supported by the bottom rolls at all times, the ends of the work can never get closer to the top roll than the distance between the points of tangency of the workpiece and the rolls. Thus, it is impossible to eliminate these flat areas by rolling (see Fig. 4a).

To minimize flat areas when using pyramid machines, the usual procedure is to preform the ends to the desired radius in a press brake or to roll an oversize blank, then trim the flat ends after. Sometimes, the shell can be returned to the rolls for truing after the seam has been joined. Occasionally, a narrow shim is placed at the ends to increase the bend radius, but care must be taken to avoid machine overload.

The techniques used in forming with pyramid rolls make it more difficult to achieve the accuracy that is obtainable with pinch-type rolls.

Capacity. Three-roll forming machines are rated by the manufacturer according to the maximum thickness and width of low-carbon steel plate the machine can form at room temperature. Values are usually given for single-pass rolling, and allowances are then made for multiple-pass rolling. For example, a machine rated at ¾ in. by 144 in. (thickness and width of plate, respectively) for work metal having a maximum tensile strength of 60,000 psi, and capable of rolling plate to a diameter of 96 in. in a single pass, can roll to a final diameter of 23 in. in multiple passes if the top roll is no larger than about 14½ in. in diameter.

If plate thickness was increased to 1 in., the same diameter restrictions would apply, but the allowable plate width would be reduced from 144 to 56 in., because of the additional power required for the increased thickness of work metal. At this point another limitation may be encountered, because as the plate becomes narrower and thicker, the load imposed on the shorter surface area can become excessive. On the other hand, assuming all other factors remain constant, if plate thickness was reduced to ⅝ in., the allowable width would revert to full capacity of the machine (144 in.), but the rolled diameter could be reduced to 16½ in.

The maximum plate thickness that can be handled by this machine depends on the pinch opening, and is rated by the manufacturer of the machine. For instance, some machines rated as described above can accommodate work 1½ in. thick, but for forming this thickness in a machine having the indicated capacity, the allowable plate width would be reduced to 21 in. because of the above-mentioned factors. All of the above calculations also take into consideration the limiting factor of roll deflection.

With all other conditions constant, power requirements increase according to the square of metal thickness. Thus, power required for forming plate 2 in. thick is four times as great as that required for forming 1-in.-thick plate of the same width.

Selection of Machine

Selection between pinch-type and pyramid-type machines depends mainly on the shape of the starting form and of the finished workpiece, the number of formed parts to be produced, accuracy requirements, and cost.

The pinch-type machine produces more accurate workpieces, and can be loaded and unloaded much faster than the pyramid-type machine. Although both machines can produce shapes other than plain cylinders, the pinch type is capable of rolling a wider range of thicknesses. However, the pyramid-type machine is often preferred for small quantities of varied work, as in a job shop. Because of the wide space that can be obtained between the upper roll and the two lower rolls in a pyramid machine, various types of dies and fixtures can be fastened to the upper roll, thereby permitting channels, angles and various other structural shapes to be rolled or bent, either hot or cold.

Rolls

Rolls used in three-roll forming machines are machined from steel forgings having a carbon content of 0.40 to 0.50% and a Brinell hardness of 160 to 210. Plain carbon steel such as 1045 has often been used; when greater strength is needed, rolls are forged from an alloy steel such as 4340. Because the modulus of elasticity is the same for all carbon and low-alloy steels of medium carbon content, roll deflection for a given force will be the same.

Although the Brinell hardness range of 160 to 210 can be obtained by annealing, rolls having a microstructure obtained by quenching and tempering, or normalizing and tempering, are less subject to surface deterioration from spalling. Therefore, the forged rolls are heat treated before being machined.

Roll diameter varies with the length and thickness of plate to be rolled. A typical top roll in a pinch-type machine, rated for forming steel plate up to 2½ in. thick and 144 in. wide, would have a minimum diameter of 30 in. Journals for rolls of this diameter are approximately 17 in. in diameter.

Crowning of rolls to compensate for deflection is common practice. The amount of crowning is not necessarily the same for all rolls in a given machine. For instance, in some machines the rolls are not all of the same diameter; under these conditions, a roll that is smaller in diameter requires more crowning than a larger roll, because the stress on all rolls is the same. When a machine is used for both light and heavy work, it is usual to crown the rolls for average conditions and then to use strips either at the center of the rolls to compensate for extreme deflection or at the ends to compensate for a lack of deflection (see the section on Roll Deflection, page 223).

Roll Maintenance. The extreme pressures to which rolls are subjected cause them to work harden. Rolls used in continuous production under high pressure sometimes elongate and reduce slightly in diameter. The amount of elongation or reduction in diameter is seldom significant, although the ends of rolls may require trimming after long periods of use.

There is no standard practice for reconditioning of rolls. In some plants, rolls that have been subjected to long periods of severe service are trued by removing some or all of the work-hardened layer by turning. When required, the diameter is built up by welding an overlay on the rolls and then finish turning them. On the other hand, some manufacturers recommend that roll surfaces should never be turned. If the surfaces are spalled or otherwise damaged, any protruding metal should be removed by grinding. Although indentations in the rolls are less likely to be harmful, they may mark polished or clad surfaces.

When rolling scaly plate, blowing away loose scale with an air lance is helpful in preventing scale from indenting the rolls or the work metal.

Bearings and Lubricants. Bronze has been successfully used for main bearings and is sometimes specified by the user. However, tin-base babbitt is superior to bronze for most applications and is now used in most machines. Tin-base bearings are more compatible with the relatively soft steel journals at the pressures and speeds involved, and their ability to absorb particles of scale minimizes the possibility of scoring journals or bearings.

Extreme-pressure (EP) lubricants are recommended for the main bearings on all rolls, and a grade containing molybdenum disulfide is especially desirable. Because environmental conditions are likely to vary considerably where three-roll forming is done, the lubricant should have good pumpability over a range of temperatures. Extreme-pressure lubricants are satisfactory for both cold and hot forming.

Preparation of Blanks

Blanks are usually cut to the desired size before forming. The length of plate (dimension of the work metal perpendicular to the axes of the rolls) required to form a given shape is determined by measuring the mean circumference (or perimeter, if the shape is other than a cylinder), which is the circumference taken at one half the distance between the inside diameter and the outside diameter of the shape to be formed. This method of calculation is the one most generally used in both cold and hot forming of plate.

Allowance for Shift in Neutral Axis. When greater accuracy is required, the more exact location of the neutral axis is considered when computing the blank, particularly if heavy plate thicknesses are involved. The neutral axis is the boundary between metal in tension and in compression and usually is a quarter to a half the thickness of the metal being bent, measured from the inside of the bend. The exact location of this axis varies to some extent with the bend radius and the mechanical properties of the metal.

During cold forming, the neutral axis shifts inward from the mean by about 26% of the plate thickness. Thus, for an 18-in.-ID cylinder, rolled from ½-in.-thick plate, the mean circumference is about 58.12 in., and for a 26% shift, the circumference at the neutral axis becomes 57.30 in. For an 18-in.-ID cylinder of ¼-in.-thick plate the mean circumference is 57.33 in., and with a 26% shift, changes to 56.93 in.; the amount of shift is about half that for the ½-in.-thick plate. Therefore, the shift of neutral axis is usually disregarded for plate thicknesses less than ½ in., except where greater accuracy is required.

In cold forming, length of the blank is calculated by using a radius that is determined by subtracting 26% of the plate thickness from the mean radius, or by adding 24% to the inside radius.

When dimensional requirements are stringent, similar allowances are made for shift of the neutral axis and for thermal expansion in hot forming of thick plates (3 to 6 in.) at 1600 F.

Cutting of blanks can be done by shearing, if shearing equipment is available for the width and thickness of the work metal. Gas cutting commonly is used for preparing blanks that are too thick for shearing. (See the articles on Shearing, page 265, and on Gas Cutting, page 278, in this volume.)

Edge Preparation. The cut edges of any plate (high-strength steel, in particular) can be a serious problem, because of cracking during cold forming, which is cause for rejection of the workpiece. When plate is sheared, the edges are rough and often have surface cracks. Gas cutting usually produces smoother edges, but frequently the edges of gas-cut steel plate will be hardened in cooling from the cutting temperature. Thus, from either method of cutting, nucleation sites for cracks are likely to be present.

The danger from cracking caused by rough edges increases as plate thickness increases and the finished diameter of the cylinder decreases.

Because the plate surface that forms the outside diameter of the cylinder is in tension during forming, cracks propagate from edges, which are in tension.

On plate 1 in. or more in thickness, the edges indicated in Fig. 5 should be removed before cold forming. This is not required prior to hot forming. Usual practice is to employ a chipping hammer and then a portable grinder to smooth the edges. The amount of metal removed is usually negligible, and a slight bevel on the critical edges is sufficient. If a substantial amount of metal is to be removed, allowance must be made for it when calculating the dimensions of the blank.

Cold vs Hot Forming

Because cold forming involves fewer problems and is less costly than hot forming, preferred practice is to form workpieces at room temperature.

In hot forming, dimensional accuracy is more difficult to control, and cost is significantly increased by:

1. Heating the blank
2. Handling both the blank and the workpiece while the metal is hot
3. Necessity for restoring acceptable surfaces by pickling, blast cleaning, or other surface treatment
4. Accelerated rate of deterioration of rolls and other equipment, because of contact with hot metal.

Forming Capacity. When carbon or low-alloy steel is heated, tensile strength decreases and formability increases. Heating the work metal thus extends the usefulness of a roll forming machine. For instance, a 10-ft-long pinch-type machine with 19½-in.-diam rolls can form a 144-in.-diam cylinder from 2½-in.-thick by 24½-in.-wide plate at room temperature in one pass (assuming the work metal has tensile strength of 60,000 psi at room temperature). With all other conditions remaining constant, by heating the work metal to a temperature high enough to reduce the tensile strength to 10,000 psi or lower, the width of plate (measured parallel to the roll axes) can be increased to 82 in. and rolled in one pass, using the same amount of power needed for rolling plate 24½ in. wide at room temperature. To reduce the tensile strength of low-carbon steel and obtain best formability, the usual practice is to heat the steel to 1600 F.

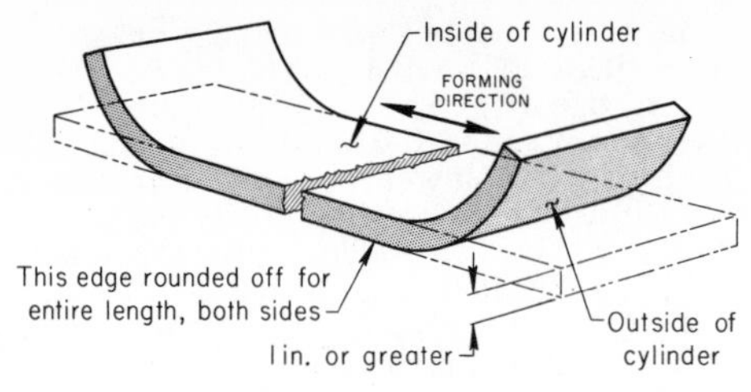

Fig. 5. Sheared or gas-cut blank, showing where metal should be removed from edges before cold forming, to reduce susceptibility to cracking

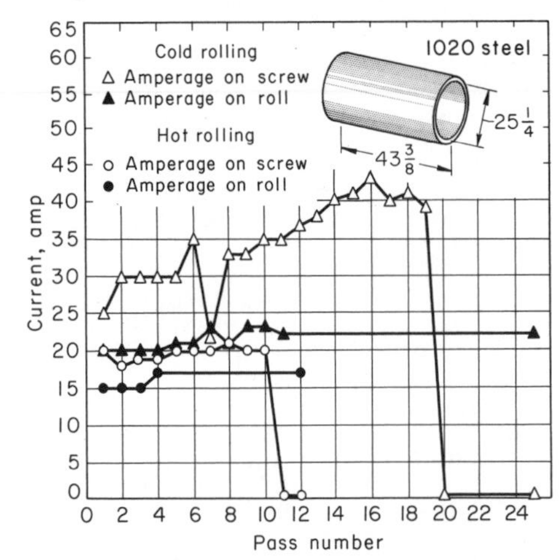

Fig. 6. Comparison of current flow (proportional to force) measured on screw and rolls during cold rolling and during rolling of 1¾-in.-thick plate preheated to 1600 F (Example 294)

Similarly, the size of machine described above is capable of cold forming a 144-in.-diam cylinder from 1¾-in.-thick by 60-in.-wide mild steel plate in one pass. Under the same conditions, except for heating to 1600 F, the thickness of the plate can be increased to 2¾ in.

One method of evaluating the difference in formability between cold and hot rolling is to measure the force required for forming a given plate. This is done on pyramid-type rolls by measuring, in terms of amperage, the downward force on the upper roll and the force required to rotate the powered rolls (see Fig. 6). The following example demonstrates the difference in current flow, number of passes, and time needed for cold and hot forming of similar cylinders.

Example 294. Cold vs Hot Forming of 1¾-In.-Thick Steel Plate (Fig. 6)

A pyramid-type machine was used to produce 25¼-in.-ID by 43⅜-in.-long cylinders from 1020 steel blanks 1¾ in. thick by 43⅜ in. wide by 84½ in. long. When forming was done at room temperature, 25 passes were required with current flow on the upper roll (screw) and power rolls as shown in Fig. 6. Rolling time was 40 min per cylinder. When blanks were heated to 1600 F and finished at 1050 F, the number of passes was reduced to 12 and rolling time to 11 min per cylinder. Current flow was also reduced, as shown in Fig. 6.

The technique described in the preceding example for increasing the effective capacity of equipment by hot forming does not apply to all metals, and the amount of decrease in tensile strength varies considerably among carbon and low-alloy steels. For example, heat-resisting alloys, by definition, resist the softening effect of heat, and many of these alloys precipitation harden in the temperature range that would be used for hot forming of carbon steel (see the article on Forming of Heat-Resisting Alloys, on page 371 in this volume). Alloys of magnesium and titanium are usually formed at the same elevated temperature that is used for forming the same alloy by other methods (see articles in this volume covering the forming of these metals). Alloys of copper and of aluminum are usually formed at room temperature. However, alloys 7075 and 7079, as well as some other precipitation-hardening alloys, must be formed within 24 hr after solution treatment. If forming cannot be done within this length of time, the work metal must be stored at −10 F to prevent precipitation hardening (see the articles in this volume on Forming of Aluminum, page 379, and Forming of Copper, page 405).

Maximum Elongation. In many applications with steel, hot forming is mandatory, regardless of the capacity of available forming equipment. Common practice is to compute a maximum elongation in the outer surface for cold forming, as determined by the formula:

$$E = \left(\frac{t}{d+t}\right)100$$

Where E is percentage elongation in the outer surface of the cylinder; d is inside diameter of the cylinder, in inches; and t is plate thickness, in inches. For example, for a cylinder having an inside diameter of 57 in. to be formed from 3-in.-thick steel plate:

$$E = \left(\frac{3}{57+3}\right)100 = 5\%.$$

Elongation of more than 5% (determined by the above formula) is seldom permitted for cold forming, and often the maximum is 3.5%. If maximum permissible elongation was 3.5% in the above example, either the minimum cylinder diameter would be near 83 in. or plate thickness would have to be reduced before cold forming would be permitted.

Maximum elongation is established by the user of the formed product, and when specifications cannot be met by cold forming, hot forming is used.

Combination Hot and Cold Forming. Sometimes, a combination of hot and cold forming is advantageous and permits elongation requirements to be met. For instance, in forming the 57-in.-diam cylinder described above, one procedure is first to hot form the 3-in.-thick plate to a circular segment of about 90 in., then allow the workpiece to cool to room temperature, and clean and finish form at room temperature. This procedure makes it possible to meet more severe elongation requirements and, at the same time, to retain some of the advantages of cold forming, such as greater accuracy.

Hot Forming Temperatures for Steel

Carbon or low-alloy steel plate is commonly heated to 1600 F for hot forming after normalizing at the mill. However, plate in the as-rolled condition is less costly. The as-rolled steel is normalized while it is being heated for forming and cooled during forming. In such an operation, the steel is heated to 1650 to 1700 F, instead of to 1600 F, before forming.

Finishing temperature is critical for some steels, especially the plain carbon grades, because of the "blue-brittle" temperature range. It is generally recommended that the finish-rolling temperature should be 1050 F or higher. If the workpiece cannot be completely formed before it cools to 1050 F, it should be removed from the machine and reheated.

Warm forming is often applied when forming requirements are too severe for room temperature, and heating to the conventional hot forming temperature cannot be permitted because mechanical properties of the steel would be impaired. A notable example is the forming of quenched-and-tempered grades of high-strength low-alloy steel. Common practice is to heat these steels no higher than the temperatures at which they were tempered, then form at once.

Power Requirements

The power required to form a given cylinder on three-roll equipment depends on the strength of the work metal, plate thickness, plate width, finished diameter of the cylinder, number of passes used, and temperature (hot or cold forming).

Strength of the work metal, plate thickness and plate width (measured parallel to the roll axes) determine the diameter of a cylinder that can be formed in a given machine. The curves in Fig. 7, for a 10-ft-long pinch-type roll machine with 19½-in.-diam rolls, represent combinations of maximum plate thickness and width that can be rolled at room temperature into cylinders of 144-in. diameter or larger in a single pass. The large influence of the strength of the steel is evident from this graph. For instance, 1.5-in.-thick low-carbon steel plate of 60,000-psi tensile strength can be rolled into 144-in.-diam cylinders in one pass in widths up to 120 in. in this machine. Under otherwise similar conditions, the width of 1.5-in.-thick high-strength low-alloy steel that can be formed to the same cylinder diameter is restricted to about 22 in. (Fig. 7). The machine used was rated at 2⅝ in. by 120 in.

Work Hardening. Most metals are susceptible to strengthening by cold work (work hardening), although the extent to which metals are affected varies widely among the various compositions. Of the steels commonly processed by three-roll forming, those of low carbon content, such as 1010, are least susceptible to work hardening and seldom present any serious problems. As carbon or alloy content increases, the rate of work hardening increases.

For metals that work harden rapidly, power consumption increases as forming proceeds. Eventually, the machine is overloaded or the work metal fractures.

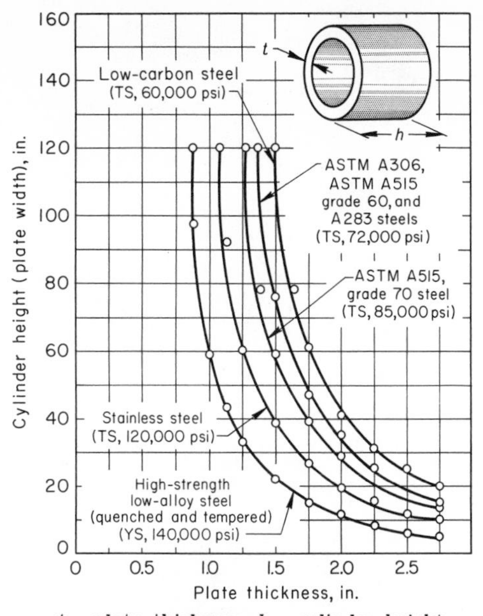

t = plate thickness, h = cylinder height

Fig. 7. Interrelation of cylinder height, plate thickness and work-metal strength for forming in a single pass in a pinch-type roll machine at room temperature

Intermediate annealing must be used when work-hardenable metal is severely formed. For steel, full annealing is usually recommended. Process (subcritical) annealing is sometimes used. However, process annealing alternated with cold work is likely to result in excessive grain growth and subsequent poor formability, despite the decreased hardness.

Cylinder Diameter. With other conditions constant, power requirements increase as cylinder diameter decreases, when the cylinder is completely formed in one pass. However, the use of two or more passes (up to 12 is not uncommon) permits rolling of smaller-diameter cylinders without increasing machine size. For instance, the curves in Fig. 7 show that 1.5-in.-thick by 120-in.-wide plate of mild steel can be formed into a cylinder 144 in. in diameter in one pass on a given machine. By using 10 or 12 passes, cylinders as small as 25½ in. in diameter have been formed from maximum thicknesses shown in Fig. 7. For plate thickness of 1$\frac{3}{16}$ in. or less, cylinders as small as 21½ in. in diameter can be formed in multiple passes.

Similarly, for carbon steel having a tensile strength up to 85,000 psi and stainless steel up to 120,000 psi, any of the plate thicknesses shown in Fig. 7 can be rolled to cylinders as small as 27½ in. in diameter. For steels having a tensile strength of about 72,000 psi, plate thicknesses of 1$\frac{3}{32}$ in. or less can be rolled to cylinders 22 in. in diameter, using the multiple-pass procedure. Limitations of plate thickness for rolling 22-in.-diam cylinders then decrease to 1$\frac{1}{64}$ in. (max) for steel with a tensile strength of 85,000 psi, and $\frac{13}{16}$ in. for stainless steel with a tensile strength of about 120,000 psi.

For quenched and tempered high-strength low-alloy steel (140,000 psi in Fig. 7), power requirements are high; in addition, there is increased probability of cracking. Suggested limits for maximum plate thickness and minimum cylinder diameter for multiple-pass rolling, regardless of power, are:

Plate thickness, in. (max)	Cylinder diameter, in. (min)
1	46
¾	35
½	32½
⅜	30½
¼	28

Temperature. Limitations imposed by steel composition and other factors shown in Fig. 7 are changed markedly when the work metal is heated (see the section on Cold vs Hot Forming and Example 294 in this article). However, it is not always possible to employ hot forming — for instance, for quenched-and-tempered high-strength low-alloy steel (see the subsection "Warm Forming", on this page).

Forming Small Cylinders

Cold forming of small cylinders by the three-roll process requires more than ordinary care, especially when the diameter of the cylinder to be formed is near that of the rolls. Rolling of cylinders having an inside diameter of less than 2 in. more than the outside diameter of the roll is not generally recommended. However, a skilled operator, by using special care, can form cylinders within 1½ in. in diameter in a pinch-type machine. The following example describes the procedure used in one application.

Example 295. Forming Cylinders to Near Roll Diameter

Cylinders 7½ in. ID and 18 in. long were formed from mild steel plate 24⅜ in. long by 18 in. wide and ¼ in. thick. A pinch-type machine with a rated capacity of $\frac{3}{16}$ in. by 6 ft and having 6-in.-diam rolls was used. For this operation, the blank was preformed in a press brake. To avoid excessive work hardening and resulting springback, it was necessary to complete the forming in one pass. The ends of the plate were tack welded together while held securely by the rolls. The cylinder was then removed from the machine and welding was completed. Any cylinder that was excessively out-of-round was rerolled. In rerolling, the rolls were opened slightly to allow passage of the weld bead. Load required for rerolling was about a third greater than that required for initial rolling.

Forming Large Cylinders

Cylinders that are large either in diameter or length can be formed by the three-roll process. Some special procedures may be required, especially when the sheet is so thin that the cylinder cannot retain a round shape without support. Under these conditions, overhead cranes or temporary braces or both can be used for support.

When flat blanks of the required length are not available, two or more sections can be welded together to obtain the required length. The following example describes this practice in the forming of large cylinders.

Example 296. Forming 186-In.-OD Cylinders in a Pinch-Type Machine

Cylinders 186 in. in diameter and 112 in. long were formed from blanks prepared by welding together three sections of copper-clad low-carbon steel. The fabricated blanks were 580¾ in. long by 112 in. wide by $\frac{9}{16}$ in. thick.

Cylinders were formed cold on a ¾-in. by 12-ft pinch-type machine. The major problem in this operation was support, because the work was not thick enough to provide natural support. Overhead cranes were used to hold the formed section of the plate during rolling. Ends of the cylinder were tack welded before the workpiece was removed from the machine. Temporary braces were then used to hold the cylinders in a near-round condition while the seam was welded. After welding, outside rounding rings made from 1½-in. by 5-in. rectangular steel bars were used to hold the cylinder shape for subsequent attachment to other cylinders. In use, welded internal parts stiffened the assembly.

Forming Truncated Cones

Pyramid-type machines are generally used in the forming of truncated cones.

There are two basic limitations on the shape of conic configurations that can be formed by the three-roll process: (*a*) the smaller diameter (A in Fig. 8) must be large enough to keep the established workpiece-to-roll relation on minimum obtainable diameter, and (*b*) the plate must be thick enough to be formed by the holdback method shown in Fig. 8, lest the pressure build-up on the holdback pin upset the plate edge or damage the holdback attachment, or both.

The size of cone that can be formed depends largely on the pitch, spacing and length of rolls, and on the diameter of the upper roll. As the cone height increases, difficulties in getting the large diameter to follow the small diameter accurately also increase. If the lower roll spacing is too wide, the size of the smaller diameter will be severely limited, because as the work metal passes the holdback pin (Fig. 8), it will curve into the housing that supports the rolls and rolling will be impossible.

Procedure. There are several significant differences between forming of conic shapes and forming of cylinders by the pyramid-type three-roll process. In the rolling of cylinders, the blank is rectangular and is rolled in a direction perpendicular to the rolls. In contrast, curved blanks are used for conic shapes and they are rolled on a curve. Also, no pin is needed in rolling cylinders, and the top roll is pitched for forming cones, whereas it is straight and level when forming cylinders.

Before the developed blank is placed in the pyramid-type three-roll machine for forming a cone, the ends of the blank are preformed in a pinch-type roll from the rear or in a press brake. For forming the cone, the top roll is pitched as shown in Fig. 8. As the rolls drive the blank, its edge drags around the pin, and the various diameters of the cone are formed. The blank is then rolled in multiple passes, dragging around the pin until the ends of the blank are closed. If the pitch of the rolls matches the pitch of the entire length of the cone, a nearly true cone will result.

Truncated cones are sometimes produced by forming two semicircular half cones and welding them together; the completed workpiece has two longitudinal seams instead of one. In another method, two or more circular tapered sections are formed and welded together. When produced by this method, the finished cone has one longitudinal seam and one or more circumferential seams.

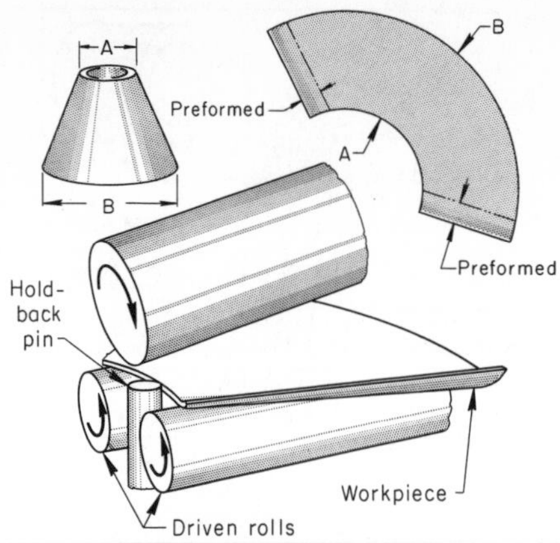

Fig. 8. Rolling a truncated cone in a three-roll pyramid-type machine from a blank with preformed ends

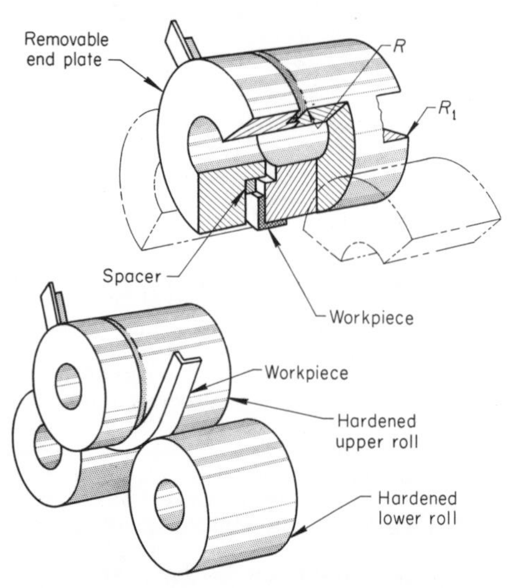

Fig. 9. Roll setup for forming an angle section into a circle. Guide rolls and guide fingers are not required for this application.

Forming Bars and Shapes

Pyramid rolls and machines having overhanging rolls are used to form bars, bar sections and structural shapes into circles. Shapes that can be processed by this method include rounds, squares, flats (on the edge or on the flat), I-beams, L-shaped structurals, and channels. Hardened roll sections that are adjustable to the thickness or cross section of the shape are used (Fig. 9). Some bars or shapes can be formed with plain, flat rolls, but more often rolls conforming to the shape of the unformed workpiece are required.

The rolls are adjusted to produce the required workpiece diameter in the same manner as in rolling cylinders from sheet or plate. Prebending the ends and rolling the workpiece back and forth are also employed in three-roll forming of bars and shapes. A significant difference in the rolling of bars and shapes is the frequent use of guide rollers or guide fingers, or both, mounted so as to contact the sides of the workpiece and prevent it from twisting during forming.

One of the most difficult shapes to form by the three-roll process is an angle with one leg inside the circle (Fig. 9). When forming this shape, spiralling, twisting, buckling of the inside leg, and reduction of the angle between the two legs are likely to occur. These difficulties can be minimized by using a hardened upper roll having a removable end plate and a spacer that is not more than $1/32$ in. thicker than one leg of the angle (Fig. 9). The radius on the upper roll (identified as R in Fig. 9) must conform to the fillet radius of the angle to be rolled. The other end of this roll (identified as R_1 in Fig. 9) can have the same radius or a radius conforming to another angle to be rolled. This end of the upper roll can be used by reversing the roll end for end. In production rolling of the same angle, common practice is to have the same values for R and R_1 (Fig. 9), thus permitting double the roll life by reversing the roll. Guide rollers and fingers (not required for the section shown in Fig. 9) also help to produce accurate circles from bar sections.

Out-of-Roundness

Out-of-roundness, or ovality, of cylinders produced by three-roll forming is caused by one or more of the following variables:

1 Varying thickness of the flat blank
2 Varying hardness within the blank
3 Overforming or underforming of the ends in the preforming operation
4 Springback of the work metal
5 Temperature of the metal being formed
6 Number of passes
7 Condition of the equipment
8 Operator skill.

The most important of the above factors is operator skill; condition of the equipment is also a major factor.

Variations in the mill product (thickness and hardness within a single sheet or plate) are seldom great enough to warrant the extra cost that would be necessary for closer-than-normal control of the work metal. Out-of-roundness and other dimensional variations in the product increase as workpiece diameter increases. Plate thickness above or below actual crown thickness of the rolls can also cause dimensional variations. For either large or small workpieces, much out-of-roundness is caused by variations in preforming the ends, regardless of whether pinch rolls or press brakes are used in preforming.

Springback is overcome by forming to a circle smaller than that required for the finished cylinder. However, overforming of high-springback material must be done with caution; as the elastic limit is exceeded, metals will take a permanent set and too much overforming can result.

Hot forming may contribute to out-of-roundness, because considerable plastic flow can take place when a steel workpiece is heated to 1600 F or higher. The amount of plastic flow varies as the bending load is applied during forming, and variations are increased by uneven cooling of the work metal. Resulting variations in plate thickness and curvature contribute to out-of-roundness.

Production Example. Without the use of special techniques or secondary operations, there is likely to be considerable variation in out-of-roundness among workpieces that are intended to be identical and are produced under the same conditions. This is demonstrated in the following example.

Example 297. Out-of-Roundness Variations in 44 Cylinders, 17 In. in Diameter (Fig. 10)

Cylinders 17 in. in diameter were produced on a pinch-type machine in one pass. Leading edges of the blanks were prebent 15° for a distance of 2 in. with a 4-in. radius. After the cylinders were formed and tack welded, measurements were taken. Out-of-roundness variation in 44 cylinders is plotted in Fig. 10.

Number of passes used to form a given cylinder can have a significant effect on out-of-roundness. In most applications, two or more passes (sometimes as many as 12) will produce cylinders that are more nearly true round than those formed in a single pass.

Methods of Correction. The most effective method for correcting out-of-roundness is to reroll the cylinder carefully before welding. This operation causes a one-third greater load on the machine than the original rolling.

For cylinders having wall thickness no greater than about ⅜ in., a draw-down type of expander applied after rolling and welding is an effective means of correcting out-of-roundness.

If design permits, beads or flanges can be rolled into the cylinder wall to reinforce it and help to maintain roundness. Oil drums are examples of the effective use of this technique.

When dimensional requirements are plus or minus a few thousandths of an inch, stock must be allowed for machine boring the cylinder to the specified diameter.

Forming Speed

Speed of forming is a critical factor in product quality. Low-carbon steel plate up to 5⁄16 in. thick is sometimes rolled at speeds up to 60 fpm. For a speed this high, however, workpiece diameter is necessarily medium to large, because it is impractical to control the machine for rolling small diameters at high speed.

The most commonly used speeds for cold forming (particularly for thick plate) range from 12 to 20 fpm. This range is usually maintained in both cold and hot forming; however, to complete hot forming with a minimum decrease in temperature of the work metal it is sometimes necessary to increase the speed of the bending roll.

Roll Deflection

Roll deflection can be calculated by standard formulas, considering the roll as a simple beam supported at both ends. On pyramid rolls, deflection is often minimized by support rollers applied to the lower rolls. These rolls act as back-up rolls.

In forming heavy plate, pressures are high and all three rolls are crowned (made larger at the centers than at the ends). Crowning is necessary because the rolls deflect under the bending load; if they were straight, all formed cylinders would bulge somewhat at the center. Because the amount of deflection depends on the bending load, usual practice is to crown the rolls enough to compensate for the average job in the plant. When forming plate thicker than the actual crown deflection, the rolls are shimmed by running strips of thin metal (16, 14, 12 or 10 gage) between

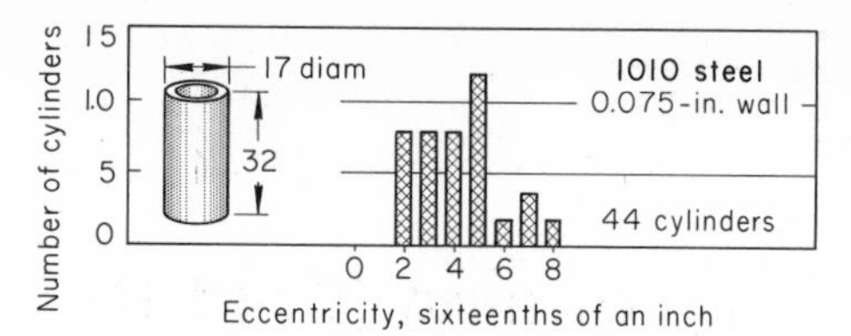

Fig. 10. Out-of-roundness variations in 44 cylinders of the same diameter produced in a pinch-type roll machine (Example 297)

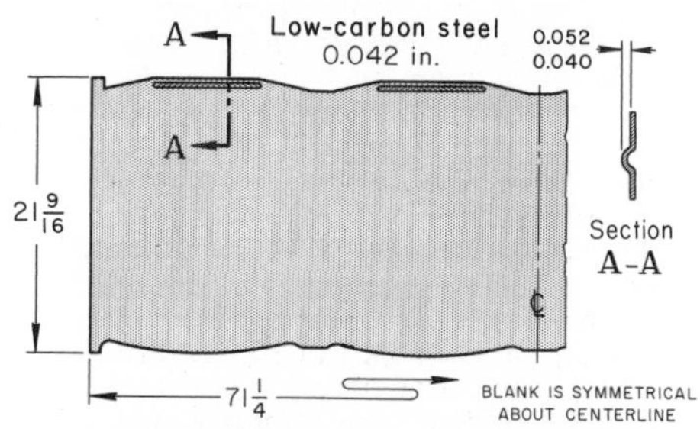

Fig. 11. Developed blank that was three-roll formed and welded to make a cylinder (Example 298)

the rolls and the inside diameter of the workpiece at the center of the rolls. This shimming compensates for excessive deflection.

When forming metal that is too thin to cause deflection of the rolls, crowning will cause the formed cylinder to be larger in diameter at the ends than in the center. Correction can be made by shimming the ends of the rolls in a manner similar to that described above for shimming the centers.

Alternative Processes

For producing large cylinders and truncated cones from heavy plate, three-roll forming is the most practical method.

Deep drawing is often the most economical method of producing small cylinders from sheet no thicker than 0.125 in. Seamless cylinders or cones can be produced by deep drawing, piercing and trimming (see the article "Deep Drawing", which begins on page 162 in this volume). However, as cylinder size or wall thickness increases, forming by deep drawing becomes impracticable.

In some applications three-roll forming and welding are preferred for producing a hollow shape from stock that is substantially thinner than 0.125 in., as described in the following example.

Example 298. Three-Roll Forming vs Deep Drawing (Fig. 11)

Because of saving in material, three-roll forming was used instead of deep drawing to produce a square tub for a washing machine. The developed blank, shown in Fig. 11, was made from a low-carbon steel 0.042-in.-thick by 43⅜-in.-wide coil that was slit in half and sheared into 71 9⁄16-in. lengths. The sheared lengths were fed into a press, which produced completed blanks, each with four draw beads.

The sequence of operations to produce the tub was as follows:

1 The developed blank was immersed in hot soap solution at 190 to 200 F, and dried in air. This left a film that served as the lubricant for the subsequent operations.
2 The lubricated blank was formed into a cylinder in one pass using a pinch-type three-roll forming machine. The machine was 36 or 48 in. wide with rolls 2½ to 3 in. in diameter.
3 The rolled cylinder was welded, using the foil butt-seam welding process.
4 The welded cylinder was loaded onto the horn of a special expanding machine, which formed the cylinder into a square.

Contour Roll Forming. Theoretically, the diameter and length of straight cylinders producible by contour roll forming are almost unlimited. In practice, however, diameter and wall thickness are limited by the size of available equipment. Contour roll forming is rarely used for rolling metal thicker than 0.250 in. and is most often used for thicknesses less than 0.125 in. Therefore, contour roll forming is impractical for producing large, heavy-wall cylinders. (See the article "Contour Roll Forming", which begins on page 224 in this volume.)

Forming two halves (semicircles) between dies in a press and then welding the two half-cylinders is sometimes practical. However, even when presses of sufficient size are available for forming large plate, die cost is likely to be prohibitive.

For limited production, a press brake is often used to produce semicircles that can subsequently be joined by welding into cylinders (see Example 129, in the article on Press-Brake Forming in this volume).

Other Applications in This Volume

The use of three-roll and other forming processes in the sequence of operations for making a container for liquids is described in Example 482 in the article on Forming of Stainless Steel. A blank with the edge radii preformed was rolled into a cylinder, then seam welded. The cylinder was rerolled to restore roundness. Roll forming a curve in a channel section made of titanium is shown in Fig. 8 on page 444, in the article on Forming of Titanium.

Safety

Forming rolls move relatively slowly, but require protection for the operator. The most positive method of protection is to cover the nip point between the feed rolls. One effective guarding device is a solid metal plate covering the nip point between the feed table and the rolls for the full length of the rolls. This plate, with a stud welded to each end, is attached to slotted vertical brackets by nuts and washers, so that it is adjustable vertically. The brackets are securely fastened to the feed table.

The height of the feed table can be made adjustable by welding a nut to the lower end of each tubular leg. A long bolt, with a large washer welded to the top of the head, is screwed into the nut to achieve the desired height. A locknut can be used to prevent the bolt from turning because of vibration.

Emergency tripping bars connected to electric cutoff switches or, preferably, to reverse electric switches, can be used to stop the rolls. The bars may be at knee level in front of the operator, or directly in front of the bottom feed roll and far enough below the feed point to avoid accidental tripping.

Feeding guides for narrow workpieces can be made of bar stock or angles that are bolted to the feed table. The guides should be slotted, for easy adjustability to various widths of workpieces.

Contour Roll Forming (Cold Roll Forming)

*By the ASM Committee on Contour Roll Forming**

CONTOUR ROLL FORMING (also known as cold roll forming) is a process for forming metal sheet or strip stock into desired shapes of uniform cross section by feeding the stock longitudinally through a series of roll stations equipped with contoured rolls (sometimes called roller dies) — two or more rolls per station. Most contour roll forming is done by working the stock progressively in two or more stations until the finished shape is produced.

The process is particularly suited to the production of large quantities and long lengths to close tolerances, with a minimum of handling. Auxiliary operations, such as notching, slotting, punching, embossing, curving and coiling, can be easily combined with contour roll forming.

Applicability

All metals that can be shaped by any of the common forming processes can be contour roll formed. The formability of the work metal controls the permissible speed of roll forming and the degree (severity) to which the metal can be formed. For instance, the speed at which the softest grade of aluminum strip can be contour roll formed may be as much as 400 times the speed permitted for rolling titanium strip into a similar shape. Roll forming of shapes that involve bending through 180° is common practice in working with soft metals such as aluminum, whereas bending of titanium through more than 90°, without employing special techniques, would be unusual.

Cold and hot finished carbon steel, stainless steel, and aluminum and copper alloys are contour roll formed in the greatest quantities. The less formable metals, such as titanium and the nickel-base heat-resisting alloys, are less frequently shaped by this process.

Stock that has been precoated with vinyl or some other organic coating, or with metal by electroplating, hot dip coating or other technique, can be contour roll formed. However, to avoid loss of adhesion or other damage to the coating, the severity of forming is usually less than on the uncoated metal, depending on the coating material, thickness and method. Also, special attention must be given to the design and surface finish of tools, the speed of forming, and the selection and application of lubricants. In some applications, particularly those in which the removal of lubricants is difficult, lubricants cannot be used.

In a special application of contour roll forming, metals and nonmetals (such as rubber or felt) can be combined to produce composites. Weather stripping is an example of a composite produced by contour roll forming (see Example 311).

Thickness Range of Work Metal. The range of work-metal thicknesses that can be shaped by contour roll forming can only be approximately given. Items such as steel measuring tape and brass radiator tubing are usually produced from strip 0.004 to 0.005 in. thick. At the opposite extreme, channels and Z-sections are produced from steel up to 0.312 in. thick. The maximum thickness of section that can be contour roll formed is usually limited by the size of machinery available and the amount of force the bearings and spindles can withstand. The length of section that can be roll formed is limited by the facilities for handling formed sections.

Shape. Under the most favorable conditions (availability of equipment and formability of work metal), it is possible to contour roll form almost any shape. However, formability of the work metal and the number of forming stations available may impose limitations on complexity of shape or severity of forming. Several examples of complex shapes and the procedure used for forming them are described later in this article.

In contour roll forming, all bends are parallel to each other and in the same longitudinal direction at the time of passing through the rolls; however, fixtures can be added to a roll forming machine that will form the workpiece into a ring or hoop. Bending shoes or roller-type benders mounted on the machine produce the desired curvature after the cross-sectional shape has been formed. Special coiling machines that coil and cut the roll formed shapes to length are also available. Wheel rims for automobiles are typical of workpieces that are formed in a straight length, passed through a bender, and cut off in one continuous operation.

Auxiliary operations can readily be incorporated in a roll forming setup, the most common being piercing and notching of the strip immediately before the first forming station or between stations. Piercing and notching are often done simultaneously with roll forming by using flying dies or a hump table or loop and a stationary die. Notches, holes and miter cuts can be made by incorporating punches or dies in the cutoff tool.

Perforating of light-gage metal (less than 0.020 in. thick, for example) can be incorporated in a roll forming setup by using perforating rolls. These rolls are costly, but are compatible with high forming speeds, and sometimes perforating rolls are more economical than an oscillating die.

Performing welding operations in conjunction with contour roll forming is common practice, particularly in continuous seam welding for producing tubing from strip or coil stock (see Examples 304 to 306).

The principal disadvantage of combining auxiliary operations with contour roll forming is that in many instances the entire operation is slowed down. Thus, each application must be studied individually to determine whether it is more economical to contour roll as fast as possible and perform auxiliary operations separately, or to sacrifice some of the potential forming speed by including one or more auxiliary operations.

In most instances of forming simple shapes from metals having good formability, the inclusion of auxiliary operations is not economical. Roll forming alone could be accomplished at rates as high as several hundred feet per minute, and most auxiliary operations would slow this potential speed down to an uneconomical rate. Alternatively, if stock thickness, metal formability, or complexity of shape is such that severe restrictions are imposed on forming speed, one or more auxiliary operations then become economically feasible.

Machines

Machines used for contour roll forming are available with shaft diameters of 1 to 15 in. and width capacities of 4 to 60 in. The number of roll stations varies from 1 to 40 for most machines, although the number of roll stations that can be used is limited only by requirements. Most of these machines are built with individual units (roll stations), so that the initial installation can be limited to immediate needs, and additional units can be added when required. The different types of machines have many features of construction in common.

Overhung-spindle machines are the simplest type used for contour roll forming. An overhung-spindle machine with one roll station is shown in Fig. 1. The rolls and roll shafts (spindles) have no outboard support. The greatest advantage of an overhung-spindle

*K. B. VALENTINE, *Chairman,* Metallurgical Engineer, Pontiac Motor Div., General Motors Corp.; BARLOW W. BROOKS, JR., Vice President, Roll Forming Corp.; HENRY P. CIPPERLEY, Roll Designer, Roll Form Products Co.; WILLIAM P. EKEY, Cleveland Roll Forming Co.; CLARK FREDENBURG, Engineer, Special Projects Engineering, Van Huffel Tube Corp.; BURTON V. PABST, President, Dieomatic Metal Products Ltd.; HARLEY SHILLING, Manager of Roll Design, Binkley Co.; WARD W. THIEL, Supervisor, Tool Engineering, E. F. Hauserman Co.; AARON J. UNGERER, JR., Chief Engineer, Product Development, Standard Products Co.; ELMER J. VANDERPLOEG, Application Engineer (retired), Yoder Co.

machine is the convenience it affords in changing rolls, because there are no outboard housings to remove. Machines of this type are available with roll-shaft diameters of 1 to 2 in. Their principal disadvantage is a lack of rigidity, which limits their capacity to a strip width of 6 in. and thickness of about 0.040 in. (for work metal not harder than low-carbon steel). Despite this limitation, overhung-spindle machines are used for forming many commercially important products, including molding and weather stripping.

Outboard supports on the roll shafts are required for rolling strip widths greater than about 6 in. and thicknesses greater than about 0.040 in. A universal type of rolling machine having roll shafts supported at both ends is shown in Fig. 2. These machines are available with roll-shaft diameters ranging from 1½ to 3 in. and various shaft lengths as required. These machines are best adapted to rolling strip no thicker than about 3⁄16 in.

In normal operation of an outboard-support machine, the outboard housings must be removed to change rolls. This is not difficult, however, because the housings are removed by sliding them off the shafts away from the driving end. Outboard housings can also be moved inward toward the driving end; the rolls then are mounted on the outside, the machine being operated as an overhung-spindle machine.

Heavy-duty machines (roll-shaft diameters up to 15 in.) are basically similar in design to the outboard-support machine shown in Fig. 2. The major difference between the two machines is that in a heavy-duty machine the roll shaft is driven by means of a coupling, instead of directly from the driving head as in Fig. 2.

Rolls and housings used in the larger machines are too heavy for changing rolls by sliding the housings in a horizontal direction. In heavy-duty machines, the cap sections of the housings are removed and the rolls are then disconnected from their couplings and lifted by an overhead crane. This permits rolls to be mounted or removed from the shafts away from the machine. When quick changeover is important, extra shaft-and-roll assemblies should be available to permit one set of rolls to be made ready while another set is in service.

Another type of heavy-duty machine that is driven through a coupling is designed with only the bottom roll shaft being driven. The major advantage of this machine, compared to those with both rolls positively driven, is its greater capacity for depth of rolled shape, which is limited only by the distance that the upper roll can be adjusted in the housings. Two advantages of contour forming with only one driven roll are that scuffing (often a problem in deep forming) is minimized, and that the initial cost of the equipment is less than for machines of similar capacity with two driven rolls.

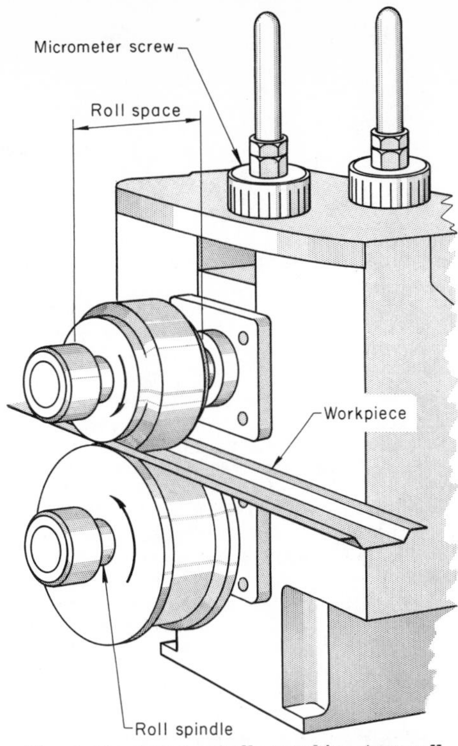

Fig. 1. Overhung-spindle machine (one roll station) for contour roll forming

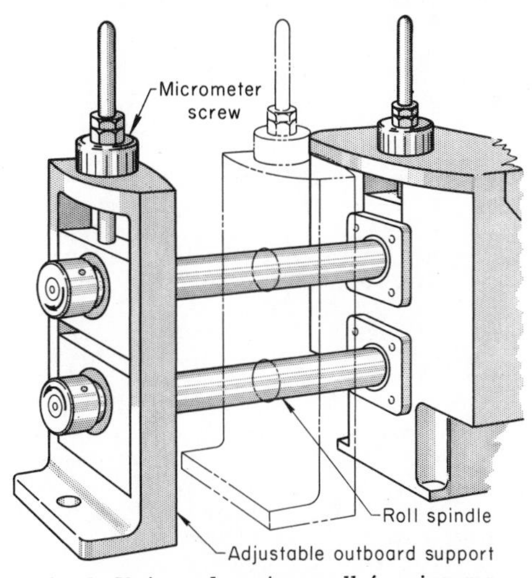

Fig. 2. Universal contour roll forming machine, with outboard support for roll shafts

Auxiliary Equipment

In addition to the machines that do the roll forming, several other pieces of equipment are usually required for production operation. Stock for roll forming is usually received in coils; thus, an electric hoist on an overhead track is needed to lift coils from skids and transfer them to a cradle or reel (another piece of auxiliary equipment). Also, equipment for welding the end of an expended coil to the lead of the next one, an entrance guide, intermediate guides, a straightening device, and cutoff equipment may be needed.

Stock reels should be equipped with an expandable arbor to fit the inside diameter of the coil, and with a friction drag. Stock reels incorporating these features and in a wide range of coil capacities are commercially available. (See the section "Coil-Handling Equipment", on pages 13 to 15 in the article on Presses.)

The friction drag is necessary to prevent the coil stock from overrunning onto the floor in the event of a sudden stoppage of the roll forming equipment. In the simplest type of motor-driven stock reel, a dancer arm and roll ride the stock in a loop-detector arrangement, which starts and stops the motor as required, supplying stock at the average rate used by the roll former. Stock speed is matched approximately by adjusting a variable-pitch sheave to prevent too-frequent stopping and starting of the a-c drive motor. This type of control on the stock reel will provide acceptable results for most applications. More elaborate controls can be used, such as a d-c motor drive with feedback control to match stock speed with machine speed. Elaborate controls are expensive and should not be considered unless they are needed to meet special workpiece requirements.

Stock reels are available with a swivel base and two arbors. A coil may be positioned on one arbor while the first coil is being used, thus reducing change time. This arrangement is advantageous when coils are relatively small and production requirements are high, because time consumed in changing coils can become a substantial portion of the total time.

Welding Equipment. Thread-up time can be eliminated by welding the end of each expended coil to the leading end of the next one, using manual methods. For stock thickness of 1⁄16 in. or over, a semiautomatic welder can be placed in the line. Regardless of the welding method used, any appreciable flash must be removed before the welded joint reaches the first roll station. Provision can be made to remove flash by installing a grinder similar to a band-saw-blade grinder.

Occasionally, welding is done "on the fly" by providing accumulator loops for use during the time the stock must be stationary in the welder and grinder. However, the initial cost of this equipment is high and it is troublesome to keep in operation. The use of welding to eliminate thread-up time should be considered only after a careful time study; the cost and time saved by welding and grinding equipment must be balanced against the cost of time lost in thread-up.

Welding "on the fly" is especially advantageous in producing electrically welded tubing, because of: (*a*) decreased scrap loss; (*b*) less tool maintenance from elimination of the wandering leading ends when "on the fly" welding is not used; and (*c*) increased production, resulting mainly from fewer tool adjustments and consequently less downtime.

Entrance guides ahead of the first forming station insure correct alignment of the work metal entering the starting rolls. This is particularly desirable when the forming is unsymmetrical in the first station and the stock could climb or shift to one side without guides. The simplest form of entrance guide consists of a flat plate with a channel milled to the proper width and depth to accept the strip at its maximum tolerance, and a simple removable lid to hold the stock in place. The mounting for this guide should permit adjustment vertically and laterally.

When wide variations in stock width are encountered, a self-centering, parallel-rule entrance guide is preferred. This guide is constructed like a navigator's parallel rule, with the crossbars pivoted and mounted at their centers with a spring, causing the side bars or rules to close on the stock under spring load.

Stock drags are occasionally used to place a slight tension on the stock and to cause it to feed more uniformly through the first few stations. The simplest form consists of two pieces of hardwood. The stock is clamped between the wooden members, which butt against the entrance guide, thus providing enough friction to keep the stock under tension. The amount of tension can be regulated by the clamping force on the wooden members.

Guides between roll stations facilitate entrance of the partly formed stock into the next station. In theory, if rolls are properly designed, guides between stations are unnecessary, because each set of rolls should accept the cross section from the preceding set of rolls. In practice, however, because of such factors as cost, lead time, and availability of space or equipment, the number of roll stations is often less than the ideal number, thus requiring more forming in each station than is consistent with best practice. Therefore, the use of guides between stations helps to compensate for lack of additional stations, and to minimize springback.

Guides between stations are seldom required to contact the entire contour of the work metal — only the critical points. Regardless of their shape, guides should be designed with removable top portions to facilitate threading. A typical guide used for a channeled workpiece is shown in Fig. 3.

Various metals may be used for guides, depending on the end use of the workpiece. For the areas contacting the moving workpiece, hardened steel (usually, case hardened low-carbon steel) is preferred from the standpoint of guide life. However, when workpiece finish is critical and hardened steel guides are likely to scratch the surface, bronze or aluminum guides are used. For some work, hard chromium plating of guides will minimize damage to workpiece surfaces and still provide acceptable guide life. When the plating becomes worn, it can be renewed.

Straightening Equipment. Usually it is necessary to straighten the workpiece after the final roll station. This is done by standard straightening guides attached to the machine beyond the last set of rolls, or by special devices designed for individual applications.

Straightening guides are usually adjustable vertically and laterally; the most versatile types can be swiveled in either elevation or azimuth and can also be rotated about an axis. Most straighteners employed for contour roll forming are of either the roll type or the shoe type.

A roll straightener consists of multiple rolls (individually adjustable) arranged to contact the stock in selected areas. A shoe straightener consists of one or more shoes, usually made of bronze, properly fitted to the contour and adjustable at least in a direction

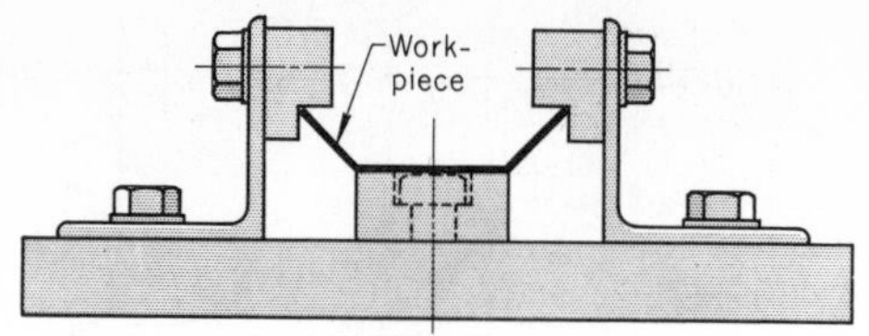

Fig. 3. Typical guide for use between roll stations

that will cramp the stock to correct for sweep or twist.

There are also applications in which a deliberate sweep (curve) is desired. A sweep guide is similar to a straightening guide, and a straightening guide often can be adjusted to give the required sweep in a constant radius. For more detailed information on straightening equipment, see the articles on Straightening of Bars, page 322, and Straightening of Tubing, page 329.

Cutoff Equipment. Because most contour rolled products are made from coil stock, a system of cutting the formed shapes to length must be provided. Flying-shear cutoff machines are built in several types and sizes.

The sliding-die cutoff machine is most commonly used. The action of this machine is similar to that of a punch press, although construction of the machine differs. The flywheel and clutch are placed below the bed, with the ram connected to the crankshaft by guide posts passing through the bed. Gibs are provided in the bed and ram to accept a gibbed die and a punch holder that permits linear movement of the die to match work-metal speed during the cutoff cycle.

Both mechanical and air clutches are used in a sliding-die cutoff machine. The air clutch is preferred, because its cycles are more uniform than those of the mechanical clutch. A "shipper rod" with an adjustable stop that determines the length of the workpiece is usually attached to the die at the exit end. The workpiece passes through the die and contacts the stop on the shipper rod, thus causing the die to move forward at the same speed as the workpiece. The die movement trips the press, cutting the workpiece to the required length. Cutting can be done either mechanically or electrically. The die is then released and returns to its original position by means of a spring or an air cylinder, and the cut length drops into a truck or is removed by a conveyor. Shock absorbers are often used to cushion and stop the die as it returns to position.

When the work-metal section is thick enough to have good beam strength, the procedure described above seldom causes serious problems, particularly when a reasonable tolerance on the cut length is permissible. Close tolerances greatly increase cutoff problems by the moving-die method; a die weighing about 2000 lb must match work-metal speed, and a slight error in timing can result in excessive variation in cut length. For example, when work-metal speed is 120 ft per min, a variation of 0.01 sec in the cutoff cycle will result in an error of 0.24 in. in length of cut. Variations in length of cut usually range from $\pm 1/16$ in. to $\pm 1/4$ in., depending mainly on rolling speed.

When the work metal is flexible and does not have enough beam strength to actuate the shipper rod, a device can be employed that consists of a pulse generator driven by movement of the stock and operating at approximately 15 kc. This is used in conjunction with an electronic counter to count the required pulses for the set length of stock, and a d-c motor to accelerate the die to line speed with proper feedback to control the acceleration rate of the motor. An error signal fed back to the counter compensates for previous error by correcting the subsequent cutoff cycle. Programers may be attached to this device so that an entire day's production can be programed. The device cuts the required number of a given length and shifts to a new length as required. Devices of this type are expensive and require constant attention by highly skilled maintenance personnel.

Roll Design

As shown in Fig. 1 and 2, the principal forming rolls are mounted on two horizontal shafts. Usually both rolls are positively driven, although for some applications one roll is driven and the other is an idler. The efficiency of contour roll forming can often be increased by adding side rolls, which may either be idlers located between or beside forming stations or be positively driven as separate forming stations.

Forming rolls are usually designed to form the work metal in an upward direction (for instance, a channel or angle is formed with the legs pointing upward), although variations in practice are sometimes required to solve operational or handling problems. The use of a flying shear for cutoff may require a specific position of the workpiece. Work metal with a highly polished or prepainted surface is often formed with the polished or painted surface on top. If the finished piece is completely closed, positioning during forming must be considered, particularly when there is danger of entrapping lubricant.

In roll design, a vertical reference line is established with respect to the number and severity of bends. On symmetrical sections this line will be on the centerline of the workpiece. On unsymmetrical sections it will be on either side of the centerline, as required, to equalize the amount of forming.

A horizontal reference line, when used, is located at the lowest point of the shape and runs straight to the last set of rolls. On complex shapes a straight reference line may be difficult to establish; however, the design should result in as nearly a straight line as possible, to insure that the metal will pass through the rolls with a minimum of slippage at the critical points where maximum pressure must be applied.

Rolls are usually designed to begin forming near the center of the work metal and to work toward the edges. This minimizes the danger of tearing the work metal, which might occur if the edges were formed first and prevented metal flow toward the center.

Diameters and speeds of upper and lower rolls may be the same for forming shallow contours. For forming deep sections, however, it is usually desirable to have the pitch diameter of the upper roll larger than that of the lower roll (assuming that forming is in an upward direction).

To prevent buckling between stations, the strip should be kept under slight tension. This is best accomplished by having each successive set of rolls larger in diameter by ½ to 1%.

One-Piece vs Split Rolls. Simple rolls are usually of a one-piece design, but as complexity of the workpiece increases, the use of split rolls should be considered. There are seldom any marked disadvantages in using split rolls, and one or more of the following advantages can often be gained:

1. Turning, grinding or other machining operations are usually easier to perform on the separate sections of split rolls than on one-piece rolls having a complex contour.
2. Sections of split rolls are less susceptible to cracking in heat treatment than single complex rolls.
3. Handling problems are simplified, particularly for large roll sections.
4. Because sections of rolls subject to excessive wear or breakage can be replaced separately, split rolls are often more economical than one-piece rolls.
5. Split rolls permit the use of different roll materials, as needed, for areas of high and low wear.
6. Split rolls allow flexibility in making different widths of the same section by the use of spacers or additional roll sections.
7. Split rolls allow for minor adjustments that cannot be made with one-piece rolls.

Figure 4 illustrates some of the above advantages of split rolls. In Fig. 4(a), the upper roll is composed of five separate sections. In addition to being easier to manufacture, split rolls of this type allow for minor adjustments (by shims or similar means) after the initial trial and before the first production run.

Figure 4(b) shows an upper forming roll made up of three sections — a narrow center section flanked by two wider sections. In use, the center section is subjected to a higher rate of wear than the adjacent flanking sections. The narrow center section of this forming roll can be replaced without changing the flanking sections, or can be made from a more wear-resistant metal.

Auxiliary Rolls. Many contour roll forming operations can be done more efficiently when auxiliary rolls are mounted either between rolling stations or beside the main forming rolls, as in Fig. 20(b). Most auxiliary rolls are idlers, although some are positively driven. For shapes such as tubing and corner-bead sections, idler rolls do much of the forming. These rolls are more satisfactory than guides, which can cause excessive heat from friction. Idler rolls should be designed to permit adjustment. Mounting of idler rolls is their most troublesome feature, because space in the machine may be limited.

Driven side rolls sometimes are the best means of forming complex shapes, particularly those shapes that have a number of sharp bends and will subsequently be completely closed (complex tubular shapes). The most common method of forming with driven side rolls is to remove the upper roll shaft from a station and replace it with an assembly similar to the one shown in

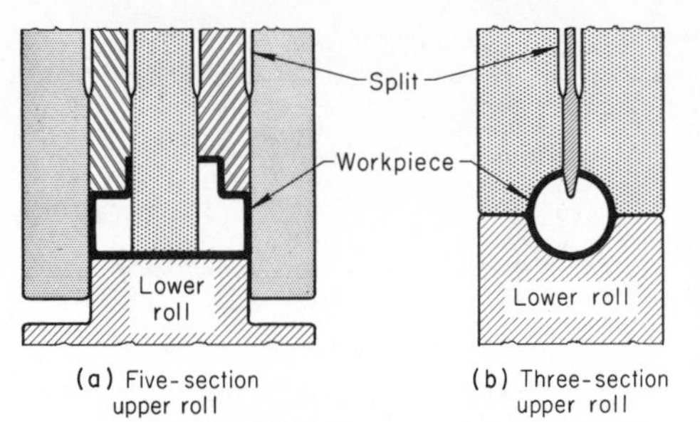

(a) Upper roll constructed in five sections allows for minor adjustments. (b) Three-section upper roll allows replacement of center section.

Fig. 4. Two types of split rolls used in contour roll forming

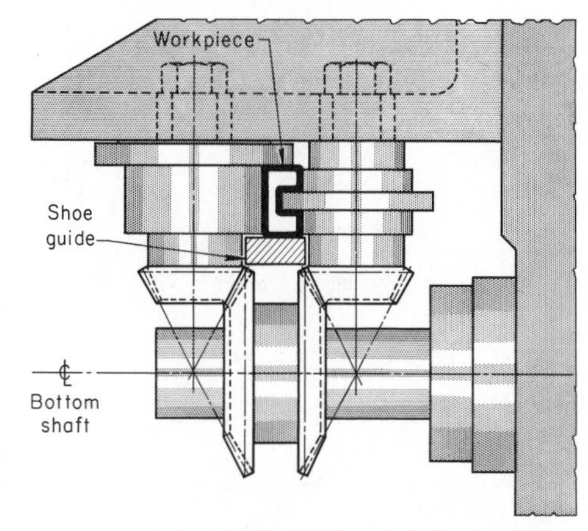

Fig. 5. Driven side rolls used in forming a complex shape

Fig. 5. The rolls are mounted to pinions that are bushed and anchored to the large bracket on the housing, and the entire side-roll assembly is bolted to the machine. Driving is accomplished by bevel gears that mesh with other bevel gears mounted on the lower roll shaft. Side-driven rolls are usually smaller than vertical rolls; consequently their speed of rotation must be greater to match the surface speed of the other rolls. This is done by proportioning the sizes of the bevel gears to give the correct ratio.

Selection of Roll Material

The materials that are most commonly used for contour rolls are:

1. Low-carbon steel, turned and polished — not hardened
2. Gray iron (such as class 30), turned and polished — not hardened
3. Low-alloy tool steel (such as O1 or L6), hardened to Rockwell C 60 to 63 and sometimes chromium plated
4. High-carbon, high-chromium tool steel (such as D2), hardened to Rockwell C 60 to 63 and sometimes chromium plated
5. Bronze (usually aluminum bronze).

Quantity to be rolled is usually the major factor in choosing the most appropriate roll material, although other factors, as noted below, also affect selection to some extent, and one or more of them may become definitive in particular production applications.

Short-Run Production. For rolling small quantities of a specific shape or when repeat orders are not expected, rolls made of either low-carbon steel or gray iron are commonly used. When the work metal is soft and corner radii are generous, low-carbon steel or gray iron rolls can be used for medium or high-production runs, because rolls are easily made from these materials and are not expensive.

Medium-Run Production. As the size of the production run increases, rolls made of hardened, ground and polished tool steel, such as O1 or L6, are usually more economical and are widely used, as indicated by the examples in this article. These steels are not expensive (base price is less than 60¢ a pound), they machine easier than more highly alloyed tool steels, and they can be heat treated by simple procedures. Rolling of four to five million feet of light-gage steel or aluminum before complete regrinding is common when using this type of tool steel. Rolls made of these steels may be plated with up to 0.001 in. of chromium to reduce galling or scratching of the work metal, or to extend tool life between grinds by decreasing roll wear or by minimizing corrosion or pitting.

Long-Run Production. For long production runs (over five million feet) or continuous high production, it is usually more economical to make rolls from one of the high-carbon high-chromium tool steels, such as D2. These highly alloyed grades cost nearly twice as much as O1, are more difficult to machine and grind, and require more complex heat treatments. However, because of their longer life between regrinds, the higher-alloy grades are usually more economical for long runs.

Factors Other Than Quantity. Three other conditions, under any one of which rolls made of steel such as D2 are often preferred (quantity becoming a secondary consideration), are: (*a*) excessively hard work metal (low formability); (*b*) excessively sharp radii or other severe forming conditions; and (*c*) work-metal surfaces that are abrasive (such as unpickled hot rolled steel) and cause excessive roll wear. Rolls made of highly alloyed tool steel may also be plated with chromium for the reasons mentioned in the section above.

Special Finish Requirements. In many applications, such as rolling light-gage stainless steel, aluminum alloy or coated stock, preservation of surface finish is of primary concern. Under these conditions, softer rolls are used to avoid damaging the work-metal surface, even though there may be a substantial reduction in roll life.

As workpiece finish requirements become more rigorous, softer rolls are required; rolls made of bronze are often used. In some applications, plating of hardened steel rolls is sufficient to prevent the marring of surface finish on the work metal.

Coiled vs Cut-to-Length Stock

Several factors must be considered in deciding whether to use coiled strip or cut lengths in contour roll forming. Some advantages of using coiled stock in preference to cut lengths are:

1. Coiled stock costs less initially and waste is reduced, thus reducing over-all material cost.
2. Tooling costs are reduced, because fewer stations are required and no extra guides are needed.
3. More intricate shapes can be formed, because guiding is kept to a minimum.

4 Results are more uniform, because ends are produced with less distortion and flare.
5 Productivity is higher, because the operation is almost continuous and handling of material is minimized.
6 Setup and changeover time is decreased, because tooling is simpler.

Some disadvantages of using coiled stock, as compared to cut lengths, are:

1 Additional equipment is required, such as for flying cutoff and prenotching.
2 Additional equipment requires more floor space.
3 Intricate or irregular notches or embossing over a large area may not be feasible in a continuous operation, thus requiring cut-to-length blanks on which these operations have already been performed.

Determining Strip Width

The width of strip required to produce a given shape is determined by making a large-scale layout, dividing it into its component straight and curved segments, and totaling the developed width along the neutral axis. The outside profile and the neutral axis of each curved segment can usually be treated as circular arcs. Also, for bends having an inside radius of up to about twice the stock thickness in low-carbon steel, the neutral plane or axis is located approximately one-third of the distance from the inside surface to the outside surface at the bend.

Accordingly, the developed width w (sometimes called "bend allowance") for a curved segment of inside radius up to about $2t$ is given by the formula:

$$w = 0.01745\alpha(r + t/3)$$

where α is angle to which the metal is bent, degrees; r is inside radius of bend, in.; t is metal thickness, in.; and 0.01745 is the factor for converting degrees to radians.

Sharp Bends. For bends having sharp inside corners, the formula is simplified by the omission of inside radius r:

$$w = 0.01745\alpha(t/3)$$

The factor $t/2$ is used when the material is less formable than low-carbon steel (as for the stainless steel shape in Fig. 6c; see calculations below).

The strip width needed for the shape with sharp inside bends shown in Fig. 6(a), which was contour rolled from 0.030-in.-thick cold rolled low-carbon steel strip, can be calculated by using the simplified formula for determining the developed width of the curved segments, as follows:

$$w \text{ for } 90^\circ \text{ bends} = 0.01745 \times 90 \times 0.010 = 0.0157 \text{ in.}$$

$$w \text{ for } 45^\circ \text{ bend} = 0.01745 \times 135 \times 0.010 = 0.0235 \text{ in.}$$

Adding the widths of the five straight and four curved segments, the total developed width for the shape in Fig. 6(a) is:

$$0.470 + 2(0.815) + 1.690 + 0.220 + 3(0.0157) + 0.0235 = 4.080 \text{ in.}$$

Radius up to 2t. The inside radius must be considered in obtaining the developed width of bends that do not have a sharp inside radius, and the original formula [$w = 0.01745\alpha(r + t/3)$] is used. For the shape illustrated in Fig. 6(b), which was contour rolled from hot rolled low-carbon steel, the calculation of developed strip width is as follows:

$$w\ (90^\circ \text{ bend}) = 0.01745 \times 90(0.125 + 0.040) = 0.259 \text{ in.}$$

and total strip width is:

$$0.875 + 1.000 + 0.750 + 2(0.259) = 3.143 \text{ in.}$$

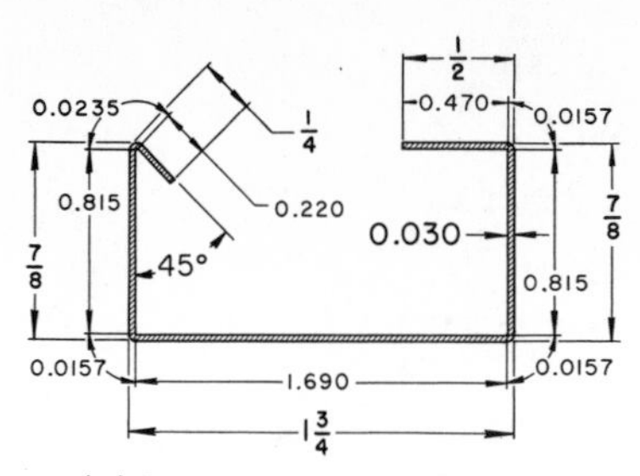

(a) Developed width, 4.080 in. Cold rolled low-carbon steel

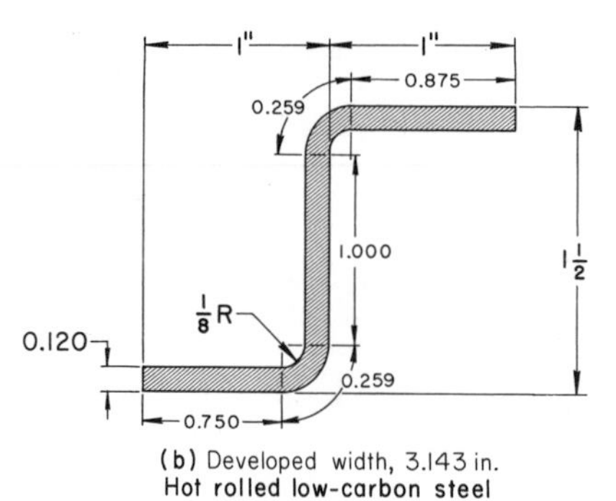

(b) Developed width, 3.143 in. Hot rolled low-carbon steel

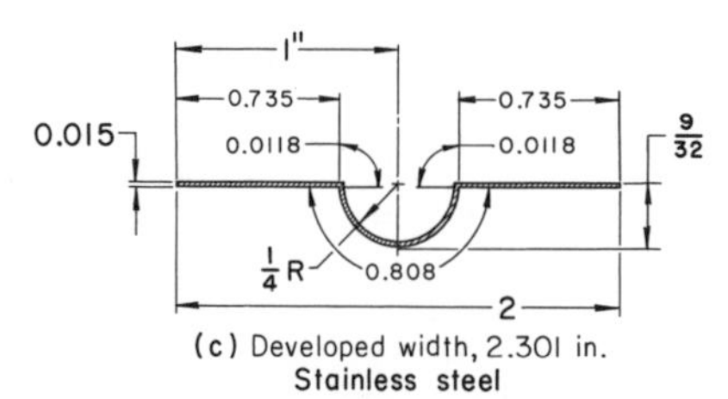

(c) Developed width, 2.301 in. Stainless steel

Fig. 6. Three contour rolled shapes for which developed widths were determined according to formulas and calculations given in the text

Radius Larger Than 2t. When the inside bend radius is larger than about $2t$ or when the material is less formable than low-carbon steel, or both, the neutral plane or axis lies approximately halfway between the inside surface and the outside surface at the bend. Developed width w of a bend is then:

$$w = 0.01745\alpha(r + t/2)$$

If the shape in Fig. 6(b) were to be contour rolled from stainless steel instead of low-carbon steel, the developed width of the strip would be:

$$0.875 + 1.000 + 0.750 + 2 \times 0.01745 \times 90(0.125 + 0.060) = 3.206 \text{ in.}$$

instead of 3.143 in., as calculated for low-carbon steel.

The strip width for the stainless steel shape shown in Fig. 6(c), which has two sharp bends and one large-radius bend, is calculated as:

$$2 \times 0.735 + 2 \times 0.01745 \times 90 \times 0.0075 + 0.01745 \times 180(0.25 + 0.0075) =$$
$$2 \times 0.735 + 2 \times 0.0118 + 0.808 = 2.301 \text{ in.}$$

Final dimensioning of stock for close-tolerance parts or for shapes in which the curved sections constitute a significant part of the over-all width is usually based on production trials.

Number of Stations

Factors that determine the optimum number of stations for contour roll forming include: work-metal thickness, composition and hardness; complexity of shape; tolerances; production quantity; available equipment; and special requirements.

Work-Metal Thickness. Usually, the number of stations required for forming a given shape increases as the thickness of the work metal increases, although not necessarily in direct proportion.

Composition and hardness of work metal (reflected in yield strength), strongly influence the number of stations required (see Examples 299 and 301). As yield strength increases, more stations are needed, assuming that other factors remain constant. Annealed work metals are usually preferred for contour roll forming, because yield strength is lowest for the fully annealed metal of any specific composition. However, there are sometimes other considerations. For instance, stretcher strains are likely to appear in fully annealed low-carbon steel after roll forming, unless the steel has been subjected to a temper pass. In some instances a roller leveler unit is installed on the contour roll machine immediately preceding the first roll station to eliminate stretcher strains (see page 326 in Volume 1 of this Handbook for additional information on stretcher strains).

The use of too few roll stations often leads to straightening problems. For instance, channel sections of 0.020-in.-thick stainless steel were produced in three roll stations, and excessive straightening was required. Addition of a fourth roll station decreased straightening requirements to an acceptable level.

Complexity of Shape. With even the most formable work metal, complexity of shape limits the minimum number of stations that can be used. A simple shape may be formed in as few as three stations; complex shapes may require 15 or more (see Example 305).

Close tolerances require one or more stations for final sizing, even though other factors may remain unchanged.

Production quantity can also influence the number of stations required. When a production run is too small to warrant the cost of installing the optimum number of stations, or when available equipment has to be used, there can be some penalties — a premium price will have to be paid for a more formable grade of work metal, wider than desired tolerances will have to be accepted, the cost of stress relieving the metal between passes will have to be absorbed, or a product that is difficult to straighten accepted.

In large-quantity production, on the other hand, output is often increased by using more stations than the minimum needed to turn out a satisfactory product. Greater operating speed is possible when less forming is done in any one station (see the section on

Forming Speed). Occasionally, the use of extra stations in continuous roll forming not only increases productivity but also replaces a conveyor that would otherwise be needed to move the work metal from one location to another.

Influence of Work-Metal Composition and Condition

The effect of work-metal formability on procedures and results in contour roll forming is generally the same as in other forming methods.

Initial yield strength and rate of strain hardening of the work metal affect contour roll forming. One measure for predicting the formability of a work metal is the Olsen cup test.

Work metals of equal thickness, with differing composition, initial yield strength, and rate of strain hardening, could require alterations in the contour rolling operation. Factors to be considered are: power requirements, number of stations, roll material, lubrication, and speed.

In contour roll forming, it is not uncommon to change the work metal but retain the same shape. In such instances, changes may be necessary in equipment and tooling.

When work-metal thickness and tooling remain unchanged, it is seldom a problem to change to a more formable work metal. For example, in changing from low-carbon steel to aluminum, major changes would be unlikely. However, it may be necessary to regrind the finish-station rolls to avoid overbending the section; this would usually be determined by a trial run.

When the change is to a metal of higher strength, one or more changes in procedure may be required to achieve desired results.

Changing the work metal from carbon steel to stainless steel is common and often poses problems. Adequate power and machine strength are primary considerations. For instance, forming type 302 stainless steel requires about twice as much power as is needed to form the same thickness and shape from 1010 carbon steel.

In forming higher-strength metals such as stainless steel, some overforming is usually required to allow for springback. Residual stress in highly cold worked metal often causes straightening problems, particularly when forming unsymmetrical shapes. A common remedy is to add roll stations to decrease the amount of forming in a given station.

The three examples that follow describe applications in which changes in work-metal composition required changes in procedure or control of the variation in composition.

Example 299. Change From Plain Carbon to High-Strength Low-Alloy Steel That Necessitated Addition of Two Roll Stations (Fig. 7)

The forming shown in Fig. 7 was successfully done in three roll stations when plain carbon steel (up to 0.25% carbon, yield strength about 35,000 psi) was the work metal. However, when the work metal was changed to high-strength low-alloy steel having a yield strength of 45,000 psi, fracturing at the point of maximum deformation was found in station 3 (Fig. 7). Examination indicated that forming had been too fast for this high-strength steel and more stations were needed. Fracturing was eliminated by adding two intermediate forming stations (Fig. 7, stations 1a and 2a).

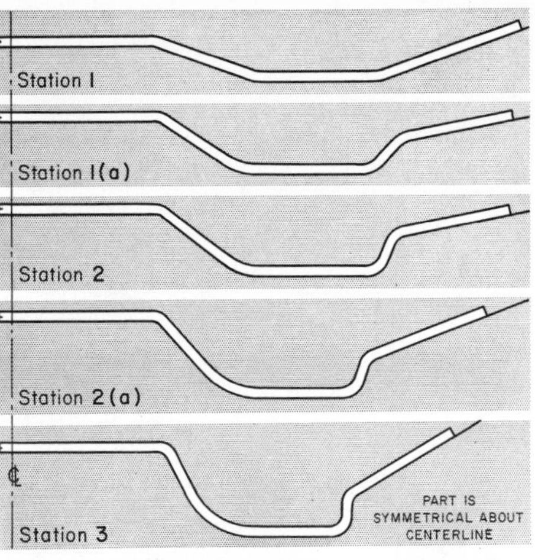

Fig. 7. Plain carbon steel was successfully formed through shapes in stations 1, 2 and 3. Intermediate stations 1(a) and 2(a) had to be added to reduce severity of bends in forming high-strength low-alloy steel. (Example 299)

Example 300. Control of Carbon Content That Eliminated Fracturing

Hat sections ½ in. deep by 1½ in. wide and having ½-in.-wide flanges were contour roll formed from 12-gage (0.1046-in.) half-hard 1020 steel using six roll stations. Sharp radii on the inside were required, which resulted in cracking on the outside. Decreasing (and controlling) the carbon content to a maximum of 0.15% permitted maintenance of sharp radii and eliminated fracturing.

Example 301. Change From Low-Carbon to Stainless Steel That Necessitated Redesign and Addition of Rolls (Fig. 8)

The shape shown in the lower left corner of Fig. 8 was originally roll formed from 1010 steel in nine roll stations, without difficulty. When the work metal was changed to type 301 stainless steel (annealed, with a 2B finish, in strips 4⁹⁄₃₂ in. wide by 0.048 ± 0.0025 in. thick), the workpiece twisted in a right-hand spiral during rolling. The problem was eliminated by redesigning the rolls in stations 7 through 9 and adding station 10. Also, the rolls were plated, the lubricant was changed, and the rolling speed was reduced.

The original and revised sequences of operation are shown in Fig. 8; processing details are given in the accompanying table.

In most instances, difficulty in maintaining size and angle tolerance increases as the yield strength of the work metal increases.

Optimum rolling speed decreases as yield strength or hardness increases (see Example 301). For instance, in changing from carbon steel to stainless, speed is usually decreased 10 to 25%, mainly to prevent rolls from galling when there is an appreciable amount of roll sweep. One method of combating roll galling without greatly reducing speed is to use EP (extreme-pressure) additives in the lubricant; or for extreme conditions, pigmented drawing compounds are added to the lubricant. The main disadvantage in using special lubricants is the difficulty and expense involved in removing them from finished workpieces.

Rolls made of aluminum bronze are often advantageous in shaping the difficult-to-form metals, because they resist galling; however, bronze rolls are softer than tool steel rolls and have shorter life. Rolls made from D2 tool steel, hardened and chromium plated, are usually best for contour roll forming of high-strength metals (see the section on Selection of Roll Material).

Joining of coils is influenced by work-metal composition, because the simplest welding methods are used for joining coils of carbon steel, whereas the tungsten-inert gas (TIG) method or other more elaborate welding methods may be required for the joining of

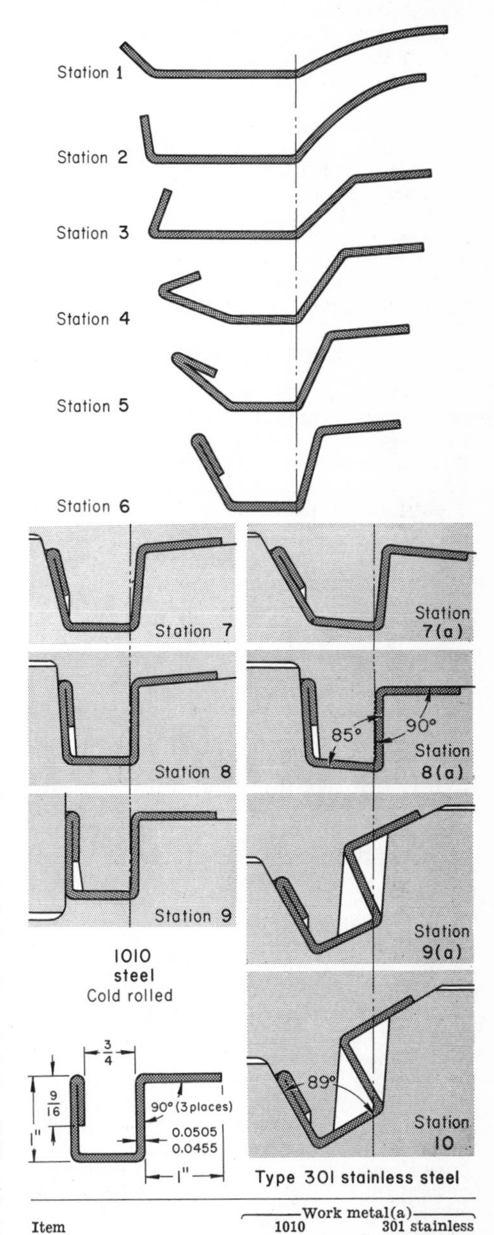

Item	Work metal(a) 1010	301 stainless
Stations(b)	9	10
Straightener	Four-roll	Shoe-type
Roll material	O1 or O6	O1 or O6(c)
Rolling speed, ft/min	120	90
Lubricant	(d)	(d)
Production, ft/hr(e)	3000	2500

(a) For both metals, surfaces of exposed areas had to be free from marks; tolerances were: ±1⁄32 in. on fractional dimensions, ±0.010 in. on decimal dimensions, ±1° on angles; maximum bow up, down and side, 0.015 in. per foot of length; maximum twist, ½° per foot of length. (b) Roller-type entry guide used. (c) Rolls were chromium plated. (d) Soluble oil mixed 1-to-12 with water, plus an EP additive for stainless steel only. (e) One operator and one helper.

Fig. 8. Shapes progressively produced in contour roll forming the same final configuration from carbon steel and from stainless steel (Example 301)

other metals, which slows down the entire coil-joining operation.

Tool cost increases when rolling harder metals (10 to 20% or more in changing from 1010 steel to stainless steel), the amount depending mainly on complexity of shape. This increased cost is accounted for mainly by the necessity of adding stations (see Example 301), although a more costly roll material is often used for the difficult-to-form work metals.

Directional properties of work metal are more critical in contour roll forming than in other methods, because all forming is done with the bend axis parallel to the rolling direction of the work metal, whereas in press forming, several different directions are usually involved. In most metals the variation in properties in different directions in the strip is not sufficient to have a marked effect on results, although such conditions can exist, and require close control of incoming work metal.

Forming Speed

Speeds used in contour roll forming can range from 1½ to 800 ft per min, although this speed range represents unusual extremes. Speeds between 80 and 100 ft per min are most widely used. One or more of the following can influence optimum forming speed:

1. Composition of the work metal
2. Yield strength or hardness of the work metal
3. Thickness of the work metal
4. Severity of the forming operation
5. Cutting finished shapes to length
6. Number of roll stations
7. Required auxiliary operations
8. Use of lubricant (coolant).

Lower speeds in the range indicated above (near 1½ ft per min) are required for contour roll forming titanium into a relatively complex shape. At the other extreme, a speed of 800 ft per min has been used in production operations in which conditions were nearly ideal; that is, for contour rolling low-yield-strength metal, such as aluminum or soft low-carbon steel, in thicknesses under 20 gage (0.0359 in.), in an operation having mild forming severity, and requiring cutoff into relatively long lengths (about 80 ft). To utilize such high speeds effectively, even though forming is not severe, more stations are usually required, to minimize the amount of forming in any one station. High speed usually precludes auxiliary operations, such as punching, notching or welding, and requires a flood of lubricant at each station.

The first four factors listed above are closely related and influence permissible forming speed. In addition, one or more of the last four factors may dictate a lower speed regardless of the otherwise permissible speed.

Cutting to length "on the fly" often necessitates a lower line speed than might otherwise be used. Since most contour-rolled lengths are cut off by a sliding die, the faster the work metal moves, the farther the die has to travel to make clean, accurate cuts. Thus, the permissible maximum speed depends greatly on cutting frequency. For instance, if the rolled workpiece is cut into 50-ft lengths, cutting off is simple and much higher speeds (the amount

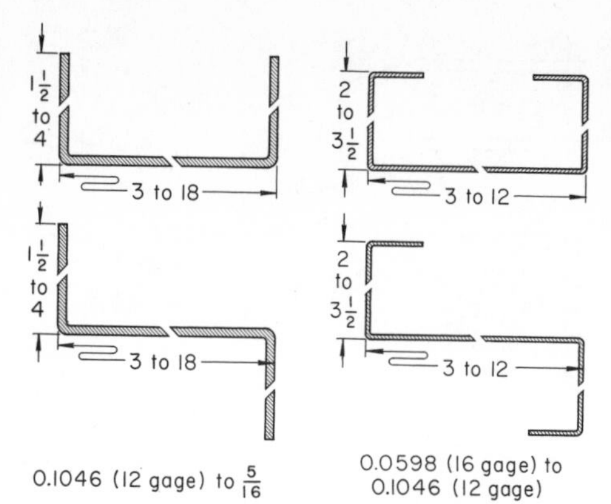

Fig. 9. Typical shapes, and ranges of size and thickness, of structural channels produced by contour roll forming

depending on cutoff equipment) can be used than when cutting 10-ft lengths.

Number of Roll Stations. With all other factors remaining constant, the number of stations in the sequence affects maximum permissible speed. However, severity and speed are so interrelated that when the number of roll stations is increased (thereby reducing the amount of forming done in one station), it is usually possible to increase the rate of travel.

Auxiliary operations, such as piercing, notching and welding, are often included in contour rolling. Although it is often the most economical procedure, inclusion of such operations may reduce the allowable speed for the entire operation.

Lubrication. Operating at high speed depends to a large extent on lubrication and cooling (the lubricant performs both functions). Lubrication is related to speed mainly because it cools the rolls as well as the work metal. In many instances specific requirements allow only a minimum amount of lubricant, or even none at all. Under these conditions speed may have to be decreased to a fraction of that which would be permitted if a flood of lubricant could be used (see the section on Lubrication, later in this article).

Influence of Application on Processing

Service requirements of the roll formed product have a marked effect on the selection of workpiece shape and of processing techniques. For instance, in structural shapes, load-carrying capacity is the most important requirement; surface finish and other appearance factors are usually of little or no importance. In architectural shapes, however, the emphasis is more likely to be on appearance rather than strength.

A selected form of strip or sheet is the initial work metal used for contour roll forming. A major application of strip is the production of tubing and pipe by roll forming and seam welding (or mechanically locking). However, for many applications, formed and welded round tubing is considered an intermediate product, because it will be reshaped into squares, triangles or other configurations by further contour roll forming. In some high-production applications, forming of the round tubing, welding and reshaping are accomplished in one continuous operation. When production quantities are small or when rolling and welding equipment is not available, common practice is to purchase the required size of rolled and welded round tubing and then to reshape as needed by additional contour roll forming.

Because of wide variations in end-use requirements, contour roll forming operations are broadly classified into:

1. Forming of structural shapes (not including seam welding)
2. Forming of architectural shapes (not including welding)
3. Forming of complex shapes from strip (including welding)
4. Forming of round pipe and tube (lock-seam or welded joints)
5. Reshaping of contour-rolled and welded tubing
6. Roll forming of composites (molding, weather stripping or similar products).

Forming Structural Shapes

Roll forming is usually selected for producing structural shapes such as Z-channels and C-channels (load-carrying members) for one or more of three reasons: (*a*) roll formed shapes provide closer tolerances than hot rolled shapes, (*b*) roll formed members can be produced to almost any desired length, and (*c*) shapes can be roll formed that are impractical to produce by other methods.

Techniques used for roll forming structural shapes are likely to differ from those used for roll forming other products, because: (*a*) thickness of work metal is usually greater, (*b*) radii are usually larger (frequently required to be larger), and (*c*) surface requirements are likely to be less critical, because the application usually requires strength rather than appearance.

Machine and material-handling facilities limit the thickness of work metal that can be formed. Roll forming of simple shapes having thicknesses up to ⅜ in. is common practice, although thicknesses up to ½ in. have been successfully roll formed.

For large production runs, a common practice is to design rolls capable of producing only one shape and size. However, structural members are more often produced by combination rolls that accommodate both Z-channels and C-channels of varying dimensions (see Fig. 9).

Plain hot finished steel, pickled-and-oiled steel, high-strength low-alloy steel, and galvanized steel are the metals most commonly rolled into structural shapes.

Springback varies among these metals, and is corrected for by side-roll adjustment, by sizing in Turk's-head rolls, or by straightening rolls. Frequently, a combination of two or more of these methods is used.

Forming Architectural Shapes

Contour roll forming is used to produce architectural components, such as posts for interior and exterior partitions, window members, door reinforcements, door frames, cornices, base and corner trim and panels. In many instances, roll forming is selected for these mass-produced articles because it results in lower cost for volume production. However, there are also many applications for which roll forming is used because the required accuracy and sharp radii are impractical to obtain by any other method.

Although architectural members must sometimes carry substantial loads, major emphasis is often placed on accuracy and surface finish. Uniformity in cross section is especially important, because in some applications two or more sections must fit together or line up with matching parts.

In most applications, surfaces of architectural shapes are exposed in their end use; therefore, surface marking from pressure or other causes must be held to limits more stringent than in most structural applications. Even when members are painted, pressure marks are likely to show through, resulting in unacceptable appearance.

Requirements for sharp bends are also unique in architectural shapes. Bends requiring outside radii less than metal thickness are not uncommon. These sharp radii are often achieved by the use of rolls having a bead around their periphery, which serves to force the metal in two directions away from the inside radius (actually undercutting), and results in a sharper outside radius (see Example 302 and Fig. 10).

To prevent chipping when beaded rolls are used, the rolls are usually made from a low-carbon steel having low hardness. However, because the use of this steel shortens roll life substantially, beaded rolls are sometimes made of a tough grade of tool steel, as in the following example:

Example 302. Contour Roll Forming a Sharp-Cornered Architectural Shape in Eight Stations (Fig. 10)

Eight rolling stations were used to complete the shape having four sharp corners shown in Fig. 10. The forming accomplished in each station is also shown. Processing details are given in the table with Fig. 10. As indicated in the sequence of operations, the upper rolls in stations 2 through 5 were beaded to undercut the inside, and allow sharp radii (about 1/32 in.) on the outside, of the workpiece.

All rolls for this operation were mounted on spindles 2½ in. in diameter. The 0.059-in.-thick cold finished 1010 steel was fed to the rolls from the coil by a roll feed. The rolled product was straightened in an adjustable stand using hard bronze blocks in the straightener, and then cut into 60-in. lengths by a slug-type cutoff die.

Combination Methods. Some workpiece shapes can be more economically produced by a combination of contour roll forming and press-brake forming. The decision of whether to finish the workpiece in a roll former or a press brake depends on the shape of the workpiece and the number of roll stations required, length of the rolled section, and quantity requirements.

Many shapes that would require several roll stations for completion can be finished on a press brake with less cost for tooling when small quantities are involved. However, for large production quantities, even the most complex shapes can usually be completed in a roll former at a lower cost than by combination methods. Length of the rolled section is also a factor and must be compatible with available press-brake equipment before a combination method can be considered.

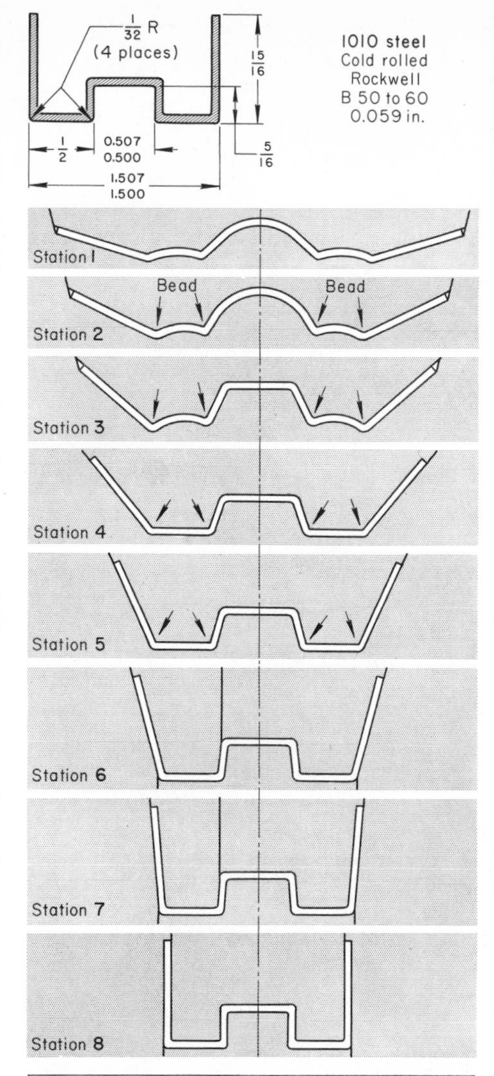

Number of stations(a)	8
Stock feed	Roll-type
Straightener(b)	Hard bronze, 4 in. long
Roll material	4370 steel at Rc 57 to 59(c)
Cost of rolls and straightener	$3900

Operating Conditions

Rolling speed	85 ft per min
Lubricant	Soluble-oil:water (1:12)
Setup and dismantling time	6.8 hr
Time for rolling 1000 pieces(d)	1.6 hr

(a) All spindles were 2½ in. in diameter. (b) Made in two halves. (c) Tool steels of similar composition, such as L6, are considered equivalent for this application. (d) Length per piece was 60 in.

Fig. 10. Roll forming sequence and processing details for producing a sharp-cornered architectural section (Example 302)

One instance in which a combination of contour roll forming and press-brake bending was the preferred method for completing a specified shape is described in the example that follows. (See also Examples 320 and 321, comparing costs of contour roll forming and of press-brake forming.)

Example 303. Combining Contour Roll Forming With Press-Brake Forming (Fig. 11)

The complex shape shown in Fig. 11 was made by first roll forming, using seven stations, and then making the final four bends in a press brake. The sequence of operations for roll forming, and the final shape produced in the press brake, are shown in Fig. 11.

The 0.048-in.-thick by 13 15/32-in.-wide cold rolled steel strip was fed into the roll forming machine (3½-in.-diam spindles) using a roller-type guide. The rolled shape was then passed through a straightener using hard bronze blocks, after which it was sawed into 120-in. lengths, and then trimmed on a punch press. The cut-to-length shapes were finally transferred to a press brake for finishing.

In this application, because production quantities were low and an adequate press brake was available, the combination of roll forming and press-brake forming proved more economical than the tooling required for completion by roll forming. Processing details for the contour roll forming are given with Fig. 11.

Forming Complex Shapes in Combination With Welding

Contour roll forming in combination with seam welding is commonly applied to the production of complex shapes used for a variety of structural applications. Usually the welding is done after the strip has passed seven or eight forming stations, although location of

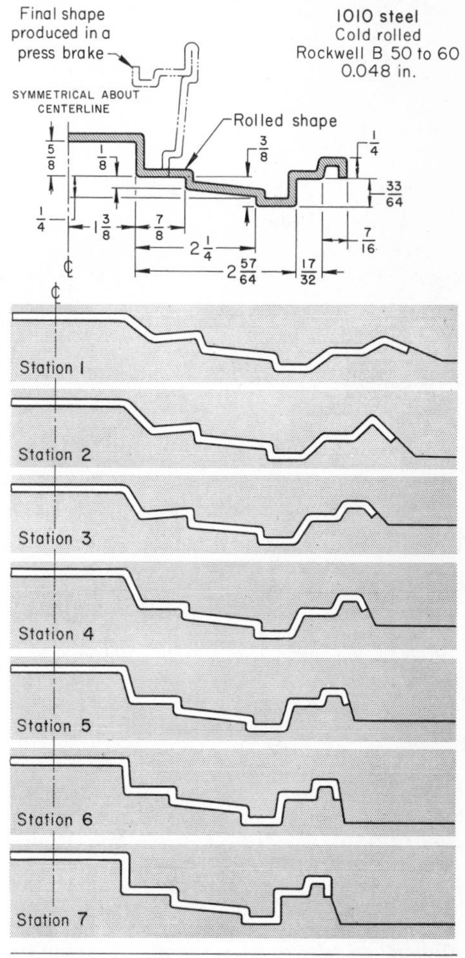

Number of stations(a)	7
Stock feed	Roll-type
Straightener	Hard bronze block
Roll material	4370 steel at Rc 57 to 59(b)
Cost of rolls and straightener	$10,000

Operating Conditions

Rolling speed	60 ft per min
Lubricant	Soluble-oil:water (1:12)
Setup and dismantling time	10.6 hr
Time for rolling 1000 pieces(c)	7.6 hr

(a) All spindles were 3½ in. in diameter. (b) Tool steels of similar composition, such as L6, are considered equivalent for this application. (c) Each piece was 120 in. long.

Fig. 11. Roll forming sequence and processing details for partly forming an architectural section prior to finish forming in a press brake (Example 303)

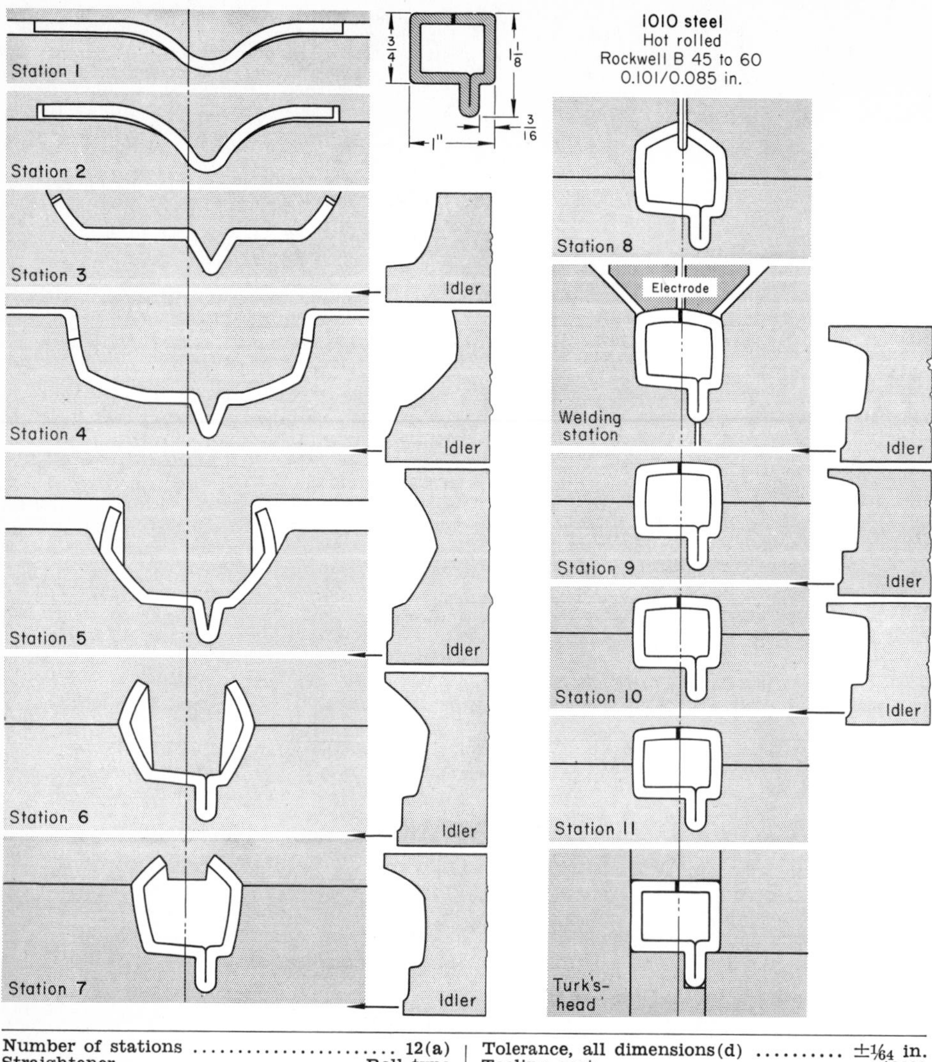

Number of stations	12(a)
Straightener	Roll-type
Roll material	O1 or L6 tool steel(b)
Roll hardness	Rockwell C 60 to 62

Operating Conditions(c)

Rolling speed	55 ft per min
Lubricant	Soluble-oil:water (1:12)
Tolerance, all dimensions(d)	±1/64 in.
Tooling cost	$3000
Production rate	2400 ft per hr

(a) Eight forming, three sizing and one Turk's-head station. (b) Chromium plated. (c) Operation performed by one operator and one helper. (d) Rolled product had to be free from bow and twist, and suitable for painting.

Fig. 12. Sequence of operations and processing details for roll forming of door-frame members (Example 304)

the welding operation in the sequence depends mainly on the shape being formed.

Mandrels are sometimes required in roll forming to back up the difficult-to-form areas. However, mandrels are troublesome and slow down the operation. By doing most of the forming before welding, and then sizing after welding, complex shapes can be produced to close dimensions without a mandrel, as shown in the two examples that follow.

Example 304. Combining Roll Forming With Welding (Fig. 12)

Completed parts having the cross-sectional shape shown in Fig. 12 served as structural members for door frames. As seen from the sequence of operations in Fig. 12, initial forming was done in eight stations with idler rolls between stations. After welding, the workpiece was sized in three conventional rolling stations (with intermediate idler rolls) and a final Turk's-head station. Tolerances were held to ±1/64 in. on all fractional dimensions. Special requirements were that the workpiece be free from bow and twist, and that all surfaces be suitable for painting. Processing details are given in the table with Fig. 12.

Table 1. Processing Details for Roll Forming a Complex Shape (With Intermediate Welding) From Steel Strip 16 1/16 In. Wide (Example 305)

Number of forming stations	22(a)
Straightener	Roll-type
Roll material(b)	O1 or L6 tool steel
Roll hardness	Rockwell C 60 to 62

Operating Conditions(c)

Rolling speed	50 ft per min
Lubricant	Soluble-oil:water (1:12)
Roll life	1 1/4 million ft
Production rate	165 pieces per hour(d)

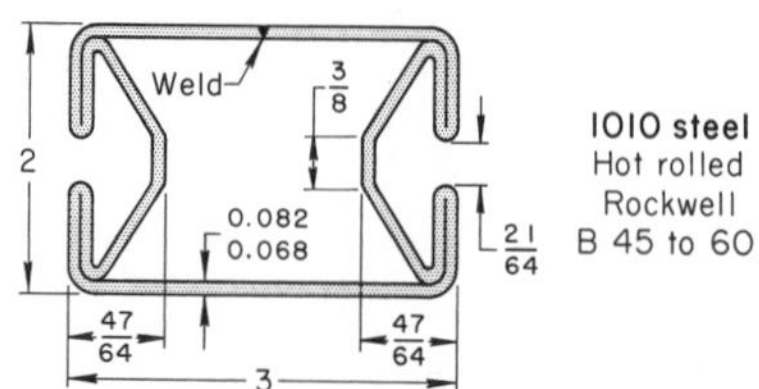

(a) Eighteen preweld forming stations and four sizing stations; plus Turk's-head and straightener. (b) Approximately 75% of the rolls were chromium plated. (c) Operation performed by one operator and one helper. (d) Formed pieces were 102 in. long.

Example 305. Producing a Complex Shape in 22 Forming Stations With Intermediate Welding (Table 1)

Completed parts having the cross-sectional shape shown with Table 1 were roll formed in 102-in. lengths from 16 1/16-in.-wide by 0.075-in.-thick (±0.007 in.) low-carbon steel strip for use as members in the construction of material-handling containers. Forming was done in 18 stations before welding. Following the welding station, sizing was done in four stations, which had provisions for four-way forming. The workpiece was then forced through a Turk's-head and roll straightened. Tolerances were held to ±1/32 in., except where otherwise noted in the sketch in Table 1. It was also necessary that surfaces be suitable for painting.

Forming Round Pipe and Tube

Welded-seam pipe and tube are formed by three methods: edge forming, center forming and true-radius forming. Edge and center forming (Fig. 13a and b) require complete sets of rolls for each size of tube, because the stations that precede welding have the final radii in the roll contours. In true-radius forming (Fig. 13c), the breakdown rolls can be used for a range of sizes, which reduces tooling cost and setup time.

For all three methods of producing welded tubing, the forming rolls are termed as breakdown and finishing rolls. Breakdown is usually accomplished in the first three or four roll stations, as indicated in Fig.13.

Optimum distance between the edges of the stock in the final finishing station (stations 6, 7, and 5 in Fig. 13a, b and c, respectively) is affected by method of welding and tube size. For resistance welding, however, the following relations of tube size to distance are typical.

3/8-in.-diam tube	Distance, 0.062 in.
1	0.124
2	0.172
4	0.250

Machine size (whether it should be a light 1 1/2-in.-spindle machine or an intermediate 4 to 6-in.-spindle machine) is determined by material thickness and tubing size. Large pipe sometimes requires a machine having 12 to 14-in.-diam spindles.

Speed of production is controlled by gage and type of work metal. Aluminum can be formed and welded as fast as 250 ft per min, whereas titanium tubing is produced at a rate of only 18 in. per min. The welding operation is often the main limitation on the speed at which tubing can be produced by roll forming.

Soluble oil is the most practical lubricant for forming tube, and should be used to prevent galling. A mixture of 25 to 40 parts water to one part oil is commonly used.

Long roll life can be expected in producing round tubing; three to four million feet between regrinds is considered normal.

Lock-seam tube has two edges folded over to form a lock (Fig. 13d). Production of lock-seam tubing is restricted to light-gage material, usually less than 20 gage (0.0359 in.), because heavier stock is too difficult to lock. The lock-seam method is used extensively for thicknesses that are impractical for welding because they are too thin. Maximum thickness is also restricted by tube diameter. As a general rule, stock thickness should not be greater than 3% of the tube diameter. For instance, 0.030 in. is about the maximum thickness of strip that should be used to produce 1-in.-OD tubing.

Minimum width of the lock should be five times the material thickness. The lock-seam method is also applicable to square tubing.

The various stages of lock-seam forming are shown in Fig. 13(d). Idlers are used between stations from station 4 to station 8. Between stations 8 and 9, a lock housing unit that is equivalent to two stations is used. Both side rolls and vertical rolls are used in the locking stand, the main purpose being to lock the two edges of work metal in the groove. A mandrel is placed inside the tube to help form the small lock. This mandrel is in the locking stand and extends beyond station 9. In the last station, two small rolls ride opposite each other on the mandrel, pushing the work metal to form a tight lock between top and bottom rolls in station 9. It is necessary to have close control over the stock thickness, because a 0.001-in. difference in thickness will result in a difference of about 0.005 in. in the outside diameter of the tube.

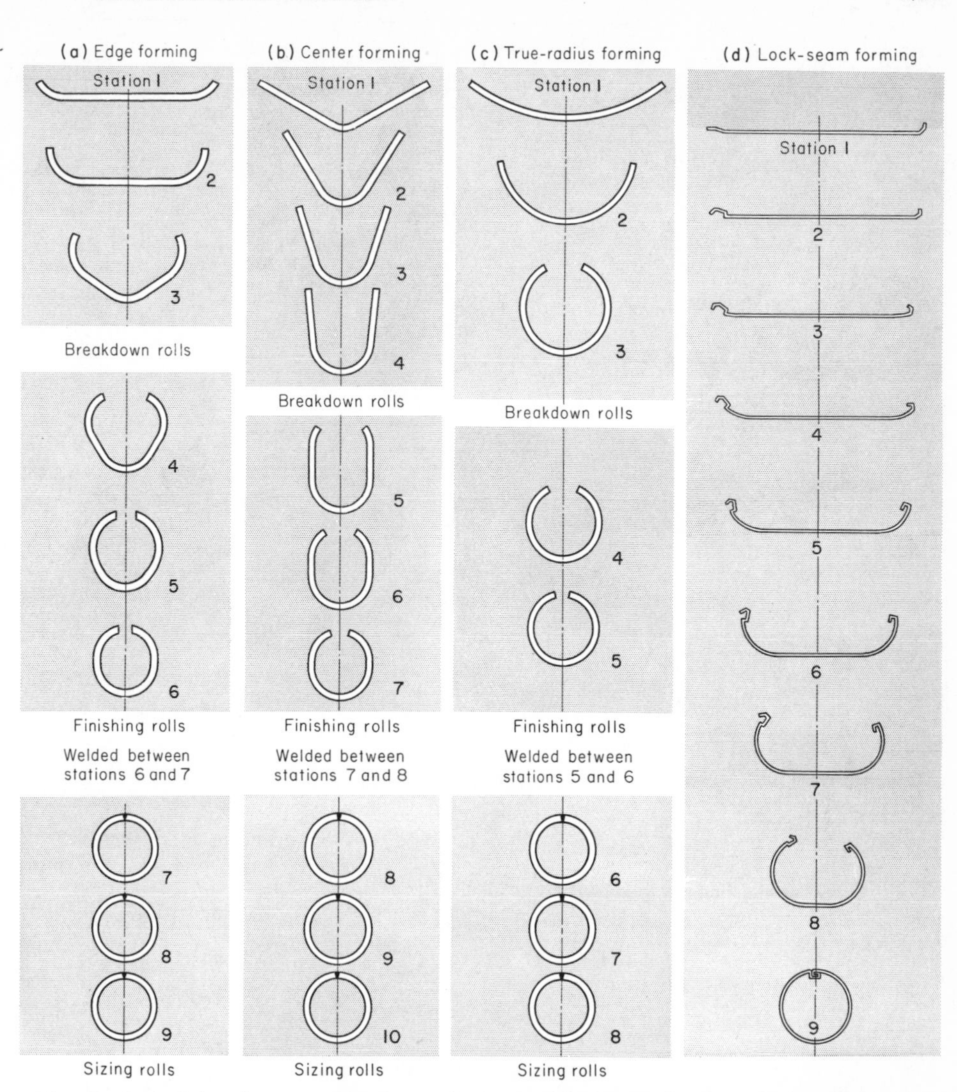

Fig. 13. Typical forming sequences for producing round pipes and tubes with a welded butt end and with a lock-seam joint. See text for discussion.

Reshaping of Round Tubing

Several cross sections that are feasible to produce by reshaping round tubing are shown in Fig. 14. Reshaping can be done in a separate operation or continuously in sequence with the production of round tubing.

On squares and rectangles, the flatness of the sides will vary with work-metal thickness and hardness. On light gages and in the harder tempers, springback results in a crown effect on the sides. This condition can be corrected by overforming in the final station. In forming rectangles, the longer sides may become convex and the short sides concave. Flatness can be controlled to a minor extent by roll adjustments in the finish station, but major correction is made by using concave or convex contours in final Turk's-head rolls.

Rolling speeds used in reshaping tubing of light-gage metal are often equal to those used in producing the basic round tube. For reshaping heavier-gage tubing (for example, over 0.035 in.), speed should be reduced by as much as 25% of that used for forming the round tube, depending mainly on the capacity of the equipment.

Tooling requirements for reshaping round tubing vary with gage, size and complexity of final shape. It is often possible to form simple squares from thin-gage round tubing in one roll station and one Turk's-head station. However, as stock thickness or complexity of shape, or both, increase, more stations are required — as in the four examples that follow.

Example 306. Square Shape That Was Produced From Light-Gage Round Tubing in Two Roll Stations (Fig. 15)

The finished square tubing shown in Fig. 15 was produced for backs for metal chairs. The basic round tube, also shown in Fig. 15, was made from a 1010 steel strip 4 11/32 in. wide by 0.035 +0.004, −0.000 in. thick. Reshaping into square tubing was incorporated as part of

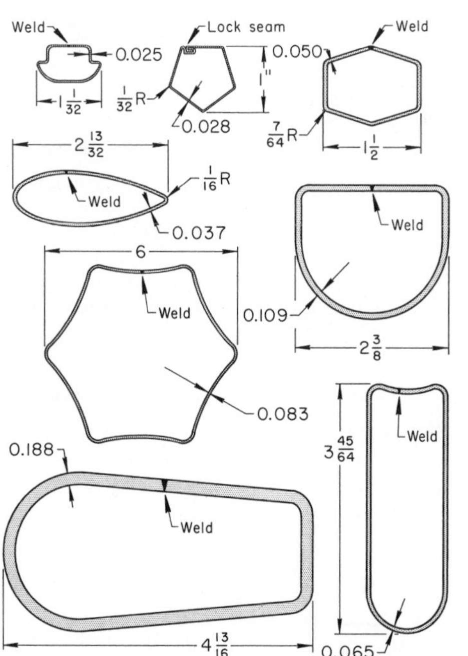

In addition to these contours, square, triangular and rectangular shapes are formed from round tubing in one or more roll stations.

Fig. 14. Cross sections showing typical contours that can be produced by reshaping welded or lock-seamed round tubing

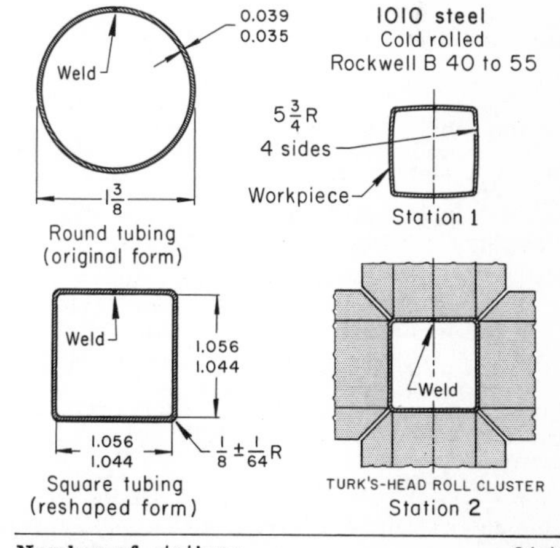

Number of stations	2(a)
Straightener	Roll-type
Roll material	O1 or L6 tool steel
Roll hardness	Rockwell C 60 to 62
Tool cost(b)	$575

Operating Conditions(c)

Rolling speed	132 ft per min
Lubricant	Soluble-oil:water (1:12)
Production rate	3500 ft per hr

(a) One roll station and one Turk's-head unit with two four-roll clusters. (b) For re-forming rolls and straightener. (c) Operation performed by one operator and one helper.

Fig. 15. Sequence of shapes in two-station forming of a square shape from welded round tubing (Example 306)

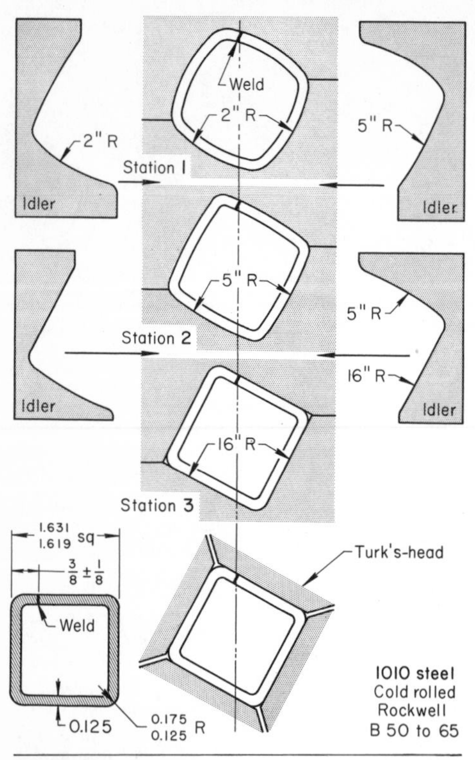

Number of stations	4(a)
Straightener	Roll-type
Roll material(b)	O1 or L6 tool steel
Roll hardness	Rockwell C 60 to 62
Tool cost(c)	$1300

Operating Conditions(d)

Rolling speed	65 ft per min
Lubricant	Soluble-oil:water (1:12)
Production rate	1800 ft per hr

(a) Three forming stations and one Turk's-head; idlers between stations 1 and 2, and 2 and 3. (b) Chromium plated. (c) Re-forming and straightener rolls. (d) Operation performed by one operator and one helper.

Fig. 16. Sequence of shapes in four-station forming of a square shape from welded round tubing (Example 307)

the continuous operation using two stations, as shown in Fig. 15, plus a straightener. One operator with a helper conducted the reshaping operation. Processing details are included in the table with Fig. 15.

The round tube was formed and welded in the first eight stations of a nine-station tube mill. The tube was reshaped into a square by the ninth roll station and by a Turk's-head unit with two four-roll clusters.

Example 307. Square Shape That Was Produced From 0.125-In.-Wall Round Tubing in Four Roll Stations (Fig. 16)

The finished square tubing shown in Fig. 16 was produced from round tubing having a 2¹⁄₁₆-in. OD and a wall thickness of 0.125 ± 0.008 in. The round tubing was reshaped in three conventional roll stations, as shown in Fig. 16, but idler rolls were utilized between stations 1 and 2, and 2 and 3. In a fourth station, final shaping was done by Turk's-head rolls. Flatness of the sides was controlled by changing convexity or concavity in the rolls at station 4 as needed. Processing details are included in the table with Fig. 16.

Examples 308 and 309. Additional Roll Stations Required to Form Complex Shapes From Welded Round Tubing

Example 308 (Fig. 17). The complex shape shown in Fig. 17 was produced from 1010 welded steel tubing having 1⁹⁄₁₆-in. OD and a 0.062-in. wall thickness, in three main rolling stations and one Turk's-head station. Idler rolls also were used ahead of station 1 and between stations 1 and 2, and stations 2 and 3. The same number of stations was required for producing the complex shape shown in Fig. 17 as for rolling the simple square described in Example 307, even though the stock used for producing the square was double the thickness used for the complex shape. Processing details for forming the complex shape are given in the table with Fig. 17.

Example 309 (Table 2). Producing the complex shape shown in Table 2 from 0.035-in.-wall welded tubing required three main roll stations with idler rolls preceding each station, a four-roll Turk's-head, and two straightening rolls. [This procedure is in marked contrast to that described in Example 306 for producing a simple square from tubing having the same wall thickness. The shape shown in Table 2 required four ¹⁄₃₂-in. radii in addition to the two 180° bends, a difficult shape to form under any conditions. Use of more stations as described in this example is usually the best procedure.]

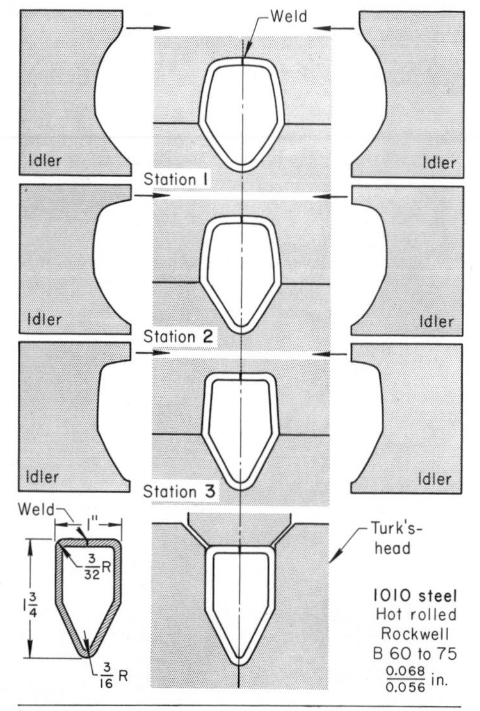

Number of stations	4(a)
Straightener	Roll-type
Roll material	O1 or L6 tool steel
Roll hardness	Rockwell C 60 to 62
Tool cost(b)	$1250

Operating Conditions(c)

Rolling speed	108 ft per min
Lubricant	Soluble-oil:water (1:12)
Production rate	2500 ft per hr

(a) Three re-forming stations and one Turk's-head. Idler rolls used ahead of station 1 and between stations 1 and 2, and 2 and 3. (b) Re-forming and straightener rolls. (c) Operation performed by one operator and one helper.

Fig. 17. Sequence of operations and processing details for forming a complex shape from round tubing (Example 308)

Table 2. Processing Details for Reshaping 0.035-In.-Wall Welded Round Tubing Into a Complex Shape (Example 309)

Number of stations	4(a)
Straightener	Roll-type
Roll material	O1 or L6 tool steel
Roll hardness	Rockwell C 60 to 62
Tool cost	$1200

Operating Conditions

Rolling speed	90 ft per min
Lubricant	Soluble-oil:water (1:12)

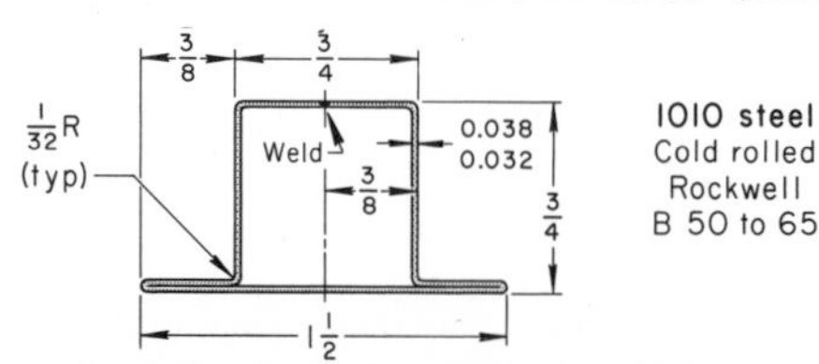

(a) Three main rolling stations, three sets of idler rolls, a four-roll Turk's-head station and two straightening rolls.

Corner Radii. Table 3 lists standard outside corner radii for square or rectangular tube reshaped from round tube of various diameters and wall thicknesses. The figures are based on 1010 or 1015 steel tube and apply for reshaping without a significant change in the outside circumference of the tube.

The data shown in Table 3 are based on a D/l ratio of 1.273 (D being the outside diameter of the round tube, and l being the length of one side of the square tube, or one-fourth the sum of the lengths of the four sides of the rectangular tube, produced from it). The square tube for which the corner is shown in Table 3 had a D/l ratio of 1.286. The 1⅛-in.-diam tube was less than the range, but the 0.174-in. radius lies within the range for a tube of this thickness. The square tube shown in Fig. 15 had a ⅛-in. radius, which was larger than the standard range for this tube thickness, as indicated in Table 3. The D/l ratio was 1.375/1.124, or 1.223.

When close control of corner radii is required, the tools must keep the metal closely confined during reshaping. When working with welded tube, the reshaping should be controlled so that the weld is not at a corner, as shown in Fig. 14 to 17. Sometimes this is not possible, but the welded area is generally less formable than the metal away from the weld.

Example 310. Special Shape Rolled From Lock-Seam Tubing in Turk's-Head Rolls (Fig. 18)

The shape shown in Fig. 18 was produced from ⅝-in.-OD lock-seam 1010 steel tubing in three stations by means of Turk's-head rolls, also shown in Fig. 18. The round tubing was forced through these undriven rolls directly from the mill that formed the round tubing from strip. After passing through station 3, the work was straightened on a shoe straightener. Processing details are included in the table with Fig. 18.

Roll Forming of Composites

Roll forming continuous sections of two or more similar or dissimilar materials is common practice. Two typical applications that utilize simultaneous roll forming of composites are described in the two examples that follow.

Example 311. Weather Stripping That Was Produced by Composite Roll Forming Four Materials (Fig. 19a)

Figure 19(a) shows a cross section of weather stripping composed of thin low-carbon steel core, rubber, wool fabric and a stainless steel bead. This composite was produced in two operations: (*a*) rubber was extruded on the low-carbon steel core and the fabric was applied, and (*b*) edge beads were formed and the stainless steel bead was applied. Roll forming was accomplished in seven stations at 100 ft per min. Rolls were made from L6 tool steel and heat treated to Rockwell C 59 to 60.

Example 312. Three-Material Composite That Was Produced by Roll Forming (Fig. 19b)

Figure 19(b) shows a section of a channel composed of galvanized steel and wool fabric locked together by stainless steel beads. This part was rolled in a 12-station machine in a single operation at a minimum speed of 100 ft per min. Rolls were made from L6 tool steel and heat treated to Rockwell C 59 to 60.

Control of End Flare

End flare occurs to some degree in nearly all roll formed shapes. It can extend back from the end as little as 2 or 3 in., or as much as 12 in. End flare can be from a few thousandths of an inch (this small amount is usually ignored) to ½ in. or more, which may pose difficult problems. Both ends may flare outward, or one end may flare outward and the other inward.

Excessive flare is caused by hard work metal, workpiece shape, too few roll stations, unsuitable roll design, or a combination of all these.

There are several means of keeping end flare within acceptable limits. Replacing a hard work metal with one that is more formable will lessen, but not always eliminate, end flare. Minor changes in shape or design of the workpiece are often feasible and should be considered when end flare is a problem. It is much better to recognize the possibility of excessive flare before designing the rolls than to attempt correction after the rolls are made. The best means of minimizing end flare is to provide enough roll stations to prevent the sides or edges of the work-metal strip from elongating.

In extreme cases, flare has been minimized to an acceptable degree by finish forming in the second-last station and then stress relieving (by heating with an induction coil) before the final station.

Lubrication

Lubricants prevent metal pickup by the rolls (thus improving finish on the work metal and prolonging roll life) and also prevent overheating of rolls and work metal. When rolls become overheated, their life is shortened. If work metal is overheated, it may warp, and require a straightening operation. When lubricants can be tolerated, rolling efficiency is usually increased by their use.

Soluble oil (in a 1-to-12 mixture with water) is the most commonly used lubricant. It is usually applied by pumping from a self-contained sump in the machine base through a manifold having flexible tubes and nozzles that direct the fluid to the required locations. Gutters are arranged around the top of the machine to catch the fluid and return it to the sump.

Other lubricants have been used satisfactorily for specific applications. However, in addition to being able to perform lubricating and cooling functions, a lubricant must be nontoxic, noncorrosive to the metal being formed (as well as to rolls and other machine components), and removable by available shop cleaning facilities. For instance, some silicone-base fluids are excellent lubricants for roll forming, but they are extremely difficult to remove from metal surfaces, which poses problems in obtaining satisfactory plating or adherence of organic coatings or adhesives. Additions of extreme-pressure (EP) lubricants are sometimes made in severe roll forming (see Example 301).

For some applications no lubricant is permitted (for example, forming of painted or otherwise coated metals,

Table 3. Standard Outside Corner Radii for Square or Rectangular Tube Reshaped From Round Tube(a)

Round tube: Outside diameter, in.	Round tube: Wall thickness, in.	Square tube, outside corner radius, in.
½ to 1½	0.028	1/32 to 1/16
½ to 2½	0.035	1/32 to 1/16
½ to 4	0.049	3/64 to 5/64
½ to 4⅛	0.065	1/16 to 7/64
¾ to 4⅛	0.083	5/64 to ⅛
1 to 4⅛	0.095	3/32 to 5/32
1¼ to 4	0.109	⅛ to 13/64
1¼ to 4	0.120	⅛ to 7/32
2 to 4	0.134	5/32 to 9/32
2 to 4	0.148	3/16 to 5/16
2 to 4	0.165, 0.180	¼ to ½

(a) Generally accepted as standard. Smaller or larger corner radii can be specified.

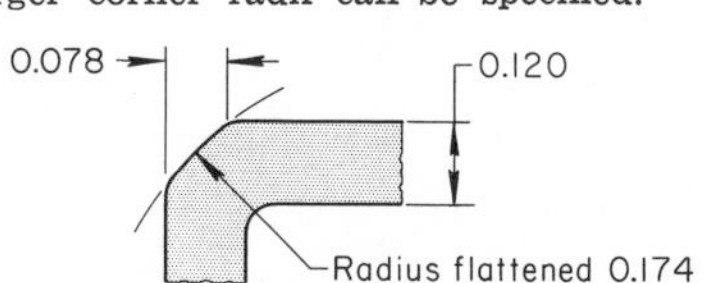

Example: ⅞-in. square (0.120-in.-wall) reshaped from 1⅛-in. round tube, one corner of which is shown above (Also, see text for additional discussion.)

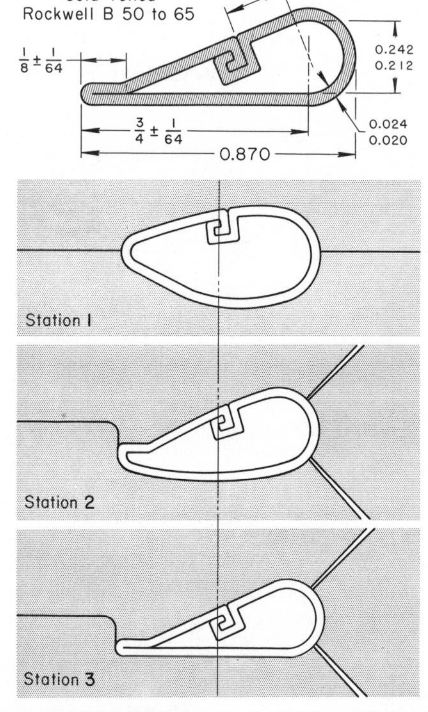

Number of stations	3(a)
Straightener	Shoe-type
Roll material	O1 or L6 tool steel
Roll hardness	Rockwell C 60 to 62
Tool cost(b)	$550

Operating Conditions(c)

Rolling speed	120 ft per min
Lubricant	Soluble-oil:water (1:12)
Production rate	1200 ft per hr

Specified Maximum Bow and Twist, In.

Vertical:	
19-in. length	0.032
23-in. length	0.039
29-in. length	0.049
Horizontal:	
19-in. length	0.024
23-in. length	0.029
29-in. length	0.036

(a) Three Turk's-head stations — one two-roll and two three-roll heads. (b) Re-forming rolls and straightener. (c) Operation performed by one operator and one helper.

Fig. 18. Reshaping of round lock-seam tubing in Turk's-head rolls (Example 310)

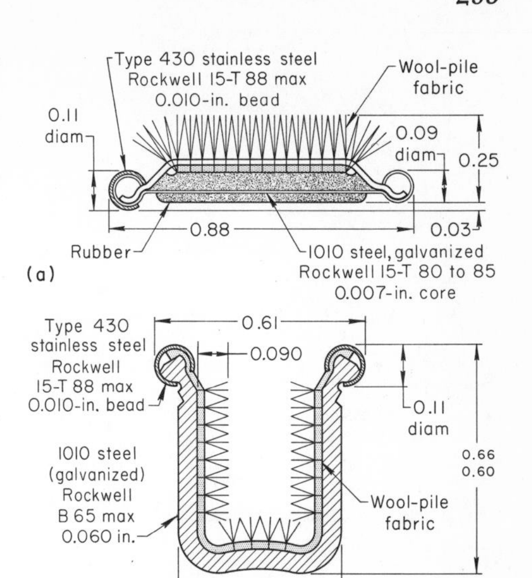

Fig. 19. Shapes produced by composite roll forming. (a) *Weather stripping produced by forming four materials.* (b) *Channel produced by forming three materials.* (Examples 311 and 312)

forming of complex shapes that would entrap lubricants, and forming of composite materials). The resulting penalty could be reduction of rolling speed or lower-quality finish, or both. However, in some instances, even though flooding with lubricant cannot be tolerated, other means can be utilized to supply some lubricant to the rolls. One method is to mount cellulose sponges in constant contact with the rolls, and to keep them wetted with lubricant by hand or by drip applicators.

Despite the fact that lubrication is helpful and often necessary in contour rolling, application and subsequent removal of lubricants are significant cost items. When roll forming steel, however, the selection of hot rolled, pickled and oiled grades of work metal has often eliminated the need for an additional lubricant.

Dimensional Accuracy

Five major factors influence dimensional accuracy in contour roll forming:

1 Initial variation of work-metal dimensions
2 Rolling technique
3 Formability of the work metal
4 Complexity of shape
5 Number of stations used.

In most applications, two or more of the above items influence the dimensional accuracy feasible in a given operation. In almost all production operations, costs are increased as tolerances become tighter.

Several methods of maintaining closer tolerances are available, and it is possible to select the most economical for a given application, as described in the following example.

Example 313. Use of Side Rolls in Finishing Station to Meet Tolerances (Fig. 20)

Figure 20(a) shows a simple shape made from 0.090-in.-thick hot rolled 1010 steel on which it was necessary to hold the 2-in. inside dimension to ±0.010 in. This was not feasible using conventional two-roll forming in the finishing station (Fig. 20a), because the commercial quality strip had a thickness variation of ±0.008 in., thus resulting in a total variation of 0.016 in. on the 2-in. inside dimension of the channel section.

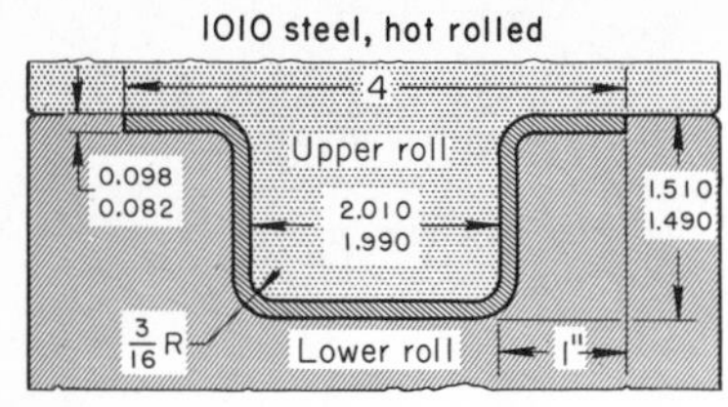

(a) Original method

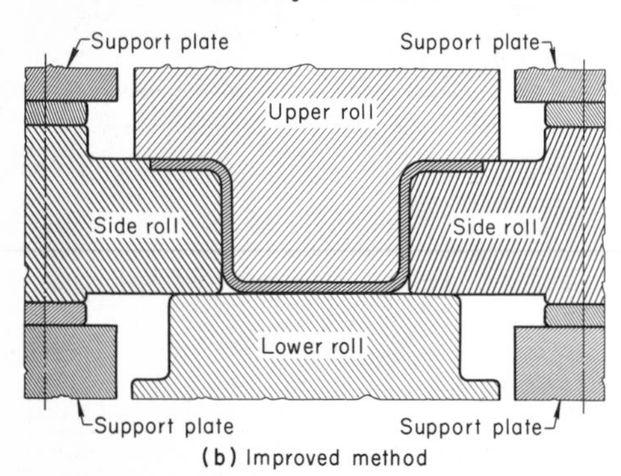

(b) Improved method

(a) Two-roll finishing station in which tolerance on inside dimension of part could not be held. (b) Finishing station with side rolls, which provided good control of inside width.

Fig. 20. Effect of tooling on dimensional accuracy (Example 313)

One means of achieving the required dimensions was to purchase close-tolerance strip, but cost was prohibitive. Another possibility was to change bottom finishing rolls to accommodate shipments of stock, which ran to the high or low side of the allowable range. This possibility was discarded as impractical.

The most practical approach was to use a four-way forming station for finishing, as shown in Fig. 20(b). The side forming rolls, supported by plates, constantly held and formed the material against the upper roll. The side plates, with their component supports at their ends, were designed to operate under tension and to deflect as work-metal gage increased. This resulted in good control of the inside width, because most of the dimensional variation was thus transferred to the outside, where it could be tolerated. Another advantage of the four-way forming principle was the elimination of sidesweep, which had been observed when using a one-piece bottom roll (Fig. 20a). Sidesweep induced scrub marks on the work metal and resulted in bottom roll galling.

The operation was done in a total of eight roll stations (seven preceding the finishing station) at a speed of 88 ft per min. Soluble oil mixed 1 to 12 with water was used as the lubricant. Rolls were made from L6 tool steel, hardened and chromium plated.

Formability of the work metal affects dimensional tolerance; in most instances, the better the formability, the closer the tolerances can be held, including end flare and straightness. When forming the harder metals, additional forming stations are helpful in achieving closer tolerances, because less forming is done in any one station.

Retaining tolerances in long production runs after specific finished workpieces are developed seldom poses problems, assuming the equipment and control of the work metal are maintained. Process capabilities in terms of holding tolerances for different shapes produced in large quantities are demonstrated in the six examples that follow.

Examples 314 to 319. Dimensional Variations in Several Shapes During Production Runs

Example 314 (Fig. 21). The 0.505/0.495-in. dimension of the simple shape shown in Fig. 21 was checked with a dial indicator at intervals of about 1000 linear feet during a production run of 101,100 ft. The histogram included in Fig. 21 shows the variations recorded on this dimension during the run. The two other formed dimensions were checked with go no-go gages; thus no measurements were recorded for those dimensions.

This same shape was produced from cold rolled 1010 steel strip and 302 stainless steel (2B finish) without change of tooling or method. The dimensional data given in Fig. 21 are for the 302 stainless.

Although both the 1010 and the stainless steels were rolled at the same speed of 83 ft per min, the 1010 steel could have been rolled at higher speed, but because only small quantities of the 1010 were rolled, compared with the quantities of stainless, the same speed was used for both. Hardness of the carbon steel was Rockwell B 55 to 65, whereas the stainless steel was Rockwell B 75 to 85. [In most instances, softer metal permits higher rolling speeds.]

Soluble oil mixed 1 to 12 with water was used for the lubricant. Rolls were made from L6 tool steel, hardened and chromium plated.

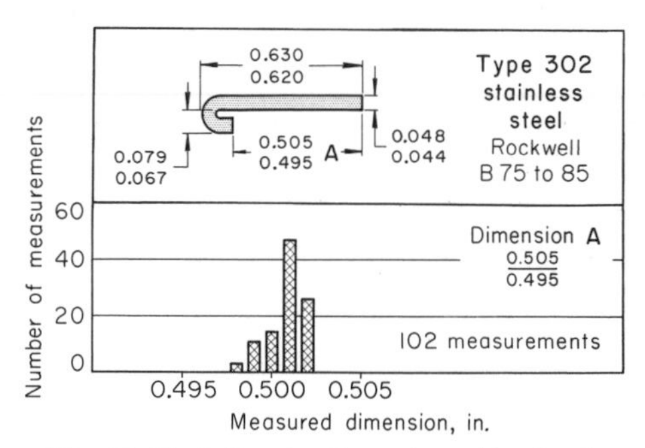

Fig. 21. Variation in dimension of a simple shape, as measured at intervals of about 1000 linear feet during a production run of 101,100 ft (Example 314)

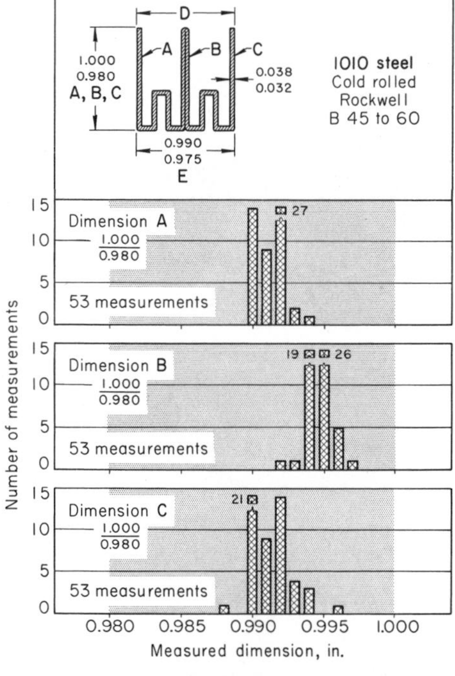

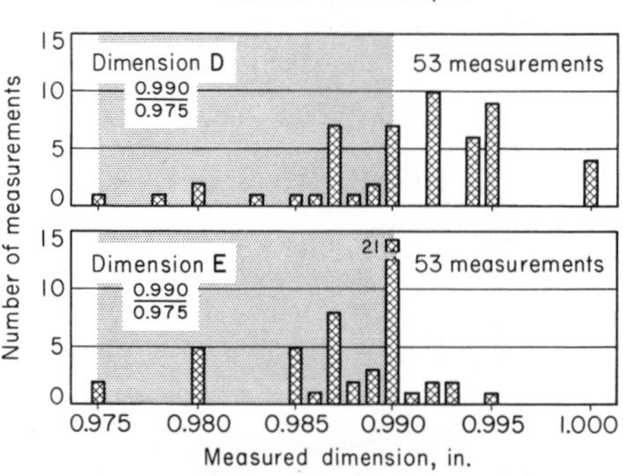

Fig. 22. Variations in dimensions of a complex shape, as measured at intervals of about 1000 linear feet during a production run of 54,800 ft (Example 315)

Example 315 (Fig. 22). The complex shape shown in Fig. 22 was produced from 0.035-in.-thick (±0.003 in.) bright-finish 1010 strip having a hardness of Rockwell B 45 to 60. The histogram included in Fig. 22 shows variation of five dimensions based on 53 measurements of each dimension during a run of 54,800 ft.

Problems in retaining tolerances must be expected when rolling shapes of this complexity (twelve 90° bends and one 180° bend), because of springback. No difficulty was experienced in maintaining the specified height, but in several instances the width (especially the top dimension, D) exceeded the prescribed maximum (Fig. 22). However, in this instance the amount of variation shown did not interfere with the end use.

Because of variation in springback among different lots of work metal, maintaining close tolerances on the shapes, as shown in Fig. 22 was almost impossible without the compressive forces applied by side rolls. In this operation, idler side rolls were used immediately preceding the final finishing station.

The shape was produced in 17 roll stations including a four-way idler preceding the final station where a bronze shoe-type straightener was included. Rolling speed was 85 ft per min, and soluble oil mixed 1 to 12 with water was used as the lubricant. All rolls (except the finisher and idler) were made from L6 tool steel, hardened and chromium plated. Finisher and idler rolls were the split-type and made from combinations of L6 and D2 tool steels (the latter steel for the high-wear portions of the rolls).

Example 316 (Fig. 23). Variations in four dimensions of a simple shape (Fig. 23), recorded during the forming period of 21 months, are indicated in the histograms shown in Fig. 23. Actual dimensions were recorded at intervals of approximately two months, gages being used for routine control of dimensions. The workpiece was produced on a continuous basis from 0.050-in.-thick cold rolled low-carbon steel in an eight-station roll former, plus a final straightening station. Rolling speed was 80 ft per min. A low-viscosity mineral oil was used as a lubricant.

Example 317 (Fig. 24). Variations in three dimensions of a simple shape (Fig. 24), recorded during the forming period of 23 months, are indicated in the histograms shown in Fig. 24. Actual dimensions were recorded at intervals of approximately two months (ten spot checks), gages being used for routine control. The workpiece was produced on a continuous basis from 0.062-in.-thick cold rolled low-carbon steel in a nine-station roll former, plus a final straightening station. Rolling speed was 60 ft per min. A low-viscosity mineral oil was used as a lubricant.

Example 318 (Fig. 25). Variations in three dimensions of a simple shape (Fig. 25), recorded during the forming period of approximately 32 months, are indicated in the histograms shown in Fig. 25. Actual measurements (ten spot checks) were seldom recorded, because gages were used for routine control of dimensions. The workpiece was produced on a continuous basis from 0.078-in.-thick cold finished low-carbon steel in a ten-station roll former, plus a straightener. Rolling speed was 60 ft per min. A low-viscosity oil was used as a lubricant.

Example 319 (Fig. 26). Deviations from parallelism and variations in camber, bow and twist in a complex 8²⁹⁄₃₂-in.-long contour roll formed shape are given in Fig. 26. Twenty-five pieces were measured for parallelism and camber, and 24 parts for bow and twist. Pieces measured were selected at random (intervals ranging from 20 to 800) from a production run of 5200 pieces.

These dimensional data were obtained with dial-indicator height gages and special checking gages on an inspection table. Pins were placed in the tracks to facilitate measuring, as shown in Fig. 26.

The rolled shape was completed in a total of 16 stations (rolling and straightening) at 44 ft per min using soluble oil mixed 1 to 12 with water as a lubricant.

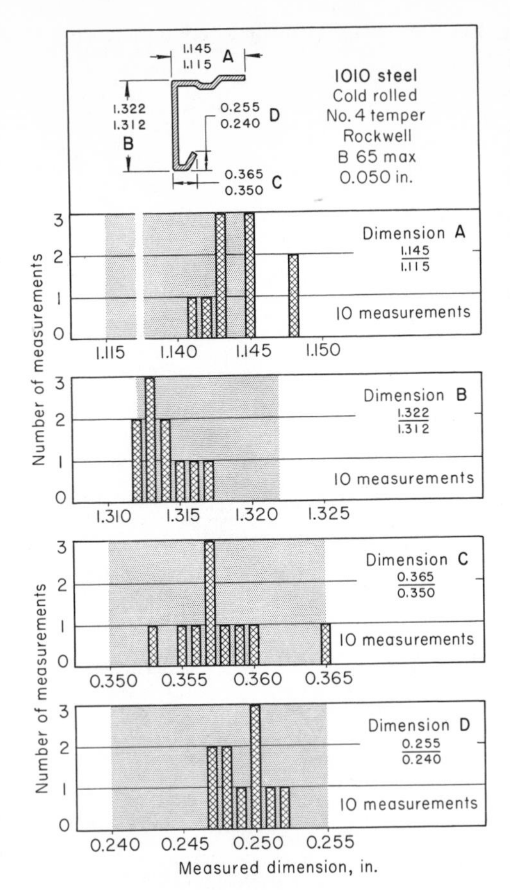

Fig. 23. Variations in four dimensions of a simple shape, based on ten spot checks over a period of 21 months (Example 316)

Surface Finish

Contour roll forming seldom improves the initial finish on the work metal. One exception is the roll forming of unpickled hot finished steel, from which much scale is removed, producing a better surface. It is usually possible to preserve the existing finish on unformed areas of the work metal. Sheet and strip ranging from unpickled hot rolled steel to highly polished stainless steel are contour roll formed with a minimum of damage to surface finish. In addition, work metals having almost every known type of coating are contour roll formed in high production with no damage to the coatings.

This does not mean that no damage to the work metal will occur if the specific applications are not carefully considered in planning the processing technique. In addition to normal precautionary measures, such as keeping the work metal clean before rolling and maintaining the equipment properly, one or more of the following must be considered and possibly adjusted when minimum damage to surface finish is a primary requirement:

1 Roll design or number of rolls in a given station
2 Number of stations
3 Roll material and finish
4 Lubricant
5 Rolling speed.

As severity of forming increases, the possibility of damage to the work-metal surface increases and may require alteration of the rolls within a station. For instance, in forming deep channels as described in Example 313, the shape could have been produced using top and bottom rolls. In this example, side rolls were added to improve dimensional tolerance. When maintenance of surface finish is a problem, the use of side rolls is helpful, because it minimizes roll sweep, which is inevitable when the shape is produced solely by top and bottom rolls. Excessive roll sweep is likely to damage both the work metal and the rolls.

Although sliding friction caused by roll sweep may damage surface finish, there is even greater likelihood of damage from excessive forming pressure in a given roll station. Therefore, as severity of forming increases, the possibility of damage to work-metal finish can be lessened by adding stations, thus decreasing the amount of forming done by a given set of rolls and reducing forming pressures.

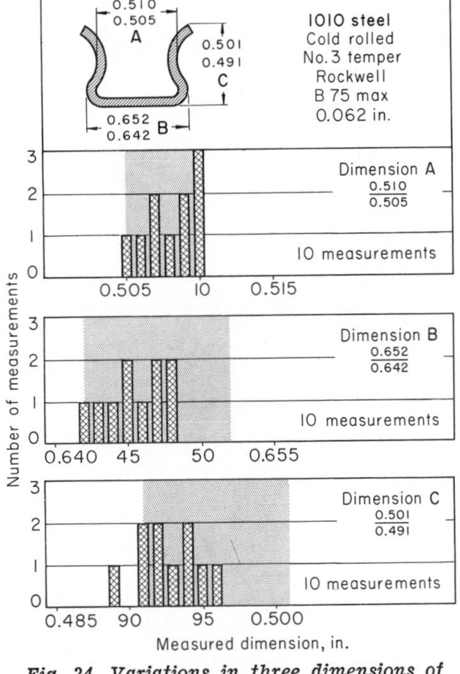

Fig. 24. Variations in three dimensions of a simple shape, based on ten spot checks over a period of 23 months (Example 317)

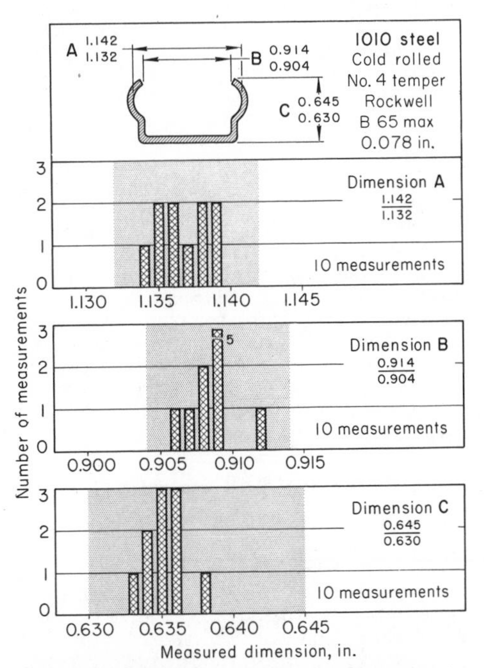

Fig. 25. Variations in three dimensions of a simple shape, based on ten spot checks over a period of 32 months (Example 318)

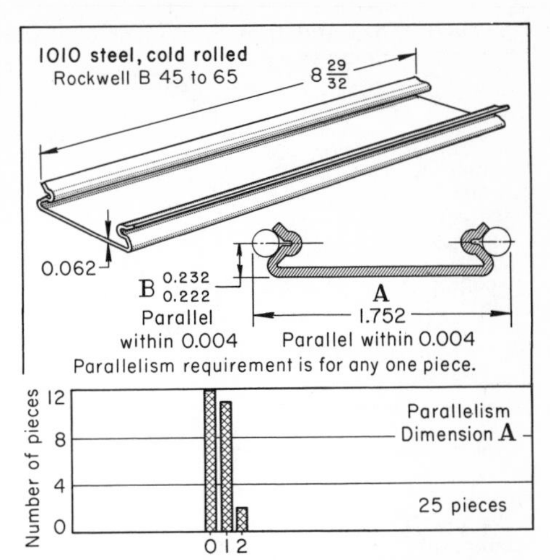

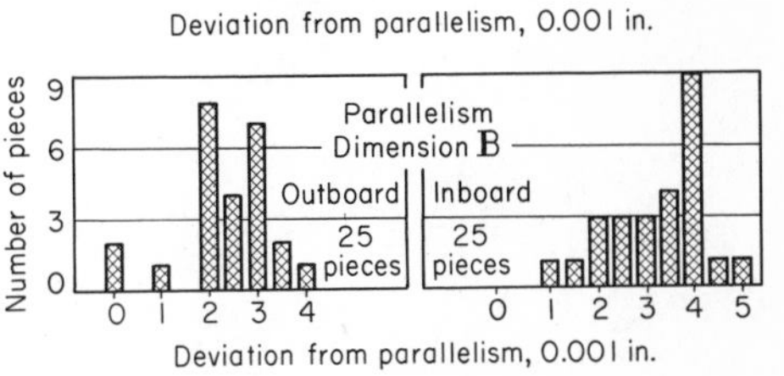

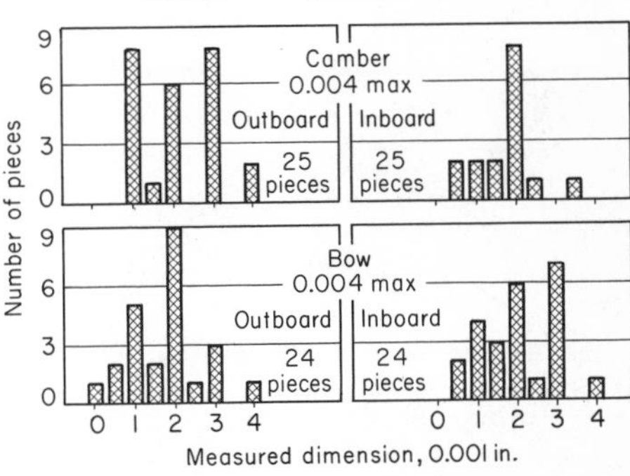

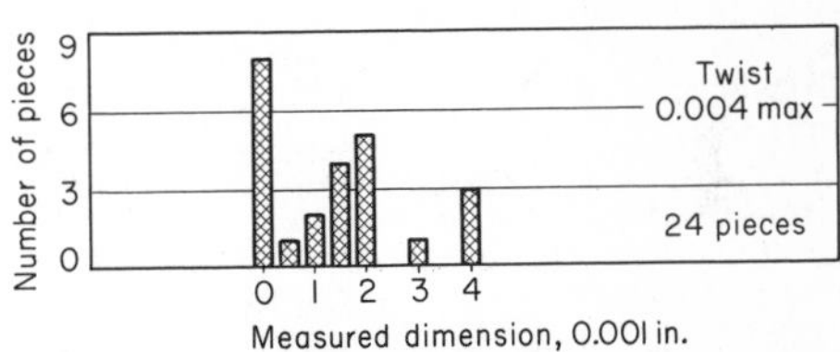

Fig. 26. Deviations from parallelism, and variations in camber, bow and twist, of a complex shape (Example 319)

Roll material and roll finish also contribute to the surface finish obtained in contour roll forming (see the section on Selection of Roll Material). Chromium-plated steel rolls or rolls made of bronze are best for preserving work-metal finish.

Lubrication is preferred in contour roll forming and has a significant effect on work-metal finish. When lubricants cannot be tolerated, as in the roll forming of coated metals, more attention must be given to roll design, additional stations, roll materials and possibly lower rolling speeds than would be used if copious amounts of lubricant were permitted.

Each metal presents a different problem in maintaining surface finish.

Table 4. Time and Cost for Producing Various Quantities by Contour Roll Forming vs Press-Brake Forming (Examples 320 and 321) (a)

Item	Production quantity, pieces: 1,000 Contour roll	1,000 Press brake	10,000 Contour roll	10,000 Press brake	50,000 Contour roll	50,000 Press brake	100,000 Contour roll	100,000 Press brake	250,000 Contour roll	250,000 Press brake	500,000 Contour roll
Example 320											
Production time, man-hr:											
Setup	7.9	2.9	31.6(b)	11.6(b)	47.4(c)	29.4(d)	47.4(c)	29.4(d)	47.4(c)	....	....
Operating (e)	2.4	35.2	24.0	352.0	120.0	1760.0	240.0	3520.0	600.0	....	....
Total	10.3	38.1	55.6	363.6	167.4	1789.4	287.4	3549.4	647.4	....	....
Cost:											
Tooling (f)	$6000	$800	$6000	$ 800	$6000	$ 800	$6000	$ 1,600(g)	$6000	....	....
Labor (h)	51	190	278	1818	837	8947	1437	17,747	3237	....	....
Total	$6051	$990	$6278	$2618	$6837	$9747	$7437	$19,347	$9237	....	....
Production cost/pc (j)	$6.05	$0.99	$0.628	$0.262	$0.137	$0.194	$0.074	$0.193	$0.037	....	....
Example 321											
Production time, man-hr:											
Setup	8.0	3.0	16(k)	6(k)	32(b)	12(b)	48(c)	18(c)	48(c)	18(c)	48(c)
Operating (m)	1.6	18.1	16	181	80	905	160	1810	400	4525	800
Total	9.6	21.1	32	187	112	917	208	1828	448	4543	848
Cost:											
Tooling (f)	$6650	$750	$6650	$ 750	$6650	$ 750	$6650	$ 750	$6650	$ 1,500(g)	$ 6,650
Labor (h)	48	105	160	935	560	4585	1040	9140	2240	22,715	4,240
Total	$6698	$855	$6810	$1685	$7210	$5335	$7690	$9890	$8890	$24,215	$10,890
Production cost/pc (n)	$6.70	$0.85	$0.68	$0.169	$0.144	$0.106	$0.077	$0.099	$0.035	$0.097	$0.021

Example 320

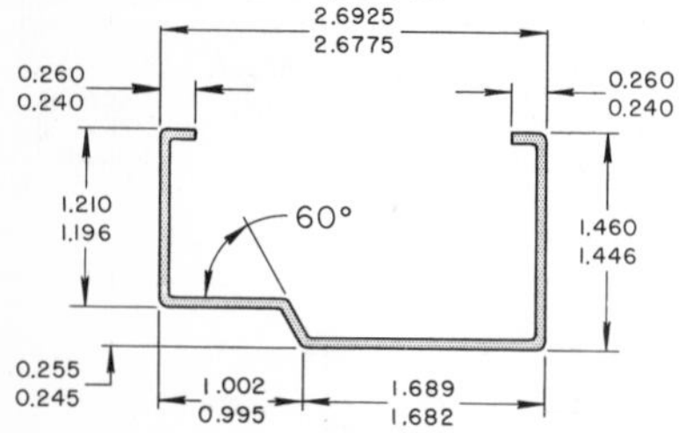

2.6925 / 2.6775; 0.260 / 0.240; 0.260 / 0.240; 1.210 / 1.196; 60°; 1.460 / 1.446; 0.255 / 0.245; 1.002 / 0.995; 1.689 / 1.682

1010 steel
Cold rolled
Rockwell B 45 to 60
0.048 in.

(a) Machine amortization and material not included in costs. (b) Four setups. (c) Six setups. (d) Ten setups. (e) Contour roll — one man needed to roll form and fly cut to 84-in. lengths. Press brake — two men needed: 8.8 man-hr to shear blanks; 9.9 man-hr to form ¼-in. flanges; 5.5 man-hr for each of three operations (form offset and two 90° bends); for total of 35.2 man-hr. (f) Contour roll — rolls and flying-cutoff die. Press brake — dies. (g) Two sets of dies used to increase tooling capacity for higher production quantities.

(h) $5 per hour for labor plus operating burden. (j) Length per piece, 84 in. (k) Two setups. (m) Contour roll — one man needed to roll form and fly cut to 36-in. lengths. Press brake — one man needed: 6.5 hr to shear blanks; 2.9 hr to do each of four forming operations (form V-pockets, 5/16-in. offset, 3/16-in. flange, and 1⅛-in. flange); for total of 18.1 man-hr. (n) Length per piece, 36 in.

Example 321

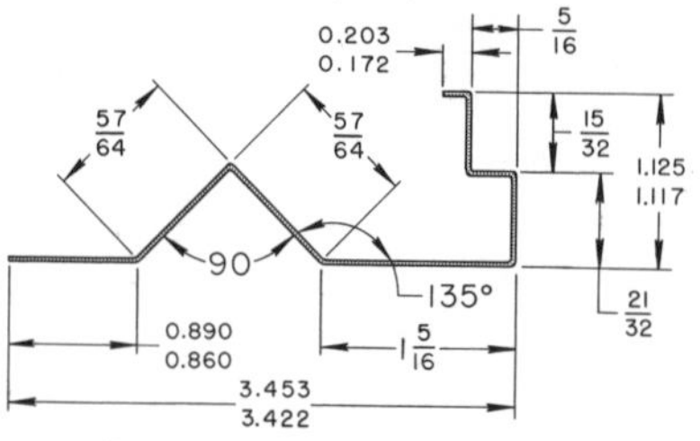

0.203 / 0.172; 5/16; 57/64; 57/64; 15/32; 1.125 / 1.117; 90°; 135°; 21/32; 0.890 / 0.860; 1 5/16; 3.453 / 3.422

1010 steel
Cold rolled
Rockwell B 45 to 60
0.024 in.

Hot rolled unpickled steel seldom offers any problem in maintaining surface finish. Rolling removes much of the scale and usually improves the finish, provided a flood of lubricant is used to flush away the scale. Otherwise, this scale will be trapped between work metal and rolls, resulting in damage to both surfaces. Rolls made from abrasion-resistant tool steel such as D2 are especially recommended for roll forming of hot rolled unpickled steel.

Cold finished carbon steel, aluminum and brass are usually rolled with a minimum of damage to work-metal finish. One or more of the conditions listed above may require special attention, depending mainly on severity of forming. A flood of lubricant is desirable in roll forming cold finished metals.

Highly polished stainless steel or aluminum can also be contour roll formed without damage to surfaces. However, each item of procedure becomes more critical than in roll forming lower-quality finishes. Greater attention must be given to roll design, fitting and maintenance. Chromium-plated rolls are usually preferred when work-metal finishes are critical. Maximum cleanness in all phases of the operation (including the use of freshly cleaned work metal) is mandatory for achieving desired results. Special lubricants are preferred for roll forming stainless steel (see Example 301) and may be essential when forming is severe and quality of finish is critical.

Galvanized Steel. Success in roll forming hot dip galvanized steel depends mainly on the quality of the zinc coating, maintenance of the rolls, and lubrication. Inferior galvanizing or severe bends, or both, cause the coating to loosen and stick to the rolls. Wipers that contact the working surfaces of the rolls will aid in preventing surface damage. Chromium-plated rolls are also helpful in minimizing damage to galvanized work metal.

Precoated metals (vinyl and other organic coatings) must be rolled without lubricant and sometimes pose problems, although by paying careful attention to the conditions listed above, precoated metals can be contour roll formed without damage to the coating surface. One of the most common applications is the forming of aluminum siding for buildings. Complete preservation of finish depends mainly on severity of forming. Sometimes it is necessary to increase radii before the particular operation is successful.

Embossed metals are also roll formed without lubricants. Shapes are designed to avoid excessive forming pressure, and bend radii not less than twice the metal thickness are used to prevent distortion of the embossing. Forming of aluminum eave troughs is an example of this operation.

Contour Roll Forming vs Press-Brake Forming

Contour roll forming is primarily a high-production method, and it is particularly well-suited for the economical production of relatively complex shapes. If two or more forming strokes would be needed in a press brake, the cost of the product in high-volume production is usually less when made by contour rolling. However, press-brake forming is often competitive in high-volume production of sections that can be formed in a single press stroke.

Quantity to be formed is most often the deciding cost factor when an acceptable product can be produced by either method. Cost of tooling for contour roll forming is usually several times that for press-brake forming. Setup time is also longer for contour roll forming. However, in most applications, productivity is much greater by contour roll forming than by press-brake forming; thus higher tooling cost can be justified for high-volume production. The following two examples compare times and costs for forming parts in varying quantities by contour roll forming vs press-brake forming.

Examples 320 and 321. Cost and Quantity Relations for Contour Roll Forming vs Press-Brake Forming

Example 320 (Table 4). The 18-gage (0.048-in.-thick) workpiece shown in Table 4 was produced from low-carbon steel in 84-in. lengths by two methods: (*a*) from coil stock in a 2½-in.-spindle contour rolling mill having eight rolling stations, a cutoff press with die, and a runout table to produce cut lengths "on the fly"; and (*b*) from sheared blanks in a press brake, utilizing a V-die for 90° bends and a special offset die for the remaining bends.

As shown in Table 4, total production time for this part by contour rolling was about ¼ to 1/12 of the time required when a press brake was used, with the difference between the two methods being greatest for the larger quantities. The longer setup time for contour rolling would make production by the press-brake method faster only for quantities less than about 150 pieces.

Because tooling cost for contour rolling is substantially higher than for the press-brake method, the production cost is less by the press-brake method for the lower quantities listed in Table 4. Above a break-even point of about 33,000 pieces, contour rolling is the more economical method.

Example 321 (Table 4). The 0.024-in.-thick workpiece shown in Table 4 could also be produced by either roll forming or press-brake forming. Roll forming from coil stock was done in an 11-station machine, cutting to length "on the fly".

Production time, tooling and labor costs varied as in Example 320. Contour rolling required less production time than the press-brake method for all the quantities listed in Table 4, and was the more economical method for quantities above about 75,000 pieces, depending on the number of setups.

The break-even quantity was over twice that for Example 320, because the labor costs for Example 320 were nearly twice as high on the press brake, mainly because two operators were needed to handle the workpieces in Example 320.

Effect of Design Changes. Although contour roll forming usually costs less than press-brake forming for mass production of parts, the probable frequency and magnitude of changes in part design, and their effect on tooling cost, must also be considered.

Before making tooling to produce a given part by roll forming, the design of the shape should be firmly established, because alterations to rolls are usually costly, and rolls may require replacement if the part design is later modified. On the other hand, dies for press-brake forming can usually be reworked at moderate cost, and sometimes press-brake dies can be altered simply by resetting the gages.

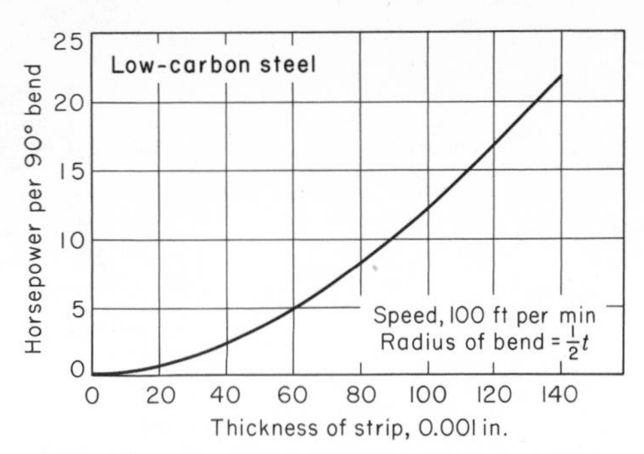

Foremost among the sources of power loss are: friction on the strip during forming; flattening of the strip between bending points; cold work on the strip resulting from variations in thickness above the nominal standard; friction between mating surfaces of the forming rolls; and the mechanical inefficiency of the roll forming machine.

Fig. 27. Power needed for contour roll forming a 90° bend in low-carbon steel

APPENDIX

Power Requirements*

The power consumed in cold forming strip into a sectional profile by contour roll forming depends on many variables; among them are the thickness and the tensile strength of the work metal, the number of stages used in forming, the efficiency of the roll-drive system, and the amount of friction of the rolls on the work metal.

Theoretical calculations for work done in forming give values that are only 10% of the power actually used in contour roll forming. Presumably, the other 90% of the power is consumed in overcoming friction and machine inefficiency. Figure 27 shows the actual power consumption in forming an experimental 90° bend in low-carbon steel at a speed of 100 ft per min with an inside radius of bend of ½t (t = work-metal thickness). The graph shows that about 20 hp is required for forming the bend in 0.128-in.-thick sheet. Experiments have shown that about 676 ft-lb of energy per foot is required for making a similar bend in 0.128-in.-thick low-carbon steel by other methods. If this forming could be done at the rate of 100 ft per min by the other methods, the power consumption would be $676 \times 100/33{,}000 = 2.05$ hp.

In one test of power consumption, a sheet 0.104 in. thick was formed into a contour with 12 separate angles, in a nine-stage contour roll former. The temperature of the metal increased 120 F between the first stage and the last stage. At a rolling speed of 43 ft per min, it was estimated that 40 hp was expended in heating the metal.

Figure 28 indicates the hardness variation in a typical section cold formed by contour rolling. As would be expected, the surface of the metal in the vicinity of the bends was appreciably harder than the metal in the flat, unformed regions of the profile.

*From E. Griffin, *Journal of the Institute of Metals,* **84** (1955-56), 181-197.

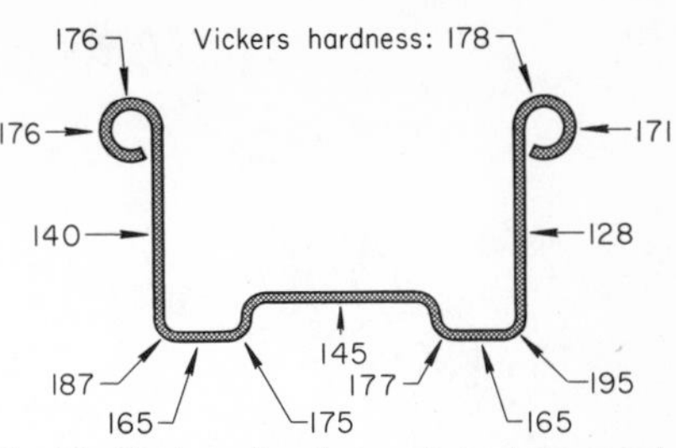

Fig. 28. Surface hardness at various points on a contour roll formed section of low-carbon steel, showing the variations in effect of cold work during forming

Stretch Forming

STRETCH FORMING is the forming of sheet, bars, and rolled or extruded sections over a form block of the required shape while the workpiece is held in tension. The work metal is stretched just beyond its yield point (generally 2 to 4% total elongation) to retain the contour of the form block.

The four methods of stretch forming are: stretch draw forming (Fig. 1a and b); stretch wrapping, also called rotary stretch forming (Fig. 1c); compression forming (Fig. 1d); and radial-draw forming (Fig. 1e). These methods are discussed separately in subsequent sections of this article.

Applicability

Almost any shape that can be produced by other sheet forming methods can be produced by stretch forming. Drawn shapes that involve metal flow, particularly straight cylindrical shells, and details that result from compression operations such as coining and embossing, cannot be made. However, some embossing is done by the mating-die method of stretch draw forming (Fig. 1b).

Stretch forming is used to form aerospace parts from steel, nickel and aluminum, and from titanium alloys and other heat-resisting and refractory metals. Some of these parts are difficult or impossible to form by other methods — for instance, the titanium alloy gas-turbine ring shown in Fig. 2. The procedure for making such a ring is described in Example 328.

Stretch forming is used also to shape automotive body panels, both inner and outer, and frame members that could be formed by other processes but at higher cost. An example is the automobile roof shown in Fig. 3, which was stretch draw formed using a blank that weighed 6.4 lb less than would have been needed for a conventional press forming process. Architectural shapes and aerospace forms that call for compound curves, reverse bends, twists, and bends in two or more planes are also produced by stretch forming.

Advantages. Stretch forming has the following advantages over conventional press forming methods:

1. About 70% less force is needed than for conventional press forming.
2. Stretch forming can reduce material cost as much as 15%. Although allowance must be made on the stock for gripping, it is gripped on two ends only. The allowance for trimming is usually less than in conventional press forming.
3. Because stretch forming is done on the entire area of the workpiece, there is little likelihood of buckles and wrinkles. Tensile strength is increased uniformly about 10%.
4. Springback is greatly reduced. There is some springback, but it is easily controlled by overforming.
5. Residual stresses are low in stretch formed parts.
6. Form blocks are made of low-cost materials — wood, plastics, cast iron, or low-carbon steel — and are about one-third the cost of conventional forming dies. If the workpiece is formed hot, the dies must be able to withstand the forming temperature. However, most stretch forming is done at room temperature.
7. Changeover is simple. Only one form block and two sets of grippers are involved. To make the same part from a different metal or another stock thickness, the same form block and grippers are used, but the tension of the stretch mechanism is adjusted.

Limitations. Stretch forming is subject to the following limitations:

1. It is seldom suited to progressive or transfer operations.
2. It is limited in its ability to form sharp contours and re-entrant angles. It is at its best in forming shallow or nearly flat contours.
3. If the piece is not pinched between mating dies, there is no opportunity to coin out or iron out slight irregularities in the surface of the metal.
4. In some applications — especially in stretch wrapping — the process is slower than competitive processes, and it is not suited to high-volume production. However, stretch draw forming with mating dies can be done as rapidly and automatically as conventional press operations. In fact, punch presses are used

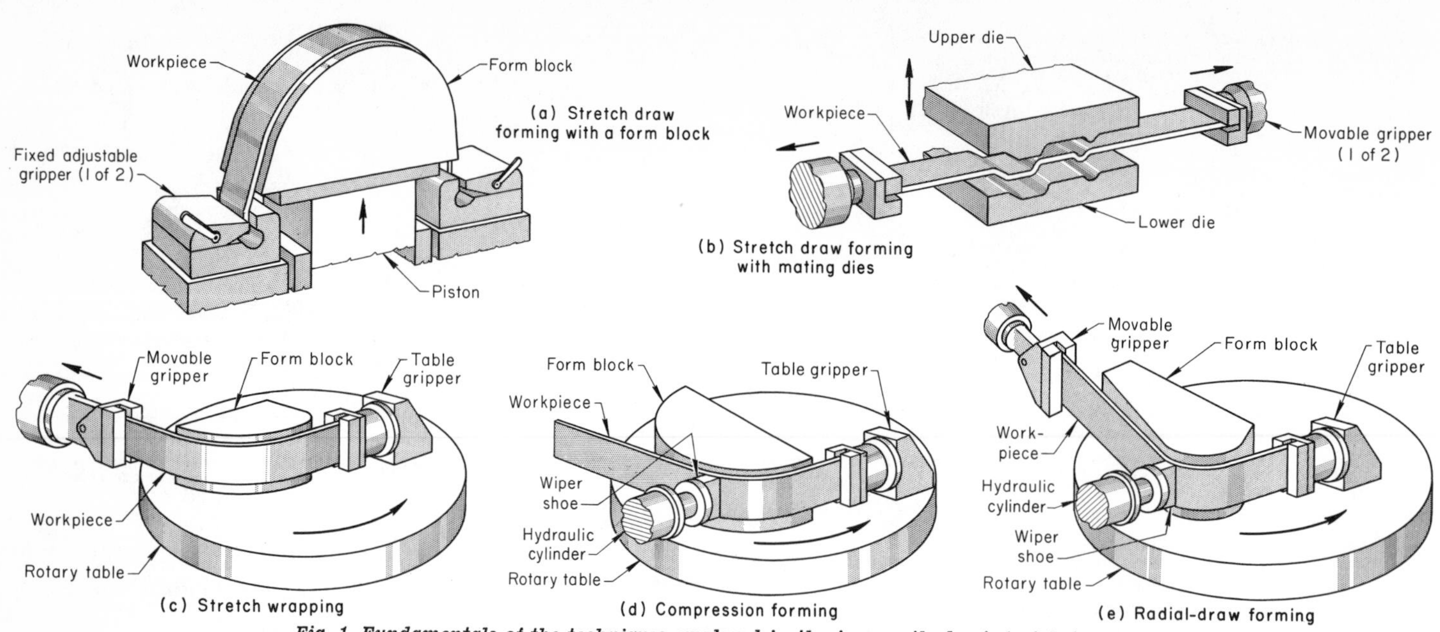

Fig. 1. Fundamentals of the techniques employed in the four methods of stretch forming

ations. In fact, punch presses are used with dies incorporating draw beads, or other means of gripping the blank, to perform some stretch forming operations (see Example 153 and the discussion of draw beads, page 125, in the article "Press Forming of Low-Carbon Steel").

5 Stretcher strains are likely to show up on the surface of some metals — notably low-carbon steel — that, because of their processing history or alloy content, do not have uniform mechanical properties throughout the sheet.

6 Metals with yield strength and tensile strength very nearly the same, such as titanium, need automatic equipment for determining the amount of strain for uniform results.

7 Best results are achieved with rectangular blanks. The aircraft industry uses trapezoidal blanks, but gives greater attention to each piece than is warranted in high-volume production.

8 Deep forming in the direction of the free edges is not practical.

Machines and Accessories

Stretch wrapping, compression forming, and radial-draw forming use rotary tables (some with sliding leaves) for mounting the form blocks, a ram gripping and tensioning or wiping device, and a mechanically or hydraulically actuated table gripper (Fig. 4). Machines used for these operations have capacities up to 1000 tons.

Stretch draw forming is done in three types of machines. In one type, the form block mounted on a hydraulic cylinder is pushed into the blank, which is held in tension by a pair of pivoting grippers. In another type, the form block is fixed to the table and the blank is drawn around it by a pair of grippers actuated by slides or a hydraulic cylinder. The third type of machine is a single-action hydraulic press equipped with a means of closing and moving a pair of grippers (see Fig. 7); a mating die is used instead of a form block. Hydraulic presses ordinarily used in stretch draw forming have capacities of 200 to 800 tons.

Accessory Equipment. Grippers and wiping shoes or rollers are made to conform to the rolled or extruded shape that is to be stretch formed. Jaws used for gripping sheet in stretch draw

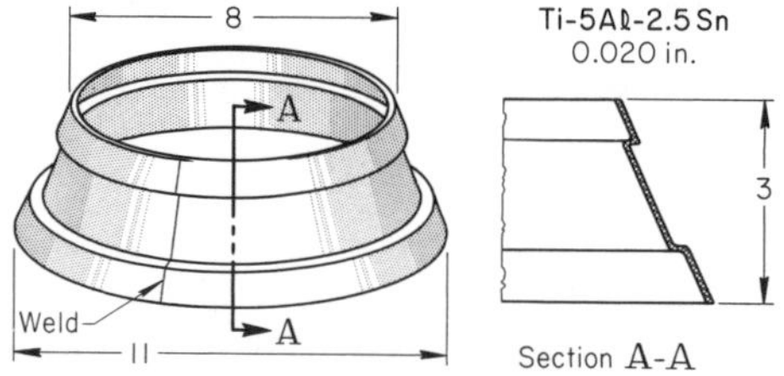

Fig. 2. Titanium alloy gas-turbine ring that was produced by compression forming

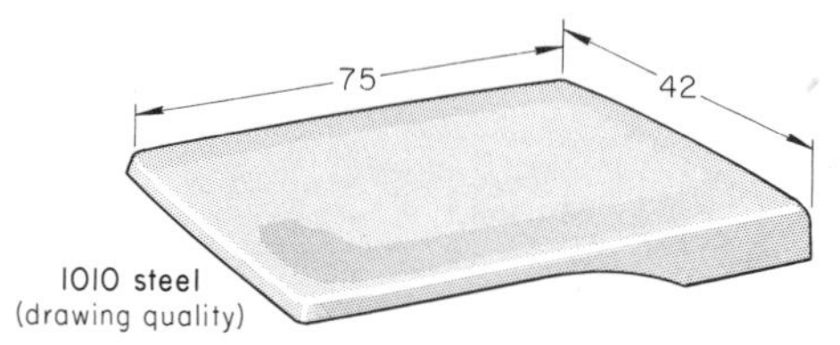

Fig. 3. Stretch draw formed automobile roof

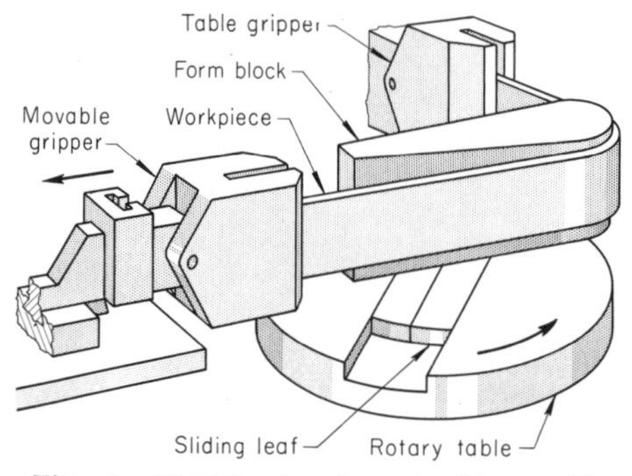

Fig. 4. Stretch forming machine with rotary table and sliding center leaf

forming can be segmented or contoured to apply equal stretch to all parts of the sheet as it is formed.

The vertical adapter shown in Fig. 5 is used with a rotary table; it is fastened to the hydraulic cylinder used for applying tension to the blank. The adapter allows wiper shoes, rollers and grippers to move up or down as needed, to accommodate work with bends in two or more planes. Lead screws or hydraulic cylinders position the grippers or wiping devices at the correct position for the forming operation (see Examples 328 and 329).

A yield detector and tension-control device (Fig. 6) provide means of automatically applying the same amount of stress to every workpiece in a production lot. This is important with metals (for example, titanium) that have yield strength and tensile strength too close for ordinary control of tension for stretch forming (see the article on Forming of Titanium, page 443 in this volume). With this type of control, scrap in stretch forming of titanium can be reduced to 2%.

The tension control uses two inputs in a null system for its output signal. One input comes from a load cell that gives a signal proportional to the stretch force on the workpiece. The other signal comes from a potentiometer that measures the elongation of the workpiece. As long as the signals are proportional, the metal is not stretched beyond its yield point, and the two inputs balance. When the yield point is reached, the input from the load cell stops rising and remains constant, while the potentiometer input continues to rise. This upsets the null balance and an output signal is given, which can be interpreted as percentage strain beyond the yield point.

Table restretch units are small short-stroke hydraulic cylinders and clamps that can be bolted to the rotary table to give a final stretch set to workpieces that need to be stretched from both ends or restretched after heat treatment. Usually the capacity of these units is equal to that of the main tensioning gripper.

Stretch Draw Forming

Stretch draw forming is done with either a form block or a mating die.

The form-block method uses either a fixed or a moving form block. A fixed form block is attached to the machine base. Each end of the blank is held by a gripper attached to a hydraulic cylinder. The grippers move to stretch the blank over the form block. This technique is illustrated in Example 535 in the article on Forming of Aluminum Alloys, in this volume.

The moving form block is attached to a hydraulic piston. A blank is held by grippers while tension is applied to it, and then the form block moves to form the part, as shown in Fig. 1(a). (See also Example 533, in the article on Forming of Aluminum Alloys.)

Although bars and structural shapes are usually radial-draw formed, Examples 536 and 537 in the article on Forming of Aluminum Alloys explain how they can be stretch draw formed by the form-block method.

The mating-die method uses a two-piece die mounted in a single-action hydraulic press (Fig. 7). This method combines the advantages of stretch forming and conventional press forming: the stretch forming sets the contours of moderately formed workpieces, and the press forming gives definition to sharply formed contours, such as beads or feature lines on automobile body parts.

Grippers preform the blank over the lower die to the curvature of the part (see Fig. 7a). There is very little metal flow; the stretching action and die form the general outline of the part. The upper die then descends to produce the details and set the contours (see Fig. 7b).

Automatic material-handling equipment can be adapted to the machine for production runs. Production rates are comparable to those obtainable for drawing in conventional single-action and double-action presses. Stretch draw press tooling for large parts, such as automobile roof panels, weighs only one-third that for a conventional double-action press, as shown below.

Item	Conventional press	Stretch press
Capacity, tons:		
Punch	900	250
Gripper (blankholder)	600	85
Tooling weight, tons	22	7
Press height, in.	288	200

Parts that are exposed to view, such as automobile outer body panels, frequently have a maximum surface roughness specification of 45 micro-in., and stretcher strain marks and other defects, which are still noticeable after painting, must be prevented. One method of avoiding strain marks is the use of segmented or curved grippers, which equalize the amount of stretching.

The following example describes production of a rear-deck lid by stretch draw forming with a mating die.

Example 322. Stretch Draw Forming an Automobile Rear-Deck Lid (Fig. 7)

Automobile rear-deck lids were produced in a stretch draw press using mating dies, as shown in Fig. 7. The blanks were commercial quality, cold rolled 1008 steel, 0.036 in. thick, 57 in. wide, and 63 in. long. Residual mill oil was the only lubricant. Production rate was 360 pieces per hour, and annual production was 400,000 deck lids.

Tension was applied to the sheet by the grippers as they moved apart. (Generally, hydraulic cylinders are used to apply the force in this operation.) The tensioned sheet (still held by the grippers) was then lowered to stretch over the lower die. Finally, the upper die was lowered, pressing the sheet into both dies to form the lid.

Cycle time was 7 sec. Finished parts showed uniformly good quality without wrinkles or buckles.

Two pounds more of sheet steel would have been needed to produce this part in a conventional double-action press.

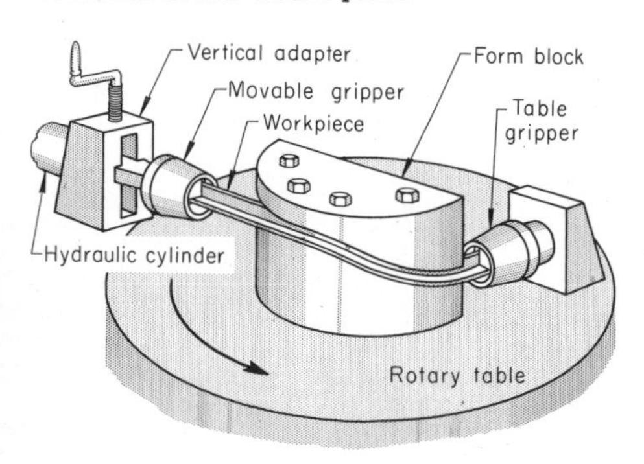

Fig. 5. Use of a vertical adapter on the tension unit to accommodate work with bends in two or more planes

If stretch drawing is used to form severe contours, the stretch limits of the metal may be exceeded in the zones of deep forming, so that the metal fractures. This may be avoided by lancing the metal in areas to be discarded later, so metal can flow in the severely formed zones — as was done in this example:

Example 323. Use of Lancing in a Severely Stretch Draw Formed Part (Fig. 8)

The truck cowl shown in Fig. 8 was stretch draw formed with mating dies from a 68-by-18-by-0.035-in. sheet of cold rolled, drawing quality, aluminum-killed 1008 or 1010 steel. Forming was severe around the ventilating air inlet, which was later cut out, and to relieve the strain so that the metal could flow into the sharp contours of the molded edge, a lancing cut was made in the scrap area. Lancing was used rather than cutting a slug,

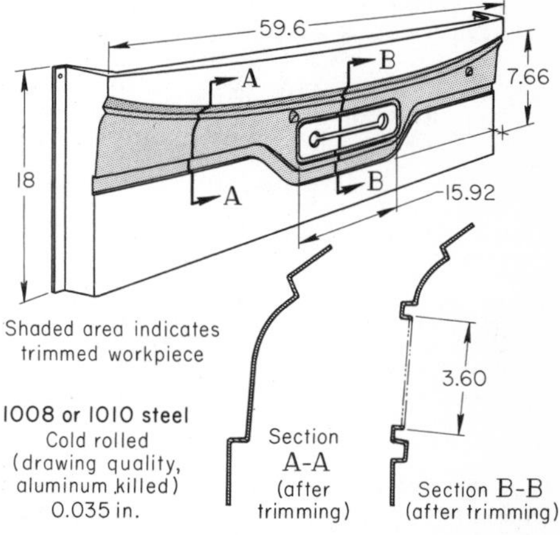

Sharp contours around the oblong ventilating air inlet could be formed because the sheet was lanced in a trim area, permitting metal to flow into die details.

Fig. 8. Truck cowl that was made by stretch draw forming with mating dies in a press (Example 323)

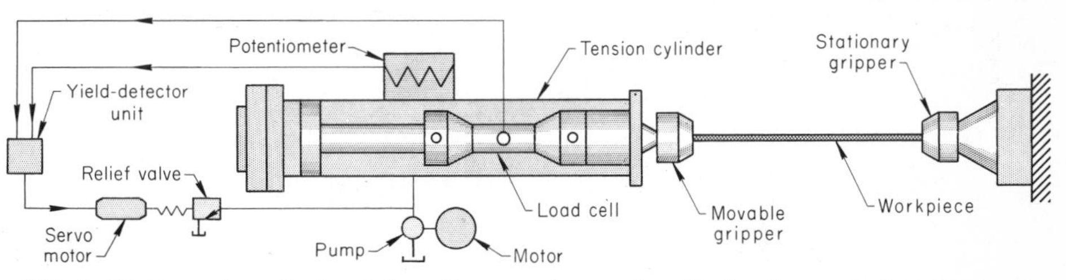

Fig. 6. Components and signal-flow diagram of an automatic tension-control system used in stretch forming

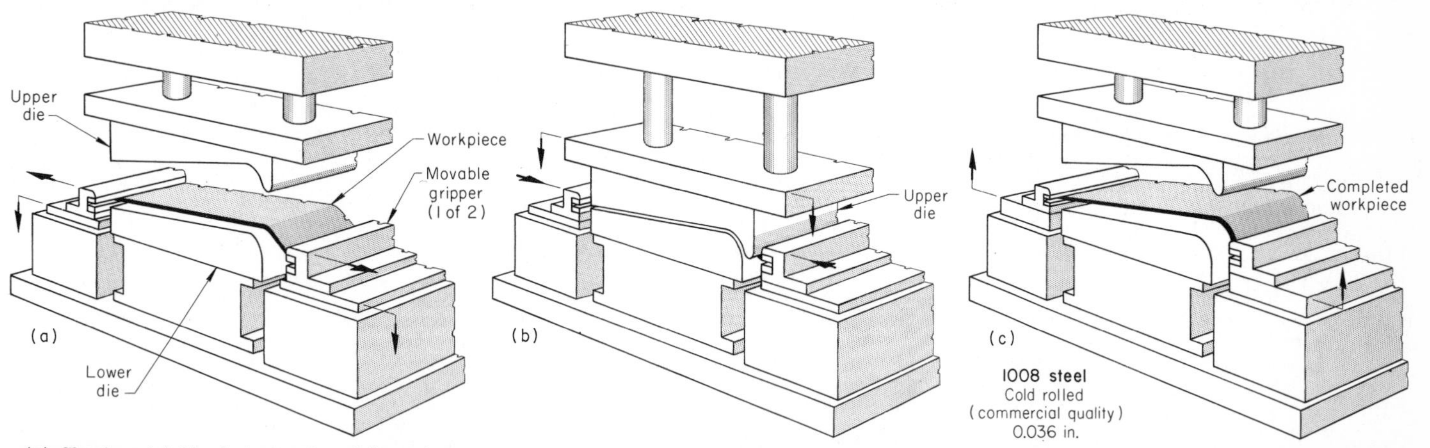

(a) Sheet-metal blank is tensioned by grippers moving apart. Grippers move down, stretching the workpiece over the lower die. (b) Upper die descends onto the workpiece, pressing the metal into both dies to form the part. (c) After forming, press opens and part is released from grippers.

Fig. 7. Production of an automobile rear-deck lid in a stretch draw forming press (Example 322)

because there was no convenient way to eject the slug. The dumbbell effect shown in Fig. 8 was caused by metal drawing away from the rounded ends of the slot during forming.

All inside radii were 0.060 in. Forming tolerances were held within ±0.030 in. Because the part would be exposed to view, the surface had to be free of blemishes.

Rate of production of the cowl by stretch draw forming was about the same as it would have been with ordinary press forming, about 100 to 150 pieces per hour. An automatic sheet loader was used to place the sheets in the grippers, which measured 72 by 1⅙ in., and the finished workpieces were unloaded automatically. The grippers could exert 70 tons of tension. Press capacity was 800 tons on the main ram. Applied stretch was 1 to 1½%. Yearly production was 25,000 pieces.

Single-operation production of a truck-cab roof having a combination of gradual curves and sharp contours is described in the following example.

Example 324. Stretch Draw Forming of a Truck-Cab Roof With Reinforcing Beads (Fig. 9)

By using stretch draw forming with mating dies, the truck-cab roof panel shown in Fig. 9 was produced in one operation. Panels were formed from cold rolled, drawing quality, aluminum-killed 1008 steel. Blanks were 60 by 32 in. by 0.035 in. thick.

With automatic material-handling equipment to load and unload the machine, production rate was 100 to 150 pieces per hour; annual production was 25,000 pieces.

The forming dies were of cast iron, with flame hardened surfaces where severe forming occurred. Design changes that would make the dies obsolete were not expected for four or five years.

Radii on the roof beads were 0.040 in.

Other examples of stretch draw forming using the mating-die and form-block methods are described in Examples 532 and 534 in the article on Forming of Aluminum Alloys.

Stretch Wrapping

In stretch wrapping, just enough tension is applied to one end of a workpiece to exceed the yield strength of the material, while the form block revolves into the workpiece with the turning of the table, as shown in Fig. 1(c). The other end of the workpiece is held in a table gripper or clamped to the end of the form block. The hydraulic cylinder applying tension to the workpiece is free to swivel, so that the tension is always tangential to the last point of contact. Thus, the work metal wraps in tension around the form block without the scuffing or friction that occurs with other forming methods. The result is an exactly formed piece with little springback, so form blocks can be made to accurate size.

Because there is no scuffing, form blocks can be made of soft metal, wood or plastic (although common die materials like cast iron are often used). Form blocks made of hardwood, masonite and epoxy also have been used. The contour of the form block can vary throughout the bend, and the workpiece will follow it accurately, provided there are no concave surfaces on the form block.

Form blocks for stretch wrapping of rolled and extruded sections are machined to the shape of the section, as well as the contour of the finished part. In this way, the shaped form block supports the section during forming. Additional support sometimes is needed for open or hollow sections. A segmented filler, a filler made of low-melting alloy, or a strip of easy-to-form metal can provide this support. A shaped form block and a segmented filler were used to form the extruded section in Example 538 in the article on Forming of Aluminum Alloys.

Return bends can be made by using extra form blocks on sliding leaves of the turntable, and reversing the table direction to produce the part, as shown in Fig. 10.

Machines for stretch wrapping consist basically of a variable-speed, power-driven rotary table and a double-action pressure-controlled hydraulic cylinder. The form block is bolted to the table. Grippers are connected to the hydraulic cylinder so that tension can be applied to the workpiece, as in Fig. 1(c).

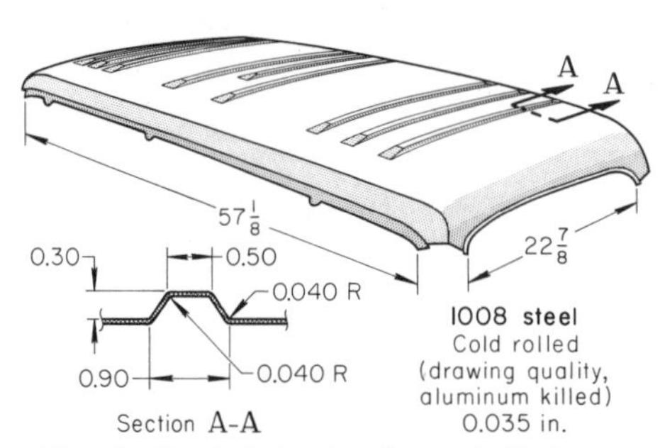

Fig. 9. Beaded truck-cab roof that was stretch draw formed with mating dies (Example 324)

Production of a typical part by stretch wrapping is described in the following example.

Example 325. Forming an Aircraft Leading-Edge Wing Panel by Stretch Wrapping

A corrugated leading-edge wing panel of aluminum alloy 6061-O was stretch wrapped in a stretch forming machine with a vertical-axis turntable. The sheet, with corrugations in the direction of airflow, was gripped at each end with grippers shaped to fit the corrugations. Tension applied was slightly above the yield strength of the work metal. The form block, bolted to the turntable, rotated slowly into the workpiece, causing it to form smoothly into the shape of the wing without flattening the corrugations. While the form block was moving into the sheet, the hydraulically restrained gripper maintained tension slightly above the yield point. The form block was made to the required final shape without allowance for springback, because only a small amount occurred.

Compression Forming

In compression forming, the workpiece is pressed against the rotating form block, instead of being wrapped around it. Generally, the process is used for (*a*) maintaining or controlling workpiece cross-sectional dimensions throughout the contour, (*b*) bending to radii small enough to exceed the elongation limits of the metal if formed by stretch wrapping, and (*c*) bending sections too heavy for the capacity of available stretch wrap machinery.

Compression forming can generally be done in the same machine as stretch wrapping, but the hydraulic cylinder is used to apply pressure instead of tension to the workpiece. The cylinder is locked in place to keep it from swiveling, and the ram head is furnished with a roller or a shoe to press the workpiece against the form block. A clamp or table gripper holds the end of the workpiece against the form block, and, as the table rotates, the shoe or roller on the hydraulic cylinder presses the workpiece into the contour of the block, as shown in Fig. 1(d). Stretch wrapping is shown in Fig. 1(c).

Compression forming can often make bends to a smaller radius than stretch wrapping in a part that has a deep cross section. If the same bend were produced by stretch wrapping, fracturing or overstressing of the outer fibers would result. The total load needed to form large-section pieces, such as crossrails and bumpers, can be as little as 2% of that needed to form them in a punch press. Total energy applied to the workpiece would, of course, be the same (neglecting efficiency), the smaller compression forming force being applied for a longer period of time. The wiping shoe or roller can hold the cross section size and shape to close tolerance throughout the contour. Parts too heavy in cross section for stretch wrapping can often be compression formed.

A typical application of compression forming is described in the following example.

Example 326. Compression Forming of Roof Bows for Railroad Coaches

Railroad coach roof bows of quarter-hard type 201 stainless steel were shaped by compression forming on a stretch forming turntable. The form block was contoured to fit the inside of the hat shape of the section from which the bow was made, and a wiper shoe on the compression ram was contoured to fit the outside of the hat shape. A typical production lot was 2000 pieces, at a production rate of 20 pieces per hour. The forming force was about 2% of the force that previously had been needed for press forming the piece from the same stock.

The hat shape had been contour roll formed from coil stock.

Blanks for stretch forming usually are made longer than the finished part so that the surfaces damaged by the gripper jaws can be trimmed off. However, end details, locating surfaces, and other considerations occasionally make it necessary to use a blank cut to the length of the finished part, and still dimensional tolerances must be met, as in the following example.

Example 327. Use of an Adjustable Form Block to Compression Form a Developed Blank (Fig. 11)

Because both ends of the piece shown in Fig. 11 had previously-produced details, the part could not be trimmed after forming. Instead of a table gripper or clamp, the blank was fastened to the form block by bolts through two 13/16-in.-diam holes pierced in one end. The blank was cut slightly shorter than the required length, because during forming the length increased from 141.81 to 142.25 in.

The 1020 steel structural shape that was being compression formed had considerable springback, which varied with each heat of steel. To obtain uniform results, the form block was made adjustable. As shown in Fig. 11, the wear plate, made of ¾-in.-thick by 8-in.-wide high-carbon steel, was backed up with jackscrews that could be adjusted to change the effective radius. One end of the wear plate was fastened to the base plate and the other end was free to move in and out of any position, supported by the jackscrews. When a new lot of steel was delivered, an experimental piece was run to determine springback, and the jackscrews were adjusted accordingly.

The work material was a hot rolled channel 6 in. wide, 10.5 lb per foot, approximating a 1020 steel in composition.

The piece was compression formed on a radial-draw former into a half circle with a 45-in. radius. The two holes in the end of the piece were used to connect this section with a fishplate on one end of a mating piece, to form an assembled ring. The sequence of operations was as follows:

1 Saw ends with a 3° bevel to developed length (141.81 in.).
2 Deburr.
3 Pierce two 13⁄16-in.-diam holes.
4 Form both ends to 45-in. radius for 6 to 8 in. of length on a press brake.
5 Bolt the workpiece to the form block by the two pierced holes. Compression form to 45-in. radius.
6 Galvanize after forming.
7 Flatten as necessary (galvanizing sometimes caused warpage).

A straight mineral oil was used as the lubricant. The over-all tolerance on the formed curve was 0.060 in. TIR.

Production time was 3 min per piece, with two operators, and setup time was 1 hr. Production lot size was 250 pieces.

When a part must have curvature in two or more planes, a vertical adapter, either hydraulic-powered or screw-actuated, is used, to permit the ram gripper to move up and down as the work requires. Thus, the work material can be fed into a spiral or other form involving rising and falling curvatures. In the example that follows, a vertical adapter with a wiper shoe was used to form a low-angle helix that was later welded into a ring.

Example 328. Producing a Ring From a Helix to Counteract Springback (Fig. 12)

Because springback in forming a titanium alloy engine ring made it difficult to weld the workpiece into a true circle after forming, the stock was compression formed into a low-angle helix by using a vertical adapter with a wiper shoe. The form block was smaller in diameter than the finished ring, and when the workpiece was removed from the form block, springback was just enough to permit welding into a true ring. The setup used for forming the ring is shown in Fig. 12.

Radial-Draw Forming

Radial-draw forming is a combination of stretch wrapping and compression forming, as shown in Fig. 1(e). As in stretch wrapping, one end of the workpiece is gripped by stationary jaws attached to the rotary table. The other end is gripped by jaws on the hydraulic cylinder. The cylinder exerts tension on the workpiece as the form block on the rotary table revolves into it. A second hydraulic unit, fitted with a wiper shoe or roller, presses the workpiece into the contour of the form block at the point of tangency. The hydraulic unit applying the compression force can be moved as necessary to keep the wiper shoe in contact with the workpiece. On large machines, an operator sometimes rides a platform on the second unit to watch the point of contact.

Joggles in rolled or extruded sections can be formed after the part has been radial-draw formed, without removing the part from the form block. When contour forming is completed, the part is held in tension while the compression unit is repositioned, and the joggle is formed by the wiper shoe. Sometimes, the wiper shoe is used to apply pressure to a loose joggle block (see Fig. 13), if the wiper shoe will not provide the correct shape for the joggle. In either case, the shape of the joggle is also machined into the form block.

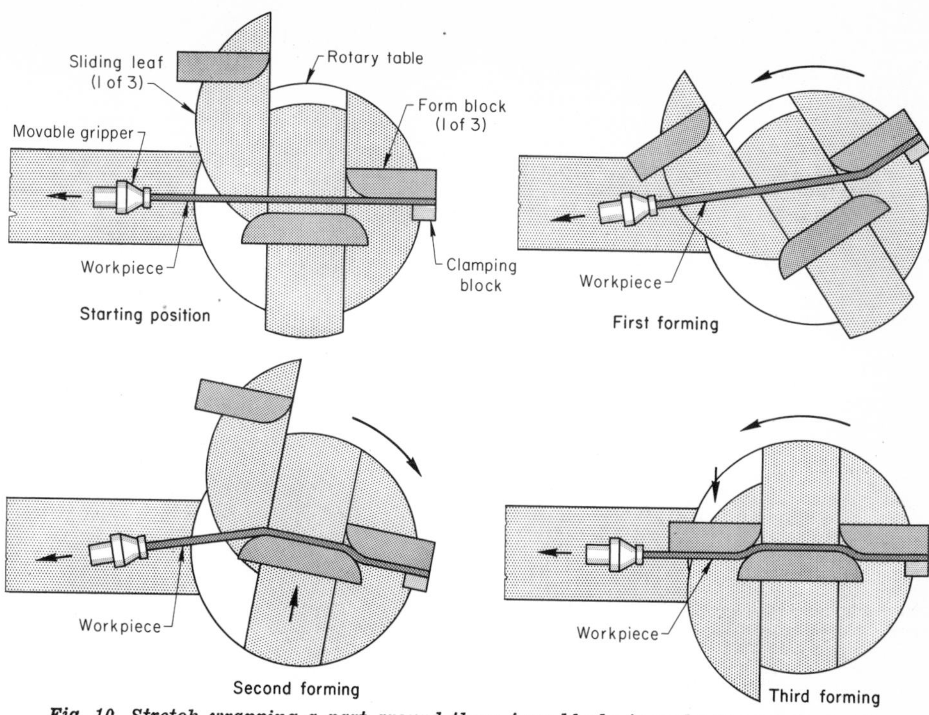

Fig. 10. Stretch wrapping a part around three form blocks to make two reverse bends

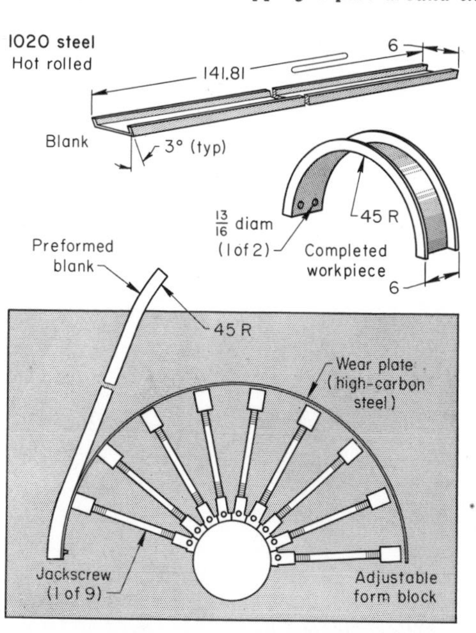

Fig. 11. Steel channel that was compression formed without trim allowance, using an adjustable form block (Example 327)

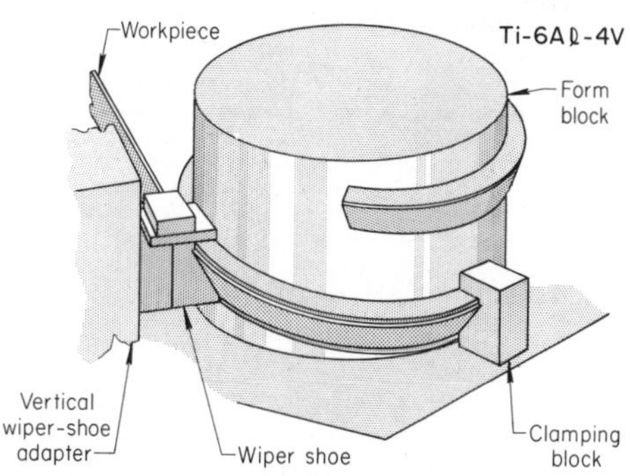

After forming, springback of the titanium alloy used brought the formed piece to a circular shape, which could be welded into a ring.

Fig. 12. Use of a vertical wiper-shoe adapter to form a helical shape (Example 328)

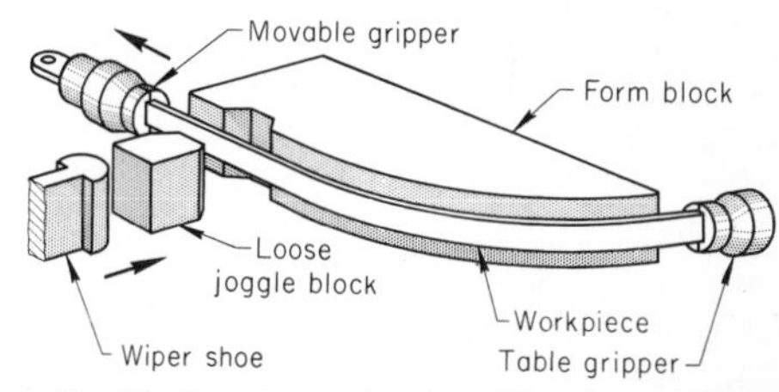

Fig. 13. Forming a joggle with a loose block and a wiper shoe after radial-draw forming

The vertical adapter shown in Fig. 5 can be used in radial-draw forming of bends in two or more vertical planes.

Architectural sections, extruded shapes, and other sections sometimes have to twist on themselves if they are contour formed through any plane other than the plane of symmetry. In radial-draw forming, this can be done by permitting the workpiece to rotate axially as the part follows the twisting contour of the form block. Rotation is obtained by slightly loosening the lock ring on the body of the gripper head, allowing the head to rotate about its own centerline. The example that follows illustrates the forming of an angle section by this method.

Example 329. Twisting an Angle Section During Contour Forming (Fig. 14)

An L-shape section for the gunwale of an air-sea rescue craft (shown in Fig. 14) had to be twisted as it was radial-draw formed. It was made of aluminum alloy 2024-T4. Forming had to be done in several planes. The locking ring of the gripper was loosened, permitting the head to rotate as the part was formed.

The usual production-lot size was 500 pieces. Parts were formed at the rate of 10 per hour.

Radial-draw forming operations on an extruded section and on a sheet are illustrated in Examples 539 and 540 in the article on Forming of Aluminum Alloys, in this volume.

Accuracy

High-strength alloys, stainless steel, and titanium can be stretch formed to over-all tolerances of ±0.010 in. on workpieces bent to about a 7-in. radius. With springback allowance, bends can be controlled within ±½°. Cross-sectional dimensions have been held within ±0.002 in. by close control of raw material, as in the following example.

Example 330. Maintaining Close Tolerances on Grooves While Forming a Guide-Vane Shroud (Fig. 15)

Because a cover strip had to slide easily, but without play, into the grooves of a stainless steel guide-vane shroud after the vanes were assembled, the width of the grooves had to be held within 0.004 in., as shown in Fig. 15.

Strip was selected that had thickness variation within ±0.0005 in., because of the close groove tolerances that had to be met. The two U-bends forming the grooves were made in a press brake, and the guide slots were pierced in another operation. Stretch forming then contoured the shrouds to a 7½-in. radius. Width of the work strip and width of the grooves were held within the specified tolerances without using a filler for support.

Shrouds were produced at the rate of 10 per hour. A typical production run was between 200 and 1000 pieces.

As shown by the preceding example, it may be necessary to control stock to a small thickness variation if close tolerances on the workpiece must be met. Ordinarily, it is good practice to allow about 25% of the finished-part tolerance as the stock-thickness tolerance, or the tolerance on any preformed dimension that could affect the accuracy of the stretch formed dimension. In Example 330, the smallest tolerance was ±0.002 in., and the stock-thickness variation was controlled to ±0.0005 in. (25% of workpiece tolerance).

Titanium is stretch formed both hot and cold (see section beginning on page 443 in "Forming of Titanium Alloys", in this volume). In cold stretch forming, shrinkage at right angles to the stretch is ordinarily controlled within ±1⁄32 in. on bends to a 9-in. radius.

Angular variation on stretch bends in all materials is held to ±½°.

In one plant, large rectangular tubing of copper alloy is stretch formed with a filler or a flexible mandrel, similar to those described in the article on Bending of Tubing, page 308 in this volume. Tubes as large as 4 to 8 in. square and up to 16 ft long with ⅛-in. to ⅜-in. walls are formed. When mandrels are not used, distortion appears as concavity in the face away from the form block and some tapering toward the concave face, as shown in Fig. 16. These tubes are stretch formed to large radii with a ±1⁄32-in. tolerance on the radius of the bend.

In the bending of large tubing, the bend is usually so shallow that the elastic limit of the metal is not reached without gross overbending, unless stretch forming methods are used. As with conventional methods, overbending leads to unpredictable results. Tolerances on shallow bends can sound deceptively large. To hold a 10-ft radius within ±1⁄32 in. in a 10° arc means holding an over-all tolerance of better than ±0.005 in.

The elevator cable guide of 1020 steel in the example that follows was held to a radius-of-bend tolerance of ±1⁄32 in.

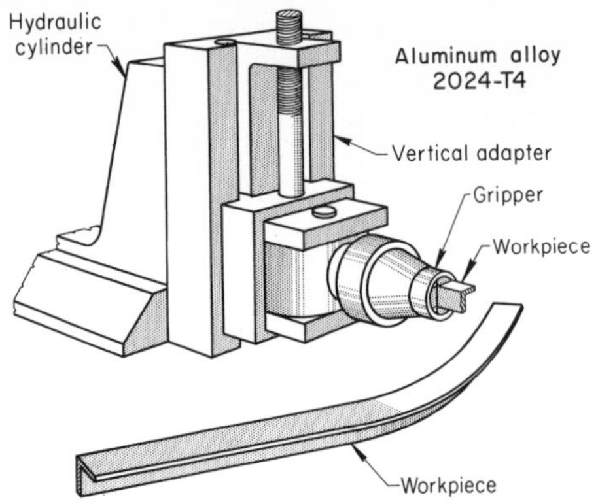

Fig. 14. Gunwale section that was produced from an L-section by a combination of twisting, stretching and forming in several planes (Example 329)

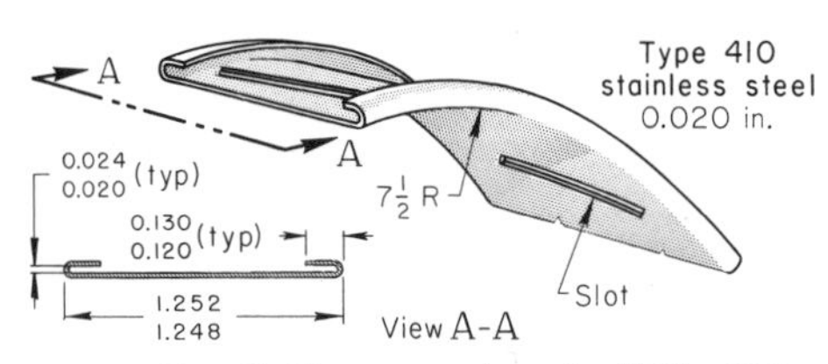

Fig. 15. Guide-vane shroud that was stretch formed without noticeable distortion to the 0.020/0.024-in. groove dimension (Example 330)

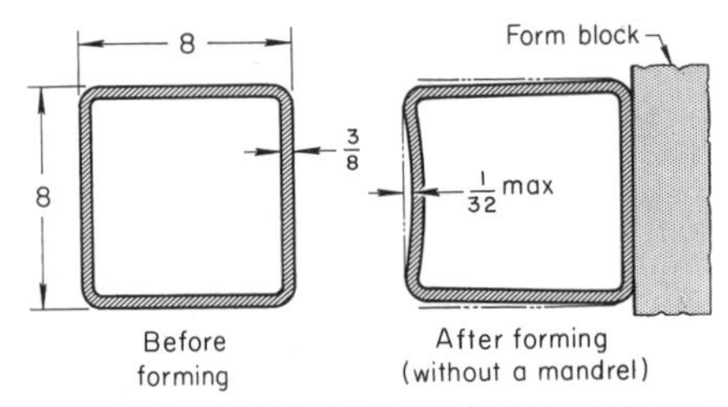

Fig. 16. Typical distortion of square copper alloy tubes in stretch forming

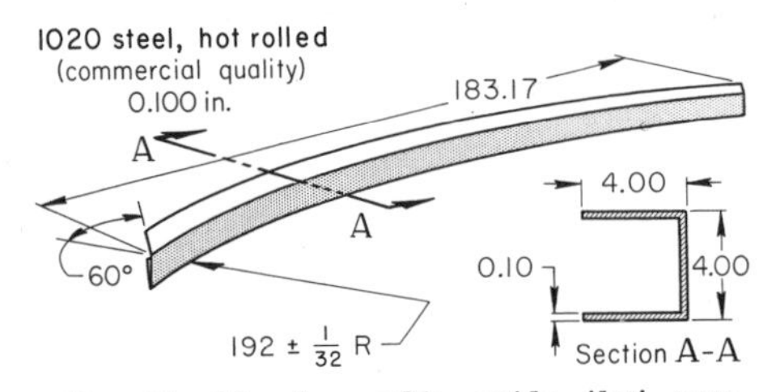

Fig. 17. Elevator cable guide that was stretch wrapped within ±1⁄32 in. of nominal radius (Example 331)

Example 331. Stretch Wrapping a Cable Guide to Close Limits (Fig. 17)

Elevator cable guides like the one shown in Fig. 17 were held to a tolerance of ±1⁄32 in. on a radius of 192 in. for a bend angle of 57°. To put enough stress on the workpiece to hold the form within tolerance, the guide was stretch wrapped in a radial-draw former.

The channel section used as the blank was made in a press brake from 1020 hot rolled steel. The only lubricant used in the stretch wrapping operation was residual mill oil.

Surface Finish

Little can be done in stretch forming to improve surface finish, because tool contact with the surface is incidental, but some practices will help to preserve the original finish, namely:

1 Avoid overstretching. With most materials, 2 to 4% stretch is sufficient to achieve the results desired in stretch forming. Overstretching some metals, such as aluminum, simply because they are ductile, is a common mistake. This leads to the appearance of stretcher strains or other surface relief effects.
2 Plastic wiper shoes can be used in compression forming or radial-draw forming of aluminum alloys to avoid marring the surface. With stainless steel workpieces, well-finished plastic wiper shoes are used with drawing compounds similar to those used for severe deep drawing.

For the parts described in Examples 533, 534 and 535 in the article on Forming of Aluminum Alloys, an extra-fine finish was needed on the surface touching the form block. Special practices used to preserve the finish included cleaning to eliminate abrasive dust particles, the use of polyvinyl chloride instead of a lubricant, and the use of special carrier sheets for protection of the surface during forming.

Table 1. Costs for Forming 40 Each of Two Different Aircraft Parts by Stretch Forming vs Drop Hammer Forming (Example 332) (a)

Process	Number of operations	Forming time, min	Cost of forming
Flap Track Fairing Half			
Stretch forming	2	372	$ 98(b)
Drop hammer forming	8	2837	$758
Cove Skin			
Stretch forming	2	335	$310(c)
Drop hammer forming	9	933	$330

(a) For each process, blanks were heat treated before forming. (b) Not including amortization of equipment. (c) Including prorated amortization of stretch draw press.

Stretch Forming vs Alternative Methods

The two examples that follow — the first from the aircraft industry, and the second from the automotive industry — compare stretch draw forming with alternative forming or drawing processes. For the products considered, stretch forming was competitive.

Example 332. Stretch Draw Forming vs Drop Hammer Forming (Table 1)

Two aircraft parts, one a complex flap track fairing half with contours in many planes and the other a moderately simple cove skin, were compared as to ease and cost of production by drop hammer forming and stretch draw forming. Forty pieces of each part were made by each process. The results are summarized in Table 1. As these data show, for both parts stretch forming required fewer operations and cost less than drop hammer forming.

Example 333. Stretch Draw Forming vs Conventional Drawing

An automotive plant that produced quarter-pillar lock panels from 0.035-in.-thick, commercial quality 1008 steel by conventional drawing investigated the relative merits of stretch draw forming for this product. In drawing, a 1000-ton double-action press with conventional draw dies produced 525 pairs of panels per hour. In stretch draw forming, an 800-ton, 108-by-60-in., straight-side, single-action mechanical press with 48-in.-long stretch grippers was used. Production rate was the same as for the conventional press when automatic loading and unloading were used, and production cost was less. The process was changed to stretch draw forming.

In high-production forming, the chief disadvantage of stretch forming is the slowness of the hydraulic units used on the grippers, unless excessively high-capacity pumps are used. Mechanical units are available that have a rapid response.

Lubrication

In most stretch forming, little or no lubricant is needed, because there is a minimum of movement between the work metal and the form block. On sheet steel, residual mill oil is usually sufficient, although some operators spray the stock with a light lubricating oil as it enters the forming area. Sometimes lubricants are purposely avoided because they attract and retain dust particles that might mar the workpiece surface (see Examples 533 and 535 in the article on Forming of Aluminum).

In compression forming of copper alloys, low-carbon steel and stainless steel, where a shoe rubs hard against the part or in applications in which there is considerable movement against the form block, white lead thinned with SAE 30 engine oil can be brushed on the workpiece before forming. In some shops, molybdenum disulfide is similarly used on low-carbon steel. Both lubricants resist heat and pressure, as well as reduce friction.

A sheet of polyvinyl chloride was used in place of a lubricant (and to embed dust particles) in the forming of microwave reflectors, as described in Example 534 in the article on Forming of Aluminum Alloys.

Other Examples of Stretch Forming Applications in This Volume

Alloy (and thickness, in.)	Type of forming	Example
Stainless Steels		
302, annealed (0.008) ..	Radial draw	484
302, ¼-hard (0.042)	Stretch wrap	485
Not specified	Stretch draw	486
Aluminum Alloys		
2024-O (extruded Y) ..	Stretch wrap	538
5050-O (0.020, to 0.040)	Stretch draw	534
5050-O (0.003)	Stretch draw	535
5050-O (0.125)	Stretch draw	533
5052-H31 (0.090)	Stretch draw	532
6061-T4 (0.032, corrug.)	Radial draw	540
6061-T4 (¾ by 11⁵⁄₁₆) ...	Stretch draw	536
6063-T5 (extruded Z) .	Stretch draw	537
7075-O (T-section)	Radial draw	539
Titanium Alloy		
Ti-5Al-2.5Sn (0.250-0.094)		618

Drop Hammer Forming

DROP HAMMER FORMING is a process for producing shapes by the progressive deformation of sheet metal in matched dies under the repetitive blows of a gravity drop hammer or a power drop hammer. Configurations most commonly formed by the process include shallow, smoothly contoured, double-curvature parts; shallow-beaded parts; and parts with irregular and comparatively deep recesses. Small quantities of cup-shape and box-shape parts, curved sections, and contoured flanged parts also are formed.

Advantages and Limitations. The main advantages of drop hammer forming are: (*a*) low cost for limited production; (*b*) relatively low tooling costs; (*c*) dies that can be cast from low-melting alloys and that are relatively simple to make; (*d*) short delivery time of product, because of simplicity of toolmaking; and (*e*) the possibility of combining coining with forming.

Against these advantages, the following limitations must be weighed: (*a*) probability of forming wrinkles; (*b*) need for skilled operators, specially trained for this process; (*c*) restriction to relatively shallow parts with generous radii; (*d*) restriction to relatively thin sheet, from about 0.024 to 0.064 in. (thicker sheet can be formed only if the parts are shallow and have generous radii).

Drop hammer forming is not a precision forming method; tolerances of less than ¹⁄₃₂ to ¹⁄₁₆ in. are not practical. Nevertheless, the process often is used for sheet-metal parts, such as aircraft components, that undergo frequent design changes.

Hammers for Forming

Gravity drop hammers and power drop hammers are comparable to a single-action press. However, they can be used to perform the work of a press equipped with double-action dies through the use of rubber pads, beads in the die surfaces, draw rings, and other auxiliary equipment.

This article was compiled from the first five references listed at the end of the article.

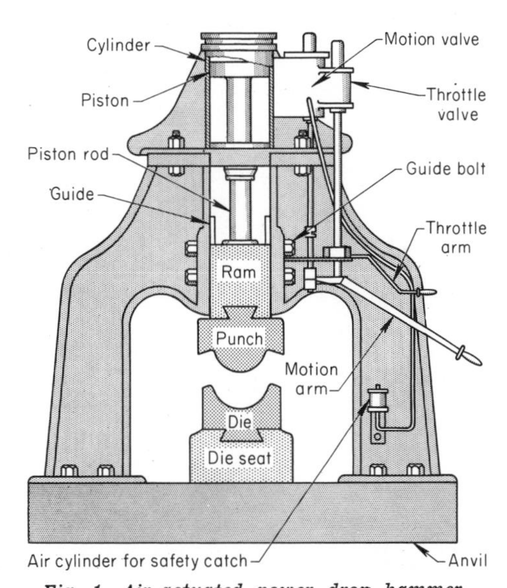

Fig. 1. Air-actuated power drop hammer, equipped for drop hammer forming

The rated sizes of commercially available gravity drop hammers range from 1000 to 10,000 lb, representing maximum energies of 3850 to 52,000 ft-lb. Power drop hammers are rated from 1000 to 35,000 lb, representing energies from 11,000 to 425,000 ft-lb. Ram dimensions and other pertinent details concerning these hammers will be found in the article "Hammers and Presses for Forging", page 1 in Volume 5 of this Handbook.

Because they can be controlled more accurately and because their blows can be varied in intensity and speed, power drop hammers, particularly the air-actuated types, have virtually replaced gravity drop hammers. A typical air drop hammer, equipped for drop hammer forming, is shown in Fig. 1.

Planishing hammers also are used for drop hammer forming. These are fast-operating air-driven or motor-driven machines that are generally used for low-production operations to form dual-curvature surfaces. They are used also to planish welds and to smooth out wrinkles or other imperfections in drawn or drop hammer formed parts.

Tooling

In general, a tool set consists of a die that conforms to the outside shape of the desired part, and a punch that conforms to the inside contour (see Fig. 1).

Tool Materials. Dies are cast from zinc alloy (3.5 Cu, 4 Al and 0.04 Mg), aluminum alloy, beryllium copper, ductile iron, or steel. The wide use of zinc alloy as a die material stems from the ease of casting it close to the final shape desired. Its low melting point (717 F) also is advantageous. All dies, regardless of die material, are polished.

Punches usually are made of lead or a low-melting alloy, although zinc or a reinforced plastic also may be used. The sharpness of the contours to be formed, the production quantity, and the accuracy desired primarily govern the choice of punch material. Lead has the advantage of not having to be cast accurately to shape, because it deforms to assume the shape of the die during the first forming trial with a blank.

Rubber Padding. In some drop hammer forming, both a working (roughing) punch and a coining (finishing) punch are used. When the working punch becomes excessively worn, it is replaced by the coining punch, and a new coining punch is prepared. Another method for achieving the same results with one punch is to use rubber pads. Rubber suitable for this purpose should have a hardness of Durometer A 80 to 90. In the positioning of pads for a particular part (see Fig. 2), the maximum thickness of rubber is situated where the greatest amount of pressure is to be applied in the initial forming. As forming progresses, the thickness of rubber is reduced by removing one or more of the pads after each impact.

Lubricants

Lubricants are used in drop hammer forming to facilitate deformation by reducing friction and minimizing galling and sticking, and to preserve or improve surface finish. Selection of a lubricant depends primarily on type of work metal, forming temperature, severity of forming, and subsequent proc-

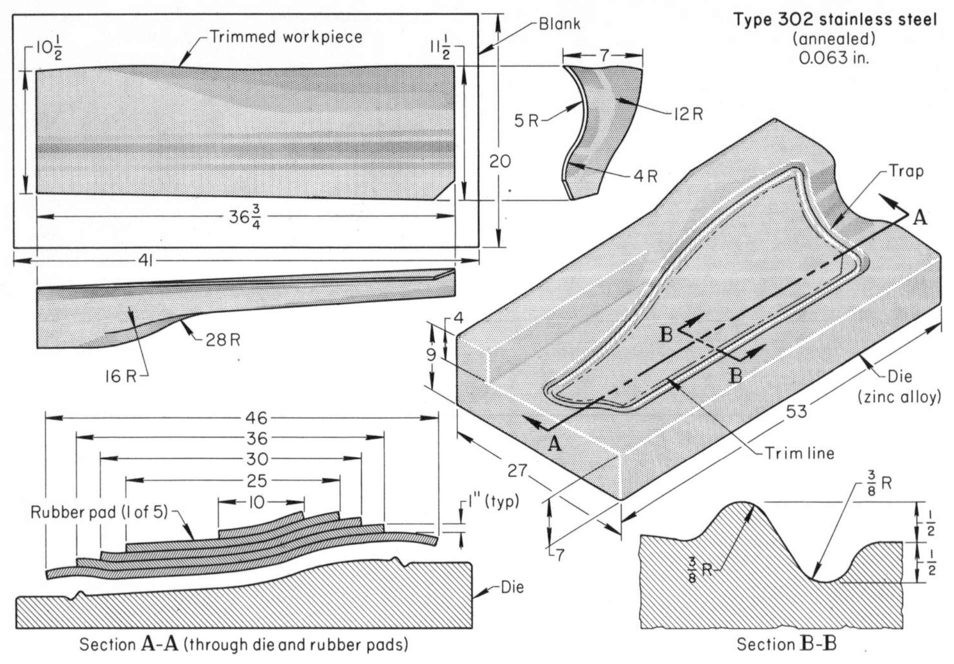

Fig. 2. A smoothly contoured stainless steel part (Part A) *that was formed in a die with a peripheral trap for hold-down* (Ref 2)

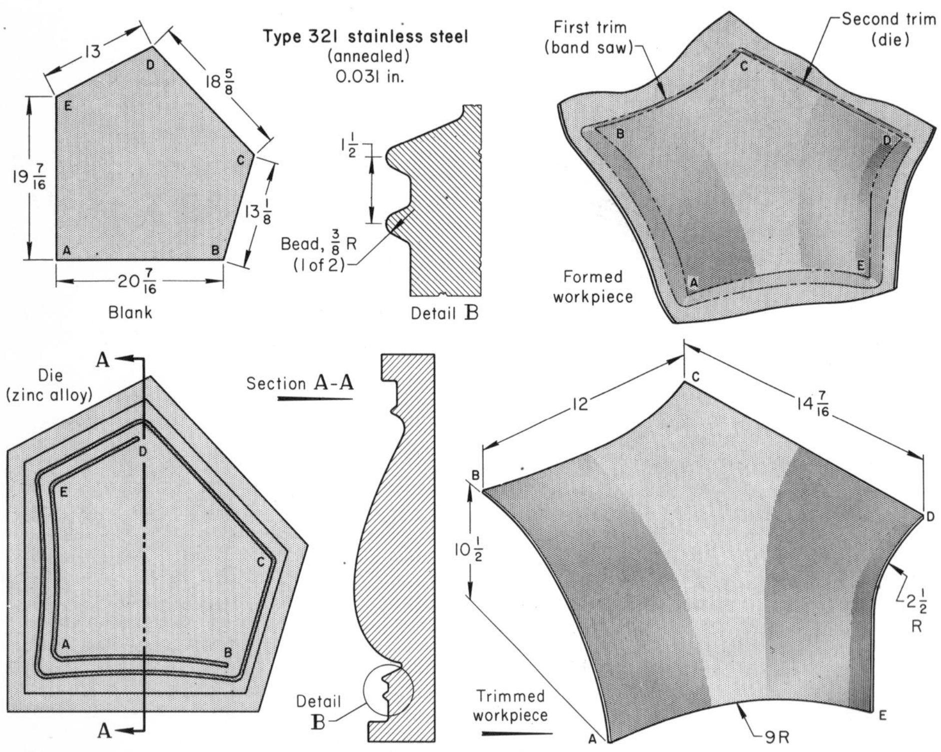

Fig. 3. Stainless steel part (Part B) *that presented a difficult springback problem. Part was formed in a die provided with beading.* (Ref 2)

essing. Recommendations for lubricants used with steels, and aluminum, magnesium and titanium alloys are given in the sections of this article that deal with processing of those metals.

Blank Preparation

The blanks for drop hammer forming generally are rectangular and are prepared by shearing. The blank should be large enough to yield a part with a flange 2 to 3 in. wide, in order to facilitate drawing of the metal during forming. When multistage forming is used, the part may be trimmed to provide a flange not less than ½ in. wide for the final forming stage.

Sheared edges are generally satisfactory for drop hammer forming, because the wide flange permits some cracking in the flange area without harming the part. The blank should be deburred to avoid possible damage to the tooling.

Drop Hammer Coining

Tableware, coins, and a variety of decorative items, produced in copper alloys, stainless steel, sterling silver, and other metals, are commonly coined by the drop hammer process. Processing details and production examples of drop hammer coining are given in the article "Coining", beginning on page 78.

Multistage Forming

With the drop hammer process, complicated parts can be formed by means of a single die and punch. However, when a large quantity of a particular part is required, it is common practice to adopt a multistage forming technique, employing several sets of dies and punches. The forming operation in any one stage is less severe than if the part were formed in a single operation. Metals that work harden appreciably are usually annealed after each operation, unless a suitable die sequence eliminates the need for annealing.

Unless contact of the work metal with lead is undesirable, the number of stage dies can be kept at a minimum by using lead pads to reduce the depth of the die cavity. Lead can be poured into the die, or lead sheet can be laid in the bottom of the recess, to the desired height; the lead is then formed to contour by a heavy blow of the punch. After the part has been preformed with the padded die, the pad is removed and the part is then formed to the full depth of the die.

Control of Buckling

Forming a deeply recessed part in thin sheet by any conventional method usually requires a high hold-down force, to prevent buckling. In drop hammer forming, the hold-down action is restricted to the end of the stroke. Thus, buckles are free to form during most of the stroke. The hold-down pressure takes effect when the punch contacts the top of the wrinkles formed in the flange and rapidly increases until the die is bottomed. The wrinkles can be removed only at the end of the stroke, and if they are not too deep.

Multistage Processing. To avoid the formation of wrinkles that are too deep to be removed in the late stages of the stroke, the forming process is divided into several forming stages. The wrinkles formed in each stage are slight and can be eliminated at the end of the stroke or, if necessary, by manual hammering. To provide adequate hold-down action at the end of each operation, it is general practice to use stage dies with surfaces that extend slightly beyond the trim line and to use punches equipped with suitable beads or traps.

Hold-Down for Deep Parts. To form deep parts, a series of plywood or metal hold-down rings may be used; one ring is removed after each blow. These rings usually vary in thickness from ¼ to 1 in. The desired metal flow may be approached during the early stages of forming, using a blank that is considerably larger than that required to form the part. The excess metal is trimmed off after several blows. The stiffness of the oversize blank prevents draw-in, and thus induces stretching, which counteracts the tendency to buckle. The die for a part with a deep recess must be designed with a horizontal surface to accommodate beading.

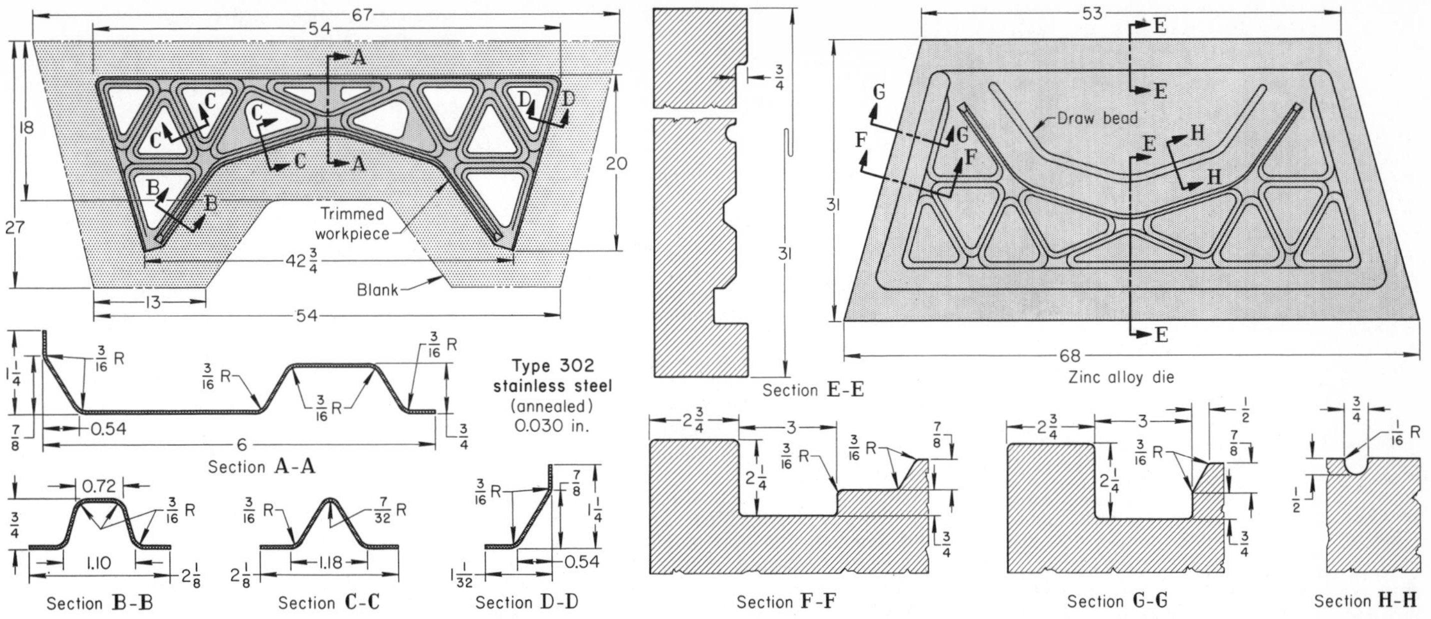

Fig. 4. Stainless steel part (Part C) *with extensive beading, formed in a zinc alloy die* (Ref 2)

Processing Steels

Carbon and low-alloy steels containing less than 0.30% carbon are the most easily formed by the drop hammer process. Higher carbon content decreases formability and promotes cracking. Although lead additions do not affect the formability of steel adversely, the sulfur additions that are characteristic of resulfurized free-machining steels promote susceptibility to cracking.

All carbon and low-alloy steels require full annealing for satisfactory drop hammer forming. Process (or mill) annealing usually is unsatisfactory, because of its inability to develop uniform softness and to avoid excessive grain enlargement.

Stainless steels that are extensively formed by the drop hammer process include austenitic types 302, 304, 305, 321 and 347. For severe drop hammer forming, grades containing not less than 10% nickel (and preferably about 12%) should be selected, to minimize cracking. All stainless steels are drop hammer formed in the fully annealed (solution treated) condition.

Sheet Thickness. The drop hammer forming of steel sheet (particularly, stainless steel sheet) less than 0.018 in. thick is impractical because of wrinkling and the difficulties encountered in attempting to planish the wrinkles. The most common range of steel sheet thickness for drop hammer formed parts is 0.024 to 0.063 in. Thicknesses up to 0.078 in. have been hammer formed.

Tool Materials. Cast zinc alloy is the most widely used die material for drop hammer forming of carbon, low-alloy and stainless steels. Alloy cast iron dies are substituted when a large quantity of parts is required. To increase the life of dies with sharp fillets and corners, inserts of an air-hardening tool steel may be used.

Punches are made either of zinc alloy or of cast iron, and ground to size. A zinc alloy punch, cast directly into the die, can be used for shallow parts, but it may be undersize (because of shrinkage on cooling) if the part contains large cavities. Lead punches also are used extensively, although they are easily distorted when used to form steels. Punch life can be increased considerably by facing the punch with an untrimmed finish-formed steel part.

Lubricants. When zinc alloy dies and zinc alloy or lead punches are employed, many steel parts can be formed without a lubricant. Harder tool materials or more severe forming may require the use of a light lubricant such as SAE 10 or SAE 30 mineral oil.

Precautions for Stainless Steels. Stainless steels, especially the austenitic grades, work harden more than do the carbon and low-alloy steels that are suitable for hammer forming. When cold forming stainless steel, it is necessary to stretch the metal rather than allow it to draw into the die. Stretching prevents the formation of wrinkles that are difficult to eliminate. By means of stretching, quarter-hard and even half-hard types 301 and 302 can be drop hammer formed, although only to a very limited extent. Part configuration must be simple and of only moderate depth; otherwise, wrinkles (in a shallow part) or distortion (in a complex shape) will occur. Although it is preferable that the part be made in a single die with a single blow, some commercial quarter-hard parts have required as many as three or four blows for successful forming.

When moderately complex parts are formed in a drop hammer in several stages, it is advisable to consider intermediate annealing, to offset the effects of work hardening. It is not necessary to pickle after each annealing treatment (provided scaling is not too heavy), except before the finish-forming operation and after the final annealing treatment. If the part is formed in zinc alloy dies, any adhering zinc particles must be removed by pickling or by treatment in a fused salt bath (caustic soda) before annealing treatments (both intermediate and final). This requirement is most important for parts that are to be welded or that will be exposed to elevated-temperature service. Failure to remove the zinc may result in cracking.

Springback. Carbon and alloy steel parts, and especially stainless steel parts, having large radii and smooth contours are more difficult to maintain in desired shape than parts with relatively sharp radii, because of greater springback under these conditions. Common practice is to compensate for this springback from the desired contour by trial and error. If this method is not successful, the part must be distorted elastically on assembly — that is, sprung into the final shape.

Parts with reverse contours ("saddleback" parts) are extremely difficult to form without excessive wrinkling.

Limits in Deep Recessing. When deeply recessed parts are to be formed in a drop hammer, the recesses are limited in both depth and contour. With a single die, a cup-shape or dome-shape part can be formed to a limiting depth of 60 to 70% of that obtainable by means of double-action dies. Square and rectangular steel boxes (even shallow ones) require a minimum corner radius of ¼ in., or five times the metal thickness, whichever is larger. For deeper boxes, progressively larger corner radii are necessary, and these minimum radii apply to boxes of any width.

Production Examples. Details of the drop hammer forming of stainless steel parts are given in Examples 480 and 481 in the article "Forming of Stainless Steel"; examples relating to drop hammer coining can be found in the article "Coining", which begins on page 78. Additional applications of drop hammer forming of stainless steel aircraft components are described in the following paragraphs.

Part A. The smoothly contoured aircraft part shown in Fig. 2 was drop hammer formed from a square-sheared, annealed type 302 stainless steel blank, 0.063 in. thick. The die and punch, both made of zinc alloy, were designed to compensate for springback. Hold-down was facilitated by a trap that bordered the periphery of the part contour in the die (Fig. 2).

Forming required seven blows of the drop hammer. For the first blow, five rubber pads, each 1 in. thick, were positioned as shown in Fig. 2. One rubber pad was removed after each of the next four blows. The sixth blow was delivered through a rubber pad 46 by 10 in. by ½ in. thick, and the seventh blow was struck with the bare punch.

Forming was done without a lubricant and without intermediate annealing, unless wrinkles developed. Wrinkled parts were annealed, and the wrinkles were removed with a power hammer. These parts were then sized in the drop hammer. After forming, parts were trimmed in a band saw.

Part B. The smoothly contoured part shown in Fig. 3 presented a difficult springback problem. Hold-down was facilitated by beading, which was lubricated with SAE 10 or SAE 30 mineral oil. The work metal was annealed, 0.031-in.-thick type 321 stainless steel sheet. The die and punch were made of zinc alloy. Except for the beading, working surfaces were not lubricated.

The square-sheared blank (Fig. 3) was preformed by hand prior to hammer forming. Forming in the drop hammer employed eight rubber pads, one of which was removed after each successive stroke. Between strokes, wrinkles were removed with a hand mallet, as required. Initial trimming was done in a band saw.

Final sizing was done in the drop hammer with the original die, a new punch, and without padding. Sizing required two light blows, followed by one heavy blow. The formed part was trimmed, and was resized by hand or restruck in the die to eliminate severe springback.

Part C. The aircraft part shown in Fig. 4 is representative of a hammer-formed contour with extensive beading. The work metal was annealed type 302 stainless steel sheet, 0.030 in. thick. The blank was prepared by square shearing and rotary shearing.

Forming was done with a zinc alloy die and punch. The die contained a draw bead (Fig. 4), to promote stretching. Initial forming required several light blows; between blows, wrinkles were flattened with a hand hammer. The final set was accomplished with one heavy blow. The lubricant was a fatty-acid type of nonpigmented drawing compound.

After forming, the part was cleaned, trimmed with a shear, pickled and passivated.

Processing Aluminum Alloys

Drop hammer forming of aluminum alloys is most suitable for limited production runs that do not warrant expensive tooling. The process often is used for parts, such as aircraft components, that undergo frequent design changes. Some forming applications also involve coining and embossing.

Work Metal. Annealed tempers of all aluminum alloys are the most suitable for hammer forming. Intermediate work-hardened tempers of the non-heat-treatable alloys are often used for channel shapes and shallow embossed panels.

Heat treatable alloys frequently are partly formed in the annealed condition. Then the part is solution heat treated, quenched, restruck to size, and artificially aged. Restriking is also necessary to remove distortion caused by quenching.

Drop hammer forming can be done on freshly quenched alloys within a few hours after quenching, or later if the alloys are refrigerated to prevent aging.

Sheet Thickness. Under comparable conditions, with the same equipment and with the same thickness of sheet, aluminum wrinkles more easily than steel under a drop hammer. To obtain results comparable to those obtained with steel, aluminum alloy sheet should be at least 40% thicker than the steel, or preferably in the approximate thickness range of 0.034 to 0.109 in.

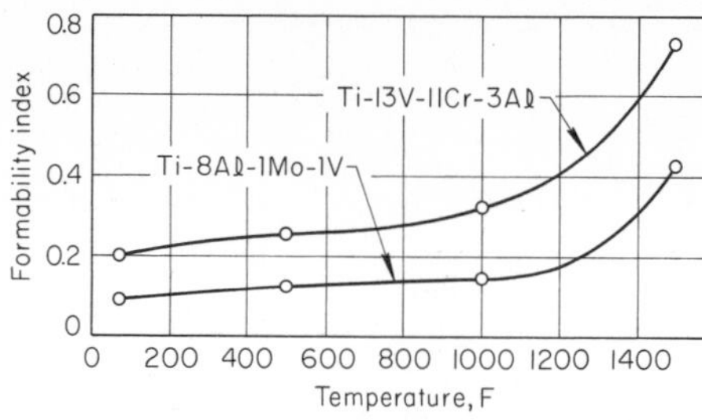

Fig. 5. Effect of forming temperature on the drop hammer formability of two titanium alloys

Equipment and Tool Materials. Aluminum alloys are drop hammer formed in gravity drop, power drop, and planishing hammers. A typical tooling setup is shown in Fig. 40 on page 396 in this volume.

Dies are cast from aluminum, zinc alloy, iron or steel. Dies for high production are usually cast in iron or steel. All dies are polished. Most punches are made of lead or a low-melting alloy, although zinc alloy or reinforced plastic also may be used. The softer punch materials have the advantage of deforming readily to assume the shape of the die during forming trials.

When planishing hammers are used, the preferred tool material is hardened, polished tool steel.

Forming Characteristics. Annealed aluminum alloys are readily formed under the drop hammer. Simple components can often be produced by a single blow. However, deep shapes require extreme care in blank development and die design. Blankholders are not used; therefore, wrinkles are difficult to avoid, especially when thin sheet is being formed.

Processing Magnesium Alloys

Drop hammer forming of magnesium alloys, which is performed on preheated sheet in heated dies, is suited for the production of formed parts having shallow depths and asymmetrical shapes, and for parts for which special springback control is required.

Work Metal. Magnesium sheet alloys in the annealed condition are preferred for drop hammer forming. The ideal sheet thickness for forming is ⅛ in., and the part should be designed so as to be formable in six stages or less. For sheet thinner than ⅛ in., ten stages or less are recommended.

Equipment and Tool Materials. Both gravity drop and power drop hammers are suitable for forming of magnesium alloys.

Zinc alloy is the preferred punch and die material, although lead punches are sometimes used for production runs of not more than 50 pieces. When lead comes in contact with magnesium sheet, there is danger of lead pickup, which can cause corrosion of the sheet. Although lead pickup may occur at room temperature, it is more likely to occur at the elevated temperatures at which magnesium alloys are formed. Therefore, if lead pickup cannot be tolerated or if the production run exceeds 50 pieces, either zinc alloy or cast iron may be substituted for lead.

Lubricants. Vegetable-lecithin oils provide good lubrication at temperatures up to 500 F. Suspensions of colloidal graphite may have to be used if temperatures are to exceed 500 F. However, these suspensions are more difficult to remove when parts are cleaned after forming.

Preheating. Magnesium parts are usually formed at temperatures of 450 to 500 F, depending on the alloy (see the article on Forming of Magnesium, which begins on page 424, for specific recommendations). Heating times are 5 min per stage for sheet up to about 0.051 in. thick, and up to 9 min per stage for thicker sheet (up to 0.125 in.).

The oven for heating parts between stages should be near the drop hammer; the decrease in temperature during transfer from the oven to the hammer will range from 30 to 45 F in 5 sec. The dies can be heated by being put in an oven conveniently located to the hammer, and then be kept at temperature by ring burners or torches during the forming of the part.

Small dies can be anchored to an electrically heated cast iron platen installed on the hammer bed, but this method is impractical for large dies. The punch and die also may be heated by electric elements or by a heat-transfer fluid. The working temperatures should not exceed those recommended.

Rubber pads may be used in the initial forming operation. At 450 F, the reduction obtainable using rubber staging is approximately 10%. Special types of rubber are available for forming at temperatures up to 600 F. The rubber pads are removed before the final blow is delivered to set the material.

Springback. One advantage of the elevated temperatures used in drop hammer forming of magnesium is the marked reduction or total elimination of springback, provided the maximum practical temperatures are always employed. The rate of deformation is important in drop hammer forming and must be controlled carefully on severe drawing or when material in the hard (H24) temper is being formed. The rate of deformation can be controlled by the operator, although not to close limits. Parts that require relatively severe forming may be started by allowing the punch to descend slowly into the die and by using subsequent strikes to set the material.

Dimensional Tolerances. Tolerances of ±0.03 in. have been held in the production of magnesium parts. However, when close tolerances are important, press forming is usually the preferred method for forming magnesium parts.

Processing Titanium Alloys

Various titanium sheet alloys have been formed by the drop hammer process, including Ti-13V-11Cr-3Al, Ti-8Al-1Mo-1V, Ti-6Al-4V, and Ti-5Al-2.5Sn. In general, the alloys containing aluminum as the principal alloying element are the most difficult to form. The minimum thickness of titanium sheet for hammer formed parts is about 0.025 in.

Tool Materials. Contact between titanium and low-melting tool materials, such as zinc alloy or lead, should be avoided — particularly when the titanium is formed at elevated temperature or must be heat treated after forming.

When these tool materials are used, contact with the workpiece can be avoided by capping the punch and die with sheet steel, stainless steel, or a nickel-base alloy. The choice of capping material depends on the tool life desired. The longest tool life is obtained by capping with Inconel 600 sheet in thicknesses of 0.025 to 0.032 in.

In general, steel and ductile iron dies are used when the tooling must be heated above 400 F. Preheating both the work metal and the tooling is not uncommon.

Rubber Pads. High-temperature rubber pads are used both in preforming operations before the final strike and as electrical insulators to prevent current loss to the tooling when the work-metal blank is heated by the electrical-resistance method.

Lubricants used in drop hammer forming of titanium should be nonchlorinated. Extreme-pressure oils, and both pigmented and nonpigmented drawing compounds are used in most operations.

Preheating Tools and Blanks. Difficult titanium parts are formed at elevated temperature (see pages 439 and 440 for recommendations and precautions). Thermal expansion of the blank and the tooling must be considered. If the tooling is not preheated, the amount it expands will depend on the length of time it is in contact with the blank. The allowance for thermal expansion used in the design of tooling for titanium is 0.006 in. per inch for a forming temperature of 1000 F. The allowance for expansion of circular or elliptical parts should be made radially, not peripherally. When hot sizing is to follow forming, the drop hammer tooling usually is made to net dimensions without consideration of thermal expansion.

If the blanks are to be heated in a furnace and then transferred to the drop hammer tools, stops should be located in the tooling for rapid and accurate location of the blank. Resistance heating may be used in drop hammer forming, but because of the electrical connections necessary, it generally requires more time for forming each part. Clearance relief for the electrical leads is necessary if the blank is shorter than the die. The dies must be insulated from the bed of the press to prevent short-circuiting. Insulating materials such as pressed asbestos-cement board or high-temperature rubber have been used satisfactorily for this application.

In resistance heating, clamping should be secure so that high resistance at the clamp-blank interface will not result in hot spots and possible melting due to insufficient clamping area for the current being transmitted. The current supplied from a low-voltage, high-amperage source, such as a welding machine, is increased until the desired temperature of the blank is obtained. The temperature of the blank can be checked with a thermocouple. The use of temperature-sensitive crayons is permitted only on the trim areas of the part, to avoid contamination of the part. As soon as the forming temperature is reached, the blank can be covered with a high-temperature rubber pad at least 1 in. thick; the

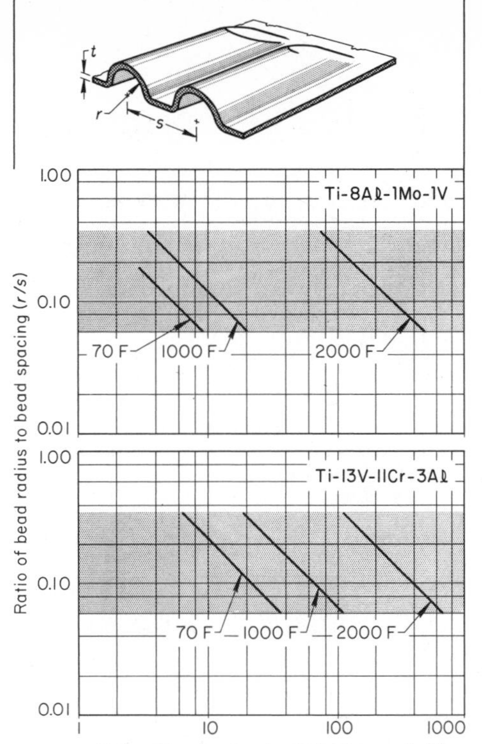

Fig. 6. Limits of formability of beaded panels from titanium alloys Ti-8Al-1Mo-1V and Ti-13V-11Cr-3Al at room temperature and at elevated temperature

electrodes are disconnected, and the part is then formed. This process is repeated for each successive blow until the part is formed to final dimensions. In the final stage, no rubber is used over the part, and the dies are closed on the part for at least 30 sec after the final blow.

Furnaces used to heat blanks should be controlled within 15 F to prevent possible damage to the titanium. The temperature to be used depends on the titanium alloy being formed. Workpieces should not be overheated, and they should be shielded so that no hot spots occur. As soon as the blank reaches the required temperature, it should be removed from the furnace and formed. The furnace should be located next to the hammer. The total time for the sequence of transfer, forming, and return to the furnace should not exceed 8 sec. After the final strike on the hammer, the dies should remain closed for about 30 sec so that the part will cool slightly in the die. In elevated-temperature forming of titanium, the total time at temperature should not exceed that permitted for the alloy. The use of an inert furnace atmosphere increases the permissible time at temperature, but should not be depended upon as a substitute for efficient operations.

A third method of heating titanium for drop hammer forming is with radiant quartz lamps. The lamps are placed close to the blank while the blank is resting on the tooling. The lamps are then moved out of the way, and the part is formed. This sequence is repeated until the part is completely formed. It sometimes helps if the edges of the blank are supported on an insulating blanket, such as asbestos, so that the heat loss to the tooling is reduced.

Formability vs Temperature. Variation of the drop hammer formability index for two titanium alloys with temperature is given in Fig. 5. It is evident from the curves that significant increases in formability can be achieved at temperatures above 1000 F.

Drop Hammer Forming Limits

The severity of permissible deformations in drop hammer forming is limited both by geometrical considerations and by the properties of the work metal. The forming limits can be predicted by considering parts of interest as variations of beaded panels. For parts characterized in this way, the critical geometrical factors are the bead radius, r, the spacing between beads, s, and the thickness of the work metal, t (Fig. 6).

Two of the forming limits depend entirely on dimensional relations and are the same for all materials: The ratio of the bead radius, r, to bead spacing, s, must lie between 0.35 and 0.06. The lower formability limit is controlled by the necessity for producing uniform stretching and avoiding excessive springback. If the r/s ratio is too small, there will be greater localized stretching at the nose of the punch.

Within the limits set for all materials by the r/s ratio, success or failure in forming beaded panels depends on the ratio of the bead radius to the sheet thickness (r/t), and on the ductility of the work metal. The part will split if the necessary amount of stretching exceeds the ductility available in the material. The splitting limit can be predicted from the elongation value, in a 0.5-in. gage length, in tension tests at the temperature of interest.

Formability limits for two titanium alloys, developed from predictability equations, are plotted in Fig. 6. Both charts were constructed on a logarithmic basis and show the marked improvements in formability resulting from better elongation values at elevated temperature.

Selected References

1. D. E. Strohecker, "Forming of Titanium and Titanium Alloys", Battelle Memorial Institute, Columbus, Ohio, DMIC Report 238, Sept 1, 1957
2. "Forming of Austenitic Chromium-Nickel Stainless Steels", Second Edition, International Nickel Co., Inc., New York, 1954
3. W. W. Wood, "Theoretical Formability", Volumes I and II, Office of Technical Services, U. S. Department of Commerce, Washington, Report No. ASD-TDR 61-191, Aug 1961
4. "Forming of Magnesium", Dow Chemical Co., Midland, Mich., 1962
5. K. R. Van Horn (editor), "Aluminum", Volume III, Chapter 6, American Society for Metals, Metals Park, Ohio, 1967.

Additional References

"Forming of Aluminium and Its Alloys by the Drop Stamp", Information Bulletin 12 (24 p), The Aluminium Development Association, London (England), 1961

A. McLeod, Soft Metal Tools for Pressing Short Run Panels, *Sheet Metal Industries*, 1941, **15** (170), 774-778, 783-785; **15** (171), 906-910, 917-920

C. J. Frey and S. S. Kogut, Drop Hammer Technique and Innovation, *Aviation*, 1942, **42** (10), 130-133, 285

"Handbook on the Fabrication of Sheet Metal Details", Section 6 — Drop Hammer, Ministry of Aircraft Production (Great Britain), 1943

A. T. Pierce, The Formation of Sheet Metal Components by Means of the Air-Operated Drop Stamp, *Sheet Metal Industries*, 1943, **18** (200), 2145-2148; 1944, **19** (201), 109-116

Explosive Forming

EXPLOSIVE FORMING changes the shape of a metal blank or preform by the instantaneous high pressure that results from the detonation of an explosive. This article is concerned only with the explosives generally termed high explosives, and not with so-called low explosives.

Systems used for explosive forming operations are generally classified as either confined or unconfined. This article deals largely with unconfined systems.

Confined systems (Fig. 1) use a die, in two or more pieces, that completely encloses the workpiece. The closed system has distinct advantages for the forming of thin stock to close tolerances, and has been used for close-tolerance sizing of thin-wall tubing. However, confined systems are generally used only for forming of comparatively small workpieces, because economic feasibility decreases as the size of the workpiece increases.

Unconfined Systems. In an unconfined system (Fig. 2), the shock wave from the explosive charge takes the place of the punch in conventional forming. A single-element die is used with a blank held over it, and the explosive charge is suspended over the blank at a predetermined distance (the "standoff" distance). The complete assembly can be immersed in a tank of water, as shown in Fig. 2, or a plastic bag filled with water can be placed over the blank.

The unconfined system is inherently inefficient, because only a small part of the total energy released by the explosion is effective as forming energy. The medium within which the explosion occurs plays an important part in determining the efficiency of the system. As the density of the medium increases, efficiency increases. For this reason, most explosive forming of large pieces is done in a medium more dense than air. Water is the most commonly used medium for ambient-temperature explosive forming. Molten aluminum has been used as the medium in explosive forming at elevated temperature.

Under normal operating conditions, it is best to detonate the explosive charge as far below the surface of the water as possible. This reduces the amount of water that is thrown by the explosion, and reduces the amount of energy lost by venting to the atmosphere the gas bubble that results from the detonated charge.

The amount of energy or peak pressure delivered can be calculated from standard formulas. Generally, a cylindrical charge (or point charge) is located near the centerline of the part and at a standoff distance that is related to the span of the workpiece over the die cavity. For large parts, it is generally impractical to use a point charge; for example, in forming large hemispheres or end closures for rocket motors, Primacord, shaped in a large loop and located close to the outer periphery of the part, is ordinarily used instead of a point charge. (Primacord is a cordlike detonating fuse that consists of a filament of explosive material covered by a protective, water-repellent coating.)

This article is a digest of "Explosive Forming of Metals", by D. E. Strohecker, R. J. Carlson, S. W. Porembka, Jr., and F. W. Boulger; DMIC Report 203, 8 May 1964.

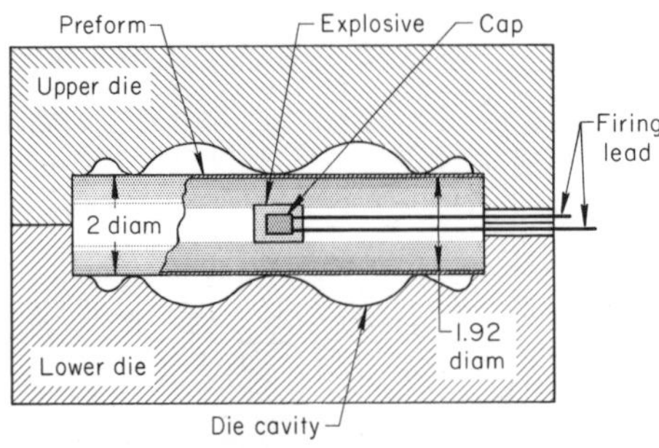

Fig. 1. Confined system for explosive forming

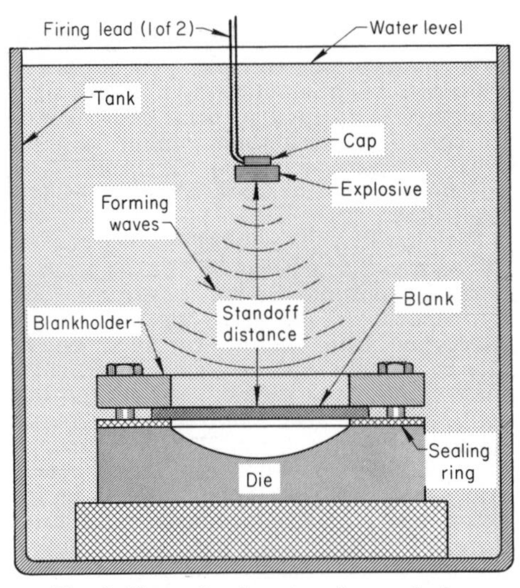

Fig. 2. Unconfined system for explosive forming

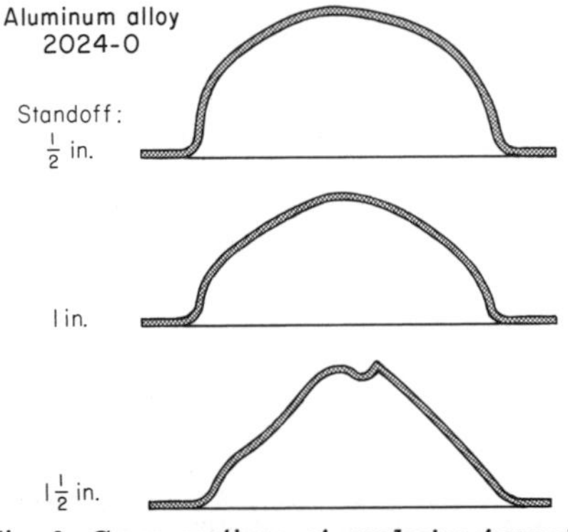

Fig. 3. Cross sections of explosive-formed workpieces, showing effect of slight changes in standoff distance at close range

The variations in energy level delivered from various shapes of charge are small when the charge is fired in a water medium, provided the standoff distance is 12 in. or more. When charges are placed very close to a blank (within 1 or 2 in.), energy-transfer mechanisms from the explosive to the workpiece change. An example of these effects is shown in Fig. 3.

Equipment

The primary equipment for explosive forming in an unconfined system consists of a water tank, a crane, a vacuum pump and a detonator.

Water Tank. The water tank must be able to withstand the repeated impacts of the explosive shock without rupturing. Many tanks are designed to be large enough so that the shocks reaching the walls from centrally placed charges are considerably reduced. The stress in a tank wall as a function of the radius of the tank for a 1-lb charge of TNT and constant wall thickness of 1 in. is plotted in Fig. 4. These data show that an increase in the diameter of the tank from 4 to 40 ft lowers the stress level in the tank wall by only about 26%, from 1650 to 1225 psi. At the same time, the weight of tank-wall material will have increased tenfold.

One of the best approaches to the reduction of tank-wall thickness is to moderate the pressure of the shock wave before it strikes the tank wall. Figure 5(a) shows the use of inflated rubber tubing for the reduction of stress in the tank walls. The rubber tubing acts as a cushion; in one application, it provided an 83% reduction in stress. To use this technique in a large tank, a considerable amount of tubing would be needed, and it would be difficult to maintain the position of the tubing and to prevent damage to the tubing during explosions. The use of an air-bubble curtain as shown in Fig. 5(b) appears to offer one of the best solutions to the problem of low-cost water-tank construction. To be effective, a uniform and closely spaced curtain of bubbles must be maintained along the walls of the water tank. The bubble curtain is controlled by the size and spacing of holes in the air line at the base of the tank, and by the air flow and pressure maintained in the line. A maximum charge size of 70 grams of TNT has been fired in an 8-ft-diam tank provided with a curtain of air bubbles with no visible signs of damage to the tank wall when the bubble curtain was operating.

The base of the tank must withstand at least as much impact as the tank walls. Placing the tank in solid rock, where possible, is advantageous. A heavy base of reinforced concrete can be used, provided it is covered by a heavy steel plate to distribute stress in the concrete evenly, preventing localized high stresses. Shock-absorbing material may be placed between the concrete and the steel baseplate; a sheet of rubber will provide some stress reduction. The use of a closely coiled, inflated rubber hose between the baseplate and the base of the tank is also effective in reducing stress. The stress in the base can be reduced by as much as 80% by this means. The hose should be inflated with only enough air to support the baseplate and the water head above it; overinflation will increase stress-wave transmission and may result in damage to the hose.

Difficulties in sealing the tank base to the tank wall must also be overcome. In some metal tanks the joint has been welded, but not with complete success. Seals of resilient plastic have provided satisfactory results, and are easy to repair if a leak develops.

Crane. A crane is usually necessary to move material around the facility and also in and out of the water tank. Ideally, the crane should be air operated, to avoid having electric power lines within the firing area. The required capacity of the crane will depend on the size and weight of the dies to be handled. One of the largest portable dies used in an explosive forming operation weighed 21,000 lb.

Vacuum Pump. A vacuum pump will probably be needed for most explosive forming operations when parts are formed under water. If the firing area is to be maintained with a minimum of electric lines, a venturi pump operating on water pressure will work satisfactorily. A mechanical pump driven by an electric motor can be used, with the vacuum lines being brought into the firing area from a pumping site remote from the firing area. An electrically driven mechanical pump is preferred, because it has a considerably greater capacity than a venturi pump and is probably more economical to operate. In a high-production facility where the application of a vacuum might be unacceptably time-consuming, a storage tank in the vacuum line will greatly assist the operation. If it is found necessary to operate an electrically driven vacuum pump in the firing area, it should have shielded wiring and a sealed motor. When a mechanical pump is used, it is important to eliminate any possibility of water entering the pump.

Detonation Circuit. Under ideal conditions, the detonator for the electric blasting caps is the only electric circuit that should be permitted in the area where explosives are handled.

A detonator should be constructed on the fail-safe principle, so that any malfunction will immediately cause the circuit to be disarmed. The following characteristics are desirable in the design of a detonator for use in explosive forming applications:

1 The device should be operable only with a key that is carried by the individual setting the charges.
2 When the device is not armed with the key, this fact should be visually discernible from the work area.
3 The lead wires to the cap should always be shorted when the circuit is not armed.
4 When the circuit is armed with the key, both a visual and an audible warning of its armed condition should be activated automatically.
5 A method of checking the continuity of the blasting circuit should be an integral part of the detonator.

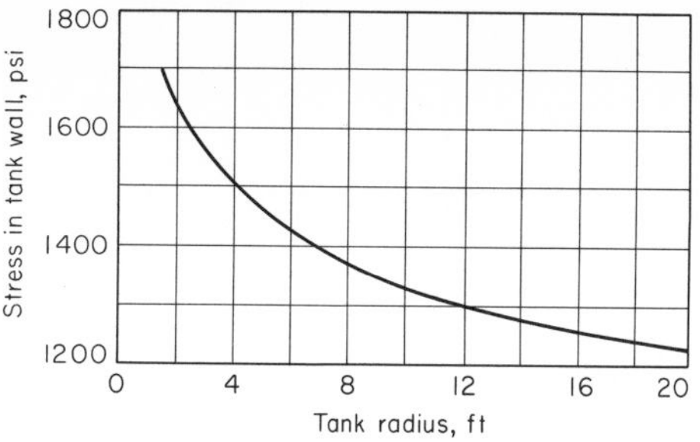

Fig. 4. Effect of tank radius on stress produced in 1-in.-thick tank wall by the detonation of 1 lb of TNT at the tank center

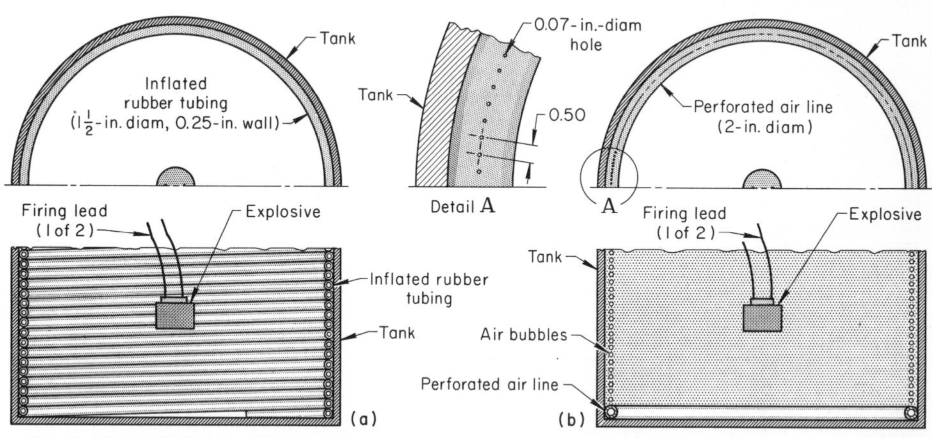

Fig. 5. Use of inflated rubber tubing, and of an air-bubble curtain, for reducing the stress in the tank walls induced by explosion

A schematic wiring diagram for a detonator that meets these requirements is shown in Fig. 6.

The current for firing the blasting caps can come from a 6-volt battery or directly from a 110-volt line. If a 110-volt line is used, it is wise to use some type of circuit breaker for protection of the lines if a short occurs during firing.

Figure 6 shows the circuit for a detonator in the unarmed condition, the condition being demonstrated by current flowing through the uppermost of the three poles in the relay, 4, to the "safe" warning light, 6. Switch 1 is actuated by a key carried by the responsible person. It operates the relay. The upper pole disconnects the "safe" warning light and connects the "armed" warning light, 5, and the horn, H. The two other poles shift to disconnect the short circuit of the line to the caps and connect its two leads to the firing circuit. Switch 3 is the detonating switch. Before it is thrown, the firing circuit is completed through the battery and the microammeter for a continuity check of the circuit. When switch 3 is thrown, the 110-volt line is connected to the firing circuit and the cap detonates. Thus, the conditions listed previously are met.

Auxiliary Equipment. During the operation of an explosive forming facility, debris will probably collect on the surface of the water or be distributed throughout the water tank. Skimming equipment, such as that used for swimming pools, serves well for the removal of material floating on the surface. Material distributed throughout the water must be removed by filtration. However, any explosive material collected in the water tank will be pumped through the filtration lines and possibly into the pump, where it may collect and later cause an accident.

In locations where water is plentiful, the tanks are emptied by gravity and refilled frequently; in other areas, the same water must be used over and over. The dumping of tank water into sewer lines should be avoided, because any explosive suspended in the water may be trapped by an obstacle in the sewer and build up a concentration that could cause a serious accident. When a misfire is detected, attempts should be made to recover as much of the undetonated explosive as possible, for later destruction. The filter material should be handled as explosive material when it is emptied.

The amount of explosive stored within the facility should always be kept to a minimum and preferably should not exceed the supply necessary for one day's operation. For temporary storage of explosives within the facility, small storage containers can be made from discarded refrigerators. The caps should be stored in one and explosives in another. The main storage of explosives for the operation should be at some distance from the facility.

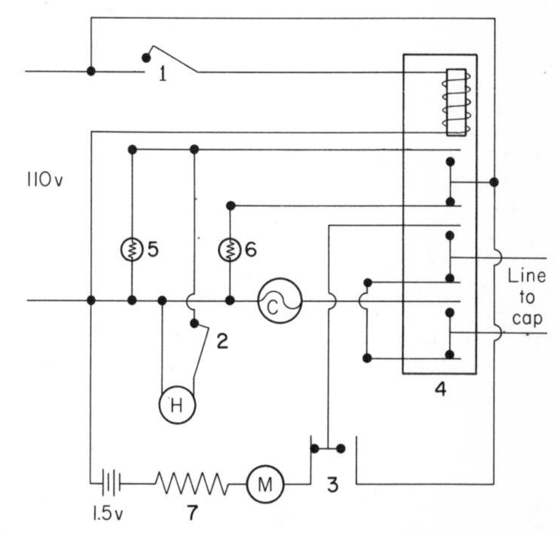

1 – Key switch; single pole, single throw. 2 – Horn switch; single pole, single throw ("momentary off" operation). 3 – Continuity and firing switch; single pole, double throw. 4 – Relay; triple pole, double throw. 5 – "Armed" warning light. 6 – "Safe" warning light. 7 – 10,000-ohm resistor. C – 5-amp circuit breaker. H – Horn. M – Microammeter.

Fig. 6. Wiring diagram for a safe detonator for explosive forming

Die Systems and Materials

Basic differences between tooling for explosive forming and for conventional forming arise from the type of loading that the die material must be able to withstand. In explosive forming, high impact loads transmit shock waves through the metal that cause unusual stress patterns within the die material, and therefore, corners should be eliminated where possible. Shock loading causes the die to fracture along lines from the corners, rather than through the thinnest section as in static fracture. Figure 7 shows the modes of fracture for conditions of static loading and dynamic (shock) loading.

Evacuating Ports and Seals. In most explosive forming, a vacuum is applied between the blank and the die cavity. If possible, some method of sealing should be made an integral part of the die. In many applications, the use of rubber projecting about 1/16 in. above the die surface has provided the necessary seal. Because explosive forming causes the metal to pick up detail from the die, the vacuum port in the die should be kept small and be located in a part of the die where its impression can be removed from the workpiece in a subsequent trimming operation. If this is not possible, the vent hole should be located so that the dimple that is formed will not be objectionable.

Blankholder Design. A blankholder is generally necessary to prevent wrinkling of the metal as the blank is drawn into the die. The size of the blankholder and the clamping pressure needed depend on the type of metal being formed. With a soft metal, such as annealed aluminum, very little blankholder pressure is needed; hard metals, such as stainless steel, need high pressures to prevent wrinkling.

Bolts are often used to clamp the blankholder to the die. In forming materials, such as aluminum, that do not need high clamping forces for the blankholder, hydraulic clamping jacks are usually efficient.

In applications in which the parts to be made are concentric and the forming is to be done in air, it may be possible to eliminate the blankholder. A taper-wall die has been used for forming cones, where the blank is situated on a taper leading into the die. This technique can provide savings when aboveground operations are used.

Materials for Solid Dies. Solid dies made from heat treated alloy steel maintain contour, surface finish and dimensional accuracy for a relatively long time. To avoid brittle fracture under overloads, a maximum hardness of Rockwell C 50 is desirable.

Where the need for long life and good surface finish does not justify the cost of alloy steel dies, low-carbon steels such as 1010 or 1020 may be good alternative choices. In practice, a light coat of lubricating oil over the steel die surface after each forming operation will provide sufficient protection from rusting. In addition, steel dies should be dried and coated with oil at the end of each day's operation.

A castable alloy containing about 95% zinc and small amounts of aluminum and manganese has been widely used when the production quantity does not exceed 100 pieces.

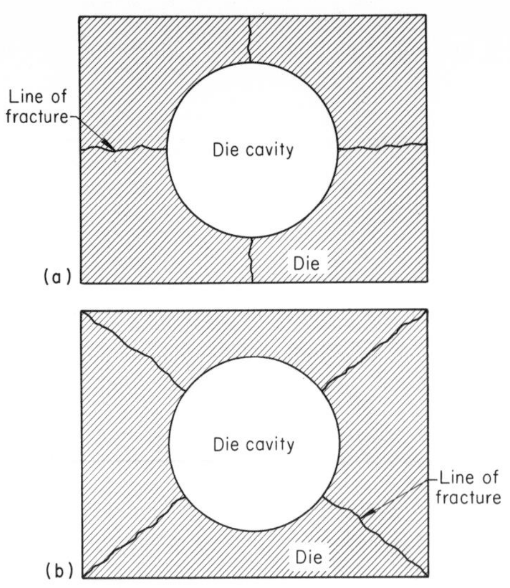

Fig. 7. Modes of fracture of a rectangular die under (a) *static load and* (b) *shock load*

Reinforced concrete has been considered for the construction of dies large enough to exceed the machining capabilities of all-metal dies. The ease of producing large concrete dies is a primary advantage. Disadvantages include low tensile strength of concrete.

Plaster has been used for one-shot dies. Because the rate of loading is very fast, the shape of the brittle die material is transferred to the metal surface before the die crumbles. Better results are produced if a plaster die is contained by a metal case so that the plaster is loaded in compression to the greatest extent possible. The case should be cylindrical, to minimize stress concentration.

Materials for Composite Dies. Epoxy facings have been used successfully on concrete dies. The epoxy may contain reinforcing glass cloth or may simply be a smoothing agent. Epoxy is easy to apply, provides a smooth surface, and, by minimizing shock-wave irregularities, helps to maintain a compressive-stress state in the concrete. Where heavy loading is encountered, the life of a plastic laminate is about 25 pieces before it starts to crack and needs to be replaced. Because replacement cost is low, this is not a serious disadvantage.

Since most concrete dies will withstand at least one impact without disintegrating, it is feasible to sweep a concrete die oversize by the thickness of a metal liner that is to be installed. The metal liner is installed by explosive forming it to the die, after which it serves as the die surface for subsequent forming operations. The two main advantages of this type of die construction are the ability to obtain a smooth die surface by polishing the liner in the flat before placing it in the die and the longer life the metal-lined die will have compared with the life of plastic-lined dies. After several shots, the concrete begins to pulverize behind the metal liner and causes progressively more dimensional variation with each formed piece after the first few.

The use of plastic laminates in zinc alloy dies of complex shapes will provide a considerable saving in diesinking time. The body of the zinc alloy die is cast roughly to shape, and then a plastic laminate made from a plaster matrix is seated in the die by backfilling with a resilient plastic.

Transmission Mediums

Most early work in explosive forming was done in air, which provided very high peak pressures for very short periods, usually a few microseconds. Consequently, the total impulse available for forming was less than that in a liquid medium, which provides slightly greater confinement of the charge and higher efficiency in terms of total impulse. The size of charge needed for forming a given part in water is approximately 80% smaller than the charge that would be needed if the part were formed in air.

Liquids. Water is one of the best mediums for explosive forming, because it is readily available in most locations, inexpensive to use, and produces excellent results. Because the energy absorbed by a medium is a direct function of its density, considerably more energy might be lost by waves transmitted through a liquid than through air. This loss of energy, however, is more than compensated for by the additional confinement of the explosive charge and the lengthening of the pulse due to the trapped energy. The net result is an increase in total impulse available in a liquid over that transmitted in a gas for the same charge size and standoff distance. When a charge is confined in a liquid medium and the charge is sufficiently far from the surface of the water, several pulses can be obtained as a result of the overexpansion and overcompression of the gas bubble from the explosive charge. The greater confinement of the explosive by the water evens out the pulse distribution and maintains a positive pressure for a period of milliseconds. Figure 8 shows pressure differences between water and air mediums, at various standoff distances, using a 4-lb charge of TNT.

Other liquids, such as oil, have been successfully used as transmission mediums. Depending on their density, they perform in the same general manner as water, but water is generally preferred because of easier handling. Higher-density liquids, such as mercury, are too expensive for general use.

Solid mediums, in the form of rubber sheets, cast plastics, or even metals, are sometimes used in explosive forming. Plastics and rubber improve the formability of some metals. The use of a plastic transmission medium has proved especially helpful in the close-tolerance sizing of tubing details.

Solid mediums give some protection to the surface of the part being formed. Sometimes, in liquid mediums or in air, small slivers of metal projected from the blasting cap, or from wire or other material used to attach the charge, may strike the surface of the blank and cause scrap. Difficulty is also sometimes experienced from slight irregularities in the shape of the explosive charge, which cause the formation of jets. The jet effect is smaller under water, and normally causes difficulty only at very small standoff distances. Probably one of the most beneficial characteristics of a solid medium is the uniform distribution of pressure over the surface of the part being formed.

Explosive forming of heated metals demands the use of some inexpensive medium that will maintain its characteristics at relatively high temperature and will not transmit much heat to the explosive charge. Several materials, including sand and small glass beads, have been used for this purpose. If sand is used, some buffer material should be placed over the blank to prevent the sand from embedding in the work metal or marking the surface.

Shock-Wave Transmission

Shock waves travel through a medium at the speed of sound. When a minimum of energy loss is desired at an interface between two different mediums, they should be selected to have a close acoustical impedance match. Since the acoustical impedance is a function of the density of the medium, as a first approximation, matching the densities of the mediums helps to increase the efficiency of the system.

The effect on the depth of draw of placing an intermediate medium, such as a sheet of rubber, over a blank is shown in Fig. 9. The increase in rubber thickness lowers the maximum depth of draw a given explosive charge will produce; but it may increase the over-all depth of draw the piece will tolerate, because of the improved distribution of forming stresses on the work metal. The use of a solid intermediate medium allows more material to draw from under the blankholder without wrinkling and without fracture of the cup at the apex.

The same reasoning applies for the impedance between the explosive charge and the medium in which it is detonated. By obtaining a reasonable impedance match between the explosive and the medium, only weak reflections occur between the explosive and the transmission medium; the stronger reflections occur at the surface of the medium container. If the container walls are shaped properly, the reflections can be used to reinforce the shock wave that strikes the workpiece. They may also be directed to areas of the workpiece that need greater amounts of energy for forming.

Forming of Sheet

Explosive forming has been used most widely for producing parts from sheet metal. For concentric shapes, the tooling and charge placement are relatively simple, and only a minimum of experience is needed to produce acceptable parts. Nonconcentric shapes, however, such as beaded panels, electrode forms, and other unsymmetrical shapes, involve techniques using uneven force distributions, shock-wave reflectors and shaped charges.

Tooling Considerations. For concentric parts, fairly simple techniques such as casting or turning can be used for the production of tools. The more complex dies used for nonconcentric parts necessitate hand finishing or profile milling. Special features can be incor-

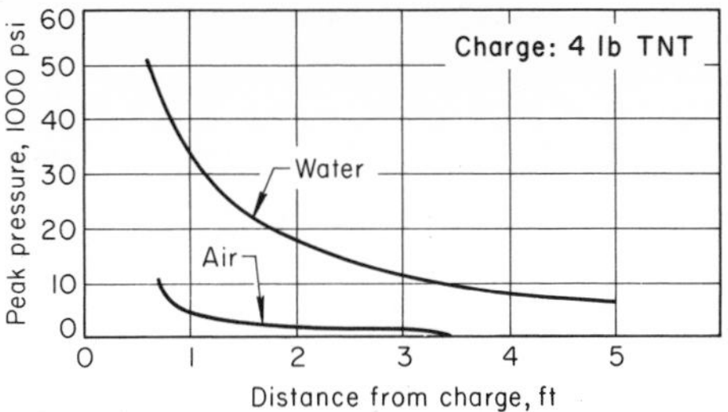

Fig. 8. Peak pressure versus standoff distance, for explosive charges fired in air and in water

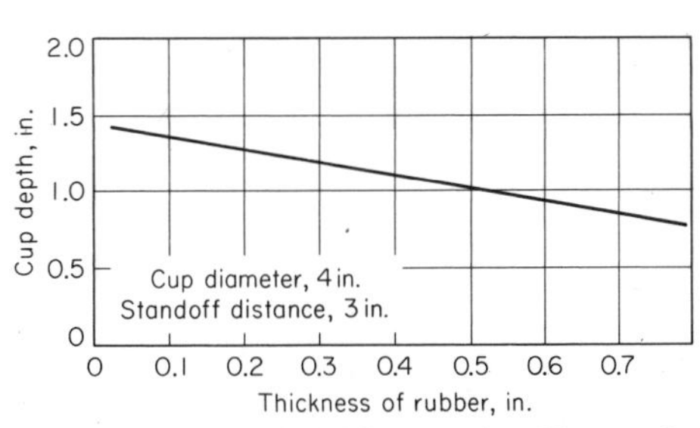

Fig. 9. Effect of thickness of rubber pad placed on blank on depth of draw of a 0.064-in.-thick PH 15-7 Mo stainless steel cup in explosive forming with 60 in. of 100-grain Primacord

porated in dies to control metal deformation and minimize buckling.

In simple drawing operations, buckling is prevented by the pressure applied to a blankholder. With concentric parts, an equal blankholder pressure is applied around the circumference, whereas with nonconcentric parts variations in blankholder pressure are needed to accommodate variations in depth of draw. Pressures can be estimated for concentric shapes, but a trial-and-error system must be used to establish the pressure patterns for nonconcentric shapes. In such systems, the blankholder pressure for the minimum depth of draw should be 2 to 4% less than for areas of maximum draw. Control of metal movement during forming can also be accomplished by using a bead around the die to induce more friction between the blank and die. This approach is much less flexible, particularly when a trial-and-error approach is used in the initial forming.

Forming of thin sheet metals can be assisted by slowly drawing a vacuum between the blank and the die and working out wrinkles with a plastic mallet as they form. This procedure represents partial forming, and often sufficient deformation is achieved so that only a light explosive charge is needed to complete the forming.

Tolerances as close as ± 0.001 in. have been met on small parts by explosive forming. However, working tolerances generally are ± 0.010 in. Variations are directly related to the amount of pressure applied in the forming operation. The use of plastic or rubber fillers over parts also has considerable bearing on the variations in workpieces. Since filler materials decrease the total pressure imposed on the part but maintain the pressure for a longer period of time, the increase in total impulse improves conformation to the die and minimizes springback. There are few applications in which explosive forming in steel dies cannot equal or better the dimensional stability of conventional forming.

Placement of Explosive Charges. Explosive forming operations usually require that the charges be at some standoff distance from the parts to be formed; a contact charge supplies a peak pressure so high that the blank may be ruptured. Positioning of the explosive charges can be performed by a number of techniques, provided several conditions are met: (*a*) the method of positioning should be substantial enough that immersion in a water tank for firing will not displace the charge, (*b*) the rigging for the charge should not break into flying projectiles that might damage the workpiece, and (*c*) any debris from the rigging should be easily recoverable from the water tank.

To meet these requirements, various types of rigging have been used. For large parts, small-gage wire is used, and generally is retrieved with the die. For smaller parts, masking tape is normally preferred for locating the charge, because it is easy to handle. Permanent steel rigging can also be used, provided the charge is separated from the rigging by at least 2 in. Cardboard tubes work well for separating the charge from the rigging if the tube is not immersed in the water longer than 5 min before the charge is fired. For longer immersion times, the tube should be sprayed with a plastic coating.

Often it is possible to obtain the same results with different types of charges. For instance, tank ends can be formed with a cylindrical charge or with an equal weight of Primacord wrapped on a cardboard tube. Similar results are obtained if the diameter of the Primacord does not exceed twice the diameter of the solid cylindrical charge. Consequently, when the supply of one type of explosive has been depleted, it is often possible to substitute another type that is on hand.

Special shapes of explosive charge are generally needed for the forming of nonconcentric shapes. The development of a special charge shape is difficult, and the shape is usually made by trial-and-error tests. Energy transmission to the part can also be varied through the use of a rubber blanket covering surface areas that need the least forming. The most widely used technique involves the use of several charges to work the metal into the die in steps.

Shock-wave reflectors are suitable for producing parts that need a deeper draw in one particular region. These reflectors become very complicated, however, if there is more than one such region in a part.

Economics of Explosive Sheet Forming. Simple shapes readily formed by conventional methods should not be considered for explosive forming; no economic advantage will be realized. More complex shapes, and metals with special properties (such as the work-hardening stainless steels), lend themselves to explosive forming. Size must also be taken into account; explosive forming can produce extremely large items that would be impractical to form by conventional methods.

Table 1 shows cost comparisons for the fabrication of five aircraft parts by

Table 1. Manufacturing Costs per Piece for Aircraft Parts Produced in Two Different Quantities by Conventional vs Explosive Forming

Part formed	Cost per piece in 100-piece lots, $ — Conventional forming	Explosive forming(a)	Increase or decrease by explosive forming, %	Cost per piece in 500-piece lots, $ — Conventional forming	Explosive forming(a)	Increase or decrease by explosive forming, %
Side-panel jet pod	80.64	89.91	+11.5	35.44	55.03	+55.3
		81.29	+0.8		49.23	+38.9
Collar-outlet housing	6.77	12.99	+91.9	2.18	6.12	+180.7
		10.79	+59.4		4.60	+111.0
Tailpipe ring	80.63	53.22	−34.0	38.40	21.68	−43.5
		50.72	−37.1		20.00	−47.9
Pan-fire shield	66.91	40.08	−40.1	22.80	19.19	−15.8
		36.19	−45.9		16.58	−27.3
Bellmouth engine tailpipe	161.47	133.54	−17.3	57.82	52.75	−8.8
		128.48	−20.4		49.34	−14.7

(a) First cost entry for each part is based on actual cost for experimental forming of the part; second cost entry is predicted cost of explosive forming as a production operation.

both explosive and conventional forming methods in sufficient quantity to establish cost information. Three of the parts examined were fabricated less expensively by explosive forming.

The number of pieces to be produced affects the relative economy. Although explosive forming often is applicable only to short production runs, as many as 20,000 pieces have been produced competitively by explosive forming.

Forming of Plate

Explosive forming of metal plate has been practical because presses large enough to form heavy plate generally are not available. Economic advantages are realized when a forming operation, prior to machining of thick parts, can reduce the subsequent machining time and the weight of raw material required. Explosives have been used to pierce holes in heavy shapes. This operation requires the use of a wave guide, with appropriately positioned and sized holes, over the workpiece.

Tooling Considerations. In order to support the higher loads required for explosive forming of metal plate, the tooling must be of heavier construction than that used in sheet forming. Usually, plates are not formed to close tolerances, particularly since they are often machined in a later operation. Forming is generally done in free-forming dies such as shown in Fig. 10.

Tolerances that can be met in explosive-formed plate materials are the same as those usually applied in explosive forming of sheet metal — that is, ±0.010 in. Ordinarily, considerably greater tolerances than this are allowed on parts that are to be machined subsequently. With free-formed plate materials, variations as great as ±0.250 in. have been considered acceptable.

Placement of explosive charges for plate forming is similar to that for sheet forming, except for the scaled-up size of the tooling, workpiece and explosive charges. Since water is the preferred transmission medium in these operations, the operations must be performed in large water tanks; or, if firing is aboveground, a large water bag can be used. In each approach, the explosive energy is transmitted to the workpiece through water.

Because of the relatively simple shapes involved in plate forming, charge shapes and placement are less complex. Normally, centrally located charges and ring charges positioned at the desired standoff distances are used.

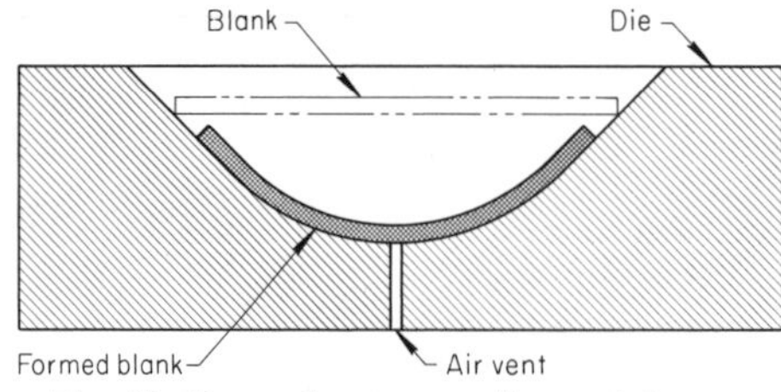

Fig. 10. Tapered-entrance die used for explosive forming of plate without a blankholder

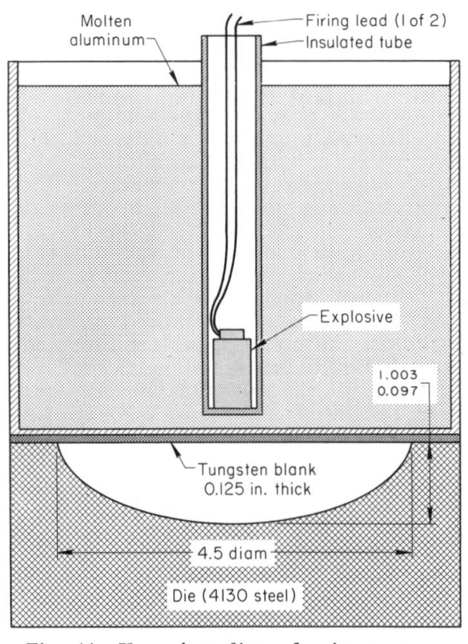

Fig. 11. Use of molten aluminum as a medium in elevated-temperature explosive forming of tungsten

Table 2. Costs for Forming Aircraft Skin Sections by Explosive Forming vs Two Conventional Methods (a)

Cost item	Cost per piece — Bulging	Shear spinning	Explosive forming
Work metal	$0.89	$1.00	$0.77
Tooling	3.60	1.00	2.40
Facilities	2.30	4.00	1.00
Total	$6.79	$6.00	$4.17

(a) Skin sections, 31 in. long, 12 in. in diameter at one end, and 5 in. in diameter at the other end, were formed from aluminum alloys 6061 and 5086.

Forming of Tubes

Explosive forces have been used successfully in tube-forming operations. This process has allowed the formation of many unique tubular shapes by beading and bulging the initial workpieces in selected areas.

Tooling Considerations. To facilitate removal of the completed tubular workpieces, it is necessary to use either split dies or split tapered die inserts, depending on the particular part to be formed. The use of split dies makes evacuation more difficult than with single dies, in that rubber seals are necessary between the die halves. The parting line between the die segments will often leave undesirable marks on the formed parts. This marking effect can be reduced either by reducing the explosive charge and increasing the number of shots, or by increasing the clamping forces on the die halves.

Some control of the amount of bulging can be attained through the use of end plugs to apply some restraining force to prevent drawing from the ends of the tube. This precaution can be critical in thin-gage tubing, which may wrinkle if the ends of the tube are not restrained.

Shock-wave reflectors can be incorporated in the tooling for explosive forming. They find best applications in tooling for nonconcentric shapes or where re-entrant angles are desired. With the use of special reflectors, the charge can be placed at one end of the tube, and a reflector can be placed inside the tube to concentrate the shock wave in certain areas. Very large bulges (350% of tube diameter) have been produced with the use of reflectors, intermediate anneals, and step-forming operations. The reflectors can vary considerably in design, ranging from a solid filler with an angled cut (to concentrate the energy on one side of the tube) to exponential shapes for re-entrant angles.

Tolerances as small as ±0.001 in. have been held in forming of small-diameter tubes, but tolerances of the order of ±0.010 in. are more generally accepted. Extremely close tolerances demand the construction of heavy, accurate dies that will withstand repeated heavy loading in production of the desired parts.

Placement of Explosive Charges. The setup for forming generally requires the use of line charges placed on the centerline of the tube. Alignment of the charge is critical, because the tube provides some reflective characteristics to the shock wave, and misalignment can cause higher pressures in the side of the tube closest to the charge. A rigid plastic tube can be used to cover the explosive charge and to keep it in line.

Normally, a die is necessary when a specific contour is wanted. Simple bulges can be formed in heavy-wall tubes without a die, but tolerances cannot be held closely, either on diameter or on the contour of the bulge.

Application. The sound-suppressor tubes used on all commercial jet aircraft represent an application that has involved the production of more than 10,000 pieces. The main economic advantage in this application is derived from the close tolerances that can be held, as well as the elimination of brazing and other manual operations normally required for the assembly of conventionally formed tubes.

Forming of Welded Sheet-Metal Preforms

Explosive forming has been used in forming components from welded preforms. Such preforms are necessary when the initial tube size is larger than that obtainable commercially, or when a specialized starting shape is needed. Because subsequent forming operations will be conducted, it is necessary that good-quality, ductile welds be made in preform fabrication. Generally, the welds are planished and the preforms are annealed prior to forming. Also, when possible, the welds are located in areas where minimum stretching is expected, to reduce the possibility of weld failure during forming.

Tooling Considerations. The size of part may limit the use of split dies and also limit the process to applications in which natural draft will permit removal of the part from the die. No other special considerations are necessary for tools except for forming of thin parts that may wrinkle when a vacuum is applied between the preform and the die. Wrinkles can be avoided by the use of sandwich blanks, or they can be removed by hammering with a mallet if they form during the time the vacuum is applied.

Tolerances for parts explosive formed from welded sheet can be held to ±0.010 in., although a more practical tolerance of ±0.032 in. is normally specified. The higher forces that would be necessary to meet closer tolerances would shorten die life and increase die costs for a given production run. Close tolerances also require a higher degree of weld finishing prior to forming.

Placement of Explosive Charges. The type and placement of explosive charges in forming welded sheet assemblies depends on the final shape of the part desired. Line charges positioned at the axis of the assembly are used for long right-cylindrical shapes. With a cone-shape part, a point charge located near the base of the cone may be preferable.

Economics of Forming Welded Assemblies. Economic advantages that may be realized in explosive forming of welded sheet-metal assemblies depend on the complexity of the part design and the number and types of operations needed in conventional fabrication. In addition, characteristics of the work metal such as ease of forming, welding and machining will influence the comparison. One economic comparison concerning the forming of welded aluminum alloy sheet preforms is summarized in Table 2. This comparison, which involved bulging, shear spinning and explosive forming, shows that explosive forming was the least expensive method for the application.

Explosive Forming of Heated Blanks

Refractory metals like tungsten are explosive formed with better results when the blanks are heated. The arrangement shown in Fig. 11 was used to form a dome from tungsten sheet that was heated to 1250 F. Molten aluminum was used as the transmission medium.

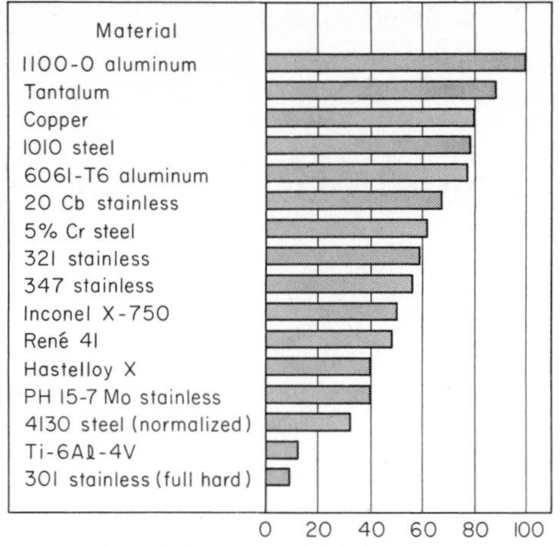

Comparison is based on forming of 0.032-in.-thick material, with explosive at 15-in. standoff distance. All metals were annealed unless indicated otherwise.

Fig. 12. Formability of various metals by explosive forming, relative to that of aluminum alloy 1100-O

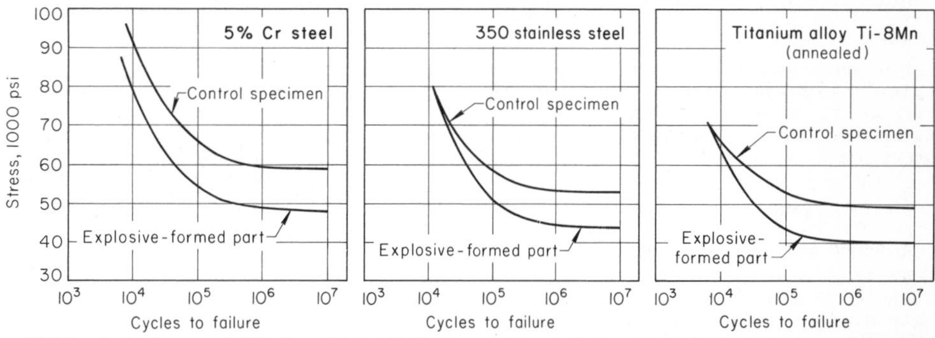

Metals tested were 0.025 in. thick. Fatigue specimens were taken from explosive-formed parts that had been stretched about 7%. The formed parts were heat treated after forming, then explosive-sized before fatigue specimens were removed for testing; about 1% stretch was produced in sizing. Control specimens were taken from the materials before forming.

Fig. 13. Decrease in fatigue strength of three different metals as a result of explosive forming

The explosive, a 12-gram charge of composition C-4 explosive (detonation velocity, 26,400 ft per sec; supplier, U.S. Government) was protected by an insulated tube to avoid premature explosion. The die was constructed from 4130 steel. A dome 4.5 in. in diameter by 1 in. high was formed within a tolerance of ±0.003 in. in one shot.

Formability

In normal explosive forming operations, the major characteristics of the work metal that determine formability are ductility and toughness. It is general practice not to exceed the elongation, as determined by tension testing, in forming a part from the same metal. Toughness criteria cannot be as readily applied, because forming represents biaxial and triaxial stressing, as compared with uniaxial stressing in the tension test. Also, the design of tooling can influence the apparent formability of a material.

Comparisons of formability of various materials by explosive forming are subject to the particular experimental design under which they are tested. As a result, absolute values of formability are not obtained, but relative behavior for use in other explosive forming operations can be established. A comparison of the formability of some metals, using annealed aluminum alloy 1100 as a basis, is shown in Fig. 12. The apparent formabilities shown can be increased through modified tooling design in other operations. Also, increasing the forming temperature will provide obvious forming advantages.

Data indicating that explosive working lowers the fatigue strength of materials are shown in Fig. 13.

Safety

In and around an explosive forming facility, any fire-producing or spark-producing equipment must be eliminated. Precautions should include the collection of all matches and lighters from any person entering any building where explosives are present. During operations, only persons absolutely necessary for carrying out the operations should be present.

Misfires during an operation are extremely hazardous and time-consuming. Precautions should be taken to make sure that an electrical short circuit does not occur during the immersion of the setup for firing in the water tank. Incorrect placement of the blasting cap or improper size of blasting cap may cause failure of the charge to explode when the cap detonates.

Precautions to be taken if the firing circuit has been energized and the charge does not go off include a check of the continuity of the circuit. If the circuit is good, another attempt should be made to fire the charge. If this fails, the firing circuit should be disconnected from the power source and the power source tested for proper output. If no failure is found in the power source, the lead wires in the firing circuit can be inspected visually from a distance to determine if any shorts have occurred. Under no circumstances should the charge be brought to the surface for examination until 15 min has elapsed from the last time attempts were made to fire the charge. All personnel should leave the area during this waiting period. After the specified time has elapsed, the charge should be brought to the surface and a new cap installed.

When defective blasting caps are found, they should be destroyed with any other scrap explosive at the close of operations each working day.

Electromagnetic Forming (EMF)

By David F. Brower*

ELECTROMAGNETIC forming, also known as magnetic pulse forming, is a process for forming metal by the direct application of an intense, transient magnetic field. The workpiece is formed without mechanical contact by the passage of a pulse of electric current through a forming coil.

The major application of EMF is for the single-step assembly of tubular parts to each other or to other components; it is used to a lesser extent for the shaping of tubular parts and the shallow forming of flat stock. Metals with high electrical conductivity are formed directly; poorly conductive metals are formed with the aid of highly conductive "drivers". Process characteristics that determine the applicability of EMF are listed in Table 1.

The basic process is covered by U. S. Patent 2,976,907, issued to G. W. Harvey and D. F. Brower in 1958; additional patents cover various aspects of the process and equipment.

Process Description

A very intense magnetic field that lasts only a few microseconds is produced by the discharge of a bank of capacitors into a coil called the forming coil. The resulting eddy currents induced in a conductive workpiece interact with the magnetic field to cause mutual repulsion between the workpiece and the forming coil. The force of this repulsion accelerates the workpiece against a die or a mandrel with enough stored energy to stress the work metal far beyond its yield strength. The reaction to this shaping force is sustained by the forming coil, which must therefore be stiff and strong enough to withstand such forces.

Basic Circuit. Figure 1 shows the basic circuit for EMF, as used for compression forming of a tubular workpiece. It consists of a forming coil, an energy-storage capacitor, switches, and a power supply of nearly constant current to charge the capacitor.

Figure 1(a) shows the flux-density pattern of the magnetic field produced by discharging the capacitor through the forming coil in the absence of an electrically conductive workpiece. The evenly spaced flux lines indicate a uniform flux density within the coil.

Figure 1(b) shows the change in field pattern that results when the capacitor is discharged through a forming coil in which a tubular workpiece of highly conductive metal has been inserted. The magnetic field is distorted and the flux density intensified by confinement to the small annular space between the coil and the workpiece (flux lines are more closely spaced).

*Manager of Magneform Department, Gulf General Atomic, Incorporated.

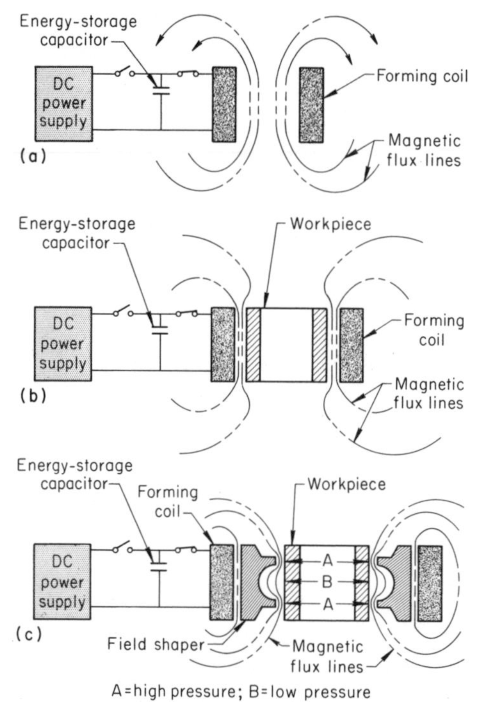

(a) Field pattern in absence of workpiece. (b) Field pattern with workpiece in forming coil. (c) Field pattern when field shaper is used.

Fig. 1. Basic circuit and magnetic field patterns for electromagnetic compression forming of a tubular workpiece

Duration of Pulse. The resistance that the workpiece offers to the magnetic field as a result of its eddy-current fields causes a net pressure on the surface of the workpiece. As the surface moves inward under the influence of this pressure, it absorbs energy from the magnetic field to do the work of forming.

In spite of the resistance of the eddy currents, in time the magnetic field permeates the workpiece, and the forming force drops to zero. In order to apply most of the available energy to forming, and the least possible fraction to permeating the workpiece material (which wastes energy by resistance heating), the forming pulse is kept short. In most forming applications, pulses have a duration of between 10 and 100 microseconds.

Field Shapers. For efficient use of stored energy, coils are designed to minimize stray inductance and to avoid flux concentrations. Field patterns are ordinarily controlled with field shapers, which are massive current-carrying conductors. Field shapers are not necessarily directly connected to the basic coil, but they may be inductively coupled to it.

Figure 1(c) illustrates the use of a field shaper to concentrate the force in certain regions of the workpiece. This technique not only produces high local forming pressures in desired areas, but also lengthens the life of the forming coil by preventing high pressures on weaker parts of the coil.

In the following example, a field shaper was used to concentrate the forming force where it was needed, and to limit it where fragile areas of the workpiece could have been damaged by it. The forming pressure along the length of a workpiece is easily con-

Table 1. Characteristics of EMF That Determine Its Applicability

1 Pressure is applied directly to the workpiece through the medium of the magnetic field, so that forming entails no physical contact. Since the magnetic field will pass through electrical nonconductors, forming can be done through a nonmetallic coating or container.

2 In contrast to most metal-forming processes, most of the forming takes place after the pressure impulse has ended. The metal is rapidly accelerated, gaining a large amount of kinetic energy by moving only a short distance during the impulse. This kinetic energy subsequently does the actual work of forming.

3 Only metals having relatively high electrical conductivity, such as copper, aluminum, carbon steel, brass and molybdenum, are efficiently formed by EMF. Metals with lower conductivity, such as stainless steel, can be formed by using an intermediate highly conductive "driver".

4 The ratio of the masses of pieces involved in assembly operations may be much more significant than their relative mechanical strength or their elastic properties. Since no static forces are involved in EMF, relatively light structures can be used for supporting the dies.

5 The magnetic field behaves much like a compressed gas. It exerts a uniform pressure that is relatively independent of variations in spacing between the workpiece and the forming coil. In swaging and expanding operations, no torque is applied to the workpiece, such as would be encountered in spinning and rolling.

6 The contact between the magnetic field and the workpiece is frictionless, so no lubricant is needed.

7 Although the pressure that can be applied by the magnetic pulse can be very high in comparison with the average pressure in mechanical forming, the peak pressure is limited by the strength of the forming-coil material to much lower values than are commonly encountered in shearing, punching and upsetting.

8 The magnetic field cannot be easily "shaped" to fit all workpiece contours. In general, it is impossible to apply a high pressure in an arbitrarily chosen area while applying a low pressure in immediately adjacent areas.

9 Being purely electromagnetic, the process is not limited in repetition rate by the mechanical inertia of moving parts. The timing of the magnetic impulse can be synchronized with microsecond precision, and machines can be made to function at repetition rates of thousands of operations per minute. The strength of the magnetic impulse can be controlled electrically with high precision.

trolled in this way; however, controlled variation of the pressure around the circumference is not always possible.

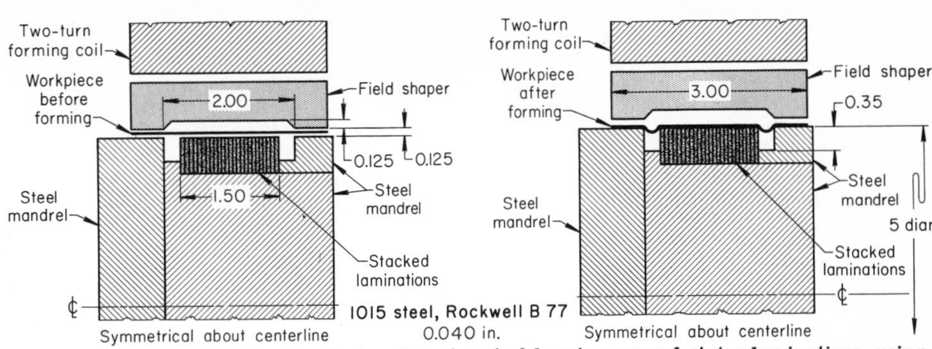

Fig. 2. Setup for electromagnetic forming of a steel housing around stator laminations, using a field shaper (Example 334)

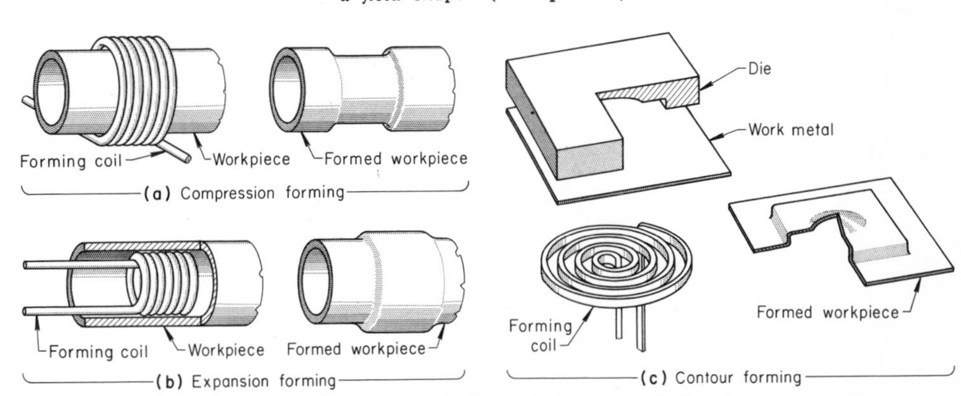

Fig. 3. Three basic methods of electromagnetic forming

Example 334. Use of a Field Shaper in Forming of a Stator Housing Over Stacked Laminations (Fig. 2)

The housing for the stator assembly of an electric motor was formed in place, as shown in Fig. 2. The steel outer band (the workpiece) was compressed onto the stacked laminations and shaped to conform to the supporting mandrel in a single EMF operation. The laminations were bound rigidly in place without the use of rivets or bolts; simultaneously, grooves (for mounting end bell housings) were formed precisely concentric with the inner surface of the laminations.

About 40 kilojoules of energy was needed, because of the high pressure required for forming the grooves. Because such a high pressure would have deformed the laminations, a field shaper was built into the coil (see Fig. 2). The pressure along the length of the workpiece in this arrangement varied approximately in inverse proportion to the square of the spacing.

In trial runs, difficulty was experienced with field leakage through the coil housing into the laminations when using a standard compression coil of the type shown in Fig. 9. To solve this problem, a special two-turn coil that provided a higher frequency was constructed.

The assembly shown in Fig. 2 was produced with this experimental tooling at a rate of 240 per hour, using manual loading and unloading. The forming was done in a 48-kilojoule machine.

Similar assemblies were mass produced at a rate of 600 per hour in a 48-kilojoule machine equipped with semiautomatic feed. Machine cost, including the feed mechanism, was about $80,000. At $10 per hour, direct labor plus overhead would cost $0.016 per assembly in this operation. If the $80,000 capital cost of the forming machine were amortized over one million operations, this would amount to an additional $0.08 per assembly, for a total of $0.096 per assembly.

Forming Methods and Coil Types. Typical forming with the three basic types of coil used for compression, expansion and contour forming is shown schematically in Fig. 3. A tubular workpiece is compressed by an external coil, as shown in Fig. 3(a), usually against a grooved or suitably contoured insert, plug, tube or fitting inside the workpiece. A tubular workpiece is expanded by an internal coil, as shown in Fig. 3(b), usually against a collar or other component surrounding the workpiece. Flat stock is almost always contour formed against a die, as indicated in Fig. 3(c).

Workpiece Design. In addition to being an electrical conductor (resistivity not greater than 15 microhm-cm), the workpiece must provide a continuous electrical path. The current in a tubular workpiece flows around the circumference. Therefore, if a tubular workpiece were slit through its length, as shown in Fig. 4(a), the interference with the current flow would reduce and distort the forming forces.

Figure 4(b) shows a tubular workpiece containing perforations, and a cut at one end that is at an angle with the axis. Such minor irregularities do not seriously interfere with the current flow, and are acceptable under many conditions. Deep slots in the end of tubes, such as those shown in Fig. 4(c), interfere with the current flow in such a way as to produce uneven pressure on the work metal.

Workpieces other than uniform tubular shapes or flat blanks usually have to be formed with specially designed

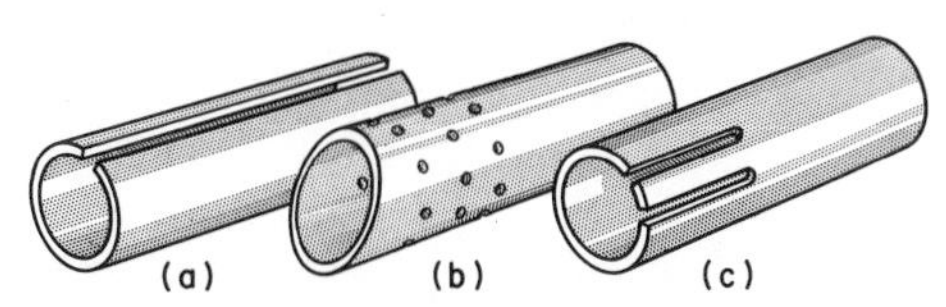

(a) Full-length slit. (b) Perforations and angular cut. (c) Partial-length slots.

Fig. 4. Design aspects of tubular workpieces that affect applicability of EMF. See text.

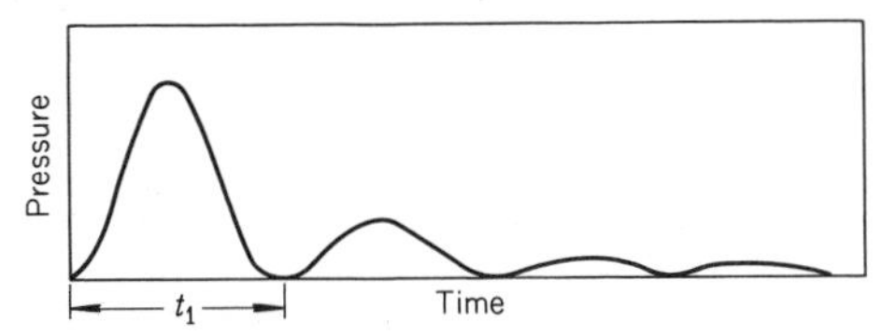

Fig. 5. Typical pressure wave form in EMF

field shapers that can be opened or expanded, and the time for loading and unloading is greatly increased.

Principles

Because of the short duration of the magnetic impulse, the pressure must be high enough to impart sufficient kinetic energy to the workpiece during the pulse to do the desired forming. Any resistance to the motion of the workpiece during the impulse reduces the amount of useful forming energy transferred. Accordingly, for high efficiency, the peak pressure should be several times that necessary to exceed the static yield strength of the workpiece and to overcome any other constraints for the duration of the impulse.

Pressure Wave Form. A forming coil is, electrically, an inductor in series with a small amount of resistance. When an energy-storage capacitor discharges through such a coil, the discharge is a momentary oscillating current. The frequency of this oscillation is often called the "ringing frequency" by electrical engineers. This oscillating current has a damped sine-wave form. The frequency is inversely proportional to the square root of the product of the capacitance of the storage bank and the inductance of the coil. The rate of decrease of the amplitude of the pulse is proportional to the resistance of the coil circuit. The pressure produced by the coil is proportional to the square of this current; thus, the pressure pulse is entirely positive and approximates a damped sine square form, as illustrated in Fig. 5.

Most of the forming energy is provided by the first wave; succeeding waves transmit less energy to the workpiece because of their lower energy content and because of the progressively widening gap between coil and workpiece as forming takes place. The portion of the energy of the electrical discharge that is not transferred to the workpiece as kinetic or deformation energy appears as resistance heating.

An energy discharge or pulse can be characterized by its peak pressure, which is that of the first wave, and by the duration of the first wave (Fig. 5). The time between successive waves changes slightly as the workpiece moves (changing the inductance of the coil) and as heating changes the resistance of the electrical circuit. However, these effects are ordinarily negligible.

Peak pressure is approximately related to other process variables as follows:

1 Directly proportional to the energy of the electrical impulse from the capacitor bank
2 Inversely proportional to the resistivity of workpiece and coil
3 Inversely proportional to the total of the volume of the workpiece and the field shaper penetrated by the electromagnetic field (skin effect) and the volume between the coil and workpiece surfaces.

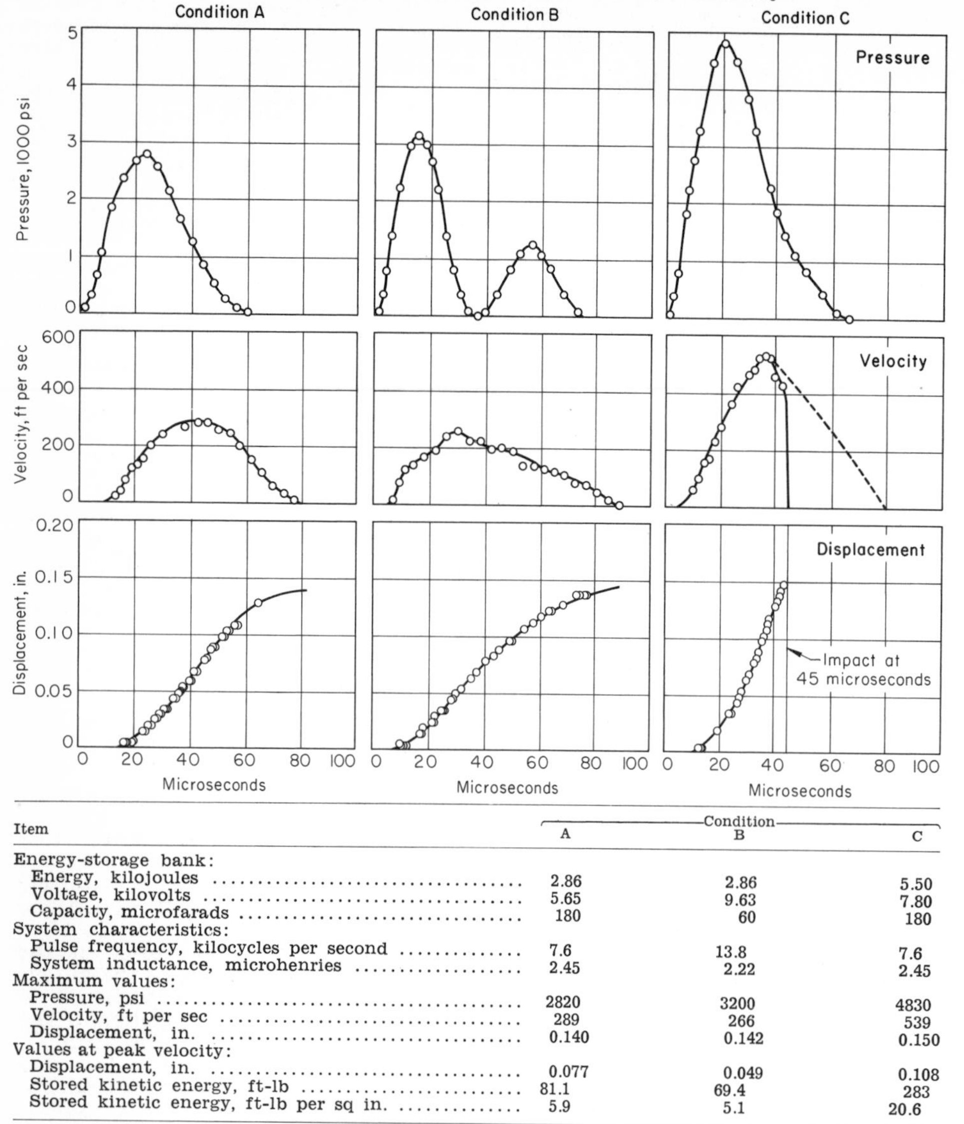

Item	Condition A	Condition B	Condition C
Energy-storage bank:			
Energy, kilojoules	2.86	2.86	5.50
Voltage, kilovolts	5.65	9.63	7.80
Capacity, microfarads	180	60	180
System characteristics:			
Pulse frequency, kilocycles per second	7.6	13.8	7.6
System inductance, microhenries	2.45	2.22	2.45
Maximum values:			
Pressure, psi	2820	3200	4830
Velocity, ft per sec	289	266	539
Displacement, in.	0.140	0.142	0.150
Values at peak velocity:			
Displacement, in.	0.077	0.049	0.108
Stored kinetic energy, ft-lb	81.1	69.4	283
Stored kinetic energy, ft-lb per sq in.	5.9	5.1	20.6

The broken line on the velocity curve for condition C shows the calculated continuing velocity if there had been no impact against the steel frame at 45 microseconds.

Fig. 6. Changes in forming pressure, workpiece velocity and workpiece displacement during electromagnetic expansion forming of identical tubes under three different conditions. See text headed "Typical Forming Cycles", for discussion.

The effect of workpiece size and electrical resistivity on peak pressure is discussed later in this article, in the section "Typical Energy Relations".

Wave duration for the first wave in a pressure pulse in the idealized situation is inversely proportional to the ringing frequency of the system: $t_1 = 1/(2f)$.

Also, to a close approximation:

$$t_1 = k\left(\frac{Cds}{l}\right)^{1/2}$$

where k is a proportionality constant, C is the capacitance of the energy-storage bank, d is the diameter of the workpiece (for the surface adjacent to the coil), l is the working length of the workpiece (width of coil), and s is the thickness of flux pattern between coil and workpiece (including skin depth of workpiece and field shaper). Thus, the wave duration increases with increasing capacitance of energy bank, diameter of workpiece nearest the coil, and spacing between coil and workpiece, but decreases with increasing length of workpiece.

The skin depth in workpiece and field shaper increases with the increasing wave duration.

Typical Forming Cycles. Figure 6 shows the forming pressure, workpiece velocity, and workpiece displacement as measured during the expansion forming of identical aluminum alloy tubes under three different combinations of conditions (detailed as conditions A, B and C in the table accompanying Fig. 6).

Only the first pressure wave is shown for condition A in Fig. 6; the second wave was not measurable in this forming operation. Although the maximum pressure was reached in 23 microseconds, maximum velocity was not attained until 44 microseconds had elapsed, and most of the deformation or displacement of the workpiece occurred after the pressure had dropped below its peak value.

In forming under condition B, the first two pressure waves were significant, and are shown in Fig. 6. The lower capacity and higher voltage of the electrical discharge (as compared with those of condition A) resulted in a higher but narrower first pressure wave, a lower maximum velocity, and a smaller amount of stored kinetic energy on reaching peak velocity.

However, because the electrical energy input for condition B was the same as for condition A, and the efficiency was nearly equal for the two forming operations, the displacement curve differed only slightly, and the total displacement of the workpiece wall was nearly the same.

Condition C in Fig. 6 represents a forming operation in which free forming took place until impact, after 45 microseconds, against an unyielding cylindrical steel frame ½ in. thick that surrounded the workpiece. In this operation, a higher input voltage charged the capacitor bank to nearly twice the level used in condition A. Thus, the capacitor discharge produced higher maximum pressure and workpiece velocity, and therefore more stored kinetic energy, at peak velocity. The kinetic energy of the rapidly moving workpiece was not used gradually to do continuing unrestricted forming (as in conditions A and B), but was used to impact the workpiece against the steel frame. The braking influence of entrapped air caused a rapid drop in velocity just before impact, as shown. The broken-line extension of the velocity curve shows the calculated continuing velocity of the wall of the cylinder in the absence of the steel frame.

Energy Sources

In ordinary applications, the power supply may need to deliver almost instantaneous power of 1000 megawatts to the forming coil. Because this much power cannot be drawn directly from the usual industrial power supplies, specially designed energy sources are needed.

Flywheel-generator combinations, inductors and batteries have been used for energy storage and pulse discharge. For EMF applications, however, capacitor banks have been the most satisfactory means of energy storage.

To charge the capacitor bank, alternating current is converted to high-voltage direct current by a suitable power supply or charging circuit. The charging rate must be fast enough to charge the capacitor bank in an interval not less than the desired repetition rate for the pulse discharge, which is usually about 4 to 30 per minute, but may be much higher. (Repetition rates of 250 to 1000 operations per minute have been used in production, and a rate of 10,000 operations per minute is considered feasible.)

For maximum energy transfer to the coil during the impulse, internal resistance and inductance in the power supply must be kept to a minimum.

Capacitor Banks. Oil-filled paper dielectric capacitors can store energy at a density of over 1200 joules per cubic foot. At this level they will average many millions of charge-discharge cycles before failure, if used in properly designed equipment. The life of energy-storage capacitors depends on the peak dielectric stress, the amount of stress reversal, the length of time spent under a high stress, and the peak current. By considering these variables and applying a suitable factor of safety, the equipment designer controls capacitor life. Economic considerations determine optimum life.

Standard commercial electromagnetic forming machines have capacitor-bank energy sources rated at 6 to 84 kilojoules. Units with capacity greater than 12 kilojoules are designed on a modular basis in increments of 12 kilojoules. Characteristics of typical energy sources are listed in Table 2.

Because production rates with manual loading and unloading are generally about 200 to 600 pieces per hour, machines for this type of operation are designed for pulse repetition rates in this range. The faster pulse repetition rate desired for use with automatic work-handling equipment is readily obtained, however, as it is limited only by the characteristics of the charging circuit and the rate at which the components of the system dissipate heat.

Standard machines use banks of capacitors that are rated at 3 kilojoules, but ordinarily operate at a maximum level of 2 kilojoules. The peak current per capacitor is 35 kiloamperes. At this level, the life expectancy is several million charge-discharge cycles. Each capacitor is switched into a parallel-plate bus (or low-inductance co-axial cable) system through individual molybdenum-anode ignitrons specially designed for pulse service. The capacitors are charged through a constant-current rectifier system.

The energy stored in the bank is precisely measured by a voltage-metering circuit. When the preset energy level is reached, the charging cycle is terminated and the switches (ignitrons) are triggered, either automatically or by an outside pulse, to discharge the capacitors into the forming coil. The storage systems are designed to have very low internal inductance, so that the maximum energy is transferred to the forming coil during the impulse. The internal inductance of a typical 60-kilojoule storage unit is about 35 nanohenries.

The maintenance of control circuits and charging circuits using solid-state components is comparable to that required in other industrial equipment of moderate to low complexity. When extreme reliability is required, all solid-state devices, and no electromechanical parts (such as relays), are used.

The average life of a capacitor at a cycling rate of 600 operations per hour at maximum energy is about three million operations. At reduced energy levels, capacitor life is much longer.

Switches and transmission lines must have very low resistance and inductance. Switches must be capable of handling voltages of about 10 kilovolts and currents of many kiloamperes. If more than one switch is used in the discharge circuit, they must be capable of being synchronized within less than 1 microsecond.

Although spark gaps and vacuum switches have been used as switches, ignitrons specially designed for the desired switching rate, capacity and synchronization are preferred for reliability, long life, compactness and freedom from noise. (Ignitrons are mercury-pool ignition-controlled rectifiers of a type commonly used in welding machines and in the control of electric motors. They use a trigger circuit to ionize mercury, which conducts the current.)

Table 2. Characteristics of Typical Commercial Energy Sources for EMF

Characteristic	Maximum energy output of source, kilojoules 6	12	60
Current pulse:			
Peak current, kiloamperes	100	200	1000
Peak voltage, kilovolts	8.3	8.3	8.3
Repetition rate, cycles per hour:			
At maximum energy setting	600	600	600
At low energy setting	1800	1800	1800

Ignitrons have a life of one to two million operations at moderate loading and about 500,000 operations at maximum rated energy and repetition rates. Ignitrons must be selected for the desired voltage and peak current and for the desired repetition rate. An ignitron capable of switching a given average load at a rate of 600 per hour might be completely incapable of handling that average load at a rate of 3600 per hour.

A variety of terminal arrangements and semiflexible cable connections are employed to adapt standard machines to different forming coils and auxiliary equipment.

Coils and Field Shapers

The three basic types of coils for compression, expansion and contour forming are shown in Fig. 3. The principle of the field shaper is shown in Fig. 1, and the use of a field shaper in a compression forming application is described in Example 334.

The three primary factors in the design of coils and field shapers are size, electrical characteristics, and strength. The theory of their design is extremely complex, and material and construction requirements are highly critical, because forming coils must accept the repetitive discharge of large amounts of electrical energy in pulses lasting only 10 to 100 microseconds and must generate uniform forming pressures as high as 50,000 psi.

Moderate to short-run compression and expansion operations are done with convenience, versatility and economy by using interchangeable field shapers with standard coils. For long production runs, coils with fixed-field shapers provide greater efficiency and durability. A variety of coils of standardized designs are available. Specially designed coils are more expensive.

Depending on the type and the application, coils can serve for a few hundred thousand up to several million operations before repair or replacement is required.

Size. The diameter of the section of the workpiece to be formed determines the diameter of the working surface of the field shaper, or of the coil when a shaper is not used.

Clearance of about 0.050 in. per side ordinarily is needed for insulation and work insertion and removal. For maximum efficiency the clearance is kept as small as possible, because the effective force varies inversely with the square of the clearance distance.

Coils for workpieces of large diameter, using moderate pressure, are usually the easiest to design and build. This is particularly true of expansion coils (like the one used in Example 335), where the large diameter allows room for supporting structures and cooling arrangements.

Usually, much less pressure is needed for the forming of large sheet or tubular structures than for forming small ones. Solenoid coils without field shapers function well for applications requiring a relatively low pressure over large areas; they are both durable and efficient.

Relatively inexpensive coils that can be placed in or over the workpiece can sometimes be used to form exceptionally large parts. A special coil of this type was used to form 50-in.-diam magnesium cylinders. A single turn sawed from ½-in.-thick aluminum plate served as an expansion coil for resizing the cylinder at a circumferential weld. Similar coils could be used to form ridges or flanges on the ends of large cylinders.

Simply constructed special coils several feet in diameter have been used also for forming flat parts.

Electrical Characteristics. To avoid loss of efficiency through excessive resistance heating, and to avoid damagingly high temperatures and temperature gradients, coil materials are usually restricted to metals having electrical resistivity not greater than about 30 microhm-cm. The total impedance of the coil (capacitance plus inductance plus resistance) must be great enough to protect the capacitance bank from too rapid a discharge.

Mechanical Strength. Coils usually are of multiturn design, with sufficient mass and strength to withstand repeated forming impacts. Mechanical strength is more important than conductivity for those parts of the coil that directly sustain the reaction to the forming force, although the materials also should have a resistivity no greater than 15 microhm-cm.

An average forming force as high as 50,000 psi is produced on the surface of the workpiece in a pressure pulse lasting 10 to 100 microseconds, and the reaction to this forming force must be sustained by the coil. Accordingly, the coil not only must be strong enough to sustain the repeated thrusts of forming energy, but also should be as massive and rigid as possible, in order to minimize its deflection under load.

The problem of building coils to withstand high load is distinctly different in each of the three basic types of coil. Because there are no stringent volume restrictions on compression coils, they can be strong and massive, regardless of the size of the workpiece.

Although simple coils like those shown in Fig. 3(a) can be used alone, in practice the coil ordinarily receives additional support from a metallic "coil body" (usually of beryllium copper) and an insulating structure (see Fig. 7, 8 and 9), which are needed for safe and efficient handling and for the efficient use of electrical energy. With such coils, the ultimate limit to the pressure that can be repetitively applied probably depends on the strength of the coil members that carry high-density current, and on the strength of their supporting structures, if any.

Expansion coils must fit inside the workpiece, and thus the space to provide a strong structure is restricted. In small-diameter coils (Fig. 3b), the conductors must be relatively small in cross section to allow space for the return flux, and the conductors must be supported by an insulating mandrel. The force that can be exerted by these coils is limited ultimately by the strength of the mandrel.

Some flat spiral coils (Fig. 3c) also depend on the strength of an insulating backing to give the conductors support, so that the peak force they can exert depends mainly on the strength of the support. Other contour-forming coils have been made with massive construction; these have the same load limitations as mentioned for compression coils.

To be capable of exerting high force, coils must be designed so that unnecessary field (pressure) concentrations are avoided. Careful tailoring of the field distribution over the coil conductors is an essential part of the design of a high-pressure coil..

The results of short-term tests of coils can be misleading, because the mass of the conductor and the short duration of the pulse limit the amount of energy that can be absorbed during a single cycle. Thus, a relatively weak but massive coil conductor structure may show no sign of failure after several forming operations, but may fail suddenly after only two or three additional cycles.

General-Purpose Compression Coil. Figure 7 shows a type of compression coil designed for ruggedness and versatility in medium-pressure applications on tubular parts up to 4 in. in diameter. The coil has interchangeable field shapers of beryllium copper, each designed for a specific workpiece.

In this 6-kilojoule compression coil, the primary conductor (A in Fig. 7) is made of 0.250-in.-OD by 0.060-in.-thick copper tubing insulated with a Teflon sheet. The insulated tubing is embedded in epoxy-fiberglass filler material and enclosed in a beryllium copper coil body (B in Fig. 7). The coil body provides rigid support for the coil windings; it causes comparatively uniform current flow on the surface of the primary conductor, eliminating stress concentrations; and it isolates the primary conductor from external effects.

A band of fiberglass rovings impregnated with epoxy resin (C in Fig. 7) is wrapped under tension over the primary coil and coil body to reinforce them against the expansive stress caused by reaction to the forming force. The band is about ¼ in. thick by 3½ in. wide. The outermost layer of the compression coil (D in Fig. 7) is a carbon steel shell ¼ in. thick.

Inside the coil body and insulated from it by a 0.050-in.-thick layer of epoxy-fiberglass is the beryllium copper field shaper (E in Fig. 7). It is highly

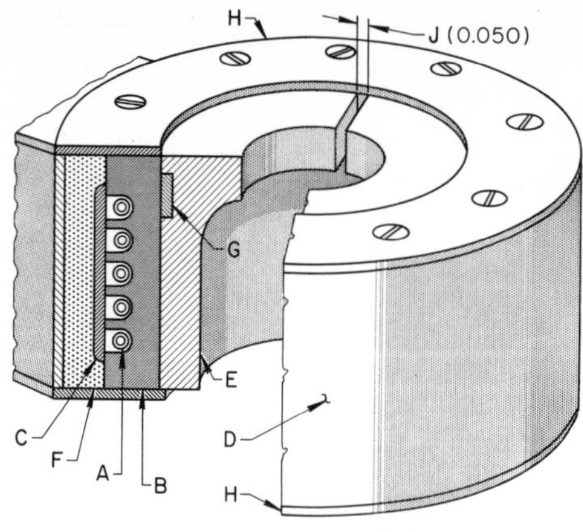

A – Primary conductor. B – Beryllium copper coil body. C – Fiberglass reinforcement. D – Steel housing and magnetic shield for coil. E – Beryllium copper field shaper. F – Fiberglass insulation. G – Fiberglass reinforcement. H – Fiberglass supporting member. J – Slot 0.050 in. wide in field shaper.

Fig. 7. General-purpose compression forming coil with a removable field shaper

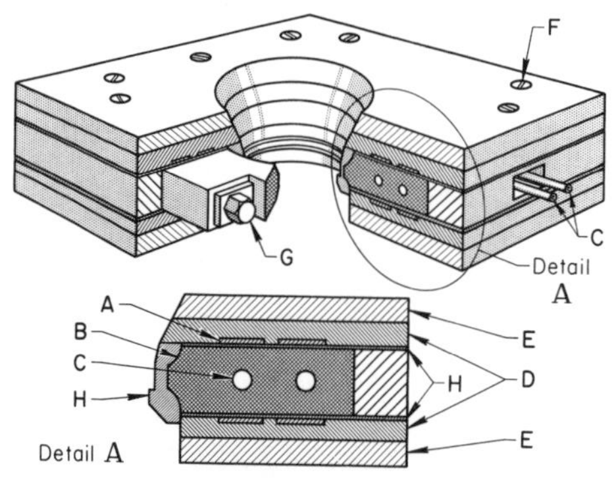

A – Primary conductor. B – Beryllium copper field shaper. C – Water passage. D – Fiberglass insulation. E – Steel backup plates. F – Press bolt. G – Shaper press bolt. H – Shaper insulation.

Fig. 8. Heavy-duty, wafer-type compression forming coil

conductive to minimize heat loss, and also strong enough to support pressure at least as great as that applied to the workpiece at the peak of the forming pulse. Between the primary conductor and the carbon steel shell is a 1-in.-thick layer of epoxy-fiberglass insulation (F in Fig. 7).

The slotted field shaper is held together with an epoxy-fiberglass band (G in Fig. 7), and supports at the top and bottom of the coil (H in Fig. 7) are also of fiberglass. These end supports are of insulating material to allow passage of the magnetic flux. The field shaper has a 0.050-in.-wide slot (J in Fig. 7).

The flux concentration at the inner wall of the field shaper causes it to heat faster than the rest of the assembly. It is cooled by convection or by forced-air circulation. In high-speed coils, the field shaper is sometimes water cooled. Heat generated in the coil body and primary conductor is removed by water circulating in the copper tubing of the primary conductor. Temperature rise in the coil is about 90 F.

Because the magnetic field near the slot in the shaper is slightly weaker than elsewhere, the workpiece is displaced toward the slot during the forming pulse. When this is objectionable, two opposing slots are provided in the shaper to give a balanced field. Sometimes the halves of the field shaper with two slots are not fastened together, to accommodate an irregularly shaped part. The movement of the shaper halves during the pulse will eventually damage the coil (they are restrained only by inertia), and so this technique is suitable only for short-run applications.

Heavy-Duty Wafer Compression Coil. Even stronger, more efficient construction is found in the heavy-duty wafer-type coil shown in Fig. 8, for which the forming pressure is limited only by the properties of the shaper material.

In this type of coil, the primary conductor (A in Fig. 8) is a closely spaced flat spiral made of copper or a copper alloy, such as beryllium copper, having a resistivity of 10 microhm-cm or less. This conductor must have much better conductivity than that required of workpieces, because of the greater difficulty of removing heat in a coil that is repetitively pulsed.

The beryllium copper field shaper (B in Fig. 8) is made of two rugged plates held together against the outward force of the magnetic impulse by shaper press bolts (G in Fig. 8). All of the cooling in this coil is provided by means of water circulating through passages (C in Fig. 8) in the field shaper. Heat generated in the primary conductor passes through an insulating sheet (H in Fig. 8) into the shaper.

The insulating plates (D in Fig. 8) are of epoxy-fiberglass. They provide an insulation-filled space through which the magnetic flux can return around the primary-conductor spiral and the field-shaper plates. The whole assembly is sandwiched between 1-in.-thick, surface-ground, carbon steel backup plates (E in Fig. 8) that provide support and magnetic shielding. These plates, together with press bolts (F in Fig. 8), clamp the coil assembly together and hold the primary conductor tightly against the field shaper during the impulse.

Wafer coils are used in energy ratings up to 60 kilojoules and pressure ratings up to 60,000 psi.

Sliding-Shaper Compression Coil. The sliding-shaper coil shown in Fig. 9 has, in most of its essentials, the same construction as the wafer coil of Fig. 8, with the exception that the beryllium copper field-shaper elements are capable of movement, and are driven by pneumatic cylinders. In operation, the halves of the shaper are separated for the insertion of a workpiece having a protuberance, after which they are brought together for the forming operation. When the field-shaper halves are close together, they are in the same relative position with respect to the primary conductor as are the shaper halves in Fig. 8.

Since the field-shaping members are not tightly clamped against the primary conductors, both the field-shaping members and the primary conductors are separately water-cooled. (The water-cooling channels are not shown in Fig. 9.)

Because of the somewhat large spacing between the field-shaping elements and the primary conductor, there is a minor loss of efficiency compared with that of the wafer coil. During the magnetic impulses, there is a slight separation of the field-shaper halves (which are not tightly bolted together). However, because of the relatively large inertia of the field-shaping members, the amount of energy transferred to them during the impulse is small and is absorbed in the reaction with the pneumatic cylinders.

Like wafer coils, sliding-shaper coils are used in energy ratings up to 60 kilojoules and pressure ratings up to 60,000 psi.

Sliding-shaper compression coils of special construction are used for high-speed assembly of automotive parts, as described in Example 337.

Expansion Coil. Light-duty expansion coils, for use at pressures up to about 7000 psi, consist of solenoid coils of beryllium copper tubing wound on fiberglass forms. They are commonly up to 10 in. in active length and 4 in. in diameter, and usually are designed for the forming of specific workpieces. Coils 2 ft long and others over 4 ft in diameter have been built, and have been applied successfully.

For short-run low-pressure expansion applications, temporary coils sometimes are made simply by wrapping a wooden form with building wire. Selection of wire size and number of turns, however, is critical in order to get a suitable inductance. Also, extreme care must be taken to avoid electrical and mechanical hazards.

Expansion coils of high strength with ceramic insulator construction, and high-pressure coils using self-supporting conductor construction, are designed to suit specific applications. The capability of these coils is limited by the strength of the coil (which must be a good conductor of electricity) and of the supporting mandrel.

Space limitations sometimes present problems in constructing high-pressure expansion coils for high-production applications. Single-turn coils with high strength and capacity can be made as described in the preceding paragraph, but their low impedance must be compensated for by using a transformer between them and the storage banks. Such a transformer will change the relatively high-voltage, low-current output of the storage bank to a lower-voltage, higher-current input usable by the single-turn coil.

In one application, a single-turn coil with an autotransformer was used to expand a 3-in.-diam, 0.040-in.-wall steel tube into the apertures of a flange to make a rigid structural assembly. Production rate was 300 to 400 assemblies per hour.

In the following example, a deep contour was formed in a hoop-shaped part by impact against a ring die, using an expansion coil.

Example 335. Electromagnetic Forming of a Grooved Hoop-Shaped Part (Fig. 10)

As shown in Fig. 10, a grooved hoop-shaped part was formed by expanding a welded band of 0.030-in.-thick steel into a ring die, without using a field shaper. The weld bead was ground smooth before forming. Because of the high velocity of the band when it struck the die, it conformed accurately to the die contour. About 40 kilojoules of energy was used.

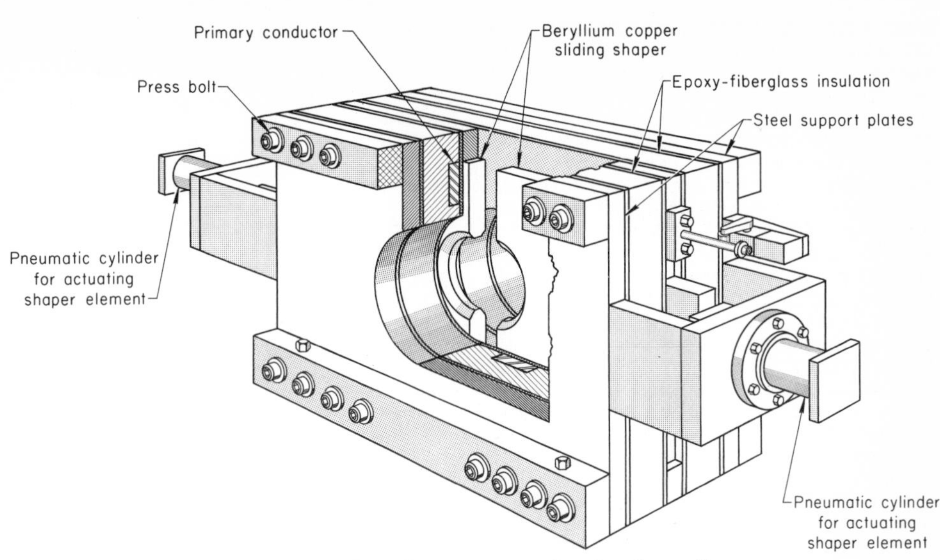

Fig. 9. Sliding-shaper compression forming coil

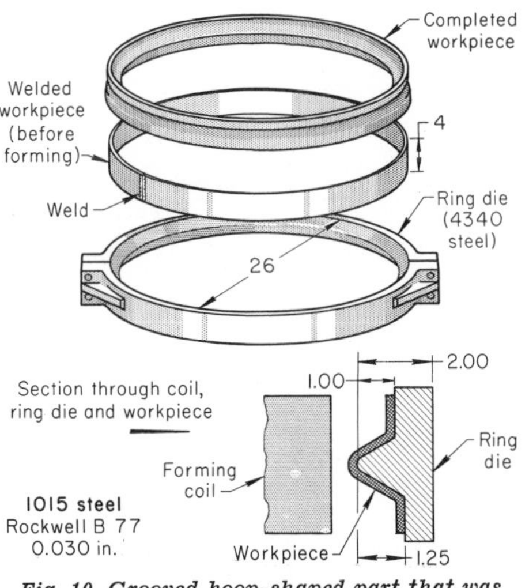

Fig. 10. Grooved hoop-shaped part that was electromagnetically formed from a welded circular band, using an expansion coil and a ring die (Example 335)

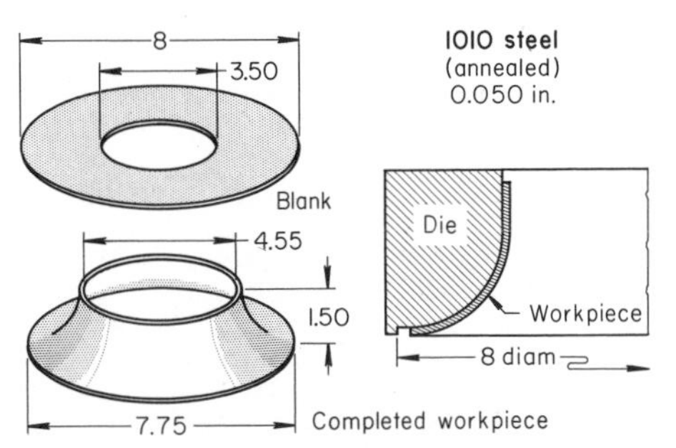

Fig. 11. Contoured part that was made from a pierced flat blank by electromagnetic forming (Example 336)

The 4340 ring die (Fig. 10) was made by rolling, welding on lugs, bolting together into a hoop shape, and then turning the inside contour in a lathe.

Because the die was not subjected to static pressure, there was no need for the sturdy construction that would have been necessary had other forming methods been used. Using the electromagnetic forming technique, it was merely necessary that the die be many times as massive as the workpiece.

Flat Spiral Coil. For contour forming of flat blanks, flat spiral coils apply essentially uniform pressure over a circular flat area, except for a small area in the center. It is difficult to achieve durability at peak pressures above 5000 psi in such coils.

The design of a flat spiral coil depends strongly on the requirements of the application. For applications that need high uniform pressure only over a ring-shaped area, rugged and durable coils have been built, capable of exerting up to 50,000 psi.

The electromagnetic forming of a contoured part from flat stock, using a flat spiral coil, is described in the example that follows.

Example 336. Electromagnetic Contour Forming of an Orifice From a Flat Blank (Fig. 11)

The fluid-flow constrictor shown in Fig. 11 was formed by the use of a flat coil in a set-up like that shown in Fig. 3(c). The annealed 1010 steel blank, a flat annular disk 8 in. in diameter, was laid on the coil under the die. The magnetic field generated pressure against the disk, driving it against the die (Fig. 11).

The forming equipment had a rating of 12 kilojoules and cost $20,000. An output of 10 kilojoules was used in forming the orifice. Production rate was 240 pieces per hour. Because of its use as a flow constrictor, the 4.55-in. orifice diameter was held accurately. It was maintained without any trimming after forming. In cross section, the formed part had an exponentially curved contour.

Direct labor plus overhead would cost $0.04 per piece, assuming a charge of $10 per hour. Amortization of the cost of the forming machine over one million pieces would add $0.02 per piece, for a total of $0.06 per piece.

Typical Energy Relations

The actual energy relations in the forming of aluminum alloy 6061-O, with a resistivity of 3.8 microhm-cm, and low-carbon steel, with a resistivity of 12 microhm-cm, are shown in Fig. 12. The data were obtained using a 12-kilojoule machine operating at rated capacity with a standard wafer compression coil of the type shown in Fig. 8. In the forming operations described, the initial gap between field shaper and workpiece was 0.060 in.

The variation of peak forming pressure with workpiece length is shown for tubular workpieces 3½ to 6½ in. in diameter with a wall thickness greater than 0.030 in.

The effects of workpiece dimensions and resistivity on peak forming pressure or pulse height were qualitatively as predicted in the section of this article on Principles. The pressure for a workpiece length of 1 in. was about half of that for a length of ¼ in.; the pressure for a workpiece diameter of 6½ in. was about two-thirds of that for a diameter of 3½ in. Peak pressure was higher for the work metal of lower resistivity: 20 to 50% higher for the 6061-O than for the low-carbon steel, with the percentage difference being greater for workpieces of larger diameter and shorter length.

Because the pressure is directly proportional to the energy, Fig. 12 is also valid for other energy levels. Thus, if the 12-kilojoule equipment produces a pressure of 14,000 psi on a workpiece 5 in. in diameter and 0.6 in. long, it will produce 10,500 psi if operated at a 9-kilojoule level, or 7000 psi at a 6-kilojoule level.

The same relations apply for other combinations of coil and storage bank, as well as for other types of coils. Qualitatively they are similar; quantitatively they depend on the actual dimensions, design of the coil, and capacitance of the storage bank.

Although the length and diameter of the workpiece have a substantial effect on the peak forming pressure, they have only a slight effect on the length of the pressure pulse, which is about 50 to 60 microseconds. The reason is that coils of the type shown in Fig. 8, to which the graph refers, are designed to have a limited range of inductance regardless of the workpiece contours. This prevents damage to the energy-storage bank as the result of excessive peak current drain.

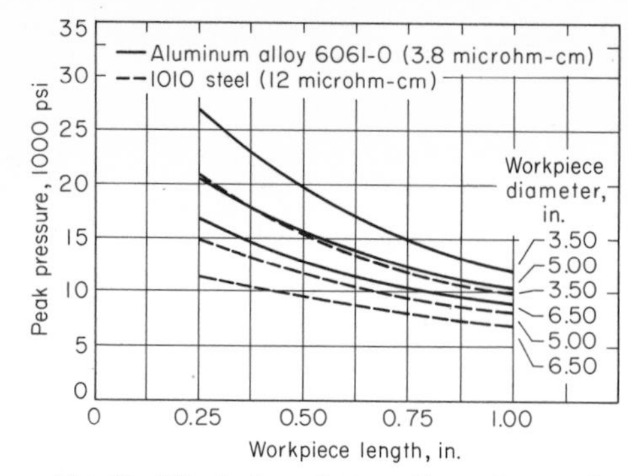

Fig. 12. Effect of workpiece dimensions and electrical resistivity on peak pressure in electromagnetic compression forming of tubular workpieces of wall thickness greater than 0.030 in.

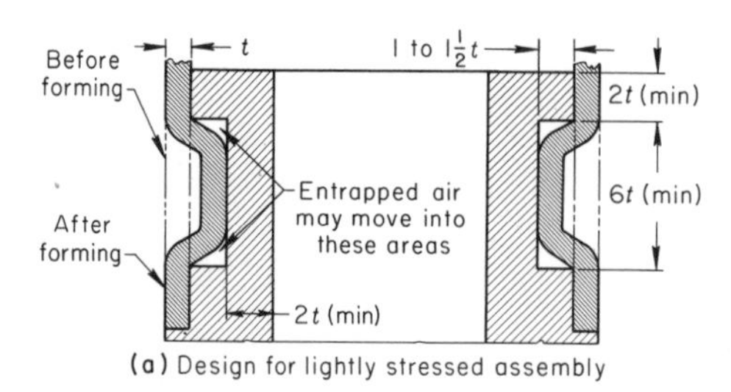

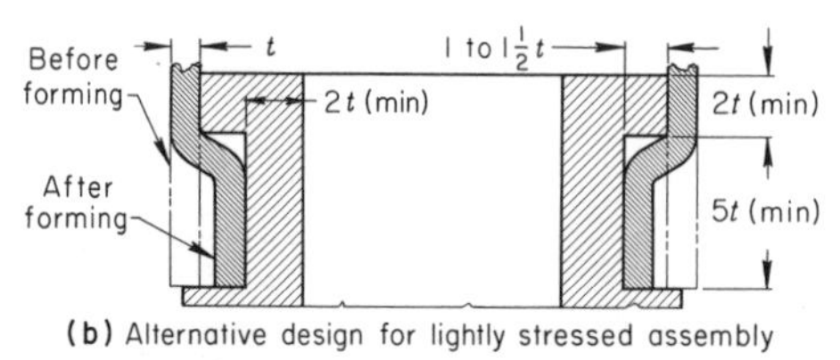

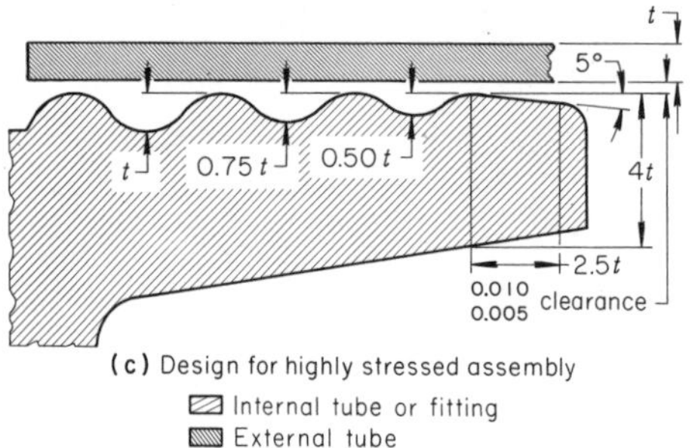

Fig. 13. Three types of axially loaded joints made by electromagnetic forming

Applications

Electromagnetic forming is used chiefly to expand, compress or form tubular shapes, and occasionally to form flat sheet; it often combines several forming and assembly operations into a single step. The method is also used for some piercing or shearing operations.

In the automotive industry, EMF is used to assemble air-conditioner components, high-pressure hoses, shock-absorber dust covers, rubber boots on ball joints, oil-cooler heat exchangers, and accessory motor packages.

Universal-joint yokes, drive linkages, wheels, cams, gears and various other linkages or fittings are assembled to drive shafts or torque tubes by EMF. In this type of application, a torque joint, tube or hollow shaft is compressed onto a fitting inside the tube, as in Example 337; or conversely, the hub of a wheel, gear or linkage is compressed onto the outside surface of a shaft. Splines, pockets or knurl configurations can be used in the fittings to provide torque resistance, depending on torque-strength requirements, type of materials, and dimensions involved.

In the manufacture of electrical equipment, components of high-voltage fuses, insulators, and lighting fixtures are joined by EMF, and heavy-duty electrical connections are made by swaging a terminal sleeve over a conductor cable.

Aircraft applications include torque-shaft assemblies, control rods and linkages, forming and assembly of cooling-system ducts, and sizing of tubing. Other uses for EMF are swaging of preformed rotating bands on ordnance projectiles and assembly of propane and liquid-gas containers and other small pressure vessels. In nuclear work, fuel-rod sheaths are compressed and sealing operations performed in remote shielded areas.

Axially loaded joints made by EMF are used in some aircraft applications and in actuator rods, where it is important to avoid excess weight. For long life under exposure to high stress and vibration, design of these joints is critical.

These assemblies are made by swaging the end of a tube into circumferential grooves in the second tube or fitting, as shown in Fig. 13. Recommended dimensional limits are also given in Fig. 13. Close tolerances and close fit on the parts to be joined are not necessary. A loose slip fit is usually satisfactory; clearance of as much as ⅜ in. has been used.

One arrangement suitable for joining lightly stressed members is shown in Fig. 13(a). A second arrangement, shown in Fig. 13(b), is equally satisfactory and requires considerably less energy for forming.

The joint contour shown in Fig. 13(c) is recommended for highly stressed, axially loaded assemblies. Three generously radiused grooves are used to avoid stress concentration. The grooves become progressively deeper toward the end of the external tube.

Tests indicate a better distribution of stress on all grooves under axial load as a result of the variation in groove depth. Tests also indicate a significantly lessened tendency for the end fitting to move relative to the tube, up to the yield point of the unformed tube section. This is important to members subjected to repeated reversals of load. Joints have been made in which the unformed section of tube failed without detectable relative joint movement. When the tube must be highly stressed in service, it is preferable that the fitting (inside part) be of higher yield strength than the tube.

The fitting must be designed with proper cross section or must be adequately supported internally, so that the difference in springback after forming will contribute to tightness of the joint. It may be desirable to reduce wall thickness of the fitting to assure deflection and springback, leaving the tube with residual hoop stress.

On large parts with appreciable groove volume, it may be necessary to draw a vacuum on the inside of the tubular component to remove air from the groove area. Otherwise, the air can be entrapped and offer considerable resistance to the high-velocity forming. A simpler way to deal with this problem, when design permits, is to provide extra volume in the form of square corners in the groove, as shown in Fig. 13(a) and (b).

Torque joints assembled by EMF are preferred to welded joints in some applications, because of the absence of scale and residual flux, because joints are easily inspected for quality, and because heat distortion is absent.

The spline joint is best suited for torque joints using tubes with heavy wall thickness. Joints made by driving the tube into pockets machined parallel to the axis of the fitting are used with thin-wall tubes. For low torque requirements, coarse knurling of the fitting before assembling to the tube is satisfactory and economical.

The use of specially designed sliding-shaper coils, as in the example that follows, enables efficient high-speed production of torque joints.

Example 337. Production of a Torque Joint for a Drive Shaft by EMF (Fig. 14)

The torque joint shown in Fig. 14 was electromagnetically formed to assemble the drive shaft for a passenger car to the universal-joint yoke. Tests showed the joint to be as strong as the drive shaft. Substituting EMF for welding significantly reduced noise and vibration in the automobile.

The drive shaft was a 3-in.-OD tube of 1020 steel with a wall thickness of 0.065 in., on which the end had been reduced in a rotary swager to a minimum inside diameter of 2.640 in., in a preliminary operation. The tube had a tensile strength of 70,000 psi and a yield strength of 38,000 psi.

In magnetic forming, the reduced end of the tube was wrapped tightly around the rectangular protrusions on the round portion of the yoke, as shown in sections A-A and B-B in Fig. 14, providing both longitudinal and axial strength in the assembly.

A special sliding-shaper coil was built to handle the assembly. Production rate was 240 assemblies per hour, using a 48-kilojoule electromagnetic forming machine that cost about $80,000.

At $10 per hour, direct labor plus overhead would cost $0.04 per assembly. Machine cost, based on amortization over one million assemblies, would be $0.08 per assembly, making a total cost of $0.12 per assembly.

Heat Shrinking. Electromagnetic forming is used to assemble heat-shrink-fitted assemblies that would be too long in relation to the diameter involved to assemble efficiently by other means, as in the following example:

Example 338. Assembly by Combination of Heat Shrinking and EMF (Fig. 15)

The assembly shown in Fig. 15 could not be made by heat shrinking alone, because of its high length-to-diameter ratio and the small dimensional change.

By combining EMF with heat shrinking, the two parts of the assembly were first machined to a loose fit (instead of the usual interference fit). Then, a 0.020-in.-wall 1100-O aluminum alloy driver was used with a compression coil, as shown in Fig. 15, to assemble the 0.035-in.-thick type 430 stainless steel sheath to the 1½-in.-OD graphite tube (a nuclear fuel element).

The stainless steel sheath was induction heated to 1500 F, the components were brought into position rapidly, and the magnetic compression was done before the stainless steel could be cooled or the aluminum driver or graphite tube heated significantly. The assembly was allowed to cool in air after the forming was completed.

A 12-kilojoule machine that cost about $30,000 was used in making this assembly.

The combination of magnetic forming with heat shrinking has also been used in making torque joints when an exceptionally hard material had to be formed into grooves in a soft or weak material; heating is used to lower the strength and improve the ductility of the hard material. In applications of this kind, the difference in thermal expansion of the two materials and the use of grooves help to make strong, rigid torque joints that will not loosen under vibration.

Combinations of Operations. Some parts that would require a number of separate conventional forming operations can be made in a single operation by EMF. For instance, simple tooling can be devised to enable blanking, piercing or other cutting operations to be done along with complex forming in one step. In the example that follows, a simple die was made to pierce two holes in an aluminum alloy tube, expand the tube and form a 180° flange on one end of the tube, all in one EMF operation.

Example 339. One-Operation Forming and Piercing by EMF (Fig. 16)

The tubular part shown at the right in Fig. 16 was produced in one EMF operation by using an expansion coil to form, flange and pierce a length of tubing against a single-piece die (setup shown at left and center in Fig. 16). The workpiece was a 4-in. length of 3¼-in.-OD, 0.035-in.-wall aluminum alloy 6061-O tubing with a yield strength of 7000 psi.

The die was turned from 4340 steel tubing with a ½-in. wall, and two holes were drilled in the die to accomplish the piercing operation. The formed part was removed from the die by means of a simple ejector.

The forming equipment had a capacity of 6 kilojoules, and cost approximately $18,000. Production rate was 240 pieces per hour, using manual loading and unloading.

Per-piece cost for labor plus overhead, based on a charge of $10 per hour, would be $0.04. Amortization of the cost of the machine over one million pieces would add $0.02 per piece, for a total cost of $0.06 per piece.

Special Equipment

Special equipment is required for economical performance in volume production applications of EMF, and for doing varied and unusual forming and assembly operations.

High-Speed Machines. Extremely high repetition rates can be attained by properly matching the characteristics of the power source, the energy-storage unit, the switching components, the forming coil, and the workpiece. A rate of 10,000 operations per minute is considered feasible, limited primarily by the ability of the components to dissipate heat, and by the power rating of the charging circuitry. Arbitrary pulse timing is possible with a precision of less than 1 microsecond.

Developmental low-energy equipment for shearing and flanging tubular aluminum can stock has been operated continuously at 1000 operations per minute for more than 1700 hr, with only minor maintenance. Such equipment can be synchronized with high precision to the operation of mechanical feeding equipment — a workpiece being fed at a rate of 100 ft per minute would move only 0.002 in. during a 100-microsecond EMF operation. (Shearing and flanging of the aluminum can stock was done in less than 50 microseconds.) The relatively simple holding and positioning devices needed for EMF also make the method well suited for high-speed, continuous-feed work.

A machine for embossing 0.006-in.-thick aluminum alloy tubular metal parts 4 in. long by 2 in. in diameter has been used on a pilot basis at 250 operations per minute.

Manual-Feed Equipment. With manual feeding, the production rate is limited by the speed at which an operator can load and unload parts.

To speed up production with manual handling, insulating fixtures into which the work is inserted may be mounted in the coil or field shaper. For assembly operations, the fixture locates the workpieces in proper position with respect to each other, as well as to the coil or field shaper.

Typically, closing a coil cover initiates the charge-and-fire cycle, and the cover automatically opens for work removal when the forming is completed. Production rates of 350 to 400 assemblies per hour are typical of those attained with this type of equipment.

Cost

Engineering cost may be high in short-run operations, especially if new applications that require coil design are being developed. However, no special skills are required of the operator in volume-production operations, in which his usual function is only to load and unload parts and to push the firing button.

Capital costs for EMF equipment are influenced chiefly by the requirements for repetition rate and for durability of energy-storage capacitors, discharge ignitrons, and forming coils.

The cost of a standard (600 operations per hour) energy-storage bank for production use in the 12-to-84-kilojoule range is about $25,000 to $100,000. Energy-storage banks for experimental use, where durability, speed, safety and control features are less critical, can be built for about $500 to $1000 per kilojoule of capacity.

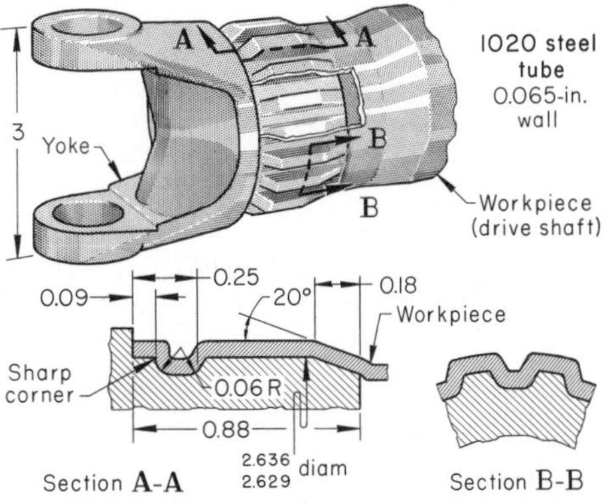

Fig. 14. Drive-shaft torque joint made by electromagnetic forming (Example 337)

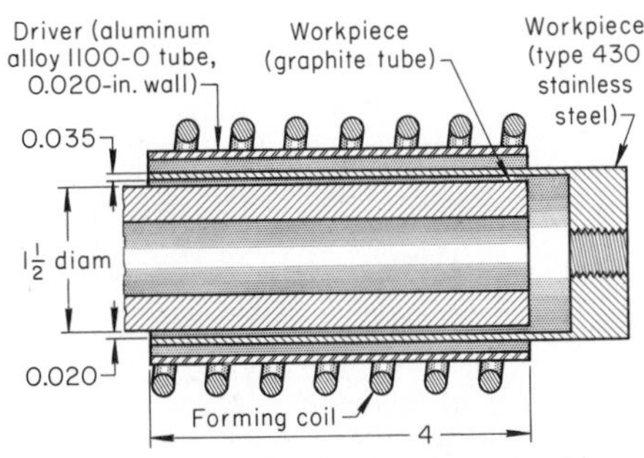

Fig. 15. Setup for assembly by a combination of heat shrinking and electromagnetic forming (Example 338)

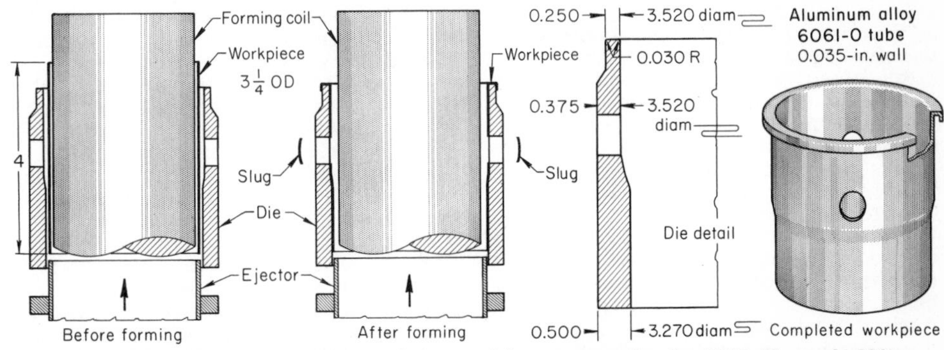

Fig. 16. Forming and piercing a tubular part in one operation by EMF (Example 339)

Coils for use in high-volume production range in cost from about $250 to $15,000. The cost of coils varies greatly with the pressure, energy, operating ratio, size and special features (such as sliding field shapers, which can multiply the cost of the coil by a factor of two or more over the cost of a coil of the fixed-shaper type).

Ordinarily, no special facilities are required. The equipment operates on 220-volt or 440-volt alternating current, 50 to 60 cycles per second, single phase. A relatively clean and dry shop environment is necessary.

Operating Costs. Estimated operating costs for typical production EMF operations at two different levels of energy are listed in Table 3. Cost in individual applications may vary substantially from these estimates, depending on requirements of the application.

The efficiency of use of stored energy ordinarily is about 4 to 10%, but may be as high as 25%. The efficiency of the electrical equipment itself is usually more than 75%.

The life of capacitors in most production applications is several million operations; that of switching ignitrons is about one million. Coil life generally ranges from half a million to ten million operations, depending on the operating stress level. Typical coil life is one million operations.

Over-All Cost. By reducing labor cost per piece, the substitution of a single EMF operation for several time-consuming operations (such as riveting, welding, brazing, spinning, rolling, swaging, drilling, pegging, press forming, cleaning, scale removal, or flux removal) can reduce over-all cost for assemblies or formed parts such as those described in this article. The cost advantage is usually greatest for high-production applications, although savings have been made in short-run job-shop or prototype applications, because tooling can sometimes be extremely simple.

In general, to achieve low over-all cost per piece, it must be possible to amortize the cost of the forming machine over a large number of operations (not necessarily on the same assembly or part). This is illustrated in the calculation of per-piece costs given in Example 334, in which the machine cost was amortized over the production of one million assemblies.

Safety

The potential hazards that attend electromagnetic forming operations may be divided into two categories: (*a*) mechanical and sonic hazards, and (*b*) electrical hazards.

Mechanical and Sonic Hazards. As can be expected of any equipment capable of exerting high pressure and of delivering energy at a high rate, electromagnetic forming equipment can cause substantial damage when its forces are misdirected. The magnetic pulse produces pressure perpendicular to the surface exposed to the field. Thus, if a cylindrical workpiece is positioned in such a way as to pass completely through a compression coil, only radial forces will be exerted on it during the forming operation. If, however, such a workpiece were inadvertently inserted only partly through the coil, force produced by the magnetic pulse on the end could be sufficient to eject the workpiece from the coil at high velocity. In the same way, improperly positioned parts can be violently ejected from an expansion coil. An appropriate shield should be provided about the coil to protect personnel if there is a possibility that the machine may operate on an improperly positioned part.

Table 3. Estimated Operating Cost for Typical EMF Operations

Item	Cost per 1000 pieces, at energy level of: 12 kilojoules	84 kilojoules
Replacement of components and tools:		
Energy-storage capacitors	$0.96	$6.72
Switching ignitrons	1.35	8.10
Forming coils	2.00	6.00
Maintenance	1.00	3.50
Electric power	0.12	0.84
Total	$5.43	$25.16

Cost data are based on operation at 100% of rated energy-storage capacity.

The sound produced in electromagnetic forming operations results from the rapid movement of the workpiece compressing the air, and ordinarily is at a moderate level. If, however, the area of the workpiece moved in the air is large and the distance moved is great, the intensity of sound generated could be great enough to cause damage to the ears of nearby workers unless a sound-absorbing barrier is placed around the work station.

The possibility of an electrical arc-over in a coil or field shaper is another potential source of mechanical or sonic hazard. In the event of an electrical arc-over, essentially all of the energy in the capacitor bank may be directed into an explosion, generating high-intensity sound and perhaps forcibly ejecting bits of insulation or metal. For a 12-kilojoule machine, a shield of ¼-in.-thick plywood or plexiglass should be sufficient to protect personnel from flying debris produced by the arc. Protection required against the sonic hazard depends on the distance of the operator from the coil. Care should be taken to prevent metallic chips from falling onto exposed parts of the field-shaper gaps, where they could produce an arc-over. Insulators should be regularly checked for wear and cracks.

Electrical Hazards. Voltages used in electromagnetic forming operations range up to 10 kilovolts, and the capacitor banks can deliver extremely high current — a lethal combination if proper safeguards are not employed. All high-voltage components of the system should be completely contained in a well-grounded, heavy-gage metal cabinet. Doors and panels should be bonded to the cabinet with heavy-duty straps. Energy-storage capacitors and associated circuitry should be interlocked with cabinet doors and panels so as to be firmly grounded when the cabinet is opened. Maintenance personnel should work on energy-storage circuitry only after firmly shorting the storage capacitors with a direct wire connection. Maintenance personnel should also observe all standard precautions when working with the high-voltage components of the machine.

Pulsed voltages of the type that appear at the coil terminals of electromagnetic forming equipment are much less dangerous than direct voltage. Normally, pulses of no more than about 1000 volts appear in any exposed portion of the equipment. The typical 10,000-cps pulse appears for less than one millisecond. However, precautions should be taken to prevent operators from being directly exposed to such voltages. The workpiece should *never* be held by hand, because the possibility always exists that an arc-over between coil and workpiece could occur. Energy-storage equipment should always incorporate resistors shunting the work-coil terminals, so that in the event of coil failure (or in the event that a coil is not connected), a potentially lethal charge cannot remain on the coil terminals.

Coils are encased in metal shells that act as eddy-current shields. As a result, the magnetic field is reduced to a very low level at a distance of a foot or so from the bore of the coil. Although there are no reports of ill effects on individuals from pulsed magnetic fields at these levels, it is probably not wise to expose parts of the body to high-field regions of a work coil (that is, within a few inches of the bore) while the coil is in operation.

Other Data on Electromagnetic Forming in This Volume

Copper and aluminum, because of their high conductivity, are particularly suitable for electromagnetic forming. The article on Forming of Copper and Copper Alloys (which begins on page 405 in this volume) presents information on the use of electromagnetic forming for making thermally and electrically conductive joints; Table 7 in that article lists terminal-joint dimensions.

Two examples in the article on Forming of Aluminum (which begins on page 379) describe electromagnetic forming of aluminum alloy tubing:

Example 551. The end of a tube of alloy 3003-O was formed with an expansion coil around a steel reinforcing ring. The coil was located just inside the end of the tube. The tube was bulged behind the ring at the same time that the end of the tube was wrapped over the ring, locking it securely in place.

Example 552. A metal-to-metal seal was produced by swaging a tube of alloy 3003-H14 onto a grooved tubular steel insert. The seal remained intact at a pressure of 4000 psi — a pressure that was sufficient to burst the tube elsewhere along its length.

Selected References

K. Baines, J. L. Duncan and W. Johnson, Electromagnetic Metal Forming, *Proceedings of the Institution of Mechanical Engineers*, 180, 93-110 (1965-1966). [Describes experiments in expanding copper and aluminum tubes, and outlines a theoretical analysis of the forces produced. Eleven references.]

H. J. Lippmann and H. Schreiner, Zur Physik der Metallumforming mit hohen Magnetfeldimpulsen, *Zeitschrift für Metallkunde*, 55, 737-740 (Dec 1964). [Calculates rates of deformation: 86 meters per second for brass, and 130 meters per second for copper. In German.]

Kenneth F. Smith, Metal Forming by Electrical Energy Release — Trends and Applications, *Transactions of the Society of Automotive Engineers*, Paper 650190, 878-890 (1966). [Illustrates 55 applications of electromagnetic and electrohydraulic forming. Thirty-two references.]

SHEARING, SLITTING, AND GAS AND ARC CUTTING

CONTENTS

Shearing of Plate and Flat Sheet

*By the ASM Committee on Shearing and Slitting**

SHEARING of sheet and plate is broadly classified by the type of blade (cutter) used — namely, straight or rotary. Straight-blade shearing is used for squaring and cutting flat stock to required shape and size. It is most often used for square and rectangular shapes, although triangles and other straight-sided shapes are also sheared with straight blades. Rotary shearing (not to be confused with slitting) is used for producing circular or other contoured shapes from sheet or plate.

Straight-Blade Shearing

In straight-blade shearing, the work metal is placed between a stationary lower blade and a movable upper blade. As the upper blade is forced down, the work metal is penetrated to a specific portion of its thickness, after which the unpenetrated portion fractures and the work metal separates (Fig. 1). The amount of penetration depends largely on the ductility and thickness of the work metal. The blade will penetrate 30 to 60% of the work-metal thickness for low-carbon steel, depending on thickness (see the subsection on Capacity, later in this article). For a more ductile metal like copper, the penetration will be greater. Conversely, the penetration will be less for metals that are harder than low-carbon steel.

A sheared edge is characterized by the smoothness of the penetrated portion and the relative roughness of the fractured portion. Sheared edges cannot compete with machined edges, but when blades are kept sharp and in proper adjustment, it is possible to obtain sheared edges that are acceptable for a wide range of applications. The quality of sheared edges generally improves as work-metal thickness decreases.

Applicability. Straight-blade shearing is the most economical method of cutting straight-sided blanks from stock no more than 2 in. thick. The process is also widely used for cutting sheet into blanks that subsequently will be formed or drawn on a punch press. Blanks can be cut to size within ±0.005 in., and strips can be cut to width within ±0.005 in. in lengths up to 12 ft.

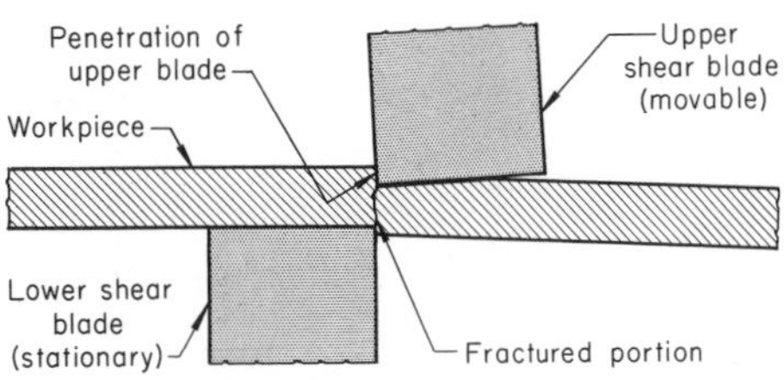

Fig. 1. Mechanics of straight-blade shearing

Straight-blade shearing is seldom used for shearing metal harder than about Rockwell C 30. When extremely soft, ductile metal (especially, thin sheet) is sheared, the edges of the metal roll and large burrs result. As the hardness of the work metal increases, blade life decreases for shearing a given thickness of metal.

In general, it is practical to shear flat stock up to 1½ in. thick in a squaring shear. Squaring shears up to 30 ft long are available (even longer shears have been built), and some types are equipped with a gap that permits shearing of work metal longer than the shear blade. Flat stock up to 2 in. thick can be sheared in an alligator shear, but this machine is extremely limited in length of cut and is not widely used for shearing large sections of flat stock.

Machines for Straight-Blade Shearing

Punch presses and press brakes are sometimes used for shearing a few pieces, or as a temporary expedient when more efficient equipment is not available. Production shearing, however, is usually done in machines, called shears, designed for this operation.

Squaring Shears. Trimming and cutting of sheet or plate to specific size are usually done in a squaring shear (see Fig. 2). Squaring shears (also called resquaring or guillotine shears) are available in a wide range of sizes and designs. Some types permit slitting by moving the work metal a predetermined amount in a direction parallel with the cutting edge of the blade after each stroke of the shear.

The sheet or plate is held rigid by hold-down devices while the upper blade moves down past the lower blade. Most sheet or plate is sheared by setting the upper blade at an angle, as shown in the lower left corner of Fig. 2. The position of each blade can be adjusted to maintain optimum clearance between blades. Squaring shears can be actuated mechanically, hydraulically or pneumatically.

Mechanical shears are the most widely used. The power train of a mechanical shear consists of a motor, reduction gears that drive a flywheel, the flywheel, a clutch that connects the flywheel and a crankshaft, and a ram actuated directly by the crankshaft. Under most operating conditions,

*PAUL K. ZIMMERMAN (deceased), *Chairman;* A. G. BAUMGARTNER, Vice President (retired), Cincinnati Shaper Co.

ROY FLOWERS, Superintendent of Fabrication, W. S. Tyler Co. Div., W. S. Tyler, Inc.; KENNETH R. KESKA, Chief Engineer, Torrance Machinery & Engineering, Inc. (formerly with Yoder Co.); STEVE MRAZ, Plant Superintendent, Cleveland Steel Service Center, Jones & Laughlin Steel Corp.; F. W. PETTERS, Chief Engineer, Joseph T. Ryerson & Son, Inc.

L. J. REGULY, Senior Mechanical Engineer, Mechanical Dept., Inland Steel Co.; RALPH H. WEISNER, Chief Engineer, Wysong and Miles Co.; ARTHUR G. ZAHN, Vice President, Chesterfield Steel Service Co.

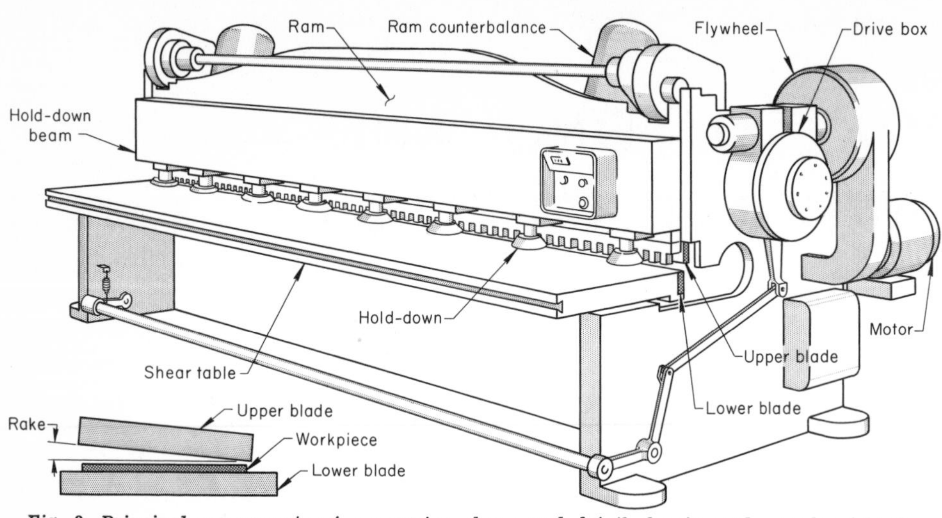

Fig. 2. Principal components of a squaring shear, and detail showing rake angle of blades

a mechanical shear can deliver more strokes per minute (spm) than can a hydraulic shear. Some mechanical shears cycle as fast as 300 spm.

Another advantage of the mechanical shear is that because of the energy stored in the flywheel, a smaller motor can be used for intermittent shearing. For instance, a mechanical shear with a "no cutting" or "free running" speed of 65 spm can make approximately six full shearing strokes (maximum thickness and length of cut) per minute with a standard motor. However, when the same shear is cutting at top speed (65 spm) and full capacity, a much larger motor is required. For such rapid cutting, there is not enough time between cuts for the smaller motor to restore the speed of the flywheel.

An additional advantage of the mechanical shear is that the moving blade travels faster than that of a hydraulic shear. Greater blade speed minimizes work-metal twist, bow and camber.

Hydraulic shears are actuated by a motor-driven pump that forces oil into a cylinder against a piston, the movement of which energizes the blade.

A hydraulic shear is capable of making longer strokes than is its mechanical counterpart. This can be an advantage, because a longer stroke allows the use of longer blades. When high rake angles are needed for long blades, the use of a mechanical shear is sometimes precluded because of insufficient stroke length. For instance, if a 10-ft-long blade set at a rake angle of ⅜ in. per foot requires a minimum stroke of 5 in., a 20-ft blade at the same rake angle will require nearly twice as much stroke length.

Another advantage of a hydraulic over a mechanical shear is that overloading causes the hydraulic shear to stop, thus avoiding breakage of blades or damage to machine components.

When shearing at full capacity (maximum length and thickness of work metal), the hydraulic shear is slow in operation. However, for shearing pieces that are short in relation to blade length, the ram stroke can be shortened and the cutting speed can be increased. For very short strokes, the hydraulic shear can approach, or sometimes equal, the strokes per minute of a mechanical shear.

Table 1. Shearing Capacities for Various Metals Compared to Low-Carbon Steel

Thickness of low-carbon steel, in.(a)	Thickness (in.) that can be sheared with same force as used for low-carbon steel: 302 stainless steel(b)	Full-hard strip steel	Aluminum and alloys
0.060	0.036	0.048	0.075
0.075	0.048	0.060	0.120
0.120	0.060	0.075	0.134
0.134	0.075	0.105	3/16
3/16	0.134	5/32	7/32
1/4	3/16	3/16	1/4
5/16	7/32	7/32	3/8
3/8	1/4	1/4	7/16
7/16	5/16	5/16	1/2
1/2	3/8	3/8	5/8
5/8	7/16	7/16	3/4
3/4	1/2	1/2	1
7/8	5/8	5/8	1 1/4
1	3/4	3/4	1 1/2
1 1/4	1	1	2

(a) Also applicable to strip steel (soft to half-hard), aluminum-clad steel, and copper and copper alloys. (b) Applicable also to most other austenitic stainless steels, normalized alloy steels such as 4130 and 8630, annealed high-carbon steel, and annealed tool steel.

Greater hold-down pressure is required for cutting the same work-metal thickness with hydraulic shears than is needed with mechanical shears. This is because the greater blade clearances and larger rake angles that often are used with hydraulic shears increase the likelihood of deflection of the work metal during shearing.

Greater blade clearance must be used to prevent the stalling of hydraulic shears when shearing work of large area, especially at or near maximum capacity of thickness. For example, in cutting a 10-by-10-ft plate into two equal parts, resistance to shearing is equal on both sides of the blade, and greater shearing force is required than for trimming a narrow strip from a 10-ft-long plate. Increasing the blade clearance reduces double shearing and permits a more natural fracture with greatly reduced force.

If hydraulic shears were built for overloading, they would lose much or all of their safety advantage. Furthermore, the cost of equipment would be considerably increased.

Mechanical shears have the extra or overload capacity to cut large-area plates with close blade clearances. However, mechanical shears sacrifice the safety feature of hydraulic shears.

Pneumatic shears are used almost exclusively for shearing thin metal (seldom thicker than 0.060 in.) in relatively short pieces (seldom longer than 5 ft).

Alligator shears have a shearing action like that of a pair of scissors. The lower blade is stationary, and the upper blade is held securely in an arm and moves in an arc around a fulcrum pin. (The two types of alligator shears are described and illustrated on page 274.)

This type of machine is the most versatile of all power-driven shears. It can shear plate, sheet and strip, although its greatest use is for shearing bars and bar sections and for preparing scrap.

Alligator shears are available in a range of sizes including those that can shear plate up to 1¼ in. thick by 30 in. long, and plate up to 2 in. thick in shorter lengths. These machines vary in weight from about 2500 to 43,000 lb. The lighter machines can be made portable; the heavier machines, however, must be anchored firmly in concrete, especially if they are to be used in conjunction with roller conveyor tables in the shearing of plate.

Capacity. Most shearing machines are rated according to the section size of low-carbon steel they can cut. The tensile strength of low-carbon steel sheet and plate is generally no higher than 75,000 psi. The use of a machine for shearing other metals depends primarily on the relation of the tensile strength of low-carbon steel to that of the metal to be sheared. Metals having a tensile strength greater than low-carbon steel almost always reduce the capacity of the machine. For example, the machine capacity for shearing high-strength low-alloy steels is reduced to about two thirds to three quarters of the rated capacity for low-carbon steel. Conversely, for shearing aluminum alloys machine capacity can range from 1¼ to 1½ times the rated capacity for low-carbon steel.

Some examples of relative shearing capacity are presented in Table 1. Metal thicknesses given in this table are based on the thickness of low-carbon steel that can be sheared with the same shearing capacity. For instance, a specific force is required to shear ¼-in.-thick low-carbon steel. Table 1 shows that the same force can shear only a 3/16-in. thickness of type 302 stainless steel, but can shear a ⅜-in. thickness of aluminum.

Ductility, measured by elongation of the work metal, also can affect machine capacity. Annealed copper, for example, because of its high elongation, requires as much shearing effort as low-carbon steel — even though copper has considerably lower tensile strength.

Power Requirements. The energy consumed during shearing depends on the product of the average stress, the cross-sectional area to be sheared, and the depth of maximum blade penetration at the instant of final fracture of the work metal. For any metal, the amount of energy consumed is proportional to the area under the shearing stress-strain curve for that metal.

Typical shearing stress-strain curves for hot rolled and cold rolled steels are shown in Fig. 3. For these metals the average stress is 73.5% of the maximum shearing stress (S_s).

As shown in Fig. 3, the distance through which the force acts (blade penetration) is near 35% of the thickness for hot rolled steel and 18.5% for cold rolled steel. Taking the curve for hot rolled steel (Fig. 3) as an example, the average stress under the curve is 73.5% of the maximum stress and the distance through which the force acts is 35% of the work-metal thickness; hence, the energy used in shearing is:

$$\text{Energy (in.-lb)} = 0.735S_s \times Wt \times 0.35t = 0.257S_s \times Wt^2$$

where S_s is maximum shearing stress, psi; W is work-metal width, in.; and t is work-metal thickness, in.

Applying the same formula to the curve for cold rolled steel in Fig. 3, the energy consumption is $0.136S_s \times Wt^2$.

The maximum instantaneous horsepower required for cutting work metal in a shear is determined by:

$$\text{Hp max} = \frac{W \times t \times S_s \times V}{33{,}000}$$

where W is work-metal width, in.; t is work-metal thickness, in.; S_s is maximum shearing stress, psi; and V is speed of shear blade, ft per min.

The average power requirement for a shear making N cuts per minute is:

$$\text{Hp avg} = \frac{W \times t^2 \times N \times S_s}{1{,}540{,}000}$$

The above formulas for maximum and average horsepower determine the net power required for actual shearing of the workpiece. The amount of power to overcome friction must be added to net power.

Friction depends on design of the shearing machine and the blade, type of bearings, alignment, lubrication, temperature of operation, and size of the machine in relation to the area of the section to be sheared. When shearing metal of nearly the maximum size for which a shear is designed, the loss of horsepower by friction for well-designed machines seldom exceeds 25% of the gross horsepower.

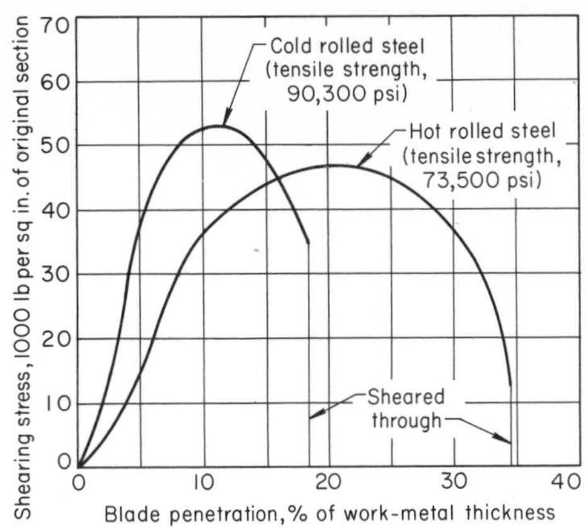

Fig. 3. Typical shearing stress-strain curves for hot rolled and cold rolled steels (F. E. Flynn and D. A. McArthur)

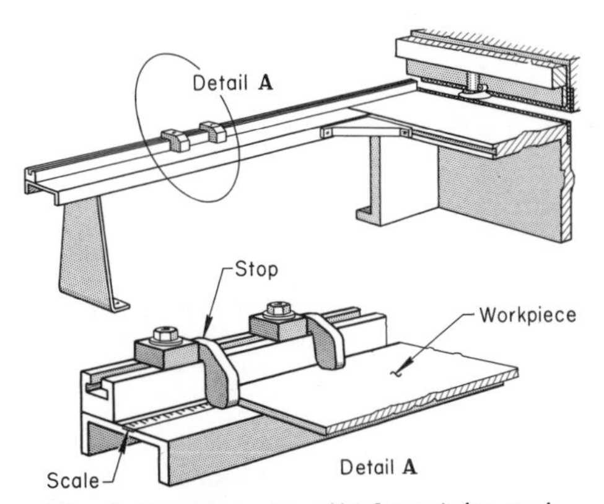

Fig. 4. Squaring-arm attachment for positioning of long pieces in a shearing machine

Accessory Equipment for Straight-Blade Shearing

Accessory equipment is useful and often required for efficient and accurate straight-blade shearing.

Hold-downs (see Fig. 2) are mechanical or hydraulic devices that hold the work metal firmly in position to prevent movement during shearing. The most efficient hold-down system is a series of independent units that securely clamp stock of varying thickness automatically and without adjustment.

The force on each hold-down foot must be substantial and can range from several hundred pounds on a machine for shearing sheet to several tons for shearing plate. Hold-downs must be timed automatically with the stroke of the ram so that they clamp the work metal securely before the blade makes contact and release their hold instantly after shearing is completed.

Back gages are adjustable stops that permit reproducibility of dimensions of sheared workpieces in a production run. These gages are controlled either manually or electrically from the operator's position at the front of the shear. Push-button control provides a selection of fast traverse speeds and slow locating movements for accurate final positioning. Accurate gage screws, compensating nuts, precision slides and guides, and decimal indicators permit gage settings to an accuracy of 0.001 to 0.002 in.

For thin sheet, magnetic overhead rollers eliminate sag and support the sheet for accurate gaging to a depth of 48 in. into the shear. For rapid and accurate cutting, back gages are equipped with electronic sensors that automatically trip the shear only when the sheet is accurately positioned.

Back gages are also equipped with retractable stops for shearing mill plate. With the stops out of the way, mill plate of almost any length can be fed into the shear and cut to the desired length. When stops are not used, the workpiece can be notched or scribed to indicate the cutoff position.

Front Gages. When gaging from the front of the machine, the operator locates the work metal by means of stops secured in the table or in the front support arms. Front gaging is often done by means of a squaring arm.

Squaring arms are extensions attached to the entrance side of a shearing machine that are used to hold long sections of work metal in the proper position for shearing. Each arm is provided with a linear scale and with stops for accurate, consistent positioning of the work metal. Squaring arms are reversible to allow use at either end of the shear and to distribute the wear on shear blades. Figure 4 shows a squaring arm attached to a squaring shear.

Straight Shear Blades

Most shear blades are made in one piece from tool steel; some are made of carbon or alloy steel with hard-faced cutting edges or with inserts of tool steel or carbide. The composition, thickness and quantity of metal being sheared are the most important factors in the selection of blade material. In Table 2, D2 tool steel is recommended in eight instances for cold shearing of metals up to ¼ in. thick, and in six of these instances it is the sole recommendation. For low-volume production or occasional shearing of metals up to ¼ in. thick (except the more highly abrasive metals such as silicon steel), blades made of W2, W3 and L6 tool steels are recommended. Blades made of A2 tool steel have been satisfactory for high-production cold shearing of soft nonferrous metals, but D2 blades are usually more economical because of better wear resistance. For cold shearing of metal more than ¼ in. thick, blades made of D2 tool steel usually are not recommended, because they are likely to break under impact loads. However, depending mainly on blade design and length of cut, blades made of D2 tool steel have been used successfully for cold shearing of aluminum alloys up to 1¼ in. thick.

Table 2. Recommended Materials for Straight Shear Blades for Cold Shearing of Flat Metal(a)

Metal to be sheared	Thickness, less than ¼ in.: Low production	Thickness, less than ¼ in.: High production	Thickness, ¼ to ½ in.: Low production	Thickness, ¼ to ½ in.: High production	Thickness, ½ in. or more
Carbon and low-alloy steels with up to 0.35 C	W2 or W3 with 1.00-1.25 C; or L6	D2	W2 or W3 with 0.85-1.00 C; or L6	A2	S2(b) S5(c)
Carbon and low-alloy steels with 0.35 C or more	W2 or W3 with 1.00-1.25 C; or L6	D2	W2 or W3 with 0.80-0.90 C; or L6	S5	S2 S5(c)
Stainless steels and heat-resisting alloys	W2 or W3 with 1.00-1.25 C; or L6	D2	S2 S5	A2	S2 S5(c)
High-silicon electrical steels	D2	D2 Carbide(f)	S2(d) S5(d)	S2(d) S5(d)	(e)
Copper alloys and aluminum alloys	W2 or W3 with 1.00-1.25 C; or L6	A2 D2	W2 or W3 with 0.85-1.00 C; or L6	A2	S2(g) S5(c)
Titanium and alloys	D2	D2	...	...	...

(a) The recommended tool materials are identified in Table 7 on page 481. (b) For low production, steel W2 or W3 with 0.70 to 0.80% C may be used for shearing low-carbon steel (less than 0.35% C) ½ to ¾ in. thick. (c) Steel S5 is preferred for work thicker than ¾ in. (d) High-silicon steel ¼ to ½ in. thick is usually sheared at about 500 F. (e) Seldom sheared in thicknesses of ½ in. or more. (f) As inserts; usually these are brazed into tempered medium-carbon or low-alloy steel. (g) For low production quantities, W2 or W3 tool steels containing 0.80 to 0.90% C may be used for shearing metal ½ to ¾ in. thick.

The W2 or W3 steels with low carbon content (0.80 to 1.00%) and L6 steel are suitable for shear blades for some cold shearing applications in which the work metal is more than ¼ in. thick, as shown in Table 2. However, the shock-resisting grades S2 and S5 are usually recommended for shearing heavy sections of all metals, although L6 is often used instead.

Length and design of the blade sometimes influence the selection of blade material. Despite the fact that water-hardening tool steels such as W1 and W2 are suitable for many cold shearing applications, heat treatment causes greater distortion in these steels than in the oil-hardening or air-hardening grades. To make a shear blade 164 in. long from D2 tool steel, a bar 163¾ in. long is required. The same blade made from W2 requires a bar 164¼ in. long. Both steels elongate when heat treated, but W2 will bow more readily than D2. Because straightening is difficult, the W2 blade must have more grinding stock. The additional grinding decreases the depth of the hardened shell and shortens the useful life of the blade.

Hardness. The rate at which a blade wears in cold shearing depends chiefly on its carbon content and hardness. Shallow-hardening tool steels such as those in the W group may equal D2 in performance until several sharpenings have ground away the hardened shell; then their hardness is lower, and life between grinds decreases accordingly.

Insufficient hardness of a blade used for cold shearing will shorten the life of the blade. In one application, a blade made of S5 tool steel with a hardness of Rockwell C 44 wore three times as fast as one with a hardness of Rockwell C 54 used under the same conditions.

Despite the desirability of having shear blades as hard as possible to minimize wear, it is often necessary to sacrifice hardness to prevent blade breakage as the hardness or thickness of the metal being sheared increases.

Recommendations for the hardness of blades for cold shearing cannot always be made without knowledge of the details of the operation. For example, a D2 blade performed satisfactorily at Rockwell C 61 in one application, whereas blades this hard broke under similar operating conditions in a different plant. Blades made of D2 steel will usually operate successfully at Rockwell C 58 to 60 for shearing low-carbon steel up to ¼ in. thick, and in many instances blades made of D2 have been used successfully at Rockwell C 60 to 62. However, in shearing high-strength low-alloy steel, the hardness of a D2 blade must be kept below Rockwell C 58 to prevent breakage.

The shock-resisting S grades of tool steel are used in the hardness range of Rockwell C 45 to 55. The higher end of this range is applicable to the shearing of steels ¼ to ½ in. thick and also to the shearing of nonferrous metals. As shock loading increases with shearing of harder or thicker metals, blade hardness is decreased toward the low side of the above hardness range. For further details on shear-blade materials, see the article "The Selection of Material for Shear Blades", pages 755 to 758 in Volume 1 of this Handbook.

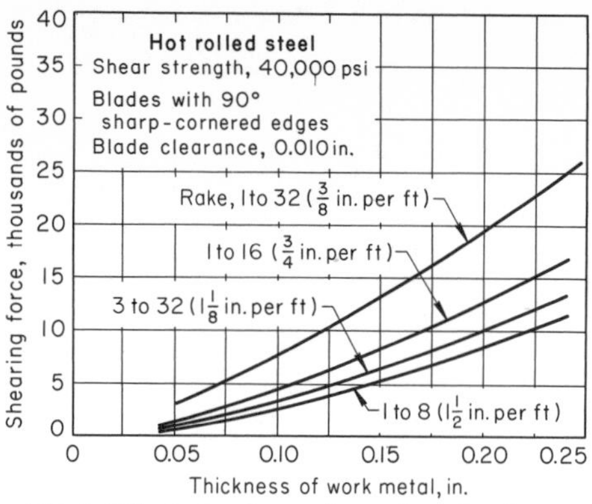

Fig. 5. Effect of rake angle on shearing force

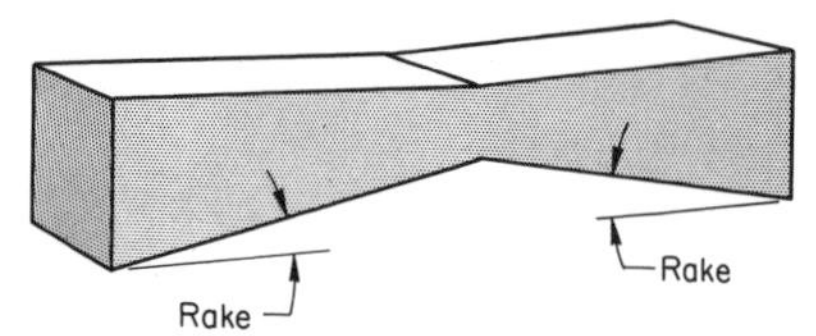

Fig. 6. "Bow-tie" shear blade, with rake in two directions

Rake is the slope of the angle formed by the cutting edges of the upper and lower blades (see Fig. 2). Rake may be expressed as the ratio of the amount of rise to a given linear measurement; for example, a rake of 1 to 16 means that the upper blade rises 1 in. for each 16 in. of linear distance along the blades. Rake is also expressed as one number; the unexpressed second number is assumed to be 1 ft of linear distance. For example, a ¾-in. rake means that the upper blade is mounted at an angle resulting in a ¾-in. rise per foot, which is the same as a 1-to-16 rake.

Rake is used to permit progressive shearing of the work metal along the length of the blade. This reduces the amount of force required and allows the use of a smaller machine than would be necessary if the cutting edges of the blades were parallel. Figure 5 shows the effect of rake angle, expressed in ratios, on force required for shearing various thicknesses of hot rolled steel sheet. Note that the shearing force is lowest for the 1-to-8 ratio (which results in the steepest rake angle), and that the force required for shearing any given thickness increases as the angle becomes flatter.

It is not possible, however, to make accurate calculations of required force for different thicknesses of work metal based solely on change of rake, because blade penetration varies for different thicknesses. Even for low-carbon steel, the amount of blade penetration before fracturing occurs can be as great as 60% of the work-metal thickness for 0.135-in.-thick (10-gage) stock and as little as 30% for ¾-in.-thick stock.

Three typical relations among metal thickness, force, and penetration for low-carbon steel are:

1 To shear ¾-in.-thick plate with a blade having a rake angle of ¾ in. per foot, the load is 141,000 lb, based on a shear-blade penetration of 31%.
2 To shear ½-in.-thick plate using a rake angle of ⅜ in. per foot, the load is 148,000 lb, based on a blade penetration of 37%.
3 To shear 0.135-in.-thick sheet using a rake angle of ⅛ in. per foot, the load is 52,000 lb, based on a blade penetration of 60%.

The main disadvantage of using a high rake angle is that it increases distortion of the work. Large rake angles can also cause slippage, and therefore require high hold-down forces.

A variation of the one-direction-rake shear blade shown in Fig. 2 is the two-direction rake produced by a "bow-tie" blade (Fig. 6). This blade equalizes side thrust because cutting begins at each side of the workpiece and progresses uniformly to the center.

A disadvantage of the two-direction-rake blade is the increased force required for making two cuts simultaneously. Another disadvantage is that many bow-tie blades are not reversible; consequently, their total life is shorter.

Clearance. Excessive blade clearance causes the work metal to be wiped down between the blades during cutting and results in heavy burring or flanging of the work metal. The burrs and deformed metal are objectionable because of their interference with subsequent processing. A more serious consequence of excessive clearance is that it can cause the workpiece to be pulled between the blades, which in turn causes overloading of the machine and may result in breakage of machine components or shear blades.

When soft metals are sheared, insufficient clearance results in double (secondary) shearing, which appears as a burnished area at top and bottom of the sheared edge, with a rough area between the burnished edges. Because of the difference in action, greater tolerances usually are required when shearing in a hydraulic machine than in a mechanical machine — all other conditions being equal. Some mechanical shears are constructed so as to operate with a fixed clearance, and no adjustments are made for variations of work-metal composition or thickness. To prevent double shearing, the ram is made to travel downward at an angle approximately 2° from the perpendicular. This causes the cutting edge of the movable blade to travel away from the ruptured section of the workpiece as indicated in Fig. 1.

In general, greater blade clearance is required for shearing hard steels than for shearing soft steels, because soft steels fracture more quickly, thus allowing a cleaner cut.

Because of deflection, clearance at the center of the blade is usually less than at the ends. The difference increases as blade length increases.

Blade clearance (except on machines using a fixed clearance) is generally increased as work-metal thickness increases. For example, in one plant a clearance of approximately 0.003 in. is used for squaring shears with a capacity of up to ¼-in.-thick low-carbon steel. To minimize blade deflection,

Table 3. Effects of Variables on the Twisting of Work Metal During Shearing

Variable increased	Effect on twisting
Thickness of work metal	Increase
Hardness of work metal	Decrease
Width of sheared backpiece	Decrease
Length of work metal	Increase
Stress in work metal	Increase
Rake angle of blade	Increase
Blade speed	Decrease

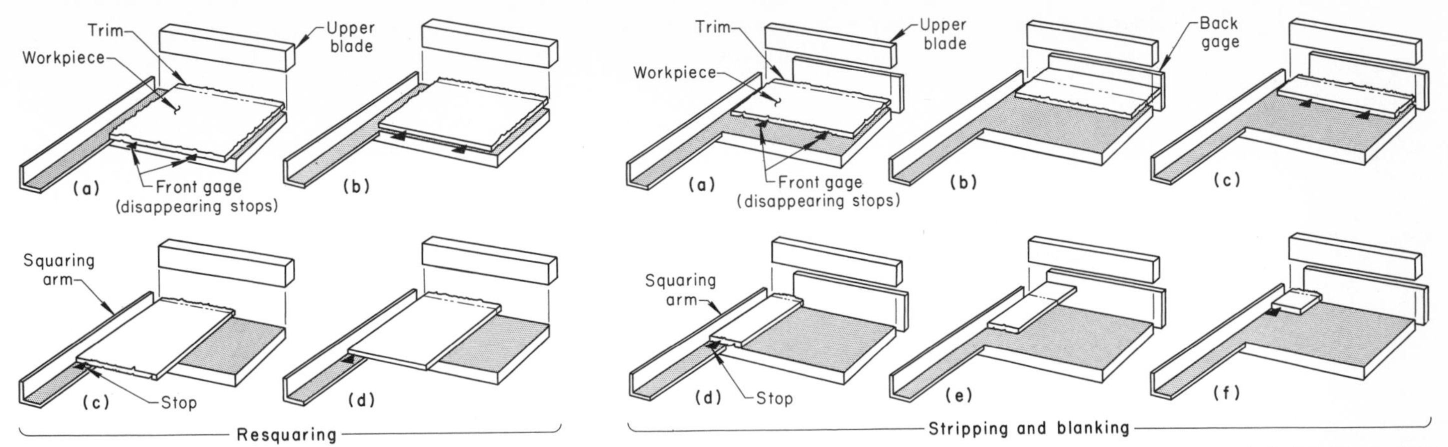

Resquaring: (a) Workpiece is placed against front gage stops; one side is trimmed. (b) Trimmed side is placed against a second pair of front gage stops; second side is trimmed to produce blank of specified width and with parallel sides. (c) One side is placed against squaring arm; one end is trimmed. (d) Second end is trimmed to produce blank of specified length. Ends are square with parallel sides.

Stripping and Blanking: (a) Workpiece is placed against front gage stops; one side is trimmed. (b) Trimmed side is placed against back gage stop to produce first strip. Procedure is repeated. (c) Final strip from original workpiece is produced by placing trimmed side against front gage stops and trimming off rough side. (d) Strip is placed against squaring arm; one end is trimmed. (e) Strip is fed to back gage stops and sheared to produce first blank of specified length. Procedure is repeated for production of subsequent blanks. (f) Trimmed end of strip is placed against front gage stop; rough end is trimmed to produce final blank of specified length from first strip.

Fig. 7. Sequence of operations for resquaring and for stripping and blanking of sheet and plate

clearance at the center of the blade is reduced to 0.002 in. For example, the clearance for shearing low-carbon steel ranging from ¼ to 1 in. in thickness is 0.014 in. at each end of the blades and 0.012 in. at the center of 10-to-12-ft-long blades used in a mechanical shear.

Ram Speed in Straight-Blade Shearing

Speed of the ram (and, in turn, of the blade) has a marked effect on results in shearing of flat stock. Low linear speed increases distortion of the workpiece and produces a rough sheared surface. As speed is increased, less distortion occurs, and a cleaner sheared surface is obtained. In general, speeds up to 70 to 80 ft per min can be used without difficulty when shearing annealed metals. Regardless of the speed used, adequate hold-down force is mandatory.

Harder work metal requires lower shearing speed, to avoid blade chipping and premature dulling. When work-metal hardness is Rockwell C 30 or higher, speeds greater than 50 ft per min are not recommended, and much slower speeds may be required for acceptable blade life (see Example 343, in the article on Shearing of Bars).

Accuracy in Straight-Blade Shearing

The dimensional accuracy obtained in shearing is influenced by the capacity of the machine, the condition of the blades, blade clearance, and the thickness of the work metal.

Squaring shears, properly set up and maintained, can cut sheet stock to a dimensional accuracy of ±0.0005 in. per foot when thickness is no greater than about 0.135 in. A tolerance of ±0.001 in. per foot is required for thicker sheet. These tolerances apply regardless of length.

Expressed as total tolerance, sheets no thicker than approximately 0.135 in. can be cut to size within 0.010 in., and strips can be sheared to width within 0.010 in. These tolerances apply to stock up to 12 ft long that is essentially free from stress and is flat within commercial limits. Sheets that are not flat or that have residual stress, or both, cannot be sheared with the same accuracy.

Greater tolerances are required in shearing plate. A total tolerance of between 0.020 and 0.040 in. can be maintained when plate is sheared in squaring shears. Dimensions can be held to a tolerance of about ±1⁄16 in. when shearing in alligator shears.

Production Practice in Straight-Blade Shearing

Procedures for two common shearing operations — namely, squaring a sheet or plate to a specified size, and cutting small rectangular pieces of a specified size from a large sheet or plate — are illustrated in Fig. 7. As shown in Fig. 7, when stripping and blanking small rectangular pieces, the large work metal is trimmed on one edge only, after which it is stripped (sheared to narrow, parallel strips). The ends of the strips are then trimmed to reduce handling.

Shearing of more than one thickness of metal at the same time is seldom done, because of the large force required. The action in shearing multiple thicknesses is that of cutting through each thickness, instead of causing each piece to break away after partial penetration by the blade as in shearing a single thickness. Shearing of multiple thicknesses thus demands more power than shearing of single pieces equivalent in thickness to a stack. Also, the edges of stack-sheared pieces are not acceptable for most fabricating operations, because of heavy burrs.

When enough power is available, multiple-thickness shearing is sometimes done in cutting up scrap, for which quality of edge is unimportant.

Problems often encountered in shearing flat stock are excessive burring, and distortion in the form of camber, twist or bow. Burrs are caused usually by dull blades, or sometimes by improper blade clearance. Camber, twist and bow can result from excessive rake of the shear blade, dull blades, improper blade clearance, condition of the work metal, or low blade speed. Seven process variables that influence twisting of the work metal are listed in Table 3, which shows the effect of an increase in these variables on the amount of twisting.

Shearing vs Gas Cutting

Straight-blade shearing or slitting is the usual method employed for cutting sheet stock. Plate stock, however, is cut by shearing, gas cutting, or electric-arc cutting (see the articles "Gas Cutting" and "Electric-Arc Cutting", on pages 278 and 301, respectively), depending largely on its thickness. In general, gas cutting is the preferred method for cutting plate 1½ in. thick or more.

For metal thicknesses up to 1 in., shearing is faster, more accurate, and more economical than gas cutting, and produces a smoother surface. In a specific operation involving steel plates 144 by 15 by ½ in., the time required for shearing was 1.8 min versus 11.3 min for gas cutting. Similar plates ¾ in. thick required 2.2 min for shearing versus 12 min for gas cutting. Setup time for shearing was approximately the same as for gas cutting.

Rotary Shearing

Rotary shearing, or circle shearing (not to be confused with slitting), is a process for cutting sheet and plate in a straight line or in contours by means of two revolving tapered circular cutters. Recommended cutter materials are given in Table 4.

For conventional cutting, to produce a perpendicular edge, the cutters approach each other and line up vertically at one point (Fig. 8). The point of cutting is also a pivot point for the workpiece; because of the round shape of the blades, they offer no obstruction to movement of the workpiece to the right or left. This feature permits cutting of circles and irregular shapes

Table 4. Recommended Blade Materials for Rotary Shearing of Flat Metal(a)

Metal to be sheared	Thickness to be sheared: 3/16 in. or less	3/16 in. to 1/4 in.	1/4 in. or more
Carbon, alloy and stainless steels	D2(b)	A2(c)	S4; S5
High-silicon electrical steels	M2(d); D2(e)	D2	...
Copper and aluminum alloys	A2; D2	A2; D2	A2(f)
Titanium and titanium alloys	D2(g); A2(h)	...	...

(a) The recommended tool materials are identified in Table 7 on page 481. (b) Steel L6 is also recommended for shearing carbon and low-alloy sheet that contains more than 0.35% C. (c) Steel D2 is also recommended for low-carbon and low-alloy sheet. (d) For sheet less than 1/32 in. thick. (e) For sheet more than 1/32 in. thick. (f) Steel S5 is recommended for sheet thicker than 1/2 in. (g) For sheet thinner than 1/8 in. (h) For sheet more than 1/8 in. thick.

that have small radii, and cutting in straight lines.

Overlapping of the cutters to the position shown in Fig. 9 permits shearing of smooth beveled edges in straight lines or in circular shapes. With the cutters positioned as shown in Fig. 9, a bevel can be cut across the entire thickness of the workpiece, resulting in a sharp edge on the bottom of the workpiece, or (by varying the overlap of the cutters) only a corner of the workpiece can be sheared off, leaving a vertical edge (or "land") for approximately half the workpiece thickness. Both conditions are illustrated in Fig. 9.

Shearing of workpieces into circular blanks requires the use of a holding fixture that permits rotation of the workpiece to generate the desired circle. For straight-line cutting in a rotary shear, a straight-edge fixture is used, mounted in the throat of the machine behind the cutter heads.

Applicability. Any metal composition or hardness that can be sheared by straight blades can be sheared by rotary cutters.

In general, rotary shearing in commercially available machines is limited to work metal 1 in. or less in thickness. There is no minimum thickness. For example, 400-mesh wire cloth made from 0.0010-in.-diam wire can be sheared successfully by the rotary method.

Circles up to 10 ft in diameter or larger can be produced by using special clamping equipment. Minimum diameters depend on thickness of the work metal and size of the rotary cutters. With material up to 1/8 in. in thickness, the minimum circle that can normally be cut is 6 in. in diameter. For 1/4-in.-thick stock, the minimum diameter is 9 in., and for 1-in.-thick stock, the minimum diameter is 24 in.

Rotary shearing is limited to cutting one workpiece at a time. As in straight-blade shearing, multiple layers cannot be sheared because each layer prevents the necessary breakthrough of the preceding workpiece.

Rotary shearing, gas cutting, and electric-arc cutting are competitive for some operations. Each can produce straight or beveled edges of comparable accuracy. Selection of one of the three processes depends largely on the thickness of the work metal. In general, rotary shearing is used for cutting sheet and plate less than 1 in. thick, and gas cutting for thicknesses of 1 in. or more.

Gas cutting is less suitable for cutting a single thickness of sheet or thin plate because the heat causes excessive distortion, but it is often feasible to minimize this problem by stack cutting (cutting several thicknesses at a time). Gas cutting is more versatile than rotary shearing; it can produce smaller circles than rotary shearing, and can produce rings in one operation.

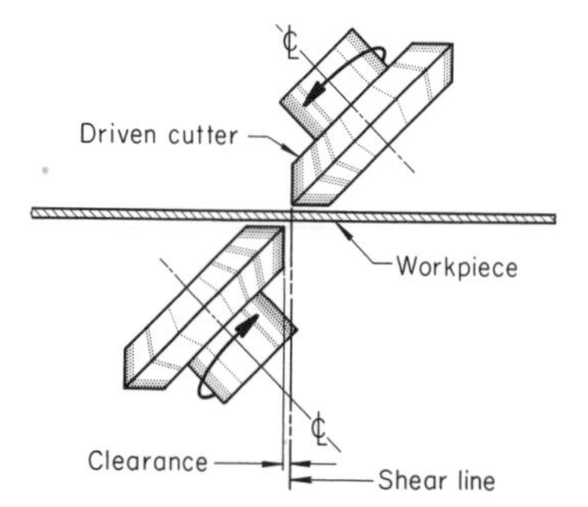

Fig. 8. Conventional arrangement of cutters in a rotary shearing machine, for production of a perpendicular edge

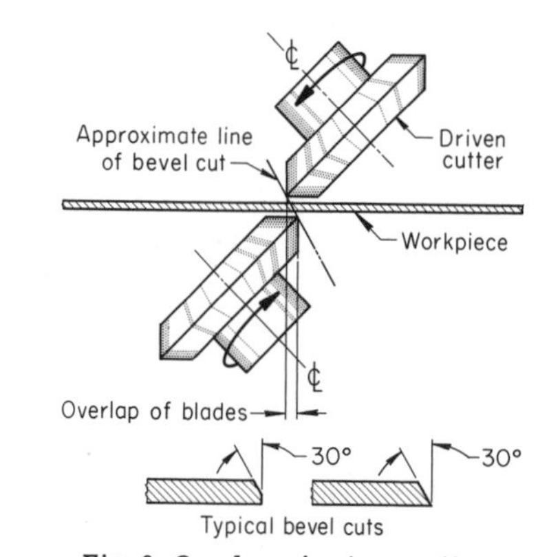

Fig. 9. Overlap of rotary cutters for production of beveled edges

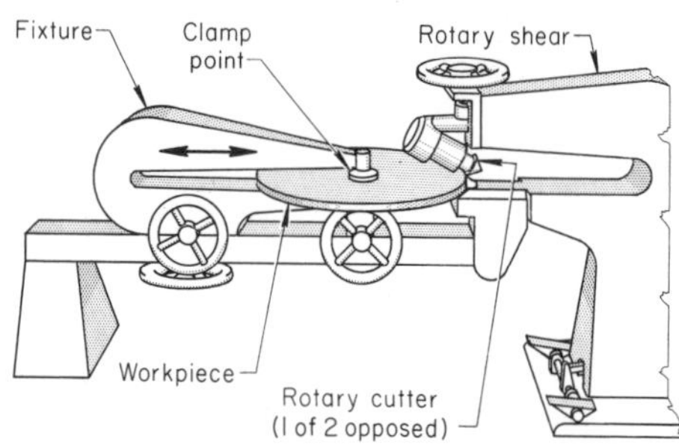

Fig. 10. C-frame fixture and rotary shearing machine for cutting a circle

Circle Generation. For cutting circles, the workpiece is placed in a special fixture consisting of a C-shaped, deep-throated frame having a rotating pin or clamp point at its outer extremity. Figure 10 illustrates one type of C-frame fixture attached to a rotary shearing machine.

The maximum circle that can be sheared is governed by the depth of the throat of the clamp, and the amount of clearance necessary to permit the rotating workpiece to clear the deep part of the C-frame on the machine. Therefore, when using square blanks, removal of the corners permits an increase in the size of the circle that can be cut.

There are two methods of holding the center point of the work metal during circular shearing. In one method, the work metal is clamped by a screw-type handwheel (Fig. 10) or by an air cylinder, each of which incorporates two pivoting pressure disks, one above and one below the workpiece. The disks permit the workpiece to rotate in a horizontal plane. The other method is by center pinning. In this method, a hole is drilled or punched in the work metal for locating and rotating it on a pin in the center clamping attachment. The hole is at the predetermined center of the circle to be produced.

Of the two methods, center pinning provides greater rigidity because the work metal cannot slip off center during shearing. The circle generated when the work metal is held by the clamping method may not be perfectly true if the clamping fixture has not been properly located or has shifted because of pressure on the cutters. The disadvantage of center pinning is that a hole must be made in the work, and must be closed by plug welding if not wanted in the finished product.

Adjustment of Rotary Cutters. The upper cutter head and drive of a rotary shear is raised and lowered by power. A clutch mechanism limits upward and downward travel. Power movement of the upper cutter is essential (especially when cutting plate stock), because the shearing edges of the cutters must be moved toward each other in proper alignment to create initial shearing action. Often in setting up, the work metal is rotated in the clamp attachment with the cutter exerting light pressure to determine whether a true circle is being generated. Additional pressure is then applied by the vertical screwdown of the upper cutter to cause shearing.

Only the upper cutter is rotated by the power-drive system. The pinching and rotating action of the upper cutter causes the work metal to rotate between the cutters, and the work metal causes the bottom cutter to rotate.

The position of the upper cutter in relation to the lower cutter is important. Figure 8 shows the setting for shearing a straight edge. Clearance between the cutters is just as important as it is with straight blades.

Overlap of the cutters as shown in Fig. 9 produces a bevel cut. The degree of bevel up to a maximum of 30° can be adjusted by changing the amount of overlap of the cutters.

Accuracy of the sheared circle depends on rigidity of the center clamping device, sharpness of the cutters, maintenance of optimum clearance between the cutters, thickness of the work metal, and cutting speed.

For work metal up to about 1/8 in. in thickness, dimensional accuracy within ±1/32 in. can be obtained when generating a 30-in.-diam circle. With proper setup of equipment, the sheared edge will show only a slight indication of the initial penetration.

Speeds of 8 to 22 ft per min are most commonly used for rotary shearing of metal up to 1/4 in. thick. For rotary shearing of metal 1/4 to 1 in. thick, speeds of 5 to 10 ft per min are used.

Flanging and Joggling. The rotary shear can be used for forming flanges and joggles on flat stock. The maximum joggle that can be produced usually is limited to the thickness of the work metal. Because the work metal is made to flow into a different shape during flanging or joggling, the amount of energy required reduces the capacity of the machine to 75% of the rated capacity for shearing.

For flanging or joggling, the cutters of a rotary shear are replaced with forming tools. A typical setup for forming a joggle is shown in Fig. 11.

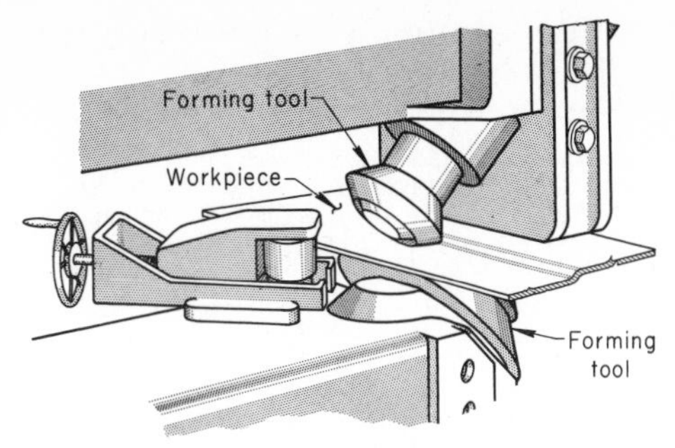

Fig. 11. Setup and tooling for forming a joggle in plate stock with a rotary shear

Safety

Shearing machines must have safety devices to protect personnel from the hazards of shear blades, flywheels, gears and other moving parts. Safety devices must be rigid enough to prevent damage from falling objects.

Squaring shears should have guards on all moving parts including flywheels, hold-downs and blades. The treadle, whether mechanical or electrical, should have a lock. Blade-guard openings should be no larger than ½ in., to keep the operator's fingers out of the danger area. Hold-downs should be similarly guarded.

Shears used for shearing plate are more difficult to guard because of the greater clearances required under the hold-down and blade guards to permit entry of the plate (especially when it is bowed or buckled). Guards on shears for plate should be of a type that rise only when the plate is inserted and then rest on the surface of the plate, thereby preventing openings for fingers or hands. When there is no workpiece in the machine, the guards rest on the surface of the table.

A sweep arm, if properly designed, has some merit as a safety device on a squaring shear. This device sweeps across the front of the machine between the blade and the operator. It must be designed so that it closes all dangerous openings into the shear prior to the stroke of the machine.

Safety regulations also cover the maximum noise level permitted from a shearing operation to prevent permanent impairment of hearing. In general, the maximum is 95 decibels.

Selected Reference

H. J. Crasemann, Kraefte in Scheren, *Werkstattstecruk,* **51,** 396-403 (Aug 1961). Examines the calculation of forces involved in shearing. (In German.)

Slitting and Shearing of Coiled Sheet and Strip

*By the ASM Committee on Shearing and Slitting**

COILED sheet or strip is cut to size for further processing, by slitting, for dividing it into narrower coils, and by shearing, for cutting it into flat pieces of specified length.

Slitting

A slitting line for cutting wide coiled stock into narrower widths consists essentially of an uncoiler for holding the coil, one or more slitters, and a re-coiler for simultaneous coiling of all slit strips (Fig. 1). Other equipment can be added to the line for scrap disposal, coil handling and packaging, leveling and edge conditioning.

Slitting is done by circular blades mounted on two arbors of the slitter.

Slitting lines are broadly classified as driven or pull-through types. In the driven type, uncoiler, slitter and re-coiler are each driven by a separate motor. The motors are synchronized to maintain constant speed of the metal as it travels through the slitting line.

In a pull-through slitting line, the drive motors on the slitter and uncoiler are used only to feed the coil stock far enough through the slitter to permit attaching the slit strips to the re-coiler. After the strips are attached, the motors for the uncoiler and slitter are disconnected and the driven re-coiler pulls the strip from the uncoiler through the slitter.

The choice between driven and pull-through lines depends largely on work-metal strength and thickness, number of slits, and slitting speed. In general, for slitting metal less than 0.010 in. thick, a driven slitter is preferred, because thin-gage metal is likely to tear in a pull-through slitter.

*For committee list, see page 265.

Power Requirements. The power needed to slit four different metals at 80 ft per minute is shown in Fig. 2. Source of the data is "Cold Roll-Forming and Manipulation of Light-Gauge Sections", by E. Griffin, *Journal of the Institute of Metals,* **84,** 1955-56, 181-197. For inclusion of pull-through and coiling power, cutting power should be multiplied by a factor of 1.5 to 2. Tension for pull-through slitting can be calculated by the formula:

$$L = nS_s t^2$$

Where L is the tension load per cut, n is the number of cuts, S_s is the shear strength, and t is the thickness of the work metal. For a strip 0.080 in. thick, about 320 lb of tension per cut is needed in low-alloy high-strength steel, 260 lb in low-carbon steel or hard brass, and about 200 lb for medium-strength aluminum or quarter-hard brass.

Stock Width and Thickness. Most coiled flat rolled steel that is slit and re-coiled is 36 to 60 in. wide and 0.020 to 0.125 in. thick. Some lines, however, can slit coils as wide as 90 in. (or as wide as the mills produce) and others can accommodate coil stock less than 1 in. wide. Slitters are used regularly for the thickest metal produced in coils.

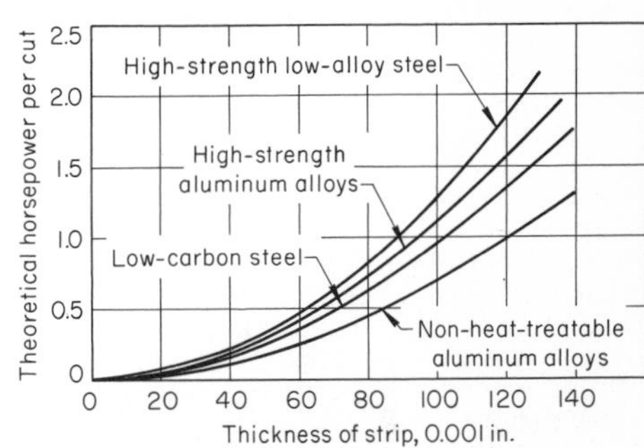

Fig. 2. Power required for slitting strip

Dimensional Accuracy. Commercial tolerances for slit widths of cold rolled low-carbon steel strip with a No. 3 edge are given in Table 1.

For hot rolled low-carbon steel strip 0.109 in. thick or less, tolerances of ±0.008 in. can be maintained on strip widths of 5 in. or less, ±0.010 in. on strip widths of 5 to 10 in., and ±0.016 in. on strip widths of 10 to 12 in.; for coil stock more than 0.109 in. thick, the tolerance that can be maintained is ±0.016 in. for all widths up to 12 in.

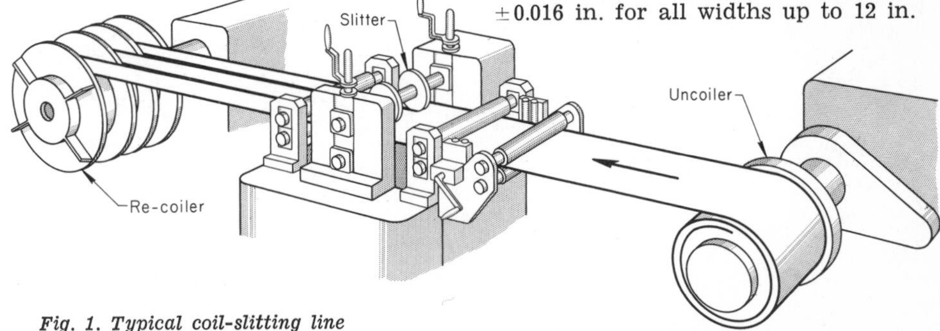

Fig. 1. Typical coil-slitting line

Table 1. Commercial Tolerances for Slit Widths of Cold Rolled Low-Carbon Steel Strip With a No. 3 Edge(a)

Thickness of strip, in.	Tolerance, in., for strip slit to width (in.) of: ½ or less(b)	Over ½ thru 6	Over 6 thru 9	Over 9 thru 12	Over 12 thru 20	Over 20 thru 23$\frac{15}{16}$
0.068 or less	±0.005	±0.005	±0.005	±0.010	±0.016	±0.020
0.069 to 0.099	±0.008	±0.008	±0.010	±0.010	±0.016	±0.020
0.100 to 0.160	±0.010	±0.010	±0.016	±0.016	±0.020	±0.020
0.161 to 0.249	...	±0.016	±0.020	±0.020	±0.031	±0.031

(a) No. 3 edge is an "approximately square edge" produced by slitting. (b) Slit strip ½ in. wide or less is called flat wire.

Closer tolerances for both hot and cold rolled low-carbon steels can be met by the use of special procedures and controls, but at an increase in cost. For instance, when slitting stock up to 0.060 in. thick to widths of less than 9 in., a width tolerance of ±0.002 in. can be maintained. However, when slitting to tolerances closer than ±0.005 in., slitters with precision bearings locked solidly in their housings must be used to minimize variation contributed by the machine. The setup must be accurate, and all operations must be performed under optimum conditions.

Burrs are normally present to some extent on slit edges. If burr-free edges are required, the slit strips are subsequently edge rolled.

Height of the burr depends mainly on rigidity and sharpness of the blades, horizontal and vertical blade clearances, rigidity of the slitting machine, variation in thickness of wide stock, and hardness of the metal being slit.

Wide stock generally varies in thickness across the width because of roll deflection during mill processing. The metal is thicker in the center than at the sides. This condition causes the arbor of the slitter to deflect and may require smaller vertical clearance between the blades to achieve acceptable slitting at the center of the strip. When compensation is made for variation in thickness and arbor deflection, the edge-trim blades often slit with improper vertical clearance, causing excessive burrs or blade pickup.

Minimum burr height can be achieved only by careful control of all variables. For example, sharp blades can be set to accurate clearances, but if the bearings of the slitter are loose, blade clearance will increase, resulting in larger burrs. Table 2 shows vertical (positive and negative) and horizontal clearances used in slitting operations at one plant.

Table 2. Vertical and Horizontal Clearances of Slitter Blades

Work-metal thickness, in.	Clearance, in.	Work-metal thickness, in.	Clearance, in.
Vertical Positive		**Vertical Negative**	
0.010	0.003	0.168	0.002
0.020	0.007	0.178	0.004
0.030	0.010	0.187	0.006
0.042	0.014	0.200	0.008
0.049	0.017	**Horizontal**	
0.059	0.022	0.008 or less .	0.000
0.068	0.020	0.009 to 0.010	0.0005
0.083	0.018	0.011 to 0.019	0.001
0.095	0.015	0.020 or more..	7 to 8% of the thickness of the work metal
0.102	0.013		
0.119	0.007		
0.134	0.005		
0.150	0.000		

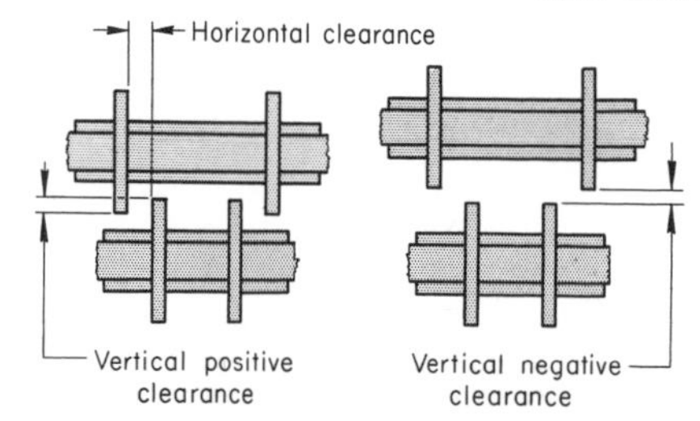

Camber, which is present to some extent in almost all coiled metal, causes strip to move laterally as it passes through the slitting line. With a properly set-up slitting line, however, if the camber of the unslit coil is small enough that the slitter trims the edge for the full length of the coil, slit coils will have less camber than the unslit coil. If the camber in the unslit coil is such that the edge is not trimmed continuously, the coil stock must be guided into the slitter, either by shifting the coil on the uncoiler or by using side guides directly in front of the slitter. When it is necessary to shift the position of the coiled metal on the uncoiler, the slitter will generally follow the camber of the unslit coil, and the slit coils will have about the same amount of camber as the unslit coil.

Camber can also be caused by variables in slitting. If the shearing pressure between blades is uneven because of a dull blade, or if there is a difference in thickness of strip at the points of contact with the blades, or if only one side of the strip is being slit, the strip will have camber in a direction away from the side at which the greatest pressure is applied.

Re-coiling of Slit Stock. Variation in thickness across the width of coil stock often causes problems in re-coiling. Coils of the thicker strands from the center section of the unslit coil will build up on the re-coiler at a faster rate than the thinner strands from the sides, resulting in tighter center coils. If the outer coils are coiled too loosely, they will sag after removal from the re-coiler. In addition, the wraps of loose coils can slip and telescope during subsequent handling. Telescoped coils are difficult to handle during uncoiling; if severe telescoping occurs, the coil can come completely apart.

One method of preventing loose coils is to insert pieces of paper or cardboard into the wraps as the strand is re-coiled. This procedure increases the diameter of the coil and the tension on the strand, thus tightening the coil.

When coils of uniform tightness must be produced, a separate re-coiler can be used for each strand, so that tension on each strand is individually controlled to insure uniform tightness of each coil. Another procedure is to provide a looping pit between the slitter and the re-coiler, in which the slit strands are allowed to sag; a drag-tension device, installed directly in front of the re-coiler, provides uniform tension on each strand as it is coiled. Each of the latter two methods requires a large additional investment in equipment.

Effect of Slitting Speed on Productivity. Slitting speed has a small effect on over-all productivity, because the slitting phase of the operation occupies only a small fraction of the total time. The greater portion of the total time is consumed in handling operations: removing bands from the coil, loading on the uncoiler, threading, placing separators on the re-coiler drum, and stripping the re-coiler.

Table 3 shows a breakdown of the time for slitting three different lengths of coils at average speeds of 325 and 650 ft per min. As these data show, doubling the slitting speed results in only a 3 to 12% reduction in over-all cycle time, for any length of coil.

Shearing

Shearing lines (also called cut-up lines, or cut-to-length lines) are high-production setups for producing accurately cut-to-length sheets from coil stock. There are two basic types of shearing lines: the stationary-shear type and the flying-shear type. These machines uncoil the strip and cut it to the required lengths.

Fig. 3. Two types of shearing lines for cutting coiled strip into flat sheets

Table 3. Effect of Speed and Coil Length on Slitting Time vs Total Cycle Time(a)

Operation	Time, minutes, at average speed of: 325 fpm	650 fpm
Coil Length, 690 Ft(b)		
Slitting	2	1
Coil handling(c)	28	28
Total cycle	30	29
Coil Length, 2000 Ft(d)		
Slitting	6	3
Coil handling(c)	28	28
Total cycle	34	31
Coil Length, 3000 Ft(e)		
Slitting	9	4½
Coil handling(c)	28	28
Total cycle	37	32½

(a) For slitting coiled sheet 36 in. wide and 0.062 in. thick, using seven cuts. (b) 32-in.-OD coil; weight, 5240 lb. (c) Removing bands from coil and loading it on uncoiler, threading, attaching six strands and placing separators on re-coiler drum, placing one band on each coil and stripping it off the re-coiler. (d) 48-in.-OD coil; weight, 15,000 lb. (e) 60-in.-OD coil; weight, 22,500 lb.

Some shearing lines include side trimmers, which provide sheets that are square and to size on all four edges. When side trimmers are used, they usually are located several sheet lengths ahead of the shear.

Stationary-shear lines (Fig. 3) consist of an uncoiler, rolls that remove the set from the uncoiled strip and feed it over a hump table, a stationary shear of the square-shear type, a gage table with a retractable stop, and a stacker that stacks the cut sheets as they are delivered from the gage table.

The retractable stop on the gage table is used to control the length of the cut sheets. As the uncoiled strand approaches the stop, it trips a limit switch that actuates the shear. After reaching the retractable stop, the strand continues to flow from the uncoiler and forms a loop over the hump table. When shearing is completed, the gage stop retracts and a cut sheet is delivered to the stacker. As the cut sheet is removed, it trips a limit switch that resets the gage stop. Then the shear opens, permitting the strand to slide out of its loop onto the gage table against the gage stop, and the cycle is repeated.

Some stationary-shear lines have measuring feed rolls instead of a hump table and a gage table. In these lines, there is a stock loop between the straightener and the feed rolls that allows the straightener to run continuously and the feed rolls to stop during shearing. Some lines have two shears that can be pivoted to cut trapezoidal blanks. The shears are timed to make alternate cuts and have two stackers for the blanks.

A stationary-shear line costs less than a flying-shear line, but it is slower if the uncoiler must be stopped to permit shearing. However, when a hump table is used, speeds up to 200 ft per min are possible, depending to a great extent on the width, thickness and length to be cut. Number of cuts per minute is a more realistic means of describing the capabilities of specific equipment than is number of feet per minute. Shearing of stock up to $\frac{3}{16}$ in. thick at a rate of up to 70 cuts per minute is common practice.

Flying-Shear Lines. One type of flying-shear cut-up line (Fig. 3) incorporates an uncoiler, straightening rolls, measuring rolls, a sliding-die shear, a runout conveyor, and a device for piling the sheared lengths. This type of flying-shear line can be operated at speeds that compare closely with those obtained with a hump-table stationary shear, for the same length of cut.

The guillotine type of flying shear also can be used for cutting a moving strand without stopping the operation. The capabilities of a guillotine-shear line are similar to those of the sliding-die type, except that a guillotine line can operate at higher speed. For a favorable length of cut (28 to 31 in.), guillotine shears can be operated as fast as 350 ft per min. For shorter lengths of cut, the maximum speed will be reduced; for instance, if the length of the cut piece were only 15 in., the speed would be reduced by 30 to 40%. Thickness of stock usually does not affect the speed of shearing, within the capabilities of a specific machine.

Machine capacity is based on a maximum thickness for a certain width of stock. If the stock width is less than maximum, the thickness can be increased so that about the same cross-sectional area of metal is sheared. For instance, a machine capable of cutting stock 80 in. wide by 0.091 in. thick could be used for stock 54 in. wide by 0.125 in. thick. To prevent overloading the shear blades at any one point, each machine has a maximum stock thickness that can be sheared. Machines of this type are available that can shear sheet as wide as 92 in. and as thick as ⅜ in.

Rotary-drum shears are used exclusively for high-production operations in sheet mills. A rotary-drum shear can handle stock up to 72 in. wide and from 0.010 to 0.090 in. thick. The length of sheet that can be cut ranges from 2 to 24 ft, and operating speeds are as high as 1000 ft per min.

The tin-plate flying shear — a special type of rotary-drum shear — is made specifically for cutting coils of tin plate into lengths for the manufacture of cans. Machines for this application can accommodate stock up to 38½ in. wide and 0.004 to 0.015 in. thick. Length of cut can be as short as 14 in. Speed can be as high as 1500 ft per min.

Dimensional accuracy of the length of cut depends on the condition of the machinery, speed and length of cut, and the condition of the coiled product (uniformity of the coil). Under best conditions, $\pm\frac{1}{32}$-in. accuracy can be maintained; "best conditions" include equipment that is in first-class repair, uniform coils, an operating speed near the center of the range for the specific equipment, and a favorable length of cut. "Favorable length of cut" is difficult to define, because it is directly related to speed and because it varies to some extent for different types of equipment. As the length of cut is increased, speed can be increased; conversely, as the length of cut is decreased, speed must be decreased. Length variations of $\pm\frac{1}{16}$ in. for constant-speed operation, and of $\pm\frac{1}{8}$ in. for conditions of acceleration and deceleration, are typical for the conditions that usually exist.

Shearing of Bars and Bar Sections

*By the ASM Committee on Shearing and Slitting**

BARS and bar sections are sheared between lower and upper blades of a machine in which only the upper blade is movable. As the upper blade is forced down, the work metal is distorted and caused to fracture. Figure 1 shows the appearance of a sheared round bar. The burnished area, or depth of shear action by the blade, is usually one-fifth to one-fourth the diameter of the bar. In visual examination of a sheared edge, the burnished portion appears smooth, whereas the fractured portion is comparatively rough.

*For committee list, see page 265.

Applicability. In general, any metal that can be machined can be sheared, but power requirements increase as the strength of the work metal increases. Further, blade design is more critical and blade life decreases as the strength of the work metal increases.

Equipment is available for shearing round, hexagonal or octagonal bars up to 6 in. in diameter or thickness, rectangular bars and billets up to 3 by 12 in. in cross section, and angles up to 8 by 8 by 1½ in.

Straight blades can be used to shear bars and bar sections, although a considerable amount of distortion occurs, as shown in Fig. 1. In addition, the concentration of shock on the blades is high when shearing with straight blades (particularly when shearing round bars). Preferred practice is to use blades that conform to the shape of the work metal, as discussed in a subsequent section of this article (see Fig. 5 and 7). Angles are usually sheared in a special machine, or in a special setup with conforming blades.

Because of the conditions illustrated in Fig. 1, the quality of edges sheared with straight blades cannot compete with edges that are sawed or otherwise machined. However, when blades are sharp and accurately adjusted, sheared edges that are acceptable for a wide range of applications can be obtained. The quality of sheared edges usually increases as thickness of the work metal decreases.

Accuracy of Cut. Workpieces properly supported on both sides of the shear blades by a roller conveyor table and placed squarely against a gage stop securely bolted to the exit side of the machine can ordinarily be cut to lengths accurate to +⅛, −0 in., on shears that can cut bars up to 4 in. in diameter. When larger shears are used, the breakaway of the metal can cause a variation of ±3⁄16 in. Fairly consistent accuracy in shearing of slugs can be obtained by careful adjustment of the gage setting, especially if the slugs are produced on a weight-per-piece basis.

Supporting the free end of the material on a spring-supported table will minimize bending during the shearing operation, thus providing better control over the length of cut.

Selection of Cutoff Method. The method of cutting off bars may be determined by the edge condition that is required for subsequent operations. Sawing usually produces a uniform cut edge with little or no damage to the microstructure in the immediate area. Gas cutting produces an edge that resembles a sawed edge in smoothness and squareness. However, the cut edge of some steels becomes hardened during gas cutting, thus making subsequent machining difficult. A sheared edge usually is easy to machine but can make fit-up of parts of a weldment more difficult and can increase warpage because of wider gaps.

The two examples that follow describe applications in which shearing was more economical than gas cutting.

Examples 340 and 341. Cost of Shearing vs Gas Cutting of Wire Cloth and Angles

Example 340 — Wire Cloth (Table 1). The costs of shearing and of gas cutting wire cloth into 60-in. squares are compared in Table 1. The cloth had 1½-in. openings and was made of ⅝-in.-diam, 1060 steel rod, tempered in a lead bath to Rockwell C 30 to 34.

As shown in Table 1, because of the higher production rate, the cost per piece for shearing was about one-fourth the cost for gas cutting.

A hydraulic shear was used having a capacity for shearing 12 ft of 1-in.-thick low-carbon steel. The blades were made of S5 tool steel and hardened to Rockwell C 56 to 58. Blade clearance was set according to manufacturer's recommendations, and the blades were parallel within 0.015 to 0.020 in. for the entire 12 ft without bow in the upper blade.

Example 341 — Angles (Table 2). Originally one leg of an angle 5 ft long by ⅜ in thick (ASTM A36 steel) was reduced in width from 3 in. to 1½ in. by gas cutting. Two disadvantages of this method were: the gas-cut edge required cleaning, and the workpiece had to be straightened after cutting. By changing from gas cutting to shearing, the cleaning and straightening operations were eliminated, and cost was reduced by about 40% (Table 2).

To facilitate shearing, it was necessary to butt weld two tabs on the leg to hold the angle in position. The tabs were ⅜ by 2 by 6 in. and were spaced to assure contact with the hold-down of the shear.

Table 1. Costs of Shearing vs Gas Cutting of Wire Cloth (Example 340)

Item	Gas cutting	Shearing
Labor, direct:		
1 operator, 8 hr at $8/hr	$64.00	$ 64.00
1 helper, 8 hr at $5/hr	...	40.00
Labor, indirect	8.00	8.00
Oxygen and acetylene	17.00	...
Regrinding of shear blades	...	2.00
Total cost	$89.00	$114.00
Pieces cut in 8 hr	8	40
Cost per piece	$11.12	$2.85

Wire cloth, made of ⅝-in.-diam 1060 steel rods spaced 1½ in. apart and tempered in a lead bath to Rockwell C 30 to 34, was cut in 60-in. squares from pieces 65 in. wide by 21 ft long.

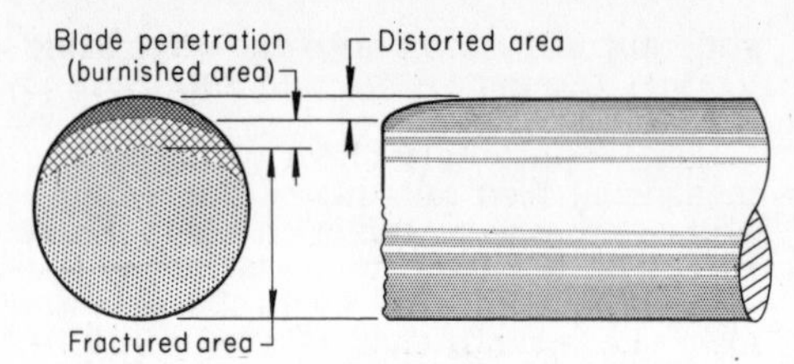

Fig. 1. Effects of shearing a round bar with a straight blade

Table 2. Cost of Shearing vs Gas Cutting for Reducing the Width of an Angle Leg (Example 341)

Item	Cost per piece
Shearing	
Material for two tabs	$0.15
Welding of tabs to angle	0.20
Shearing	0.30
Total	$0.65
Gas Cutting	
Cutting and cleaning	$0.75
Straightening	0.30
Total	$1.05

Power Requirements. The net horsepower required for shearing may be estimated from the following formula:

$$Hp = \frac{AVS}{33{,}000}$$

where A is the cross-sectional area of the workpiece, sq in.; V is the speed of the shear blade, ft per min; and S is the shear strength of the work metal, psi. The 33,000 is foot-pounds per minute per horsepower. It may be necessary to increase the calculated value as much as 25% to compensate for machine inefficiency.

Although the above formula is used for estimating, it is of limited value because it does not take into consideration the ductility of the metal. The formula is based on shearing low-carbon steel. Copper, for example, is more ductile than steel; therefore the distance of blade penetration before fracture in copper will be greater than in steel. Conversely, when shearing metals that are less ductile than low-carbon steel, the distance of blade penetration before breakaway will be less. Power requirements also are affected by the ductility of the work metal.

Cutting Speed. The speed at which material is subject to shearing action without adverse effect can range from almost zero to 70 or 80 ft per min. However, as speed increases above 20 to 25 ft per min, problems are encountered in holding the workpiece securely at the blade without the far end whipping, especially with material ¼ in. thick or more. When bars harder than Rockwell C 30 are cut at speeds of 40 to 50 ft per min or higher, chipping of the blade is common (see Example 343).

Machines

Production shearing of bars and bar sections is usually done in machines with a throat opening designed for large, bulky workpieces. These machines include alligator and guillotine shears, and a multipurpose machine with interchangeable punches and dies for shearing, punching and coping. Squaring shears, normally used for sheet and plate, can also be used for cutting bar stock to length. Punch presses and press brakes can be provided with appropriate tooling for shearing operations.

Alligator shears are so named because the action resembles that of an alligator's jaw. In an alligator shear, the lower blade is stationary and the upper blade, held securely in an arm, moves in an arc around a fulcrum pin (Fig. 2). The shearing action is similar to that of a pair of scissors. A crankshaft transmits power to the shearing arm, and the leverage applied produces the force for shearing. Maximum shearing force is obtained closest to the fulcrum, and the mechanical advantage decreases as the distance between the point of shearing and the fulcrum increases. Thus, with the maximum opening (largest rake angle), capacity is maximum for any shear. As the blade begins downward travel and rotation about its fulcrum, the cross-sectional area engaged by the blade is increased; therefore, more energy is expended, and the upper blade is slowed down until the breakaway point is reached. At this point the mechanical forces have overcome the resistance of the metal and the remainder of the cross-sectional area breaks off.

The capacity of an alligator shear is designated as the maximum cross-sectional area of flat plate or round bar that can be sheared, based on work

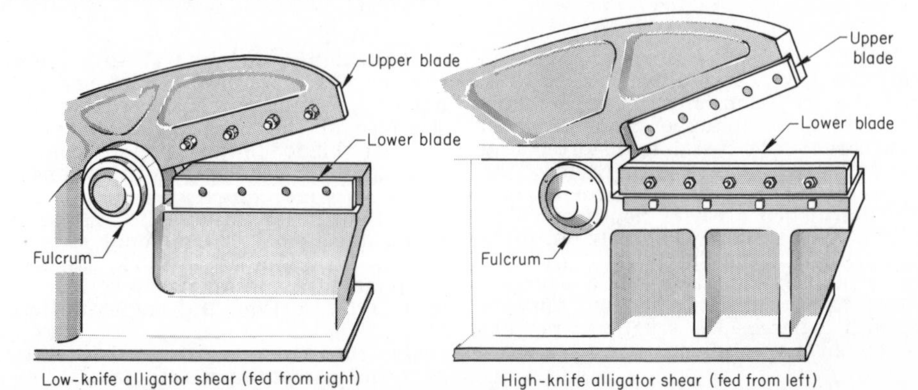

Fig. 2. Two types of alligator shears. See text for discussion.

metal having a tensile strength of 40,000 psi.

An alligator shear not only can shear bars and bar sections, but can also be used for plate, sheet and strip within the limitations of the blade length of the machine. Alligator shears are used extensively for preparing scrap, because the single pivot point allows the blades to open wide enough to accept bulky objects. For instance, on a machine with 12-in.-long blades, the opening between upper and lower shear blades is approximately 5¼ in.; on a machine with 36-in.-long blades, the opening can be as great as 11 in.

The two types of shearing arms used on alligator shears are low-knife and high-knife (Fig. 2). In the low-knife type, the cutting edge of the lower blade is in line with the center of its fulcrum pin; in a high-knife shear, the cutting edge of the lower blade is on a plane above the centerline of the fulcrum pin. In general, the low-knife shear is preferred for cutting bars and bar sections. The high-knife shear is preferred for cutting flat stock and for use in scrap yards. A high-knife shear, by making successive cuts, can shear flat stock that is wider than the length of the shear blades.

An alligator shear is further classified as either right-hand or left-hand (each is illustrated in Fig. 2), depending on the side from which it is fed.

The weight of alligator shears ranges from about 2500 to 43,000 lb. The lighter shears can be made portable on wheels, on a sled-type skid, or on blocks. The heavier machines must be anchored in concrete.

The speed of alligator shears ranges from approximately 50 strokes per minute for the smallest power-driven machine to about 18 strokes per minute for the largest heavy-duty shear. Except for small hand-operated types, alligator shears are usually mechanically driven; a flywheel provides uniform, sustained power during cutting.

The number of strokes per minute can be reduced by changing either the motor speed or the diameter of the flywheel pulley. An increase in the number of strokes may affect the stored energy of the flywheel and reduce the shearing capacity. On continuously cutting shears, greater speed will reduce workpiece-positioning time for the operator, and thus may reduce output rather than increase it. On single-stroke machines, cutting time is minimal compared to the time required for accurate positioning of the stock.

Guillotine shears are designed for cutting bars and bar sections to desired lengths from mill stock, and are used extensively throughout the fabricating industry. Two general types are available — open-end (Fig. 3) and closed-end. The shear illustrated in Fig. 3 is called "open-end" because it has a C-frame construction with one end open and unsupported. Open-end shears are either single-end, for one operator, or double-end, for two operators. On double-end machines, both ends can be right-hand or left-hand, or one end can be right-hand and the other end left-hand, depending on the type of shearing to be done.

A closed-end guillotine shear is basically the same as the one illustrated in

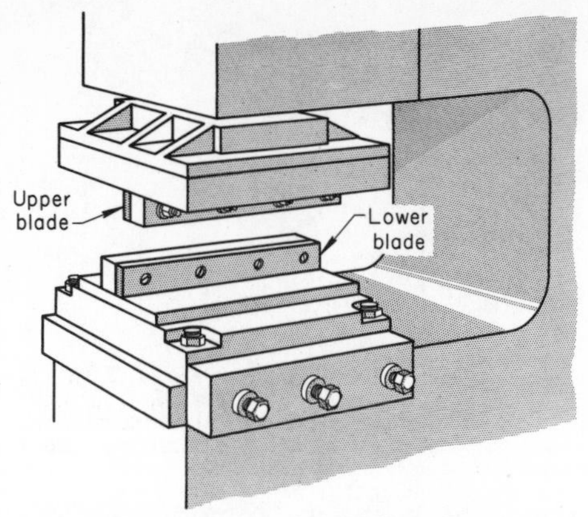

Fig. 3. Open-end guillotine shear

Fig. 3 except that it has frame supports on both sides.

An open-end shear has the advantage of giving the operator a clear view of the blades. However, because one end is open, a heavier frame and more floor space are required than for a closed-end shear of equal capacity.

Guillotine shears for bars and angles are available in capacities up to 300 tons. Either intermittent or continuous operation is possible. Guillotine shears can be equipped with simple straight blades (Fig. 3), or with two or more short blades having specific shapes.

Guillotine shears are actuated mechanically, hydraulically or pneumatically. Hydraulic and pneumatic machines are lighter in weight for a specific shearing power, are more economical, and operate with less vibration than mechanical shears. Hence, hydraulic or pneumatic machines up to 10-ton capacity are completely portable, and units of 200 to 300-ton capacity are semiportable (need not be solidly mounted in concrete).

Combination machines are multipurpose machines used primarily in metal-fabricating shops where there is a constant need for shearing small quantities (often two or three pieces) of a variety of shapes and sizes from bars or bar sections. Some combination machines can also be used for punching, slotting and notching.

Many combination machines incorporate several devices within the frame for performing different operations, so that a new setup is not required for each. A holder for an interchangeable punch and die is located in an area with a deep throat. This facilitates punching of holes, slots or notches in plates and bars, and in webs or legs of structural members.

A slide moving at 45° from vertical carries a blade for shearing angles. The support bed is on a swivel so that the ends of the angle section can be varied as desired from 45° to 90°. In two strokes of the machine, angles can be sheared to produce miter joints for subsequent welding (see the subsection "Shearing of Angles", on page 277).

Combination machines can be used for cutting square and rectangular notches in the leg of an angle. These machines can be set up to cut a 90° V-shaped notch in angles that subsequently will be bent into frames. Other shapes, such as beams and channels, can be notched in a similar manner, provided the machine can accommodate the vertical height between the upper and lower legs of the workpiece.

Provision is also made for shearing bars with guillotine-type blades or special blades (see the discussion relating to Fig. 5 in this article).

Combination machines are available in capacities ranging from 12 to 100 tons. The 12-ton machine can punch a 9⁄16-in.-diam hole through a ¼-in.-thick section, and can shear 3-by-3-by-¼-in. angles, ⅞-in.-diam rounds, ¾-in. squares, and 4-by-¼-in. flats.

The 100-ton machine can shear 6-by-6-by-⅝-in. angles, 2¼-in. rounds, 2-in. squares, and 8-by-¾-in. flats.

Punching and shearing machines are deep-throat C-frame machines for punching, shearing, notching or coping of plates, bars and structural sections. Shoes, into which punches, dies and shear blades can readily be inserted, are mounted on the bed and ram.

The shoes either rest on the bed or are overhung; the overhanging type is designed so that structural shapes may be punched in both web and flange. The plain type of shoe is used primarily for plate work; however, plates can be worked with the overhanging shoes. Both types of die blocks are fitted with die sockets that hold dies of different inside diameters. The punch holder is adjustable to suit the location of the dies. Table 3 lists the capacities for punching and shearing with this type of machine.

Fixturing is an important consideration in the shearing of bars. For safety and the proper functioning of open-end shears (Fig. 3), and for shearing units like those shown in the center and at the right in Fig. 7, hold-down fixtures are essential. Guide pins are also helpful, especially when shearing with conforming blades as shown in Fig. 7.

Shear Blades

Shock-resisting tool steels such as S2 or S5 are most commonly used as blade materials for cold shearing, although L6 has also been successfully used for some applications. Some plants use shear blades made from carbon or alloy steel with hard faced shearing edges.

The hardness of tool steel blades usually ranges from Rockwell C 45 to 55 (sometimes as high as Rockwell C 58, as in Example 342). The upper end of

Table 3. Maximum Workpiece Dimensions That Can Be Accommodated in Vertical Open-Gap Punching and Shearing Machines of Various Tonnage Ratings

Machine rating, tons	Punching		Shearing				Size of angle, in.	
	Hole diam, in.	Plate thickness, in.	Plate thickness, in.	Size of bar section or plate, in.	Diameter of round, in.	Size of square, in.	Cutting on square	Cutting on angle
50	13⁄16	¾	½	5 by ½	1½	1¼ by 1¼	3 by 3 by ⅜	4 by 4 by ⅜
97½	1¼	1	⅞	6 by 1	2	1½ by 1½	4 by 4 by ½	6 by 6 by ⅜
156	2	1	1⅛	8 by 1	2½	2 by 2	6 by 6 by ½	....
312½	2½	1½	1½	10 by 1½	3½	3 by 3	8 by 8 by ¾	....
500	4	1½	2	10 by 2½	5	3½ by 3½	8 by 8 by 1¼	....
700	6	1½	2½	12 by 3	6	4¼ by 4¼	8 by 8 by 1½	....

this range can be used when work-metal thickness does not exceed ½ in. As work-metal thickness increases, hardness of the blade should be decreased to the lower end of this range, but not below Rockwell C 45 unless experience with previous applications warrants it. The practice in most plants is to start with blades near the lower end of the range, increasing their hardness only after experience proves it safe. Excessive blade wear is usually preferable to blade breakage.

Blade Material for Hot Shearing. Ordinarily blades for hot shearing of bar stock are made of H11, H12 or H13 hot work tool steel. There are no data to prove the superiority of one of these steels over the others. H21 and H25 are sometimes used, but they are more costly and are recommended only when H11 has been tried and found to be inadequate.

Hardness of blades for hot shearing varies considerably with thickness and temperature of the metal to be sheared, and the type and condition of the shearing equipment. However, hardness is usually kept at Rockwell C 38 to 48.

For high-alloy metals to be sheared at high temperatures, higher-alloy blades may be needed. High-temperature engine-valve alloys have been sheared with T1 high speed steel blades.

Hard faced blades are satisfactory for hot shearing and are used exclusively in some plants. Material for the blade body is usually 1030 or 1045 steel. Hard facing alloys have the following nominal compositions:

1 – 0.50 C, 0.90 Si, 4.75 Cr, 1.20 W, 1.40 Mo
2 – 0.75 C, 0.50 Mn, 0.65 Si, 4.00 Cr, 1.00 V, 1.20 W, 8.00 Mo
3 – 3.00 C, 1.00 Si, 28.00 Cr, 4.00 Mo.

Blade Profile. The cross section of an alligator shear blade for cutting bars and shapes is normally rectangular. Light-duty blades are about 1¼ in. wide by 4 in. deep by 12 in. long. Blades for machines of about maximum size are commonly about 2 by 5 by 36 in. For mounting, blades are provided with countersunk holes as shown in Fig. 4 that allow bolt heads to be sunk sufficiently to prevent interference between blades.

Blade clearance for shearing bars and bar sections ranges from 0.005 to 0.015 in. The smaller clearance is used for shearing clean work metal; the larger clearance is preferred for shearing scaly products, to prevent scale or other foreign material from lodging between blades and scoring the surfaces.

Blades for alligator shears are available with grooves across the width to prevent forward movement of the work metal when the upper blade descends; thus more of the cutting length of the blade can be utilized.

Most blades have four cutting edges ground identically (Fig. 4), so that by inverting the blade and reversing its direction, all four cutting edges can be used before the blade is returned for sharpening. Resharpening any of the four edges requires grinding of one or both faces of an edge. Therefore, a blade that shows severe damage, such as breakout of a section, must be ground to a new, clean and sharp edge. To avoid such major regrinding, blades

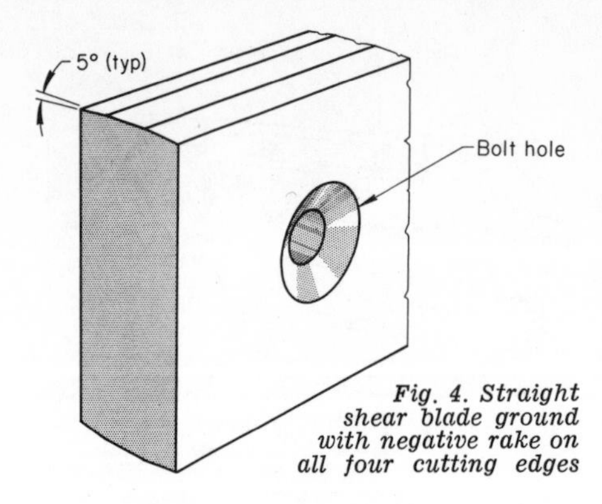

Fig. 4. Straight shear blade ground with negative rake on all four cutting edges

should be kept free from large nicks and "mushrooming".

Most blades are ground to a slight negative rake as shown in Fig. 4. The intent is to cause the work metal to begin to flow from a slight bending action before actual shearing takes place. Blades provided with a negative rake of 5° to 10° are often less susceptible to chipping at the cutting edge than those ground with a 90° edge (zero rake).

Shear Blade Life. Service data on shear blade life are scarce because maintenance programs in most high-production mills call for removal of blades and redressing during scheduled shutdowns, regardless of the condition of the blades at the time. Blade life in number of cuts before regrinding has been variously reported as 5000 to more than 2 million. Even when an attempt is made to make blade material and cutting conditions as nearly identical as possible, variations in blade life of 100% or more have been reported.

Blade life depends to a great extent on the composition and hardness of the work metal (see the article "The Selection of Material for Shear Blades", page 755 in Volume 1 of this Handbook, for specific data on blade life).

Angle of the cutting edge often affects blade life, and in some instances shearing speed has a marked effect on blade life. For instance, harder work metal usually requires a lower shearing speed, to avoid blade chipping and premature dulling. When work-metal hardness is Rockwell C 30 or higher, speeds greater than 50 ft per min are not recommended, and much slower speeds may be required for acceptable blade life.

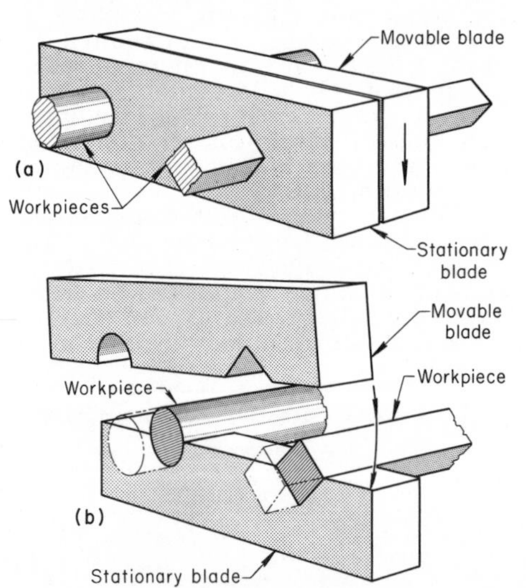

Fig. 5. Two types of blades for shearing of bars. See text for discussion.

The two examples that follow demonstrate the effects of blade angle and speed on blade life.

Example 342. Negative Rake for Prolonged Blade Life

Shear blades that were provided with a negative rake of 10° almost eliminated the problem of chipping at the cutting edge when shearing 5⁄16-to-5⁄8-in. round 1060 steel bars tempered to Rockwell C 30 to 34. Previously, blades ground to 90° (zero rake) chipped excessively and required frequent replacement. The life of blades with negative rake was substantially longer than that of zero-rake blades.

Shearing was done in a hydraulic shear at slow speed (less than 5 ft per min) for both the zero and the 10° negative-rake blades. The blades were made of S5 tool steel and heat treated to Rockwell C 56 to 58.

Example 343. Reduction in Speed for Prolonged Blade Life

When 1085 flat spring steel, ⅛ and 3⁄16 in. thick and 2 in. wide, ranging in hardness from Rockwell C 30 to 34, was sheared to lengths of 4 and 5 ft at a blade speed of 70 ft per min in a punch press, blades had to be replaced every 2 to 3 weeks (200 to 500 cuts) because of chipping. In addition, regrinding during this period was required. When the procedure was changed to shearing at 10 ft per min in a C-frame shear, blade life was increased to an average of 10,000 cuts before regrinding was required, and chipping was eliminated. Blades for both the punch press and the shear were made from S1 tool steel and ranged in hardness from Rockwell C 54 to 56.

Cost. Because of the relatively small amount of machining needed to make a shear blade, compared with the machining needed to make an intricate impression in a die block or a forming die, cost of the material is an important part of the total cost of a blade. A blade made from S2 tool steel costs about 1.8 times as much as one made from W2 tool steel, and 0.7 times as much as one made from D2 tool steel.

Blade Design and Production Practice

The straight-edge blades described in the preceding section and illustrated in Fig. 4 can shear almost any bar or shape that is within the capacity of the machine. However, unacceptable distortion may result in some shapes of workpieces when sheared with blades that are not designed for cutting specific shapes.

Conforming Blades. One method of minimizing distortion in sheared bars employs two hardened blades mounted face-to-face, with identical holes through each blade. The holes should conform to the shape of the work metal and should be large enough to allow easy passage through the blades (Fig. 5a). One blade is movable vertically and one is stationary. Relatively little movement of the machine is required when blades of this type are used. In addition, because the blades completely encircle the work metal, hold-downs are not needed. However, these blades are usually limited for use on specially built or combination machines.

Shearing of round and square bars is more frequently done with the open-type blades illustrated in Fig. 5(b). Each blade is contoured to accommodate half the cross section of the work metal. The upper blade moves in a

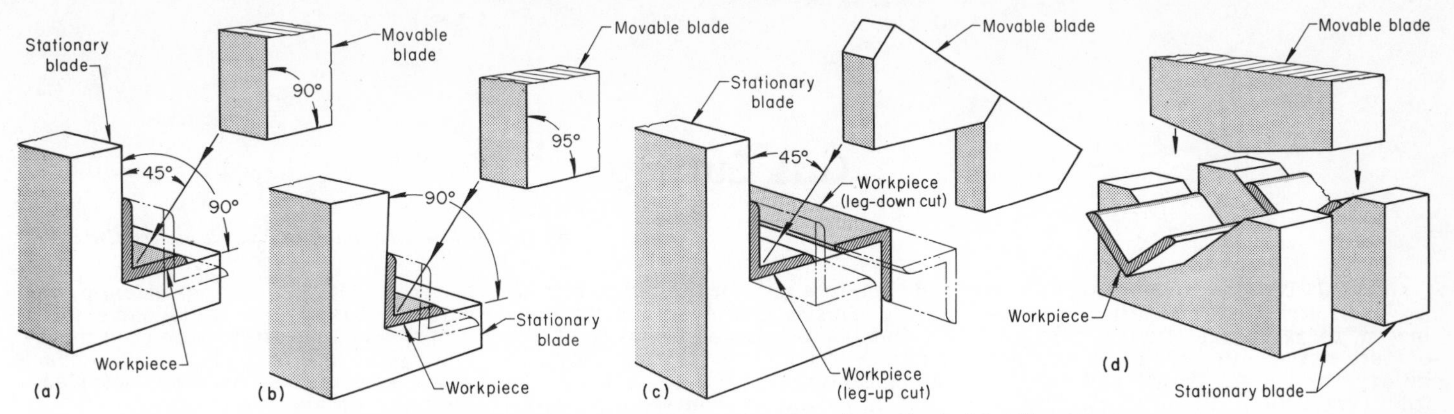

Fig. 6. Four types of blades for shearing of angle sections. See text for discussion.

vertical direction, while the lower blade remains stationary. When using this technique, some type of hold-down is needed. Because of the stiffness of the work metal, the hold-down for bars should permit slight movement of the work metal in the axial direction to avoid double shearing. The hold-down can be a simple set screw (to permit adjustment) in a bracket, or a more elaborate unit, such as a handwheel assembly utilizing an Acme thread.

For shearing square bars with any type of blade, the work metal should be placed so that the movement of the blade is across the diagonal of the square. With this technique the shearing force is applied to four sides instead of two, resulting in a smoother sheared surface. Shearing across the diagonal provides support on two sides of the square shape, which minimizes distortion, and also permits more than one size of bar stock to be sheared in a given hole.

Best practice for shearing round bars is to use blades with holes for each size of stock to be cut. Blade holes appreciably larger than the stock size cause excessive distortion of the workpiece.

Shearing of angles is done either in a combination machine or by double cutting. In a combination machine — the more common method — two blades such as those shown in Fig. 6(a) are used. One blade, usually the one that is stationary, is L-shaped and is positioned as shown. The movable blade is square or rectangular and is mounted with its two cutting edges parallel to those of the stationary blade. Figure 6(a) also shows that the space between the blades in the loading position is the same shape as the workpiece.

The movable blade travels at 45° toward the stationary blade, and both blades contact the work metal uniformly. Shearing by this technique is essentially a blanking cut, and distortion of the workpiece is minimal. One disadvantage of the method is that all cutting occurs at once, resulting in a high shear load. This condition is not important when small angle sections are cut; however, for work metal larger than 4 by 4 by ½ in., the movable blade should be provided with rake to prevent excessive loading.

To provide a rake angle between the movable and stationary blades, the included angle between the cutting edges of the upper or movable blade is increased to 95°, as shown in Fig. 6(b). Shearing begins at the extremity of each leg and progresses toward the root of the angle. The increase in the included angle of the movable blade results in some distortion of the drop-cut piece; the amount of distortion is about equal to the difference in angle between the movable and stationary blades (5° is normal). The part remaining on the table or stationary blade is not distorted.

Most combination shearing machines use a more versatile blade arrangement than those shown in Fig. 6(a) and (b). The setup shown in Fig. 6(c) provides for shearing angle sections in both the leg-up and the leg-down positions. A swiveling table locates and holds the workpiece during shearing. With the swiveling table and two positions for the workpiece, mitering of the flanges to any specific angle can be done easily. For instance, when shearing angle sections for a frame having the leg on the inside, the table would be set and locked at 45°. One end is mitered by placing the section in a leg-down position on the table and shearing off enough to make a clean cut. The other end is mitered by placing the section leg-up on the table and shearing to the proper length. The opposite positions are applicable when angle sections for a frame having the leg on the outside are being cut.

Shearing at a 45° angle reduces the capacity of the machine, because a greater length of metal is cut at one time when a 90° cut is made. For example, a machine with a capacity of 8 by 8 by 1¼ in. when making a 90° cut, has a capacity of only 8 by 8 by 1 in. when cutting at 45°.

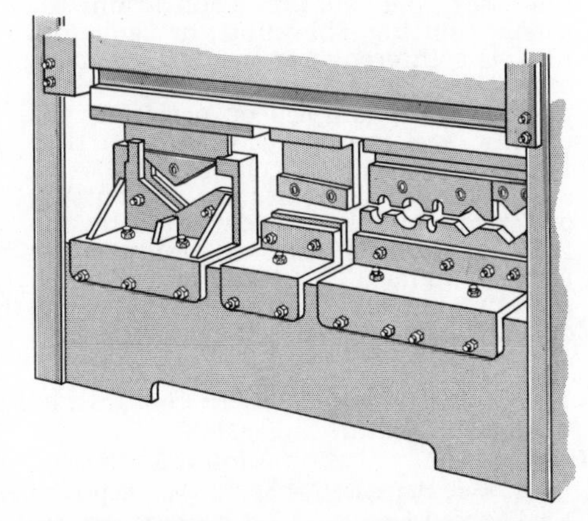

Fig. 7. Multiple setup for various types of shearing, singly or in combination

Double cutting of angle sections, also called slugging, is used less frequently than shearing in a combination-type machine. This technique uses two stationary blades, spaced ½ in. apart, and one movable V-shaped blade arranged as shown in Fig. 6(d). The movable blade has a shallow V-shape that does not conform to the shape of the workpiece. Shearing starts at the extremity of each leg and progresses to the root of the angle, producing a ½-in.-wide slug that is pushed out the bottom between the stationary blades.

In the double-cutting method of shearing, distortion occurs only in the slug, because the work metal is supported by the two stationary blades. The disadvantages of using the double-cutting method are: (*a*) increased power is required for making two cuts at the same time, and (*b*) some metal is lost in the slug.

The two stationary blades must be firmly supported to prevent their spreading during the cutting operation.

A similar tool can be used for shearing a channel section. The stationary blades should closely fit the contour of the channel section. Double cutting is adaptable to a guillotine shear, a combination machine, or a press.

The importance of square ends produced on angle sections by double cutting is shown in the next example:

Example 344. Double Cutting That Eliminated Out-of-Square Ends

When steel angles, 3 by 2 by ½ in., were sheared by the conventional (single-cut) method, the cut ends were out-of-square. This condition caused a fitup problem when the cut angles were placed in a welding jig for fabricating a rectangular frame. The out-of-square ends required an excessively large weld bead. During cooling, contraction of the weld bead caused distortion of the welded assembly.

The improved method consisted of double cutting the angles in a punch press. Pieces sheared by this method allowed acceptable fitup for welding and eliminated distortion by minimizing the amount of heat required to apply the weld bead.

Multiple Setups. Fabricating shops often must shear small quantities to a variety of shapes. To handle such work, many shops use a machine with a multiple setup like the one shown in Fig. 7. Without changing blades, the following operations can be performed: double shearing of angle sections (Fig. 7, left), straight-blade shearing (Fig. 7, center), and shearing of round and square bars and single shearing of L-sections (Fig. 7, right). All movable blades are attached to a single ram.

Gas Cutting

*By the ASM Committee on Gas and Arc Cutting**

GAS CUTTING is a chemical reaction in which preheated metal is cut, or removed, by rapid oxidation in a stream of pure oxygen. Preheating is attained by oxygen-fuel gas flames and oxygen-iron combustion. Preliminary furnace heating is used when needed. The cutting of oxidation-resistant metals is aided by the addition of certain chemical fluxes or metal powder to the oxygen stream.

The simplest gas-cutting equipment consists of two cylinders (one for oxygen, one for the fuel gas), gas regulators and gages, gas-supply hoses, and a cutting torch with a set of replaceable cutting tips. This manually operated equipment is portable and inexpensive.

Higher production rates and better quality of cutting are obtained with machines that guide the operation and control its speed. In large installations, the gases are supplied from a bank of gas cylinders or bulk storage tanks, which are isolated for safety.

Many types of gas cutting are unsuited to machine operation. However, mechanized cutting is important for profile cutting — the cutting of regular and irregular shapes from flat stock. Gas cutting can cut carbon and low-alloy steel plate in any thickness that can be rolled.

Gas cutting is essentially a process of controlled oxidation of metal. Because of the properties of iron and its oxidation at elevated temperature, gas cutting is most efficient in cutting carbon, low-alloy, and some high-alloy steels. Many high-alloy steels and most nonferrous metals either resist continuous oxidation or in other ways upset the delicate balance of physical and chemical reactions required for uniform cutting. As a result, cutting of such materials becomes more a matter of progressive melting than of controlled oxidation, and the cut edges generally are round and irregular. To overcome this, chemical flux or metal powder (principally iron powder) can be added to the oxygen jet to provide the reactions necessary for controlled cutting. Chemical fluxes and metal powders are used for cutting stainless steel, cast iron, and nonferrous metals in mills, foundries and fabricating shops. Equipment for such cutting is somewhat awkward, and speeds are lower than those of some arc-cutting processes.

Arc-cutting processes (see the article "Electric-Arc Cutting", on page 301 in this volume) do not depend solely on the principle of controlled oxidation and therefore are not limited to ferrous metals. This is true even though some arc cutting processes use oxygen. For instance, plasma-arc cutting may use supplementary oxygen to increase the speed in cutting carbon steel. However, the speed with which the plasma-arc process can cut square-edged profiles in stainless steel and aluminum, for instance, is not matched by gas cutting. Plasma-arc cutting is competitive with gas cutting of carbon and low-alloy steels if large quantities of straight-line cutting are involved, and if the work metal is limited to thicknesses that will permit a comparable quality of cut. The higher costs for plasma-arc equipment and operation usually are justified by its greater speed.

Terminology. Various gas-cutting processes have been known as *flame cutting, burning, oxy-fuel gas cutting,* and *oxygen cutting*. Many authorities agree that *oxy-fuel gas cutting* and *oxygen cutting* more accurately describe the processes than do the other terms. However, all the terms mentioned above are in popular use. Moreover, the rapid development of new processes has caused some shift in the boundaries of older definitions. For instance, *plasma-arc cutting* has been called *flame cutting* and, in certain applications, *flame machining*. At least two arc-cutting methods use oxygen to assist cutting. In another form of oxygen cutting, a laser beam is passed through the window of an oxygen-pressurized chamber and out a small orifice at the other end.

For these reasons, an attempt has been made in this article to use the accepted terminology that seems most consistent. The term *flame machining* is not used, for several reasons. First, every gas-cutting operation can be considered as similar to, or replacing, one of the conventional machining operations such as sawing, slitting, milling, planing and drilling. Operations in precision gas cutting are not separate processes, but simply applications of profile cutting, beveling or gouging. Also, the inference of accuracy associated with machining might be misleading. Several examples of precision gas cutting are presented in this article (see Examples 350, 353, 354 and 363).

The various processes for gas cutting of ferrous metals are identified by the fuel gas that is used to produce the preheat flame. The commercially important processes are: oxyacetylene cutting, oxy-natural gas cutting, oxy-propane cutting, and oxy-Mapp gas cutting. (Mapp is a trade name for a proprietary mixture of stabilized methylacetylene and propadiene.) Other fuel gases used include hydrogen, ethylene, methane, ethane and butane.

For gas cutting of stainless steel and nonferrous metals, and for faster cutting of cast iron and oxidation-resistant ferrous alloys, two other methods are available: chemical-flux cutting and metal-powder cutting.

Other gas-cutting methods may be identified by the special purposes for which they are intended, such as oxy-fuel gas gouging, oxygen-lance cutting, and underwater gas cutting.

Principles of Operation

Principles of operation are the same for all the gas-cutting methods named in the three preceding paragraphs. A small area on the surface of the metal is heated quickly to a bright red heat (about 1400 to 1600 F) by the oxy-fuel gas flame. A jet of oxygen is directed at the preheated spot, causing rapid oxidation of the heated metal with evolution of a large amount of heat. The heat thus generated melts the oxide and a thin film of metal adjacent to it. The oxygen jet, assisted by gravity, flushes away the molten oxide, exposing fresh surfaces for cutting. Only the metal in the path of the oxygen jet is acted upon. As the cut progresses, a narrow slot, or kerf, is cut through the metal.

During the operation, oxygen and fuel gas are supplied separately to a cutting torch at pressures usually determined by pressure regulators, adjusted by the operator, at the points of supply. The cutting torch contains the necessary ducts, mixing chamber, and control valves to supply an oxy-fuel gas mixture and a pure oxygen stream to the cutting tip. By adjusting the control valves, the operator is able to provide the precise oxy-fuel gas mixture desired. By depressing a cutting-oxygen lever, he is able to initiate the cutting-oxygen flow. Cutting tips contain a single cutting-oxygen orifice centered within a ring of smaller oxy-fuel gas exit ports. The operator is able to change the cutting capacity of the torch by changing the cutting tip for one of different size. This usually requires a new series of adjustments of pressure regulators and control valves.

Because different fuel gases have different combustion and flow charac-

*Roger S. Babcock, *Chairman,* Staff Engineer, Linde Div., Union Carbide Corp.; A. L. Cooper, Supervisor of Manufacturing Engineering, Large Rotating Apparatus, Westinghouse Electric Corp.

W. L. Elliott, Manager of Materials Engineering, John Deere Harvester Works; E. H. Franks, Atomic Power Equipment Dept., General Electric Co. (formerly Chief Welding Engineer, Electric Boat Div., General Dynamics Corp.); H. B. Hartline, Chattanooga Div., Combustion Engineering, Inc.

John R. Kelly, President, Harris Calorific Sales Co.; George R. Spies, Jr., Supervisor, Advanced Engineering Dept., Central Research Laboratories, Air Reduction Co., Inc.; J. L. Vieira, Manufacturing Assistant, Electro-Motive Div., General Motors Corp.

teristics, the construction of cutting tips, and sometimes of mixing chambers, varies according to the type of gas. However, the function of these components remains basically the same, and the operator makes the same basic adjustments.

Oxy-fuel gas flames start the oxidation reaction and sustain the reaction by continuously heating the metal at the line of cut. The flame also helps to clean the metal of scale and dirt that would impede or distort the jet of gas.

In gas cutting, a relatively large mass of metal surrounds the flame at the cutting face, making the rate of heat transfer in the metal a factor in the heat balance needed for cutting. As the thickness of the metal to be cut increases, more heat is conducted from the preheat area. To compensate for this heat loss, either the oxy-fuel gas flow must be increased or the cutting speed must be reduced.

Oxygen flow must also be increased as the thickness of the metal to be cut increases. To maintain a steady-state reaction at a satisfactory cutting speed, the velocity and volume, as well as the shape of the oxygen jet, must be closely controlled. Because the cutting-oxygen jet is surrounded by preheating flames, it is affected by these gases and the surrounding atmosphere. The jet must have sufficient volume and velocity to penetrate the depth of the cut and still maintain its shape, force and effective oxygen content.

The limits within which the cutting reaction can operate effectively are determined by many factors besides those mentioned. Gas cutting involves control of more than twenty variables. Suppliers of cutting equipment provide tables that give approximate gas pressures for various sizes and styles of cutting torches and tips, along with recommended cutting speeds; these are the variables that the operator can control. Other variables include type and condition of material, thickness of cut, type of fuel gas, and quality and angle of cut. (When not otherwise defined, a cut is usually taken to mean a through or "drop" cut, made in horizontal plates with the cutting tip in the vertical position.)

It is not possible to cut at maximum speed without sacrificing economy and quality; nor is it possible to obtain maximum economy without some sacrifice of speed and quality.

Process Capabilities

Developments in mechanization have greatly increased the industrial importance of the gas-cutting process. Cutting machines with electronic tracing tables and accurate, low-inertia guidance equipment have made multiple-torch cutting more useful in steel fabrication. Shape-cutting machines of this type are discussed in the section on Equipment in this article (see pages 288 and 289).

Materials. Gas cutting is used primarily for cutting carbon and low-alloy steels. Although other iron-base alloys and certain nonferrous metals can be gas cut, some process modification is required, and results are not always the same as those obtained in

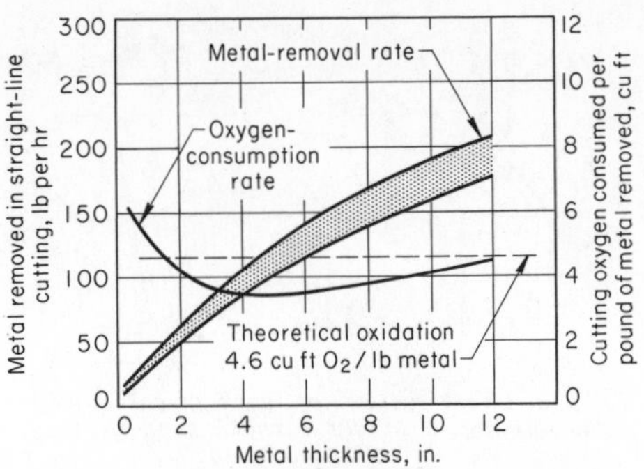

Fig. 1. Effect of metal thickness on consumption of cutting oxygen and on metal-removal rate

cutting the more widely used grades of steel. The effects of alloying elements in steel on its cuttability are given in the section on Effect of Alloying Elements in this article (page 286).

Unlike other metals, iron and its oxides have the chemical and physical properties required for self-sustaining and controllable combustion. Oxides of carbon steel and low-alloy steel melt at about the same temperature as the parent metal, and are therefore easily moved by the force of the flame.

Special problems exist in the cutting of high-alloy steels, cast iron, and nonferrous metals, because they do not readily oxidize and therefore do not provide enough heat for a continuous reaction.

Some metals oxidize more readily than iron, but their oxides form a tough, adherent film with a melting point considerably higher than that of the parent metal. Such oxide films act as a barrier between the oxygen and the metal, and resist the dislodging action of the cutting flame.

As the carbon and alloy contents of the steel to be cut increase, preheating or postheating treatments (of the entire workpiece) often are necessary to overcome the effect of the heat cycle, particularly the quench effect.

Some of the high-alloy steels, such as the stainless steels, and cast iron are cut successfully by injecting metal powder (usually iron) or a chemical additive into the oxygen jet. The metal powders not only supply combustion heat, but also break up oxide films. Chemical additives combine with oxides to form lower-melting products that can be flushed away.

Cast iron can be cut, but with less precision, by an oscillating technique described on page 294.

Applications. A wide variety of steel products can be cut with relative ease and precision by the oxy-fuel gas processes. These include all types of rolled shapes, forgings and castings. Large-scale applications of the processes are found in shipbuilding, building construction, earthmoving, materials handling, and machinery building, and in the fabrication of pressure and storage vessels.

Many machine structures, formerly made from forgings and castings, can be made at less cost by redesigning them for welding and gas cutting, with the advantages of quick delivery of material from steel suppliers, low cost of gas-cutting equipment, simplicity of operation, and flexibility of design.

Machine parts, such as gears, sprockets, handwheels, clevises and frames, and tools, such as wrenches, can be cut by gas torches. Often these products can be used as-cut. However, when cutting medium-carbon or high-carbon steels or other metals that harden by rapid cooling, the hardening effect must be considered, especially if the workpiece is to be subsequently machined. Hardening and distortion are discussed on pages 285 and 286.

Thickness Limits. Although gas torches can cut steel less than 1/8 in. thick and over 60 in. thick, some sacrifice in quality occurs near both ends of this range. As thickness increases, the system becomes more sensitive to small variations that affect the flame and the heat distribution through the cut. Even a highly skilled operator may have difficulty in avoiding gouges in kerf walls of heavy cuts when imperfections are encountered in the steel, or when the direction of the cut changes abruptly. With very thin material, it is difficult to control the heat input to avoid melting the kerf edges. Although steel as thin as 0.075 in. can be cut, the kerf is likely to be of uneven width, with cut edges either rounded or encrusted with slag. Steel that is less than 1/4 in. thick often is stacked for cutting. Stack cutting is described on pages 292 and 293.

Chemistry of Cutting

When carbon or low-alloy steel is heated to ignition temperature and supplied with oxygen, the steel in the path of the oxygen oxidizes rapidly. The principal oxidation product is the black iron oxide Fe_3O_4. Since the iron content of these steels is 95% or more, the chemical equation:

$$3Fe + 2O_2 \longrightarrow Fe_3O_4 + 267{,}000 \text{ calories}$$

can be used as a guide to oxygen requirements and heat evolvement, based on the oxidation of 3 gram-formula weights or moles of iron to Fe_3O_4. (The amount of heat evolved in this reaction has been incorrectly shown in a number of publications as 26,700 calories.) The above relation can also be expressed as:

$$1 \text{ lb Fe} + 4.6 \text{ cu ft } O_2 \longrightarrow 1.38 \text{ lb } Fe_3O_4 + 2870 \text{ Btu}$$

Accordingly, for the complete oxidation of iron (with oxygen volumes at 68 F and at 1 atmosphere):

1 lb of iron requires 0.38 lb, or 4.6 cu ft, of oxygen.
1 cu in. of iron requires 0.109 lb, or 1.31 cu ft, of oxygen.
1 lb of oxygen requires 2.62 lb, or 9.19 cu in., of iron.
1 cu ft of oxygen requires 0.22 lb, or 0.76 cu in., of iron.

In gas cutting, not all of the iron removed from the cut is oxidized. Some of it (up to 30 or 40%) is blown out of the cut as molten iron, along with the oxide, and becomes a part of the slag.

Oxygen consumption varies widely in practice, depending on whether maximum economy, speed or accuracy is sought. As shown in Fig. 1, for average straight-line cutting of low-carbon steel, the consumption of cutting oxygen per pound of metal removed varies with the thickness of the metal, and is lowest at a thickness of 4 to 5 in.

The amount and distribution of heat from the chemical reaction can be roughly calculated by assuming that, for every unit mass of iron oxidized, an equal mass of iron is melted. The heat evolved is 2870 Btu per pound of iron oxidized. About 680 Btu is required for melting 1 lb of iron (taking 2800 F as the melting point, 0.2 Btu per pound per °F as the average specific heat, and 117 Btu per pound as the heat of fusion). Only a small part of the total heat could be used in melting the iron; about 2100 Btu per pound is available for further distribution. Some of this heat is used to superheat the molten product, some is conducted into the workpiece, and some is lost through radiation and convection. Most of the heat is finally flushed out of the cut in the molten mixture of iron and iron oxides together with residual hot gases. The heat balance must be kept within limits for controlled cutting.

As the cutting oxygen flows down through the cut, the quantity available for reaction decreases. If the flow of oxygen is relatively large and sharply coherent, the rate of cutting through the depth of the cut is not affected; that is, the cutting face will remain vertical if the oxygen is in excess and the cutting speed is not too great.

If the oxygen flow is insufficient, or cutting speed too high, the lower portions of the cut will react more slowly. As a result, the cutting face will become curved, as shown in Fig. 2. The horizontal distance between the points of entry and exit is called "drag". Drag often is expressed as a ratio or as a percentage of the metal thickness.

Drag can be stabilized; at the proper drag ratio, the heat from the molten metal flowing down the curve is used most efficiently. Drag is a rough measure of cutting quality and of economy in oxygen consumption. In metal thicknesses up to 2 or 3 in., a 10 to 15% drag is associated with good quality of cut and economy. Higher quality demands less drag; more drag indicates poorer quality and low oxygen consumption. Too much drag may lead to incomplete cutting.

In very thin sections, drag has little meaning; the main problem is control of high heat input compared to low heat sink. In very thick sections, the opposite is true; the problem is to avoid excessive drag. All the input variables controlled by the operator (size and type of cutting tip, preheat flames, oxygen flow, and cutting speed) can be used to control drag.

Oxygen purity, as well as the alloy content of the steel being cut, affects the chemical reaction in gas cutting. Oxygen purity also affects combustion heat. The oxygen supplied from cylinders for gas cutting usually is at least 99.5% pure. A 0.5% departure from this purity (99% O_2) decreases the cutting efficiency. At 90% purity, cutting is very difficult, and at lower purities it is often impossible. The impurities consist of inert gases and water vapor. The effective purity of oxygen can also be reduced by gaseous combustion products from the preheat flames and from the metal being cut.

Alloying of iron affects gas cutting primarily by changing the rate of oxi-

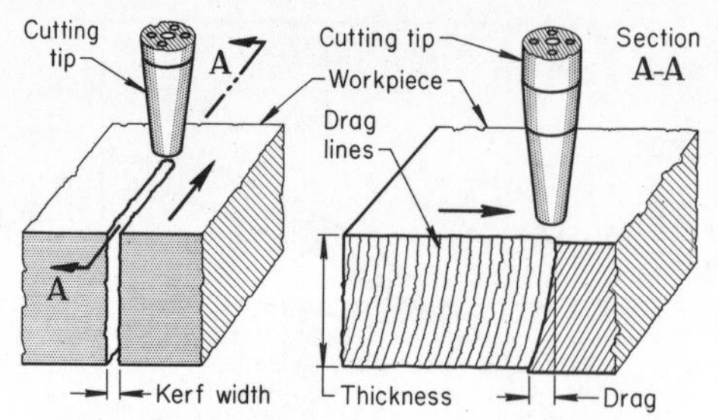

Fig. 2. Cross section of work metal during gas cutting, showing curvature on cutting face, called drag

dation. The total alloy content in low-alloy steel usually does not exceed 5%, and the effect on cutting speed is slight. In more highly alloyed steel, the oxidizing characteristics of alloying elements and the constituents formed in alloying may make controlled oxidation difficult or even impossible. In any steel, the chemical reaction is accelerated by preheating the workpiece; the higher-alloy steels, therefore, are preheated to promote cutting. Preheating in this sense differs from the preheating that is done by the oxy-fuel gas flames, which usually are called preheat flames.

Preheating as explained in the above paragraph ranges from warming a cold workpiece with a torch to furnace heating the work beyond 1000 F. For some alloy steels, preheat temperatures are 400 to 600 F. Carbon steel billets and other sections are occasionally cut at temperatures of 1600 F and higher.

Preheating is not intended solely to promote the chemical reaction in cutting, because both the mechanical and metallurgical properties of even some low-alloy steels are affected by the heat cycle of cutting. These effects usually can be controlled by preheating and postheating treatments (see the section on Heat Effects, page 284).

Chemical reactions are used in such methods as flux cutting and metal-powder cutting to overcome the adverse effects of some alloying elements. Chemical fluxes combine with refractory oxides to form lower-melting compounds. Metal powders such as iron, or iron and aluminum mixtures, burn with a high evolution of heat, which aids in the rapid cutting of metals that normally resist oxidation.

Combustion of Gases

Fuel-gas combustion produces the preheat flames, which serve two main purposes. When burning alone, they help to initiate the cutting operation. During cutting, the flames surround the oxygen stream and help sustain the operation. Specific functions of preheat flames are to:

1 Heat the surface of the workpiece to the ignition temperature for cutting
2 Descale and clean the workpiece
3 Supply the workpiece and cutting oxygen with enough heat to maintain the heat balance needed for continuous cutting
4 Protect the oxygen stream from turbulent interaction with the air.

Because the steel surface will ignite in oxygen at any point where the proper temperature is reached, the control, accuracy and quality of the cut depend on the uniformity of the preheat flames. These gases issue from ports that surround the cutting-oxygen orifice in the cutting tip. For uniform flow, both the ports and the oxygen orifice must be kept free of foreign matter — especially scale and slag particles that may be ejected from the cut.

The fuel gases used for preheating are listed in Table 1, which also gives their combustion constants in oxygen. Because these gases differ greatly in heat content and combustion, equipment is designed for particular fuels. Operators trained in the use of one gas usually require additional training in the use of another.

Table 1. Specific Volumes and Combustion Constants of Fuel Gases in Oxygen

Gas	Specific volume, cu ft per lb(a)	Heat value, Btu per cu ft(a)	Temperature of flame in oxygen, F(b)
Acetylene	13.75	1556	5600-6300
Natural gas(c)	22.5	1000	4600-5500
Propane	8.15	2627	4600-5650
Mapp(d)	8.85(e)	2384(e)	5300
Hydrogen	178.23	344	5000-5060
Butane	6.25	2999	5000-5300
Coke gas	...	500	4600
Oxygen	11.21	...	...

(a) Cubic feet at 32 F, 1 atmosphere. (b) Values are approximate. Different authorities cite the higher or the lower values of the ranges shown. (c) Average mixture, principally methane. (d) Stabilized methylacetylene-propadiene. (e) Cubic feet at 60 F, 1 atmosphere.

The most important preheat fuel gases are acetylene, natural gas, propane and Mapp. These gases are hydrocarbons, which give off carbon dioxide and water vapor as the products of complete combustion. Flames of hydrocarbon gases are complex, displaying successive cones as a result of stepped chemical reactions. With acetylene, the products of complete combustion cannot exist at the temperature of the inner cone. Combustion is completed in the cooler outer sheath of the flame. Chemical equations for combustion reactions of hydrocarbon gases often are simplified by treating the reactions as though the products were formed in only one step.

Acetylene (C_2H_2) combustion produces a hot, short flame with a bright inner cone at each cutting-tip port; the hottest point is at the tip of this inner cone. Combustion starts in the inner cone and is brought to completion in a cooler, blue, outer flame. The sharp distinction between the two flames helps in adjusting the ratio of oxygen to acetylene.

Depending on this ratio, the flame may be carburizing (reducing), neutral or oxidizing. A neutral flame results when just enough oxygen is supplied for primary combustion, yielding carbon monoxide (CO) and hydrogen (H_2). These products then combine with oxygen in ambient air to form the blue outer flame, yielding carbon dioxide (CO_2) and water (H_2O). The neutral ratio of oxygen to acetylene is about 1 to 1, and the flame temperature at the tip of the inner cone is about 5500 F.*
This flame is used for manual cutting.

*Temperatures cited in this article for combustion are approximate. Various authorities differ by 10% or more, as indicated in Table 1.

When the oxygen-to-acetylene ratio is reduced to about 0.9 to 1, a bright streamer begins to appear, and the flame becomes carburizing, or reducing. A carburizing flame is sometimes used for rough cutting of cast iron.

When the oxygen-to-acetylene ratio is increased to more than 1 to 1, the inner cones are shorter, "necked in" at the sides, and more sharply defined; this flame is oxidizing. Flame temperature increases until, at a ratio of about 1.7 to 1, the temperature is maximum, or somewhat over 5600 F at the tip of the cones. An oxidizing flame can be used for preheating at the start of the cut, and for cutting very thick sections.

According to the equation:

$$2C_2H_2 + 5O_2 \rightarrow 4CO_2 + 2H_2O$$

an oxygen-to-acetylene ratio of 2.5 to 1 is required for a complete reaction. For complete combustion, however, as much as 1.5 parts of oxygen is taken from ambient air. In oxyacetylene cutting, part of this oxygen may be supplied from the cutting oxygen, but total oxygen consumption is relatively low — an advantage of acetylene over natural gas and propane. Operation of oxyacetylene equipment in confined spaces, such as the inside of a closed tank or vessel, requires forced ventilation to supply the additional air needed for breathing and for flame combustion.

Acetylene must be used at pressures below 15 psi, which is a stable operating range. Safety codes specify equipment and handling practices for acetylene. When supplied in special cylinders, acetylene is dissolved in acetone, which is contained in a porous mass that fills the cylinder. This technique eliminates the sensitivity of acetylene at pressures over 15 psi. Such cylinders can be filled to pressures exceeding 15 psi, but not greater than 250 psi. Acetylene may also be supplied from generators. With either means of supply, safety regulations must be observed to avoid sudden decomposition and explosion.

Despite some disadvantages, acetylene has been used for cutting for a longer time than any other gas. Its performance is well understood, equipment for it is perfected and widely marketed, and it is readily available. It has become the standard against which other gases are compared.

Typical conditions for manual oxyacetylene cutting are shown in Table 2; conditions for machine oxyacetylene cutting are given in Table 3.

Natural gas is a mixture of gases, but consists principally of methane, and therefore usually is given the chemical symbol for methane (CH_4). One source defines the most widely used mixture as 85% methane (CH_4), 4% ethane (C_2H_6), and 11% (N_2, H_2, O_2, H_2O). Some wells produce natural gas with large proportions of ethane and propane.

The chemical equation for complete combustion:

$$CH_4 + 2O_2 \rightarrow CO_2 + 2H_2O$$

indicates an oxygen-to-methane ratio of 2 to 1; this ratio is used for the preheat flame. Maximum flame temperature at the tip of the inner cones is about 5000 F. Both higher and lower temperatures have been reported; also,

Table 2. Typical Data for Manual Oxyacetylene Cutting of Low-Carbon Steel Plate

Plate thickness, in.	Diameter of cutting orifice, in.	Oxygen pressure, psi	Cutting speed, ipm(a)	Gas consumption, cu ft(b)(c) — Per hr: Oxygen	Per hr: Acetylene	Per linear ft: Oxygen	Per linear ft: Acetylene
⅛	0.0380-0.0400	15-23	20-30	45-55	7-9	0.37-0.45	0.06-0.07
¼	0.0380-0.0595	11-20	16-26	50-93	9-11	0.63-0.72	0.08-0.11
⅜	0.0380-0.0595	17-25	15-24	60-115	10-12	0.80-0.96	0.10-0.13
½	0.0465-0.0595	20-30	12-22	66-125	10-13	1.10-1.14	0.12-0.17
¾	0.0465-0.0595	24-35	12-20	117-143	12-15	1.43-1.95	0.15-0.20
1	0.0465-0.0595	28-40	9-18	130-160	13-16	1.78-2.89	0.18-0.29
1½	0.0595-0.0810	35-48	6-14	143-178	15-18	1.96-3.18	0.21-0.33
2	0.0670-0.0810	22-50	6-13	185-231	16-20	3.55-6.16	0.31-0.53
3	0.0670-0.0810	33-55	4-10	240-290	19-23	5.80-12.00	0.46-0.95
4	0.0810-0.0860	42-60	4-8	293-388	21-26	9.70-14.64	0.65-1.05
5	0.0810-0.0860	53-70	3.5-6.4	347-437	24-29	13.66-19.83	0.91-1.37
6	0.0980-0.0995	45-80	3.0-5.4	400-567	27-32	21.00-26.70	1.19-1.80
8	0.0995	60-77	2.6-4.2	505-615	31.5-38.5	29.30-38.84	1.83-2.42
10	0.0995	75-96	1.9-3.2	610-750	36.9-45.1	46.90-64.20	2.57-3.84
12(c)	0.1200	69-86	1.4-2.6	720-880	42.3-51.7	67.70-103.00	3.98-6.05

(a) Lowest speeds and highest gas consumptions are for inexperienced operators, short cuts, dirty or poor material. Highest speeds and lowest gas consumptions are for experienced operators, long cuts, and clean and good material.
(b) Because the pressure of acetylene for the preheating flames is more a function of torch design than of the thickness of the part being cut, pressure data have been omitted from this table. For acetylene pressure data, see charts of manufacturers of apparatus.
(c) Beyond 12-in. thickness, the critical data of manual cutting practices are greatly affected by the condition of the metal and the skill of the operator, resulting in wide ranges of data. In view of this, the table has been terminated at the 12-in. thickness. In Table 3, on machine cutting, thickness range is extended to 36 in.

Table 3. Typical Data for Machine Oxyacetylene Cutting of Low-Carbon Steel Plate(a)

Plate thickness, in.	Diameter of cutting orifice, in.	Oxygen pressure, psi	Cutting speed, ipm(b)	Gas consumption, cu ft(b)(c) — Per hr: Oxygen	Per hr: Acetylene	Per linear ft: Oxygen	Per linear ft: Acetylene
⅛	0.0250-0.0400	15-23	22-32	40-55	7-9	0.34-0.36	0.05-0.06
¼	0.0310-0.0595	11-35	20-28	45-93	8-11	0.34-0.66	0.07-0.08
⅜	0.0310-0.0595	17-40	19-26	82-115	9-12	0.86-0.89	0.08-0.09
½	0.0310-0.0595	20-55	17-24	105-125	10-13	1.04-1.24	0.11-0.12
¾	0.0380-0.0595	24-50	15-22	117-159	12-15	1.45-1.56	0.14-0.16
1	0.0465-0.0595	28-55	14-19	130-174	13-16	1.83-1.86	0.17-0.19
1½	0.0670-0.0810	25-55	12-15	185-240	14-18	3.20	0.23-0.24
2	0.0670-0.0810	22-60	10-14	185-260	16-20	3.70-3.72	0.29-0.32
3	0.0810-0.0860	33-50	8-11	240-332	18-23	6.00-6.04	0.42-0.45
4	0.0810-0.0860	42-60	6.5-9	293-384	21-26	8.53-9.02	0.58-0.65
5	0.0810-0.0860	53-65	5.5-7.5	347-411	23-29	10.97-12.62	0.77-0.84
6	0.0980-0.0995	45-65	4.5-6.5	400-490	26-32	15.10-17.78	0.98-1.16
8	0.0980-0.0995	60-90	3.7-4.9	505-625	31-39	25.52-27.30	1.59-1.68
10	0.0995-0.1100	75-90	2.9-4.0	610-750	37-45	37.50-42.10	2.25-2.55
12	0.1100-0.1200	69-105	2.4-3.5	720-880	42-52	49.70-60.00	2.97-3.50
12	0.1935	30	(e)	1274	85	(d)	(d)
14	0.221	25	(e)	1458	98	(d)	(d)
16	0.221	30	(e)	1683	98	(d)	(d)
18	0.250	25	(e)	1838	134	(d)	(d)
20	0.250	30	(e)	2098	134	(d)	(d)
22	0.250	35	(e)	2358	134	(d)	(d)
24	0.290	25	(e)	2467	174	(d)	(d)
26	0.290	30	(e)	2772	174	(d)	(d)
28	0.290	35	(e)	3077	174	(d)	(d)
30	0.332	25	(e)	3125	204	(d)	(d)
32	0.332	30	(e)	3425	204	(d)	(d)
34	0.332	35	(e)	3775	204	(d)	(d)
36	0.332	40	(e)	4125	204	(d)	(d)
Cutting With One-Piece Divergent Nozzles (High-Speed Tips)(f)							
¼	...	120	26	70	14	0.54	0.109
½	...	100	22	100	18	0.91	0.163
¾	...	100	20	120	18	1.00	0.18
1	...	110	18	130	18	1.44	0.20
1½	...	100	16	170	25	2.11	0.31
2	...	100	13	230	25	3.52	0.39
3	...	85	10	270	32	5.4	0.64
4	...	85	9	330	35	7.3	0.78
5	...	110	8	395	35	9.7	0.87
6	...	125	7	435	35	12.4	1.00
7	...	80	6	495	36	16.5	1.20
8	...	100	5½	580	36	21.2	1.32

(a) Column values do not necessarily vary in exact proportion to plate thickness, because straight-line relations do not exist among pressure, speed, and orifice sizes.
(b) Lowest speeds and highest gas consumptions are for inexperienced operators, short cuts, dirty or poor material. Highest speeds and lowest gas consumptions are for experienced operators, long cuts, clean and good material.
(c) Because the pressure of acetylene for the preheating flames is more a function of torch design than of the thickness of the part being cut, pressure data have been omitted from this table. For acetylene pressure data, see charts of manufacturers of apparatus.
(d) The data for 12 to 36 in. are for torches with large tips, using large volumes of oxygen at low pressures. Because the speed depends on the condition of the material being cut and the skill of the operator, no figures are given for gas consumption per linear foot.
(e) Cutting speeds vary from 4 ipm for light sections to 2 ipm for heavy sections.
(f) These data are for divergent orifices that have controlled expansion tips, permitting the use of relatively high oxygen pressures so as to expand the cutting oxygen through the orifices. Thus the gas stream has high velocity and is relatively narrow. Higher speeds and lower specific consumption of oxygen result.

Table 4. Typical Data for Manual Oxy-Natural Gas Straight-Line Cutting of Low-Carbon Steel Plate (a)

Plate thickness, in.	Diameter of cutting orifice, in.	Oxygen pressure, psi	Minimum natural gas pressure, oz per sq in.	Cutting speed, ipm (b)	Approximate gas consumption, cu ft per hr: Oxygen	Natural gas
1/8	0.046	15	3	20 to 28	25	8
1/4	0.046	18	3	18 to 28	35	10
3/8	0.046	20	3	16 to 20	45	14
1/2	0.059	30	3	13 to 17	50	18
3/4	0.059	35	3	10 to 15	75	20
1	0.059	40	3	9 to 13	100	24
1 1/2	0.067	40	3	7 to 12	145	26
2	0.067	45	3	6 to 10	190	28
2 1/2	0.067	50	3	6 to 9	245	30
3	0.093	50	3	5 to 8	270	32
4	0.093	55	3	5 to 7	320	36
5	0.093	60	3	4 to 6	400	40
6	0.110	60	3	4 to 6	470	48
7	0.110	70	3	3 to 5	520	52
8	0.110	80	3	3 to 4	580	56
10	0.110	90	3	3 to 4	850	60
12	0.110	100	3	2 to 3	1000	64

(a) Using injector-type torch and two-piece tips. (b) Variations in cutting speeds may be caused by mill scale on plate, variation in oxygen purity, flame adjustment, condition of equipment, impurities in steel, and variation in heat content of natural gas.

Table 5. Typical Data for Machine Oxy-Natural Gas Shape Cutting of Low-Carbon Steel Plate 1/4 to 8 In. Thick (a)

Plate thickness, in.	Diameter of cutting orifice, in.	High preheat: Oxygen, psi	High preheat: Natural gas, psi	Low preheat: Oxygen, psi	Low preheat: Natural gas, oz per sq in.	Cutting oxygen, psi	Cutting speed, ipm (b)	Width of kerf, in. (approx)
1/4	0.036	28	3	7 to 12	1	70 to 75	18 to 28	0.08
3/8	0.037	28	3	7 to 12	1	70 to 80	18 to 26	0.08
1/2	0.039	34	3	7 to 12	1	75 to 80	16 to 24	0.09
5/8	0.039	34	3	7 to 12	1	75 to 80	16 to 23	0.09
3/4	0.046	46	3	8 to 12	1	80 to 85	16 to 22	0.10
1	0.046	48	3	8 to 12	1	80 to 85	14 to 20	0.10
1 1/4	0.054	44	3	8 to 12	1	80 to 85	14 to 18	0.12
1 1/2	0.054	44	3	8 to 12	1	90 to 95	13 to 18	0.12
1 3/4	0.054	45	3	8 to 12	1	90 to 95	12 to 17	0.12
2	0.054	45	3	8 to 12	1	100	10 to 15	0.12
2 1/4	0.055	46	3	8 to 12	1	100	9 to 15	0.13
2 1/2	0.055	46	3	8 to 12	1	100	8 to 14	0.13
2 3/4	0.067	46	3	8 to 12	1	100	8 to 13	0.14
3	0.067	46	3	8 to 12	1	100	7 to 13	0.14
3 1/2	0.073	50	3	10 to 14	1	105	6 to 12	0.15
4	0.073	50	3	10 to 14	1	110	6 to 11	0.15
4 1/2	0.082	50	3	10 to 14	1	110	5 to 10	0.17
5	0.082	50	3	10 to 14	1	115	5 to 10	0.17
5 1/2	0.096	50	3	10 to 14	1	115	5 to 9	0.18
6	0.096	50	3	10 to 14	1	120	5 to 9	0.18
6 1/2	0.096	50	3	10 to 14	1	120	4 to 8	0.18
7 1/2	0.096	50	3	10 to 14	1	120	4 to 8	0.18
8	0.096	50	3	10 to 14	1	120	3 to 7	0.18

(a) Two-piece tips for high-speed machine cutting. (b) Variations in cutting speeds may be caused by mill scale on plate, variation in oxygen purity, flame adjustment, condition of equipment, impurities in steel, and variation in heat content of natural gas.

Table 6. Typical Data for Machine Oxy-Natural Gas Drop Cutting of Shapes From Low-Carbon Steel Plate 10 to 21 1/2 In. Thick (a)

Plate thickness, in.	Diameter of cutting orifice, in.	Preheat: Oxygen, psi	Preheat: Natural gas, psi	Cutting oxygen, psi (b)	Cutting speed, ipm	Cutting oxygen, cfh
10	0.250	35 to 45	5	27	3.25	1400
12 3/4	0.281	35 to 45	5	28	3.25	1750
15 1/2	0.281	35 to 45	5	30	3.0	1900
18	0.312	35 to 45	5	28	4.25	2245
21	0.312	35 to 45	5	28	3.0	2245
21 1/2	0.312	35 to 45	5	30	3.75	2365

(a) Two-piece recessed tips with milled preheat flutes (heavy preheat) and straight-bore cutting-oxygen orifices. (b) Pressure measured at torch inlet.

Table 7. Typical Data for Machine Oxy-Propane Straight-Line Cutting of Low-Carbon Steel Plate 8 to 44 In. Thick (a)

Plate thickness, in.	Diameter orifice, in. of cutting	Operating pressure, psi: Cutting oxygen	Preheat oxygen	Propane	Cutting speed, ipm	Gas consumption, cfh: Cutting oxygen	Preheat oxygen	Propane
8 to 12	0.1562	40 to 65	20 to 40	10 to 15	3 to 6	715 to 1210	200 to 375	55 to 105
10 to 16	0.1875	30 to 60	20 to 40	10 to 15	3 to 5	840 to 1500	200 to 375	55 to 105
15 to 25	0.250	30 to 60	20 to 40	10 to 15	2 to 3 1/2	1500 to 2510	200 to 375	55 to 105
20 to 32	0.2812	30 to 60	20 to 60	10 to 20	2 to 3	1900 to 3150	220 to 425	60 to 115
24 to 36	0.3125	25 to 55	20 to 65	10 to 25	1 1/2 to 2 1/2	2080 to 3650	250 to 450	60 to 125
28 to 44	0.3437	25 to 55	20 to 65	10 to 25	1 1/2 to 2 1/2	2570 to 4400	250 to 450	60 to 125

(a) Two-piece recessed tips with milled preheat flutes (heavy preheat) and straight-bore cutting-oxygen orifices.

optimum oxygen-to-gas ratios have been put at 2.1 to 1. The flame is more diffuse than with acetylene; heat intensity is lower; and adjustment for carburizing, neutral and oxidizing flame is less clearly defined. Cutting speeds are slower, and oxygen consumption is greater. Also, more time is required for preheating with natural gas than with acetylene. An excess of oxygen shortens preheat time, but increases consumption of oxygen. Furthermore, natural gas cannot be used for welding of steel, so extra installations will be needed if this operation is to be performed.

Despite these disadvantages, the use of natural gas for cutting has increased. Natural gas is the lowest-cost commercial fuel gas, although the price is much higher in cylinders than for the same gas from a pipeline.

Neither acetylene nor natural gas accumulates in low pockets. When burned alone in air, the flame of natural gas does not produce soot.

Typical data for manual oxy-natural gas cutting are given in Table 4; for machine cutting, in Tables 5 and 6. Corresponding tip sizes from different manufacturers differ in performance because construction is not the same.

Propane (C_3H_8) is a petroleum-base fuel usually supplied as a liquid in storage tanks from which it is drawn off as a gas. The gas is dispensed from bulk storage tanks through pipelines. It has a narrow range of flammability and is relatively stable, but is heavier than air. Complete combustion requires an oxygen-to-propane ratio of 5 to 1. However, about one-half to three-fourths of the oxygen needed is taken from the ambient air. When the ratio of oxygen to propane is 4.5 to 1, the flame temperature is about 5000 F at the tip of the inner cones. At 4.25 to 1, the flame temperature is about 4800 F. Flame properties are similar to those of natural gas, as to diffuseness, heat intensity, flame adjustment, and cutting speed. When burned alone in air, the flame is soot-free. Propane cannot be used for welding steel.

Cutting torches and tips used with propane are the same as those used for natural gas. Therefore, the data shown in Table 4 for natural gas can be used for manual oxy-propane cutting by selecting a propane pressure (about 3 to 10 psi) depending on the size of tip used. Under these conditions, propane flow is about 50% of natural gas flow.

Data for machine oxy-propane cutting of heavier thicknesses are given in Table 7.

Comparison of Gases. The following two examples describe studies conducted in two plants on the comparative performance of acetylene, natural gas, and propane. The first example covers a range of thicknesses; the second is a cost comparison for a single thickness.

Example 345. Acetylene vs Natural Gas vs Propane for Cutting 1020 Steel (Table 8)

Performance of acetylene, natural gas, and propane was compared in a series of tests on hot rolled 1020 steel plate, 1/4 to 6 in. thick. Straight-line cuts 20 ft long were made in 4-by-26-ft plates from the same mill heat. All cutting was done in a multiple-torch cutting machine, using a single torch. For acetylene

Table 8. Test Conditions and Results in Cutting Hot Rolled 1020 Steel Plate Using Three Fuel Gases (Example 345) (a)
(A = Acetylene; N = Natural gas; P = Propane)

Plate thickness, in.	Tip drill number			Cutting oxygen, psi			Preheat gas, psi			Cutting speed, ipm(b)			Gas consumption, cu ft per hour: Cutting oxygen			Gas consumption: Preheat oxygen			Gas consumption: Total oxygen			Gas consumption: Preheat gas			Piercing time, sec: Minimum			Piercing time, sec: Maximum		
	A	N	P	A	N	P	A	N	P	A	N	P	A	N	P	A	N	P	A	N	P	A	N	P	A	N	P	A	N	P
¼	73	68	68	125	85	85	4	½	½	25	25	25	54	55	55	15	50	44	69	105	94	14	28	10	3	3	3	5	6	6
½	68	64	64	110	85	85	4	½	½	21	21	21	83	75	75	19	53	45	102	128	120	18	30	11	3	3	3	6	7	7
1	64	60	60	115	90	90	4	½	½	17	17	17	120	110	110	19	56	49	139	166	159	18	32	12	3	3	3	7	8	7
3	53	54	54	115	95	95	5	½	½	9	10	10	246	231	231	34	59	52	280	290	283	32	30	13	4	4	4	9	10	9
5	51	51	51	125	95	95	5	½	½	8	8	8	374	356	356	37	68	57	411	424	414	34	34	13	5	5	5	10	11	10
6	51	49	49	125	95	95	6	½	½	7	8	8	410	395	395	42	74	71	452	469	466	35	37	15	5	6	6	11	12	11

(a) Both natural gas and propane produced lighter slag adherence and better surface condition in cutting plates 2 in. or more in thickness. (b) Cutting speeds were assumed normal for operating one to four cutting torches on plate with tight scale of light to medium thickness. Operation of additional torches or heavier scale could require reduction of 1 to 3 in. per minute in cutting speed.

cutting, high-speed cutting tips were used. For natural gas and propane, divergent-type, high-speed, two-piece tips were used, with injector-type cutting torches and a high-low preheat-control system called a "gas saver".

Recording flowmeters were used to determine consumption rates of the fuel gases and of preheat and cutting oxygen. A total of 18 test plates (three of each size) was used.

Table 9. Cost of Gases Consumed in Cutting 1¼-In.-Thick Hot Rolled 1020 Steel at a Speed of 17 In. per Min (Example 346)

Gas	Fuel gas: Acetylene(a)	Propane(b)	Natural gas(c)
Gas Consumption, Cubic Feet per Hour			
Oxygen(d)	155	167	167
Fuel gas	25	11	20
Cost of Gas, per Hour			
Oxygen	$1.91	$2.05	$2.05
Fuel gas	0.80	0.09	0.015
Total(e)	$2.71	$2.14	$2.065

(a) At $3.20 per 100 cu ft. (b) At $0.82 per 100 cu ft. (c) At $0.075 per 100 cu ft. (d) Cutting plus preheat oxygen, at $1.23 per 100 cu ft.
(e) With two machines having four cutting heads each, operating 50% of the time, it was estimated that a saving of about $20 per 8-hr shift could be realized by changing from acetylene to natural gas.

The results given in Table 8 are for cutting 60 ft and are averages of three cuts in each plate thickness for each oxy-gas mixture used. The cuts were spaced well apart, and the plates were rotated, to avoid the effect of residual heat, which might confuse results. Because of the large finished sizes of the cut plates, there was little or no distortion from differential heating.

Example 346. Cost Comparison for Three Fuel Gases (Table 9)

In one plant, acetylene, at $3.20 per 100 cu ft, was being used in large quantities for machine gas cutting of hot rolled 1020 steel plate. Natural gas was available at $0.075 per 100 cu ft, and propane at $0.82 per 100 cu ft. Although it was realized that (*a*) the cost of the preheat gas is only one factor in the over-all cost of gas cutting (because different gases require different amounts of preheat and cutting oxygen), and (*b*) cutting speed and quality of cut vary with the preheat gases used, the price differential among the three gases prompted a restudy of the cutting process.

In the study, each gas was used to cut samples of 1¼-in.-thick plate at the same cutting speed (17 in. per min). Gas flows (preheat oxygen, cutting oxygen, and fuel gas) could then be adjusted to the minimum required for an acceptable quality of cut. Because cutting times would be equal, labor and overhead would be equal, and over-all costs would be in proportion to relative costs of gas consumed. Test results are given in Table 9.

Cutting with natural gas or propane showed additional savings: less cleaning time was needed because less slag adhered to the plate. Cutting tips were the two-piece fluted-nozzle type shown in Fig. 8(b). With these gases, tips had longer life and required less cleaning; tips and regulators were interchangeable. The study resulted in changing to natural gas.

Mapp gas (stabilized methylacetylene-propadiene) is a proprietary gas mixture; it is shipped and stored as a liquid, either in bulk storage tanks or in portable cylinders.

Both methylacetylene and propadiene have the chemical symbol C_3H_4 and by themselves are unstable, giving off their heat of formation during decomposition. As with acetylene, this heat is in addition to the heat of combustion. However, the methylacetylene-propadiene mixture in Mapp gas is stabilized by the addition of other hydrocarbons. The composition of Mapp gas is not disclosed, so that the chemical equation for complete combustion in oxygen is not given. However, when the flame is neutral, the ratio of oxygen to fuel gas is about 2.3 to 1; the normal operating ratio for cutting varies from 2.17-to-1 to 3-to-1, depending on speed and thickness. Maximum flame temperature at the tips of the inner cones, reported as 5300 F, occurs at oxygen-to-fuel ratios of 3.5-to-1 to 4-to-1. Flames can be adjusted for carburizing, neutral or oxidizing conditions. Settings for oxy-Mapp gas cutting with standard-pressure tips and with high-speed tips are given in Table 10.

Mapp gas is heavier than air, but it has a strong odor to reveal its presence if it is leaking or has collected in low pockets. It is less likely than acetylene to burn back into the torch or supply lines (flashback).

In comparing the cost of Mapp gas with the cost of acetylene, the difference in cylinder yields and consumption rates is a consideration. A 120-lb cylinder of Mapp gas yields 620 cu ft of gas, whereas a 240-lb cylinder of acetylene yields only 260 cu ft of gas. In addition, acetylene is consumed at a faster rate. Thus, storage, transportation, and time and labor for changing cylinders become important cost factors.

In the following example, the merits of natural gas, propane, acetylene and Mapp gas are compared. The comparison is based on the fastest cutting speed obtainable with each gas while maintaining the same standard of cut quality. Thus, labor is a cost factor. In contrast, labor costs did not enter into the comparison described previously in Example 346. All cuts were made at the same speed in Example 346, and only gas flows were varied to produce the same quality of cut.

Table 10. Typical Data for Oxy-Mapp Gas Cutting of Low-Carbon Steel Plate, Using Standard-Pressure Cutting Tips or High-Speed Cutting Tips(a)

Plate thickness, in.	Cutting tip No.(b)	Cutting speed, ipm	Oxygen: Cutting pressure, psi(c)	Oxygen: Cutting rate of flow, cfh	Oxygen: Preheat pressure, psi	Oxygen: Preheat rate of flow, cfh	Methylacetylene-propadiene: Cutting pressure, psi	Methylacetylene-propadiene: Cutting rate of flow, cfh	Kerf width, in.
Cutting With Standard-Pressure Tips									
⅛ ...	75	30 to 36	40 to 50	12 to 15	5 to 10	7 to 25	2 to 10	2 to 10	0.025
3/16 ..	72	26 to 32	40 to 50	20 to 30	5 to 10	7 to 25	2 to 10	2 to 10	0.03
¼ ...	68	24 to 30	40 to 50	30 to 40	5 to 10	7 to 25	2 to 10	2 to 10	0.04
½ ...	61	22 to 28	40 to 50	55 to 65	5 to 10	12 to 25	2 to 10	5 to 10	0.05
¾ ...	56	16 to 22	40 to 50	60 to 75	5 to 10	12 to 25	2 to 10	5 to 10	0.06
1	56	14 to 20	40 to 50	60 to 75	5 to 10	12 to 25	2 to 10	5 to 10	0.06
1¼ ...	54	13 to 17	50 to 60	105 to 120	10 to 20	20 to 35	2 to 10	8 to 15	0.08
1½ ...	54	12 to 16	50 to 60	105 to 120	10 to 20	20 to 35	2 to 10	8 to 15	0.08
2	52	10 to 14	50 to 60	145 to 190	10 to 20	20 to 35	2 to 10	8 to 15	0.09
2½ ...	48	9 to 13	50 to 60	210 to 265	10 to 30	20 to 50	6 to 10	8 to 20	0.10
3	48	8 to 13	50 to 60	210 to 265	10 to 30	20 to 50	6 to 10	8 to 20	0.10
4	46	7 to 12	60 to 70	290 to 330	10 to 30	25 to 50	6 to 10	10 to 20	0.15
5	46	6 to 10	70 to 80	330 to 405	10 to 30	25 to 50	6 to 10	10 to 20	0.15
6	42	5 to 8	60 to 70	375 to 470	10 to 30	25 to 50	6 to 15	10 to 20	0.16
8	35	4 to 7	60 to 70	485 to 590	30 to 50	40 to 100	10 to 15	20 to 45	0.19
10	30	3 to 6	40 to 70	500 to 625	30 to 50	40 to 100	10 to 15	20 to 45	0.20
12	30	3 to 5	50 to 85	645 to 865	30 to 50	60 to 150	10 to 15	30 to 60	0.21
Cutting With High-Speed Tips									
⅛ ...	75	32 to 38	60 to 70	20 to 25	5 to 10	7 to 25	2 to 10	3 to 10	0.025
3/16 ..	72	28 to 32	70 to 80	30 to 40	5 to 10	7 to 25	2 to 10	3 to 10	0.03
¼ ...	68	26 to 32	70 to 80	55 to 65	5 to 10	7 to 25	2 to 10	3 to 10	0.05
½ ...	61	24 to 30	80 to 90	75 to 95	5 to 10	12 to 25	2 to 10	5 to 10	0.06
¾ ...	56	20 to 26	80 to 90	115 to 130	5 to 10	12 to 25	2 to 10	5 to 10	0.07
1	56	18 to 24	80 to 90	115 to 130	5 to 10	12 to 25	2 to 10	5 to 10	0.07
1¼ ...	54	16 to 20	70 to 80	155 to 170	10 to 20	20 to 35	2 to 10	8 to 15	0.08
1½ ...	54	15 to 19	80 to 90	170 to 180	10 to 20	20 to 35	2 to 10	8 to 15	0.08
2 ...	52	14 to 18	80 to 90	215 to 255	10 to 20	20 to 35	2 to 10	8 to 15	0.09
2½ ...	52	12 to 17	80 to 90	215 to 255	10 to 20	20 to 35	2 to 10	8 to 15	0.09
3	48	10 to 15	80 to 90	335 to 400	10 to 20	20 to 35	6 to 10	10 to 15	0.10
4	46	9 to 14	80 to 90	375 to 425	10 to 20	20 to 35	6 to 10	10 to 15	0.12

(a) All recommendations are for straight-line cutting with a three-hose torch perpendicular to work. (b) All tips are of design recommended by the supplier. (c) Pressure of cutting oxygen measured at the torch.

Table 11. Operating Conditions and Comparative Costs for Straight-Line Gas Cutting of Low-Carbon Steel Plate With Four Fuel Gases (Example 347) (a)

Item	Acetylene	Mapp(b)	Propane	Natural gas
Cutting ½-In.-Thick Plate				
Type of cutting tip	45(c)	68(d)	361(c)	361(c)
Cutting-oxygen orifice:				
Tip No.	1	...	1	1
Drill-size No.	68	68	68	68
Diameter, in.	0.031	0.031	0.031	0.031
Optimum cutting speed, ipm(e)	35	35	32	31
Fuel-gas pressure, psi	5	10	9	4.5
Fuel-gas flow, cfh	23	13	27	45
Preheat oxygen(f):				
Pressure, psi	8	30	20	30
Flow, cfh	28	39	110	75
Ratio of oxygen to fuel gas	1.2 to 1	3 to 1	4 to 1	1.7 to 1
Cutting oxygen(f):				
Pressure, psi	100	110	100	100
Flow, cfh	75	85	75	75
Time per 100 ft cut, hr	0.571	0.571	0.625	0.645
Fuel cost per 100 ft cut	$0.33	$0.15	$0.04	$0.02
Cost of preheat and cutting oxygen per 100 ft cut:				
Oxygen at $0.18 per 100 cu ft	$0.11	$0.13	$0.21	$0.17
Oxygen at $0.50 per 100 cu ft	$0.29	$0.36	$0.58	$0.48
Oxygen at $1.00 per 100 cu ft	$0.59	$0.71	$1.16	$0.97
Direct labor cost per 100 ft cut(g)	$2.85	$2.85	$3.12	$3.22
Total cost of gas and direct labor per 100 ft cut:				
Oxygen at $0.18 per 100 cu ft	$3.29	$3.13	$3.37	$3.41
Oxygen at $0.50 per 100 cu ft	$3.47	$3.36	$3.74	$3.72
Oxygen at $1.00 per 100 cu ft	$3.77	$3.71	$4.32	$4.21
Cutting 1-In.-Thick Plate				
Type of cutting tip	45(c)	61(d)	361(c)	361(c)
Cutting-oxygen orifice:				
Tip No.	2	...	3	3
Drill-size No.	62	61	57	57
Diameter, in.	0.038	0.039	0.043	0.043
Optimum cutting speed, ipm(e)	24	24	21	21
Fuel-gas pressure, psi	8	10	7	4.5
Fuel-gas flow, cfh	30	16	25	45
Preheat oxygen(f):				
Pressure, psi	16	30	20	25
Flow, cfh	32	50	100	80
Ratio of oxygen to fuel gas	1.1 to 1	3.1 to 1	4 to 1	1.8 to 1
Cutting oxygen(f):				
Pressure, psi	115	100	95	95
Flow, cfh	120	130	140	140
Time per 100 ft cut, hr	0.833	0.833	0.952	0.952
Fuel cost per 100 ft cut	$0.63	$0.27	$0.06	$0.03
Cost of preheat and cutting oxygen per 100 ft cut:				
Oxygen at $0.18 per 100 cu ft	$0.23	$0.27	$0.41	$0.38
Oxygen at $0.50 per 100 cu ft	$0.63	$0.75	$1.14	$1.05
Oxygen at $1.00 per 100 cu ft	$1.27	$1.50	$2.28	$2.09
Direct labor cost per 100 ft cut(g)	$4.16	$4.16	$4.76	$4.76
Total cost of gas and direct labor per 100 ft cut:				
Oxygen at $0.18 per 100 cu ft	$5.02	$4.70	$5.23	$5.17
Oxygen at $0.50 per 100 cu ft	$5.42	$5.18	$5.96	$5.84
Oxygen at $1.00 per 100 cu ft	$6.06	$5.93	$7.10	$6.88
Cutting 2-In.-Thick Plate				
Type of cutting tip	45(c)	54(d)	361(c)	361(c)
Cutting-oxygen orifice:				
Tip No.	4	...	4	4
Drill-size No.	55	54	55	55
Diameter, in.	0.052	0.055	0.052	0.052
Optimum cutting speed, ipm(e)	18	18	16.5	16.5
Fuel-gas pressure, psi	5	10	8	4.5
Fuel-gas flow, cfh	28	15	31	45
Preheat oxygen(f):				
Pressure, psi	16	30	20	25
Flow, cfh	33	46	125	80
Ratio of oxygen to fuel gas	1.2 to 1	3 to 1	4 to 1	1.8 to 1
Cutting oxygen(f):				
Pressure, psi	100	95	105	105
Flow, cfh	220	260	245	245
Time per 100 ft cut, hr	1.11	1.11	1.21	1.21
Fuel cost per 100 ft cut	$0.78	$0.34	$0.09	$0.04
Cost of preheat and cutting oxygen per 100 ft cut:				
Oxygen at $0.18 per 100 cu ft	$0.51	$0.61	$0.81	$0.71
Oxygen at $0.50 per 100 cu ft	$1.40	$1.70	$2.24	$1.97
Oxygen at $1.00 per 100 cu ft	$2.81	$3.40	$4.48	$3.93
Direct labor cost per 100 ft cut(g)	$5.55	$5.55	$6.05	$6.05
Total cost of gas and direct labor per 100 ft cut:				
Oxygen at $0.18 per 100 cu ft	$6.84	$6.50	$6.95	$6.80
Oxygen at $0.50 per 100 cu ft	$7.73	$7.59	$8.38	$8.06
Oxygen at $1.00 per 100 cu ft	$9.14	$9.29	$10.62	$10.02

(a) Costs per 100 cu ft of bulk fuel gases were: acetylene, $2.50 (estimated; in-plant generated); Mapp gas, $2.03; propane, $0.25; natural gas, $0.07. (b) Stabilized methylacetylene-propadiene. (c) Two-piece, high-speed cutting tip. (d) Two-piece, high-speed cutting tip different in design from tip used with the other fuel gases. (e) Optimum cutting speed was fastest speed consistent with maintaining acceptable quality without loss of cut. (f) Total oxygen required for cutting includes both preheat oxygen and cutting oxygen. (g) At $5/hr.

Example 347. Acetylene vs Mapp Gas vs Propane vs Natural Gas (Table 11)

Four fuel gases were evaluated as to performance and economy in cutting by a manufacturer of structurals for buildings and bridges. Cutting data were first obtained in the laboratory. Laboratory results were then checked out in a six-month shop trial.

The objective of the laboratory tests was to determine the fastest cutting speed that could be attained by each of the gases while meeting shop-quality cut standards. Fuel gas and oxygen consumption were then carefully measured at these optimum cutting speeds while cutting steel plate ½, 1 and 2 in. thick. These data were translated into costs per 100 ft of cut.

Testing procedure was such as to neither favor nor penalize the cutting qualities of the gases. A carriage-driven, three-hose cutting torch was used, permitting independent regulation of fuel gas, preheat oxygen, and cutting oxygen. Gas consumption was measured by flowmeters and was checked by weighing cylinders before and after tests. Cutting tips were two-piece or high-speed types recommended by the manufacturer for the three plate thicknesses cut. All cuts were square, straight-line cuts made in steel of the same quality, surface condition, and temperature, and at the same edge distance.

Results of the test for each plate thickness are shown in Table 11. Of the data shown, cutting-tip data, fuel-gas and oxygen pressures, and ratios of oxygen to fuel gas did not enter into calculations but were recorded for reproducibility and verification.

Table 11 indicates that optimum speeds for acetylene and Mapp were 9 to 14% faster than those for propane and natural gas. Thus, at optimum cutting speeds, the differences in labor costs were significant. To reflect these differences, a labor rate of $5.00 per hour was assumed, and direct labor costs per 100 ft of cut were calculated (Table 11).

Fuel gas costs were based on bulk prices; oxygen costs, on a spread of three prices to show how different prices affect total costs.

Mapp gas showed lowest total cost, except at $1.00 oxygen and 2-in. plate, where acetylene was cheaper. Acetylene was next cheapest, except at $0.18 oxygen and 2-in. plate — where natural gas took second place. Generally, as oxygen prices increased, the difference between Mapp and acetylene decreased, but the advantage of Mapp and acetylene over natural gas and propane increased. Both natural gas and propane showed cost improvement at $0.18 oxygen and 2-in. plate.

To determine if shop personnel would, on their own, maintain laboratory cutting speeds, several shop operations were converted from bulk and cylinder acetylene to Mapp gas. Data obtained after six months confirmed the laboratory tests, and the entire plant was converted to Mapp.

It should be emphasized that the conclusions of this test were based on obtaining maximum cutting speeds at a quality of cut that was satisfactory for trimming and for weld edge-preparation in structural fabrication. Had the shop not used the higher cutting speeds, the savings might not have been realized.

Heat Effects

In gas cutting of steel, the temperature of a narrow zone adjacent to the cut face is raised considerably above the transformation range. As the cut progresses, the steel cools again through this range. The cooling rate depends on the heat conductivity and the mass of the surrounding metal, on the loss of heat by radiation and convection, and on the speed of cutting. When the steel being cut is at room temperature, the rate of cooling at the cut is sufficient to produce a quenching effect on the cut edges, particularly in heavier cuts involving large masses of cold metal.

When etched and polished specimens of gas-cut edges are examined under the microscope, the grain structure usually is found to be altered. Normal pearlitic steel is transformed into one or more structures, ranging from spheroidized carbides in ferrite to the harder constituents, depending on the amount of carbon and alloying elements present, and on the rate of cooling. The heat-affected zone may be $\frac{1}{32}$ to $\frac{1}{4}$ in. deep for steels $\frac{3}{8}$ to 6 in. thick. Some increase in hardness usually is detected at the outer margin of the heat-affected zone in nearly all steels.

Low-Carbon Steels. For low-carbon steels (0.25% C or less) cut at room temperature, the hardening effect usually is negligible, but it may become noticeable at the upper carbon limit if subsequent machining is required. Short of preheating or annealing the workpiece, this hardening effect may be lessened by making sure that the cutting flame is neutral to slightly oxidizing and is burning properly, and that the inner cones of the flame are at the correct height. By increasing the machining allowance slightly, a first cut usually can be made deep enough to get below the hardened zone in most steels.

In general, the mechanical properties of low-carbon steels are not affected adversely by gas cutting.

Medium-carbon steels (0.25% to 0.45% C) are affected only slightly by hardening caused by gas cutting. Steels ranging up to 0.30% C, with very low alloy content, show some hardening of the cut edges, but generally not enough to cause cracking. If gas-cut steel plate is to be subsequently welded, the carbon may range to 0.35%; the heat of welding obliterates the marginal structure produced by gas cutting. All other steels in this medium-carbon group should be preheated to 500 to 600 F to avoid cracking. If the gas-cut edges are to be machined, all of the medium-carbon steels should be preheated.

Higher-Carbon and Alloy Steels. Gas cutting of higher-carbon (over 0.45% C) and hardenable alloy steels at room temperature may produce, on the cut surface, a thin layer of hard, brittle material that is susceptible to cracking from the stress of cooling. The cooling stress that causes cracking is similar to the stress that causes distortion (see discussion starting at end of page).

Microcracks, or even incipient cracks, can be dangerous, because in service under tension they can develop into large fractures. The problems of hardening and the formation of residual stress can be alleviated by preheating and annealing.

Preheating serves three purposes:

1 Preheating reduces the temperature gradient near the cut during cutting. This lowers differential expansion, which may cause distortion or upsetting of the metal. Metal upset during the heating cycle can produce excessive stress in cooling.
2 Preheating increases the cutting speed and improves the surface of the cut, especially in heavier sections and in the difficult-to-cut steels.
3 Preheating reduces the cooling rate in the annealing range for the heat-affected portion of the cut during the cooling cycle. By slower cooling, more ductile microstructures are obtained and the formation of the hard martensitic structures is suppressed.

If the higher-carbon and alloy steels are adequately preheated (and, in certain instances, annealed afterward), no cracks will occur. Ordinarily, a preheat temperature of 500 to 600 F is sufficient for the carbon steels; alloy steels may require preheating to as high as 1000 F, or may not require preheating at all.

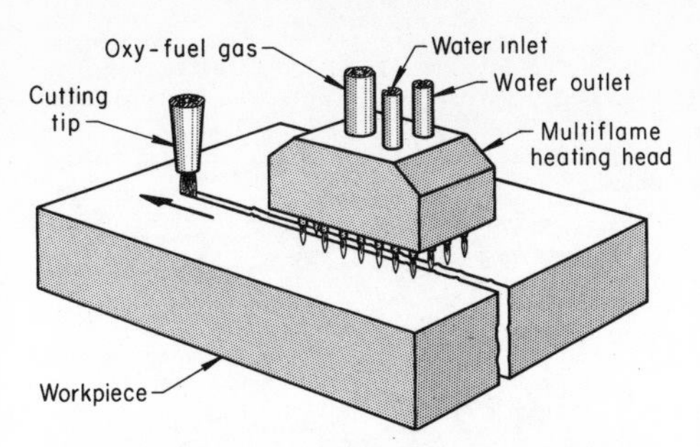

Fig. 3. Local annealing using a multiflame heating head mounted behind a machine-guided cutting tip. For local preheating, the heating head would be mounted ahead of the cutting tip.

Care must be taken to maintain the preheat temperature throughout the cutting. In cutting thick preheated sections, the work should be completed as soon as possible after the piece has been withdrawn from the furnace. If the piece partly cools in air before cutting, the interior will be considerably hotter than the exterior. The cutting flame may start to cut easily, but as it goes deeper, it may produce a cavity, because of the increased oxidation. As a result, the flame will flare up. This can often be corrected by lowering the oxygen pressure.

Local preheating involves heating that area of the workpiece that encloses what will become the heat-affected zone of the cut. If the area to be heated is small, and the section is not too thick, the preheating flame of a cutting torch may be used, but usually a special heating torch is required.

Local preheating is used when it is impossible or impractical to preheat the entire workpiece. It is important to heat the workpiece uniformly through the section to be cut, without causing too steep a temperature gradient. A multiflame heating torch is sometimes mounted ahead of the cutting torch in machine-guided cutting. The setup is similar to the local annealing setup shown in Fig. 3, except that the heating torch precedes the cutting tip.

Annealing serves two main purposes in controlling the effects of gas cutting in carbon and low-alloy steels. It restores the original structure of the steel, whether it be predominantly pearlitic or predominantly ferritic with spheroidized carbide, and it also provides stress relief. Many steels do not require annealing if they have been properly preheated. (See Volume 2 of this Handbook for annealing practices for specific steels.)

Local annealing, also called flame annealing, is a localized postheat treatment that can be used to prevent hardening or to soften an already hardened cut surface. Either the preheating flame of the cutting torch or a special heating torch may be used for local annealing, depending on the mass of the workpiece and the area to be covered. The heat-affected portion of the workpiece should be heated uniformly, and the temperature gradient at the boundary of the heated mass should be gradual enough to avoid distortion of the workpiece.

Local annealing is not a substitute for preheating, because damage done during cutting (such as upsetting of the metal or cracking at the cut edges) cannot be rectified by any form of annealing; the total adverse effect of such damage can only be mitigated. Flame heating also is used to maintain preheat temperature during cutting.

Local annealing is similar to local preheating when multiflame heating torches are used after a machine-guided cutting torch (see Fig. 3). This method, however, is limited to steel plate up to $1\frac{1}{2}$ in. thick. For steel plate from $1\frac{1}{2}$ to 3 in. thick, heating torches must be applied to both sides of the plate. The method is not suitable for thicknesses over 3 in.

If the local annealing cannot be done simultaneously with cutting, the cut edges can be tempered after cutting, using a suitable heating torch. Both local annealing and tempering temperatures depend on the steel. For data on heat treating of various types of steel, see Volume 2 of this Handbook.

Austenitic stainless steels (except stabilized types) are affected by the heat of the metal-powder or chemical-flux cutting processes. Carbide precipitation occurs in the heat-affected zone about $\frac{1}{8}$ in. from the edge, where the metal has been in the range of 800 to 1600 F long enough for dissolved carbon to migrate to the grain boundaries and combine with the chromium to form chromium carbide. The chromium-poor (sensitized) grain boundaries are subject to corrosion in service, the ultimate effect being continuous corrosion parallel to the cut edge.

This is one effect that is not always completely canceled by subsequent welding at the cut edge. However, this type of corrosion can be prevented by a stabilizing anneal, which will put the carbon back into solution. One of the disadvantages of a stabilizing anneal is that distortion can be caused by quenching through the sensitizing temperature range.

The problem of carbide precipitation also can be avoided by using stabilized or extra-low-carbon grades of stainless steel, which inhibit the formation of chromium carbide.

Another method of dealing with this problem is by water quenching the cut edge directly behind the cutting torch. Because it takes only about 2 min at sensitizing temperature for carbide precipitation to occur, water quenching must be done immediately. Distortion is more likely with this method than with the stabilizing anneal. Still another method is to remove the sensitized zone entirely by chipping or machining.

(For data on annealing, and for a comparison of the relative merits of using stabilized and extra-low-carbon grades of stainless steels in place of annealing, see pages 243 and 244 in Volume 2 of this Handbook.)

Distortion. In most gas cutting of steel plate, distortion of the finished part is not a problem. In plate over $\frac{5}{16}$ in. thick, the distortion usually is so slight as to be negligible, or at least tolerable. The conditions under which distortion can become a problem are:

(*a*) the cutting of thin plate, (*b*) the cutting of long narrow widths, (*c*) the cutting of profiles that require close tolerances, and (*d*) the cutting of plates that contain high residual stress. Gas cutting either may remove some of the restraint to locked-in stress or may add new stress; in either case, some warping of the surface of the plate may occur, especially if the plate is thin. Plates in the annealed condition before being cut have no residual stress.

The ability to predict distortion is important to the success of some cutting operations. Distortion often appears complicated because of the deformation reversal between the heating and cooling portions of the thermal cycle. With experience, however, both the direction and the approximate amount of distortion can often be estimated.

Stages of Deformation. Figure 4 shows the successive stages of deformation that occur as a result of the heating and cooling cycles when gas cutting a narrow strip from a plate having large restraint on one side and little on the other (Fig. 4a), and a narrow plate having little restraint at either side of the kerf (Fig. 4b). The gas-cutting thermal cycle changes the shape of the narrow sections and causes residual stress in the large section. Because temperature changes in heating and cooling are equal, it might seem that the plates should return to their original shape. This would occur if the entire plate were uniformly heated and cooled; but the temperature gradient near the cut is steep, ranging from about the melting point at the cut, to room temperature a short distance away from it.

As the metal is heated, it expands, and its yield strength begins to decrease. From about 400 to 1600 F, the tensile yield strength of low-carbon steel drops from maximum to negligible values. In compression, the range may differ by 200 to 300 F.

As the hotter metal expands, it is compressed by the surrounding cooler and stronger metal. The hotter metal continues to expand elastically in all directions until its compressive yield strength is reached, at which point it yields plastically (upsets) in all directions not under restraint. The portion of this upset metal that is above 1600 F is virtually stress-free; the remainder is under compressive stress equal to its yield strength.

There is also a smaller compressive stress in the metal that expanded but did not upset. It is the net stress on the heated (kerf) side of the neutral axis that causes the bowing of a narrow plate during cutting, as shown in Fig. 4.

As the heated metal begins to cool, it contracts, and its strength increases. At first, the contraction only reduces the compressive stress in the still-expanded metal. By the time the compressive stress is reduced to zero and the plate resumes its original shape, the previously upset metal has regained considerable strength. This contracting metal is now in tension as it cools, and its tensile yield strength increases. The tension increases until the metal reaches room temperature. It is the residual tensile stress in the cooling (kerf) side of the neutral axis that causes the bowing of narrow plates after cooling, as shown in Fig. 4. Thus, final distortion can be traced to the upsetting in heating. Controlled upsetting is the basic principle of flame straightening.

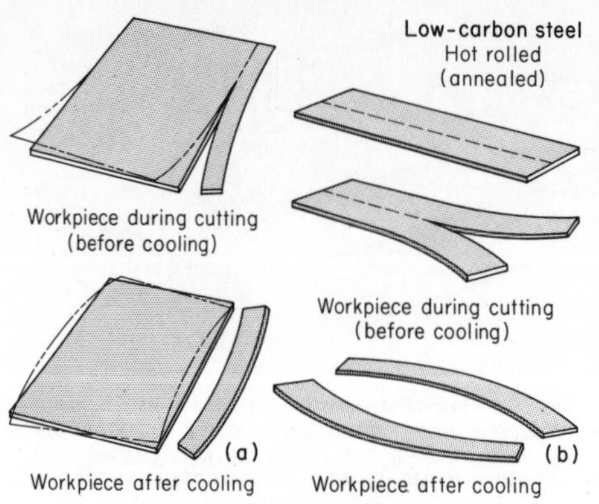

(a) Plate with large restraint on one side of kerf, little restraint on other side. Phantom lines indicate direction of residual stress that would cause deformation except for restraint. (b) Plate with little restraint on either side.

Fig. 4. Deformation (exaggerated) that occurs in gas cutting

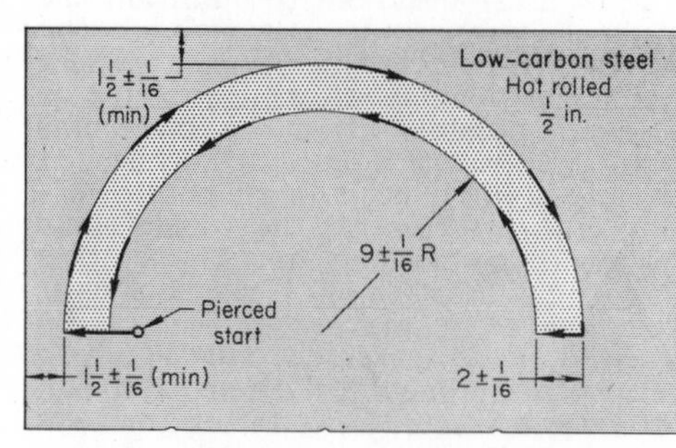

Fig. 5. Layout for single-torch cutting of a half ring, to minimize distortion. The scrap outside the ring prevented unequal heating; the stock inside the ring provided restraint. (Example 348)

Preventing Distortion. If the strength of a plate through its section is low, it may warp or buckle in gas cutting. If the strength of the section is high but the heated metal is embrittled, it may crack in tension. Both possibilities can be lessened by preheating the workpiece before cutting; preheating will reduce differential expansion, thereby decreasing the stress gradient that will be set up. Steels subject to embrittlement are discussed on the preceding page of this article, under "Higher-Carbon and Alloy Steels".

The strength of structural shapes such as flats, I-beams and channels often is used to prevent bowing when these members are split. Instead of cutting continuously, the cut is interrupted at intervals, leaving a series of connections about ½ in. long to prevent distortion. The connections then are cut after the member cools. The disadvantage of this method is that a series of pierce cuts must be made carefully, because there is no adjacent edge or scrap plate to start from. Sections also may be clamped back-to-back for added strength in cutting.

When a long, narrow shape is to be drop cut from a larger plate, the cutting sequence usually is chosen to make maximum use of the restraint of the stock material, as shown in the following example:

Example 348. Cutting a Half Ring (Fig. 5)

For gas cutting an 18-in.-ID half ring (Fig. 5) with a single-torch machine, the ring was laid out on the stock plate so as to restrain distortion. Cuts were then taken so that the ring was restrained until the final cut.

As shown in Fig. 5, the layout provided a minimum allowance of 1½ in. at the outside edge, to avoid unequal heating of the ring. The cut was started across one bottom leg, then went around the outside and across the other leg, leaving the ring attached to the large portion of the plate until the final cut. Stress in the outside arc was largely offset by opposing stress in the inside arc.

The cumulative effect of length on distortion can be avoided by water quenching the cut directly behind the cutting torch; however, the hardening effect that results may be undesirable.

One of the best practices for cutting long narrow shapes with parallel sides is to use two torches simultaneously. The residual stresses, being equal and opposite, will prevent bowing. Any method that distributes stress equally about a neutral axis can accomplish the same result.

One of the problems in shape cutting is movement of the shape within the outline of the kerf because of expansion and contraction during cutting. When a large plate is used to produce a number of small shapes, the shapes are likely to move in relation to the plate, resulting in inaccuracy in shape. Such inaccuracy is slight, and usually can be tolerated. For closer tolerances, either the template can be adjusted to allow for the error, or wedges can be used to prevent it. Both preventive measures are described in Example 354.

Effect of Alloying Elements

Alloying elements, in quantities normally present in low-carbon, medium-carbon and low-alloy steels, have little or no effect on ease of cutting by any of the gas-cutting processes. In larger quantities, most alloying elements impede gas cutting by being relatively poor oxidizers (copper, nickel), producers of refractory oxide (aluminum, chromium), or gas producers (graphite, sulfur).

Unlike machining with edge tools, gas cutting is insensitive to mechanical properties such as hardness and toughness. Some of the effects of the common alloying elements on the cuttability of steel are summarized in the paragraphs that follow.

Aluminum. Gas cutting is not impeded by content up to about 2%. Aluminum content of 10% or more resists ordinary gas cutting, but metal-powder cutting may be used.

Carbon. In amounts found in carbon steels (under 1.7%), carbon does not hinder gas cutting. However, to prevent hardening and cracking at cut edges, carbon steels containing 0.30% C or more should be preheated between 500 and 600 F or should be heated after cutting (before the cut surface cools to normal temperature), or both. The carbon effect varies with other alloying elements present.

Chromium. Straight-chromium steels with up to 1.5 or 2% Cr cut like low-carbon steel, but content of 4 to 6% Cr requires preheating up to 900 F and a carburizing flame. At about 10% Cr and over, metal-powder cutting or chemical-flux cutting is used.

Copper content of 3% or less in steel does not adversely affect gas cutting.

Manganese. Steels that contain up to 14% manganese, with 1.3% C, can be cut readily either by conventional gas cutting or by metal-powder cutting. However, some high-manganese steels require preheating.

Molybdenum. A content of 0.25%, as in chromium-molybdenum aircraft steels, does not hinder cutting. Steel with 5.5% Mo, 8% W and 1% C resists ordinary gas cutting but may be cut by metal-powder cutting.

Nickel. Steel with as much as 7% Ni can be gas cut, when plates are to be subsequently welded. When nickel is present with chromium in stainless steels, metal-powder cutting or chemical-flux cutting is used.

Phosphorus content of 2% or less does not prevent good gas cutting.

Silicon content of 2.90% or less does not hinder ordinary gas cutting, but preheat of 500 F minimum must be maintained to prevent edge cracking. Transformer iron, containing 4% Si or less, can be gas cut, but a high silicon content reduces speed. Preheating and annealing are necessary with some silicon steels in the higher carbon and manganese ranges, to prevent or minimize air hardening.

Sulfur in usual amounts has no effect on gas cutting. Higher percentages reduce cutting speed and produce sulfur dioxide fumes.

Titanium in amounts present in steels has no effect on gas cutting. Titanium alloys respond to gas cutting much faster than steel.

Tungsten content of 10% or less, together with 5% Cr, 0.2% Ni and 0.8% C, does not hinder gas cutting. At 17%, tungsten resists ordinary gas cutting.

Vanadium in amounts present in steel has no effect on gas cutting.

Equipment

Methods of supplying, storing and distributing the gases used in gas cutting depend on the type of gas and its method of production, as well as on consumption requirements. Except for natural gas, commercial gases are commonly supplied and stored in compressed-gas cylinders; natural gas is supplied by pipeline from gas wells and may be stored in accumulators. Acetylene may also be supplied from on-site generators. For heavy consumption requirements, banks of gas cylinders are usually joined by a pipe manifold and piped directly to the point of use.

The design, construction and use of compressed-gas cylinders, acetylene generators, and the piping systems that conduct the gases to the cutting station are governed by federal and local laws and by the rules of insurance underwriters and various safety organizations.

Equipment used for manual gas cutting is usually marketed as a package, and consists of gas regulators, gas hoses, cutting torch, cutting tips and a multipurpose wrench. Auxiliary equipment may include a hand truck, tip cleaners, a radius-bar attachment (for cutting circles), and tinted operator's goggles.

Machine cutting equipment varies from simple carriages to complex electronic scanning devices that automatically control a series of cutting torches through a coordinate-drive system. The essential equipment for both manual and machine cutting is described below.

Regulators. Whether gases are taken directly from compressed-gas cylinders or supplied from a pipeline terminal, pressure and rate of flow must be adjusted to the requirements of the cutting operation. Gas regulators do this by accepting gas at a range of pressures and delivering it to the hose-torch-tip system at the particular operating pressure required to force the gas through the system at the desired rate of flow. This required pressure is set by manual adjustment on the regulator, so that when the pressure delivered drops below the set pressure, sufficient gas is released to restore pressure to the required level. During a cutting operation, this continuous self-adjustment by the regulator keeps pressure oscillating in a narrow range about the pressure setting, so that no flicker in the gas flames is apparent.

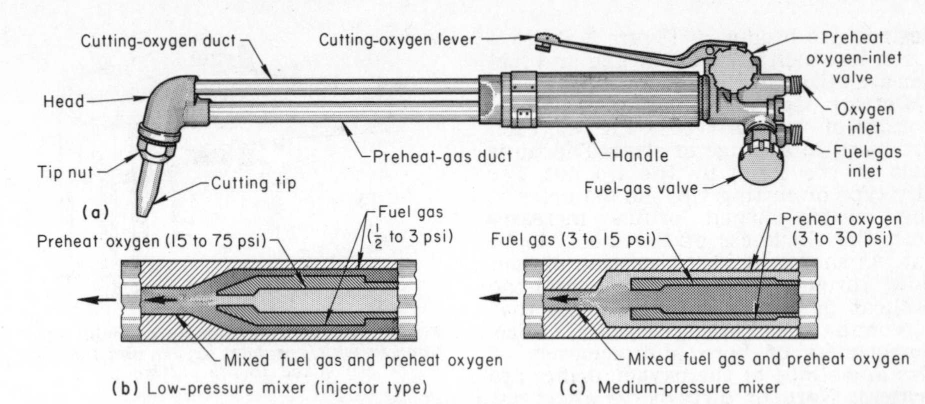

Fig. 6. (a) *Typical manual cutting torch in which preheat gases are mixed before entering torch head.* (b) *and* (c) *Sections through preheat-gas duct showing two types of mixers commonly used with the torch shown. Injector mixer* (b) *is used for low-pressure fuel gases.*

Gas regulators vary in design, performance and convenience features. Some have dial pressure gages to indicate the pressure at the supply and the discharge (operating) ends. Others indicate only the operating pressure, by means of the position of the adjusting screw. When a single-stage regulator is connected to a single compressed-gas cylinder, as the cylinder is depleted, the operating pressure and flow decrease (for nozzle-type regulators) or increase (for stem-type regulators), necessitating periodic readjustment. Two-stage regulators (and equivalent designs) maintain a constant delivery until almost all of the cylinder gas is depleted.

Regulators are designed for use with specific types of gas and for specific pressure ranges. A portable oxyacetylene setup requires an oxygen regulator at the oxygen cylinder and an acetylene regulator at the acetylene cylinder. These regulators are not interchangeable. If the gases were taken from pipe terminals, at much lower pressures, a different set of regulators probably would be required.

High-Low Regulators (gas savers) are used mainly to conserve preheat oxygen when natural gas or propane is used as the preheat fuel in gas cutting. Because these gases burn with a lower heat-transfer intensity than that of acetylene, they require a longer time to start a cut. To reduce preheat time, a high flow rate of oxygen and fuel gas is required at the start. However, if this flow rate were maintained during the cutting, the cost per linear foot of cut would be very high. Because it takes less heat to maintain a cut than to start it, considerable savings result from reducing the initial gas flow rate. High-low regulators permit the starting (preheat) flow rates to be reduced to a predetermined level when the flow of cutting oxygen is initiated. This operation may be done manually or automatically, depending on the regulator design.

When the regulator is switched from high to low, the preheat cutback may range from 75% to 25% as plate thicknesses increase from ⅜ in. to 8 in. High-low regulators are used for both manual cutting and machine cutting with either natural gas or propane.

Hoses. Flexible hoses of standard sizes (⅛ to ½-in. ID), with standard fittings, carry the gases from the regulator to the cutting torch. Oxygen hoses are generally green, and the fittings have right-hand threads. Fuel-gas hoses are red, and the fittings have left-hand threads; a groove is cut around the fitting for identification. In heavier operations, two oxygen hoses sometimes are used, one for preheat and one for cutting oxygen. Multitorch cutting machines often have three-hose torches.

Cutting Torches. The functions of a gas-cutting torch (see Fig. 6a) are to (*a*) control the cutting oxygen, (*b*) control the mixture and flow of the preheat oxygen and fuel gas, and (*c*) discharge these gases through a cutting tip with the proper velocity and volumetric rate of flow. These functions, which can be controlled partly by the operator, are limited by the pressure of the gases at the torch inlets, and by the size and design of the cutting tip at the other end.

An oxygen inlet control valve and a fuel-gas inlet control valve permit the operator to adjust gas flow. The fuel gas flows through a single duct and mixes with the preheat oxygen; the mixed gases then flow to the preheating-flame orifices in the cutting tip. The oxygen is divided, part mixing with the fuel gas and part going through the cutting-oxygen orifice in the cutting tip. The cutting-oxygen flow is initiated by a lever-actuated valve on the manual torch, and by panel controls in machine cutting. Although torches are of various designs, all have these basic features.

As shown in Fig. 6, cutting torches can be divided into types according to the method of mixing the preheat gases. Cutting torches must supply preheat gases mixed in the proper ratio, and must supply this mixture in quantities large enough to produce the amount of heat needed for the job. To do this when fuel gases are supplied at low pressure, an injector-type mixer is required that will aspirate or draw more fuel gas than would otherwise flow. Aspirating or mixing efficiency can be varied to suit fuel-gas pressures by redesign of the mixer as shown in Fig. 6(b) and (c).

Because torch performance depends on matching the mixer with the fuel-gas pressure available, several mixer designs are produced. Figure 7 shows a torch in which preheat oxygen and fuel gas are mixed in the cutting tip.

Cutting tips are precision-machined nozzles of various types (Fig. 8), each produced in a range of sizes. The tip is held in the torch by the tip nut. For any type of cutting tip, the diameter of the cutting-oxygen orifice increases with the thickness of the metal to be cut. As shown in Fig. 8, cutting oxygen flows through the center hole, and the preheat gas flows through ports that surround the cutting-oxygen orifice. Smoothness of bore and accuracy of size and shape of the oxygen orifice are critical. Worn or dirty bores affect cut quality by causing distortion or turbulence in the cutting-oxygen stream.

The size of the cutting-tip orifices determines the final rate of flow and the velocity of the preheat gases and cutting oxygen. The gas flow to the cutting tip can be varied by adjusting the torch inlet valve or the regulator, or both.

The tips shown in Fig. 8(a) and (c) are designed for acetylene and are not efficient when used with natural gas or propane, because of differences in burning characteristics. The two-piece tip shown in Fig. 8(b) is designed for slower-burning gases, such as natural gas and propane. As shown, the tip end of the insert is recessed in the shell to form a "skirt", which promotes flame stability. This tip would overheat with acetylene and cause flashbacks.

Cutting-oxygen flow cannot be progressively increased solely by increasing the oxygen pressure, without reaching a point where turbulence in the cutting oxygen reduces the cutting efficiency. Turbulence in the cutting oxygen causes wider kerfs, slower cutting, greater oxygen consumption, and poorer quality of cut. This is one reason why larger cutting tips are required for making heavier cuts.

The flow of cutting oxygen can be improved greatly by changing the cutting-oxygen orifice from the straight-drilled type shown in Fig. 8(a) and (c) to a type in which the exit nozzle flares outward or diverges. General-purpose, or straight-drilled, tips are intended primarily for manual cutting. They perform well, but they cannot equal the results of divergent tips in cutting machines.

Divergent cutting tips are based on principles of gas flow through a venturi. High velocities are reached, and as the gas emerges from the venturi nozzle there is little or no differential pressure between the effluent and the atmosphere. The result is a more coherent oxygen stream than can be obtained from the straight-drilled nozzle. Divergent tips, often called high-speed tips, operate at higher cutting-oxygen pressure, in the range of 100 psi, and provide cutting jets of supersonic velocity. They are precision made and are more expensive than straight-drilled tips, but they produce the best results. Because of their high speed, they are best suited to machine cutting. Divergent tips give superior cutting in metal up to about 6 in. thick, but beyond this thickness their advantage decreases; they are not recommended for cutting metal more than 10 in. thick.

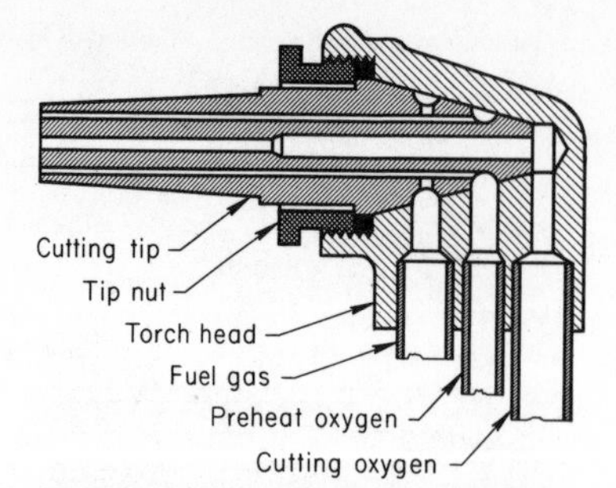

Fig. 7. Head and cutting-tip assembly of a torch in which preheat oxygen and fuel gas are mixed in the cutting tip

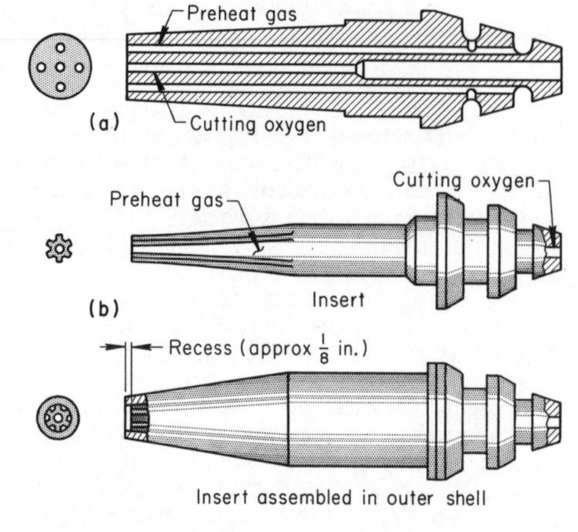

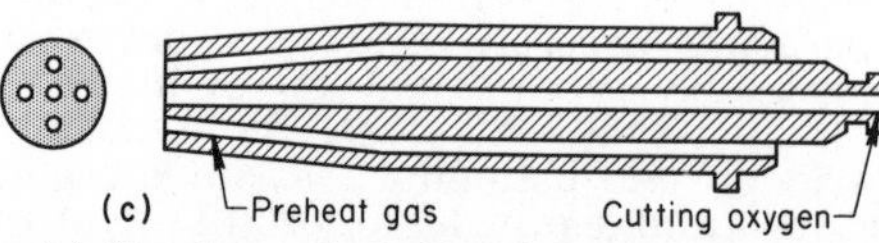

(a) Simple nozzle used mainly with acetylene; (b) two-piece nozzle used with natural gas or propane; (c) one-piece nozzle used mainly with acetylene and when preheat gases are mixed before entering the cutting head.

Fig. 8. Three types of cutting tips

Selection Factors. Natural gas and propane operate most efficiently with high-low gas regulators, injector-type cutting torches, and two-piece, divergent, recessed cutting tips.

Acetylene cutting is more efficient with divergent (but not two-piece) tips, and, if acetylene is supplied from low-pressure generators, with injector-type cutting torches. High-low regulators are not normally required for acetylene.

Mapp gas may be used with two-piece, divergent cutting tips, but the tip recess is less than for natural gas or propane. Injector-type torches and high-low regulators are not needed.

Guidance Equipment. The use of various devices for guiding the cutting torch distinguishes precise cutting from ordinary severing. In freehand cutting, the operator can usually follow a layout accurately at low speeds, but the cut edges may be ragged because of small variations in manual control. At higher speeds (usually over 10 in. per min), the operator has more difficulty in following a layout. For accurate manual cutting, the torch tip must be guided by a metal straightedge or the edge of a template. Circles and circular arcs are cut with the aid of a radius bar (a light rod that is adjustably clamped to the torch at one end while the other end is held at the circle center).

Portable Track-Guided Cutting Machines. Cutting torches can be mounted on portable track-guided cutting machines. These machines have electric variable-speed carriages that run on a portable track. Used without the track, the machines also can follow a radius bar. Although manual cutting torches can be mounted on portable cutting machines, torches designed for these machines are more satisfactory. Machine cutting torches are more rugged. Ducts and valves are encased in a single tube, the cutting tip is mounted axially with the tube, and the spring-loaded cutting-oxygen lever of the manual torch is replaced with a valve knob or a lever-operated poppet valve.

Machine torches may be either a two-hose or three-hose type. In the three-hose type, fuel gas, preheat oxygen, and cutting oxygen are supplied by individual hoses. The three-hose type is more commonly used on stationary cutting machines; the two-hose type is usually used on portable carriages.

On some portable machines, the gases are supplied to connections on the carriage, rather than directly to the torch, to avoid hose-drag effects on the torch. Short hoses are used from machine connections to the torch. Some carriages can accommodate two or more torches operating simultaneously, for trimming and beveling.

When cutting with portable track-guided equipment, the operator must follow the carriage to make adjustments as needed. When plates are wavy or distorted, the trackage will span the low spots, making it necessary to adjust torch height to avoid losing the cut. This condition is aggravated when cutting bevels, because the torch is at an angle. When carefully operated, track-guided torches can produce cuts at speeds and quality closely approaching the best obtainable with stationary cutting machines.

Portable Shape-Cutting Machines. These machines are motor-driven but hand-guided, and usually carry a single cutting torch. The torch rides on a guide wheel, which is steered by hand to follow an outline. In some applications, outline templates and guide bars are used. With these, an idler wheel or stylus on the tracing head runs on the edge of the template. The tracing head is propelled by knurled wheels that are driven by a variable-speed motor. Good to excellent cuts can be achieved in various plate thicknesses, but cutting speeds and accuracy are limited by skill of the operator. These machines normally are used for small lots, or jobs requiring portability. Operator fatigue can be a problem, and the operator is not free to make torch adjustments.

Stationary shape-cutting machines use a pantograph follower, or a motor-driven coordinate drive that has separate carriages for longitudinal and transverse travel.

Both types of machines come in various sizes and with different controls for precision and reliability. Some machines can operate over widths of 200 in. or more, for any length. The machines usually can accommodate one to twenty torches simultaneously. Some machines have motor-driven torch

Table 12. Comparison of Four Tracing Systems Used for Machine Gas Cutting

Item	Magnetic edge tracing	Manual edge (spindle) tracing	Manual line tracing	Electronic line tracing
Cutting speed	30 ipm, provided 15-lb magnetic pull is not exceeded by machine inertia	14 ipm max on parts exceeding operator's reach	14 ipm max	30 ipm usual, 140 ipm available
Tolerances(a)	Equal to Table 13	Equal to Table 13, but subject to template wear	Equal to Table 13 for material over 3 in. thick; ±1/8 in. for material up to 3 in.	Equal to Table 13 with jute-paper template
Close-tolerance cutting (+0, −1/32 in.)	Yes, with more costly templates	Not easily performed	No	Yes. Jute paper fair; polyester sheet best
Control of accuracy	Function of template	Function of template and operator skill	Function of template and operator skill	Function of template
Template	Steel required; most expensive	Soft metal, wood or hardboard; moderate cost	Least expensive; lines drawn on paper	Least expensive; lines drawn on paper
Outside corner radii	90° corner requires special latch(b); other radii, not less than follower radius	Radius not less than follower radius	Approx 3/16 in.	Sharp
Inside corner radii	90° corner not possible; other radii, slightly less than follower radius	90° corner not possible; other radii, slightly less than follower radius	Approx 3/16 in.	90° corner requires corner loop(b); other radii, 3/32 to 1/8 in.
Adjustment of machine settings during cut	Easily performed	Operator can make with difficulty	Operator can make with difficulty	Easily performed
Piercing starts	Require special template construction or freehand lead to template after pierce	Require special template construction or freehand lead to template after pierce	Easily performed; operator follows the lead-in line to template	Same as manual line tracing except electronic follow (operator, free from tracing duty, can better control pierce)
Preheat warpage of 1/2-in. and thinner plate	Less, as maximum speed can be used to minimize effect of heat flow into piece	More than in magnetic edge tracing, because of lower speed and greater heat input	More than in magnetic edge tracing, because of lower speed and greater heat input	Less, as maximum speed can be used to minimize effect of heat flow into piece
Operator fatigue	Average	High	High	Least
Flame-outs, loss of cut by nonuniform speed and tracing	Moderate	High	High	Least
Automatic torch shut-off if template line is lost	No	No	No	Yes (optional feature)
Chain cutting; full plate layout	Difficult; template cost high	Difficult; template cost not as high as magnetic edge tracing	Not as difficult as for manual edge tracing; template cost low; causes higher operator fatigue	Easy; template cost same as manual line tracing
Plate utilization; nesting of pieces	Function of operator discretion	Function of operator discretion	Template made for full plate	Template made for full plate
Operation of two machines by one operator	Difficult	No	No	Yes; requires good work-station layout
Use of multiple torches	Yes	Yes	Yes	Yes
Finish of cut surface(c)	Average to good	Average to poor	Average to poor	Best

(a) Tolerances generally acceptable for machine gas-cut parts are given in Table 13. (b) The tracing is made to loop out around the corner in order to avoid having the stream of cutting oxygen cut off the corner of the workpiece. (c) As a function of tracing and uniform speed.

holders that may be operated manually or automatically to adjust for plate warp. Hinged torch holders may be used to facilitate cleaning or replacement of cutting tips.

Tracing may be manual, magnetic or electronic. The simplest machines usually have one or two torches using manual or magnetic tracing.

Manual tracing may be done by steering an idler wheel or a spindle around a template. Another method is to guide a wheel or a focused light beam around an outline on paper. Cutting speed is controlled by setting the speed of the tracing head (pantograph type) or by setting the speed of the torch carriage (coordinate drive). Maximum speed in manual tracing (about 14 in. per min) depends on operator skill.

Magnetic tracing is done with a knurled, magnetized, rotating spindle against the edge of a steel template. Magnetic force of about 15 lb is sufficient to drive, at preset speeds, a low-inertia pantograph system. Direct-reading tachometers, showing cutting speed in inches per minute, can be helpful in making adjustments to cutting speeds.

Electronic tracers use a photoelectric cell that scans the reflection of a beam of light directed on the outline of a template. Templates may be line drawings on paper, white-on-black paper cutouts, or photo negatives of these, depending on the scanning principle involved and the durability required. When tolerances closer than 1/16 in. must be held repetitively, templates of plastic film, glass cloth, or other durable and dimensionally stable material are used.

In scanning the edge of a white-on-black template, the circuit through the photoelectric cell is balanced when the cell sees an equal amount of black and white. Any change from this balanced light sends an impulse to a motor that moves the tracing head back to balance. In line tracing, the photoelectric cell scans the line from side to side. As long as the light is reflected equally from both sides of the line, the steering signals balance. When the photocell scans more light on one side of the line than on the other, the scanner rotates to balance.

Some electronic tracing heads have adjustments that permit parts to be cut about 1/32 in. larger or smaller than the template. This feature, known as kerf adjustment, is useful for cutting to close tolerances, especially when the template has insufficient kerf allowance.

Coordinate drives often use a sine-cosine potentiometer (directional resolver) to coordinate separate drive motors for longitudinal and transverse motion of the torch carriages. These drives can translate motion in a 1-to-1 ratio, or in other ratios when convenient. The system, known as ratio cutting, permits the use of templates in any proportion from full-scale to one-tenth size.

Tape Control. Computerized cutting machines may be controlled by punched tape. These machines need no templates. The information usually is programed from an accurate outline. After the tape is punched, it may be used repetitively with single or multiple machines.

Many combinations of cutting features may be found in a single machine. Table 12 compares four tracing systems used for machine gas cutting. Although the simpler cutting machines lack the speed, versatility and other features of the more complex types, their lower cost often makes them better suited to low production.

Starting the Cut

Whenever possible, cuts are started at the outer edge of the workpiece. The cutting torch is placed so that the ends of the inner cones in the preheating flame just clear the work metal. When a spot of metal at the top of the edge has been heated to a bright red, the jet of cutting oxygen is turned on. The reaction forms a slot in the plate edge and the torch is moved steadily along the desired line of cut.

In manual cutting, the oxygen is turned on by depressing the cutting-oxygen lever. In machine cutting, the buttons that control the cutting oxygen and the travel are pressed in sequence, the time interval depending on material thickness. Machines that do not have automatic control of tip-to-work distance usually require constant operator attention to allow for warped metal.

Piercing. The technique of starting a cut at a point inside the edge of a plate is known as "piercing". More time is required to bring the spot to ignition temperature, and more care is needed to prevent molten metal from splashing back and fouling the tip. Piercing starts are necessary when cutting holes and slots, and when cutting shapes that cannot be started from the edge. The pierce is made in the portion that will become scrap, at a point that will conveniently allow a short lead-in to the cutting line.

In manual piercing, when the spot is heated bright red, the torch is raised about ½ in. above the normal cutting distance and the cutting oxygen is turned on slowly. As soon as the metal is penetrated, the torch is lowered to cutting height and the cutting is continued. Drilled holes are used for some work, particularly to furnish a starting edge for a heavy internal cut.

Machine torch piercing is the same as manual piercing (described above) except that the torch travel begins when the cutting oxygen is slowly turned on and the piercing starts to eject molten slag. The initial pierce action will not completely penetrate the plate, so that the completed pierce will cover a short distance (depending on plate thickness), and will form a sloping trough with molten slag ejected behind and away from the torch. The length of the lead-in must be increased for heavy plate; for example, about 3 in. is required in 5-in.-thick plate.

Light Cutting

Light cutting (work metal less than ⅜ in. thick) requires extra care in selecting the tip, keeping the tip clean, and controlling the gas pressure. Conditions for light cutting using oxyacetylene, oxy-natural and oxy-Mapp gas are given in Tables 2 to 5 and in Table 10. In general, the techniques described in the section on Medium Cutting (the next section) are also applicable to light cutting.

There is little or no control over quality of cut when gas cutting steel that is thinner than ⅛ in. The main problems are wide, uneven kerf, ragged edge, and distortion — all caused by excessive heat buildup. Where no other cutting method is available, gas cutting of single sheets has been done under water. Cutting tips with a single leading preheat flame also have been used, although this limits maneuverability.

In thicknesses ⅛ in. and over, for straight or large-radius cuts, the cutting torch sometimes can be slanted forward to increase the distance through the cut and to deflect some of the heat input. When cutting shapes, however, the torch must be vertical.

That ⅛-in. thicknesses are practical for production cutting is demonstrated by the experience described in the following example.

Example 349. Gas Cutting of Cab Sections From Thin Stock

Cab sections for industrial trucks and earth-moving equipment were cut from 1020 carbon steel up to 96 in. wide, 156 in. long, and ⅛ to ¼ in. thick. The sections, including frames for doors, windows and windshields, were gas cut by electronically controlled machines, using full-scale ink tracings and one or two oxy-acetylene torches. Cutting speeds up to 30 in. per min were obtained with tips having small preheat flames, using low oxygen pressure (18 to 20 psi). The cuts were slag-free, and distortion was negligible.

One of the most important techniques for cutting of thin sections is stack cutting. This technique, which is described in the section on Stack Cutting (page 292), not only avoids the problems inherent in light cutting, but also increases production rates. The sections stacked for cutting must be flat and closely clamped together.

Medium Cutting

In medium cutting (work metal ⅜ to 10 in. thick), gas cutting achieves its highest efficiency and produces the most satisfactory cuts. Conditions for medium cutting with oxyacetylene, oxy-natural gas, oxy-propane and oxy-Mapp gas are presented in Tables 2 to 5, and in Tables 7 and 10.

Commercial Cuts. To be acceptable, commercial cuts must meet the following requirements:

1. Drag must be short; that is, the line markings on the face of the cut should approach the vertical. Drag should not be so large as to prevent the final corner from being cut and the piece from dropping.
2. Sides of the cut should be smooth — not fluted, grooved or ragged.
3. No slag should adhere to the bottom of the cut. With proper adjustments, only loose slag is left, or none at all.
4. Upper and lower edges should be sharp enough to meet quality requirements.
5. Cost must be moderate.

The tolerances that can normally be obtained in commercial gas cutting are shown in Table 13. For some products, more liberal tolerances than those shown in Table 13 are acceptable. For more stringent tolerances, see the section on Close-Tolerance Cutting, on page 298 in this article.

The following conditions are necessary to obtain satisfactory commercial cuts: (*a*) suitable cutting tip, with cutting orifice of correct type and size, and proper degree of preheat; (*b*) suitable oxygen and fuel-gas pressures; (*c*) correct cutting speed; (*d*) uniformity of torch movement; (*e*) clean, smooth-bore cutting orifice and preheat holes; (*f*) high-purity oxygen; and (*g*) proper angle of the cutting jet in relation to the upper edge of the cut.

Table 13. Dimensional Tolerances Normally Obtainable in Production Gas Cutting of Plate

Plate thickness, in.	Tolerance, in.
Up to ½ inclusive	±1/16
Over ½ to 1⅛	±3/32
Over 1⅛ to 3	±⅛
Over 3 to 5	±5/32
Over 5 to 6	±3/16
Over 6 to 8	±7/32
Over 8 to 10 inclusive	±¼

For machine cutting with equipment in good working condition, and with adequate control for minimizing distortion in cutting shapes and long, narrow pieces.

Surface finish for gas-cut production parts is judged by comparison with samples of various degrees of good or poor practice. One such group of machine-cut samples is shown in Fig. 9. Here, sample A represents high quality, with drag varying about 2 to 7%. Sample C shows the effect of speed on drag — which, in this case, is about 15 to 17% of the thickness. The surface of sample C is good, being only slightly rougher than that of sample A. The small uncut triangle and the surface defect at the left end of the cut are typical of long-drag cuts; the remedy is to slow the torch when approaching the end of the cut, which was not done in cutting this sample. The other samples show typical defects resulting from improper torch settings, as noted in the legend of Fig. 9.

Tip Design. When selecting cutting tips, consideration must be given to tip design. General-purpose, or cylindrical-bore, tips usually operate best with cutting-oxygen pressures of 30 to 60 psi; a pressure of 40 psi is a good initial adjustment. Divergent-orifice tips operate with cutting-oxygen pressures of about 100 psi, but variations to ±20 psi may give better results. Because the tip size controls the width of the kerf, a smaller tip can be used for a narrower kerf, but the part may not drop free and slower speed must be used. Tips larger than usual may be used when the metal is covered with thick scale.

Cutting speed is one of the most important factors affecting quality. Within recommended speed ranges, cuts of the best quality are obtained at the slower end; higher speeds are for maximum output. The optimum cutting speed can be determined by observing the products of the cut issuing from the underside of the work. When speed is too slow, the cutting stream does not issue clearly, but forms a series of slag drippings. Excessive speed is indicated by a stream trailing at a sharp angle to the bottom of the workpiece. The highest-quality cutting occurs when a single, continuous stream issues from the underside for about ¼ in., then breaks into a uniform spray. This condition often is accompanied by a sound like that of ripping canvas.

Preheat flames and their purpose are described on page 280, in the section on Combustion of Gases. Usually, less preheat is needed to continue a cut than to start it. When optimum quality is desired, the amount of preheat should be reduced after starting. Commercial devices are available for this purpose. Although in heavy thicknesses the amount of preheat affects the quality of the entire cut face, in thicknesses

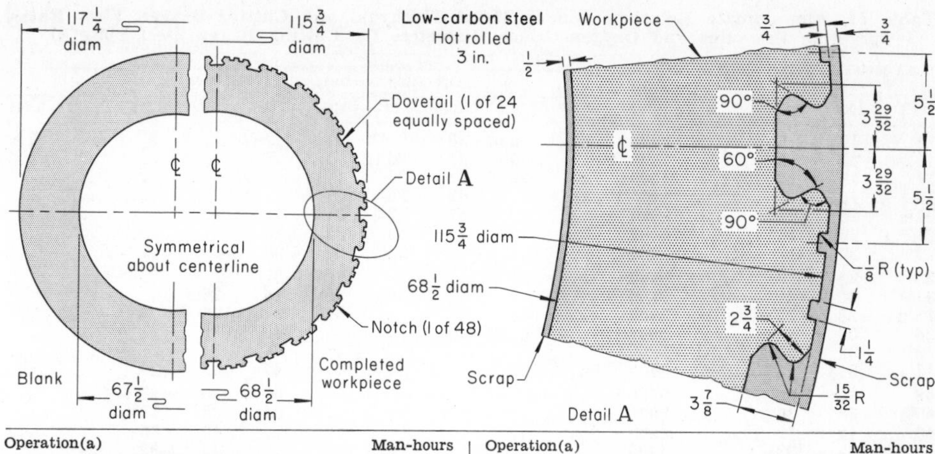

Operation(a)	Man-hours
Gas Cutting From Plate	
First paper template (for cutting circular blank)	0.25
Metal template (shear, lay out, saw and file)	4.00
Second paper template (draw complete shape outline, using metal template)	1.25
Gas cut circular blank and clean	2.07
Gas cut to final size	2.96
Total, per piece	10.53

Operation(a)	Man-hours
Machining From Casting(b)	
Center casting, rough and finish machine OD and ID in boring mill	27.20
Lay out 48 slots	2.40
Mill 48 slots	21.00
Total, per piece	50.60

(a) Only nonidentical operations in the two methods are compared; all other operations were identical. (b) Dovetails were cast on cores; no machining was required.

Fig. 10. Large notched and dovetailed ring that was machine gas cut from plate, using scrap movement for dimensional control. Table compares production times per piece for gas cutting and for previous method of producing the ring. (Example 350)

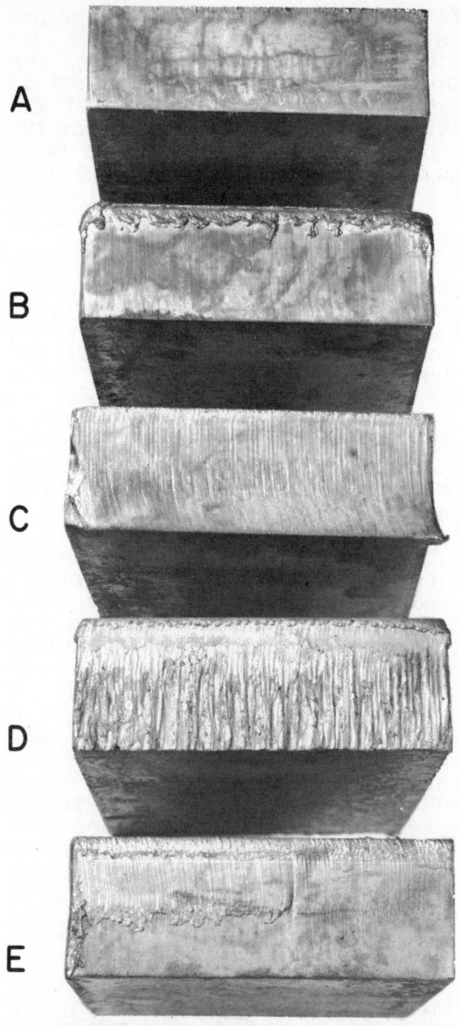

A — Proper speed, preheat, and cutting-oxygen pressure (see table below). Note clean face and nearly straight drag lines.
B — Proper speed and cutting-oxygen pressure, but too much preheat. Note excessive slag, and rounding of top edge.
C — Proper preheat and cutting-oxygen pressure, but too much speed. Note increase in drag, and uncut corner at lower left.
D — Proper speed and preheat, but too much cutting-oxygen pressure. Note extremely rough surface, and melted-down top edge.
E — Proper preheat and cutting-oxygen pressure, but speed too slow. Note burned slag adhering to cut surface.

Torch Settings for Bar A(a)

Preheat-oxygen pressure:	
High (edge starting)	45 psi
Low (cutting)	8 to 12 psi
Preheat-natural-gas pressure:	
High (edge starting)	3 psi
Low (cutting)	Under 1 oz per sq in.
Cutting-oxygen pressure	100 psi
Cutting speed	10 to 15 in. per min

(a) Settings for bars B, C, D and E were varied as noted in the legend above. All bars were cut with two-piece divergent-nozzle (high-speed) tips with 0.054-in.-diam cutting-oxygen orifice. All cutting was done with low preheat settings, except for bar B, which was cut with both preheat gases set higher than for starting.

Fig. 9. Gas-cut surfaces of 2-by-6-in. bars of hot rolled 1015 steel, as affected by cutting speed, preheating conditions, and cutting-oxygen pressure

up to 2 in. the effect of preheat on quality is limited to the top corner of the cut. An excessive amount of preheat causes this top corner to melt and roll over. An insufficient amount of preheat will result in loss of cut. The preheat for best quality is that which provides a continuous reaction with a sharp, clean top edge of the cut.

Kerf Compensation. Allowance for kerf width may have been made in the template design; if not, allowance must be made by the operator. Kerf compensation is the allowance of half the kerf width on the outline of the template; this amount is added for outside cuts and subtracted for inside cuts. In straight-line cutting or in following a layout, the operator may make this compensation; in machine cutting, kerf compensation should be incorporated in the template.

Machine Accuracy. When the machine is properly adjusted, the guidance system governs accuracy. Mechanical followers are highly accurate when properly adjusted. However, compensation for the diameter of the follower wheel or spindle must be made in the same manner as for kerf width when making a template.

Kerf angle, the small deviation of the kerf wall from a right angle, may be caused by failure to set the torch perpendicular to the work, or it may be a natural result of the cutting-oxygen stream. In the latter case, the width of the kerf increases from the top to the bottom of the cut; this may be corrected for in straight cutting by angling the torch slightly, to make one wall of the kerf perpendicular. In shape cutting, however, this cannot be done; here, kerf angle can be corrected for by slightly reducing the pressure of the cutting oxygen.

Plate movement is either vertical, caused by warp, or lateral, caused by planar expansion and contraction of the part by heat. Vertical movement requires either manual or automatic control of torch height (a very slight allowance can be made in the initial setting of the tip-to-work distance). Lateral movement can be controlled by (*a*) fixing or weighting the part to be cut on the plate support; (*b*) wedging the cut within the stock plate; or (*c*) allowing only a small amount of scrap trim around the part, so that the scrap will move instead of the workpiece. The example that follows describes an application in which scrap movement was used to help maintain close tolerances in the gas cutting of a complex shape.

Example 350. Accuracy Within 1/32 In. in Cutting a Large Complex Shape (Fig. 10)

The large notched and dovetailed ring shown in Fig. 10 was gas cut from 3-in.-thick low-carbon steel plate, using oxy-natural gas in a machine equipped with an electronic tracer. The 24 dovetails and 48 notches had to be accurate within 1/32 in. To meet the tolerance, a circular blank was cut with a stock allowance of 1/2 in. on the inside radius and of 3/4 in. on the outside radius before making the final cut. This permitted the scrap to move during final cutting, rather than the workpiece.

Three templates were required; two of light-buff jute paper (17 sq ft per lb), and a master template of sheet metal. Because atmospheric conditions affect the dimensional stability of jute paper, template preparation and gas cutting were scheduled so that no paper template was in use for more than 4 hr. The first template was two concentric circles, with kerf compensation of 1/16 in. for both cuts. A sheet-metal master template was made of a 45° segment of the finished part (detail A of Fig. 10). This metal template was used for progressively drawing the outline on the second paper template.

After the circular blank had been cut and the scrap removed, the second paper template was drawn with an inside circle of correct diameter and kerf compensation, a lightly traced outside diameter, and a centerline. The metal template was then placed on the paper and aligned with the inside circle, and the outside outline was drawn for the segment; these steps were repeated until the full template was made.

The final template was placed on the machine and aligned with the circular blank; test notches were made to check torch and machine operation. The outside cut was made with a pierce start in the scrap of a dovetail, and the cut proceeded in a clockwise direction until the outside was completed. The inside cut was then made, starting from an inside

Table 14. Approximate Relations Among Metal Thickness and Cutting-Oxygen Flow Rates, Operating Pressures and Oxygen-Orifice Diameters for Cutting Heavy Steel Plate(a)

Work-metal thickness, in., for thickness-range basis(b) of: 80t	100t	120t	Flow rate, cfh	Cutting oxygen — Operating pressure, psi, at torch entry, for orifice diameter, in., of: 0.147	0.1695	0.1935	0.221	0.250	0.290	0.332	0.375	0.422	0.468
12	10	8	1000	56	39	28	..	..	..	..	..	..	..
14½	12	9½	1200	..	49	35	26	..	..	..	..	..	..
17	14	11	1400	..	59	42	31	..	..	..	..	..	..
19	16	13	1600	..	..	49	36	27	..	..	..	..	..
21½	18	14½	1800	..	..	57	42	31	..	..	..	..	..
24	20	16	2000	..	..	..	48	35	26	..	..	..	..
27	22	17½	2200	..	..	..	53	39	28	..	..	..	..
29	24	19	2400	..	..	..	..	44	31	..	..	..	..
31½	26	21	2600	..	..	..	..	49	34	24	..	..	..
33½	28	22½	2800	..	..	..	..	54	37	26	..	..	..
36	30	24	3000	..	..	..	..	..	40	29	..	..	..
38½	32	25½	3200	..	..	..	..	..	43	31	..	..	..
41	34	27	3400	..	..	..	..	..	47	33	25	..	..
43	36	29	3600	..	..	..	..	..	50	36	27	..	..
45½	38	30½	3800	..	..	..	..	..	54	38	29	..	..
48	40	32	4000	..	..	..	..	..	..	40	30	..	..
..	42	33½	4200	..	..	..	..	..	..	43	32	24	..
..	44	35	4400	..	..	..	..	..	..	45	34	25	..
..	46	37	4600	..	..	..	..	..	..	48	36	27	..
..	48	38½	4800	..	..	..	..	..	..	50	38	28	..
..	..	40	5000	..	..	..	..	..	..	53	40	30	..
..	..	41½	5200	..	..	..	..	..	..	..	42	31	24
..	..	43	5400	..	..	..	..	..	..	..	44	32	25
..	..	45	5600	..	..	..	..	..	..	..	46	34	26
..	..	46½	5800	..	..	..	..	..	..	..	48	35	27
..	..	48	6000	..	..	..	..	..	..	..	50	37	28

(a) Data are based on gas cutting of plate 8 to 48 in. thick at speeds of 2 to 6 in. per minute, using a straight-drilled torch tip of the type and with the dimensional relationships illustrated at right.
(b) Based on the approximate formula that oxygen flow in cubic feet per hour will range from 80 times metal thickness (80*t*) to 120 times metal thickness (120*t*) in heavy cutting. Cutting-oxygen consumption for shape cutting is generally near, or slightly above, 120*t*; straight-line cutting will use 80*t* to 100*t*.

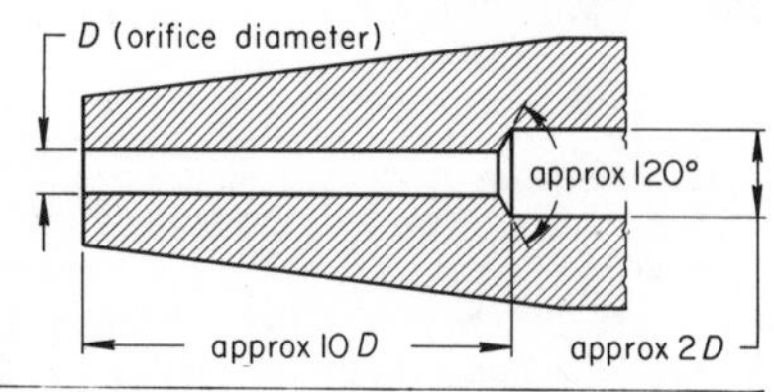

edge. During piercing or start of cut, high preheat was used: 46-psi preheat oxygen and 3-psi natural gas. After the cut was established, cutting conditions were as follows: cutting tip orifice, 0.067 in.; preheat oxygen, 10 psi; natural gas, 1 oz per sq in.; cutting oxygen, 100 psi; and cutting speed, 10 in. per min. No machining was required on the gas-cut surface.

This part had previously been made from a steel casting. The mold had to be cored for the dovetails, and the casting had to be machined on the outside and inside diameters and on the notches. The man-hours required for producing the part by gas cutting and by machining it from a casting are compared in the table that accompanies Fig. 10. For the operations compared, gas cutting resulted in a saving of nearly 80% in labor time.

Heavy Cutting

The cutting of metal 10 in. or more in thickness requires that particular attention be paid to gas flow, preheat-flame setting, drag, and starting techniques. Standard cutting torches can be used to cut steel up to 18 or 20 in. thick; heavy-duty torches are used to cut steel up to 60 in. thick. Pieces over 20 in. thick are rarely cut outside of steel mills. Torch settings for gas cutting of heavy low-carbon steel plate are given in Tables 3, 6 and 7.

Gas-Flow Requirements. Heavy cutting requires a uniform supply of high-purity oxygen and fuel gas at constant pressure, and an adequate volume of cutting oxygen. Torches should have three hoses — one for the cutting oxygen, one for the preheat oxygen, and one for the fuel gas. This will allow proper pressures to be set independently for preheating and cutting. Cutting-oxygen hoses should be at least ½ in. in diameter, to insure an adequate volume of oxygen at the low pressure settings. Regulators must be capable of providing the large volumes of gas required. Cutting-oxygen flow requirements in cubic feet per hour will vary roughly from 80*t* to 120*t*, where *t* equals the thickness to be cut, in inches. Table 14 gives typical cutting-oxygen flow rates, and operating pressures for various orifice diameters, for cutting plate 8 to 48 in. thick, using cylindrical-bore tips of the type shown in the table. Cutting-oxygen consumption for shape cutting generally will be nearer 120*t*, or slightly more, whereas for straight-line cutting it will be between 80*t* and 100*t*.

Preheating. In heavy cutting, the preheat flame must be large enough to extend almost to the bottom of the thickness to be cut; otherwise, the cut will have excessive drag. When sufficient preheat cannot be obtained from the cutting torch, an auxiliary heating torch can be used or the work can be preheated to 200 to 800 F.

Figure 11(a) shows the proper torch position for preheating. Figure 11(b) shows an improper position for preheating (torch too far onto the work), which results in the action of cut shown in Fig. 11(c) and in an uncut corner (Fig. 11d). Height above the work is important; if the tip is too close, excessive melting and rounding of the top edge will occur; if too far, improper preheat and cutting conditions will occur. Generally, 1 to 2 in. of separation is satisfactory.

The edge corner should be thoroughly preheated, with the preheated zone extending far down the face (Fig. 11a). As soon as some metal has melted, the flow of cutting oxygen and the cutting motion should be started simultaneously. Speed should be normal. The cut should progress down the face at a constant rate until it breaks through the bottom. When the cut breaks through, the drag will be long, but it will shorten to normal as soon as the cut is confined. The effects of too little or too much speed at starting are shown in Fig. 11(e) and (f). Too slow a speed will cause a shelf; too great a speed will result in incomplete penetration or an extremely long drag.

Drag. In completing the cut (for drop cutting), it is important that only minimum drag exist, as shown in Fig. 12(a). Too much drag will result in the condition shown in Fig. 12(b), where an uncut corner remains. Figure 12(c) and (d) show the effects of angling the torch forward to minimize drag and thus prevent an uncut corner. If the torch angle is too great, the condition shown in Fig. 12(e) may occur, leaving an uncut corner. Angled cutting may be used in straight-line work, but for shape cutting, the torch must be perpendicular to the work. Test cuts should be made before starting production cuts.

Starting. Extra care is needed in starting a heavy cut, to avoid leaving an uncut corner or pocketing the flame in the lower portion of the cut. Starting sometimes is facilitated by first undercutting the forward edge of the material with a hand torch (Fig. 13).

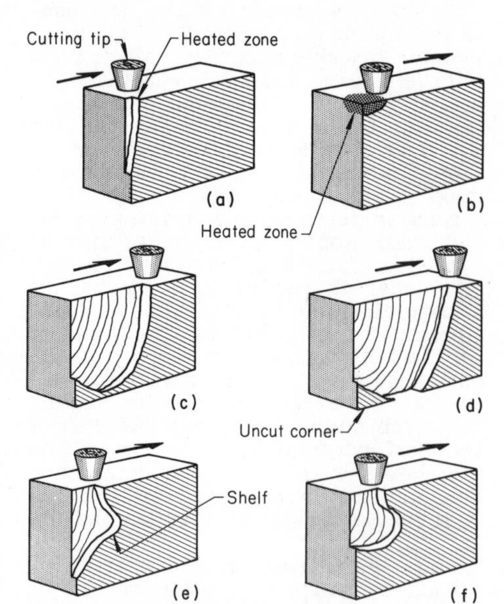

(a) Proper torch position; preheat is primarily on starting face. (b) Improper start; cutting tip is too far onto work, which results in action of cut as shown in (c) and in uncut corner as shown in (d). (e) Action of cut at too low a speed. (f) Action of cut at too high a speed.

Fig. 11. Proper and improper techniques for starting a heavy cut

Stack Cutting

Stack cutting is a practical means of cutting sheets too thin for ordinary cutting, but it also can reduce the cost of cutting thicker material. Savings are multiplied by using multitorch machines for stack cutting. Several torches can be used, each cutting up to 30 pieces of ⅛-in.-thick material simultaneously. Thicknesses most practical for this technique are 20 gage (0.0359 in.) to ½ in., although material ¾ in. thick has been stack cut. Shapes made by stack cutting usually have sharper edges than those cut singly.

Material for stack cutting should be clean and free from loose or heavy scale. The sheets or plates must be clamped tightly in a pile with edges aligned where the cut is to start. Air gaps between pieces will interfere with the cutting flame. The most practical total thickness for the stack is 5 or 6 in., although 10-in. stacks have been cut. The risk of a costly mishap increases with the thickness to be cut and the number of pieces.

When stack cutting pieces less than 3/16 in. thick, a waster plate of 1/4-in. material is clamped atop the stack. The waster plate insures better starting and a sharper edge for the top. It also prevents buckling.

In addition to increasing productivity, stack cutting also reduces materials handling, grinding and cleaning costs, gas consumption, and floor-space requirements. However, savings must justify the time for stacking and clamping. The method is best used when the flat sheets are bundled in stacks at the steel mill.

An application of stack cutting, as practiced in a diesel engine plant, is described in the example that follows.

Example 351. Stack Cutting of Cooling-Fan Side Plates (Fig. 14)

The cooling fan of a direct-current main generator for a diesel locomotive consisted of two side plates, 52 in. OD by 30 in. ID by 3/16 in. thick, between which 24 fan blades were riveted. The assembled fan was 6 1/4 in. wide. The side plates (Fig. 14) were cut in stacks of 20 to 30 in a two-torch gas cutting machine with an electronic tracer, using only one cutting torch. An injector-type torch with a two-piece divergent cutting tip was used with the oxy-natural gas process. Torch settings and other processing details are shown in the table with Fig. 14, together with alternative production methods.

When comparing stack cutting with multitorch machine cutting, the deciding factor in making the choice is not the actual cutting time per piece. The saving includes reduced material handling, less grinding and cleaning, and lower gas consumption. The example that follows describes an application in which stack cutting required less time than multitorch cutting of small lots of a simple shape.

Example 352. Stack Cutting vs Multitorch Machine Cutting (Fig. 15)

A six-torch gas-cutting machine with an electronic tracer was used to cut the 18-in. perimeter of the 3/8-in.-thick triangle shown in Fig. 15. At a cutting speed of 19 in. per min, six pieces were cut in 0.95 min, or 0.158 min per piece. However, each piece required 0.5 min of light grinding to clean the edges. Total time for these two operations was 0.658 min per piece. With setup time of 2.3 min per piece added, total time per piece was 2.958 min.

When stack cutting was used, the material came from the mill in bundles of 13 plates. The plates were supplied in sizes for convenient multiples of the nested shape, the total quantity being based on estimated needs for several months. Bundles were stored as received and used as required. Each bundle of 13 plates made a stack 4 7/8 in. high.

A single torch was used for stack cutting. At a cutting speed of 7 in. per min, 2.571 min was required for cutting the stack, or 0.198 min per piece. This was about 25% longer than it took with the multitorch machine. However, only the bottom plate of each stack required light grinding, making the cleaning time per piece 0.038 min. Setup time was 1.662 min per piece. Total time per piece for all operations was therefore 1.898 min — or 36% less than by the six-torch method.

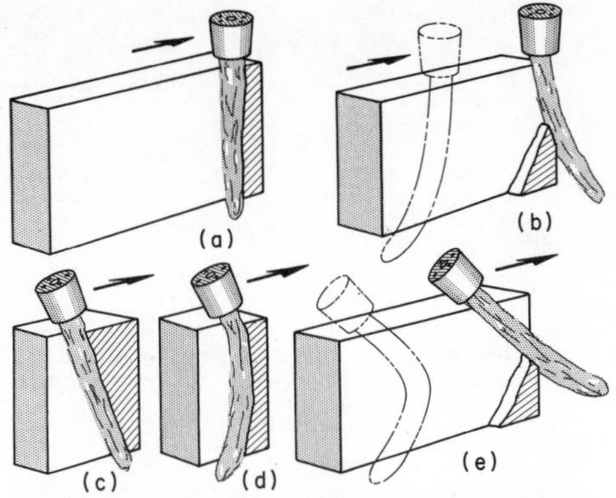

(a) Minimum drag (typical of balanced conditions) permits flame to break through cutting face uniformly at all points.
(b) Excessive drag (phantom lines), typically caused by insufficient oxygen or excessive speed, results in an uncut corner.
(c) and (d) Forward angling of torch to minimize drag and thus avoid an uncut corner.
(e) Excessive forward angling of torch, which results in an uncut corner.

Fig. 12. Proper and improper techniques for completing a heavy cut

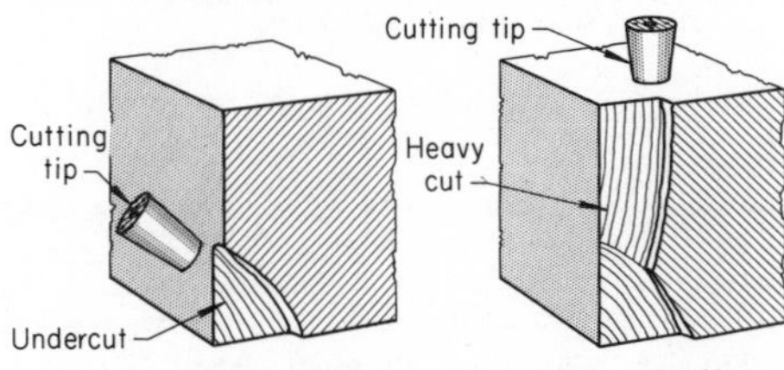

Fig. 13. Undercutting as an aid in starting a heavy cut

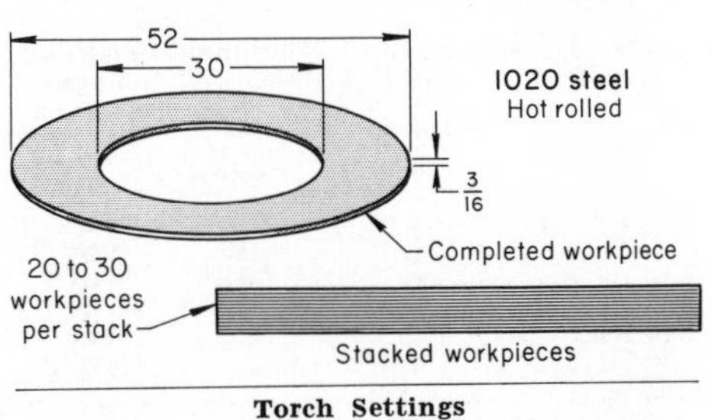

Torch Settings

Cutting tip .... Two-piece divergent type
Diameter of cutting-oxygen orifice .... 0.067 in.
Flow rates (approx):
Natural gas preheat .... 34 cu ft per hr
Preheat oxygen .... 68 cu ft per hr
Cutting oxygen .... 356 cu ft per hr
Cutting speed (25 pieces) .... 6 in. per min

Alternative Production Methods

Up to 10 pieces .. Nibble, saw, machine turn(a)
10 to 25 ..... Stack gas cut (portable machine)
25 to 1000 .. Stack gas cut (stationary machine)
Continuous production(b) .... Die blank

(a) Methods listed in descending order of preference. (b) Minimum quantity, 1000 pieces per year, two years' production.

Fig. 14. Stack-cut flat ring (Example 351)

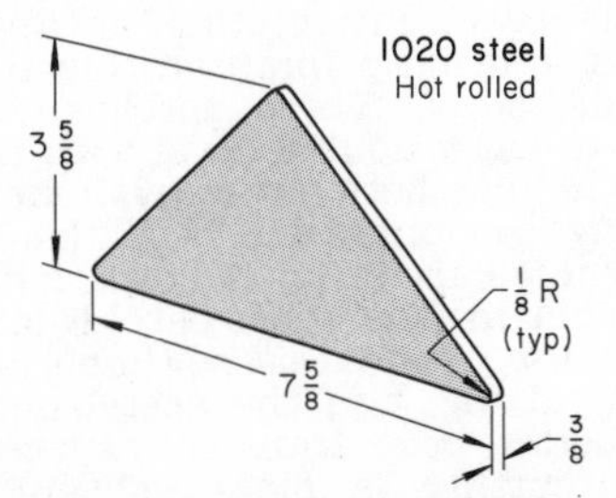

Fig. 15. Triangle that was produced in 36% less time when gas cut in stacks of 13 with a single torch than when six pieces were individually gas cut at one time with a six-torch machine (Example 352)

Preparation of Weld Edges

Steel plates to be welded are resquared, trimmed to size, cut to shape, and beveled by gas cutting, often in one operation. Some cutting also is done on forgings and castings to prepare them for welding. Cutting accuracy can be held to 1/4 or 1/8 in., and squareness and smoothness of the cut edges are usually satisfactory. Adherence of slag to the underside of the cut can be closely controlled; however, a light cleaning operation may be needed. If so, a wide-blade chisel, a grinding wheel, or a wire brush may be used.

Bevel cutting differs from ordinary profile cutting in that the cut edge, instead of being square with the plate surface, is at an angle. Bevel cutting is used primarily to prepare the edges of plate for welding. Some bevels are cut to remove a sharp corner or (as in Example 361) to cut shapes.

Single and double bevel cuts usually vary from 30° to 45°, measured from the square, uncut edge. Low-quality cut surfaces may result for bevels of less than 10° unless an extra scrap allowance is made. For bevels greater than 60°, it is difficult to maintain proper preheat temperature.

Standard cutting equipment is used for cutting bevels in straight-line cutting and in cutting circles. Most shapes cannot be bevel cut by standard machines, because there is no provision for rotating the torch with a change in direction. Some tape-controlled machines have a rotating-torch mechanism for cutting beveled shapes. Circular bevel cutting can be done with portable equipment that can use a radius bar. Sometimes, the workpiece can be rotated past a stationary cutting torch.

Cutting-tip selection for beveling requires special consideration, for two reasons: (*a*) when the cutting tip is inclined to the metal surface, heat transfer to the plate is reduced; and (*b*) because of the angle, the actual cutting thickness is greater than the plate thickness.

Preheating for Bevel Cutting. Torch inclination does not affect the oxidizing action of the cutting-oxygen stream if preheat is adequate. Therefore, tip size (size of cutting-oxygen orifice) and cutting-oxygen flow are selected on the basis of the as-cut thickness. Preheat gas flow, however, is affected in two ways: (*a*) as the angle of inclination increases, heat transfer becomes less efficient and more preheat gas flow is required; and (*b*) in contrast to perpendicular cutting, more preheat is required for thinner materials. (The latter effect may be related to the percentage of heat deflected and to the higher speeds at which thinner materials are cut; the effect disappears in metal thicknesses greater than 4 in.)

Because preheat is important in bevel cutting, several techniques, in addition to increased preheat gas flow, are used to obtain proper preheat. The best position for oxyacetylene cutting is that in which the uppermost cones of flame touch the plate surface while the lower cones extend into the cut. A second torch may be used to precede the cutting torch, for additional preheat. Also, extra preheat tips, called bevel adapt-

Table 15. Torch Settings for Various Bevels, Using Extra Preheat Tip (Bevel Adapter) in Oxy-Natural Gas Cutting (a)

Bevel dimensions, in. A	B	C	Cutting-oxygen orifice diam, in. (b)	Pressure, psi Oxygen	Natural gas	Speed, ipm
Bevel Angle (α) of 45°						
¼	¼	⅜	0.037	45	10	13
⅜	⅜	½	0.037	45	10	13
½	½	11⁄16	0.054	60	10	12½
¾	¾	1 1⁄16	0.054	60	10	11
1	1	1 7⁄16	0.054	60	10	11
1¼	1¼	1¾	0.055	60	10	11
1½	1½	2⅛	0.055	65	10	10
2	2	2 13⁄16	0.073	70	10	9
2½	2½	3½	0.073	70	10	6½
3	3	4¼	0.073	80	10	6
Bevel Angle (α) of 30°						
5⁄32	¼	5⁄16	0.054	60	10	15
7⁄32	⅜	7⁄16	0.054	60	10	14
¼	7⁄16	½	0.054	60	10	14
9⁄32	½	9⁄16	0.054	60	10	14
⅜	21⁄32	¾	0.054	60	10	14
7⁄16	¾	⅞	0.054	60	10	14
½	27⁄32	1	0.054	60	10	13
9⁄16	31⁄32	1⅛	0.054	60	10	13
¾	1¼	1½	0.054	60	10	12
⅞	1½	1¾	0.054	60	10	11
1	1¾	2	0.054	60	10	10½
1 5⁄32	2	2 5⁄16	0.055	65	10	10
1¼	2 5⁄32	2½	0.055	65	10	9
1 7⁄16	2½	2⅞	0.055	70	10	9
1½	2 19⁄32	3	0.055	70	10	7
1¾	3 1⁄32	3½	0.073	75	10	7
2	3 15⁄32	4	0.073	75	10	6½

Partial bevel — Full bevel

(a) Extra preheat tip to be set ¼ to ⅜ in. above plate surface. For proper torch setting, adjust preheat for slight whistle, then reduce oxygen slightly. (b) Two-piece tips for high-speed machine cutting. Corresponding tip sizes of different manufacturers vary in performance because of differences in construction of torches and mixers.

Fig. 16. Cutting a bevel with an extra preheat tip, or bevel adapter. For beveling in the opposite direction, an opposite-hand adapter is needed.

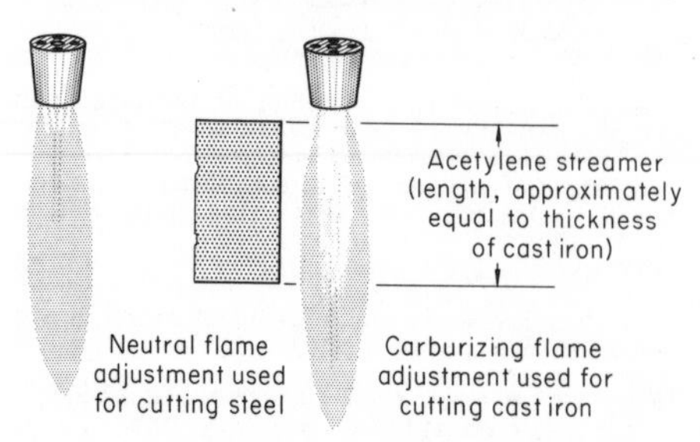

Fig. 17. Flame adjustments for cutting steel and cast iron

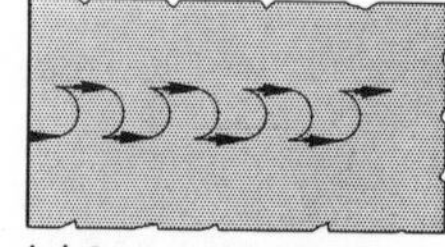

(a) Cutting thin cast iron

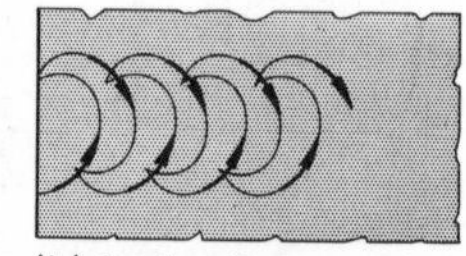

(b) Cutting heavy cast iron

Fig. 18. Movement of torch when cutting cast iron

Table 16. Recommended Minimum Dimensions for Machine Gas-Cut Holes and Slots (a)

Work-metal thickness, in.	Minimum hole diam, in. Rough cuts (b)	Accurate cuts (c)	Minimum slot size, in. (c)
¼ to 7⁄16	1	1¼	½ by 1½
½ to 15⁄16	¾	1¼	½ by ¾
1 to 1⅞	¾	1¼	¾ by 1
2 to 2⅞	1	2	1 by 1½
3 to 4⅞	2	...	1½ by 2
5 to 7¾	3	...	1½ by 3

Start — Start — Arrows indicate direction of cutting

(a) Holes or slots are cut from pierced starts as illustrated above. Torch settings are as indicated in tables of cutting conditions for the fuel gas used. (b) Accuracy will be somewhat less than normal tolerances shown in Table 13. (c) Normal production tolerances shown in Table 13 will be maintained. Minimum sizes of holes are larger than those of slots because circular holes are more difficult to cut.

ers, are available. These adapters have a special heating nozzle offset from the cutting tip so that, when the cutting tip is inclined at 45°, the heating tip is normal to the plate, as shown in Fig. 16. Bevel adapters are right-hand or left-hand; therefore, two may be needed. Much beveling is done, however, without special equipment.

Data for bevel cutting with adapters, using natural gas preheat, are shown in Table 15. This table also can be used when cutting bevels without the use of extra preheat tips, by selecting the next larger tip to provide the extra preheat needed, due to torch inclination. For example, a 45° bevel having a ⅜-in. A and B dimension requires a 0.037-in.-orifice tip with an adapter; the same bevel without an adapter would require a 0.054-in.-orifice tip and the settings listed for it. The cutting-tip height for oxy-natural gas beveling should be about ⅛ to ¼ in. at the closest point above the work. For bevels larger than those for which dimensions are given in Table 15, the torch-to-work distance usually is increased.

When a plate must be trimmed to size as well as partly beveled, both operations can be done at the same time, using two torches close together, with the perpendicular torch leading. Special multitip bevel-cutting heads are also available for this purpose. Two torches may similarly be used for cutting a double bevel intersecting at an edge, with the leading torch cutting the underside bevel. Three torches can be used to cut a double bevel with a short vertical face between bevels; the torch cutting the underside bevel leads, the perpendicular torch follows, and the torch cutting the upper bevel is last.

Because preheat is so important in bevel cutting, and the acetylene flame has better heat transfer, oxyacetylene bevel cutting is more efficient than oxy-natural gas or oxy-propane bevel cutting in thicknesses up to 4 in. Mapp gas has also proved advantageous for bevel cutting.

J-Grooving. A type of gas cutting known as J-grooving sometimes is used to prepare the edges of heavy pressure vessels for welding. The purpose is to provide a groove with less cross-sectional area than an angular bevel would provide in a heavy plate, thus saving time, labor and filler metal in welding. The cutting tips used in this operation are gouging tips; hence, J-grooving is discussed in the section on Oxy-Fuel Gas Gouging, page 299.

Cutting Cast Iron

Because of high carbon content, cast iron resists ordinary gas cutting. Gray iron contains some carbon in the form of flakes of graphite and some in the form of iron carbide, both of which hinder oxidation of the iron. For this reason, gray iron is classed as oxidation-resistant with respect to gas cutting. High-quality production cuts typical of steel are not expected; iron castings usually are gas cut to remove gates, risers and defects, to repair or alter castings in service, or for scrap.

Techniques. Cutting is done manually, using more preheat and cutting oxygen than is used in cutting equal thicknesses of steel. The increased gas flow is obtained by using a larger tip. The preheat flames are adjusted to be carburizing, with the excess acetylene streamer approximately equal to the thickness being cut, as shown in Fig. 17. This adjustment helps to maintain preheat in the cut, because the excess acetylene combines with cutting oxygen beyond the tip. (The same principle is used to some extent in cutting thick steel sections.)

Before the cut is started, the area of the initial cut is preheated, the point of starting is heated to melting, and then the cutting oxygen is released.

In cutting, the torch is advanced in half-circles, as shown in Fig. 18. The size of the half-circles and the speed of advance depend on the thickness of the cut. This oscillating technique helps the cutting jet to get behind and blow out the slag and molten metal at the cut. The kerf is wider and the cut edges are considerably rougher than in cutting steel. Also, oxygen and acetylene consumptions are greater.

Other methods for cutting cast iron, more effective than ordinary gas cutting, are metal-powder cutting and chemical-flux cutting. These methods are frequently used in foundries for removing gates, risers and sprues, or for breaking up ladle skulls. Metal-powder cutting and chemical-flux cutting are discussed on page 299 in this article.

Applicable Shapes

Irregular shapes may be cut by special techniques, or may be beyond the practical limits of gas cutting.

Bars and Structural Shapes. When round steel bars are cut, gas pressures are set for the maximum thickness or diameter, and the cut is started at the side. As the cut progresses, the torch is raised (and lowered) to follow the circumference. Starting is aided by nicking the bar with a chisel to make a burr at the point where the cut is to begin. Gas cutting of round bars is usually manual, so the cut surface is rough. The chief advantage of gas cutting over sawing is that the torch can be brought to the work.

The same advantage applies to gas cutting of various structural shapes, although cutting can be smoother and sharper because it can be guided on the flanges and webs. Extra care must be taken when cutting thick filleted sections. These cuts usually are satisfactory for welding, but may require light grinding if exposed to view. Columns that require end capping usually are machined to exact size.

Circular holes can be gas cut, rather than drilled, if the hole wall does not require a machined finish, and if the roundness and concentricity have wide tolerances. The following types of holes can be made by gas cutting: clearance holes for piping and bolting; concrete grouting holes; holes for piping where the pipe is welded to the piece containing the hole; inspection or access holes; and holes for plug welds.

Holes can best be gas cut with the aid of electronic tracers. Accuracy depends on template accuracy. Hole location and hole size in plate up to 3 in. thick can be held readily to the tolerances listed in Table 13. As shown in Table 16, the cut is advanced from a pierced starting hole. In piercing, the slag must be removed from any area that the flame will later touch. This is particularly important for small holes.

Recommended minimum hole diameters are shown in Table 16. The two levels of quality shown indicate the influence of hole size on accuracy. Normal production tolerances (Table 13) are difficult to maintain in thicknesses over 3 in., because of kerf angle. Holes larger than those listed can be gas cut to normal production tolerances.

Slots. The procedure for gas cutting of slots is the same as that for gas cutting of holes. Table 16 lists minimum slot sizes that can be cut to normal tolerances, and contains a sketch that illustrates torch movement.

Slots can be made at less cost by gas cutting than by profile end milling, if a machined edge is not mandatory. Table 17 compares the times for producing slots in material ¼ to 7¾ in. thick by gas cutting and by profile end milling.

Borderline Shapes. The next four examples illustrate shapes that are borderline for gas cutting. The first example concerns a shape in which two sides had to be exactly perpendicular. In the second example, three sides of a shape were required to hold a tolerance of $+0, -\frac{1}{32}$ in. In the third example, a shape with a narrow pointed end was required to maintain sharp edges and corners. The fourth example describes a shape that contained a long slot, narrower than the minimum recommended for normal accuracy in Table 16.

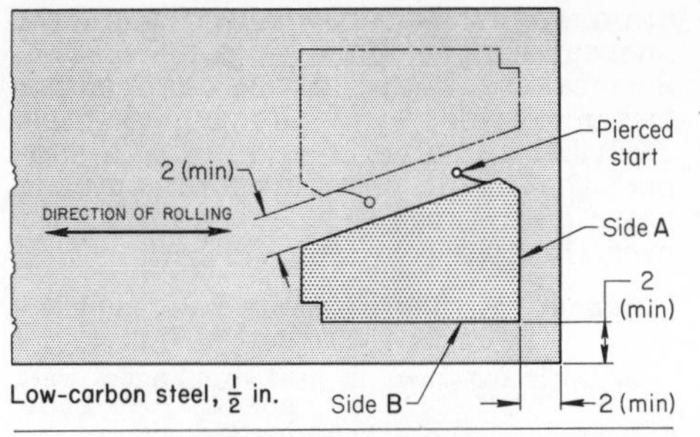

Operating Procedure

1 Ink trace paper template from master template. Use magnets to hold template for tracing and cutting.
2 Locate and space items on template and plate as shown.
3 Set torch tip ½ to ¾ in. above plate.
4 Cut in clockwise direction.
5 Inspect first piece on each plate.
6 Destroy paper template 4 hr after it is made.

Torch Settings

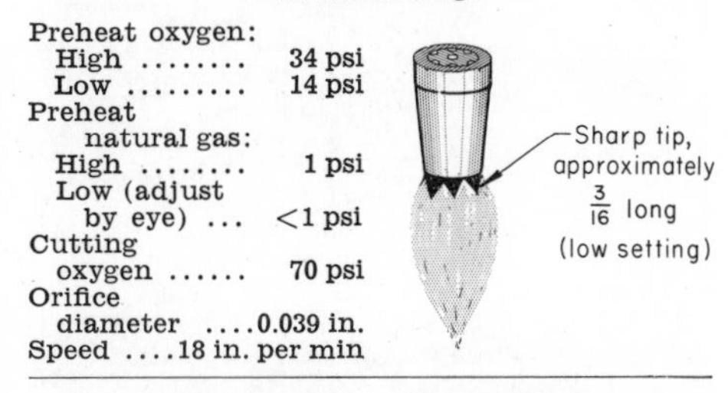

Preheat oxygen:
High .... 34 psi
Low .... 14 psi
Preheat natural gas:
High .... 1 psi
Low (adjust by eye) ... <1 psi
Cutting oxygen ...... 70 psi
Orifice diameter ....0.039 in.
Speed ....18 in. per min

Fig. 19. Gas cutting a gusset with two perpendicular sides (Example 353)

Table 17. Comparison of Times for Producing Slots by Machine Gas Cutting and by Profile End Milling

Work-metal thickness, in.	Slot size, in.	Production time, hr: Gas cutting(a)	Production time, hr: End milling(b)
¼	½ by 1½	0.031	0.1540
⅜	½ by 1½	0.031	0.1630
½	½ by ¾	0.031	0.1645
¾	½ by ¾	0.032	0.1793
1	¾ by 1	0.032	0.2829
1½	¾ by 1	0.036	0.3085
2	¾ by 1	0.041	0.3441
2½	1 by 1½	0.048	0.4163
3	1 by 1½	0.052	0.4422
4	1½ by 2	0.067	0.7143
5	1½ by 2	0.072	0.7684
6	1½ by 3	0.105	0.9402
6½	1½ by 3	0.112	0.9891
7¾	1½ by 3	0.117	1.1112

(a) Includes time for piercing of starting hole, removal of slag from pierced start, cutting of slot, and removal of slag from finished slot. (b) Includes time for layout of slot, drilling of starting hole (or holes), and profile end milling of slot. For material up to 5 in. thick, one starting hole is drilled and slot is milled with a two-lip end mill; for material 6 to 7¾ in. thick, two starting holes are drilled and slot is milled with a four-lip end mill.

Example 353. Two Perpendicular Sides (Fig. 19)

The gusset shown in Fig. 19 was gas cut from ½-in.-thick low-carbon steel so that sides A and B would be 90° to each other. By positioning the part a minimum of 2 in. from any edge of the plate and cutting in a clockwise direction, the restraint of the uncut portion of the plate was used to keep the two adjacent sides of the gusset in position during machine gas cutting. As shown in Fig. 19, the cut was started clockwise, from a pierced start, along the noncritical side. The shorter side A, then side B, were cut so that they could not move in relation to each other. The noncritical sides were cut last.

The cutting machine was equipped with an injector torch for use with low-pressure natural gas. A high-speed, two-piece cutting tip was used, together with high-low gas regulators. The operating procedure and torch settings used are given in the table that accompanies Fig. 19.

Example 354. Three Close-Tolerance Sides (Fig. 20)

Figure 20 shows the layout for gas cutting a part that had to fit a welding fixture. Two methods were used to hold the contour bounded by surfaces A, B and C to a tolerance of $+0, -\frac{1}{32}$ in.: (*a*) wedges were inserted into the kerf, locking the shape to the plate for maximum restraint; and then (*b*) the effects of distortion that remained were overcome by making allowances in the template. The latter was accomplished by making cutting tests, and measuring and adjusting the master aluminum template until the proper shape was developed. The master template was used only for preparing the template used on the job.

The equipment for cutting was the same as that described in Example 353. Operating procedure and torch settings are given in the table that accompanies Fig. 20. Although the procedure mentions the use of a paper template, a plastic template was substituted later, to extend template life to more than 4 hr.

When gas-cut shapes have rounded top edges (rollover), the cause usually is excessive preheat. However, this condition can also occur when the cutting path surrounds too small a mass of the shape being cut, causing excessive heat accumulation, as in the application described in the example that follows.

Example 355. Shape With Narrow Pointed End (Fig. 21)

The 7½-in.-thick shape shown in Fig. 21 included a narrow portion where the cutting path doubled back. Although the finished

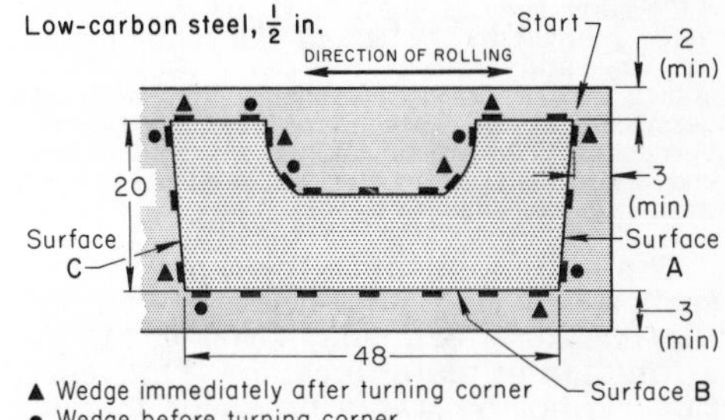

Operating Procedure

1 Ink trace paper template from master template. Use magnets to hold template for tracing and cutting.
2 Set torch tip ½ to ¾ in. above plate.
3 Cut in clockwise direction with single torch.
4 Wedge approximately ½ in. behind cutting tip.
5 Reset previously placed wedges, where possible, after setting new wedges.
6 Inspect first piece on each plate.
7 Destroy paper template 4 hr after it is made.

Torch Settings

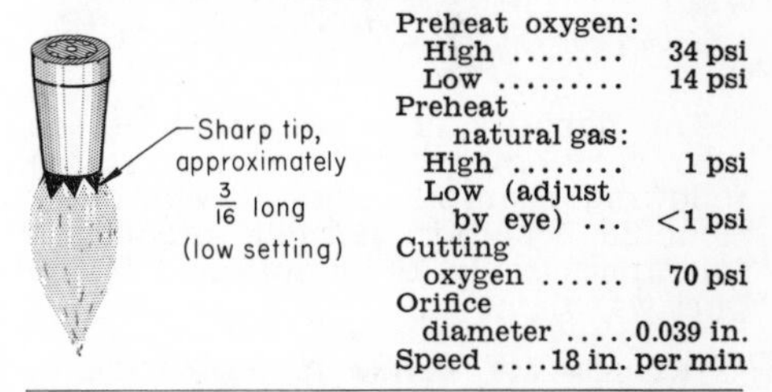

Preheat oxygen:
High .... 34 psi
Low .... 14 psi
Preheat natural gas:
High .... 1 psi
Low (adjust by eye) ... <1 psi
Cutting oxygen ...... 70 psi
Orifice diameter .....0.039 in.
Speed ....18 in. per min

Fig. 20. Gas cutting a part with three sides held to close tolerances (Example 354)

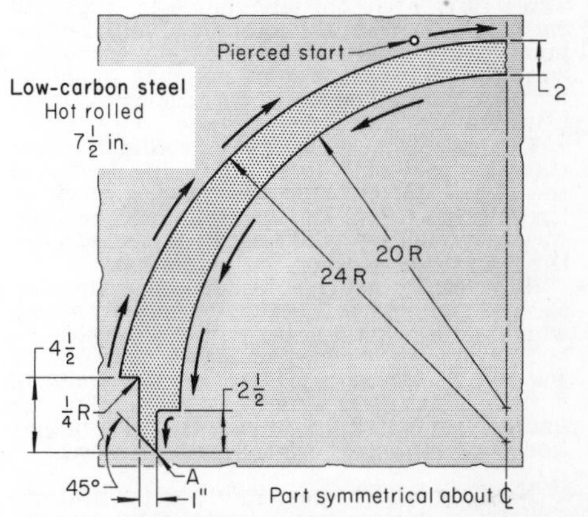

Fig. 21. Gas-cut shape on which the narrow projection was subject to melting at the edges (Example 355)

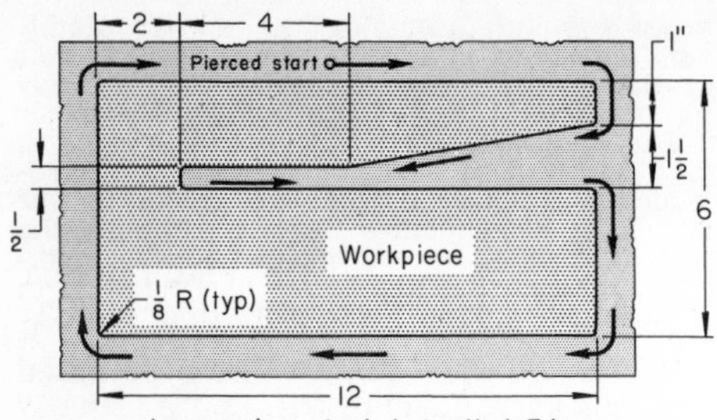

Fig. 22. Shape that was gas cut to normal tolerance (±⅛ in.) for 3-in. plate thickness, despite narrow re-entrant slot and thin projection, which ordinarily are subject to melting at the edges (Example 356)

shape was within the tolerances given in Table 13, a slight rounding of the top edge of the 1-in.-wide projection and of point A (Fig. 21) was observed. From top to bottom, the kerf width increased 1/16 in. per side, making the 1-in. projection ⅞ in. wide at the bottom with a kerf angle of about ½°.

To start the cut for this shape, a hole was flame pierced to the left of the centerline at the top, and from it the cut progressed as shown in the sketch. Because of the deviations described above, this shape was considered borderline insofar as process capability was concerned, in spite of the fact that tolerances were not exceeded.

The minimum width for a projection, such as on the shape that was cut in the foregoing example (see Fig. 21), is a function of plate thickness. This relation cannot be stated precisely, mainly because the rounding of corners is also a function of the size of the tracing follower and the diameter of the cutting flame. The following table, however, may be used as a guide:

Plate thickness, in.	Minimum projection width, in.
¼	⅜
½	½
1	¾
1½	1
2	1¼
3	1½
3 to 7¾	2

The opposite of a projection is the narrow re-entrant cut described in the following example. Here it was questionable whether normal production tolerances could be maintained if the part was flame cut.

Example 356. Narrow Re-entrant Cut (Fig. 22)

The 3-in.-thick shape shown in Fig. 22 was cut within ±⅛ in. (the tolerance given in Table 13), even though the ½-in.-wide slot was narrower than the minimum width recommended in Table 16, and the 1-in. projection was less than the 1½-in. nominal minimum for 3-in. stock. The shape was cut by machine, using natural gas preheat fuel.

Two problems were anticipated. One was that the heat buildup in the ½-in. portion of the slot would burn up the scrap, causing an irregular path for the cutting flame. The other was that melting would occur at the edges of the 1-in.-wide area of the projection.

However, by using a high-speed cutting tip at the high end of the cutting-speed range, which is 7 to 13 in. per min (see Table 5), both problems were overcome. A narrow kerf was cut in the slot, leaving a scrap width of ¼ in., which was sufficient to confine the flame. Heat buildup at the end of the projection was minimized by the cutting speed.

Nesting of Shapes. Savings in material, labor, and gas consumption can be made by nesting parts in the stock layout for single-torch or multitorch operation. Savings can be realized whenever one cut can be made in place of two. Sometimes a shape can be changed for better nesting. The following example describes a change in contour of a support that made possible more complete nesting and saved the manufacturer over $10,000 a year.

Example 357. Design Change for Complete Nesting of Supports (Fig. 23)

Supports for tubes in heat exchangers were cut from ASTM A212, grade B, steel plate, using a two-torch gas-cutting machine of the pantograph type. A magnetic follower was used to trace a steel template. As shown in Fig. 23(a), each torch cut the top edge of the shape, and then doubled back to cut the bottom edge. The dimensions of the support varied according to the size, spacing and number of tubes, but the basic design was the same for all supports. Because of the incomplete nesting of the supports, a third of the material was lost as scrap.

By changing the design of the support to that shown in Fig. 23(b), each torch (after the first cut) could cut a support in a single pass. Labor and gas consumption were reduced 45% and 40%, respectively, and production rate was almost doubled. Scrap losses were negligible.

An estimate of dollar savings was made on the basis of an average-length support (48 in.) and the number of supports made in one year. These data are presented in the table that accompanies Fig. 23. It was later found that the new design permitted the use of four torches instead of two, thus reducing labor and overhead approximately 50% more.

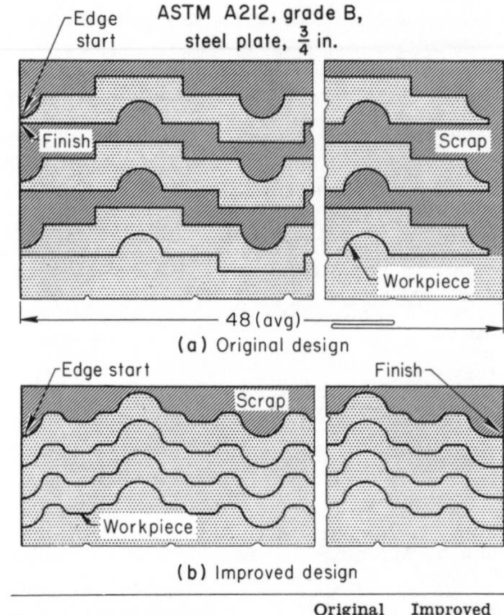

Item	Original design	Improved design
Production time per piece, hr	0.12	0.066
Material per piece, lb	25.5	17
Comparison of Costs per Piece		
Labor and overhead, at $5/hr	$0.60	$0.33
Material, at $0.066/lb	1.59(a)	1.12(b)
Acetylene, at $3.20/100 cu ft(c)	0.05	0.03
Oxygen at $0.36/100 cu ft(d)	0.05	0.03
Total(e)	$2.29	$1.51
Annual production, 13,200 pieces	$30,274	$19,962
Saving per year	...	$10,312

(a) After deduction of $0.09 for value of scrap. (b) No scrap. (c) Flow rate, 14 cu ft per hr. (d) Flow rate, 120 cu ft per hr. (e) Cost based on average-size support bar, illustrated above.

Fig. 23. Redesign of heat-exchanger tube support bar for more efficient gas cutting (Example 357)

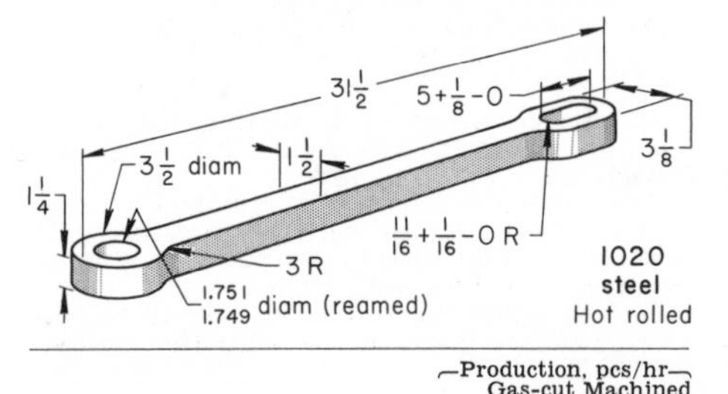

Operation	Production, pcs/hr — Gas-cut plate	Production, pcs/hr — Machined forging
Gas cut hole, slot and profile(a)	48.4	...
Light grind cut edges(b)	45.6	...
Ream cut hole to 1¾-in. diam	28.9	...
Drill and ream 1¾-in.-diam hole	...	13.6

(a) A six-torch gas-cutting machine with electronic tracer was used. (b) A portable disk grinder was used.

Fig. 24. Suspension bar that was produced faster by gas cutting of steel plate than as a machined forging (Example 358)

Gas Cutting vs Alternative Methods

Gas-cut parts sometimes are used to replace castings or forgings, and gas cutting may replace certain machining operations. Provided the properties and dimensional accuracy of gas-cut plate are acceptable, gas cutting is selected in preference to alternative methods when it can provide one or more of the following advantages:

1 Reduced labor and overhead costs
2 Reduced material costs
3 Reduced tooling costs
4 Faster delivery.

When required dimensional accuracy cannot be obtained with gas cutting alone, a combination of processes can be used: rough cutting can be done by gas cutting, and finish cutting can be done by machining.

The five examples that follow compare the results obtained in gas cutting and in alternative production methods.

Examples 358 and 359. Gas-Cut Steel Plate vs Forgings

Example 358 (Fig. 24). The suspension bar shown in Fig. 24 was originally produced as a machined forging from 1020 steel. To reduce costs, gas cutting from hot rolled 1020 steel was considered as an alternative method, but it was important that no loss in production rate should result.

When forgings were used, only two machining operations were required: drilling and reaming the 1¾-in. hole. When gas-cut plate was used, a 1 11/16-in.-diam hole and the oval slot were pierced and cut when the bar profile was cut. The gas-cut edges were lightly ground, and the 1 11/16-in. hole was reamed to 1.749/1.751 in. in diameter.

Gas cutting was done in a six-torch machine with an electronic tracer. Travel speed was 15 in. per min, using a cutting tip with a No. 60 drill-size (0.040-in.-diam) orifice. Gas cutting, grinding and reaming were done in parallel operations, so that the production rate depended on the slowest operation. As shown in the table with Fig. 24, the gas-cutting procedure provided a faster production rate — more than double the pieces per hour.

Example 359 (Fig. 25). Two methods were acceptable for making bearing supports for commutator-end housings: (*a*) forging in closed dies and then machining to the shape shown in operation 4 of Fig. 25; or (*b*) gas cutting a blank and then completing it by machining and press forming, as shown in Fig. 25.

Choosing between the two methods depended on conditions in the shop at the time the parts were needed. Forging and machining was the more costly of the two methods. However, it was preferred when the shop was extremely busy, because the forgings were purchased and then machined in the shop as needed. As noted in the table with Fig. 25, more time per piece was required for facing and turning the

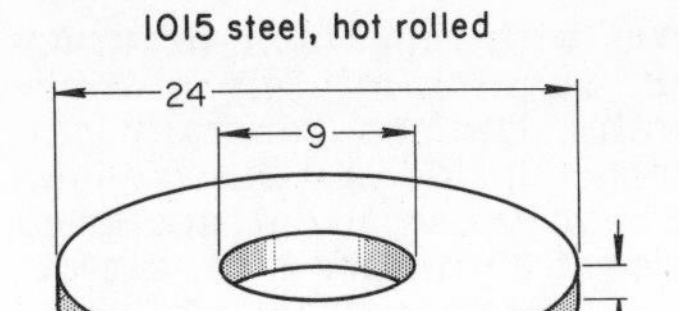

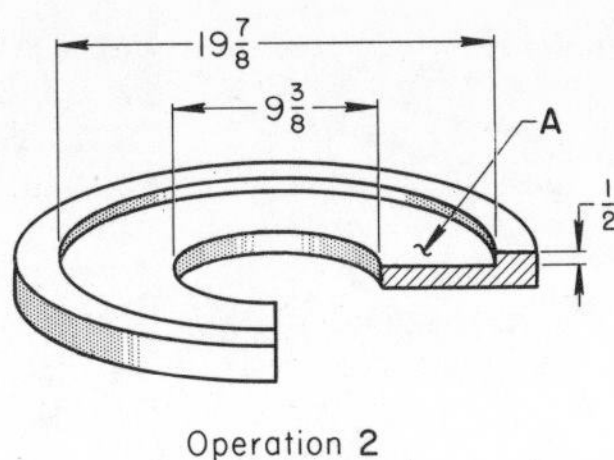

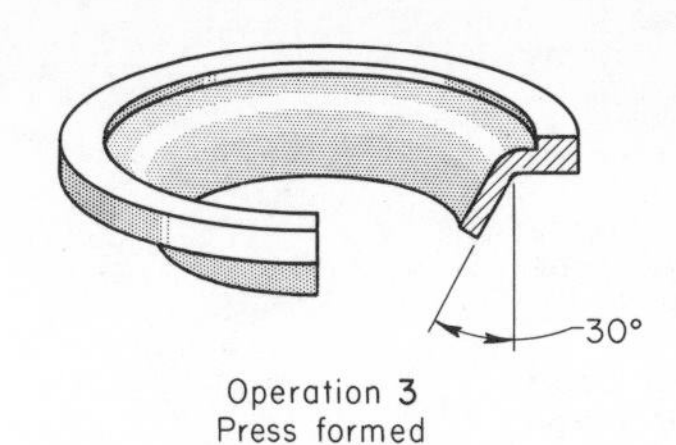

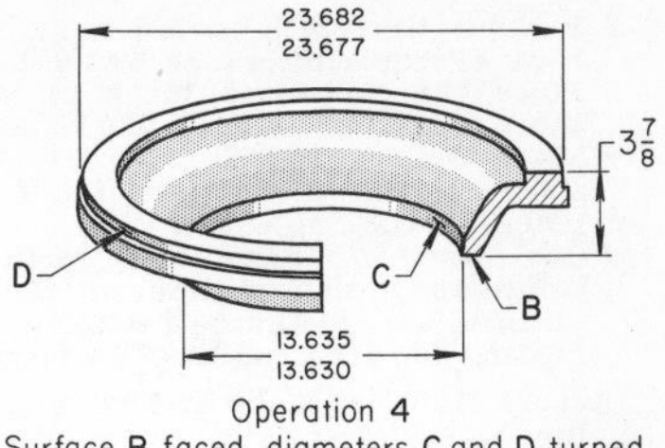

Operation 1 – Gas cut both the inside diameter and the outside diameter, using a four-torch gas-cutting machine with an electronic tracer (production rate, 19.2 pieces per hour). Operation 2 – Turn recess A in a vertical turret lathe (3.06 pieces per hour). Operation 3 – Press form in a 1900-ton hydraulic press (production rate, 22.6 pieces per hour). Operation 4 – Face B, turn C and D in a vertical turret lathe (4.6 pieces per hour for the gas-cut plate; 3.3 pieces per hour for the forging).

Fig. 25. Bearing support that could be made by forging and machining, or by gas cutting, machining and press forming (Example 359)

forgings because there was more stock to be removed than when the alternative method was used. When the shop was less busy, method (*b*) above was preferred, because cost of the part was less and it provided needed work in the shop.

Gas cutting was done in a four-torch machine with an electronic tracer. All machining was done in a vertical turret lathe. Forming was done in a 1900-ton press, using 950 to 1000 tons of force.

Various machine parts, such as bases, housings and frames, are made from gas-cut parts that are welded together, rather than purchased as castings. Empirical methods are frequently used to determine whether or not a weldment can be produced more economically than a casting. For instance, if it does not take too many secondary operations to produce a weldment from components that have been previously gas cut from plate, it is estimated that the cost of the finished weldment probably will be 2 to 2½ times the price of the raw material used. Assuming that low-carbon steel at mill price costs one-sixth to one-fourth as much as a purchased steel casting, the cost advantage of the weldment is obvious. The example that follows discusses the production of a part that cost less as a weldment than as a steel casting.

Example 360. Weldment vs Steel Casting (Fig. 26)

The body center-plate bearing support shown in Fig. 26(a) and (b), for a diesel locomotive underframe, was fabricated as a weldment from hot rolled 1020 steel. Total plate stock for this part was 1416 lb; finished weight of the part was 998.5 lb. The steel casting (Fig. 26c) previously used weighed 1097 lb. Two such supports were welded to the locomotive underframe to be the load-bearing and pivot points for each set of trucks.

Seven pieces of gas-cut plate made up the assembly. A multitorch cutting machine with an electronic tracer was used in the sequence given below:

1. Cut the profile of the baseplate (Fig. 26a) from 2-in. plate, using three torches, cutting three pieces at one time. Cutting speed, 11 in. per min; cutting tip, No. 56 drill size (0.0465 in.).
2. Cut inner diameter and outer diameter of the 2-in.-thick bearing ring (Fig. 26a), using four torches at the same speed and with the same size cutting tip as for step 1.
3. Cut support gussets (Fig. 26b) from 1-in. plate, using six torches. Cutting speed, 14 in. per min; cutting tip, No. 60 drill size (0.040 in.).
4. Cut holes, then cut the profile of the center gussets (Fig. 26b) from 1-in. plate. Cutting speed, 14 in. per min; cutting tip, No. 60 drill size.
5. Assemble parts, using a fit-up jig and tack weld. Weld joints in a weld positioner, using gas metal-arc equipment with a flux-cored electrode.
6. Stress relieve. Machine-turn the bearing face and machine the top of the gussets to clean up the 13 7/16-in. dimension. This same operation would have had to be performed on a casting.

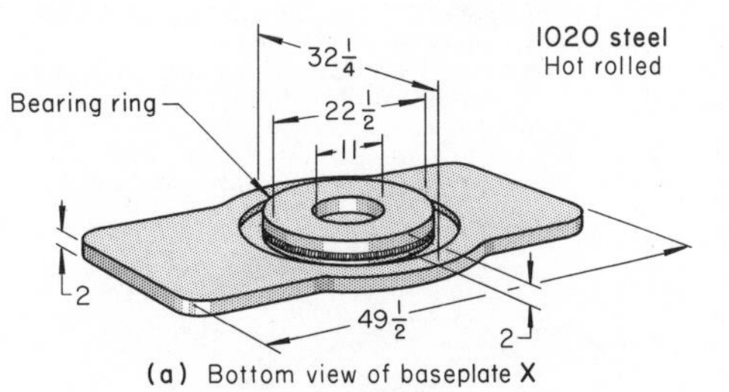

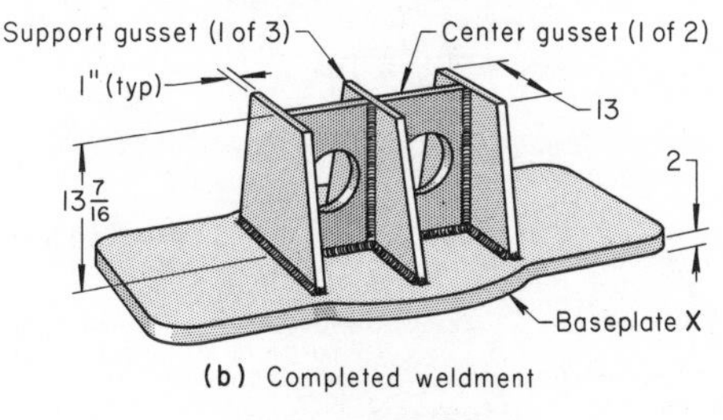

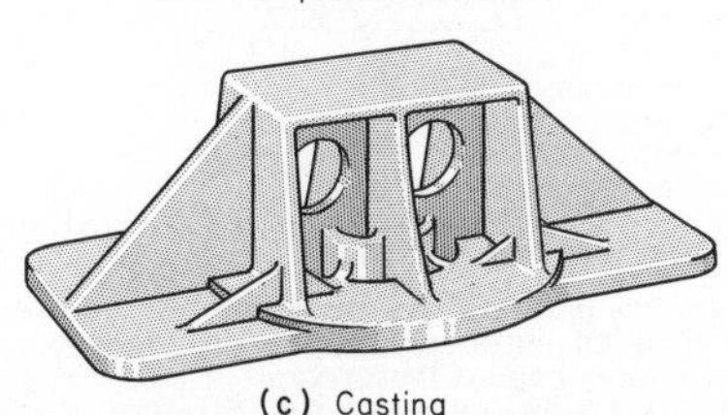

Fig. 26. Bearing support for locomotive wheel trucks that was produced at less cost as a welded assembly of gas-cut components (a) *and* (b) *than as a casting* (c) (Example 360)

There are few gas-cutting operations that cannot be performed by some type of machining. Machining may produce more accurate results, but time and cost may be saved by gas cutting. The two examples that follow describe applications in which gas cutting was used to remove a large quantity of metal, either to eliminate machining or to minimize the time required for machining to final size. (See also Example 365, in the section on Metal-Powder Cutting, and Example 366, in the section on Oxy-Fuel Gas Gouging. Example 365 compares metal-powder cutting with milling for the removal of excess stock from an Inconel part; Example 366 compares oxy-fuel gas gouging with planing for cutting the J-groove edges for the welded joint on thick-wall pressure vessels made of ASTM A212, grade B, steel plate.)

Example 361. Gas Cutting vs Band Sawing (Fig. 27)

The cross shown in Fig. 27(a) originally was rough cut by band sawing and then rough and finish milled to size. The cross was cut from a piece of forged 4340 steel, 19¼ by 11½ by 5¼ in. thick. Because the shape could be traced by a single line set at the proper angle, gas cutting was substituted for band sawing, to save time. The cross was cut 0.30 in. oversize to allow for machining. A pantograph-type machine with a magnetic tracer was used for gas cutting. After a few trials to establish the best cutting sequence, the following operations were set up:

1. Set the torch to a compound angle consisting of a 32.5° bevel and left-to-right inclination of 13.75°. [The inclination angle caused some concern because the flame would lead the cut at faces X and Y (Fig. 27b), and such a condition could possibly cause gouging.]

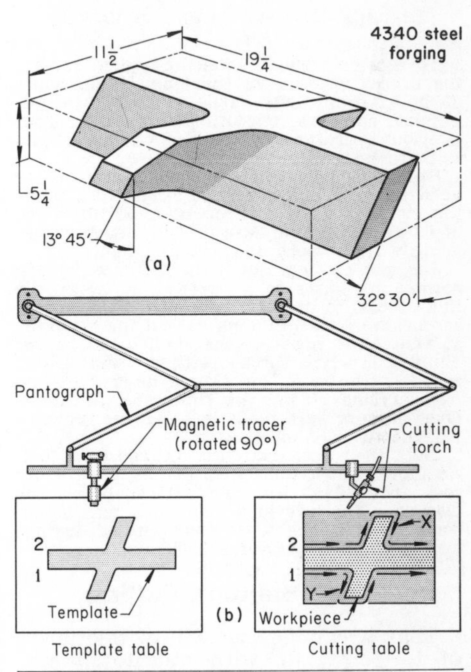

Operating Conditions for Gas Cutting

Cutting tip	Heavy-duty
Diameter of cutting-oxygen orifice	0.1065 in.
Diameter of preheat orifices (six)	0.0465 in.
Cutting-oxygen pressure	60 to 70 psi
Cutting-oxygen flow rate	600 to 680 cfh
Preheat-oxygen flow rate (2-hose torch)	77 cfh
Acetylene pressure	6 psi
Acetylene flow rate	70 cfh
Cutting speed	4 to 6 in. per min

Man-Hours per Piece, Band Sawing

Drill starter holes	1.557
Band saw (rough size)	3.780
Rough mill (size, comparable to gas cut)	3.617
Total	8.954

Man-Hours per Piece, Gas Cutting

Load and unload furnace; set up block	0.113
Gas cut to size	0.495
Grind (clean up); handling	0.128
Total	0.736

Fig. 27. Cross (a) *that was gas cut, by method shown in* (b), *in about 8% of the time formerly required for producing it by band sawing* (Example 361)

2 Preheat the block to 800 F and soak for 6 min. (Permissible range was 600 to 900 F.)
3 Place the preheated block on the cutting table and align with a fixed steel template.
4 Make cuts 1 and 2 from left to right as shown in Fig. 27(b). (Details of cutting are listed in the table with Fig. 27.)
5 Cool in air to room temperature, allowing complete transformation of the cut faces. (Immediate postheat treatment caused increased hardness of the cut faces.)

Actual time saved by gas cutting over band sawing was determined by comparing man-hours for both methods. This comparison, shown in the table that accompanies Fig. 27, indicates that gas cutting required less than one-twelfth the time needed for band sawing.

Many boiler drums for steam generators in power plants are made from two semicylindrical half shells welded together longitudinally to form a cylinder. The ends of the cylinder are then closed with formed heads joined to the shell by a circumferential weld. The half shells are hot formed in a press from flat steel plate. After forming, the excess material at the longitudinal joints must be removed before the shells are welded together; either planing or gas cutting can be used for this removal. The following example illustrates a saving that was achieved by gas cutting.

Example 362. Gas Cutting vs Planing (Fig. 28)

To establish the cost advantage in removing excess metal from the longitudinal joints of boiler-drum half shells (Fig. 28) by gas cutting, as compared with planing, data from previous operations on shells of various lengths and thicknesses were compared.

Data for the planing operation were averaged from 83 half-shell operations. The planing cut was made at a speed of 23 sfm, feed of 0.040 in. per min, and 0.75-in. depth of cut, using a high speed steel cutting tool.

For gas cutting, the half shells were submerged in water to a depth 1 in. below the line of cut, to prevent distortion. Two cutting torches were used in a special cutting machine, so that both edges of the shell could be cut simultaneously. Torch settings and travel speed were based on standard straight-line oxyacetylene cutting of the same thickness. Over 60 cuts were made in the same range of thicknesses used for planing.

Data then were translated into cost per foot. As shown in the table with Fig. 28, gas cutting cost about 64% less per half shell, on the average. The previous 12-month production was 795 half shells, so that annual savings were estimated at over $18,000.

Close-Tolerance Cutting

Shapes can be gas cut to tolerances of 1/32 to 1/16 in. with multitorch machines of the pantograph or coordinate-drive type if these conditions are met:

1 The operator is well-trained and experienced.
2 The machine is properly adjusted, so that it can trace and retrace a pattern with accuracy of ±0.005 in., running in a given direction.
3 The workpiece is reasonably flat and free of dirt, scale, grease and oil.
4 The workpiece is supported or restrained to prevent movement of the shape during cutting.
5 The cutting tip is selected for high-quality, narrow-kerf cutting.
6 The material thickness does not exceed 2 in., and cutting speed is commensurate with material thickness, fuel gas, and equipment.

Some of the above conditions are illustrated by the cutting operations described in Examples 350, 353 and 354. The part discussed in the following example was produced regularly to a tolerance of +0, −1/16 in. on the slots.

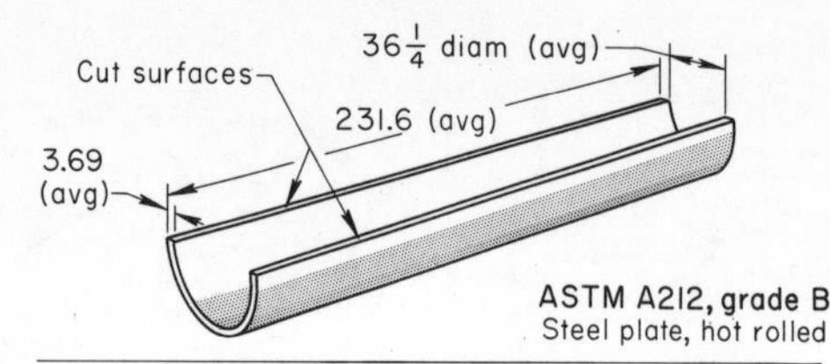

Item	Planing	Gas cutting
Removal cost per ft ..	$1.83	$0.27
Removal cost per half shell	$35.32	$12.61(a)
Annual cost(b)	$28,079	$10,025

(a) Including extra setup cost of $7.40 per half shell. (b) 795 half shells per year.

Fig. 28. Half shell from which excess metal of 3.05-in. average depth was removed by gas cutting at less cost than by planing (Example 362)

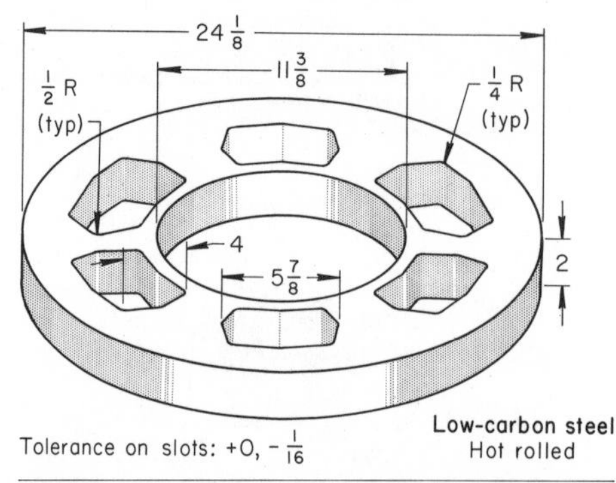

Torches	Low-pressure injector-type
Tip	Two-piece divergent type
Diameter of cutting-oxygen orifice	0.045 in.
Fuel gas	Natural gas
Pressure:	
Preheat gas	1/2 psi(a)
Preheat oxygen	10 psi
Cutting oxygen	95 psi
Cutting speed:	
Slots	10 in. per min
Inside and outside diameters	12 in. per min

(a) Preheat-gas pressure would be about 9 psi with an equal-pressure torch; however, with a low-pressure injector-type torch, a greater amount of gas is siphoned through the regulator in operation.

Fig. 29. Part containing slots that were gas cut to close tolerances (Example 363)

Example 363. Gas Cutting Close-Tolerance Slots for Broaching (Fig. 29)

The workpiece shown in Fig. 29 is a part of a harmonic balancer for a diesel engine crankshaft. The part was made by gas cutting from a 2-in.-thick plate of hot rolled low-carbon steel, maintaining dimensional accuracy of the slots within +0, −1/16 in. (The slots were finished by broaching to final size.)

Starting holes for the outside and inside diameters and for slots were drilled. Plates were supported on the cutting table with stops at one end and one side. Cover support bars were used on the cutting table to insure over-all contact of the plate within 1/16 in. Cutting was done with Mylar line-tracing templates, a new template being required after 130 pieces were cut (approximate production for an 8-hr shift). Slots were cut first, and then the inside and outside diameters were cut. After one slot was cut, the slot opposite it was cut, which helped to maintain required accuracy. A six-projection go-no-go plug gage was used to check the size and location of the slots. Four pieces were cut at a time in a multitorch machine with an electronic tracer. Cutting conditions are tabulated with Fig. 29.

Use of Tracing Equipment. Electronic tracing has several advantages over other tracing methods for close-tolerance work. Electronic devices do not touch the template. They can follow a pencil or ink line 0.025 in. wide on paper or plastic, with repeatable accuracy of ±0.005 in., running in a given direction. Electronic systems generally can produce sharper inside and outside corner radii. For instance, if cutting speed does not exceed 30 in. per min, a template with an outside corner radius of 3/32 in. should produce a completely sharp corner. A 3/32-in. inside radius on the template would produce a somewhat larger radius in the workpiece, depending on thickness and cutting tip.

Magnetic tracers can produce square outside corners if a corner latch unit is employed; otherwise, the cut will equal the radius of the magnetic follower. A latch provides a surface for the follower to ride past the corner point. When the follower reaches the point where its direction should change, the latch flips over to the new direction. With magnetic tracing, inside radii in the cut piece will be slightly smaller than the follower radius. The magnetic follower must be large enough to produce about a 15-lb force.

In manual tracing, accuracy is a problem when a spindle is used to trace a solid template, or when a drive wheel is used to trace a line. Accuracy of the cut piece depends on the operator, although edge tracing, like magnetic tracing, is inherently more accurate than line tracing. Maximum manual tracing speeds are about 14 in. per min.

Special equipment sometimes is used for production jobs requiring unusual accuracy, as in the following example.

Example 364. Cutting to Tolerance of ±0.015 In. (Fig. 30)

Twenty-four air-intake ports had to be cut to ±0.015 in., in the diesel-engine cylinder liner shown in Fig. 30(a). The ports, each 5/8 in. wide by 1 1/4 in. long, were equally spaced around the circumference of the 10 3/4-in.-diam section of the 1-in.-thick cylinder made of a 1020 steel forging. Ports were cut at 10° to a radial line, so that air would swirl upon entering the cylinder. Surface finish and accuracy had to be between a rough and a semifinished machine cut. Nicks or gouges could not be tolerated.

A fixture was constructed to produce the parts by gas cutting. The only machining anticipated on the port walls was blending of the walls into the periphery of the cylinder with a 3/16-in. radius, as shown in Fig. 30(b).

The cutting machine had a two-torch pantograph driven by an edge tracer. For positive tracing accuracy, the drive spindle and the template were geared together. The fixture consisted of a tank partly filled with water, two coordinately driven shafts and two automatic drill heads. An air-operated expanding mandrel was mounted on each shaft, to hold a liner. The drills made starting holes for cutting each port and were indexed to cycle with the gas cutting. The liner was partly submerged in cooling water; this minimized deformation and resulting errors in spacing. The setup, as shown schematically in Fig. 30(c), was completely automatic, once loaded. The sequence of operations was:

1 Load two liners into the machine and clamp them on expanding mandrels.
2 Start machine; advance drills, drilling 1/4-in. holes in approximate centers of ports.
3 Index liners 120° for cutting.
4 Ignite automatic torches by spark. Preheat 2 sec, then start gas cutting. Advance drills and drill the next holes.
5 Repeat indexing until all holes have been cut. Machine shuts off automatically.

Torch settings are given in the table that accompanies Fig. 30. Factors that contributed to maintaining dimensional tolerances of ±0.015 in. were:

1 Maintenance of all equipment in excellent working order
2 Use of a positive-tracking template
3 Machining of outside surface of the cylinder liner to eliminate surface contaminants that

might interfere with the action of the cutting flame
4 Drilling of starting holes, to avoid metal expulsion that might affect the cutting tip or interfere with the cut
5 Use of matched torch tips designed for high-quality cutting
6 Rigid support of workpieces
7 Cooling workpieces to minimize distortion.

Metal-Powder Cutting

In metal-powder cutting, finely divided, iron-rich powder, usually airborne, is directed into the gas flame. The iron powder passes through and is heated by the preheat flames so that it burns in the oxygen stream. Heat generated by the burning iron particles, together with the driving force of the resulting iron oxide, greatly improves the cutting action. Cuts can be made in stainless steel and cast iron at speeds only slightly slower than in equal thicknesses of carbon steel. By adding a small amount of aluminum powder, cuts can be made through copper and brass. Even concrete up to 12 in. thick can be cut, at speeds of 2 to 3 in. per min.

Equipment. Metal-powder cutting can be done with a standard cutting torch using an external powder attachment, or by a modified cutting torch with built-in powder passages. A powder dispenser, air supply, and powder hose are required, in addition to the normal fuel and oxygen lines. The equipment may be used in hand cutting for removing metal, such as risers from castings, or it may be mechanized for straight-line or shape cutting in machines.

Powder-cutting torches mounted on standard gas-cutting machines are used to cut stainless steel. Accuracy is less important in powder cutting of stainless steel than in gas cutting of carbon steel, since allowance usually is made for machining or grinding to size.

Thickness. In plate in the thickness range of 1 to 4 in., powder cuts can be produced mechanically with an accuracy of 1/32 to 1/16 in., under favorable conditions. Heavier sections seldom are cut except for the trimming of castings, and in this application hand cutting requires greater allowances to avoid damage. For this reason, risers often are cut 1/8 in. above the surface of the casting.

Quality of Cut. In powder cutting, the kerf has a layer of scale which, on stainless steel, gradually flakes off as the piece cools to room temperature. The surface exposed after scale removal has the texture of worn coarse-grit sandpaper. A light grind normally is sufficient to smooth high spots and remove iron particles and oxide. Carbide precipitation in unstabilized austenitic stainless steels can be restored by heat treating, or it can be removed by machining off a layer of metal. The amount removed depends on the subsequent use of the piece, because, in welding, there may be further carbide precipitation; however, a 1/8-in. allowance usually is satisfactory.

Powder-cut cast iron develops a hardened case at the surface, which may require annealing or removal by grinding.

Applications. Typical powder-cutting applications include removal of risers; cutting of bars, plates and slabs to size; demolition of heavy sections; and scrapping. With heavy-duty torches

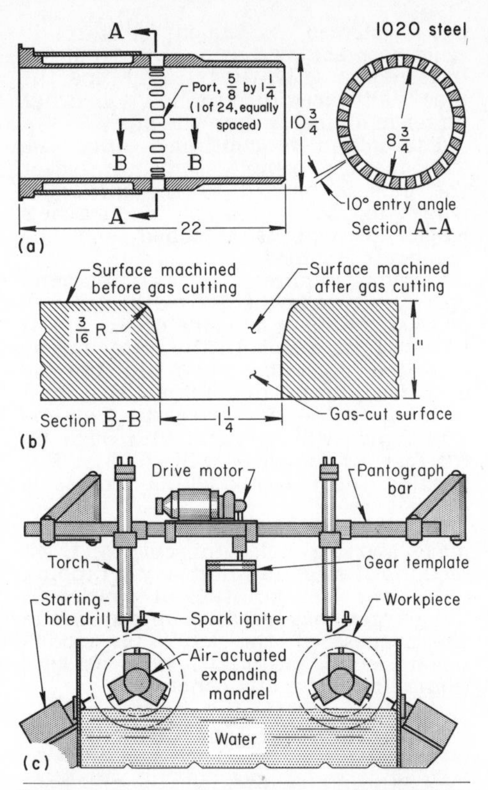

Torch	Injector-type
Cutting tip	Two-piece divergent type
Diameter of cutting-oxygen orifice	0.040 in.
Pressure of preheat natural gas	8 psi
Pressure of preheat oxygen	26 psi
Pressure of cutting oxygen	85 psi
Cutting speed	13 to 14 in. per min

Fig. 30. Close-tolerance cutting of intake ports in a cylinder liner (Example 364)

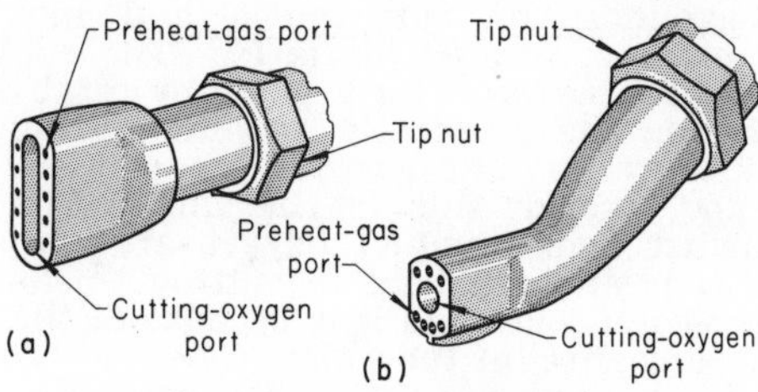

Fig. 31. Two types of gouging tips: (a) *tip for cutting flat grooves;* (b) *tip for cutting round grooves*

and equipment, the process can cut stainless steel up to 48 in. thick, cast iron up to 56 in. thick, and steel-mill ladle skulls up to 72 in. thick.

Operating Conditions. Normal operating conditions for powder cutting of 18-8 stainless steel 4 in. thick are: oxygen, 550 cu ft per hr; acetylene, 30 cu ft per hr; powder, 18 lb per hr; and cutting speed, 6 in. per min.

Kerf width and kerf angle (see page 291) may vary considerably, and should be established for specific shapes and for torch and powder-feed settings.

Powder Cutting vs Milling. The following example compares removal of excess stock from an Inconel plate by milling and by powder cutting.

Example 365. Powder Cutting vs Milling for Removing Excess Stock From Inconel Plate

Face milling was used to remove 1 in. of stock from the edge of a 1-in.-thick, 12-in.-long Inconel plate. Four 1/4-in.-deep cuts were taken with a 9-in.-diam face-milling cutter having 12 teeth. Cutting speed was 50 sfm and feed was 0.008 in. per tooth. Total milling time was 24 min (6 min per cut). Allowing for normal delay, over-all time was 26.4 min. In comparing this time with that for iron-powder cutting, it was decided that one powder-cutting pass would be followed by a 1/8-in. finish cut with the face mill. This was done to obtain the required finish and to avoid contamination by the powder. Standard oxy-acetylene cutting equipment was used with a separate tube feeding iron powder into the cutting stream at a rate of 6 lb per hour.

Powder cutting removed 7/8 in. of excess stock in 0.96 min. An additional 6.60 min was required for removal of the remaining 1/8 in. of stock by face milling. The total time of 7.56 min for powder cutting followed by milling was 3½ times faster than face milling alone.

Chemical-Flux Cutting

In this method of gas cutting materials that form refractory oxides, finely pulverized flux is injected into the cutting oxygen before it enters the cutting torch. The torch has separate ducts for preheat oxygen, fuel gas, and cutting oxygen (see Fig. 7). When the flux strikes the refractory oxides, which are formed when the cutting oxygen is turned on, it reacts with them to form a slag of lower-melting compounds. This slag is driven out, enabling oxidation of the metal to proceed.

The chemical-flux method is used less than the metal-powder method in cutting of stainless steel, but it is preferred in certain applications because it produces no iron buildup. A surface layer of chemical-flux-cut stainless steel approximately 1/16 in. deep must be removed before subsequent welding.

When cutting materials such as stainless steel, toxic fumes are created, requiring ventilation. The operator should have an approved respirator.

Oxy-Fuel Gas Gouging

Oxy-fuel gas gouging differs from ordinary gas cutting in that, instead of cutting through the material in a single pass, the process makes grooves or surface cuts. Special cutting torches are required for most applications, although some gouging is done with standard torches and a special tip.

Special cutting tips for gouging vary in design, to suit the size and shape of the desired groove or surface cut.

A gouging tip for cutting flat grooves is shown in Fig. 31(a). Tips of this type are made in various sizes and shapes for manual or mechanical scarfing of billets and slabs, or for the removal of defects, pads and fins from castings. Torches for these applications may include attachments for dispensing iron powder to increase the speed of cutting or to permit the scarfing of stainless steel. Gas consumption, especially of oxygen, is much greater than in ordinary gas cutting.

A gouging tip for cutting round grooves is shown in Fig. 31(b). The bent tip makes it possible to hold the torch so that the cutting flame will strike at a low angle. This type of gouging tip is used to remove defects from metal, such as in welds, or to cut a weld groove. A weld groove can be cut on the back of a welded joint to expose clean, sound metal for the final welding pass. Similarly, a weld groove can be cut in a butt joint between two plates.

J-Grooves. The tip shown in Fig. 31(a) also has been used to prepare the edges of thick-wall pressure vessels for welding by cutting a J-groove. Where plate edges with opposing J-grooves are butted together, a weld groove is formed (see Fig. 32) that is more efficient, in thick sections, than a conventional V-groove. J-grooves are often made by planing, but oxy-fuel gas gouging can be used to cut these grooves by a single pass in material up to 4 in. thick, and by two passes in thicker material.

J-grooves have been oxy-fuel gas gouged in flat plates supported horizontally, so that dross from the cut at the vertical edge is driven out by the combined forces of the flame and gravity. However, the following example describes an attempt to cut the grooves in formed half shells, supported in a U-position with the joint edges horizontal. This was done to reduce setup cost, because the half shells had already been sized by gas cutting.

Example 366. Cutting J-Grooves by Gouging (Fig. 32)

After excess stock had been removed from boiler-drum half shells by gas cutting (see Example 362 and Fig. 28), preparation of weld edges was required. Edge preparation consisted of cutting a J-groove along the longitudinal edges of the half shells. This was usually done by planing. In this application, however, large cost savings were possible if oxy-fuel gas gouging could be used. The cost advantage would accrue mainly from using the same equipment and setup as was used for gas cutting to remove the excess stock.

The groove was changed slightly to accommodate the gouging technique. The objective was to provide a groove large enough to permit weld deposit into the root of the joint, but to minimize the cross-sectional area of the groove to reduce welding costs. Critical variables included gas flow and the position of the cutting tip relative to the cut. The tip was of the type shown in Fig. 31 (a).

The three important angles of approach lay in planes taken through the axis of the tip. The vertical angle was in a plane at right angles to the surface to be cut, and it determined the angle of incidence of the flame to this surface. The horizontal angle determined the direction in which the molten slag would be driven from one side of the plate. The tip angle was the angle of rotation of the tip about its axis, and it determined the slope of the groove.

Other important dimensions were tip height (the distance of the tip from the surface), and tip offset, which determined the size of the root or uncut "land" on the surface to be cut.

A typical weld groove formed by abutting J-grooves gouged in this operation is shown in Fig. 32; conditions used for oxyacetylene gouging are listed in the accompanying table.

Gas gouging proved to be borderline for a trade-off with planing. A very high degree of skill was required to control all the variables in order to produce repetitive high-quality cuts. Material costs and the critical nature of the joints placed a heavy penalty on errors and defects. Because planing depended less on skill, and was quite dependable, this plant continued to use it for cutting J-grooves.

Oxygen-Lance Cutting

An oxygen lance is essentially a length of black iron pipe with suitable valve, hose and oxygen supply. An experienced operator can pierce or cut through sections several feet thick by oxygen lancing. Protection is needed from flying sparks and molten slag or metal.

The discharge end of the iron pipe is preheated to ignition temperature, the valve at the opposite end of the pipe is opened gradually, and the oxygen burns off the end of the pipe, which is pressed gently against the metal to be cut or pierced. As the metal starts to react with the oxygen or melt from the heat generated by the burning pipe, the pipe is advanced to cut a hole somewhat larger in diameter than the pipe.

The action is continued until the work metal is completely penetrated or the pipe is burned to the minimum length for safe operation. Then a new length of pipe is attached and the process is resumed.

Severing requires a series of piercing operations along the desired line of cut, or washing along one side of the initial hole to form a slot. In the latter method, care must be taken to provide continual drain of molten slag and metal from the cut; otherwise, the entering pipe will overheat and burn up too fast, or the dross will solidify. Restarting the cut on solidified dross is difficult.

An oxygen lance is often used to make starting holes for cutting thick sections of steel and in heavy scrapping operations. The addition of powder to the oxygen has greatly improved the effectiveness of the lance on oxidation-resistant materials, such as cast iron, refractories and concrete.

Underwater Gas Cutting

In underwater gas cutting, an oxyhydrogen flame usually is preferred to oxyacetylene for preheat. Hydrogen is stable and the flame is easily controlled at the higher pressures required for underwater operation. Oxy-natural gas cutting is also used in underwater gas cutting, for the same reason.

The flame and the oxygen jet are shielded from the water by a cup that surrounds the cutting tip and into which compressed air is fed. The cup shield also serves as a guide by establishing the proper tip-to-work cutting distance. Air and gaseous products escape through slits in the shield. The higher heat input of oxygen-arc cutting is more efficient in cutting thicknesses of 3/8 in. and less, because of the cooling effect of the water.

Safety

The hazards of combustion or possible explosion associated with the gases used in gas cutting, as well as the possible presence of toxic gases and dusts, make it necessary for the user to follow established safety precautions. When this is done, and when equipment is used correctly, gas-cutting operations proceed without undue risk. However, the operation of gas-cutting equipment by untrained personnel is an invitation to trouble or disaster.

In the bibliography that follows, the last ten references are on the subject of safety in gas cutting.

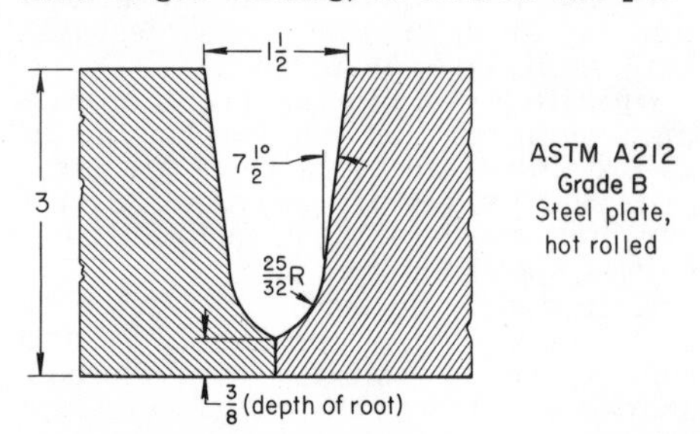

Pressure of preheat oxygen	30 psi
Pressure of preheat acetylene	11 psi
Pressure of cutting oxygen at nozzle	22 psi
Consumption of cutting oxygen	6500 cfh
Vertical tip angle	19°
Horizontal tip angle	11½°
Tip rotation angle	0°
Tip height	0
Tip offset	5/16 in.
Cutting speed	35 in. per min

Fig. 32. Weld groove formed from two J-grooves made by oxyacetylene gouging (Example 366)

Selected References

General Sources

George V. Slottman and Edward H. Roper, "Oxygen Cutting", McGraw-Hill Book Co., Inc., New York, 1951. [A comprehensive textbook of the chemistry of gas cutting and the effects of cutting on metals. Plant facilities, types of equipment, and classes of cutting are described with photographs, charts and drawings.]

E. Seymour Semper, "Oxygen Cutting", Louis Cassier Co., Ltd., London, 1949. [A review stressing the practical aspects of gas cutting, the process, types of equipment, making of templates, and classes of cutting. Photographs and drawings complement the text material.]

"The Oxy-Acetylene Handbook", Second Edition, Linde Div., Union Carbide Corp., New York, 1960. [Part 1 (142 pages) gives a general description of the chemistry and history of the oxyacetylene flame, principles and operation of equipment, and safe practices in setting up and operating equipment. Part 5 (56 pages) describes in detail oxygen cutting by hand and machine for all classes of cuts and a variety of materials. Part 7 (81 pages) consists of charts, diagrams, tables, and formulas useful in gas welding and cutting. Included is a description of procedures for powder cutting. Book is well illustrated.]

N. J. Normando and J. E. Waring, The Application of Numerical Control to Oxygen Cutting, *Welding Journal*, 42 (5), 285 to 293 (1963). [Principles and advantages of both manual and computerized numerical control for gas-cutting machines are described. The classes of work that can economically use numerical control are reviewed, together with types of equipment.]

R. L. Deily, Mechanization Applied to Oxygen Cutting, *Welding Journal*, 34 (5), 433 to 439 (1955). [A review of many areas showing historical development of machine-cutting equipment in steel fabricating, scarfing, hot cutting, and lancing.]

A. N. Kugler, "Oxyacetylene Welding and Oxygen Cutting Instruction Course", Revised Edition, Air Reduction Co., Inc., New York, 1966. [This text is divided into Book 1 (Lectures) and Book 2 (Exercises). It is a practical course in gas cutting and welding. The book includes the development and chemistry of the gas-cutting process, and both lectures and exercises on the construction, proper operation, and safe use of equipment, mainly for manual cutting and welding. The exercises cover practical shop problems. Drawings and photographs illustrate the text material.]

A. A. Wells, Iron-Oxygen Combustion Process, *British Welding Journal*, 2, Sept 1955, 392 to 400; Further Studies of Iron-Oxygen Combustion in Gas Cutting, *ibid*, 8, Mar 1961, 79 to 85. [The factors influencing rates of cutting and oxygen consumption were studied.]

J. D. Hembree, R. W. Belfit, H. A. Reeves, and J. P. Baughman, A New Fuel Gas — Stabilized Methylacetylene-Propadiene, *Welding Journal*, 42 (5), 395 to 404 (1963). [A report on Mapp fuel gas, giving chemical and physical properties, field and laboratory test results, and cost comparisons with other fuel gases.]

J. C. Worthington, Natural Gas-Oxygen Cutting, Theory and Application, *Welding Journal*, 39 (3), 229 to 235 (1960). [Cost comparisons of natural gas, acetylene and propane as fuel gases are made. Charts of oxygen pressures, natural gas pressures, tips and cutting speeds are shown for various cutting operations and materials.]

Lynn C. Denny, Lester L. Luxon, and Barbara E. Hall (Editors), "Handbook of Butane-Propane Gases", Fourth Edition, Chilton Co., Los Angeles, 1962. [A handbook of properties, storage, distribution, and uses of LP gas. Chapter 22 (19 pages) compares butane-propane and acetylene as fuel gases, and describes cutting equipment used in oxy-butane-propane gas cutting.]

Safety

Frank E. McElroy (Editor), "Accident Prevention Manual for Industrial Operations", Fifth Edition, National Safety Council, Chicago, 1964. [A comprehensive text of safety and accident prevention consisting of 45 chapters. Chapter 29 (28 pages) discusses welding and cutting processes, safety in installation and operation, hazards, personnel protection, and safety training. Chapter 28 (66 pages) describes local exhaust systems of many types, for both general and special needs. Chapter 32 (33 pages) deals with safety measures for use, handling, and storage of flammable and combustible liquids. Chapters 33 (31 pages) and 34 (31 pages) outline principles of fire protection and extinguishment. Chapter 39 (41 pages) introduces the subject of industrial hygiene, including sources, evaluating, measuring, and controlling of hazards. Chapter 40, "Elements of Industrial Toxicology" (59 pages), and Chapter 41, "Table of Chemical Hazards" (24 pages), supplement Chapter 39. Other chapters have information on safe practices that supplements the referenced chapters.]

"Oxygen-Fuel Gas Systems for Welding and Cutting", National Fire Protection Assoc., Boston, Bulletin No. 51, 1964. [Standards for installing and operating oxygen-fuel gas welding and cutting systems.]

"Fire Prevention in Use of Cutting and Welding Processes", National Fire Protection Assoc., Boston, Bulletin No. 51B, 1962. [Basic and special precautions for prevention of fire in welding and cutting.]

"Storage and Handling of Liquefied Petroleum Gases", National Fire Protection Assoc., Boston, Bulletin No. 58, 1965. [Standards for both storing and handling liquified petroleum gases.]

"Safety in Welding and Cutting", American Welding Society, New York, Bulletin Z49.1, 1967. Also available from U. S. A. Standards Institute, New York. [Standards for installing and operating oxygen-fuel gas systems, fire prevention and protection, protection of personnel, ventilation, and health protection.]

"Allowable Concentration of Toxic Dusts and Gases", U. S. A. Standards Institute, New York, Z37 Series of Bulletins, 1941 through 1967. [The subject of each booklet is contamination levels for one substance or, in some instances, a group of substances.]

"Recommended Safe Practices in Cutting and Welding", Air Reduction Co., Inc., New York, Booklet No. ADE 872M, 1967. [A pocket-size outline of safe practices in welding and cutting, for field or plant use, with illustrations of safe and unsafe practices.]

"Safe Handling of Compressed Gases", Compressed Gas Assoc., Inc., New York, Pamphlet P-1, Third Edition, 1956. [General rules for handling, moving, storing, and using compressed gases, for both cylinders and tank cars.]

"Gas and Electric Cutting and Welding", American Petroleum Institute, New York, Accident Prevention Manual No. 3, Second Edition, 1953. [Booklet outlines suggested provisions for the protection of persons from injury and the protection of property from damage by fire that might arise during the operation of electric and gas welding and cutting equipment in and around petroleum operations.]

"Safe Practices — Gas Welding and Cutting Equipment", U. S. Dept. of Labor, Bureau of Labor Standards, Washington, D. C., Occupational Safety Chart No. 5. [Illustrated chart of safe practices in gas cutting and welding, suitable for posting in plant or field.]

Electric-Arc Cutting

*By the ASM Committee on Gas and Arc Cutting**

ELECTRIC-ARC CUTTING is a method of melting or oxidizing metal by applying heat from an electric arc to the work-metal surface along a line of cut. Because of the extremely high temperature developed, the electric arc can be used to cut any metal that conducts electricity. Modifications of the basic process include the use of compressed gases to cause rapid oxidation (or to prevent oxidation) of the work metal, thus incorporating some aspects of gas cutting.

Electric-arc cutting is classified into seven processes, only three of which are of commercial importance. These are: (*a*) air carbon-arc cutting, (*b*) oxygen-arc cutting, and (*c*) plasma-arc cutting. The remaining four processes, which largely have been superseded by the above, are briefly described in the last section of this article.

Electric-arc cutting can be used on ferrous and nonferrous metals for rough severing, such as removing risers or scrap cutting, as well as for more closely controlled operations. Each process has particular capabilities and limitations. Special applications include shape cutting, grooving, gouging and underwater cutting. Maintaining the squareness of cut edges, particularly in sections more than 2 in. thick, is generally more difficult in electric-arc cutting than in gas cutting.

Air Carbon-Arc Cutting

Air carbon-arc cutting is a method of cutting or gouging metal by melting with heat from an electric arc and blowing away the molten metal with a high-velocity jet of compressed air. A special holder is used to clamp the solid carbon-graphite electrode in a position parallel to the air stream, which is emitted from orifices in the electrode holder. The air strikes the molten metal immediately behind the arc. The electrode holder also contains an air-control valve, an air hose, and a cable. The cable is connected to the welding machine and the air hose to a source of compressed air.

Cutting may be done manually, but for accurate work, special electrode holders are mounted on motor-driven carriages.

Power Supply. Constant-voltage direct current, with a flat to slightly rising voltage characteristic, is best for most applications. It is important to select a power source having sufficient capacity. Recommended current levels for various sizes of electrodes are given in Table 1. Steel, stainless steel, and various cast irons can be cut using alternating current, although direct current is preferred. For copper alloys, alternating current is preferred, although direct current with reverse polarity can be used.

Table 1. Recommended Current Levels for Graphite Electrodes of Various Sizes Used in Carbon-Arc Cutting

Electrode diameter, in.	Current, amp	Electrode diameter, in.	Current, amp
5/32	80 to 150	3/8	300 to 550
3/16	110 to 200	1/2	400 to 800
1/4	150 to 350	5/8	600 to 1000
5/16	200 to 450	3/4	800 to 1600

Air Supply. Compressed air, from a shop line or a compressor, is usually supplied at 80 to 100 psi, although pressure as low as 40 psi can be used for light work. Pressures up to 125 psi are needed for making deep grooves in thick metal. Air hoses should have a minimum inside diameter of 1/4 in. and no constrictions. Pressure is not critical in air carbon-arc cutting, but a sufficient volume of air is important to ensure a clean slag-free surface. The amount of air required depends on the type of work: 3 to 33 cu ft per min for manual operations; 25 to 50 cu ft per min for mechanized semiautomatic operations. The electrode should extend no more than 6 in. beyond the holder, which has airflow-metering orifices to suit the capacity.

Electrodes used in air carbon-arc cutting are composed of a special mixture of carbon and graphite, and are usually coated with copper to increase life and current-carrying capacity, and to reduce radiated heat.

Carbon is an amorphous, hard material, highly resistant to abrasion and erosion, whereas the opposite is true of graphite. Graphite has a higher oxidizing temperature but a lower rate of oxidation and lower electrical and thermal conductivity than carbon. There is also some difference in density between carbon and graphite. Because some properties of both carbon and graphite are desired in electrodes for air carbon-arc cutting, the most suitable electrode contains a combination of the two materials.

Technique. Depth and contour of the cut or groove are controlled by the lead angle of the electrode, speed of cut and amount of current. The usual procedure is to hold the electrode at an angle, striking an arc between the end of the electrode and the work metal. The air blast is directed immediately behind the point of arcing, and the electrode is pushed forward.

Details of the technique used depend to some extent on whether the operation consists of through-cutting or of gouging out grooves. This process is especially well adapted to gouging.

For through-cutting, the electrode is held at a steeper angle (almost vertical) than for gouging. When plate thickness is greater than 1/2 in., two or more passes may be required.

Grooves as deep as 1 in. can be made in a single pass. A steep angle, approaching that used for through-cutting, and a rapid advance produce a deep, narrow groove, whereas a flatter electrode orientation and a slower advance produce a wide, shallow groove. Groove width is influenced also by electrode diameter, and is usually slightly greater if the electrode is moved in a forward direction only. A wide groove can be made with a small electrode, using an oscillating motion as in welding. Gouging or cutting can be done in all positions of the electrode. In overhead work, the electrode must be held to one side to prevent molten metal from dropping on the operator.

*For committee list, see page 278.

In removing excess metal, such as risers and pad stubs, or in surfacing, a washing or weaving motion is recommended. Smoothness of the kerf is determined largely by how steadily the electrode is held and advanced during the cutting operation.

Application. Air carbon-arc cutting is most extensively used in steel foundries for removing light gates and risers and for removing defects from castings. The process also is widely used for removing welding defects, cleaning out roots of welds, widening grooves, and preparing plate for welding. Another application is for alteration work in mills and refineries. In shops where heavy plates are prepared for welding, the plates are butted together and a U-groove is then gouged in both sections simultaneously as shown in Fig. 1.

Oxygen-Arc Cutting

Oxygen-arc cutting is a combination of melting, oxidizing, diluting, fluxing, and mechanical ejection. A flux-covered, tubular steel electrode is used. The covering serves as insulation against arcing from the sides of the cut. Low-carbon steel and other ferrous metals are raised to the kindling temperature by the arc and are burned away by the oxygen stream. The oxidation or combustion reaction liberates additional heat, which supports continuing combustion of sidewall material as the cut progresses. The preheat necessary to obtain and maintain ignition is provided by the electric arc at the point where the oxygen jet strikes the surface of the work metal.

When cutting oxidation-resistant metals, more of a melting action takes place. Under these conditions, the covering on the electrode acts as a flux and helps the flow of molten metal from the cut. This function of the electrode covering is of considerable importance and is similar to that of powdered flux or powdered metal injected into the gas flame in the flux-injection method of gas cutting stainless steel. Figure 2 shows the setup and principal components of an oxygen-arc electrode.

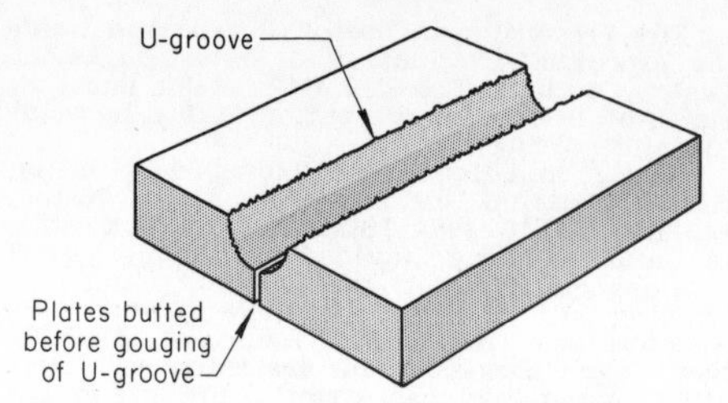

Fig. 1. Butted plates in which U-groove was produced by air carbon-arc gouging, in preparation for welding

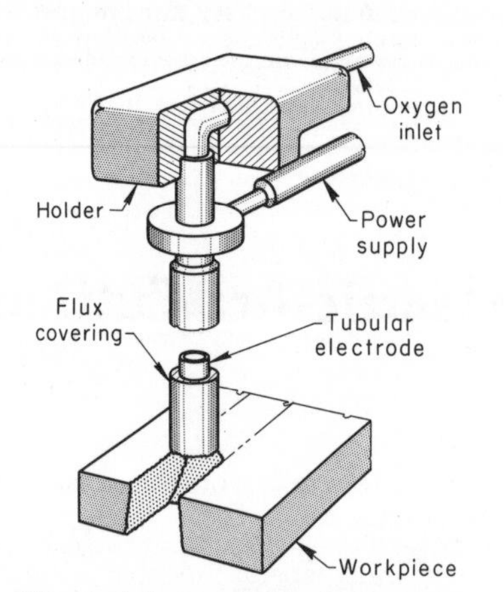

Fig. 2. Setup and principal components of an oxygen-arc electrode

Equipment. Oxygen-arc cutting can be done with either direct or alternating current, although direct current with straight polarity (negative electrode) is preferred, because a more rapid cut is possible. Both the electrode and the electrode holder must be of special design, because they must convey the electric current and oxygen to the arc (Fig. 2). A fully insulated holder is always necessary and, for underwater cutting, a flashback arrester is also needed.

Electrodes. Tubular steel electrodes used in oxygen-arc cutting are available in 3/16-in. and 5/16-in. diameters, with bore diameters of approximately 1/16 in. and 1/10 in., respectively. The 3/16-in.-diam tube is 18 in. long, and the 5/16-in.-diam tube is 14 or 18 in. long. The covering is extruded to a thickness comparable to that of a low-carbon steel welding electrode.

For underwater cutting, the electrode is given a final coating of a plastic that renders the covering impervious to fresh water or seawater for several hours of submersion at depths exerting static pressures up to 100 psi.

Technique. In oxygen-arc cutting, the tip of the electrode is scratched or tapped on the work metal to strike an arc, and the oxygen is released. No specific arc length is held, and the electrode is dragged along the plate surface at a speed dictated by the progress of the cut. The inclination of the electrode and the speed are adjusted as required, to give the most efficient and highest-quality cut.

The use of a template guide is common; because the electrode is insulated, it can be pressed against the template guide without likelihood of arcing. Straight-line cutting is done with a straight-edged guide clamped parallel to the line of cut. The cut is made by holding the electrode against the guide and the work metal at the same time. Circular openings in tanks have been cut using the circumference of a pipe as a template.

The speed of cutting varies with the thickness and composition of the work metal, oxygen pressure, amount of current, and dimensions of the electrode. When steel up to 3 in. thick or nonferrous metal up to 1/2 in. thick is cut with an electrode 3/16 or 5/16 in. in diameter, the electrode is dragged along the line of cut as slight pressure is applied. In underwater cutting, regardless of thickness, positive pressure must be maintained against the work metal.

Application. Oxygen-arc cutting was developed primarily for underwater use, but has been advantageously applied to cutting in air. In cutting either in air or under water, the process can be used for all ferrous and many nonferrous metals of almost any thickness. However, the cut edges of the metal are somewhat uneven, and require surface preparation before welding.

Plasma-Arc Cutting

Plasma-arc cutting is done with a high-velocity jet of high-temperature ionized gas. The relatively narrow plasma jet melts and displaces the workpiece material in its path. Because plasma-arc cutting does not depend on a chemical reaction between the gas and the work metal, and because temperatures are extremely high, it can be used on almost any material that conducts electricity, including those that are resistant to oxy-fuel gas cutting. This process is used extensively for profile cutting of stainless steel plate and, to a lesser extent, on aluminum.

Principles. At temperatures above about 10,000 F (as in a welding arc), gases are partially ionized, and exist as a plasma, or mixture of free electrons, positively charged ions, and neutral atoms. The plasma torch confines the plasma-forming gas in an arc chamber, while the arc supplies a large input of electrical energy. The central zone of the plasma reaches a temperature of

Table 2. Operating Conditions and Recommended Gas-Flow Rates for Plasma-Arc Cutting of Steel and Cast Iron

Work-metal thickness, in.	Cutting speed, ipm(a)	Current, amp	Nozzle size, in.	Gas flow, cu ft per hr: Air(b)	Combined: Nitrogen	Combined: Hydrogen	Dual flow(c): Nitrogen	Dual flow(c): Oxygen
1/4	40 to 200	100 to 420	0.125 to 0.187	200	120 to 150	10	...	...
1/2	30 to 150	150 to 800	0.140 to 0.250	200	130 to 225	15	60	400
1	20 to 50	250 to 650	0.161 to 0.250	300	130 to 225	15	60	400
2	5 to 25	450 to 850	0.187 to 0.250	350(d)	150 to 225	15	100(e)	400(e)
3	5 to 10	600 to 800	0.218 to 0.250	...	170 to 225	20	...	...

(a) Higher cutting speeds can be obtained using larger nozzle sizes and corresponding increases in power and gas flow. (b) Multiport nozzles used with compressed air. (c) Inner shield of nitrogen used to protect electrode (see text). (d) From 250 to 500 amp. (e) From 350 to 750 amp.

Table 3. Operating Conditions and Recommended Gas-Flow Rates for Plasma-Arc Cutting of Stainless Steel and Aluminum

Work-metal thickness, in.	Cutting speed, ipm	Current, amp	Nozzle size, in.	Gas flow, cu ft per hr — Combined: Argon	Combined: Hydrogen	Combined: Nitrogen	Combined: Hydrogen
Stainless Steel							
1/2	25 to 140	150 to 500	0.140 to 0.218	...	..	110 to 180	10
1	20 to 90	210 to 650	0.187 to 0.218	130	70	150	15
3	5 to 16	500 to 750	0.218 to 0.250	130	70	180 to 225	20
Aluminum							
1/2	80 to 200	200 to 600	0.140 to 0.218	65	30	110 to 180	10
1	20 to 90	200 to 550	0.140 to 0.218	65	35	110 to 180	10
2	10 to 60	275 to 750	0.161 to 0.250	100	50	120 to 225	15 to 20

20,000 to 50,000 F, and is completely ionized.

Figure 3 shows the essential components and mechanics of a plasma-arc cutting torch. It is similar to a tungsten-inert gas welding torch with the tungsten electrode recessed into a nozzle with a small opening, but it is more rugged. A high-frequency pulsing potential is used to initiate a pilot arc between the tungsten electrode (cathode, negative) and the copper nozzle (anode, positive), both of which are water cooled. The pilot or internal arc initiates an external or "transferred" arc between the torch electrode and the workpiece, which is connected as an anode (positive). The pilot arc is then shut off, and the external arc supplies the energy. Some nonconductive materials can be cut with the plasma jet produced by the internal arc alone, but less cutting energy is available.

The design of plasma-arc torches varies among different manufacturers. In the torch illustrated in Fig. 3, the gas is introduced around the electrode at the top. Passage through the lower half of the electrode chamber causes the gas to swirl around the walls of the nozzle, helping to stabilize and constrict the arc. The layer of cooler gas next to the nozzle acts as a thermal and electrical insulator and prevents melting of the nozzle.

The plasma jet heats the workpiece by bombardment with electrons (anode spot effect) and by transfer of energy from the high-temperature, high-energy gas. The plasma-arc-constricting orifice in the torch nozzle focuses the arc energy on a small area of the workpiece, and heats the area to melting temperature. The molten products are removed continuously by the jet.

Selection of Gas. Any gas or gas mixture that does not adversely affect the tungsten electrode or the workpiece can be used in the plasma-arc torch. The most frequently used gases are compressed air, argon, nitrogen, hydrogen and oxygen, or mixtures of these gases. Stainless steel, and aluminum and other nonferrous metals, are cut with argon-hydrogen or nitrogen-hydrogen mixtures. Carbon steels, alloy steels, and cast irons are cut with a nitrogen-hydrogen mixture, compressed air, or a nitrogen-oxygen mixture. Torches supplied by one manufacturer use oxygen as an outer sheath with nitrogen plasma as an inner sheath to protect the electrode.

Flow rates of the gases and setting of the arc current are regulated according to work metal, thickness of cut, and type of gas, to produce the maximum cutting rate consistent with an acceptable quality of cut.

Typical total gas flow rates are between 70 and 400 cu ft per hour. Arc currents range between 150 and 1000 amp for typical cutting rates of 10 to 70 in. per min. The diameter of the orifice (usually 1/16 to 1/4 in.) depends on the arc current and gas flow required. Table 2 gives recommended rates of flow for gas mixtures and for air, based on work-metal thickness, cutting speed, amount of current, and nozzle size, for cutting steel and cast iron.

Mixtures of argon and hydrogen, or of nitrogen and hydrogen, are generally used for cutting stainless steel, and aluminum and other nonferrous metals. Table 3 gives recommended rates of gas flow for cutting stainless steel and aluminum, based on work-metal thickness, cutting speed, amount of current, and nozzle size.

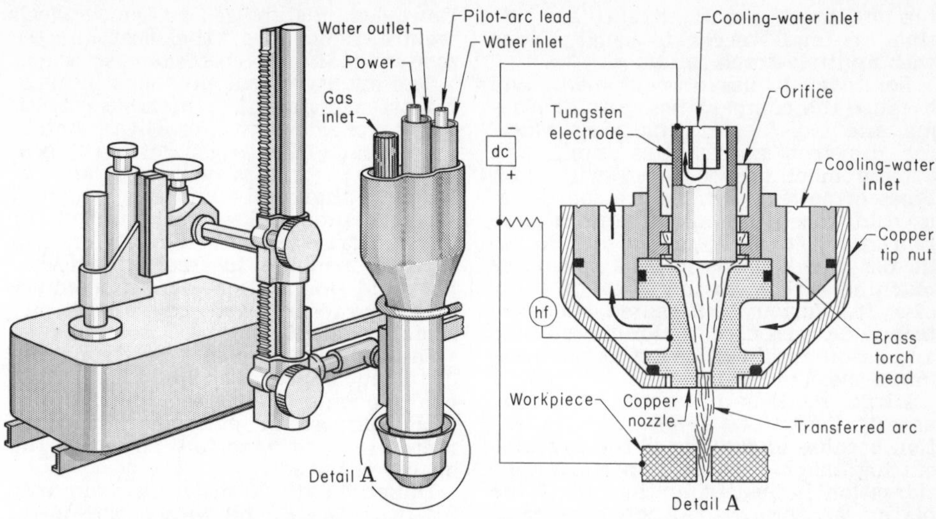

Fig. 3 Essential components and mechanics of a typical plasma-arc cutting torch

Table 4. Typical Current Levels Used for Plasma-Arc Cutting of Steel, Stainless Steel, and Aluminum at Various Thicknesses

Cutting speed, ipm	Current, amp Steel	Stainless	Aluminum
1/4-In. Thickness			
20	200	250	200
40	250	260	200
70	275	270	200
100	275	275	250
150	275	300	250
1/2-In. Thickness			
20	250	250	250
40	275	300	250
70	275	350	250
100, 150	...	...	275
1-In. Thickness			
10	250	300	300
20	275	300	325
40	275	350	350
70	...	...	350
100	...	...	375
2-In. Thickness			
5, 10	500	400	350
20	550	475	375
3-In. Thickness			
5	...	...	400
10	...	500	425
4-In. Thickness			
5	...	475	400
10	...	500	450
5-In. Thickness			
5	...	550	450
10	...	...	475

Nozzle Construction. Special nozzle construction is needed when an outer sheath of oxygen is employed. Multiport nozzles with a ring of smaller orifices around the central orifice are used with compressed air, or when it is desired to reduce the taper of the cut.

Power Supply. Direct-current power sources rated at about 400 volts (open-circuit) or 200 volts (under load) are necessary. The circuit is basically the same as that used for tungsten-arc welding, except that a lead is taken from the ground through a resistor to the nozzle of the torch for the high-frequency pulse used to initiate the pilot arc.

Current demand depends on type and thickness of the work metal, and on cutting speed. Current levels based on these variables are given in Tables 2, 3 and 4. Other variables, such as equipment, can influence current demand.

Work Metals. Plasma-arc cutting is used mainly on stainless steel and aluminum alloys; in these metals, it produces comparatively smooth cuts, free from contaminants. Oxy-fuel gas cutting of stainless steel requires the addition of iron powder or chemical flux. Aluminum alloys cannot be cut by the oxy-fuel gas method. Heavy-duty plasma torches can cut stainless steel up to 6 in. thick and aluminum alloys up to about 8 in. thick.

Other metals that are resistant to oxy-fuel gas cutting are also cut by the plasma method, including magnesium, copper, nickel, and copper-nickel alloys.

Titanium can be cut by either method, but is cut more rapidly by the oxy-fuel method. This is because titanium has a great affinity for oxygen, and therefore reacts with the gas cutting stream at a rate faster than the rate of melting by the high-intensity plasma arc. Although gas cutting is faster, plasma-arc cutting with inert gas mixtures is less likely to contaminate the titanium next to the surface.

Because of its rapid cutting rate, a plasma arc is economical for cutting of carbon steels 1/2 to 3 in. thick.

Cutting Speed. Figure 4 compares cutting speeds of a plasma arc at five different power levels with conventional gas cutting of carbon steel. The speeds shown for cutting of work metal 1 in. thick or less can be as much as five or more times as great for plasma arc as for conventional gas cutting. For metal 3 in. thick, speeds for both processes are about equal; for metal more than 3 in. thick, gas cutting is faster.

Workpiece Size and Shape. The reduction in cutting time (and saving in labor cost) compared with gas cutting is more likely to be realized on long continuous cuts such as are required in bridge construction, shipbuilding and tank fabrication. The relative economy of shorter cuts, which require frequent starts, will depend on the number of torches that is practical, since gas cutting of small pieces is usually done with multiple-torch setups.

For efficient use of equipment, and because the comparative costs of plasma and oxy-fuel cutting vary widely for different applications, multitorch cutting machines equipped with both types of cutting torches are sometimes used in warehouse cutting and in plate fabricating. Cutting speeds of 2 to 240 in. per min have been used on a large machine with a cutting area of 44 by 82½ ft. Various automated guidance techniques are used for profile cutting, and 0.8-in. radii can be cut at the maximum speed of the machine.

Large sections of work metal are usually limited to single-torch operation because of the size of the available cutting machine — an important consideration in justifying the use of the plasma-arc process. Although there is no theoretical limitation to multitorch operation, it is usually practical to limit plasma-arc installations to a maximum of two torches, because (*a*) power demands for plasma-arc cutting are high, and installations using more than two torches usually develop prohibitive power requirements; (*b*) limited visibility is imposed on the operator by the need for darker eye shields, which presents difficulty in monitoring multiple torches; and (*c*) greater damage to equipment can result from delayed detection of malfunction. Therefore, for cutting small sections of carbon steel, which requires a large number of torches, gas cutting is generally more practical than plasma-arc cutting.

Technique. With a mechanically operated plasma-arc torch, the standoff distance from the work metal is between ¼ and ⅝ in. Current and rate of gas flow are set in accordance with conditions shown in Tables 2 to 4.

In manual operation, the current and rate of gas flow are set according to cutting conditions. The arc is struck by pressing a button on the torch, which is guided manually over the work metal. At the end of the cut, the arc automatically extinguishes, and the control opens the contactor and closes the gas valves. The operator can extinguish the arc at any time by moving the torch away from the work metal.

To avoid damage to the torch, the metal nozzle of the torch must never be allowed to touch the work metal. For manual cutting, the nozzle is insulated to prevent accidental contact between the work metal and the torch metal.

Quality of Cut. Surfaces of plasma-arc cuts are usually smoother than those obtained by gas cutting, but the top edges may be rounded. Also, the walls of the cut often have a V-shaped included angle, which may be 5° to 10°; multiport nozzles, properly operated, reduce this bevel to 1° to 2°.

This angle must be acceptable in shape cutting or other applications in which the torch must be kept vertical. However, when only one side of the kerf is critical, the V-angle can be compensated for by keeping the torch at an angle while cutting.

When cutting stainless steel, the plasma arc produces smooth, clean edges. Only light grinding to remove discoloration is required before welding. Unwelded, unstabilized austenitic steels require removal of the heat-affected zone to maintain corrosion resistance.

The quality of cut produced by plasma-arc cutting of nonferrous metals varies considerably. For these metals, no comparison with gas cutting is possible. Cut surfaces will generally be rougher than all but the roughest surfaces produced by machining. For mechanical assemblies, it is often necessary to machine to final dimensions. For weld preparation, access openings, and clearances, parts are usually acceptable as cut.

In all plasma-arc cutting, the quality of the cut improves as speed is reduced, but reducing the speed defeats the main purpose of plasma-arc cutting; therefore, it is important to define the quality required.

Dimensional variation is ordinarily ±3⁄32 to ±⅛ in., and with close control can be held to ±1⁄16 in. The depth of the heat-affected zone depends on the type of work metal, its thickness, and the cutting speed; maximum depth on stock up to 1 in. thick is about 3⁄16 in., and is much less at high cutting speeds.

Width of kerf is greater than that produced by conventional gas cutting. Although work-metal thickness, nozzle size and cutting speed influence the width of a plasma-arc kerf, the range is usually 3⁄16 to ⅜ in. For thick work metal, width of kerf may exceed ½ in. The minimum inside radius that can be formed depends on kerf width. Under optimum conditions — using thin work metal, small nozzle size, and slow speed — the minimum inside radius for plasma-arc cutting is 3⁄16 in.

Bevel cutting for weld preparation is an important application of plasma-arc cutting. The intense heat makes it suitable for all types of beveling at a higher efficiency than gas cutting. The plasma-arc process produces surfaces of acceptable quality, and, because of the natural V-shaped cut, it is sometimes considered more efficient for bevel cutting than for perpendicular cutting. Torch equipment and settings are the same for both types.

Safety Precautions. The plasma arc is a much brighter source of radiation than the gas cutting flame, and is more closely related to the arcs of gas tungsten-arc and gas metal-arc cutting. Helmets and eye protection used for the latter processes must also be employed when plasma-arc cutting. Generally, shades 11 and 12 of protective lens are recommended. Similarly, because of the intensity of ultraviolet radiation of the plasma arc, all skin areas of the body should be protected by dark, substantial clothing to prevent ultraviolet burns. Otherwise, the precautions for plasma-arc and gas cutting are similar. Good maintenance and proper operation of the plasma equipment are essential, not only to avoid gas leaks, but also to guard against electrical hazards.

Natural ventilation is usually adequate in high-roofed, industrial structures. However, plasma fumes are generated rapidly at the high cutting speed that can be attained, and forced ventilation may be required if the fume concentration reaches dangerous levels, as in confined areas with poor natural ventilation.

During some plasma-arc cutting, noise levels may be high enough to warrant the use of ear protectors, such as earmuffs and earplugs, by the operator and by other personnel in the immediate vicinity who might be affected by such noise level. If the normal speaking voice must be raised to be understood, ear protection is recommended unless a noise survey by a qualified analyst indicates otherwise.

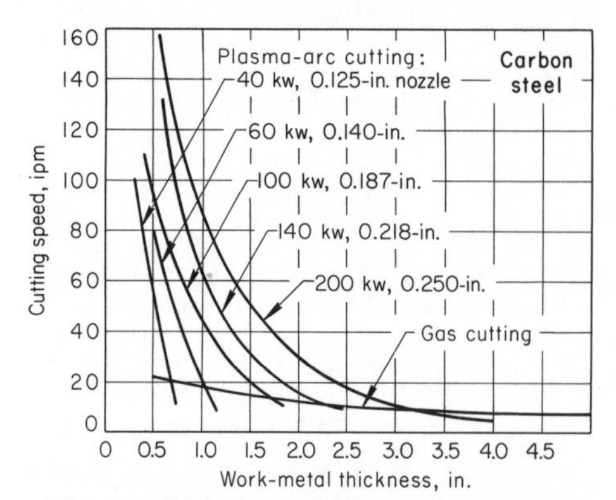

Fig. 4. Effect of work-metal thickness on cutting speed for plasma-arc cutting at five different power levels, compared with conventional gas cutting

Seldom-Used Electric-Arc Cutting Processes

The four electric-arc cutting processes described in this section either are almost obsolete or have never been used extensively. However, these processes are sometimes used for highly specialized applications or when equipment for more suitable methods is not available.

Carbon-arc cutting is one of the oldest electric-arc cutting methods. This process uses the heat generated by the carbon arc to melt metal progressively to produce a kerf. The melted metal is removed from the cut by gravity or by the force of the arc, or by both.

The use of carbon-arc cutting is limited to cutting up of scrap and dismantling of structural steel assemblies.

Shielded Metal-Arc Cutting. Metal can be cut by a shielded metal arc, using flux-covered stick electrodes. The molten metal is removed from the cut by gravity or by the force of the arc, or both.

Shielded metal-arc cutting is most commonly used for removing gates and risers from castings and for cutting up scrap. The process can also be used for underwater cutting with specially processed (waterproof) electrodes.

Gas Metal-Arc Cutting (MIG). In this process, heat is obtained from an electric arc formed between a continuously fed wire and the work metal. The molten metal is continuously blown from the kerf by the shielding gas. The process is used mainly on stainless steel and aluminum, although other metals can be cut by this method.

Gas metal-arc cutting is most often used in fabricating shops where gas metal-arc welding is done, as the same equipment can be used for both cutting and welding. Gas metal-arc cutting is limited in application, because the rate of wire consumption is high, and the thickness of sections that can be cut is limited to about 1½ in. for stainless steel and about 3 in. for aluminum.

Gas tungsten-arc cutting (TIG) is similar to gas tungsten-arc welding, except that higher amperages and voltages are used. The same basic circuit and similar shielding gases are used for both processes.

Although gas tungsten-arc cutting can be used for cutting most ferrous and nonferrous metals, it is largely confined to the cutting of stainless steel and aluminum ½ in. or less in thickness. The quality of the cut is usually good enough to permit welding without machining the cut surfaces.

FORMING OF BARS, TUBE AND WIRE

CONTENTS

Bending of Bars and Bar Sections

*By the ASM Committee on Bending of Bars and Tubing**

BARS are bent by four basic methods: draw bending, compression bending, roll bending, and stretch bending.

Draw Bending. In draw bending, the workpiece is clamped to a rotating form and is drawn by the form against a pressure die, as shown in Fig. 1. The pressure die can be either fixed or movable along its longitudinal axis. A fixed pressure die must be able to withstand abrasion caused by the sliding of the work metal over its surface. A movable pressure die, because it moves forward with the workpiece as it is bent, is less subject to such abrasion. It provides better guidance and more uniform restraint of the work material. (See Fig. 10 on page 446 in the article on Forming of Titanium Alloys.)

On power bending machines, draw bending is used more than any other bending method.

Compression Bending. In compression bending, the workpiece is clamped to a fixed form, and a wiper shoe revolves around the form to bend the workpiece (Fig. 1). Compression bending is most useful in bending rolled and extruded shapes. A bend can be made close to another bend in the workpiece without the need for the compound dies required in draw bending. Although compression bending does not control the flow of metal as well as draw bending, it is widely used in bending presses and in rotary bending machines.

Roll bending uses three or more parallel rolls. In one arrangement using three rolls, the axes of the two bottom rolls are fixed in a horizontal plane. The top roll (bending roll) is lowered toward the plane of the bottom rolls to make the bend, as shown in Fig. 2. The bottom rolls are power driven; the top roll is an idler and is moved up or down by a hydraulic cylinder. (For other three-roll arrangements, see the article "Three-Roll Forming", page 217 in this volume.)

A roll arrangement for four-roll bending is shown in Fig. 3. The bar enters between the two powered rolls on the left. The lower bending roll is then adjusted in two directions according to the thickness of the bar and the desired angle of bend.

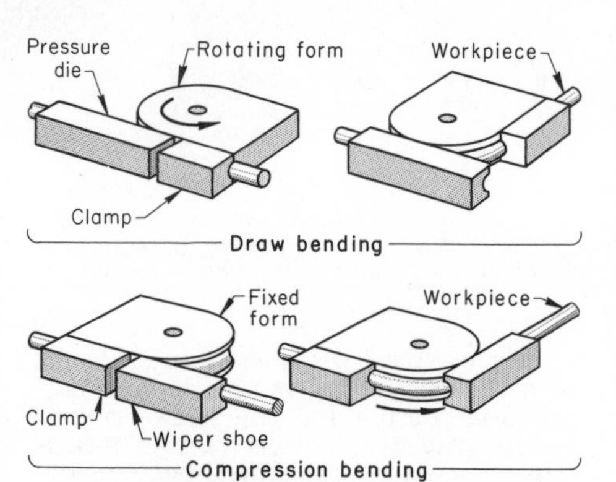

Fig. 1. Essential components and mechanics of draw bending and compression bending of bars and bar sections

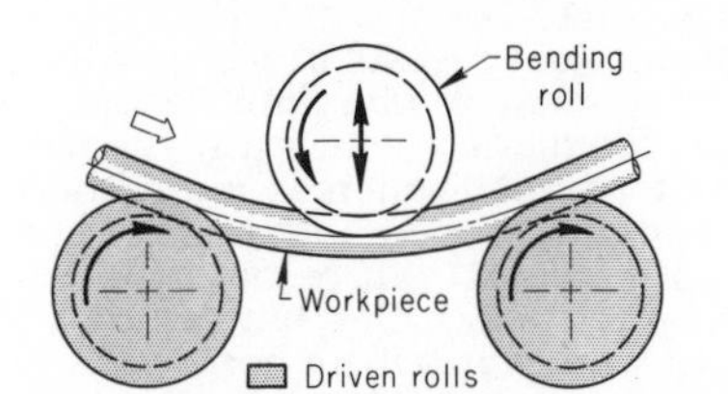

Fig. 2. Operating essentials in one method of three-roll bending

Hoops, arcs of any length, and helixes are easily made in a roll bender. Usually, the bend radius must be at least six times the bar diameter or the section thickness in the direction of the bend. To limit distortion in roll bending of asymmetrical sections, a double section can be made and split in two after bending. Sometimes rings are made by roll bending helixes and cutting them into rings for welding.

Roll bending is impractical for making more than one bend in a bar. It is difficult to control springback in a roll bender, and it may take several passes through the rolls to make the needed bend. Therefore, this method of making bends is slower than other methods. Another disadvantage of roll bending is that a short section of each end of the bar is left straight. For three-roll bending, the ends can be preformed in a press before bending, or the straight parts can be trimmed off.

The following examples describe two production applications of three-roll bending. The second example compares three-roll bending with gas cutting.

Example 367. Three-Roll Bending of a Structural Section

A 10-hp three-roll bender was used to bend a steel angle 3 by 3 by ⅜ in. into a circular reinforcing flange 60 in. in diameter. The angle was of hot rolled ASTM A107 steel. The top roll of the bender was a plain cylinder; each of the two bottom rolls consisted of two cylindrical sections held apart by a spacer to provide a recess for the edge-bent flange. The operations were performed in this order:

1 Cut angle to developed length plus 10 in.
2 Set rolls to bend correct radius; roll 360°.
3 Cut off ends of the rolled bar.
4 Weld the bar into a hoop.
5 Grind the weld flush.
6 Roll the ring in the three-roll bender to make it a true circle.

*J. H. Robinson, *Chairman,* Works Metallurgist, Springfield Works, Motor Truck Div., International Harvester Co.; Andrew C. Dickson, Chief Manufacturing Engineer, AP Parts Corp.

Sidney H. Feldman, Development Engineer, Sawhill Tubular Div., Cyclops Corp.; M. F. Fireoved, President, Wayne Fabricating Corp.; Craig C. Johnson, Pines Engineering Co., Inc.; E. C. Kingsland, Methods Engineer, Boiler Div., Babcock & Wilcox Co.

J. M. Lowe, President, Whitley Products, Inc.; Hugh G. Lusher, Chief Engineer, Elbeeco Plant, Aircraft Div., Aeroquip Corp.; John J. Vett, Manager, Product Development, Youngstown Sheet & Tube Co.

Example 368. Roll Bending vs Gas Cutting of Large Steel Rings (Table 1)

Two different methods — gas cutting, and rolling and welding — were used for producing large rings (60-in. OD by 52-in. ID by 1 in. thick) from hot rolled ASTM A107 steel. Rolling and welding provided considerable savings in cost and time, as shown by the comparative data in Table 1.

The gas-cut ring was cut from 1-in.-thick plate, 61 in. square. The gas-cut surface was acceptable without machining, but the cutting flash had to be ground off.

The rolled ring was formed in a three-roll bender by edge-bending a bar, 1 in. by 4 in. by 15½ ft, weighing 13.6 lb per foot. (The setup for roll bending is shown in Fig. 9 on page 222 in the article "Three-Roll Forming", in this volume.) The ends required trimming, beveling, welding on two surfaces, and flush-grinding of the welds. The bending rolls were assembled with 1-in. spacers to provide slots for supporting the bar during bending.

Table 1. Cost and Time for Three-Roll Bending vs Gas Cutting of a Ring (Example 368)

Item	Gas cutting	Three-roll bending	Saving
Cost of material per piece	$54.66(a)	$16.06	$38.60
Labor, man-hr:			
Setup(b)	0.75	0.25	0.50
Fabrication	1.7(c)	0.9(d)	0.8

(a) Cost of the 1-in.-thick plate, 61 in. square, was $86.16 (1077 lb). Salvage value of the unused portion was estimated at $31.50. Net cost thus was $54.66. (b) For making the first piece. (c) Includes grinding. (d) Includes welding.

Stretch bending is used for bending large irregular curves. The workpiece is gripped at the ends, stretched, and bent as it is stretched around a form. Usually, less springback occurs when the work is bent while it is stretched. The gripped ends are customarily trimmed off. This method can do in one operation what would otherwise take several operations, and sometimes does it better. The result is a possible saving in time and labor, even though stretch bending is a slow process. The tools, form blocks, or dies for stretch bending are simpler in design and less costly than conventional press tooling.

Stretch bending of bars is described in more detail in the article on Stretch Forming, which begins on page 239.

Bending Machines

The machines used for bending of bars include the following: devices and fixtures for manual bending; press brakes; conventional mechanical and hydraulic presses; horizontal bending machines; rotary benders; and bending presses. Shapers have also been used to perform specific bending operations.

Manual Bending. Hand-powered machines or fixtures are used in many shops for making bends that do not require much energy to form. This equipment is supplied with ratchets, levers or gears to give the operator mechanical advantage. Different types of fixtures are used for manual draw bending, stretch bending, or compression bending. Roll bending is seldom done by hand. The same tools are used as those on some power bending machines.

The maximum sizes of low-carbon steel bars that can be manually cold bent are given in Table 2.

Press brakes are used for all types of bending, especially in small-lot production (25 to 500 pieces), when standard tooling or low-cost special tooling can be used. Often the punch is not bottomed in the die, but the stroke is controlled, and the bar is bent "in air" (Fig. 4). With this technique, various bend angles can be made with the same die (see also the article "Press-Brake Forming", which begins on page 101 in this volume).

Mechanical presses are generally used only for mass production, because only large production lots can justify the cost of tooling, which is more than for most standard bending tools. Figure 5 shows a round bar being bent into a U-bolt in a press. The bar is first cut to length and pointed at both ends (preliminary to a later threading operation). The bar is then loaded into the press and held in a grooved die that bends the bar into a U in one stroke. In the setup of Fig. 5, more than one workpiece can be bent at a time.

The two examples that follow describe applications of a mechanical press in bending bars.

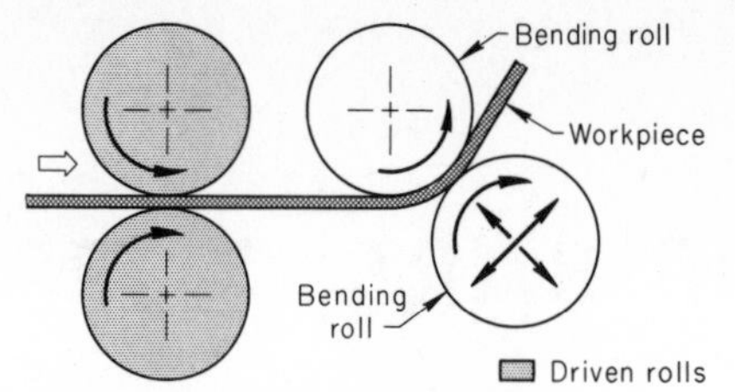

Fig. 3. Operating essentials in four-roll bending

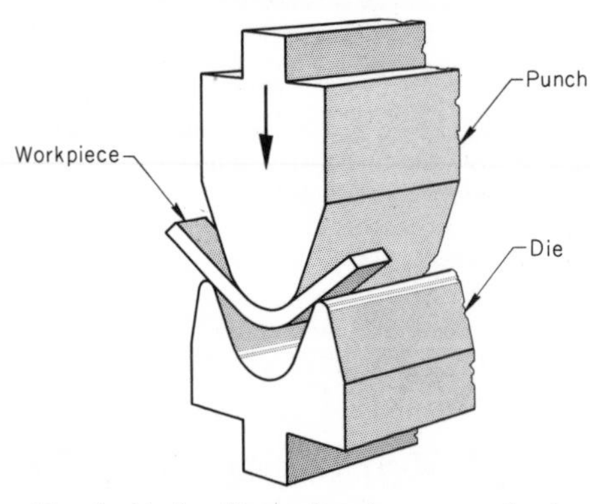

Fig. 4. Air bending a bar in a press brake

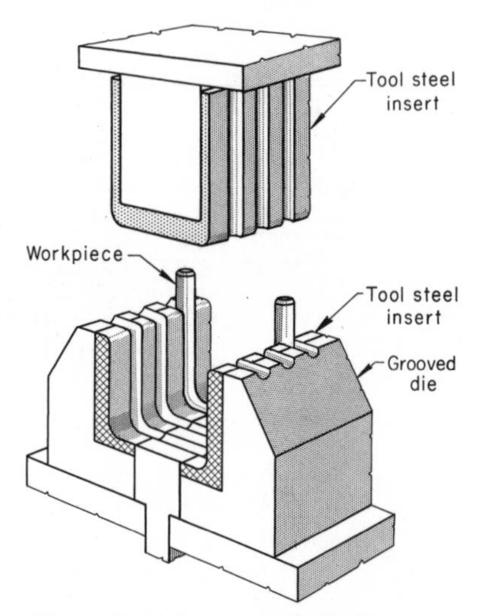

Fig. 5. Use of a grooved die in a mechanical press for bending a round bar into a U-bolt in one stroke

Table 2. Maximum Sizes of Low-Carbon Steel Bars for Manual Bending

Shape	Size, in.
Rounds	1 (diam)
Squares	¾ (per side)
Flats bent on flat	⅜ by 4
Flats bent on edge	¼ by 1
Angles	3/16 by 1 by 1
Channels	3/16 by ½ by 1

Example 369. U-Bolts Made in a Mechanical Press

U-bolts ¾ in. in diameter were bent hot in a fast single-action press using a grooved die (see Fig. 5). The ¾-in.-diam hot rolled bars of 1541 (formerly 1041) steel were sheared to length and pointed at both ends. The bars were taken on a chain conveyor to a furnace and heated to 1550 F. They were then loaded in the press, bent into the U-shape, and dropped in a quench tank, at the rate of one piece every 8 sec.

Example 370. Bending a Welded Assembly in a Mechanical Press (Fig. 6)

The wheel spider shown in Fig. 6 had three 10-in.-long spokes of 0.375-in.-diam low-carbon steel. The spider was assembled by welding the three spokes to a ½-in.-thick steel hub. The assembly was loaded into a 75-ton mechanical press, a double bend (joggle) was made in the spokes, and the short straight surface between the two bends was flattened to ¼ in. thick. Next, the wheel rim was welded to the spokes as shown in Fig. 6(d). The assembly was then loaded into another press where the legs were sheared flush with the outer edge of the rim and a ⅛-in.-diam hole was pierced in the flattened area of each spoke. Production rate was 25 per minute.

Hydraulic presses are often used to bend bars in much the same manner as mechanical presses. Although hydraulic presses are usually slower than mechanical presses, they have the advantage of exerting full force over a long stroke. Therefore, deep bends can often be made on a hydraulic press much smaller than the mechanical press that would be required. In the next example, a hydraulic press needed so little head room that a closed shape could be bent over it.

Example 371. Bending a Double-Bar Structure in a Hydraulic Press

A double-bar structure was constructed of two 7/16-in.-diam bars that were connected by welded cross members to form a ladder-like structure. A rectangular shape was formed by making four 90° bends having ⅝-in. inside radii. The two bars (sides of the ladder-like structure) were bent simultaneously, using a punch that forced the bars between rollers. By using a small (3-ton) vertical hydraulic press, the four bends could be made consecutively, allowing the workpiece to encircle the press ram as bending was completed. The overhead clearance would not have been available with a mechanical press.

This technique permitted making 360 double bends (90 frames) per hour.

Horizontal bending machines for bending bars consist of a horizontal bed with a powered crosshead that is driven along the bed through connecting rods, crankshaft, clutch, and gear train. Dies are mounted on the bed, and forward motion of the crosshead pushes the bar through the die. The long stroke and generous die space make this machine useful for a variety of cold and hot bending operations, although speeds are lower than for mechanical presses of like capacity. Horizontal benders are available in capacities from 10 to over 300 tons.

Rotary benders, either vertical or horizontal, are used for draw, compression, or stretch bending of bars. Such machines consist of a rotary table in either a horizontal or vertical position on which the form block or die is mounted (see Fig. 1). Suitable hydraulic or mechanical clamping, tensioning, or compressing devices are provided to hold the workpiece while the die rotates to the required position, or while the workpiece is bent about the central forming die. Some machines can make bends by two, or all three, methods.

Bending presses are most widely used for bending tubing (see page 311 in the article "Bending and Forming of Tubing", for a description and an illustration of a bending press). There are occasions, however, when bending presses are used for bending bars, as in the next example.

Example 372. Making a Double Crank in a Bending Press (Fig. 7)

Double cranks like the one shown in Fig. 7 were made in a bending press from round bars 5⁄16 or 3⁄8 in. in diameter. The bars were cut to length and fed into the press to flatten the ends and pierce the holes. The two sharp bends were made one at a time in the same press with a V-die. A bearing bracket was assembled on the crank, followed by a double-staking operation in the same press. Greatest demand on the press was in the end-flattening operation, which required a press capacity of 100 to 150 tons.

Shapers can be tooled for bending operations. One method is to have the fixed die, or anvil, held on the knee of the shaper and the punch mounted on the ram (Fig. 8). The shaper must make one stroke only. The stroke can be adjusted to allow for springback in the workpiece, and therefore the work can be bent to fairly close limits.

The setup shown in Fig. 8 is used to correct for springback in formed parts such as J-bolts, U-bolts and rings. A V-punch and die mounted in the shaper can make bends of various kinds.

Also, a shaper can be provided with a rack and pinion to produce rotary motion for bending (see Fig. 9). Bend radius can be varied by the use of center pins of different diameters.

Typical uses of a shaper in the bending of bars are described in the two examples that follow.

Examples 373 and 374. Shapers vs Presses for Bending Bolts

Example 373. Originally, U-bolts were press bent cold in a die from 3⁄8-in.-diam hot rolled merchant bars of 1025 steel, cut to length. Permitted variations in the material caused differences in springback, resulting in unacceptable parts. The work was transferred to a shaper, in which the stroke could be adjusted for springback at the beginning of each production run, or of each new lot of material.

Example 374. Originally, J-bolts were press bent cold in a die from sheared lengths of 1⁄2-in.-diam hot rolled merchant bars of 1025 steel. The press made the J-bolts by bending the bar into a half circle with one long arm. The unbalanced support caused variations in bending, so that some parts were unacceptable.

The job was put on a shaper. For this operation, the stock was sheared to double lengths, which the shaper bent into a circular loop with two long arms (the ends). The looped bar was then sheared in half. The cost of tooling for the shaper was much less than for the press.

A rack-and-pinion-actuated fixture similar to that shown in Fig. 9 was used for bending the bar into a circular loop. The bar stock was placed in the fixture at a slight angle, to allow one leg to pass the other during forming. After the bar was cut in two, the J-bolt was finished in a setup like that in Fig. 8.

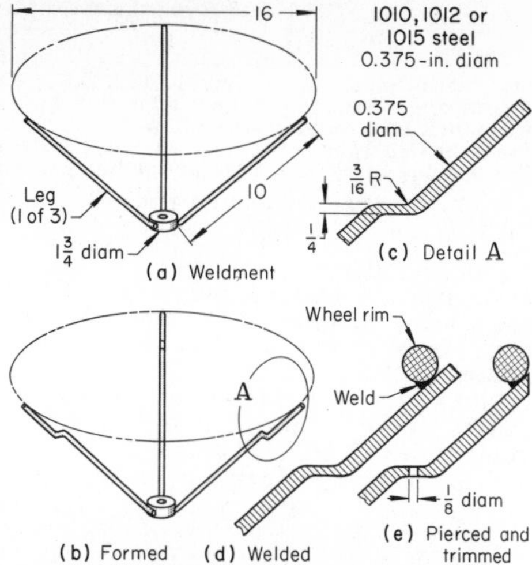

Fig. 6. Welded bar assembly that was formed by bending in a mechanical press (Example 370)

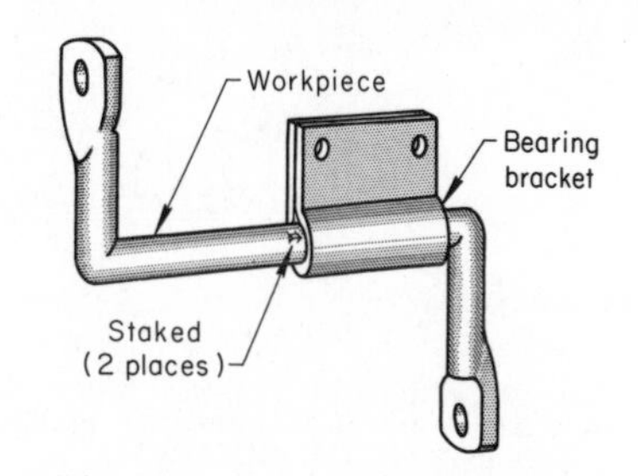

Fig. 7. Double crank produced in a bending press (Example 372)

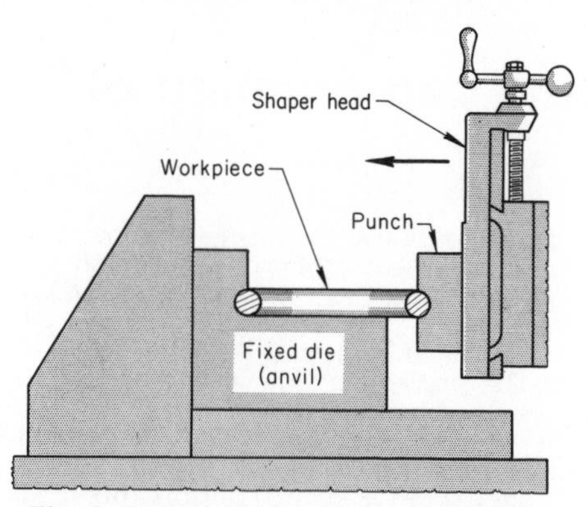

Fig. 8. Use of a shaper for correction of springback in U-bolts, J-bolts or rings

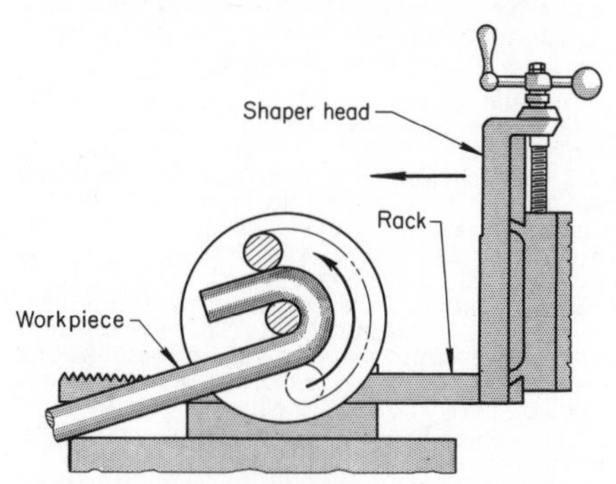

Fig. 9. Bending with rotary motion in a shaper

Tools

Tools for draw and compression bending are shown in Fig. 1. The form used in both processes is shaped to the contour of the bend. Usually, it is grooved to fit the work. Often, the form is part of a right cylinder whose straight portion (frequently, an insert) provides the surface against which the work is clamped. Hydraulic or mechanical pressure holds the clamp against the workpiece. Annular grooves or roughened surfaces grip the bar or bar section.

To allow for springback, the bend radius is made smaller on the form than is required for the workpiece. The form is also designed for a greater angle of bend than is needed. These two adjustments permit overbending the piece to allow for springback. Such adjustments are made by trial. The form is tested and corrections are made before it is heat treated.

Finish on the form (rotating or fixed) should be just good enough to avoid marring the workpiece. For most bar bending, a machined finish is sufficient. For decorative stainless steel and polished aluminum, grinding or polishing of the form surfaces may be needed. However, the clamping area should not be ground or polished unless necessary. The smoother the finish in the clamping area, the greater the danger that the workpiece will slip through the clamp. The pressure die and wiper shoe require a good finish (usually ground), because the work metal must slide along them.

When air bending bars in a press brake, simple V-blocks will suffice for the female dies. The opening of the V-blocks should be eight times stock thickness for standard sections, and ten times stock thickness for heavy sections. The upper die (punch) is shaped to the inside radius of the bend, and the angle of bend is controlled by the length of stroke. The same die set can be used for making various bends, and for various stock thicknesses, by adjusting the stroke.

Press brakes can use rubber pads for tooling on bends that need support (see "Press-Brake Forming", page 101). Completely shaped dies for bottoming can also be used in a press brake, as shown in Fig. 10.

Most dies used in conventional mechanical or hydraulic presses are completely shaped bottoming dies, which makes them more expensive than tooling for other bending machines. Tooling for bending presses is specially designed to fit the needs of the machine and the work to be done. Dies for bending presses are simple to construct and relatively inexpensive.

Tools for stretch bending are dealt with in the article "Stretch Forming", which begins on page 239 in this volume. See especially Fig. 1, 4, 5, and 10 to 14 in that article.

Die Materials. For production of thousands of pieces per month, dies are usually of hardened steel. Tool steel is used for small one-piece dies. Larger dies are made of low-carbon steel, and then carburized and hardened. Clamping inserts are made separately.

For moderate production of a few hundred pieces per month, unhardened carbon steel is often used. If only a few parts are needed, wood or an aluminum alloy may be strong enough for dies.

For bottoming dies in presses, hardened tool steel is always used. For cold bending, A2 tool steel hardened to Rockwell C 58 to 62 is most often selected. A hot work tool steel, such as H11, hardened to Rockwell C 45 to 50, is usually the choice for hot bending.

Bend Allowance

From the radius of curvature at the neutral axis and from the angle of the bend, the stock consumed in a bend can be computed. A formula often used for this computation is:

$$W = 0.01745\,\alpha(r + \delta)$$

where W is the bend allowance; α is the angle of bend, in degrees; r is the radius of bend to inner stock surface; and δ is the distance from the inner surface to the neutral layer (a commonly used approximation when this figure is not known is ⅓ to ½ stock thickness). The constant 0.01745 is a conversion factor changing degrees to radians.

When bar stock for a workpiece whose ends are within, or very near, the bend area is cut square to the neutral axis, the ends, after forming, will not be square to the neutral axis. The basic reason for this is the difference in circumference of the outer and the inner surfaces of the bend. Additional deviation from squareness can be expected because all of the material toward the outside of the bend from the neutral axis has undergone a tensile load and the material inside this line has been under compressive load. Unless compensation can be made for these variations, the ends of the formed part must be trimmed if they are to be square to the axis.

Blank preparation of a structural channel prior to forming into a semicircle is described in Example 327 in the article on Stretch Forming; in this application, the ends of the blank were cut in such a way that trimming after forming was unnecessary.

Table 3. Typical Lubricants for Bending Various Metals

Work metal	Lubricant
Low-carbon steel	Water-soluble, vegetable-oil-base drawing oil(a)
Stainless steel and other high-alloy iron-base alloys	Mineral-oil-base drawing oil(a)
Aluminum alloys and copper alloys	Mineral oil
Brass (severe bends)	Soap solution(b)
Hot bending of carbon, alloy and stainless steels	Molybdenum disulfide

(a) Available as proprietary material. (b) Creamy mixture of laundry soap and water.

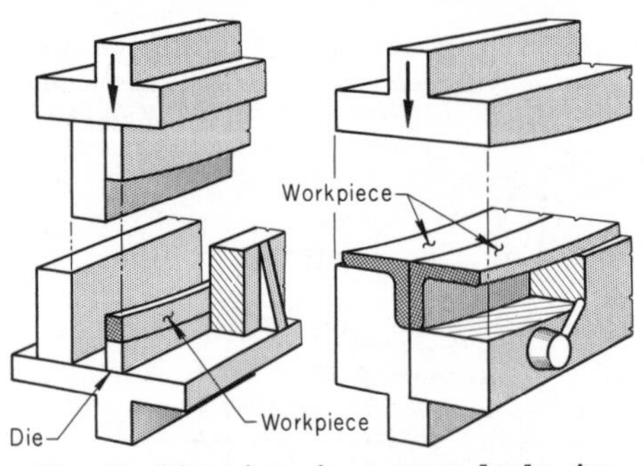

Fig. 10. Die setups in a press brake for edge-bending a bar (left), and for bending two structural angles (right)

Lubrication

Successful bending depends to a large extent on the type of lubricant used. No one lubricant works equally well on all materials. Selection of a lubricant varies among different shops. Typical lubricants for bending specific metals are listed in Table 3.

Overlubrication, in either quantity or type of lubricant, must be avoided. Not only is excessive lubrication likely to cause wrinkling, but the cost of removal must be considered. It is never good practice to use a pigmented compound if successful results can be obtained with an unpigmented compound, because pigmented compounds are more difficult to remove.

Wiper dies are lubricated with a very small quantity of high-grade drawing lubricant. It is important not to overlubricate pressure dies and wiper shoes.

Bending and Forming of Tubing

*By the ASM Committee on Bending of Bars and Tubing**

THE PRINCIPLES for bending tubing are much the same as for bending bars (see the article on Bending of Bars, page 305 in this volume). Two important additional features in bending of tubes are that internal support is often needed, and sometimes support is needed on the inner side of a tube bend.

Wall thickness of the tubing affects the distribution of tensile and compressive stresses in bending; a thick-wall tube will usually bend more readily to a small radius than a thin-wall tube.

Table 1 gives the minimum practical inside radii for cold draw bending of round steel or copper tubing, with and without various supports against flattening and wrinkling.

Selection of Bending Method

The four most common methods of bending tubing are basically the same as those used in the bending of bars (see page 305): compression bending, stretch bending, draw bending, and roll bending. The method selected for a particular application depends on the equipment available, number of parts required, the size and wall thickness of the tubing, the work metal, the bend radius, the number of bends in the workpiece, the accuracy required, and the amount of flattening that can be tolerated.

* For committee list, see page 305.

Hand vs Power Bending. The bending methods and tooling in hand bending are the same as for power bending. Steel tubing as large as 1.50-in. OD with 0.065-in. wall can be bent by hand, but the process is slow and repeatability is questionable. Some hand benders use an adjustable friction device, a kind of sliding brake, to prevent sliding of the tubing. The friction prevents wrinkles and other defects in bending.

Examples 375 to 377. Effect of Production Quantity on the Selection of Hand or Power Bending

Example 375. Bending equipment was needed to produce a U-shaped furniture part with two 90° bends from ¾-in.-OD 1010 steel welded tubing with a 0.049-in. wall. The two bends were made to a 2-in. radius as measured on the tube centerline. A small amount of flattening was tolerated. Production rate was 500 pieces per month.

Because no great accuracy was needed, and the production volume did not warrant more than a minimum investment, a bending fixture for compression bending by hand was selected, with tooling to allow for both bends to be made in one setup. Had production volume been larger, a power-driven bender or a bending press might have been selected.

Example 376 (Fig. 1). Eight parts, bent from welded steel tubing with 1½-in. OD and 0.065-in. wall, were required as samples. Each part consisted of an 80° arc at the end of a short straight piece of tubing (see Fig. 1).

The eight samples, and a subsequent order for 35 prototypes, were produced in a manual bender. However, a third order for production of 35,000 pieces justified the use of an automatic bending press with a high-speed ram. Costs and operating conditions for the hand and machine bending procedures are compared in the table with Fig. 1.

Example 377. In the production of hydraulic lines for machine tools, from ⅜-in. and ½-in.-OD steel tubing and from ¼-in.-OD copper tubing, hand bending required 6400 man-hr per year for 44,000 bends. A change to power bending reduced the man-hours needed to 450, saving $20,000 per year.

Tools

Tools used for the bending of tubes are similar to those used for the bending of bars (see page 307 in the article on Bending of Bars). One important difference is that tools for tubes need carefully shaped guide grooves to support the sidewalls and preserve the cross section during the bend.

Form blocks, or bending dies, resemble those described in the article on Bending of Bars (see page 307). They either rotate or are fixed, depending on the arrangement of the machine in which they are used. One end of the tube is clamped at the end of the groove in the form block, and the tube is bent by being forced around the block and into the groove.

For round tubes, the depth of the groove in the form block should be half the outside diameter of the tube, to provide sufficient sidewall support.

The block becomes the template for holding the shape of the bend. Form blocks can be made of wood, plastic or

Table 1. Minimum Practical Inside Radii for Cold Draw Bending of Annealed Steel or Copper Round Tubing to 180° (a)

	Minimum practical inside radius, in.		
	Grooved bending tools		Cylindrical bending block
Tubing OD, in.	With mandrel; ratio, <15(b) (best conditions)	With mandrel or filler; ratio, <50(b) (normal conditions)	without mandrel; ratio, <30(b) (poor conditions)
⅛	1/16	¼	½
¼	⅛	5/16	1
⅜	3/16	⅜	2
½	¼	7/16	3
⅝	5/16	9/16	4
¾	7/16	11/16	6
⅞	½	¾	8
1	9/16	⅞	10
1¼	11/16	1	15
1½	13/16	1⅛	20
1¾	15/16	1¼	27
2	1 1/16	1⅜	35
2½	1⅜	1⅝	..
3	1⅝	1⅞	..
3½	1⅞	2⅛	..
4	2⅛	2⅜	..

(a) Radii can be slightly less for a 90° bend, but must be slightly larger for 360°. (b) Ratio of outside diameter to wall thickness of tubing.

hardboard; if they are to be used for an extensive production run, they can be made of tool steel and hardened.

Clamping blocks hold the end of the tube to the form block and maintain the holding force necessary to make the bending action effective. Although the groove in the clamping block should be well formed, the finish should not be so fine that the tube will slip. Ordinarily, the as-machined finish will do, but sometimes ridges or serrations are machined into the clamp to increase the holding force. Rosin can be applied to the tube to prevent it from slipping in the clamp.

If the clamped area is to be a part of the finished piece, care must be taken to prevent scratches or mars. If the clamping groove has to be ground or polished to provide a good surface, the portion of the tube to be clamped will have to be longer to better distribute the higher clamping force. When the clamping length is short, the end of the tube is sometimes plugged to prevent it from deforming from high clamping forces. Table 2 lists typical clamping lengths for bending steel tubing.

Pressure dies are used in draw bending of tubing to press the workpiece into the groove in the form block and support the outer half of the tube. The most commonly used pressure die is as long as the developed length of the bend, plus some allowance for holding, and does not slide over the tube, but travels with it as it moves toward the bend area (see Fig. 1 in the article on Bending of Bars, page 305 in this volume). In one face, it has a groove with a depth that is slightly less than half the outside diameter of the tube.

Table 2. Typical Clamping Lengths for Bending Steel Tubing

Radius of bend centerline	Wall thickness of tube, in.	Typical length clamped
1 × OD	Under 0.035	4 to 5 × OD
	0.035 to 0.065	3 to 4 × OD
	Over 0.065	2 to 3 × OD
2 × OD	Under 0.035	3 to 4 × OD
	0.035 to 0.065	2 to 3 × OD
	Over 0.065	1½ to 2½ × OD
3 × OD	Under 0.065	2 to 3 × OD
	0.065 and over	1 to 2 × OD

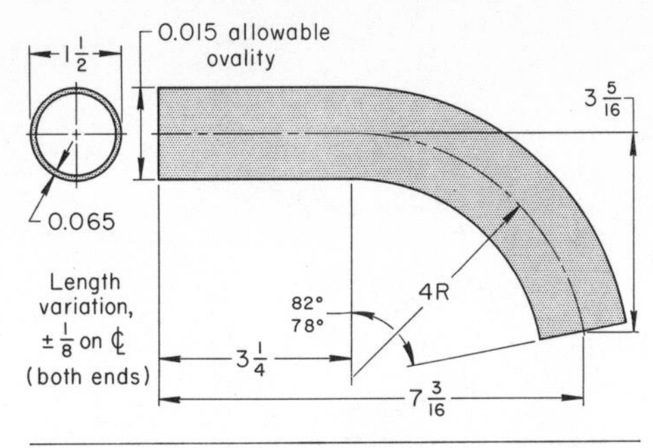

Item	Hand bending(a)	Machine bending(b)
Tooling cost	$40	$180
Setup time, hr	1	3
Production, pcs/hr ..	100(c)	450
Pieces per setup	35	35,000

(a) Prototype pieces. (b) Production order. (c) 0.6 min per piece.

Fig. 1. Bend in welded steel tubing produced by hand or by machine (Example 376)

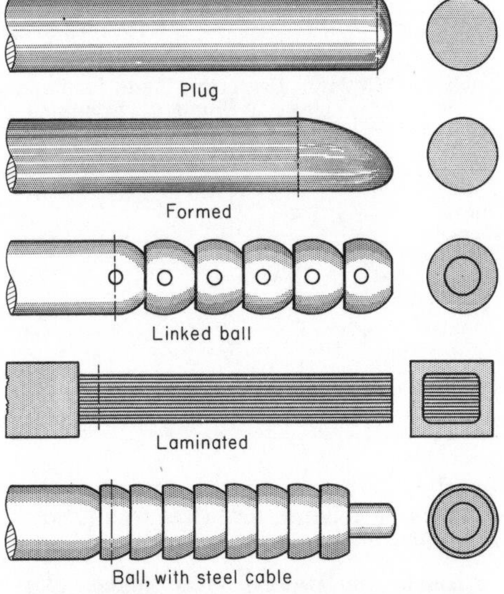

Fig. 2. Five types of mandrels used in bending of tubing. Broken vertical lines are points at which bends should be tangent to mandrel centerlines.

On noncritical work, a stationary pressure die can be used, or even a roller. Either has a tube-forming groove machined in its face. Most stationary pressure dies are made from low-carbon steel, which can be case hardened to resist wear. Tool steel such as O1, A2 or D2, hardened to Rockwell C 55 to 60, or aluminum bronze is commonly used for sliding dies.

On compression bending equipment, where the tube is clamped to a nonrotating form block, a wiper shoe replaces the pressure die. Its relation to the workpiece is similar to that of the stationary die described above in that the wiper shoe slides over the workpiece. However, instead of being fixed, the wiper shoe revolves around the stationary form block, progressively pressing the tube into the form block groove. For most applications, the length of the wiper shoe is from three to five times the outside diameter of the tube. The wiper shoe is made of tool steel and hardened to Rockwell C 55 to 60, or of a bearing bronze.

Wiper dies are stationary, straight-groove dies (not to be confused with the wiper shoes described above) sometimes needed in draw bending to support the tube on the side opposite the pressure die as the tube is about to be drawn into the contour of the form block. Metal that will form the inside of the bend undergoes severe compression that is transmitted back toward the as-yet-unbent end of the tube, where it could cause wrinkles were it not for the support of the wiper die.

The wiper die has a groove that is machined and ground to conform to the tube being bent and to fit the groove and lips of the form block, ending in a feather edge pointing toward the tangent point of the bend and extending to within ⅛ to ½ in. of the tangent point. Although it is difficult to maintain this distance without deflection, it must be done meticulously if the wiper die is to prevent compression wrinkles. Wiper dies are machined from 52100 (or L2 tool steel) for low-carbon steel tubing, or from aluminum bronze for stainless steel tubing. Wiper dies are never hardened.

Mandrels, which are described in detail in the following section of this article, are of three general types—rigid, flexible, and articulated—and are made to support the inside of the tube during bending.

Rigid mandrels fit the interior of the tube, and sometimes are shaped to conform to the start of the bend. However, because they are rigid, they support the entire circumference of the tube only as far as the point of bending and not beyond the tangent of the bend. Plug mandrels and formed mandrels are included in this category.

Flexible mandrels bend with the tube. They are generally built up of shims or laminae. This type of mandrel is sometimes used with square tubes and box sections where only a few bends are needed. Inserting and removing flexible mandrels usually is difficult.

Articulated mandrels include round-ball mandrels, discussed in a later section, and various other shaped mandrels that are used in much the same way as ball mandrels.

Loose fillers like sand and various low-melting alloys also serve as mandrels for low-production applications.

Dies used in press-type bending machines are similar to those described on page 307 in the article on Bending of Bars. Dies, including wing dies for bending presses, may have grooves for one to six tubes to be bent in one press stroke (see Examples 389 and 390).

Formed rolls are used in roll bending of tubes. Grooves corresponding to the outer surface of the tubes to be bent are cut or ground into the outer surfaces of the rolls so that they fit the surface of the tube as it is bent. For a more complete description of rolls used in roll bending, see page 219 in the article "Three-Roll Forming".

Bending Tubing With a Mandrel

Mandrels are sometimes used in bending to prevent collapse of the tubing or uncontrolled flattening in the bend. A mandrel cannot correct failure in bending after the failure has begun, nor can it remove wrinkles.

Five types of mandrels used in the bending of tubing are shown in Fig. 2.

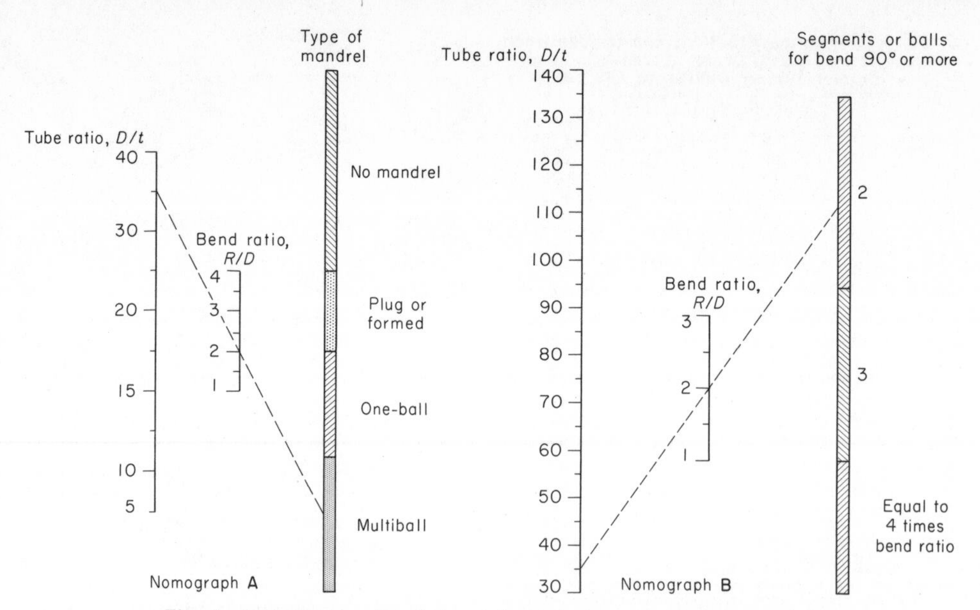

Fig. 3. Nomographs for determining when a mandrel is needed and the correct type to use. (See text for explanation.)

The plug mandrel and the formed mandrel are rigid, but the three other types shown are flexible or jointed to reach farther into the bend.

The largest diameter of the rigid portion of the mandrel should reach a short distance into the bend, the distance that it extends (past the tangent straight portion) depending on the kind of mandrel and the size of tube, and usually being established by trial. If the mandrel extends too far, it can cause a bulge in the bend. Conversely, if the mandrel does not extend far enough, wrinkles may form or the outer tube surface may flatten in the bend area.

The need for a mandrel depends on the tube and bend ratios. The tube ratio is D/t, where D is outside diameter and t is wall thickness. The bend ratio is R/D, where R is the radius of bend measured to the centerline.

Table 3 can be used to determine whether or not a mandrel is needed for bending steel tubing, and Fig. 3 shows the usual conditions that require the use of a mandrel and what type of a mandrel is needed.

The nomographs given in Fig. 3 are used as follows:

1 In nomograph A, find the tube ratio and the bend ratio in the left-hand and center scales, and lay a straightedge across them. The zone on the right-hand scale where the straightedge falls shows whether or not a mandrel is required, and what type. Bends for which D/t is more than 40 always require a multiball mandrel.
2 If a multiball mandrel is indicated, refer to nomograph B in Fig. 3. As before, find the tube ratio and the bend ratio in the left-hand and center scales and lay a straightedge across them. The number of balls needed in the multiball mandrel will be indicated on the right-hand scale.

Plug and formed mandrels are fixed, and the tube is drawn over the tip of the mandrel in forming. This action work hardens the tube so that it resists flattening during bending. Clearance between the mandrel and the inside of the tube should not be more than 20% of the wall thickness. If the mandrel is too tight, the tube is likely to fail in the bend. The use of plug and formed mandrels is shown in the three examples that follow.

Example 378. Use of a Plug Mandrel in Bending Welded Low-Carbon Steel Pipe

A short length of ¾-in. pipe (1.050-in. OD by 0.113-in. wall) of welded low-carbon steel was bent 90° to a 2-in. radius. In spite of the thick wall, the small bend radius made it necessary to use a plug mandrel to support the pipe against flattening. Other tools used were a form block, a clamp and a pressure die. Total tool cost was $300.

The bending machine was a power-driven, rotary draw bender, rated for a maximum of 1-in. extra-strong seamless low-carbon steel pipe (1.315-in. OD by 0.179-in. wall). The bends were made at the rate of 300 per hour.

Example 379. Use of a Formed Mandrel in Bending Low-Carbon Steel Tubing

A U-shape was formed by making two 90° bends in 1¼-in.-OD welded low-carbon steel tubing with a 0.065-in. wall. Radius of the bends was 2⅜ in. Wrinkles, shear marks, or other visible defects were not permitted.

The part was formed in a power-driven draw bender at the rate of 300 bends per hour. The bender was rated for 3½-in.-OD by 0.083-in.-wall steel tubing with 40,000-psi yield strength. A formed mandrel was used with a lubricant. Tool cost was $300.

Mandrels are more necessary in tubes other than round, in order not to distort the cross section. In the following example, a formed mandrel was used in an oval tube.

Table 3. Minimum Centerline Radii for Bending Steel Tubing Without a Mandrel

Tubing OD, in.	Minimum centerline radius, in., for tubing with wall thickness, in., of: 0.035	0.049	0.065	0.083	0.093	0.120
3/16 ...	5/16	¼	3/16	...		...
¼	½	⅜	5/16	...	...	...
5/16 ...	⅞	¾	⅝	...	...	...
⅜	1½	1¼	1⅛	1	...	...
½	2¼	2	1¾	1½	...	...
¾	4	3	2½	2	...	...
1	8	6	4	3	2	2
1½	...	...	12	10	8	6
2	...	...	...	24	20	16
2½ ...	...	...	...	...	24	20
3	...	...	...	...	...	25

Example 380. Bending Oval Tubing With a Formed Mandrel

Oval tubing, 1-in. by 4⅜-in. outside dimensions by 0.065-in. wall, was bent on edge to make a U-shape with two 90° bends at a 9-in. radius. The tubing was welded hot rolled low-carbon steel. Wrinkles, shear marks, or other visible defects were not permitted.

The bends were made in a draw bender rated for 3½-in.-OD by 0.083-in.-wall steel tubing with 40,000-psi yield strength. This piece, bent with a formed mandrel, form block, clamp, and pressure die, demanded the full rated torque of the machine. The mandrel was lubricated. Tool cost was $2000, and 250 bends were made per hour.

Ball mandrels with one or more balls are used for many bends. During bending, the metal is stretched tightly over the mandrel, making withdrawal difficult. Withdrawal mechanisms are needed. In thin-wall tubing of softer metals, as the mandrel is withdrawn it sizes the bend somewhat, smoothing the stretched metal and correcting the shape of the cross section.

The bodies and balls of one-ball mandrels used on most tubing are commonly made of carburized mild steel, hardened, ground and polished. For bending of stainless steels, they are made of polished aluminum bronze.

One-ball mandrels used in the bending of tubes up to 1¼-in. OD generally have a body that is undersize 0.005 to 0.007 in., with a ball 0.010 to 0.014 in. smaller than the inside diameter of the tube. Square or shaped tubes require a mandrel that fits closer. If the bends are in one plane, the body and the ball of the mandrel can be grooved to clear weld flash or seams. More commonly, a mandrel is made undersize to clear the obstruction. When the workpiece must be bent in several planes, it can be reinserted with the seam in the groove, but it is usually better to specify tubing with a controlled weld flash.

Ball mandrels are often made with several balls, as shown in Fig. 2. The balls or segments are always smaller than the body, and can be jointed by links and pins, ball joints, or steel cable. Usually, a linked or jointed mandrel is stronger than a comparable mandrel joined by steel cable. The linked mandrel bends in only one plane, and is easier to load than one that is less rigid. The ball-jointed mandrel is also in wide use, and has the advantage of having rotating balls to equalize wear. Ball-jointed ball mandrels are made in many sizes, down to one for tubes as small as 0.222-in. ID.

Ball-jointed and steel cable ball mandrels cannot be grooved to clear weld flash and seams, because the mandrel segments rotate.

Many multiball mandrels make bends with a centerline radius that equals the outside diameter of the tubing. Ball mandrels can be used on bends not possible with formed mandrels:

Example 381. Multiball vs Formed Mandrel in Forming a U-Shaped Bend

A U-shape was produced by making two 90° bends in 1¼-in.-OD welded tubing of low-carbon steel in both 0.049 and 0.065-in. wall thicknesses. The bend radius for both types of tube was 2⅜ in. Wrinkles, shear marks, or other visible defects were not permitted.

For the 0.065-in.-wall tubing, the bend was made with a formed mandrel, which adequately supported tubing of this wall thickness. However, a formed mandrel could not be used for the 0.049-in.-wall tubing. For the thinner-wall tubing, the D/t ratio was so large that it was necessary to use a well-lubricated three-ball mandrel and wiper die. The ball mandrel was required to support the outer wall in the bend area, and the wiper die was required to prevent wrinkling caused by compression in the inner wall of the bend.

The machine used was a draw bender rated for steel tubing with 3½-in. OD, 0.083-in. wall, and a yield strength of 40,000 psi. Tooling costs and production rates for bending the two wall thicknesses of tubing were:

Tube size, in.	Tooling cost	Bends per hour
1¼ by 0.049 wall	$450	200
1¼ by 0.065 wall	300	300

In the foregoing example, if the formed mandrel had been used in bending the 0.049-in.-wall tube, the tube would have deformed excessively from inadequate support. A formed mandrel would have to be advanced farther into the bend area than is normally done. This would cause a hump and greater thinning of the tube wall where the outside of the bend was stretched over the end of the mandrel. When wall thickness is less than approximately 0.049 in., this technique should not be used, because there is not enough metal to take the stretch without breaking.

Clearances for mandrels vary from none at all (to produce some bends the mandrel is forced into thin-wall tubing) to 0.095 in. or more. The clearance needed depends on stock material, wall thickness, bend radius, and quality of the bend. The better the bend, the more closely the mandrel must fit.

Mandrels are even more necessary in bending nonround tubing than they are in the bending of round tubing (see Example 380). Segmented mandrels must be used in almost all bending of square, hexagonal and octagonal tubing. The number of segments that are needed in the mandrel usually depends on the wall thickness of the tubing.

Chromium plating extends the life of some mandrels, and the plating can be renewed for further use. Platings should not be more than 0.0003 to 0.0005 in. thick, as thicker plates may flake off. Plated mandrels should be stripped and replated when the plating is worn through at any point.

Polished mandrels usually work best, but ground or machined surfaces are satisfactory when slight marking on the inside of the tube is acceptable.

The bending of a fragile thin-wall tube may need the careful use of a multiball mandrel and a wiper die. If the bend is changed to a larger radius or if a stronger or thicker-wall tube is substituted, the mandrel can be changed to a less complicated one, and the wiper die may not be needed. Sometimes a plug or form mandrel can be used instead of a multiball mandrel, even when the bend is made to the minimum practical radius, as shown in the following example.

Example 382. Forming 90° Bends in Stainless Steel and Aluminum Tubes With Plug and Multiball Mandrels

Four tubes were bent 90° for comparison, two of stainless steel (321, welded tubing) ¼-in. and 1-in. OD, and two of aluminum (6061-O, seamless tubing) ¼-in. and 1-in. OD. The 1-in. aluminum tube had a 0.049-in. wall, and the three other tubes 0.035-in. walls. The stainless steel was annealed and descaled. All bends were made cold with a lubricated mandrel in a 1-in.-capacity draw bender. Tolerances and quality met the required standards.

A plug mandrel was used in the ¼-in. tubes, and a multiball mandrel in the 1-in. tubes. A wiper die was used with the multiball mandrel in the 1-in. stainless steel tube. The ¼-in. tubes were bent to 0.375-in. centerline radius, and the 1-in. tubes to 1-in. centerline radius.

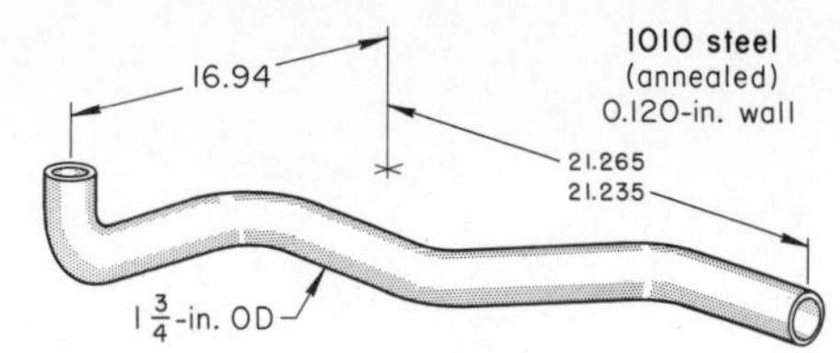

Fig. 4. Manifold tube that was bent to an accuracy of ±1° on each of four bends (Example 383)

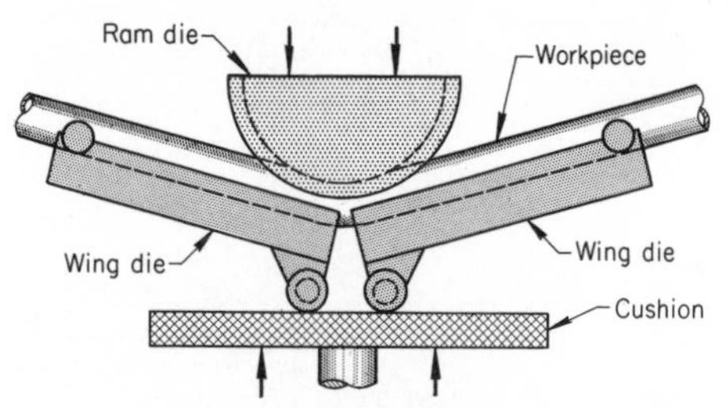

Fig. 5. Essential components and mechanics of a bending press

These were the sharpest bends practical by this method. The ¼-in. tubes flattened by 10%; the 1-in. tubes by 5%. All of the tubes thinned at least 20% in the outer wall. Other results were:

Item	Outside diameter, in. — Stainless ¼	Stainless 1	Aluminum ¼	Aluminum 1
Bending torque, lb-ft	30	150	20	100
Springback	3°	2°	2°	1°

Dimensional Accuracy. Regardless of other conditions, when accuracy is important, the use of a mandrel is mandatory. The example that follows describes an application that illustrates the degree of accuracy that can be achieved by the use of a mandrel.

Example 383. Use of a Plug Mandrel to Hold Close Tolerance on Four Bends (Fig. 4)

The tube shown in Fig. 4 was used in a return-line manifold of a high-pressure hydraulic system on a large tractor. The radius of each of the four bends was required to be within ±1°. Over-all length was required to be within ±0.015 in.

To achieve this degree of accuracy, a considerable amount of tool adjustment was required during each setup. From two to six tubes were bent before acceptable tubes were produced. To produce a lot of 40 tubes, 2½ man-hr was required, setup included.

Bending was done in a powered draw bender, using a round-end plug mandrel. The mandrel had a drilled hole to deliver a constant flow of lubricant inside the tube during bending. The lubricant was a mixture of lard oil and low-viscosity mineral oil.

Mandrel Materials. Most mandrels are made of tool steel (W1, O1, A2 and F1 are typical selections) and hardened to Rockwell C 55 to 60.

Bending Tubing Without a Mandrel

It is cheaper to bend tubing without a mandrel. Trial bending is generally necessary to find what bends can be made. Tubing with thick walls is more likely to be bendable without a mandrel than thin-wall tubing. Bends with large radii are more likely to be formable without a mandrel than those with small radii. Slight bends are more feasible than acute bends. Wide tolerances on permissible flattening make a bend easier to form without a mandrel.

Springback is greater without a mandrel, but it can be compensated for by overbending, or lessened by increasing force on the pressure die.

The following example compares power bending without mandrels of two sizes of tubing in stainless steel and aluminum alloy.

Example 384. Bending Stainless Steel and Aluminum Tubing Without a Mandrel

Four tubes were bent to 90° for comparison — two welded tubes of type 321 stainless steel, and two seamless tubes of 6061-O aluminum alloy. There was one ¼-in.-OD tube and one 1-in.-OD tube of each metal. Wall thickness of all four tubes was 0.035 in. Tolerances and quality met standards for commercial aircraft. The stainless steel was annealed and descaled.

All the bends were made cold without a mandrel and without lubrication, in an automatic hydraulic draw bender with 1-in. capacity. The ¼-in. tubes were bent to 1-in. centerline radius, and the 1-in. tubes were bent to 8-in. centerline radius. (These are the sharpest bends ordinarily recommended for this technique.) All the bends flattened 10%. Results were:

Item	Outside diameter, in. — Stainless ¼	Stainless 1	Aluminum ¼	Aluminum 1
Bending torque, lb-ft	20	60	15	45
Springback	8°	12°	5°	10°

Machines

The machines used in the bending of tubes are essentially the same as those used in the bending of bars (see page 306 in the article on Bending of Bars). In general, bending machines fall into three categories: rotary benders (stretch, compression and draw bending); press benders (stretch and compression bending); and roll benders.

Powered rotary benders are commonly used to bend tubing as large as 8 in. OD. At least one machine can bend tubing as large as 12 in. OD with a ¼-in. wall, and a few special power benders can bend 18-in. pipe.

Boilermakers normally use power benders that can bend 3-in.-OD steel tubing with ½-in. wall to a centerline radius as small as 3 in.

The next two examples describe the use of rotary benders.

Example 385. Forming a Boom for a Front-End Loader From Rectangular Tubing

A tapered rectangular tube with a 0.112-in. wall was bent to make the boom for a front-end loader. A tapered segmented mandrel was made to fit the tube. The tube was edge bent in a powered draw bender. This machine was also used to bend thick-wall 3-in. pipe for other parts of the tractor frame.

Example 386. Bending Steel Tubing for Automobile Seat Frames

Steel tubing with 1-in. OD and 0.049-in. wall was bent 90° to make the frame for automobile seats. The inside of the bend was collapsed into a dimple for clearance, but most of the column strength was kept by holding the shape of the outside of the bend. This was done in part by collapsing the inner wall of the tube over a convex punch instead of a conventional groove. Centerline radius of the 90° bend was ⅝ in. The bends were made, two at a time, in a fast rotary bender.

Bending presses are hydraulic machines made especially for bending both bars and tubes, but most often for tubes. The ram of a bending press can be stopped at any point in the stroke. Wing dies and a cushioning device help to wrap the work around the ram die, as shown in Fig. 5. When the ram moves down, it causes the wing dies to pivot by a sort of camming action and wrap the workpiece around the ram die. The wing dies wipe the work to control the flow of metal; a compression bend is made on each side of the ram die, without wrinkles or distortion.

A bending press can usually make bends much faster than machines that are not made especially for bending. The open design of the press makes possible the bending of complex shapes in one setup. Single bends can be made sequentially, or the press can make several bends simultaneously. Bends can be made to various angles and in various planes. Usually the bar is passed through the press in one direction, and the press makes a sequence of bends automatically. The work is held against stops to locate each bend.

When several bends are made in one or more workpieces at each stroke of the press, all bends are in the same plane. Different angles and bend radii also can be made in the same workpiece, and the angles and spacing of bends can be adjusted. One disadvantage of the bending press is that it causes a slight reduction in the thickness of the workpiece at the bend.

Automatic bending presses are used for production bending. Capacities are 3 to 40 tons for bends that generally do not exceed 165°. Bends in the same plane should be separated by a distance equal to twice the outside diameter of the tube. Bends in different planes should be separated by a distance equal to at least three times the outside diameter of the tube. If the bent portion is to be joined with another bend into an accurate circle, length of the straight legs on each end of the bend should be at least twice the outside diameter of the tube. Bends can be made beyond these limits, but at greater cost. Bends are usually made in dies that are a little tight on the tubes to prevent flattening and wrinkling.

Exhaust pipes for automobiles, with bends in various planes, are made in automatic bending presses, as in the following example.

Example 387. Forming Automobile Exhaust Pipes From 1010 Steel Welded Tubing (Fig. 6)

An exhaust pipe 82 in. long with bends to bypass the obstructions on the underside of a vehicle is shown in Fig. 6. These pipes were made of hot rolled or cold rolled 1010 steel welded tubing with 1¾-in. OD and 0.060-in. wall. Hardness was Rockwell B 63 to 78.

Bending was done in an automatic 20-ton hydraulic bending press, using a punch with a 5-in. centerline radius in the groove, and two wing-die shoes. Locating fixtures and a checking fixture (off the press) were also used.

The press made different angles of bend by using turret-mounted stops to control the stroke. The location of the bend was set by backstops at the right side of the press. Counting the plane of the first bend as 0°, the radial position (roll of the tube) for the plane of each bend in turn was located by stops along a bar on the left of the machine. In loading the tubes for the first bend it was important to keep all weld seams in the same place, so all tubes would bend alike.

The tube was nested in the wing die shoes for the first bend, and then the work was moved by hand for each of the other bends. All the bends were standard. Tolerances were:

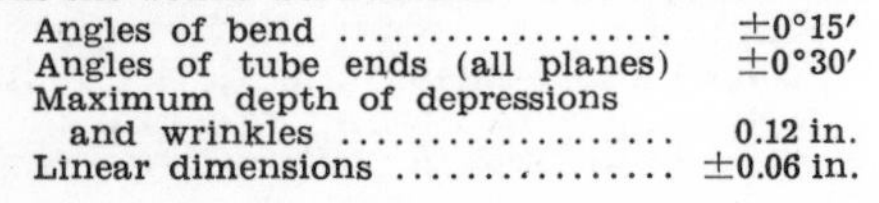

Angles of bend	±0°15′
Angles of tube ends (all planes)	±0°30′
Maximum depth of depressions and wrinkles	0.12 in.
Linear dimensions	±0.06 in.

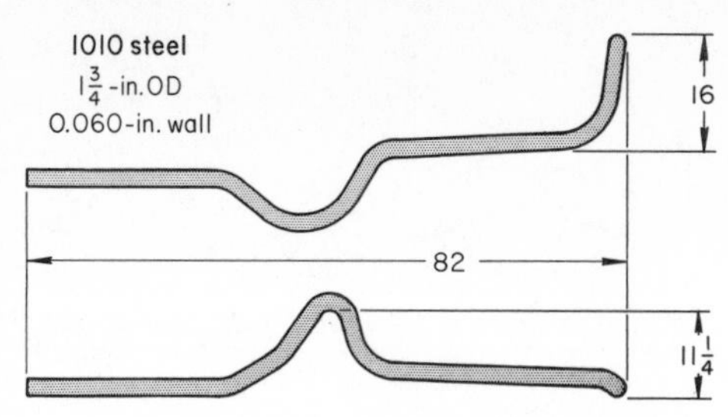

Fig. 6. Automobile exhaust pipe produced in an automatic, hydraulic bending press (Example 387)

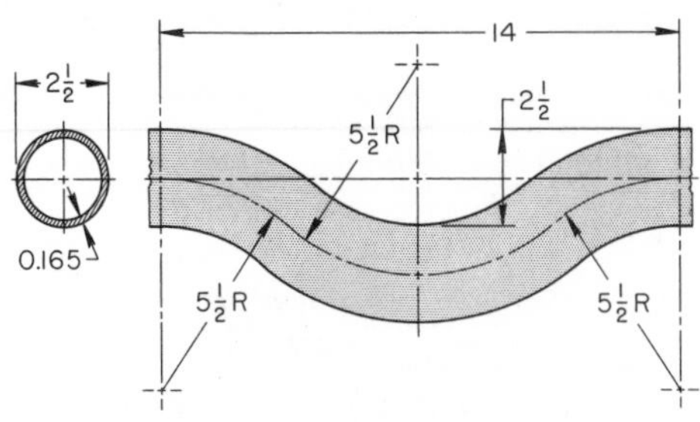

Fig. 7. Offset and return shape that was produced from thinner-wall steel tubing and in less time by press bending than by rotary bending (Example 388)

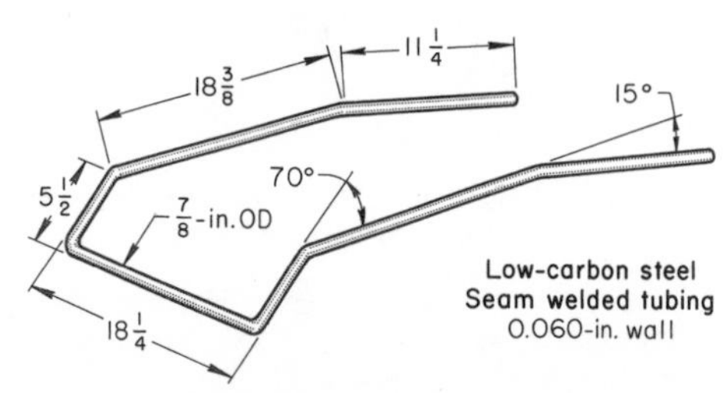

Fig. 8. Handle for a supermarket cart that was bent in an open-back inclinable press (Example 391)

All the bends were made cold. The punch was set to clear the work by ½ in. for loading, and the total machine time to make five bends was 0.1305 min. Production was 130 pieces per hour on a 10,000-piece order. Total cost of the punch and the two die shoes was $175.

Examples 388 to 391 describe other applications of press bending:

Example 388. Press vs Rotary Bending of Three Bends in a 2½-In.-OD Tube (Fig. 7)

An offset and return composed of three bends, as shown in Fig. 7, was made in a 2½-in.-OD tube. Maximum offset at the center of the middle bend was 2½ in. Centerline radius was 5½ in. for all three bends, and there was no straight section between bends. Length of the formed section was 14 in. Length of the tubing averaged 24 ft.

Originally, a rotary compression bender was used to make the bends with special clamping dies formed to the curve of the bent section. Even with this precaution, it was difficult to bend the tubes accurately. Extra time was needed to rework the tubes to required shape.

A press die set was developed that made all three bends in one stroke, improved the quality of the bends and eliminated rework. Also, the press was able to make the bends in the 0.165-in.-wall stock specified by the design, whereas 0.220-in.-wall stock had been required for the rotary bender. Tooling cost of $1200 for press bending was justified because several thousand pieces were needed each year. Comparative costs for the two methods were:

Item	Rotary bending	Press bending
Tube cost per foot	$1.07	$0.92
Labor, man-hr (two men) (a)	0.5	0.1

(a) Includes all piece handling and rework.

As this comparison shows, for an initial investment of $1200 for tools, $3600 was saved in material on each thousand pieces, and 400 man-hr of labor.

Example 389. Bending Low-Carbon Steel Tubing Into U-Frames for Dinette Chairs in a Hydraulic Bending Press

Tubing of 1010 steel with ¾-in. OD and 0.049-in. wall was bent into U-shaped frames for dinette chairs. The U-shape was composed of two 90° bends with 1¾-in. centerline radius. Two tubes at a time were loaded side by side into the press so that four bends were made with each stroke. Production rate was 500 pieces per hour at 250 strokes per hour. The press had sufficient capacity to bend two 1-in.-OD by 0.065-in.-wall tubes at the same time.

Example 390. Bending Square Tubing Into Trunk-Hinge Brackets for an Automobile in a Hydraulic Bending Press

Rectangular low-carbon steel tubing (¾ by 1 in., 0.060-in. wall) was bent to a shape resembling the outline of a dipper for automobile trunk-hinge brackets. The shallow-angle bends were first formed in one cycle of a 20-ton bending press. Then the pair of brackets was completed in a single stroke by bending them side by side on a second press. In the second stroke, the die formed a detent on them, thus saving a separate operation. Production rate was 600 pieces per hour.

Example 391. Use of a Press for Making Six Bends in Welded Tube (Fig. 8)

Tubes like the one shown in Fig. 8 were bent in high production for handles for supermarket carts. All bends were made in an open-back inclinable press. Bends were made in pairs, producing one part (six bends) in three press strokes. The sequence of operations and production rates for each were:

Operation	Pieces per hour
Cut to length	150
Deburr inside diameter	200
Make U-bend	100
Make 70° bends	200
Make 15° bends	225

Dies were hardened W1 or W2 tool steel. Low-viscosity mineral oil was the lubricant.

Roll benders for bending tubes are similar to those used for bending bars, as described on page 305, but tolerances are more critical on the rolls and spacing. (Roll benders are described on page 217 of this volume.) The contour of the rolls must match that of the tube to minimize wrinkling or flattening. Tubes of sizes up to 8-in. OD by 0.240-in. wall can be bent into arcs, circles or helixes. Helix coiling is described in the following example:

Example 392. Coiling a Helix of Round Steel Tubing in a Three-Roll Bender (Fig. 9)

Steel tubing of 2-in. OD and 0.240-in. wall was coiled in a three-roll bender into a helix 24 in. in mean diameter with 2½-in. pitch and 20 turns, as shown in Fig. 9. The tubing, 126 ft long, was made by welding together random lengths 10 to 24 ft long. The welds were then ground flush. The form rolls were contoured to fit the 2-in. OD of the tubing. The tubing was started into the rolls so that it coiled without stop until the helix was completed. Had the coiling been stopped, the diameter of the helix might not have been constant. After coiling, the helix was removed and trimmed to length.

Rings are easily made on three-roll benders. In the following example, techniques are compared for making a torus by two methods of bending.

Example 393. Three-Roll vs Press Bending for Forming a Seal Ring

Two different methods were used for making a seal ring 24 in. in mean diameter by bending and welding a steel tube (2-in. OD, 0.148-in. wall) into a torus. In the first method, semicircular bends were made in a bending press, the straights were trimmed, and the ring was completed by welding the two halves together with two joints. In the second method, one weld was eliminated by rolling the tube in a three-roll bender, making a 360° bend. After trimming the straights, the ring was completed with a single weld, and was trued by rerolling in the bender. Time and costs per piece for the two methods were:

Item	Two welds	One weld
Setup, man-hr(a)	0.5	0.5
Production, man-hr	3.4	1.9
Material cost	$2.40(b)	$1.86(c)

(a) Setup time is for the first piece. (b) Tubing was cut to developed length plus 12 in. (c) Tubing was cut to developed length plus 10 in.

Hot Bending

Most of the bends described so far in this article have been made by cold bending (workpiece at room temperature). There are obvious advantages to cold bending: heating equipment is not needed, benefits of previous heat treatment are not destroyed, subsequent cleaning or descaling is less likely to be needed, workpiece finish is better, and thermal distortion is avoided.

On the other hand, cold bending demands more energy than hot bending for the same bend. There is more springback after a cold bend and more residual stress in the tube. Bends cannot be made to as small a radius cold as they can hot.

Tubes are bent hot to make bends of small radius, adjacent bends with little or no straight tube between them, bends in material with little cold ductility, bends that take too much power to bend cold, and bends in fragile assemblies where the force of cold bending might cause damage.

Temperatures and procedures in the hot bending of carbon, low-alloy, medium-alloy, and stainless steel tubes are summarized in Table 4.

Disadvantages of bending tubes hot include high cost, slow production, and poor finish on bends.

Tubes of carbon steel and of most alloy steels can be bent to a much smaller radius by hot bending than by cold bending. A bend radius of 0.7 to 1.5 times the outside diameter of the tube can usually be made by hot bending. The wall thickness of the tube affects this range. The tube wall must not be so thin that it will distort or thin excessively in the outer wall. If the tube ratio (outside diameter divided by wall thickness) is more than 10, the tube probably needs internal support in bending, unless there is some upsetting of the tube that thickens the wall.

Figure 10 shows the tube relations that can usually be successfully bent hot in a die but without a mandrel, and Fig. 11 shows the tube relations that can usually be successfully bent hot with a mandrel or filler. Figure 10 applies to tubes 1.5 to 3 in. in diameter; Fig. 11 is for tubes of all diameters.

If a mandrel is not practical for internal support of the tube, the tube can be packed with dry sand. First, a plate is welded to one end of the tube to block the end. The tube is filled with sand, and is tamped or vibrated to make sure the sand is packed tight. Another plate is welded to the open end, the tube is heated, and the bend is made. Finally, the plates are cut off and the sand is emptied out.

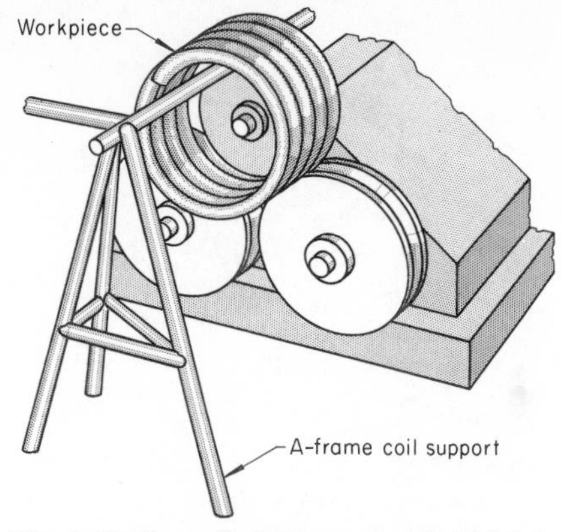

Fig. 9. Coiling a helix from round steel tubing by three-roll bending (Example 392)

Various specialized techniques for bending tubes hot are described in Examples 394, 395 and 396, which follow.

Example 394. Five-Step Bending of 2-In.-OD Tube to 1½-In. Centerline Radius

Return bends for the coils of a boiler were made by bending 2-in.-OD carbon steel tube 180° on a 1½-in. centerline radius. The tube had a 0.260-in. wall. The sequence of operations was:

1 Bend 180° on 4½-in. centerline radius in a conventional rotary bender.
2 Heat the bend area to between 1800 and 2000 F in a furnace.
3 Reshape the bend to 2-in. radius in a bending press.
4 Close legs to 3 in. between centers in a vertical press.
5 Restrike in the vertical press to make bend radius 1½ in.

Operations 3, 4 and 5 were performed in rapid sequence so that all bends were made before the tube cooled below 1600 F. Production rate was 30 pieces per hour.

Thinning of the outer wall can sometimes be controlled better in hot bending by heating only the part of the workpiece that will be the inner wall of the bend. This reduces its compressive strength so that the bend causes very little stretch of the outer wall. This method makes good bends with centerline radii of 1.3 to 1.5 times the outside diameter of the tube with the usual tooling in a rotary bender.

Boiler tubes are bent by heating one side for one third of the way around the tube. The heated portion becomes the inside of the bend, and because it yields more easily in compression, thinning of the outer wall is limited. The tubes are bent to a U-shape in a bending machine. The U can then be reheated on the inside as before, and the bend can be squeezed in a press in one or more steps, to make a narrower U, as in the following example dealing with the bending of boiler tubing.

Example 395. Localized Heating for a Compression Bend (Fig. 12)

Return bends were made for use in the economizer of a boiler. The tube was made of carbon steel, 2-in. OD by 0.284-in. wall. The operations were:

1 Heat the tube to 1300 to 1350 F in a special burner that heated the bottom 120° of the tube for an 18-in. length where the bend was to be made (Fig. 12).
2 Bend the tube in a rotary bender 180° to 7½ in. between centers with the heated portion on the inside of the bend.
3 Squeeze the tube between dies in a hydraulic press to 6 in. between centers.
4 Squeeze as in step 3 to 4¾ in. between centers.
5 Squeeze as in step 3 to 3½ in. between centers.
6 Reheat the entire surface of the bend for 8 in. on each side.
7 Size in a die.
8 Squeeze as in step 3 to 2½ in. between centers.
9 Normalize.

Production rate, with three men working, was 20 bends per hour.

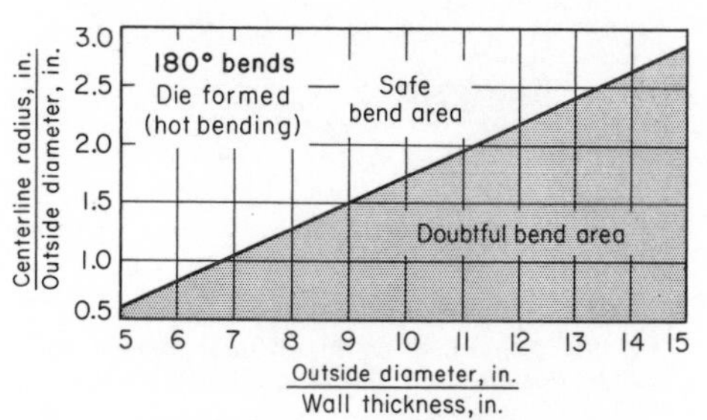

Fig. 10. Chart for determining conditions for successful hot bending of tubes 1.5 to 3 in. in diameter without the use of a mandrel

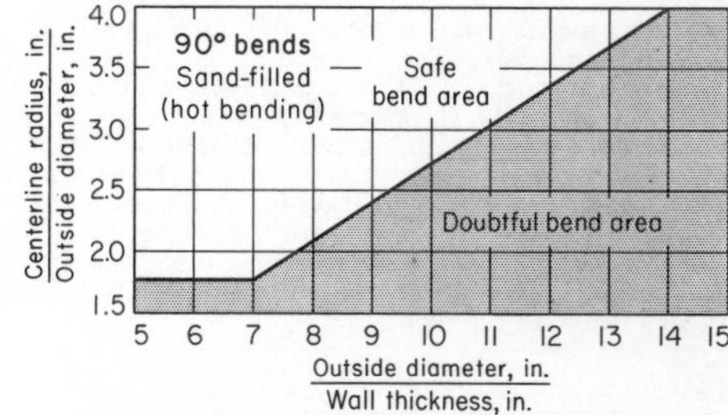

Fig. 11. Chart for determining conditions for successful hot bending of tubes of all diameters with use of a mandrel or filler

Table 4. Temperatures and Procedures for Hot Bending of Steel Tubes

Steel	Temperature, F	Procedures
Carbon Steels		
ASTM A106, A178, A192, A210	1800 to 2000 (or <1350)	Do not heat beyond 2000 F and do not bend between 1350 and 1600 F(a).
Low-Alloy Steels		
ASTM A209, A213 (gr T11 and T22), A335 (gr P2)	1800 to 2000 (or <1350)	Do not heat beyond 2000 F and do not bend between 1350 and 1600 F(a).
Alloy Steels		
ASTM A213 (gr T5 and T9)	1800 to 2000	Do not heat beyond 2000 F and do not bend between 1350 and 1600 F(a). Heat treat after bending, 1350 to 1375 F.
Stainless Steels		
Types 304, 310, 321	>2100	After bending, heat treat to 2000 to 2050 F. Furnace cool to 600 F; air cool(b).
Type 446	>2100	Do not bend at less than 1600 F. Heat treat at 1450 to 1600 F; water quench.

(a) Ductility is sometimes low in this range; thus, the range should be avoided for hot bending. (b) This treatment has proved best for maximum strength in service at elevated temperature.

Large tubes are commonly bent hot while they are filled with dry sand. The bending is done on a bending table that is made of cast iron plates. The plates have a continuous pattern of cored holes. A bending form for whatever radius is needed is bolted to the bending table. Steel pins or stops can be placed in the holes in the table to keep the work in line. A clamshell furnace in sections is the usual source of heat. Winches, jacks and hoists supply the bending force. A typical application is described in the following example:

Example 396. Hot Bending a Large Tube on a Cast Iron Bending Table (Fig. 13)

A 180° bend with a 15-in. radius was made near the center of a 15-ft length of steel tube, 7¼-in. OD by 1-in. wall. A plate was welded to one end of the tube to close it. The tube was dropped, closed-end down, into a pit, and was filled with sand. The tube was vibrated and tamped to make sure the sand was well compacted, and the open end was closed with another welded-on plate.

The bending table was set up for the bend. The proper form block was bolted to the table, and lines tangent to the bend were laid out for proper location of stop pins (Fig. 13).

The tube was heated to between 1800 and 2000 F in a clamshell furnace and set on the bending table. One end was clamped down to the table. The other end was pulled by a cable, which, guided by a series of strategically located pulleys fastened to the table, bent the tube incrementally around the form block to the final position shown in Fig. 13.

When the bend passed inspection, the ends of the tube were cut off and the sand was poured out. The entire process, including preparation and handling, took 45 min.

Choice of hot or cold bending can depend on available equipment, cost of new equipment, labor costs, and urgency of the job order, as well as on the size of the production lot.

Example 397. Hot vs Cold Bending for Forming Z-Shapes in Carbon Steel Tubes (Fig. 14)

Fifty pieces of carbon steel tube (ASTM A210), each 20 ft long, were to be bent 4 ft from each end at 60° on a 15-in. centerline radius to make Z-shaped pieces (Fig. 14). Equipment was available for hot bending; cold bending would have required the purchase of $1200 worth of tooling. Twelve bends per hour could be made by cold bending, whereas by hot bending only 1.5 bends per hour could be made. The cost analysis for making the 50 pieces was as follows:

Item	Hot bending	Cold bending
Fuel cost	$3.50	...
Tooling cost	$350	$1200(a)
Total man-hr(b)	132.5	12.5(c)
Total production time, hr	33⅓	4⅙

(a) Total cost advantage for hot bending was $846.50. (b) Includes setup and handling time. (c) Total labor advantage for cold bending was 120 man-hr.

In the preceding example, if 33⅓ hr could be spared to make the 50 pieces, the next consideration would be cost. To amortize the $846.50 net additional cost over the 120 man-hr saved, the hourly wage rate would have to be about $7. A larger order, greater urgency, or a backlog of other urgent jobs could have made cold bending more advantageous than hot bending.

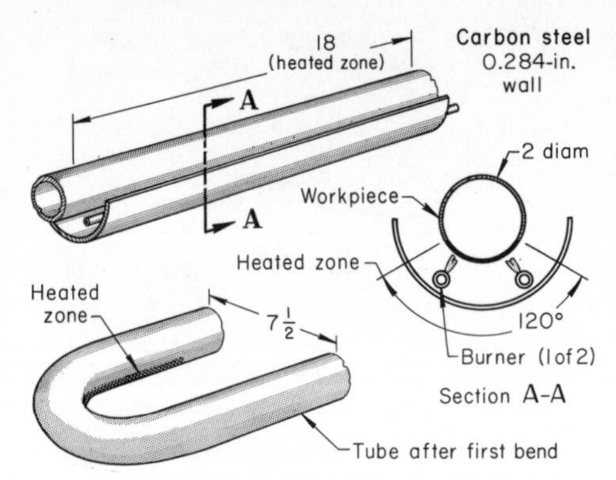

Fig. 12. Compression bend produced in tubing, and special burner used for localized heating of the workpiece before bending (Example 395)

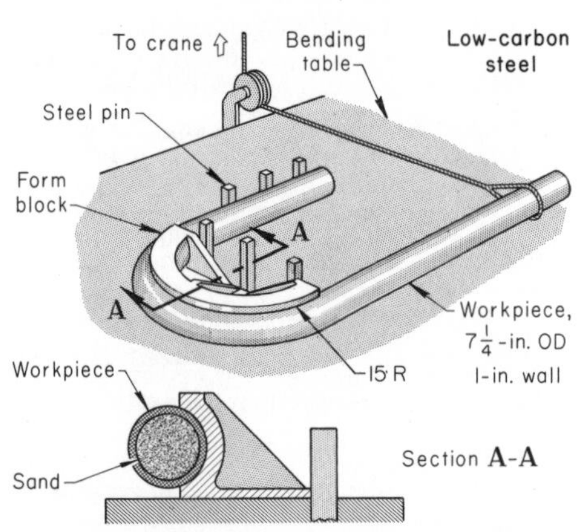

Fig. 13. Final position in hot bending of a large sand-filled tube (Example 396)

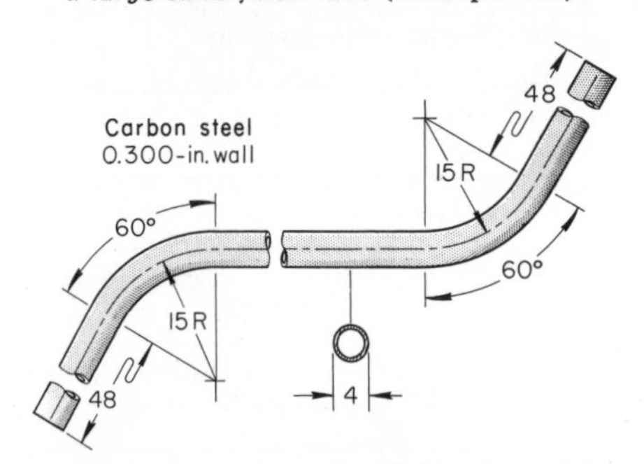

Fig. 14. Z-shaped part suitably formed by either hot or cold bending (Example 397)

Tube Stock

Tubes are classed as seamless, welded, lock-seam, butt-seam and jacketed.

Steel tubing is available both seamed and seamless. Seamed tubing with internal flash demands special consideration when a mandrel is to be used in bending (see the section on Bending Tubing With a Mandrel, page 309).

Lock-seam tubing can be bent if the seams are tight: a test is to twist a 3-ft-long section of tubing in the hands; any grating or slipping indicates a seam too loose to make good bends.

Butt-seam tubing is similar to welded tubing, but with no weld at the joint, and it is seldom used. To make good bends it must be accurate in dimensions, have no scale, and be bent with the seam in the plane of the bend. A mandrel must always be used. It is more economical to use welded tubing.

Stainless steel jacketed tubing is made by roll forming a sheet of stainless steel onto a butt-seam tube of mild steel. The stainless steel jacket is rolled into a lock seam in the open seam of the inner tubing. For best bending, the stainless steel jacket should be at least 0.020 in. thick, and the two layers should be rolled tightly together. Tools for bending such jacketed tubing cost more than tools for bending plain tubing: it takes a wiper die of aluminum bronze, a hardened steel mandrel, and unusually high pressure on all tools — all of which add to the cost of the tooling. Also, the seam must be in the plane of the bend, either inside or outside.

Galvanized steel tubing can be bent to a radius as small as four times the outside diameter. For tube to be bent to smaller radii, galvanizing should be done after bending, because the galvanized coating is likely to flake if galvanized stock is used.

Aluminum-coated tubing (hot dipped) can be bent by essentially the same techniques used for uncoated tubing of the same diameter and wall thickness, using slightly higher clamping pressures to avoid slipping (see the section on forming hot dip aluminum-coated steel, page 138 in this volume).

Seamless tubing should be free of scale or rust. Wall thickness, concentricity and hardness vary in seamless steel tubing. These variations are likely to cause variable springback, wrinkles, and excessive flattening.

Common pipe in all sizes and thicknesses is easily bent if it is clean and free of rust or scale, inside and out.

Stainless steel tubing can be bent to a greater angle, at a given radius, than low-carbon steel. Austenitic types in the 300 series are most commonly bent, because they are strong and ductile. Tubing in a stabilized condition at a temper no higher than quarter hard will make good bends with low scrap rates. Both welded and seamless tubing are available. Thin-wall tubes should have exact diameter and wall thickness specified. Annealing is usually recommended after bending operations.

Copper alloy tubing is usually extruded. It is easily bent in the annealed condition, and it has little springback. Copper and some brasses may not need to be annealed. Copper-nickel alloys, however, are more difficult to bend and have greater springback.

When copper alloys are annealed, as most of them are, oxides should be removed by pickling before the tube is bent, to protect the tooling. Oxides increase friction and wear in bending.

Aluminum alloy tubing, like copper alloy tubing, is usually extruded, or extruded and drawn. Soft aluminum may tear or collapse on bending. The oxide coating that forms on exposed surfaces of aluminum alloys is abrasive to tooling. Lubrication prolongs tool life.

Anodized aluminum and decorated aluminum can usually be bent without harm to the finish. Aluminum pipe is bent by hand to a radius usually not less than four times the outside diameter. For examples of bending aluminum tubing, see the article "Forming of Aluminum Alloys", which begins on page 379 in this volume.

Bending Thin-Wall Tubes

Techniques used to bend thin-wall tubes are the same as those used to bend standard tube and pipe, but they are more carefully applied. A tube can be classed as thin wall if the ratio of outside diameter to wall thickness (D/t) is greater than 30 to 1. The wall thickness, if not related to the tube diameter, is a meaningless measure. For instance, a tube wall 0.020 in. thick would be a standard wall for a tube of ⅛-in. OD. But for a 6-in. tube it would be a very thin wall. The centerline radii given in Table 5 for bending tubing of various D/t ratios with a ball mandrel and a wiper die are conservative and often are exceeded.

Table 5. Average Practical Centerline Radii for Bending of Thin-Wall Steel Tubing Using a Ball Mandrel and Wiper Die

Tubing OD, in.	Average centerline radii, in., for tubing with wall thickness, in., of: 0.035	0.049	0.065	0.083	0.093	0.120
½	½ (a)	½ (a)	...	...	...	...
⅝	⅝ (a)	⅝ (a)	...	...	...	...
¾	¾	¾ (a)	¾ (a)	...	...	...
⅞	1¼	1⅛	1 (a)	...	...	...
1	1¾	1½	1¼	1⅛ (a)	...	...
1⅛	2½	2	1¾	1½	...	...
1¼	3⅞	3½	3	2½	2	...
1½	5	4¼	3¾	3¼	2¾	2¼
2	9	8	7	6	5	3½
2½	12	10½	9¼	8	6½	5
3	15	13	11	10	9	8

(a) No wiper die required

Machines used to bend thin-wall tubing have a greater capacity than is necessary, so that they will be stable and rigid. Their bending action must be smooth and steady. Runout on machine spindles should not exceed 0.0005 in. Mandrel rods must be heavy enough that they do not stretch or buckle when the slip-fitting mandrel is inserted into the tubing.

Auxiliary equipment includes: means for pressurizing the tubes with air or hydraulic oil (hydrostatic mandrel) to keep them from necking after they are drawn past the last mandrel ball; hydraulic feed on pressure dies to hold tubes in compression; and mandrel oscillators that move the mandrel back and forth to keep the tubes from necking down. Amplitude of mandrel oscillation can be adjusted from ⅛ to 1 in., and frequency, from 1 to 500 cpm.

Tools must be more accurately made than for bending standard tubes. The form block or bending die should have a runout at the bottom of the groove of not more than 0.001 in. The depth of the groove should equal 55% of the outside diameter of the tube. The width of the groove should equal the outside diameter of the tube plus 10% of the wall thickness. The width of the clamping groove on the bending die should equal the outside diameter of the tube minus 10% of the wall thickness. The length of the clamping groove should be five to six times the outside diameter of the tube unless special clamping provisions like flaring or clamping cleats are included. The clamp and the bending die can be keyed or doweled for perfect alignment. Clamping plugs are sometimes used; these either should be slip fitted in the tube or should be expandable.

The pressure die should have a groove wider than the tube outside diameter by an amount equal to 15% of the wall thickness. The width should not vary from end to end by more than 0.0005 in. Variation in the groove will cause a pinching or relieving effect. If all tools are properly adjusted, only light pressure is needed on the pressure die, which can be adjusted against a solid bar with the same diameter as the outside diameter of the tube.

The wiper die has a groove of width equal to the outside diameter of the tube plus 10% of the wall thickness. The groove should be highly polished and have a thin coat of light oil. Too much or too heavy oil will cause wrinkles. The groove must be a full half-circle in cross section to support the whole inner half of the tube. The groove must also fit closely to the form die for at least 15° back of the point of bend so that it cannot be forced away by the pressure buildup of the compressed inner wall of the bend. Failure to maintain the position of the wiper die can cause wrinkles.

Mandrels used with thin-wall tubes are generally multiball mandrels. They have a clearance no greater than 10% of the wall thickness of the tube. The mandrel must be positioned very carefully so that the full diameter of the body is just at the start of the bend (first ball of cable or ball-socket mandrels at the bend tangent). A template should be used to set the mandrel. If auxiliary oil or air pressure in the tube is not used, there must be enough balls to reach completely around the bend.

Interlock tooling is sometimes used for bending thin-wall tubes. The clamp is keyed to the form block; the wiper die is locked to the pressure die; and the pressure die is locked into alignment with the form block. Interlock tooling was developed specifically for automatic bending, but it has some advantages in general bending. The tools will not crush the work nor mark it; setup time and scrap can be reduced.

Material should be especially uniform in thin-wall tubing to be bent, and should all be from the same source — preferably from the same heat. Because tooling dimensions are held closely, close-tolerance tubing is recommended, in spite of its added cost.

Production Examples. Thin-wall tubing is frequently bent to elbows that have a centerline radius equal to the diameter, and it is not uncommon for the diameter to be as much as 90 times greater than the wall thickness (for instance, a 6-in.-diam tube with an 0.065-in.-thick wall). Many such elbows are used in vacuum-line service, where no wrinkles are permitted. They are commonly made from 1020 steel tubing in the as-received condition. Bends are made using ball mandrels and wiper dies, and an oil-base lubricant. Some manufacturers of elbows use chromium-plated tools to minimize tool wear.

It is often difficult to prevent thin-wall tubing from slipping during bending. Methods used to provide adequate clamping are described in the next examples:

Examples 398 and 399. Procedures to Prevent Slipping of Tubes During Bending

Example 398 — Tube for Hydraulic Circuit (Fig. 15). The tube shown in Fig. 15 was used in a high-pressure hydraulic circuit of an earthmover. Five bends, ranging from approximately 20° to 86°, were made in a powered compression bender. All bends were made on a 6-in. centerline radius.

The 86° bend posed a problem because only 5 in. of tube was available for clamping; adjacent bends were in other planes. Surfaces of the clamps were rough, but the tube slipped during bending, causing unacceptable bends. The first approach was to line the clamps with emery cloth, but this did not add enough friction to prevent slipping. A second approach was to increase the force on the clamp. Until a hydraulic cylinder could be installed to provide this force, a factory lift truck was used. Acceptable bends were produced by increasing force on the pressure die.

The tubing had a phosphate coating. A three-ball mandrel with an oil hole provided a constant supply of lubricant (a mixture of lard oil and mineral oil) to the inside of the tube. Tools were of W1 or W2 tool steel, hardened.

Example 399 — A 90° Bend. A smooth 90° bend was to be made in the center of a 12-in.-long tube. This tube was 2¼ in. in OD and had a wall thickness of 0.048 in. It was made from seam welded low-carbon steel. Centerline radius of the bend was 4⅝ in.

In conventional bending, the tubes slipped, resulting in unacceptable marking of the workpieces. The first attempt to solve the problem involved threading the clamping surfaces of the tools. This prevented slipping, but the threads marked the tubes. A second approach was to bore shallow grooves in the clamping surfaces to provide a series of flattring surfaces. The grooves, ⅛ in. wide by 0.010 to 0.015 in. deep, were spaced ⅛ in. apart along the full length of the cylindrical clamping surfaces. The clamping tools (W1 or W2

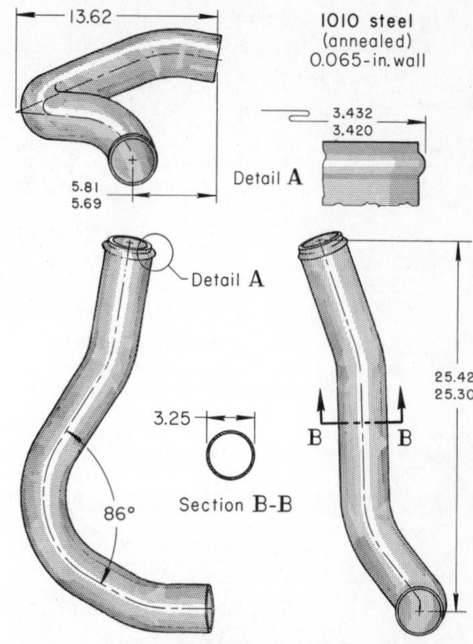

Fig. 15. Component of a hydraulic system that required five bends (Example 398)

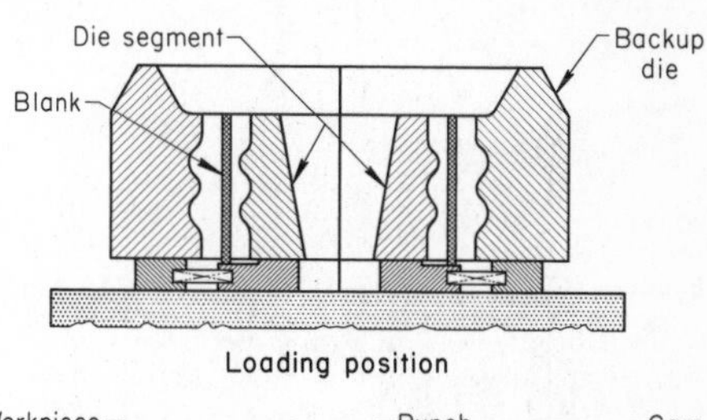

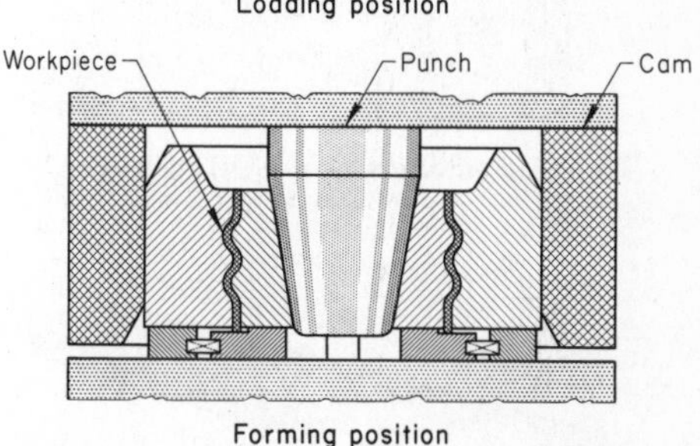

Fig. 16. Use of segmented dies for expanding a section of tubing in a press

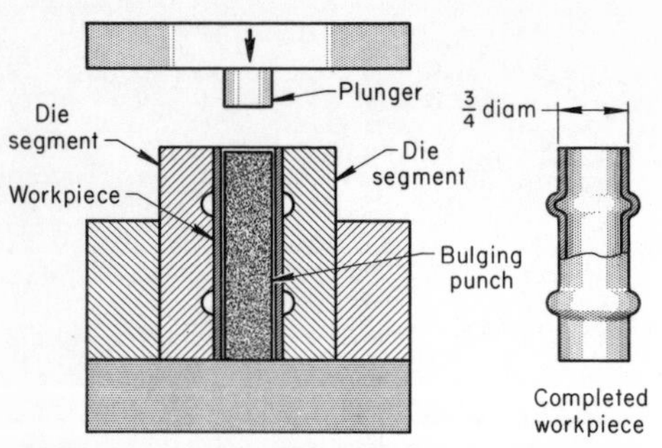

Fig. 17. Bulge-forming beads on a coupling tube, using a rubber punch in a segmented die (Example 400)

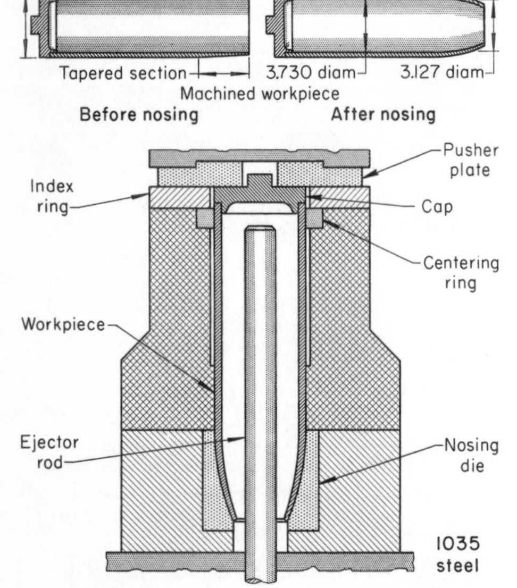

Fig. 18. Reduction of a shell by nosing (Example 401)

tool steel) were hardened and ground in the usual manner. With tools thus prepared, marking of the workpieces was eliminated.

Other tooling used included a two-ball mandrel that was plated with chromium and a wiping die of hard bronze. A heavy oil was used as the lubricant. Production lots ranged from 250 to 500 pieces. Production was at a rate of 175 pieces per hour.

Lubrication for Tube Bending

Where a mandrel is used, both the mandrel and the interior of the tube are heavily coated with a thick lubricant. Pigmented lubricants are useful for adding body between the mandrel and the tube. Sometimes, thick lubricants are heated to 250 F and sprayed onto the inner surface of the tube. An oil hole in a mandrel can be used to lubricate the inside of a tube during bending (see Example 398).

The wiper die, on the other hand, needs only a very light lubricant, applied sparingly, if at all. Nothing must interfere with the close fit between wiper die and tube, which prevents compression wrinkles.

Not all metals react to lubricants in the same way. In general, mineral oils are always acceptable, and so are organic fats. Certain sulfur and chlorine additives can cause staining or corrosion of stainless steel or copper, and should be used with caution. For aluminum, special additives have been developed to be used with light or medium mineral oil; the same formulations work well on copper and brass.

Tube Forming

Tubular sections are converted into a variety of products. One or more forming processes may be used. These processes include: press forming, contour roll forming, tube spinning, rotary swaging, hydraulic bulging, explosive forming, electromagnetic forming, and electrohydraulic forming.

Press Methods. Expanding with segmented dies (Fig. 16) is a method often used for forming configurations in sidewalls of drawn shells or sections of tubing. With this method, the forming segments are contracted by compression springs, and expanded radially by a tapered punch. The backup, or outer, die is made of two segments, held apart by compression springs. In operation, as the press ram descends, cams move the two segments of the backup die together. The punch then moves the inner segments outward, forming the shapes in the sidewall. As the press ram is raised, springs return the die parts to their original positions, and the workpiece is rotated 45° for a restrike operation. Restriking is required to remove flat spots resulting from the stretch across the gaps between the forming segments in the expanded position. The size of the gap can be decreased by increasing the number of segments. The presence of the gaps is one of the drawbacks of this method and is the reason that an alternative method, such as rubber-pad forming, is sometimes used. The example that follows describes forming of a tube section by the rubber-pad method.

Example 400. Bulging by Rubber-Pad Forming in a Segmented Die (Fig. 17)

The hose-coupling tube shown in Fig. 17 was formed by bulging two beads with a rubber punch in a segmented die. The workpiece, with the rubber punch in it, was held in the die on the bed of the press while a closely fitting plunger was lowered into the tube by the upper ram. The compression of the rubber punch caused outward expansion of the tube walls into the two grooves in the die, thus forming the part.

Tubing is often used for making mortar shells by nosing. Shells are machined before instead of after nosing and may be reduced as much as 30% of their original diameter by nosing. An example of nosing practice follows.

Example 401. Reducing Ammunition Shells by Nosing (Fig. 18)

Figure 18 shows a mortar shell before and after nosing. The original workpiece was a section of ½-in.-wall 1035 seamless steel tubing. The workpiece was prepared for nosing by being machined both inside and out. Inside dimensions and concentricity were maintained, and the need to machine the inner contour after nosing was eliminated. The outer surface was machined with a taper, which provided a developed contour to yield the required dimensions in the nosed section.

The die setup used for nosing is shown in Fig. 18. The centering ring controlled concentricity of the straight wall section. The index ring controlled the length of the shell by serving as a stop for the pusher plate. The nosed shell was stripped from the die by the press-actuated mechanical ejector rod.

A 200-ton hydraulic press was used, although the nosing operation required only 91 tons capacity. The die had a carbide insert; lubricant was chlorinated oil. The cap was secured to the shell by silver brazing.

Tubing is commonly pierced and flanged on a press (see Example 555 in the article "Forming of Aluminum Alloys", page 400 in this volume).

Contour roll forming is not only used to make seam welded tubing, but also to produce a variety of cross sections by reshaping the tubing. This process is

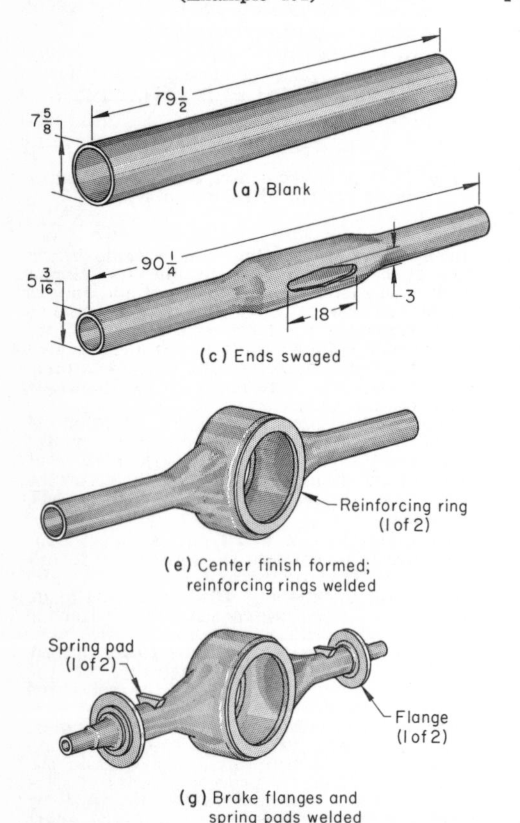

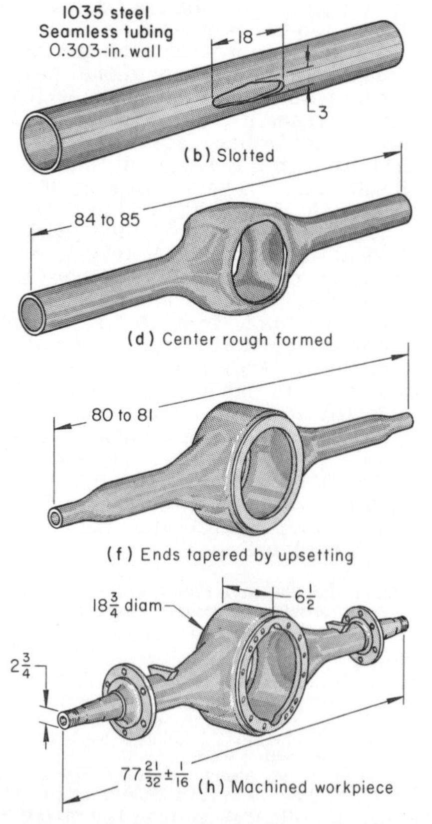

Fig. 19. Steps in production of a rear-axle housing from a tubular blank (Example 402)

discussed in the section on Reshaping of Round Tubing (which includes Examples 306 to 310), on pages 233 and 234 in the article "Contour Roll Forming", in this volume.

Tube spinning is an established method for altering the shape of tubing, most commonly to produce a tubular part having two or more wall thicknesses. Very often tube spinning precedes some other forming operation. Practice is covered in the article "Tube Spinning", which follows. (See also Examples 497 and 503, on pages 374 and 375 in the article "Forming of Heat-Resisting Alloys".)

Rotary Swaging. Shaping of tubing by rotary swaging, with or without a mandrel, is common practice. Procedures for tube swaging are covered in the article "Rotary Swaging of Bars and Tubes", page 333 (note especially Examples 427, 430, 431 and 432).

Hydraulic bulging of tubing is common practice for producing a variety of shapes. Typical practice is described in Example 601, on page 423 in the article on Forming of Copper Alloys.

Explosive forming is sometimes used for reshaping of tubular sections. Specific applications are described in Examples 498, 501 and 503, on pages 374 and 375 in the article "Forming of Heat-Resisting Alloys", and in Example 547, on page 398 in the article "Forming of Aluminum Alloys".

Electromagnetic forming can also reshape tubing. Typical applications are described in Example 339, on page 263 in the article "Electromagnetic Forming", and Example 551, on page 399 in "Forming of Aluminum Alloys".

Electrohydraulic forming can likewise be used for reshaping tubing, as demonstrated by Examples 548 and 549, on pages 398 and 399 in the article "Forming of Aluminum Alloys".

Combination Procedures. Often a tubular blank can be used effectively to produce a specific shape by several different operations, which may include piercing, reducing, expanding and upsetting. The rear-axle housings described in the next example were made in seven steps from tubular blanks. Several types of forming were involved.

Example 402. Rear-Axle Housing Formed From a Tubular Blank (Fig. 19)

The rear-axle housing shown in Fig. 19 was produced from 1035 steel tubing in seven manufacturing operations. The 79½-in.-long tube (Fig. 19a) was first pierced to form the slot (Fig. 19b). Each end was then reduced (at room temperature) from 7⅝ to 5¾6 in. in diameter, as shown in Fig. 19(c). This operation increased total length to 90¼ in. and increased wall thickness in the reduced sections to 0.365 in. (from 0.303 in.). The workpiece was then heated to approximately 1400 F in a gas-fired conveyor-type furnace. In the heated condition, the center section of the workpiece was rough formed (Fig. 19d) by means of an expanding bar that was inserted through the slot, rotated 90°, and expanded with a tapered shaft. While the workpiece was still hot, the tapered transition sections were formed by pulling a shaped plug into each throat area.

The circular section was formed by cold rolling (Fig. 19e). At the same time the flanges were flattened. The flanges were machined and reinforcing rings were welded on as shown in Fig. 19(e). The wheel ends were tapered, reduced in diameter, and increased in wall thickness by hot upsetting (Fig. 19f). The housings were machined to locate the brake flanges and the spring pads, which were welded on (Fig. 19g). Other machining followed. The machined housing is shown in Fig. 19(h).

Tube Spinning

*By the ASM Committee on Spinning**

TUBE SPINNING is a rotary-point method of extruding metal, much like cone spinning, except that the sine law (see page 203) does not apply. Because the half angle of a cylinder is zero, tube spinning follows a purely volumetric rule, depending on the practical limits of deformation that the metal can stand without intermediate annealing (see Table 2 in the article on Spinning, page 204). Tube spinning is also limited by the smallest percentage reduction in thickness that will ensure complete flow of the metal. This minimum reduction is usually 15 to 25%, depending on the metal and on the thickness of the original tube.

Applicability. Spinning is one method of reducing the wall thickness of tubular shapes and increasing their strength, particularly for aircraft and aerospace applications. Producing specific shapes from tubing is a major function of tube spinning. For instance, one or more flanges can be spun at selected areas on a tube, often at savings in the cost of labor and material when compared with other processes, such as machining. Tube spinning also has been used because ring forgings having the desired relation between wall thickness and length were not available (see Examples 405 and 406).

All ductile work metals are suitable for tube spinning; the practical ranges of compositions and strengths are approximately the same as for power spinning of cones. Metals as hard as Rockwell C 35 have been successfully spun. Most tube spinning is accomplished without heating the workpieces.

The amount of wall reduction that can be accomplished without intermediate annealing is given for a number of metals in Table 2 in the article on Spinning, page 204. The amount of permissible reduction is often greater for spinning of tubes than for spinning of cones or hemispheres.

The range of tube sizes that can be spun depends primarily on the available equipment. Tubelike preforms that have an inside diameter in a range from 1¾ to 70 in. have been successfully spun. Wall thicknesses of the starting tubes are often as great as 1.0 in. for steel and 1.25 in. for aluminum.

The minimum size of tube that can be spun is more likely to be a limiting factor than the maximum size, because of machine characteristics. For instance, a large machine is not well suited to spinning small tubing, because it has insufficient spindle speed. The relation of spindle speed and tube size should be such that a minimum of 400 sfm can be obtained.

Preform Requirements. Preform is the name commonly applied to a tube or a tubular shape before it is spun. A preform may be a straight, symmetrical tube, or it may have been changed in shape by the addition of an internal flange for clamping.

Tubular shapes used for spinning include forged or centrifugally cast tubes (both of which are completely machined before spinning), welded tubing, seamless tubing, and extruded tubing.

For spinning, the inside diameter should vary no more than ± 0.002 in. on tubes up to 3 in. in inside diameter, or than ± 0.006 in. on tubes with inside diameters of more than 3 in.

Wall thickness of the preform should be within ± 0.003 in. unless the preform is machined all over, when wall thickness should be within ± 0.001 in. Ovality should be within 0.002 in. for small-diameter preforms (say, less than 3 in.) to within 0.012 in. for large diameters.

Methods of Tube Spinning

Two distinctly different methods or techniques are used for tube spinning — namely, backward and forward. They are so termed because of the directional relations of metal flow and tool travel. In both methods, the workpiece is fixed in one position at one end, and the remaining length is free to slide along the mandrel.

Backward Spinning. In backward spinning, the workpiece is held against a fixture on the headstock, the roller advances toward the fixed end of the workpiece, and the work metal flows in the opposite direction, as illustrated in Fig. 1(a). Two advantages of backward spinning over forward spinning are: (*a*) the preform is simpler for backward spinning, because it slides over the mandrel and does not require an internal flange for clamping; and (*b*) the roller traverses only 50% of the length of the finished tube in making a 50% reduction of the tube wall, and only 25% of the final length for a 75% reduction. The latter advantage not only increases production, but also allows workpieces to be spun that are beyond the normal capacity of the machine. For instance, a machine having only a 50-in. length of stroke can produce a workpiece 100 in. long using a 50% reduction.

The major disadvantage of backward tube spinning is that the first portion of the spun tube must travel the greatest distance and is, therefore, the most susceptible to distortion (Fig. 2). This disadvantage is seldom critical when

*For committee list, see page 201.

spinning tubes of constant wall thickness. However, when the preform has weld sculptures of substantially greater thickness than the tube wall (as in solid fuel cases) distortion can be a problem. For example, in backward spinning of the tube shown in Fig. 2, one side became an inch longer than the other, even though the preform was essentially perfect and the mandrel was accurate within 0.0015 in. TIR.

Forward Spinning. In forward spinning, the roller moves away from the fixed end of the workpiece, and the work metal flows in the same direction as the roller, usually toward the headstock, as shown in Fig. 1(b). The main advantage in forward spinning compared with backward spinning is that it will overcome the problem of distortion (Fig. 2). In forward spinning, closer control of length is possible because as metal is formed under the rollers it is not required to move again, and any variation caused by variable wall thickness of the preform is continually pushed ahead of the rollers, eventually becoming trim metal beyond the finished length.

Disadvantages of forward spinning are: (*a*) some arrangement such as the one illustrated in Fig. 1(b) must be made for clamping the preform to the mandrel at the tailstock end, and (*b*) production is slower in forward spinning because the roller must traverse the finished length of the workpiece.

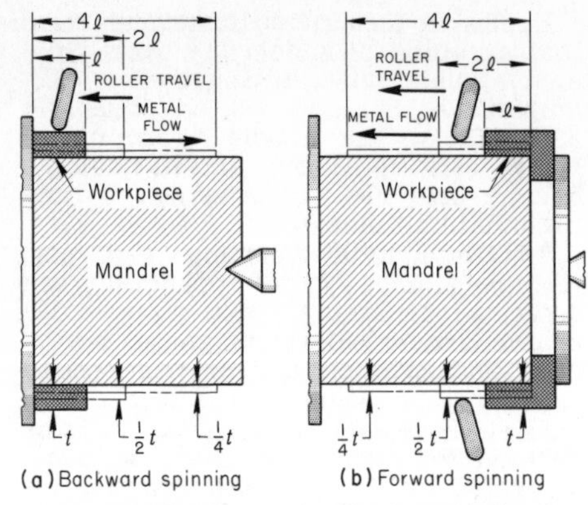

Fig. 1. Metal flow and roller travel in backward and forward spinning of tube

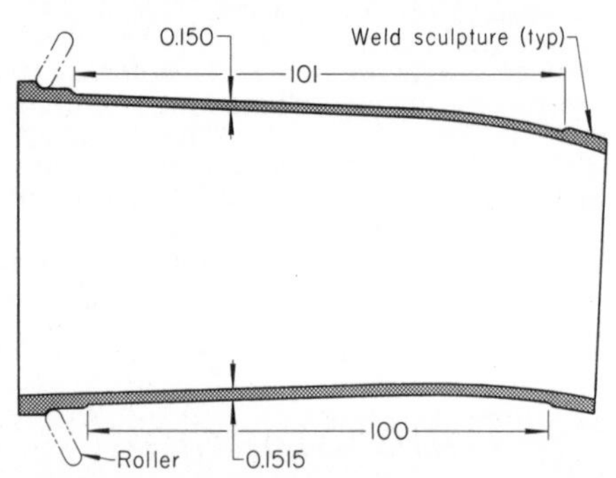

Fig. 2. Example of distortion in backward spinning of tube (see explanation in text)

Machines for Tube Spinning

Machines used for tube spinning are usually the same as those used for power spinning of cones or other shapes. The few special features that are required for tube spinning are normally specified and can be supplied on all power spinning machines. A power spinning machine will have the same size capacity for tube spinning as for cone spinning. A 75-by-100-in. machine has the capacity to spin a tube 75 in. in diameter by 100 in. long. Machines available for tube spinning range in size capacity from 18 in. in diameter by 15 in. long to 120 in. in diameter by 150 in. long. The length dimension applies to the travel of the roller, or tool carriage, so that by using the backward tube-spinning process it is possible to produce a workpiece much longer than is indicated by the size of the machine. The maximum size of the workpiece that can be produced using the backward technique is limited by two considerations:

1. The amount of reduction possible to take on the final spinning operation (a 50% reduction would result in a tube twice as long). The machine force capacity and work-metal characteristics will determine the possible reduction.
2. The clearance provided for workpiece removal. A machine with a capacity of 50 in. usually has enough tailstock motion so that a workpiece 50 in. long can be removed from a mandrel 50 in. long. Many machines have been built with greater-than-standard tailstock clearance so that backward tube spinning can be used to the greatest advantage.

The capacity in terms of force for spinning cones is seldom specified for tube spinning. A machine with the force capability for spinning a 1-in.-thick plate into a cone through a 50% reduction in one operation, does not have the capability of reducing a tube with a 1-in.-thick wall 50% in one pass. Most tube spinning is, therefore, done in smaller reductions per pass.

Cone spinning is a function of shear and the forces necessary to move metal on the shear plane, whereas tube spinning is similar to extrusion, which requires higher compressive forces. This has been determined by sectioning blanks, scribing the surfaces in block patterns, silver brazing them together, spinning them (both shear and tube), and resectioning to expose the scribed surfaces. In the shear-spun parts, the material is displaced along the shear plane, the square blocks resembling parallelograms; in the tube-spun parts, the squares are elongated in the direction of the axis of the tube, but compressed in the radial direction.

Most tube spinning is done on machines with two opposed rollers. This practice minimizes the deflection caused by spinning with one roller, when the length-to-diameter ratio of the mandrel and workpiece is large. Even on machines employing opposed rollers, when the length-to-diameter ratio is excessively large, deflection of the mandrel is often a problem because the mandrel and workpiece are pushed off center. To counteract this problem, machines have been built with more than two rollers. When three or more rollers are used they have the same centering effect as a steady rest. One three-roll tube-spinning machine now in use has a rated capacity of 25-in. diameter by 40-ft length, with special provision for allowing the workpiece to extrude beyond the machine bed.

Because most power-spinning machines used for tube spinning are the same as for cone spinning, they have tracer-control devices so that section thickness can be varied. However, most tube spinning is straight. For spinning straight tubes, mechanical stops are used to limit the travel of the cross-slide units, thereby controlling the diameter of the workpiece.

Tools for Tube Spinning

Tools required for tube spinning are: a mandrel, rollers (two are usually required), a puller ring (for removing the workpiece from the mandrel), a drive ring (which can also be used as a puller ring), tracer styluses (two are required when a tracer is used), and tracer bars (two are required).

Mandrels. Figure 3 shows a typical mandrel for tube spinning, and gives usual ranges of dimensions. Many mandrels are made solid, although as size increases and weight becomes excessive, the usual practice is to hollow them out, either by coring, if made from castings, or by boring if made from forgings or bars. Mandrels are sometimes fabricated from several machined components, as in Example 405.

Mandrel wear is a major problem because of the severe service to which mandrels are subjected. Wear increases as the strength of the work metal increases or wall thickness of the workpiece decreases. The only means of minimizing mandrel wear or deterioration is to make the mandrels from extremely wear-resistant metals.

Alloy cast iron (usually hardened to about Rockwell C 58) is often used as a mandrel material for limited-production spinning. In many instances, alloy cast iron (sometimes used as-cast) has given acceptable results even for medium-production spinning, provided the work metal is easy to spin and the wall of the as-spun workpiece is not too thin. Conversely, when the application is more severe, alloy cast iron mandrels have been known to fail by spalling and pitting after spinning only a few pieces.

Mandrels made of steels such as 4150 and 52100, hardened to about Rockwell C 60, have proved successful for many spinning applications, particularly when severity, as determined by work metal and wall thickness, is considerably less than maximum. In some applications, it has been desirable to sacrifice some wear resistance to gain toughness in the mandrel. Under these conditions, a hot work tool steel such as H12 hardened to Rockwell C 52 to 55 has been used (Examples 405 and 406).

Tool steels such as D2 or D4 hardened to approximately Rockwell C 60 to 62 have proved best for mandrels when service is rigorous, particularly for high-production spinning.

Regardless of what mandrel material is used, best practice calls for a light polishing of the mandrel after every 10 to 20 workpieces, to remove any metal pickup and thus prevent scratches on the inside diameter of the workpiece.

Rollers used for tube spinning are subjected to rigorous service. A typical roller used for tube spinning is illustrated in Fig. 4. The lead angle of the roller shown in Fig. 4 is given as 22°, but this angle is often larger when conditions require a larger angle. A surface finish of 10 micro-in. or better is preferred.

Most rollers used for tube spinning are made from D2 or D4 tool steel, hardened to Rockwell C 60 or slightly higher. Rollers made in accordance with this practice have been known to last for 4000 to 5000 hr when spinning hot rolled tubes of 1020 to 1025 steel. The higher-vanadium types of high speed steels, such as M4 hardened to approximately Rockwell C 62, have also proved to be acceptable roller materials for production spinning.

Staggered rollers that have relatively large radii have been successfully used for forward spinning of workpieces such as missile cases. The two rollers shown in Fig. 5 are staggered radially so that each takes a portion of the total "bite". When this practice is used, the lead roller takes approximately 30% of the total "bite", and the second roller takes the remainder. The large radii on the rollers have the effect of increasing the feed, which results in greater production. The only disadvantage is that more power is required because more metal is moved per unit of time.

Auxiliary Tools. Stock pullers and drive rings are usually made from a low-carbon steel such as 1020. Tracer templates must be made to accurate dimensions; the material composition is not critical, and low-carbon steels are most commonly used. Styluses are made from hardened tool steel, or ball bearings can be used.

Cost of spinning tools depends mainly on their size and the materials from which they are made. For mandrels, the total cost will also depend considerably on whether they are solid or cored. Typical costs for several spinning tools are given in Table 1.

Tube Wall-Thickness Limitations

Limitations on the wall thickness of the preform that is practical for tube spinning are influenced by the formability characteristics of the work metal and available power. Depending on the characteristics of the work metal, the minimum reduction for the first pass is approximately 15% but for many metals it is greater than 15%. Assuming that results can be obtained in reducing wall thickness by 15% on the first pass, the thickness of the displaced layer of metal is 0.075 in. for a 0.500-in.-thick wall, and because the reduction must always be a percentage of wall thickness, power consumption increases as wall thickness increases.

Metals that can usually be spun satisfactorily using a wall reduction of 15% on the first pass include low-carbon and medium-carbon steels, alloy steels (including high-strength steels like D-6ac), and all of the low-carbon stainless steels. Using the largest standard machine presently available, the maximum starting wall thickness for the above metals is about 1.125 in.

Successful spinning of the softer metals, such as the aluminum alloys, requires a higher percentage of reduction per pass (30% minimum) or a large burr will form at the leading edges of the rollers. However, less force is required for spinning aluminum. Thus, for spinning aluminum alloys 2014 and 2024, using the largest available machine, the wall thickness of the preform can still be as great as 1.125 in.

Table 1. Typical Costs of Tools for Spinning Tubes

Tool	Size, in.	Material	Cost
Mandrel	3¼ OD, 72 long	4150 steel	$400
	30 OD, 72 long	Gray iron(a)	$6000
Drive ring	3¼ ID	1020 steel(b)	$30
	30 ID	1020 steel(b)	$375
Stock puller	3¼ ID	1020 steel	$50
	30 ID	1020 steel	$600
Rollers	14 OD, 10 ID, 2¼ wide	D2 tool steel	$350 each
Templates, tracer bars	Up to 12 long; ½ thick	Cold rolled steel	$50 per pair
	Over 12 long; ½ thick(c)	Cold rolled steel	$75 per pair

(a) Cored. (b) Case hardened. (c) Average.

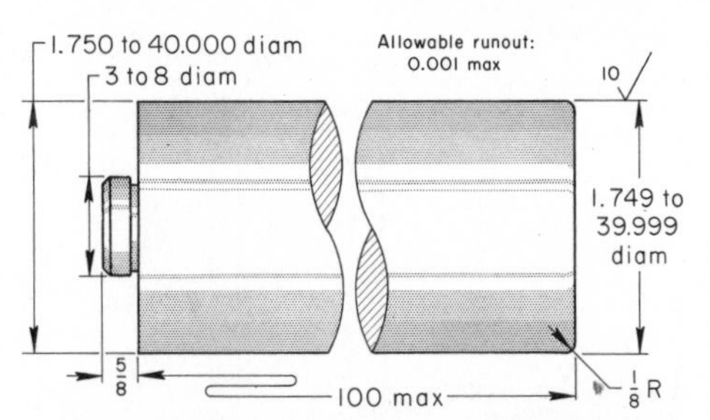

Fig. 3. Typical mandrel for tube spinning, showing usual ranges of dimensions

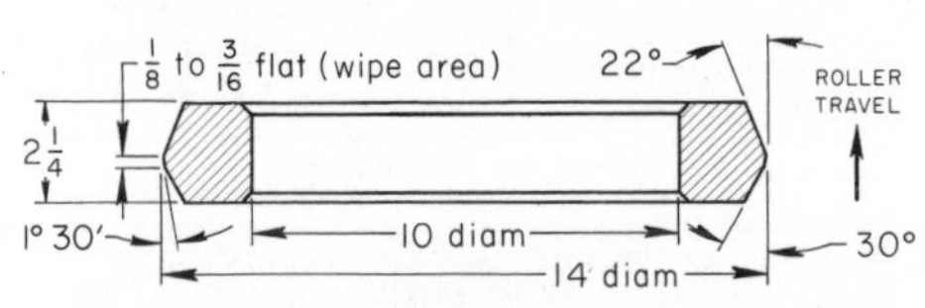

Fig. 4. Details of a typical roller for tube spinning

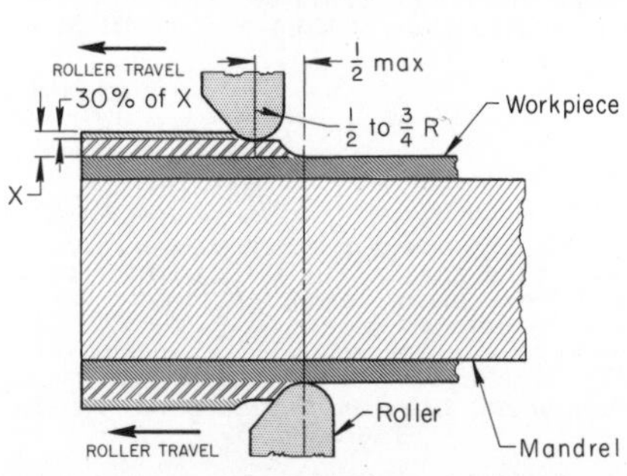

Fig. 5. Large-radius rollers staggered radially for forward spinning of tube, showing how each roller takes a portion of the total bite ("X" in illustration)

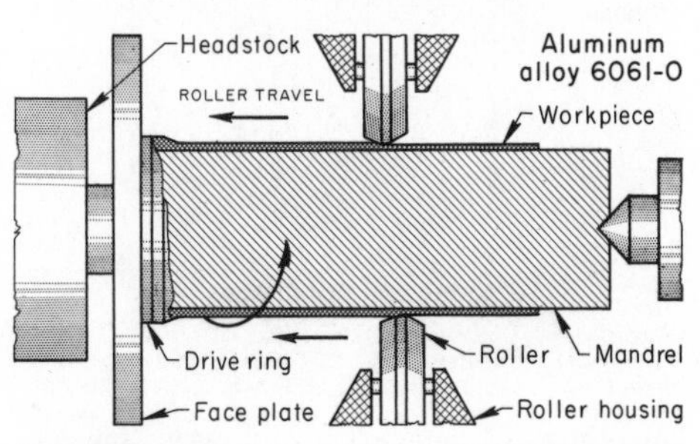

Preform:
- Length .... 19 in.
- Inside diameter .... 20.482 to 20.490 in.
- Wall thickness .... 0.627 to 0.633 in.

Spun tube:
- Length .... 55.5 to 56.5 in.
- Inside diameter .... 20.482 to 20.490 in.
- Wall thickness .... 0.214 to 0.215 in.

Total wall reduction 66%
Number of passes 3
Speed .... 130 rpm (740 sfm, approx)
Feed .... 4 ipm
Lubricant .... Proprietary spinning oil
Time per piece (three passes) .. 21 min (approx)
Tool materials and hardness:
- Mandrel .... Alloy cast iron, Rockwell C 60
- Roller .... D2 tool steel, Rockwell C 60

Fig. 6. Setup for three-pass spinning of a machined aluminum preform (Example 403)

even though the percentage reduction is greater than for higher-strength metals.

To spin extremely soft metals such as 3003 aluminum, percentage reduction per pass must be increased. For spinning this grade of aluminum or other metals at a similar hardness, about 0.500 in. is the maximum wall thickness of the preform. Spinning of thicker-wall preforms of soft metals has been accomplished, but subsequent machining operations were required to produce acceptable surfaces.

Minimum Wall Thickness. The minimum thickness of preform wall that can be successfully spun is not clearly established, although small preforms having walls as thin as 0.040 in. have been spun. Need for spinning extremely thin-walled preforms is infrequent.

Dimensional accuracy of the wall after spinning is not appreciably affected by preform thickness, provided total reduction between process anneals is no greater than 80%.

Production Practice

The five examples that follow describe commercial practice used for tube spinning of aluminum, low-carbon steel and high-strength steel. In all of these examples, either forged or machined preforms were used.

Example 403. Three-Pass Spinning for 66% Reduction of Machined Aluminum Preforms (Fig. 6)

The tool setup used for backward spinning of a machined aluminum preform is shown in Fig. 6. In three passes, the tube wall thickness was reduced by 66% and a final length nearly three times greater than the length of the preform was achieved. Processing details are tabulated with Fig. 6.

Example 404. Three-Pass Spinning for 80% Reduction of Steel Ring Preforms (Fig. 7)

Rolled carbon steel rings were machined to the dimensions of the preform shown in Fig 7. In three spinning passes, the wall thickness of the preform was reduced by 80% and the length was increased from 6 to 22½ in., as shown in Fig. 7. The same procedure was used for spinning similar rings of type 304 stainless steel. Processing details are given in the table that accompanies Fig. 7.

Examples 405 and 406. Cost of Missile Components Made by Use of Spinning

Example 405 (Fig. 8). The forged and machined preform shown in Fig. 8(a) was used to produce a component of a motor case for a solid-propellant missile by spinning. After spinning, mechanical sizing produced the final shape shown in Fig. 8(b). The mandrel was constructed from three pieces fastened together mechanically (Fig. 8c).

The sequence of operations was as follows:

1. Machine the preform from a forging.
2. Spin in three passes to final wall thickness and profile shown in Fig. 8(b), but to inside diameter approximately ½% undersize.
3. Stress relieve at 1200 to 1250 F in a controlled-atmosphere furnace.

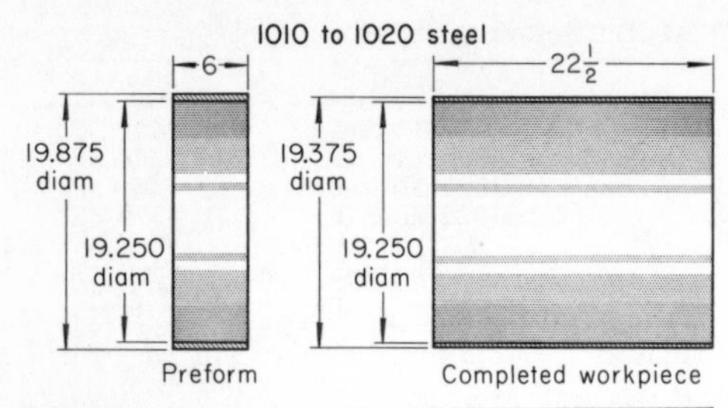

Reduction in:
- First pass ....0.3125 to 0.203 in. (35%)
- Second pass ....0.203 to 0.107 in. (47%)
- Third pass ....0.107 to 0.062 in. (42%)

Total reduction ...(0.3125 − 0.062)/0.3125 = 80%
Speed ....180 rpm (940 sfm, approx)
Feed ....4 ipm
Lubricant ....Proprietary spinning oil
Time per piece (three passes)..16 min (approx)
Tool materials and hardness:
- Mandrel ....Alloy cast iron, Rockwell C 60
- Roller ....D2 tool steel, Rockwell C 60

Roller shape ....22° lead, 3° wipe(a), 3/16-in. flat

(a) Wipe is the 3/16-in. flat on these rollers that is at 3° to the horizontal axis (see Fig. 4).

Fig. 7. Original preform and spun workpiece (Example 404)

4 Blast clean to remove scale resulting from the lubricant or stress relieving.
5 Mechanically size to expand the workpiece approximately ½%, upsetting the thicker ends to divide the thickness equally between the inside and outside diameters, as shown in Fig. 8(b). A diameter tolerance of +0.010, −0.000 in. was maintained.
6 Hold on inside diameter with expanding fixture to maintain roundness while the workpiece is machined to length.

Workpieces were spun in three different makes of machines; two-roller tools were used for all three. The forward-spinning technique was used on two of the three machines.

Alternate methods of producing these missile components proved impractical, mainly because thin-wall forgings 95 in. long were not available. Thus, an alternate method would require a girth weld at approximately the midpoint of the length. However, additional welds were not desired and also the cost would have been more than double (see table with Fig. 8).

Example 406 (Fig. 9). The motor-case section shown in Fig. 9 was produced by essentially the same processing procedure as the larger component described in Example 405 (Fig. 8), except that five spinning passes were used instead of three. The smaller motor-case component could have been made to specifications by machining from a large forging, but this procedure would have been more costly than forging, machining and spinning. Costs for spinning and estimated costs for machining the component from a forging are compared in the table accompanying Fig. 9.

Example 407. Five-Pass Spinning for 89% Reduction in Wall Thickness of High-Strength Steel Preforms (Fig. 10)

Five spinning passes were required to spin a forged and machined alloy steel preform (Fig. 10a) to the shape shown in Fig. 10(b). The workpiece was in the spheroidize-annealed condition before spinning and was stress relieved between the third and fourth spinning passes. Mechanical properties before and after spinning were:

	Before	After
Tensile strength, psi	110,000	277,000
Yield strength, psi	77,400	232,000
Elongation in 2 in., % ..	19.3	9
Rockwell C hardness	20	36

Spinning was done in a 100-hp machine that had a pressure of 2000 psi available on the main and cross slides. Additional processing and tool details are tabulated with Fig. 10.

Sometimes tube spinning is combined with manual spinning or other forming processes to manufacture a part. One such instance is described in Example 275, page 208, in the article on Spinning, where aluminum alloy tank halves were produced by manual spinning, machining and tube spinning.

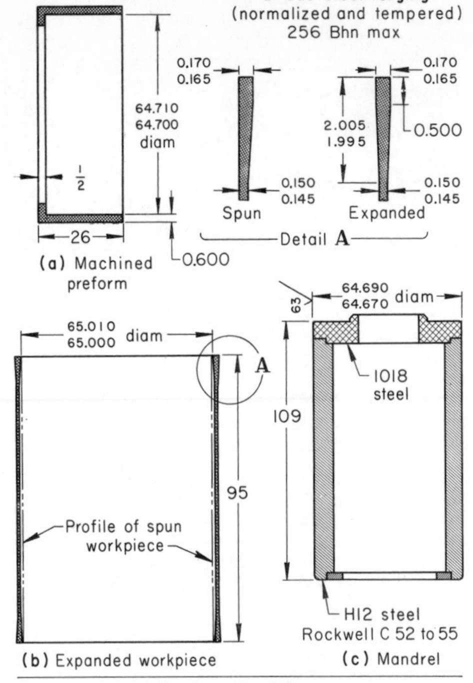

Spinning Conditions

Number of passes 3
Total wall reduction ....0.600 to 0.150 in. (75%)
Speed ....40 to 44 rpm (690 to 755 sfm)
Feed: 1 ipm (pass 1), 2 ipm (pass 2), 3 ipm (pass 3)
Lubricant ..Proprietary high-pressure lubricant
Mandrel material ....H12 tool steel, R_C 52 to 55
Roller material(a) ....D2 tool steel, R_C 57 to 62

Costs

	Spinning	Alternative method(b)
Material	$3000	$10,500
Processing	3500	3,000
Total	$6500	$13,500

(a) Both standard and large-radius types were used (Fig. 4 and 5). (b) Estimated for producing the workpiece entirely by forging, machining and welding.

Fig. 8. Preform and missile motor-case component spun on a fabricated mandrel (Example 405)

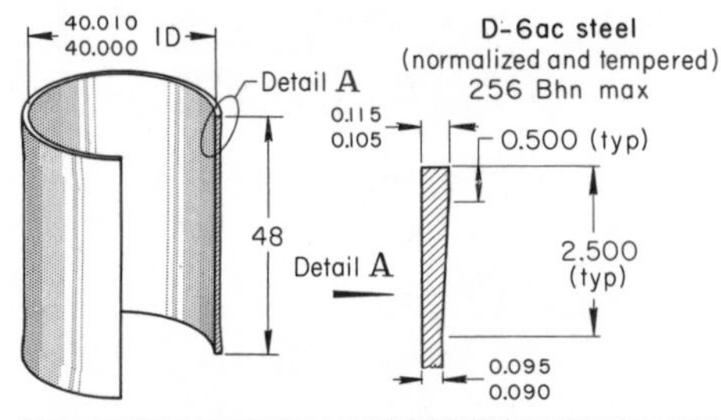

Spinning Conditions

Number of passes ....5(a)
Total wall reduction .....0.500 to 0.090 in. (82%)
Speed ....190 rpm
Feed ....(b)
Lubricant ...Proprietary high-pressure lubricant
Time per piece (five spinning passes) .....2 hr
Mandrel material ....H12 tool steel, R_C 52 to 55
Roller material ....D2 tool steel, R_C 57 to 62

Costs

	Spinning	Alternative method(c)
Material	$ 800	$1800
Processing	700	300
Total	$1500	$2100

(a) After the third pass, the workpiece was process annealed at 1250 F for 4 hr. (b) Feed was 0.060, 0.060, 0.030, 0.080 and 0.045 ipr for passes 1, 2, 3, 4 and 5, respectively. (c) Estimated cost of machining the workpiece from a large forging.

Fig. 9. Center section of a solid-propellant motor case spun from a forged and machined preform (Example 406)

Effect of Machine Variables in Tube Spinning

The two basic machine variables that affect workpiece accuracy are feed per revolution and machine deflection.

Feed per revolution is of concern during the development phase of a tube-spinning operation, because it directly affects finished wall thickness, surface finish, and workpiece diameter. Increased feed per revolution will produce a workpiece having greater wall thickness, smaller inside diameter (inside diameter tighter to the mandrel), and rougher surface finish.

Because feed per revolution and roller radius or bite are interrelated, the effect of changes in feed per revolution can be modified by changes in the dimensions of the roller. An increase in roller radius produces thicker walls, larger inside diameters, and finer surface finishes on spun parts. Therefore, except for the effect on wall thickness, an increase in roller-to-workpiece contact area through the use of increased roller radius has the same effect as a decrease in feed per revolution. Similarly, increasing feed from 0.030 to 0.050 ipr, and roller radius from 0.250 to 0.500 in., may cause an increase in wall thickness but will have little or no effect on inside diameter and surface finish.

To maintain uniform wall thickness, the distance between the roller and the mandrel must be decreased to compensate for increased roller deflection that results from increases in feed per revolution or from increased area of roller contact (larger radius).

Machine deflection varies among different machines and must be determined by experimentation for each different setup. To some extent, deflection can be established for a particular size of machine. For instance, it has been determined that a 42-by-50-in. movable-slide machine will have approximately 0.025-in. deflection when reducing D-6ac steel from a wall thickness of 0.115 to 0.070 in. However, roller shape, roller setting, and feed per revolution can cause a variation in deflection ranging from 0.010 to 0.050 in. Whether or not rollers are staggered (see Fig. 5) has a marked effect on the magnitude of machine deflection.

Further variation in deflection among makes and models of machines can result from slight variations in the mechanical condition of slides, roller synchronizing systems, hydraulic circuits, or gear trains. These variables primarily affect uniformity of feed per revolution — which, if not maintained during spinning, will result in a workpiece with varying wall thickness.

Deflection must be compensated for. One technique for controlling workpiece diameter is by adjustments in feed per revolution. For instance, in Example 406, to permit removal of the workpiece from the mandrel and to compensate for shrinkage during annealing, the third-pass feed was reduced to 0.030 in. per revolution — resulting in a growth of approximately 0.090 in. on the inside diameter. The fourth pass was then run at a feed of 0.080 in. per revolution to shrink the workpiece back on the mandrel, and the fifth pass was made at 0.045 in. per revolution to provide a controlled diameter and a surface finish of 80 micro-in. or better.

Machine variables cause the most difficulty in unit or low production. Once settings have been established for spinning a given workpiece on a specific machine, it remains only to adjust for any changes in roller shape, roller wear, or feed rate. If these adjustments are made, machine variables will not appreciably affect workpiece accuracy during production runs.

Finish of Tube-Spun Parts

Roller radius, composition and condition of work metal, feed per revolution, and lubricants affect the surface finish of tube-spun workpieces.

Roller Radii. Standard rollers for tube spinning, such as that shown in Fig. 4, can be modified for a specific application to produce workpiece finishes as good as 40 to 80 micro-in. Optimum results are usually obtained by modifications in lead angle, relief angle, and width of flat, depending on the work metal and the reduction per pass. When surface finish is of secondary importance, the standard type of roller is preferred because the contact area is low, thus minimizing horsepower requirements. The main disadvantage of standard rollers is that any given shape is restricted to a narrow range of bite; when there is a marked difference in reduction per pass and finish is highly important, it may be necessary to change rollers between passes.

In most tube spinning, optimum surface finish is obtained by using large-radius rollers staggered and offset as shown in Fig. 5. Surface finish of 20 to 40 micro-in. is common when using this type of tooling. The large-radius rollers are also better adapted to producing consistent surface finishes where there is substantial variation in percentage of reduction per pass than are the standard rollers. However, power demand is greater for large-radius rollers than for standard rollers.

Work-Metal Variables. Composition and condition of the work metal affect the surface finish obtained in tube spinning. Some work metals are extremely susceptible to burring and tearing. For instance, 6061-O aluminum alloy can be reduced only a small amount in one pass because of its susceptibility to burring. However, when this alloy is solution treated and aged, good surface finish can be obtained using reductions of 25 to 30% per pass. For best surface finish on some work metals (notably cast preforms of stainless or maraging steels), a common technique is to make one relatively heavy spinning pass (say 30%), and then take a light machining cut to remove burrs and tears prior to additional spinning passes.

Thick walls in conjunction with very small preform diameters, regardless of other conditions, are likely to result in unacceptable surface finish.

Feed per revolution has a marked effect on surface finish in tube spinning. For an otherwise established set of conditions, surface finish becomes rougher as feed rate is increased. In most tube spinning, dimensional accuracy is more important than finish and must be given primary consideration in establishing rates of feed (see the preceding section in this article).

Lubricants. The effect of lubrication on surface finish is less important than might be expected, although efficient lubrication is recommended for obtaining best finish.

During tube spinning, the most reliable indication of lubricant efficiency is obtained by observing the lubricant pattern on the mandrel after workpiece removal. A thin, even film is ideal. Dry spots indicate poor application, or breakdown during forming. Such conditions will result in scratches in the workpiece inside diameter and excessive deterioration of the mandrel.

Lubricants and coolants for all power spinning are discussed on page 207 in the article on Spinning.

Speeds and Feeds for Tube Spinning

The technique for controlling speed is less complex for tube spinning than for cone spinning because in tube spinning there is no substantial change in diameter during a spinning cycle.

In tube spinning, best results are obtained by using speeds considerably higher than would be used for most metal-cutting operations. Speeds used in practice vary widely and depend greatly on the capabilities of the machine; 400 sfm is about the minimum speed for best results in any tube-spinning operation, and speeds much higher than 400 sfm are usually preferred. The minimum speed of 400 sfm often limits the minimum size of the tube that can be spun because of limitations of spindle speed.

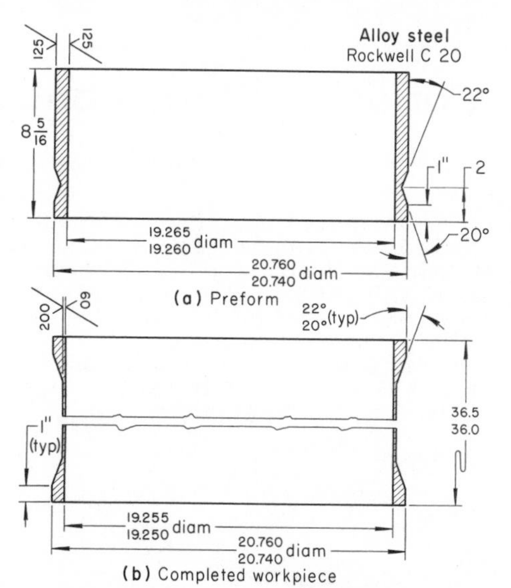

Spinning Conditions

Number of passes 5
Reduction in:
First pass .... 0.750 to 0.616 in. (17%)
Second pass .... 0.616 to 0.418 in. (32%)
Third pass .... 0.418 to 0.220 in. (47%)
Fourth pass .... 0.220 to 0.133 in. (39%)
Fifth pass .. 0.133 to 0.066/0.063 in. (50 to 53%)
Speed .... 200 rpm (1090 sfm, approx)
Feed .... 4 ipm (avg)
Lubricant .... Proprietary spinning oil

Tool Material and Costs

Mandrel construction .... Cored type
Mandrel material .... 52100 steel, R_C 60
Roller material .... D2 tool steel, R_C 60
Cost of:
Mandrel $6000
Rollers (two) 500
Driver-pull ring 300
Templates for tracer 100
Total tool cost $6900

Fig. 10. Forged and machined preform and spun workpiece of high-strength alloy steel (Example 407)

Table 2. Effect of Increasing Reduction in Wall Thickness on Mechanical Properties of 1015 Steel Tube 7¼-In. OD by 6¼-In. ID

Wall thickness, in.	Total reduction, %	Tensile strength, psi	Yield strength, psi	Elongation in 2 in., %
0.501(a)	0	56,000	33,200	34½
0.412	17½	78,500	69,400	13½
0.328	35	83,000	76,200	12½
0.193	61	86,800	78,600	11
0.173	66	87,500	80,400	11

(a) Starting thickness of tube wall

Speeds of 600 to 1200 sfm are most common, mainly because this range is more compatible with spindle speeds for the size of the work being spun.

Maximum speed is not critical for tube spinning. Likewise, there is no close correlation between work-metal composition and spinning speed. This is apparent in the details of Examples 403, 404 and 407. In Example 403, aluminum was spun at 740 sfm, whereas a higher speed was used for spinning low-carbon steel (Example 404) and a still higher speed for spinning a high-strength alloy steel (Example 407). These examples represent the practices used in different plants.

Feeds for tube spinning may be expressed either as inches per revolution (ipr) or as inches per minute (ipm). Feeds used in practice cover a range as great as from 1.5 to 15 ipm. In terms of ipr, feeds vary from approximately 0.003 to 0.080. However, most tube spinning is done at the lower rates of feed. For instance, in Examples 403, 404 and 407, feeds are given as 4 ipm but speeds vary, so the feeds in ipr for the three examples are 0.031, 0.022 and 0.020, respectively.

A higher feed rate usually results in coarser finish on the workpiece. Feeds are often adjusted as required to obtain a specified dimension (see Example 406 and the discussion under Effect of Machine Variables, on the facing page).

Effects of Tube Spinning on Work-Metal Properties

Tube spinning cold works the metal and has a marked effect on its properties; the magnitude of change depends on the percentage reduction and the susceptibility of the metal to work hardening. Table 2 shows how percentage reduction affects the tensile strength, yield strength, and elongation of 1015 steel tube.

The change in strength and ductility for several metals after various percentages of reduction of wall thickness is given in Table 3; the influence of composition is evident. For example, 4130 steel during a wall reduction of 80% increased 72% in tensile strength and decreased 71% in ductility (measured by elongation). In contrast, type 304 stainless steel subjected to the same wall reduction increased 202% in tensile strength and decreased 88% in elongation. (For a further discussion

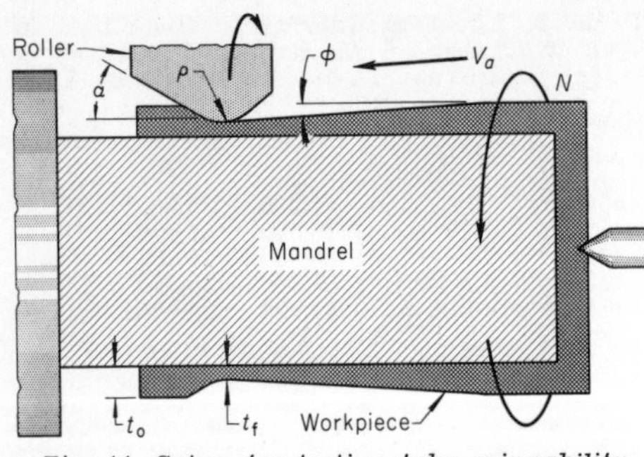

Fig. 11. Setup for testing tube spinnability

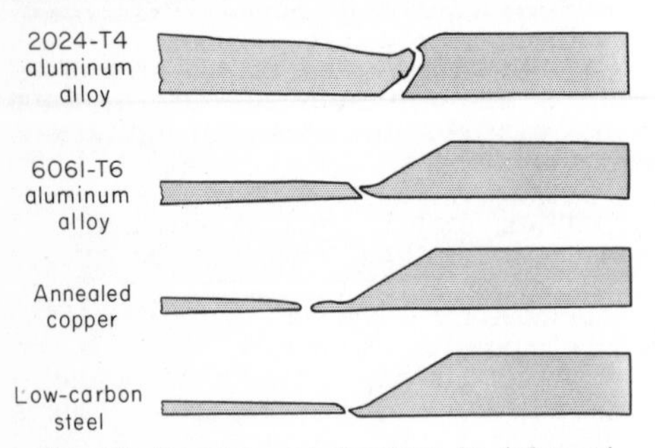

Fig. 12. Location of fracture in tubes of four different metals tested for spinnability

of the effect of spinning on various properties of the work metal, see page 207 in the article on Spinning.

Table 3. Mechanical Properties of Various Metals Before and After Power Spinning

Metal	Reduction in wall, %	Tensile strength, psi Before	Tensile strength, psi After	Yield strength, psi Before	Yield strength, psi After	Elongation in 2 in., % Before	Elongation in 2 in., % After
Carbon steels:							
1010 to 1020 HR	50	56,000	87,000	33,200	78,500	34½	11
1020 CR	65	61,000	110,000	45,000	90,000	30	9
1045	70	75,250	115,000	51,250	102,000	30	8
Alloy steel(a)	91	110,000	277,000	77,400	232,000	19.3	9
4130 steel	80	81,250	140,000	52,250	104,500	28	8
304 stainless steel	80	86,000	260,000	33,800	170,000	65.6	8
Titanium alloy(b)	80	149,000	219,000	140,300	206,000	17.4	5

(a) 0.44 C, 1.49 Si, 1.98 Cr, 0.48 Mo. (b) Ti-13V-11Cr-3Al.

Tube Spinnability

The spinnability of a metal is the maximum reduction it can withstand before failure during spinning.

A test setup for determining tube spinnability by forward spinning is shown in Fig. 11. The roller path was set at an angle, ϕ, of 2° to 4° such that the wall thickness of the tube was gradually reduced from t_o to t_f, where the tube failed. Typical sections from the tests (Fig. 12) show that 2024-T4 aluminum fractured under the roller in a brittle manner, whereas 6061-T6 aluminum, annealed copper, and low-carbon steel all failed in tension behind the roller. A similar transition in the type of failure has also been observed in shear spinning (see Fig. 19 in the article on Spinning, page 207). Experimental data for tube spinnability are included in Fig. 20 in the article on Spinning, page 208, for the case of $\alpha = 30°$, $\rho = 1/8$ in., $\phi = 2°$, $V_a = 3$ ipm, $N = 150$ rpm, and feed $= 0.02$ ipr. The complete agreement between maximum reduction in shear and tube spinning is noteworthy. Thus, as in shear spinning, maximum reduction in tube spinning can be estimated from the reduction of area in a tension test.

In studies of the effects of feed, roller corner radius and roller angle on maximum tube-spinning reduction, only feed had an adverse influence; the other variables had no appreciable influence.

Up to a tensile reduction of area of approximately 45%, maximum reduction in tube spinning depends on the ductility of the metal, and beyond this range there is a maximum spinning reduction of about 80% regardless of the ductility of the work metal (see Fig. 20 in the article on Spinning, page 208).

Straightening of Bars, Shapes and Long Parts

*By the ASM Committee on Straightening of Bars and Tubing**

BARS, bar sections, structural shapes and long parts are straightened by bending, twisting or stretching.

Deviation from straightness in round bars may be expressed either as camber (deviation from a straight line) or as total indicator reading (TIR), per foot or for some other convenient length. Total indicator reading, which is twice the camber, is measured by rotating a round bar on its axis on rollers or centers and recording the needle travel on a dial gage placed in contact with the bar surface, generally midway between the supports. The indicator reading divided by the distance in feet between the supports gives the straightness in TIR per foot. Alternatively, the deviation is expressed in terms of the distance between the supports. The effect that changing the distance between supports has on the reading is illustrated in Fig. 1; the difference in readings illustrates the importance of including support distance and location of indicators in a straightness specification.

Sections other than round are usually checked for camber by placing a straightedge against the bar and measuring with suitable gages the distance between the straightedge and the bar at the midpoint of its length.

In flat bars and structural members, camber is sometimes referred to as the deviation from straightness parallel to the width, and bow as the deviation parallel to the thickness (see Fig. 2).

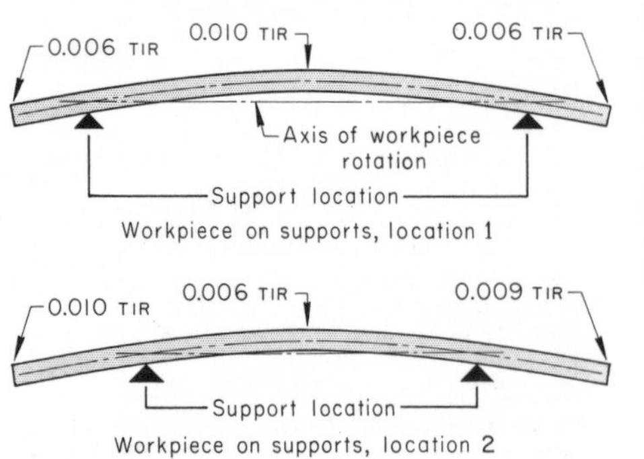

Fig. 1. Effect of distance between supports on straightness readings for round bars

Scant runout is seen at nodes of curvature. If a bar has compound curvature, checking for camber or total indicator reading only at the midpoint of the bar length can be misleading. Serious errors may result unless dial-gage readings are taken at short intervals over the entire length of the bar, or unless gangs of indicators are used at short intervals along the bar.

Straightness Tolerances. Federal Specification 48 ("Tolerances for Steel and Iron Wrought Products") establishes the straightness tolerances on some steels as:

1 Hot rolled carbon steel bars: ¼-in. deviation in any 5 ft or 0.050 in. per ft
2 Hot rolled alloy steel and high-strength low-alloy steel bars: ⅛-in. deviation in any 5 ft or 0.025 in. per ft
3 Hot rolled stainless steel and heat-resisting steel bars for machining: ⅛-in. deviation in any 5 ft, but not to exceed 0.025 in. per ft

*E. GAMMETER, *Chairman,* Chief Metallurgist, Tubular Products Div., Babcock & Wilcox Co.; A. J. BOYLAN, Chief Metallurgist, Michigan Seamless Tube Co.; NORMAN N. BREYER, Professor of Metallurgical Engineering, Illinois Institute of Technology, (formerly, Manager of Technical Products Div., Research and Development Dept., LaSalle Steel Co.); R. E. EIRONS, Chief Metallurgist, Union Drawn Div., Republic Steel Corp.

S. O. EVANS, Manager of Product Planning and Development, Tubular Products Div., Babcock & Wilcox Co.; FRED HEINZELMAN, JR., Vice President, Fred Heinzelman & Sons, Inc.; CECIL J. MCCLURE, General Foreman, Paulo Products Co.; MYNARD MCCONNELL, President, Taylor-Wilson Manufacturing Co.; ROBERT RICHMOND, Assistant Vice President, Midwest Div., Bliss & Laughlin Steel Co.; RAY M. SCHNEIDER, Sales Manager, Bar and Tube Machinery, Foundry and Mill Machinery Group, Blaw-Knox Co.

O. J. SKAWDEN, Vice President, Sutton Engineering Co.; M. F. STEELHAMMER, Superintendent of Rod and Wire Mill, Alloy Metals Products Div., H. M. Harper Co.; M. W. TUFTS, Director of Research, Wyckoff Steel Div., Screw and Bolt Corp. of America.

4 Cold finished carbon steel bars; turned, ground and polished bars; or drawn, ground and polished bars: machine straightened within limits reasonable for satisfactory machining in an automatic bar machine.
5 Cold finished stainless steel and heat-resisting steel bars for machining: 1/16-in. deviation in any 5 ft, but not to exceed 0.0125 in. per ft
6 Carbon steel, stainless steel and heat-resisting steel structural shapes (except wide flange sections): 0.025-in. deviation per ft
7 Wide flange sections used as beams: 0.0125-in. deviation per ft
8 Wide flange sections used as columns: up to 45 ft long, 0.0125-in. deviation per ft, but not over 3/8 in.; over 45 ft long, 3/8 in. plus 0.0125 in. per ft beyond the 45-ft length.

Manual Straightening

The original method of hand straightening is still used extensively when accuracy and precision are required or when the shape of the bar or part makes machine straightening impractical.

The tools used in manual straightening include hammers and mallets, anvils, surface tables, vises, levers, grooved blocks, grooved rolls, twisting devices, various fixtures, and heating torches. The use of a grooved block (Fig. 3a) illustrates the basic principle of manual straightening by bending.

Shafts for centrifugal irrigation pumps are an example of parts that usually must be manually straightened, because of the accuracy required and the necessity for doing the work at the installation site. Most of these shafts are 10 to 20 ft long, have diameters of 3/4 to 2 in., and are of cold drawn 1045 steel. The steel supplier generally straightens the cold drawn stock within 0.005 or 0.010 in. TIR in 10 ft, but the shafts are often bent slightly in transport and in handling. It is common to hand straighten the shafts at installation, within 0.005 in. TIR in 20 ft. The shafts are rotated on supports and are deflected by using a lever.

Special cold drawn sections as long as 12 ft are commonly straightened manually. Many special sections are enough like standard flats that they can be straightened in standard two-direction roll straighteners, but quantities often are too small to warrant the cost of special rolls. Other special sections may be too complex in shape for machine straightening.

Special sections almost always have twist after cold drawing. The twist must be removed before the section can be straightened. One end of the section is held in a vise or in a special fixture while the other end is twisted with a wrench or special handle. When the twist is corrected, the bar can be straightened to remove camber and bow.

Example of Practice. The example that follows describes an application of manual straightening in which a change in procedure that eliminated one operation saved money.

Example 408. Original and Improved Procedures for Manual Straightening After Heat Treatment (Table 1)

An aircraft bar wing of modified 4330 steel was heat treated to Rockwell C 46 to 49. A straightness tolerance of 0.015 in. was required on the over-all length of 34¼ in. Originally, the piece was manually straightened twice, once after martempering and again after double tempering in a fixture.

An improved method, using the same heat treating procedures as in the original method, reduced cost by 37½% by eliminating the first straightening operation, a subsequent stress-relieving treatment, and the holding fixture used during double tempering. The double-tempering time was cut in half for each period because the holding fixture was not used. Less time was required for the single straightening operation than for the two straightening operations in the original procedure. A cost comparison for the two methods is given in Table 1.

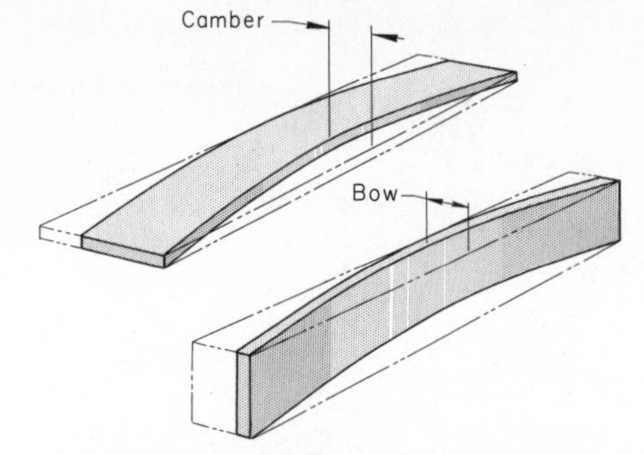

Fig. 2. Camber and bow in flat bars

Table 1. Cost Comparison for Two Methods of Hand Straightening of an Aircraft Part (Example 408)

Item	Cost per piece — Original method	Cost per piece — Improved method
Load parts	$ 0.50	$ 0.50
Heat treat and martemper	3.00	3.00
Straighten	1.00	...
Stress relieve	1.00	...
Clean	1.50	1.50
Clamp in fixture(a)	1.00	...
First temper	4.00	2.00
Second temper	4.00	2.00
Unload fixture	1.00	...
Rockwell test	0.50	0.50
Hand straighten	1.50	2.00
Hone	1.00	1.00
Total	$20.00	$12.50

(a) Four pieces per fixture

Straightening by Heating

Alloy steel bars and shapes with a hardness greater than Rockwell C 50, and fabricated stainless steel parts, frequently warp because of stress set up during fabrication, machining or heat treatment. These items can usually be straightened by the application of heat and, in most instances, of force. The heat can be localized in the area to be straightened, or the entire piece can be heated — either to the tempering temperature or to about 50 F below it. Low-carbon steel bars can also be straightened by heating.

Localized Heating. Torches are used to apply heat to the convex side of warped parts. A small area is heated to a dull red. The localized heating causes the workpiece to expand, but during cooling some straightening occurs. Skillful heating, cooling and gaging of the workpiece can result in reasonable straightness.

Torch heating causes soft spots in hardened steel workpieces; also, localized heating with a torch can cause localized residual tensile stress that can be undesirable even in an unhardened workpiece if it is subjected to cyclic loading.

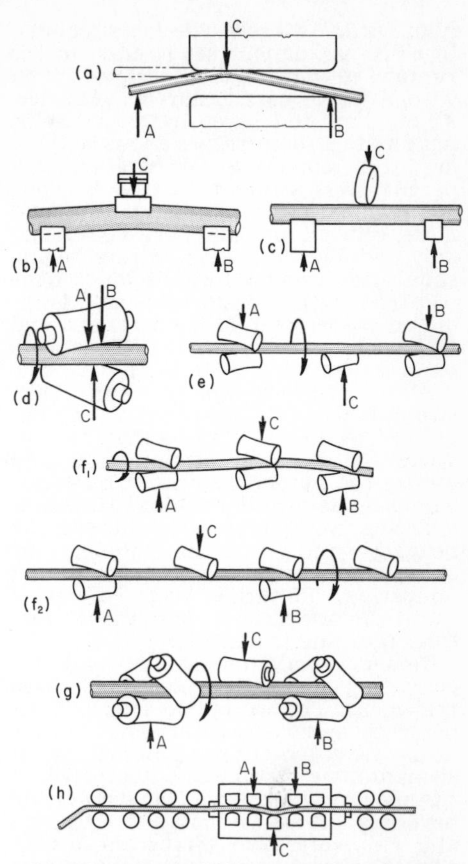

(a) Manual straightening with a grooved block. (b) Straightening in a press. (c) Simplest form of rotary straightening. (d) Two-roll straightening. (e) Five-roll straightening. (f_1 and f_2) Two arrangements of rolls for six-roll straightening. (g) Seven-roll straightening. (h) Wire straightening.

In all methods shown, the bar is supported at points A and B, and force at C on the convex side causes straightening. (See text and later illustrations for details of the straightening methods shown here.)

Fig. 3. Principle of straightening by bending

In press straightening with the use of localized heat, the workpiece is supported at each end with suitable blocks. A stop block is placed directly under the ram to limit the amount of deflection. With the high points of its curvature up, the workpiece is pressed down until it rests lightly on the stop block, and then heat is applied. For a heat treated workpiece, the amount of heat is usually governed by the original tempering temperature, and the distance the workpiece can be deflected and released without fracture depends on the type and hardness of the steel, heat treatment, and shape of the workpiece. Another method of controlling deflection without breakage is to place the workpiece on shims on a flat surface and to apply pressure to the surface of the workpiece, heat and release. If the workpiece still is not straight, either use more shims and reheat or allow the workpiece to cool longer before releasing the pressure.

Where a flame cannot be effectively directed, or may damage the metal, a small weld bead can sometimes be used as the source of heat. Weld beads are applied to the convex area, allowed to cool, and machined off if necessary.

Heating Below Tempering Temperature. Heating and press straightening are not generally applicable to steel at high hardness levels. The force required to cause permanent set is close to the rupture strength of the steel, and even with extreme care failure is probable. At medium and lower hardness levels, heating to a temperature about 50 F below the tempering temperature will permit press straightening to be done successfully. Straightening becomes more difficult as the part cools, and only slight corrective straightening should be attempted at the lower temperature levels. Considerable skill is required to perform such operations and to hold tolerances within 0.003 to 0.010 in. over a length of 18 to 48 in.

After the workpiece has been straightened it is tempered to the required hardness. Tempering relieves stress set up during straightening and during the hardening cycle. This stress will often deform the workpiece; consequently, workpieces straightened by heating and pressing should be clamped in restraining fixtures during tempering. Fixturing can correct a slight distortion and also prevent distortion during tempering.

Temper straightening is used for correcting distortion caused by heat treatment. The workpiece first is tempered to a hardness somewhat higher than required, then clamped in a straightening fixture and tempered to the required hardness. The greater the hardness difference between the first and the corrective tempering operations, the more accurate the dimensions will be. Temper straightening is most successful at hardness levels of Rockwell C 55 and lower.

Deep-hardening alloy and tool steels that are being martempered to minimize distortion should be held straight during the cooling period after austenitizing and until the completion of martempering. If straightness is not maintained throughout martempering, the workpiece will warp as martensite continues to form. Straightening should be done below 900 F. Cold bars or chills contacting the high side will more rapidly extract the heat from the workpiece and aid in straightening.

Straightening in Presses

Round bars up to 2 in. in diameter and from 2 to 10 ft long are often straightened in an arbor press. Larger workpieces are similarly straightened in power presses, which may have power rolls and hoists to move the work.

The principle of press straightening is illustrated in Fig. 3(b). The bar to be straightened is supported at points A and B with the convex side of the bow or kink toward point C. Sufficient force is applied at C to cause the bar to become bowed in the opposite direction. The force must be great enough to exceed the elastic limit of the material, but it must set up just enough strain in the bar to allow it to return to the straight position (but no farther) when the pressure is released. The greater the bow in the bar and the higher its elastic limit, the greater the force required to produce the correct amount of strain. To straighten a bar by press straightening, the metal must be capable of cold deformation, and it must strain harden.

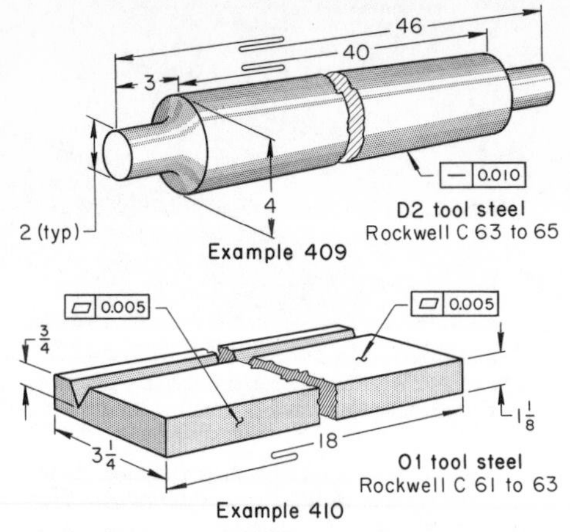

Fig. 4. Shaft and grooved bar that were press straightened after heat treatment (Examples 409 and 410)

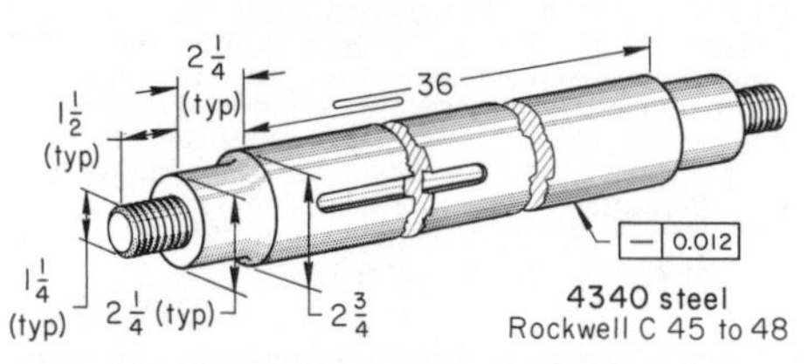

Fig. 5. Shaft that was straightened by pressing and fixture tempering (Example 411)

In press straightening, the operator usually locates kinks or bows in round bars by holding a piece of chalk close to the surface of the bar and then rotating the bar so that any high spots will be marked by the chalk. The high spot is then brought under the ram of the straightening press, and sufficient force is applied to take out the kink or bow. In shapes other than rounds, the out-of-straight condition must be detected by eye or with the aid of a straightedge. This type of straightening requires considerable skill on the part of the operator. A straightening press is sometimes referred to as a "gag press" and the straightening operation as "gagging".

Hydraulic or mechanical presses are used for straightening bars, shapes and shaftlike parts before, between and after heat treating operations. Some bars that are roll straightened do not meet straightness requirements and must receive a final press straightening. Presses are also used to straighten large-diameter bars in preparation for turning or grinding. Finish ground or turned products with highly finished surfaces are press straightened to avoid the spiral marks produced by rotary straightening. Press straightening does not change the size of the bar, whereas rotary straightening, by the rolling action, or the alteration in residual stress caused by bending, or both, may cause a change in bar size.

Some high-strength steels and stainless steels are too hard to be straightened in any way except in a press, and some metals are too hard to be straightened without heat, unless the bar is first annealed. Cold straightening bars of these metals may cause the bars to break.

Press straightening is easier when the bar has a hardness of less than Rockwell C 40. The bar can be retempered to relieve the stress introduced in straightening.

In a straightening press, a round bar usually is set on spring-loaded rollers near the ends of the bar. Thus, the bar can be rotated on its axis while a dial gage shows any deviations from straightness. As the press ram moves down, it presses the bar into V-blocks that support the straightening pressure. This action is repeated, sometimes with the bar shifted or the roller supports moved, until the bar is straight enough to meet specifications. The V-blocks and roller supports can be moved to change the leverage and to adjust the application of the force. A straightening press is better suited to the correction of short bends and kinks than to the correction of long bends.

A straightening press can hold distortion of heat treated bars and shafts to 0.010 in. or less, as shown in the following three examples.

Examples 409, 410 and 411. Straightening of Heat Treated Bars and Shafts in a Press

Example 409 (Fig. 4). A D2 tool steel shaft with a hardness of Rockwell C 63 to 65 and a straightness specification of 0.010 in. TIR is shown in Fig. 4. The shaft was hung in a vertical furnace, preheated to 400 F, 1000 F and 1500 F, before heating at 1850 F. The part was air cooled to 500 F. Since inspection at that temperature showed distortion of 0.015 to 0.025 in. TIR, the bar was straightened in a manual hydraulic press to 0.007 in. TIR before it cooled to 400 F. At 150 F, the shaft was again straightened to within 0.007 in. TIR.

The shaft was clamped in a V-block for tempering at 300 F for 6 hr, then given a subzero treatment and straightened to within 0.008 in. TIR. The shaft was again clamped in the V-block, using shims for straightening, while being retempered at 300 F for 6 hr. Final straightening in the press was to 0.007 in. TIR, which was better than was required.

Example 410 (Fig. 4). A flat bar of O1 tool steel having a ¾-in.-deep V-groove along one edge is shown in Fig. 4. The specified hardness was Rockwell C 61 to 63. The top and sides had to be flat within 0.005 in.

The bar was preheated to 1100 F, heated at 1480 F and marquenched at 375 F. The bar was then clamped in a fixture and cooled to 100 F. Inspection showed 0.006-in. maximum variation for the top and side. The bar was reclamped in the fixture, and was tempered at 300 F to a hardness of Rockwell C 63 to 64. The bar was reclamped with shims to straighten it, and was retempered at 325 F to a hardness of Rockwell C 61 to 62. The bar was then straightened in a press within 0.005 in. at the top and side.

Example 411 (Fig. 5). A 43½-in.-long shaft of 4340 steel is shown in Fig. 5. Specified hardness was Rockwell C 45 to 48. Straightness was to be held within 0.012 in. TIR.

The shaft was hung in a vertical furnace, preheated to 1100 F, heated to 1560 F, then martempered at 450 F.

Inspection showed a straightness error of 0.055 in. at the keyway. The shaft was straightened in a mechanical press within 0.012 in. It was then clamped in a fixture and tempered at 700 F, which reduced the straightness error to 0.010 in TIR. The shaft was reclamped with shims to straighten, and was retempered at 775 F to the specified hardness. The shaft was then straight within 0.008 in. TIR.

If the workpieces in Examples 409, 410 and 411 had been heat treated without being clamped, they would have been free to distort and would have needed more press straightening. Straightening of bars and shafts during transformation and during tempering is more efficient and costs less, and it is sometimes the only way in which straightness specifications can be met.

Structural parts for aircraft are commonly straightened by a combination of methods, as shown in the five examples that follow.

Examples 412 to 416. Straightening of Structural Shapes by a Combination of Methods

Example 412 (Fig. 6). A structural aircraft part called a cap was made from modified 4330 steel bar 3⁄16 in. thick by 66 in. long (Fig. 6). The part was channel shaped with one flange removed for a portion of its length to produce an angle section. Holes ⅛ in. in diameter were made in both sides of the angle section and in the channel section. Heat treatment consisted of suspending the workpiece by the angle end in a salt bath at 1550 F for ½ hr, quenching in salt at 470 F, and air cooling. After being heat treated, the parts were cleaned and checked for hardness (aim was Rockwell C 46 to 49). With hardness less than Rockwell C 50, a subzero treatment was given prior to tempering; with hardness of Rockwell C 50 or harder, the workpiece was clamped in a fixture, tempered at 600 F for 5 hr and finally air cooled. The workpiece warped about 1 in. in 66 in. after quenching, and a warp of about ¼ in. remained after fixture tempering. A camber of ¼ in. was easily removed manually, but a workpiece with a camber of more than ¼ in. was retempered in the fixture before straightening. Shape and straightness were checked in a fixture using a 0.020-in. feeler gage. After being tempered at 600 F, the workpiece had a hardness of Rockwell C 46 to 49.

Rotation of about 60° was required to correct for 0.030-in. twist. A 10-ton hydraulic press was used to correct short bends. The workpiece was supported on slotted blocks, placed about 14 in. apart, which gave support to the flanges while pressure was applied. A force of about 3000 lb deflected the channel section ⅜ to ½ in. for a camber correction of 0.020 in. per 6 in. A force of 1000 to 1500 lb on the angle section produced about the same deflection and correction.

Stretching was used to maintain spacing and alignment for the ⅛-in.-diam holes. Because of the thin sections, the part shrank 0.030 to 0.040 in. after quenching in salt at 470 F. To correct this shrinkage, the part was preheated at 550 F for ½ hr, then clamped in the tempering fixture and heated at 600 F for 5 hr. As the fixture expanded from the heat, the part was stretched. After slowly cooling in the fixture, the part had a permanent stretch of 0.020 to 0.030 in., which corrected hole alignment and spacing.

About 8 min was required for clamping the part in the tempering fixture, and 22 min for hand straightening.

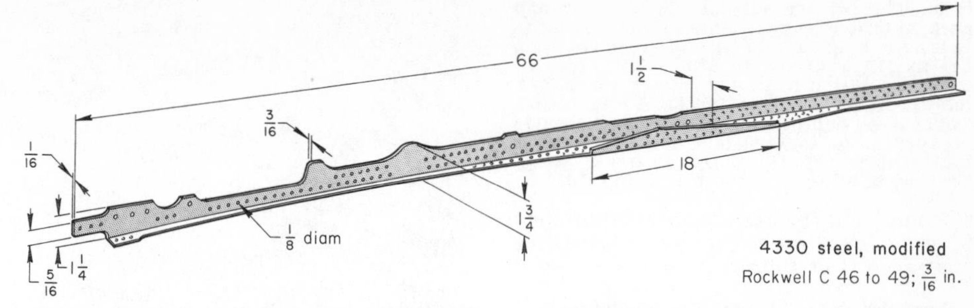

Fig. 6. Aircraft part that was straightened by a combination of methods (Example 412)

Example 413 (Fig. 7). A welded double-channel structural member made of 4340 steel, 72 in. long and weighing 11.5 lb (Fig. 7) was austenitized at 1525 F for 40 min, martempered at 470 F, stress relieved at 400 F, and cleaned. The unusual feature of this operation was the simultaneous straightening, bending and tempering.

The workpiece was machined on a straight plane and then fixture bent 7° on one end during tempering. The fixture was constructed with various gibs and filler blocks milled to fit the contours of the workpiece, including allowance for the 7° bend, which extended for approximately 12 in. (Fig. 7). The workpiece was then placed on the fixture, and all holding clamps were placed in position. The fixture-and-workpiece assembly was then heated to 600 F. At this time all clamps were tightened, thus making the 7° bend at one end. The assembly was then heated (tempered) to 1000 F for 4 hr.

After tempering, the channel was straightened in a hydraulic press to achieve final alignment within 0.030 in. A special gage was used to inspect alignment and the bend. Time for straightening and gaging was 30 min.

Example 414. An aircraft bar wing ⅝ by 1¼ by 34¼ in. and weighing 5 lb was made of 4330 steel bar. The bar was preheated to 1200 F, austenitized at 1575 F for 40 min, martempered in salt at 470 F, and tempered twice at 600 F for 2 hr each time to a hardness of Rockwell C 46 to 49. After the second temper and while still hot, the part was placed in a vise and straightened by hand within 0.040 in.

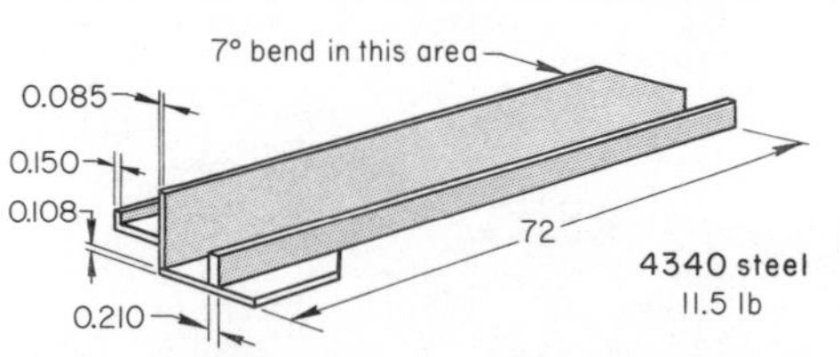

Fig. 7. Welded structural member that was straightened during and after heat treatment (Example 413)

Using a wrench to twist the bar, 45° corrected a twist of 0.030 in. As quenched, the bar was usually warped ¼ in., which required as much as a 6-in. deflection to straighten. Short bends were removed in a 10-ton hydraulic press, with the bar supported on blocks 14 in. apart. A 3000-lb force was applied in the 1¼-in. direction and a 1000-lb force in the ⅝-in. direction, with a total deflection of 1 to 1½ in. The part was moved, rotated and pressed until the camber was within 0.015 in. About 10 min was required for straightening each bar.

Example 415 (Fig. 8). A structural bar with a tapered-width channel, 3⁄16 in. thick and 66 in. long, was made of 17-4 PH stainless steel (Fig. 8). The part was solution treated to Rockwell C 39 to 42, finish machined, and then aged for 1 hr at 900 F. It was straightened to within 0.015-in. camber in a hydraulic press upon removal from the aging treatment. The part could be straightened only until it cooled to 700 F, which took 10 min. Since 20 min was required to straighten the part, reheating to 900 F was necessary.

The channel was supported on two blocks 16 in. apart while force was applied by a pressure ram through a block fitted to the inside contour (upper view in Fig. 8). A force of 3000 lb deflected the part about 1 in. for a correction of 0.020 in. Force was applied at 2-in. increments along the bar.

Two 5-ton hydraulic presses mounted on a large steel table were used to remove the twist. One ram held one end of the part against a block on the table while the second ram untwisted the part (Fig. 8, lower view). A slotted bar served as a lever to twist the channel 30° for a permanent correction of 0.020 in. for each 24 in., or 0.050 in. for the entire length.

Example 416 (Fig. 9). A welded, I-beam-shaped aircraft longeron of 17-4 PH stainless steel with maximum dimensions of 6 by 6 by 72 in. is shown in Fig. 9. The longeron was solution treated at 1900 F for 30 min, cooled to 1200 F, then clamped in a holding fixture on the shims shown in Fig. 9 for cooling to 300 F. In addition to warped flanges, the part had a full-length camber of about ½ in. after solution treatment and about ⅛ in. after cooling in the fixture.

After cooling to 300 F in the fixture, the part was removed and aged at 1050 F for 4 hr, then manually straightened to within 0.060 in. While still hot, the part was placed in a 100-ton hydraulic press on ½-in.-thick shims, spaced 36 in. apart. To remove the camber, the part was pressed to the baseplate, held a few seconds, then released. This was repeated over the entire length by moving the part 6 in. each time until it was straight within 0.060 in. Badly warped parts required the use of chill blocks to shrink the heated metal while it was being deformed by pressure. Chill blocks were especially useful at the round welded section, because the part could fracture easily in this area.

A long, thin rectangular bar was heat treated and straightened in a press by the procedure described in the following example:

Example 417. Straightening a Long, Thin Rectangular Bar in a Hydraulic Press

A rectangular bar of 17-4 PH stainless steel was 3 in. wide, 84 in. long, and ¼ in. thick (except for 3 in. at each end, where it was 1 in. thick). The bar was solution treated and finish machined, which caused a bowing of

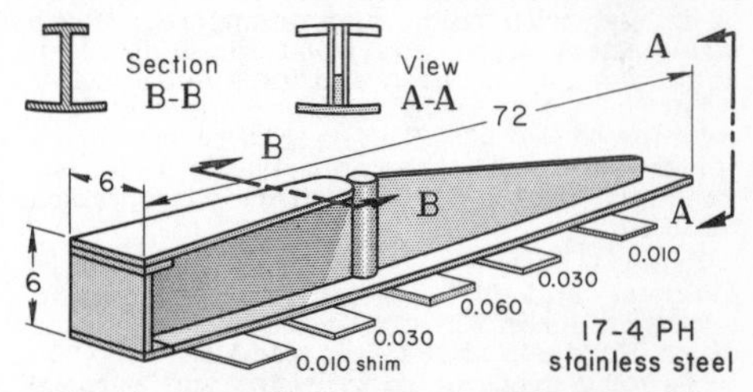

Fig. 9. Aircraft longeron weldment with warped flanges and excessive camber, which required both fixture and press straightening (Example 416)

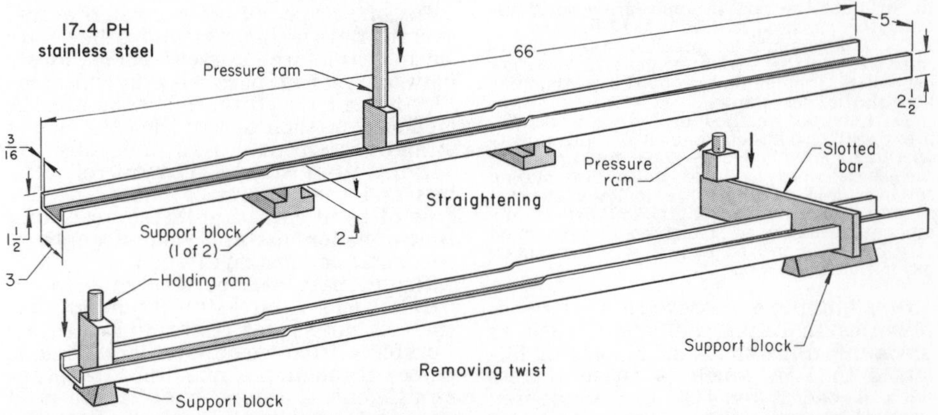

Fig. 8. Setups for straightening and removing twist from a stepped channel (Example 415)

¼ in. The bar was clamped in a fixture and aged at 900 F, which reduced the bowing to ⅛ in. After aging, the bar was removed from the fixture, reheated to 800 F, and straightened in a 10-ton hydraulic press, using 3000-lb force between support blocks 16 in. apart. This caused deflection of ¾ in. for a correction of 0.030 in. It took 20 min and two to three ram strokes per 16-in. setup, and 5 setups per bar, to straighten the bar within 0.060 in.

Round shafts are often straightened before they are ground, as in the three examples that follow:

Examples 418, 419 and 420. Straightening of Shafts in Preparation for Grinding

Example 418. A shaft of medium-carbon steel, 4 in. in diameter by 20 ft long, was heat treated to 269 to 321 Bhn, straightened for turning, turned in a lathe, and then straightened for centerless grinding. The shaft lay on rollers beneath the ram of the press, which permitted it to be rotated and also to be moved along its axis. Spring-loaded blocks supported the rollers so that straightening pressure would first deflect the springs, letting the shaft down on movable V-block anvils for straightening. The springs pushed the rollers up, lifting the shaft off the anvils when the ram moved up. The shaft was rotated under a dial indicator to find the high spots. The spots were marked with chalk so that they could be moved beneath the ram. The shaft was straightened within tolerance by pressing, moving the shaft, and pressing again. In an 8-hr day, 5 to 15 shafts were straightened.

Example 419. After being heated to 1850 F and air cooled, a shaft of D2 tool steel, 2 in. in diameter by 66 in. long, was straightened within 0.020 in. The straightening began when the shaft had cooled to 900 F from 1850 F. A 10-ton hydraulic press applied 2000-lb force to the shaft, which was supported on anvil blocks 18 in. apart. The shaft was continuously gaged with dial indicators as it was rotated on its axis, to check the location of the high and low points.

Between 900 and 500 F the shaft deflected easily, 2000 lb causing a deflection of ⅛ in. per 20 in. When the shaft cooled further, straightening was more difficult and required increased force and a longer holding time.

Gaging and straightening continued until the shaft had cooled to 150 F; then the shaft was tempered at 900 F for 2 hr, resulting in a hardness of Rockwell C 59 to 60. Sometimes a difficult shaft was clamped to a 3 by 3 by 72-in. bar with shims and retempered. If the straightness error was 0.080 in., a 0.060-in. shim was used on each end for a deflection of 0.140 in. (0.060 + 0.080 in.), and the shaft was retempered at 925 F. The higher tempering temperature made the shaft slightly softer but generally straightened it within the specified 0.020 in.

Example 420. Shafts of 1045 steel, ⅝ in. in diameter and 21⅝ in. long, were induction hardened 1¾ in. on one end and 2 in. on the other. Hardness at the ends was Rockwell C 56 to 60 for a depth of 1/32 to 1/16 in., and warpage was 0.010 to 0.030 in. The straightness tolerance was 0.005 in. Originally, a hand arbor press was used for straightening the shafts, and stationary V-blocks were used for supports. The operator moved the shafts back and forth under the ram to apply pressure. A dial indicator was used to locate the high and low spots. The amount of pressure was undeterminable, and the amount of deflection was not controlled. Production rate by this method was two shafts per minute.

An improved method used an air-operated press with stroke-length control and a foot-operated control valve. V-blocks for supporting the shaft were mounted on a free-moving carriage, making it possible to lower the ram at any point on the shaft and deflect any amount necessary to straighten it. Production rate by the improved method was four shafts per minute.

Straightening presses are used as accessories to other equipment, such as blooming mills that roll blooms or billets 5 to 7 in. thick. A 200-ton press with a bed 2 by 4 ft can straighten such blooms or billets within ¼ in. per 6 ft in lengths as great as 16 ft, without the use of spacers or shims. Many blooms or billets do not need straightening — for instance, if they are to be cut into pieces for forging stock.

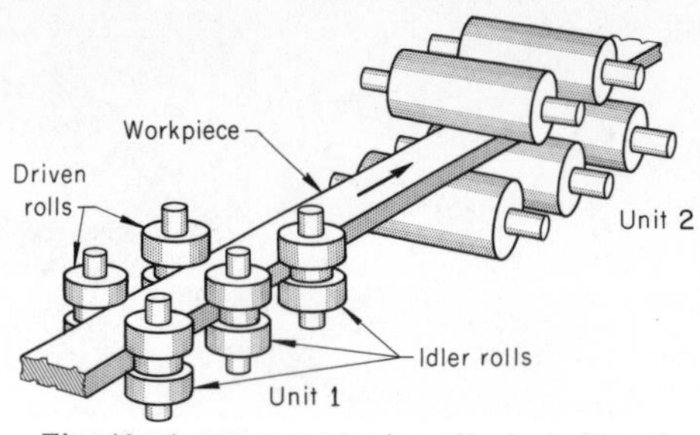

Fig. 10. Arrangement of vertical-shaft and horizontal-shaft rolls in a roll straightener for straightening a rectangular-section bar

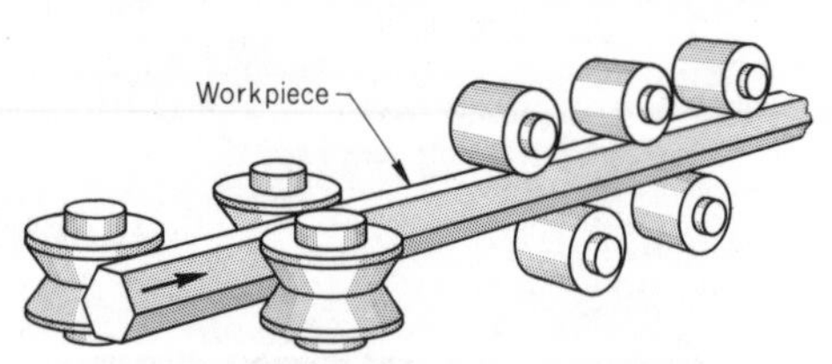

Fig. 11. Straightening of a hexagonal bar in a two-plane roll straightener

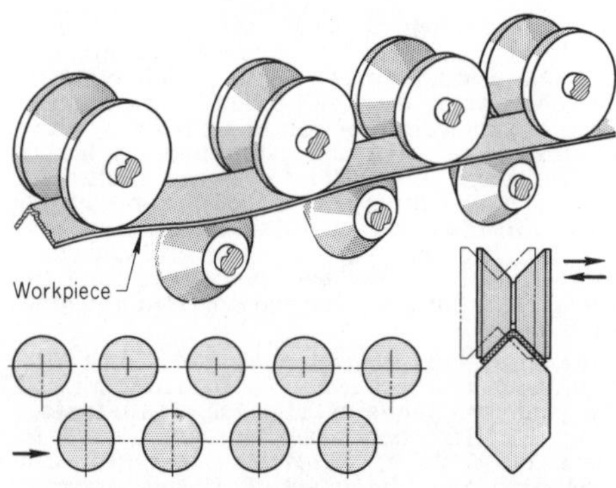

Fig. 12. Roll straightening of a structural angle. The top rolls can be adjusted horizontally and vertically.

Parallel-Roll Straightening

Roll straightening is a cold finishing mill process by which bars and structural shapes are provided with straightness adequate for most applications. For bars and shapes on which close tolerances must be maintained, roll straightening may be followed by press straightening.

In one type of roll straightening, square, flat, hexagonal and other flat-sided bars are passed continuously between sets of parallel-axis rolls (see Fig. 10 and 11). Uniform bends are introduced in such a way that the bar is straight when it leaves the rolls. By varying the distance between roll centers and the amount of offset, the degree of bend can be adjusted according to the section size and yield strength of the metal being straightened.

Round bars can be straightened on parallel-axis roll straighteners, but there is no way of restraining a round workpiece from turning on its axis as it passes through the machine. In rotary straighteners, round bars rotate and advance through the rolls so that the bars are bent uniformly in all planes; the rolls are adjustable so that the bars emerge straightened. Rotary straighteners for round bars usually consist of rolls that can be set at variable angles to each other (see Fig. 14 and 15).

Parallel-Roll Straighteners. Square, flat, hexagonal and other flat-sided bars can be straightened in both directions in one pass through a straightener having two sets of parallel rolls in planes 90° to each other (see Fig. 10), or in two passes through a straightener having a set of parallel rolls in only one plane, by turning the bar 90° on its axis between passes.

In machines with a single straightening plane, the rolls are mounted on horizontal shafts as shown in unit 2 of Fig. 10. If the horizontal rolls are grooved (like the vertical rolls of unit 1 in Fig. 10), the straightening in one plane also produces some straightening in a plane 90° to the first plane.

For high accuracy of straightness and high production rate, a second unit is added in a plane perpendicular to the first unit (see Fig. 10). Unit 1 has vertical shafts for straightening curvature in the horizontal plane; unit 2 has horizontal shafts for straightening curvature in the vertical plane. The two driven rolls rotate but otherwise are stationary; the three idler rolls are adjustable away from and toward the workpiece.

The first driven roll contacted by the bar is set with enough space between the first two idler rolls to curve the bar uniformly with the concavity toward the first driven roll. As the bar passes over the second idler roll and is held in position by the second driven roll, the concave side of the bar is reversed. The amount of reversal can be controlled by the position of the second idler roll, and with that roll properly positioned, the bar will emerge straight from the third idler roll. With a greater number of rolls, the most severe curvatures are reduced at the entry end of the machine. This leaves less work for the remaining rolls and provides for better straightening of small curvatures.

The number of rolls in a set of straightening rolls ranges from four to as many as 13; the most common number is eight or nine.

The amount of adjustment in roll spacing is determined by:

1 The resistance of the work metal to deflection beyond its elastic limit. The greater the resistance, the farther apart the rolls must be spaced to provide sufficient shaft and bearing capacities.
2 The distance must be short enough to produce a permanent set in the smallest bar and to straighten it.
3 If sections with high width-to-thickness ratios are being straightened, the distance must be great enough so that pressure from the rolls does not upset the edges of the bar.

Machines are built with both fixed and adjustable roll-center distances. In adjustable-center-distance machines, a separate housing carries the roll assembly to permit positioning along the straightener bed. These housings either reduce the space for the shafts or limit the minimum distance between the rolls.

Most sections can be straightened adequately in two planes. A flat bar is shown in Fig. 10 as it passes between grooved straightening rolls on vertical shafts and then through plain-face rolls on horizontal shafts. The bar passes first through the vertical-shaft unit because it is natural for the bar to enter with the flat side lying against the feed table. It is natural also to straighten in the grooved rolls first because the grooves that guide the bar also produce some straightening in the second plane and assure proper entry of the bar into the second unit. If the machine were reversed, it would be desirable to groove the rolls on the horizontal shafts to make certain that the bar would not "walk off" the rolls.

Grooving the rolls for thin flat bars helps to reduce upsetting of the edge and twisting of the bar. A hexagonal bar is shown in Fig. 11 as it passes between grooved straightening rolls on vertical shafts and through flat-face rolls on horizontal shafts. This roll arrangement follows the same principles as those for flat bars.

Sections that are symmetrical in both planes are easier to roll straighten than nonsymmetrical sections. Sections that are symmetrical in one plane but nonsymmetrical in the plane at 90° are usually best straightened in the symmetrical plane. Axial adjustment of some of the rolls to produce additional straightening in the nonsymmetrical plane is necessary in this method, as in the straightening of the angle section shown in Fig. 12.

Angles are best straightened in horizontal-shaft rolls with the apex of the angle up and roll adjustment made in the vertical plane. The angle lies naturally on the feed table and is straightened in both directions. To take out bends 90° to the plane in which the angle is straightened, one or two top rolls are adjusted axially to deflect the angle in this direction.

A structural channel can be passed through horizontal-shaft rolls with the flanges of the channel up or down. The upper rolls are staggered vertically and horizontally to remove camber in both planes.

Square or nearly square bars can be straightened on the diagonal in a single-plane machine using V-shaped upper and lower rolls (Fig. 13a) similar to the upper rolls used for straightening the angle shown in Fig. 12. In this method of straightening, only the shaded portion of the cross section shown in Fig. 13(b) is stressed beyond the elastic limit; therefore, the results may not be satisfactory. A square is better straightened in a two-plane machine, in which the areas stressed beyond the elastic limit are greater and more nearly symmetrical, as shown in Fig. 13(c). Square and hexagonal bars as large as 4 in. and flat bars as wide as 12 in. are straightened in roll straighteners. Larger bars are usually straightened in presses.

Bars of low-carbon steel seldom change size in straightening. Steel having 0.30% carbon, or more, may enlarge slightly in section because straightening redistributes the stress that remains from previous operations. For instance, a bar of 1045 steel, 1 3/16 in. square, may enlarge 0.002 in. in one pass through a roll straightener, and 0.004 in. in two passes. The bars shorten as they enlarge

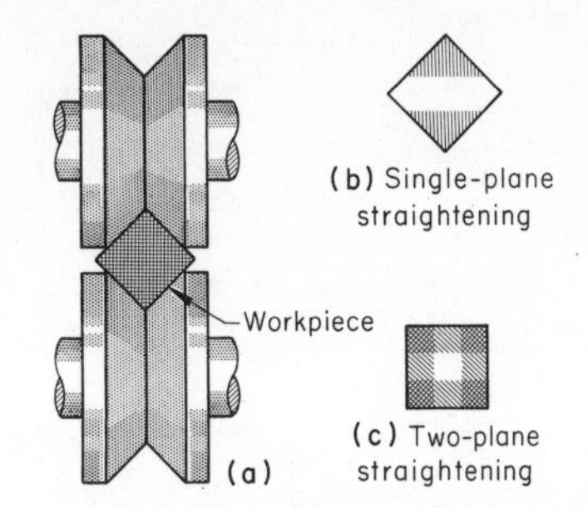

(a) Setup for single-plane roll straightening. (b) and (c) Stress patterns that result from single-plane and two-plane straightening.

Fig. 13. Roll straightening of square bars

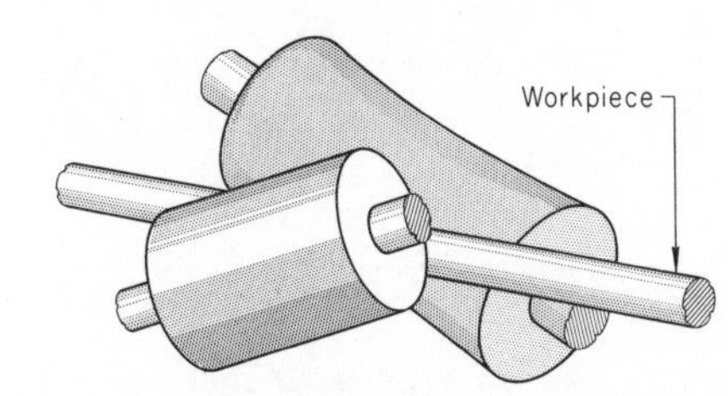

Fig. 14. Arrangement of rolls in a two-roll rotary straightener (top and bottom guides not shown)

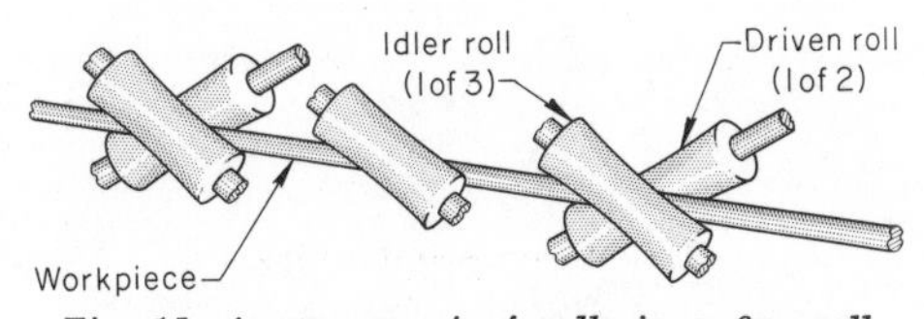

Fig. 15. Arrangement of rolls in a five-roll rotary straightener

in section, in accordance with the Poisson's ratio of the material.

Sometimes, square, hexagonal and flat bars up to 3/4 in. in cross section are cold drawn from coils of hot rolled stock. The drawn bars are straightened in roll straighteners and sheared to length. To correct the curvature resulting from coiling, two-plane straighteners are used, with sets of six to eight rolls in each plane.

Rotary Straighteners

Round bars or shaftlike parts of all types of metal are straightened in rotary straightening machines of two basic types: crossed-axis-roll machines and rotary-arbor machines.

The basic principle of rotary straightening is that the workpiece is fed forward and deflected beyond its elastic limit by crossed-axis rolls that also impart the rotary motion. The surface of the bar is alternately subjected to tensile and compressive stresses as it rotates in the straightener. Rotary straighteners are available with two to nine rolls.

A two-roll rotary straightener consists of two rolls directly opposed and positively driven. One of the rolls is concave and the other has a straight face, as shown in Fig. 14. The angularity adjustment of the rolls at opposite inclinations rotates and feeds the bar through the machine. Straightening is accomplished by flexing the workpiece into the throat of the concave roll by the modified straight-face roll (Fig. 3d). The bar is positioned vertically by means of a bottom guide, or top and bottom guides (not shown in Fig. 14), so that the axis of the bar coincides with the centerline of its path between the rolls.

The amount of bend given a bar as it passes through the machine depends on two adjustments made by the operator: (*a*) the angle of the rolls to the axis of the bar; and (*b*) the roll pressure, which is selected by adjusting one of the rolls toward or away from the other. Roll-angle adjustments and pressure adjustments depend on the size of the bar being straightened and its mechanical properties. In general, the larger the bar, the greater the roll angle — provided the mechanical properties are about the same. A heat treated bar (tensile strength of 125,000 to 150,000 psi) will require a smaller roll angle and more pressure than a bar of the same size and grade that has been annealed, or annealed and cold drawn.

In two-roll rotary straightening, the workpiece is subjected to a continuous straightening action from the point of entrance to the work rolls to the end of the workpiece as it leaves the rolls. Therefore, there is no variation in size within the bar, as is sometimes encountered with multiroll straighteners. Two-roll straighteners can be used for short workpieces such as rocker-arm shafts and chain-link pins, because all of the flexing is contained within the cavity of one roll. Two-roll straighteners are also used for sizing or correction of out-of-roundness in hot rolled bars. Extremely soft metal may be reduced in diameter if too much pressure or too large a roll angle is used.

Two-roll straighteners will remove end kinks and will round-out squashed ends, both of which sometimes occur when bars are cold sheared to length prior to straightening.

Two-roll rotary straighteners inherently have a lower through speed than multiroll straighteners. The roll inclination must be kept lower (about 20°) in two-roll straighteners, and therefore the rotational speed of the bar is much higher in relation to the forward speed.

The span over which bending takes place is considerably shorter in two-roll machines than in multiroll rotary straighteners, because in two-roll machines all bending takes place within the length of the rolls and not from roll to roll. With such a short span, much more force must be applied to the bar by the bending equipment than with multiroll machines.

Bars from 1/16 to 10 in. in diameter can be straightened in two-roll rotary machines.

In addition to finish straightening, the two-roll rotary machine can (*a*) rough straighten hot rolled round bars, which may be very crooked and may have sharp hooks and rough and scaly surfaces; (*b*) straighten and size cold drawn round bars, which may be bowed but have no sharp bends; and (*c*) polish or burnish to improve surface finish after grinding. Extra rolls should be kept for straightening only, sizing only, and polishing only.

Multiroll Rotary Straighteners. Another type of machine used in the straightening of bars is the multiroll rotary straightener. Figure 15 shows a five-roll rotary straightener, which consists of two driven rolls and three idler rolls. The two end idlers oppose the driven rolls, and between them is located the middle or pressure roll. All rolls are concave in shape, and the roll inclination is adjustable in order to obtain the maximum length of contact between the roll surface and the workpiece (see also Fig. 3e). Bottom cast iron guide shoes are located at the entry and exit ends between the driven rolls and their respective opposing idlers to position the bar properly.

A six-roll rotary straightener has a roll arrangement similar to that of a five-roll machine; the sixth roll is placed either opposite the middle roll or outboard of the exit-end powered rolls (see these roll arrangements in Fig. 3f). Seven-roll arrangements consist of two three-roll clusters with a middle idler roll (Fig. 3g). Small cluster-roll straighteners have been used extensively for specialty work on small workpieces like valve push rods (approximately 5/16 in. in diameter) and rocker-arm shafts; however, they are used most for straightening large tubing (2⅜ to 24 in. in diameter).

In operation, the rolls are angularly adjusted to accommodate various bar sizes. With the average angle selected as 30°, the adjustment may vary from about 28° to 30°, depending on the size of the bar being straightened.

In a five-roll straightener, the middle idler roll is adjusted to put enough bend in the bar to exceed the elastic limit of the metal. As the bar is fed through the straightener and rotated by the entrance and exit rolls, the adjustment of the pressure roll causes the bar to bend beyond its elastic limit in all directions perpendicular to its longitudinal axis. This action produces a straight bar with symmetrical stresses.

Optimum settings of roll angle vary somewhat with bar size. Typical settings are given in Table 2.

Cold drawn bars that are straightened in a multiroll rotary straightener usually increase in diameter during the straightening operation. Low-carbon steel bars with up to about 0.15% carbon show a negligible increase in diameter. However, as the carbon content increases, the amount of change increases. It is not uncommon for 2-in.-diam cold drawn bars of 1050 steel to increase as much as 0.004 in. in diameter. These bars will decrease in length about ½ in. in 12 ft as a result of the increase in diameter. This shortening must be considered when bars are cut to exact lengths before straightening.

When cold drawn bars are to be straightened in a multiroll rotary straightener, selection of the cold drawing die size is important if the bars are to be held within standard size tolerances. Most grades, particularly those having high carbon content, should be drawn to the low side of the diameter tolerance to compensate for the increase during straightening. The extreme ends of the bars, which do not get the full effect of the bend by the pressure roll, do not increase in diameter. After straightening, the bar ends will remain the same size as when cold drawn.

Straightening in a multiroll rotary straightener does not work harden the

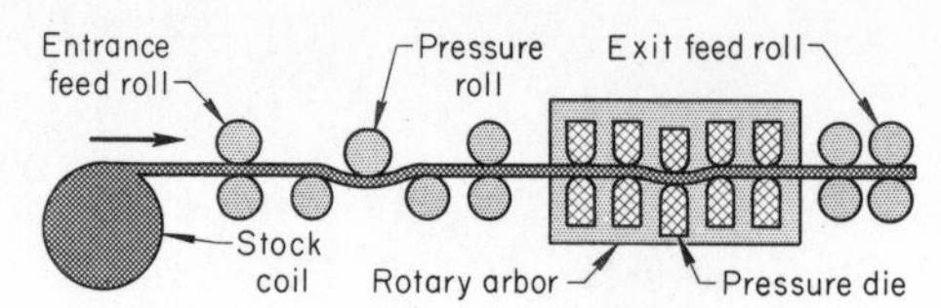

Fig. 16. Arrangement of rolls and dies in a rotary-arbor straightener used for the straightening of coiled rod or wire

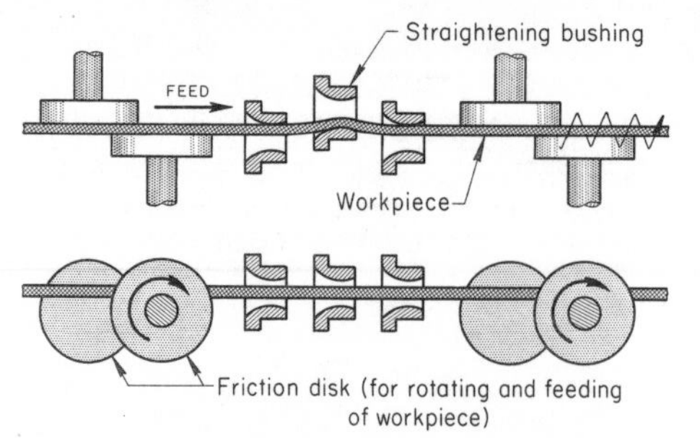

Fig. 17. Plan and side views of a mechanism for straightening cut lengths of bars

Table 2. Typical Settings of Roll Angle for Five-Roll Rotary Straighteners for Use on Bars of Various Diameters

Diameter of bar, in.	Setting of roll angle	Diameter of bar, in.	Setting of roll angle
¾	26⅝°	2¾	28½°
1	26⅞°	3	28¾°
1¼	27°	3¼	29°
1½	27¼°	3½	29¼°
1¾	27½°	3¾	29½°
2	27¾°	4	29⅝°
2¼	28°	4¼	29⅞°
2½	28¼°	4½	30°

Recommended settings for the starting setup; these will vary slightly in the actual setup used.

bar stock to any appreciable extent. This is desirable when the bars are to be cold headed or cold extruded.

The basic five-roll straightener has been modified so that four of the rolls are driven and only the middle pressure roll is an idler. The heavier feeding pressure that is obtainable with driven entry and exit pressure rolls is advantageous in that a polishing effect can be obtained on products such as cold drawn steel. In addition, the driven rolls provide more traction so that a heavier deflection can be exerted by the middle straightening roll.

In a further modification of the five-roll straightener, all five rolls are driven. This eliminates the need for guides between the rolls, but roll speed synchronization becomes important.

Hot rolled round steel bars are generally straightened commercially in two-roll or multiroll rotary straighteners. Bars as large as 10 in. in diameter and having yield strengths up to 100,000 psi have been straightened in these machines. Some machines are modified by adding hydraulic loading to the straightening mechanisms and by adding a shear pin to provide for any shock loading that might be encountered because of extreme out-of-roundness of large hot finished bars.

Rotary-arbor straighteners are used to straighten coiled rod or wire up to ⅝ in. in diameter. The straightening is done by an arbor rotating around the wire as it passes through the machine, as shown in Fig. 16 (see also Fig. 3h). The arbor encloses five pairs of cast iron straightening dies. The dies are equally spaced in a fixed spacing that relates to the size capacity of the machine. The greater the capacity, the greater the fixed spacing of the dies.

The dies, bell-mouthed for easier entrance of the wire, are locked in place by adjusting screws. The pairs of dies at the two ends of the straightener arbor are set so that the wire is always at the center of the arbor in these dies. The middle die is called the pressure die because it is set to bend the wire slightly, as shown in Fig. 16. The dies on either side bend the wire slightly in the opposite direction.

The machine is set by trial. If the wire comes out bowed, usually the pressure die has not been set to bend the wire enough. If the wire comes out wavy, the pressure die may be bending the wire too far. Helical marks may be caused by lack of lubrication, imperfect dies, or an embedded sliver of metal.

Growth. During straightening in a rotary-arbor machine, most grades of cold drawn carbon steel, and of alloy steel with more than 0.15% carbon, will increase in diameter (as much as 0.006 in.), unless the wire has been stress relieved before straightening.

Speed of straightening in rotary-arbor straighteners is usually 75 to 200 ft per min, depending on the size capacity of the machine and on the type of wire.

Cut lengths of bars are straightened in mechanisms like the one shown in Fig. 17. A helical motion is imparted to the bars by pairs of rotating, offset friction disks, which burnish the bar as they feed it through three straightening bushings that turn freely in bearings. The middle bushing is adjusted to deflect the bar, just enough for good straightening action. Such a machine made in various size capacities can straighten bars 5/64 to 1¼ in. in diameter at speeds of 92 to 164 ft per min.

Straightening Stainless Steel for Cold Heading. Coiled stainless steel wire (series 300 and 400) 0.062 to 0.610 in. in diameter requires moderate straightness while being fed into cold heading machines. Wire 0.040 to 0.125 in. in diameter can be hand straightened sufficiently for entering the feed rolls. The feed rolls then pull the wire with enough tension to remove the coil radius as the wire leaves the coil reel. For parts having a length-to-diameter ratio of 4-to-1 to 8-to-1, no further straightening is necessary. The feed rolls provide sufficient straightness to permit the blank to be cut to length and transferred to the die station. After cold heading, the part has the straightness obtained in the heading operation.

Parts up to 6 in. long cold headed in open-die headers require a straightness of 0.004 in. in 4 in. A single-plane five or six-roll straightener placed 90° to the feed roll is usually used.

Single-plane and two-plane straighteners mounted on portable pedestals are available as machine accessories.

Stretch Straightening

Many bars and shapes that are difficult to straighten by other methods can be straightened easily by stretching. However, this technique is usually confined to straightening of shapes that are uniform in cross section and length.

Advantages of stretch straightening include low costs for tooling and for maintenance, simplicity of operation, and (usually) completion of straightening in one operation. Disadvantages include waste by trimming 6 to 18 in. from the ends of bars damaged by gripping; the need (usually) for two men to do the straightening; the need for cutoff equipment; and production of only 30 to 40 bars per hour.

A stretch straightener has two heads with grips that clamp on the ends of the bar. One head can be adjusted to suit the workpiece length. The other head (tailstock) is powered for stretching and also for rotation to correct twist in the workpiece.

Stretching machines are made in sizes to exert stretching forces of 15 to 500 tons to workpieces that may be from 20 to 100 ft long. Stretching must stress the work beyond its yield strength. For complete straightening, the bar should be stretched 2%. To do this, and also to overcome the greater strength caused by work hardening, the stretching machine needs a capacity of 10 to 15% beyond the yield strength of the bar.

Some straightening can be done by stretching only to the yield strength of the work, but this would not be enough to remove completely some sharp bends and twists. A stretcher with a capacity of 150 tons can straighten, to some extent, a low-carbon steel bar with a cross section of 15 sq in., or 10 sq in. of austenitic stainless steel, or 7 sq in. of ferritic stainless, and can do complete straightening on 13 sq in. of low-carbon steel, 8 sq in. of austenitic stainless, or 6 sq in. of ferritic stainless steel. Figure 18 shows the relation of stretcher force to the area of cross section of the bar. Deviation that remains after stretch straightening can sometimes be corrected by manual straightening.

Most hot rolled bars can be straightened by stretching. Straightening by stretching also works well on rolled and extruded bars of aluminum and austenitic and ferritic stainless steels, but not on martensitic stainless steels unless they are first annealed. Low-carbon steels are easy to stretch straighten, but annealing before stretching becomes more necessary as the carbon content increases.

Stretch straightening and detwisting of steel extrusions are described in the two examples that follow:

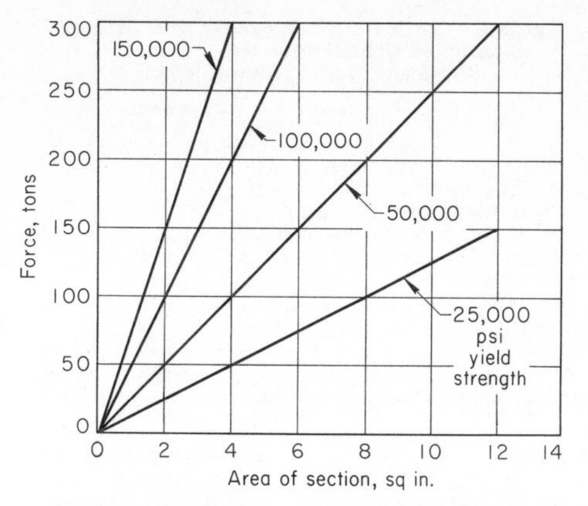

Fig. 18. Relation of stretcher force to area of bar cross section in stretch straightening steel bars of various yield strengths

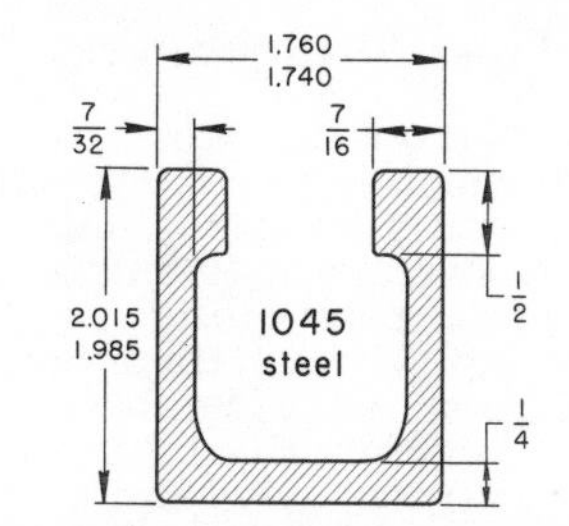

Fig. 19. Cross section of a 14-ft-long extrusion that was stretch straightened and detwisted (Example 421)

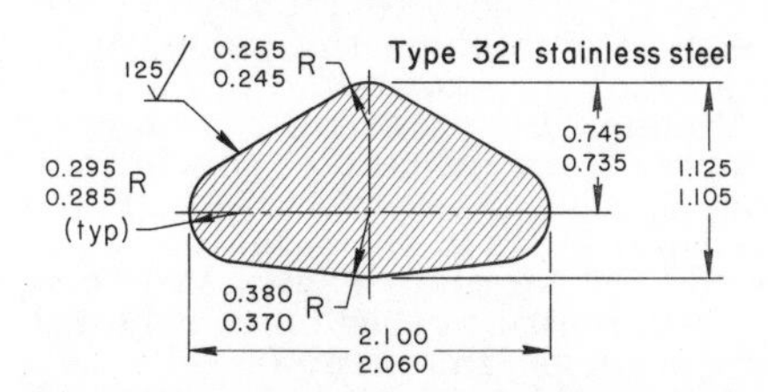

Fig. 20. Cross section of a 25-ft-long extrusion that was stretch straightened, cold drawn to dimensions shown, then press straightened (Example 422)

Example 421. Stretch Straightening of a 1045 Steel Extrusion (Fig. 19)

The 1045 steel channel-shaped extrusion shown in Fig. 19 was stretch straightened and detwisted in a 120-ton press at the rate of 20 pieces per hour.

The section was extruded in 28-ft lengths, cut in half, and annealed (30 min at 1500 F, slow furnace cool to 1100 F, air cool) to 209 Bhn. It was then stretch straightened to within 1/8 in. in 10 ft, cut into pieces 13 5/16 in. long, and press straightened to maintain the 1.750 ± 0.010-in. dimension across the open end.

As extruded, the bar had 12-in. camber and 10° twist in 14 ft. Annealing was required because the extrusion had been allowed to cool in air from the extrusion temperature and consequently had increased in hardness and decreased in ductility. A 30-ton tensile load was required to straighten the extrusion. Go no-go snap gages were used to check the 1.750-in. and 2.000-in. dimensions.

Example 422. Straightening a Stainless Steel Extrusion Before and After Cold Drawing (Fig. 20)

A 25-ft-long extrusion of 321 stainless steel was stretch straightened to within 1/8 in. in 5 ft before being cold drawn to the dimensions shown in Fig. 20. As extruded, the bar had a combination bow and camber of 12 in. in 10 ft and a yield strength of 60,000 to 70,000 psi. Twenty-five pieces per hour were stretch straightened and detwisted in a 120-ton press.

After cold drawing, the bar had a camber of 12 in. in 25 ft and a bow of 1/8 in. in 5 ft. A 50-ton hydraulic press was used to reduce the camber to 1/16 in. in 5 ft at a rate of 15 pieces per hour. The support points varied from 3 to 6 ft. Only slight improvement was obtained in bow, but this was sufficient to maintain straightness within tolerance when the extrusion was cut into pieces 5/8 in. long.

Straightening of Tubing

*By the ASM Committee on Straightening of Bars and Tubing**

TUBING of any cross-sectional shape can be straightened by using equipment and techniques that are basically the same as those discussed in the preceding article, on Straightening of Bars.

In general, a round tube that has warped in annealing or other heat treatment is given a rough-straightening pass in a press or a roll straightener, followed by one or more passes in a rotary straightener and, if required, a finish pass in a press straightener.

Rough straightening eliminates excessive bow that would cause whipping in the inlet trough. Because the tube does not rotate during rough straightening, almost any amount of bow can be accepted; thus, both roll and press straightening can be used. If the tube is only slightly bowed, initial rough straightening can be omitted.

*For committee list, see page 322.

A rotary straightening pass is necessary for finish straightening but need not be used when the tube requires another cold drawing operation. Two rotary passes may be required when the tube has developed excessive out-of-roundness, bow or multiple kinks in previous processing.

If the tube is considerably out-of-round, a normal straightening pass, with only a middle roll offset, will not be effective. A preliminary pass with no offset in the middle rolls and all rolls set to ovalize may be required before the normal straightening pass.

Most tubing, especially the smaller sizes (1 1/4-in. OD and under), requires only one or two rotary straightening passes. For larger-diameter tubing (1 1/2-in. OD and over), or when straightness better than standard is required, additional work can be done in a press straightener to remove short end hooks or to secure precision straightness. Press straightening converts long, gentle bows into a series of short bows ending at each point where the punch hits.

Straightening of tubing having shapes other than round is done in roll or press straighteners with much the same considerations governing the choice as those for similar solid shapes.

Table 1. Straightness Tolerances for Round Seamless Mechanical Steel Tubing (a)

Size limit of tubing: Outside diameter, in.	Wall thickness: Min, % of OD	Wall thickness: Max, in.	Maximum camber: In any 3 ft, in.	Maximum camber: In any length, in./ft(b)
5 or less	3	0.5	0.030	0.010
Over 5, to 8	4	0.75	0.045	0.015
Over 8, to 10 3/4	4	1.0	0.060	0.020

(a) Tolerances apply generally to unannealed, finish-annealed and medium-annealed, cold finished and hot finished tubes of carbon steel with 0.45% C max, and alloy steel with 0.25% C max. (b) For welded steel tubing, maximum camber is 0.010 in. per ft.

Asymmetrical sections such as airfoil or teardrop designs require press straightening. Stretch straighteners are helpful in detwisting and straightening asymmetrical shapes.

Straightness tolerances for round tubing are given in Table 1. Tubes requiring tolerances closer than those shown demand special straightening operations and special inspection.

Effect of Tubing Material

Procedures and tooling are influenced by the tubing material. The principal factors are composition and condition of the work metal, wall thickness, type of tubing (seamless or welded), and type and extent of distortion. Greater force and more rugged equipment are required for straightening tubes with thick walls and high elastic limit.

Wall Thickness. The amount of distortion that occurs in the hollow section where it bears against the straightening tools is relatively small in thick-wall tubes, which approach solids in their behavior. Distortion becomes significant as tube walls become thinner, making precautions against permanent distortion necessary. Damage to thin-wall tubing appears as spot dinges or ovality from punch straightening, or as spiral dinges (called "rings") or ovality from rotary straightening.

Type of Tubing. Seamless tubes often have a nonuniform wall thickness, which makes the straightening operation more difficult. In a welded tube, the weld and adjacent material may have mechanical properties differing considerably from the rest of the tube. Residual stress from welding may also affect straightening.

Type and Extent of Distortion. Crookedness in tubing can result from distortion during heat treatment or cooling, from distortion during cold drawing as the result of eccentric wall, from hooked ends on hot finished tubes (usually caused by misalignment or roll wear in the hot sinking mill), or from accidental bending during processing.

End hooks are pronounced bends that usually appear close (18 in. or less) to the leading or trailing ends of some tubular products.

Control of Straightening Pressure

Pressure exerted on the workpiece by the straightening rolls must be carefully controlled to prevent permanent damage, especially to thin-wall tubing. This can be done by increasing the distance between the points at which the tool contacts the workpiece, thus reducing the total force, or by increasing the contact area between tool and tubing and thereby reducing the unit pressure on the workpiece.

In rotary straightening of thin-wall tubing, the length of contact between the roll and the tube, and the distance between sets of rolls, should be maximum, and care should be exercised in the adjustment of opposed rolls to avoid excessive ovalizing and pressure on a short section of tubing. In a two-roll machine, the length of curve is limited to the length of the roll, and tubing with very thin walls may be subject to ringing at the roll shoulders where the pressure is greatest. This limits the two-roll machine to a maximum diameter-to-wall thickness ratio of about 15 to 1 for full straightening.

Table 2. Costs for Carburizing and Straightening of Cold Drawn Steel Tubes in 150-Piece Lots (Example 425)

Operation	Carburizing method: Liquid	Pack
Load tubes into bath	$ 5	...
Load tubes into box	...	$ 6
Turn tubes end for end	60	...
Pack box with carburizer	...	90
Clean	5	...
Straighten	75	...
Reheat to temper	50	50
Clean	5	5
Straighten	150	75
Total	$350	$226

Press Straightening

The straightening press can rough straighten tubing prior to roll straightening or rotary straightening, or can completely straighten tubing by removing end hooks that cannot be removed easily by any other method. Sometimes end hooks and large cambers must be removed to permit the tubing to enter the rotary straightener and to prevent dangerous whipping of the work. A press can also be used to straighten welded tubing before the bead is reduced. It is best to reduce the bead before straightening the welded tubing in a rotary straightener.

Tooling. In press straightening of thin-wall tubing, there should be a wide spacing between saddles. If there are short kinks in the tube, the spacing is dictated by their length, and operator skill must be relied on to obtain the best possible straightening.

Rolls with a semicircular groove for holding the tubing are sometimes used for end supports. The spacing of these rolls can easily be adjusted to suit the length of the bow. The pressure shoe attached to the press ram is flat, with a semicircular groove to distribute force over a greater area. The diameter of the groove should approximate the diameter of the tube, to avoid flattening of the tube under pressure.

Applications. Straightening presses are used on tubes to remove kinks, camber and other distortions caused by mishandling, cutting off and heat treatment. Techniques used to remove excessive camber resulting from heat treatment of various sizes and lengths of round tubing are described in the following example.

Example 423. Press Straightening Tubes of Various Sizes and Lengths

Seamless tubes of 52100 steel, 2½ to 6 in. in outside diameter, 30 to 72 in. long, and with wall thickness of ¼ to ½ in., were austenitized at 1575 F for ½ hr and quenched in molten salt at 350 F for 10 min. Heat treatment caused a camber of ⅛ to 3/16 in., which should have been no more than 0.020 in. Hardness was Rockwell C 60 to 61.

Straightening was done in a 10-ton hydraulic press while the tubes, supported in U-shaped saddles, cooled from 350 F to above 90 F. The ram block had a half-circle contour to prevent the tube from flattening while pressure was applied. Tubes of 4½-in. OD and larger, with walls less than ½ in. thick, were straightened with a plug in the center under the ram and in each end. A handle was welded to the center plug to make its positioning and removal easy. [A nut and bolt can be used as an adjustable vertical post inside the tube. Unscrewing the nut tightens the fit.]

Tubes were straightened in about 20 min while still hot from the quench. A force of 1000 lb straightened a tube with a 2½-in. OD and a ¼-in.-thick wall, in saddles 30 in. apart. Before the tube cooled to 150 F, it was deflected 3/16 in. and released quickly. After the tube had cooled to below 150 F, it could be deflected only ⅛ in. in the 30-in. span and had to be held down a few seconds to effect a set. Straightening continued until the tube cooled to 90 F.

After tempering, the tube was straightened again, using a force of 2000 lb and a longer holding time. Each ⅛-in. deflection straightened the tube 0.001 to 0.002 in. per ft. The tubes were pressed at the high point and about 15° on each side of the high point at 3-in. intervals. If the tubes cooled to 90 F before being satisfactorily straightened, they were heated to 350 F and the operation was continued, often with forces of 2500 to 3000 lb. Frequently a tube would flatten or break if force was applied at the high point only, although turning the tube to each side of the high spot helped considerably. The more difficult bends were removed by heating a narrow ring around the tube to 450 F. In this area, the hardness was Rockwell C 58 to 59. While hot, the tube was deflected ⅛ in. in a 24-in. span.

Larger-diameter and thicker-wall tubes required as much as 10,000-lb force to straighten after quenching, and 20,000 lb after tempering. Severely warped tubes were fully annealed, straightened and rehardened.

Straightening difficulties were attributed to overheating, poor quenching technique, straightening at too low a temperature, or wide variations in wall thickness. Tubes with wall thickness varying from ⅜ to 7/16 in. warped as much as ⅜ in. in 5 ft. One troublesome tube, which finally broke, had a wall thickness varying from ⅜ to 9/16 in.

Straightening presses can be used to reduce the out-of-roundness of tubing. The following example illustrates how correction for roundness, after carburizing and before hardening, reduced press time.

Example 424. Correcting Out-of-Roundness in Short, Large-Diameter Tubes

Tubular sleeves of 8620 steel, 8-in. OD by 8 in. long with a ½-in. wall thickness, were heated to 1700 F for 6 hr in molten carburizing salt, quenched, and tempered at 350 F. The sleeves had a 1/16-in.-deep case with a hardness of Rockwell C 62 to 64, and were out-of-round from 0.040 to 0.060 in. Roundness tolerance was 0.005 in. The sleeves were straightened to this roundness in a press by heating the inside of the tubes at the high spots and then pressing them ⅛ in. with 4000-lb pressure. Usually it took three pressings with six hot spots to round up each sleeve. This took 25 min and cost $2.50 per sleeve.

An improved method was devised. The parts were carburized in the same way except that they were cooled in air instead of being quenched. The sleeves were then rounded within 0.003 in. while they were soft. The parts were reheated to 1550 F, quenched, tempered at 350 F and rounded again. The out-of-roundness was only 0.020 to 0.030 in., which needed less time to round up. The first operation took 7 min, and the second took 10 min, for a total of 17 min and a cost of $1.70 per sleeve.

Some carburizing and other heat treating methods or procedures cause more distortion in long tubes than other methods. In the following example, carburizing procedures were changed so that the part was heat treated in a straight, unstressed position, resulting in reduced distortion.

Example 425. Change in Method of Carburizing and Hardening of Tubes That Reduced Straightening Time (Table 2)

Cold drawn steel tubes, 1¼-in. OD by 7 ft long with ⅛-in. wall thickness, made in 150-piece lots, were liquid carburized at 1700 F for 3 hr, making a carburized case 0.040 in. deep.

One end of the tubes protruded from the bath, so that the hot tubes had to be turned end for end in order to be carburized the full length. This resulted in a double case at the middle of each tube. After the tubes cooled in air, they were distorted enough so that each tube had to be straightened before tempering. Straightening to 1/16-in. maximum camber took 5 min per tube. After tempering, the tubes again required straightening. The second straightening took 10 min per tube, and some of the tubes broke in straightening to the specified 1/16 in.

In an improved method, the tubes were pack carburized in long boxes in a gas furnace, 2 hr at 1500 F and 4 hr at 1700 F, then cooled in the pack. The tubes received an even depth of case and did not need straightening until after tempering. Straightening to 1/16 in. took 5 min per tube, and none of the tubes broke.

Operations and costs of the liquid and pack methods for carburizing and straightening 150-tube lots are compared in Table 2.

Parallel-Roll Straightening

Single-plane and two-plane roll straighteners for tubular products are basically the same as those for solid bars. Machines for tubular products may have somewhat longer center distances than bar straighteners and at the same time may not require as large shafts and bearings. The roll-center distance is generally a function of the outside dimensions of the tube, and increases approximately as the outside dimensions of the tube increase.

Less force is required for straightening tubes than solid bars of equal outside dimensions.

Round tubing is best straightened on machines equipped with semicircular grooved rolls. The grooves must conform closely to the tube size, and each size must have its own set of rolls, or set of grooves in a multigrooved roll. Round tubing may revolve slightly in the rolls, thus avoiding the effect of straightening and resulting in rough straightening only.

Tubing that is badly warped can be rough straightened as easily in a roll straightener as in a press. The roll straightener operates faster than the press but takes longer to set up. When straightening 2-in.-diam tubes 20 ft long, for instance, the roll straightener can process 250 to 400 pieces per hour, compared to 100 to 120 pieces per hour in a press. However, changeover time for a roll straightener is 16 min, whereas a press setup can be changed in as little as 6 min.

The cost of roll straighteners increases greatly for the larger tube sizes, so that a large tonnage of tubes must be processed to justify the cost of machines for straightening tubes that are larger in outside diameter than approximately 3 in.

Square and rectangular tubing is commonly straightened in either single-plane or two-plane machines (see Fig. 10 and 13 in the article "Straightening of Bars, Shapes and Long Parts" in this volume). If the rolls of a single-plane machine are grooved to fit the tube, an appreciable straightening effect in a plane spaced at 90° is provided. When additional straightening is required, square tubes are turned 90° for a second pass through the rolls. A two-plane roll straightener is better suited to rectangular tubing than a single-plane roller, because the rolls need not be reset for the second pass.

Two-Roll Rotary Straightening

The principle employed in rotary straightening of round tubes is basically the same as for solid round bars. The driven rolls, set at a predetermined angle, rotate the tube while conveying it in a lineal direction. The crest of the bow is stressed to, or beyond, the elastic limit once during each revolution, and the maximum stress point is repeated spirally along the length of the tube. The distance between each stress point depends on the lineal travel for each revolution of the tube. Approximate values for lineal travel can be determined by multiplying the tube circumference by the tangent of the angle of the rolls.

Two-roll rotary straighteners (see Fig. 3d and 14 in the article "Straightening of Bars, Shapes and Long Parts") are used primarily on tubes having a diameter-to-wall thickness ratio of no more than 15 to 1. The machine is equipped with two skewed rolls, between which two guide shoes are mounted. One roll has a concave contour; the other is straight or convex. The rolls may be arranged in a horizontal or a vertical plane. Machines with rolls arranged in the vertical plane are of relatively new design.

The tube is held between the guide shoes while the straight or convex roll bends the tube between the ends of the concave roll. The maximum deflection depends on the depth and the skew angle of the concave roll.

Two concave rolls have also been used to straighten tubes. The concave rolls are set to make full-length contact along the surface of the tube, and the crest of the bow is ovalized between the rolls several times before the tube emerges from the machine.

Straightening of End Hooks. The two-roll machine can remove most of the sharp bend at the end of tubing if the rolls are ground to suit the deflection requirements of the tube material and are set at an angle to suit the size of tube and length of end hook. The resulting curve in the rolls is suitable for a specific range of tube sizes with a specific elastic limit. Wider variations in tube size and grade of material are processed by changing the angle setting of one or both rolls to produce the required deflection.

The design of the two-roll machine permits the rolls to be set at a small angle with the centerline of the stock. The smaller the angle, the less through feed per revolution of the tube, and because of the small helix angle created by feed per revolution, a large portion of the tube is subject to maximum bending stress.

Short bends and end hooks can be straightened more easily in a two-roll machine than in a multiple-roll machine, because all bending takes place within the length of the rolls and not from roll to roll. The short span greatly increases the load necessary for straightening, which partly explains why a two-roll machine is unsuccessful in straightening thin-wall tubing.

Roll Angle. Contoured rolls are designed for a specific range of tube sizes and materials. This is approximately the same range of conditions that can be handled by the equivalent multiple-roll straighteners. For most applications the rolls are set at an angle of 15° to 25°. The contour of the rolls can be varied to suit specific applications. For instance, a roll of shallow concavity is used for metal having a low elastic limit, whereas for straightening metal having a higher elastic limit, a roll of deeper concavity is used.

Limitations. The two-roll machine is not ordinarily used to finish-straighten tubing if the ratio of outside diameter to wall thickness is greater than 15 to 1. The crushing strength of a thin-wall tube in the short span of a two-roll straightener is such that the tube will crush or "ring" before it bends if the rolls are set to remove the maximum bend. However, if the amount of bend to be removed is reduced by a preliminary rough-straightening operation, the machine can be used to finish-straighten tubing having a diameter-to-wall thickness ratio considerably greater than 15 to 1, depending on the amount of straightening done in the preliminary operation.

Polishing of the tube surface can be either beneficial or detrimental. The hourglass shape of the rolls presents different diameters to the surface of the tube, resulting in some slipping. This burnishing action improves surface finish, although excessive slipping can produce a burnished spiral on the work surface.

Scratches may result when foreign material becomes embedded in the guide shoes. The use of nylon shoes and a soluble oil as a lubricant will reduce scratches.

Sizing After Derodding. Producers of cold drawn tubing use internal mandrels to control the inside diameter, and two-roll crossed-axis machines are used to extract the mandrel (derod) after the drawing process. The identical rolls apply heavy pressure on the workpiece, thus expanding the tubing to allow removal of the mandrel.

The expanded tubing does not always return to its drawn diameter. The external dimensions of tubing can be corrected by drawing the tubing through dies that are undersize by an amount equal to the amount by which the tubing expands during derodding.

Multiple-Roll Rotary Straightening

Rotary straighteners with five, six or seven rolls are also used in straightening of tubing. The five-roll machine (see Fig. 3e and 15 in the article "Straightening of Bars, Shapes and Long Parts") consists of two two-roll clusters and a middle deflecting roll. This machine has two large rolls on one side that are opposed by three small rolls on the other. Two of the three small rolls and the two large rolls function as entry and exit feed rolls. The third small roll located between the other two small rolls functions as a deflecting roll. The rolls may be arranged in the horizontal or in the vertical plane.

In some machines, only the two large rolls are driven; in others, all rolls except the deflecting roll are driven, and sometimes all five rolls are driven. When more than two rolls are driven,

Table 3. Typical Equipment Used for Rotary Straightening Various Sizes of Tubing Made of Different Metals

Type of metal	Size of tubing to be straightened, in. Outside diameter	Wall thickness	Rotary straightener Type	Speed, fpm	Hp	Weight, lb
Low-carbon steel	½ to 4, nominal pipe size(a)		Five-roll(b)	250 to 1000	75 to 100(c)	65,000
	6⅝ to 24(d)	0.280 to 1.230	Seven-roll(e)	40 to 120	400(f)	600,000
Alloy steel, 4137, 4340, 52100	3½ to 7½(d)	Up to 1½	Seven-roll(e)	40 to 160	200(c)	170,000
Stainless steel, titanium	9⁄16 to 2	Up to 0.300	Five-roll(b)	20 to 100	15(g)	10,000
Copper	½ to 2⅝	Various	Five-roll(b)	100 to 400	10(g)	10,000

(a) Butt-welded pipe. (b) All rolls driven. (c) Adjustable-speed, constant-potential, d-c motor. (d) Seamless tubing. (e) Three-roll clusters (see Fig. 1). (f) Constant-hp, adjustable-speed, d-c motor. (g) Motor having a mechanical speed variator with a ratio of 5 to 1.

speed-matching of roll surfaces becomes important. Matching can be obtained by keeping correct relationship between roll diameters or, more easily and accurately, by a differential drive between the two roll banks or, in some machines, by driving the rolls with individual motors having relay, continuous-feedback, or similar controls.

The six-roll machine has two middle deflecting rolls, opposed to one another, similar to the entry and exit rolls in the five-roll straightener, but it differs from the five-roll straightener in that all rolls are of equal diameter (see Fig. 3f1 in the article "Straightening of Bars, Shapes and Long Parts"). Normally, four or all six of the rolls are powered. Another type of six-roll straightener has a roll arrangement similar to that of a five-roll straightener with an extra outboard roll (see Fig. 3f2 of the above article).

A seven-roll rotary straightener has two three-roll clusters — one at the entry end and one at the exit end of the straightener — and a middle deflecting roll (Fig. 1). Normally, the two bottom rolls are driven and the five others are idlers. The middle roll (deflecting roll) moves vertically, and the four end idler rolls move in a circular path about pivot points in the base and apply pressure to the tube for feeding and straightening.

Various other multiple-roll straighteners have been built for specific applications.

The general principles that apply to the use of multiple-roll machines are the same as those already described for two-roll straighteners.

Middle-roll offset straightening bends a straight tube by an amount that stresses the outer fibers of the tube to the elastic limit. When the straightening load is released, the tube "springs back" to its initially straight position. The outer fibers of an initially bowed tube are stressed beyond the elastic limit, and the tube "springs back" to a straight position.

Straightening of tubing in this manner could be termed single-pass straightening. It is possible, however, to arrange the rolls in the multiple-roll machine to double-straighten each tube as it is conveyed through the machine. The middle roll stand is offset to deflect a bowed tube and to stress its outer fibers beyond the yield point, and, in a similar manner, the tube is deflected over the third roll stand by an auxiliary roll or by the discharge table. The tube is stressed at both the middle and third roll stands — or, in effect, double-straightened — with each pass through the machine.

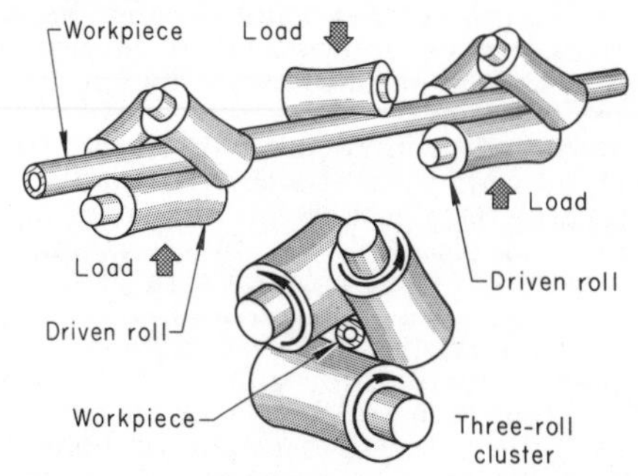

Fig. 1. Arrangement and principles of operation of three-roll clusters in a seven-roll rotary straightener

Bending the tube, however, creates an area of strain or cold work directly under the bending load. The rotation of the tube as it goes through the machine generates a spiral of strained area around the periphery of the tube. The centerline of the third roll stand should be spaced in such a way that no one point on the tube duplicates itself at the same location on both the middle and third rolls, thereby eliminating the possibility of reworking the strained area.

Applications. Multiple-roll machines are advantageous in processing thin-wall tubes, and thick-wall tubes having a high ratio of diameter-to-wall thickness. This is because of the lower unit loading on the workpiece that is applied across the longer bending spans between adjacent rolls. The multiple-roll straightener has an additional advantage in higher throughput speeds than other rotary straighteners, because of the higher angularity settings of the rolls. Thus, multiple-roll straighteners are widely used in tube mill production lines.

Multiple-roll machines ordinarily are used for applications in which the primary purpose is sizing or rounding up of the workpiece, or burnishing of the workpiece. They do not straighten as accurately as two-roll machines, nor do they remove end hooks as effectively.

Long bows in medium and heavy-wall tubes are removed by closing each roll pass and bending the tube with the middle roll. Closed-pass rolling provides full-length support within each roll stand. Straightening in this manner requires less deflection and spreads the bending load over the full length of each roll.

Long bows can sometimes be removed from extra-heavy-wall tubes by opening each roll stand and bending the tube between the two bottom rolls with the top middle roll. The object is to exert a minimum load on the tube.

Thin-wall tubes should be processed with low unit loads applied to the surface of the tube and with minimum deflection. High loads and excessive deflection will "ring" the interior of the tube. The bending load can be spread across the surface of the tube by angling the middle roll toward the centerline of pass. Ovalizing and spreading the roll contact lower the required amount of deflection to produce a straight tube. Deflecting a tube over a long span requires a large offset that can make it difficult to convey the tube through the machine. However, proper roll design and roll spacing make it possible to process a wide range of outside diameters in the multiple-roll rotary straightening machine.

Example 426. Straightening of Tubes in a Five-Roll Rotary Straightener

A production lot of 16 tubes of type 316 stainless steel, at Rockwell B 96 to 98, was straightened for centerless grinding after being cold drawn to 2.015-in. OD. The tubes were 20 ft long with a wall thickness of 5⁄16 in. Tube diameter varied 0.003 to 0.004 in. as shown by measurements taken 90° apart at 6-ft intervals along the tubes. Straightness was required to be within 1⁄16 in. in 5 ft, but preferably within 0.003 in. per ft.

The five-roll straightener had two driven rolls and three idler rolls. Speed was 60 ft per min with the rolls set at 28½°. One pass through the rolls improved the straightness of the tubes to ¼ in., with end hook remaining in three pieces. Roundness improved to 2.014/2.016 in., from the previous 2.013/2.018 in. A second straightening made the tubes straight within ⅛ in., with end hook still remaining in three pieces. A third straightening made the tubes straight within 0.080 in. except for three pieces that returned to ⅛ in. The latter were given two more straightening passes. The fourth pass increased the bend, and the fifth pass restored the conditions as they had been after the third pass.

End hook can be removed from thin-wall and medium-wall tubes by ovalizing and bending the tube in the middle roll pass.

Removing end hook from thick-wall tubing on multiple-roll straighteners is difficult because the center-to-center distance between the No. 1 and 2 roll stands is usually greater than the length of the end hook. This is demonstrated in Example 426 above.

The roll angle of a straightening machine depends on the outside diameter of the tube to be straightened. In general, a machine used for small-diameter tubing in the range of ¼ to ¾ in. may have a roll angle of 40° to 45°. In some special high-speed straighteners, when the tubing is almost straight to begin with and is easy to straighten, a 40° angle may be used for tubing as large as 2 in. For machines in the range of 2 to 6 in., a common angle is 30°. For very large tubing 18 to 24 in. in diameter, the angle may be as low as 17½°.

To fit a large tube within the size range of the machine to the roll contour, the angle between the centerline of the tube and the roll must be greater than that required for a small-diameter tube. The angle may be adjusted from 2° to 3° on either side of the nominal angle for a given machine — the lowest angle for the smallest size and the largest angle for the largest size.

Tube Deflection. The amount by which the middle roll or rolls must be offset from the entry and delivery rolls varies inversely with the outside diameter of the tube to be processed. This is shown by the following equation:

$$\delta = Sl^2/6ED$$

where S is the yield strength of the metal (psi), l is the distance between the outboard rolls (in.), E is the modulus of elasticity, and D is the outside diameter of the tube (in.).

As the diameter of the tube decreases, the deflection requirements increase over a given span. Thus, the factor that determines the smallest-diameter tube that a machine can process is the deflection requirement of the tube over the span of the rolls. Approximately ¾ in. is the maximum deflection that can be applied to most tubes without adversely affecting travel of the tube through the rolls of a rotary straightening machine.

Typical sizes and types of multiple-roll straighteners used for straightening various sizes and types of tubing are given in Table 3.

Entry and Delivery Tables. Well-designed entry and delivery tables are important in the rotary straightening of tubular products. The rotary straightening machine is designed to support, guide and straighten a tube within the length between the first and last roll stands. It is not designed to feed, support or confine a long tube over its full length.

Entry-table guides confine the portion of the tube that is beyond the limits controlled by the rotary straightening machine so as to minimize rotary whipping of the unstraightened portion. The table guides must be designed to suit the size range, grade of material, and travel rate of tube that is to be processed. A combination of entry and delivery tables and guides keeps the amount of straightener deflection, or offset, to a minimum, increases the range of sizes that can be straightened in any one machine, and decreases the possibility of damaging the tube.

The entry table should also feed the tube into the rotary straightener with skewed rolls, so that the tube will be rotating and moving lineally when it enters the straightener.

Ovalizing in Rotary Straighteners

A straightening effect can be produced in some tubular products not only by bending, but by squeezing them slightly out-of-round between the straightening rolls as the tubes are processed through a rotary straightening machine. The rolls have a concave curvature whereby a line of contact is produced between the roll and the workpiece for almost the full length of the roll.

Machines having two-roll and three-roll clusters are used to combine bending and ovalizing in straightening of round tubes.

Collapse Strength. The cold working of a tubular product by bending and ovalizing in a rotary straightening machine can reduce the collapse strength or external-pressure resistance of the tube. Therefore, cold working should be kept to a minimum. Designing the rotary straightener to produce as low a bending and ovalizing force as possible helps to produce a more satisfactory tubular product.

Rotary Swaging of Bars and Tubes

*By the ASM Committee on Rotary Swaging**

ROTARY SWAGING is a process for reducing the cross-sectional area or otherwise changing the shape of bars, tubes or wires by repeated radial blows with one or more pairs of opposed dies. The work is elongated as the cross-sectional area is reduced. Usually the workpiece (starting blank) is round, square or otherwise symmetrical in cross section, although other forms, such as rectangles, can be swaged.

Most swaged workpieces are round, the simplest being formed by reduction in diameter. However, swaging can also produce straight and compound tapers, produce contours on the inside diameter of tubing, and change round to square or other shapes.

Applicability

Swaging has been used to reduce tubes up to 14 in. in initial diameter and bars up to 4 in. in initial diameter.

Hardness, tensile strength and reduction in area of the work metal have the most significant effect on swageability. Type and homogeneity of microstructure also influence the ease of swaging and the degree to which a metal can be swaged. Maximum reduction in area for various metals is given in Table 1.

Work Metals. Of the plain carbon steels, those with a carbon content of 0.20% or less are the most swageable. These grades can be reduced up to 70% in cross-sectional area by swaging. As carbon content or alloy content is increased, swageability is decreased. Alloying elements such as manganese, nickel, chromium and tungsten increase work-metal strength and thus decrease the ability of the metal to flow. Free-machining additives, such as sulfur, lead and phosphorus, cause discontinuities in structure that result in splitting or crumbling of the work metal during swaging.

In cold swaging of steel (at room temperature), maximum swageability is obtained when the microstructure is in the spheroidized condition. Pearlitic annealed microstructures are less swageable than spheroidized microstructures, depending on the fineness of the pearlite, and on the tensile strength and hardness of the steel. Fine pearlitic microstructures, such as are found in patented music wire and spring wire, can be swaged up to 30 to 40% reduction in area.

Figure 1 shows the relation of hardness to carbon content for pearlitic and

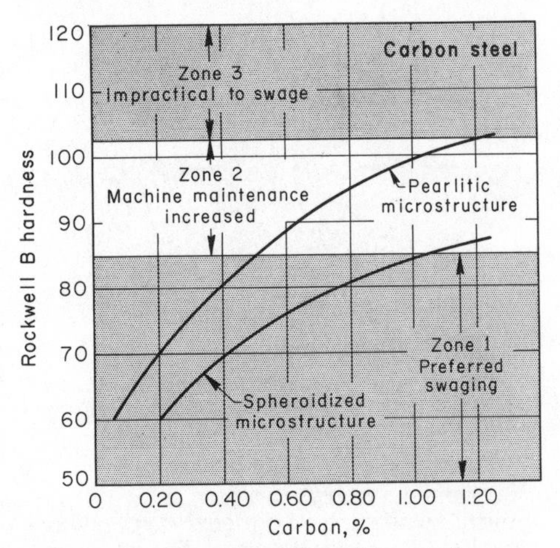

Fig. 1. Swageability of carbon steel, as a function of microstructure, hardness and carbon content

Table 1. Maximum Reduction in Area Obtainable in Several Metals by Cold Swaging

Work metal	Reduction in area, %	Work metal	Reduction in area, %
Plain Carbon Steels(a)		**Aluminum Alloys**	
Up to 1020	60	1100-O	70
1020 to 1050	50	2024-O	20
1050 to 1095	40	3003-O	70
Alloy Steels(b)		5050-O	70
		5052-O	70
0.20% C	50	6061-O	70
0.40% C	40	7075-O	15
0.60% C	20	**Other Alloys**	
High Speed Tool Steels(b)		Copper alloys(c)	60-70
All grades	20	A-286	60
Stainless Steels(c)		Cb-25Zr	60-70
		Hipernik	80
300 series	50	Hipernom	80
400 series:		Inconel X-750	60
Low-carbon	40	Kovar	80
High-carbon	10	Vicalloy	50

(a) Low-manganese steels, spheroidize annealed. (b) Spheroidize annealed. (c) Annealed.

ELTON MAYHEW, *Chairman*, Chief Engineer, Swaging Machine Div., Torrington Co.; WALTON E. BRUSH, Metallurgist, Lamp Div., Westinghouse Electric Corp.; FRANK GORSLER, Senior Research Engineer, Physical Research Dept., Cincinnati Milling and Grinding Machines, Inc.; WILLARD B. GREEN, JR., Assistant Chief Metallurgist, Research Dept., Torrington Co.; CLARENCE J. MILLER, Manager, Swaging Sales, Abbey Etna Machine Co.; ROBERT W. SELWOOD, GFM Co.; GEORGE SHARP, President, George Sharp, Inc.; MARTIN J. TOBIN, President, Martin J. Tobin Co.

R. E. WIEN, Supervisor, Special Projects, Headquarters Manufacturing Laboratory, Research & Development Center, Westinghouse Electric Corp.; JOSEPH E. ZAHODY, Tube Mill Foreman, Atlas Steels Co. Div., Rio Algom Mines Ltd.

spheroidized microstructures and also shows three zones of swageability, indicating that a hardness of Rockwell B 85 is the maximum preferred for carbon steels, and that when hardness exceeds Rockwell B 102 swaging is impractical. In Fig. 2, the influence of cold reduction on tensile and yield strengths of several metals is shown.

Workpieces that require reductions greater than can be accomplished with one swaging pass must be stress relieved or reannealed after the first pass to restore ductility in the metal for further reduction. Stress relieving of steel by heating to 1100 to 1250 F often restores ductility, although excessive grain growth may develop when extensive cold working is followed by heating within this temperature range. Under these conditions, stress relieving is of little value, and it is necessary to fully anneal the material.

Metal Flow During Swaging

Metal flow during rotary swaging is not confined to one direction. As shown in Fig. 3, more metal moves out of the taper in a direction opposite to that of the feed than through the straight portion (blade). Some metal flow also occurs in the transverse direction, but it is restricted by the oval or side clearance in the dies (see Fig. 9).

Feedback. The action of the metal moving against the direction of feed is called feedback, and results from slippage of the workpiece in the die taper when it is too steep. Feedback is manifested as heavy endwise vibration offering considerable resistance to feeding of the workpiece.

Workpiece Rotation. Unless resisted, rotation is imparted as the dies close on the workpiece, and the speed of rotation is the speed of the roller cage. If rotation is permitted, swaging takes place in only one position on the workpiece, causing ovaling, flash, and sticking of the workpiece in the die. Resistance to rotation is manual when the swager is hand fed; mechanical means are used with automatic feeds.

Machines

Rotary swaging machines are classified as standard rotary, die-closing, and stationary-spindle types. All these machines are equipped with dies that open and close rapidly to provide the impact action that shapes the workpiece. Die-closing and stationary-spindle type swaging machines can be altered to produce a slower, "squeeze-type" action of the dies (see opposite page).

Selection of Machine. A standard rotary swager is recommended for bar stock or tubing when swaging consists of a straight reduction in stock diameter or when it is used for tapering round workpieces.

When swaging bars or tubes that cannot be fed into the machine in the usual manner (see workpiece in Fig. 5), a die-closing swager is recommended.

A stationary-spindle machine is used when swaging involves changing of the cross-sectional shape of a bar or tube to a different shape (such as a round to a square, or a square to a triangle), or when swaging the end of coiled wire.

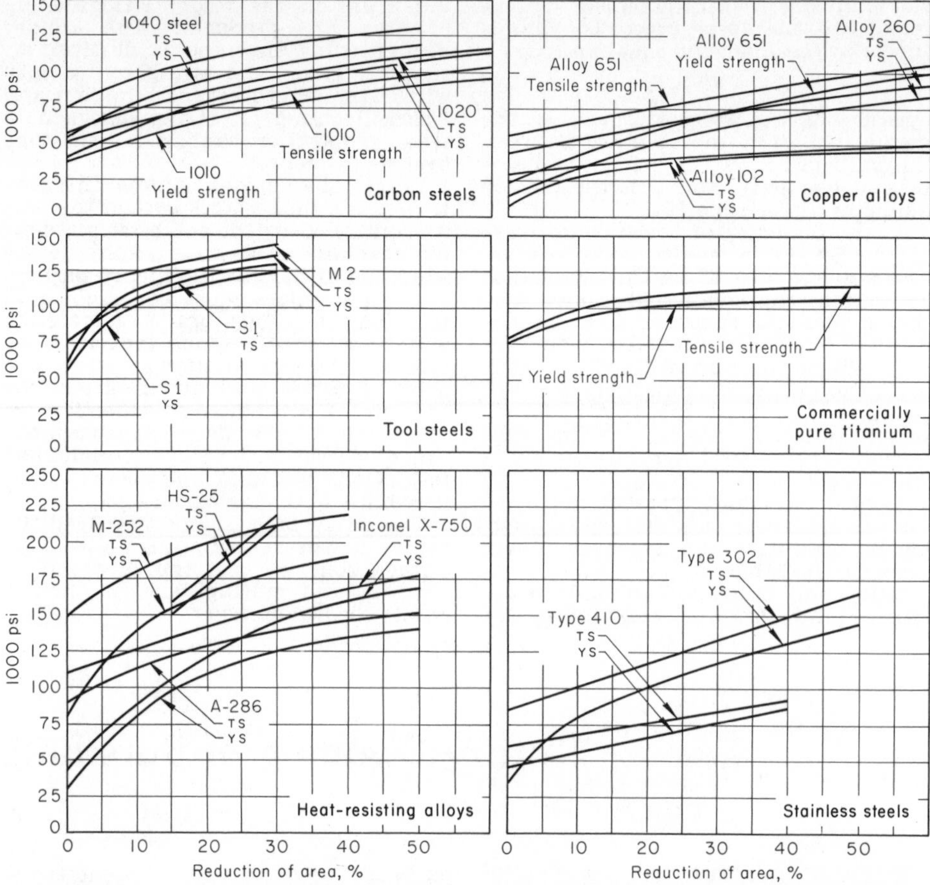

Fig. 2. Influence of cold reduction by swaging on mechanical properties of various metals

Fig. 3. Direction of metal flow in workpiece during rotary swaging

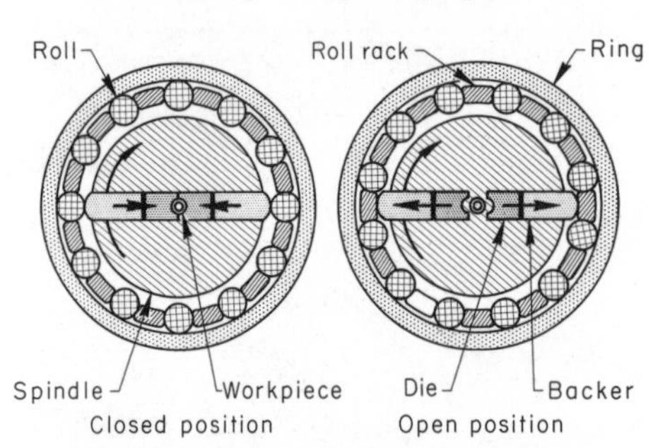

Fig. 4. Principal components and directions of movement in a standard two-die rotary swager. See text for discussion.

Standard rotary swagers, stationary-spindle swagers and squeeze-type swagers allow the work to be fed into the taper entrance of the swaging dies. The amount of diameter reduction per pass is limited by the design of the entrance taper of the dies or the area reduction capability of the machine. The results are expressed in terms of diameter reduction. Several swaging reductions may be necessary before the maximum area reductions are reached, because of die design.

The two methods of calculating reduction are:

Percentage diameter reduction = $100[1-(D_2/D_1)]$

Percentage area reduction = $100[1-(D_2^2/D_1^2)]$

A die-closing type of swager has dies made with side relief great enough to allow the dies to come directly down on the work. The maximum side relief that can be used limits the reduction in diameter per swaging pass to 25%. The die-closing type of swager may have a front entrance angle and can be used as a standard rotary swager. When used in this manner, the diameter and area reduction per pass are the same as for a standard rotary swager. However, diameter reduction should not be confused with area reduction.

Standard Rotary Swagers. The basic rotary swager is a mechanical hammer that delivers blows (impact swaging) at high frequency, thus changing the shape of a workpiece by metal flow. This machine is used for straight reducing of stock diameter, or for tapering round workpieces.

A standard rotary swager consists of a head that contains the swaging components and a base that supports the head and houses the motor. Figure 4 shows the principal components and directions of movement in the head of a typical two-die rotary swager. A hardened and ground steel ring, about 0.020 in. larger in diameter than the bore of the head, is pressed into the head so that the ring is in compression.

The spindle, centrally located within the ring, is slotted to hold the backers and dies and is mounted in a tapered roller bearing. Flat steel shims are placed between the dies and backers. A roll rack containing a set of rolls (usually 10 to 20) is located between the press-fitted ring and the backers. (A conventional impact-type backer is shown in Fig. 7.) The spindle is rotated by a motor-driven flywheel keyed to the spindle. During rotation of the spindle, the dies move outward by centrifugal force and inward by the action of the backers striking the rolls. The number of blows (impacts) produced by the dies is 1000 to 5000 per minute, depending on the size of the swager. The impact rate is approximately equal to the number of rolls times the speed (rpm) of the swager spindle times the factor 0.6, which allows for creep of the roll rack.

The amount of die opening when the dies are in the open position — backers positioned between the rolls (see Fig. 4) — can be changed to some extent during operation by a mechanical device that restricts the amount dies and backers can move under centrifugal force. Changing the closed position of the dies — backers positioned on the rolls (see Fig. 4) — however, cannot be done during operation; the swager must be stopped and shims inserted between the dies and the backers. The severity of the blow can be varied by using shims of different thicknesses. The dies should be shimmed tight enough to obtain a reasonable amount of interference between the backers and the rolls when the dies are in the closed position.

The amount of shimming should be sufficient to bring the die faces together, and generally 0.002 to 0.020 in. preload may be added, according to the size of machine. A swager is shimmed too tightly, or has too great a preload, when it stalls in starting while the swager hammers are off the rolls. The lightest possible shimming should be used; overshimming increases machine maintenance. Additional shimming will not produce a smaller section size, because section size is controlled by the size of the die cavity when the dies are in the closed position. Insufficient shimming, however, will increase the section size and cause variation in results, particularly in dimensions and surface conditions.

Die-closing swagers are used when the dies must open more than is possible in a standard rotary swager to permit loading. Die-closing swagers are essentially of the same construction as the standard rotary swagers described above. Both have similar components, such as dies, rolls, roll rack, inside ring, spindle and shims.

The main difference between die-closing and standard rotary swagers is the addition of a reciprocating wedge mechanism that forces closure of the taper-back dies, as shown in Fig. 5. The wedge mechanism consists of a wedge for each die that is positioned between the die and the backer. The rotating dies open by centrifugal force and are held open by springs or other mechanical means when the power-actuated wedge mechanism is in the back position. Wedge control of the die opening permits the work to be placed in the machine in a predetermined position

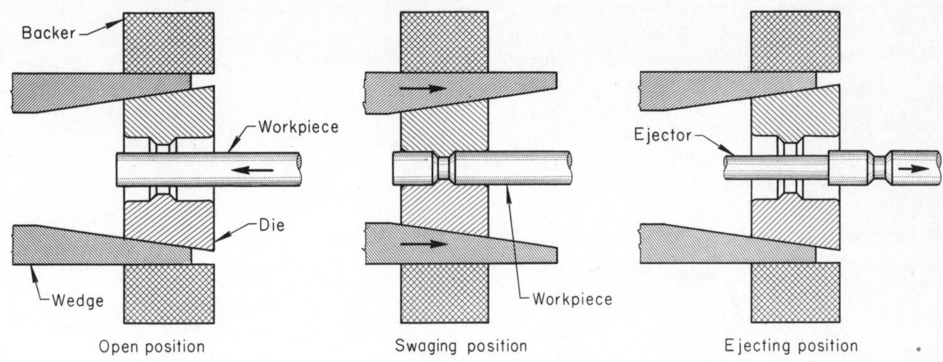

Fig. 5. Principal components and directions of movement in a die-closing swager

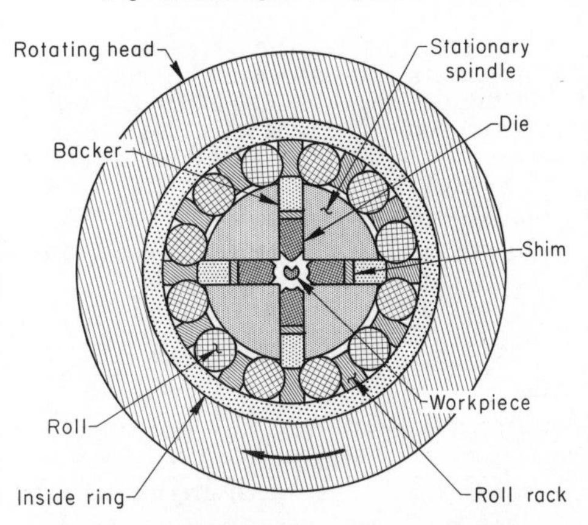

Fig. 6. Principal components of a stationary-spindle rotary swager

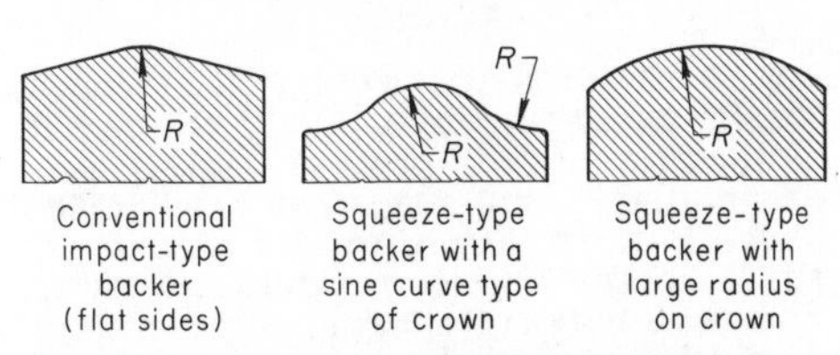

Fig. 7. Designs of three different backer cams used in rotary swaging

when the dies are open. Reduction per pass is limited to 25% of the original diameter of the workpiece. The wedge angle of dies should not exceed 7½°.

Stationary-spindle swagers are sometimes called inverted swagers, because the spindle, dies and work remain stationary while the head and roll rack rotate. These machines are used for swaging shapes other than round.

The reciprocating action of the dies is the same as in swagers in which the spindle is rotated and the roll rack remains stationary. Principal components of a stationary-spindle machine are shown in Fig. 6.

The stationary-spindle swager consists of a base that houses the motor and supports a bearing housing containing two tapered roller bearings. The head, fastened to a rotating sleeve mounted in the tapered roller bearings, is motor-driven and acts like a flywheel. The spindle is mounted and held stationary by a rear housing that is fastened to a bearing housing.

As the head rotates, the rolls pass over the backers, which in turn cause the dies to strike the workpiece in a pulsating hammer-type action. Die opening may be controlled by the forward feed of the workpiece, although springs are sometimes used to open the dies. Maximum outward travel of the dies in the open position is regulated by a mechanical device in the front of the machine. Shims are used between the dies and the backers in the same manner as in swagers with rotating spindles.

Swaging by Squeeze Action. The impact action common to standard rotary swagers can be slowed to produce a squeezing action by employing a backer cam. The design of the crown and width of the backers are such that at least one roll is always in contact with the backer. The shape of the crown can be a single curve (Fig. 7), or two radii that approximate a sine curve (Fig. 7). When using this type of backer, the machines have fewer rolls than a standard swager.

Swaging with squeeze action is used to obtain greater reduction in area than normally produced by impact action and to produce intricate profiles on internal surfaces with the aid of a mandrel.

Compared to impact forming with standard swagers, squeeze forming produces less noise and vibration, requires less maintenance of rolls and backers, and can produce greater reductions and closer tolerances. Standard swagers, however, are simpler to operate and lower in cost, require less floor space, and are faster for small reductions.

Rolls and backers used for cold swaging are made from tool steel. The grade of tool steel used varies considerably, although many rolls and backers are made from one of the shock-resisting grades, such as S2, and then hardened and tempered to Rockwell C 55 to 60.

Almost all rolls and backers become work hardened, to a degree that depends on the severity of reduction of the swaged workpiece, the swageability of the work metal, the material used for the rolls and backers, total operating time, and adjustment of the machine. To reduce the effects of work hardening and to prolong service life, rolls and backers used in cold swaging are stress relieved periodically at 350 to 450 F for 2 to 3 hr. The stress-relieving temperature used must not be higher than the original tempering temperature, or softening will result. The frequency of stress relieving depends on the severity of swaging. Under normal conditions, rolls and backers should be stress relieved after every thirty hours of operation.

Stress relieving is usually not required for rolls and backers used for hot swaging, because some stress reliev-

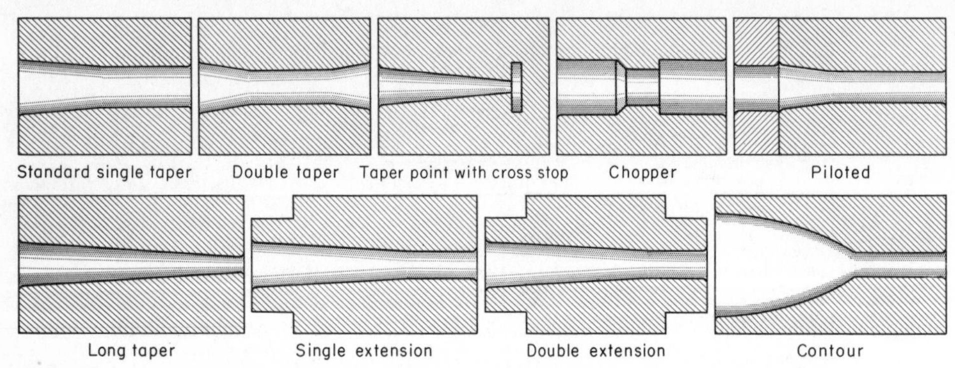

Fig. 8. Typical die shapes used in rotary swaging. See text for discussion.

ing occurs each time heat transfers from the hot workpiece to the rolls and backers. Also, work hardening of these components is less than in cold swaging, because less force is required to form the part by hot swaging.

The rolls and roll rack of a four-die machine are subject to about 1½ times as much wear as those in a two-die machine, and therefore must be replaced more often. (Other elements, such as the spindle and cap, liner plates, backers and dies, have about the same rate of wear in both types of machine; however, replacement cost of these components is less for a two-die machine.)

The number of rolls in a four-die machine must be divisible by four, so that they can be placed at 90° spacing. Thus, a ten-roll machine is limited to using two dies.

A stationary-spindle machine generally has 12 rolls, and two, three or four dies can be used.

Number of Dies. Most swagers have either two or four dies, although three-die machines are available. Most swaging is done in two-die machines, because they are less costly to build and simpler to set up and maintain.

Four-die swaging machines have some advantages. Slightly greater reductions can be made more readily, and cold working of the dies is reduced, because less ovality or side clearance is required than for two dies. Four-die machines are especially useful for swaging workpieces from a round to a square cross section. Four dies should not, however, be used for workpieces less than 3⁄16 in. across (in either round or square section), because the dies would be too weak. Four dies are used primarily in stationary-spindle swaging machines.

To change the number of dies in a swager, generally the spindle must be changed, because the slots in the spindle accommodate only the number of dies used.

Machine Capacity. The rated capacity of a swaging machine is based on the swaging of solid work metal of a designated tensile strength, and is expressed as the diameter, or the average diameter of a taper, to which the machine can swage a workpiece made from that material.

Machine capacity is influenced greatly by the strength of the head. The load on the head is approximately equal to the projected area of the workpiece under compression times the tensile strength of the work metal.

For example, if the strength of the head limits the safe working load of a two-die machine to 112,500 lb, the rated capacity (specific diameter) of the machine for a 3-in.-long die in swaging solid work metal of 60,000-psi tensile strength can be calculated as follows:

$$\text{Load (lb)} = \text{projected load area (sq in.)} \times \text{tensile strength (psi)}$$
$$= \text{specific diameter (in.)} \times \text{die length (in.)} \times \text{tensile strength (psi)}$$

Therefore:

$$\text{Specific diameter} = \frac{\text{Load (lb)}}{\text{Die length (in.)} \times \text{tensile strength (psi)}} = \frac{112{,}500}{3 \times 60{,}000} = 5/8 \text{ in.}$$

For work metal of a higher or lower tensile strength, the capacity or specific diameter would be proportionately lower or higher, in accordance with the above formula. For a greater die length, the machine capacity would be lower. To swage parts to a larger final average diameter in this two-die machine, it would be necessary to decrease the working length of the die, proportionately, and thus to decrease the area of work metal under compression.

For swaging a tube, the capacity of the machine is limited by the cross section of the die and the compressive strength of the tube, and sometimes by the size of hole through the spindle of the machine. Swaging of tubes with a wall thickness greater than 0.040 in. over a mandrel is considered the same as swaging of solid bar stock. Tubes with thinner walls require greater force, depending on tube diameter and length of die, because friction traps the metal between the die and mandrel, and there is no bulk metal to move.

Machines with dies that produce a squeezing action are rated according to their radial load capacity. Usually the capacity is limited by the stress at the line of contact between the roller and backer. For a reasonable component life, this stress should not exceed about 170,000 psi. Assuming this stress as maximum when rollers and backers are made of steel, the radial load capacity is determined by the following formula:

$$L = 1.38Nl\left(\frac{D_r \times D_b}{D_r + D_b}\right)$$

where L is the radial load capacity, in tons; N is the number of backers; l is the effective roller length, in inches; D_r is the diameter of each roller, in inches; and D_b is the diameter of the backer crown contacting the rollers, in inches. The constant converts the standard Hertz stress formula to tons of force when a value of 170,000 psi is used for maximum stress.

For example, a four-die machine having 4-in.-diam rolls with an effective length of 10 in. and with a 36-in.-diam backer crown would have a radial load capacity (L) of almost 200 tons, determined as follows:

$$L = 1.38 \times 4 \times 10\left(\frac{4 \times 36}{4 + 36}\right) = 199 \text{ tons}$$

Swaging Dies

Resistance to shock and wear are the primary requirements for cold swaging dies. Sometimes it is necessary to sacrifice some wear resistance to prevent die breakage from lack of shock resistance. In many applications, shallow-hardening tool steels such as W1 are used, because it is possible to develop extremely high surface hardness and a softer, tougher core with these steels. Another advantage in using the W grades of tool steel for swaging dies is that they are available in different carbon ranges (0.60 to 1.40%). It is usual to vary the carbon content in accordance with die size. For instance, steels for small dies (½ by ¾ in. in cross section) have a carbon content of about 1.4%, those for medium-size dies (2 by 2 in. in cross section) have about 0.95% carbon, and a 0.60% carbon content is used for large dies (5 by 8 in. in cross section).

When using the practice outlined above, a zone about 9⁄64 in. in depth hardened to Rockwell C 62 to 65 is recommended. This can be obtained by water or brine quenching the W grade tool steels (see page 225 in Volume 2 of this Handbook).

Dies are often plated with about 0.0002 in. of chromium to improve resistance to wear and galling.

Numerous other materials have been used for swaging dies, such as the shock-resisting tool steels (S group) at Rockwell C 55 to 60, and L6 tool steel hardened to about Rockwell C 60. Carbide is used for some high-production applications. Sometimes tool steel dies are hardened only at critical areas, by flame or induction methods.

Dies for hot swaging must be made from metal that resists tempering at elevated temperature. Hardened high speed steels, such as M2, cast cobalt-base alloy tool materials, and shock-resisting grades of carbide are suitable die materials for hot swaging.

Types of Dies. Depending on the shape, size and material of the workpiece, dies range from the simple, single-taper, straight-reduction type to those of special design. Figure 8 illustrates nine typical die shapes. Specific applications for each are as follows:

Standard single-taper dies are the basic swaging dies designed for straight reduction in diameter. One common use is to tag bars for drawbench operations.

Double-taper dies are designed for plain reductions, such as those made in the standard single-taper die described above. A double-taper die can be reversed to obtain twice the life of a single-taper die.

Taper-point dies are used for finish forming a point on the end of the workpiece or for forming a point prior to a drawbench operation. The built-in cross stop insures equal length of all swaged points.

Chopper dies are made of heat-resisting metal and are used exclusively for hot swaging.

Piloted dies insure concentricity between the unswaged section and the reduced section of the workpiece. The front part of the die acts as a guide; reduction occurs only in the taper section.

Long taper dies are designed with a taper over their entire length; however, the length of the taper produced on the work will be slightly less than that of the die.

Single-extension dies are used for high reduction of solid bars and tubing of low tensile strength. This die produces a longer tapered section than a standard die.

Double-extension dies are extended at both ends to facilitate the swaging of thick-wall tubing, and to provide a longer taper section.

Contour dies are used to produce special shapes on tubes and bars.

Die Clearance. Swaging die sets are usually two, three, or four-piece, depending on the type of swaging machine used. Practically all swaging dies require clearance in the form of relief or ovality in the die cavity. Without clearance, the flow of metal is restricted, and this results in the workpiece sticking to the die.

Ovality in Two-Piece Dies. Oval dies are oval in both the taper and blade sections. This ovality provides the necessary clearance for the die to function. Also, oval dies are useful for applications in which maximum work hardening of the metal being swaged is desired. The disadvantages of using ovality to obtain clearance are: (*a*) close tolerances are difficult to maintain, (*b*) dies wear rapidly, and (*c*) finish on work is inferior to that produced with dies having side clearance.

Ovality in two-piece dies is produced by placing shims between the finished die faces and boring or reaming the assembly to the desired clearance. Smoothly blending the two contours gives an approximately oval shape to the reassembled die. An alternative procedure for producing ovality is to bore the two die blocks oversize, and then to grind the die faces until the groove in each half is of the proper depth to produce the desired swaged diameter.

The amount of ovality required varies with the characteristics and size of the work metal to be swaged. Table 2 gives nominal values for determining the amounts of ovality for swaging solid materials from 1/32 to 3/4 in. in diameter, and for tubing covering a range of outside diameters. The following sample calculation shows how Table 2 is used to determine the die ovality required for swaging 1/2-in.-diam 1020 steel bar to a diameter of 0.375 in. using a die with a taper of 8° included angle. From Table 2, the ovality for the die taper for swaging low-carbon steel is 0.001 in. per degree of taper plus 0.5% of the maximum diameter of the bar before swaging. Therefore:

$$\text{Ovality of die taper} = (0.001 \times 8) + (0.005 \times 0.500) = 0.008 + 0.0025 = 0.0105 \text{ in.}$$

According to Table 2, ovality of the blade section of the die is 0.003 to 0.004 in. less than the ovality of the taper section. Therefore:

$$\text{Ovality of die blade} = 0.0105 - 0.003 = 0.0075 \text{ in.}$$

Table 2. Nominal Values for Use in Computing Ovality, and Corner Radius on Groove, of Dies for Swaging of Bars and Tubing

Work metal	Amount of shimming recommended for die diameter (in.) of: Between 3/4 and 1/4	3/16	1/8	1/16	1/32
Dies for Swaging of Bars					
Low-C steels; hard brass; copper	For die taper: 0.001 in./deg + 0.5% of max work diam For die blade: Above value less 0.003 to 0.004 in.	2% (a)	3% (a)	4% (a)	(b)
High-C and alloy steels	125% of value for low-C steels	2% (a)	3% (a)	4% (a)	(b)
Lead	No shimming required	...	...	...	...

Dies for Swaging of Tubing

When OD equals a minimum of 25 times wall thickness, use no shimming.
When OD equals 10 to 24 times wall thickness, use 60% of values for bars (see above).
When OD equals 9 times wall thickness or less, use same values as for bars (see above).

Corner Radius on Die Groove

For solid work metal: 1/16 of blade diameter to nearest 0.005 in.
For tubular work metal: Corner radius equal to the wall thickness.

(a) Per cent of average diameter of work. (b) Stone edges of die groove.

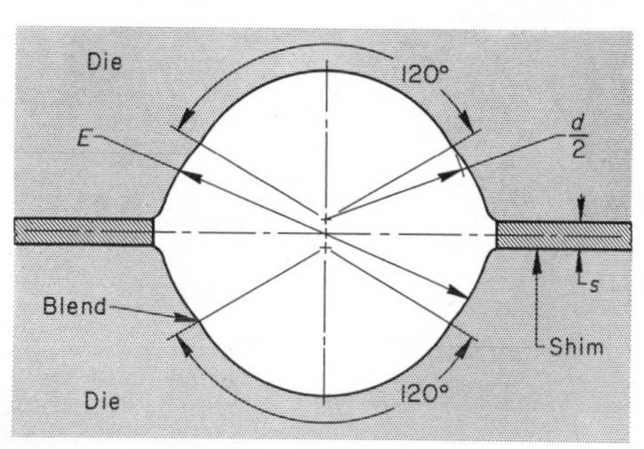

Fig. 9. Design of die with side clearance. See text for discussion.

These calculated values determine the thickness of shims that must be used between the die faces during machining of the cavity to produce a die of proper ovality for swaging 1020 steel bars. These values also apply when the alternative method of producing ovality is used.

In addition to ovality, die halves should be provided with a corner radius at the exit end of the blade section as well as at the die entrance. Table 2 shows that the corner radius on the groove should be 1/16 of the blade diameter to the nearest 0.005 in. for swaging solid sections, or equal to wall thickness for swaging of a tube. Thus, the die for swaging the 1/2-in.-diam 1020 steel bar referred to in the sample calculation above would require a corner radius of about 0.025 in. (1/16 of 0.375).

The included angle for the taper section of oval dies should be no more than 30°; an included angle of 8° or less is preferred.

Two-Piece Dies With Side Clearance. Two-piece dies that contact the workpiece over two 120° segments of the circle (Fig. 9) in both the taper and blade sections are superior to the oval dies previously described. Workpieces swaged in 240°-contact dies have better surface finish and closer tolerance. The life of these dies is longer, and the work metal is cold worked less rapidly than in oval dies. Dies with 240° contact can be used for straight reductions of solid bars or of thick-wall tubing.

Figure 9 shows the design of 240°-contact dies with side clearance. The dies are first bored or ground without shims to produce the area of work contact. Shims are then inserted to produce side clearance only. Side clearance is then bored or ground until dimension E, measured diagonally across the mouth of the die, is equal to:

$$\sqrt{d^2 + ds + s^2}$$

where d is the initial diameter of the taper at the entrance to the die, and s is the thickness of the shim stock placed between the die faces. The maximum thickness of the shim should be one-third of the swaged diameter of the workpiece. This will produce a total contact of 240° along the taper and blade sections. The intersection between the taper and blade must be well blended for best results in feeding and finishing.

When swaging tubing, the shim thickness varies with the ratio of outside diameter to wall thickness (D/t ratio), so that the side clearance is nearly zero for thin-wall ($D/t = 30$ or more) tubing.

The same procedure is followed in determining the side clearance for the blade. The diameter of the swaged workpiece is used instead of the large diameter of the taper. The same shim is used for both taper and blade.

Ovality in Four-Piece Dies. Each piece of a four-piece die makes approximately 90° contact with the surface of the workpiece when the die is not provided with ovality or side clearance. Dies without ovality are used for sizing thin-wall tubes ($D/t = 30$ or more). For swaging solid sections or thick-wall tubing, or for mandrel swaging, oval dies are required; ovality influences circumferential flow of the work metal and reduces the load on the machine.

Ovality is produced by grinding the dies held by a fixture mounted on a rotating face plate of an internal grinder. The taper is produced by pivoting the grinding wheel slide to the appropriate angle and traversing the surface. During grinding, the dies are separated by shims of a thickness that will produce the required diameter in the blade section when ground with a wheel of predetermined size. Thinner shims are used when assembling the dies in the swaging machine. The amount of ovality usually ranges from 2 to 10%.

Auxiliary Tools

Swaging machines require auxiliary tools for guiding and feeding the workpiece into the die, holding it during swaging, and ejecting it. These tools

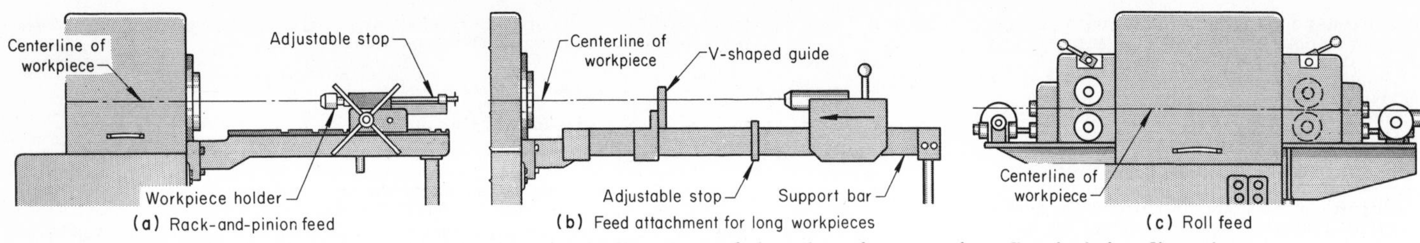

(a) Rack-and-pinion feed (b) Feed attachment for long workpieces (c) Roll feed

Fig. 10. Three types of mechanisms for feeding the workpiece in rotary swaging. See text for discussion.

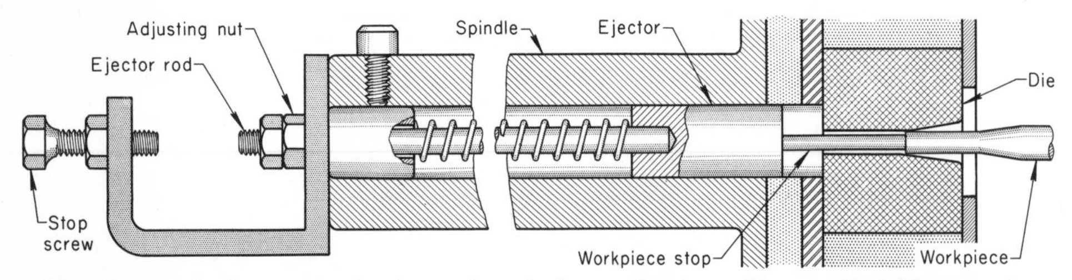

Fig. 11. Principal components of a spring ejector mechanism with an adjustable rear stop

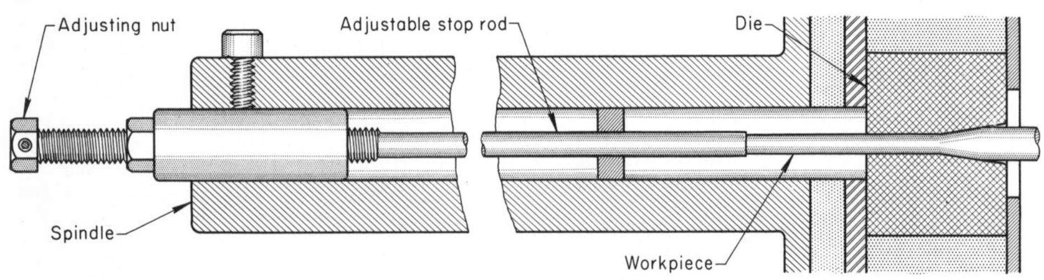

Fig. 12. Principal components of an adjustable stop-rod mechanism

range from simple hand tools to elaborate power-driven mechanisms. Some of the common types of auxiliary tools are illustrated in Fig. 10 through 14; their uses are described in the paragraphs that follow.

Rack-and-pinion feed mechanisms (Fig. 10a) are designed for manual operation and provide more force for feeding the workpiece than can be obtained by hand feeding. With these mechanisms, operator fatigue is reduced, and the workpiece is guided straight along the centerline of the machine.

Feed attachments for long workpieces (Fig. 10b) consist of a carriage with antifriction rollers that is mounted on a fixed bar that extends from a bracket on the entrance side of the machine for the length of the longest workpiece to be swaged. Alignment of the outer end of the bar is made by leveling screws in the base of a triangular support. The carriage provides a means for attaching plain or antifriction workpiece holders and adapters, and a handle for manual feeding toward the swager. An adjustable limit stop is provided on the support bar to control the length of the swaged section and to reproduce accurate tapers.

Roll-feed mechanisms have rolls at the entrance and at the exit end of the swager (Fig. 10c). The rolls at the entrance feed the workpiece, and the rolls at the rear pull the workpiece from the machine. Roll-feed mechanisms are used for continuous swaging. Rolls can be made from either metal or a nonmetallic material (such as rubber). Some roll-feed mechanisms have four soft rubber rolls at the entrance to the swager and no rolls at the rear. This arrangement is ideal for swaging small-diameter bars whose surface finish is critical, because it prevents marking of the swaged surfaces when the bars are pulled from the rear of the machine.

V-shape work guides (see Fig. 10b) are used to support and center the ends of long tubes or bars as they enter the dies. This type of guide is mounted on the front of the machine and can be adjusted vertically to accommodate a range of workpiece diameters up to the capacity of the machine.

Spring ejectors are required for the removal of short workpieces when size prevents manual withdrawal from the dies or when workpieces are swaged over their entire length and cannot be passed through the spindle to the exit end. Figure 11 shows the principal components of a spring ejector mounted on the rear of a swaging machine spindle. As the workpiece enters the die against the workpiece stop, the ejector rod is forced backward until it contacts the preset stop screw. As soon as the swaging cycle is completed, the spring-loaded ejector forces the workpiece from the front of the machine.

Spring ejectors reduce operator fatigue and shorten the swaging cycle in many applications. A similar mechanism may be used on large machines with power feed. The ejector maintains contact with the workpiece stop on the return stroke, thus supporting the workpiece until it is free from the dies.

Stop rods are often used to improve uniformity of swaged pieces in production runs. These rods can be adjusted and locked so that subsequent workpieces will have swaged sections of equal length (Fig. 12). The swaged length can be held within 0.001 in., depending on speed and feed pressure.

Manual workholders are used for holding and feeding workpieces during swaging. There are many designs of manual workholders; four commonly used types are illustrated in Fig. 13. The type shown in Fig. 13(a) contains a latch for gripping the head of a short workpiece and for retracting the workpiece from the dies. The workpiece is released from the holder by pressing the thumb pad attached to the latch. The holder shown in Fig. 13(b) acts as a pusher for feeding the workpiece, which fits into the socket of the holder. Its counterpart used for swaging tubes is shown in Fig. 13(c). The combination tool shown in Fig. 13(d) functions as a holder, a front mandrel, and a stop for the workpiece.

Work adapters and holders (Fig. 14) are used with rack-and-pinion feed mechanisms or with attachments for feeding long workpieces (see Fig. 10a and b). Figure 14(a) shows an antifriction rotating workholder that fastens to the feed plunger. The work fits into the adapter of the rotating head and is manually frictioned to prevent rotation at spindle speed. The holder illustrated in Fig. 14(b) incorporates a spring-loaded friction shoe over which a tubular workpiece is fitted before swaging. The socket-type holder in Fig. 14(c) is stepped to accommodate several sizes of solid or tubular workpieces. The holder shown in Fig. 14(d) can be used for tubing; the holder in Fig. 14(e) can be used for tubing or bars. Figure 14(f) is an adapter that can be attached to the main feed rack or piston rod of rack-and-pinion feed mechanisms (Fig. 10a) to contain the holders illustrated in Fig. 14(c), (d) and (e).

Tube Swaging Without a Mandrel

Tubes are usually swaged without a mandrel to attain one or more of the following: (*a*) a reduction in inside and outside diameters or an increase in wall thickness, (*b*) the production of a taper, (*c*) the conditioning of weld beads for subsequent tube drawing, (*d*) increased strength, (*e*) close tolerances, (*f*) a laminated tube produced from two or more tubes.

The usual limit on the diameter of tubes that can be swaged without a mandrel is 30 times the wall thickness. Tubes with an outside diameter as large as 70 times wall thickness can be swaged, but under these conditions the included angle of reduction must be less than 6°, and the feed rate must be less than 15 in. per min. Under any conditions, the tube must have sufficient column strength to permit feeding. Squareness of the cut ends, roundness, and freedom from surface defects also become more critical as the ratio of outside diameter to wall thickness increases.

Types of Tubes for Swaging. Seamless and welded tubing can be swaged without a mandrel. Seamless tubing is available in greater wall thicknesses in proportion to diameter than welded tubing. However, seamless tubing is the more expensive and may have an irregular and eccentric inside diameter, which will result in excessive variation in wall thickness of the swaged product. When purchasing seamless tubing, it is possible to specify two of the three dimensions: outside diameter, inside diameter, and wall thickness. Thus, the disadvantage of varying dimensions can be partly overcome by specifying the two dimensions that must be controlled for an acceptable product.

Welded tubing usually has a more uniform wall thickness than seamless tubing, and thus has an inside diameter that is more nearly concentric with the outside diameter. Swaging certain types of welded tubing can result in bending, because the metal in the weld area flows less readily than the remainder of the tube material. If the weld is defective or if the metal in the weld area is harder than the remainder of the tube, splitting will occur during swaging. Welded tubing must be held on the centerline of the feed direction during swaging to produce a straight product. Seamless and welded tubes must be free of open seams and cracks, because such defects will become enlarged during swaging.

Die Taper Angle. In best practice when swaging low-carbon steel, the included angle of die taper should not exceed 8° when using manual feed. For thin-wall tubing of low-carbon steel or for more ductile tubing, such as annealed copper, the included angle may be as great as 15°, provided both pressure and feed are decreased proportionately. When the angle of taper exceeds 15°, mechanical or hydraulic feed should be used.

Reduction per Pass. Small reductions can be made in one pass when taper does not exceed 30° included angle. Multiple passes are required to swage tubing in dies with a taper exceeding 30°. Large taper angles generate excessive heat and pressure, which may result in metal pickup by the dies. This condition is more pronounced when swaging aluminum tubing and sometimes occurs when the included angle of die taper is no greater than 20°.

Effect of Reduction on Tube Length. In swaging tubes without a mandrel, an increase in length through the swaged section is usually a minor consideration. Lengthening of about 5 to 15% can be expected for typical swaging operations on low-carbon steel, copper, aluminum or other readily swageable metal tubes with outside diameters of 15 to 25 times wall thickness. Lengthening increases as the amount of reduction per pass increases. Because of the uncertainty as to the relative amounts of radial and axial movement of metal, percentage reduction is frequently designated in terms of diameter reduction rather than area reduction. When the tube is reduced to the extent that it approaches a solid, the endwise flow of metal increases. When total reduction in area is greater than 65 to 75% (depending on the ratio of outside diameter to wall thickness), the tube should be considered a solid, for swaging, and swaging dies should be designed accordingly.

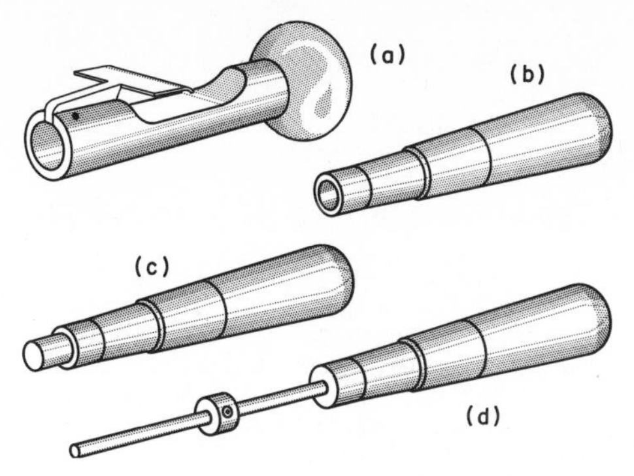

Fig. 13. Four types of hand tools for holding and feeding a workpiece for rotary swaging. See text for discussion.

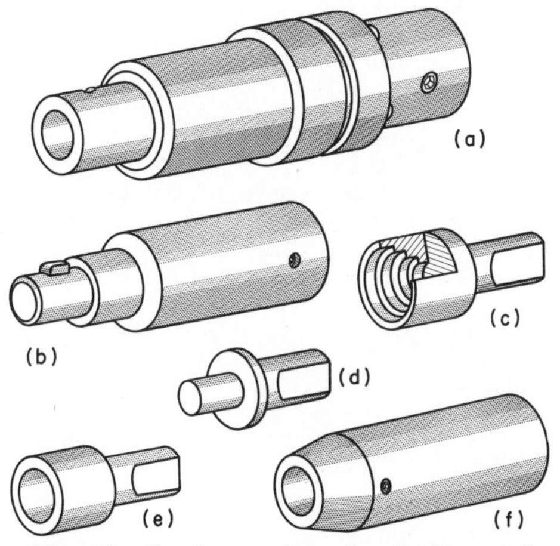

Fig. 14. Six types of work adapters and holders used with the feeding mechanisms shown in Fig. 10. See text for discussion.

Effect of Reduction on Wall Thickness. Swaging of tubing without a mandrel results in an increase in wall thickness. The increase in wall thickness is greater for larger reductions in outside diameter. In general, the wall thickness of the swaged section increases as ductility of the work metal increases.

The wall thickness that will be produced by swaging a tube without using a mandrel can be calculated to about ±10% from the empirical relation:

$$t_2 = D_1 t_1 / D_2$$

where D_1 is outside diameter before swaging, D_2 is outside diameter after, t_1 is wall thickness before swaging, and t_2 is wall thickness after.

Swaging of Long Tapers. The method used for swaging long tapers depends on work-metal hardness, outside diameter, wall thickness, and over-all length, because these variables determine required machine size, die design, and type of feed mechanism.

Welded tubing sometimes causes difficulty in swaging long tapers, because of variations in hardness between the welded seam and the remainder of the tube. Annealing after seam welding is recommended when swaging long tapers from welded tubing.

Almost any reasonable length of taper can be swaged on any length of tube that has a diameter within the capacity of the machine. Long tapers usually require multiple operations.

Table 3 compares the lengths of taper that can be formed in a single operation and in multiple operations on tubes with an outside diameter of 2¼ in. or less, using standard-length and extended-length dies. Standard-length dies refer to manufacturers' catalog sizes, whereas extended lengths are greater than those shown as standard. Note that the longest taper formed in a single operation is fairly close to the length of the die. However, when dies of the same length are used in multiple operations, a smaller portion of the usable length is used for forming the taper, because of the allowance required for blending.

The number of operations needed to produce a specified taper, in addition to the length of taper and length of dies used, is influenced by the following:

1 Minimum length of die entrance is ⅜ in.
2 Each succeeding taper must overlap the preceding taper by 1 in. to permit blending.
3 All operations except the last must allow a straight section (blade), with a minimum length of 1 in., on the tube in addition to the taper being swaged.

The following example illustrates the use of the information contained in Table 3 and in the above list.

Example 427. Forming a 30-In.-Long Taper in Four Operations (Fig. 15)

Figure 15 shows the sequence of operations for swaging a 1¼-in.-OD low-carbon steel tube to ½-in. diameter over a taper length of 30 in. Extended dies (9⅞ in. long) were used for the first three operations and a standard die (8⅜ in. long) for the final operation. An allowance of ⅜ in. was made for die entrance, 1-in. overlap was used for each succeeding taper, and each operation except the last allowed a blade section to remain. The same machine (an 8¾-in. swager) was used for all four operations.

In each operation, the tube was fed through the die to a stop, reducing the tube in each operation to the diameters shown in Fig. 15. Each feed length was controlled by a stop, so that the newly formed taper blended with the preceding one.

Figure 16 shows how a taper 30 in. long can be formed in two operations by dies 18 in. long.

Rate of feed for swaging long tapers is usually 1 in. per sec, withdrawal time is 4 in. per sec, and handling time requires about 4 sec per operation.

An accurate feeding attachment is necessary to swage long tapers. The attachment must feed the tube to the proper length for each operation to produce a uniform taper. This is accomplished by registering the infeed position of the tube from the butt end by means of stops on the attachment (see Fig. 15).

Manually operated feed attachments are generally used for producing tapers longer than 16 in. For tapers up to about 16 in., either hydraulic or air-actuated feed attachments are more convenient.

Cost is the deciding factor between using standard or extended dies, and usually determines the number of operations to be used, for swaging a given taper. However, when tapers exceed 20

Table 3. Comparison of Taper Swageable on Tubes of 2¼-In. Maximum Outside Diameter in Single and Multiple Operations

Die length, in.	Length of taper swaged, in. — Single operation	Multiple operations — First operation	Intermediate operations	Final operation
Standard Die Lengths				
4½	4⅛	3⅛	2½	3½
6⅜	6	5	4⅜	5⅜
8⅜	8	7	6⅜	7⅜
15	14¾	...	...	...
18	17¾	...	...	...
24	23	...	...	...
Extended Die Lengths (Standard Plus 1½ In.)				
6	5⅝	4⅝	4	5
7⅞	7½	6½	5⅞	6⅞
9⅞	9½	8½	7⅞	8⅞

in. in length, there is no alternative but to use multiple operations, because few swaging machines can hold dies longer than 20 in.

Any swaging machine can handle extended dies (see Example 427) that are longer than standard for the machine size. A given machine can also accommodate shorter dies when die-box fillers are used. Thus, each machine has considerable flexibility as to the length of dies it can handle.

Extended dies cost more than standard dies (usually about one-third more). Therefore, it must be decided if it would be more economical to pay the higher cost for extended dies and use fewer operations, thereby increasing productivity, or to use less expensive dies and accept lower productivity.

Similar consideration must be given to using a larger machine that will accommodate a longer standard die.

Tube Swaging With a Mandrel

For some applications it is necessary to reduce the wall thickness of tubing by swaging over a mandrel. This can be done if the final wall thickness is not less than 0.025 in. and the thickness of metal under compression (tube plus mandrel) at any one time is not more than ten times the wall thickness.

A mandrel is used to maintain the inside diameter of a tube during swaging of its outside diameter, to support thin-wall tubes during reduction in diameter, and to form internal shapes. When extended through the front of the dies, a mandrel can also serve as a pilot to support one of the tubes that are to be joined by swaging.

Music wire is generally used for small mandrels (0.003 to 0.062 in. in diameter). Ordinarily, these small mandrels are used only once. Larger mandrels are made from shock-resisting tool steel, hardened, ground and polished, and sometimes plated with about 0.0002 in. of chromium to improve wear resistance and surface finish on the inside diameter of the tube. A combination of hardness and toughness is needed for the larger mandrels.

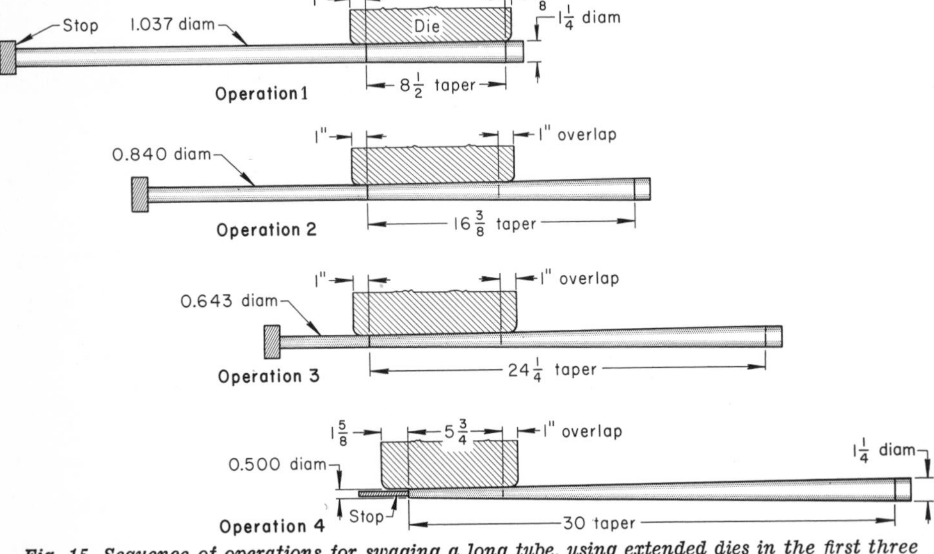

Fig. 15. Sequence of operations for swaging a long tube, using extended dies in the first three operations and standard-length dies in the final operation (Example 427)

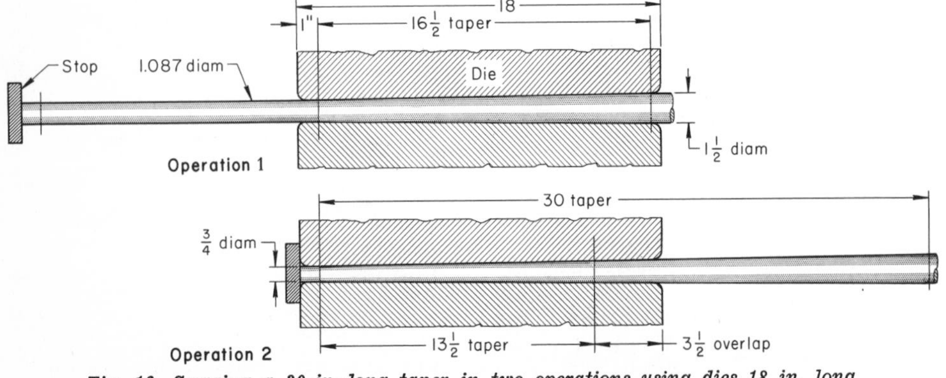

Fig. 16. Swaging a 30-in.-long taper in two operations using dies 18 in. long

Some tool steel manufacturers recommend a tool steel in the S group, hardened to Rockwell C 59 to 61; others recommend A2 or W1 tool steel hardened to Rockwell C 60 to 62 and ground to a finish of 2.5 to 3 micro-in.

Types of mandrels most often used are illustrated in Fig. 17 and are described in the paragraphs that follow:

Plug-type mandrels are fastened to a mandrel rod that is substantially smaller in diameter than the inside diameter of the tube to be swaged. The mandrel is usually about the same length as the swaging die. The mandrel is placed in the die in a fixed position, and the tube is fed over the mandrel into the swager. The mandrel and mandrel rod are removable to permit loading of the tube. A typical setup is illustrated in Fig. 17(a).

Spindle-type mandrels are mounted on a rotating mandrel holder that permits the workpiece and mandrel to rotate independently of the machine spindle. This arrangement is shown in Fig. 17(b). The tube is fed into the die while the mandrel is fixed.

Low-melting alloys are often used for mandrels that support thin-wall tubing during swaging (Fig. 17c). After swaging, the supporting metal is melted out. There are a number of commercially available alloys with melting temperatures ranging from 117 to 477 F (see page 864 in Volume 1 of this Handbook), which is a suitable melting temperature range for these mandrels.

Mandrels for thin-wall tubing are mounted in fixed holders in front of the dies. The mandrel slides back to permit loading of the tube onto the mandrel, after which it slides forward into the die. The feed collar on the mandrel then feeds the tube into the die. Sufficient clearance between the die and mandrel is maintained to permit feeding of the workpiece into the die. Figure 17(d) shows loading and working positions of this type of mandrel.

Full-length mandrels are hardened and ground steel bars made slightly longer than the finished length of the swaged tube. The mandrel is inserted into the tube, and both are passed through the machine (Fig. 17e).

Machine Capacity. Mandrels alter the machine capacity requirement for swaging. When a mandrel is used, the workpiece must be considered as a solid bar, and selection of a swaging machine should be based on its capacity to reduce solid work metal. For example, a machine with a capacity sufficient for swaging a ⅝-in.-diam solid bar is satisfactory for swaging a 1-in.-diam tube with a ¼-in. wall thickness without a mandrel. However, when a mandrel must be used in the 1-in.-diam tube, a machine capable of swaging a 1-in.-diam solid bar must be used. (For calculation of machine capacity, see Appendix on page 346.)

Dies for mandrel swaging must have more ovality than those used for swaging tubing without a mandrel or for swaging a solid bar. Dies that have a nearly round cavity will swage a tube on a mandrel so closely that removing the mandrel is difficult. Ovality overcomes this problem. The amount of die ovality required is proportional to tube wall thickness and diameter.

Internal shapes can be produced in tubular stock by swaging it over shaped mandrels. Workpieces are generally classified as: (*a*) those with uniform cross section along the longitudinal axis, and (*b*) those with axial variations, such as internal tapers or steps.

Workpieces in the first category can be made from long tubular stock swaged over a plug-type mandrel. After swaging, the tube is cut into two or more pieces of the desired length. When swaging shapes with spiral an-

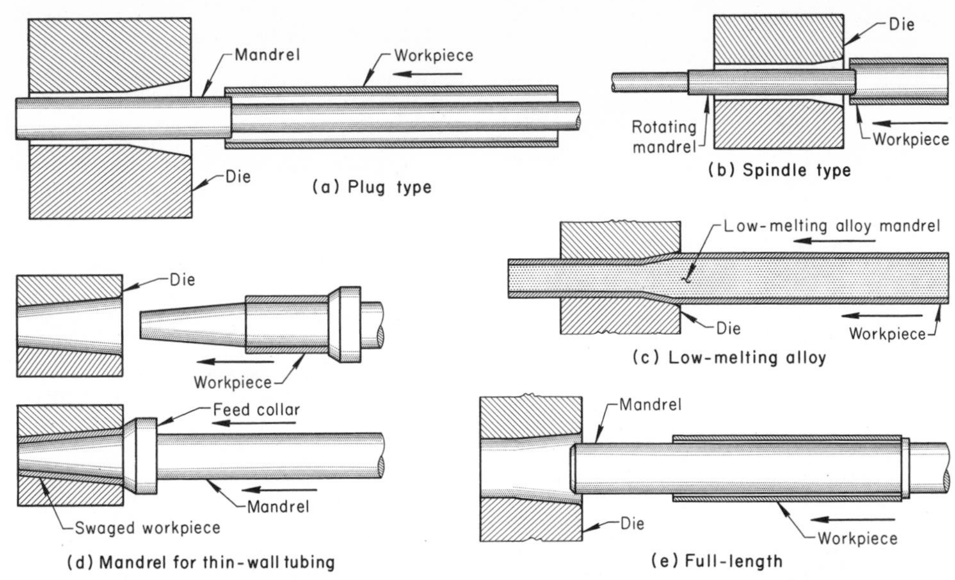

Fig. 17. Five types of mandrels most often used in rotary swaging of tubes

gles, the angles should not exceed 30° as measured from the longitudinal axis, although angles up to 45° have been used for some internal shapes.

Sectional views showing typical internal shapes of workpieces with uniform cross section along the longitudinal axis are shown in Fig. 18. These shapes are made from tubular blanks with inside diameter 0.020 in. larger than the largest diameter of the mandrel. In addition, the difference between the largest and smallest internal diameters of the swaged workpiece is added to the outside diameter of the swaged piece to obtain the correct blank diameter.

For example, an internal ¾-in. square is to be swaged into a 1½-in.-OD tube. The diagonal of a ¾-in. square is 1.06 in. Therefore, the inside diameter of the tubular blank should be 0.020 in. larger, or a total of 1.08 in. The difference between the maximum and the minimum internal diameters of the swaged piece is 1.06 − 0.75 in., or 0.31 in. Thus, the outside diameter of the tubular blank stock should be 1.50 + 0.31 in., or 1.81 in.

To prevent breakage of the mandrel and to obtain the best tangential flow of metal, a swaging machine equipped with a four-piece die and with accurate timing of the blows is preferred for producing internal splines in workpieces with the same cross section at any point along the axis. The dimensional accuracy of workpieces with internal splines is improved when they are swaged in a four-die rather than in a two-die setup, because less work metal is forced into the clearances of four-piece dies. Internal squares or hexagons are less sensitive to the differences between two-piece and four-piece dies.

Figure 19 illustrates several typical workpieces in which the internal shapes require axial variations of the cross section. Internal shapes that contain stepped contours may require preshaped blanks when the differences between the steps are large. For some shapes that terminate as blind holes, axial back pressure is required to influence metal flow during swaging.

Gun barrels are frequently rifled by broaching. Instead, however, they can be rifled by being swaged with a fluted mandrel, as in the next example.

Example 428. Use of a Fluted Mandrel to Rifle the Bore of a Gun Barrel (Fig. 20)

Gun barrels were originally produced by gun drilling 0.222-in.-diam holes in ¾-in.-OD bar sections and then rifling the bore by broaching. After broaching, the gun barrels were turned to a ⅝-in. OD.

By the improved method, 18½-in.-long blanks (Fig. 20) were gun drilled so that their inside diameter was 0.234 in. They were then turned on centers to obtain precise concentricity between inside and outside diameters. In the first swaging operation, the workpieces were reduced in outside diameter to 0.798 in. and in inside diameter to 0.230 in. while length was increased to 22½ in. (operation 1 in Fig. 20). In operation 2 (Fig. 20), a fluted mandrel was inserted to form the rifling as swaging further reduced the outside and inside diameters of the workpieces and increased the length to 24³⁄₁₆ in.

The workpieces were swaged in a 7½-hp two-die machine capable of delivering 1800 blows per minute. Entrance taper of the die was 6° included angle, and over-all length of the die was 3 in. A semiautomatic hydraulic feed mechanism was used, barrels being manually placed into a spring-loaded chuck. The feed was started by the operator, the mandrel being positioned and held in place by an air cylinder. The workpiece was hydraulically fed over the mandrel and disposed of at the rear of the machine, after which the mandrel returned ready for reloading.

The work metal for the part shown in Fig. 20 was 1015 steel, although other steels ranging from lower-carbon steels (such as 1008) to medium-carbon alloy steel have been used for gun barrels. Regardless of the composition, complete spheroidization is essential for the most satisfactory swaging.

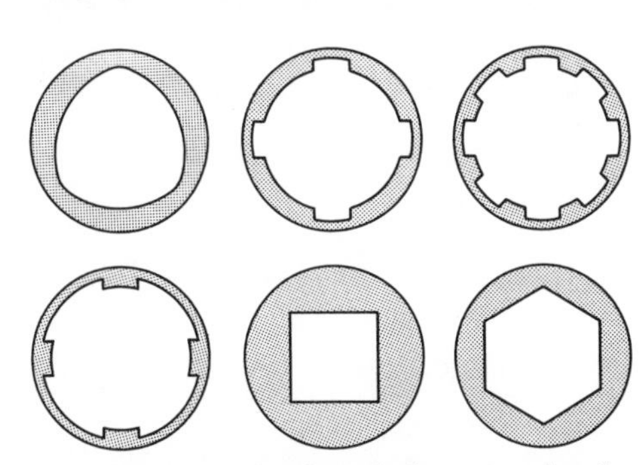

Fig. 18. Typical internal shapes produced in tubular stock by swaging it over shaped, plug-type mandrels

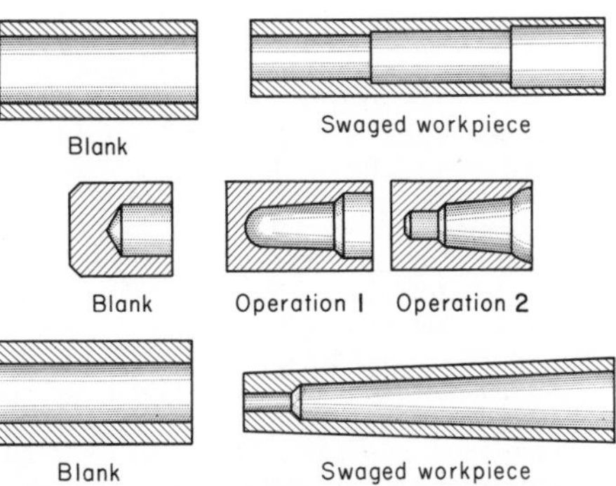

Fig. 19. Internal shapes of nonuniform axial cross section produced by swaging over a mandrel

Tool life is often the limiting factor in producing internal shapes. As the amount of reduction increases and tools (mandrels, specifically) become more delicate, swaging sometimes becomes economically impractical because of short tool life.

Lubrication between mandrel and the workpiece is essential for most mandrel-swaging operations. Only a thin film,

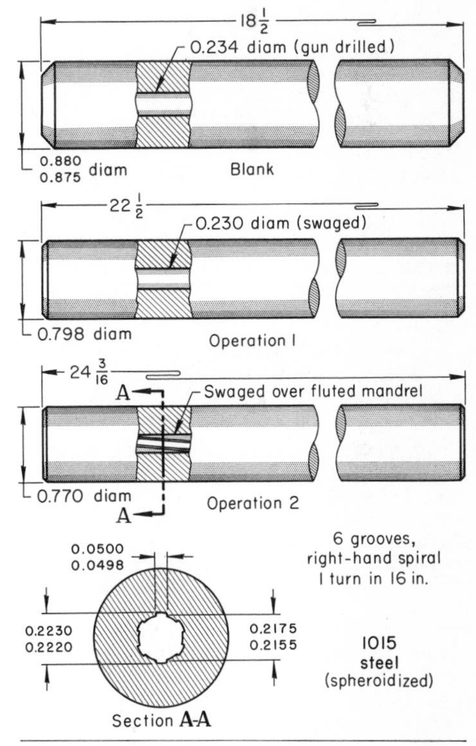

Operating condition	Gun drilling	Turning
Speed, rpm	1750	500
Speed, sfm	343	98
Feed	2¾ ipm	0.015 ipr
Cutting fluid	Sulfurized oil	None
Tool material	Carbide	Carbide
Setup time, min	10	10
Total tool life, pcs	50,000	100,000
Production, pcs/hr	19	60

Swaging Conditions

Spindle speed	300 rpm
Workpiece speed	150 rpm
Feed	30 ipm
Lubricant	None
Setup time	10 min
Die life, total	40,000 pieces
Mandrel life, total	50,000 pieces
Production rate	80 pieces per hour
Surface finish	Burnished

Fig. 20. Progression of a gun-drilled and turned blank through two-operation swaging, including rifling with a fluted mandrel, to make a gun barrel (Example 428)

Table 4. Methods for Removing Surface Contaminants From Metals Prior to Swaging

Metal	Cleaning method
Steel and stainless steel	Vapor degreasing, acid pickling (for removal of scale), alkaline cleaning, solvent cleaning
Aluminum	Vapor degreasing, acid cleaning, solvent cleaning
Copper	Vapor degreasing, acid cleaning, mild alkaline cleaning, solvent cleaning
Brass	Vapor degreasing, mild alkaline cleaning, solvent cleaning

such as applied with a wiping cloth, is used on the mandrel. Generally, the tube and dies are wiped clean before starting the operation. (See the section on Lubrication, on this page.)

Reduction of Solid Workpieces

The percentage reduction in cross-sectional area of a solid bar produced by a given swaging operation is determined as follows:

$$R = 100\,[1 - (D_2^2/D_1^2)]$$

where R is the percentage reduction in area, D_1 is the original diameter, and D_2 is the diameter of the swaged section.

The following sample calculation exemplifies the use of the above formula in determining the procedure for reducing a 0.500-in.-diam bar of 1050 steel to a diameter of 0.250 in. In the fully annealed condition, this steel can be swaged to 40% reduction of area in one pass. However, the total reduction in area from 0.500 to 0.250 in. in diameter is 75% and is determined thus:

$$R = 100[1 - (0.250^2/0.500^2)] = 75\%$$

Therefore, it will be necessary to stress relieve the metal after each 40% reduction in area until final size is obtained. The first swaging pass of 40% reduces the diameter to 0.388 in.:

Area of 0.500-in. diam = 0.1964 sq in.
Area remaining after 40% reduction
= 60% of 0.1964, or 0.1178 sq in.
= 0.388-in. diam.

Therefore, in the first swaging pass the bar diameter is reduced from 0.500 to 0.388 in. However, final swaged diameter is established at 0.250 in., which means that stress relieving is required before further swaging. Again using the formula, it is found that reducing a 0.388-in. diameter to a 0.250-in. diameter is a 58% reduction in area and too great for one pass. Therefore, by calculation and by keeping reduction at a maximum of 40% per pass, the diameter is reduced to 0.300 in. in the second pass, after which the workpiece is again stress relieved.

By further calculation, it is found that reducing the 0.300-in. diameter to 0.250 in. involves a final reduction in area of 31%.

Effect of Feed Rate

The rate of feed used for rotary swaging may range from 10 in. per min to 200 in. per min; about 60 in. per min is probably the most common feed. The extremely low rate of 10 in. per min has been used when swaging internal configurations from tubing, or for tubing having a diameter-to-wall thickness ratio of 35 or more, whereas in swaging simple tapers on a readily swageable metal, the rate of feed is sometimes as high as 200 in. per min.

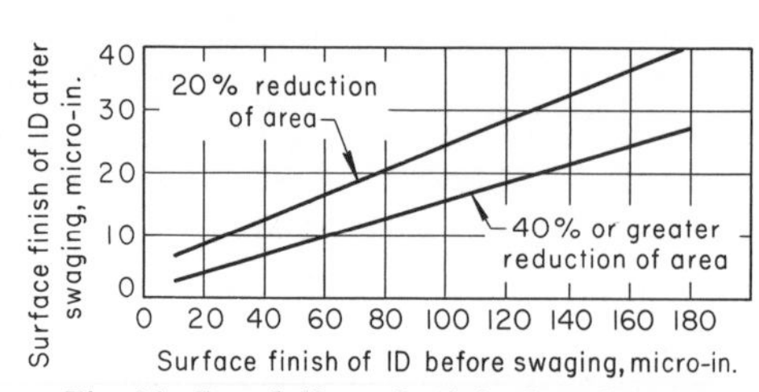

Fig. 21. Correlation of original and swaged surface finishes on the inside diameter of tubes for two different reductions

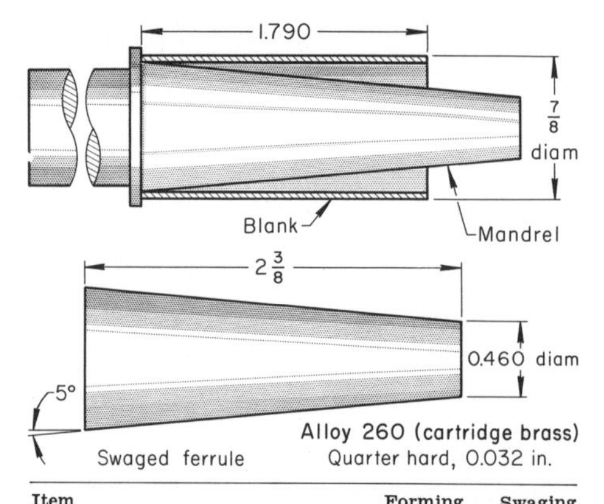

Item	Forming	Swaging
Tool costs (for 5000 pieces)	$1300(a)	$400(b)
Tool cost per piece	$0.26	$0.08
Production, pieces per hour	500	750

Swaging Conditions

Spindle speed	250 rpm
Workpiece speed (approx)	125 rpm
Feed	60 ipm
Lubricant	None
Setup time	8 min
Die life, total	50,000 pieces
Tolerance (plug gaged)	+0.0005, −0.0000 in.
Surface finish	Burnished

(a) Blanking dies, $500; drawing dies, $400; taper-forming tools, $400. (b) Dies, $150; workholder, $250.

Fig. 22. Swaging a ferrule from tube stock in preference to press forming (Example 431)

In general, high rates of feed have an adverse effect on dimensional accuracy and surface finish. A spiral pattern on the workpiece surface suggests excessive rate of feed.

Effect of Die Taper Angle

In rotary swaging, the angle of the taper at the die entrance influences the method of feeding the workpiece into the die. When the included angle is in the range of 6° to 8°, manual feeding is practical for cold swaging of small production quantities, but mechanical feeding is more practical for high-volume production. When the included angle of the die-entrance taper is 8° to 30°, power feeding is required.

When the included angle of the taper at the entrance of the die is between 16° and 30° and swaging time is greater than handling time, production can sometimes be increased by swaging the workpiece in two passes and reducing the angle of die taper for the first pass, as in the following example:

Example 429. Reduction of Die Taper Angle That Decreased Swaging Time

Thirty-two seconds was required for swaging a ½-in.-diam bar to a final diameter of ¼ in. in one pass through a die with an entrance taper of 30°. An additional 4 sec was required for handling. Swaging time was reduced to a total of 12 sec when the bar was reduced in two passes of 8 and 4 sec, respectively. The die for the first pass had an entrance taper of 8° included angle. For the second pass the die had an entrance taper of 30° included angle. Handling time was 4 sec for each pass.

Although the first-pass die in Example 429 had an entrance taper angle of 8° (included), an angle of 6° is more generally used.

Effect of Surface Contaminants

Residues from drawing lubricants, oxides, scale, paint and other surface contaminants should be removed before swaging, because they retard feeding of the workpieces into the swager and also load the dies and other moving components of the equipment.

Abrasive cutoff wheels should not be used for preparation of tubular products, because abrasive dust from the wheels is detrimental to the swaging dies and machine. Although the abrasive dust can be removed from the outside surface of the tube if enough clean wiping cloths are used, it may be difficult to remove from the inside surface and the cut edge of the tube.

Cleaning of the workpiece before swaging is essential and can be done by standard procedures. Table 4 lists methods that can be used for several metals. For further details on metal cleaning, see the article "Selection of Cleaning Process" in Volume 2 of this Handbook, and the articles in Volume 2 that deal with the cleaning and finishing of specific metals.

Lubrication

The adverse effect that lubricants have on feeding conditions eliminates lubricants from use in many swaging operations (except between mandrels and workpieces). If a lubricant can be used, a better finish and longer tool life generally result.

Lubricants used include oils specifically prepared for swaging operations, phosphate coatings, molybdenum disulfide, kerosine, and Stoddard solvent, which is especially useful for swaging aluminum.

The main disadvantage in using lubricants is that excessive feedback can occur, especially when dies have a large entrance angle. Feedback is less likely to occur when large machines are used (about 200 tons or more), because they are equipped with automatic feed units capable of exerting several tons of force on the end of the blank.

Usually, a lubricant can be employed safely when the entrance angle of the swaging die does not exceed 6° (included). When this angle is more than 8°, the lubricant can accumulate in the entrance taper and result in violent feedback. This reaction cannot be tolerated in manual feeding. An automatic feed must be sufficiently rigid and powerful to overcome feedback.

Mandrel lubricants must be used during mandrel swaging to prevent seizure between the work and the mandrel. Where the entrance angle of the dies exceeds 8° included, the work is kept free from oils by wiping the work and the swaging dies clean before any swaging is attempted. It is important to select a mandrel lubricant that will adhere to the mandrel and to use it in such amounts that it does not drip into the dies during the swaging operation. Most mandrel lubricants have this adhering quality. The lubricant selected must not contaminate the blade and entrance section of the die by forming gummy residues, because the dies must be kept clean. Resistance to heat is also desirable for mandrel lubricants.

If a mechanical feed with ample power is used, lubricants can be tolerated on the work, regardless of the entrance angle of the dies. With manual feeding, lubricants on the outside of the work present a hazardous feeding condition.

Lard oil or a one-to-one mixture of machine oil and kerosine is satisfactory as a mandrel lubricant for most swaging operations. Drawing lubricants, such as chlorinated extreme-pressure lubricants (available as proprietary compounds), or those containing fatty oils or castor oil, also are satisfactory for mandrels. Another effective lubricant is graphite mixed with a quick-drying liquid that floats the graphite into the tube and immediately dries.

Dimensional Accuracy

Dimensions that can be maintained in normal swaging of steel products in a wide range of sizes are listed in Table 5. These dimensional tolerances apply to solid bars, and to tubes swaged over a mandrel. The tolerances listed in Table 5 apply only to the main sections of swaged workpieces. Dimensions at the ends of swaged sections will vary because metal flow is greater, causing the ends to be slightly bell-mouthed. When uniform dimensions are necessary throughout the entire length of the workpiece, suitable allowances must be made for cutting off the ends of the swaged workpiece.

For swaging to close tolerances, the workpiece must be within the capacity of the machine and the work metal must be as ductile as possible to prevent recovery (springback) to a larger diameter than required.

Tolerances for cold swaged tubular products can be held to closer limits than the tolerances applicable to the outside diameter of standard tubing. The inside diameter, however, cannot be held as close, because of variations in the original wall thickness and because the wall thickens during swaging. When a tube is swaged without a mandrel or without prior reaming, the tolerance for the inside diameter should be twice that for the outside diameter. An exception is welded tubing made from flat stock held to close tolerances on thickness and width. Dimensional accuracy of the inside diameter can be greatly improved by using a mandrel.

In the following example, a mandrel held the diameter to within 0.005 in.

Table 5. Tolerances on Diameter When Swaging Solid Bar Stock or When Swaging Tubing Over a Hardened Mandrel

Nominal outside diameter, in.	Tolerance, in.
1/16	±0.001
1/8	±0.002
1/4	±0.003
1/2 to 1	±0.005
2 to 3	±0.007
3 to 4½	±0.010
4½ and over	±0.015

Data were compiled using low-carbon steel samples, but are generally applicable to other swageable metals. Tolerances apply only to main sections of swaged workpieces, and are based on use of a feed rate of 60 in. per min; tolerances given can be reduced by about 50% by reducing feed rate to 30 to 40 in. per min.

Example 430. Use of Mandrel Swaging to Hold Tolerances on Diameter and Wall Thickness

Extruded 304 stainless steel tubes 10 to 20 ft long were reduced from a nominal 3.75-in. OD to a 3.500/3.505-in. OD. Wall thickness of the extruded tubes ranged from 0.225 to 0.275 in. and was required to be within 0.200 to 0.232 in. after reduction. A maximum roughness of 60 micro-in. was specified for the outside surface of the reduced tubes.

Because these requirements were beyond the capabilities of any available drawbench operation, swaging was used to reduce the extruded tubing. A mandrel was used to control the wall thickness.

This application required an area reduction of 20%. Thus, one pass was sufficient, using a feed rate of 28 in. per min, head rotation of 210 rpm, and workpiece rotation of 125 rpm. The dies were constructed with a 5° entrance angle. A chlorinated extreme-pressure oil was used as a lubricant.

Surface Finish

In general, rotary swaging improves the surface finish of the workpiece, producing finishes comparable to those obtained in cold drawing operations.

Swaging in a squeeze-type machine usually causes a distinct spiral pattern on the outside surface of the workpiece. The pitch of the spiral increases as the rate of axial feed increases and as the relative rotation between the die and workpiece decreases. The intensity of the pattern on the inside surface depends on wall thickness. As the wall thickness increases, the spiral pattern gradually fades out. The surface finish of the inside diameter is related to the surface finish before swaging, surface finish of the swaging mandrel, amount of reduction, feed rate, rotational control of the tube during swaging, the lubricant employed, and mechanical characteristics of the work metal.

Figure 21 correlates the surface finish on the inside diameter of tubes before and after swaging to reductions of 20 and 40%. The values shown are based on tooling that was axially polished to a finish of 2 to 4 micro-in. and the use of a lubricant that was capable of preventing metal pickup. Note that the higher reduction resulted in a finer surface finish on the inside diameter.

Figure 21 summarizes data for several different tube materials. Starting material was "as received" — sometimes seamless tubing that was pickled and sometimes as-welded tubing. This accounts for the range of finish on the inside diameter before swaging.

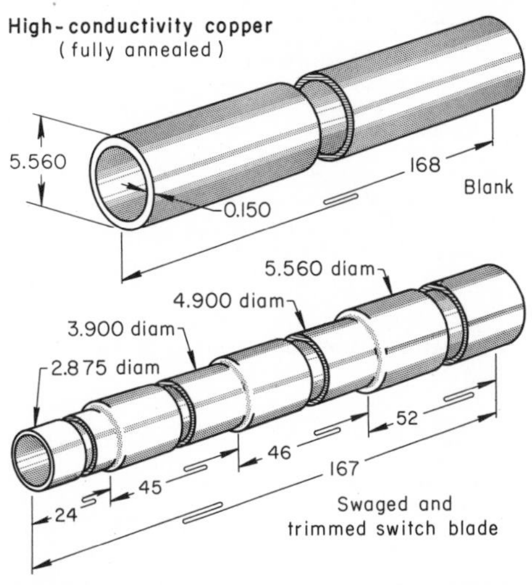

Spindle speed	178 rpm
Workpiece speed	5 to 10 rpm
Feed	24 ipm
Lubricant	None
Setup time	15 min(a)
Die life, total	500 pieces
Production rate	2 pieces per hour
Tolerance	±1/32 in.
Surface finish	Burnished

(a) Includes changing of dies and guides.

Fig. 23. High-voltage-switch blade (bottom) that was swaged from tube stock (top) in three operations, in preference to spinning (Example 432)

Swaging vs Alternative Processes

There are numerous applications for which swaging is the best method of producing a given shape, and is thus selected regardless of the quantity to be produced. Conversely, there are many workpiece shapes that can be produced successfully by swaging, but can be produced equally well by other processes, such as press forming, spinning and machining.

In Example 430, swaging was chosen because it was the only practical method of producing tubing to the required tolerances and surface finish. Applications comparing swaging with alternative processes are described in the four examples that follow.

Example 431. Swaging vs Press Forming (Fig. 22)

The ferrule illustrated in Fig. 22 was originally produced in a press by drawing disks into cups, redrawing to form the taper, and trimming the ends. With this procedure 500 ferrules per hour were produced and tooling cost was $1300.

The improved method consisted of cutting the blanks from tubing, then swaging them in a 5-hp, two-die rotary machine. Dies with an included taper angle of 9° 56′ and 0.005-in. ovality were used. Tools for swaging cost only $400 and the production rate was increased to 750 pieces per hour. Additional details for press forming and swaging are given in the table with Fig. 22.

Example 432. Swaging vs Spinning (Fig. 23)

Blades for high-voltage switches were swaged from annealed copper tubes (Fig. 23) in three operations using a two-die rotary machine. Each die was 7¾ in. long, 7⅛ in. wide and 5 in. high. The tapered section in each die had a 15° included angle, and side clearance was used instead of ovality. Tubes were fed into the swager by a hydraulically actuated carriage on a long track. An intermediate steady rest moved along the track to help maintain tube alignment.

In the first operation, the tube was swaged through a 4.900-in. die up to the first step. In the second operation a tube length of 45 in. was swaged to 3.900-in. OD, and in the third operation the end portion was swaged to 2.875-in. OD. In a final operation, the large end was trimmed to obtain an over-all workpiece length of 167 in. Operating conditions for swaging are given in the table with Fig. 23.

Formerly, these blades had been produced by spinning 168-in. lengths of annealed copper tubing 2.875-in. OD by 2.500-in. ID. By changing to swaging, production cost was reduced 10%. Swaging provided two additional benefits: (*a*) the center of rotation was shifted toward the large diameter of the workpiece, thereby reducing the number of counterweights required to balance the switch blade when in operation; and (*b*) the small end received the most cold work, thus strengthening this portion to the desired condition.

Example 433. Swaging vs Turning (Fig. 24)

The tapered workpiece illustrated in Fig. 24 was originally produced by lathe turning, at the production rate of only 200 pieces per hour. A substantial loss of work metal as chips made this method impractical.

By changing to swaging it was possible to produce 1200 pieces per hour with no loss of metal. The operation was performed in a 7½-hp rotary swager using dies with an over-all length of 6⅜ in., 1° taper, and side clearance (no ovality). An inside spindle stop fastened to a straight rod mounted in and rotated with the spindle allowed adjustment by means of a screw at the rear of the spindle. The work blanks were hand fed and no special holder or feeding mechanism was used. Additional operating details are listed with Fig. 24.

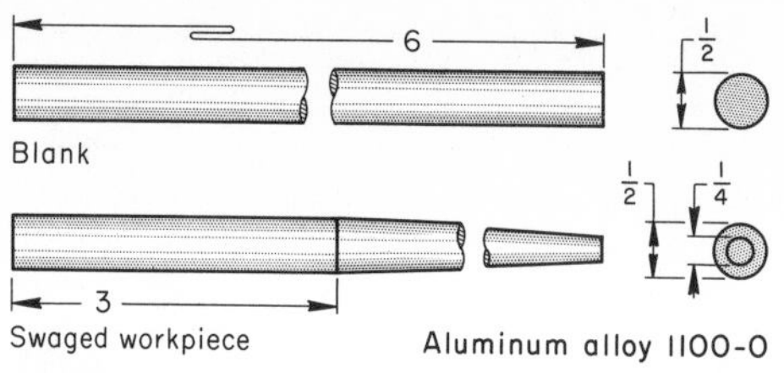

Spindle speed	250 rpm
Workpiece speed	150 rpm
Feed	60 ipm
Lubricant	None
Setup time	10 min
Die life, total	50,000 pieces
Production rate	1200 pieces per hour
Tolerance	±0.001 in.
Surface finish	Burnished

Fig. 24. Tapered aluminum workpiece that was produced by swaging without the loss of metal and the low production rate of lathe turning (Example 433)

(Example 435, below, describes an application in which combining swaging with turning yielded a considerable increase in production rate over that obtained in turning alone.)

Example 434. Swaging vs Milling (Fig. 25)

Grooves (flutes) were originally milled in socket-type clutch-head screwdrivers (Fig. 25) at a rate of 200 pieces per hour. A change of procedure to swaging in a stationary-die machine increased the production rate to 1100 pieces per hour.

The work was swaged in a 3-hp four-die machine capable of delivering 1500 blows per minute. Entrance taper of the die was 20° included angle; manual feed was used. Other operating details are tabulated with Fig. 25.

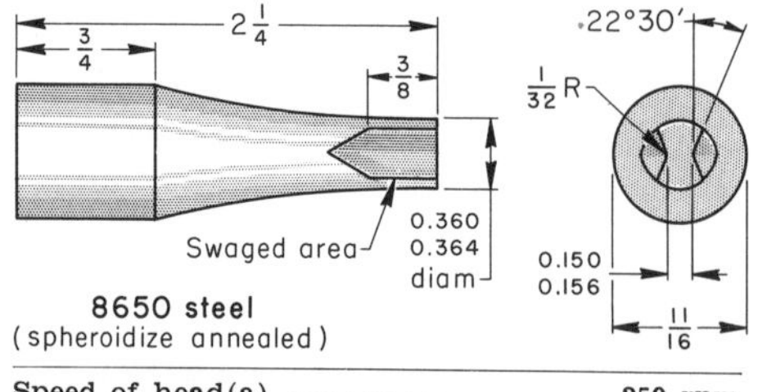

Speed of head(a)	250 rpm
Feed	60 ipm
Lubricant	None
Setup time	10 min
Die life, total	40,000 pieces
Production rate	1100 pieces per hour
Surface finish	Burnished

(a) Stationary-die machine

Fig. 25. Socket-type clutch-head screwdriver in which the groove was previously milled, but when the operation was changed to rotary swaging in a stationary-die machine, the production rate increased from 200 to 1100 pieces per hour. (Example 434)

Swaging Combined With Other Processes

In some applications the most practical method of producing a given workpiece is to combine two or more processes. Combined processes are used for the following reasons: (*a*) to increase the rate of production, (*b*) to avoid otherwise costly tooling, (*c*) to decrease or eliminate the loss of work metal, (*d*) to provide closer dimensional tolerances, or (*e*) to provide improved surface finish.

The three examples that follow describe applications in which the above advantages influenced the decision to combine machining operations with swaging operations.

Example 435. Combination Turning and Swaging for Increased Production (Fig. 26)

The firing pin shown in Fig. 26 (lower view) was originally produced by turning in an automatic lathe at a rate of 60 pieces per hour. Not only was the rate of production unacceptably low, but also the required tolerance of ±0.002 in. could not be met consistently. In addition, the finish-turned workpieces showed tool marks.

The above conditions were improved by rough turning the 3140 steel blank (upper view in Fig. 26) in an automatic lathe, then swaging the blank to the firing-pin shape. With this procedure, 180 pieces per hour were produced on the automatic lathe and 300 pieces per hour on the swager (two passes per piece). Other improvements that resulted from the change in method were closer tolerance (±0.001 in.), burnished finish, and a metal saving of 22%.

The blanks were swaged in a 5-hp rotary swager using dies designed with 30° side clearance and no ovality. The first die had a blade length of 1⁵⁄₁₆ in.; the second, a 2-in. blade length. Additional manufacturing details are tabulated with Fig. 26.

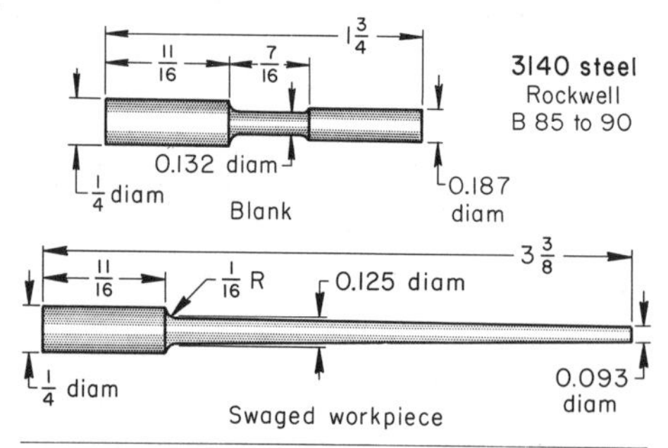

Operating Conditions for Rough Turning

Speed	110 sfm
Feed	0.001 ipr
Depth of cut (max)	0.059 in.
Cutting fluid	Sulfurized oil
Tool material	High speed steel
Setup time	6 hr
Tool life per sharpening	1400 pieces
Production rate	180 pieces per hour

Operating Conditions for Swaging

Spindle speed	250 rpm
Feed rate	60 ipm
Lubricant	None
Setup time	10 min
Die life, total	50,000 pieces
Production rate	300 pieces per hour(a)
Tolerance	±0.001 in.
Surface finish	Burnished

(a) Two passes per piece

Fig. 26. Rough-turned blank for a firing pin (top) and pin that was produced from it by swaging (bottom). Production rate increased over 200% when pin was produced by turning and swaging instead of by turning only. (Example 435)

Example 436. Combining Drilling and Mandrel Swaging to Produce 0.036-In.-Diam Holes (Fig. 27)

The copper blank shown in Fig. 27 was produced by drilling six ⅛-in.-diam holes in bar sections 1¹⁄₁₆-in. OD by 3½ in. long. After drilling, six 0.036-in.-diam mandrels were inserted into the holes, and the blank was swaged to increase its length to 4 in., reduce its outside diameter to ⅝ in., and reduce the holes to 0.036-in. diameter. The mandrels were withdrawn after swaging.

The blank was drilled in a specially built horizontal machine, and was swaged in a rotary swager using manual feed. The dies had 0.010-in. ovality and entrance angle of 8° (included). Over-all length of the die was 3 in.; blade length was 1¼ in. Operating conditions for drilling and swaging are given in the table that accompanies Fig. 27.

Example 437. Combining Machining With Swaging (Fig. 28)

The completed workpiece shown in the lower portion of Fig. 28 was originally designed for production in one piece by turning. However, it was estimated that only four pieces per hour could be produced by turning in a lathe.

The workpiece was redesigned as two components (Fig. 28), each of which was made in an automatic bar machine. The two components were then swaged together as shown in Fig. 28, in a 5-hp rotary swager using conventional dies with side clearance (no ovality). Workpieces were fed by hand, using a gripping tool that prevented the workpiece from rotating at excessive speed. The swager was equipped with a spring-loaded ejector that exerted end pressure against the collar, thus retarding its spinning and simultaneously helping to keep the collar straight and square against the holding tool. Additional operating details are tabulated with Fig. 28.

Special Applications

The difficulties of attaching terminals and fittings to cables by welding or soldering are often overcome by the use of swaging. Four types of swaged attachments are illustrated in Fig. 29. The plain ball swaged in position (Fig. 29a) will resist movement from a force equal to 80% of the rated breaking strength of the cable. The ball with single shank (Fig. 29b) is used when the load stress is applied in one direction only. The ball with double shank (Fig. 29c) is used when load stress is applied in opposite directions. In Fig. 29(d) and (e), the plain shank terminal is assembled on the cable and staked in position before swaging.

Swaging can also be used to form wire or tubing from metals that are not strong enough to be formed completely by wiredrawing or tube drawing. Solder, for example, can be reduced only about 10% in cross-sectional area by wiredrawing, whereas a reduction of up to 60% can be obtained by swaging.

Swaging is applicable to forming of small-diameter thin-wall shells that are difficult to make by drawing in presses. Shells can be drawn in presses provided the drawing force does not exceed the tensile strength of the material. If the tensile strength is exceeded, the bottom of the shell will be pushed out. This factor limits the length and wall thickness to which small-diameter shells can be formed by drawing. In swaging, the length of shell that can be produced is limited only by the ability of the wall to withstand thinning.

Hot Swaging

Hot swaging is used for (*a*) metals that are not ductile enough to be swaged at room temperature, or (*b*) greater reduction per pass than is possible by cold swaging.

The tensile strength of most metals decreases with a rise in temperature; the amount of decrease varies widely with different metals and alloys. The tensile strength of carbon steels at 1000 F is approximately half the tensile strength at room temperature, and it is about one-fourth of room-temperature strength at 1400 F and one-tenth at 1800 F.

In practice, reductions greater than those indicated in Table 1 are sometimes possible by cold swaging without intentionally heating the work metal, because sufficient heat is generated during swaging to cause a substantial decrease in strength and increase in ductility of the work metal.

The decrease in strength at elevated temperature does not make possible unlimited reductions at high temperatures. Because of the design and capabilities of swaging machines, the work metal must be strong enough to permit feeding of the workpiece into the machine. When the work metal has lost so much of its strength that it bends rather than feeds in a straight line, chopper dies must be used (see Fig. 8). This type of die limits the reduction of area to 25% regardless of work-metal ductility.

The temperature to which a work metal is heated for swaging depends on the material being swaged and the desired reduction per pass. Table 6 lists a number of metals that must be swaged at elevated temperature and gives the working temperature range for each.

Alloy steels harder than Rockwell B 90 are difficult to cold swage and can cause premature failure of the dies and machine components. For these steels, hot swaging should be considered. For metals that work harden rapidly and require intermediate annealing during cold swaging, hot swaging is often more economical.

Tungsten must be worked at elevated temperature because of its low ductility at room temperature. Because of the small size of the ingot and the high working temperature involved (Table 6), special techniques are employed for feeding a tungsten workpiece into the swager, as in the following example.

Example 438. Hot Swaging of Tungsten

Tungsten ingots of a common size (0.5 by 0.6 by 21 in.) were swaged to ⅛-in.-diam bars for wire drawing by the following procedure.

After heating, each ingot was grasped in tongs and manually fed into the machine until about half the ingot had been swaged. Then the other half was reheated and swaged. Dies were changed and the procedure of heating and swaging was repeated until the ingot attained a length (about 5 ft) suitable for mechanical feeding.

For continuous swaging of elongated ingots, a gas-fired furnace about 3 to 4 ft long was mounted in front of the entrance to the swager. In addition, a set of drag rolls for gripping the work metal emerging from the swager was installed at the exit end of the machine in line with the spindle hole. After reaching the proper temperature, the work metal was pushed manually with a push rod through the furnace and through the operating swager until gripped by the drag rolls, which pulled the workpiece through the swager. Each pass reduced the area 25 to 30%.

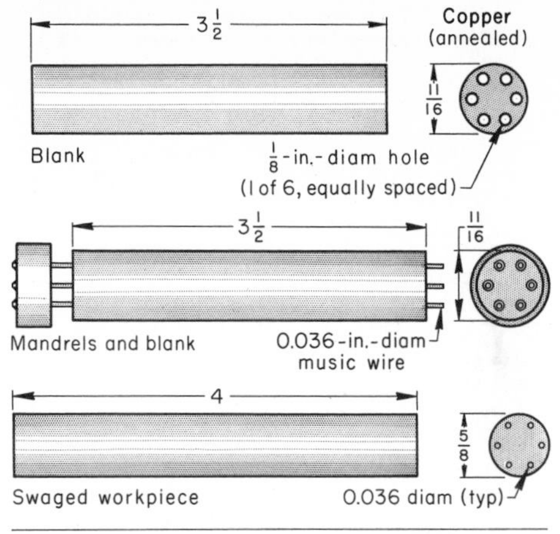

Operating Conditions for Drilling

Speed	8000 rpm (262 sfm)
Feed	0.002 ipr
Cutting fluid	Mixture of mineral and lard oil
Setup time	8 min
Tool life per grind	10 pieces
Production rate	10 pieces per hour(a)

Operating Conditions for Swaging

Spindle speed	250 rpm
Workpiece speed	125 rpm
Feed	60 ipm
Lubricant	(b)
Setup time	8 min
Die life, total	50,000 pieces
Production rate	500 pieces per hour
Tolerance on hole diameter	±0.002 in.
Surface finish	Burnished

(a) Approximate. Six holes per piece. (b) Mandrel was wiped with a cloth that had been saturated with an extreme-pressure lubricant.

Fig. 27. Blank with drilled holes (top) that was swaged over music-wire mandrels (center) for increase in length and reduction of outside diameter and hole diameter (bottom) (Example 436)

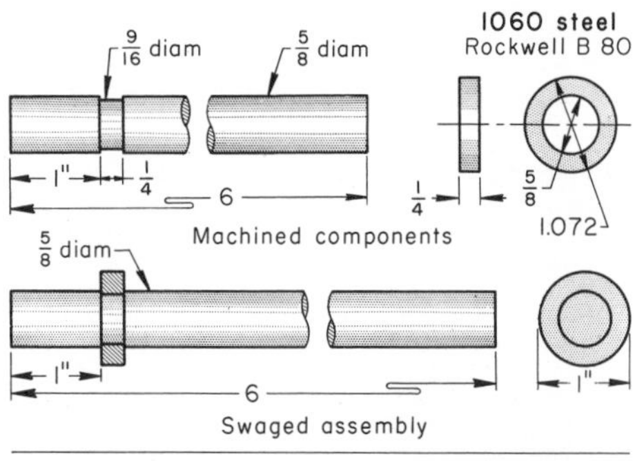

Operating Conditions for Machining(a)

Speed	500 rpm (82 sfm)
Cutting fluid	Sulfurized oil
Tool material	T1 high speed steel
Setup time	6 hr
Tool life per sharpening	1000 pieces
Production rate	90 pieces per hour

Operating Conditions for Swaging

Spindle speed	250 rpm
Workpiece speed	50 rpm
Lubricant	None
Setup time	10 min
Die life, total	50,000 pieces
Production rate	600 pieces per hour

(a) Conditions apply to each of the two components made in different setups in an automatic bar machine.

Fig. 28. Two machined parts swaged into one assembly (Example 437)

Table 6. Operating Temperatures for Hot Swaging of Various Materials

Material	Working temperature range, F
Hafnium	1300 to 1650
Hiperco 27, 35 and 50	1300 to 1650
K-42-B	1550 to 1825
Molybdenum(a)	1125 to 2600
Permendur	1300 to 1650
Puron	1100 to 1475
Refractaloy 26	1475 to 1750
Tungsten(a)	1650 to 2925
Zircaloy-2 and Zr (pure)	1300 to 1650

(a) At the start of the swaging operation, the temperature should be near the top of the range, and may be lowered as the bars or ingots are reduced in cross-sectional area.

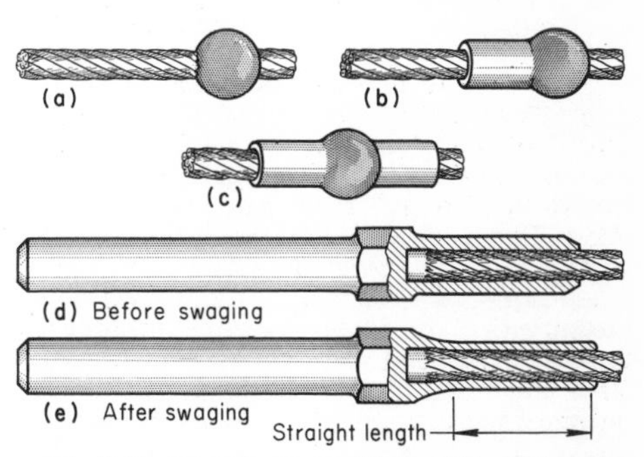

(a) Ball swaged in position. (b) Ball with single shank. (c) Ball with double shank. (d) Shank terminal before swaging. (e) Shank terminal after swaging.

Fig. 29. Four types of terminals attached to cables by swaging

A tungsten ingot usually is swaged to about ⅛ in. in diameter (although it can be swaged to a diameter of 0.040 in.), after which it is ductile enough to be hot drawn.

Molybdenum. Procedure for swaging molybdenum is essentially the same as for tungsten.

Equipment for Hot Swaging. All machines employed for cold swaging can be used for hot swaging by incorporating either a water jacket or a flushing system. A water jacket is simply a groove in the bore of the swager head in the area of the inside ring. The groove is connected to a continuous water supply to dissipate the heat.

A flushing system introduces a cooling compound at the upper rear of the head. The compound is pumped through the machine and exits at the lower front, from which it flows by gravity through a water cooler before entering the supply tank. This tank is equipped with a filter through which the cooling medium passes before reentering the machine.

In addition to cooling, the flushing system removes accumulated foreign matter and lubricates the working parts of the swager. Although flushing removes foreign substances such as scale and sludge, it is important that the method used for heating the workpiece be of a type that will produce the least possible oxidation.

Dies for hot swaging must be made of material that will resist softening at elevated temperature. High speed steel, cast cobalt-chromium-tungsten alloys, and carbide are satisfactory materials for hot swaging dies.

Procedure. The following procedure is recommended for setting up the machine for hot swaging:

Setup for swager blow:

1 Roll flywheel to free backers from rolls.
2 Open gate of machine.
3 Insert dies.
4 Loosen backer bolts.
5 Estimate thickness of shims, and insert the shims.
6 Roll flywheel back and forth so that die faces just touch.
7 Remove shims, and replace with shims that are 0.010 in. thinner.
8 Check swager blow by placing 0.010-in.-thick feeler gage between die faces; roll flywheel over; die faces should just touch feeler gage.

Setup for die opening:

1 Roll flywheel off rolls to open the die.
2 Place unswaged workpiece between die faces and tighten backer bolts.
3 Remove work and close gate, thus completing the setup for operation of the machine.

A common production procedure for hot swaging is the tandem arrangement of several swagers, each of which is equipped with a heating furnace in front of the machine and close to the dies. The furnaces are mounted so that they can be pushed aside for quick changing of the dies. Drag rolls are mounted at the rear of each swager to pull the workpiece through the furnace and the machine. Each drag-roll mechanism is equipped with a variable-speed drive to regulate the rate of feed into the swaging machine. Feed for this type of operation ranges from a minimum of 5 ft per min to a maximum of 20 ft per min.

Lubrication. In addition to preventing seizure between the dies and the workpiece, lubricants minimize wear of the backers, shims, dies, spindle side plates, back plates, rolls and swager gate. However, the flow of the lubricant must be controlled to prevent excessive cooling of the workpiece.

A mixture of semisynthetic solvent with water (1 part solvent to 25 parts water) is recommended as a lubricant for hot swaging operations; it should be free from chlorine and sulfur.

Noise Suppression

The noise from rotary swaging operations is so great that special protection of the operator is required. Noise intensity of the average swager in a range of up to 20 hp is about 93 to 95 decibels at frequencies of 1000 to 3000 cps. For most factory conditions, a level no higher than 85 decibels should be permitted.

The following list includes several methods of protecting personnel against excessive noise:

1 Earmuffs are effective, but are uncomfortable to wear for prolonged periods.
2 Earplugs made from various materials are fairly effective, but can cause infection of the ear.
3 Machines can be insulated during manufacture. The use of insulating blocks between the head and rear bearing and the base, undercoating of the guard, and lining of the base and covering the rear panel with ½-in.-thick structural-insulation fiberboard can decrease noise to an acceptable level.
4 Housing the machine is the most effective and acceptable method of confining noise. The housing consists of a frame made from lumber 2 to 4 in. thick and covered inside and outside with ½-in.-thick structural-insulation fiberboard. The housing has a door to give access to the rolls, backers and dies. A small opening can also be provided for long workpieces. The space between the fiberboard covering can be filled with loose insulating material if desired. A ventilating system equipped with a fan and piped to the outside atmosphere is necessary to prevent overheating of the motor. A rubber cushion should be used under the housing where it contacts the floor, to eliminate noise leaks. This type of housing reduces the noise level to 78 decibels at 1000 to 3000 cps. The housing is inexpensive and can be constructed easily.

Special insulating materials ranging from 12 to 15 in. in thickness are unnecessary. Installations using them are considerably more expensive than is warranted.

Machines placed on floors above other work areas should have vibration dampers under the base. Vibration dampers for machines mounted on ground-level floors have no effect on the noise level in surrounding areas if the floors are solid and soundly built.

Swaging Problems and Solutions

Work feeds hard:

1 Material too hard; anneal or stress relieve to remove effects of cold working.
2 Material too oily or greasy; thoroughly clean workpiece and die grooves.
3 Dies and backers sticking in swager spindle.
4 Die entrance too small to allow work to enter properly.
5 Backer bolt setting improper. Too small an opening will cause work to feed hard. Too large an opening will cause work to flow between die faces, resulting in fins and retarded feeding. Backer bolts should be set so that dies will open one or two thousandths of an inch for each degree of included angle of the die entrance taper.
6 Steps may be worn in die taper; remachine the dies.
7 Side clearance inadequate. Dies made for thin-wall tubing cannot be used for solid work, because there is no side clearance. If the workpiece is being contacted by more than half of each die cavity, increase side clearance.
8 Oxide scale or discoloration may retard feeding; remove by pickling.

Work feeds but has rough surface:

1 Stone the die edges to prevent clipping the work. Clipping is caused by too little side clearance or dies made for thin-wall tubing.
2 Work adhering to die entrance taper can be prevented by wiping every fourth or fifth workpiece with graphite or molybdenum disulfide powder.
3 Polish or stone the dies to remove high spots.
4 Avoid overfeeding.
5 Long spiral effect is produced by too much ovality, or by whipping of work as it leaves the die.
6 Stone the rear exit of swaging die.
7 Improper blending of taper and straight blade causes small dents in a uniform spiral pattern.
8 Small, unevenly distributed dents are caused by dirt and scale in die. Clean the dies and pickle the work metal to remove loose particles.

Work sticks in dies and rotates with swager spindle:

1 Side clearance of both taper and blade of die inadequate.
2 Pilots may fit work too closely.
3 Crooked workpiece.

Peeling:

1 Excessive pressure in die grooves.
2 Die groove too long. Straight blade of swaging die should not exceed ten times work diameter.

Scouring and picking up (scuffed areas, tearing, and metal adhering to dies, particularly of aluminum workpieces, but other metals also):

1 Lubricate work with kerosine or graphite.
2 Polish or chromium plate the dies.
3 Increase ovality or side clearance.

Cracking of solid workpiece:

1 Longitudinal cracks are usually caused by seams or pipes in work metal; may require upgrading work-metal quality.
2 Short cracks running in all directions indicate the work metal is too hard. Anneal or stress relieve to relieve previous work hardening.
3 Too much reduction per pass. Reduce amount of reduction and stress relieve between operations.

Cracking of tubing:

1 Inside surface may have lines or scratches that become cracks as tube is swaged.
2 Material too hard; stress relieve before swaging.
3 If using welded tubing, weld seam may be too hard; stress relieve before swaging.
4 Rework dies to remove all ovality; use side clearance only.
5 Use mandrel and do minimum amount of ironing on mandrel.

Wrinkling or corrugating of tubing (usually on outside of tube with a diameter of more than 30 times wall thickness):

1 If reduction is on one end of tube only, fill die with mandrel, leaving enough room for tube to slide over mandrel when swaged (see Fig. 17).
2 Dies have too much ovality; use round die groove.
3 Use slower feed and set die backer bolts to minimum die opening.
4 Work metal too hard; stress relieve or anneal before swaging.

Workpiece sticks to mandrel:

1 Increase ovality in dies.
2 Mandrel improperly hardened causing flat spots or sinks.
3 Inadequate lubrication on mandrel.

Mandrels break:

1 Mandrel material not suited to high shock.
2 Allow mandrel to float and rotate with workpiece.
3 Taper mandrel about 0.001 in. for entire length for ease of removal.

APPENDIX

Calculating Machine Capacity for Tube Swaging

Two operations are performed in tube swaging with a mandrel: (*a*) reduction of the diameter in the tapered zone (sinking), and (*b*) forming of the tube wall against the mandrel (forming). If the ratio of diameter to wall thickness before swaging is 8 or more, the following considerations are used in calculating machine capacity for tube swaging:

1 The sinking zone is considered to exert ⅓ as much force as the forming zone.
2 The blade is considered to exert 0.7 times as much force as would be computed for the contact area taken as a whole.
3 If the die is relieved, it will contact the workpiece over a fraction of the circumference. This fraction is called the contact ratio; the ratio is affected by feed rate in the tapered zone, and by the yield strength of the work metal in the blade zone.

The following formulas are based on these considerations:

$$L_t = 0.79(D_1+D_2)(p+q/3)r_tS$$
$$L_b = 1.1D_2r_bS_yl$$
$$L = L_t + L_b$$

Where D_1 is outside diameter before swaging (inches); D_2 is outside diameter after swaging (inches); L is total radial load (tons); L_t is radial load on the tapered zone (tons); L_b is radial load on the blade zone (tons); p is the length of the forming area (inches); q is the length of the sinking area (inches); r_t is the contact ratio in the tapered zone; r_b is the contact ratio in the blade zone; S is tensile strength (ksi); S_y is yield strength (ksi); l is blade length (inches).

Forming of Wire

*By the ASM Committee on Forming of Wire**

WIRE FORMS are used to give high strength-to-weight ratio, an open construction (as in fan guards or baskets), resilience to absorb shock, and economy of automatic production of formed parts. Where production quantities are small or the size of the finished article is large, the wire may be straightened and cut to length as a preliminary operation before the individual pieces are fed into hand benders, kick presses, power presses equipped with appropriate dies, or coiling devices. For large quantities, the wire is straightened as it comes from the coil and is fed directly and continuously into power presses, automatic forming or spring-coiling machines, multiple-slide machines, or special machines actuated by cams or air or hydraulic cylinders.

Operations other than bending that are performed on wire include:

Threading with single-head or multiple-head chasers, or with flat-die or rotary-die roll threaders. Roll dies can also be used for knurling, pointing and chamfering.

Heading in open-die rod headers, to make a variety of heads such as flat, round, slotted, indented hexagon, tee and ball.

Swaging or extruding of long points or reduced-diameter sections on rotary-die swagers or long-stroke headers.

Welding with resistance, arc or gas.

Speed of Forming. Increasing the speed of forming can result in out-of-tolerance parts, increased springback, and more wear on the tools and machine caused by increased force and torque. In machines where some of the tools are air-actuated and some are not, enough time must be allowed for the air-actuated tools to cycle, or the machine will be out of phase. For example, a machine with a mechanical drive and air-actuated tools was constantly out of phase when making 70 formed and welded assemblies per hour. By reducing the speed about 5%, the air valves and cylinders had time to complete their cycles, and were in phase with the mechanical devices. Table 1 shows the effect of machine speed on the dimensions of a part formed in a multiple-slide machine.

Tools used for forming wire should be made of tool steel hardened to Rockwell C 56 to 61. Water-hardening tool steels, such as W1, are usually adequate. For more severe forming and for longer tool life, D2 tool steel is recommended. Surfaces contacting the wire should be polished to prevent marking. They can usually be hardened after tryout in the soft state.

Springback is variable and difficult to control in the forming of wire, as it is in most pressworking operations. The amount of springback will vary with the type and temper of wire and may be different for each lot of a specific type and temper. The most practical way to determine springback is to make trial bends before the tools have been hardened or on temporary tools. Final correction for springback must usually be made at the final tool setup, after the tools have been hardened.

Effect of Material Condition

Most wire forming is done at room temperature. Wire made of low-carbon steel is usually formed in the as-drawn condition. Medium-carbon steel wire (1035 to 1060) is usually annealed before severe forming and heat treated after forming.

Surface Finish. A rough surface on the wire may cause short tool life. Plated wire is as easily formed as bare wire except that, if the plating loosens or peels, it may damage the tools. Platings of gold, tin, solder, or other soft metals may show marks readily; however, soft plating may act as a lubricant during the forming of wire. Whether the wire can be plated before forming may depend on the severity of forming and the subsequent fabricating operations. Welding, for instance, may require that plating be done after forming.

Properties. Strength of the wire is important in forming, especially in the making of steel springs. The required tensile strength is developed in spring wire (*a*) by cold drawing through a series of dies with up to 85% reduction in cross section, or (*b*) by heat treating steel containing 0.60 to 0.70% carbon, quenching in oil, and tempering the wire. The elastic limit in torsion of spring wire is more important to its use in a spring than is its tensile strength. For information on the mechanical properties of steel spring wire, see the article that begins on page 160 in Volume 1 of this Handbook.

Table 1. Effect of Machine Speed on Dimensions of a Wire Part Formed in a Multiple-Slide Machine

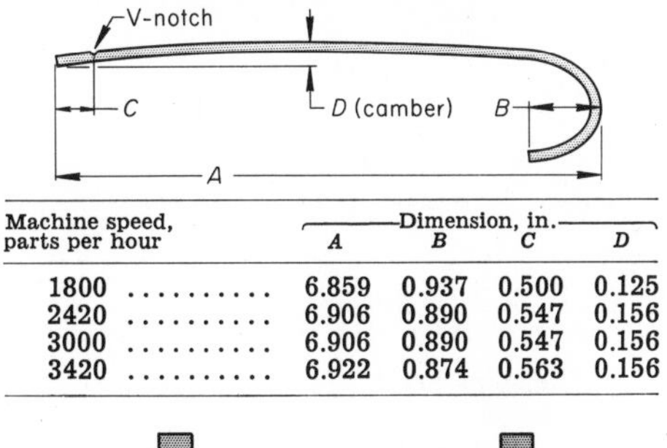

Machine speed, parts per hour	Dimension, in. A	B	C	D
1800	6.859	0.937	0.500	0.125
2420	6.906	0.890	0.547	0.156
3000	6.906	0.890	0.547	0.156
3420	6.922	0.874	0.563	0.156

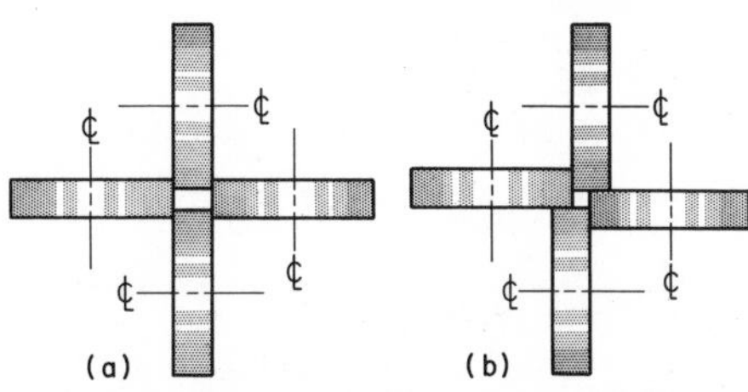

Fig. 1. Turk's-head rolls: (a) *positioned in line to form a rectangular cross section, and* (b) *offset to form a square section*

Rolling of Wire in a Turk's-Head Machine

A Turk's-head machine generally has four rolls that will accommodate wire of one cross-section (generally, round) and cold roll it to another shape. Uses of the machine are:

1. To make accurate square and narrow rectangular wire directly from round wire
2. To finish special shapes from round or preformed rough shapes
3. To put edge contours on flat metal ribbon.

Operation of Machine. The machine has a cluster of four rolls whose axes are in the same plane and at right angles to each other as shown in Fig. 1. In operation, a coil of wire is supported in a payoff reel; the wire is pulled through the rolls by a capstan and then is re-coiled. A drawbench can be used for pulling short lengths (up to 100 ft) through the rolls.

The narrow rolls can be centered (opposed) to form some shapes, as in Fig. 1(a), or they can be offset for some other shapes, as in Fig. 1(b). Although the rolls shown are plain cylinders, these can be replaced with rolls ground to any shape that will form a section, simple or complex. Some sections are formed in several passes. It may take two passes to roll an accurate sharp-cornered square wire, and three or more passes through the Turk's-head machine may be needed to make a complex section fill properly.

Simple or complex shapes may be drawn through a Turk's-head machine as fast as 600 ft per min, depending on the force and speed available in the

*J. G. WEISS, *Chairman,* General Superintendent – Wire Mills, Keystone Steel & Wire Co.; PAUL DILLON, Manager, National Technological Center, Simmons Co.; J. F. KINAL, Works Manager, Merrill Manufacturing Corp.

BURTON F. LEWIS, Vice President – Business Development, U. S. Baird Corp.; GEORGE F. MEYER, Assistant Works Metallurgist and Spring Engineer, West Pullman Works, Farm Equipment Div., International Harvester Co.; DAVID B. ROBERTSON, President, Robertson Steel & Iron Co.; A. F. SPERDUTI, Chief Engineer – Research & Development, Fenn Manufacturing Co.

OTTO STOLL (deceased), Tooling Supervisor, North & Judd Manufacturing Co.; RICHARD P. WAUGH, Senior Engineer – Parts Div. Engineering Laboratory, Sylvania Electric Products, Inc.; HARRY WOLF, Manager – Advance Products, Dishwasher and Disposall Dept., General Electric Co.

drawbench, and on the amount of heating in the operation.

Some of the cross sections formed in Turk's-head rolls are shown in Fig. 2. In general, the sections that can be formed depend on the ductility of the wire, and are limited to shapes that can be ground into the rolls, shapes suited to the roll design, symmetrical shapes, and shapes no wider than twice the thickness (unless preformed wire is used).

Some Turk's-head machines have three rolls to make triangular shapes and other shapes suited to a three-roll design.

Accuracy of forming in a Turk's-head machine depends on:

1 Accuracy and uniformity of the initial round wire in size, shape, smoothness, hardness and ductility
2 Dissipation of heat caused by cold working
3 Smooth operation of drive in accelerating, running and decelerating
4 The amount of reduction in area or change in section in one pass.

Any variation in size of the round wire pulled through the rolls may cause changes in size and shape of the product. If the round wire is oversize in a portion of its length, it may cause a sharper corner in the shape and thus a longer cross-corner dimension, or it may form a fin. If the round wire is undersize, the shape will not be so well filled, and the cross-corner dimension will be decreased.

Variations in the hardness and ductility of round wire also can cause variations in the cross-corner dimension of a shape. Hard spots increase the cross-corner dimension; soft spots decrease it. A rough or unlubricated surface increases cross-corner size; a smooth, oiled surface makes it smaller. Heating of the rolls caused by cold working may enlarge the rolls, making the product smaller. A coolant is frequently used to remove heat from the rolls.

Nonuniform acceleration, running and deceleration of the capstan, and changes in tension on the wire, may also cause variations in the formed shape. The greater the reduction in section size of the wire as it is drawn through the Turk's-head rolls, the greater are the chances of variations in the formed shape.

Accuracy of a Turk's-head machine in ordinary production is ±0.002 in., but ±0.0005 in. is a reasonable tolerance if all important factors are controlled. The two examples that follow illustrate the accuracy obtained in forming wire in Turk's-head rolls.

Example 439. Square Wire of Monel

Round Monel wire, 0.435 in. in diameter, was formed into square wire in two passes through Turk's-head rolls. The dimension of the square wire was accurate within ±0.0005 in., the corners being filled out so that the cross-corner size was within 0.009 in. of the theoretical size for a square with sharp corners. The square was 0.2850 ± 0.0005 in. on a side, and the diagonal was 0.395 ± 0.001 in., with 0.403 in. being the theoretical cross-corner dimension for a sharp-cornered square.

Example 440. Rectangular Wire of Phosphor Bronze

Phosphor bronze was formed into rectangular wire in a Turk's-head machine with rolls 2$\frac{9}{16}$ in. in diameter. The corners of the rectangle were fairly sharp, with 0.003-in. maximum radius. The use of preformed wire (formed in the Turk's-head machine and annealed) resulted in accurate products, three typical outputs being wire with the following cross sections:

1: 0.0160 +0.0002, −0.0003 in. by 0.0980 +0.0003, −0.0005 in.
2: 0.0226 +0.0003, −0.0002 in. by 0.0615 ± 0.0003 in.
3: 0.0306 +0.0003, −0.0002 in. by 0.0616 ± 0.0006 in.

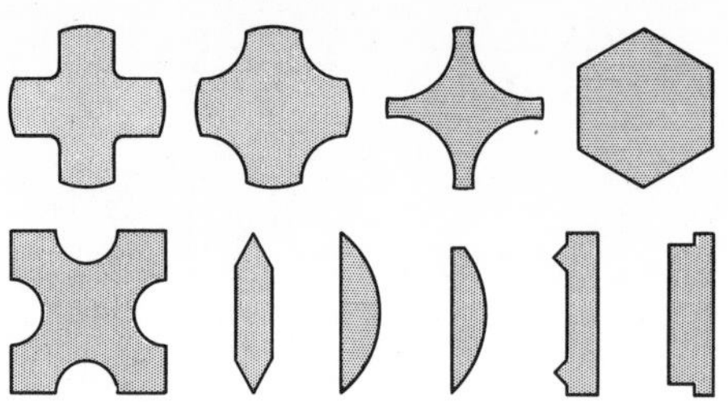

Fig. 2. Typical cross sections of wire formed in Turk's-head rolls

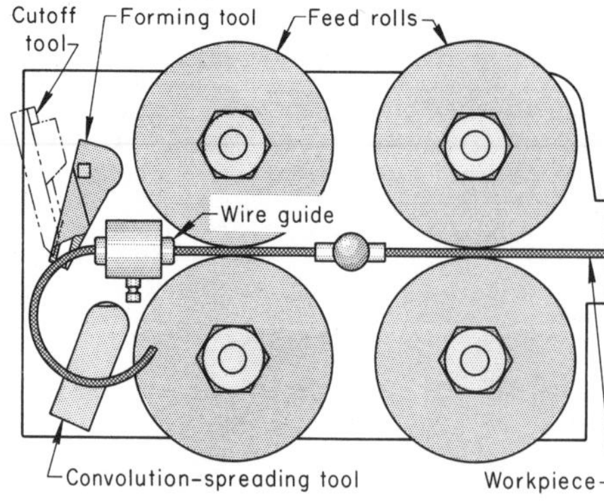

Fig. 3. Mechanism for winding springs that have coils of varying diameters

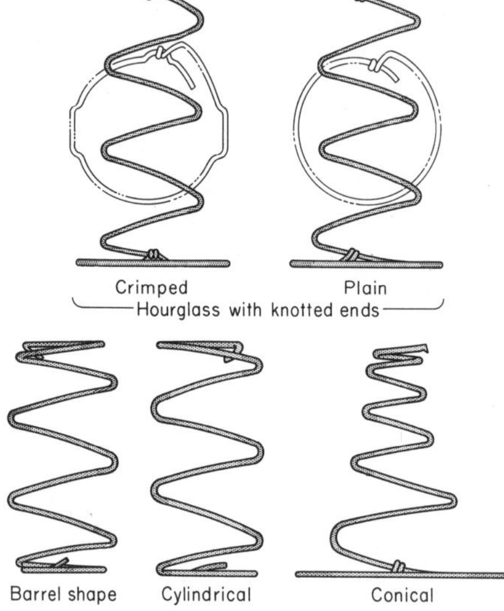

Fig. 4. Five types of compression springs for upholstery

Spring Coiling

Small quantities of springs may be coiled in a lathe. The arbor around which the spring is wound is held in the chuck, and two wooden friction blocks are mounted on the cross slide. Numerous hand-operated devices are also used. Production coiling is done in single-purpose automatic spring coilers.

In a standard spring-coiling machine a pair of feed rolls pushes a calculated length of straightened wire through restricting guides against a coiling point and around a fixed arbor into a coil. At the end of the coiling cycle, the feed rolls stop and a cutoff mechanism actuates a knife, which severs the completed spring against the arbor as an anvil. A mechanism for winding springs whose coils vary in diameter is shown in Fig. 3. A flying knife separates the completed spring from the wire strand.

Standard spring-coiling machines range in size from those that can coil only fine wire to those that can form ¾-in.-diam cold drawn or ⅝-in.-diam pretempered wire. Each coiler can process a range of wire diameters dependent on the number and size of half-round grooves in the feed rolls. A set of feed rolls usually has grooves of three or four different sizes. For example, a machine might coil wire 0.0915 to 0.207 in. in diameter and make a spring with an index (ratio of mean spring diameter to wire diameter) ranging from 3 to 18. The length of wire fed is controlled by the feed rolls.

A coiler equipped with a variety of attachments and cams can produce almost any type of spring, including tight-wound extension springs, common compression springs with open ends or ends closed for grinding, barrel-type springs of various contours, tapered springs, single-coil springs, variable-pitch compression springs, and torsion springs.

A tight-wound extension spring is wound in a standard coiler, but the end loops are formed in one of three ways:

1 One or more of the end loops are opened up or pulled out in a secondary operation to form the required end hooks.
2 End loops are automatically formed by deflecting the wire into shape as a part of the coiling operation.
3 Automatic handling equipment and attachments are incorporated as additions to a regular coiler to make the loops.

The second method is less complicated to set up and operate, but both it and the third method are limited to wire less than 0.050 in. in diameter and, because of setup time, to production runs of not less than 10,000 pieces.

A machine equipped with a torsion-spring attachment forms straight extended arms; these arms can be formed and looped as desired in a second operation.

Compression springs are wound in standard coilers equipped with a pitch tool located under the first formed coil. This tool, controlled by cams, regulates the spacing between the coils, which may be either uniform or variable. The ends of compression springs may be plain, plain and ground, squared, or squared and ground.

The use of round wire predominates in making compression springs, although square, rectangular or special-section wire is necessary in some applications. Square or rectangular wire is used to obtain the maximum load capacity for a given space. Wire with square corners before coiling will upset at the inside of the coil and become trapezoidal in section after coiling. This limits the deflection per coil, especially in small ratios of mean diameter to wire thickness. The use of wire that is keystone-shaped before coiling overcomes the problem, but such wire is costly — particularly in small quantities.

The two following examples describe production applications of spring coiling from cold drawn round wire.

Example 441. Coiling an Extension Spring

A simple tight-wound extension spring, formed of 0.080-in.-diam cold drawn steel spring wire, was wound into a coil ½ in. in diameter, and 3 in. long. The coil was within the range of the machine; thus only one additional tool was needed — a solid carbide arbor on which to coil the spring. Setup was simple and quick. Production was 40 to 60 springs per minute per machine. One operator set up and ran two or three machines.

Example 442. Coiling a Tapered Spring

From 0.378-in.-diam cold drawn steel spring wire, a 13-in.-high spring was coiled that tapered from 8-in. ID to 1-in. ID and had a uniformly decreasing pitch from top to bottom. Several hours of setup time were required to enable production of a spring that met the specifications for height and load. Each part had to be gaged in production, which was at the rate of seven springs per minute.

Accuracy. The cams, gears and other parts of a coiling machine become worn as the machine is used, resulting in a less accurate product. Some product inaccuracies can be reduced by control of the speed of the machine.

Dimensional variations, from the standpoint of materials, are caused by variations in springback and distortion during heat treatment. Variations in pitch and diameter depend on the speed of coiling. Dimensional variation also depends on the ratio of wire size to diameter, and the ratio of pitch to spring diameter. By increasing the limits slightly, coiling speed and production rate may be increased.

Many springs are acceptable with inaccuracies or with a wide tolerance on dimensions and in performance, but some (valve springs, for instance) must be more accurate. Variations in mechanical properties of the wire will result in nonuniform springs. Standard spring wire has a permissible tensile-strength variation of 25,000 to 35,000 psi; wire for valve springs has a limit of variation of 20,000 psi. The range in any one coil seldom exceeds 5000 psi.

Coiling must be fast enough to produce an even flow of wire from the payoff reel. If the wire flow is jerky or nonuniform, the dimensions of the spring may vary excessively.

A spring coiler can be set up to coil 0.192-in.-diam wire into a compression spring with closed ends and evenly spaced coils (a valve spring) of 1.300 ± 0.010-in. OD, and 3.000 ± 0.015 in. long. Accuracy must be held in a valve spring because the load may be specified within 6 lb at a specified compressed length. A change of 0.010 in. in length may be enough to change the load by 2 lb, with no other variations.

Upholstery Springs. The compression coils used in mattresses and box springs, and in furniture and automobile seating, are illustrated in Fig. 4. The ends of the springs are squared, and some are knotted, for better supporting characteristics. The top and bottom coils of some springs are crimped to provide a straight length for joining the coils into a unit or onto a frame.

Lacing or spiraled spring wire is used to lace upholstery-spring coils into a unit or to lace the outside coil rows of upholstery units to a border wire.

The compression coils are formed in a machine similar to a standard spring coiler. A flying shear cuts the coil from the incoming wire. The forming and

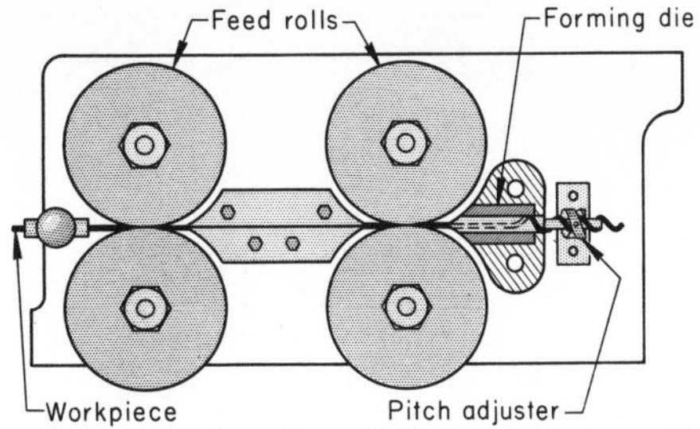

Fig. 5. Forming-die coiler for production of helical springs

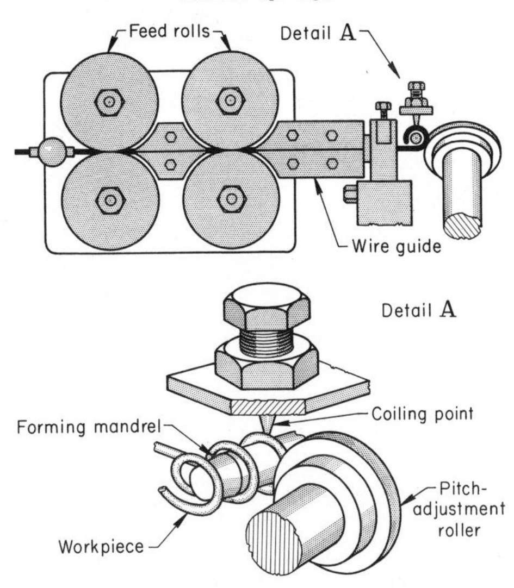

Fig. 6. Roll-forming coiler for producing helical springs

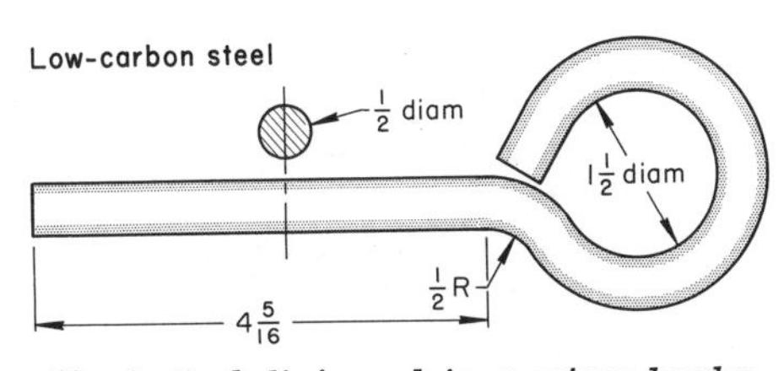

Fig. 7. Eyebolt formed in a rotary bender

knotting of the top and bottom coils is done at a separate forming station arranged like a multiple-slide machine.

Wire can be fed into the coiling machines at a speed as high as 170 ft per min, but knotting and crimping operations will slow the production rate.

Lacing coilers are of either the forming-die type or the roll-forming type. The wire is drawn through straightening rolls by the feed rolls and then is forced through a forming die and pitch adjuster, as shown in Fig. 5. A finish-sizing operation is used in heavy gages to set the final pitch. A flying shear cuts the lacing to length.

Roll-forming tooling is shown in Fig. 6. The feed rolls pull the wire through the straightening operation, and the wire is guided against a coiling point (sizing point) and around a mandrel. Pitch is controlled by the pitch-adjustment roller. In forming a close-wound spring, the roller is not used.

The wire-feed speed of the forming-die helical generator is about 250 ft per min; the roll-forming coiler has a speed up to 500 ft per min. Pitch and outside diameter are more accurately held in the forming-die coiler.

Tight-wound extension springs are wound on roll-forming tooling. Loops or end hooks usually are then put on the springs in a press operation.

The tensile strength of wire used in upholstery coils that are not tied ranges from 220,000 to 295,000 psi, depending on wire size. For springs with knotted and formed end coils, the tensile strength ranges from 180,000 to 220,000 psi. The coils are stress relieved at 475 to 525 F after forming. Tensile strength of the lacing wire is 225,000 to 290,000 psi, depending on wire size.

The diameter of the largest coil on the upholstery spring is held to ±1/32 in. The height is held to +¼, −0 in.

Manual and Power Bending

Manual and power bending is done in rotary benders, air-actuated or hydraulically actuated formers, and special fixtures to locate the bend and hold the part. The blanks are straightened and cut to length before forming.

A rotary bender can be manual or power-operated. The precut blank is placed between a center pin or form block and a stop pin. The arm supporting the wiper block is rotated clockwise, thus forming the wire around the center pin. An adjustable stop controls rotation of the arm so that uniformity is maintained from piece to piece. The eyebolt shown in Fig. 7 was formed in a rotary bender from ½-in.-diam cold drawn stock at a production rate of 300 pieces per hour.

The center pin can be changed to suit the bend radius. Form blocks can be used for larger radii. The stop pin is movable to accommodate different bend radii and stock thicknesses. Round, square or rectangular wire can be bent in this equipment.

A more complex wire form such as the scroll shown in Fig. 8 can be formed around blocks mounted in a rotary bender. The compact shape at each end could be formed by holding the wire taut while it is wrapped around a rotating form block, or in a

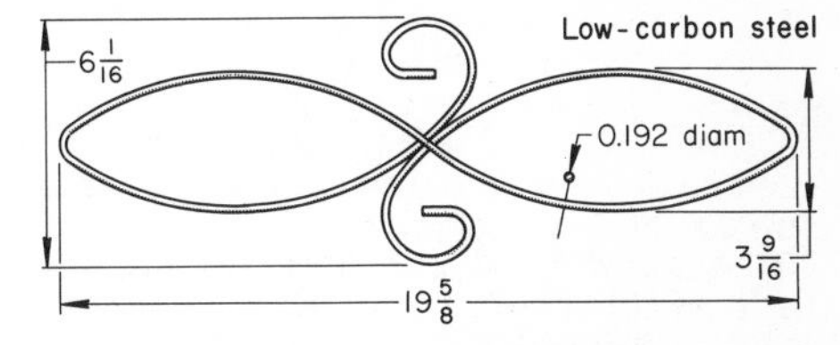

Fig. 8. Complex wire scroll formed in a rotary bender

machine with a spring-loaded or air-loaded wiper block. Another form block could be used for the long curves. The form blocks in these two operations must be designed to compensate for springback. The sharp bends at the outer ends can be made in a rotary bender around a center pin.

Forming in Multiple-Slide Machines

Multiple-slide machines are automatic mass-production machines that make completed wire products from coiled stock. They can straighten, feed, cut, stamp and form the wire, all in one continuous operation. Attachments are used for additional opera-

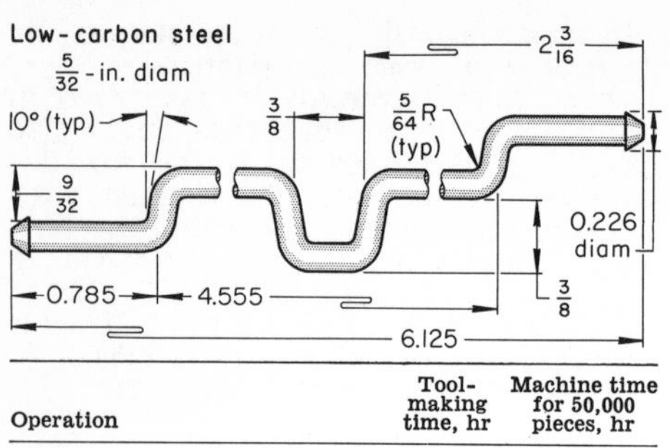

Operation	Tool-making time, hr	Machine time for 50,000 pieces, hr
Original Method		
Straighten and cut off	..	15
Head each end in header .	12	70
Form in press	50	62
Setup	..	2
Total	62	149
Improved Method (Multiple-Slide Machine)		
All operations	110	40
Setup	..	5
Total	110	45

Fig. 9. Headed part produced in 70% less machine time in a multiple-slide machine than in a cold header and a forming press (Example 443)

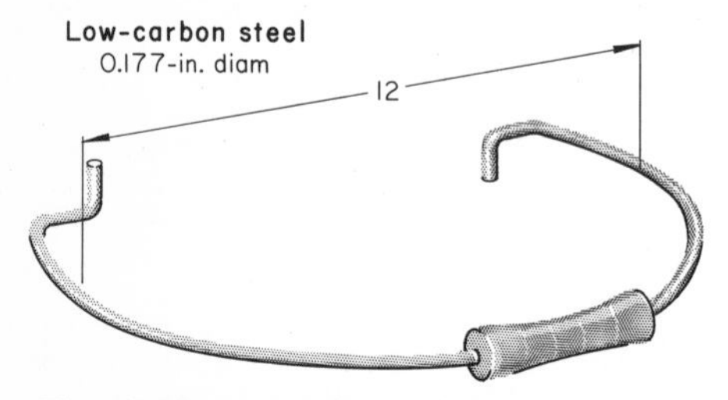

Fig. 10. Wire bail with wooden handle automatically assembled and formed in a multiple-slide machine (Example 444)

tions on wire up to ½ in. in diameter. Feed lengths of wire to make one part may be as much as 36 in.

Most multiple-slide machines are horizontal, but some are vertical and some inclinable. Production lots of 10,000 pieces usually justify the use of a multiple-slide machine, but smaller lot sizes may also be economical.

A multiple-slide machine usually includes a wire straightener, feed mechanism, and stock clamp, and has a bed with four forming slides, a center post, and a stripper. The bed has room for a press head (an attachment that does presswork) and may provide for other attachments. Discussion and illustrations of the machine and the tooling, and examples of forming strip stock, are presented in the article on Multiple-Slide Forming, which begins on page 154; on page 96 in "Press Bending of Low-Carbon Steel"; on page 113 in "Press Forming of Low-Carbon Steel"; on page 136 in "Press Forming of High-Carbon Steel"; and on page 416 in "Forming of Copper and Copper Alloys", in this volume.

A multiple-slide machine can be used for three-dimensional forming as well as for the automatic production of simple parts, as in the applications described in the three examples that follow.

Example 443. Multiple-Slide Machine vs Cold Header and Forming Press (Fig. 9)

The 5/32-in.-diam low-carbon steel part shown in Fig. 9 was made in large quantities, and its usage was expected to extend over several years. Originally, the ends of the part were upset in an open-die header, and the

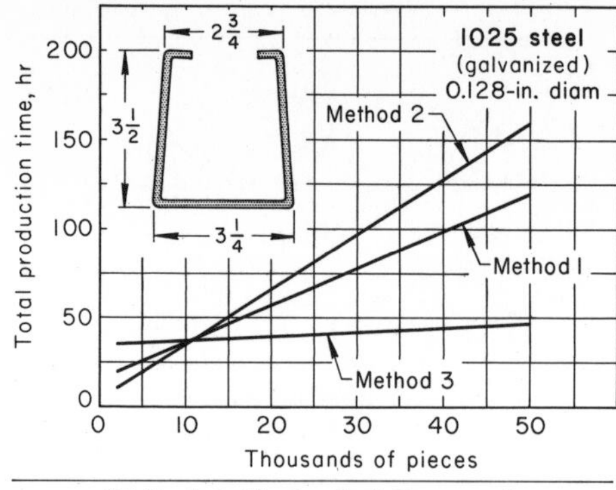

Method 1. Mechanical Press and Air-Actuated Tools

Straighten and cut off	5000 pcs/hr
Press form two inside bends	2000 pcs/hr
Bend ends	667 pcs/hr
Setup time	3 hr
Tooling time	10 hr

Method 2. Air-Actuated Tools

Straighten and cut off	5000 pcs/hr
Form two inside bends	667 pcs/hr
Bend ends	667 pcs/hr
Setup time	2 hr
Tooling time (tools on hand)	None

Method 3. Multiple-Slide Machine

Form complete	4000 pcs/hr
Setup time	4 hr
Tooling time	30 hr

Fig. 11. Effect of production-lot size on total production time for making a wire form by three different methods (Example 445)

other forming was done in a mechanical press. Total machine time was 2.95 hr per thousand parts. Changing the production to a multiple-slide machine reduced the machine time to 0.8 hr per thousand parts. Total machine time to make 50,000 parts including setup, and the time to make tools for the two methods, are compared in the table accompanying Fig. 9. The amount of material used was the same for both methods.

Example 444. Bail Wire Inserted Through Handle and Formed in a Multiple-Slide Machine (Fig. 10)

Figure 10 shows a simple curved bail made of 0.177-in.-diam low-carbon steel wire 26 in. long. The two right-angle bends at each end were made after the wire was fed through the hole in the wooden handle. A standard long-stroke multiple-slide machine was used for the part.

The handle was fed into position from a magazine with an escapement actuated by the front slide. The wire was then fed through the hole in the handle and cut to length. The front slide finished its stroke, then the side tools formed the large curve. Hinged tools on the side tools formed a right-angle bend at each end. Another set of hinged tools, mounted on the rear portion of the stationary forming post, was actuated by the forward motion of the rear slide to make the second right-angle bend at each end, thus completing the bail. The vertical motion of the stripper helped to unload the workpiece after the tools had been withdrawn.

Example 445. Comparison of Three Methods of Making a Wire Form (Fig. 11)

A wire form was made of 0.128-in.-diam galvanized 1025 steel by the three methods outlined in the table below Fig. 11. The charted time included the production time, setup time and time required to make the tooling. For method 1, a mechanical press with a new die was used to make the two inside bends at once, and the ends were bent using available air-actuated tools. In method 2, available air-actuated tools were used for all four bends. For method 3, a multiple-slide wire-forming machine that required new tools was used. Cost of forming was the same for all three methods at a total production of 11,000 pieces, as shown in Fig. 11. Up to a production of 11,000 pieces, method 2 was most economical, since there were no tooling costs, and setup costs were low, when available tools were used. Method 3 was the most economical for quantities over 11,000 pieces.

Resistance welding attachments for multiple-slide machines are commonly used for these types of wire parts:

1. Simple parts
2. Parts that leave room enough in the machine for the needed electrical insulation of the tooling
3. Parts that, after forming, can be transferred easily to a lower level for the welding operation. Welding at a lower level allows a longer welding cycle with simpler, stronger tools that can do the best work.
4. Parts that let the welding electrodes press the wire ends together for the weld
5. Parts that can be welded as fast as they are formed.

Welding in a multiple-slide machine is described in the example that follows.

Example 446. Forming and Resistance Welding Simultaneously at Two Levels in a Multiple-Slide Machine (Fig. 12)

Figure 12 shows the tooling setup for a bottle opener that was formed on the upper level and resistance welded on the lower level of a multiple-slide machine. With this arrangement, less complicated tools were used and the application of welding pressure in a direct line with the weld joint assured good control with minimum attention.

The work material was 0.156-in.-diam low-carbon steel wire. Forming was done with standard cams at the rate of 60 pieces per minute. The welding unit was single-phase, synchronous NEMA S1H type spot welder control and a 50-kva welding press package transformer.

The cams used to control the electrode movement also initiated the cycling of the welding timer. Welding and forming were done simultaneously, thus providing maximum time for welding without increasing the cycle time.

Swaging of nibs and stamping of lettering were done in a second operation, since the machine used did not have a press station. A complete opener could have been made in a multiple-slide machine that had both a press station and a forming station.

Quality and accuracy depend on the quality and accuracy of the stock that is fed into the machine. If the tensile strength of the wire varies, the work will usually be less accurate. The completed work must be inspected often, because the strength of the material may vary. The tools may need adjustment to improve product quality.

Accuracy of the work may be affected by the straightener. The usual roll straighteners may not be good enough for work that takes long lengths of wire. A rotary straightener may do a better job.

Curves with large radii need more tolerance than do sharper bends, but bends with radii smaller than twice the thickness or diameter of the wire may also give trouble, such as overstressing and breaking the wire.

Accuracy of the work is often affected by the speed of the machine (Table 1). For each part there is one best operating speed that will produce the most parts per day with the least scrap. Faster speeds may make more scrap or parts out of tolerance. Increasing the speed may increase the springback and make the tools and machine wear out faster, all of which may cause the product to be unacceptable. Optimum speed for a part is found by trial.

Small parts can be made to tolerances of ±0.002 in. from wire accurate in diameter within 0.001 in. and of uniform temper, provided feed length is less than 4 in. For average work in a multiple-slide machine forming wire ⅛ to 3/16 in. in diameter, with feeds of 10 in. and more, total tolerance of 1/32 to 1/16 in. is usually satisfactory. Springback becomes a larger factor with wire of greater strength. Wider tolerances permit the work to proceed with less adjustment and less tool maintenance.

Smaller tolerances may increase production time and cost, as shown in the following example.

Example 447. Effect of Tolerances on Production Time in a Multiple-Slide Machine (Fig. 13)

The door-operating hanger shown in Fig. 13 was made of 0.192-in.-diam, zinc-coated, medium-hard 1010 steel wire in a multiple-slide machine. With the liberal tolerances shown in Fig. 13, 4000 pieces per hour were easily produced. Close quality control and inspection were not required.

Because of problems in application, it was recommended that the tolerances be reduced to ±1/64 in. To have better control over springback and deformation during ejection, the machine speed was reduced to 2800 pieces per hour. Also, a press trimming operation was added to hold the 19/32-in. dimension to the new tolerance. For ease of trimming, the developed length was increased from 9 to 9½ in.

A comparison of time, cost and material for producing 10,000 hangers to each set of tolerances is given in the table with Fig. 13.

Typical accuracy of work in a multiple-slide machine is shown in Table 2. The accuracy shown in the table is for work done in machines that are in good operating condition and are supplied with wire uniform in mechanical properties and dimensionally accurate within ±0.002 in. With ideal conditions, simple forming, and more accurate wire, tolerances could be half those shown in Table 2.

Forming in Special Machines

Special machines may be used to form wire and then to weld the formed part automatically. Such machines make only one product, or a small range of products. To make a different item, a special machine must be taken apart so that its components can be changed and reassembled into a new machine. The examples that follow describe applications for special machines.

Example 448. Forming Wire Into Welded Frames

Bright, clean, round wire of 1008 steel, 0.120 in. in diameter, was formed and welded into rectangular frames in a special machine. The frames were made in four sizes ranging from 9 to 19 in. in one direction, and 19 to 20½ in. in the other; the ends of the wire were butt-welded in the middle of a side. The operations were done in this order:

1 Cut wire to length.
2 Bend 90° in two places; form part into a U with air-powered tools.
3 Transfer work to a second forming station; form into a rectangle.
4 Transfer to a third station; butt-weld ends.
5 Eject frame.

The machine made 425 pieces per hour, with labor costing 60¢ per hundred pieces. Setup time to change to another size of frame was 1.5 hr. Cost of the machine was $25,000.

Example 449. Multiple-Slide vs Special Machine (Fig. 14)

Figure 14 shows a formed and welded product consisting of 36 wire forms (fingers), eight straight lengths of wire (rails), and an octagonal wire frame. The components could be bent and welded by hand or welded by loading wire forms into a magazine, or the entire product could be formed and welded

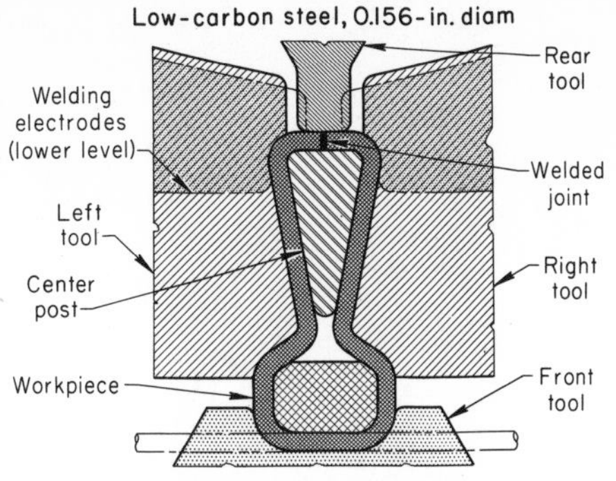

Fig. 12. Tooling setup for forming and resistance welding a bottle opener in a multiple-slide machine (Example 446)

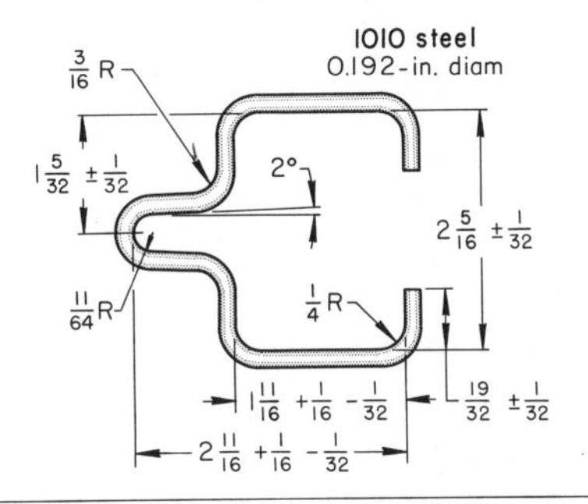

Item	Production of 10,000 pieces to tolerances: As shown	Of ±1/64 in.
Setup time, hr	6.0	6.0
Forming time, hr	2.5(a)	3.6(b)
Press trimming time, hr(c)	...	10.0(d)
Total time, hr	8.5	19.6
Tool cost	$150	$308
Extra material for trimming(c)	...	5.6%

(a) 4000 pieces per hour. (b) 2800 pieces per hour. (c) For holding the 19/32-in. dimension to ±1/64 in. (d) 1000 pieces per hour.

Fig. 13. Door-operating hanger formed in a multiple-slide machine. Table shows increase in time, cost and material for reducing all tolerances shown on drawing to ±1/64 in. (Example 447)

Table 2. Typical Dimensional Accuracy of Work Formed in a Multiple-Slide Machine

Machine rating: Capacity (wire diam), in.	Feed length, in.	Accuracy of formed dimensions, in.
1/32	0 to 4	±0.005 to ±0.010
1/16	2 to 8	±0.010 to ± 1/64
⅛	3 to 10	±1/64 to ± 1/32
3/16	4 to 24	±1/32 to ±3/64
¼	6 to 30	±1/32 to ±3/32
⅜	6 to 24	±1/32 to ±1/16
½	8 to 24	±1/32 to ±1/16

Accuracy of Formed Angles

Length of formed leg, in.	Tolerance obtainable
Up to 3	±1°
3 to 6	±2°
Over 6	±3°

automatically in a special machine. For annual production of 100,000 assemblies (3.6 million formed fingers), the automatic method was best. Until the special machine was ready, the fingers were formed in a multiple-slide machine. Rails were precut; the frame, of thicker wire, was precut and formed, and butt-welded by hand; the parts were assembled and manually welded together.

The automatic machine made the part completely, starting with 3000-lb coils of round steel wire in two sizes. The fingers were made one at a time of 0.120-in.-diam wire by rotating pins and by cam followers. The fingers were carried by a magnetic slide and were indexed to the welding position by two alternating barrel cams, one four-place and one five-place. The ends of the fingers were trimmed by air power. The fingers were welded to the rails and frame by the TIG (tungsten inert-gas) method. The rail wire was notched. The 0.187-in.-diam frame wire was cut to length and bent into an octagon. The work was ejected after welds had cooled.

Example 450. Effect of Quantity on Use of a Multiple-Slide vs a Special Machine (Fig. 15)

The part shown in Fig. 15 was used in two different welded assemblies of dish racks. One rack used two parts; the other used five. Parts for the first rack were made in a multiple-slide machine; $1200 was spent on tooling. Labor cost was 10¢ per 100 pieces.

The second rack was made in greater quantity, 100,000 per year for five years. This rack was made in a special automatic machine that cost $60,000. It made 140 complete racks per hour, at 3¢ each for labor.

Production Problems and Solutions

Problem: A small garment eye was produced at the rate of 300 parts per minute, but desired flatness was not obtained. The eye was to be formed in one plane.

Solution: The tooling was changed to form the eye on a plate, confining the wire. Forming sections were supported in the plate and were retracted below the surface of the plate before ejection.

Problem: Broaching of a flat on a small formed part for a business machine caused fine chips to collect in the forming tools, interfering with the work.

Solution: Forming was done on the upper level, and broaching on the lower level, of the machine. A small jet of air blew the chips down, away from the forming tools.

Problem: A small electronics part was formed around a fragile center post that broke after a few thousand pieces.

Solution: Tooling was changed so that the part was made in two stages. A heavy center post was used for the first form, where the greatest pressure was exerted. A center post having the shape of the smaller section controlled final closing of the part.

Problem: Ordinary forming tools could not form brass wire of 0.040-in. diameter into a 0.374/0.376-in.-OD ring.

Solution: The formed ring was sized by being pushed through a die below the forming level, by means of a ring-setting attachment.

Problem: Steel wire 0.225 in. in diameter was formed into seat wire in a large multiple-slide machine, using 34-in. feed length. The front tool was 20 in. wide. The bearings of the front shaft became hot, and the cam roller of the front forming slide had to be replaced often.

Solution: The addition of auxiliary front slides at each side of the standard front slide provided more direct application of the forming pressure, with three motions from the front position, reducing the load on each tool. Forming loads were exerted at different points in the machine cycle, reducing bearing pressure and allowing faster machine speed.

Problem: Automated machines had too much downtime because a pair of seven-roll straighteners could not straighten the wire properly to prevent jamming. The wire, cold drawn 1008 steel, 0.120 in. in diameter, was fed in 36-in. lengths, which were pulled by serrated jaws operated by a crank; 1750 parts per hour were automatically cut off and cam formed.

Solution: A rotary straightener and cutoff machine was adapted to cut parts to length and drop them into a hopper, with an escapement timed by the automated machines.

Problem: A specially arranged multiple-slide machine for forming and welding handles from low-carbon steel wire 3/32 in. in diameter made imperfect welds, and there were variations in forming. The wire varied in diameter and tensile strength, which affected the feed length and forming. Operators had not been trained to adjust and maintain the machine.

Solution: The wire was specified to closer tolerances, and inspected before use. Operators were trained, and a program of preventive maintenance was begun. Production efficiency increased to 75% from as low as 25%.

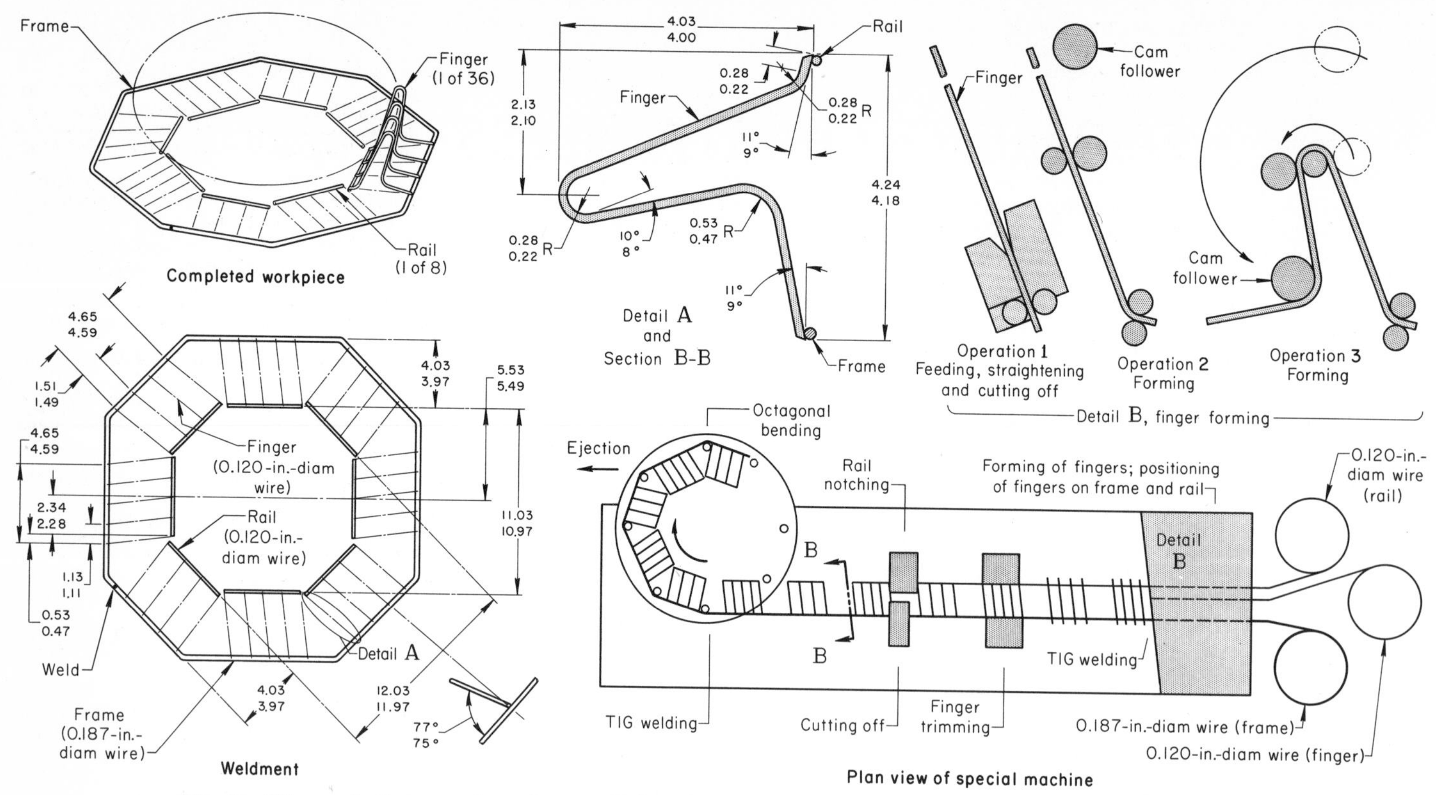

Fig. 14. Wire rack that was formed, assembled and welded automatically in a special machine (Example 449)

Lubricants

Requirements of lubricants for wire-forming operations are more severe than for most other metalworking operations. The exceptionally high working pressures that may be reached require special lubricants to prevent galling, seizure or fracture of the wire, and to prevent excessive tool wear. Improper lubricating oils or compounds interfere with close-tolerance work and cause variations in the finished parts. The lubricant varies with the type of wire. Aluminum, copper alloys, basic steel wire, and steel spring wire each require a different lubricant.

Lubricants for wire forming can generally be classed in three groups: inorganic fillers, soluble oils, and boundary lubricants.

Inorganic fillers include solids such as white lead, talc, graphite, and molybdenum disulfide in a vehicle such as a neutral oil or paraffin oil.

Soluble oils include mineral oils to which agents such as sodium sulfonates have been added to make the oil emulsifiable in water. Soluble oils are good for cooling and corrosion prevention.

Boundary lubricants are thin adsorbed films and are usually subjected to high unit pressures. Thin-film lubricants are of two basic types:

1. **Polar Lubricants.** Lubricants, or constituents of lubricants, capable of either physical or chemical adsorption on a solid surface to form a thin film that resists mechanical removal and provides lubrication under high unit pressures.
2. **Extreme-Pressure Lubricants.** Lubricants capable of reacting chemically with solid surfaces under rubbing conditions, to prevent welding and to provide lubricant reaction products on the surface. Extreme-pressure lubricants permit high unit loading with a minimum of surface wear and damage.

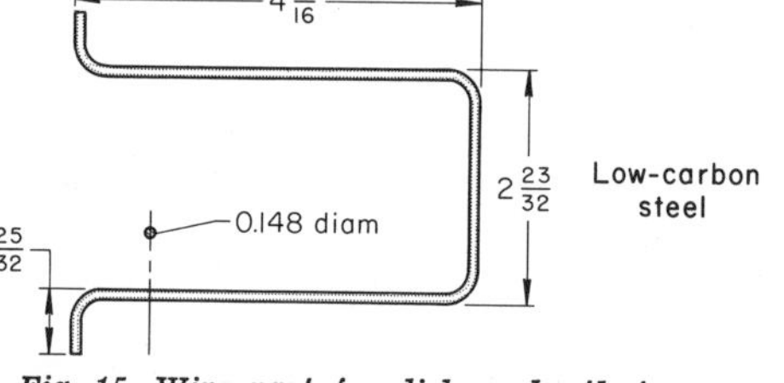

Fig. 15. Wire part for dish racks that was produced in two different types of machines, depending on production quantity (Example 450)

Chemically active constituents of typical boundary lubricants are sulfur, chlorine and phosphorus compounds.

Applications. Certain types of oil, wax and tallow are used to lubricate aluminum and scaly steel wire. Mixtures of lard oil and of paraffin oil in kerosine, or of oil and a soap solution, have been used as lubricants for wire forming.

Often the lubricant used in drawing wire is expected to stay on the drawn wire in a quantity that is adequate for subsequent forming operations. Many severe operations, such as upsetting and spring coiling, may be done without additional lubrication, but additional lubricant may be used in some press and rolling operations.

The lubricant remaining after wiredrawing should be enough to lubricate the wire in forming over a form tool or a mandrel. The lubricant should be a hard dry coating, such as a mixture of lime and metallic soaps. This will protect the wire from damage in forming, and will extend the life of the tools without sticking to them.

Zinc phosphate is often used to coat wire before it is redrawn into smaller sizes. It is also used in coiling thick, high-tensile spring wire into a closed helix. In other difficult forming, like a large upset, a zinc phosphate coating is a good lubricant for all tools.

Wire for forming into products to be electroplated is usually drawn with a lubricant that can be removed easily and that does not contain small particles that could become embedded in the surface of the wire. After drawing, the wire may be sprayed or dipped in thin oil. The oil protects the wire from corrosion and serves as a lubricant in the forming operations.

Steel wire with a metal coating, such as zinc, tin, copper, brass and lead, is often used in forming. In some operations, the metal coating provides all the lubrication necessary.

When lubricant must be added to the wire, it can be applied at the uncoiler or at the tools. Soluble oil or wax in water is most practical and is easy to remove in cleaning. Some formed wire must be completely clean.

Spring wire is supplied with a coating to act as a lubricant. This coating may be a mixture of soap and lime, borax or phosphate, or a plating (or displacement coating) of cadmium, zinc, tin or copper. When the coil is to be electrically normalized, a borax coating is specified; other coatings insulate the wire from good electrical contact.

The most unusual lubricant may be the one that comes on the oil-tempered grade of valve spring wire. During heat treatment, oxidation of the surface is permitted under carefully controlled conditions. The scale thus formed acts as a lubricant during coiling. Its characteristics must be carefully controlled with respect to thickness, adherence, and flakiness of the scale, for not only must it supply the required lubrication during coiling, but it should detach from the surface at the same time.

FORMING OF STAINLESS STEEL AND HEAT-RESISTING ALLOYS

CONTENTS

Forming of Stainless Steel

*By the ASM Committee on Forming of Stainless Steel**

STAINLESS STEELS are blanked, pierced, formed and drawn in basically the same press tools and machines that are used for other metals. However, because stainless steels have higher strength and are more abrasive than low-carbon steels, and have a surface finish that often must be preserved, the techniques used in the fabrication of sheet-metal parts from stainless steels are more exacting than those used for low-carbon steels.

In general, stainless steels have the following characteristics, as compared with carbon steels:

1 Greater strength
2 Greater susceptibility to work hardening
3 More abrasiveness
4 Higher probability of welding and galling
5 Lower heat conductivity.

Selection of Alloy

The properties and selection of stainless steels are discussed in Volume 1 of this Handbook, in the articles "Wrought Stainless Steels" (pages 408 to 431) and "Wrought Heat-Resisting Alloys" (pages 466 to 488), and in the articles on the selection of stainless steels and heat-resisting alloys for specific applications (pages 552 to 636). The influence of formability, power requirements and over-all cost is discussed in Volume 1 in the article "Selection of Stainless Steel Sheet for Formability", on pages 543 to 552.

General ratings of the relative suitability of the commonly used austenitic, martensitic and ferritic types of stainless steels to various methods of forming are given in Table 1. These ratings are based both on formability and on the power required for forming.

As the table shows, the austenitic and ferritic steels are, almost without exception, well suited for all of the forming methods listed. Of the martensitic steels, however, only types 403, 410 and 414 are generally recommended for cold forming applications. Because the higher carbon content of the remaining martensitic types severely limits their cold formability, these steels are sometimes formed warm. (Warm forming also may be employed to good advantage with other stainless steels in difficult applications.)

Formability. Characteristics of stainless steel that affect its formability include yield strength, tensile strength, and ductility, and the effect of work hardening on these properties. Chemical composition of stainless steel also is an important factor in formability.

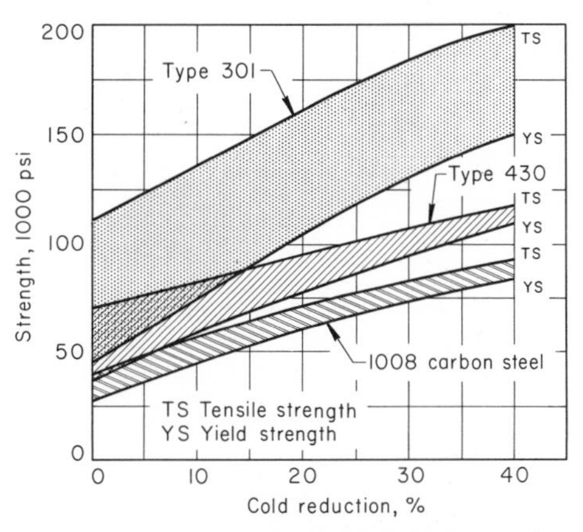

Fig. 1. Comparison of work-hardening qualities of type 301 austenitic stainless steel, type 430 ferritic stainless steel, and 1008 low-carbon steel

Figure 1 compares the effect of cold work on the tensile strength and yield strength of type 301 (an austenitic alloy), type 430 (a ferritic alloy) and 1008 low-carbon steel sheet.

Austenitic Types. Type 301 stainless steel has the lowest nickel and chromium contents of the austenitic types; it also has the highest tensile strength in the annealed condition. The extremely high rate of work hardening of type 301 results in appreciable increases in tensile strength and yield strength with each increase in the amount of cold working, as measured by cold reduction (see Fig. 1). This response to work hardening is particularly important for structural parts, including angles and channel sections—which, after fabrication, are expected to have additional strength and stiffness. On the other hand, for deep drawing applications, a lower rate of work hardening is usually preferable and can be obtained in the austenitic alloys that have higher nickel contents—notably types 304, 304L and 305.

In general, the austenitic alloys are more difficult to form as the nickel content or both the nickel and the chromium contents are lowered, such as in type 301. The presence of the stabilizing elements columbium, titanium and tantalum, as well as higher carbon contents, also exerts an adverse effect on the forming characteristics of the austenitic stainless steels. It is for this reason that the forming properties of types 321 and 347 stainless steel are less favorable than those of types 302, 304 and 305.

Ferritic Types. The range between tensile strength and yield strength of type 430 narrows markedly as cold work increases, as is shown in Fig. 1. This response is typical of the ferritic alloys and limits their formability (in comparison with the austenitic alloys). Nevertheless, type 430, although lacking the formability of type 302, is widely used in applications that require forming by blanking, bending, drawing or spinning. One of the most important applications for type 430 stainless steel is in automotive trim or molding.

Comparison With Carbon Steel. The curves for 1008 low-carbon steel are included in Fig. 1 as a reference for the evaluation of stainless steels. The decrease in formability of 1008

*CHARLES B. ALLEN, *Chairman,* Manager of Laboratory, Railway Div., Budd Co.; KENNETH ARMAGOST, Supervisor of Die Design, Ranco Inc.; SIDNEY J. BARBER, Assistant Vice President, E. F. Houghton & Co. HAROLD BLOOMFIELD, Secretary, Bloomfield Industries Inc.

C. KENNETH DIVERS, Director of Research and Development, Automotive and Appliance Manufacturing Div., Gulf & Western Industries, Inc. (formerly with Ternstedt Div., General Motors Corp.); ROBERT E. FRANKENBERG, SR., Service Metallurgist, Stainless and Strip Div., Jones & Laughlin Steel Corp.; RALPH S. GOLDEN, Manufacturing Engineer, Commercial Aircraft Div., Cessna Aircraft Co.; WALTER T. HILLER, General Sales Manager, Kerns United Corp.; G. W. HINKLE, Stainless Metallurgical Engineer, Central Alloy District, Republic Steel Corp.; WESLEY KALITA, Engineering Services Dept., Allegheny Ludlum Steel Corp.

C. R. MAYNE, International Nickel Co., Inc.; RICHARD N. MCCARTEN, Process Engineer, Parker Pen Co.; ROSS W. TEEGUARDEN, Supervisor of Industrial Engineering, South Wind Div., Stewart-Warner Corp.

Table 1. Relative Suitability of Stainless Steels for Various Methods of Forming (a)
(A = Excellent; B = Good; C = Fair; D = Not generally recommended)

Steel	0.2% yield strength, 1000 psi	Blanking	Piercing	Press-brake forming	Deep drawing	Spinning	Roll forming	Coin-ing	Emboss-ing
		Suitability for:							
Austenitic Steels									
201	55	B	C	B	A-B	C-D	B	B-C	B-C
202	55	B	B	A	A	B-C	A	B	B
301	40	B	C	B	A-B	C-D	B	B-C	B-C
302	37	B	B	A	A	B-C	A	B	B
302B	40	B	B	B	B-C	C	...	C	B-C
303, 303(Se) ..	35	B	B	D(b)	D	D	D	C-D	C
304	35	B	B	A	A	B	A	B	B
304L	30	B	B	A	A	B	A	B	B
305	37	B	B	A	B	A	A	A-B	A-B
308	35	B	...	B(b)	D	D	...	D	D
309, 309S	40	B	B	A(b)	B	C	B	B	B
310, 310S	40	B	B	A(b)	B	B	A	B	B
314	50	B	B	A(b)	B-C	C	B	B	B-C
316	35	B	B	A(b)	B	B	A	B	B
316L	30	B	B	A(b)	B	B	A	B	B
317	40	B	B	A(b)	B	B-C	B	B	B
321, 347, 348 ..	35	B	B	A	B	B-C	B	B	B
Martensitic Steels									
403, 410	40	A	A-B	A	A	A	A	A	A
414	95	A	B	A(b)	B	C	C	B	C
416, 416(Se) .	40	B	A-B	C(b)	D	D	D	D	C
420	50	B	B-C	C(b)	C-D	D	C-D	C-D	C
431	95	C-D	C-D	C(b)	C-D	D	C-D	C-D	C-D
440A	60	B-C	...	C(b)	C-D	D	C-D	D	C
440B	62	...	...	...	...	D	...	D	D
440C	65	...	...	...	...	D	...	D	D
Ferritic Steels									
405	40	A	A-B	A(b)	A	A	A	A	A
430	45	A	A-B	A(b)	A-B	A	A	A	A
430F, 430F(Se)	55	B	A-B	B-C(b)	D	D	D	C-D	C
442	..	A	A-B	A(b)	B	B-C	A	B	B
446	50	A	B	A(b)	B-C	C	B	B	B

(a) Suitability ratings are based on comparison of the steels within any one class; thus it should not be inferred that a ferritic steel with an A rating is more formable than an austenitic steel with a C rating for a particular method. (b) Severe sharp bends should be avoided.

steel with cold work appears to fall between that of type 430 and that of the more formable type 301. Figure 1 shows also that cold work does not increase the strength of 1008 as rapidly as it does that of types 301 and 430 stainless steel.

Stress-Strain Relations. Figure 2 shows load-elongation curves for six types of stainless steel: four austenitic (202, 301, 302 and 304), one martensitic (410), and one ferritic (430). The information was obtained by drawing cups of the shape shown. The type of breakage in failure of the austenitic types was different from that of types 410 and 430, as shown in Fig. 2. The austenitic types broke in a fairly clean line near the punch nose radius, almost as if the bottom of the drawn cup were blanked out; types 410 and 430 broke in the sidewall in sharp jagged lines, showing extreme brittleness as a result of the severe cold work.

As shown in Fig. 2, the power required to form type 301 exceeds that required by the other austenitic alloys; also, it will withstand maximum elongation before failing. Types 410 and 430 require considerably less power to form but fail at comparatively low elongation levels.

Power requirements for forming of stainless steel, because of the high yield strength, are greater than for low-carbon steel; generally, twice as much power is used in forming stainless. Because the austenitic steels work harden rapidly in cold forming operations, the need for added power after the start of initial deformation is greater than that for the ferritic steels. The ferritic steels behave much like plain carbon steels once deformation begins, although higher power also is needed to start plastic deformation.

Over-All Cost. Differences in formability among stainless steels sometimes have a substantial effect on production rates, scrap losses and over-all manufacturing cost. However, because of the great difference in cost among the various stainless steels, the per-pound cost of raw material is often an overriding factor in the selection of an alloy. In the following example, a considerable saving per piece resulted when ferritic stainless steel was substituted for the austenitic type previously used.

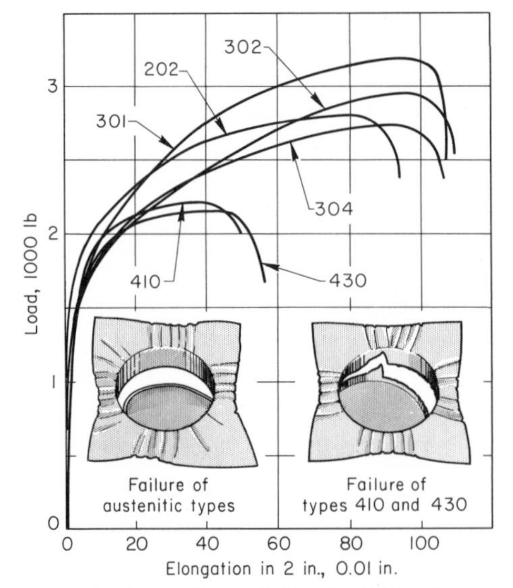

Fig. 2. Comparison of the ductility of six stainless steels, and of the types of failure resulting from deep drawing

Example 451. Effect of Change in Material on Cost of Product (Table 2)

A sugar-dispenser cap (see sketch in Table 2) was originally produced from type 302 stainless steel. However, by changing to type 430 stainless steel, it was possible to reduce material cost by $0.0076 per piece, for a saving of $1140 per production run of 150,000 pieces.

For both steels, a 60-ton open-back inclinable press was used to blank and draw the workpiece (see Table 2). The draw radius of the die was increased for type 430 without any change in the configuration of the piece. Coil stock 0.018 in. thick by 4⅜ in. wide was fed to the press by a roll feed. The stock was roller coated with a drawing compound as it was fed into the press.

Type 430 stainless was purchased in a No. 2B bright-finish coil, which reduced buffing time to 20% of that shown in Table 2.

Table 2. Costs of Forming a Sugar-Dispenser Cap From Type 302 vs Type 430 (Example 451)

Operation	Production, pcs/hr	Labor per 100 pcs, hr	Tool cost
Data for Both Steels			
Blank & draw(a) ..	2050	0.049	$1575
Trim(a)	975	0.103	700
Roll thread & bead(b)	2350	0.043	75
Wash	5000	0.020	...
Buff	250	0.400	475
Total		0.615	$2825
Cost of Steel per Piece			
Type 302			$0.05225
Type 430			0.04465
Saving by use of type 430			$0.00760

Type 302 or 430, Rockwell B 80, 0.018 in.

(a) In a 60-ton press. (b) Using a thread roller.

Lubrication

Lubrication requirements are more critical in forming stainless steels than in forming carbon and alloy steels, because it usually is necessary to preserve the high-quality surface on stainless steels, and because stainless steels have higher strength, greater hardness, lower thermal conductivity, and higher coefficient of friction. In forming stainless steels, galling and spalling occur more readily, and higher temperatures are reached in a larger volume of the workpiece. Local or general overheating can change the properties of the work metal.

Table 3 lists the lubricants ordinarily used in forming stainless steel by various processes. Except for the special-purpose lubricants graphite and molybdenum disulfide, they are listed in the approximate order of increasing ability to reduce galling and friction. The ratings in Table 3 also consider other suitability factors such as cleanliness and ease of removal.

Mineral oils, soap solutions, and water emulsions of general-purpose soluble oils are omitted, since they are ineffective in most forming of stainless.

The recommended lubricants are discussed further in the sections that deal with the individual forming processes in the remainder of this article.

As a precaution, all lubricants should be removed, and the parts thoroughly dried, after completion of the sheet metalworking operation. Most lubricants must be removed before the formed parts are heat treated; this applies particularly to those containing insoluble solids, sulfur or chlorine.

Blanking and Piercing

The shear strength of stainless steel is about twice that of low-carbon steel. Therefore, the available force for blanking or piercing stainless steel should be 50 to 100% higher than for equivalent work on carbon steel.

Tools and power can be saved if the stock can be blanked at about 350 F. Finish will also be better. Power requirements can also be reduced by using angular shear on the punch or the die. (For details, see page 33 in the article on Blanking, and page 48 in the article on Piercing, in this volume.)

Die Materials. Cutting edges must be of a hard, strong material. Recommended die materials, in order of suitability for increasing quantities, include O1, A2, D2 and D4 tool steels, and carbide. (For detailed information, see the article "Selection of Material for Blanking and Piercing Dies".)

The use of carbide for high-volume production in applications that do not require the impact resistance of tool steels is illustrated in the next example:

Example 452. Use of a Carbide Die to Form a Miniature Piece (Fig. 3)

The cathode shown in Fig. 3 was produced in a three-stage progressive die made of carbide, by piercing, blanking and forming. The piece was trough-shaped, ¼ in. long, of type 304 stainless steel, 0.003 in. thick. One end was rounded, and the other was V-shaped. The difference in contour of the two ends kept the pieces from stacking. Before forming, the blank was ⅜ in. wide. The piece was pierced with 68 holes, each 0.012 in. square. In this operation, the material was displaced by a pointed punch, rather than being removed by a flat-nose punch. The pieces were cut from 6-in.-wide strip, producing 16 pieces at a stroke. The press was a 15-ton mechanical press that ran at 240 strokes per minute.

Clearance between punch and die should be about the same as for blanking and piercing of cold rolled low-carbon steel. Some manufacturers use less than 0.001 in. per side; others specify 5 to 10% of stock thickness per side for sheet and 10 to 15% of stock thickness for plates and bars. Studies have shown, however, that larger clearances — 12.5 to 13.5%, and even up to 42%, of stock thickness — have resulted in increased die life (see "Use of Large Clearance", page 47 in this volume).

Cutting edges should be carefully aligned, sharp, clean and free of burrs. The importance of sharpness of cutting edges cannot be overemphasized.

Deburring. Generally, stainless steel does not shear clean, but leaves a rough work-hardened edge that is dangerous to handle and may affect subsequent operations adversely. Flat pieces can be rolled or pressed between dies adjusted exactly to the thickness of the stock, or the burrs can be removed by grinding, stoning, or filing.

Lubrication. Blanking and piercing of stainless is often done dry, but the lubricants indicated in Table 3 are sometimes used to prolong die life. Lubricants containing sulfur or chlorine are the most effective for this purpose; for high-speed work, emulsions are used.

Dimensions. Pierced holes should not be smaller than the thickness of the stock. Holes larger than ⅛ in. should be spaced so that the distance between centers is not less than 1½ times the hole diameter. Small holes should have a distance between centers of at least 1¾ times the diameter of the holes. Holes should never be closer together than one stock thickness, nor should the edge of blanks be less than one stock thickness from the edge of the stock. For progressive-die operation, edge distances should be between 1½ and 2 times stock thickness.

Nibbling. In some applications, an irregular contour is cut out by punching a series of overlapping holes along the contour. This process is called nibbling. A variety of unusual shapes can be cut at 300 to 900 strokes per minute by a press equipped with either a round or a rectangular punch.

Table 3. Suitability of Various Lubricants for Use in Forming of Stainless Steel
(A = Excellent; B = Good; C = Acceptable; NR = Not recommended) (a)

Lubricant	Blanking and piercing	Press-brake forming	Press forming	Multiple-slide forming	Deep drawing	Spinning	Drop hammer forming	Contour roll forming	Embossing
Fatty oils and blends(b)	C	B	C	A	C	A	C	B	B
Soap-fat pastes(c)	NR	NR	C	A	B	B	C	B	C
Wax-base pastes(c)	B	B	B	A	B	B	C	B	A
Heavy-duty emulsions(d)	B	NR	B	A	B	B	NR	A	B
Dry film (wax, or soap plus borax)	B	B	B	NR	B	A	B	NR	A
Pigmented pastes(c)(e)	B	NR	A	B	A	C	NR	NR	NR
Sulfurized or sulfochlorinated oils(f)	A	A	B+	A	C	NR	A	B	A
Chlorinated oils or waxes(g):									
High-viscosity types(h)	A(j)	NR	A	NR	A	NR	A(k)	A	NR
Low-viscosity types(m)	B+	A	A	A	B	NR	A(k)	A	A
Graphite or molybdenum disulfide(n)	NR	(p)	(p)	NR	(p)	NR	(p)	NR	NR

(a) Ratings consider effectiveness, cleanliness, ease of removal, and other suitability factors. (b) Vegetable or animal types; mineral oil is used for blending. (c) May be diluted with water. (d) Water emulsions of soluble oils; contain a high concentration of EP sulfur or chlorine compounds. (e) Chalk (whiting) is commonest pigment; others sometimes used. (f) EP types; may contain some mineral or fatty oil. (g) EP chlorinated mineral oils or waxes; may contain emulsifiers for ease of removal in water-base cleaners. (h) Viscosity of 4000 to 20,000 SUS. (j) For heavy plate. (k) For cold forming only. (m) Viscosity (200 to 1000 SUS) is influenced by base oil or wax, degree of chlorination, and additions or mineral oil. (n) Solid lubricant applied from dispersions in oil, solvent or water. (p) For hot forming applications only.

Table 4. Typical Bending Limits for Six Commonly Formed Stainless Steels

Type	Minimum bend radius: Annealed, to 0.187 in. thick (180° bend)	Quarter hard, cold rolled: To 0.050 in. thick (180° bend)	Quarter hard, cold rolled: 0.051 to 0.187 in. thick (90° bend)
301, 302, 304	½t	½t	1t
316	½t	1t	1t
410, 430	1t	..	..

t = stock thickness

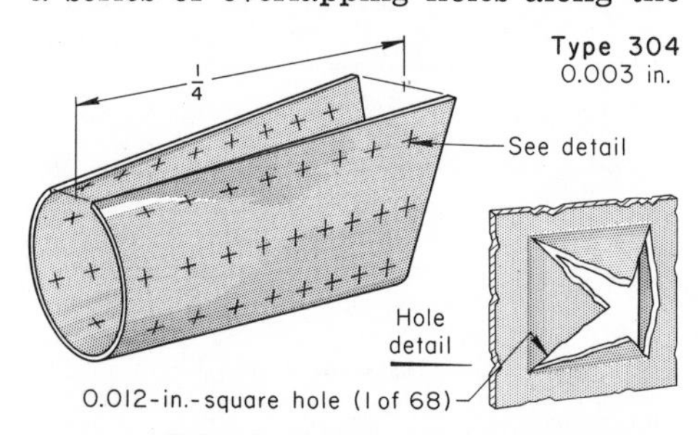

Fig. 3. Cathode produced in a progressive die with carbide tools (Example 452)

Press-Brake Forming

All of the austenitic stainless steels in the soft condition can be bent 180° over one stock thickness, but need up to 50% more power to form than low-carbon steel. Springback is more severe than with low-carbon steel, and must be allowed for. Work-hardened austenitic steel can be press-brake formed only to a very limited degree. If austenitic stainless steel is heated to about 150 F, it can be formed with appreciably less power than is required when it is cold, and yet can be handled easily.

The straight-chromium grades of stainless steels vary in their response to press-brake forming. The low-carbon stainless steels containing 12 to 17% chromium bend readily but, like the austenitic steels, need more power for bending than is needed for low-carbon steel. High-chromium, low-carbon types (like 446) bend better when heated to 350 to 400 F. High-carbon, heat treatable stainless steels are not recommended for press-brake forming, even if in the annealed condition.

Typical bending limits for the major stainless steels are shown in Table 4. A completely flat bend can generally be made in the 18-8 and similar alloys.

Dies. Press brakes can use dies with cross sections like those shown in Fig. 4

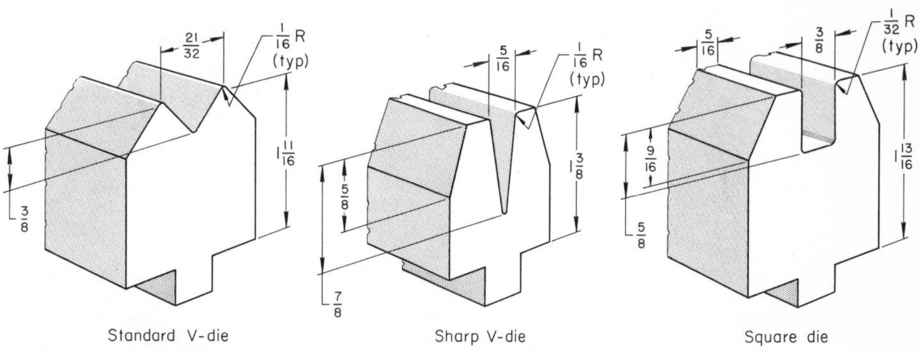

Fig. 4. Typical dies for press-brake forming of stainless steel sheet up to 0.035 in. thick

for forming stainless steel in sheets up to 0.035 in. thick. Adjustable dies like the one shown in Fig. 5 can be used for forming 180° bends in stainless steel sheet 0.012 to 0.018 in. thick.

Springback is a function of the strength of the material, the radius and angle of bend, and the thickness of the stock. Table 5 shows the relation between radius of bend and springback for three austenitic stainless steels. Ferritic steels usually exhibit less springback than do austenitic steels, because the rate of work hardening of ferritic steels is lower.

Springback can be controlled by reducing the punch radius, by coining the line of bend (if the shape of the die is such that bottoming is feasible), and by overbending. Sometimes, for overbending, it is necessary only to make the punch angle smaller than the desired final angle of the workpiece, as in the following example.

Example 453. Setting a Flange Angle in a Press Brake (Fig. 6)

The bracket shown in Fig. 6 was preformed in a U-die from a developed blank of type 302 stainless steel, half-hard, 0.040 in. thick. Only the punch angle needed to be reduced to set the angle on the flange.

As the bracket came from the U-die, the springback in each flange was 15°. To correct this spread, the piece was put in a restrike die in a press brake, which set each angle separately. The restrike die angle was 90° with a ⅛-in. radius. The restrike punch was made to an angle of 86° with a 3⁄32-in. radius to coin the bend, so that the flanges would form to 90° ± 1°.

The lubricant was a water-soluble pigmented drawing compound. The workpiece was degreased after forming.

Lubricants. For ordinary press-brake operations (chiefly, bending and simple forming), lubricants are not used as frequently as with higher-speed press operations. Convenience of use is a major factor in selecting lubricants for this type of press-brake forming; pigmented lubricants are not favored, and cooling effectiveness is of little significance at low production rates. For severe forming and for operations that would ordinarily be done in a press, if available, the recommendations in the "Press forming" column in Table 3 apply.

Table 5. Springback of Three Austenitic Stainless Steels Bent 90° to Various Radii

Steel and temper	Springback for bend radius of: 1t	6t	20t
302 and 304, annealed	2°	4°	15°
301, half-hard	4°	13°	43°

t = stock thickness

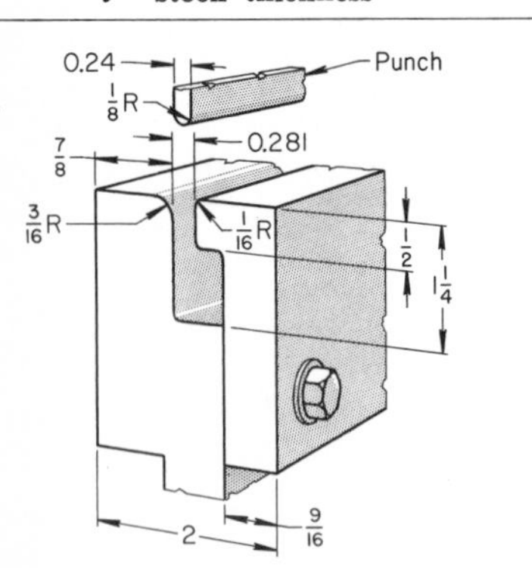

Setup can be used for forming bends to ⅛-in. inside radius in sheet 0.012 to 0.018 in. thick, and will produce 5⁄32-in.-radius bends in half-hard stainless steel. Detachable side of die can be shimmed for bending thicker sheet or for bending with larger-radius punches.

Fig. 5. Adjustable press-brake die for forming 180° bends in stainless steel sheet

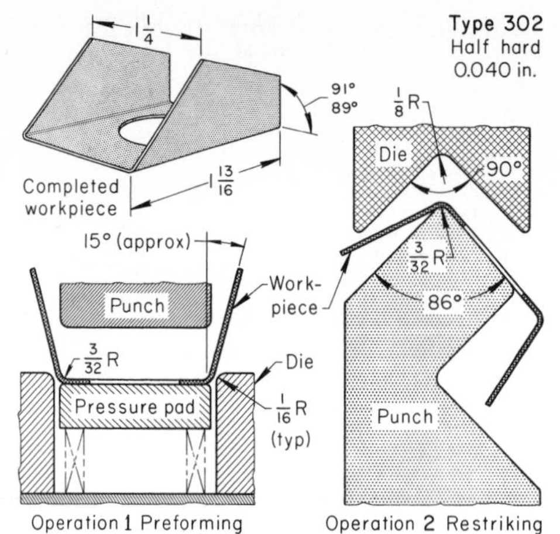

Fig. 6. Production of a U-shape bracket from a developed blank by preforming, and restriking to set flange angles, in a press brake (Example 453)

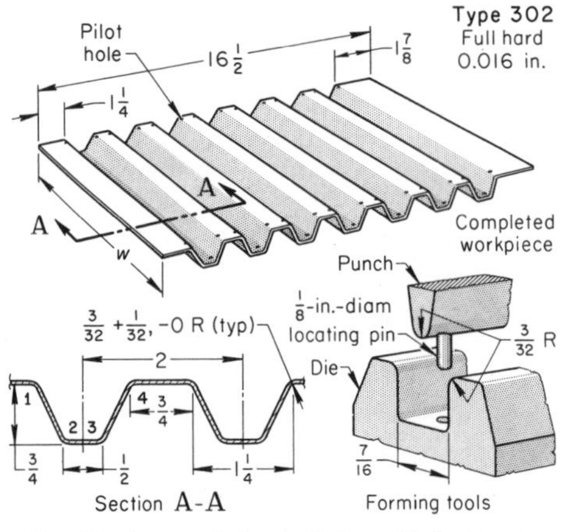

Fig. 7. Corrugated sheet in which corrugations were formed one at a time in a press brake, using tools shown (Example 454)

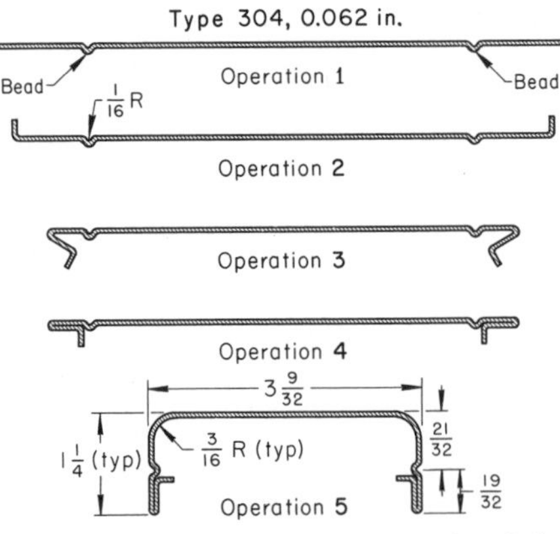

Fig. 8. Shapes progressively produced in five-operation forming of a handrail in a 400-ton press brake (Example 455)

Applications of press-brake forming are described in the three examples that follow.

Repetitive bends, as in corrugated stock, are frequently made one at a time in a press brake, if the quantity of production is not sufficient to warrant a special die, as in the next example.

Example 454. Press-Brake Forming of Corrugations (Fig. 7)

The corrugated sheet shown in Fig. 7 was formed from 0.016-in.-thick full-hard type 302 stainless steel. The finished sheets, after bending, were 16½ in. long, as shown, but the width (w) dimension varied according to the use of the piece.

The corrugations were made one at a time by air bending in the tooling shown at the lower right in Fig. 7. Pilot holes in the workpiece and locating pins in the punch helped to keep the workpiece aligned. Deviation from flatness in the pieces was corrected by restriking some of the bends.

Irregular contours on long, narrow parts are conveniently produced by bending in a press brake; because of the strength of stainless steels, the forming often must be divided among several successive operations:

Example 455. Forming Stainless Steel Handrails in a Press Brake (Fig. 8)

Figure 8 illustrates the shapes produced in five successive operations that were required for forming a handrail from 0.062-in.-thick type 304 stainless steel. Because of flatness requirements and the resistance of the metal to bending, a 400-ton press brake was used.

Forming the 1⁄16-in.-radius beads (operation 1, Fig. 8) was particularly troublesome because of the difficulty in retaining flatness. A force of 600 tons, which exceeded the rating of the press brake, was used to form the beads.

The second and third operations presented no problems, but the fourth operation was difficult, because the workpiece had to be held without marring the polished surface. Similar parts were produced from low-carbon steel without difficulty.

Although press-brake forming is generally limited to straight bends, more complicated shapes can also be made:

Example 456. Press-Brake Forming a Stretch Flange and Bending in Two Directions (Fig. 9)

An L-shape mounting channel (Fig. 9) was formed of 0.028-in.-thick type 347 stainless steel. After annealing, the developed form was blanked and deburred. The ¼-in. radius that was to be formed into a stretch flange was polished.

The piece was then formed in two operations in a press brake. The first operation formed all flanges around the periphery, and the second set the 37° closed angle.

Tools were made of oil-hardening tool steel. The lubricant was water-soluble nonpigmented drawing compound.

Press Forming

Stainless steels are press formed with the same kind of equipment as is used in the forming of low-carbon steel. However, although all stainless steels are not the same in strength or ductility, they all need more power to form than do carbon steels. In general, presses should have the capacity for 60% more ram force than is needed for equivalent work in low-carbon steel, and frames should have the rigidity and bulk to withstand this greater force.

Dies. Besides wearing out faster, dies may fracture more readily when used with stainless steel than when used with low-carbon or medium-carbon steel, because of the greater forces needed to work stainless steel.

For the longest service in mass production, the wearing parts of the dies should be made of carbide, D2 tool steel, or high-strength aluminum bronze. Carbide can last ten times as long as most tool steels, but carbide is more expensive and does not have the

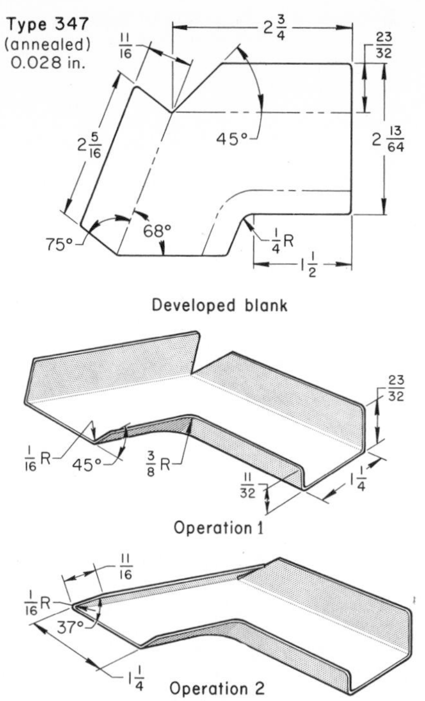

Fig. 9. Mounting channel with a stretch flange and bends in two directions that was formed in two operations in a press brake (Example 456)

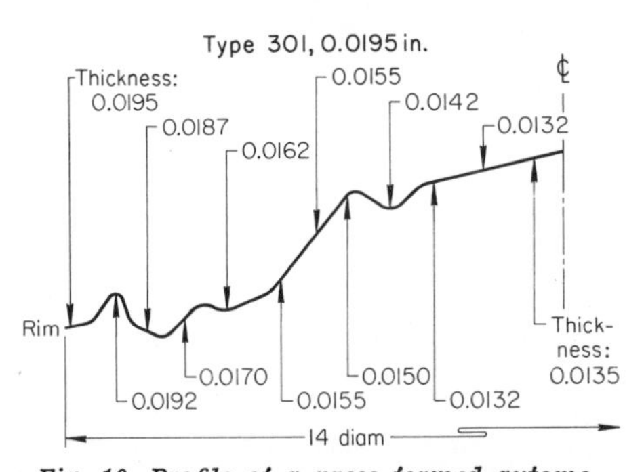

Fig. 10. Profile of a press formed automobile wheel cover showing thinning purposely produced by severe stretching

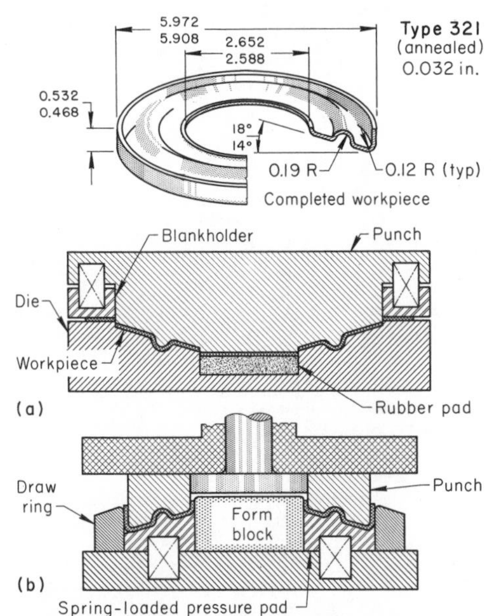

Fig. 11. Severe forming of an austenitic stainless steel aircraft-muffler header, to produce work hardening that would increase the rigidity and fatigue strength of the part (Example 457)

shock resistance of tool steels and aluminum bronze. Tool steels such as D2 are preferred when resistance to both shock and wear is required.

Aluminum bronze offers the most protection against galling and scuffing of the workpiece. An oil-hardening tool steel such as O2 can be used for short production runs.

Austenitic Alloys. Workpieces can be stretched by applying high blankholder pressures to the flange areas to prevent metal from flowing into the die. This causes severe thinning, but work hardening may cause the thinned metal to be as strong as or stronger than the thicker unworked sections. Figure 10 shows a section of an automobile wheel cover, made of type 301 stainless steel, in which the central portion was purposely thinned and work hardened by stretching.

In the application described in the example that follows, one of the principal reasons for stressing the workpiece to the limits of formability was to work harden it for increased strength.

Example 457. Severe Forming for Intentional Work Hardening (Fig. 11)

The material for a muffler header (Fig. 11) for a small aircraft engine was intentionally stressed nearly to the limits of formability, to increase rigidity and give it the necessary fatigue strength. The headers were made in two operations in a 60-ton open-back-inclinable mechanical press having a 5-in. stroke. Each operation used a tool steel die, hardened to Rockwell C 59 to 62. Production was 400 pieces per month.

The first die (Fig. 11a) was a compound die that formed the dish of the part, formed the bead in the dish, and blanked the inside and outside diameters. The blankholder at the outer edge of the workpiece was spring loaded, and a rubber pad supported the inner surface of the workpiece against the center blanking punch. The sequence was programed so that the forming was completed before the outside and inside diameters were blanked, thus making the flange dimensions more accurate and concentric than would have been possible otherwise. Die life was approximately 20,000 pieces.

The second die (Fig. 11b) formed both the inner (stretch) flange, and the outer (compression) flange. A spring-loaded pressure pad maintained correct gripping pressure against the muffler-header body during this operation.

The blank was annealed type 321 stainless steel, 0.032 in. thick, sheared to 8½ in. square. The bead formed in the first die was used as a locating surface in the second die. The dies were brushed with oil between pieces.

The production rate for both operations was seven pieces per minute; at $8 per hour, the labor cost was nearly $0.02 per piece. Setup time for the first operation was 0.17 hr, and 0.31 hr for the second operation.

Stainless steel has high ductility but wrinkles easily in compression. Therefore, if there is a choice in direction of metal flow during forming, a better part is likely to be produced by stretching than by compression, as in the following example.

Example 458. Use of Clamping Plates and Bead to Control Metal Flow (Fig. 12)

The dome section shown in Fig. 12 was formed from a tapered blank of annealed type 302 stainless steel in a 250-ton double-action hydraulic press. It was desirable to maximize metal flow from the narrow end of the blank in order to cause stretching rather than contraction in the metal and thus avoid wrinkles.

The dies could not be oriented to let the blank lie flat, because of the necessity for forming the re-entrant angle next to the lower clamping plates. Both the upper and the lower edges of the blank were held between steel

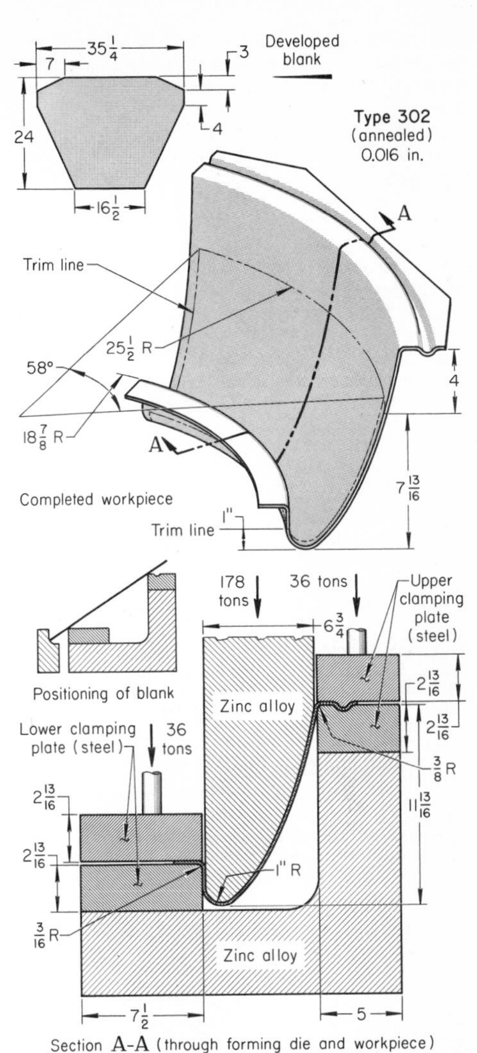

Fig. 12. Tools and clamping plates for controlling metal flow in press forming the part shown (Example 458)

plates during forming. Clamping force on each pair of plates was 36 tons. Since the upper plates were twice as long as the lower and two-thirds as wide, the clamping force was distributed over a larger area and could have permitted the major part of the metal flow from the larger end, with attendant wrinkling of the work metal. Addition of a bead to the upper clamping plates improved holding at that end and caused the major part of the metal flow to occur at the small end of the blank. The application of a fatty-acid-type, nonpigmented drawing compound to the lower plates further encouraged metal flow from the small end of the blank.

Scrap loss because of tearing over the relatively sharp lower die radius was 3%.

Ferritic Alloys. The formability of ferritic stainless steels, particularly the higher-chromium types, can be improved by warm forming at 250 to 400 F, rather than cold forming. The metal is more ductile at the higher temperatures, and less power is needed in forming. Some pieces that cannot be made by cold forming can be made successfully by warm forming.

Lubrication. The lubricant used most often in press forming of stainless steel is the chlorinated type. It has unexcelled chemical EP activity; and the ability to adjust this activity and viscosity independently over an extremely wide range makes it the most versatile lubricant for this purpose. All chlorinated lubricants are readily removable

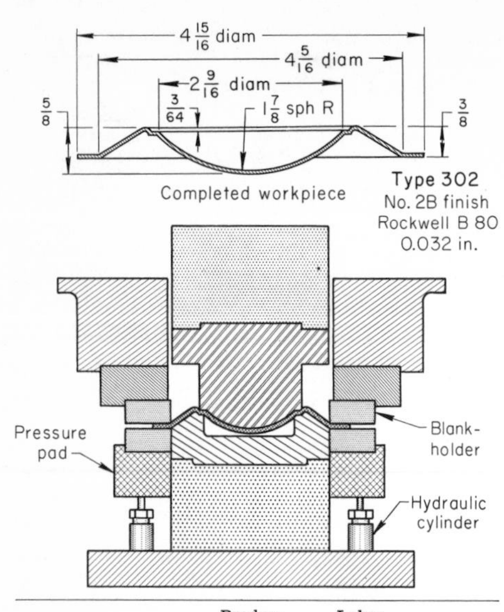

Operation	Production, pcs/hr	Labor per 100 pcs, hr	Tool cost
Blank(a)	1500	0.067	$ 700
Draw(b)	250	0.400	750
Trim(c)	450	0.222	700
Wash	3000	0.033	...
Total		0.722	$2150

(a) In a 60-ton press. (b) In a 150-ton double-action toggle press. (c) In a 60-ton open-back inclinable press.

Fig. 13. Cover half that was forward formed in two combined operations in the tooling setup shown, in a double-action press (Example 460)

in degreasers or in solvents, and emulsifiers can be added to them for easy removal in water-base cleaners.

As shown in Table 3, pigmented pastes, sulfurized or sulfochlorinated oils, and dry wax or soap-borax films are also highly effective lubricants for press forming, but are less convenient to use. Heavy-duty emulsions, because of their superior characteristics as coolants, are preferred for high-speed operations.

In the following example, both high chlorine content and high viscosity were needed to produce acceptable parts. (See also Example 470, in which a low-viscosity chlorine-base lubricant replaced a viscous mineral oil.)

Table 6. Production Rates and Labor Time for Making a Severely Drawn Shell (Example 461)

Operation	Production, pcs/hr	Labor per 100 pcs, hr
Blank and draw(a)	922	0.108
Restrike(a)	1429	0.070
Pierce center hole; trim(b) ..	845	0.118
Pierce side holes(c)	786	0.127

(a) In a compound die, in a 45-ton mechanical press with an air cushion. (b) In a 22-ton mechanical press. (c) In a horn die in a 22-ton mechanical press.

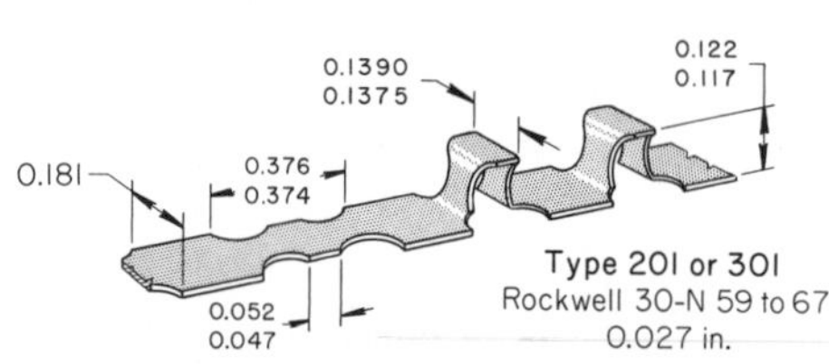

Fig. 14. Section of a piston ring that was notched and formed with corrugations in a progressive die, then annealed and formed into a circle before being cut off from the strip stock (Example 462)

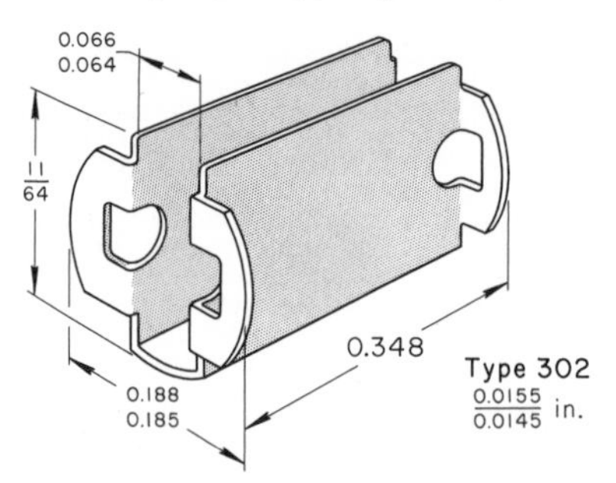

Fig. 15. Bracket that was made by hand feeding stock into a progressive die to avoid the jamming that would have been likely from automatic feeding (Example 463)

Example 459. Increase in Chlorine Content and Viscosity of Lubricant That Improved Results in Forming

A wheel cover was made from a type 302 stainless steel blank 18 in. in diameter by 0.028 in. thick, in two operations: draw, then trim and pierce. At first, a lightly chlorinated oil (10% Cl) of medium viscosity (1500 SUS at 100 F) was used in drawing. Even though the draw was shallow, 12% of the wheel covers were rejected for splits and scratches.

A change was made to a highly chlorinated oil (36% Cl) of much higher viscosity (4000 SUS at 100 F). As a result, the rejection rate decreased to less than 1%. After forming, the wheel covers were vapor degreased.

Combined Operations in Compound and Progressive Dies

The use of compound and progressive dies for mass production of parts that require many operations, or for an operation too severe to be done economically in a single-operation die, is discussed in the article "Press Forming of Low-Carbon Steel", on pages 114 and 115 in this volume. The same principles apply to their use on stainless steel for blanking, piercing, bending, forming, drawing, coining, or embossing, or combinations of these operations.

Both compound and progressive dies must be made of die materials hard enough to withstand the most severe demands of blanking, and tough enough for the most severe forming or coining operations. The lubricant must have enough body for the most severe draw, and yet be light enough not to interfere with the production of coined or embossed details, or to gum up cutting edges.

In a compound die in a double-action press, two draws can be made in stainless steel provided the press capacity is not exceeded, as in the next example.

Example 460. Forming in Two Forward Draws in a Compound Die, Using a Double-Action Press (Fig. 13)

The 5¼-in.-diam blank for the cover half shown at the top in Fig. 13 was made from type 302 stainless steel coil stock 5⅝ in. wide, in a 60-ton press. The cover halves were formed at the rate of 250 pieces per hour in a 150-ton double-action press. Two forming operations were required.

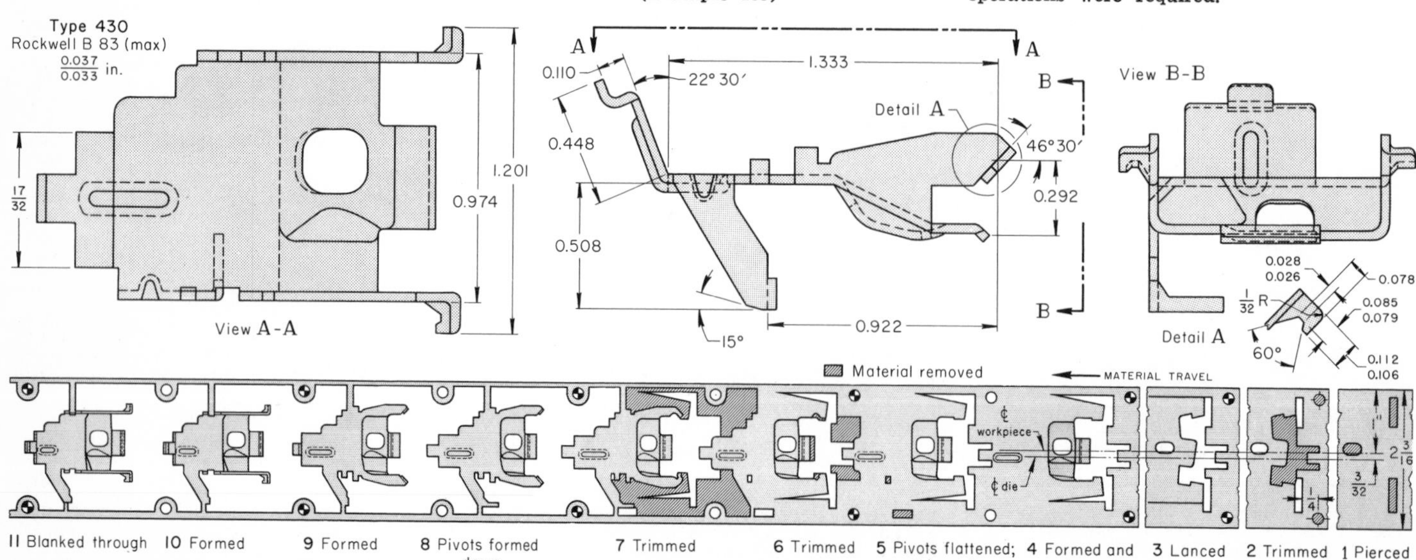

Fig. 16. Bellows lever produced in an 11-station progressive die in the sequence of operations indicated on the strip development shown. Final forming was done in a separate die. (Example 464)

The small size of the die made it impractical to apply the pressure-pad force with the die cushion, and an adequate uniform force could not be obtained from springs. For this reason, a hydraulic system was used to apply force to the pressure pad.

A valve in the hydraulic circuit controlled and held constant the amount of force on the blank, which was held between the blankholder and pressure pad. Downward motion of the outer slide formed the cone. The outer slide dwelled while the inner slide punch formed the offset and the spherical radius. The dies were made of D2 tool steel and had a life of 500,000 pieces. A high-pressure drawing compound was used on the blanks.

The workpiece was trimmed to a $4\frac{15}{16}$-in. final diameter in a 60-ton press, and then washed. Annual production was 15,000 pieces. Production rates, labor time, and tool costs are given in the table accompanying Fig. 13.

The next example demonstrates the near-maximum severity of forming that can be achieved in a blank-and-draw compound die.

Example 461. Blanking and Severe Drawing in One Operation in a Compound Die (Table 6)

The shell illustrated in Table 6 was blanked and drawn in a severe forming operation in a compound die, at the rate of 16,000 pieces per year. The die was used in a 45-ton mechanical press with an air cushion. The formed piece was restruck in the same die to sharpen the draw radius and to flatten the flange within 0.006 in. The die was made of A2 tool steel and had a life of 50,000 pieces per grind. An emulsified chlorinated concentrate was used as lubricant.

After forming, the piece then was moved to a 22-ton mechanical press, where the 0.093-in.-diam hole was pierced and the flange was trimmed to an oval shape. A second piercing operation, in a horn die in a 22-ton mechanical press, pierced two 0.062-in-diam holes in the side of the shell. Air ejection was used in all operations except the final piercing, where the piece was picked off.

The material was type 302 stainless steel, 0.037 in. thick and $2\frac{1}{4}$ in. wide, which had been annealed. Table 6 gives production rate and labor time for each of the four operations.

Small, complex parts that must be made in large quantities are well suited for production in progressive or transfer dies. A transfer die uses a minimum of material and can accept coil stock, loose blanks, or partially formed parts. Scrap removal problems are lessened. A progressive die is preferred when the piece can remain attached to the strip, as in the following example.

Example 462. Notching and Forming a Piston-Ring Strip in a Progressive Die (Fig. 14)

A corrugated strip, used for an oil piston ring, was formed from type 201 or 301 stainless steel. Coiled strip 0.181 in. wide was slide fed into a four-ram press. Each ram had a capacity of 6 tons. Only two rams were used; the strip was notched by the second ram and formed by the third. As the strip emerged from the forming die, it was annealed by induction heating, and then was passed onto a coiling shoe, where it was formed into a circle and cut off.

The press made 450 strokes per minute. A ring was completely formed in three press strokes. After about 500,000 strokes (roughly the work of two shifts), the dies were cleaned and reconditioned.

The profile of the strip before and after forming the corrugations is shown in Fig. 14.

In the following example, piercing, blanking and forming were combined in a seven-stage progressive die. Although progressive, it was hand fed — a rather unusual combination.

Example 463. Producing a Small Bracket in a Progressive Die With Hand Feeding (Fig. 15)

The small bracket shown in Fig. 15 was made in a seven-station progressive die from $\frac{3}{8}$-in.-wide stock that was hand fed into the 6-ton press. Hand feeding was done because close operator attention was required to prevent jamming, which would have damaged the frail dies. The sequence of operations was as follows:

1 Feed strip to finger stop; pierce
2 Feed to notch-die opening; pierce
3 Notch and trim lugs
4 Form lugs
5 Form and cut off
6 Unload by blast of air.

The parts were barrel finished to remove burrs and to provide a smooth finish and high luster. Production rate was 2175 pieces per hour. Annual production was 2 million pieces. A chlorinated and inhibited oil was used as lubricant.

Often there is a choice as to whether a stainless steel piece is to be made in a progressive die or in a series of single-operation (simple) dies. Deep forming, which makes the workpiece more three-dimensional in form than flat, usually presents difficulties in designing and constructing efficient and long-life progressive dies. The cost and delay involved in developing progressive tooling was justified for producing the bellows lever and the frame described in the examples that follow, in quantities of 100,000 or more per year.

Examples 464 and 465. Use of Progressive Dies for High-Quantity Production

Example 464 — Bellows Lever (Fig. 16). A bellows lever was pierced, embossed and partly formed in an 11-station progressive die, as shown in Fig. 16, from type 430 stainless steel, $2\frac{3}{16}$ in. wide and 0.035 in. thick. The long flange was bent, and at the same time, a corner-stiffening bead was formed and the pivot points were further flattened in a final-forming die.

The progressive die was set up in a 75-ton mechanical press, which produced 5000 pieces per hour. The final-forming die ran in a 30-ton press at a rate of 652 pieces per hour. Annual production was 150,000 levers.

The lever could have been made in a series of six individual dies, which would have cost about $7500, or $4500 less than the $12,000 cost of tooling for the progressive-die method. However, for the progressive-die method, press time (0.1733 hr per 100 pieces) was considerably shorter than it would have been with individual dies (estimated at 0.6115 hr per 100 pieces), and variation on the critical dimensions was less.

Had production requirements been only 10,000 to 20,000 levers per year, however, the use of the less costly individual dies might have been the more economical method.

Example 465 — Frame (Fig. 17). The frame shown in Fig. 17 was made of 0.022-in.-thick type 430 stainless steel coil stock, $3\frac{3}{4}$ in. wide. The maximum hardness was Rockwell B 83.

A nine-station progressive die pierced and flanged holes, embossed stiffening beads on the two legs, trimmed and formed tabs, coined identification data, and blanked the part from the strip. Then stops were lanced and formed and bottom flanges were formed in a forming die, and a final-forming die was used for the deep side flanges.

The progressive die was run in a 75-ton mechanical press at a rate of 5000 pieces per hour. The first and second forming dies were run in a 30-ton press at speeds of 984 and 936 pieces per hour, respectively.

The annual production was 90,000 frames, and demand was expected to increase. This, plus the short press time (0.2284 hr per 100 pieces, as against an estimated 0.6665 hr per 100 pieces if produced in eight separate dies) and the greater accuracy obtainable in the progressive die, justified the higher tooling cost for the progressive-die method ($12,000, compared with an estimated $7500 for separate dies).

The dies were made of A2 tool steel and had a life of 50,000 to 75,000 pieces between regrinds.

The lubricant was an emulsifiable chlorinated oil concentrate.

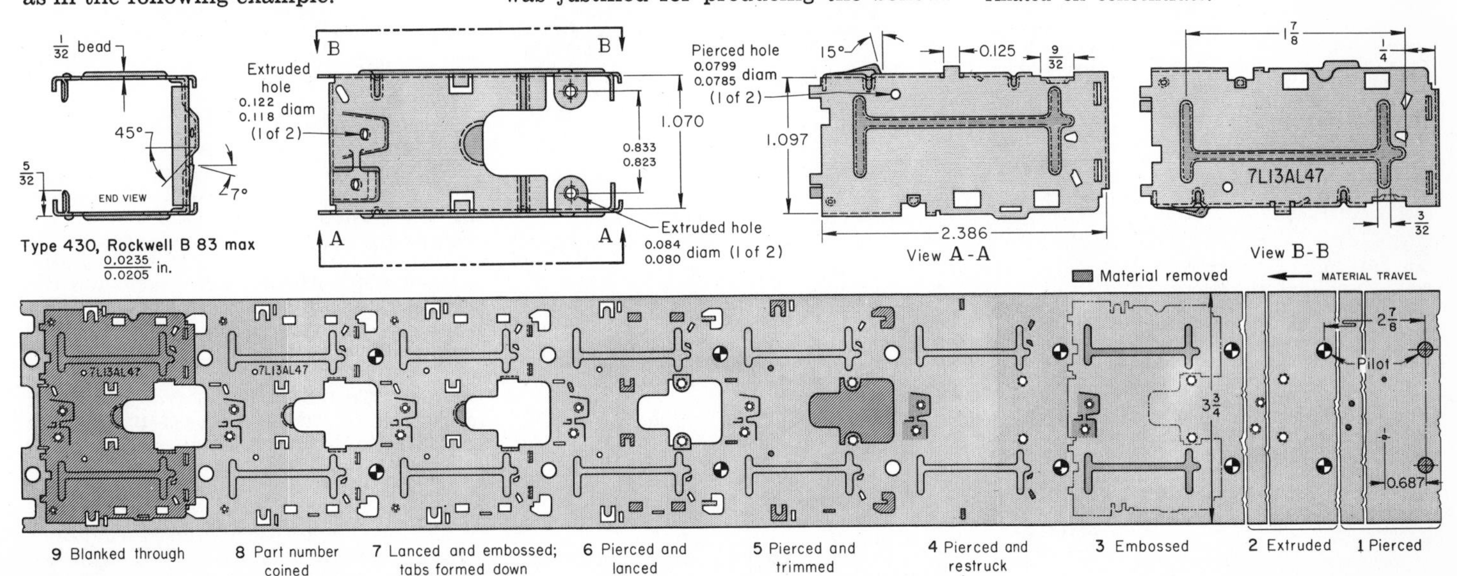

Fig. 17. Frame produced in a nine-station progressive die in the sequence of operations indicated on the strip development shown. Final forming was done in separate dies. (Example 465)

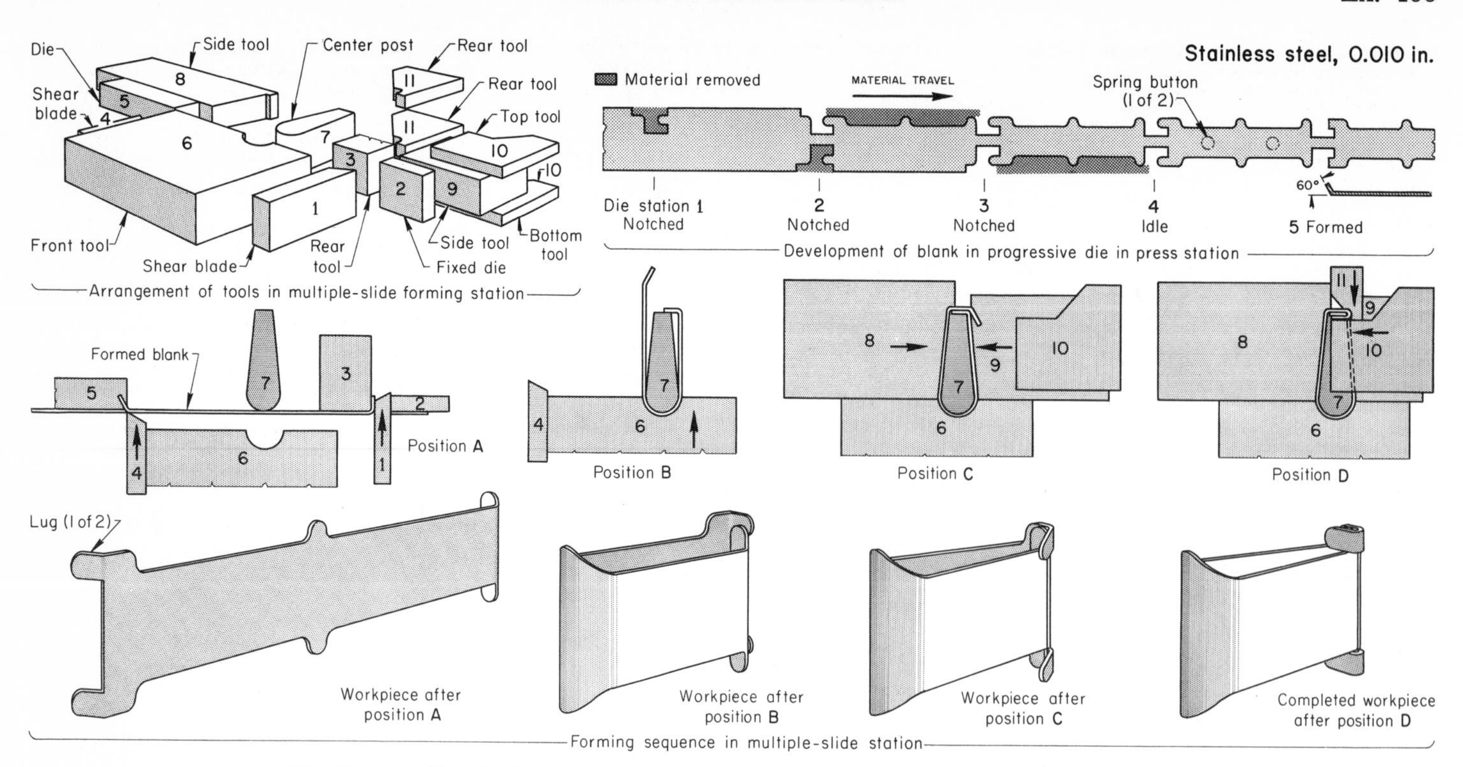

Fig. 18. Operations in forming a wristband link in a multiple-slide machine (Example 466)

Multiple-Slide Forming

Small high-production stainless steel parts sometimes can be formed in multiple-slide machines with the same kinds of tools as are used for forming low-carbon steel. (For information on multiple-slide forming, see the article that begins on page 154 in this volume.) The following example describes the forming of a link for a flexible expanding wristband.

Example 466. Multiple-Slide Forming of a Wristband Link (Fig. 18)

The workpiece shown in Fig. 18, a link for an expanding wristband, was formed in a multiple-slide machine from stainless steel strip 0.010 in. thick by 0.354 in. wide, and was locked in shape by bent lugs. Production rate was 6000 pieces per hour.

The blank for the link was made in a five-station progressive die mounted in the press station of the machine. As shown in the upper right corner of Fig. 18, the strip was notched in stations 1, 2 and 3 by four small heeled punches. For support against side thrust, the heels entered the die before engaging the stock. An air blast entering through holes in the punches removed the scrap, to protect the die and the feed mechanisms. In the fifth die station, two lugs on the blank were bent 60°. Spring-actuated lifters stripped the blank from the bending section of the die after the lugs were bent. The workpieces were held together by a narrow strip of stock that was left to index the workpiece through the stations of the progressive die.

The blank was then fed to the forming station, so that it was edge-up between the center post 7 and front tool 6 (position A in Fig. 18). As the blank entered the forming station, the center post moved upward into forming position. Then, shear blade 1 moved forward against fixed die 2 to trim off the joining strip. Blade 1 also bent the end of the blank against the auxiliary rear tool 3, which then retracted. The other end of the blank was cut off by shear blade 4 against die 5, as shown in position A in Fig. 18.

After the blank was cut off by shear blade 4, front tool 6 bent the workpiece around center post 7 (see position B in Fig. 18).

In position C, the workpiece was formed on the center post by side tools 8 and 9, while still being held by tool 6. Tool 6 was wide enough to form the full width of the workpiece, including the lugs, but tools 8 and 9 were narrower, leaving exposed the top and bottom lugs that had been formed in the last press-die station.

In position D, tools 6, 8 and 9 held the part against center post 7 while rear tools 11 flattened the top and bottom lugs against the center post. Then the center post was lowered from the workpiece. Side tool 9, which was spring loaded, slid between top and bottom tools 10, permitting them to advance to form the top and bottom lugs into a U-shape. Tool 9 held the workpiece against tools 6 and 8 while tools 10 tucked in the lugs.

With all the other tools holding the closed position against the workpiece, rear tools 11 moved slightly to press the lugs closed against tools 10. Then, as the tools opened, the completed link was ejected by an air jet.

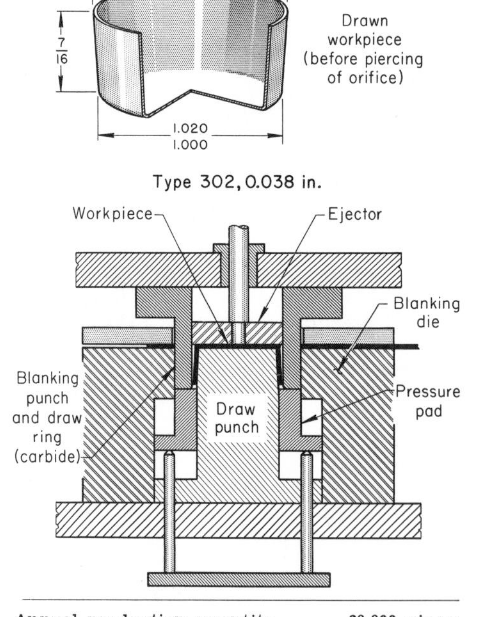

Annual production quantity	60,000 pieces
Production rate, blanking and drawing	670 pieces per hour
Production rate, piercing	153 pieces per hour
Die cost, blanking and drawing	$685
Die cost, piercing	$295

Costs per Piece

Material	$0.027
Dies (blank-and-draw, and pierce) (a)	0.016
Labor, blanking and drawing	0.002
Labor, piercing	0.018
Overhead, blanking and drawing	0.005
Overhead, piercing	0.035
Total cost per piece	$0.103

(a) Total cost of dies amortized over one year's production of 60,000 pieces

Fig. 19. Forming an orifice cup in a blank-and-draw die with a carbide punch and draw ring. Orifice was pierced in a second operation. (Example 467)

Deep Drawing

Percentages of reduction (blank diameter to inside diameter of cup) obtainable in deep drawing range from 40 to 60% for the chromium-nickel (austenitic) stainless steels of best drawability and from 20 to 30% for the straight-chromium (ferritic) grades. The amount of reduction obtainable varies greatly with the radius of the die and to a lesser extent with the radius of the punch nose. As the die radius decreases, the drawability decreases, as shown in Table 7 for austenitic stainless steel. Typically used punch and die radii are five to ten times metal thickness. With the ferritic grades, the drawability and ductility usually decrease with increasing chromium content. To offset this, steels with high chromium content are often warmed moderately before drawing.

Presses used for deep drawing stainless steel differ only in power and rigidity from those used for low-carbon steel; because of the higher work-hardening rate of stainless steel and its inherent higher strength, presses used for deep drawing stainless steel often

Table 7. Effect of Die Radius on Reduction Obtainable in Deep Drawing of Austenitic Stainless Steel(a)

Die radius(b)	Reduction in drawing, %
15t	50 to 60
10t	40 to 50
5t	30 to 40
2t	0 to 10

(a) Per cent reduction = $100(1 - d/D)$, where D is the diameter of blank, and d is the inside diameter of the drawn piece. (b) t = stock thickness.

need 100% more ram force and the necessary frame stiffness to support this greater force.

Dies for drawing stainless steel must be able to withstand the high force and to resist galling. For ordinary service, D2 tool steel dies give a good combination of hardness and toughness. On long runs, carbide draw rings have exceptionally long life. Where friction and galling are the chief problems, draw rings are sometimes made of high-strength aluminum bronze.

The example that follows describes an application in which the selection of tool material was critical, in order to avoid scoring of the workpiece and to obtain acceptable die life in drawing.

Example 467. Use of a Carbide Blank-and-Draw Ring (Fig. 19)

An orifice cup, 1 in. in diameter by 7/16 in. deep, was blanked and drawn in one operation. A 0.053-in.-diam orifice was pierced in the cup in a second operation. The specifications called for the sides of the cup to be free of score marks from the die. The blank was 1.575 in. in diameter, cut from 0.038-in.-thick type 302 stainless steel strip 2 in. wide.

The blank-and-draw tooling shown in Fig. 19 was originally made of tool steel of a grade no longer used. It produced fewer than 50 pieces without scoring of workpieces. The combination blanking punch and draw ring was chromium plated in an attempt to increase its durability. Adhesion of the plating was not satisfactory; the chromium started to peel after 180 pieces had been produced. Next, a draw ring made of graphitic tool steel was tried, but this also scored the workpieces.

Finally, a new draw ring was made of sintered carbide consisting of 81% tungsten carbide, 15% cobalt and 4% tantalum — a composition especially recommended for draw dies. The new ring, used with a chlorinated oil-base lubricant, withstood the heat and pressure generated by the severe blank-and-draw operation, and produced mar-free parts. Maintenance was negligible, and after three years the carbide draw ring had produced 180,000 pieces, with little evidence of wear.

The blanking punch-to-die clearance was 0.002 in. per side. Drawing punch-to-die clearance was 0.0335 in. plus 3° taper per side on the draw punch. The punch nose radius was 0.015 in., and the draw radius was 0.093 in.

The following example shows how the gradual wear of carbide draw rings in severe drawing affected the outside diameter of drawn shells.

Example 468. Effect of Wear of a Carbide Draw Ring on the Diameter of a Drawn Shell (Fig. 20)

The carbide draw ring used in deep drawing a shell for pens and pencils made more than 225,000 pieces before it was replaced. Measurements of the pieces were made at production intervals, as plotted in Fig. 20.

Shortly after 225,000 pieces had been drawn, shells began to be produced that would no longer enter the "go" ring gage freely, because of wear on the draw ring. The worn draw ring, which permitted excessive springback, was replaced before the beginning of the next production run.

The shell was drawn from a blank of type 317 stainless steel 1.906 in. in diameter and

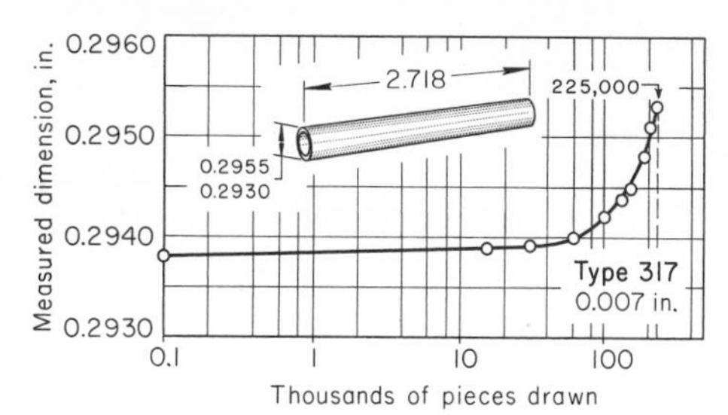

Fig. 20. Variation in diameter of a deep drawn shell that resulted from wear of the carbide draw ring used (Example 468)

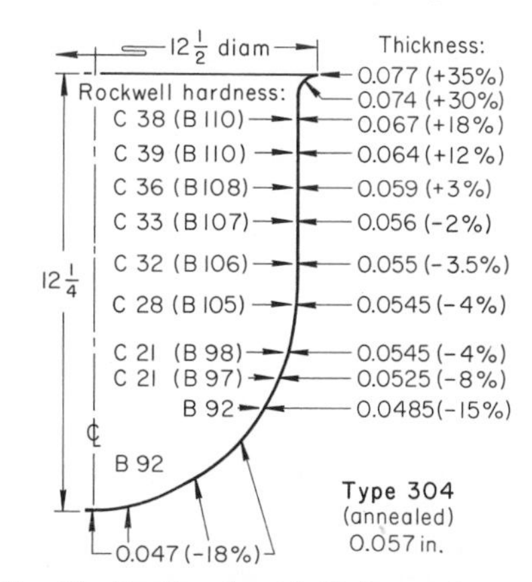

Fig. 21. Profile of a shell drawn from an austenitic stainless steel, showing variations in hardness and thickness produced by drawing

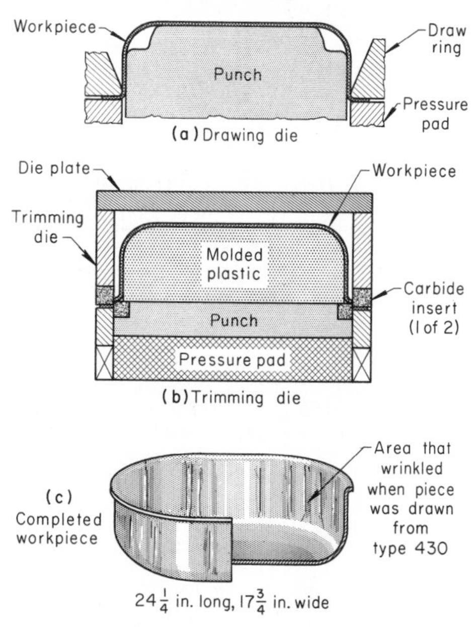

Die clearance (0.055 in. per side) and draw-ring radius (1/4 in.) were not changed when 0.031-in.-thick type 430 was substituted for 0.050-in.-thick galvanized carbon steel as the work metal, and wrinkles resulted in drawing.

Fig. 22. Setups for drawing and trimming a basin (Example 469)

0.007 in. thick to a finished depth of 2.718 in. using chromium-plated punches. The shell was made in eight single-station dies, seven drawing and one end forming, at a rate of 600 per hour. The punches had a 0.090-in. nose radius and the draw dies had a 90° conical entrance angle with a 0.060-in. radius blending the corners. A mixture of three parts inhibited hydraulic oil and one part chlorinated oil was used as lubricant.

Die clearance for heavy draws is 35 to 40% greater than the original metal thickness for austenitic alloys; for the ferritic alloys, which thicken less, 10 to 15% is generally adequate.

Figure 21 shows a profile of an austenitic stainless steel drawn part that illustrates the thickening pattern observed in drawing a cup from this material. If the process is one of stretching more than of drawing, the clearances do not have to compensate for natural thickening.

Clearances of less than the metal thickness generally are not used with stainless steel, because they result in "ironing" or squeezing of the metal between the male and female dies. The austenitic stainless steels are not suited to ironing, because their high rate of work hardening promotes scoring and rapid wear of the dies. Also, any substantial ironing in drawing austenitic stainless steels greatly increases the likelihood of fracturing the workpiece.

The example that follows describes an application in which the work metal was changed from galvanized carbon steel to a thinner ferritic stainless steel without a revision of die clearance. The resultant problems were solved by substituting an austenitic stainless steel that was better suited to the original clearance even though it had the same thickness as the ferritic steel.

Example 469. Matching Work Metal to Die Clearance (Fig. 22)

Using the tooling shown in Fig. 22, basins were made at the rate of 10,000 to 15,000 pieces per year from galvanized carbon steel, 0.050 in. thick. The press was a 1000-ton hydraulic press with an air-over-oil pressure pad and a draw rate of 6 in. in 5 sec. The punch, draw ring, and pressure pad for the drawing die (see Fig. 22a) were hardened cast iron. Carbide inserts were used as cutting edges on the trimming punch and die (Fig. 22b). The locator on the trimming die was molded plastic, and the die plate was cast iron. Both dies were used side-by-side in the press at the same time, since it had enough capacity to draw and trim in one stroke. Thus, a finished piece was produced with each stroke of the press, using manual transfer.

To produce a more corrosion-resistant basin, type 430 stainless steel was substituted for the galvanized carbon steel. To minimize the increase in cost of material, the type 430 was only 0.031 in. thick; however, the same tooling was used, because the relatively low annual quantity did not warrant the cost of retooling. Because the hold-down forces were not suitable for the ferritic stainless steel, several hundred pieces out of the first run were fractured in drawing.

When the hold-down pressure was adjusted to a level suitable for a ferritic stainless steel, contraction wrinkles formed where the material entered the throat of the die (see Fig. 22c), because the die clearance was too great. Corners of the blank were cropped, viscosity of the lubricant was changed, and hold-down pressures were more closely adjusted in an effort to control wrinkling.

Data given for noncylindrical draws in a diemakers' handbook provided both an explanation for the difficulties encountered in changing the work metal and guidance for the selection of a suitable stainless steel:

Stock thickness (t), in.	Work metal: Carbon steel	Type 430	Types 302 and 304
Die Clearance per Side, In.			
0.050	0.055	0.055	0.090
0.030	0.033	0.033	0.054
Draw-Ring Radius, In.			
0.050	1/4 to 3/8	1/4 to 3/8	4t min
0.030	3/16 to 5/16	3/16 to 5/16	4t min

These data showed that the thickness of type 430 stock that could best be formed by the die would be the same as that of the carbon steel previously formed, and that if the stock thickness were reduced, an austenitic steel like type 302 could be used. The die clearance was 0.055 in. per side, and the draw-ring radius was ¼ in. Thus, the die was suited for the 0.050-in.-thick carbon steel, but not for the 0.031-in.-thick type 430. However, 0.031-in.-thick type 302 would be closely matched to the die capacity.

A change was made to type 302 stainless steel 0.031 in. thick with no further difficulty. A change to 0.050-in.-thick stock of type 430 might have been successful.

Speed of drawing has an important bearing on the success of the draw. A rate of 20 to 25 ft per minute makes a good compromise between the rate of work hardening and the uniform distribution of stress. With proper forming techniques, the rate of fracture at this speed is often less than 2%.

Lubricants. Ordinarily, both sides of the workpiece need to be lubricated for each draw. If too little lubricant is used, tools may build up enough heat during a production run to cause the work metal to fracture due to galling. In tests with a minimum of lubricant, failures occurred after 25 draws.

Both chemical type and viscosity or body of the lubricant are important. Either chemical or mechanical EP activity (see pages 23 and 24) is needed for severe deep drawing of stainless steel.

Viscosity or pigment loading must not be too high or too low. Too thick a lubricant can cause wrinkling of compressed metal; too thin, seizing or galling.

The same characteristics that make chlorinated oils and waxes useful for press forming of stainless steel (see page 357) also make them useful for deep drawing these alloys. Table 3 lists other lubricants used in deep drawing stainless steel. Pigmented pastes and dry films are also effective (and in some instances, superior) in deep drawing.

In the following example, changing from a viscous mineral oil to a low-viscosity mineral-oil blend of a chlorinated wax eliminated wrinkling and galling.

Example 470. Effect of Reducing Viscosity and Adding Chlorinated Wax to Mineral Oil Lubricant in Deep Drawing

A coffeepot was deep drawn from a type 302 stainless steel blank 14 in. in diameter by 0.032 in. thick, in two deep draws and one bulging operation. At first, the blanks were lubricated by brushing both sides with mineral oil having a viscosity of 6000 SUS at 100 F. The workpiece wrinkled in the first draw, and galled in the second draw and in bulging.

The lubricant was replaced with a thinner mineral oil (viscosity, 500 SUS at 100 F) that was fortified with a chlorinated wax. The lubricant was brushed on, as before. Not only did the use of the modified lubricant eliminate the wrinkles in the first draw, but enough lubricant remained on the surface to prevent galling in the two other operations. Even though a fluid of much lower viscosity was used, the tenacity imparted by the chlorinated wax permitted the retention of sufficient lubricant for the subsequent bulging and deep drawing operations.

Sometimes, however, there is no substitute for the physical separation and equalization of pressure provided by pigments, as in the following example.

Example 471. Pigmented Paste vs Chlorinated Oil for Deep Drawing

For easy cleaning in a vapor degreaser, highly fortified oils were specified for deep drawing a rectangular shell from 0.035-in.-thick type 304 stainless steel. Chlorinated and

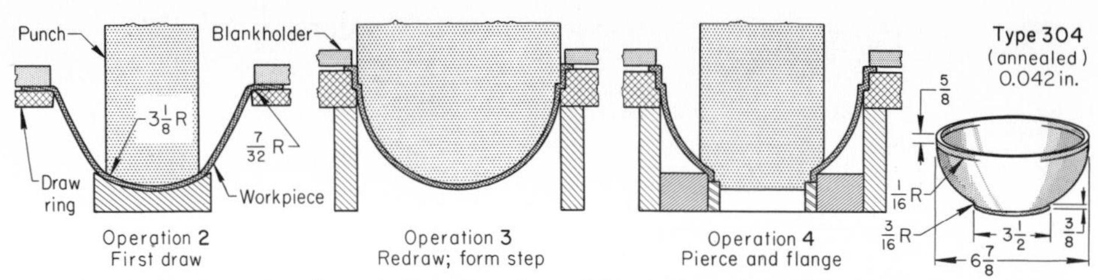

Fig. 23. Production of a stepped-diameter, flanged hemisphere, in which a narrow punch was used in predrawing of dome. Piece was drawn from an 11⅛-in.-diam blank produced in operation 1 (not shown). (Example 474)

Table 8. Force Required for Drawing Two Stainless Steels and Low-Carbon Steel of 0.050-In. Thickness to Various Diameters

Diameter of piece, in.	Approximate drawing force required, tons — Stainless steels — Austenitic, type 18-8	Ferritic, 17% Cr	Low-carbon steel
5	39	20	18
10	78	59	39
20	157	117	78

sulfochlorinated oils with viscosities of 4000 to 20,000 SUS at 100 F failed to eliminate welding to the dies and splitting of the workpiece at the corners. The shell, a well for a steam table, was deep drawn from a rectangular blank, 30 by 23 in., with corners trimmed at 45°. The shell was drawn in one operation and then the flange trimmed. Interior dimensions of the drawn shell were 20 by 12 by 6 in. Bottom corners had ⅝-in. radii; vertical corners, 1⅛-in. radii; and the flange, a ¼-in. radius. The shell had approximately 3° taper on each side. Clearance between the punch and die was equal to the stock thickness.

The oil-type lubricant was replaced by a highly pigmented water-miscible fatty paste, diluted with two parts of water, which was applied to both sides of each blank by rollers. This lubricant eliminated the welding, and allowed enough metal flow to prevent splitting. The drawn parts were cleaned with hot alkaline solution in a soak tank.

Drawing Cylindrical Parts. When a part is made in several drawing operations, the amount of reduction in redrawing is related to the condition of the metal in the first drawing operation (cupping). If the material is highly stressed because of excessive blankholder pressure or because of small die radius, very little reduction can be made in the second operation.

General practice on the more formable grades of austenitic stainless steel is to allow 40 to 45% reduction in the first operation, followed by a maximum of 30% in the second operation, if the workpiece is not annealed between draws. With an anneal, the second reduction usually is 30 to 40%. On some parts, it may be preferable to spread the reduction over four draws before annealing: for example, making successive reductions of 35, 30, 20 and 10%.

There is usually a decrease in drawability on redrawing, and the greatest total reduction in a two-draw operation is most often produced by having the first-stage reduction as large as possible. During redrawing, it is advisable to use a tapered or rounded-end internal blankholder or sleeve to allow easy flow of metal into the die, as indicated in Fig. 31 in the article "Deep Drawing", page 177 in this volume. An internal blankholder with small-radius 90° corners causes the metal to be bent severely through two 90° bends before flowing into the die.

Optimum drawability is available at ram speeds of not more than 20 to 30 ft per minute. Work hardening of stainless steel is minimized by slow forming.

The following two examples describe applications in which small shells were deep drawn in several steps to reduce the amount of work done in a single operation. Because production quantities were low, individual dies were more economical than a transfer die.

Example 472. Seven-Step Deep Drawing of a Fountain-Pen Cap

Fountain-pen caps of various closely related designs were made on the same production line by one blanking and cupping operation and six redraws. A flat blank of type 302 stainless steel having a hardness of Rockwell 15-T 83 to 88 was used. The first five draws ordinarily were the same for any of the caps made on the line; therefore, to set up for a different size of cap, only the compound blank-and-cup die and the last die (or, for some caps, the last two dies) needed to be changed; hence, changeover time was only about 45 min.

In the first operation, which was done in an 18-ton mechanical press, a compound blank-and-cup die equipped with a rubber die cushion cut circular blanks from 0.0105/0.0110-in.-thick strip and drew them into a cup. To make a typical cap, 3½ in. long by 0.3365/0.3375-in. OD, a blank 2.200 in. in diameter was cut from stock 2¼ in. wide, and was drawn into a cup ¾ in. deep by 1.250 in. in diameter — a 43% reduction in diameter. Reductions in the subsequent redraws were, respectively, 27, 22, 18, 18, 16 and 15%. All except the last redraw were done in 4-ton hydraulic presses with 6-in. strokes. The final redraw was made in a 6-ton hydraulic press with a 12-in. stroke.

The draw dies were carbide inserts ½ to ⅝ in. thick. The die openings had a 3/16-in. radius blending with a 1/16-in.-wide land. There was a 2° relief per side below the land. The high speed steel punches had a 3/32-in. nose radius and were chromium plated for smoothness and wear characteristics. The workpiece was pushed through the die and stripped from the punch by a split stripper plate under the draw die. The strippers were closed by cam action from the press stripper rod.

Because production quantities of any one part were small, this technique was preferable to making a transfer die for each of the several caps produced on this line. Operations were set up in machines in the line as they were needed and as the machines became available.

The final draw, which was the deepest, governed the final production rate of 575 pieces per hour. However, when there was a backlog of pieces, this operation was set up on two machines at the same time.

The blank-and-cup die made about 45,000 pieces before resharpening. The draw rings were used for 150,000 to 200,000 pieces before wear was too great. Dies in the first few draws were allowed to wear over a fairly wide range. As the die opening increased, clearance was maintained by increasing the thickness of the chromium plating on the punch. When the die openings were 0.004 to 0.005 in. oversize, the dies were replaced, and punches were returned to original size by stripping, polishing and replating.

The lubricant was a mixture of one part sulfur-free chlorinated oil with three parts inhibited hydraulic oil having a viscosity of 250 SUS at 100 F. It was furnished to all presses through a central pumping system.

Critical tolerances on these fountain-pen caps were ±0.001 in. on outside diameter and ±0.0005 in. on inside diameter. Holding the clearance between the draw die and punch to 10% greater than stock thickness helped maintain these tolerances.

Example 473. Production of a Pencil Cap by Deep Drawing in a Press Line

A cap for an automatic pencil, 0.3795/0.3805-in. OD by 0.3595/0.3605-in. ID by 2.100/2.110 in. long, was produced in 5000-piece lots from a blank 1.875 in. in diameter in a line similar to that described in Example 472. The line differed from that for the production of the pen cap in only two respects: closer tolerances were needed on the length of the pencil cap, and provision had to be made for a hole and locking lug for the lead-extending mechanism. Therefore, the piece was trimmed twice, and the end was pierced. Operations subsequent to deep drawing consisted of piercing the 0.201-in.-diam end hole, finish trimming the open end, and shearing the clip-locking lug. Some of the pen and pencil caps had a taper on the end; this taper was formed during the final draw.

The operations were: blank and cup; first redraw; second redraw; first trim; third redraw; fourth redraw; fifth redraw; form profile in end; pierce end; trim open end to length; shear clip-locking lug.

The cap was made of type 302 stainless steel, having a hardness of Rockwell 15-T 83 to 88, in dies ordinarily used for precious metals. Because die clearances, entrance angles and radii for forming stainless steel are usually different from those used for forming precious metals, tooling for the four redraws and for profile forming had to be changed for the stainless steel caps. However, dies for the following operations could be used with either stainless steel or the precious metals: blank and cup; first trim; pierce 0.201-in. hole; trim to length; shear clip-locking lug.

Only 5000 caps of this style were ordered at a time; therefore, the production schedule depended on the operation of the precious-metal line, which had individual machines producing 500 pieces per hour. If 200,000 or more pieces had been produced per year, tooling for automatic transfer equipment would have been economical, and production would have been about 1500 pieces per hour.

Estimates of the drawing forces necessary to form an austenitic stainless steel, a ferritic stainless steel and low-carbon steel are compared in Table 8. These drawing forces, in tons, are based on the formula $S\pi Dt$, where S is the tensile strength of the metal in tons per square inch; D is the blank diameter, in inches; and t is the metal thickness, in inches.

Blankholding pressures for the austenitic alloys must be much higher than for the ferritic types or low-carbon steels. For austenitic alloys, the pressure (P) on the metal under the blankholder is about 1000 psi, and for the ferritic alloys, 200 to 500 psi. Thinner material and larger flange areas generally require greater pressure.

Drawing Hemispherical Parts. The drawing of hemispherical, or dome-shape, parts demands special attention to blankholder pressure to prevent wrinkling, because so much of the metal surface is not in contact with any die surface for most of the draw. Only the very tip of the punch is in contact with the work at the start of the stroke, and the surface between that tip and the blankholder draws or stretches free until the punch descends far enough to contact it.

Sometimes an undersize punch can be used to draw or stretch the blank into a preform before the dome-shape punch makes the final draw, as in the following example.

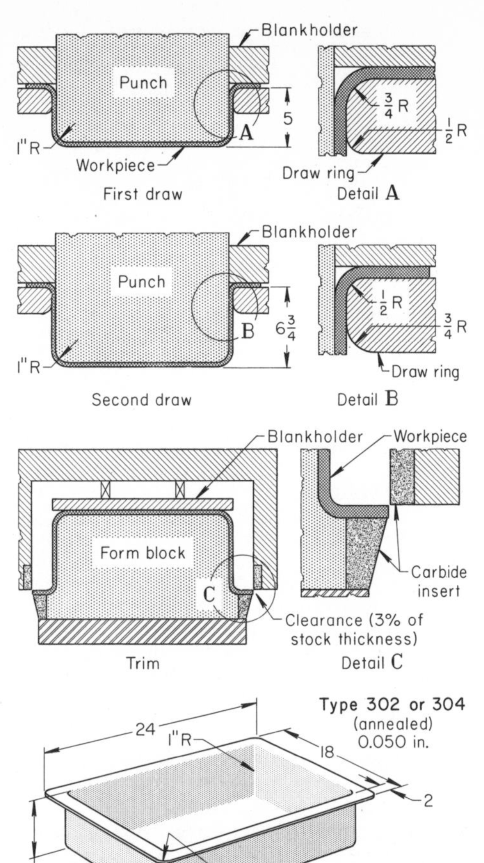

Fig. 24. Production of a flat-flanged sink basin by drawing and redrawing (using a two-radius, reversible draw ring) and trimming (Example 475)

Example 474. Two-Stage Drawing of a Stepped-Diameter Hemisphere (Fig. 23)

One of the critical points in the production of the vacuum-bottle top shown in Fig. 23 was the forming of the shoulder at the large end of the dome-shape top. The stepped inside diameter of this shoulder had to be an exact fit with the body of the vacuum-bottle jacket. The pierced hole at the small end also had to be accurately formed, to conform to the mouth of the inner container.

The stock was 11.375-in.-wide annealed type 304 stainless steel strip, 0.042 in. thick. A single-action mechanical press with a spring-loaded pressure pad was used to cut 11⅛-in.-diam blanks from the strip, leaving ⅛-in. minimum scrap on each side of the strip.

The first draw was made in a 250-ton double-action mechanical press. The punch was 3¼ in. in diameter; therefore, much of the surface of the dome was drawn free (see Fig. 23, operation 2). This required careful control of the blankholder pressure to prevent puckers and wrinkles. Blankholder pressure had to be adjusted for every lot of steel; it varied from 800 to 1000 psi. The die radius also had to be held closely (5.2 times the stock thickness). The first draw produced a cup 6⅞ in. in diameter with a 9¼-in.-diam flange.

The second draw also was made in the 250-ton double-action press. The punch for the second draw was shaped to the required inner contour of the part, including the step at the base of the dome, which was formed as the press bottomed at the end of the second draw stroke (see Fig. 23, operation 3). This operation formed the dome shape of the bottle top by reshaping, mostly by stretching, the cup formed in the first draw. The metal for the cylindrical area above the step was drawn from the flange metal remaining after the first draw.

In the fourth operation, the hole in the top of the dome was pierced, and an internal stretch flange was formed around the hole. This was done with a spring-loaded piercing die, which gave sufficient resistance to let the piercing punch shear the material, and then retreated under pressure from the flange-forming part of the punch. Both ends of the part were later trimmed in a lathe.

Drawing Rectangular Parts. During the deep drawing of a box-shape part, the metal in the corners of the part and in the flange around the corner undergoes a change much like that which takes place when a round shell is drawn from a circular blank. Metal is compressed at the corners, and significant thickening occurs where the metal flows into the corners. The sides of the box undergo essentially no thickening, because there is no compression of the metal in the flange areas as it flows or bends over the die radius.

Clearances in the sides between the punch and die ordinarily are about 10% greater than the metal thickness, to compensate for gage variations and to allow for metal flow. At the corners, punch-to-die clearances are similar to those used for cylindrical parts, to allow for thickening.

Blankholding devices are almost always used in producing deeply recessed box-shape parts, to control the metal movement — particularly in the corners. The corners are under severe strain because of the intense compression of the flange metal, and most fracturing, if it does occur, takes place in the lower wall corner sections.

Punch and die radii are generally the same for rectangular draws as for circular draws. Some fabricators prefer to make the punch and die radii at the corners larger than along the sides, in order to equalize the stress in the metal at the corners. The top surface of the draw die and the draw radii should be polished smooth, free of grind marks and well blended, to prevent localized retardation of metal flow with consequent uneven drawing of the metal. Burrs and bent edges on the blank often restrict metal flow or movement along the blankholder surface to such a degree that vertical wall fractures can occur.

Semideveloped blanks usually produce better results than rectangular ones. There are a number of patterns for trimming the corners, ranging from a simple 45° trim to patterns with a carefully developed area containing the optimum volume and area of metal.

The economic success of the run is related to tool wear as well as to scrap rate. The following example describes a combination of tool materials that has given satisfactory performance in terms of parts or draws per regrind and redress. The same tooling can be used for both drawing operations, with the draw ring reversed to present a different radius for the second draw, as in the following example.

Example 475. Use of a Reversible, Two-Radius Draw Ring for Drawing and Redrawing of a Flanged Rectangular Shell (Fig. 24)

The flat-flanged, single-sump kitchen sink shown in Fig. 24 was formed in four operations: blank, draw, redraw and trim. Forming the part was a combined draw-and-stretch operation. Because several different models, with drain holes in various locations, were made from the same drawn part, the drain hole was not pierced in the trimming operation, but was made separately. Production was 50,000 to 100,000 pieces per year.

The material was annealed type 302 or 304 stainless steel coil stock, 29 in. wide and 0.050 in. thick, with a No. 2D sheet finish. Blanks 25 in. long were sheared from the coil at the rate of 40 per minute in a single-action mechanical press. Corners of the blanks were trimmed at 45°, removing 2 in. from each edge of the blank at each corner. Clearance for this trimming was kept at less than 5% of metal thickness, in order to minimize edge distortion and burrs.

The draws were made in a 400-ton double-action mechanical press with 250 tons available for blank holding. The draw punch was made of alloy tool steel, and the blankholder was made of alloy cast iron. The reversible draw ring (see Fig. 24) was made of hard aluminum bronze and had a ¾-in. draw radius on one side for the first draw, and a ½-in. draw radius on the other side for the redraw. The workpiece was annealed in an inert atmosphere at 1950 F between the first and second draws, and air cooled rapidly to room temperature.

Depth of the sink after the first draw was 5 in.; after the second draw it was 6¾ in. Draws were made at a punch speed of approximately 21 ft per minute, with less than 2% of the workpieces fracturing.

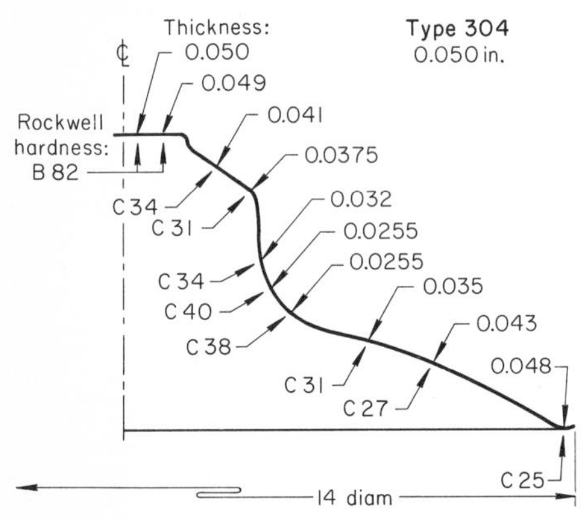

Fig. 25. Profile of shape, hardness and thickness of a manually spun part that often fractured in its thinnest section

A similar 400-ton press was used to trim the piece. Carbide inserts provided shearing edges for the trimming operation. The sink was held on a form block of molded plastic or cast iron for trimming.

The second draw operation sharpened the bottom and flange corner radii, and stretched the bottom surface and the side walls to remove any loose metal. Little or no metal was drawn into the part from the flange during the second draw.

Spinning

Stainless steel parts such as cups, cones and dished heads can be readily formed by manual or power spinning, although more power is required than for spinning of low-carbon steel. (Equipment and techniques for these processes are described in the article "Spinning", which begins on page 201 in this volume.)

Manual Spinning. The amount of thinning that occurs during manual spinning is related to the severity of the formed shape. A cross section of a manually spun piece that thinned out to such a degree that it often fractured is shown in Fig. 25. This piece was excessively worked, and the midcenter area was work hardened beyond the capacity of the material, causing the workpiece to fracture. The piece was later made by press drawing the dome-shape cup and spinning the broad flared flange.

The approximate limits of stretch in manual spinning are given in Table 9. These are for 0.062-in.-thick fully annealed stock. The second stretch after annealing is about 8% less than the first. The amount of stretch is not necessarily uniform over the entire part; it varies with the severity of the form.

All series 300 stainless steels can be formed by spinning, but the low-work-hardening types 302, 304 and 305 can be spun to greater reductions than other stainless steels before intermediate annealing becomes necessary. All anneals must be followed by pickling to remove oxides, thus restoring the clean, smooth surface. The No. 1 strip or 2D sheet finish is best for severe applications, because the metal is in the softest, stress-free condition and will take the greatest amount of working.

The following example demonstrates the spinnability of type 305 stainless.

Table 9. Approximate Limits of Stretch in Manual Spinning of Stainless Steels 0.062 In. Thick

Type	Stretch (max), %	Type	Stretch (max), %	Type	Stretch (max), %
305	45	321	35	202	25
302	40	309	30	301	25
304	40	310	30	405	25
302B	35	317	30	446	25
316	35	430	30	403	20
316L	35	201	25	410	20

These limits are for stretching during one spinning pass; after being annealed, the metal can be respun to 8% less than the first stretch.

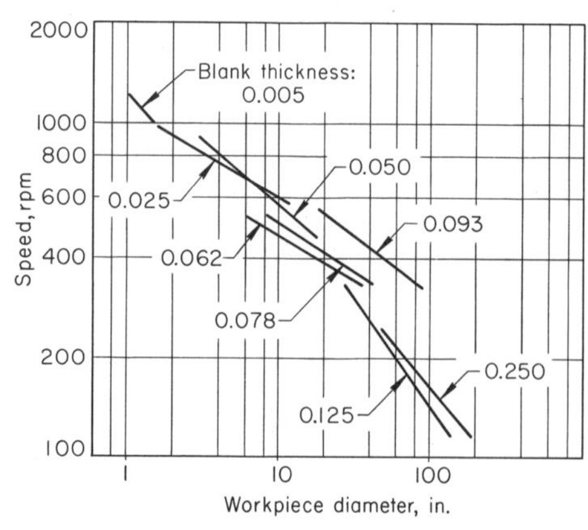

Fig. 27. Effect of workpiece diameter and blank thickness on rotational speed for manual spinning of austenitic stainless steel

Example 476. Four-Pass Manual Spinning of a Cone From Type 305 Stainless Steel (Fig. 26)

The 14-in.-diam cone shown in Fig. 26 was produced in eight operations, including four manual spinning passes, from a 16-in.-diam blank of 0.037-in.-thick annealed type 305 stainless steel that had a No. 2D sheet finish or a No. 1 strip finish. Other types of austenitic stainless steel could have been used, but the reduction per pass would have been lower, in proportion to the increase in rate of work hardening.

As shown in Fig. 26, the mandrels for spinning were made of wood or steel. The spinning roller was made of hardened steel. Pressure was applied to the entire blank in the first spinning pass. In the three other passes, the outer inch of the blank was not spun. This caused the edge to thicken to 0.070 in. and helped hold the outer shape. Thinning was greatest at the middle of the cone, to about 0.027-in. wall thickness (28% reduction). The surface area of the piece was increased 40%. The drastic working that accompanied the thinning and the increase in area made two anneals necessary (see sequence of operations with Fig. 26). Annual production quantity was 500 pieces.

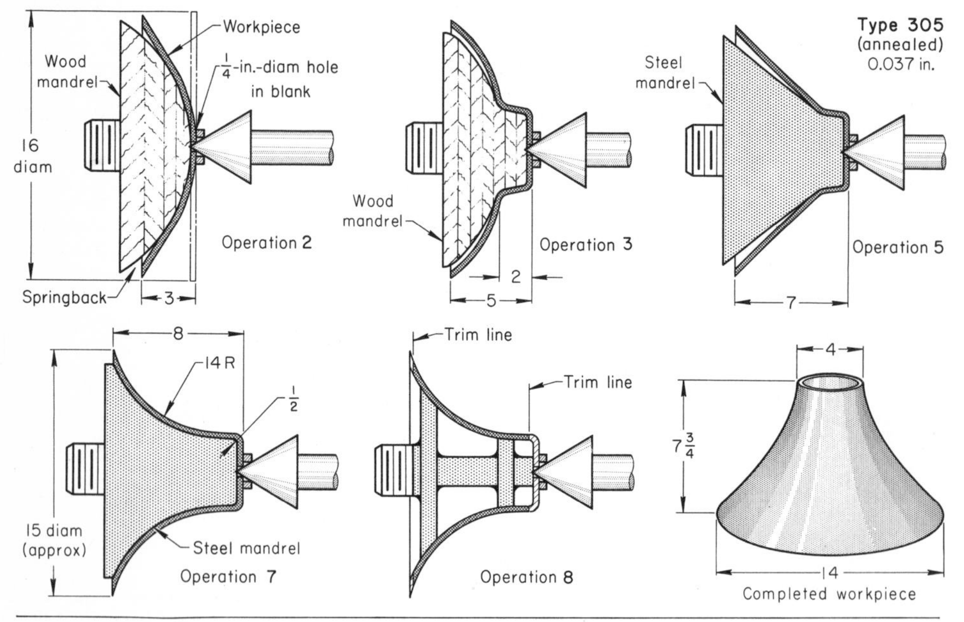

Sequence of Operations

1 Drill a ¼-in.-diam center hole in a 16-in.-diam blank, 0.037 in. thick.
2 Spin to 3-in. depth on a laminated hardwood mandrel at 300 rpm, applying manual pressure on lever and roller.
3 Spin to 5-in. depth on a second laminated hardwood mandrel, to within 1 in. of edge.
4 Anneal in hydrogen atmosphere at 1900 F; air cool.
5 Spin to 7-in. depth on a steel mandrel, to within 1 in. of edge.
6 Anneal as in operation 4.
7 Spin to 8-in. depth and final shape on a steel mandrel.
8 Lathe-trim top and bottom ends to 7¾-in. final height of cone.

Fig. 26. Production of a stainless steel cone by four-pass manual spinning (Example 476)

The series 400 stainless steels, because of their relatively low ductility, do not adapt themselves readily to manual spinning, especially when the deformation is severe. The high pressure of the forming tool causes wear of the work metal, resulting in early thinning and fracturing.

The surface of severely spun parts is often very rough because of the action of the tools on the metal, and the production of a buffed or highly polished finish on a part spun from a series 400 stainless steel can be expensive. It is generally necessary to rough grind the material to smooth out the irregularities before polishing and buffing.

Manual spinning is usually done at relatively low speeds (see Fig. 27). Because of this, the action of the forming tool causes extensive wear of the metal being formed, and significant work hardening occurs.

The usual stock thicknesses of stainless steel for manual spinning are 0.012 to 0.125 in., although stainless steels as thin as 0.005 in. and as thick as 0.250 in. have been spun by hand. The corner radius should be at least five times the thickness of the work metal. Allowance must be made in the size and shape of mandrels for springback and for heat-induced dimensional changes.

Power spinning is used for severe reductions, and for work that cannot be done by hand. Stainless steels in both the 300 and 400 series are readily formed by power spinning, but the low-work-hardening types 302 and 305 are superior. Much larger reductions of type 430 can be made by power spinning than by manual spinning.

Spinning can be done hot or cold, although the severe reduction accompanying power spinning may cause so much heat that the spinning that began cold becomes warm spinning.

Hot spinning, done only above 1450 F, is commonly used for work 3⁄16 to ½ in. thick. The need for careful control of the temperature makes it difficult to hot spin metal that is less than ¼ in. thick. Thicker stainless steel can be hot spun as easily as low-carbon steel.

Cracking at the edge is the major problem in power spinning the austenitic stainless steels. The edge of the blank may need to be ground smooth to prevent cracking. A generous trim allowance is helpful, so that the cracked edge can be cut off. Cracking and distortion can be prevented by keeping a narrow flange on the work.

If the size of the spun piece is not correct after it cools (because of springback and heat expansion), the piece can be annealed and spun to size while it is still above 300 F.

Considerable thinning can be produced by power spinning, as indicated by the cross section of a deeply spun vessel shown in Fig. 28. The thickness of the vessel was reduced from 0.075 in. to 0.026 in. in one spinning operation. A preformed cup 6 in. in diameter and 3 in. deep, drawn on a conventional press, was used as the starting shape. Note that the top of the vessel is much thicker than the wall. Thickening of the rim occurred during drawing, and because there was essentially no deformation in this region during spinning, it remained thick.

The surface on power-spun pieces is rough and requires extensive finishing to make it smooth and bright. The spun surface is rough because the roller usually imparts a spiral or helical groove to the surface as the roller is fed into the metal while it rotates. Except for this disadvantage, power spinning is an excellent way of forming pieces from stainless steel.

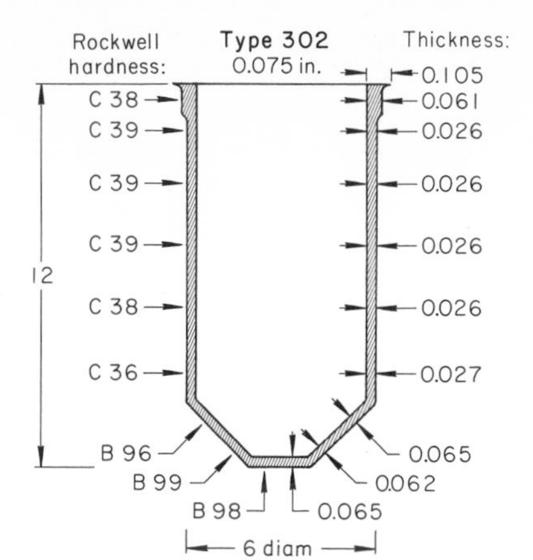

Fig. 28. Variations in hardness and thickness of a shell that was power spun from a preform drawn from stainless steel 0.075 in. thick

Table 10. Operations and Costs for Producing a Bowl by Power Spinning (Example 477)

Operation	Production, pcs/hr	Labor per 100 pcs, hr	Tool cost
Shear blank(a) ..	1125	0.089	...
Spin(b)	90	1.111	$ 600
Trim flange(c) ..	90(d)	(d)	975
Stamp name(c) ..	90(d)	(d)	90
Total		1.200	$1665

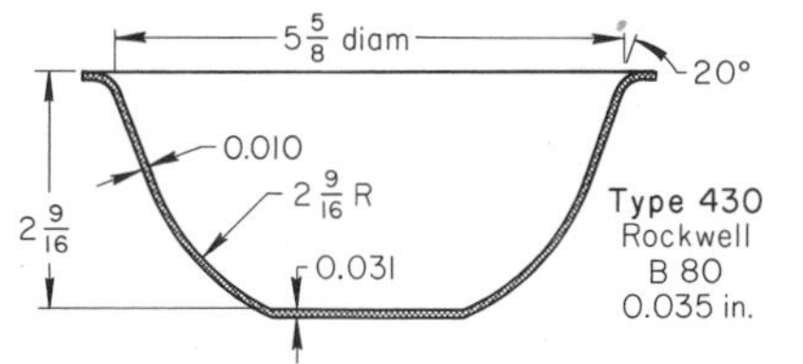

(a) To length of 8⅝ in. from 8⅝-in.-wide coil stock. (b) Power spinning in an automatic machine. (c) In a 60-ton press. (d) Trimming and stamping were done on a spun bowl during automatic spinning of another bowl.

Lubricants (see Table 3) are used to reduce friction and minimize galling and tool drag, as well as to provide cooling. For manual spinning, firmly adherent lubricants are preferred; for power spinning, coolant action is more important. Lubricants containing sulfur or chlorine are usually avoided; they are difficult to remove completely and have harmful effects on heated stainless surfaces.

Applications for which power spinning was preferable to deep drawing are described in the next two examples.

Example 477. Power Spinning a Bowl (Table 10)

The small mixing bowl illustrated in Table 10 was made in an automatic power spinning machine. The blank, 8⅝ in. square, was sheared from 0.035-in.-thick type 430 stainless steel coil stock with a No. 2B finish. Two press operations, trim and stamp name, were done on a spun bowl while another bowl was being spun. Table 10 lists production rates, labor time, and tool costs for the four operations in the production of these bowls.

The spinning could be done from a flat blank in one operation because the side of the bowl made an angle of 20° with the spin axis. If the angle had been 15° or smaller, however, a second spinning pass would have been required. (See "Mechanics of Cone Spinning", page 203 in the article on Spinning.)

The bowl could have been produced by deep drawing, but spinning was selected because the annual production quantity (25,000 to 30,000 pieces) was too low to warrant the cost of a blanking die and drawing tools.

The tools were made of D2 tool steel. The blanks were coated with a wax before spinning.

Example 478. Reduction in Cost by Change From Deep Drawing to Power Spinning (Table 11)

A cocktail-shaker cup (illustrated in Table 11), formerly made by five deep drawing operations and one restrike, was made at lower cost, by power spinning a drawn and restruck preform. Table 11 lists production and cost data for the two methods.

The spun cup, in addition to being stronger (because of the severe cold working in spinning), required fewer draw-press operations and did not require annealing.

The cup was made of type 302 stainless steel, drawing quality, with a No. 2B finish, but the thickness and width of the coil stock differed for the two methods. The drawn cup was made from stock 0.025 in. thick and 10 1⁄16 in. wide; the diameter of the blank was 9 15⁄16 in. The stock for the spun cup was 0.062 in. thick by 6 5⁄16 in. wide; blank diameter was 6 1⁄16 in.

The spun cup had to be made from a drawn preform because the wall of the cup was nearly parallel with the axis. Had the wall been at a greater angle (included angle of more than 15°), the cup could have been spun in one pass from a flat blank.

The tool material was D2 tool steel hardened to Rockwell C 58 to 60. Die life was 500,000 pieces. A wax coating was used on the blank for spinning, a wax emulsion on the drawn blank.

Table 11. Deep Drawing vs Power Spinning (Example 478) (a)

Operation	Production, pcs/hr	Labor per 100 pcs, hr	Tool cost
Deep Drawing			
Blank to 9 15⁄16 ID(b) ..	1000	0.100	$ 850
Cup to 6 ID(c)	250	0.400	600
Redraw to 4.718 ID(d)	120	0.833	575
Redraw to 3.562 ID(d)	120	0.833	575
Redraw to 3.062 ID(e)	400	0.250	450
Redraw to 2.500 ID(e)	400	0.250	450
Wash	2000	0.050	...
Anneal	...	4.500	...
Restrike(d)	180	0.553	1075
Shimmy trim(e)	375	0.265	400
Polish and buff	38	2.600	275
Total		10.634	$5250
Power Spinning			
Blank and draw(f) ...	1500	0.067	$1050
Restrike(d)	250	0.400	600
Spin; shimmy trim(g)	75	1.333	525
Wash	2000	0.050	400
Polish and buff	50	1.980	275
Total		3.830	$2850

Item	Deep drawing	Power spinning
Labor and Material Costs per Piece		
Labor, at $5 per hr ..	$0.5317	$0.1915
Material	0.4023(h)	0.3607(j)
Total	$0.9340	$0.5522
Savings per piece		$0.3818

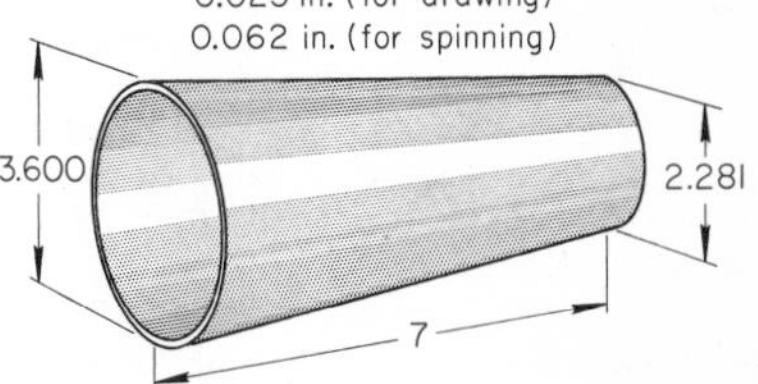

(a) Data are based on production of the part illustrated above, a cocktail-shaker cup, in annual quantities of 100,000 pieces. (b) From 0.025-by-10 1⁄16-in. coil stock, in a 150-ton press. (c) In a 150-ton double-action press. (d) In a 150-ton hydraulic press. (e) In a 95-ton OBI (open-back inclinable) press. (f) In a 150-ton press. Blank, 6 1⁄16 in. in diameter, was made from 0.062-by-6 5⁄16-in. coil. stock. (g) Power spinning was done in a 15-in. machine; trimming, in a 150-ton press by power spinning operator (h) 0.745 lb per piece, at $0.54 per pound. (j) 0.715 lb per piece, at $0.5045 per pound.

The power spinning and shimmy trimming operations were done by the same operator, since there was time between loading and unloading the power spinner.

Rubber-Pad Forming

Annealed austenitic stainless steels, types 301, 302, 304, 305, 321 and 347, are rubber-pad formed in thicknesses up to 0.050 in. Most of the operations are straight flanging — especially in thicker workpieces. With auxiliary devices, like wedges or rollers, pieces up to 0.078 in. thick can be formed. Flanges must be wide enough to develop adequate forming force from the unit pressure on their surface. For annealed stainless steels, the following minimum flange widths beyond the bend radius are recommended for successful forming:

Thickness, in.	Flange width, in.	Thickness, in.	Flange width, in.
0.016	0.250	0.040	0.360
0.020	0.270	0.051	0.410
0.025	0.290	0.064	0.480
0.032	0.330	0.072	0.510

In quarter-hard temper, types 301 and 302 up to 0.032 in. thick can be flanged provided the flange is at least ⅝ in. wide.

Rubber-pad forming of contoured flanges in stainless steel requires more powerful equipment than that used for flat flanges. Most forming of contoured flanges is done on annealed stainless steel, but a limited amount is done on quarter-hard stock.

Stretch flanges are readily formed on annealed stainless steel up to 0.050 in. thick. Rubber-pad-formed stretch flanges of thin metal are generally smoother and more accurately formed than those formed by single-action dies. Die-formed flanges often curl outward, requiring considerable hand work for correction.

Hydraulic presses used in the Guerin process develop up to 5000 psi forming pressure. Narrow stretch flanges that require pressures greater than 5000 psi are formed with the aid of auxiliary devices, such as traps and wedge blocks, that raise the forming pressure locally (see the article "Rubber-Pad Forming" on page 209 in this volume).

Thin metal can be formed by means of a simple form block, but if the web is narrow, the workpiece should be protected by a cover plate to avoid distortion. The following example demonstrates the limits of rubber-pad forming of stretch flanges in stainless steel: (*a*) the stock was quarter-hard type 302; (*b*) the workpiece had a narrow web, and therefore required the use of a cover plate in forming; (*c*) the workpiece had external hole flanges; (*d*) the stretch flange was only 5⁄16 in. wide; and (*e*) the curved workpiece was nearly 38 in. long. (If a stainless steel part of this shape is more than 24 in. long, it is almost impossible to prevent the springback of the flange material from bowing the part unless curved dies are used.)

Example 479. Use of a Curved Die With Cover Plates in Rubber-Pad Forming (Fig. 29)

The strut shown in Fig. 29 had a 5⁄16-in.-wide stretch flange and external 65° flanges on two lightening holes at the large end. It was rubber-pad formed from a quarter-hard type 302 stainless steel blank 0.016 in. thick.

The zinc alloy die used was made with a curve to offset the springback of the flange (see Fig. 29). Right-hand and left-hand pieces were flanged at the same time in the same die. A steel cover plate protected the thin web of each piece from distortion during forming. No lubricant was used. Pressure developed by the rubber was 1500 psi.

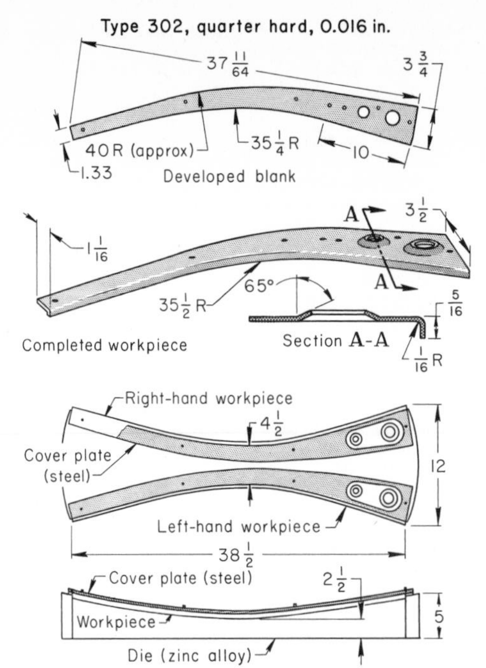

Fig. 29. Long narrow strut with a contoured stretch flange that was made by rubber-pad forming in a curved die with cover plates, to prevent springback (Example 479)

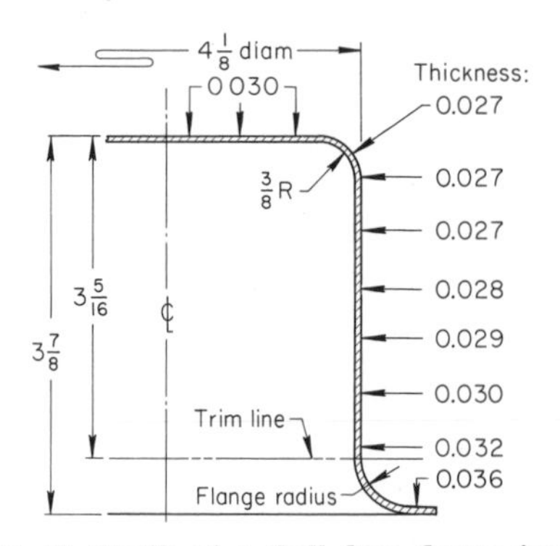

Fig. 30. Profile of a shell deep drawn from 0.030-in.-thick stainless steel by the rubber-pad method, showing relatively uniform wall thickness obtained

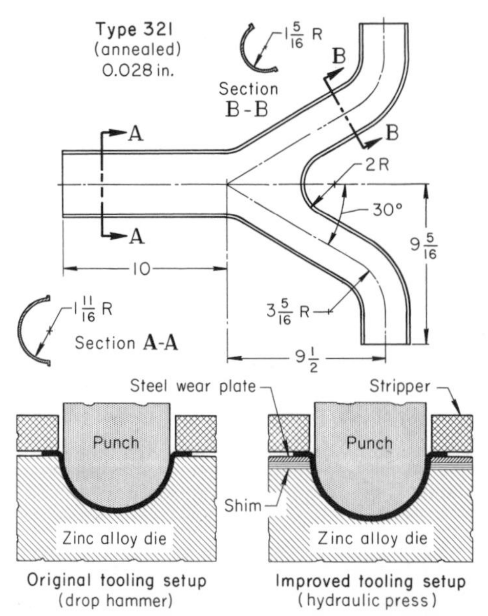

Fig. 31. Aircraft tailpipe half that was formed by the drop hammer and hydraulic press tooling setups shown (Example 480)

Deep Drawing. By the rubber-pad and rubber-diaphragm processes, stainless steels in both the 300 and the 400 series can be deep drawn to greater reductions than can be achieved with conventional methods. For extremely deep sections, the lower-work-hardening austenitic types 302 and 305 are recommended.

Two characteristics of rubber-pad methods make this great depth of draw possible: controlled, continuously adjustable pressure on the blankholder or hold-down mechanism; and continuously variable "draw-ring" radius. There is no draw ring as such, but the rubber that forms around the workpiece functions as a draw ring and conforms to the radius that will apply equal pressure to the entire surface of the workpiece. This minimizes both thinning at the punch radius and work hardening as the flange metal is drawn into the cup.

Figure 30 illustrates the relatively uniform wall thickness that can be produced by drawing using the rubber-pad method. (Compare with Fig. 21, which shows the much greater variation in wall thickness produced by conventional deep drawing.)

For more information on deep drawing by rubber-pad techniques, see the article "Rubber-Pad Forming", which begins on page 209 in this volume. Note especially the sections "Marform Process" and "Rubber-Diaphragm Forming" in that article.

Drop Hammer Forming

A wide variety of sizes and shapes can be formed in thin stainless steel by drop hammer forming. Advantages of this method include high impact energy (which often means that a piece can be formed by one blow, in contrast to four or five by other processes) and suitability to low-volume and experimental production.

Dies. Die material for drop hammer forming is less critical than for press forming. The dies are made of steel, plastic, zinc alloy and lead. Zinc alloy is widely used.

Punches are often made of lead, because it can be cast directly on the lower die, and because its weight adds energy to the stroke of the drop hammer. Although the lead is reusable, the number of pieces that can be made from each cast punch is small — about 200. Plastic punches and dies impart a finish to formed parts that would be difficult to attain otherwise. Steel dies are used for high production and for coining and sizing (see the article "Coining", page 78 in this volume).

Die designs are generally similar to those for press forming, with the same punch and die radii to reduce stress on the work metal. Die design for forming of beads and methods of relieving entrapment to insure good metal flow in

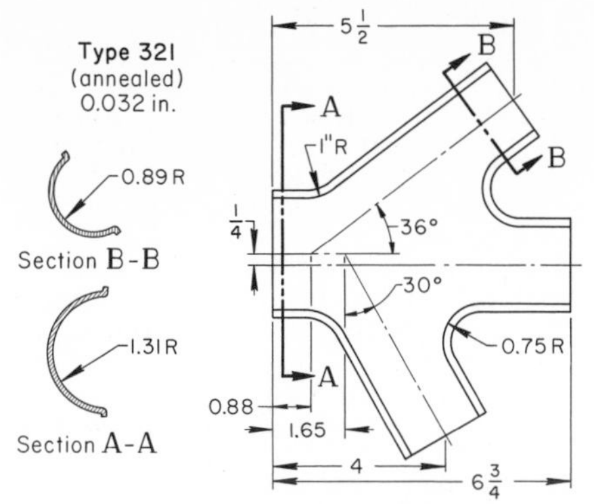

Fig. 32. Exhaust collector half that was formed in a drop hammer (Example 481)

drop hammer forming are also similar to those used in press forming.

A trapped-rubber technique somewhat similar to the Guerin process is described in the article "Rubber-Pad Forming" in this volume.

Quality of Product. Dimensions of workpieces formed in a drop hammer are less consistent than those made by other processes, because the degree of impact is subject to operator skill, and because the punch can shift under localized high loads. However, springback is less pronounced in drop hammer forming than in other forming methods, because of the high impact and forming speed.

Lubrication. The lubricants that can be used in drop hammer forming are listed in Table 3. If working is severe enough to require annealing between stages, contaminants like graphite or sulfur, from the lubricant, or zinc or lead, from the die, must be removed from the work surface. If these contaminants are left on the surface of the stainless steel when it is heated, they can cause serious surface deterioration.

Comparison With Press Forming. Press forming, although done rapidly, is inherently an operation in which ram speed and holding pressures can be closely controlled — in contrast to drop hammer forming, where the only way to form a part is by sudden impact. In some applications, production difficulties are overcome by the high rate of energy release in a drop hammer. In others, especially those where blankholder pressure is critical, press forming produces better parts more economically if the die is properly made, as in the following example.

Example 480. Change From Drop Hammer to Press Forming That Eliminated Wrinkling and Reduced Cost (Fig. 31)

The tailpipe half shown at the top in Fig. 31 was originally produced in a drop hammer, using the tooling setup shown at the lower left in Fig. 31. The operation was unsatisfactory, however, because wrinkles occurred at the intersection of the 30° risers, and six operations totaling nearly 2 min per piece were required to complete each piece.

The tools were redesigned for use in a 500-ton hydraulic press (see lower right view in Fig. 31). The zinc alloy die used in the drop hammer was reused in the press, but to withstand the abrasion of press forming with stainless steel, the die was faced off and a low-carbon steel wear plate was installed. The 1¹¹⁄₁₆-in. radius had formed well in the drop hammer, with very little springback; but springback in the press made it necessary to deepen the die. This was done by inserting shims between the die and the wear plate.

The press produced pieces that were completely free of wrinkles, at the rate of two pieces per minute. This was a 1½-min saving per piece, which, computed at average shop rates, meant a saving of 15¢ per piece.

The blank for both methods was annealed type 321 stainless steel, 20 by 24 in. and 0.028 in. thick. No lubricant was required for drop hammer forming; a wax emulsion was used for the press operation. Trimming after forming was done in a second press.

Ordinarily, a drop hammer is used for prototypes, and a press, using the prototype or improved dies, is used for mass production. If the quality of the prototype die is good, the drop hammer can be used for low production, as in the following example.

Example 481. Forming an Aircraft Exhaust Component in a Drop Hammer (Fig. 32)

Figure 32 shows a collector half used in the engine exhaust system of a small aircraft. This part is typical of the low-production work made in a drop hammer. It was produced to tolerances of ±0.032 in. on all dimensions, and ±2° on angles, from 0.032-in.-thick annealed type 321 stainless steel.

The drop hammer had a 30-by-24-in. bed and a 34-in. stroke. A lead punch was used with a die of zinc alloy. The blank was 12 by 9 in. Setup took 1.15 hr, which included the time to clear the drop hammer of a previous setup. It took five blows of the hammer to form the part. Rubber was used as a blankholder to distribute the pressure on the work. (The finished part did not need a smooth blankholder flange.) The thickness of rubber was reduced following each of the first four strokes, allowing the die to bottom in the last stroke. Then the parts were trimmed in a punch press.

It took 1.75 hr to form 100 pieces with the drop hammer (one man working). The zinc die had a life of 5000 pieces before major maintenance was needed, and the lead punch was replaced after 200 pieces. Heavy oil (600W) or a proprietary drawing compound was brushed onto the form curves of the die.

The zinc alloy die had been intended for experimental parts, but the die was not replaced for production forming, because demand was less than 150 parts per month and the results obtained were excellent.

Three-Roll Forming

Three-roll forming of stainless steel is, in general, similar to three-roll forming of other metals (see the article "Three-Roll Forming" on page 217 in this volume). Springback is a major problem with austenitic stainless steels, mainly because of the large radii involved and work hardening. It is important that the equipment be set up so that the desired curvature can be made in one pass. Because of the high rate of work hardening of austenitic stainless steels, subsequent passes are sometimes difficult to accomplish and control, unless heavy equipment is used.

The response of annealed ferritic stainless steel to three-roll forming is quite similar to that of hot rolled low-carbon steel.

Three-roll and two-roll formers can be put in sequence with contour roll formers to make a cross-sectional shape and bend or coil it, all in one production line.

The following example describes an application in which three-roll forming was combined with press forming and hydraulic expansion forming.

Example 482. Use of Three-Roll Forming in Production of a Container for Liquid (Fig. 33)

Figure 33 shows eight of the 14 operations entailed in the production of a container for liquids by press forming and hydraulic expansion forming of a welded cylinder made from a radiused flat blank by three-roll forming in pyramid-type rolls. The six other operations are identified in the table that accompanies Fig. 33. These containers were produced in annual quantities of 10,000 to 100,000 pieces, from annealed type 304 stainless steel coil stock 0.031 in. thick and 23.0625 in. wide.

Blanking the rectangular sheets for three-roll forming gave the workpiece the uniform square edges needed for maintaining the welded seam of the tube in axial alignment. The blanking tools were hardened high-car-

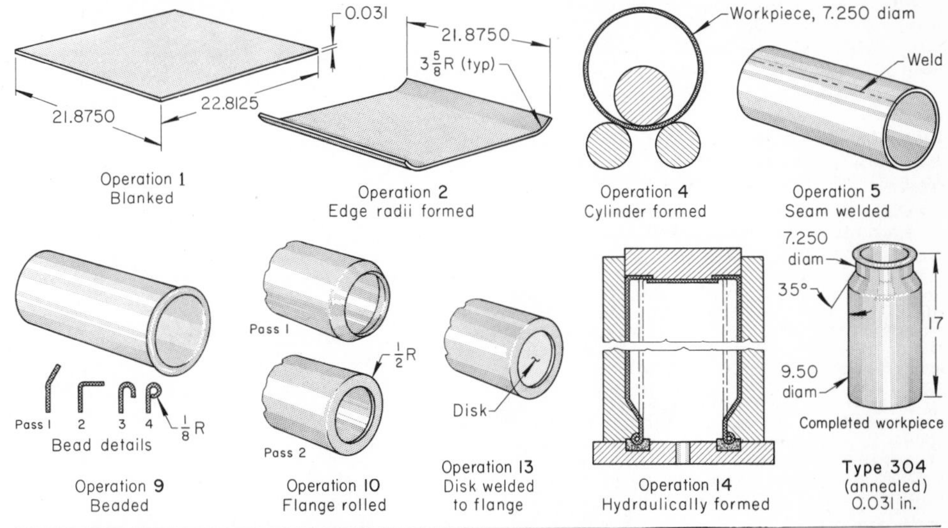

Sequence of Operations

1 Blank in die, in single-action press.
2 Form edge radii on blank, in a press brake.
3 Vapor degrease, to remove lubricant used in operations 1 and 2.
4 Roll cylinder, in three-roll former.
5 Weld cylinder seam, in automatic Heliarc setup using starting and stop-off tabs.
6 Trim tabs.
7 Hammer weld to induce compressive stress, using an air hammer at 45 psi.
8 Restore roundness of cylinder by rerolling several times in three-roll former.
9 Form bead on one end of cylinder, in four passes in an edger.
10 Roll flange on opposite end of cylinder, in two passes.
11 Trim flange.
12 Vapor degrease.
13 Weld (Heliarc) disk to inside of flange.
14 Expand and form to final shape (30% reduction in wall thickness), in a hydraulic expansion die (final pressure, 700 psi).

Fig. 33. Use of three-roll forming in conjunction with press forming and hydraulic expansion forming, in the 14-operation production of a container for liquids (Example 482)

bon high-chromium tool steel; clearance was 0.003 in. per side. The stock was lubricated for blanking and edge radiusing, but the blanks were vapor degreased before three-roll forming.

Contour Roll Forming

Stainless steel ordinarily is contour roll formed in the annealed condition. Types 410 and 430 are usually roll formed on equipment similar to that used for carbon steel, with No. 2 finish generally specified. Speeds are generally in the range of 25 to 100 ft per minute, the heavier gages and more difficult sections being roll formed at the slower speeds.

Stainless steels in hard tempers, such as quarter-hard and half-hard type 301, also are frequently roll formed. Increased power over that used for forming the same steels in the annealed condition is necessary, because of the higher initial strength of the strip. Springback must be compensated for by adequate overbending. Longitudinal cracking can be a problem with the hard tempers if adequate radii are not included in the design of the part.

Distortion or warpage of straight sections causes the greatest problem in roll forming the series 300 steels, particularly when the steel is thick. The distortion can be minimized by using more sets of rolls, or more passes, for greater control during each stage of bending. However, the skill of the operator is all-important in controlling distortion. Various straightening devices are usually attached or used on the last pass as the section emerges from the machine. In some applications, sections are deliberately curved.

With the chromium-nickel stainless steels, pickup on the rolls and galling of the strip sometimes occur. Highly polished rolls or bronze rolls are used with lubrication to minimize this problem when high pressure is needed. Heavy-duty emulsions containing chlorine offer the best combination of chemical EP and coolant activity (Table 3). Chlorinated oils or waxes are easy to use, but less effective as coolants. For severe forming, the cushioning effect of pigments is sometimes needed (as in the next example) as well as efficient cooling.

Example 483. Nine-Station Contour Roll Forming of Annealed 304 Stainless Steel (Fig. 34)

Figure 34 shows the sectional shapes progressively produced in nine-station roll forming of a sheave track from annealed type 304 stainless steel strip, 2.648 in. wide by 0.031 in. thick, with a No. 2 finish. In a tenth station, the formed track was straightened. As the track left the tenth station, it was clamped to a moving table that conveyed it to an abrasive wheel for cutoff into lengths of 10 to 20 ft. The material weighed 0.278 lb per ft; annual production was 400,000 lb.

During forming, the developed width of the section measured along the neutral axis increased only 0.040 in. (to 2.688 in.) — corresponding to only 1.5% stretch. The stretch was limited because the metal was restrained by the six pinch beads that were rolled into the strip before it was bent (see stations 1, 2 and 3 in Fig. 34). Each bead, 1/16 in. wide by 0.030 in. deep, permitted a sharp bend at that point without tearing or breaking the steel. (The 50 to 55% elongation property of austenitic 304 stainless steel made it unlikely that the metal would break in bending.) The strip was rolled with the slitting burr down, so that the burr was flattened by the shoulders of the bottom roll of station 2.

The forming rolls were made of hardened steel, and the straightening rolls of hard bronze, for a good finish. Rolling speed was 55 ft per minute. The lubricant was a pigmented water-soluble oil.

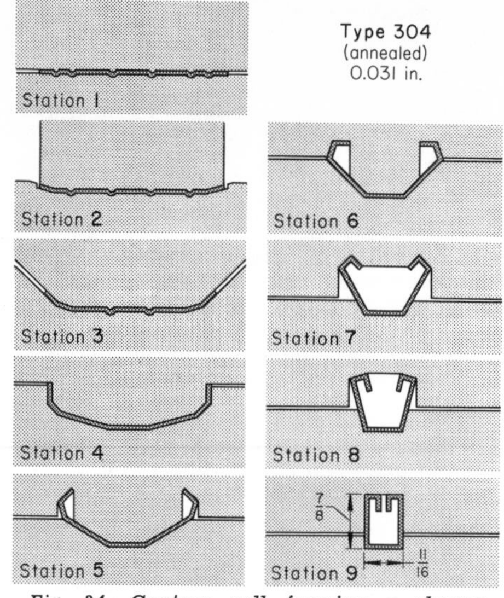

Fig. 34. Contour roll forming a sheave track in nine stations (Example 483)

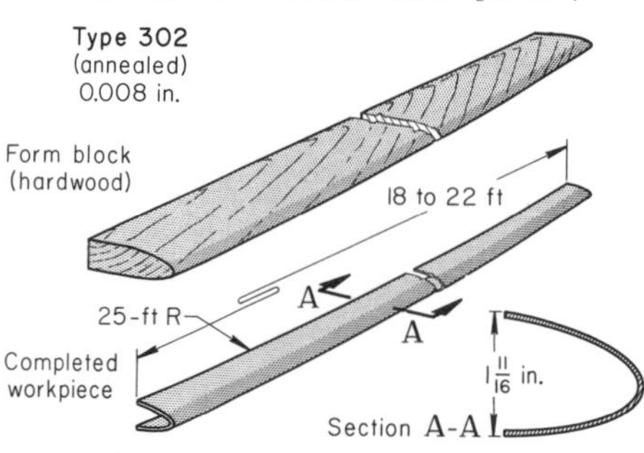

Fig. 35. Airfoil on which the leading edge was stretch formed to a long convex shape without lubricant in a radial-draw former (Example 484)

Plastic protective coatings are sometimes applied to the strip to minimize or prevent scratches and scuffing when high pressures are used and surface-finish requirements are critical. On light-gage material (especially type 430), such protection generally is unnecessary if the fabricator is experienced in processing stainless steel.

For a detailed discussion of the equipment and techniques employed in contour roll forming, see the article that begins on page 224 in this volume.

Stretch Forming

The tools and techniques for stretch forming described in the article "Stretch Forming" (page 239) are applicable to stainless steel. Machines used for stretch forming of stainless steel require 60 to 100% more power than is needed for similar operations on low-carbon steel of the same thickness.

Because of the abrasiveness of stainless steels, forming tools must be especially abrasion resistant. Wiping dies, wiping shoes, mandrels and wear plates must be made of wear-resistant tool steel, carbide, or a bearing grade of bronze, to avoid galling and welding.

Although the series 300 stainless steels are especially suitable for stretch forming because of their high work-hardening rate and ability to take large elongations, the series 400 steels are usable only for shallow stretched shapes. Type 301 is the austenitic steel best suited to stretch forming. Because of its high rate of work hardening, forming should be done slowly, to derive maximum benefit from the ductility of type 301.

Maximum percentages of stretch for one-directional forming of various kinds of austenitic stainless steels are as follows:

- Annealed types 301, 302, 304, 305, 316, 321 and 347 — 20% typical; possibly 30% on symmetrical and solid sections
- Quarter-hard types 301 and 302 — 15% typical; possibly 20% on optimum sections
- Half-hard types 301 and 302 — 5% typical; possibly 10% on optimum sections
- Full-hard type 301 — possibly 2% on optimum sections.

These figures should not be confused with permissible stretch in bending, nor are they the limits to which these stainless steels will stretch (which are considerably greater). Instead, these percentages, which determine the possible curvature of stretch formed sectional shapes of stainless steel, are based on the distortion susceptibility of severely stretched stainless steel.

The upper limits can be extended by very slow stretching and forming, especially with hardened metal. In addition, to get maximum stretch from the harder tempers, workpieces should be carefully deburred. Automatic programming is valuable in applying continuously increasing tension to overcome the continuously increasing strength as work hardening takes place during stretch forming.

Lubricants. If there is little or no movement after contact between workpiece and form block, as in stretch wrapping or single-die draw forming, little or no lubricant need be used except when deformation is severe. A low-viscosity chlorinated oil or wax provides both excellent chemical EP action and convenience of use. If there is considerable movement of the work metal against the dies (such as against the wiper shoe in radial-draw forming), pigmented lubricants are sometimes used.

The example that follows describes an application in which no lubricant was used in stretch forming of a sharply contoured part.

Example 484. Dry Stretch Forming of an Airfoil Leading Edge (Fig. 35)

The leading edge of an airfoil was stretch formed dry from a type 302 stainless steel blank, 0.008 in. thick, 4½ in. wide and 18 to 22 ft long, that had been roll formed to the air-foil contour shown in section A-A in Fig. 35. The blank had been annealed before roll forming, and it was stretch formed, without further annealing, to a 25-ft radius with the heel of the contour pointing out (see Fig. 35).

The airfoil was stretch formed in a radial-draw former, over a hard-maple form block with the airfoil contour carved into its surface (Fig. 35). Lubricant was not used because it previously had caused local variations in friction. Time for forming was 10 min per piece with three men working. Setup time was 2 hr. A typical production lot was 100 pieces.

The rolled contour had to be held within ±0.005 in. after stretch forming, and the envelope tolerance on the stretch formed shape was 0.030 in.

Springback. In sharply contoured pieces that have a relatively deep, wide cross section, some springback cannot be avoided, even in annealed metal.

During severe stretch forming, considerably higher strength (and therefore, appreciably higher elastic recovery) is developed in the more highly stressed convex surface.

Springback in regular, symmetrical sections usually can be offset by overbending the piece. Dimensional variations in workpieces are caused chiefly by variations in springback, which in turn are caused by variations in mechanical properties from sheet to sheet.

If the workpiece is irregular in cross section, or if preformed flanges are to be held to a certain angular position, or if the curve of the form varies in severity, springback may cause twist or irregular distortion of the workpiece. Various methods of blocking, pretwisting or overforming are used to prevent or correct this distortion. In the following example, an unsymmetrical cross section was twisted during forming to offset the twist caused by springback.

Example 485. Use of Twisting to Compensate for Springback in Stretch Forming (Fig. 36)

The curved channel section shown in Fig. 36 was stretch formed from quarter-hard type 302 stainless steel strip, 0.042 in. thick, that had been preformed in a press brake. Although the channel fit closely in the groove of the form block, springback caused considerable twist in the finished piece.

Elastic recovery of the outer flange and the metal near the outer edge of the web caused buckling and twisting in the part as forming tension was released. To overcome this, the part was canted by the form block and tension on the part was gradually increased during forming.

To establish a compensating initial reverse twist in the workpiece, spacers were added to the built-up form block, to wedge the section to a 5° angle as shown in Fig. 36. At the same time, a fiber filler strip with maple filler blocks was closely fitted into the channel to hold the cross-sectional contour. Details of the tooling are shown in Fig. 36.

Applied tension during stretch forming was 18,700 lb at the start; 19,550 lb at 45° bend; 20,400 lb at 90°; 21,250 lb at 135°; and 22,100 lb at the completion of the bend. A nonpigmented fatty acid was used as the forming lubricant. After forming, the workpiece was trimmed to a 145° arc with a band saw.

Equalizing Stretch. In stretch forming of sheets to a curvature in two directions (especially in stretching tempered material when the limits of stretch are very close), the quality of the product can be controlled much better if the stretch is uniform all across the workpiece. One means of obtaining uniform stretch is to provide compensating contours (which are later trimmed off) at the end of the form block, as in the following example:

Example 486. Redesign of Form Block to Equalize Strain in Stretch Forming (Fig. 37)

First attempts to stretch form the faired cover sheet shown in Fig. 37 produced unacceptable strain lines over the crown of the bend. Strain was then equalized by lengthening the form block and providing hollow contours at the end (Fig. 37). Viewed in longitudinal section, these contours were beveled sections that reduced the length of the finished section progressively toward the severely formed center section with the crown of the compound curve. As a result, the formed workpiece measured the same length at the sides and center and anywhere in between. The extra length was later trimmed off.

To prevent the blank from slipping in the gripping jaws, a ⅛-in.-diam brass rod was folded into each end, as shown in Fig. 37, to give the jaws more purchase. Because of continued difficulty in gripping, the job was

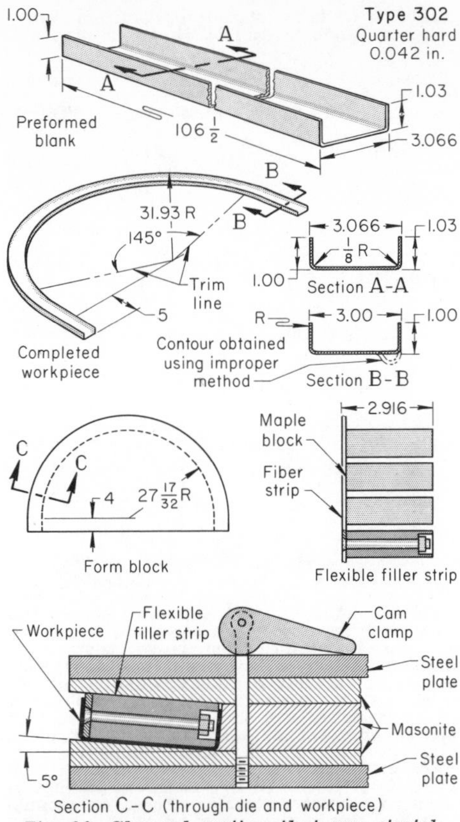

Fig. 36. Channel section that was stretch formed from a preform produced in a press brake, and details of tooling used in stretch forming, which provided reverse twist to compensate for springback (Example 485)

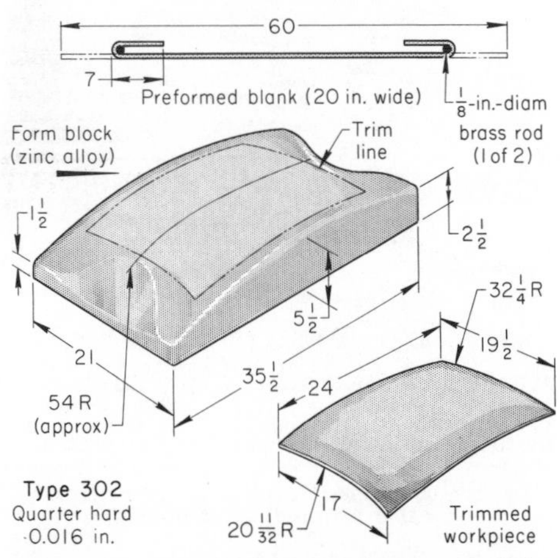

Fig. 37. Cover sheet that was stretch formed from a preformed blank on a form block designed to stretch the part evenly across its entire width by forming contours on the ends of the blank that were later trimmed off (Example 486)

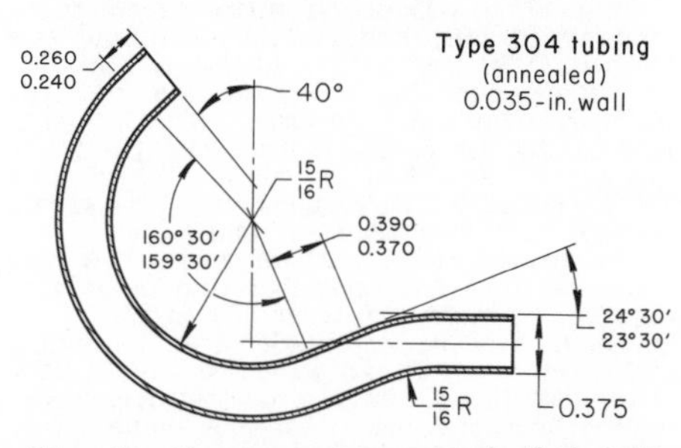

Fig. 38. Aerospace component that was bent from stainless steel tubing, with the use of a low-melting alloy as a filler during bending (Example 487)

transferred to a double-action press that gave the jaws a high hold-down pressure. The lubricant was a nonpigmented fatty acid.

Bending of Tubing

Austenitic stainless steel tubing can be bent to a centerline radius of 1½ times tube diameter. As the ratio of tube diameter to wall thickness (D/t) increases, it becomes increasingly necessary to provide both internal and external support to keep the tube from collapsing as it is bent. When D/t is greater than 30, the tube is classed as a thin-wall tube. Interlocked tooling, and bending machines of a greater capacity than required for thick-wall tubes, are strongly recommended for thin-wall tubing. (See the section "Bending Thin-Wall Tubes", page 314 in this volume.)

For bending of stainless steel tubing, wiper dies and mandrels often are made of aluminum bronze or a chromium-plated tool steel. Lubricants for the mandrel should be fairly heavy. Viscous or pigmented oil-base lubricants containing emulsifiers for ease of removal are used. Only the very lightest of lubricants should be used between the wiper die and the tube. A thin application of very light chlorinated mineral oil can be used in some bending operations without causing wrinkling.

The two examples that follow describe techniques used in bending of stainless steel tubing.

Example 487. Bending Difficult-to-Form Tubing Into an Aerospace Component (Fig. 38)

The bent tube shown in Fig. 38, used in an aerospace assembly, was difficult to form within the specified tolerances (dimensions within ±0.010 in., angles within ±½°, and flattening of the tube at bends not more than 0.002 in.).

The piece was produced from type 304 stainless steel tubing in nine operations, in the following sequence (times shown are for the production of 100-piece lots):

1 Cut tubing into lengths of 6¼ in. with an abrasive cutoff wheel; deburr roughly. (3 hr)
2 Fill each workpiece with low-melting alloy. (8 hr)
3 Make 160° bend in powered draw bender; gage the bend. (5 hr)
4 Make 24° bend in hand bender; gage the bend. (5 hr)
5 Trim ends to length in a cutoff fixture, using an abrasive wheel. (3 hr)
6 Melt out the filler. (6 hr)
7 Deburr by hand, using a grinder and a drill. (3 hr)
8 Passivate in a chemical dip. (1 hr)
9 Inspect 100% with gage and by rolling an accurate ball through the completed part. (2 hr)

Springback in bending, about 5°, was corrected by overbending to a degree that was established in trial bends.

Example 488. Bending Miniature Tubing

Ink tubes used in polygraphs and other recording instruments were made from type 304 stainless steel tubing 0.032-in. OD by 0.005-in. wall. One such ink tube had a straight length of 3 in., and a leg at each end 0.75 in. long bent 120°. Both bends were in the same plane and had a centerline radius of 3⁄16 in.

Because of springback, which was severe and sometimes erratic, the bends were made around a tool with a radius of 1⁄16 in. The bends were made by hand as compression bends in special miniature tools of low-carbon steel, including a miniature form block and a miniature clamp.

The tube was produced in four operations, as described in the following list (times shown are for 100-piece lots):

1 Cut to length (established by trial), using an abrasive wheel 0.021 in. thick. (0.5 hr)
2 Deburr inside of tube with a special tool, and outside with a fine brass wire brush. Inspect tube for burrs with a magnifying glass. (1.5 hr)
3 Make first bend. (2 hr)
4 Unload tube, turn it end for end and make second bend. (4 hr)

Setup time was 45 min. A layout was used for gaging the part. Tolerances were ±0.010 in. on lengths and ±2° on angles. After bending, the tubes were cleaned by ultrasonic washing in ethyl trichloride and then rinsed in warm water.

Other Forming Operations on Tubing

Stainless steel tubing can be flared easily to increase the diameter 25 to 30%, if it is annealed. The diameter can be reduced by rotary swaging, or it can be increased by bulging or beading. Rubber punches are often used for this purpose, as described on page 215 in the article "Rubber-Pad Forming".

Tubing of austenitic stainless steels can be hot formed by heating to between 2150 and 2300 F. Work should be halted when the tube has cooled to 1700 F, and the tube should then be cooled rapidly to minimize the precipitation of carbides.

Because austenitic stainless steel tubing is stronger than carbon steel tubing and work hardens rapidly, warm forming (below the recrystallization temperature) is also used on this material. The temperature for warm forming should be kept below 800 F to prevent the formation of carbides.

Tubing of ferritic stainless steels, such as types 430 and 446, is less easily formed than similar tubing of austenitic stainless steels. Ferritic tubing is hot formed at 1900 to 2000 F, and forming is stopped when the tubing cools to 1500 F. For best results, the range from 1500 to 1800 F should be avoided, because ductility and notch toughness are progressively impaired as the tube cools through that range. Hot shortness may be encountered in the upper part of the range. Tubing of ferritic stainless steels is warm formed at 250 to 400 F.

Forming vs Machining

Although forming ordinarily requires expensive tooling and bulky equipment, it is a high-speed process and for most parts that can be formed from sheet is more economical than machining for mass production. The following example shows how production techniques can vary with the size of the production lot, to make the best use of each technique.

Example 489. Influence of Change in Quantity on Production Method and Product Design (Table 12)

A threaded cap was made of type 347 stainless steel by three different methods, each entailing a change in design. Costs for the methods are compared in Table 12, and the designs are shown in the inset illustration.

The original order was for 100 caps, with an anticipated design change on future orders. The quickest and most economical production method was to machine the cap in one piece from bar stock (see method A in Table 12).

The next order was for 1000 caps. The design and manufacturing method were revised so that the cap was produced as an assembly of two components, one press formed from sheet and the other machined from bar stock (see method B in Table 12). Cost per piece, however, was not significantly changed.

When requirements increased to 5000 caps, a cost reduction was essential to obtain the order against a competitor's bid. The part was redesigned for production entirely from sheet, by press forming and partial machining (see method C in Table 12). Although the tools cost more than for either of the first two methods, amortizing this cost over 5000 parts resulted in the lowest tooling cost per piece. Labor cost and cost of material also were the lowest of all three methods. As a result, over-all cost was reduced nearly 50%.

The press-formed part of method B was made in a 45-ton open-back-inclinable mechanical press at a rate of 200 to 250 pieces per hour. The die was made of oil-hardening tool steel and had an expected life of 1200 pieces. Method C used a 60-ton open-back-inclinable mechanical press that made 300 to 350 pieces per hour. The die was made of air-hardening tool steel and had an expected life of 7500 pieces. Mineral oil was used as a lubricant in both methods.

Table 12. Costs for Machining vs Press Forming for Producing a Cap (Example 489) (a)

Cost item	Cost per piece: Method A	Method B	Method C
Material	$1.48(b)	$0.77(c)	$0.45(d)
Labor, at $7.50/hr	0.56	0.84	0.55
Tooling	0.30(e)	0.75(f)	0.22(g)
Total	$2.34	$2.36	$1.22

$2\frac{11}{64}$ diam
Type 347
Bar
Sheet
$\frac{7}{8}$
$2\frac{3}{16}$-in.-diam bar
Method A
$1\frac{1}{4}$ – 12 UNF – 2B
$1\frac{1}{2}$-in.-diam bar and 0.0625-in. sheet
Method B
0.093-in. sheet
Method C

(a) In method A, cap (illustrated above) was completely machined from bar stock; in method B, cap (redesigned) combined components press formed from sheet and machined from bar stock; in method C, entire cap (again redesigned) was press formed from sheet, then partly machined. (b) 1.187 lb per piece, at $1.25 per pound. (c) Bar stock at $0.63 per piece, plus sheet at $0.14 per piece. (d) 0.45 lb per piece, at $1 per pound. (e) Based on production quantity of 100 pieces. (f) Based on production quantity of 1000 pieces. (g) Based on production quantity of 5000 pieces.

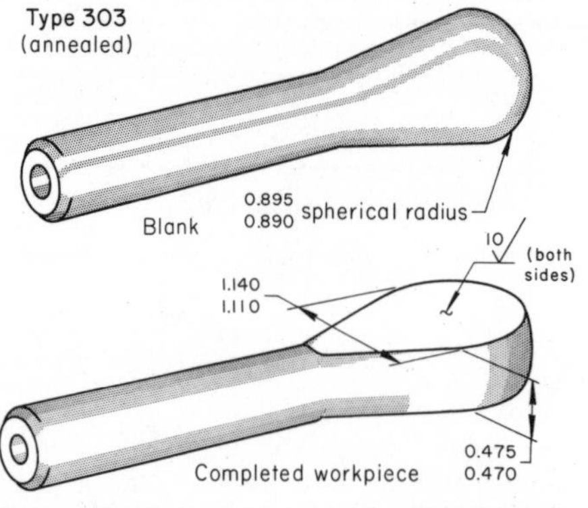

Type of press	Mechanical
Type of tools	Single-station
Die material	D3 tool steel
Die lubricant	SAE 20 oil, applied intermittently

Fig. 39. Machined blank and formed rod-end cable terminal (Example 490)

In the following example, labor and material costs for producing rod-end cable terminals were reduced when straddle milling and deburring were eliminated by the use of press forming.

Example 490. Use of Press Forming to Eliminate Straddle Milling (Fig. 39)

A rod-end cable terminal was press formed from a ground and drilled blank (upper view in Fig. 39) of annealed type 303 stainless

Table 13. Labor, Tool and Material Costs for Three Methods of Producing a Deep Drawn Piece (Example 491)

Method A (Actual)	
Labor time per 1000 pieces, man-hours:	
Shear strip	0.25
Shear blanks(a)	1.84
Draw	3.67
Vapor degrease	1.50
Saw trim top boss(b)	22.00
Saw trim bottom flange and notch	63.92
Drill 0.515-in. hole(c)	20.00
Deburr	20.00
Pickle and steam clean	3.00
Total	136.18
Labor cost per piece at $7.50/hr	$1.02
Tool cost:	
Zinc alloy draw die	$ 425.00
Saw fixtures (2)	433.20
Drill jig	171.60
Total	$1029.80
Tool cost per piece for 500 pieces	$2.06
Material cost per piece at $1.41/lb	$0.41
Total cost per piece	$3.49
Method B (Estimated)	
Labor time per 1000 pieces, man-hours:	
Shear strip	0.25
Shear blanks(a)	1.84
Draw	3.67
Pierce hole in top	3.30
Form 2.025-in. flange	3.30
First trim (2 strokes)	6.60
Final trim (2 strokes)	6.60
Pierce 0.515-in. hole	3.30
Vapor degrease	1.50
Total	30.36
Labor cost per piece at $7.50/hr	$0.23
Tool cost:	
Zinc alloy draw die	$425.00
Piercing die (top hole)	650.00
Hole-flanging die	450.00
First-trim die	575.00
Second-trim die	575.00
Piercing die (0.515-in. hole)	325.00
Total	$3000.00
Tool cost per piece for 500 pieces	$6.00
Material cost per piece at $1.41/lb	$0.41
Total cost per piece	$6.64
Method C (Estimated)	
Labor time per 1000 pieces, man-hours:	
Shear strip	0.25
Cut off and draw	3.30
Cam pierce two holes and trim	3.30
Finish trim	3.50
Form hole flange	3.50
Vapor degrease	1.50
Total	15.35
Labor cost per piece at $7.50/hr	$0.12
Tool cost:	
Cutoff and draw die	$ 900.00
Cam pierce and trim die	1200.00
Finish trim die (cam)	975.00
Hole-flanging die	650.00
Total	$3725.00
Tool cost per piece for 10,000 pieces	$0.37
Material cost per piece at $0.924/lb	$0.27
Total cost per piece	$0.76

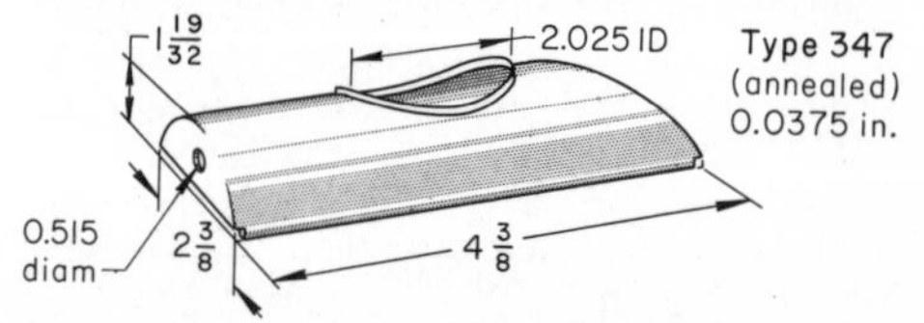

(a) Blank size, 4½ by 6 in.; weight 293.6 lb per thousand pieces. (b) Hand tool with fixture. (c) Using drill jig.

steel. The thickness of the formed portion (see completed workpiece in Fig. 39) was held within 0.005 in., and width of profile within 0.030 in. Forming refined the surface finish from 32 micro-in. (as-ground finish) to 10 micro-in.

Less preparatory form machining was needed than for the method previously used; straddle milling and deburring were eliminated — resulting in a labor saving of about 72% and a work-metal saving of 24%.

Example 491. Press Methods vs Shearing and Sawing (Table 13)

Alternate methods were considered for making the drawn collector shown in Table 13 from 0.0375-in.-thick annealed type 347 stainless steel with a No. 2D sheet finish. The sequences of operations and data on costs for the three methods are given in Table 13.

Because the total requirement for this part was only 500 pieces in three years, tooling cost had to be kept low. Method A, which was adopted for production, included sawing to trim the top boss and the bottom flange, and notch and jig drilling of the 0.515-in.-diam hole. Total cost was $3.49 per piece, of which the tool cost made up 59%.

Method B, which included press trimming in four strokes and piercing the 2.025-in.-diam top hole and the 0.515-in.-diam hole, would have cost nearly twice as much as method A for 500 pieces, in spite of a much lower labor cost, because tool cost was estimated at nearly three times that of method A.

Costs were estimated also for method C, on the basis of a hypothetical demand for a total of 10,000 pieces. With this method, four special dies, two of them compound dies, would divide six operations as follows: cutoff and draw, cam pierce and trim, finish trim, and flange holes. Use of method C would reduce the total cost per piece to about 22% of that for method A.

Oil-hardening tool steel was estimated for the dies of method B, and air-hardening tool steel for method C. A 100-ton open-back-inclinable mechanical press would have been used for both methods. Mineral oil was used for method A, and would have been used for methods B and C. The larger quantity of material purchased for method C would have reduced material costs, as shown in Table 13.

Forming of Heat-Resisting Alloys

*By the ASM Committee on Forming of Heat-Resisting Alloys**

WROUGHT heat-resisting alloys (iron-base, nickel-base and cobalt-chromium-nickel-base) can be formed by techniques similar to those used for the series 300 austenitic stainless steels, but with greater difficulty. Despite the wide differences in composition among heat-resisting alloys, all are strongly susceptible to work hardening. Figure 1 compares degree of work hardening of four nickel-base alloys with A-286 (iron-base), type 304 stainless steel, and low-carbon ferritic steel.

The differences in composition of the various heat-resisting alloys cause differences in their formability. Alloys that contain the greatest amounts of cobalt, such as HS-25 and Elgiloy, are more difficult to form than iron-base or low-cobalt nickel alloys. Most alloys that contain substantial amounts of molybdenum or tungsten for strengthening, such as Hastelloy B or René 41, are more difficult to form than alloys having low amounts of these elements.

Most of the iron-base and nickel-base alloys contain less than 0.15% carbon; more carbon than this causes excessive carbide precipitation (19-9 DL with 0.30% carbon is an exception). Small amounts of boron are used in some of the heat treatable nickel-base alloys, such as René 41 and U-700, to prevent precipitation of carbides at grain boundaries; too much boron causes cracking during forming.

Sulfur causes hot shortness of nickel-base alloys. Silicon should be less than 0.60%, and preferably less than 0.30%. More than 0.60% silicon causes cracking of cold drawn alloys, and may cause cracking of welds in some others. Usually, alloys with less than 0.30% silicon present no difficulties in forming.

Cold forming is preferred for heat-resisting alloys, especially in thin sheets; most of these alloys can be hot formed effectively only in a narrow temperature range between about 1700 and 2300 F. It is usually better to add intermediate anneals between cold forming operations than to heat the alloys for forming.

Rolling Direction

Depending on the size, amount and dispersion of secondary phases, the age-hardenable alloys show greater directional effects (Fig. 2) than alloys that are not age-hardenable. However, vacuum melting and solution annealing serve to reduce directional effects (anisotropy). As shown by data for press-brake bending in Fig. 7, directional effects contribute erratically to cracking and surface defects. In the next two examples, rolling direction seriously affected the bending and forming characteristics of iron-base alloy A-286.

Example 492. Effect of Rolling Direction in Bending A-286 (Fig. 3)

A small bracket was made by shearing blanks from sheet and bending a flange at right angles (Fig. 3). Originally, the brackets were made of type 321 stainless steel, which was formed without problems. When the same part was made of A-286 sheet, many pieces were rejected because of cracks in the bend The sheared blank for the bracket was square, and no attention had been paid to rolling direction in subsequent bending. By marking each blank to show the rolling direction, and then forming with the axis of bend at right angles to the rolling direction, cracking was eliminated. The A-286 sheet was mill annealed, and was formed in a press brake without the use of a lubricant.

Example 493. Effect of Rolling Direction in Bulging A-286 (Fig. 4)

A contoured exhaust cone (Fig. 4a) was made by cutting a flat blank from mill annealed A-286 sheet, rolling and welding a cone from the blank, and then bulging the cone into final shape. Developed blanks for two cones were cut from one sheared rectangle (Fig. 4b), with little waste of stock.

Several lots of A-286 produced good parts, but one lot of material cracked in bulging. As shown in Fig. 4(a), cracks occurred in the cone adjacent to the weld at the location where the forming stresses were parallel to the rolling direction (which also was the direction of minimum elongation). The good and inferior lots of A-286 were compared as to elongation with and across the rolling direction, and the inferior lot showed substan-

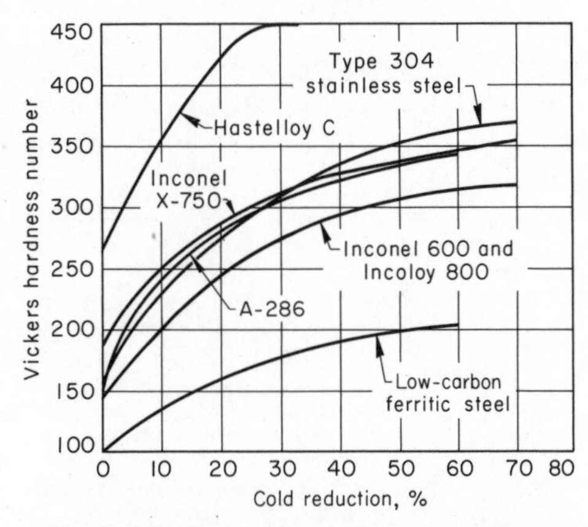

Fig. 1. Effect of cold reduction on hardness of heat-resisting alloys, type 304 stainless steel, and low-carbon ferritic steel

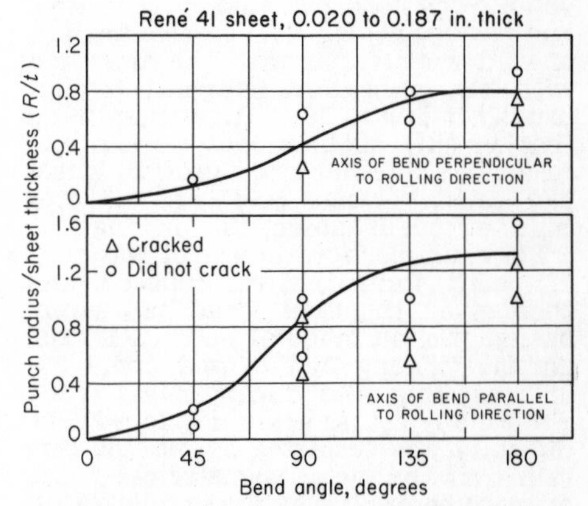

Fig. 2. Effect of direction of rolling on the formability of René 41 in press-brake bending. (See also Fig. 7.)

*A. F. HOFSTATTER, *Chairman,* Manager, Materials & Process Laboratories, Ryan Aeronautical Co.; ROBERT F. BRANDT, Special Products, Austenal Div., Howmet Corp. (formerly with International Nickel Co., Inc.); ROY L. CAMP, Manager, Manufacturing Engineering, Lycoming Div., Avco Corp.; R. P. CULBERTSON, Assistant General Manager, Refractory Metals Center, Stellite Div., Union Carbide Corp.

FRANK DONALDSON, Manufacturing Engineering Dept., Wright Aeronautical Div., Curtiss-Wright Corp.; BARRY FRANCE, Supervisor, Test and Development Laboratory, Bristol Aerospace Ltd.; ALAN K. HEGEDUS, Application Engineer, Lamp Metals & Components Dept., General Electric Co.; ARMAND LAPLANTE, Metallurgist, Missile Systems Div., Raytheon Co.

J. D. LASHBROOK, Supervisor, Tool Engineering, Marquardt Corp.; E. A. LAUCHNER, Metallurgical Engineering, Norair Div., Northrop Corp.; RONALD T. TORGERSON, Research Specialist, Space Div., Aerospace Group, Boeing Co.; ARTHUR E. WAGNER, Manufacturing Specialist (formerly with Brush Beryllium Co.).

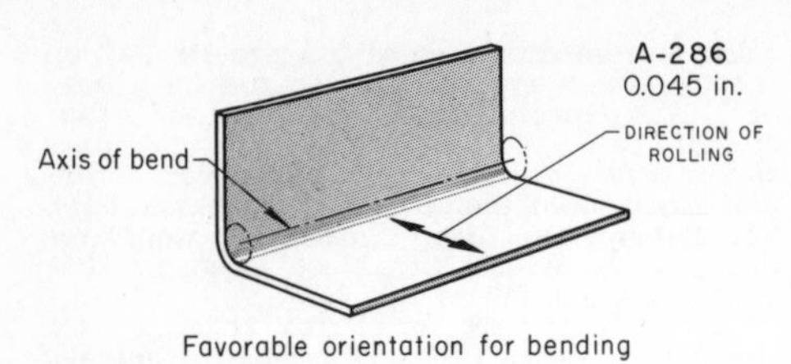

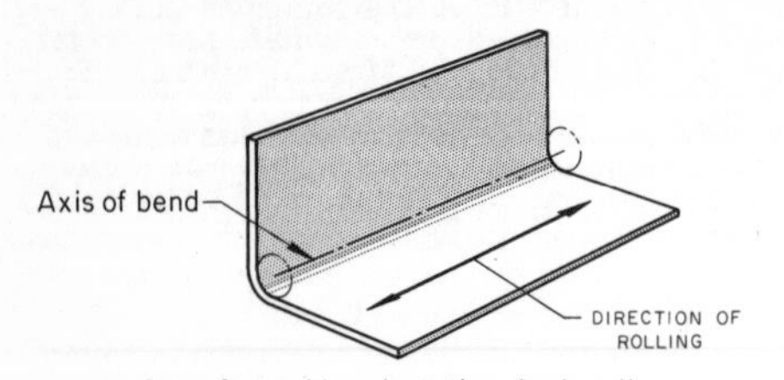

Fig. 3. Effect of rolling direction in bending (Example 492)

tially greater difference in elongation between the two directions of stress:

	Good A-286	Inferior A-286
Elongation, %:		
Across rolling direction	41.0	43.5
With rolling direction	38.5	37.2
Difference	2.5	6.3

Annealing the welded cones before bulging them reduced the number of cracked cones, but not by a satisfactory percentage. A higher percentage of acceptable cones resulted when the blanks were cut with their edges oriented to the rolling direction as shown in Fig. 4(c). Cones made from these blanks had less abrupt change in the rolling direction on each side of the weld, and the forming stresses were never parallel to the rolling direction; however, there was more scrap material from cutting the blank.

When a revision of production techniques at the mill reduced the elongation difference in the two directions of stress, it was possible to use the more economical blank layout shown in Fig. 4(b).

Effect of Alloy Condition

For the fine grain structure that is best for cold forming, heat-resisting alloys must be cold worked (reduced) beyond a critical percentage reduction, and then annealed. The critical amount of cold work varies with the alloy and with the annealing temperature, but usually it is 8 to 10%. Reheating metal that is only slightly cold worked can result in abnormal grain growth, which can cause "orange peel" or "alligator hide" effects in subsequent forming.

For example, a workpiece of Hastelloy X, partly formed, stress relieved, and then given the final form, had severe orange peel on much of its surface. The partial forming had caused about 5% cold working, and during stress relief, abnormally coarse grain developed. The difficulty was corrected by making certain that the metal was stretched 10% or more before it was stress relieved. In addition, stress relieving was done at the lowest temperature and shortest time that could be used, because higher temperatures and longer times increased grain growth. Optimum time and temperature were determined by hardness testing.

Severely cold formed parts should be fully annealed after final forming. If annealing causes distortion, the work can be formed within 10% of the intended shape, and then annealed, pickled, and given the final forming.

Table 1. Recommended Forming Speeds for Three Heat-Resisting Alloys

Alloy	Forming speed, ft per sec, for: Tensile forming	Bulge forming	Draw forming
A-286	100 to >425	0 to >700	0 to 775
René 41 .	0 to >350	0 to >700	0 to 750
HS-25 ...	50 to 275	....	650 to 825

SOURCE: W. W. Wood and others, U. S. Air Force AFML TR 64-411, Jan 1965, Project 8-143.

Mill annealed products are soft enough to permit mild forming. If the mill annealed alloy is not soft enough for the forming operation, an annealing treatment must be used that will remove the effects of cold work and dissolve the age-hardening and other secondary phases. Some control of grain size is sacrificed, but if cooling from the annealing temperature is fast enough, the age-hardening phases will be retained in solution. Further annealing after forming may be done at a lower temperature to decrease the risk of abnormal grain growth. Several intermediate anneals may be required in severe forming, but the high-temperature anneal need not be repeated. Annealing should be performed at a temperature that produces optimum ductility for the specific metal, as shown in the two examples that follow.

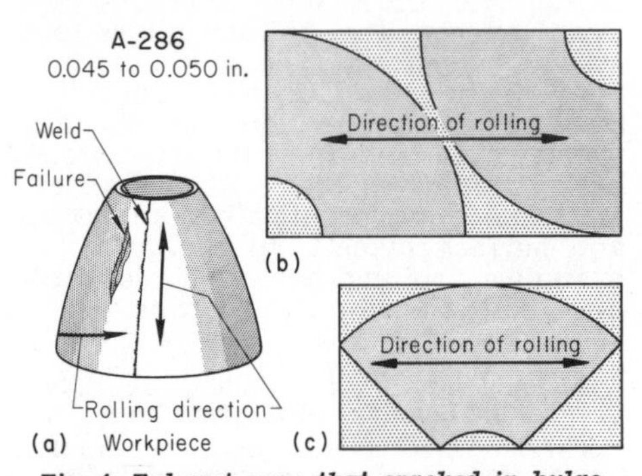

Fig. 4. Exhaust cone that cracked in bulge forming, and the two layouts used in cutting the cone blanks from sheet (Example 493)

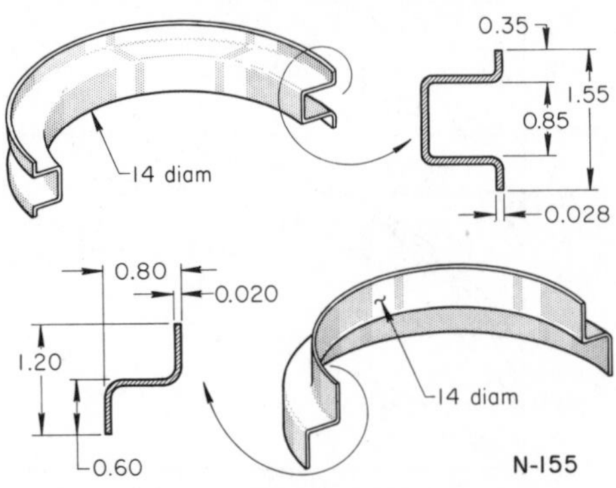

Fig. 5. Shapes formed into half-rings by stretch forming (Example 495)

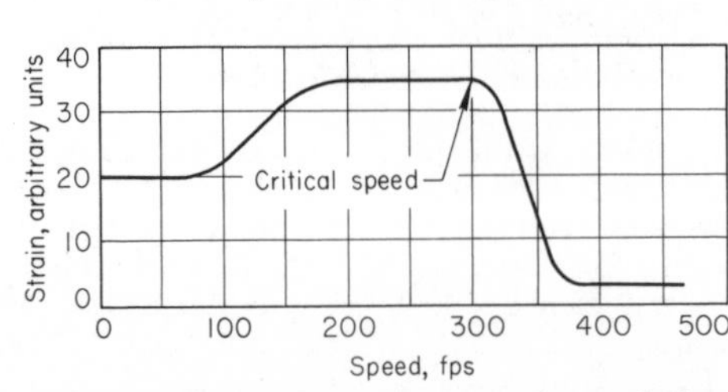

Fig. 6. Effect of forming speed on strain (typical) (SOURCE: same as for Table 1)

Examples 494 and 495. Changes in Heat Treating Practice to Eliminate Cracking

Example 494. A large manifold was made by welding together two drawn halves into a doughnut shape. Each half was drawn to a depth of 5 in. from 0.250-in.-thick René 41 that had been solution treated at 2150 F and water quenched. Drawing of the plate stock on a 7000-lb drop hammer press produced severe work hardening, and cracking occurred frequently. Three forming operations were used, with a 1975 F anneal before the second and the third.

Forming characteristics of the René 41 plate were greatly improved by modifying the solution treatment. The revised treatment consisted of first soaking the alloy at 1000 F and then transferring it to a gantry furnace and holding it at 1975 F for 30 min. The work was then lowered rapidly through the bottom of the furnace into a salt bath at 400 to 500 F. By this means, the elapsed time between leaving the high-temperature zone and entering the quench was kept to 4 or 5 sec.

By this procedure, the alloy was in the precipitation range (1100 to 1850 F) for a minimum time, and maximum softness was obtained. Hardness of the annealed material was Rockwell C 16 to 21. The salt bath provided a more uniform quench and a more ductile alloy than did the original water quench. With the revised method, because of the better ductility of the alloy, the manifold halves could be formed in two operations. The sequence of operations was: solution anneal, form, process anneal, and form.

Example 495 (Fig. 5). Half-rings having two different cross sections (Fig. 5) were stretch formed of N-155, stress relieved at 2150 F, acid pickled for removal of scale, and then stretch formed to final size. Some of the rings broke during final sizing. Breakage was eliminated by decreasing the stress-relieving temperature from 2150 F to 1800 F and by insuring a rapid cooling rate from 1800 F to room temperature. The scale formed at 1800 F was less tenacious and was removable in a less severe pickling treatment that did not attack the metal preferentially at grain boundaries.

Effect of Speed on Formability

The speed at which a metal is deformed affects its formability. In general, each metal has a critical speed of forming. In some cases, the strain rises until this critical speed is reached, after which the strain decreases sharply with increasing speed, as indicated by the typical curve in Fig. 6. This curve has a plateau of maximum strain where ductility is greatest. This plateau seems to be broad for most heat-resisting alloys. The breadth of the plateau is dependent on the use of biaxial or triaxial loading of the material during forming. Table 1 gives optimum speeds for three heat-resisting alloys and three different forming operations.

Formability-Design Relations

Because the system of applied forces is different in each method of forming, the response of a given metal (its formability) varies with the method; an alloy that is more formable than another alloy in one process may be less formable in another process. The response of the metal cannot be computed precisely from its mechanical properties, and therefore it is customary to describe formability in terms of the dimensions (or ratios of dimensions) of the part design being formed.

The charts in Fig. 7 show results of tests made in one plant on the formability of five heat-resisting alloys in press-brake bending. Each data point represents five to ten tests. Iron-base alloy A-286 was more formable than any of the other metals tested. None of the A-286 specimens cracked, even in 180° bends made with a punch of almost zero radius, and only three of the 12 groups of A-286 specimens showed orange peel or strain indications.

Although nickel-base alloys vary considerably in formability, they are generally less formable than iron-base alloys. Hastelloy X is less formable than Inconel X-750; René 41 is less formable than Hastelloy X. Cobalt-base HS-25 is more formable than nickel-base Hastelloy X and much more formable than cobalt-base J-1570.

Springback of heat-resisting alloys, even when annealed, is greater than that of most carbon or stainless steels. However, the modulus of elasticity is about the same. Because so many variables are involved, it is advisable to make samples of heat-resisting alloy parts before deciding what forming methods and tools to use.

Methods and Tools

Few applications in forming heat-resisting alloys involve quantities that warrant the use of high-production methods and tools. Usually, only a few to a few hundred parts are needed. Therefore, methods that require a minimum of tooling, such as press-brake forming (see Example 492), drop-hammer forming, spinning (see Examples 496, 497, 500, 501 and 503), and explosive forming (see Examples 498, 501, 502 and 503), have been used more than other methods. Presses or other machines are the same as those used for forming steel, but more power is needed to form heat-resisting alloys because of their higher strength. Power required for forming a given workpiece is from 50 to 100% more for heat-resisting alloys than for low-carbon steel.

Safety in Explosive Forming. Operations involving explosives and pressure vessels are governed by state, county and municipal regulations. The requirements and restrictions of these regulations should be taken into account in tool design and operational setup for explosive forming.

Tools for forming heat-resisting alloys are usually the same as for forming stainless steel in similar quantities (see the article "Forming of Stainless Steel", which begins on page 353). Clearance between punch and die is generally the same as for stainless steel. Heat-resisting alloys also resemble stainless steels in that they are likely to adhere to dies or mandrels, resulting in galling or tearing of the dies and workpieces. To minimize adherence, steel dies, punches or mandrels can be plated with approximately 0.0002 to 0.0005 in. of chromium. However, small production quantities seldom justify this practice. Cast iron has proved adequate and nongalling for many low-production forming tools. If a heat treatable grade of iron is used, areas in which high wear is anticipated can be locally hardened.

Lubrication

Some lubrication is usually required for best results in drawing, stretch forming, or spinning. In press-brake forming, lubrication is seldom needed

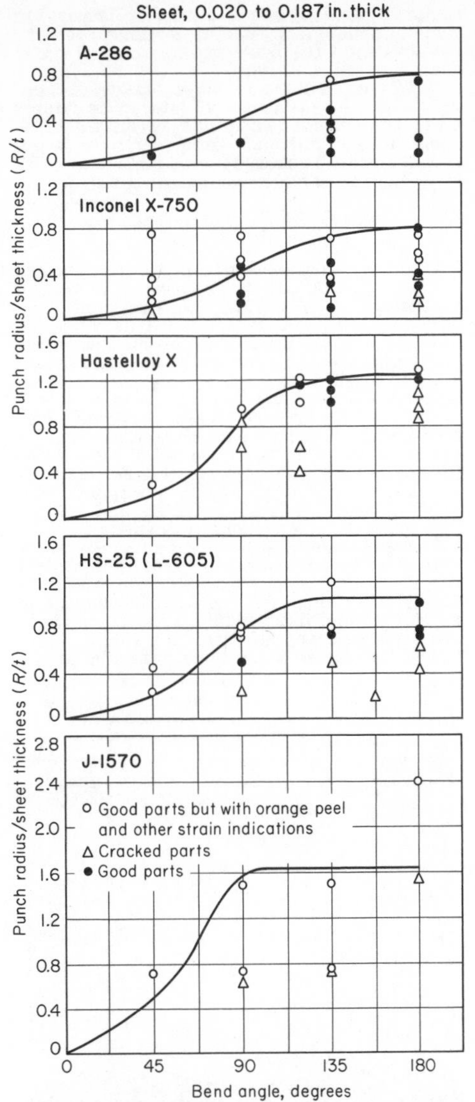

All material was air melted and was formed in the mill annealed condition. Each point represents five to ten specimens. Each chart includes bending both across and parallel to the rolling direction.

Fig. 7. Limit curves for press-brake bending of several heat-resisting alloys at room temperature

for V-bends, but will greatly improve results if a square punch is used. Mild forming operations — for example, those no more severe than a 10% reduction — can usually be accomplished successfully with unpigmented mineral oils and greases. However, polar lubricants, such as lard oil, castor oil, and sperm oil, are preferred for mild forming. They will usually produce acceptable results and are easily removed. For more severe forming, metallic soaps, or EP (extreme-pressure) lubricants such as chlorinated, sulfochlorinated or sulfurized oils or waxes are recommended. They may be pigmented with a material such as mica for extremely severe forming.

A chlorinated oil was used without added pigment for press forming an A-286 end cap in Example 496.

Lubricants that contain white lead, zinc compounds, or molybdenum disulfide are not recommended, because they are too difficult to remove before annealing, or before high-temperature service. At high temperatures, any sulfur or lead on the surface of the alloys can be harmful. Sulfurized or sulfochlorinated oils may be used if the work is carefully cleaned afterward in a degreaser or an alkaline cleaner. Work that has been formed in zinc alloy dies should be flash-pickled in nitric acid before heat treatment, to prevent the possibility of zinc embrittlement.

In spinning, tenacity is an additional property that a lubricant must have or it will be thrown off the workpiece by centrifugal force. Metallic soap or wax applied to the workpiece before spinning is usually satisfactory. In power spinning, a coolant should also be used during the process (see the article "Spinning", which begins on page 201 in this volume).

Occasionally it is advantageous to use two kinds of lubricant in the same operation. In one stretch forming application, the strain at the middle of the work was 3 to 4%, but near the ends, where the metal pulled tangent to the die, the strain was 10 to 12%. A light coat of thin oil was adequate for most of the work, but an EP lubricant was used at the ends.

For information on lubrication in forming nickel-base heat-resisting alloys, see page 432.

Forming Practice for Iron-Base Alloys

Alloy A-286, the most widely used precipitation-hardening iron-base heat-resisting alloy, has work-hardening characteristics similar to those of type 304 stainless steel (Fig. 1) and slightly lower formability. Most other iron-base heat-resisting alloys are somewhat less formable. Typical forming practice is described in the next three examples.

Example 496. Spinning vs Press Forming of A-286 End Caps (Fig. 8)

Initial trials indicated that aerospace end caps could be produced most economically by spinning (original method in Fig. 8), mainly because of the lower tooling cost (about 40%

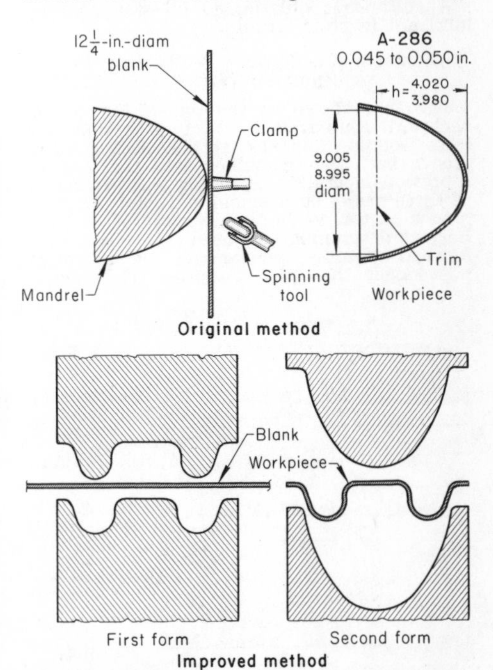

Fig. 8. Setup for producing an end cap by spinning (original method) and by press forming (improved method) (Example 496)

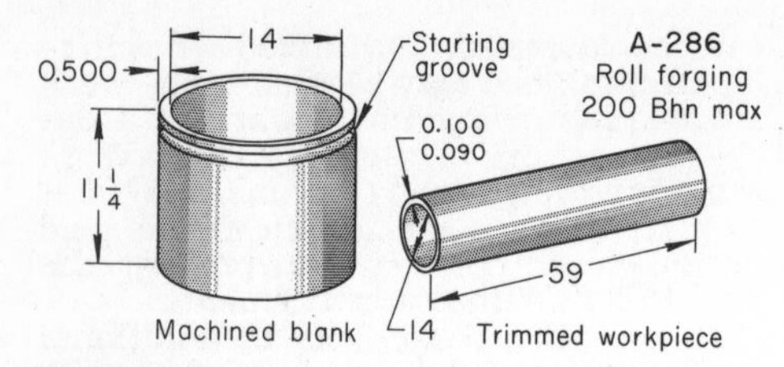

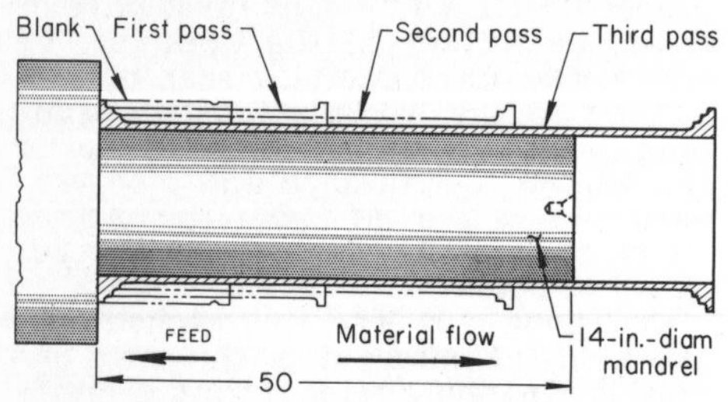

Speed	200 rpm (735 sfm, approx)
Feed	4 ipm
Lubricant and coolant	(a)
Reduction, first pass	40%
Reduction, second pass	40%
Reduction, third pass	44%
Spinning time per piece	75 min (est)
Mandrel material	Cast iron
Mandrel hardness	Rockwell C 54
Roller material	D2 tool steel
Roller hardness	Rockwell C 60 to 64

(a) Extreme-pressure (EP) lubricant on mandrel; flood of soluble-oil emulsion (1 part oil to 20 parts water) on tools and workpiece

Fig. 9. Backward tube spinning of A-286 (Example 497)

of that for press forming). In order to produce the required contour with minimum thinning, some springback was inevitable. The springback varied, and it was not possible to maintain the 9-in. diameter within the required ±0.005 in. Acceptable workpieces could be obtained by two-stage forming in a press (improved method in Fig. 8), with the following sequence of operations:

1 Cut 12¼-in.-diam blank (mill annealed).
2 First form (partial).
3 Stress relieve at 1650 F; cool in air.
4 Pickle.
5 Complete first form.
6 Second form reverse bulge (partial).
7 Stress relieve at 1650 F; cool in air.
8 Complete second form.

A sulfur-free chlorinated oil was used as lubricant in press forming.

Example 497. Forming A-286 Tube by Spinning (Fig. 9)

The tube shown at the top of Fig. 9 was backward spun from a roll forging that had been solution annealed at 1800 F. A starting groove had been machined into the tube in a previous operation. Spinning was performed in three passes on a machine capable of spinning a part 42 in. in diameter and 50 in. long. Backward spinning was used in preference to forward spinning because (*a*) the workpiece was longer than the mandrel; (*b*) forward spinning would have required a change in workpiece design to permit hooking over the mandrel; and (*c*) backward spinning is faster than forward spinning.

It was convenient to leave flanges at both ends and to trim these off later. The flanges prevented bell-mouthing and permitted trimming of the portions likely to have small radial cracks. Processing and tool details are given in the table accompanying Fig. 9.

Example 498. Explosive Forming of A-286 (Fig. 10)

A tubular workpiece was explosively formed inside a die (Fig. 10) to produce a part having an internal flange. Had this part been produced by other methods, such a flange would have had to be welded on. A-286 sheet was rolled into a round cylinder 16 in. in diameter, welded, solution treated, and descaled. Tolerance on the diameter was ±0.030 in.

The tools (die and blast deflector) cost $800 and were used to form 30 workpieces. It was estimated that the tools would have lasted for at least 30 more workpieces. Forming required 6 man-hr for each workpiece, and welding, heat treating, trimming and inspection required an additional 4 man-hr.

The explosive was gel dynamite. Six shots were used to form the workpiece. For shots 1 and 2, 15 grams of explosive were used; for shot 3, 18 grams; for shot 4, 20 grams; and for shots 5 and 6, 25 grams. After three shots, the workpiece was solution annealed and descaled (see list of operations with Fig. 10).

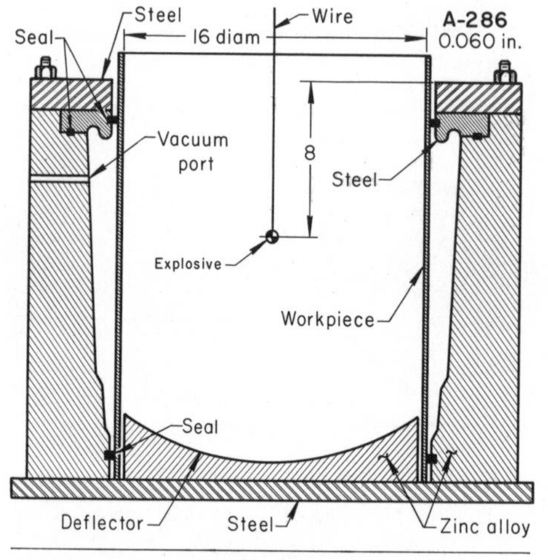

Operations

1 Die cleaned and degreased
2 Annealed workpiece loaded into die
3 Vacuum pumped (29.5 in. Hg)
4 Explosive charge set as shown above, suspended on stiff wire
5 Die and its contents submerged in water
6 Charge exploded
7 Die lifted from water and work inspected
8 Operations 3 to 7 repeated until workpiece was fully formed. Workpiece annealed and descaled after the third of six shots.

Fig. 10. Explosive forming a case from alloy A-286 (Example 498)

Forming Practice for Nickel Alloys

Two types of annealing treatments are used to soften the age-hardenable nickel-base alloys for forming, predicated on the ductility needed for forming and, if subsequent welding is required, on the avoidance of adverse metallurgical effects during and after welding. A high-temperature anneal is used to obtain maximum ductility and when no welding will be done on the formed part. A lower-temperature anneal, resulting in some sacrifice in ductility, is used when the part will be welded.

For instance, solution annealing of René 41 at 2150 F, followed by quenching in water, gives maximum ductility. However, parts formed from sheet annealed in this way should not be welded; during welding or subsequent heat treatment they are likely to crack at the brittle carbide network developed in the grain boundaries. A lower annealing temperature, preferably 1950 to 1975 F, results in less sensitization during welding, decreasing the likelihood of network cracks. Formability is reduced by 10 to 20%, but is adequate for most forming operations.

Typical practice for forming nickel-base alloys is described in the following three examples.

Example 499. Forming and Slotting Hastelloy X (Fig. 11)

The 88 flutes in the workpiece shown in Fig. 11 were finish formed and slotted one at a time with hand indexing in a 50-ton mechanical press at the rate of one piece every 14.6 min, including setup. Slots were required to be within 0.02 in. of true position.

The work metal was 0.040/0.044-in. Hastelloy X sheet. Before the mechanical press operations, the sheet had been formed by a rubber-diaphragm process, electrolytically cleaned, annealed to Rockwell 30-T 74.5 to 81.5, pickled, restruck in the forming press, and trimmed. The flutes were partially formed in this series of operations.

In choosing a method of finish forming, it was decided that the only way to form the flutes to the required shape was to use a solid tool. The rubber-diaphragm forming process, however, was the best way to form the main contours of the part. The flutes could not be fully formed by a conventional die alone because the percentage elongation exceeded the limits for Hastelloy X (38 to 42% elongation in 2 in.). By making use of the natural tendency of the blank to form wrinkles, the flutes were preformed during rubber-diaphragm forming, but pressures were only enough to form them 75% complete. However, the amount of elongation needed in the final die-forming operation was lowered, and definite locations for flutes were provided, so that each flute could be produced in one stroke of

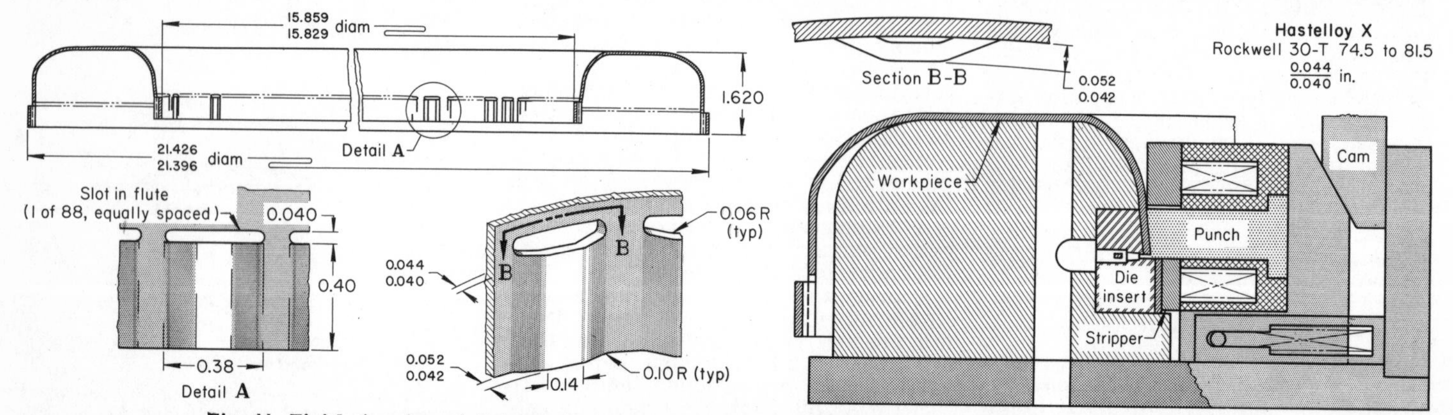

Fig. 11. Finish forming of flutes and piercing of slots one at a time in a mechanical press (Example 499)

Table 2. Time and Cost Details for Forming a Flanged Workpiece by Two Methods (Example 500)

Operation	Production rate, pieces per hour	Labor cost per piece
Original Method(a) (Spinning)		
Partly form 1.470-in. wall	8.4	$1.20
Anneal	20.0	0.49
Finish form 1.470-in. wall	7.7	1.30
Anneal	19.0	0.52
Form remainder of contour	5.5	1.87
Total		$5.38(b)
Improved Method(c) (Hydroforming)		
Form 1.470-in. wall	22.0	$0.46
Anneal	23.0	0.43
Form 1.490-in. wall	17.7	0.57
Total		$1.46(d)

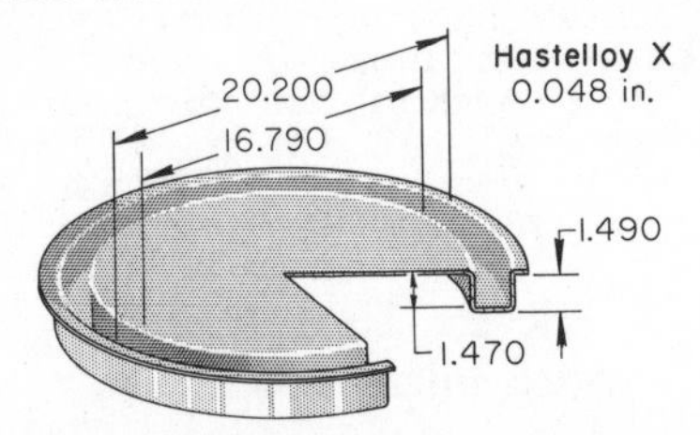

(a) Tool cost was $480. Soap was used as a lubricant. (b) Cost of $10 for three machine setups not included. Production was 150 pieces per setup. (c) Tool cost was $2185. Proprietary drawing compound used as a lubricant. (d) Cost of $20 for two machine setups not included. Production was 150 pieces per setup.

the mechanical press. The tooling (shown at the right in Fig. 11) consisted of a die and a cam-actuated punch of high-carbon high-chromium tool steel hardened to Rockwell C 58 to 60, and die inserts, stripper, and cam sections of lower-alloy air-hardening tool steel. The punch pierced the slot and flattened the bulge above the flute. The stripper formed the flute when struck by the punch holder.

Example 500. Rubber-Diaphragm Forming vs Spinning for Producing a Flanged Part From Hastelloy X (Table 2)

The completed part shown in Table 2 was originally produced by three spinning operations from a flat blank 0.048 in. thick and 26.250 in. in diameter. To reduce cost, the method was changed. Rubber-diaphragm forming was used instead of spinning, with the advantages shown in Table 2. The cost comparison does not include material cost, tool cost or overhead. As indicated by footnotes (a) and (c), the tool cost for the improved method was about 4½ times as much as for spinning.

Example 501. Explosive Forming of Inconel 718 (Fig. 12)

Fully annealed Inconel 718 sheet 0.072 in. thick was used to make the flame deflector shown in Fig. 12. The sheet was rolled into a cylinder, with the grain direction at right angles to the long axis. A 4.5-in.-OD by 32-in.-long tube was TIG welded from the cylinder, using René 41 filler rod. The weld was made flush on the inside, and the outside was ground flush to +0.005 in. The tube was spun to the dimensions shown in Fig. 12; it was fully annealed at 1750 F, and grit blasted. (An outstanding characteristic of this alloy is its slow response to age hardening, which enables it to be welded and annealed with no spontaneous hardening unless cooled slowly.)

Explosive forming of the flame deflector was accomplished by three successive charges in a split die, as follows:

- Charge 1: 60 grams of PETN (pentaerythritol tetranitrate) at an average standoff distance (distance from sheet to explosive) of 2 in.
- Charge 2: 80 grams of PETN at an average standoff distance of 2½ in.
- Charge 3: Proprietary mixture in sheet form, equal to 135 grams of TNT at a standoff distance of 1 in.

The workpiece was fully annealed after explosive forming.

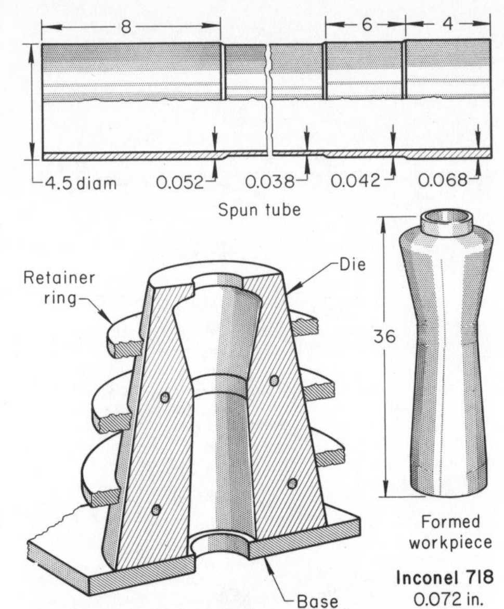

Fig. 12. Flame deflector produced by explosive forming in three successive charges (Example 501)

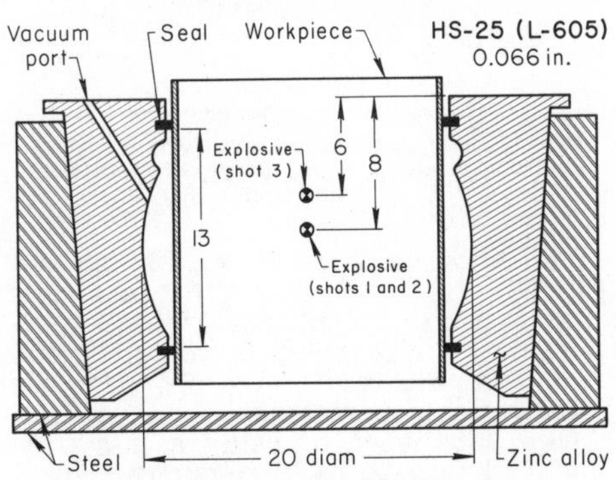

Fig. 13. Welded cylinder in position for explosive forming (Example 502)

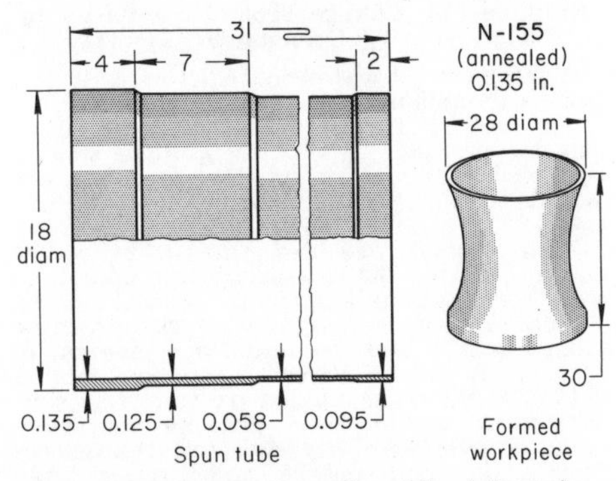

Fig. 14. Exit nozzle produced by tube spinning and explosive forming (Example 503)

Forming Practice for Cobalt-Chromium-Nickel-Base Alloys

Forming the cobalt-chromium-nickel-base alloys requires more force because usually they are stronger than the iron-base and nickel-base alloys. The cobalt-chromium-nickel-base alloys with less than 20% Ni, such as Elgiloy and HS-25, are more difficult to form. N-155, a more formable alloy, has a tensile strength of 120,000 psi, 0.2% yield strength of 60,000 psi, and elongation of 40%. These alloys, like most of the nickel-base alloys, are age hardened for elevated-temperature service.

Practice used for forming HS-25 and N-155 parts is described in the three examples that follow.

Example 502. Explosive Forming of HS-25 (Fig. 13)

Figure 13 shows the setup used for explosive forming a tail-pipe ball from HS-25 sheet. The sheet was TIG welded (butt) into a cylinder, and the shape was formed by three explosive charges. No annealing was done between welding and the first two shots of explosive forming, but after the first two shots (50 grams of dynamite for each), the assembly was removed from the water tank, and the workpiece was withdrawn from the die, annealed at 2150 F, and descaled. The workpiece was returned to the die for further forming. The third explosive charge used 62 grams of dynamite. Tolerance on diameters was maintained within ±0.010 in.

Explosive forming was preferred over forming on an expanding mandrel because the mandrel left flats on the wall of the workpiece and explosive forming did not. The entire procedure for explosive forming required 4 man-hr for each piece.

Example 503. N-155 Exit Nozzle Produced by Tube Spinning and Explosive Forming (Fig. 14)

The exit nozzle shown in Fig. 14 was produced from fully annealed 0.135-in.-thick N-155 sheet. The sheet was rolled into a cylinder, with grain direction at right angles to the long axis, and it was TIG welded. The weld was ground flush on both the inside and outside, after which the cylinder was tube-spun to the various wall thicknesses shown in Fig. 14. The workpiece was then placed in a die and explosively formed to the shape shown at the right in Fig. 14.

The underwater explosive-forming technique was used, with a vacuum of 24 in. Hg between the workpiece and the die. The explosive charge was equal to 620 grams of TNT and was placed at an average distance of 7½ in. from the workpiece walls. The first shot produced approximately 90% of the final shape. A second shot, using the same size charge, completed the workpiece, after which it was fully annealed.

N-155
(annealed)
0.078 in.

Operations

1. Blank; polish blank contour
2. First form (250 tons on ram, 20 tons on cushion)(a)
3. Anneal (2125 to 2175 F, 20 min)(b)
4. Second form (300 tons on ram, 20 tons on cushion)(a)
5. Anneal (2125 to 2175 F, 20 min)(b)
6. Restrike (250 tons on ram)(a)
7. Pierce holes and trim.

(a) Fatty chlorinated oil was used as a lubricant. (b) Heated in dissociated ammonia and cooled to 1000 F or lower in 2 min.

Fig. 15. Turbine-nozzle pipe formed in a die in two forming operations and a restrike (Example 504)

Example 504. Press Forming a Turbine Component From N-155 (Fig. 15)

Power-recovery turbine-nozzle pipes (Fig. 15) were formed from flat blanks of 0.078-in.-thick N-155 sheet. Workpieces were completed in two forming operations and one restrike, with a full anneal following each forming operation. The processing sequence is given below Fig. 15.

Forming was done with conventional tool steel dies operated by hydraulic presses having capacities up to 300 tons and speeds of 35 and 51 in. per min.

An alternate method of producing these parts was by precision casting, but this method would have cost about 20% more than press forming. This estimate included tool amortization based on producing 5000 parts.

Forming of Refractory Metals

*By the ASM Committee on Forming of Heat-Resisting Alloys**

REFRACTORY METALS are generally worked in small quantities, production rates are low, each piece is handled separately, and the forming process is closely controlled.

Table 1 shows the compositions of refractory alloys available as sheet. Typical conditions for bending sheet 0.020 to 0.050 in. thick are given in Table 2. Tensile forming parameters for sheet materials are summarized in Table 3.

Formability

Columbium and tantalum alloys generally are formed at room temperature in the annealed (recrystallized) condition, although the stress-relieved alloys are sufficiently ductile for most forming operations. Work hardening, especially of the stronger alloys, often necessitates annealing after severe forming.

Strong alloys of columbium, which are made in limited quantity, are not listed in Table 1. These alloys have varying degrees of brittleness at low temperature, but can be formed by the same procedures used for molybdenum.

Molybdenum and tungsten are more difficult to form than columbium and tantalum, but if they are heated and certain precautions are taken, even complex parts can be formed. The greatest difficulty in forming these metals is their tendency toward brittle fracture (cracks and ruptures that occur with little or no plastic deformation), and delamination (a type of brittle behavior that produces cracks or ruptures parallel to the plane of the sheet). Tungsten can be hot formed only; it is brittle at room temperature.

At slow strain rates in tension and in bending, molybdenum, Mo-0.5Ti and TZM are ductile at room temperature, becoming brittle at lower temperatures. However, because of the high variable strain rates and tri-axial stresses in the usual forming processes, these metals are usually hot formed, to decrease the probability of brittle fracture. Molybdenum and tungsten blanks must have prepared edges to prevent cracking and splitting during forming.

Molybdenum and tungsten are generally stress relieved before forming. Recrystallization raises the transition (ductile-to-brittle failure) temperature.

Effect of Composition

Columbium and tantalum are severely embrittled by oxygen, nitrogen and hydrogen, even in minute amounts. However, the usual melting and processing techniques keep the metals pure enough for good formability.

Some of the columbium alloys are more resistant to grain growth at high temperature than high-purity columbium. Alloys such as FS-80, Cb-752 and Cb-753 are high-strength materials that resist grain growth at high-temperature. These alloys have fine grain and elongate uniformly for forming and drawing operations.

*For committee list, see page 371.

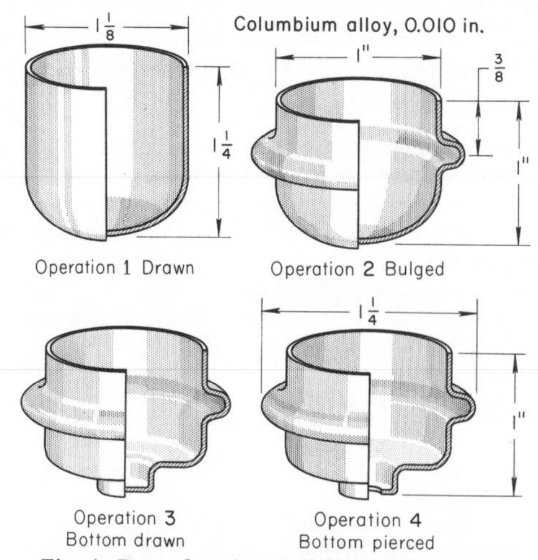

Fig. 1. Deep drawing, bulging and piercing columbium alloy sheet in four operations (Example 505)

The advantage of using a less pure material instead of high-purity columbium sheet for deep drawing, is shown in the following example.

Example 505. Change From High-Purity to Lower-Purity Columbium (Fig. 1)

A formed shell was produced from 0.010-in.-thick columbium sheet in four operations, as shown in Fig. 1. The operations were: draw cup, bulge sides, draw bottom into a smaller cup, pierce the smaller cup. The lubricant was a mixture of graphite and oil.

When high-purity columbium (200 parts per million oxygen) was used, the bottom of the cup tore during the second drawing operation, with localized necking and ductile failure. Failure was caused by low work-hardening characteristics and low uniform elongation in tension. Sheet of lower purity (columbium with 900 parts per million oxygen) was substituted to obtain better drawing characteristics. The lower-purity sheet was harder, of finer grain, more ductile, and stronger than the original material.

Surface Contamination

The most common causes of surface contamination are failure to clean the surface properly and failure to provide the proper atmosphere in heat treatment. Columbium and tantalum are usually acid pickled, and are heat treated in a vacuum or an inert-gas atmosphere. (For details of heat treating refractory metals, see page 267 in Volume 2 of this Handbook.)

Generally, the high-strength alloys are more severely embrittled by surface contamination than are the lower-strength alloys.

Molybdenum and tungsten are much less susceptible to surface contamination by oxygen and nitrogen than are columbium and tantalum. Pure dry hydrogen does not affect molybdenum or tungsten; however, stress-relieving of molybdenum alloys in an atmosphere of cracked ammonia (an atmosphere containing both hydrogen and nitrogen) may contaminate the surface, and this contamination must be removed by grinding or pickling. Molybdenum and tungsten are cleaned in an acid pickling bath or a caustic solution, and then heat treated in dry hydrogen.

Factors That Affect Mechanical Properties

Major variables that affect mechanical properties and formability are working temperature, temperature of anneals between operations, percentage

Table 1. Nominal Compositions of Refractory Alloys Available as Sheet (a)

Alloy	Zr	Ti	V or Hf	W	Others
Columbium-Base Alloys					
FS-80	1.0	...	...	...	...
FS-82	1.0	...	...	...	33.0 Ta
FS-85	1.0	...	...	11.0	28.0 Ta
C-103	...	1.0	10.0 Hf	...	...
C-129Y	...	...	10.0 Hf	10.0	0.10 Y
B-66	1.0	...	5.0 V	...	5.0 Mo
D-14	5.0	...	...	...	...
D-36	5.0	10.0	...	...	...
D-43	1.0	...	...	10.0	0.10 C
Cb-752	2.5	...	...	10.0	...
Cb-753	1.2	...	5.0 V	...	...
Tantalum-Base Alloys					
Ta-10W	...	...	...	10.0	...
Ta-8W-2Hf	...	...	2.0 Hf	8.0	...
Ta-30Cb-7.5V	...	...	7.5 V	...	30.0 Cb
Molybdenum-Base Alloys					
Mo-0.5Ti	...	0.5	...	...	0.03 C
TZM	0.1	0.5	...	...	0.03 C

(a) Commercially pure Cb, Ta, Mo and W sheets are also available.

Table 2. Conditions for Press-Brake Forming of Refractory Metal Sheet 0.020 to 0.050 In. Thick (a)

Metal or alloy (b)	Forming temperature	Minimum bend radius (c): Test data	Minimum bend radius (c): Preferred	Springback
Columbium-Base Alloys (Annealed)				
FS-82, C-103, C-129Y	Room	$<1t$	$1t$	2°- 6°
D-36	Room	$1t$-$2t$	$2t$	3°-10°
Tantalum-Base Alloys (Annealed)				
Tantalum	Room	$<1t$	$1t$	...
Ta-10W	Room	$<1t$	$2t$	1°- 5°
Molybdenum-Base Alloys (Stress Relieved)				
Mo-0.5Ti, TZM	300 F	$2t$-$5t$	$5t$	3°-8°
Tungsten (Stress Relieved)				
Tungsten	600 F	$2t$-$5t$	$5t$	2°-8°

(a) Formed to a 120° bend angle in a 60° V-die at a ram speed of 10 to 120 ipm. (b) See Table 1 for compositions. (c) t = sheet thickness.

Table 3. Elongation and True Strain in Forming Refractory Metal Sheet of Various Thicknesses and Grain Directions(a)

Alloy	Condition(b)	Thickness, in.	Forming temperature, F	Grain direction(c)	Elongation, % in: 1 in.	Elongation, % in: 2 in.	True strain(d) ε_m	True strain(d) ε_c
Columbium-Base Alloys								
FS-82	Ann	0.010	70	L	32.0	26.0	0.180	0.230
				T	30.0	25.0	0.170	0.230
C-103	SR	0.030	70	L	18.0	14.0	0.122	0.145
				T	6.0	4.0	0.041	0.046
	Ann	0.030	70	L	30.0	24.0	0.152	0.232
				T	26.0	21.0	0.150	0.197
Tantalum-Base Alloy								
Ta-10W	Ann	0.040	70	L	39.0	30.5	0.180	0.283
				T	38.0	30.0	0.197	0.282
Molybdenum-Base Alloys								
Mo-0.5Ti	SR	0.020	70	L	19.0	15.0	0.102	0.164
				T	11.0	9.0	0.052	0.089
TZM	SR	0.035	70	L	19.0	15.0	0.074	0.130
		0.040	70	L	16.0	11.5	0.060	0.075
Tungsten								
Tungsten	SR	0.035	1100	T	4.0	2.5	0.019	0.022
			1800	T	3.5	...	0.021	0.023

(a) Based on testing one heat of material for each alloy. (b) Ann = annealed; SR = stress relieved. (c) L = longitudinal; T = transverse. (d) ε_m = true strain at maximum load; ε_c = maximum true strain at maximum true stress.

reduction after the final anneal, and temperature of final heat treatment.

Rolling. Refractory metal sheet is generally made by hot forging or extruding billets to make sheet bars, which are rolled to sheet at high temperature. The final rolling of columbium and tantalum alloys is done below 1000 F, often at room temperature. The cold worked sheet is given a final recrystallization anneal to improve formability and ductility. Finish rolling of molybdenum and tungsten is done at high temperature, and final heat treatment is usually for stress relief only.

Cross-rolled sheet is generally more formable, because cross rolling makes ductility almost equal in all directions.

Heat Treatment. In the annealed (recrystallized) condition and in the ductile range, refractory metals behave much like steel. For instance, recrystallized tungsten, although brittle at low temperature, has 35% uniform elongation and 50% total elongation at 750 F. Cold working strengthens molybdenum and tungsten, reduces the temperature at which they become brittle, and makes them less formable. Although molybdenum and tungsten are given a final stress-relief, they retain their cold worked structure.

Figure 2 shows the effect of heat treatment and strain hardening on the ductility (and the ductile-to-brittle transition temperature range) of unalloyed molybdenum. The curves in Fig. 2 show that the ductile-to-brittle transition for unalloyed molybdenum is between 0 and −50 F for the stress-relieved condition, between 80 and −10 F for the stretch-strained condition, and at approximately 80 F for the recrystallized condition.

Transition Temperature. Columbium, tantalum and their most frequently used alloys are readily formable, and are ductile at temperatures as low as − 320 F. Molybdenum, Mo-0.5Ti, and TZM, in the stress-relieved condition, have transition temperatures just below room temperature. Molybdenum may fracture or delaminate at room temperature under the high deformation rates and stresses generally encountered in forming practice. Therefore, molybdenum alloys are generally formed at moderate to high temperatures. Stress-relieved tungsten has a transition temperature of 300 to 600 F, so that all forming of tungsten must be done at high temperatures.

Figure 3 shows how temperature changes the strength and elongation of a typical high-strength columbium alloy with good formability. A slight rise in temperature reduces yield strength, but also reduces ductility. The ductility is lowest at about 1200 F and then increases with increasing temperature. This reduced ductility is caused by strain aging, which is characteristic of body-centered cubic metals.

Figure 4 shows how temperature changes the ductility of four typical refractory metals. The ductility minimums lie between 1000 and 2000 F. The tantalum and columbium alloys in Fig. 4 were annealed (recrystallized), and the molybdenum alloy and tungsten were stress relieved. Tests above 500 F were conducted in a vacuum.

Effect of Forming Temperature

Annealed columbium and tantalum alloys are formed at room temperature. Heating these alloys would reduce their formability, because of strain aging, and would cause oxidation and possible surface contamination.

Tungsten is brittle at room temperature, so thin tungsten sheet is formed at 600 to 1000 F, and thicker sheet or complex shapes are formed at 1000 to 1500 F after stress relief.

Molybdenum and molybdenum alloys, in thin sheets, can be formed cold to some extent, but heating helps to prevent fracture and delamination. As shown in Fig. 4, the TZM alloy is most ductile at 200 F (just above the ductile-to-brittle transition temperature). Further rise in temperature decreases the ductility, because of strain aging. Most molybdenum is formed at 200 to 600 F, but thicker metal or complex shapes are formed at 600 to 1200 F.

Figure 5 shows the effect of heating on the bending of Mo-0.5Ti sheet. It is

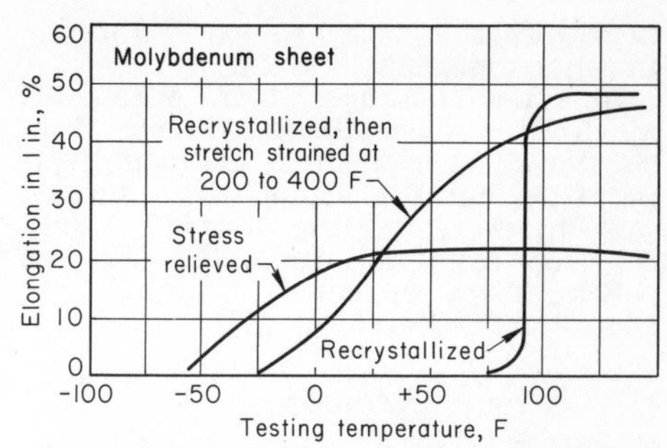

Fig. 2. Effect of heat treatment and strain hardening on the ductility (and the ductile-to-brittle transition temperature range) of unalloyed molybdenum sheet, as determined by tension tests

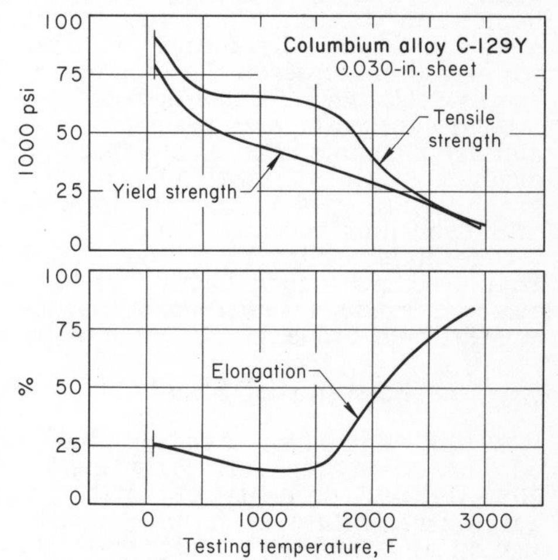

Fig. 3. Effect of temperature on strength and elongation of vacuum-annealed (recrystallized) columbium alloy sheet

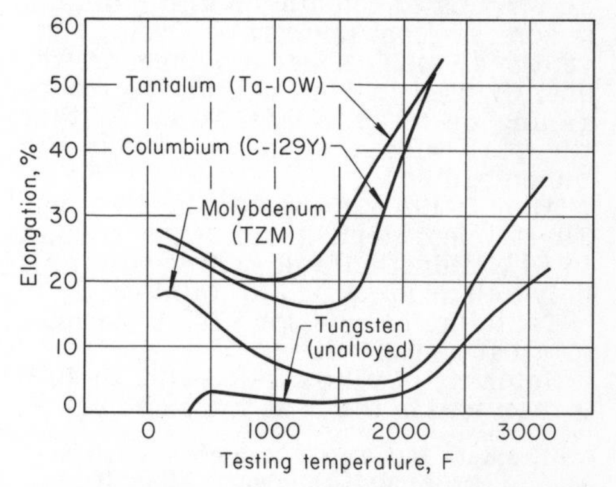

Fig. 4. Effect of temperature on the ductility of four refractory metals

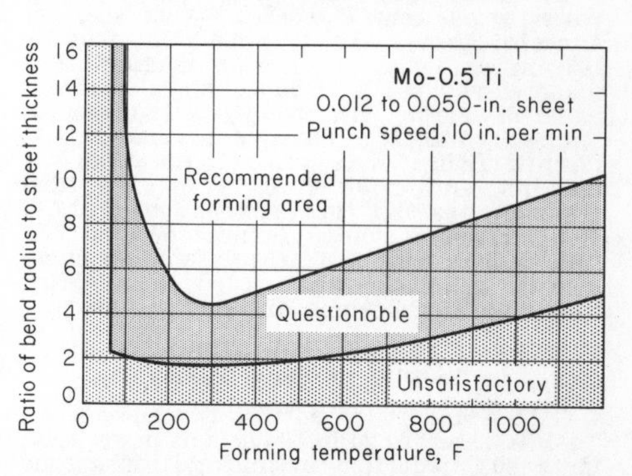

Fig. 5. Effect of temperature on the formability of Mo-0.5Ti sheet, as indicated by ratio of bend radius to sheet thickness

most formable at 200 to 400 F. Forming in other zones may crack it.

In one instance, two sheets of Mo-0.5Ti required beading. One sheet shattered when formed at room temperature, but the second sheet formed well in severe forming at 300 F. Erickson cup tests had indicated the two sheets to be of equal formability at room temperature.

Lubricants

The types of lubricants used include oils, extreme-pressure lubricants, soaps, waxes, silicones, graphite, molybdenum disulfide, copper plating, and an acrylic enamel coating made by suspending powdered copper in acrylic resin.

Ordinary oils and greases are commonly used in the forming of columbium and tantalum, because these metals are generally formed at room temperature. For severe forming operations petrolatum is frequently used.

Solid lubricants and suspensions of suitable pigments, such as molybdenum disulfide with or without colloidal graphite, are used in the hot forming of molybdenum and tungsten.

Chlorinated lubricants and others that decompose upon heating to form toxic or noxious fumes must not be used without proper safety precautions.

Forming of Sheet

All the common sheet forming methods are used for refractory metals. However, the necessity of using elevated temperature in forming molybdenum and tungsten usually precludes stretch forming and rubber-pad forming of these two metals.

Columbium and Tantalum. Almost all forming of columbium and tantalum is done at room temperature using conventional tools. A backup sheet is frequently used in a press brake to reduce galling or to provide support, so that the part will more closely follow the punch radius.

Alloy C-103 is more ductile than type 310 stainless steel; it can be power spun to 60% reduction and deflects the rolls only half as much as 310 stainless.

Tantalum can be spun in thicknesses as great as 0.620 in.

Spinning of alloys C-103 and Ta-10W is discussed in the next two examples.

Example 506. Power Spinning a Large Cone From Columbium Alloy in One Pass (Fig. 6)

The 34-in.-diam cone shown in Fig. 6 was power spun from a 0.068-in.-thick sheet of annealed (recrystallized) columbium alloy C-103, in one pass on a cone mandrel. The mandrel had a 50° included angle, and was made of ductile cast iron at a hardness of Rockwell C 58. The rollers, which had a ⅜-in. forming radius, were set 0.028 in. from the mandrel, and deflected 0.011 in. The final thickness was 0.033 in. (a reduction of 51.4% from starting thickness). Spindle speed was 200 rpm, with a feed of 6 in. per min. No intermediate reheating was needed. A lubricant containing molybdenum disulfide was used.

Example 507. Spinning 0.620-In.-Thick Ta-10W in Three Passes

Galling and rough surface developed when Ta-10W sheet, 0.620 in. thick, was power spun for a 50% reduction in thickness on a cone mandrel with 60° included angle, in one pass. Unacceptable workpieces were the result of insufficient machine capacity.

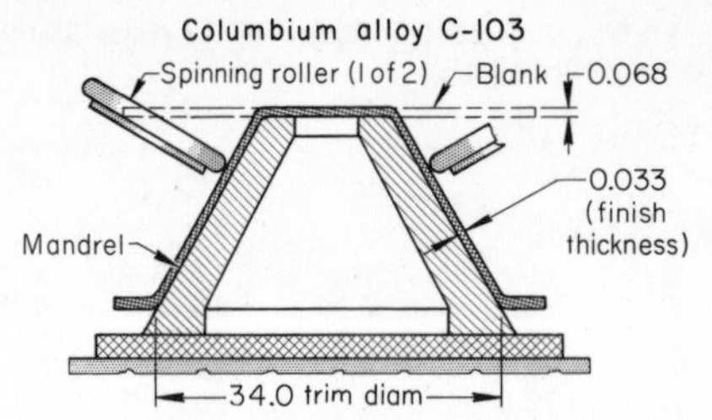

Fig. 6. Large columbium alloy cone that was power spun in one pass without intermediate reheating (Example 506)

These problems were eliminated by spinning the sheet in three passes. Reduction in the first pass was 30%, on a mandrel with 90° included angle. In the second spinning pass, a 60° cone was spun for a total reduction of 50%, followed by a third spinning on a 30° mandrel for 75% total reduction in thickness. All spinning was done hot. Oxyacetylene torches preheated the tools to 500 to 600 F and heated the work to 700 to 800 F during spinning. Intermediate heating was unnecessary. Approximately 40,000 lb of the rated machine force of 50,000 lb was used in the spinning operation. As lubricant, a paste-like mixture of graphite in light machine oil was applied to the inner and outer surfaces with a brush before spinning.

Molybdenum and Tungsten. All the common sheet-metal forming methods except rubber-pad forming and stretch forming are used for molybdenum and tungsten. These metals are formed at high temperature to prevent cracking and delamination that occur when forming at room temperature. Stretch forming has not been successful, because of the difficulties in adapting high temperatures to the process. Some rubber-pad forming of molybdenum is done, but not of tungsten, because of the higher temperatures required.

Proper preparation of the edges of blanks is necessary in forming molybdenum and tungsten. All edges in tension during forming must be rounded or polished to prevent fracture. Shearing and sawing cause edge cracking and delamination, which must be removed before forming.

Power and manual spinning are widely used for working tungsten sheet. Complex contoured or deeply recessed parts are often produced by drop-hammer forming. All work is done with heated tools and work-metal temperatures ranging from 1100 to 2000 F. Many failures in forming tungsten are caused by the stressing of edge defects in the starting blanks. These defects originate in sawing, shearing or blanking and are difficult to detect visually.

Tools and workpiece blanks are heated by electrical-resistance elements, heat lamps, and gas torches. An allowance for the difference in thermal expansion between steel dies and a tungsten or molybdenum workpiece is required for all parts whose shape or dimensions will be out of tolerance because of forming at high temperature. Hot work tool steels are satisfactory die materials. A bronze facing is recommended for steel dies if galling becomes a problem. Aluminum tooling is not recommended, because of its high thermal expansion.

The following table lists the approximate coefficients of thermal expansion for molybdenum and tungsten, and three common tool materials (steel, bismuth alloy, and aluminum).

Metal	Micro-in./in./°F
Molybdenum	2.7
Tungsten	2.6
Steel	6.5
Bismuth alloy	15.2
Aluminum	13.1

Localized deformation and wrinkling of complex parts formed from molybdenum and tungsten are generally a result of die design and operation. These problems can be avoided by proper die clearance, staging and contours, and mechanical support. A steel backup sheet is sometimes used to insure that the part more closely follows the punch, or to reduce galling.

Tungsten can be power spun in machines that are capable of power spinning steel. Spinning tungsten sheet that used the full capacity of the machine is shown in the next example.

Example 508. Power Spinning of Tungsten to 50% Reduction in Thickness

A 0.645-in.-thick tungsten sheet was power spun to approximately 50% reduction in thickness (0.347 in.), on a cone mandrel having a 60° included angle. The machine used was capable of power spinning 0.750-in.-thick low-carbon steel.

The mandrel was preheated to 600 to 800 F, and the workpiece was heated to 2000 F during spinning, by oxyacetylene torches. Mandrel speed was 250 rpm.

The rollers had a ¾-in. forming radius, and were set 0.325 in. from the mandrel.

The total machine rating of 50,000-lb force was applied to the rollers, and as spinning progressed, feed decreased from 5 to 1 in. per min.

After spinning, the cone was stress relieved at 2150 F for 1 hr in a vacuum of 10^{-4} mm Hg.

Forming of Preformed Blanks

Refractory metals preformed and welded into shaped blanks, cones or cylinders can be formed by the same process used for unwelded blanks of common sheet metals. The welds must be of high quality to avoid defects or embrittlement. Chemical blanking, electrical discharge machining, abrasive cutting, and milling are preferred for making blanks. The sequence of operations generally used in preforming is:

1 Form intermediate shape.
2 Weld by TIG method.
3 Grind weld flush and inspect.
4 Stress relieve or anneal.
5 Form to final shape.

Forming of a C-103 welded preform is described in the following example:

Example 509. Bulge Forming a Conical Preform of Columbium Alloy

A conical preform was bulge formed to produce a thrust cone for a rocket engine.

The preform consisted of three sections of columbium alloy C-103 sheet, 0.030 in. thick, press formed and TIG welded. It was not necessary to stress relieve or anneal the weld prior to forming. The welds were cleaned, ground and inspected for defects. The preform had a base diameter of 56 in. and tapered to a top diameter of 30½ in.; length was 28 in.

Bulge forming was done in a hydraulically actuated mechanical die. After forming, a nozzle extension ring of alloy C-129 was welded to the cone.

Weldments of molybdenum and tungsten are generally formed at temperatures 200 to 300 F higher than unwelded sheet of the same metals, and the weldments usually are stress relieved before forming. In some extreme applications, parts are stress relieved before and after welding, and after forming.

FORMING OF NONFERROUS METALS

CONTENTS

Forming of Aluminum Alloys

*By the ASM Committee on Forming of Aluminum Alloys**

ALUMINUM and its alloys are among the most readily formable of the commonly fabricated metals. There are, of course, differences between aluminum alloys and other metals in the amount of permissible deformation, in some aspects of tool design, and in details of procedure. These differences stem primarily from the lower tensile and yield strengths of aluminum alloys, and from their comparatively slow rate of work hardening. The compositions and tempers of aluminum alloys also affect their formability. This article emphasizes those aspects of commercial forming processes and equipment that apply specifically to aluminum alloys. Basic information on the forming of metals in general is given in other articles in this volume.

Alloy Selection

The factors involved in selecting an alloy for a specific manufacturing application are discussed in detail in the article "The Selection and Application of Aluminum and Aluminum Alloys", on pages 866 to 888 in Volume 1 of this Handbook.

Ratings of general formability or workability of the commercially available alloys in the various tempers, and comparative ratings of alloys and tempers for specific types of forming, are tabulated under specific forming processes in this article. Such ratings provide generally reliable comparisons of work metals, but at best are only an approximate guide to forming limits in any specific application. Trial runs and evaluative techniques developed for specialized applications are needed in borderline or critical situations.

Choice of temper may depend on the severity of the forming operations. The annealed temper may be required for severe forming operations such as deep drawing, or for roll forming or bending to exceptionally small radii. Usually, the strongest temper that can be formed consistently is selected. For less severe forming operations, the intermediate tempers, or even full-hard work metal, can be used.

Non-Heat-Treatable Alloys. Alloys 1100 and 3003 are frequently used in forming applications, because of their excellent workability and low cost. If somewhat higher strength is required, alloys containing magnesium are commonly used (for example, in order of increasing strength, alloys 3004, 5052, 5154 and 5086).

If superior finishing characteristics are needed in addition to higher strength, an alloy containing a small amount of manganese in addition to magnesium (alloy 5053, 5252 or 5457) can be used. Holding impurities at a low level in alloys used for decorative and finishing purposes also helps in developing bright, uniform finish.

Heat treatable alloys are used in applications for which a high strength-to-weight ratio is required. These include alloys 6061, 2014, 2024, 7075 and 7178, in approximate order of increasing strength.

The annealed temper (O) is the most workable condition for forming, but it entails the greatest expense in subsequent heat treating and straightening. Alloys that have been freshly solution heat treated and quenched (W temper) are nearly as formable as when annealed, and can be given increased strength after forming by natural or artificial aging, without reheating and consequent exposure of the finished part to warping. Alloys can be stored in the W temper for a reasonable period at a low temperature. (Almost no aging occurs in most alloys at −20 F.)

Material that has been solution heat treated at the mill, but not artificially aged (T3, T4 or W temper), is generally suitable only for mild forming operations such as bending, mild drawing, or moderate stretch forming.

Solution heat treated and artificially aged (T6 temper) alloys are seldom used for forming, other than bending to standard radii and forming of very shallow shapes. Although alloys in the T6 temper are much stronger, they have lost so much ductility in hardening that they are apt to fracture in even moderately severe forming.

Equipment and Tools

Most of the equipment used in the forming of steel and other metals is suitable for use with aluminum alloys. Because of the generally lower yield strength of aluminum alloys, however, press tonnage requirements are usually lower than for comparable operations on steel, and higher press speeds can be used. Similarly, equipment for roll forming, spinning, stretch forming, and other forming operations on aluminum

*JAMES C. HERR, *Chairman,* Chief of Process Control, General Dynamics/Fort Worth; ELDON COOPERRIDER, Chief Plant Engineer, Lennox Industries Inc.

GEORGE F. FARLEY, President (retired), Spincraft Inc.; RICHARD T. KENNEDY, Product Engineering Manager, Sunbeam Corp.; C. E. MCHAN, Group Engineer, Manufacturing Research, Lockheed-Georgia Co. Div., Lockheed Aircraft Corp.; F. G. MCKEE, Manager of Metal Working Div., Alcoa Process Development Laboratories, Aluminum Company of America; PAUL R. O'BRIEN, Director of Automotive Section, Reynolds Metals Co.; ARTHUR L. PAGE, Engineer, Talon, Inc.

WALTER PAJERSKI, Manufacturing Process Engineer, Mine Safety Appliances Co.; SCOTT F. REEKIE, Manager of Metals and Plastics Plant, Tektronix, Inc.; R. A. RIDOUT, Director of Technical Services, Kaiser Aluminum & Chemical Sales, Inc.

need not be so massive or rated for such heavy loading as for comparable operations on steel.

Tools. Total wear on tools used in forming aluminum is somewhat less than with steel. This results in part from the lower force levels involved, and in part from the smoother surface condition that is characteristic of aluminum alloys. Accordingly, tools can sometimes be made from less expensive materials, even for relatively long runs.

However, a higher-quality surface finish is generally required on tools used with aluminum alloys, to avoid marking. The oxide film on the surface of aluminum alloys is highly abrasive, and for this reason many forming tools are made of hardened tool steels. As a rule, these tools, even if otherwise suitable, should not be used interchangeably to form steel parts, because this could destroy the high finish on the tools.

Most aluminum alloys require smaller clearances between punches and dies in blanking and piercing than do steels. They require larger clearances but about the same radii on drawing tools, to allow free flow of metal and avoid excessive stretching.

The amount of springback in forming aluminum alloys is generally less than in forming low-carbon steel, and this must be considered in tool design. The amount of springback is roughly proportional to the yield strength of the metal.

The slower rate of work hardening of aluminum alloys permits a greater number of successive draws than is possible with steel.

Lubricants

Lubricants must be selected specifically for their compatibility with aluminum alloys and their suitability for the particular forming operation. A lubricant suitable for use on a steel part will not necessarily be suitable for use in the forming of a similar aluminum alloy part.

Properly formulated lubricants take into account the special requirements of regulation of moisture content in nonaqueous systems, corrosion inhibitors, and pH control, in order to prevent staining or corrosion of aluminum alloys and to make duration of contact with the workpiece less critical.

The lubricants most widely used in the forming of aluminum alloys are listed in Table 1 in approximate order of increasing effectiveness. The use of various special-purpose lubricants is discussed in sections of this article that deal with individual forming processes.

The kerosine used as a lubricant is less irritating to the hands than the one used as a fuel.

Table 1. Typical Lubricants Used in the Forming of Aluminum Alloys

(Listed in approximate order of increasing effectiveness) (a)

1 Kerosine
2 Mineral oil (viscosity, 40 to 300 SUS at 100 F)
3 Petroleum jelly
4 Mineral oil plus 10 to 20% fatty oil
5 Tallow plus 50% paraffin
6 Tallow plus 70% paraffin
7 Mineral oil plus 10 to 15% sulfurized fatty oil plus 10% fatty oil
8 Dried soap films or wax films(a)
9 Fat emulsions in aqueous soap solutions plus finely divided fillers(b)
10 Mineral oil plus sulfurized fatty oil plus fatty oil plus finely divided fillers(b)

(a) For some applications, dried soap or wax films (lubricant No. 8) are less effective than lubricants No. 5, 6 and 7. (b) Typical fillers are chalk, lithopone, white lead, talc, mica, zinc oxide, clay, sulfur and graphite.

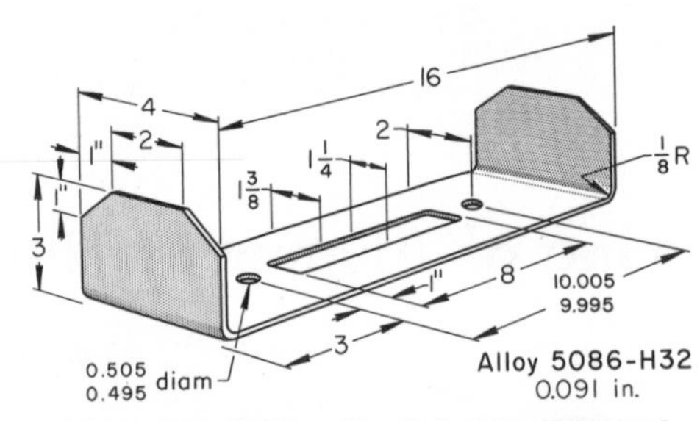

Fig. 1. Bracket produced in quantities of 100 to 500 by shearing, piercing, and forming. Piercing was done with tooling normally used for high production, to obtain dimensional accuracy. (Example 510)

Blanking and Piercing

Blanking and piercing of aluminum alloy flat stock are ordinarily done in punch presses, because of their high production rates and ability to maintain close tolerances. Press brakes are sometimes used, particularly for experimental or short-run production.

Because of the generally lower shear strength of aluminum alloys, lower-tonnage presses or press brakes are usually required than for comparable operations with steel. Total shearing force needed can be calculated as the product of shear strength, total length of cut, and metal thickness, but allowance must be made for different alloys, for dulling of the cutting edges of punches and dies, and for variation in clearance between punch and die. The shear strength of the commonly used aluminum alloys ranges from 9000 to 49,000 psi, whereas that of low-carbon steel is from 35,000 to 67,000 psi.

Tool Materials. A discussion of materials for blanking and piercing dies is given on pages 69 to 77 in this volume. Aluminum alloys are classed with other soft materials, such as copper and magnesium alloys. In general, for a given tool material, tool life will be longer for blanking and piercing aluminum alloys than for steel.

In some applications, a less expensive die can be used than with steel parts, particularly for relatively short runs. Cast zinc dies, which cost only about one-fifth as much as tool steel dies, are used for runs of up to about 2000 parts. Steel-rule dies and template dies also reduce tooling costs for short runs or moderate-length runs. For example, an aluminum alloy blank 19.5 by 12 in. by 0.040 in. thick was made in a steel-rule die having an expected life of 150 pieces. For the production quantity, the burr height did not exceed 0.005 in. Punches and die buttons for seven pierced holes of 5⁄32, 3⁄16 and 1⁄4-in. diameter were incorporated in the die.

Low-carbon steel or cast iron dies sometimes replace hardened tool steel dies, even for long runs.

Punches are usually made from annealed or hardened tool steel, depending on the size and complexity of the part and on the length of the run.

Carbide tools are seldom required, even for extremely long runs.

Tolerances. A tolerance of ±0.005 in. is normal in the blanking and piercing of aluminum alloy parts in a punch press. Using a press brake, it is possible to blank and pierce to a location tolerance of ±0.010 in. or less, although tolerances for general press-brake operations usually range from ±0.020 to ±0.030 in.

For economy in tool cost, specified tolerance should be no less than is actually necessary for the particular part. A tolerance of ±0.005 in. would probably require that the punch and die be jig-ground, adding 30 to 40% to their cost. A tolerance of ±0.002 in. may require the addition of a shaving operation. Besides the cost of an extra die, labor costs would be increased by the additional operation.

For extremely accurate work, an allowance must be made for the shrinkage of holes and expansion of blanks resulting from the elasticity of the stock. This allowance, made to both punch and die, does not change the clearance between them, and is primarily a function of stock thickness:

Stock thickness, in.	Allowance per side, in.
0.010 to 0.030	0.00050
0.030 to 0.060	0.00075
0.060 to 0.135	0.00100

For large sizes and for normal tolerances, this correction is not very important.

Unacceptable distortion or mislocation of existing holes in a part by subsequent operations must be avoided. In the following example, special tooling was used to maintain close tolerances between a large pierced opening and adjacent holes.

Example 510. Use of a Compound Die for Accurate Piercing of a Low-Production Part (Fig. 1)

The mounting bracket shown in Fig. 1 was produced in quantities of 100 to 500 pieces by shearing, piercing and forming, as follows:

1 Shear blank to size in a square shear (1200 pieces per hour)
2 Miter shear four corners in a square shear (650 pieces per hour)
3 Pierce rectangular opening and two round holes, in one stroke in a punch press, using a compound die (850 pieces per hour)
4 Form two flanges in two strokes in a press brake, using a standard 90° V-die (550 pieces per hour).

Dimensional tolerances (±1⁄32 in.) could be met by using low-production utility tooling for shearing and forming. However, it was necessary to pierce the rectangular opening and the two round holes in a single press stroke with a compound die, rather than to punch these openings successively in separate dies (normal low-production procedure), to maintain the accurate hole location shown in Fig. 1.

For lot sizes of up to 10,000 brackets, trimming the four corners of the sheared blank was incorporated into the compound die for the two holes and rectangular cutout. Another die bent both flanges in one press stroke. Maximum production rate was 850 pieces per hour. A three-station progressive die was estimated capable of producing 1600 pieces per hour.

Special requirements on press construction and maintenance, and on tool material and design, are sometimes imposed by tolerances and other workpiece specifications, as shown in the example that follows.

Example 511. Blanking, Drawing and Piercing a Gas-Mask Spacer to Close Tolerances (Fig. 2)

A spacer for a gas-mask filter can (Fig. 2) had to be produced to close tolerances on outside dimensions, and without burrs or sharp edges that could cut through the mineral wool that was wrapped over the outer edge of the spacer, as filter material, before it was inserted in the can.

To save the cost of an extra trimming or edge-turndown operation, the spacers were produced by blanking, drawing and piercing in a compound die. As the blanking sections of the die dulled, however, objectionably large burrs were produced, resulting in sharp outside edges and oversize parts.

To eliminate these problems, the blanking sections of the die were made from high-carbon high-chromium tool steel. Also, a four-post die set was used, and the operation was done in a press with minimum clearance in the gibs. The parts were checked regularly throughout the run for dimensional accuracy and burred edges.

The extreme outer dimensions were maintained satisfactorily by controlling the inside dimensions to the tolerances shown in Fig. 2.

Originally, aluminum alloy 3003-O was used, because of its drawability. A change was made to 3003-H14 because of its ability to hold closer tolerances, although scrap loss was higher because of fractures. The spacer also was successfully produced from aluminum alloy 5052-O.

For notching and piercing to close tolerances, an alternative to the use of a precision die in a punch press is the use of a tape-controlled turret punch press equipped with standard utility punches and dies, as described in the following example. Where such equipment is available, this technique is usually less expensive for relatively short runs, and is capable of maintaining tolerances of ±0.005 in.

Example 512. Cost of Close-Tolerance Piercing and Notching in a Punch Press vs a Tape-Controlled Turret Press (Fig. 3)

A cost comparison of two methods of piercing and notching a part to hole-location tolerance of ±0.008 in. is given in Fig. 3. The graph in Fig. 3 shows that a tape-controlled turret punch press with standard tooling produced parts more economically than a conventional punch press and precision compound die, for up to about 4000 pieces.

If the part design had been modified, the cost of a new tape for the tape-controlled press would have been only $43, compared with about $200 or more for modifying the precision die. Therefore, limited quantities of the modified part would have been produced at a lower unit cost by the tape-controlled press, but for large quantities, parts would be produced more economically by the conventional press method.

Production data applicable to both methods are given in the table with Fig. 3. They show the costs used in plotting the graph.

Sheared blanks 5.75 by 9.75 in. were used in both methods. The compound die was capable of holding dimensional tolerances within ±0.002 in., and the turret punch press within ±0.005 in.

If tolerances permit, holes in the sidewalls of formed parts can sometimes be pierced before forming. This can reduce costs by eliminating the need for one or more horn dies or cam-actuated dies and the resultant slow handling of parts.

An initial blank layout can be calculated from formulas used for determining bend allowance (see "Blank Size" on page 109 in "Press-Brake Forming"). The final blank layout is usually developed by successive trials and modifications. Trial blanks can be marked with a grid pattern to determine accurately the pattern and the dimensions of metal movement. (No holes should be pierced in areas of metal movement if the hole shape is important.) The part described in the following example was produced by using a bend-allowance formula to determine flat pattern dimensions, and to determine flange hole locations on the blank.

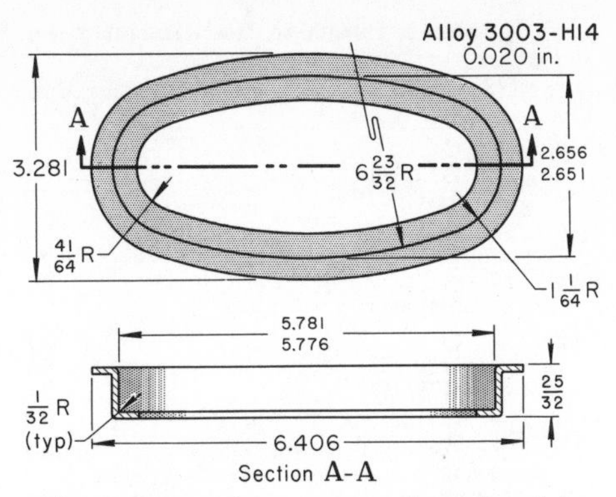

Fig. 2. Spacer for a gas mask produced to close tolerances by blanking, drawing and piercing in a compound die (Example 511)

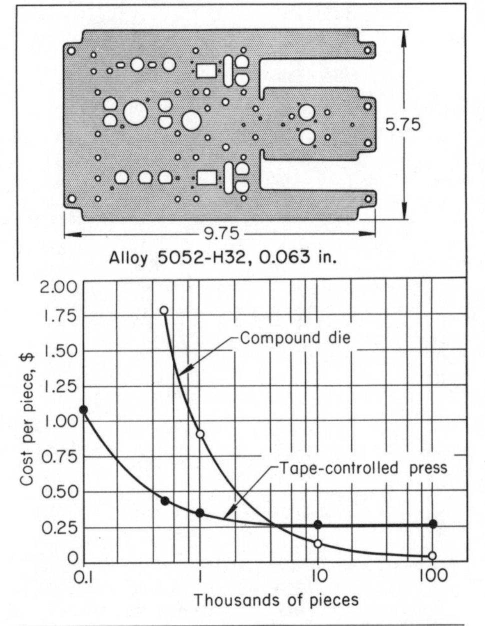

Item	Type of punch press: Conventional, with precision compound die	Tape-controlled turret type, with standard tooling
Die cost	$850	...
Tape cost	...	$ 43.30(a)
Labor costs (1000 pcs):		
Setup(b)	$18.32(c)	$ 38.44(d)
Production	30.23(e)	269.08(f)
Total (labor)	$48.55	$307.52

(a) Cost of 10 hr for production of tape, at $4.33 per hour for labor and overhead. (b) Four setups; 250 pieces per setup. (c) Based on ½ hr for each setup, at $9.16 per hr for labor and overhead. (d) Based on 1 hr for each setup, at $9.61 per hour for labor and overhead. (e) Based on 0.0033 hr per piece, at $9.16 per hour for labor and overhead. (f) Based on 0.028 hr per piece, at $9.61 per hour for labor and overhead.

Fig. 3. Cost comparison of two methods used to produce a flat part by blanking, piercing and notching (Example 512)

Example 513. Rectangular Box Produced From a Flat Pierced Blank (Fig. 4)

The shallow rectangular box shown in Fig. 4 was produced by drawing a flat blank that had previously been blanked and pierced in a compound die.

The blank layout, also shown in Fig. 4, was developed to meet a tolerance of ±0.008 in. on the hole locations and length, width and height dimensions of the box, except at the corners, where compound metal movement took place during forming. Variations in metal thickness and hardness made it necessary to trim the four corners after forming to assure a uniform height. By using the conventional bend-allowance formula to determine the stock to allow for the flat blank, the flange widths and hole locations (after forming) were within the ±0.008-in. tolerance allowed.

The shape of the blank (as shown in Fig. 4) satisfied the requirement for a simple blanking-die contour and a minimum of trimming after forming. The areas of metal movement during the drawing operation are also shown on the blank layout in Fig. 4.

Clearance between punch and die must be controlled in blanking and piercing, in order to obtain a uniform shearing action. Clearance is usually expressed as the distance between mating surfaces of punch and die (per side) in percentage of work thickness.

Correct clearance between punch and die depends on the alloy as well as the sheet thickness. Suggested punch-to-die clearances for blanking and piercing the common alloys are listed in Table 2.

The character of the shearing action also depends on the sharpness of the tools. Dull cutting edges on punch and die have effects similar to those of excessive clearance, with the effect on burr size being particularly pronounced.

With proper clearance, the fractures proceeding from the punch surface and from the die surface of the work meet cleanly without secondary shearing and excessive plastic deformation. Secondary shearing indicates that the clearance is too small; a large radius or dished contour at the sheared edge and a stringy burr indicate that the clearance is too great.

For additional information on punch-to-die clearances, see the article "Piercing of Low-Carbon Steel", which begins on page 44 in this volume.

Die Taper. The walls of die openings in blanking or piercing dies are often tapered ½° from the vertical to minimize sticking of the blank or slug in

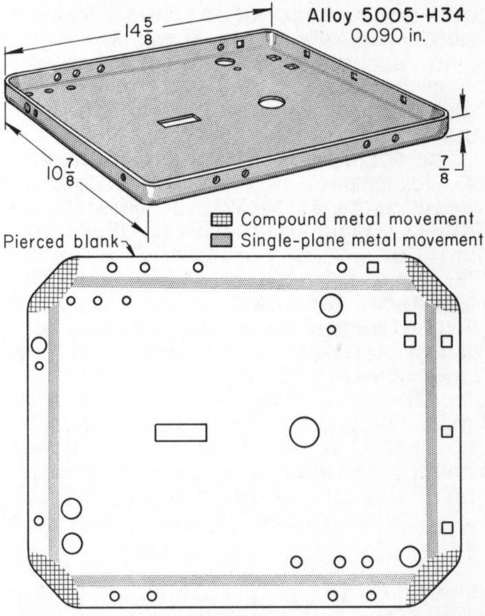

Fig. 4. Shallow rectangular box produced by drawing a flat blank that had been blanked and pierced in a compound die (Example 513)

the die. A straight vertical section of at least ⅛ in. (or equal to the metal thickness for stock thicker than ⅛ in.) is usually left at the upper end of the die opening, to provide for sharpening without changing the clearance. Tapered die relief is usually more suitable for piercing aluminum than counterbore design relief.

Stripping force of 3 to 20% of the total blanking and piercing tonnage is used for aluminum alloys. The force needed depends on the alloy, temper and stock thickness. Sharpness of cutting edges on punch and die, clearance between punch and die, lubrication, and uniformity of application of stripper-plate pressure also affect stripping force.

Lubricants are normally used in blanking or piercing aluminum alloy parts, to reduce sticking of slugs or blanks in the die opening, and to facilitate clean stripping from the punch without buckling. Lower tool-maintenance costs and smoother edges on blanks or holes can be obtained with suitable lubrication. The lubricants most commonly used include the first four types listed in Table 1, or proprietary compounds based on them.

Table 2. Punch-to-Die Clearances for Blanking and Piercing Aluminum Alloys

Alloy	Temper	Clearance per side, %t(a)
1100	O	5.0
	H12, H14	6.0
	H16, H18	7.0
2014	O	6.5
	T4, T6	8.0
2024	O	6.5
	T3, T36, T4	8.0
3003	O	5.0
	H12, H14	6.0
	H16, H18	7.0
3004	O	6.5
	H32, H34	7.0
	H36, H38	7.5
5005	O	5.0
	H12, H14, H32, H34	6.0
	H36, H38	7.0
5050	O	5.0
	H32, H34	6.0
	H36, H38	7.0
5052	O	6.5
	H32, H34	7.0
	H36, H38	7.5
5083	O	7.0
	H323, H343	7.5
5086	O, H112	7.0
	H32, H34, H36	7.5
5154	O, H112	7.0
	H32, H34, H36, H38	7.5
5257(b)	O	5.0
	H25	6.0
	H28	7.0
5454	O, H112	7.0
	H32, H34	7.5
6061	O	5.5
	T4	6.0
	T6	7.0
7075	O	6.5
	W, T6	8.0
7178	O	6.5
	W, T6	8.0

(a) t = thickness of sheet. (b) Also alloys 5357, 5457, 5557 and 5657.

Table 3. Springback Allowances for 90° Bends in 2024 and 7075 Aluminum Alloy Sheet

Sheet thickness, in.	Springback allowance, in degrees, for bend radius, in., of: 3/32	1/8	3/16	1/4	5/16	3/8	7/16	1/2
2024-O and 7075-O								
0.020	3	4	5½	7½	8½	9	9½	12
0.025	2¾	3¾	5½	6½	8	8¼	8¾	10¾
0.032	2¼	3	4¾	6	6¾	7	7½	9½
0.040	2	3	4	5	6	6¼	6¾	8¾
0.051	2	2½	3½	4	5	5¼	5¾	7½
0.064	1½	2	2¾	3¾	4½	5	5½	6¾
0.081	1	1½	2	2½	3¼	3½	4	4¾
0.094	...	...	1¾	2½	3	3¼	3¾	4½
0.125	...	...	1½	2	2¼	2¾	3	3¾
2024-T3								
0.020	10	12	15½	19	22½	24	27¼	33½
0.025	8¾	10½	14	16¾	17¾	21	23	28½
0.032	7¾	8¾	12	14½	16¾	17¾	19¼	24
0.040	7¼	8¼	10¾	12¾	14½	15¼	17	20½
0.051	...	...	9	10½	12¼	13	14½	16¾
0.064	...	...	8	9¾	11¼	12	12¾	15
0.081	...	...	...	...	9½	10½	11¼	13
0.094	...	...	...	...	8¾	9¾	10½	12

SOURCE: "Die Design Handbook", 2nd Edition, ASTME, McGraw-Hill, 1965

Press-Brake Forming

The press-brake forming techniques used with aluminum alloys are similar to those used with steel and other metals, differing only in some details of tool design.

Tolerances in press-brake forming are larger than those in punch-press operations. For simple shapes that are relatively long and narrow, a tolerance of ±1/32 in. can usually be maintained. On larger parts of more complex cross section, the tolerance may be as much as ±1/16 in.

Springback, or partial return to the original shape upon removal of the bending forces, occurs in most bending operations. (For a detailed discussion of springback, see page 108 in the article "Press-Brake Forming".)

The amount of springback depends on the yield strength, the bend radius, and the thickness of the stock. Table 3 shows the effects of these variables, giving springback allowances in degrees of overbending that have been used for high-strength aluminum alloys 2024 and 7075.

The springback allowance, or number of degrees of overbending required, ranges from 1° to 12° for 2024-O and 7075-O (yield strength of 11,000 psi min), and from 7¼° to 33½° for 2024-T3 (yield strength of 50,000 psi). The allowance increases with increasing yield strength and bend radius, but varies inversely with stock thickness. The allowance for bends of other than 90° can be estimated on a proportional basis. For bend angles of less than 90°, the springback may be greater unless the bend radius is decreased, because the metal in the bend area may not have been stressed beyond its yield point.

Radii to which bends can be made depend on the properties of the metal, and on the design, dimensions and condition of tools. For most metals, the ratio of minimum bend radius to thickness is approximately constant, because ductility is the primary limiting factor on minimum bend radius. This is not true of aluminum alloys, for which the ratio increases with the thickness.

Table 4 shows the experimentally determined variation of minimum bend radius with alloy, temper and thickness for most of the commonly used aluminum alloys, in conventional bending operations with rigid dies.

Table 5 lists the common aluminum alloys and tempers that are capable of 180° cold bends over zero radius, and shows the maximum sheet thickness at which such bends can be made.

Minimum bend radii recommended for several groups of aluminum alloys in press-brake and hydraulic forming are given in Tables 6 and 7 on page 872 of Volume 1 of this Handbook.

With special tooling, aluminum alloys can be bent to smaller radii than indicated in standard tables. Bottoming dies, and dies that combine bottoming with air bending, are used for this purpose. Hydraulic forming, forming with rubber-pad dies, and high-energy-rate forming also produce good small-radius bends.

Sometimes it is possible to take advantage of the grain direction in the work metal: The most severe bends can be made across the direction of rolling. If similar bends are made in two or more directions, it is recommended that all bends be made at an angle to the direction of rolling, if possible.

Local heating along the bend lines can sometimes be used to produce small bend radii without fracture; this is particularly useful in bending plate.

The maximum temperature that can be used without serious loss in mechanical properties is 300 to 400 F for cold worked material. Reheating of naturally aged aluminum alloys 2014 and 2024 is not recommended unless the part will be artificially aged. Generally, any reheating sufficient to improve formability will lower the resistance to corrosion to an undesirable degree, except with alclad sheet.

Blank Development. For relatively simple parts, particularly where close tolerances are not required, the blank layout can be developed directly by using bend-allowance tables or mathematical formulas (see page 109, and Table 2 on page 110, in the article "Press-Brake Forming"). As a general rule, the initial calculated blank layout and die design are developed into final form by successive trial and modification.

Lubricants are needed for nearly all press-brake forming of aluminum alloys. The light protective film of oil sometimes present on mill stock is often adequate for mild bending opera-

Table 4. Minimum Recommended Radii for 90° Cold Bends in Aluminum Alloy Sheet (a)

Alloy	Temper	Minimum bend radius in 1/32 in., for sheet thickness, in., of: 0.016	0.025	0.032	0.040	0.050	0.063	0.090	0.125	0.190	0.250
1100	O	0	0	0	0	0	0	0	0	0	0
	H12	0	0	0	0	0	0	0	0	3	6
	H14	0	0	0	0	0	0	0	0	3	6
	H16	0	0	0	0	1	2	3	4	8	16
	H18	1	1	2	2	3	4	6	8	16	24
2014	O	0	0	0	0	0	0	0	0	3	6
	T6	2	4	4	5	7	8	15	20	36	64
2024 & alclad 2024	O	0	0	0	0	0	0	0	0	3	6
	T3	2	3	4	5	7	8	15	20	30	48
3003, 5005, 5357 and 5457, at tempers listed at right	O	0	0	0	0	0	0	0	0	0	0
	H12 or H32	0	0	0	0	0	0	0	0	3	6
	H14 or H34	0	0	0	0	0	0	1	2	4	8
	H16 or H36	0	0	1	2	2	3	5	6	12	24
	H18 or H38	1	1	2	2	3	5	9	12	24	40
3004, alclad 3004, 5154, 5254 and 5454, at tempers listed at right	O	0	0	0	0	0	0	0	2	3	8
	H32	0	0	0	1	1	2	3	4	9	18
	H34	1	1	1	2	2	3	5	6	12	24
	H36	1	1	1	2	3	4	6	9	18	24
	H38	1	1	2	3	4	6	9	16	30	40
5050	O	0	0	0	0	0	0	0	0	0	0
	H32	0	0	0	0	0	0	0	2	3	8
	H34	0	0	0	0	0	1	2	4	6	12
	H36	1	1	1	2	2	3	6	8	16	24
	H38	1	1	2	3	4	6	9	12	24	40
5052 and 5652	O	0	0	0	0	0	0	0	2	3	4
	H32	0	0	0	0	1	2	3	4	6	12
	H34	0	0	0	1	1	2	4	5	9	16
	H36	1	1	1	2	3	4	5	8	18	24
	H38	1	1	2	3	4	6	9	12	24	40
5086 and 5155	O	0	0	0	0	0	1	2	3	6	8
	H32	1	1	1	2	2	3	5	6	12	16
	H34	1	1	2	2	3	3	6	8	18	24
6061 & alclad 6061	O	0	0	0	0	0	0	0	2	3	4
	T6	1	1	2	2	3	4	6	9	18	28
7075 & alclad 7075	O	0	0	0	1	1	2	3	5	9	18
	T6	2	2	4	8	10	12	18	24	36	64
7178 & alclad 7178	O	0	0	0	1	1	2	3	5	9	18
	T6	2	3	4	8	10	12	21	28	42	80

(a) These radii represent average values for forming in conventional equipment with tools of good design and condition. The minimum permissible radii in a forming operation on a specific part are subject to several variables and can be determined only by forming under shop conditions.

Table 5. Maximum Thicknesses of Aluminum Alloy Sheet That Can Be Cold Bent 180° Over Zero Radius

Alloy	Temper	Max sheet thickness, in.	Alloy	Temper	Max sheet thickness, in.
1100	O	1/8	5005	H34	1/32
	H12	1/16	5050	O	1/8
	H14	1/16		H32	1/16
	H16	1/64		H34	1/32
Alclad 2014 ..	O	1/16	5052	O	1/8
2024	O	1/16		H32	1/32
				H34	1/64
3003	O	1/8	5086	O	1/8
	H12	1/16			
	H14	1/16	5154	O	1/16
3004	O	1/8		H32	1/32
	H32	1/32	5457	O	1/8
	H34	1/64		H25	1/32
5005	O	1/8	6061	O	1/16
	H12	1/16		T4	1/32
	H14	1/16			
	H32	1/8	7075	O	1/32

tions, but when this is not sufficient, a lubricant is usually applied to the working surfaces of the tools and to the bend area of the workpiece to prevent scoring and metal pickup.

Depending on the severity of forming, the lubricant would generally be one of the first seven given in Table 1, or a proprietary compound based on one of these materials.

Tools. The bending, forming, piercing and notching dies used in press brakes for aluminum alloys are much the same as those used for low-carbon steel. To prevent marring or scratching of the workpiece, tools used for bending steel should be carefully cleaned and polished before being used for aluminum alloys. Rubber pads used in press-brake dies, when clean, will not scratch the surface of an aluminum sheet.

Because of the differences in tensile strength and springback, shut-height settings for aluminum alloys may be different from those for low-carbon steel.

Examples of Applications. The versatility of press brakes is shown in the following six examples.

Example 514. Forming a Curtain-Wall Panel in a Press Brake (Fig. 5)

The curtain-wall panel shown in Fig. 5 was formed by joggling and bending 1/8-in.-thick and 3/16-in.-thick clad aluminum sheets (5005 core and 6061 cladding) in a press brake. Panels ranged in width from 10 to 54 in., and in length from 118 to 200 in.

Joggling was done in a 200-ton press brake with 16-ft span between columns, using a standard joggle die. To prevent ram deflection from causing the joggle line to bow across the sheet, guide posts were attached to each end of the joggle-die shoes, and two heel blocks were fastened along the back edge.

The flanges were formed in the same press brake used for joggling, with a V-bending punch and die 18 ft long.

The ram was adjusted for the 1/8-in. and 3/16-in. sheets when joggling and flanging.

The joggle-relief notch also shown in Fig. 5 was made in the part to facilitate bending the flanges after the sheet had been joggled. The centerline of the notch corresponded to the bend line of the flange. Two notches were pierced in one stroke of a 25-ton press brake having a 60-in. bed. The punch had a 5° shear angle to reduce shock to the ram. The same punch and die were used for both the 1/8-in. and 3/16-in.-thick sheets.

After joggling and bending, the gap in the corner at the joggle was welded, and the panel was anodized. The 6061 cladding was used because of its ability to be anodized to the black tone specified.

Example 515. Use of Cast Plastic Blankets for Bending Corrugated Sheet (Fig. 6)

A top of an aircraft cargo container was formed from corrugated sheet of aluminum alloy 6061-T4 by making two 45° bends across the corrugations (Fig. 6). Bending in air or in a rubber-pad die caused the corrugations (which also had been formed when the metal was in the T4 temper) to flatten excessively.

To keep the corrugations from flattening, 18-in.-wide plastic blankets were cast to fit on each side of the sheet. The plastic, which

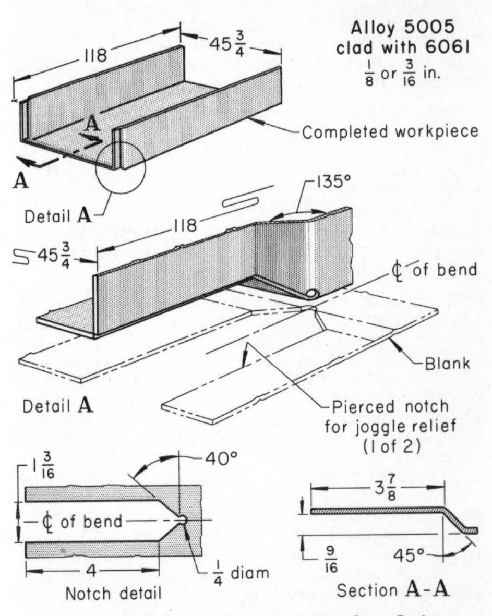

Fig. 5. Curtain-wall panel produced from clad aluminum sheet by joggling and bending in a press brake (Example 514)

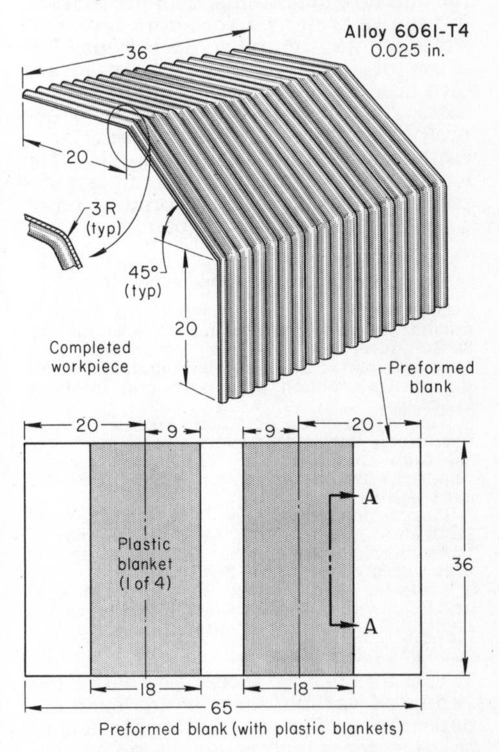

Fig. 6. Top of an aircraft cargo container formed from a corrugated aluminum blank that was encased in plastic blankets for bending in a standard V-die (Example 515)

was formulated from a polyamid resin and a plasticizer, had enough body to support the corrugations, but was flexible enough to follow the bend. The blankets were reusable, because they returned to the flattened condition after being removed from the formed workpiece.

The 45° bends were press-brake formed in air with a standard V-die and a punch with a 2-in. radius. The outside radius on the bends was 3 in., and the bent portions were held within an over-all total tolerance of 0.030 in. Springback was controlled to keep the bend angle within 1°.

Production rate was four containers per hour, and lot size was about 300 a month. Larger widths of corrugated stock (to 72 in.) also were formed, depending on the dimensions of the container needed.

The next example illustrates a technique to produce bend radii that are too small to be obtained satisfactorily with normal practice.

Example 516. Change in Punch Design That Eliminated Fracture in Forming a Small-Radius 90° Bend (Fig. 7)

In producing a bracket for an electronics application (Fig. 7), 5005-H34 alloy sheet 0.090 in. thick had to be bent 90° to an inside radius not to exceed 0.060 in. When the bracket was formed in a press-brake V-punch or with a punch of conventional design (Fig. 7) in a punch press, fracture occurred along the bend line. No significant improvement was obtained by increasing the punch radius.

Fracturing was eliminated by providing the wall of the punch with a 15° lead angle, as shown in Fig. 7. Springback as well as fracturing decreased progressively as the lead angle was lengthened from ⅛ in. to the 7/16 in. shown in Fig. 7. Beyond that length, no further improvement was obtained.

Quantity often determines whether a press brake or punch press will be used for bending operations. The press brake is usually preferred for short runs and experimental or pilot operations, because of its versatility, ability to get into production quickly, and low tooling costs. The punch press offers higher production rates and lower unit labor costs, and therefore is better suited for long runs. The following example compares two methods in the production of a part requiring a simple bend.

Example 517. Press Brake vs Punch Press for a Simple Bending Operation (Fig. 8)

Only simple bending was required for producing the reinforcing member shown in Fig. 8. Standard dies in a press brake were used for small quantities; a specially designed forming die in a punch press was used for large quantities.

The press-brake method required three operations, with adjustment of ram and gage for each operation; the punch-press method required only one operation, with no need for gage setting.

The minimum number of pieces that would justify the higher tooling costs for the punch-press method was 20,000, as shown by the break-even chart in Fig. 8.

Tools for both methods were made of 4130 or 4140 steel at Rockwell C 32; tool wear was negligible after many thousands of pieces. No lubrication was required in forming.

The number of pieces per setup depends on various factors. For example, determining factors can be the length of time for which a punch press or a press brake is needed on one production schedule, or a possible need for a continuous flow of parts to a subsequent operation, or factors that control work flow to the forming operation.

Other production considerations may override the cost factor. In Example 517, close dimensional tolerances on the finished parts could have required the use of the punch-press method, even for fewer than 20,000 pieces, because the press-brake method, with three setups and three stock-gage changes, provided a greater likelihood of variation in dimensions.

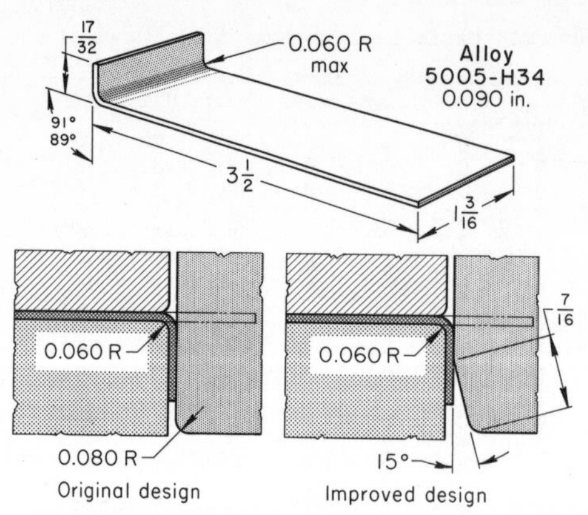

Fig. 7. Bracket, and original and improved design of punch for forming the small-radius bend without fracture (Example 516)

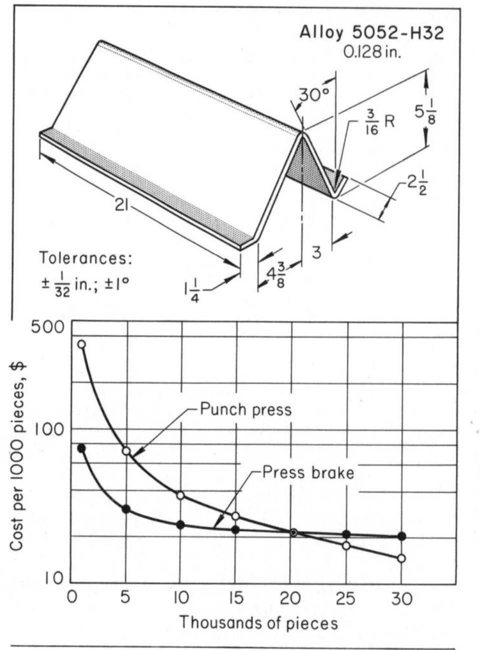

Item	Forming method: Press brake	Punch press
Production, pcs/hr	200	900
Number of setups	3(a)	1
Total setup cost	$3	$1.75
Pieces per setup	1000	5000
Setup cost per piece	$0.003	$0.00035
Labor cost per piece	$0.015	$0.0033
Die cost	$60	$350

(a) One setup for each of the three operations that were required for press-brake forming.

Fig. 8. Reinforcing member that was formed in small quantities (up to 20,000 pieces) in a press brake, and in large quantities (20,000 pieces or more) in a punch press (Example 517)

Immediate availability of equipment capable of handling parts of an extreme size or requiring a length of stroke greater than average will sometimes be of prime importance. The small quantity of parts required in the following example was produced more economically in a press brake, but it was necessary to do one bending operation in a gap-frame press, because of the need for an unusual depth of stroke to form a channel.

Example 518. Three-Operation Short-Run Forming of a Housing in a Press Brake and a Gap-Frame Press (Fig. 9)

Because the total quantity required was relatively low (fewer than 2000 pieces), the housing shown in Fig. 9 was formed most economically by making maximum use of available general-purpose equipment and tooling. As shown in Fig. 9, the first two of the three operations were done in a press brake using standard dies, which met the specified tolerance of ±1/32 in. Because of the depth of the channel, however, it was necessary to use a gap-frame press for making the U-bend. As shown in Fig. 9, a simple forming punch was mounted on a plate, with a stripper plate in the upper portion of the die.

Maintaining the 1/16-in. radius specified for the bends presented no problem as long as the stock was sheared so that the bends were made across the grain. No lubrication was needed for any of the forming operations. Tool wear was negligible throughout the production run.

The following example illustrates the accuracy to which parts can be formed in a press brake by using special equipment and techniques.

Example 519. Production of Aluminum Cabinet Tops in Seven Bends in a Press Brake (Fig. 10)

The cabinet top shown in Fig. 10 was completed by bending previously notched blanks (Fig. 10, detail A) in a press brake. Blanks were cut in a power shear, then notched and pierced in a punch press. After the press-brake operations, corners were completed by shielded-arc welding and grinding.

Although the side flanges were simple to bend, their accuracy influenced the front lip enclosure; consequently, all bends had to be closely controlled. When standard tooling and normal shop practice were employed, the product lacked the required accuracy. The problem was solved by developing a special gage that allowed control of each bend within ±0.005 in. (±0.020 in. over-all). This gage used adjustable stops that were positioned by operating dials, which were placed at the front of the die for the operator's convenience. Ten positions on the dials enabled the operator to set the stops quickly to the required position. Press-brake operations and time required for each are tabulated with Fig. 10.

Contour Roll Forming

Aluminum alloys are readily shaped by contour roll forming, using equipment and techniques similar to those used for steel (see the article "Contour Roll Forming", page 224 in this volume). Operating speeds can be higher for the more ductile aluminum alloys than for most other metals. Speeds as high as 800 ft per min have been used in mild roll forming sections 50 to 100 ft long made of 1/32-in.-thick alloy 1100-O coil stock.

Power requirements for roll forming of aluminum alloys are generally lower than for comparable operations on steel, because of the lower yield strength of most aluminum alloys.

Tooling. The design of rolls and related equipment, as well as the selection of tool materials, is discussed in the article "Contour Roll Forming", page 224 in this volume. The most commonly used material is L6 tool steel, a low-alloy nickel-chromium grade with excellent toughness, wear resistance, and hardenability. For extremely severe forming operations or exceptionally long runs, a high-carbon high-chromium grade such as D2 is preferred because it has superior resistance to galling and wear. These tool steels are hardened to Rockwell C 60 to 63. The tools are highly polished, and are sometimes chromium plated to prevent scratching and to minimize the pickup of chips when surface finish of the work is critical.

For short runs and mild forming operations, rolls can be made of turned and polished gray cast iron (class 30 or better) or low-carbon steel. For light-gage metals, tools made of plastics reinforced with metal powder, or made of specially treated hardwood, have occasionally been used.

For some applications in the roll forming of light-gage alloys where quality of surface finish is the primary concern, use has been made of cast zinc tools, at the cost of shorter tool life.

Extremely close tolerances are required on tool dimensions. Allowance for springback must be varied with alloy and temper, as well as with material thickness and radius of forming, as indicated in Table 3. Final adjustments must be made on the basis of production trials.

Layout and tool dimensions incorporate bending allowances, as described on page 228 in the article "Contour Roll Forming" in this volume.

The final strip width must be established on the basis of production trials if tolerances are close or if the curved segments constitute a substantial portion of the strip width.

Severity of Forming. Limits on severity of forming are similar to those for press-brake forming discussed in the previous section. However, minimum bend radii can be approximately half the values shown in Table 4. This is possible because of the combined effects of: (*a*) a restricted amount of forming in each stage, (*b*) the use of biaxial working of the metal on the outside of the bends, (*c*) edge compression, (*d*) highly polished rolls, and (*e*) suitable lubrication.

Similarly, the capability of forming 180° cold bends over zero radius can be extended beyond the limits given in Table 5.

Non-heat-treatable alloys are preferred for economy, and the hardest temper that will meet the forming requirements with a satisfactory yield is usually selected.

Tolerances of ±0.005 in. are common, and ±0.002 in. can be maintained on small, simple shapes formed from light-gage metals. One or two final sizing stations may be required where the contour is intricate or where springback effects are large. Several techniques for maintaining tolerances in difficult situations are described in the article "Contour Roll Forming", page 224 in this volume.

Lubricants are required in nearly all contour roll forming of aluminum alloys, as discussed in the article "Contour Roll Forming" in this volume.

For high-speed or severe forming operations, the rolls and the work may be flooded with a liquid that functions both as a lubricant and as a coolant. A soluble oil in water is preferred for this type of operation. When a more effective lubricant is required, a 10% soap solution or an extreme-pressure (EP) compound may be used. These are better suited for minimizing tool wear and producing a high finish, but are more difficult to remove. Lubricants like

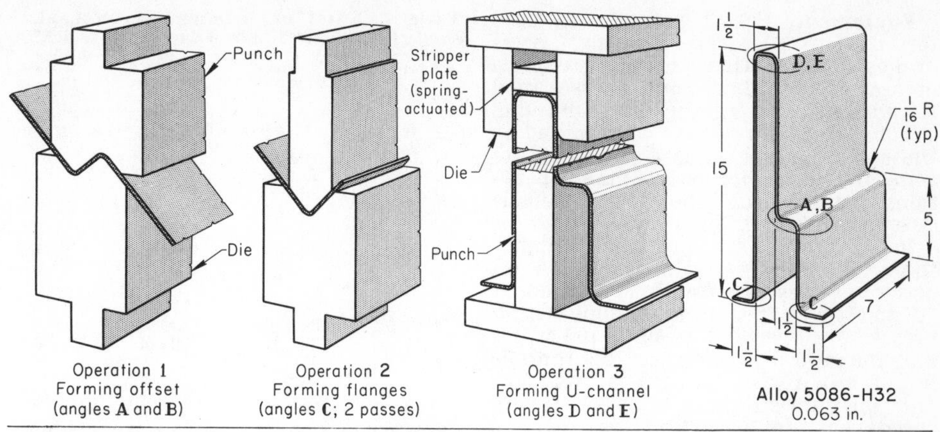

Operation	Machine	Setup time, minutes	Production, pieces/hr	Cost per piece(a)
1 Form offset	Press brake(b)	8	900	$0.0038
2 Form flanges (2 passes)	Press brake(b)	8	550	0.0059
3 Form U-channel	Punch press(c)	16	420	0.0072
Total forming cost per piece				$0.0169

(a) Direct labor cost for setup (amortized over 1000 pieces) plus production cost. (b) 30-ton mechanical press brake with 2-in. stroke and 6 ft between frame members, using standard 90° dies with 1/16-in. radius (tool material, 4130 or 4140 steel at Rockwell C 32). (c) 75-ton mechanical gap-frame press with 5-in. stroke and shut height of 15 to 18 in., using a special channel-form die and a 1/16-in.-radius punch (tool material, 4130 or 4140 steel at Rockwell C 32).

Fig. 9. Use of a press brake and a gap-frame press for low-cost forming of a housing in small quantities (Example 518)

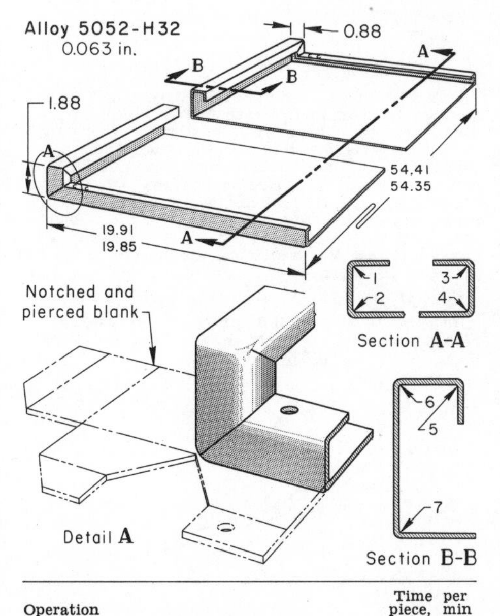

Operation	Time per piece, min
First Handling	
Remove formed piece; position blank	0.2079
Make 1st bend, one side (3 hits)	0.0880
Shift workpiece	0.0433
Make 2nd bend, one side (3 hits)	0.0880
Turn workpiece 180°	0.0856
Make 3rd bend (3 hits)	0.0880
Shift workpiece	0.0433
Make 4th bend (3 hits)	0.0880
Second Handling	
Transport and reposition piece	0.2079
Make 5th bend (2 hits)	0.0748
Shift workpiece	0.0433
Make 6th bend (2 hits)	0.0748
Shift workpiece	0.0433
Make 7th bend (2 hits)	0.0748
Net total	1.2510
Plus allowance of 5%	0.0626
Total production time	1.3136

A special adjustable gage controlled by dials on the front of the machine (so that it could be set quickly by the operator) was used to obtain the necessary degree of accuracy for producing a good closure on the front lip.

Fig. 10. Cabinet top formed in seven bends in a press brake (Example 519)

those numbered 1, 2, 4 and 7 in Table 1 are also used to some extent.

Applications. Roll formed aluminum alloy parts made from sheet or coiled strip include furniture parts, architectural moldings, window and door frames, gutters and downspouts, automotive trim, roofing and siding panels, and shelving.

Tubing, in sizes ranging from 3/4 in. to 8 in. in outside diameter, and from 0.025 to 0.156 in. in wall thickness, is made in a combined roll-forming and welding operation. Linear speeds of 30 to 200 ft per min are used in this process. Applications are irrigation pipe, condenser tubing, and furniture parts.

A modification of the roll-forming and welding process is used to make cable sheathing. Cable and strip are fed into the machine simultaneously; the strip is formed into a tube surrounding the cable, and then welded. The assembly is next passed through a sizing mill, which reduces the tubing slightly in size, and produces a waterproof and gastight sheath.

Other applications of contour roll forming include the forming of patterned, anodized or pre-enameled material. Such applications impose stringent requirements on tool design and maintenance, and lubrication sometimes cannot be used because of the nature of the coating or because of end-use requirements.

Deep Drawing

Equipment, tools and techniques used for deep drawing aluminum are similar to those used for other metals, and are described in detail in the article "Deep Drawing", which begins on page 162.

This section deals with those aspects of deep drawing that are peculiar to aluminum alloys. It is restricted to procedures using a rigid punch and die. Other procedures are described in subsequent sections of this article.

Equipment. Punch presses are used for nearly all deep drawing; press brakes are sometimes used for experimental or very short runs. Presses used for steel are also suitable for aluminum.

Tonnage requirements, determined by the same method as used for steel, are generally lower for comparable operations because of the lower tensile strength of aluminum alloys.

Press speeds are ordinarily higher than for steel. For mild draws, single-action presses are usually operated at 90 to 140 ft per min. Double-action presses are operated at 40 to 100 ft per min for mild draws, and at less than 50 ft per min for deeper draws, with low and medium-strength alloys. Drawing speeds on double-action presses are about 20 to 40 ft per min with high-strength alloys.

Tool Design. Tools for deep drawing are the same in general construction as those used with steel, but there are some significant differences. Aluminum alloy stock must be allowed to flow without undue restraint or excessive stretching. The original thickness of the metal is changed very little. This differs from deep drawing of stainless steel or brass sheet, which may be reduced as much as 25% in thickness in a single draw.

Clearances between punch and die are usually equal to the metal thickness plus about 10% per side for drawing alloys of low or intermediate strength. An additional 5 to 10% clearance may be needed for the higher-strength alloys and harder tempers. Typical clearances for multiple operations in drawing cylindrical and rectangular shells are given in Table 6.

Table 6. Typical Clearances Between Punch and Die for Successive Drawing Operations

Draw	Clearance per side, % of stock thickness
Cylindrical Shells	
First	110
Second	115
Third and subsequent	120
Final (tapered shells only)	100
Rectangular Shells	
First and subsequent	110
Final	100

With circular shells, clearance is usually increased with each successive draw, because of the metal thickening that occurred in the previous operation. The restrictions imposed on the drawing of rectangular shells by metal flow at the corners make equal clearances for each draw satisfactory. The final operation with tapered and with rectangular shells serves primarily to straighten walls, sharpen radii, and size the part accurately. Therefore, the clearance for these operations is equal to the thickness of the stock.

Excessive clearance may result in wrinkling of the sidewalls of the drawn shell; insufficient clearance will burnish the sidewalls and increase the force required for drawing.

Radii on Tools. Tools used for drawing aluminum alloys are ordinarily provided with draw radii equal to four to eight times the stock thickness. Punch nose radius is sometimes as large as ten times the stock thickness.

Table 7. Effect of Drawing on Mechanical Properties of Aluminum Alloys 3003 and 5052

Number of draws	Tensile strength, psi	Yield strength, psi	Elongation in 2 in., %
Alloy 3003			
0	16,000	6,000	30
1	19,000	17,000	11
2	22,000	21,000	9
3	23,500	22,000	8
4	24,500	22,500	8
(a)	(29,000)	(27,000)	(4)
Alloy 5052			
0	28,000	13,000	25
1	34,500	32,000	6
2	39,500	36,000	6
3	43,000	37,000	6
4	44,000	38,000	6
(a)	(42,000)	(37,000)	(7)

(a) Values in parentheses are typical values for these alloys in the full-hard condition.

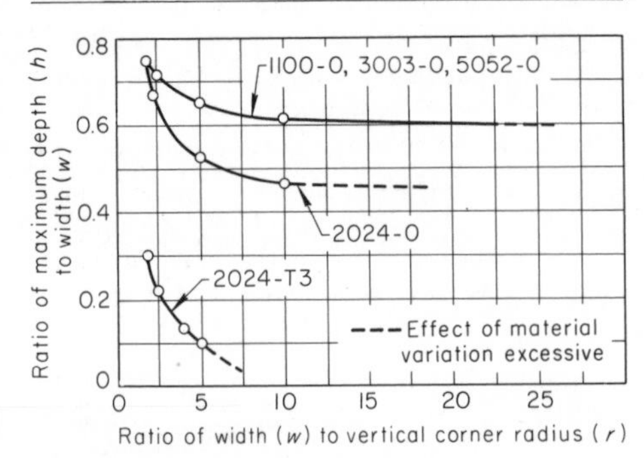

For cylindrical cups, width w equals the diameter, and vertical corner radius r equals half the diameter. Thus, the w/r ratio is 2, and values for h/w can be obtained from the graph. For rectangular boxes, width w equals the square root of the projected bottom area (width times length). If length is more than three times width, drawing limits will be more severe than limits shown in the above graph. For flanged boxes, the width of the flange must be included in depth h.

Fig. 11. Drawing limits for one-operation forming of cylindrical cups or rectangular boxes from aluminum alloy sheet 0.026 to 0.064 in. thick

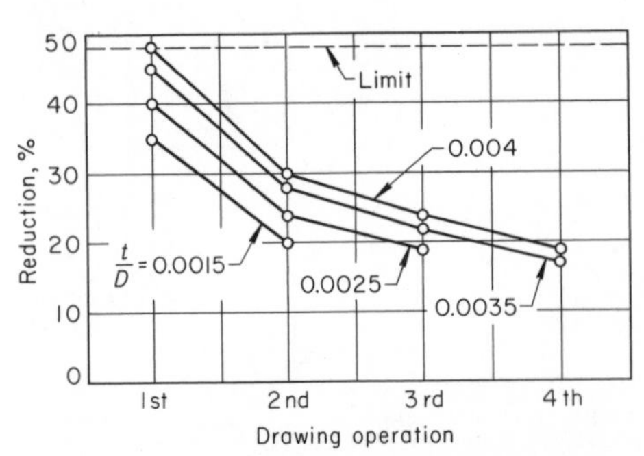

t = metal thickness. D = blank diameter.

Fig. 12. Effect of the relation of metal thickness to blank diameter on percentage reduction for successive drawing operations without intermediate annealing, for low-strength alloys such as 3003-O

A die radius that is too large may lead to wrinkling. A punch nose radius that is too sharp will increase the probability of fracture, or may leave objectionable circular shock lines that can be removed only by costly polishing.

Failure by fracture can sometimes be eliminated by increasing the die radius, or by making the drawing edge an elliptic form instead of a circular arc (see the section on Restraint of Metal Flow, on pages 172 to 175 in the article "Deep Drawing").

Surface Finish on Tools. Draw dies and punches should have a surface finish of 16 micro-in. or less for most applications. A finish of 3 or 4 micro-in. is often specified on high-production tooling for drawing light-gage or precoated stock. Chromium plating may also be specified to minimize friction and prevent pickup of dirt or other particles that could damage the finish on the part.

Tool Materials. The selection of materials for deep drawing tools is discussed in the article beginning on page 194 in this volume. Materials for small dies are chosen almost entirely on the basis of performance, but cost becomes a significant factor for large dies. Local variation in wear on tools is an important factor in tool life. A twentyfold variation in rate of wear can be observed on the die radius.

Lubricants for deep drawing aluminum alloys are usually commercial products based on the compositions listed in Table 1. Lubricants for deep drawing must allow the blank to slip readily and uniformly between the blankholder and the die, and must prevent stretching and galling while this movement takes place.

The drawing compounds can be applied only to the areas that will be subjected to a significant amount of cold working, unless local application interferes with the requirements of high-speed operation. Uniformity of application is critical, especially to enable the maintenance of correct blankholder pressure all around the periphery of the die.

Shallow drawing operations can usually be carried out with the use of lubricants 2, 3, or 4 in Table 1, in order of increasing severity of draw. Viscosity of mineral oil is increased as drawing severity increases. Lubricants 5, 6 and 7 in Table 1 are generally adequate for medium-depth draws, and for drawing operations of maximum severity.

Other factors besides percentage reduction in diameter (or depth of draw) and sharpness of radii must be considered in assessing the relative severity of deep drawing operations. Heavy-gage material necessitates higher deformation forces and therefore requires more effective lubrication. High-strength alloys exert a similar effect, and the more highly alloyed materials may also need a heavier, more effective type of lubricant, because of their generally thicker oxide coatings. To prevent scratching, heavier lubricants must be used with cast iron or low-carbon steel tools than with hardened, highly polished tools.

Drawing Limits. The reduction in diameter in a single operation possible with aluminum alloys is about the same as with drawing-quality steel. For deep drawn cylindrical shells, the following approximate reductions in diameter can be obtained with good practice.

	Reduction,
First draw	40%
Second draw	20%
Third and subsequent draws	15%

The part can usually be completely formed without intermediate annealing. Four or more successive draws without annealing can be performed on such alloys as 1100, 3003 and 5005, with proper die design and effective lubrication. The amount of reduction is decreased in successive draws because of the loss in workability due to strain hardening. The total depth of draw thus obtainable without intermediate annealing exceeds that obtainable from steel, copper, brass or other common metals.

For high-strength aluminum alloys, the approximate amount of permissible reduction in a single draw is:

First draw .... Reduction,	30%
Second draw	15%
Third draw	10%

Local or complete annealing is usually necessary on alloys such as 2014 and 2024 after the third draw, before further operations can be performed.

Alloys 3004, 5052 and 6061 are intermediate in behavior.

The rate of strain hardening is greatest for the high-strength alloys and least for the low-strength alloys. Table 7 shows the changes in mechanical properties that result from successive draws with alloys 3003 and 5052. The major portion of the change is accomplished in the first draw. The rate of strain hardening is more rapid with high-strength, heat treatable alloys such as 2014 and 2024.

Practical limits for single-operation deep drawing of cylindrical cups and rectangular boxes have been expressed in terms of dimensional ratios as shown in Fig. 11. (Reverse redrawing can be used to obtain a deeper shell than indicated by the limits in Fig. 11 for conventional drawing methods.)

The relation of the metal thickness (t) to the blank diameter (D) is an important factor in determining the percentage reduction for each drawing operation. As this ratio decreases, the probability of wrinkling increases, requiring more blankholding pressure to control metal flow and prevent wrinkles from starting. Figure 12 shows the effect of this ratio on percentage reduction of successive draws, without intermediate annealing, for low-strength alloys such as 3003-O.

Multiple-Draw Operations. The following four examples describe production procedures designed to take advantage of the formability of aluminum alloys. In all four examples, several deep draws were performed in succession without intermediate annealing.

If annealing were required, cleaning to remove drawing lubricant would be necessary before annealing, and descaling might also be needed, depending on the annealing procedure. In some applications the savings possible by the elimination of annealing and related operations can result in a lower overall cost with an aluminum alloy than with steel, even though the cost of the raw material is higher.

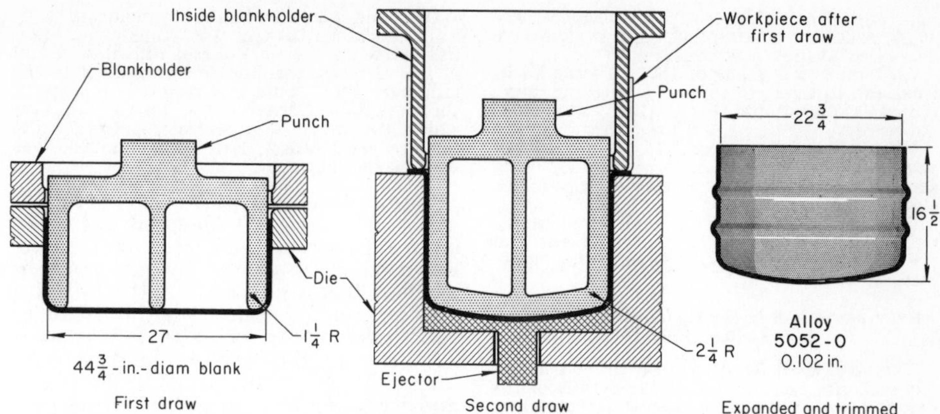

Fig. 13. Two-draw forming of a drum shell half. After being expanded and trimmed, matching halves were butt welded to make a 55-gal drum. (Example 520)

Example 520. Two-Draw Forming (Fig. 13)

Figure 13 shows the tooling setups used for two-operation deep drawing of shells, pairs of which were butt welded together to make 55-gal drums. The shells were drawn in long-stroke double-action presses of 300-ton to 400-ton capacity. Reduction was 40% in the first draw and 15% in the second.

Tools were of fine-grain cast iron hardened to Rockwell C 45 to 48 and were highly polished. This tooling and the application of a suitable grade of drawing lubricant (mineral oil base with sulfurized fatty oil and finely divided fillers) made possible a good surface finish and a low rejection rate.

After each shell was drawn, reinforcing beads were formed in the sidewalls with a segmented expanding tool, and the edges were trimmed for butt welding (see Fig. 13).

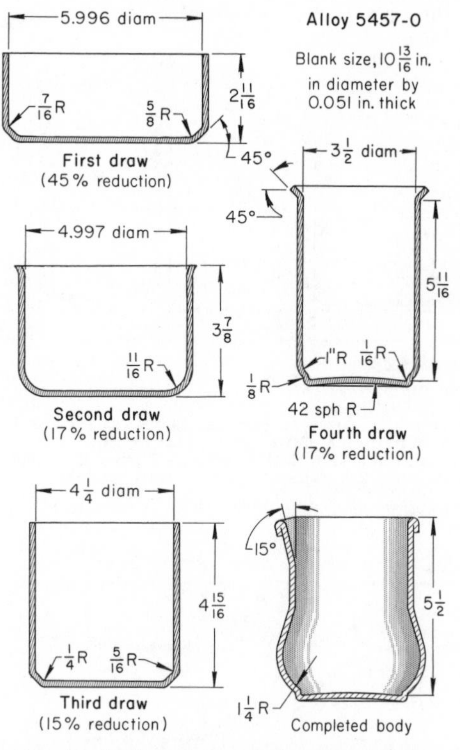

Fig. 14. Water-pitcher body formed from a 10¹³⁄₁₆-in.-diam blank in four draws without intermediate annealing (Example 521)

Example 521. Four-Draw Forming Without Intermediate Annealing (Fig. 14)

The water-pitcher body shown in Fig. 14 was formed from an alloy 5457-O blank, 0.051 in. thick and 10¹³⁄₁₆ in. in diameter, in four successive draws in double-action presses, without intermediate annealing.

The steel tools were made with generous radii, and a medium-weight mineral oil that contained 10 to 20% fatty oil was used as the lubricant. The drawing operations were designed to allow the metal to flow with a minimum of restraint and without excessive stretching.

After drawing, the workpiece was trimmed and flanged in a lathe with a curling tool. The flange was subsequently flattened in a lathe with a roll flattening tool.

The bulge in the lower portion of the pitcher was produced by a rubber punch and split die in a single-action press, and the pouring lip was formed with male and female tools in a horn press. Finally, the exterior of the pitcher was polished and the handle was riveted to the shell.

Example 522. Six-Draw Forming Without Intermediate Annealing (Fig. 15)

Figure 15 shows the sequence of shapes in the eight-operation production of a seamless angel-cake pan for commercial bakeries. Despite the severity of some of the six draws required, the use of alloy 5052-O for the pans permitted successful production without intermediate annealing.

Before the first draw, blanks were coated with a heavy, clinging drawing compound similar to No. 10 in Table 1. For each operation, production rate was 350 pieces per

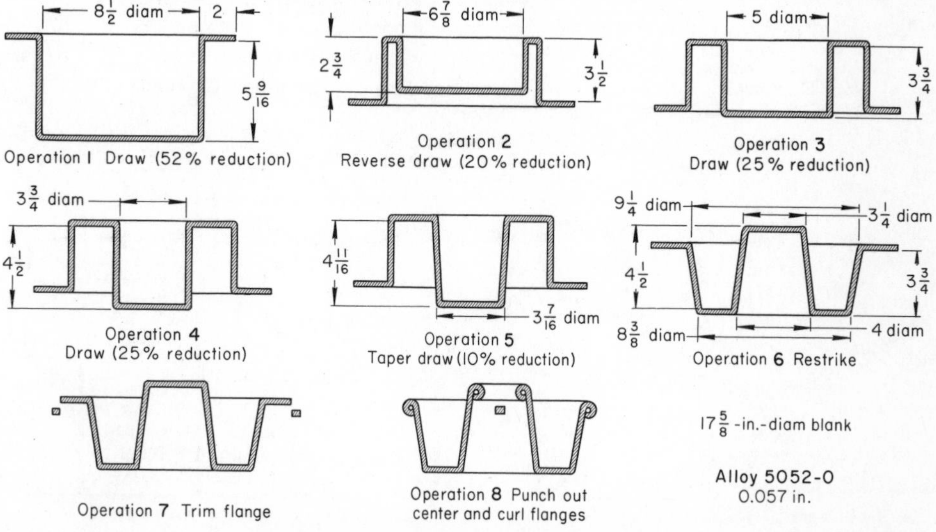

Fig. 15. Production of a seamless angel-cake pan in six draws without intermediate annealing (Example 522)

hour and direct-labor cost per 1000 pieces was $6.50. After the final operation, the pans were degreased by hot spray washing.

All tooling was made of D2 tool steel, hardened to Rockwell C 60 to 64 and chromium plated. Conventional draw rings and hold-downs were used in the draw operations. The relatively low production, 15,000 pieces per year, was most economically reached by using successive operations in presses equipped with simple dies.

Originally, the pans were made by spinning, but the sidewalls thinned to the extent that the pans were not suited to heavy-duty commercial service.

Example 523. Reverse Redrawing vs Direct Redrawing (Fig. 16)

The steps used for drawing a coffee percolator shell are shown in Fig. 16; details of the drawing and two reverse redrawing operations are given below the illustration. By reverse redrawing, it was possible to effect reductions of 19.4% and 22%, respectively, whereas it was estimated that only 15% could have been obtained by direct drawing.

Dies and blankholders were made of gray iron. Clearance between the punches and dies was 1¼ times the work-metal thickness. Radii of the dies and blankholders were kept to the minimum that would not result in tearing of the workpiece. Corner radius on the die, over which the metal flowed, was 3⁄16 in. for the final redraw. Tallow, lard oil or kerosine was used as the lubricant.

Blank development is of particular importance in the deep drawing of large rectangular and irregular shapes. Excessive stock at the corners must be avoided, because it hinders the uniform flow of metal under the blankholder and thus leads to wrinkles or fractures. With suitable tooling and careful blank development, large rectangular and irregular shapes can often be produced economically in large quantities by deep drawing. Smaller quantities are made in sections with inexpensive tooling, and then assembled by welding.

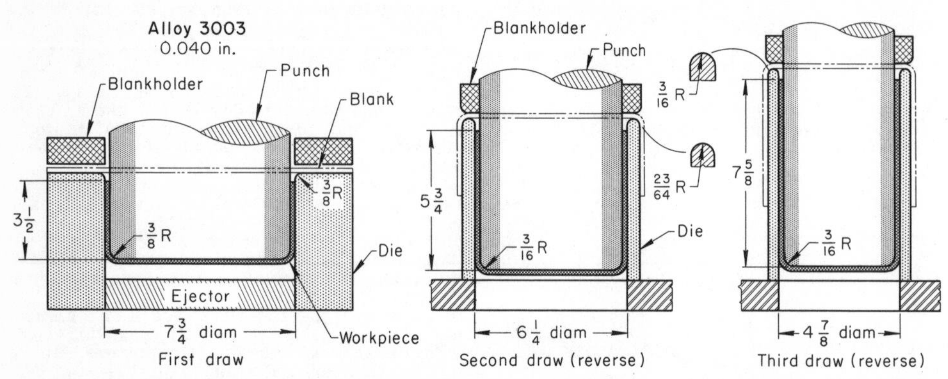

First draw — Load lubricated 12-in.-diam blank into die. Draw to cup as shown (35.4% reduction). Lift with ejector pad. **Second draw** — Turn cup upside down and place on die. Reverse redraw to cup as shown (19.4% reduction). Push through die. **Third draw** — Turn cup upside down and place on die. Reverse redraw to cup as shown (22% reduction). Push through die.

Fig. 16. Use of two reverse redraws in the production of a percolator shell (Example 523)

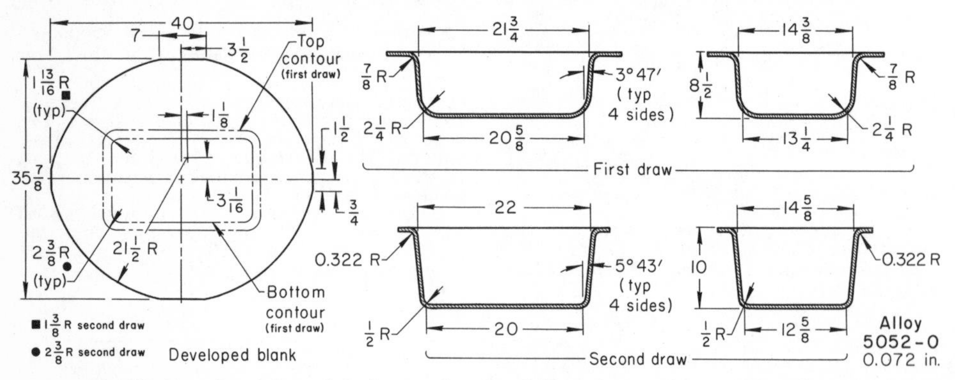

Fig. 17. Forming a large box from a developed blank in two draws (Example 524)

Both the welding operation and the subsequent grinding and polishing of the weld areas are time-consuming and costly.

The two examples that follow describe the use of deep drawing for the production of large rectangular boxes. In the second of these examples, the boxes were originally produced by drawing, press-brake forming, and welding, but as the production quantity increased, the method was changed to deep drawing.

Example 524. Deep Drawing of Large Rectangular Boxes (Fig. 17)

A large rectangular tote box was produced by two deep drawing operations from a developed blank of 0.072-in.-thick aluminum alloy 5052-O, as shown in Fig. 17. Final operations were trimming and beading.

The punch and die for the first draw were designed with radii of ten times the metal thickness, or more, to avoid overstressing. The additional stretching in the second draw was helpful in wiping out buckles and sharpening corner radii. Hardened and polished (16 micro-in. max) tool steel was required for the punches and dies to produce a high-quality finish on the boxes.

The lubricant, a mineral oil that contained 10 to 15% sulfurized fatty oil and 10% fatty oil, and that was specially compounded for use on aluminum, also was helpful in minimizing drawing difficulty.

The rectangular boxes described in Example 524 could have been formed in sections by press-brake forming and the sections welded together. This method would be economical if only 4000 boxes were required in a two-year period, or if presses capable of forming the complete box were not available.

Example 525. Deep Drawing vs Drawing, Press-Brake Forming, and Welding of Rectangular Bins (Fig. 18)

A large rectangular bin was originally made in small quantities at a minimum of tooling cost, by drawing a rectangular pan 20⅝ in. long by 18⅝ in. wide by 6⅛ in. deep, trimming it to 5-in. depth, and welding it to a 17½-in.-high sidewall that was formed in a press brake. The bottom pan was drawn from alloy 3004-O, and the sidewall was formed from 3004-H32; sheet thickness was 0.102 in. This method entailed expensive hand operations, particularly in welding and in the finishing of welds. Consequently, when production volume was increased, tools were designed for making the bins entirely by drawing.

A round-cornered blank was developed from the more formable alloy 3003-O, and tools and a drawing procedure were perfected to change the workpiece gradually from a circular to a rectangular shape in three draws, as shown in Fig. 18. For the one-piece drawn bin, larger radii at the bottom, corner and flange were required than for the welded bin (see Fig. 18).

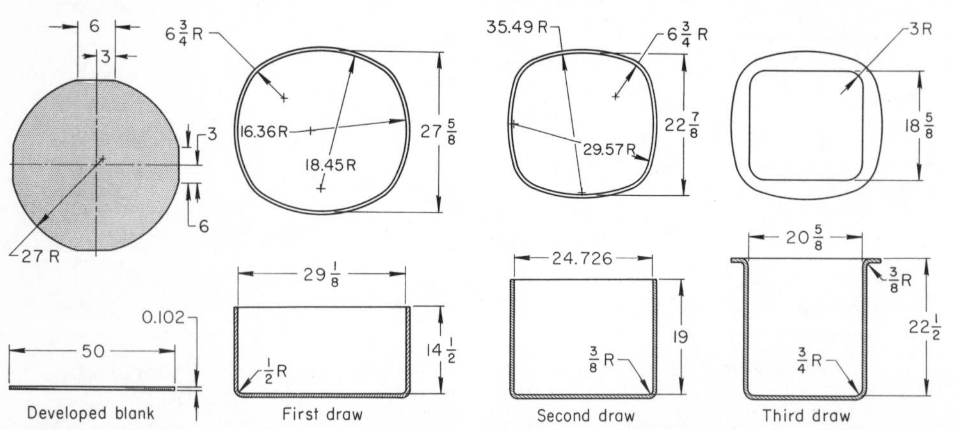

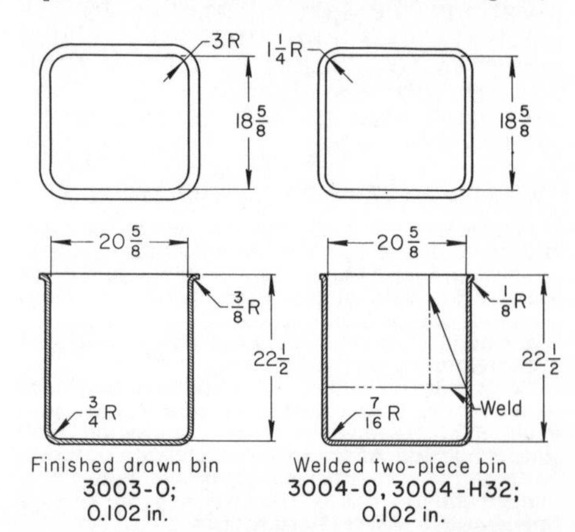

Fig. 18. Three-draw production of a rectangular bin (near right) that previously had been made as a welded assembly of a drawn base and a press-brake-formed sidewall (far right) (Example 525)

The tools were made from close-grain cast iron, and were polished to a 16 micro-in. finish. They required regular maintenance, and a heavy oil-base drawing compound was used, to prevent galling and high scrap losses.

The three dies were mounted on three separate presses so that as soon as one operation was finished, the part could be moved to the next operation and any variations in procedures or tooling that adversely affected the other operation or the part could be discovered immediately and corrected. For instance, excessively severe working in the first or second draw could have led to fractures in the third draw.

Tooling costs for deep drawing were amortized in less than three years by savings in labor costs over the previous method.

Warping. The nonuniformity of stress distribution in the drawing of rectangular or irregular shapes increases the tendency toward warping. Bowing or oil-can effects on the major surfaces become more pronounced with increasing size of the part.

Changes can sometimes be made in dimensional details of the drawing tools to eliminate these defects without the need for extra forming operations, as is demonstrated in the example that follows.

Example 526. Redesign of Punch, Pressure Pad and Subplate That Prevented Distortion of a Shallow Drawn Panel (Fig. 19)

A shallow drawn panel, shown in Fig. 19, was produced with warped, out-of-vertical sidewalls and with oil-can effect on the large flat surface.

Recessing the face of the punch to a depth of 0.030 in. (except for the outermost 0.062 in. on the periphery of the face), as shown in Fig. 19, produced straight, vertical sidewalls, but only partly corrected the oil-can effect on the face of the panel.

To correct the remaining curvature of the face, grooves were milled in a diamond pattern in the underside of the pressure pad to provide the effect of hinged corners, and the four corners were forced upward by a contoured subplate (machined with raised corners) under the pressure pad, as shown in Fig. 19. The subplate was 1 in. thick at the corners and 0.015 in. thinner in the central flat diamond-shape area. The high corners caused the pressure pad to flex sufficiently to apply an increased force on the part. The die was made of tool steel; the pressure pad was heat treated to a spring temper.

The same technique was applied to similar parts. The amount of corner elevation on the subplate varied, being developed on the basis of the part size.

The drawing of lithographed parts requires that the parts be accurately formed, with no marks or scratches on the finished surface. Drawing with a rubber die preserved the metal surface, in the following example.

Example 527. Mar-Free Drawing With a Rubber Die (Fig. 20)

The graduated-scale indicator dial shown in Fig. 20 was drawn from photoprinted and grained blanks. Accurate drawing and freedom from marring were necessary to maintain the calibrations and legibility of the scale.

The tooling consisted of a conventional punch made of soft steel, a pilot pin, a blankholder, and a rubber die 10 in. square by ¾ in. thick, machined to an inside diameter slightly smaller than the outside diameter of the punch. A rubber pressure pad, 2⅛ in. high with walls ¾ in. thick, was used under the blankholder. Inverted construction was used for the die. With the rubber tooling, accurate register of the scale was maintained and surface marring, which had occurred in conventional drawing, was eliminated. Drawing time with rubber tooling was reduced 50%, compared with conventional drawing. Also, various thicknesses of metal could be handled in the same die.

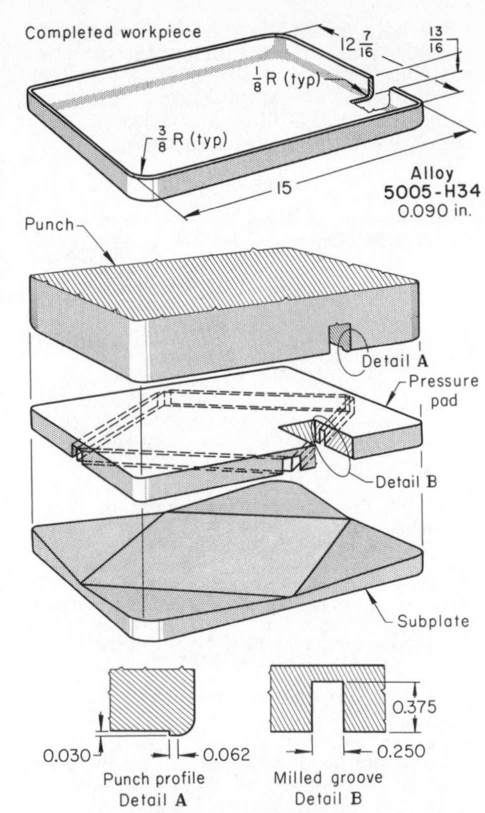

Fig. 19. Shallow panel that was drawn without distortion by using a recessed punch, grooved pressure pad, and contoured subplate (Example 526)

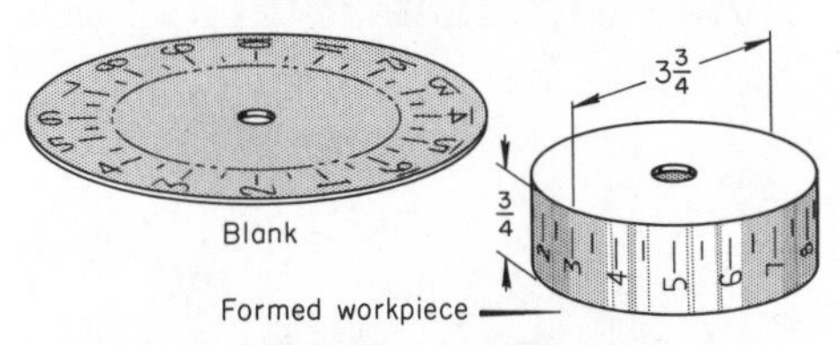

Fig. 20. Indicator dial that was drawn from a photoprinted and grained flat aluminum blank using a rubber die (Example 527)

Miscellaneous Shapes. Other shapes often produced by deep drawing (besides cylindrical and rectangular shells) include hemispherical shells, flat-bottomed hemispherical shells, and tapered shells.

Hemispherical shells with a final inside diameter less than about 150 times the original metal thickness can be drawn in one operation. For inside diameters of more than 150 times thickness, two draws will usually be required, to avoid wrinkles. Local thinning must be avoided in the first draw if the second draw is to be successful.

Flat-bottom hemispherical shells, unless very shallow, require at least two draws. The first draw produces a rounded shape, with a larger radius in the bottom area than on the side areas. The final draw flattens the bottom and gives the sides a uniform curvature of the radius required.

Tapered shells require more drawing operations for a given depth of draw than most other symmetrical shapes. The number of steps required increases with the taper angle.

The bottom edges, except for the final operation, do not have the contour of a circular arc. The profile consists of essentially flat sections at an angle of about 40° to 50° from the horizontal. Stepwise reductions are made along the line of final contour as shown in Fig. 21, and the final draw straightens out the sidewalls to the desired shape.

Each operation after the first is restricted to a shallow draw to minimize strain hardening. With alloys of low and intermediate strength, this procedure makes it possible to complete the series of draws without annealing. Contrary to normal practice, the amount of reduction per draw need not be lowered after the second draw.

Polishing or burnishing is often required on the completed shell to obtain a good-quality finish on the sidewalls.

Ironing is avoided in most deep drawing applications with aluminum alloys, but can be used to produce a shell with a heavy bottom and thin sidewalls.

The shell is first drawn to approximately the final diameter. The drawing lubricant is then removed, and the shell is annealed, bringing it to temperature rapidly to minimize the formation of coarse grains in areas that have been only slightly cold worked.

The sidewalls can then be reduced in thickness by 30 to 40% in an ironing operation. By repeating the cleaning, annealing and ironing steps, an additional reduction of 20 to 25% can be obtained, with good control over wall thickness.

A typical use of ironing is shown in Fig. 22. Here a cylindrical shell is produced with a thick bottom and thin sidewalls by a single deep draw and two successive ironing operations. The approximate final diameter and about half the final depth are obtained in the drawing operation. Wall thickness is reduced 33% in the first ironing step and 19% in the second.

Supplementary Forming. Various supplementary beading, bulging, necking and other forming operations are performed on drawn shells (see Examples 520, 521 and 522). In the following example, the use of a strong alloy (5154) not well suited to forming a radius equal to the sheet thickness necessitated annealing the drawn shell before subsequent offset forming of a bead on the circular edge.

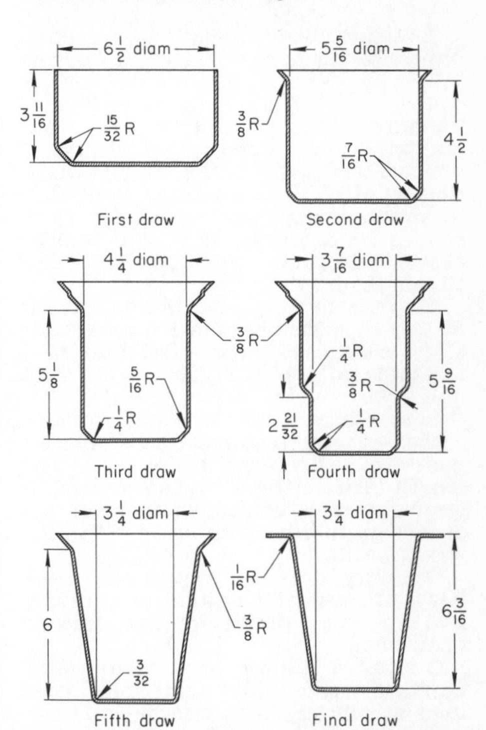

Fig. 21. Typical progression of shapes in multiple-draw forming of a tapered shell from an aluminum alloy blank 0.064 in. thick and 11½ in. in diameter

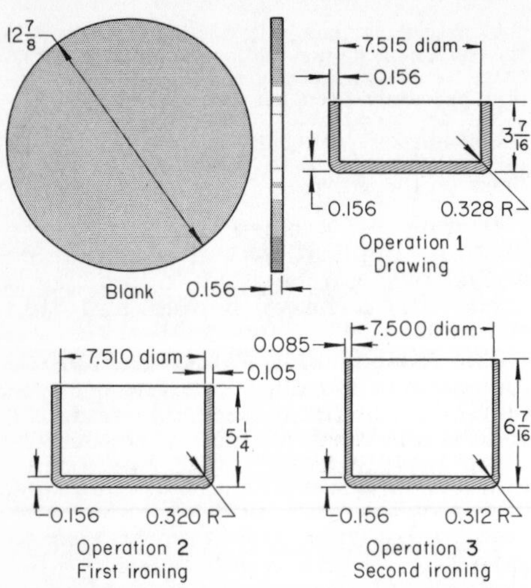

Fig. 22. Progression of shapes in producing a shell with a thick bottom and thin sides in one draw and two ironing operations

Example 528. Drawing and Supplementary Offset Forming of a Pressure Vessel (Fig. 23)

The pressure vessel shown in Fig. 23 was produced from alloy 5154-O sheet by blanking, deep drawing, annealing and forming.

The blank, 25 in. in diameter, was produced by a steel blanking die in a 600-ton mechanical press. The hemispherical shape of the workpiece (see Fig. 23) was drawn from the blank by a lubricated draw die in one operation in a 600-ton mechanical press.

After drawing, the workpiece was annealed for 2 hr at 650 F. Annealing was necessary to prevent cracking or excessive springback during subsequent forming of the circular edge between offset rolls.

The part was then trimmed by standard roll cutters to 9½ in. and formed between rolls, to produce an offset with an inside radius equal to the work-metal thickness. Both trimming and final forming were done in a bead-and-trim machine using interchangeable rolls.

Hot Drawing

Severe drawing operations are often impossible to perform at room temperature on large and relatively thick shapes made from high-strength aluminum alloys. However, the lower strength and increased ductility at temperatures above the recrystallization point of the alloy make it possible to produce large and relatively thick shapes by hot drawing. There is little or no advantage when stock is less than 0.125 in. thick.

Alloys frequently used in applications of this type include non-heat-treatable alloys 5083, 5086 and 5456, and heat treatable alloys 2024, 2219, 6061, 7075 and 7178.

Heavy-duty presses and related equipment are required. Drawing temperatures range from 350 to 600 F. The length of time the workpiece is held at temperature is controlled to avoid excessive grain growth in areas with little strain hardening.

Ordinary drawing compounds break down or burn at elevated temperature, and are not suitable for hot drawing operations.

Graphited tallow and hard yellow naphtha soap have sometimes been used as lubricants at intermediate elevated temperature. Lubricants that remain stable above 500 F include graphite and molybdenum disulfide. These materials can be used in the colloidal form with a volatile vehicle, they can be mixed with other lubricants, or they can be applied to the die as powders.

Examples of Applications. The two examples that follow describe production applications of hot drawing.

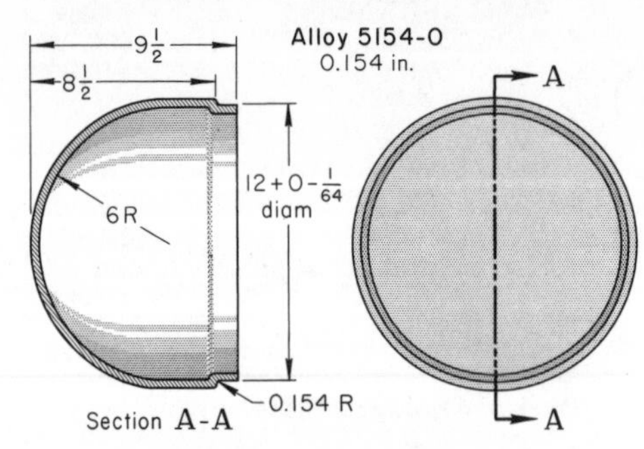

Fig. 23. Pressure vessel produced by deep drawing and forming with intermediate annealing (Example 528)

Table 8. Sequence of Operations and Manufacturing Details for Hot Drawing of a Flanged Circular Base for a Container (Example 529)

Sequence of Operations

1 – Shear. 2 – Cut circular blanks. 3 – Preheat blanks to 500 F. 4 – Preheat dies to 350 F. 5 – Lubricate blank and dies(a). 6 – Hot draw. 7 – Spin flange flat. 8 – Trim.

Manufacturing Details

Press	400-ton hydraulic(b)
Material for drawing tools(c)	Cast iron
Setup time	20 hr total
Production rate, drawing(d)	6 pcs per hour
Labor cost, all operations	$20 per piece

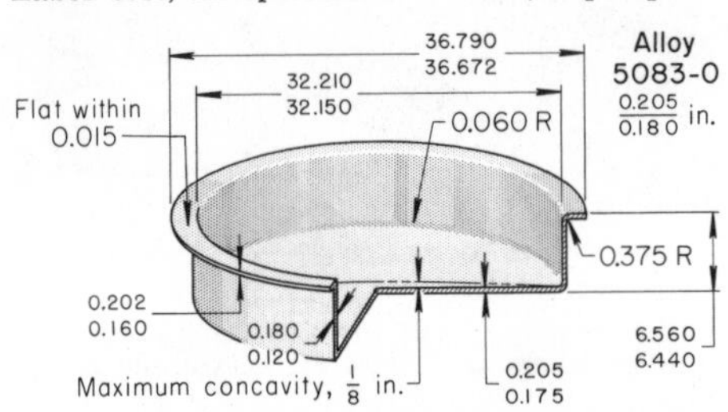

(a) Lubricant was a heavy refined mineral oil plus 10% acidless tallow. Dies were lubricated after each two parts. (b) Having a bed 60 by 48 in. (c) Die, punch and blankholder. (d) Includes time for reheating and lubricating dies.

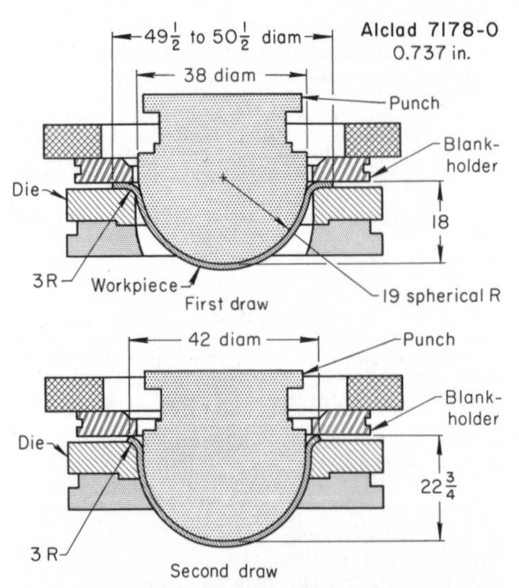

Fig. 24. Two-draw forming of a hemispherical shell. Workpiece was heated to 450 F for second draw. (Example 530)

Example 529. Hot Drawing a Large Circular Base for a Container (Table 8)

A large flanged circular base for a shipping container (see illustration in Table 8) was produced in quantities of 150 to 750 pieces by hot drawing alloy 5083-O blanks 45½ in. in diameter and 0.190 in. thick.

The sequence of operations and other manufacturing details are given in Table 8. As drawn, the flange was uneven and required flattening. This was done by spinning, using a hollow hardwood mandrel with a steel ring; larger quantities would have warranted the cost of additional press dies for flattening.

Originally, the base had been produced in 6-to-10-piece lots by spinning, but specified minimum wall thicknesses (see Table 8) were difficult to maintain.

Example 530. Use of Hot Drawing in Two-Draw Production of a Large Hemispherical Shell (Fig. 24)

A hemispherical shell was formed in two draws from a 60-in.-diam blank cut from alclad 7178-O plate 0.737 in. thick, as shown in Fig. 24. This shell was half of an underwater sonobuoy sphere designed to withstand external pressure of at least 4000 psi.

Both draws were made in a 1300-ton double-action hydraulic press with one set of tools. Die clearance was about 15% greater than work-metal thickness, and die radius was four times work-metal thickness.

For the first drawing, or preforming operation, the blank was at room temperature. The blank was lubricated with an aluminum drawing compound. The partly formed shell was then degreased and heated in a circulating-air furnace for about 20 min to 450 F, removed from the furnace, coated with a high-temperature lubricant, and drawn to full depth at 400 to 450 F. Wall thickness ranged from 115% of the nominal value at the top of the drawn shell to 90% at the bottom.

After forming, the shells were solution heat treated and artificially aged to the T6 temper to meet strength requirements.

Spinning

Spinning is often used for forming of aluminum alloy shapes that are surfaces of revolution. The manual lathes, automatic spinning machines, chucks and tools used for aluminum alloys are essentially the same as those used for steel and the other metals commonly formed by spinning (see the article "Spinning", which begins on page 201 in this volume).

Hand spinning lathes and simple tools are suitable for forming aluminum alloy blanks 0.020 to 0.081 in. thick; stock as thin as 0.004 in. can be spun with careful operation. For thicker and larger blanks, auxiliary equipment is used to apply pressure to the workpiece. This equipment varies from a simple scissors arrangement to feed screws to control tool advance, and air or hydraulic cylinders to provide pressure against the work.

Blanks up to ¼ in. thick can usually be spun at room temperature. For greater thicknesses, semimechanical to fully mechanical equipment is used, and the work metal is heated. Work metal 1 in. or more in thickness requires special heavy-duty machines and hot spinning.

Aluminum alloy parts 3 in. thick have been spun experimentally. Equipment is available for the spinning of parts as large as 16 ft in diameter.

Tolerances for spinning of aluminum alloys are essentially the same as for other common metals.

Alloys. A number of aluminum alloys are widely used in spinning applications. Desirable properties are ductility, relatively low ratio of yield strength to ultimate strength, slow rate of work hardening, and small grain size.

The alloys of low and intermediate strength that are spun most frequently include 1100, 2219, 3003, 3004, 5052, 5086 and 5154. Annealed blanks are generally used for severe forming; however, a harder temper is sometimes preferred, if it is sufficiently formable, to avoid a tendency to ball up ahead of the tool. A harder temper also may be used when forming is not severe enough to give the product its necessary strength by work hardening.

Heat treatable alloys used for high strength in the finished part are 2014, 2024 and 6061. If the forming is extensive, these alloys often must be annealed several times during spinning, or they may be spun hot.

One method used frequently for spinning heat treatable alloys is:

1 Spin annealed blank to approximate form.
2 Solution heat treat and quench.
3 Spin to final form at once, before appreciable age hardening.

If spinning to the final form cannot be done after solution heat treating and quenching, the quenched parts should be placed in a refrigerator, or packed in dry ice, and held as close to 0 F as possible until they can be spun. The parts are aged to the T6 temper after spinning has been completed.

Speeds. Typical spindle speeds for spinning flat blanks and drawn shells of various diameters are listed in Table 9. Rotational speed is decreased as blank diameter increases, so that peripheral speed is maintained in the same range regardless of the size of the workpiece. Peripheral speed ordinarily averages about 3000 ft per min for aluminum alloys. This is somewhat faster than the speeds normally used in spinning copper, brass, stainless steel and low-carbon steel.

Lubricants are needed in nearly all spinning operations. Beeswax, tallow, and petroleum jelly are suitable for most small parts. Hard yellow naphtha soap is an effective lubricant for larger workpieces. Colloidal graphite in kerosine, or compounds containing molybdenum disulfide, are used in hot spinning. Lubricating compounds used must be easily removable from the finished part without costly treatments.

Applications. Parts produced from aluminum alloys by spinning include tumblers, pitchers, bowls, cooking utensils, ring molds, milk cans, processing kettles, reflectors, aircraft and aerospace parts, architectural sections, tank heads, and streetlight standards.

Spinning is often selected in preference to drawing when quick delivery of small quantities is important, because the spun parts can usually be delivered before drawing tools have been made. Cones, hemispheres, tapered shapes, and parts with complex or re-entrant contours (if surfaces of revolution) are often more readily formed by spinning than by other methods. Spinning is also used for very large parts when suitable press equipment and tools are not readily available or are too costly.

Spinning is not usually economical for quantities of more than 5000 to 10,000 pieces, because of comparatively low production rates and resulting high unit labor costs. There are exceptions, especially in the power spinning of truncated cone-shape parts having included angles of 40° or more. Spinning is capable of producing such parts at lower cost than deep drawing and gives a uniform wall thickness and a surface free from wrinkles, and increases the tensile strength of the work metal as much as 100%.

Examples 553 and 557 illustrate the relationship between quantity and cost in forming aluminum alloy parts by spinning versus deep drawing.

Example 531, which follows, describes the use of hot power spinning of 1¼-in.-thick plate to produce small quantities of a 4-ft-diam shell. Large presses and costly tools would be required to make these parts by deep drawing.

Table 9. Typical Spindle Speeds for Spinning of Aluminum Alloy Flat Blanks and Drawn Shells of Various Diameters

Diameter of blank, in.	Spindle speed, rpm
Flat Blanks	
Up to 12	600 to 1100
12 to 24	400 to 700
24 to 36	250 to 550
36 to 72	50 to 250
72 to 120	25 to 50
120 to 180	12 to 25
180 to 210	12
Drawn Shells	
10 to 14	1000 to 1200
14 to 20	650 to 800
20 to 30	475 to 550
30 to 40	325 to 375
40 to 50	250 to 300
50 to 70	200 to 210
70 to 90	150 to 175

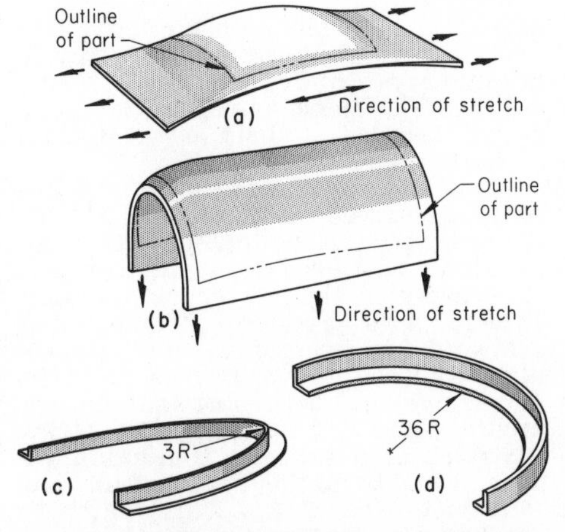

(a) Longitudinal stretching. (b) Transverse stretching. (c) Compound bend from extrusion. (d) Long sweeping bend from extrusion.

Fig. 25. Typical stretch formed shapes

Example 531. Hot Power Spinning of 48-In.-Diam Halves of a Spherical Buoy From 1¼-In.-Thick Plate

Hot power spinning was used to form the two halves of a 48-in.-diam spherical buoy from 1¼-in.-thick alloy 6061-O plate. The sequence of operations was as follows:

1 Cut 65-in.-diam circles from 66-in.-square plate stock with a band saw.
2 Lay out and drill 1-in.-diam center hole.
3 Rotate spinning mandrel at 24 rpm; heat mandrel with torches to 450 F, checking with temperature-sensitive crayons.
4 Clamp blank to mandrel with steel follower; rotate at 24 rpm.
5 Heat rotating blank with torches to 600 F; check with temperature-sensitive crayons. Continue to heat mandrel while blank is brought to temperature.
6 Increase speed to 78 rpm. Spin blank down against mandrel, making multiple forward and backward passes and using hydraulic power-assist tool with 1½-in.-radius roller. Maintain temperature with torches.
7 Rough trim by hand while hot.
8 Allow to cool to 250 F.
9 Finish trim to depth.
10 Machine edge for welding.
11 Contour-machine outside surface, to wall thickness of ¾ to 1 in.
12 Weld required fittings in place. Weld two hemispheres together.
13 Heat treat to T6 temper.

The mandrel was a ribbed hemisphere made of gray iron, which was stress relieved and then machined to approximately 46 in. in diameter. It had a 1-in.-diam center pin for holding the blank.

The procedure described in Example 531 was used for low-quantity production. For quantities of 25 or more buoys, time would be saved by performing a preliminary breakdown operation over another cast mandrel, and cost could be reduced by the use of templates and tracer-machining fixtures.

Stretch Forming

Almost all of the aluminum alloys can be shaped by stretch forming. In this process, the work metal is stretched over a form and stressed beyond its yield point to produce the desired contour. (For a detailed description of this process see the article "Stretch Forming", which begins on page 239 in this volume.)

Typical shapes produced by stretch forming are shown in Fig. 25. These include large shapes with compound curvature formed by longitudinal and by transverse stretching of sheet, and compound bends or long sweeping bends formed from extrusions.

Alloys. Properties desirable for stretch forming are high elongation, wide forming range (spread between yield strength and tensile strength), toughness, and fine grain structure.

Table 10 shows the effect of elongation and forming range on stretch-

Table 10. Mechanical Properties and Stretchability Ratings for Aluminum Alloys Most Commonly Used in Stretch Forming

Alloy	Tensile strength, psi	Yield strength, psi	Forming range, psi(a)	Elongation in 2 in., %	Stretchability rating(b)
7075-W(c)	48,000	20,000	28,000	19	100
2024-W(c)	46,000	18,000	28,000	20	98
2024-T3	64,000	44,000	20,000	18	95
6061-W(c)	35,000	21,000	14,000	22	90
7075-O	32,000	14,000	18,000	17	80
2024-O	27,000	11,000	16,000	19	80
6061-O	18,000	8,000	10,000	22	75
3003-O	16,000	6,000	10,000	30	75
1100-O	13,000	5,000	8,000	35	70
7075-T6	76,000	67,000	9,000	11	10

(a) Tensile strength minus yield strength. (b) Relative amount of stretch permissible in stretch forming, based on 7075-W as 100. (c) Freshly quenched after solution heat treatment. (SOURCE: ASME Handbook, Metals Engineering Processes, 1st Edition, 1958, page 135)

Table 11. Practical Elongation Limits for Several Aluminum Alloys in Stretch Forming

Alloy	Maximum elongation, %(a)
2014-O, 2014-T3, 2024-O, 2024-T3 and 7075-O	8 to 10
2014-W, 2024-W, 7075-W and 7178-W(b)	10 to 14
6061-W(b)	15

(a) Measured over total length subject to stretch. (b) In the W temper, alloy is freshly quenched after solution heat treatment.

Fig. 26. Motor-coach body panel with formed features in both the horizontal and the vertical planes that was stretch drawn with shaped grippers (Example 532)

ability ratings for the alloys most commonly used in stretch forming. The stretchability rating varies directly with the forming range, except for 6061-W (which has somewhat higher elongation than adjacent alloys) and 7075-T6 (which has by far the lowest elongation listed). Alloys 1100-O and 3003-O, with the highest elongation shown, nevertheless are less desirable for stretch forming than the alloys above them in the list. Their low strength and the narrow spread between yield strength and tensile strength make them particularly susceptible to local necking and premature failure in stretch forming.

Table 11 gives percentage elongation limits for some alloys in stretch forming, based on industrial practice. Actual elongation in local areas can be much higher than the average over the entire stretched area; the limits in Table 11 are about 40 to 70% of the tensile elongation in a 2-in. gage length.

On the basis of the data in Tables 10 and 11, the following conclusions can be drawn:

1. Stretch-forming capability is influenced by tensile strength and the spread between yield strength and tensile strength, as well as by elongation.
2. Non-heat-treatable alloys perform best in the annealed temper, but many have good workability in the intermediate tempers.
3. The heat treatable alloys are most suitable for stretch forming when in the fresh W temper. This has the added advantage of producing high strength without the exposure to warping that would accompany heat treatment after forming.
4. Although the low-strength alloys 1100 and 3003 excel for most forming operations, they are inferior to the O, W and T3 tempers of the high-strength, heat treatable alloys in stretchability.
5. The artificially aged tempers of all alloys can be stretch formed less severely than the W tempers.

Tools. The materials used for the form block or die depend on the production quantities required, the severity of local stress and wear on the die, and the thickness and wear properties of the alloy to be formed. Materials include wood, plastics, faced concrete, cast zinc alloys, aluminum tool and jig plate, cast iron, and (rarely) steel or chromium-plated steel.

Lubricants are recommended in the stretch forming of aluminum alloys.

Water-soluble oils are commonly used, with viscosity dependent on the severity of forming. Lubricants of types 9 and 10 in Table 1 are also used, along with calcium-base greases, paraffin, beeswax and commercial waxes. The application of too much lubricant can result in buckling of the workpiece.

Sometimes a layer of sheet rubber, glass cloth, or plastic between die and workpiece serves as a lubricant. Because of their inherent lubricity, dies made of zinc alloys require only a minimum of lubrication. Smooth-surfaced plastic dies may require no lubrication, because of their low coefficient of friction against aluminum.

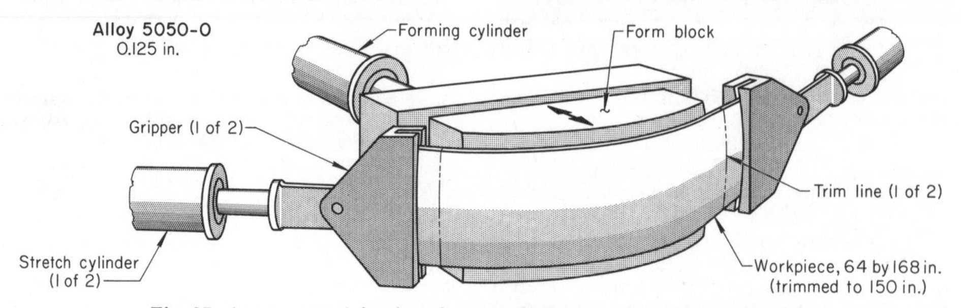

Fig. 27. Arrangement for forming parabolic reflectors (Example 533)

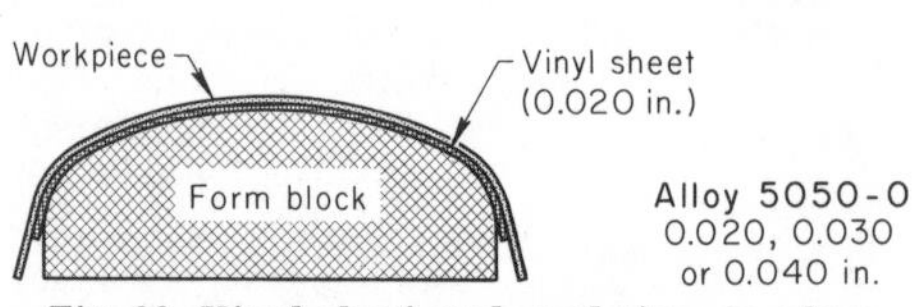

Fig. 28. Vinyl sheet and workpiece in place on form block after forming a parabolic microwave reflector (Example 534)

Applications. The various stretch-forming techniques (including stretch drawing, stretch wrapping, and compression and radial drawing) are used extensively in the aerospace industry. Typical parts produced include wing-skin and fuselage panels, engine cowlings, window and door frames, and trim panels used in aerospace, automotive, architectural and appliance industries.

Stretch draw forming of aluminum is done using both the matched-die and form-block techniques. The matched-die method uses a single-action hydraulic press equipped with a means of closing and moving the jaws that grip each end of the blank. The punch is attached to the bed of the press and the die is attached to the ram.

The other method uses a form block that is attached to a stationary bed or to a hydraulic cylinder. With this method, the blank is gripped with jaws that hold it in tension or draw it over the form block.

The part in the following example was formed with matched dies in a stretch draw press.

Example 532. Use of Shaped Jaws for Two-Way Forming of a Coach Body Panel (Fig. 26)

The body panel for a motor coach shown in Fig. 26 was formed in a stretch draw press using matched dies. The part had contour features in both the horizontal and the vertical planes. The alloy 5052-H31 blank was 33.05 by 15 in. by 0.090 in. thick. Jaws that followed the faired contour of the coach panel gripped the blank and drew it over the punch to form the contour of the panel as well as the feature lines at the sides. The blank was stretched 1 to 1½% before forming. After the contour was formed, the press closed, striking the panel with the mating die to set the contours. The punch and die were made of cast iron.

Cost of the stretch draw die was about one-third that of a conventional press die. Production rate was approximately equal to that of a conventional process. Yearly production was 25,000 panels for each side of the coach.

The blanks were loaded into the jaws and the formed parts removed from the press with automatic material-handling equipment.

The formed panels were bright dipped and anodized by a sulfuric acid process.

Stretch drawing with form blocks was used for forming the parts for large parabolic reflectors described in the three examples that follow. No wrinkles, scratches or blemishes were permitted in the formed panels.

In the first example, the blank was held in a vertical position while a thoroughly cleaned moving form block shaped the part. A polyvinyl chloride sheet acted as lubricant between the blank and form block in the second example. In the third example, a support sheet was used during forming and for carrying the formed, unbonded honeycomb workpiece to the assembly area.

Example 533. Stretch Drawing a Parabolic Microwave Reflector (Fig. 27)

By stretch drawing, a three-dimensional parabolic curve was imposed on an alloy 5050-O sheet 64 by 168 in. by 0.125 in. thick, as shown in Fig. 27. A 196-ton horizontal stretch press with a form block actuated by a hydraulic cylinder was used. The crown of the curve was 9 in. high. Because the finished part was a microwave reflector, extreme care was used in handling and forming the sheet to keep it free of dust particles that might mar its mirror-smooth finish. Care also was necessary to prevent kinking or bending of the sheet while the press was being loaded.

The form block was epoxy-fiberglass molded on a steel frame. The contour was swept on with a form template.

All forming was done dry so that lubricant would not attract dust particles to the form block or workpiece. The form block was cleaned and inspected for imperfections before each piece was formed.

A prestretch of 3 or 4 tons was applied to the workpiece before the main ram of the press forced the form block into the sheet. Time for forming was 7 min floor-to-floor. Additional time was needed to prepare the blank and clean the form block. Setup time was 2 hr. A typical production lot was 150 to 200 pieces.

Example 534. Use of a Vinyl Sheet as Lubricant in Stretch Drawing a Parabolic Reflector (Fig. 28)

A parabolic microwave reflector was formed in a horizontal stretch draw press using a stationary form block, as shown in Fig. 28. The alloy 5050-O blanks were 50 in. wide by 220 in. long by 0.020, 0.030, or 0.040 in. thick.

A thin sheet of polyvinyl chloride was placed between the form block and the blank to act as a lubricant and to prevent dust particles that settled on the surface of the form block from being imbedded in the mirror-smooth surface of the workpiece.

The zone, or over-all, tolerance for the formed panel was ±0.030 in. The contour of the form block was accurate within 0.020 in. No allowance was made for springback. The time needed to form each part was 7 min, plus die and blank preparation time. Production-lot sizes were 150 to 200 pieces, but only about 70 panels were needed each month.

Example 535. Stretch Draw Forming of Skins for a Honeycomb Panel (Fig. 29)

A parabolic microwave reflector 30 ft in diameter was made of honeycomb panel with 0.003-in.-thick alloy 5050-O skins on each surface of the honeycomb. For ease in fabrication, the reflector was made in pie-shape sections 24 in. wide at the heel. Rectangular sheets 0.003 in. thick by 24 in. wide by 17 ft long for the reflecting surface were stretch draw formed in a 150-ton vertical stretch press, as shown in Fig. 29. First, a carrying sheet of 0.060-in.-thick alloy 5050-O was stretch drawn on the form block, and became the forming surface for the foil sheet. The workpiece foil was delivered on a roll. The end was unrolled, doubled, and inserted into the grippers at one end. The foil was unrolled over the forming surface; the other end was doubled and inserted into the grippers at the other end.

After the workpiece was formed, it was delivered on the carrying sheet to the assembly area, where it was trimmed to the tapering pie-shape form of the reflector section. Later, the honeycomb was bonded to it.

Outer skin sections were stretch formed in the same way as the reflector sections. After each outer section had been formed, it was taped to a preformed carrier sheet for transport to the honeycomb panel for bonding. The undersheet used as the forming surface for outer sections remained on the form block.

Even in a dust-free room, constant vigilance had to be maintained to keep surfaces of form blocks and carrying sheets free of dust. Receiving surfaces were cleaned before forming, before trimming and before assembly. Because of the cleaning and inspection involved, the extreme care needed to handle the sheets, and the high scrap rate (80 to 85%), production rates varied considerably.

Extruded or roll formed structural shapes, rods and bars are usually stretch formed in a radial draw former, but they can be stretch formed in a stretch draw press, as in the following two examples.

Example 536. Use of a Stretch Draw Press to Edge Bend Frame Members (Fig. 30)

Reinforcing frames for microwave reflectors (see Fig. 30) were made from alloy 6061-T4, ¾ in. thick by 11¹⁄₁₆ in. wide by 150 in. long. They were edge bent to conform to the parabolic contour. Before bending, each strip was trimmed in an arbor saw to the varying angle at which the frame member would meet the parabola of the reflector. Since the curve was parabolic, the radius of curvature varied continuously, but greatest distance from arc to chord was 9 in.

The frame member was stretch formed in a horizontal stretch draw press equipped with a low-carbon steel form block with an 11-in.-deep by ¾-in.-wide groove for the framing member. No lubricant was used. Life of the form block was indefinitely long. Setup time was 2 hr. Forming time for each piece was 7 min, using three operators. There was no particular limit to the production-lot size that could have been run, but to match the skin production, lots were usually 700 pieces or less.

Example 537. Stretch Draw Forming of an Extruded Section (Fig. 31)

An extruded Z-bar of alloy 6063-T5, 1½ by 1½ by ³⁄₁₆ in., was annealed and then stretch drawn to make the roof stiffener shown in Fig. 31. The form block was machined to match the cross-sectional shape of the Z-bar so that it could support the flanges during forming.

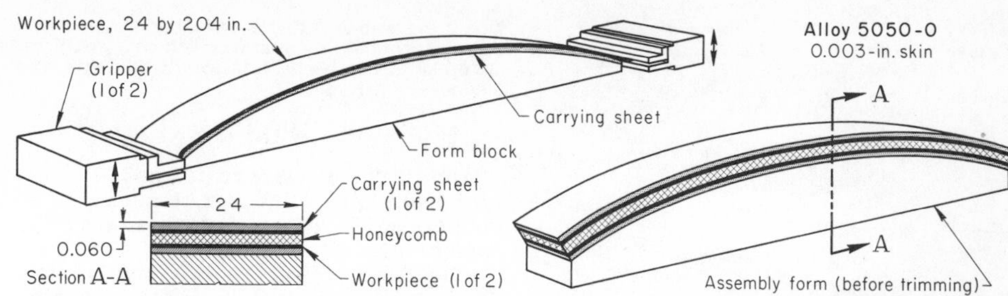

Fig. 29. Stretch draw forming 0.003-in.-thick skins for a honeycomb panel (Example 535)

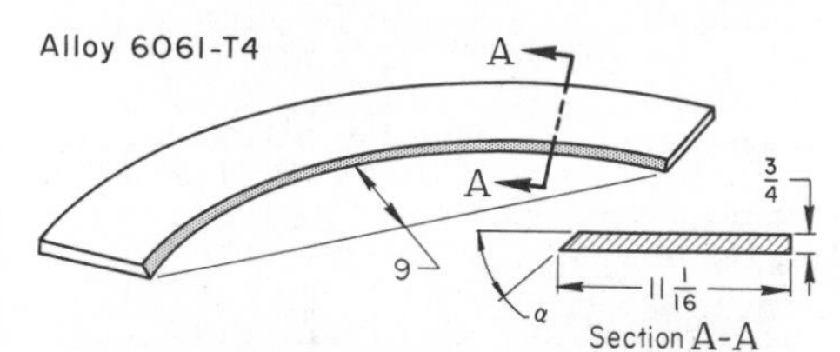

Fig. 30. Reinforcing frame member for a microwave reflector that was edge bent in a stretch draw press (Example 536)

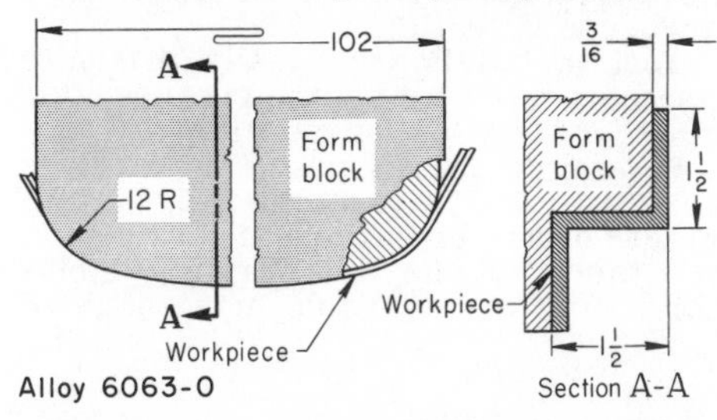

Fig. 31. Roof stiffener produced from an extruded Z-bar by stretch draw forming (Example 537)

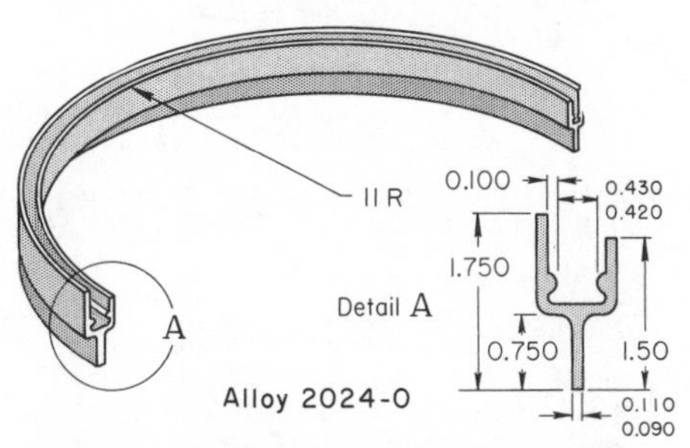

Fig. 32. Extruded section that was stretch wrapped with both a shaped form block and a segmented filler (Example 538)

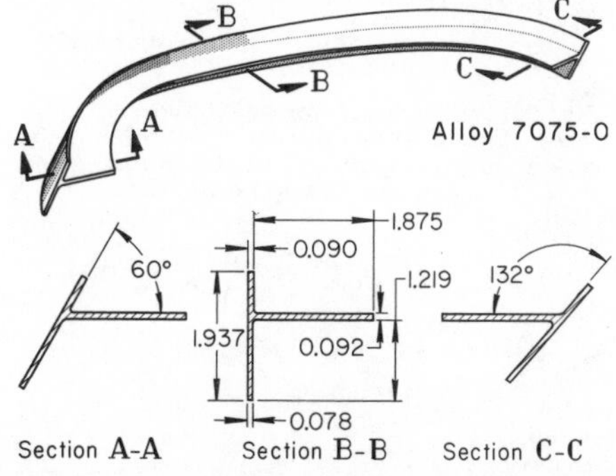

Fig. 33. Radial-draw formed T-section with radical changes in angle between leg and flange (Example 539)

The metal was stretched beyond its yield point and took a permanent set to the contour of the form block with little or no springback.

The blank was cut 8 in. longer than the required length to provide stock for gripping in the jaws. After the workpiece was stretch formed, 4 in. was trimmed from each end.

The bar could have been roll formed, using a template, and then trimmed to length. Man-hours for producing the stiffener by stretch forming and roll forming are compared below.

	Stretch forming	Roll forming
Setup time, man-hr	4.0	0.5
Time per piece, man-hr	0.1	0.5

Stretch wrapping uses a form block that is bolted to a rotary table. One end of the blank is clamped to the form block or to a table-mounted gripper. A hydraulic cylinder or a gripper applies tension to the other end of the blank while the form block revolves into it with the turning of the table. Sheets and extruded or rolled shapes are formed by this method. The forming of an aluminum panel is described in Example 325 in the article on Stretch Forming, page 242 in this volume.

Shaped form blocks that match the contour of extruded or rolled sections are used for support during forming. Filler strips, either segmented or made of low-melting alloys or strips of aluminum, are used to prevent the collapse of sections. In the following example, an extruded section was stretch wrapped using a shaped form block and a segmented filler.

Example 538. Support of Extruded Section During Stretch Wrapping (Fig. 32)

The extruded section shown in Fig. 32 was stretch wrapped into an arch that was used as the front frame member for an aircraft cockpit canopy. The material was alloy 2024-O, which was stretch wrapped using a segmented filler and a contoured form block to support the extruded section around the bend. After solution heat treating to the W temper, the workpiece was stretch wrapped again and checked in a fixture. Formed contour and changes in shape of the cross section were held within ±0.010 in.

The form block was made of zinc alloy for ease in machining the contour, and between 5000 and 6000 pieces were made on it with no signs of deterioration. Lubrication was residual mill oil. Setup time was 1 hr. Production time was 9 min per piece with two operators working. A 250-piece lot was processed every three months.

Radial-draw forming is a combination of stretch wrapping and compression forming. The workpiece is pressed against the form block by a roller or shoe while being wrapped around the turning form block. This method can be used to form a flange to a compound curvature while forming a leg, as in the following example:

Example 539. Radial-Draw Forming a T-Section Having Angular Changes Between Flange and Leg (Fig. 33)

As shown in Fig. 33, the canopy part made of a T-section varied in shape throughout its length. Originally, it was assembled and welded from three separately formed pieces. However, using radial-draw forming, the part was made from one piece of a T-shape extrusion of alloy 7075-O. The flange was given the compound curvature of the form block by a swiveled compression shoe. The leg of the T-section was stretch wrapped into a

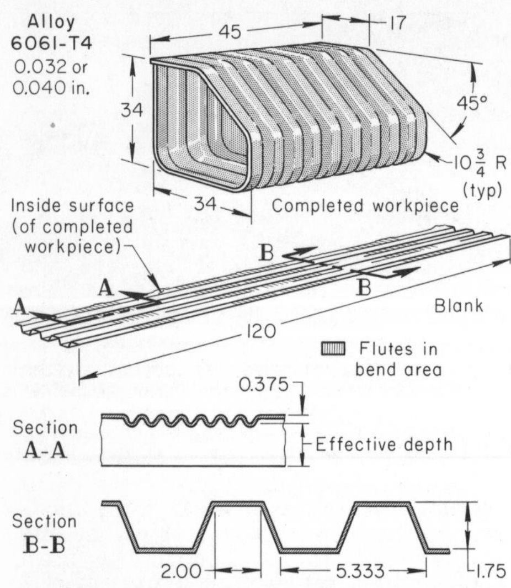

Fig. 34. Cargo container that was radial-draw formed from a commercial V-beam by fluting crests of corrugations to reduce stress in the bend zones (Example 540)

slot in the form block. Thus, the bending and twisting of the T-section were set at the same time by the combination of stretch wrapping and compression forming. Production rate was 15 pieces per hour.

Stretch forming is practical as long as the stresses on the inner and outer surfaces of the formed workpieces are kept below the tensile strength. Generally, difficulty arises when forming deep structural shapes or edge-bending pieces in one operation. Preformed sheet metal pieces with sections that are deep in relation to stock thickness may also be difficult to form. The parts can be formed in two or more steps with an intermediate anneal, or by altering the cross section to reduce the depth and nature of the bending zone, as in the following example.

Example 540. Use of Fluted Corrugations to Reduce Depth of Bend Zone (Fig. 34)

Corrugated 6061-T4 sheet was radial-draw formed to 90° and 45° bends to make the aircraft cargo container shown in Fig. 34. The stock was a commercial V-beam 120 in. long by 45 in. wide and 0.032 or 0.040 in. thick, with corrugations 1¾ in. deep repeated every 5.333 in. The 45° bend was formed successfully by radial-draw forming, but attempts to make the 90° bend failed, either by collapse of the inner ridges or, if enough stretch was applied to support them, by tearing of the outer crests.

To eliminate collapsing of the inner ridges at the 90° bends, a series of ⅜-in.-deep flutes was formed on each inner ridge in the bend zone. These flutes changed the nature of the bend and reduced the effective depth of the cross section by ⅜ in. As the 90° bends were made, the tension in the outer ridge was reduced and the flutes in the inner ridge were closed by compression. For the sake of appearance, flutes were also added to the 45° bends. The blanks were wiped as clean and free of lubricant and dust as possible, because lubrication had a deleterious effect on stretch forming of this piece.

The form block was made of epoxy-fiberglass on a steel base. The form was wiped into the epoxy with a template cut to the basic dimensions of the commercial V-beam contour. Wiping shoes and clamps of epoxy-fiberglass were cast against the form block. The epoxy-fiberglass form block had a life of 5000 pieces.

Inside radius of all bends was 9 in.; outside radius was 10¾ in. Contour tolerance on the outside surface of the bend was 0.030 in., because it had to fit to the contour of the aircraft fuselage. The 90° bends were overwrapped 20° to allow for springback; angular variation on bends was kept within 1°. Production time was 15 min floor-to-floor with three men working — one operator and two handlers. Setup time was 1½ hr, and production rate was 300 pieces per month.

Rubber-Pad Forming

Aluminum alloys are formed by several techniques that can be classified as rubber-pad forming. A general description of processes, equipment, tools and applications is given in the article "Rubber-Pad Forming", which begins on page 209 in this volume.

Alloys for rubber-pad forming are selected on the same basis as for similar bending or deep drawing operations. With non-heat-treatable aluminum alloys, the temper that will meet the forming requirements and give the maximum strength in unworked areas is usually chosen.

Heat treatable aluminum alloys ordinarily are either formed in the annealed temper and then solution heat treated, or formed in the freshly quenched W temper.

Tool materials are usually masonite for short runs and aluminum alloy, zinc alloy, or steel for longer runs.

Several different types of rubber have been used as the pad material. Certain grades of rubber have particularly good resistance to oils and forming lubricants, and are available in a range of hardness, tensile strength, and deflection characteristics to meet different forming requirements.

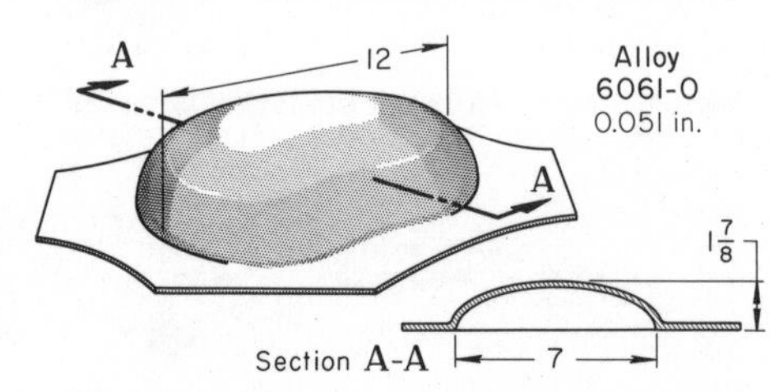

Fig. 35. Shallow part that was drawn with a rubber pad and a rigid female steel die in one operation

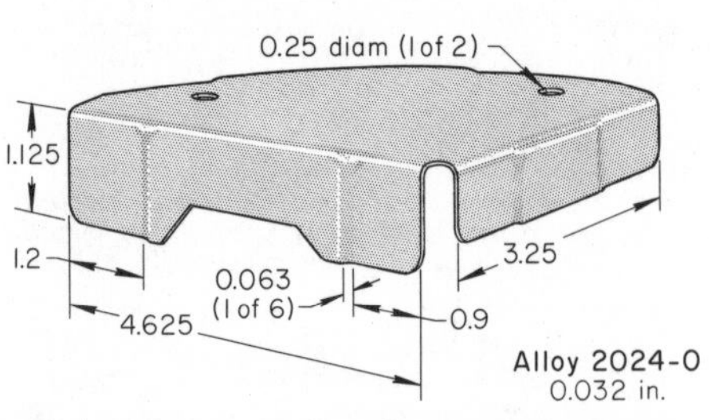

Fig. 36. Rubber-pad formed bulkhead with three flanges (one at rear, not shown) in which joggles had to set by hand after forming (Example 541)

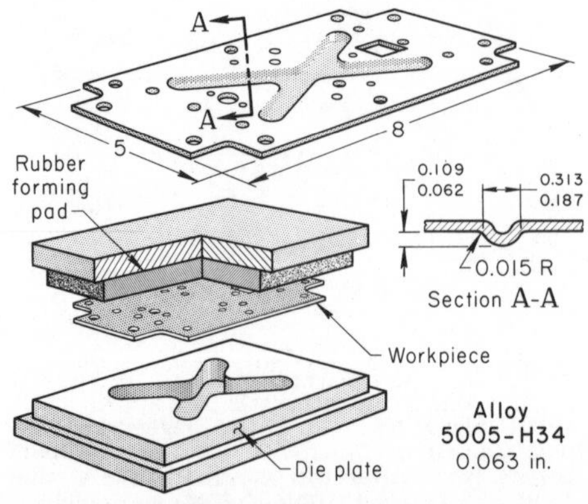

Fig. 37. Rubber-pad forming of beads in a pierced flat part (Example 542)

Capabilities. A given alloy and temper can sometimes be formed more severely by rubber-pad forming than with conventional tools, because of the multidirectional nature of the force exerted against the workpiece. Also, the variable radius of the forming pad assists in producing a more uniform elongation of the workpiece than in conventional forming operations.

Forming the shallow part shown in Fig. 35 with a rubber pad and a rigid female die used the variable radius to an advantage. The development of wrinkles was almost eliminated, because the rubber acted as a blankholder and kept the work in contact with the flat and contoured die surfaces as the drawing progressed. A drawing compound was used on the blank.

Limitations. The simpler types of rubber-pad forming have relatively low production rates and correspondingly high unit labor costs, compared with punch-press operations. However, the rubber-diaphragm process is adaptable to automatic loading equipment and thus has fairly high production rates.

Applications. Rubber-pad forming is widely used in the aerospace industry, especially for structural parts and skin components. Products made in other industries include appliance parts, license plates, numerals, lighting reflectors, skin panels for buildings, moldings, utensils, and parts drawn from prefinished sheet.

Most rubber-pad forming is done on material 1⁄16 in. or less in thickness, with only a small percentage being thicker than ¼ in. However, aluminum alloy parts ⅝ in. thick have been formed in special heavy-duty equipment of the rubber-diaphragm type.

Some bulkheads and brackets have both straight and curved flanges with joggles at both ends. The form blocks for such parts are sometimes interchangeable between the Guerin and Verson-Wheelon rubber-pad processes (see pages 209 and 212 in the article "Rubber-Pad Forming", in this volume). Handwork is usually necessary to set the joggles and to smooth small buckles in the shrink flanges:

Example 541. Use of Handwork to Finish Rubber-Pad Formed Pieces (Fig. 36)

Joggles at the ends of the three flanges in the aluminum alloy bulkhead shown in Fig. 36 had to be set by hand after the part was formed by the Verson-Wheelon process. The part was made of 0.032-in.-thick alloy 2024-O from a developed blank that was cut with a high-speed router and deburred by hand.

The form block was made of aluminum alloy 1⅞ in. thick, and had two ¼-in.-diam locating pins. A ¼-in.-thick cover plate was used to keep the web flat during forming. The cover plate was beveled and rounded on the edges to aid the flow of the rubber around the flanges. The rubber pad of the fluid cell was protected by a 1-in.-thick throw sheet. Forming pressure was 3000 psi. Cycle time was 2 min per piece. Production lots were 25 pieces.

The same part was formed by the Guerin process using the same tooling with a forming pressure of 600 psi. In the Guerin process, a ½-in.-thick throw sheet protected the rubber pad. The only significant difference in quality between the two processes was the forming of larger compression buckles in the shrink flange with the Guerin process. The joggles also had to be finished by hand, as in the Verson-Wheelon process.

The simultaneous blanking and piercing of flat stock can also be done with rubber-pad tooling. This type of operation is limited to aluminum alloy sheet no thicker than about 0.064 in.

The control of metal movement that can be obtained with rubber-pad forming not only permits more severe forming than with conventional tools, but also is applicable to beading operations. Beads are frequently used to obtain rigidity on large surfaces without increasing the metal thickness.

With a conventional steel punch, die and blankholder, metal is moved from the edges of the workpiece toward the bead, making the edges somewhat concave, and sometimes producing warping or oil-can effects. Some movement of metal toward the formed area is usually desirable, in order to prevent excessive thinning or cracking of the beads. In the forming of some parts, however, it may be necessary that metal movement be restricted to the immediate vicinity of the beads:

Example 542. Change From Conventional to Rubber-Pad Forming for Accuracy in Producing Beads in a Pierced Sheet (Fig. 37)

Figure 37 shows a beaded part in which the holes, produced to close tolerances on location and dimensions, had to be pierced before the beads were formed. When the part was formed conventionally with steel punch, die and blankholder, the holes distorted out of location, and the relatively large, flat surface warped. Also, irregular movement of the blank interfered with the accuracy of a subsequent press-brake flanging operation, which depended on the over-all dimensions of the part and the squareness of the edges.

Roughening the steel blankholder or otherwise restricting metal movement did not correct the problem.

Finally, the use of a rubber forming pad (Fig. 37) localized the forming operation to the immediate area of the beads, thereby solving the problem. It was not necessary to confine the rubber pad. Tooling costs were lowered by more than 80%, and rejections were reduced to a minimum.

With this improved method, it was only necessary to machine straight-sided grooves in a steel die and to provide two pilot pins for locating the workpiece. A female die restricted metal movement more effectively than a male die, and was used for this operation. Length of press stroke was not critical, and stock of various thicknesses could be formed on the one die.

A rubber slab of controlled properties, 1½ in. thick and with a hardness of Durometer A 90, was used for both the punch and blankholder. (This thickness and hardness combination is suitable for most beading operations on the more ductile aluminum alloys.) No lubrication was required. Tool life was about 100,000 pieces.

The deep drawing capabilities of rubber-pad processes vary with the different types of equipment. The severity of drawing possible with heavy-duty rubber-pad drawing by the Marform process (see page 213 in "Rubber-Pad Forming") is compared below with that possible in conventional drawing. The comparison is based on the drawing of alloys 1100-O and 3003-O.

Drawing severity	Reduction in diameter, %	Ratio of depth to diameter
Rubber-Pad Drawing		
Typical	57	1.1
Maximum	72	3.0
Conventional Drawing		
Maximum	40	0.45

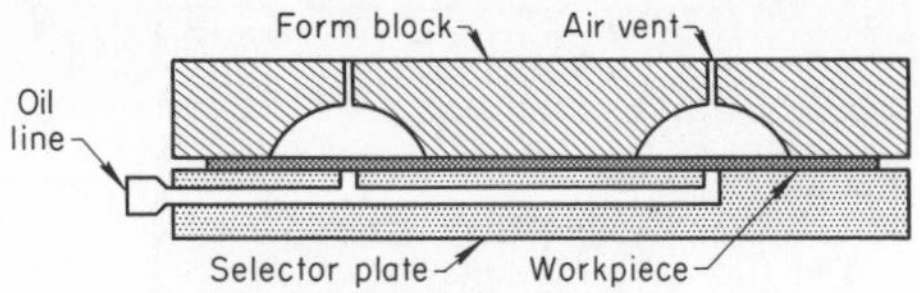

Fig. 38. Typical tooling setup for hydraulic forming of multiple beads in flat stock

Hydraulic Forming

True hydraulic forming by direct oil pressure against the surface of the workpiece has been applied to aluminum alloy flat stock. The process has been used mainly for the drawing of multiple beads on small quantities of large, flat sheets of thin material for aerospace applications. As shown in Fig. 38, a form block attached to the ram of the press holds the workpiece tightly against a selector plate, through which oil is introduced into channels at the bead locations.

In typical applications, up to 20 beads have been drawn in parts 20 to 30 in. wide by 60 to 80 in. long and about 0.012 in. thick, made from alloy 2024. Clamping force required is about 300 tons, and forming oil pressure about 1000 psi. Vents are provided in the form block to allow the escape of air from each bead cavity. The oil film left on the form block after each operation provides sufficient lubrication to draw the next part.

The technique is limited to short runs because production rate is slow. (Although 20 beads could be drawn in three seconds, total handling time for a panel was 3 to 4 min.)

Forming by Shot Peening

The major application of shot peening is to increase the fatigue life of metal parts by producing a uniform compressive stress in the surface layers. Shot peening is sometimes used as a metal-forming process, and is especially useful in the forming of large, irregularly shaped parts from aluminum alloy sheet stock.

General information on the process, equipment, and applications is given in the article "Shot Peening", pages 398 to 405 in Volume 2 of this Handbook.

Shot. When steel shot is used to peen-form aluminum alloy parts, the parts are usually treated chemically after forming to remove particles of iron or iron oxides that may be embedded in the surface.

Slugs cut from stainless steel or aluminum alloy wire are sometimes used. When peening with aluminum alloy slugs, no subsequent chemical treatment is needed, and the danger of overpeening and high localized residual stress (which sometimes occurs with steel or iron shot) is also eliminated.

Automatic or semiautomatic devices are available for the separation and removal of fines and undersize shot, and for the addition of new shot. Manual handling of shot and batch replacement may be more feasible for small-scale operations. The proportion of full-size shot in the system is usually maintained at a minimum of 85%.

Control. The effectiveness of shot peening depends on the size, shape, material and velocity of the shot, and on the quantity of shot striking a unit area per unit time. The combined effect of these variables is known as peening intensity, which is measured on standard steel test strips according to SAE J442, and is expressed as an Almen-gage reading.

The angle at which the shot strikes the work also affects the peening intensity, which is proportional to the sine of the angle of impingement. The amount of breakdown of the shot will, of course, also affect peening intensity.

The extent of surface coverage as measured by visual or instrumental techniques is often used, together with Almen test strips, to control peening operations.

Applications. One of the earliest forming applications of shot peening was the contour forming of integrally stiffened aircraft-wing panels. Because of their extreme length and variable thickness, these parts are ill-suited for forming by mechanical processes. The shot peening of an aircraft-wing panel is described in the following example.

Example 543. Forming Integrally Stiffened Wing Panels by Shot Peening (Fig. 39)

Shot peening was used for contour forming integrally stiffened aircraft-wing panels (Fig. 39) ranging up to 24 in. in width and up to 50 ft in length. The panels were machined from alloy 7075-T6 after having been stretcher leveled. Basic thickness of the panel between the ribs ranged from 0.09 to 0.18 in. for tapered skins, and up to 0.312 in. thick for straight (no taper) skins. One surface of the panels had stiffening ribs spaced a few inches apart, and also a number of ¾-in.-thick "pads" for attaching the panels to the frame or for attaching inboard equipment to the panels. This structure made it almost impossible to press form the panels to the required smoothly curved contours.

Before being peen formed, the panels were first shot peened with SAE 230 cast steel shot, to improve fatigue resistance by cold working to a depth of 0.006 to 0.008 in. The panels were then peen formed on the same worktable, without being removed from the machine. Larger cast steel shot (SAE 550 or 930) was used to form the thicker sections of a panel and to obtain a greater depth of cold work (up to 0.016 in. on pad areas). Irregular curves were produced by peening selected local areas as needed, sometimes on the reverse side of the panel as well as on the outer surface. Gradual blending of areas was necessary to obtain smooth contours.

Oscillating air nozzles were used with air pressure up to 90 psi. Peening intensity was determined by means of Almen A test strips. Forming time per panel was 2 to 3 hr. After peening, the panels were chemically treated to remove ferrous residues and to improve corrosion resistance.

Other parts formed by shot peening include honeycomb panels and large tubular shapes. Large, irregularly shaped parts are conveniently formed by this method.

The process is usually carried out as a free-forming technique, without dies

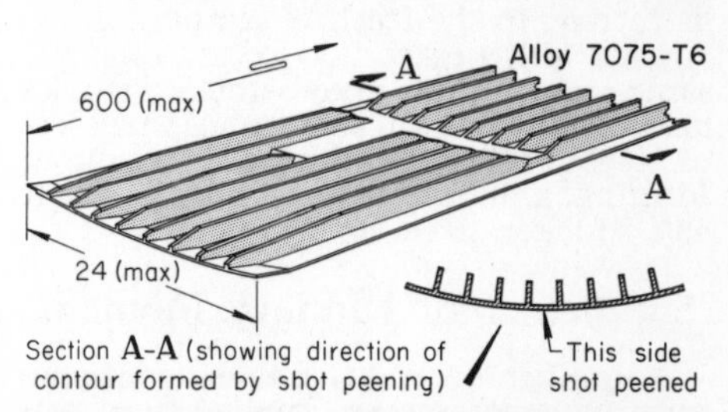

Fig. 39. Integrally stiffened wing panel that was formed by shot peening (Example 543)

or form blocks. Contour is checked against a template.

If a part is deformed beyond the specified amount, the contour can be corrected by peening the reverse side. Also, peening can be used as a salvage procedure to correct the contours of bent or distorted parts.

The peening intensity and the number of passes are varied depending on the material and the severity of forming required. Local areas can be subjected to the required treatment.

Drop Hammer Forming

Drop hammer forming is of value for limited production runs that do not warrant expensive tooling, and is often used in experimental work to make trial parts and parts that are expected to undergo frequent design changes.

Tooling costs are low, and finished parts can be produced quickly. However, only relatively shallow parts with liberal radii can be drawn, and material thickness must be in the range of about 0.024 to 0.064 in. Also, wrinkling occurs frequently, and a high degree of operator skill is required.

Equipment and Tools. Air-operated hammers with sensitive and accurate control are usually preferred to hammers operated by gravity or by steam.

The material is formed in a sequence of small steps. In a typical setup (Fig. 40) several plywood or rubber spacers are stacked on the die face, and one or more are removed after each stroke to form the workpiece progressively.

In a variation of this procedure, a series of dies can be used to accomplish the progressive forming. Only the last of these dies requires close tolerances. A rubber pad several inches thick is sometimes used between workpiece and punch in all except the final step.

Dies are simple and inexpensive. Bottom dies are cast from zinc alloy, and punches can also be made from zinc alloy. If requirements on sharpness of radii and accuracy of contour are not stringent, punches cast from lead are used for short runs. These need not be cast accurately, because they deform to the shape of the bottom die in a few strokes. For longer runs, tools can be made of cast iron or cast steel.

Lubrication requirements are similar to those for drawing operations.

Alloys used most frequently are 1100, 3003, 2024, 5052, 6061 and 7075. Annealed tempers permit the greatest severity of forming. Intermediate tempers of the non-heat-treatable alloys are often used for channel shapes and shallow, embossed panels. Heat treatable alloys can be partly formed in the annealed condition and given a restrike operation after heat treatment, or they can be formed in the fresh W temper.

With all processing conditions the same, aluminum alloy stock wrinkles more readily than the same thickness of steel sheet. For comparable results in forming, aluminum alloys must be about 40% thicker than steel.

Supplemental Forming Methods

A number of additional conventional forming processes are applied to aluminum alloy sheet, strip or wire in conjunction with the processes already described in this article. Among the supplemental processes are embossing, coining, stamping, curling, expanding or bulging, contracting or necking, hole flanging, and beading or ribbing.

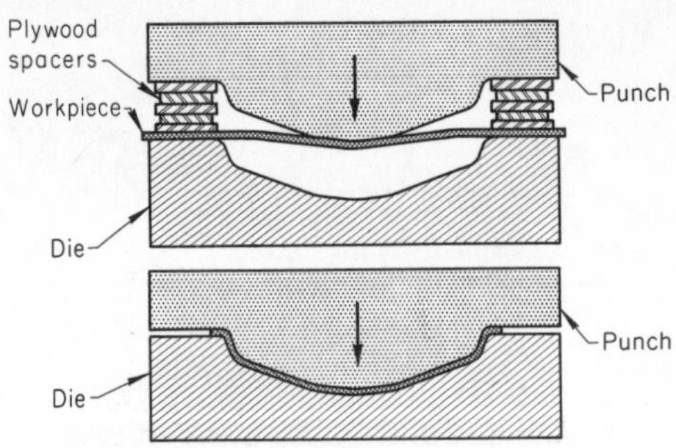

Fig. 40. Tooling and setup for drop hammer forming

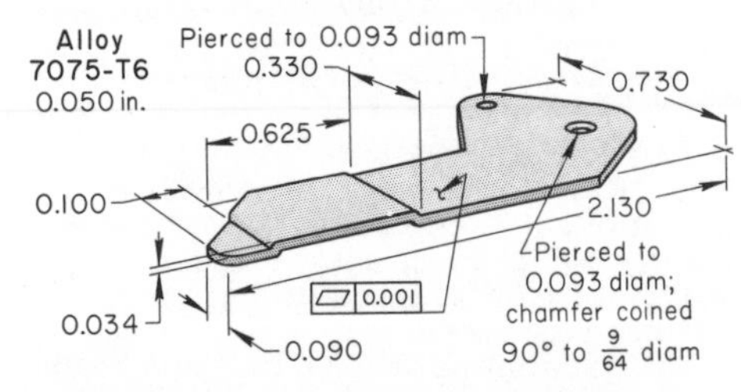

Fig. 41. Lever that was produced from solution heat treated and aged alloy 7075 strip by embossing, piercing, coining and blanking in a progressive die (Example 544)

Embossing, Coining and Stamping. These three closely related methods for making shallow impressions and patterns by compression between a punch and a die are frequently combined with drawing. In these operations, the material must yield under impact and compression, and it must be ductile to avoid fracture in tension.

Uniform thickness in all areas of the workpiece generally is maintained in embossing; however, some stretching occurs. Simple designs are produced with light pressure, using a punch of the desired shape and an open female die. Complex patterns require high pressure and a closed matching female die or a rubber female die.

Coining differs from embossing in that metal is made to flow, thus producing local differences in metal thickness. The design on top and bottom surfaces may be different. Very high pressure is required.

Stamping produces cut lines of lettering or patterns in one side of the workpiece, to 0.020 to 0.040-in. depth. The depth of penetration must be carefully controlled to minimize distortion and to prevent the design from appearing on the opposite side. Outline or open-face stamps are preferred.

Alloy and temper are usually selected to have high elongation, the required tensile strength, and as low a yield strength as possible. The annealed temper yields the most accurate impressions, but a harder temper may be required for other reasons, as in the example that follows.

Example 544. Embossing and Coining of Alloy 7075 in the T6 Temper (Fig. 41)

The lever shown in Fig. 41 was produced from 0.050-in.-thick alloy 7075-T6 strip 2¾ in. wide, in the following sequence of operations in a progressive die of hardened tool steel:

1 Emboss the 0.034-in. offset.
2 Pierce two 0.093-in.-diam holes.
3 Coin one hole to a 90° chamfer and 9/64-in. diameter (Fig. 41).
4 Shave chamfered hole.
5 Blank and flatten.

These operations were done in a 45-ton mechanical press operating at 125 strokes per minute. The punch for coin-chamfering the hole was designed to push the metal into the hole, because stock thickening around the hole was not permitted. The hole was shaved after coining to maintain size. After blanking and flattening, the part was tumbled in an abrasive medium for removal of burrs.

Although alloy 7075 is not recommended for cold working after being solution heat treated and aged (T6 temper), the flatness tolerance of 0.001 in. over the full length of the lever could not be maintained when the part was produced from alloy 7075 strip in the annealed condition and then heat treated.

Tools must be hard and tough. (For a detailed discussion and recommendations on the selection of die materials, the reader is referred to the article "The Selection of Material for Coining Dies", pages 717 to 719 in Volume 1 of this Handbook.) With stamping tools, only the punch is hardened, and the die or anvil is usually made of a low-carbon steel.

Tool surfaces must be highly polished and free from local imperfections. Lubrication is avoided if possible; when lubrication is necessary, alcohol or a similar volatile liquid should be used as the lubricant. Tools and blank must be kept free from any foreign particles.

Knuckle-joint presses with a precisely controlled short stroke, and designed to exert extremely high pressure at the bottom of the stroke, are most suitable for this application. Special precautions are taken to prevent the feeding of oversize blanks or of two blanks at once, and dies are sometimes mounted on hydropneumatic pressure-equalizing cushions to avoid breakage of the die or press frame.

Embossing, coining and stamping frequently impose special demands on tool design, particularly when done in combination with other forming operations. The following example describes an unusual tooling arrangement developed for embossing a zipper component.

Example 545. Use of Spring-Actuated Embossing Punches in Four-Operation Production of a Zipper Component (Fig. 42)

Figure 42 shows the progression of shapes that resulted from notching, piercing, forming and embossing of alloy 5056-O roll-formed wire in the production of a small zipper component. Forming, which was of the simple pressure-pad type, was done before embossing, to avoid distortion or cracking of the embossed area. Kerosine was the lubricant.

The tooling setup for embossing is also shown in Fig. 42. The upper punch and the separate auxiliary punches on each side of it were separately spring actuated. The lower, or embossing, punch was highly polished and, because of part design, had only a very small radius on the top corners. A 0.005-in. ledge was provided on each side of the lower punch to help supply additional metal in this location, and thus to prevent the development of cracks along the radius on each side of the embossing. The lower embossing punch also had a wider shoulder to prevent the workpiece from becoming distorted and undersize below the embossed area.

Curling or false wiring can be done in a variety of machines, such as press brakes, single-action punch presses, lathes, roll-forming machines, or special beading machines. The selection of machine depends on the shape and the number of parts required. Circular parts are usually curled on spinning lathes, and rectangular parts in presses. Long, relatively narrow parts can be curled in press brakes or roll-forming machines. Various types of machines have been built specifically for curling in high production quantities.

The edge to be curled should be of uniform height and free from roughness on the outside of the curl, and preferably should be rounded slightly before beginning the operation. The minimum radius for curling should be 1½ to 4 times the metal thickness, depending on alloy and temper.

Expanding or bulging of aluminum alloy parts can be carried out by several different methods, including segmented mechanical dies, rubber punches, or hydraulic pressure.

Segmented mechanical expanding dies are relatively inexpensive and are capable of high production rates, but are limited to certain shapes and may produce marks on thin stock and low-strength alloys.

Rubber punches are widely used and are applicable to extremely difficult operations or those impossible to do by other means. (Additional information on the use of rubber punches for bulging is given on page 216 in the article "Rubber-Pad Forming", in this volume.) Rubber is selected at hardness, tensile strength, and deflection most suitable for the workpiece shape. The rubber punch or pad must be correctly shaped and located to apply pressure to the shell wall at the required points; it must be kept free from oil; and it should be lubricated with talc, pumice, or other powder-type lubricant.

Water and oil can also be used to exert pressure directly against the workpiece, but this technique requires expensive tooling and controls, and is often messy.

Annealed alloys can be expanded more readily than tempered alloys. With alloys 1100-O, 3003-O and 5050-O, the diameter of a shell can be increased about 25%. Large increases in diameter can be made in two or more operations with intermediate annealing.

Different types of expanding or bulging operations are shown in Fig. 13 and 14. Bead-rolling machines are available for forming beads such as on the part in Fig. 13.

Contracting or necking operations reduce the diameter of a shell, usually at the open end. This entails reductions ranging in severity from the forming of a shallow circumferential groove to the forming of a bottle-neck shape.

The reduction in diameter, in a single operation, should not exceed 8 to 15%, depending on alloy, temper, and extent of prior work hardening. The angle from the body to the necked diameter should be less than 45°, to prevent collapse of the shell. It may be necessary to anneal the workpiece locally.

Rotary swaging is often used to reduce the diameter of thick-wall shells. This process is described in the article that begins on page 333 in this volume.

Hole flanging, the forming of a flange or collar around a hole in sheet stock, can be a critical operation. The hole should be punched from the side opposite the intended flange. This avoids splitting the severely stretched outer edge of the flange, which could be initiated by the burred edge of the hole.

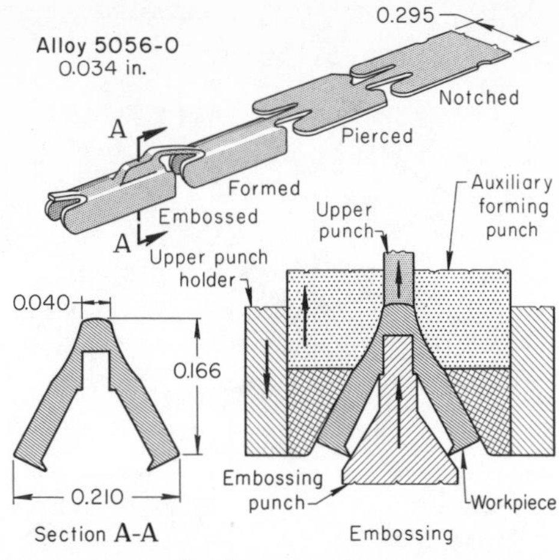

Fig. 42. Production of a zipper component from flat wire in four operations, using spring-loaded punches for embossing (Example 545)

Shallow-flanged holes can be produced in a single pierce-and-flange operation with a stepped punch. The edges of the pierced hole should also be as smooth as possible.

Low-strength, ductile alloys in the annealed temper will permit forming the deepest flanges and the sharpest bend radii. For more information on hole flanging, see the article on Bending of Low-Carbon Steel, page 89.

Beading or ribbing is usually the most economical way to provide stiffness and avoid oil-can or buckling effects in large panels. Beads that extend from edge to edge of the workpiece are conveniently formed by bending in a press brake or with corrugating rolls. Table 4 gives minimum bend radii for 90° cold bends, and thus provides an approximate guide to shape and dimension of beads formed by bending.

Beads that do not extend all the way across the part require a stretching or forming operation with a rubber-pad die or in a punch press with a rigid punch and a rigid die. A double-acting die and a blankholder can be used to prevent wrinkling at the ends of the beads, and deep parallel beads are often made one at a time.

Rubber-pad forming can also be used. Example 542 describes a situation in which a female die was preferred to a male die because it restricted metal movement to the immediate vicinity of the beads and thus helped to maintain critical dimensions.

Figure 38 illustrates the use of hydraulic forming to produce multiple beads or ribs on large flat parts made of thin material.

Drop hammer forming can be used for beading small quantities of parts.

Explosive Forming

Explosive forming is one of the high-energy-rate forming (HERF) methods that are employed in the production of aluminum alloy parts, mainly in the aerospace industries. It is often used to produce parts whose size exceeds the limits of conventional equipment or whose thickness requires pressures not obtainable with conventional equipment. It is also used to form small quantities of complex parts that would be more costly to produce by conventional techniques.

Deformation velocities are several hundred feet per second, as compared with 0.5 to about 20 ft per sec for conventional forming processes. The time required for the workpiece to deform to its final shape is a few milliseconds, with working pressures of several thousand to several hundred thousand pounds per square inch. Water usually serves as the pressure medium.

For details of equipment, tools and procedures, the reader is referred to the article that begins on page 250 in this volume, and to "Explosive Working of Metals", by Rinehart and Pearson (Macmillan, 1963).

Capabilities. Types of operations include panel forming (bending), piercing, flanging, shallow dishing, deep drawing, and cylindrical bulging. Part dimensions range from 1 in. to about 50 ft; work-metal thickness, from several thousandths of an inch to about 6 in.

Alloys. The process can be used with any aluminum alloy. Formability is a direct function of the ordinary tensile elongation values, but the function is different for each alloy, because of different strain-rate behavior. Alloy 1100-O is rated the most formable of all common metals by explosive forming.

Effect on Mechanical Properties. Changes in mechanical properties as a result of explosive free-forming operations are essentially the same as those observed with conventional forming techniques to produce the same part. Explosive forming in a die, however, often causes the metal to strike the die at extremely high velocity. The resulting high interface pressures can increase the yield and tensile strengths substantially. Forming capability is increased when critical forming velocities are exceeded.

Dies. Only a forming die or cavity is needed for explosive forming, because the shock wave acts as a punch. Some direction and concentration of the shock wave is obtained with suitably shaped and positioned "reflectors".

Cast iron and cast steel are the most frequently used die materials. A variety of other materials and combinations of materials are used, depending on the impact of the shock wave and of the workpiece against the die, the size of the die, dimensional tolerances on the part, and quantity of parts. These materials include low-melting cast alloys and plastics, reinforced concrete, concrete faced with plastic-glass composites, and high-impact steel.

The air between the workpiece and die cavity must be evacuated before forming, because the forming speed is so great that the air will be trapped between the workpiece and die rather than displaced as in conventional press forming. Trapped air and excessive lubrication cause malformed areas. The vent holes for evacuating the air must be placed in noncritical areas; otherwise, marks will appear on the formed parts. In thinner parts, the forming force will pierce holes in the parts, using the vent hole as a piercing die.

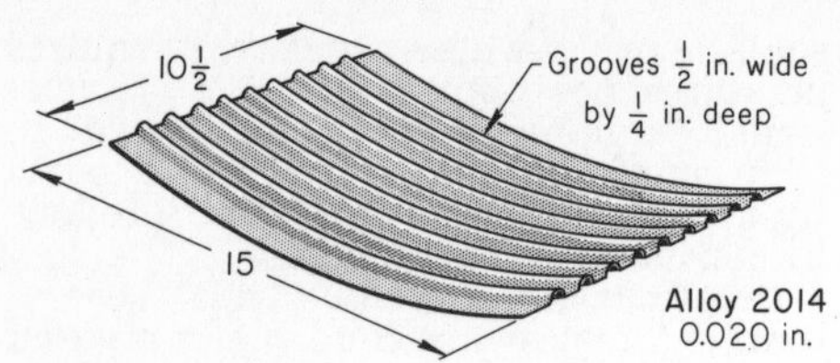

Fig. 43. Curved corrugated panel produced by explosive forming

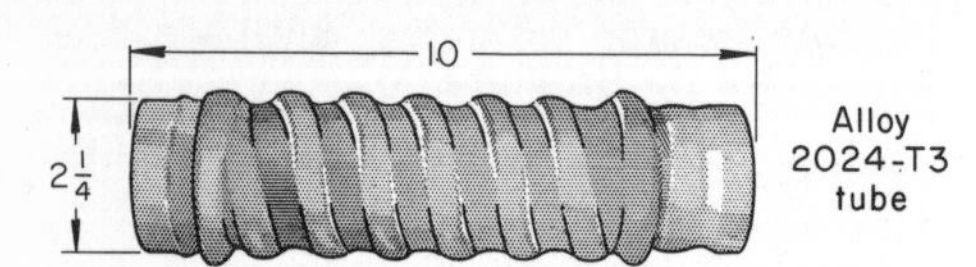

Fig. 44. Tubular part on which spirals were produced by explosive forming

Surface finish of the die cavity is important, because it is reproduced in mirror image on the workpiece.

Lubricants, if used, are usually extreme-pressure (EP) types such as No. 7, 9 or 10 in Table 1, or a mixture of paraffin and mineral oil. Because of the high velocity of forming and the extreme pressures, excessive lubrication must be avoided. Dies of low-melting alloys or dies with smooth surfaces require little or no lubrication.

Springback is of importance in die design. Increasing the explosive charge or reducing the standoff distance reduces springback. However, this increases die wear and may also fracture the more brittle die materials, and a compromise is often required.

Compensation is sometimes made for die wear by reducing charge size or increasing standoff distance to produce a controlled amount of springback and maintain dimensional tolerances.

Studies on alloy 2219 have shown springback to increase with decreasing sheet thickness between 0.250 in. and 0.032 in., and also to increase substantially with the application of a lubricant. Incremental forming has been observed to reduce the extent of springback. Draw radius, draw depth, and die material have shown no significant effects on springback behavior.

Examples of Applications. The forming of flat and moderately curved shapes has been one of the most useful applications of explosive forming. These have included parts ranging from small, detailed items a few square inches in area to large panels with areas in excess of 30 sq ft.

The curved corrugated panel shown in Fig. 43 was formed from alloy 2014 in the O, T4 and T6 tempers in a laminated epoxy-fiberglass die. The panel was formed in a single shot, using a detonating fuse as a source of energy.

Tubular parts are readily shaped by explosive forming, using a length of detonating cord suspended along the axis of the tube. For example, spirals were formed on the alloy 2024-T3 tube shown in Fig. 44. These spirals were ¼ in. high by ½ in. wide, with a 1-in. pitch. A tolerance of ±0.001 in. was maintained in forming.

The following two examples of parts produced by explosive forming give an indication of the versatility of the process. As in most explosive forming, water was used as the medium for transmittal of energy.

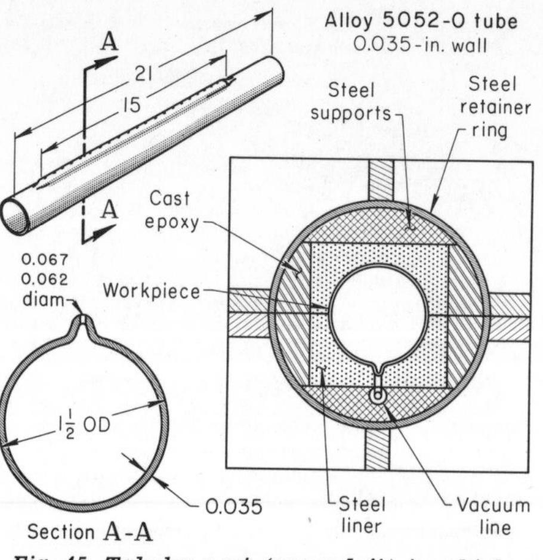

Fig. 45. Tubular part (upper left) in which 48 nozzles were produced by simultaneous explosive forming and piercing in a reinforced steel die (right) (Example 547)

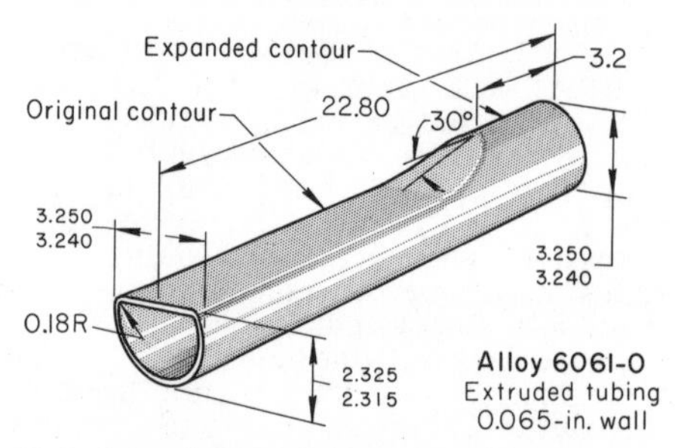

An alternative method would be to draw the expanded shape and weld it to the tubing.

Fig. 46. Adapter tube on which transitional shape was produced by electrohydraulic forming (Example 548)

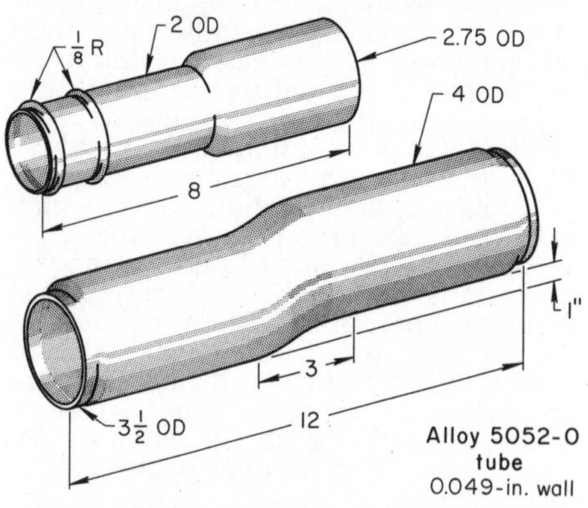

Fig. 47. Stepped tube and offset tube, originally produced as welded assemblies, that were produced as one-piece units by electrohydraulic forming (Example 549)

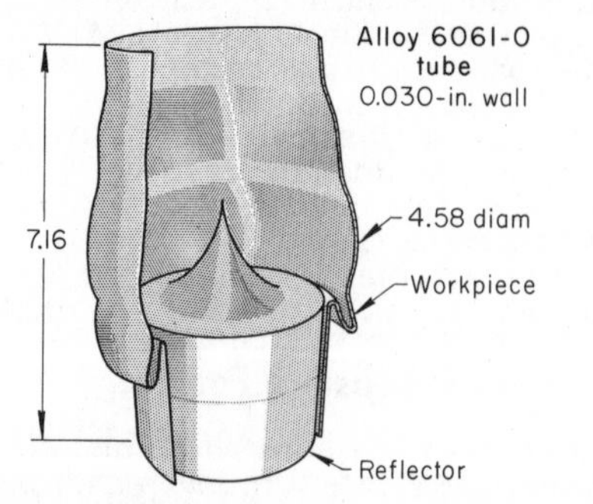

Energy-releasing spark gap was positioned at the free end of the tube. Shock waves reflected by the cone made the wall fold.

Fig. 48. Use of a shock-wave reflector for electrohydraulic free-forming of a fold in a rolled and welded tube (Example 550)

Example 546. Precision Explosive Forming of a Large Radar Lens

An approximately spherical radar lens, 78 in. in diameter by 22 in. deep, was explosive formed from an 0.087-in.-thick oversize sheet of alloy 6061-O.

A ring-shaped charge of plastic sheet explosive was located parallel with and directly above the blank, which was held against an evacuated die by a hold-down ring. The entire assembly was submerged in a tank of water.

The lens was formed approximately to required contour in two operations, and a final sizing operation was done immediately after solution heat treatment and quenching. The contour on the finished lens was held to a tolerance of ±0.007 in. at all points.

Example 547. Simultaneous Explosive Forming and Piercing (Fig. 45)

Figure 45 shows a tubular part in which 48 nozzle holes, on 0.30-in. centers, were produced in one operation by simultaneous explosive forming and piercing in a reinforced steel die. Previously, this part had been produced by attaching 48 nozzles to a tube, but air flow through the nozzles was unsatisfactory.

A water tank was not used in this operation. Instead, the tube was plugged at one end, placed in the upright die (Fig. 45) and filled with water. A partial vacuum was maintained between the tube and die during forming.

The explosive charge consisted of a 15-in. length of 50-grains-per-foot detonating cord enclosed in heavy-wall rubber hose. The tube and die were covered with a rubber mat 48 in. square by ½ in. thick. Tooling cost was $800. Production time was 6 min per piece.

Electrohydraulic Forming (EHF)

Another high-energy-rate forming (HERF) method used in the fabrication of aluminum alloy parts is electrohydraulic forming (EHF). In this process, either a spark-gap or an exploding bridgewire is employed to discharge electrical energy in water or another liquid. This generates an extremely high pressure and a shock wave similar to those produced in explosive forming. Once the energy is released in the transfer medium, the remainder of the operation is essentially the same as for explosive forming.

Capabilities of electrohydraulic forming differ somewhat from those of explosive forming. The spark-gap method can apply programmed repetitive shock waves of varying magnitude without removal of the workpiece from the die.

The exploding-bridgewire method is less readily automated, but the shock wave can be localized and directed by the shape and placement of the wire.

Dimensional tolerances can be held to lower limits than with explosive forming, because the discharge of energy is more closely controlled. For this reason, electrohydraulic forming is sometimes used for a restrike or sizing operation after preliminary explosive forming to an approximate contour.

Commercial equipment is available that can produce about 3000 small or medium-size pieces per week.

Examples of Applications. The two examples that follow describe the application of electrohydraulic forming to aluminum alloy parts. Details of the operation are given in the first example.

Example 548. Use of EHF for Producing a Transitional Shape in Extruded Tubing (Fig. 46)

The adapter tube shown in Fig. 46 was produced by expanding a D-section of alloy 6061-O extruded tubing by the bridgewire method of electrohydraulic forming. The tube was formed in a two-piece split die that had a steel outer shell and a cast epoxy liner. A longitudinal seal and an O-ring seal at each end enabled evacuation of the space between the workpiece and the die. The entire assembly was immersed in water.

Two shots at 4000 joules each were needed, using a 6-in. length of alloy 6061 wire 0.030 in. in diameter. The part was lubricated with a proprietary compound based on a medium-weight mineral oil. Production rate was three pieces per hour; each piece required 15 min for setup and 5 min for fabrication. Total quantity produced was 300 pieces. Tooling cost was approximately $3000.

An alternative method considered for the production of this tube was hydraulic forming, but this was ruled out, because of high die costs and the localized forming required. Another alternative method was to form the expanded portion by drawing and then to weld it to the tube, but the weld area could not be consistently finished to quality requirements.

Each of the two parts discussed in the following example would normally be produced as a welded assembly of two drawn pieces, but each was made in one piece by EHF.

Example 549. Use of EHF That Eliminated Welding in the Production of Tubular Parts (Fig. 47)

Originally, the offset tube shown in Fig. 47 was made by drawing two longitudinal sections with an outside diameter of 3½ in. and welding the sections together, and the in-line stepped tube also shown in Fig. 47 was made by welding sections of 2-in. and 2.75-in. diameter to a preformed transition ring.

The two tubes were produced more economically as one-piece units by electrohydraulic forming. Production costs were reduced by eliminating trimming, welding, and grinding of welds. Dimensional variation was reduced and surface finish was improved.

Certain types of parts can be made by free-forming techniques, without the use of a die. These may involve the use of a reflector, in addition to the placement of the spark gap or bridgewire, to direct and concentrate the effect of the shock wave:

Example 550. Free-Forming an Annular Fold in Rolled and Welded Tube (Fig. 48)

The part shown in Fig. 48 was formed without a die from an 8½-in. length of rolled and welded tube 3 in. in diameter. The workpiece was plugged at one end with a pointed low-carbon steel reflector, as shown in Fig. 48, and at the other end with the energy-releasing spark gap. The part was filled with water.

The contour and dimensions of the reflector were developed to expand and fold the tube wall as shown in Fig. 48. Dimensions were reproducible to 0.06 in.

Electromagnetic Forming (EMF)

Operations generally similar to those described for the preceding two HERF methods can be carried out by electromagnetic forming (also called magnetic-pulse forming). In this process, the discharge of a capacitor through a coil generates an intense magnetic field. This field interacts with the electric currents induced in a conductive workpiece to produce a force perpendicular to the workpiece surface.

Details of the process and of equipment, tools and procedures are described in the article "Electromagnetic Forming", which begins on page 256.

The method is suitable for aluminum alloys because of their formability and high electrical conductivity.

Examples of Applications. The following two examples give an indication of the range of application of electromagnetic forming to aluminum alloys.

Example 551. Reverse Forming of a Tube Around a Steel Reinforcing Ring (Fig. 49)

By the use of electromagnetic forming, a 2-in.-OD, 0.050-in.-wall tube of alloy 3003-O was wrapped around a steel reinforcing ring and was simultaneously bulged to lock the ring tightly in place in a permanent assembly (see Fig. 49). An expansion coil was located just inside the end of the tube. The end section of the tube accelerated to a high radial velocity in the first few thousandths of an inch of movement during the magnetic impulse. The major portion of the forming resulted from the kinetic energy of the metal, which caused the tube to wrap itself around the ring in a whiplike motion to produce the final form.

This assembly could not be produced economically by any method other than electromagnetic forming.

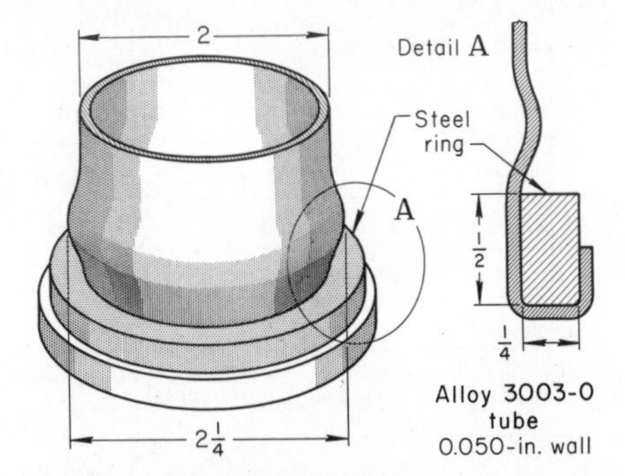

Fig. 49. Assembly produced in one step by electromagnetic reverse forming (Example 551)

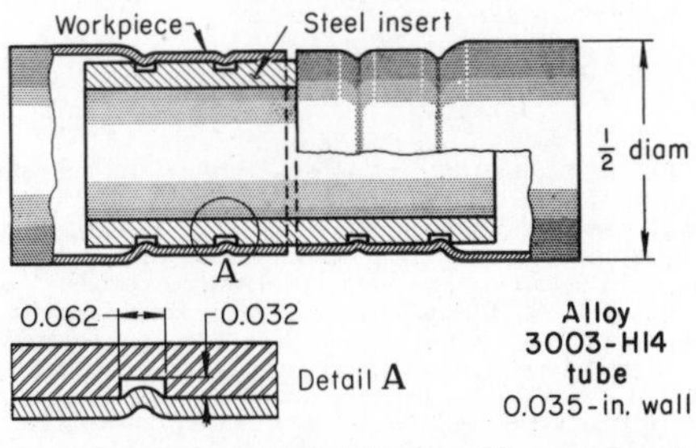

Fig. 50. Pressure-tight assembly produced by electromagnetically swaging an aluminum alloy tube onto a grooved steel insert (Example 552)

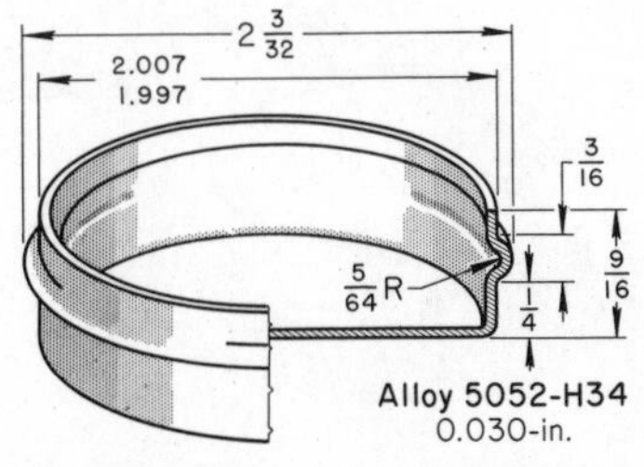

Fig. 51. Part that was produced at less cost in a punch press than by spinning (Example 553)

Pressure-tight joints, electrically or thermally conductive joints, torque joints, and structural joints between metals can be produced by EMF techniques in a variety of shapes. Joints between tubular members are the most common type. An example of such a joint is given below:

Example 552. Electromagnetic Swaging of a Tube Onto a Grooved Steel Insert (Fig. 50)

A metal-to-metal seal was produced by magnetic swaging of an alloy 3003-H14 tube onto a grooved tubular steel insert, as shown in Fig. 50, using a work coil and field-shaping insert that encircled the joint area. This seal remained intact at a pressure of 4000 psi, which was sufficient to burst the tube.

Selection of Method on the Basis of Quantity and Cost

The shape and size of the part to be formed usually limit the choice of a forming method to two or three techniques. Production cost for the given quantity then determines the method.

Punch-press operations are best suited for long runs, because of high production rates, whereas spinning, press-brake forming, circle shearing, routing, and other operations with low tooling costs are preferred for short runs.

The following five examples illustrate specific production situations.

Example 553. Spinning Replaced by Lower-Cost Forming in a Punch Press for Quantity Production (Fig. 51)

The part shown in Fig. 51 was initially purchased in quantities of about 500 per year from an outside source, which produced it by spinning. When demand for this part increased to 5000 per year, tooling was obtained for its in-plant production in a punch press. The use of a blank-and-draw die costing $425 and a bulging die costing $325 made it possible to produce the part for 25% of the former purchase price of 30¢ per piece. Blank size was developed to control the depth at 9⁄16 ± 1⁄64 in. and thereby avoid a final trimming operation.

Example 554. Production of a Barrel-Shape Bowl by Drawing, Trimming and Nosing in a Punch Press (Fig. 52)

A barrel-shape bowl was produced in annual quantities of 20,000 by drawing, trimming and nosing in separate operations in a punch press. The tooling setup for nosing is illus-

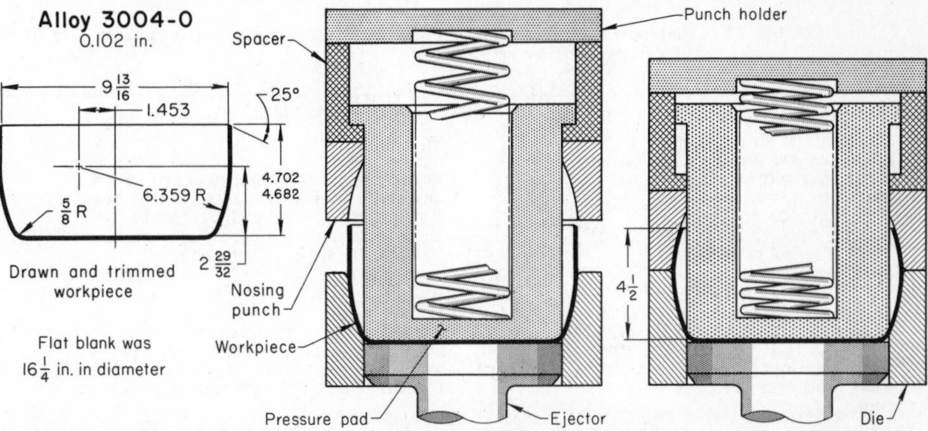

Fig. 52. Nosing a drawn and trimmed shell in a punch press to form a barrel-shape bowl (Example 554)

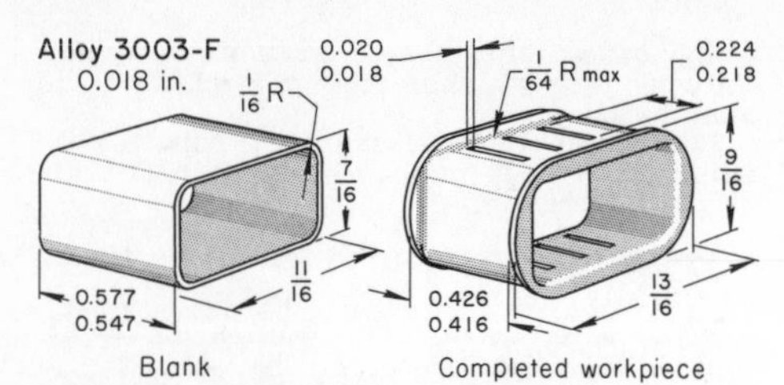

Fig. 53. Blade holder that was flanged and pierced in a punch press from a blank cut from rectangular tubing (Example 555)

trated in Fig. 52. The bowl was produced at the rate of 300 pieces per hour.

To accomplish a 40% reduction of diameter in the drawing operation, while maintaining the surface contour and smoothness required, several aspects of tool design and procedure were critical. To avoid excessive work hardening, draw-die radius was about five times, and punch-nose radius about six times, the work-metal thickness. Also, precise trimming was necessary to make top and bottom surfaces parallel for the nosing operation, and a pressure pad held the shell rigidly in place for nosing (Fig. 52), because any variation in height around the bowl could have produced local concentrations of stress and caused the sidewall to buckle.

Example 555. Production of a Blade Holder From Rectangular Tubing by Flanging and Piercing in a Punch Press (Fig. 53)

The blade holder shown in Fig. 53 could have been made from a flat blank in a press brake and then welded. This method, however, would have been too slow for the economical production of 700,000 pieces per year.

A procedure was developed for producing the part in a punch press from a blank cut from rectangular tubing (Fig. 53). Blanks were cut at the rate of 3400 per hour. Both flanges were formed in a single operation in a double-flanging die, and the six slots were pierced, three per side, in two operations. Flanging and piercing were both done in a 10-ton mechanical punch press. Flanging was done at 1400 pieces per hour; piercing, at 600 pieces (1200 sides) per hour.

Because extruded rectangular tubing with 0.018-in. wall thickness could not be obtained, it was necessary to special-order alloy 3003 tubing cold drawn in nine mill operations. Material cost was $2.23 per pound. Alloys of lower ductility would have cold worked excessively and split during the severe flanging.

Example 556. Effect of Quantity on Method of Producing a Semicircular Flanged Cup (Table 12)

Table 12 compares the sequence of operations, the tooling and equipment, and the production rates for low-quantity and high-quantity production of a flanged semicircular shield from alloy 6061-O sheet 0.190 in. thick. The use of a draw die was required even for the lowest quantity (100 pieces), because there was no simpler means by which the shield could be drawn.

As shown in Table 12, the high-quantity method substituted individual press operations for circle shearing, for trimming with a router and drilling holes, and for band-saw cutting. The restrike operation, needed for control of dimensions in the low-quantity method, was eliminated by the use of a hydraulic press instead of a mechanical press for drawing in the high-quantity method.

Sometimes the use of press equipment for high-volume production offers other advantages in addition to the expected higher production rates and lower unit labor costs. Ability to produce to closer dimensional tolerances is one. The following example describes three other advantages obtained in the production of a specific part.

Example 557. Effect of Quantity on Cost of a Housing Formed by Manual Spinning vs Deep Drawing (Fig. 54)

The unit costs for a dust-cover housing produced in various quantities by manual spinning and by deep drawing in a press are compared in Fig. 54. As shown, the quantity above which the more expensive press tooling was economically justified was about 500 pieces.

Three additional benefits besides lower unit labor costs and higher production rates were realized by the use of deep drawing for large quantities: (*a*) stock of 0.040-in. thickness could be used, instead of the 0.050-in. stock required for spinning (to compensate for thin-out); (*b*) blank diameter was 21¹⁵⁄₁₆ in., compared with 23 in. for spinning; and (*c*) blanking from strip of a suitable width also permitted a layout with less waste of material than with the sheet stock used for spinning. The net result was that deep drawing required 31% less metal per piece than was used in spinning.

Additional production details and the sequence of operations for each method are given in the table that accompanies Fig. 54.

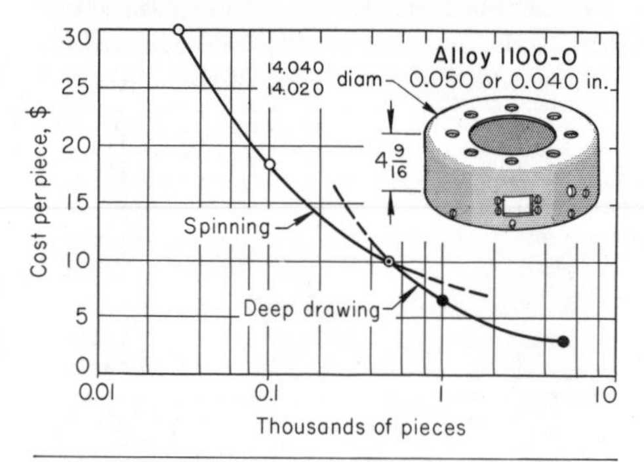

Item	Spinning(a)	Deep drawing(b)
Stock form	Sheet	Strip
Stock thickness, in.	0.050	0.040
Stock size, in.	96 by 48	22¼ wide
Diameter of blank, in.	23	21¹⁵⁄₁₆
Tool cost	$560	$3300
Setup time, hr	4	5½
Lubricant	Grease(c)	Mineral oil(d)

(a) Sequence of operations: shear; cut circle; spin, in a 3-hp manual spinning lathe with 26-in. swing; trim; mill slot, in a milling machine; drill holes, in a drill press; pierce holes, in a 5½-ton open-back inclinable press. (b) Sequence of operations: blank, in a 125-ton punch press; draw, in a 300-ton toggle press or a 400-ton hydraulic press; trim; pierce and slot, in a 125-ton punch press. (c) Aluminum-spinning type. (d) With proprietary additive.

Fig. 54. Cost of a dust-cover housing in various quantities when formed by manual spinning vs deep drawing (Example 557)

Compound dies and automated handling devices are commonly used in high-volume production. Compound dies replace utility tools and simple dies; automatic load and unload devices replace manual handling; coil stock with roll feed replaces individual blanks. Production procedures can be tailored for maximum economy at several different levels of production, as shown in the following two examples.

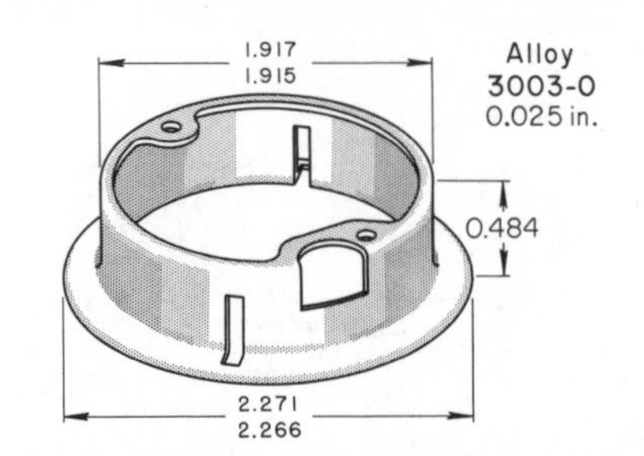

Fig. 55. Retainer ring produced by two different methods, depending on annual quantity required (Example 558)

Example 558. Comparison of Methods for Producing a Retainer Ring in Annual Quantities of 5000 and 50,000 Pieces (Fig. 55)

When the retainer ring shown in Fig. 55 was produced in annual quantities of 5000 pieces, strips sheared from sheet material were used as the stock, and presses were hand fed. The sequence of operations was as follows: shear sheet into strips; blank and draw; redraw and pinch trim; and pierce holes and slots. The cost per piece was comparatively high, but additional investment in tooling to reduce labor costs could not be justified for the relatively low annual production.

When annual demand for the ring increased to 50,000 pieces, a new manufacturing procedure was developed, in which coil stock replaced sheared strips, but with the sequence of operations otherwise unchanged. A roll feed was substituted for hand feeding the blank-and-draw operation, and production rate for that operation was thereby increased tenfold. Equipment was added to speed loading and

Table 12. Comparison of Procedures Used for Producing a Flanged Half Cup in Low and High Quantities (Example 556)

Sequence of operations	Equipment and tooling	Production, pcs/hr(a)	Completed workpiece
Quantities of 100 to 2000 Pieces			
1 Shear sheet stock to 25 by 25 in.	Square shear	(180)	
2 Shear square sheet to 24½-in. circle(b)	Circle shear	(90)	
3 Draw flanged circular cup(c)	Draw die in 600-ton mechanical press	(220)	
4 Restrike drawn cup	Draw die in 600-ton mechanical press	(250)	
5 Trim outside contour	Swing-arm router with template	(120)	
6 Saw in half, to make two pieces	Band saw with template	90	
7 Drill five holes in flange	Swing-arm drill with template	60	
Quantities of 2000 Pieces or More			
1 Shear sheet stock to 25 by 25 in.	Square shear	(180)	
2 Blank square sheet to 24½-in. circle	Blanking die in punch press	(300)	
3 Draw flanged circular cup(c)	Draw die in 650-ton hydraulic press	(200)	
4 Trim contour; pierce ten holes in flange	Trim-and-pierce die in 600-ton mechanical press	(240)	
5 Part into two pieces	Parting die in 600-ton mechanical press	220	

Completed workpiece: Alloy 6061-O, 0.190 in.; 0.447/0.437 diam (typ of 5 holes); 1.56; 5.96; 13.38

(a) Production rates in parentheses represent operations done on workpieces that were subsequently cut in half to make two finished parts, and therefore rates in terms of finished parts are twice these values. (b) For quantities of 500 to 2000 pieces, this operation was replaced by blanking the 24½-in. circle in a punch press, using a blanking die. (c) A wax drawing compound was applied to both sides of the workpiece.

unloading for the piercing operation, and the output of pierced parts was increased by 300%. As a result of these changes in manufacturing procedure, the cost of each piece was reduced to about one-third of the cost per piece produced by the original method.

Example 559. Tooling and Procedure for Four Methods of Producing a Panel in Increasing Annual Quantities (Fig. 56)

Four different methods were developed for the economical production of the panel shown in Fig. 56. Total quantity considered was between 500 and one million pieces to be produced annually in four equal runs. Each method was designed for production of the panel at minimum unit cost in a specific quantity. The effect of quantity on cost per piece by the four methods is plotted in Fig. 56.

In method A, intended for annual production of 500 pieces, eight operations were needed: two shearing operations; three piercing operations; trimming corners before drawing; drawing; and trimming corners after drawing. Available general-purpose tooling, including a draw die, was used for all operations. All of the holes were pierced in a multiple-station turret punch press, except the large-diameter hole, the six holes on the bolt circle, and the large rectangular hole. A new stylus template cost $40. Production time per piece was 7.5 min.

Method B, developed for annual production of 2500 pieces, used ten operations, seven of which were the same as in method A. The turret punch-press operation became three operations. One pierced all the small holes in the top of the panel using a die that cost $985. Two operations, using available tools, pierced ten holes in the flanges after forming and trimming. Total production time for each piece was 2.4 min.

Method C, which further reduced production time per piece to 0.96 min, was intended for annual production of 10,000 to 100,000 pieces. In this four-operation method (shear to width; blank, trim and pierce; draw; and trim corners), a compound die that cost $1600 was used for blanking and trimming, and for piercing all holes and openings. The panels were drawn and corners were trimmed with tools that were available.

For very long runs (about one million pieces), the purchase of highly automated equipment at an estimated cost of $22,500 was proposed (method D). This method would produce the panel from coil stock instead of sheet and would require only three operations (blank and pierce; draw; and shimmy trim), for a total production time of 0.48 min per piece. The proposed equipment would include a coil-stock reel, a combination roll feed and straightener, a compound blank-and-pierce die with an unloader, and a shimmy trim die. Using coil stock reduced the material cost to 99¢ per piece.

Progressive dies are often used to reduce costs in high-speed production of large quantities of formed parts. The smaller number of operations can reduce labor costs for handling and result in a net savings, in spite of high tooling costs.

The following three examples describe specific applications of progressive-die tooling.

Example 560. Use of a Progressive Die That Eliminated the Need for Expensive Perforated Stock (Fig. 57)

For minimum tooling cost at an initial annual production quantity of 100,000 pieces, a top plate for a gas-mask cartridge (Fig. 57) was produced from perforated coil stock. The part was blanked, drawn and formed in a compound die. When production requirements reached 750,000 pieces per year, a progressive die was purchased at a cost of $1000, and was used to pierce, form and blank the part from unperforated coil stock. The change in method not only lowered costs appreciably but, by piercing only the needed 135 holes in the plate (Fig. 57), also eliminated the jagged edges that had been obtained with perforated stock, and thereby improved the handling characteristics of the plate.

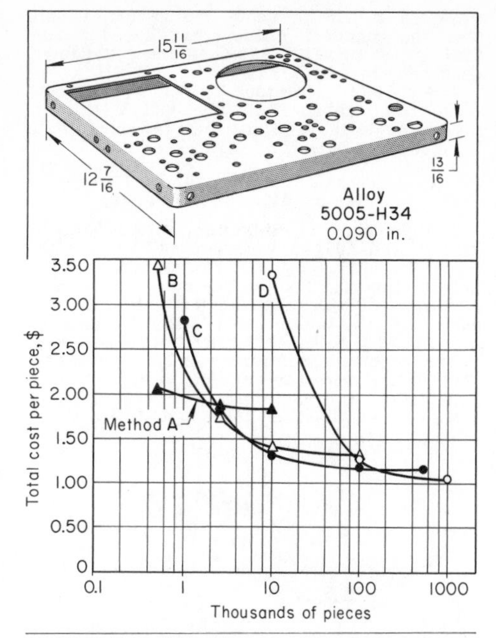

Method A — 500 Pieces per Year

Number of operations	8
Setup time	3.1 hr
Production time per piece	0.125 hr
Tooling cost	$40
Setup cost, total(a)	$74.40
Material cost per piece	$1.07
Production cost per piece(b)	$0.75

Method B — 2500 Pieces per Year

Number of operations	10
Setup time	3.1 hr
Production time per piece	0.040 hr
Tooling cost	$985
Setup cost, total(a)	$74.40
Material cost per piece	$1.07
Production cost per piece(b)	$0.24

Method C — 10,000 to 100,000 Pieces per Year

Number of operations	4
Setup time	1.5 hr
Production time per piece	0.016 hr
Tooling cost	$1600
Setup cost, total(a)	$36
Material cost per piece	$1.07
Production cost per piece(b)	$0.096

Method D — 1 Million Pieces per Year (Est)

Number of operations	3
Setup time	9.5 hr
Production time per piece	0.008 hr
Tooling cost	$22,500
Setup cost, total(a)	$228
Material cost per piece	$0.99
Production cost per piece(b)	$0.048

(a) Four setups per run of any quantity, at $6 per hour. (b) At $6 per hour.

Fig. 56. Effect of quantity on cost of a drawn and pierced panel produced by four different methods (Example 559)

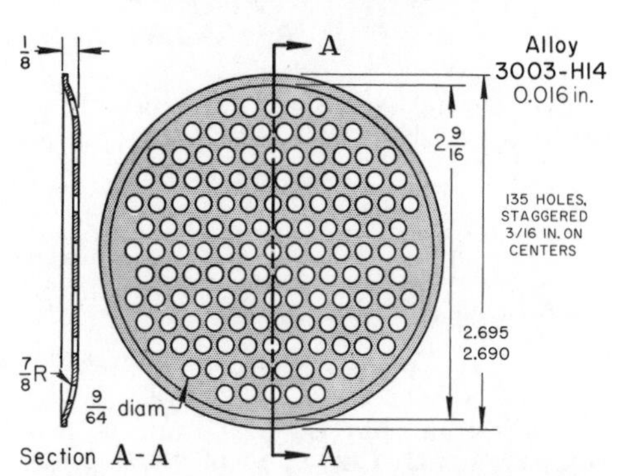

When production was low, perforated stock saved on tooling costs, but extra holes caused rough edges on the blank, making handling difficult.

Fig. 57. Plate for a gas-mask cartridge that was produced from unperforated coil stock in a progressive die (Example 560)

Example 561. Change to the Use of a Fully Progressive Die for High-Volume Production (Fig. 58)

When the mine-lamp part shown in Fig. 58 was produced in annual quantities of about 5000 pieces, only the initial forming operations were done in a progressive die. Because it was difficult to form the short leg to the 0.068-in. and the 0.132-in. dimensions within tolerances, that leg was initially blanked oversize. Additional dies were used for trimming the leg, forming the hook, and sizing the hook, in three separate operations after initial forming in the progressive die.

When production requirements increased to 50,000 pieces per year, the three separate die operations resulted in high labor costs, tied up presses needed for other work, and led to safety problems. For production in this annual quantity, a progressive die was developed to produce a completely formed part. The 0.068-in. leg was blanked to size, the first forming die was modified, and a second forming operation was developed to produce the 0.132-in. dimension directly. With the use of the progressive die for all operations, the over-all cost per piece was reduced, and the production and safety problems were eliminated.

Example 562. Cost of a Zipper Component Produced in Various Quantities in Hand-Fed Dies vs a Progressive Die (Fig. 59)

Figure 59 shows a zipper component and plots the cost per thousand pieces for producing it in various quantities in simple hand-fed dies and in a progressive die. The hand-fed dies were used for temporary production, until a progressive die could be designed, constructed and put into service for an annual production of 20 to 25 million of these components. As shown by the curves for the two methods in Fig. 59, the permanent tooling was economically justified for a quantity of about 260,000 pieces, which was only two to three days' output for the progressive die.

The temporary tooling consisted of three separate dies (for blanking and cutoff; forming; and embossing) and a ½-ton press. Total cost was $1000, and maximum capacity was 200 pieces per hour. The permanent tooling — the progressive die (for blanking; forming and embossing; and cutoff) and a 1½-ton roll-feed press — was developed and constructed at a total cost of $12,000, and was rated at 13,200 pieces per hour. Labor cost per thousand pieces was reduced from $42 to 13¢ when the progressive die was used.

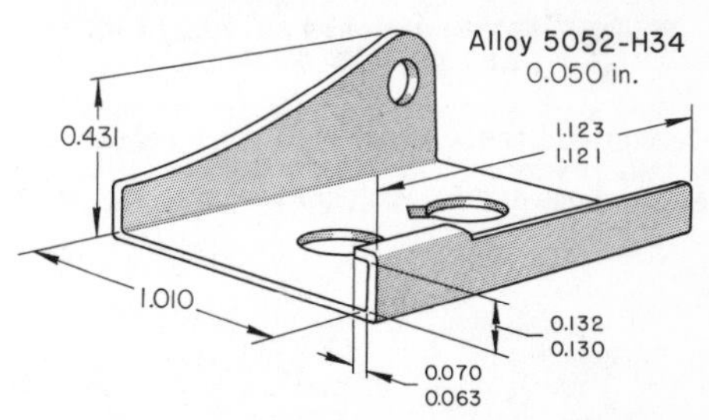

Fig. 58. Mine-lamp part formed completely in a progressive die (Example 561)

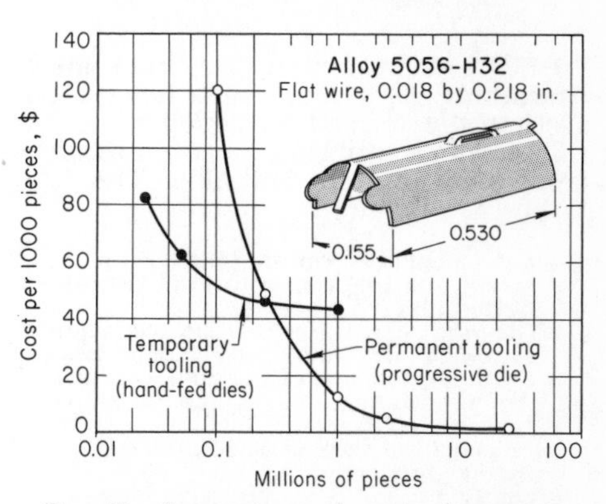

Fig. 59. Comparison of costs for mass-producing a zipper component with temporary and permanent tooling (Example 562)

Bending of Bars and Tubing

Aluminum alloy bars and tubing are bent with tools similar to those used for low-carbon steel bars and tubing (see the articles on Bending of Bars, page 305, and Bending of Tubing, page 308, in this volume). Most aluminum bars and tubing are bent in the annealed temper. Heat treated alloys can be bent, by using more bending force.

Tools should be polished to prevent marring the surface of the workpiece.

Lubrication is more critical in bending aluminum than for similar bends in steel. Aluminum is more likely to gall, especially when annealed. Mineral oil, with additives (see Table 1) to improve lubricity, is used.

Examples. Techniques and results in bending of aluminum alloy tubing are described in the next four examples.

Example 563. Application of Lubricants in Bending Alloy 6061-O Tubing (Fig. 60)

Fractures in the outer wall caused a 50% scrap rate when bending aluminum alloy 6061-O tubing with a 2-in. OD and 0.035-in. wall thickness. The tube was bent 90° on a 2½-in. centerline radius (Fig. 60). No wrinkles were allowed along the inner radius, and flattening could not exceed 10% in the bend area.

The piece had been bent in a rotary bender using a three-ball mandrel. Attempts to eliminate fracturing by reducing the force on the pressure die caused wrinkles.

The number of balls in the mandrel was reduced from three to two, and the mandrel and inside of the tube were thickly coated with a drawing compound. A very thin film of light mineral oil with a proprietary additive to improve lubricity was applied to the wiper die. With these precautions, the pieces could be bent without tearing, provided that (*a*) tooling was accurate and free of wear, (*b*) the form block was carefully centered to turn concentric with the machine, and (*c*) pressure actuating the pressure die was kept within 25 psi of that specified. (A reduction of 25 psi was sufficient to cause wrinkles; an excess of 25 psi caused fracture.)

Example 564. Bends of 90° in Alloy 6061-O and 6061-T6 Tubing

Bends of 90° were made in tubing of alloys 6061-O and 6061-T6 using a rotary bender and a ball mandrel. The tubing had a ½-in. OD and a 0.065-in. wall thickness. The bends were made to a 1.25-in. centerline radius, which was the smallest radius practical for the 6061-T6 tubing. The 6061-O tubing could have been bent to a radius as small as ½ in.

The 6061-O tubing took 25 lb-ft of torque to bend, and thinned 25%. The 6061-T6 tubing needed 40 lb-ft of torque, but the outer wall thinned only 20%.

Example 565. Bends of 90° in Three Different Aluminum Alloys

Tubing made of aluminum alloys 6061-O, 3003-O and 5052-O was bent 90° to a 1-in. centerline radius using a rotary bender with a ball mandrel. The tubing had a ½-in. OD and a wall thickness of 0.065 in. In the bend area, the tubing was slightly flattened to an oval with a 5% difference in diameters.

The important differences in bending of the three alloys were the bending torque and the amount of wall thinning. The 6061-O tube bent with 30 lb-ft of torque, and the outer wall thinned 30%. The two other alloys bent with 20 lb-ft of torque, but the outer walls thinned 55%.

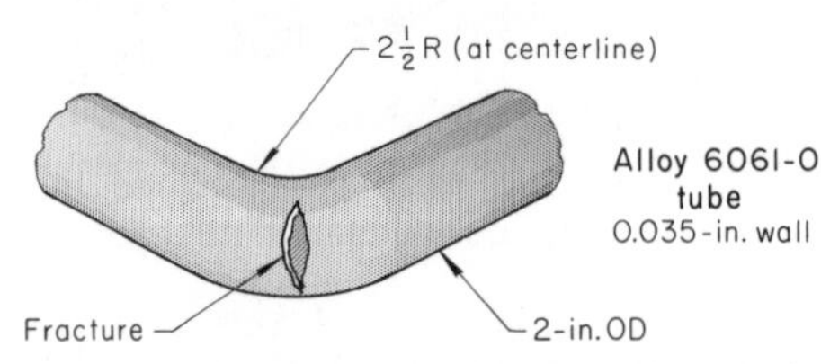

Fig. 60. Bend in aluminum tubing that required the use of a lubricant on both inside and outside surfaces to prevent fracture (Example 563)

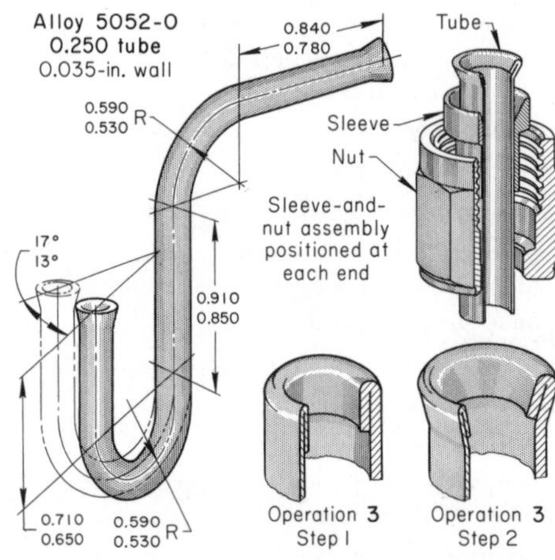

Fig. 61. Tubing bent to close dimensional and angular tolerances (Example 566)

Dimensions can be held to ±0.030 in., and angles to ±2°, as in this example:

Example 566. Bending Aluminum Tubing to Close Tolerances (Fig. 61)

The tube for an aerospace assembly shown in Fig. 61 was made of alloy 5052-O and had a 0.250-in. OD and 0.035-in. wall thickness. Fifty tubes were bent to a dimensional tolerance of ±0.030 in. and angular tolerances of ±2°. The length of tubing was determined by trial. Operations were as follows:

1. Cut tubing to length with a saw.
2. Deburr ends in a deburring machine.
3. Double flare one end.
4. Anodize.
5. Slide nut and sleeve on tube, to flared end.
6. Set up indexing bender; make trial bends.
7. Make all bends.
8. Slide second nut and sleeve onto tube, and double flare other end.

Production time for the 50 pieces was 4 hr 50 min for all operations except anodizing.

Straightening of Bars

Aluminum bars are straightened by the methods described in the article "Straightening of Bars, Shapes and Long Parts", which begins on page 322.

Stretching is used extensively as a mechanical method for stress relieving and to correct major contour deviations in rolled and extruded parts. The residual stress in a quenched part is reduced when it is stretched beyond the yield strength of the metal. The maximum rate of stress relief is obtained in the first 0.5% of permanent set. No net stress relief occurs after approximately 2% permanent set.

Aluminum alloys are normally stretched after solution heat treatment and before aging. For maximum effectiveness, the part should have a uniform cross section throughout the length and uniform mechanical properties throughout the cross section and along the length, to prevent excessive yielding in localized regions. Cold working subsequent to stretching, such as localized straightening operations, should be avoided, because it reintroduces residual stress.

Forming of Beryllium

*By the ASM Committee on Forming of Heat-Resisting Alloys**

BERYLLIUM and a beryllium alloy containing 38% aluminum have been successfully formed by bending, three-roll forming, joggling, deep drawing, creep forming, and spinning. The following are required:

1. Equipment that can be controlled at slow speeds and that can withstand the use of heated dies
2. Dies that can withstand the temperature at which beryllium is commonly formed
3. Facilities for preheating and controlling the temperature of dies and workpieces
4. In some applications, facilities for stress relieving the work at 1300 to 1450 F
5. Special lubrication
6. Safety precautions when grit blasting is required for cleaning after forming.

*For committee list, see page 371.

The three beryllium materials that are dealt with in this article are:

1. Ingot sheet (beryllium sheet that has been cross-rolled directly from a cast ingot)
2. Powder sheet (beryllium that has been extruded or cross-rolled from sintered powder metallurgy products)
3. A Be-38% Al alloy called Lockalloy.

Formability

The formability of beryllium is low compared with that of most other metals. Ingot sheet and powder sheet have hexagonal close-packed crystal structures; thus, there are relatively few slip planes and plastic deformation is limited. For this reason, all beryllium products belonging to these two categories should be formed at elevated temperature (generally 1000 to 1500 F) and at slow speeds.

The Be-38Al alloy has somewhat better formability than ingot or powder sheet beryllium, because this alloy has lower strength, higher ductility, and a cubic crystal structure. The Be-38Al alloy also is less notch sensitive at room temperature than pure beryllium, and some mild forming can be done without heating the work. Thus far, however, all production forming of this alloy has been done at elevated temperature, 400 to 800 F being the common range.

Temperature, composition, strain rate, and prior fabrication history have marked effects on the results obtained in forming beryllium.

Effect of temperature on formability (in terms of bend angle at fracture) of ingot sheet, two grades of powder sheet, and the Be-38Al alloy is shown in Fig. 1. Although these data show the effect of temperature on bendability, maximum strain on a $2t$ bend radius is not achieved at less than 90°. Therefore, it should not be assumed that the quantitative results shown in Fig. 1 can always be applied directly in practice.

Most forming of beryllium ingot or powder sheet is done above 1000 F; the most common range is 1200 to 1300 F, although forming temperatures as high as 1500 F have been used.

The Be-38Al alloy begins eutectic melting at 1193 F and should not be heated above 1000 F for any forming. It is usually formed below 800 F.

Effect of Composition. The oxide content of ingot and powder sheet has a significant effect on formability, as shown by the curves for the ingot sheet and the two grades of powder sheet in Fig. 1. As the oxide content increases, yield strength increases and ductility decreases.

Effect of Strain Rate. Strain rate greatly influences the formability of beryllium and the beryllium alloy. For instance, the stroke of a press brake is too fast for making sharp bends in hot beryllium. Therefore, slow bending, by means of equipment such as a hydraulic or air-operated press, is usually used. Minimum bend limits for the press-brake method and the slower-press method are compared in Fig. 2 for bending of cross-rolled powder sheet.

In a laboratory, a radius of $2\frac{1}{2}t$ was bent in beryllium sheet at the rate of 2 in. per minute, and a radius of $5\frac{1}{2}t$ at 12 in. per minute. Forming temperature in both cases was 1375 F.

Effect of Fabrication History. Sintered beryllium products subjected to vacuum hot pressing have low ductility, even at a theoretical density of 100%. The ductility of sintered and hot pressed beryllium can be increased by hot mechanical working.

Although Fig. 1 shows a marked difference in formability between ingot and powder sheet, this is due mainly to the difference in oxide content.

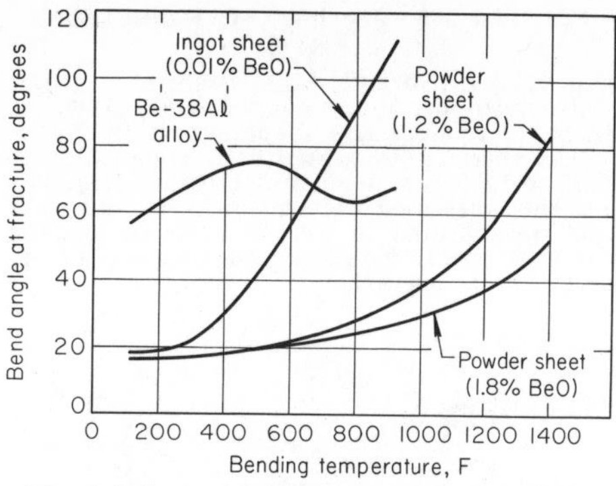

Fig. 1. Effect of temperature on bend angle of beryllium sheet, using a 2t bend radius. Angle plotted is the angle through which the sheet was bent before fracture occurred.

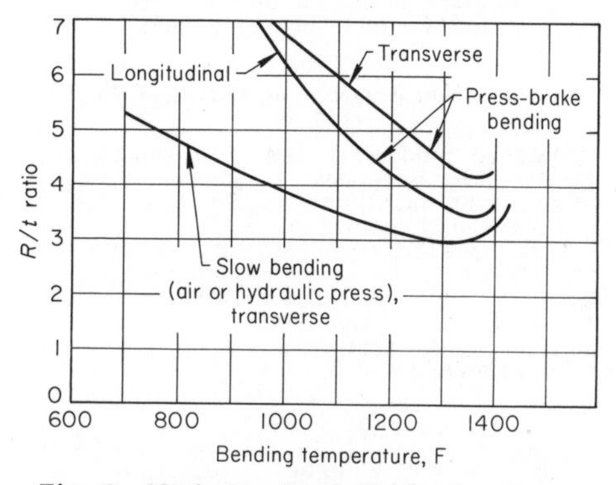

Fig. 2. Minimum bend limits for press-brake versus slower bending of cross-rolled beryllium powder sheet 0.060 to 0.068 in. thick. (R: bend radius; t: sheet thickness.)

Equipment and Tooling

Presses operated by air or hydraulic systems are usually used for forming beryllium, because of the slow speeds required. Standard mechanical presses or other fast forming presses are not suitable.

Critical components of the equipment must be protected against damage by the heat of forming. This protection usually is achieved by means of simple insulation.

Tooling. Because the tools used for forming beryllium will be heated, allowances must be made for thermal expansion, high-temperature strength, and oxidation when selecting tool material and designing tools. Tooling requirements for forming beryllium are similar to those for hot forming titanium (see the article beginning on page 437 of this volume). When only a few pieces are required, mild steel is usually used for dies. However, mild steel oxidizes rapidly at elevated temperature, and when more than a few identical pieces are to be formed, the best practice is to make dies from stainless steel or one of the nickel-base or cobalt-base heat-resisting alloys.

For forming the Be-38Al alloy below 800 F, the tooling practice used for hot forming magnesium is satisfactory (see the article beginning on page 424).

Heating Dies and Workpieces

In most forming applications, both the die and the workpiece must be preheated. Dies are specially constructed to permit heating; heat may be supplied by either electrical elements or gas burners. Although sometimes torches are satisfactory for heating the work (as when heating sheet for spinning), usually a furnace is preferred. No specially prepared atmosphere is needed.

At the maximum temperature used for forming beryllium, surface oxidation is usually negligible. However, if desired, to prevent surface discoloration (hard oxide layer), the workpiece can be coated with a film of commercial heat-resisting oil. After forming, the film of oil can be removed by wet blasting, or by degreasing with an agent such as trichlorethylene.

In the forming of thin sheet (under about 0.040 in.), cooling of the work between the furnace and the forming equipment is often a problem. Overheating to compensate for this heat loss is not recommended. One satisfactory solution is to "sandwich" thin sheets of beryllium between two sheets of low-carbon steel. This sandwich is retained through heating and forming.

Stress Relieving

Stress relieving between stages of forming, or after forming is completed, is needed only rarely. In forming of relatively thick sheet, or in severe forming, it may be necessary to use intermediate stress relieving. In Example 574, in forming a hemisphere from 0.140-in.-thick sheet by nine-stage spinning, the workpiece was stress relieved between stages. In contrast, no stress relieving was used for the part produced by spinning 0.040-in. sheet in Example 573 or for producing a hemisphere by deep drawing 0.100-in. sheet in Example 571.

For some finish formed parts, stress relieving has proved an effective means of counteracting "oil canning" or excessive warpage. When stress relieving is used, regardless of whether it is an intermediate step or a final operation, holding at 1300 to 1450 F for 20 min is recommended. No specially prepared atmosphere is needed.

Lubrication

As shown by the examples in this article, lubrication or coating of some type is needed in a majority of forming operations. For less severe operations, such as bending, powdered mica has been used (see Example 567).

For operations like joggling, forming in matched dies, or deep drawing, colloidal graphite in oil is commonly used. Colloidal graphite in oil is used also for spinning (see Examples 572 and 573). However, for severe multiple-stage spinning, such as in Example 574, glass is preferred as a lubricant.

Safety Practice

No special precautions or safety measures are required in forming of beryllium, because: (*a*) no fines or oxide dust is created in forming; and (*b*) the maximum temperature (1500 F) used for preheating causes the formation of only a thin film of hard oxide, which under normal operating conditions will not harm personnel.

However, if parts require cleaning after forming, and if grit blasting is used, the wet method is recommended. Wet blasting minimizes the possibility that beryllium oxide dust will contaminate the surrounding atmosphere.

The usual precautions observed in working with beryllium must be taken. Details on protection can be obtained from the publication "Health Protection in Beryllium Facilities", United States Atomic Energy Commission.

Bending

To achieve consistent results in bending beryllium, slow speeds are required; thus, rapid methods such as press-brake bending cannot be used. As indicated in Fig. 2, the minimum bend radius (ratio of radius, R, to sheet thickness, t) is far lower for low-velocity methods of bending. Although the R/t ratio changes to some extent for different thicknesses, the data in Fig. 2 can be used as a guide.

Secondary forming strains, which can be large in press-brake bending, are minimized in low-velocity methods such as roll bending or bending between matched dies in a slow-acting press.

Typical practices for bending beryllium sheet are described in the two examples that follow.

Example 567. Bending in Matched Dies (Fig. 3)

Matched dies actuated by an air-operated arbor press were used to bend cross-rolled beryllium powder sheet of two different thicknesses to produce the shape shown in Fig. 3.

The sheets were heated to 1250 F without a protective coating. The dies, which were made of mild steel, were heated to 1200 F prior to bending the work metal. Powdered mica was used as a lubricant. This operation was performed successfully without the need for stress relieving after bending.

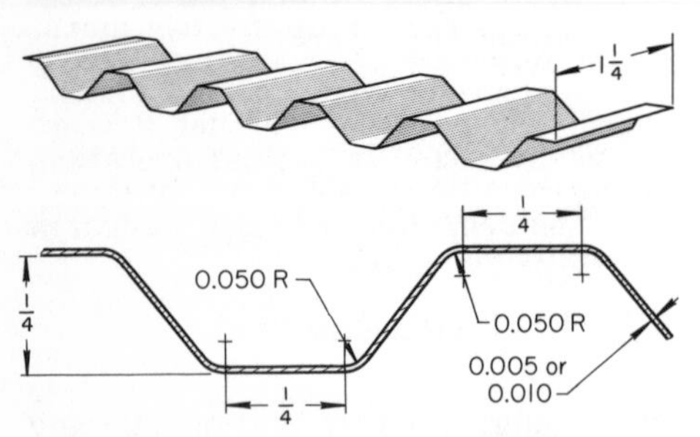

Fig. 3. Part produced by bending in matched dies (Example 567)

Example 568. Bending of Six Different Thicknesses (Fig. 4)

An air-operated press was used for bending cross-rolled beryllium powder sheet of six different thicknesses (range, 0.010 to 0.067 in.) to produce the shape shown in Fig. 4.

The sheets were heated to 1375 F, after being given a high-temperature oil-base protective coating. The dies, of austenitic stainless steel, also were heated to 1375 F prior to bending the work metal. No lubricant other than that afforded by the coating was used, nor were the workpieces stress relieved.

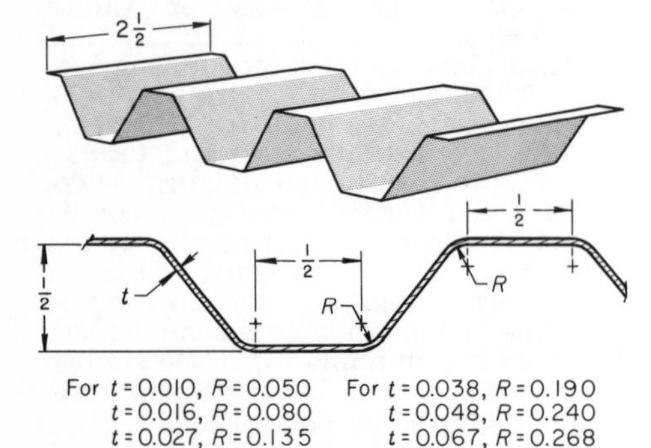

Fig. 4. Part produced from six different sheet thicknesses by bending in an air-operated press (Example 568)

Joggling

Joggles have been successfully formed in beryllium sheets up to 0.080 in. thick and in some extrusions. The work metal is heated to at least 1200 F; temperatures as high as 1275 F are used. Forming pressure must be applied slowly, thus requiring the use of an air-operated or hydraulic press and precluding the use of most mechanical presses. By observing these precautions, manufacturers have been able to form conventional joggles in beryllium with reasonable success.

The procedures described in the next two examples typify joggling practice.

Example 569. Joggling of Rolled Sheet (Fig. 5)

A 200-ton hydraulic press was used to joggle cross-rolled beryllium powder sheet 0.080 in. thick, to produce the shape shown in Fig. 5.

The sheets were heated with a gas torch to 1250 to 1275 F without protective coating. The matched dies used were made from mild steel, and were heated to 1200 F prior to joggling the work metal. No stress relieving was necessary in this operation.

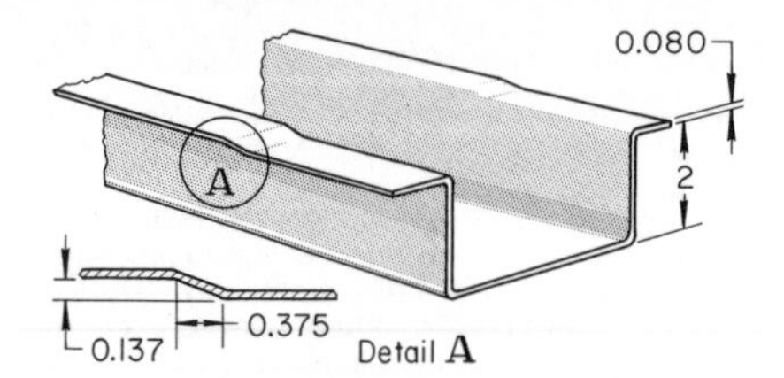

Fig. 5. Part produced by joggling cross-rolled sheet (Example 569)

Example 570. Joggling of Extruded Angles (Fig. 6)

Matched mild steel dies in a 200-ton hydraulic press were used to joggle angles extruded from beryllium powder compacts, to produce the shape shown in Fig. 6.

The extrusions, coated with a high-temperature oil-base material, were heated with a gas torch to 1200 F. The dies were heated to 1050 F. No lubricant was used, other than that provided by the protective coating. Parts were stress relieved after forming.

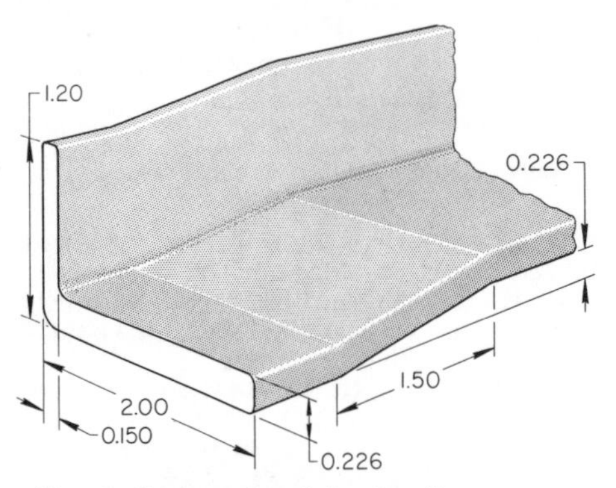

Fig. 6. Part produced by joggling an extruded angle (Example 570)

Deep Drawing

Cross-rolled beryllium sheets ranging in thickness from 0.040 to 0.250 in. have been successfully deep drawn. Drawing should be done with the work metal and dies in the temperature range of 1100 to 1250 F, in a slow-acting hydraulic or air-operated press.

Figure 7 plots combinations of conditions under which hemispherical or dish-shaped parts, with no flanges, have been successfully deep drawn from cross-rolled beryllium sheet. It is unsafe to assume that parts can be successfully deep drawn if dimensional combinations are other than shown on this plot, which is from limited data.

The procedure for drawing bowl-shape parts described in the following example represents typical practice.

Example 571. Deep Drawing of Rolled Sheet (Fig. 8)

Cross-rolled beryllium powder sheet of 0.100-in. thickness was deep drawn in a 200-ton hydraulic press to the shape shown in Fig. 8. Prior to the forming operation, which was accomplished without hold-down pressure, the uncoated sheets and the dies of H12 tool steel were heated to 1250 F. A high-temperature oil-base lubricant was used. No stress relieving was required.

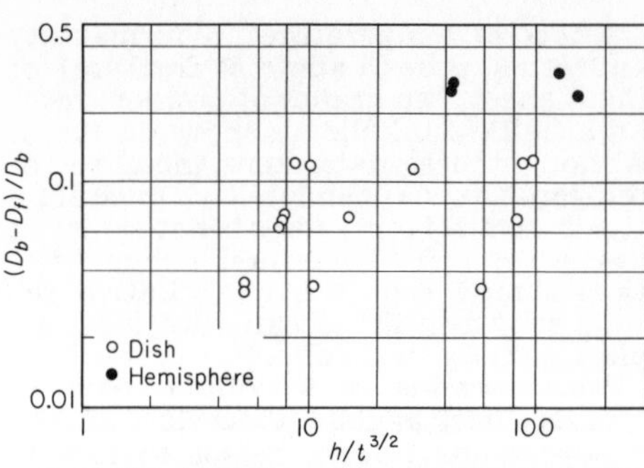

D_b is the diameter of the blank; D_f is the diameter of the deep drawn dish or hemisphere; h is the height of the dish or hemisphere; and t is the thickness of the sheet before drawing.

Fig. 7. Dimensional combinations for successful deep drawing of cross-rolled beryllium powder sheet

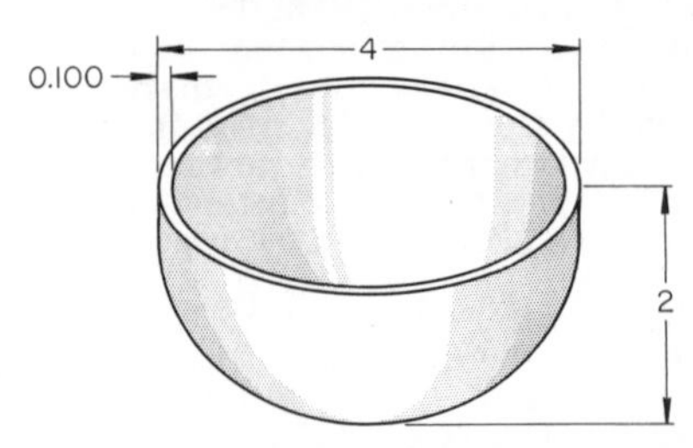

Fig. 8. Part produced by deep drawing (Example 571)

Creep Forming

Many common bending operations can be successfully accomplished under dead weight in a furnace at 1350 F. For example, the weight of the top section of a forming die is often sufficient to bend the work metal into the desired shape. Creep forming can also be used to minimize springback, by holding the formed part under pressure in hot tooling for 15 min.

Spinning

Beryllium sheets up to 0.200 in. thick have been successfully formed by spinning. For sheets less than about 0.040 in. thick, a common practice is to sandwich the beryllium between two 0.060-in.-thick sheets of low-carbon steel and heat the sandwich to 1150 F for spinning. The steel sheets not only help to maintain temperature, but also help to prevent buckling. Beryllium sheets more than about 0.040 in. thick usually are not sandwiched between steel sheets for spinning, and are heated to 1350 to 1500 F.

Hemispherical shapes have been spun in as many as nine stages with no adverse effect on the properties of the beryllium. Commonly, the part and mandrel are torch-heated during spinning.

Lubrication is especially important in spinning. Colloidal graphite or glass is usually used. Wet blasting is the recommended means of cleaning workpieces after spinning.

Figure 9 plots combinations of conditions under which parts of a variety of shapes have been successfully produced by spinning cross-rolled beryllium powder sheet. The points plotted, however, represent only limited data, and many more points would have to be estab-

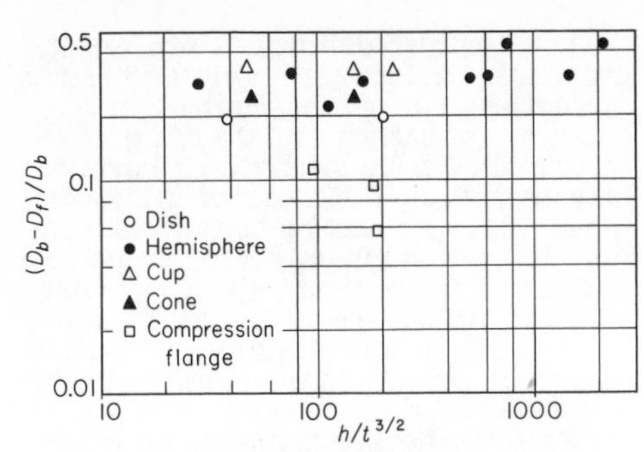

Fig. 9. Dimensional combinations for successful spinning of cross-rolled beryllium powder sheet. Symbols D_b, D_f, h *and* t *are identified below Fig. 7.*

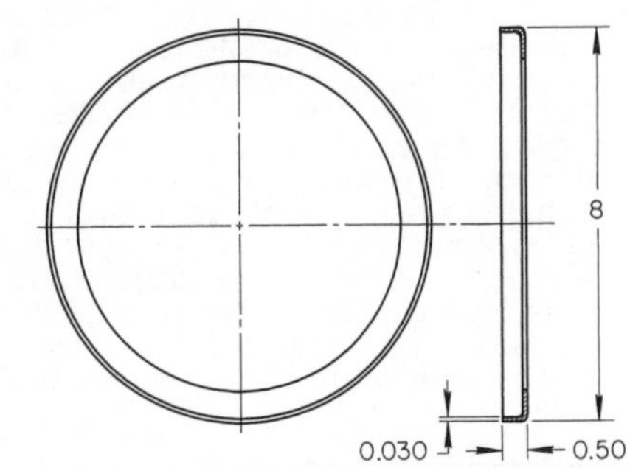

Fig. 10. Part produced by single-stage manual spinning (Example 572)

lished before it would be safe to designate dimensional limitations for spinning specific shapes.

Practice that has proved successful for spinning shapes from various thicknesses of beryllium sheet is described in the three examples that follow.

Example 572. Single-Stage Manual Spinning (Fig. 10)

The part shown in Fig. 10 was produced from cross-rolled beryllium powder sheet by single-stage manual compression spinning. Each beryllium sheet, 0.030 in. thick, was sandwiched between two 0.060-in.-thick sheets of cold rolled steel. Prior to spinning, the

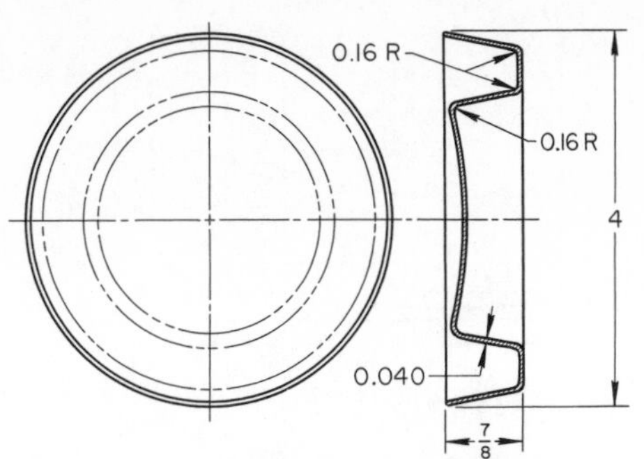

Fig. 11. Part produced by two-stage manual spinning (Example 573)

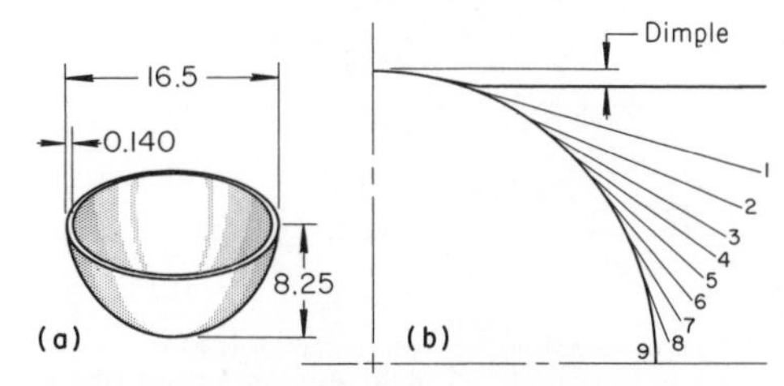

Fig. 12. Part produced by nine-stage manual spinning (Example 574)

sandwich was coated with colloidal graphite and heated to 1100 to 1200 F by an oxyacetylene torch; the mandrel, of mild steel, was heated to 900 to 1100 F.

The metal was spun at 420 rpm, using a 4½-in.-diam forming tool with a work-surface radius of 0.35 in. Colloidal graphite also was used as a lubricant in spinning. Slight buckling of the part during spinning was corrected by the use of a backup bar. Parts were not stress relieved after spinning.

Example 573. Two-Stage Manual Spinning (Fig. 11)

Parts were formed to the contour shown in Fig. 11 by two-stage manual compression spinning of 0.040-in.-thick cross-rolled beryllium powder sheet with a colloidal graphite coating. An acetylene torch was used to heat the sheet to about 1400 F and the mild steel mandrel to 1100 F. The metal was spun at 600 rpm; colloidal graphite was used as a lubricant. Stress relieving of the parts after spinning was not required.

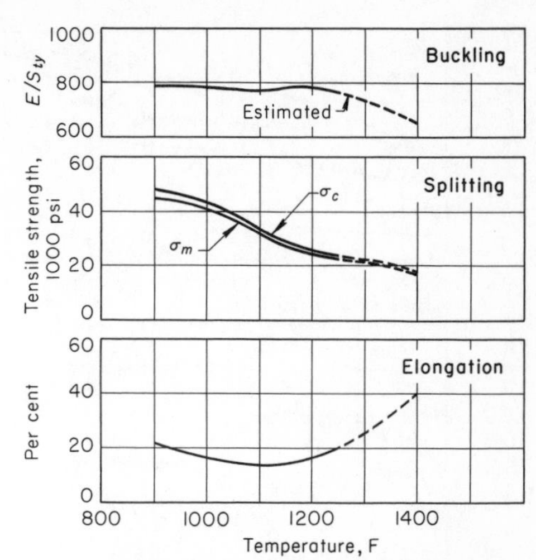

Fig. 13. Effect of temperature on forming indices for cross-rolled beryllium sheet

Example 574. Nine-Stage Manual Spinning (Fig. 12)

Glass-coated cross-rolled beryllium powder sheets were formed by nine-stage manual compression spinning to produce the hemisphere shown in Fig. 12(a). An oxyacetylene torch was used to maintain the sheets at a forming temperature of 1100 to 1500 F, and to heat the gray iron mandrel to 1100 F.

After being dimpled, parts were spun at 100 to 200 rpm in nine stages as shown in Fig. 12(b). Between stages, parts were stress relieved. The forming tool was a 2½-in.-diam spherical roller. Glass was used as a lubricant as well as for a protective coating.

Forming Parameters

The ratio of modulus of elasticity (E) to tensile yield strength (S_{ty}) is an index of buckling. The true stress at maximum load (σ_m) and maximum true stress (σ_c) are useful for representing resistance of a metal to splitting. Buckling and splitting parameter curves and their dependence on temperature are shown in Fig. 13 for cross-rolled beryllium powder sheet.

Forming of Copper and Copper Alloys

*By the ASM Committee on Forming of Copper and Copper Alloys**

COPPER AND COPPER ALLOYS are readily formed into complicated shapes, even in foil thickness. The copper alloys commonly formed are characterized by strength and work-hardening rates intermediate between those of steel and of aluminum alloys.

Alloys

Compositions of the copper alloys most commonly formed are listed in Table 1, together with their bendability and formability ratings. Grouping by major alloying elements reflects the effect of composition on physical and mechanical properties, and thus on forming behavior. Alloys with the same general rating in Table 1 may nevertheless have differences in bendability or formability that are significant in specific applications, as is demonstrated by Example 577, where alloy 170 proved to be more formable than alloy 172.

Temper Designations. Copper alloys are supplied in annealed (soft) tempers and in cold worked (hard) tempers. The standard temper designations are defined in Table 2.

The forming behavior of material in the annealed tempers depends on grain size, which is controlled in production by the temperature of the final anneal. Higher annealing temperatures produce larger grain sizes, which usually correspond to lower hardness, lower

*W. D. FRANCE, *Chairman,* Research Director, Metals Research Dept., Mill Products Div., Scovill Manufacturing Co.; W. E. ALLAN, Works Manager, Fabricated Metal Goods Div., Anaconda American Brass Co.

GEORGE L. CHASE, Tool Superintendent, General Manufacturing Div., Scovill Manufacturing Co.; RUSSELL N. DEAN, Chairman of the Board, Empire Spring Co.; A. R. ESSENBERG, Senior Engineer, Indianapolis Works, Western Electric Co., Inc.; J. J. HINES, Superintendent of Fabricating Engineering, Olin Brass Div., Olin Mathieson Chemical Corp.; JOHN M. LEE, Supervisor of Tool Design, Appliance Control Dept., General Electric Co.; DONALD A. PERRY, Chief Metallurgist, Engineering Dept., Harrison Radiator Div., General Motors Corp.; ALBERT RAITZER, Chief Metallurgist, Trane Co.

F. F. RIMMLER, Vice President, Volkert Stampings, Inc.; THOMAS SCIMONE, Tool Room Superintendent, Eagle Electric Mfg. Co., Inc.; R. E. STEVENS, Tool Engineer, Oneida Ltd.; ROBERT J. VAN VLAANDEREN, Engineer, Instrument Specialties Co., Inc.

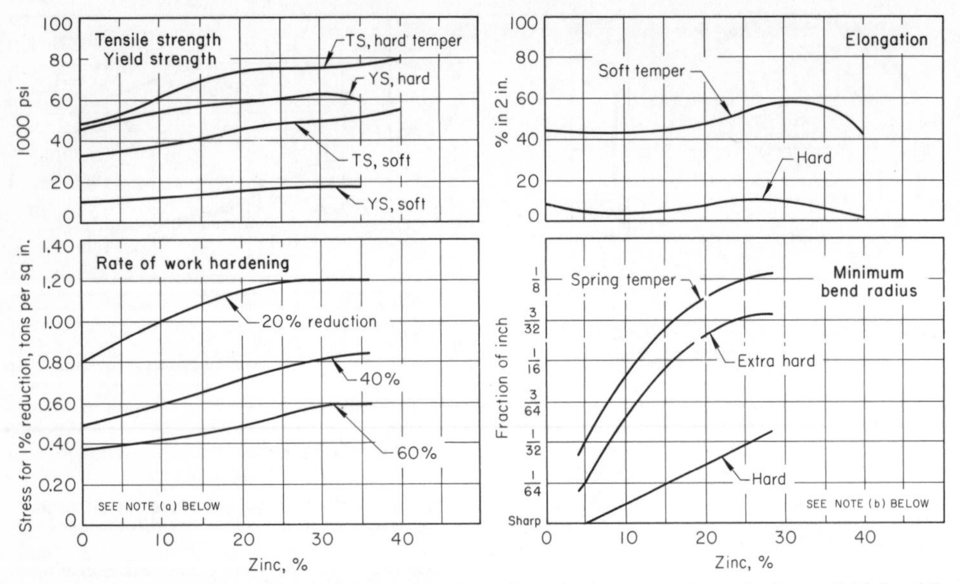

(a) Rate of work hardening is expressed as true stress in tons per square inch required for 1% reduction, averaged for the total reduction shown. (b) Minimum bend radii are for bends made axially at right angles to the direction of rolling, in 0.040-in.-thick sheet.

Fig. 1. Effect of zinc content on mechanical properties, rate of work hardening and minimum bend radius of copper-zinc alloys

These temper definitions are an approximate guide to sheet and strip properties. For closer control of mechanical properties and forming characteristics, tensile strength or hardness may be specified. Ranges of grain size, tensile strength and percentage elongation for the commonly used annealed and rolled tempers are given for many alloys in ASTM specifications. It is often possible to control properties within narrower limits than those of the standard rolled tempers.

Effect of Alloying Elements on Formability. In general, the addition of alloying elements to copper increases tensile and yield strength and the rate of work hardening, thus affecting forming characteristics. The effect of zinc content on the properties of copper-zinc alloys, as shown in Fig. 1, illustrates this behavior. Tensile strength, yield strength, and work-hardening rate are shown to increase with increasing zinc content over the range covered in Fig. 1, except that yield strength levels off or drops slightly when zinc content is between 30 and 35%. Maximum elongation is shown to occur at about 30 to 35% zinc for both strength, and increased ductility. (See page 284 of Vol. 2 of this Handbook.)

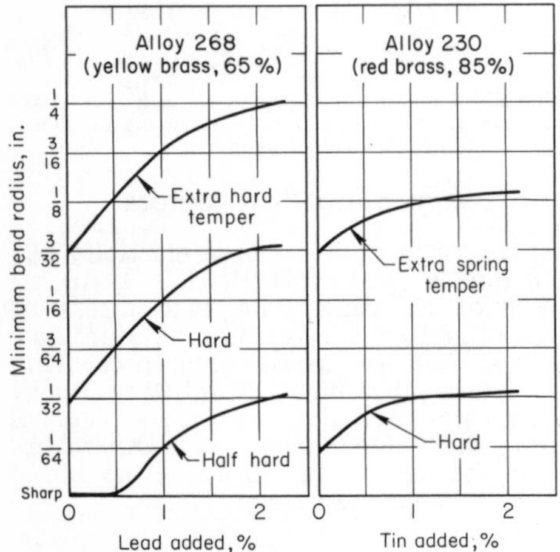

Fig. 2. Effect of additions of lead or tin on minimum bend radius of 0.040-in.-thick copper-zinc alloy sheets

Material in the annealed temper is classified by average grain size into the six grades shown in Table 2. Special annealed tempers can sometimes be produced to meet particularly critical forming requirements by modifying standard mill procedures. For example, the standard brasses are available in strip of extremely fine grain size, intended for bending and shallow drawing applications, in addition to the standard annealed tempers. This material has an unusual combination of ductility, smoothness and strength, but the small grain size (below 0.010 mm) reduces ductility enough to limit the use of the material to shallow forming applications.

Cold worked material is classified on the basis of the amount of cold reduction in rolling after annealing. The seven standard temper designations, and the corresponding reduction in thickness for each, are listed in Table 2. The harder tempers, caused by greater reduction, are stronger and less ductile.

Table 1. Compositions, Bendability and Formability Ratings of the Most Commonly Formed Copper Alloys

Alloy No.	Alloy name	ASTM specification(a)	Cu	Zn	Pb	Sn	Ni	Bendability(b)	Formability(c)
			Nominal composition, %						
110	Electrolytic tough pitch copper	B152	99.9	...	...	...	...	70	E
170	Beryllium copper, 1.7%	B194	98	(1.7 Be)		(d)		90(e)	G
172	Beryllium copper, 1.9%	B194	97.8	(1.9 Be)		(d)		90(e)	G
210	Gilding, 95%	B36(1)	95	5	...	...	...	100	E
220	Commercial bronze, 90%	B36(2)	90	10	...	...	...	90	E
226	Jewelry bronze, 87.5%	...	87.5	12.5	...	...	...	90	E
230	Red brass, 85%	B36(3)	85	15	...	...	...	70	E
240	Low brass, 80%	B36(4)	80	20	...	...	...	70	E
260	Cartridge brass, 70%	B36(6)	70	30	...	...	...	60	E
268	Yellow brass, 65%	B36(8)	65	35	...	...	...	60	E
280	Muntz metal, 60%	...	60	40	...	...	...	40	F
335	Low-leaded brass, 64.5%	B121(2)	64.5	35	0.5	...	...	50	G
340	Medium-leaded brass, 64.5%	B121(3)	64.5	34.5	1	...	...	40	G
342	High-leaded brass, 64.5%	B121(5)	64.5	33.5	2	...	...	20	F
353	High-leaded brass, 62%	B121(4)	62	36	2	...	...	20	F
356	Extra-high-leaded brass, 62%	B121(6)	62	35.5	2.5	...	...	20	P
408	Gilding bronze, 95%	...	95	3	...	2	...	80	E
413	Tin brass, 1%	...	90	9	...	1	...	70	E
430	Spring bronze, 2%	...	86	12	...	2	...	60	E
434	Spring bronze, 0.8%	...	85	14.2	...	0.8	...	60	E
464	Naval brass	B171	60	39.2	...	0.8	...	40	F
510	Phosphor bronze, 5% – A	B103(A)	95	...	...	5	...	60	E
521	Phosphor bronze, 8% – C	B103(C)	92	...	...	8	...	50	G
544	Free-cutting phosphor bronze	B103(B2)	88	4	4	4	...	20	G
614	Aluminum bronze, D	B169(D)	91	(7 Al, 2 Fe)				40	G
651	Low-silicon bronze, B	B97(B)	98.5	(1.5 Si)				70	E
655	High-silicon bronze, A	B97(A)	97	(3 Si)				70	E
706	Copper nickel, 10%	B171	88.7	(1.3 Fe)		...	10	90	G
715	Copper nickel, 30%	B122(5)	70	...	...	...	30	80	G
735	Nickel silver, 72-18	B122(1)	72	10	...	...	18	50	E
745	Nickel silver, 65-10	B122(3)	65	25	...	...	10	50	E
752	Nickel silver, 65-18	B122(2)	65	17	...	...	18	50	E
754	Nickel silver, 65-15	...	65	20	...	...	15	50	E
757	Nickel silver, 65-12	...	65	23	...	...	12	50	E
770	Nickel silver, 55-18	B122(4)	55	27	...	...	18	40	G

(a) Nearest applicable specification. Number or letter in parentheses designates a specific alloy composition of several covered by the indicated ASTM specification. (b) Based on alloy 210 as 100. (c) E = excellent; G = good; F = fair; P = poor. (d) Nickel and/or cobalt, 0.2% min; nickel plus cobalt plus iron, 0.60% max. (e) Solution heat treated condition.

Table 2. Standard Temper Designations for Copper Alloy Flat Stock

Average grain size, mm(a): Nominal	Minimum	Maximum	Standard designation	Nominal reduction in thickness, %
Annealed (Soft) Tempers(b)			**Rolled (Hard) Tempers**	
0.015	(c)	0.025	Quarter hard	11
0.025	0.015	0.035	Half hard	21
0.035	0.025	0.050	Three-quarters hard	29
0.050	0.035	0.090	Hard (full hard)	37
0.070	0.050	0.100	Extra hard	50
0.120	0.070	(d)	Spring	60
			Extra spring	68

(a) Usual range; other limits can be specified. (b) The larger the grain size, the lower the hardness. (c) Although no minimum grain size is required, the material must be fully recrystallized. (d) Not usually specified.

hard and soft tempers, but the changes are relatively small for the hard alloys.

The minimum bend radius for the tempers shown in Fig. 1 increases with increasing zinc content. This effect is smaller for the hard temper than for the extra-hard and spring tempers.

Springback is affected by increasing zinc content, in the same way as yield strength. This effect is particularly pronounced for the harder tempers, reaching a maximum at about 30% zinc.

The addition of zinc to copper (brasses) results in greater strength for the same percentage of reduction, without adversely affecting the high ductility, excellent forming behavior, ease of finishing, and the characteristic color of copper alloys.

Different alloying elements added to copper vary in their effectiveness in increasing strength and are also specific in their effects on other properties.

Beryllium, chromium and silicon, in amounts of about 2%, strengthen copper by approximately the same amount as 30% zinc. About 5% aluminum or 8% tin will also produce about the same improvement in tensile strength. Bismuth produces brittleness if present in amounts greater than 0.001%.

The addition of nickel to copper produces greater strength, lower ductility and a lower rate of work hardening than alloying with an equal amount of zinc. Alloy 715 (copper nickel, 30%) has exceptionally good corrosion resistance.

Inherently strong alloys, such as the aluminum bronzes (5 or 8% aluminum) or the silicon bronzes (1.5 or 3% silicon), are often used for plate or other heavy sections that cannot be cold worked to improve strength.

The addition of about 1% lead or tellurium greatly improves machining characteristics, but at the cost of some loss in ductility and formability.

The addition of a third alloying element to a binary alloy has effects similar to those produced by adding the same alloying element to copper. The effect on minimum bend radius of adding lead or tin to copper-zinc alloys is shown in Fig. 2. The addition of lead results in a substantial loss in formability, but tin has a lesser effect.

The substitution of varying amounts of nickel for some of the zinc in copper-zinc alloys produces the stronger but less ductile nickel silver alloys.

Effect of Temper on Formability. Soft or annealed tempers are required in forming operations that involve severe cold working. They are often required also in forming operations that involve comparatively light cold working, especially with leaded alloys and with high-strength alloys such as phosphor and silicon bronzes and nickel silvers.

Annealed alloys with the larger grain sizes often develop a rough "orange peel" surface in severe stretching or deep drawing. This can be corrected by ironing or subsequent finishing operations, or can be avoided by the use of modified forming procedures with special grades of fine-grain material.

A guide for the preliminary selection of annealed (soft) tempers of some of the common alloys for different types of forming applications is given in Table 3. Final selection of temper usually requires that trial runs be made.

Table 3. Guide for Selection of Annealed (Soft) Tempers of Copper Alloys for Forming

Alloy No. (see Table 1 for common names of numbered alloys)	Standard temper (nominal grain size, mm) for work-metal thickness of: 0.020 in. or less	Over 0.020 to 0.050 in.	Over 0.050 to 0.090 in.	Over 0.090 to 0.180 in.	Over 0.180 in.
Bending, Shallow Drawing, Contour Roll Forming, Embossing and Stretch Forming					
240, 260 and 268	0.015	0.025	0.035	0.050	0.070
210, 220, 226 and 230	0.015	0.025	0.035	0.035	0.035
110	0.015	0.015	0.015	0.015	0.025
Spinning and Deep Drawing					
240, 260 and 268	0.025	0.035	0.050	0.070	0.120
210, 220, 226 and 230	0.025	0.035	0.035	0.035	0.050
110	0.025	0.025	0.025	0.025	0.035
Severe Drawing					
240, 260 and 268	0.035	0.050	0.070	0.070	0.120
210, 220, 226 and 230	0.025	0.050	0.050	0.050	0.050
110	0.025	0.025	0.035	0.035	0.035
Coining and Extremely Severe Drawing					
240, 260 and 268	...	0.050	0.070	0.120	0.120
210, 220, 226 and 230	...	0.050	0.050	0.050	0.070
110	...	0.035	0.035	0.035	0.035

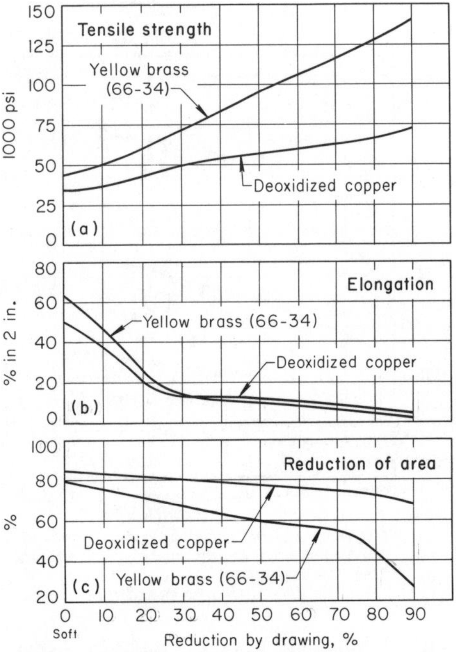

Fig. 3. Effect of cold drawing on tensile strength, elongation, and reduction of area of copper and yellow brass

The hard tempers are suitable for forming operations that require light or moderate cold working. The hardest temper that consistently yields an acceptable product is usually selected, in the absence of special requirements.

Precipitation-hardening alloys, such as beryllium copper, can be used for severely formed parts that require extremely high strength or spring properties. Forming is done in the annealed or solution treated condition, and the completed part is then heat treated to develop required strength.

Hot rolled material has microstructures and forming behavior like those of annealed cold rolled material, but is usually less uniform. It is used mainly for structural applications, rather than for severe cold forming or for applications in which surface finish is critical.

Work Hardening

Work-hardening effects for copper and yellow brass are shown in Fig. 3; tensile strength, percentage elongation in 2 in., and percentage reduction of area are plotted against percentage cold reduction. Although these data were derived from standard tension tests on wire, they provide a guide to the forming behavior of flat stock.

Tensile Strength. The curves of tensile strength in Fig. 3(a) indicate the rate at which the two metals harden during cold working. On this basis, copper work hardens at a rate equivalent to an increase of about 400 psi in the tensile strength for each 1% reduction of area by drawing. In comparison, yellow brass work hardens at a rate equivalent to an increase of about 1000 psi for a 1% reduction in area.

In general, the rate of work hardening is greater for alloys that have higher tensile strength in the annealed condition (for example, about 1400 psi increase for each 1% reduction for some of the aluminum bronzes). A notable exception is alloy 715 (copper nickel, 30%), which work hardens at about the same rate as alloy 230 (red brass, 85%).

Alloys that work harden slowly during cold reduction are preferred for redrawing without intermediate annealing. The curves of tensile strength also provide a rough guide to the forces needed for forming.

Elongation. The elongation curves in Fig. 3(b) indicate the remaining capacity for stretching or drawing material of a given temper, or the percentage reduction that can be done in a single operation. However, they give no indication of the number of redraws that can be performed without benefit of an intermediate anneal.

Reduction of area in the tension test (Fig. 3c) is the most useful guide to redrawing capability. Alloys with high values for this property and with a relatively flat curve usually can be cold formed repeatedly without annealing. The curves in Fig. 3 show copper to have a redrawing capability markedly superior to that of yellow brass. Multiphase alloys (such as Muntz metal, naval brass, leaded alloys, and beryllium copper) are usually inferior to single-phase alloys in redrawing capability. This is not always evident from the shape of the curve for reduction of area versus reduction by drawing, as in the case of deoxidized copper and 66-34 brass in Fig. 3(c), nor is it always evident from standard measurements of mechanical properties.

Formability of Copper Alloys vs Other Metals

Because of the variety of mechanisms involved in forming almost any given part, there is no single material property that completely defines formability.

Rate of Work Hardening. One commonly used index of formability is shown in Fig. 4, which compares the rates of work hardening of copper and other metals by plotting tensile strength and hardness against percentage reduction by cold rolling. Copper, and brasses up to alloy 260 (cartridge brass, 70%), are shown by the slopes of the curves in Fig. 4 to be substantially more formable than type 18-8 austenitic stainless steel, slightly more formable than 1010 steel, and slightly less formable than aluminum alloy 1100. The absolute values of tensile strength and hardness show the relative amounts of force required for forming the various materials. These comparisons are most reliable for operations that require severe deformation, such as deep drawing, spinning, coining or swaging. (See page 417 and Fig. 22, comparing work-hardening rates, and Fig. 21, comparing percentage elongation, for single-phase copper alloys.)

Minimum draw-die radius, as determined in an empirical test procedure, is also used to compare the forming characteristics of metals. Table 4 shows the results obtained in forming a cup 1 in. deep and 1 in. in diameter, from 2-in.-diam annealed blanks of different metals in thicknesses of 0.010 to 0.060 in. Alloy 260 (cartridge brass, 70%), 1010 steel, and aluminum alloy 1100 all show the same minimum draw-die radii, which are about 40% smaller than the radii that can be used for annealed type 18-8 stainless steel.

Comparison Examples. The example that follows illustrates the superior formability of alloy 260 (cartridge brass, 70%), compared to that of steel, in an application of deep drawing.

Example 575. Cartridge Brass vs Steel for Deep Drawing (Fig. 5)

The rectangular shell shown in Fig. 5 was deep drawn from alloy 260 (cartridge brass, 70%) in preference to steel, because of lower production and tool-maintenance costs.

The shell was made from 3⅛-in.-wide by 0.029-in.-thick strip annealed to a grain size of 0.025 to 0.050 mm (hardness, Rockwell F 65 to 76) by the sequence of operations given in the table with Fig. 5. Wall thickness was reduced by 0.008 in. in six drawing operations, with five intermediate anneals.

Inside corner radii were 0.010 in. (maximum), and a flat bottom was required. Range of wall thickness could not exceed 0.002 in. on the same shell, and final hardness could not exceed Rockwell B 71. Defects in surface finish that would interfere with the legibility of drop hammer marking after buffing were not acceptable.

A temporary shortage of copper led to the production of this part from low-carbon steel. The stringent requirements on the part could then be met only by sawing off the bottom and brazing on a new bottom piece. Because of the higher cost of the steel shells, brass was again used when it became available.

High-strength phosphor bronze can be more readily formed to close tolerances than most other metals. Precipitation-hardening alloys, such as the beryllium coppers, can be formed with a minimum of springback in the annealed condition and then heat treated in holding fixtures to develop high strength, as in the next example.

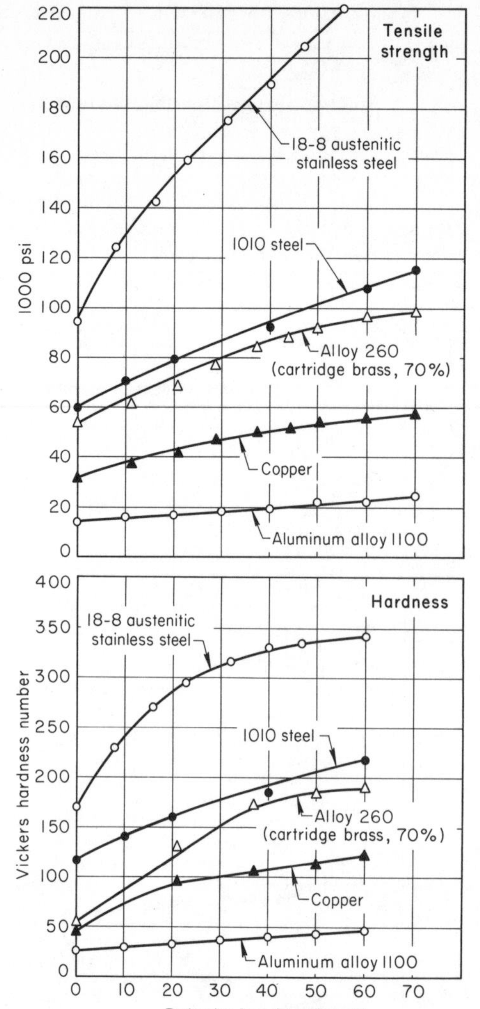

Fig. 4. Comparative rates of work hardening of copper and other metals, as shown by effect of reduction by cold rolling on tensile strength and hardness

Table 4. Minimum Draw-Die Radii for Copper Alloy 260 and Various Other Work Metals(a)

Work-metal thickness, in.	Minimum draw-die radius, in. — Alloy 260(b), 1010 steel(c) & Al alloy 1100(d)	18-8 stainless steel(e)
0.010	0.05	0.08
0.020	7/64	3/16
0.040	7/32	3/8
0.060	5/16	1/2

(a) Minimum die radii for drawing a cup 1 in. deep by 1 in. in diameter from a 2-in.-diam annealed blank. (b) Cartridge brass, 70% (tensile strength, 49,000 psi). (c) Tensile strength, 47,000 psi. (d) Tensile strength, 13,000 psi. (e) Tensile strength, 90,000 psi.

Example 576. Beryllium Copper vs Type 440A Stainless Steel (Fig. 6)

Originally, the high-strength precision diaphragm shown in Fig. 6 was to be formed from annealed type 440A stainless steel, and then heat treated to develop a high yield strength. Test runs were made on this metal, using three operations in a progressive die to blank, preform and final form. However, excessive dimensional variation occurred; this was attributed to different degrees of springback in forming and to uncontrollable distortion during heat treatment.

Alloy 172 (beryllium copper, 1.9%) was selected to replace the stainless steel after trial runs using a number of different metals. This alloy had a minimum elongation of 40% when annealed, and composition was controlled to give a minimum yield strength of 140,000 psi after heat treatment. The annealed alloy 172 showed negligible springback in forming, and a holding fixture restrained distortion satisfactorily during heat treatment.

Equipment and Tooling

Equipment that is used to form other commonly formed metals is used also for copper alloys. High-speed production, long runs, and small part size are characteristic of the production of commercial items from copper alloy flat stock. Size and tonnage requirements are generally lower than those for the forming of steel or aluminum alloys such as 5657. Small, high-speed eyelet presses are widely used for forming of copper alloys.

Copper alloys can be formed in dies designed for other metals of approximately the same strength and formability. Dies designed for deep drawing or severe bending of low-strength aluminum alloys or low-carbon steels can be used with little or no modification for copper and the readily formable brasses, although for shallow drawing or mild bending it may be necessary to make die adjustments to compensate for the smaller amount of springback with these copper alloys. To use the dies for high-strength copper alloys, additional forming stages and die modifications may be required in order to maintain dimensions; completely new dies may be needed in some instances. Dies designed for high-strength aluminum alloys or high-strength steels are generally suitable for use on high-strength copper alloys.

Most drawing dies designed for aluminum alloys do not reduce stock thickness by more than 10%, and redesign of dies and forming procedures for a reduction in thickness of 40 to 50% is sometimes desirable to take full advantage of the forming characteristics of copper alloys.

Tool design is described in articles in this volume on the individual forming methods; the selection of tool materials is discussed in the articles beginning on pages 69, 145 and 194.

Lubrication

The principles of selection and use of lubricants in forming copper alloy flat stock are the same as for aluminum alloys (see the article on Forming of Aluminum Alloys, which begins on page 379 in this volume).

Water-base and oil-base lubricants used in various forming operations on copper alloys are given in Table 5. They are listed in order of their increasing effectiveness.

Water-Base Lubricants. The soap-plus-fat paste compounds have the widest range of usefulness of the water-base lubricants, because they are readily modified by adjustment of the extent of dilution and by the addition of pigments. These pigments are of particular help in severe draws with copper-nickel alloys or heavy-gage brass, and in other heavy-duty applications where some mechanical separation between tools and workpiece is needed.

Emulsions of oils in water (soluble oils) are widely used for forming operations in which the pressure is relatively low. They are less effective as lubricants than the soap-plus-fat compounds, but their greater fluidity makes them more effective as coolants in high-speed press operations, and their lubricity can be improved by introducing small amounts of fats and other additives.

Soap solutions have good wetting and lubricating properties, and also are readily removable by hot water. Dry soap is used in deep drawing of brass shell cases and in similar operations with heavy-gage copper alloys.

Oil-base lubricants are often preferred to water-base lubricants, because oil-base lubricants are less likely to stain the work if allowed to remain on it for an extended time.

The use of volatile solvents without an additive (fatty oil or wax), or with only a small amount, completely eliminates the need for cleaning in some applications, but provides adequate lubrication for only the mildest forming operations. Precautions must be taken to provide adequate ventilation and fire protection when using volatile solvents.

Low-viscosity mineral oils provide somewhat better lubricity, and the use of mineral oils of medium and high viscosity, as well as the addition of fatty oils and small amounts of free fatty acids, extends the range of effective lubrication to include bending and drawing operations of medium severity.

Fatty oils that contain small amounts of free fatty acid are suitable for severe bending and drawing, and pigmented or chlorinated compounds are used for deep drawing operations of maximum severity.

Special Factors in Selection. In assessing the severity of forming operations as a basis for selecting a lubricant, consideration must be given to other factors in addition to the extent of deformation.

Heavy-gage materials require higher deformation pressure and make lubrication more difficult. High-strength alloys, such as silicon and phosphor bronzes and beryllium copper, also require higher deformation pressure than brasses, and need lubricants of definite acidity. No. 1 lard oil (which contains 15 to 18% free fatty acid) is commonly used to provide the required acidity.

Copper is more susceptible to cold welding than are brasses in similar forming operations, and hence lubrication requirements for copper are usually more critical than for brasses.

With a large number of materials available in each of the two groups, selection of a lubricant is often based on secondary considerations, such as cost, staining tendency, ease of application and removal, and versatility.

Water-base lubricants are more likely to stain or corrode the work metal than oil-base lubricants, in most of which the fatty oils and fats contain less than 2% free fatty acid to avoid corrosion.

Lubricants that contain active sulfur are avoided, because they can form tenacious black sulfide films. Chlorinated compounds are effective in extreme-pressure lubrication, but they are difficult to remove and must be stabilized to prevent decomposition to hydrochloric acid. In some electronics and decorative applications, the use of nontarnishing formulations or prompt removal of lubricant is necessary.

Pigments may settle out in circulating systems and clog the lines, or they may load up recesses in parts or dies, where their insolubility in cleaners makes them extremely difficult to remove. Chalk has an advantage over the other common pigments in that it can be removed in an acid dip.

Removal of Lubricants. The processes for removing lubricant residues are discussed in the articles that begin on pages 307 and 635 in Volume 2 of this Handbook. Complete removal of residues is necessary before annealing or other heat treating operations, and before electroplating and related finishing operations.

Cadmium Plating. Limited use is made of cadmium plating as a lubricant and to increase tool life. In high-volume production of small beryllium copper parts, conventional lubricants cause the lightweight parts to adhere to the tools, reducing production rates. Without lubrication, tool wear becomes a significant factor in high-volume production, because of the abrasiveness of the beryllium oxide surface. Because cadmium is soft, and because plating requires complete oxide removal, cadmium plating is beneficial in certain applications. However, the advantage of cadmium-plated over unplated beryllium copper should be determined by comparing plating cost with savings from longer tool life.

Blanking and Piercing

Blanking, piercing and related operations are done with press tools and are frequently combined with other press operations. The procedures, equipment and tooling used on copper alloy flat stock are similar to those described in the articles on Blanking and on Piercing in this volume.

Alloy and temper are normally dictated by the intended use of the part, or by subsequent manufacturing opera-

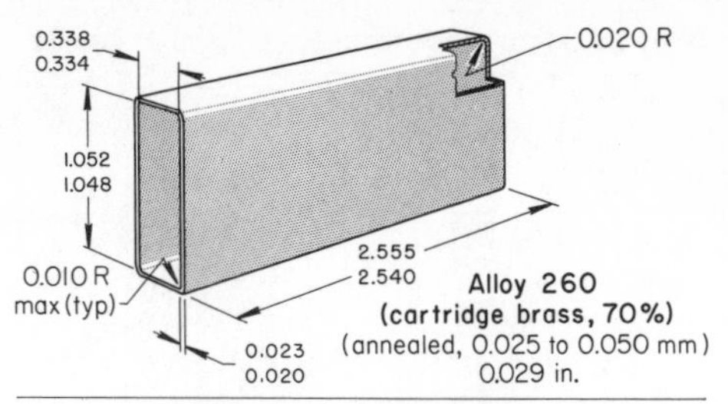

Sequence of Operations

1	Blank and cup	9	Fourth redraw
2	Anneal and pickle	10	Stamp bottom(a)
3	First redraw	11	Anneal and pickle
4	Anneal and pickle	12	Fifth redraw
5	Second redraw	13	Clean
6	Anneal and pickle	14	Flatten bottom(a)
7	Third redraw	15	Saw to length(b)
8	Anneal and pickle	16	Clean

(a) Hand press. (b) Table saw.

Fig. 5. Rectangular shell that was deep drawn from brass in preference to steel (Example 575)

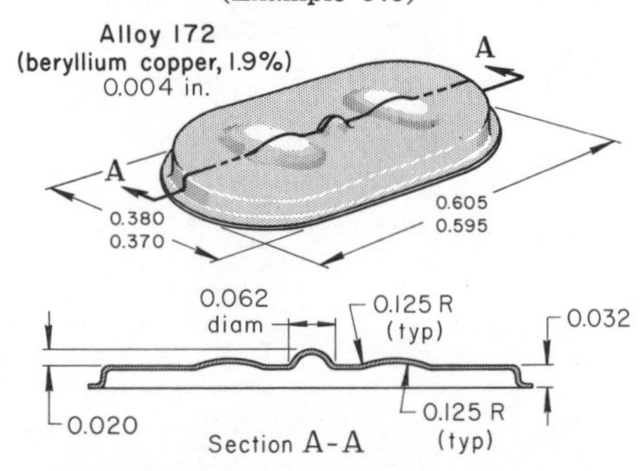

Fig. 6. High-strength precision diaphragm that was formed from heat treatable beryllium copper in preference to type 440A stainless steel (Example 576)

Table 5. Lubricants Commonly Used in Forming of Copper Alloys
(Listed in order of increasing effectiveness)

Water-base lubricants	Oil-base lubricants
Blanking and Piercing, Mild Bending, and Shallow Drawing (Less than 10% reduction in diameter)	**Blanking and Piercing, Mild Bending, and Shallow Drawing** (Less than 10% reduction in diameter)
1 Dilute soap solutions (0.3 to 2%) 2 Emulsions of 5 to 10% soluble oil(a) or fat(b) in water	1 Volatile solvents (mineral spirits, isopropanol, chlorinated solvents) (d) 2 Volatile solvents plus 1 to 10% fatty oil (d,e) or wax 3 Mineral oil (40 to 100 SUS at 100 F)
Medium Bending and Drawing (10 to 30% reduction in diameter)	**Medium Bending and Drawing** (10 to 30% reduction in diameter)
3 Dilute soap solutions (1 to 2%) plus 1% fat plus 0.25% free fatty acid(c) 4 Emulsions of soluble oils (may contain fats and other additives) 5 Soap solution (5%)	4 Mineral oil (100 to 300 SUS at 100 F) plus 10 to 20% fatty oil 5 Mineral oil (250 to 300 SUS at 100 F) plus 2 to 5% free fatty acid
Severe Bending and Drawing, and Spinning (30 to 50% reduction in diameter)	**Severe Bending and Drawing, and Spinning** (30 to 50% reduction in diameter)
6 Diluted soap-plus-fat pastes (2 to 20% final fat content; may contain mineral oil or free fatty acids) 7 Pigmented soap-plus-fat pastes (chalk, talc, mica)	6 Fatty oils containing 2 to 5% free fatty acid
Maximum-Severity Deep Drawing, and Spinning (More than 50% reduction in diameter)	**Maximum-Severity Deep Drawing, and Spinning** (More than 50% reduction in diameter)
8 Dry soap (applied from hot 10 to 15% solution)	7 Pigmented mineral oils, fatty oils, or blends of these 8 Stabilized chlorinated oils (30 to 50% combined chlorine; may be diluted with up to 20% mineral oil)

(a) Soluble oil is a mineral oil to which has been added an agent that makes it emulsifiable in water.
(b) Fats are fatty oils, such as tallow, that are made water soluble by the addition of an emulsifier. (c) Fatty acid is usually stearic, oleic or palmitic acid, or a mixture of these. (d) Precautions must be taken in handling, storage and use, to avoid hazards of fire and toxicity.
(e) Fatty oil is usually prime lard oil with less than 2% free fatty acid; also lanolin, sperm oil, castor oil or rapeseed oil.

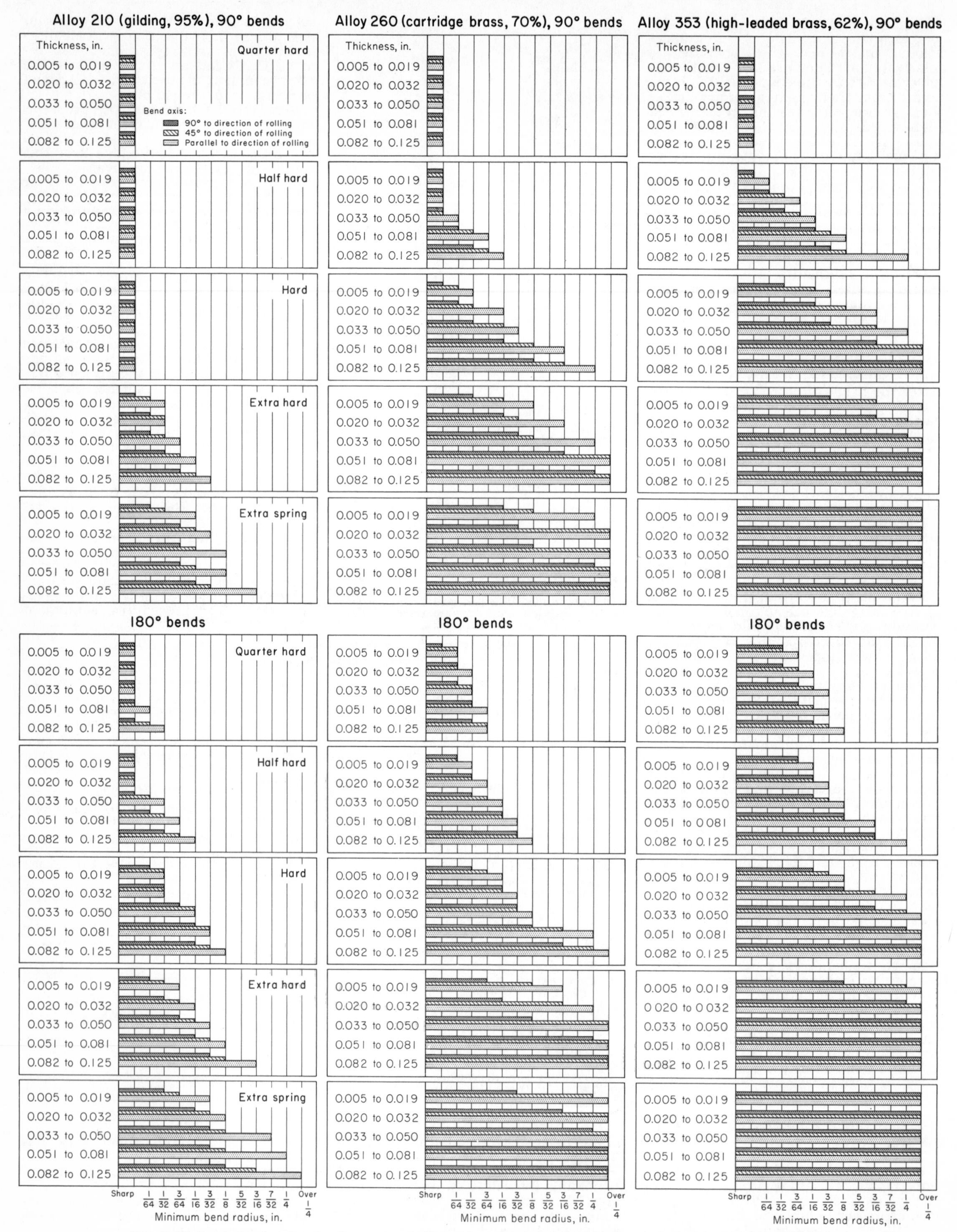

Fig. 7. Minimum bend radius for three copper alloys. (See explanatory and instructional notes on the next page.)

tions on the part. The leaded brasses and other leaded alloys are preferred for applications in which ductility is secondary to shearing characteristics and in which freedom from distortion and burrs is of particular importance. Alloys with 0.5 to 4% lead can be used, depending on whether formability or shearability is more important.

The use of alloy 330 (low-leaded tube brass) to eliminate problems encountered in piercing alloy 260 (cartridge brass, 70%) is described in Example 17 (Fig. 22) on pages 970 and 971 in Volume 1 of this Handbook. In that application, burrs were produced and slugs were not released in punching 0.040-in. holes in alloy 260 tubing without a mandrel; the difficulty was eliminated by changing to the leaded alloy.

Die Clearances. Copper and copper alloys can be readily blanked and pierced with a wide range of die clearances from 1 to 35% of the work-metal thickness. In practice, the clearance per side between punch and die is usually held between 3 and 12% of work-metal thickness for all copper alloys and tempers, 0.020 to 0.060 in. thick.

For burr-free and distortion-free blanking and piercing, alloys in the annealed tempers require smaller clearances than those in the harder tempers, and less latitude in the actual value is permitted. Die clearances up to 5% are recommended for annealed-temper alloys 0.020 to 0.060 in. thick. For alloys in harder tempers, which shear cleaner but require greater shearing forces, clearances up to 12% may be used to minimize tool-edge wear and to decrease the pressure required for blanking and piercing.

For stock thicker than 0.060 in., minimum clearance should be 0.010 in.; for stock thinner than 0.020 in., the clearance should be 0.002 in. or less. Exact clearance values for specific operations must be determined by production trials. (For additional information on punch-to-die clearance, see the article "Piercing of Low-Carbon Steel", which begins on page 44 in this volume.)

Edge Condition. Blanks that will undergo subsequent forming must have smooth edges. Blanks with rough edges are likely to crack when bent, even when the bend radii are much larger than those that properly sheared or deburred metal can withstand.

Notes for Fig. 7

1 Minimum bend radius is "sharp" for all annealed tempers. Values may be interpolated for tempers not shown.
2 Values shown for minimum bend radii are based on short bend lengths and high bending speeds, and they assume severe service conditions for the part.
3 Use next lower radius for: (*a*) slow bending speeds; (*b*) bend length greater than ten times work-metal thickness; (*c*) combination of conditions (*a*) and (*b*); and (*d*) nonfunctional bend (no subsequent finishing and not subject to load).
4 Use second lower radius for combination of nonfunctional bend and conditions (*a*), (*b*) and (*c*) in note 3.
5 See text and Table 6 for effect of prior plating, polishing, or other finishing operations on minimum bend radius.
6 Do not lower bend radius if value shown in Fig. 7 is over ¼ in.
7 Do not lower bend radius if bend is functional (subsequently finished, or subject to loading, or both).

Rough edges are likely to occur if tools are dull, damaged, or improperly aligned, or if clearance is excessive. The effect is more pronounced with hard tempers, thick stock, sharp bend radii, and short bend lengths. Only the most ductile material can withstand sharp bends, if the edges are rough.

Equipment and Tools. Press tonnage capacities are intermediate between those required for comparable operations on aluminum alloys and on steels, varying approximately in proportion to the shear strength of the material. In blanking or piercing of material thicker than 0.100 in., operating force is sometimes reduced by grinding the end of the punch or the die to provide shear action, or by staggering punch height in multipunch equipment.

Tool design is described in the articles on Blanking (page 31) and Piercing (page 44); the selection of tool materials is discussed in the article that begins on page 69.

Lubricants. The selection and use of lubricants is discussed in the section on Lubrication in this article (page 408). Table 5 in that section lists the types of lubricants that are commonly used in blanking and piercing.

Layout and Handling. Stock layout for blanking is usually based only on the most efficient use of material consistent with economical handling of the material and parts at the desired production rate. Additional restrictions are sometimes imposed on layout, because of directionality effects on subsequent or simultaneous bending operations. This behavior is discussed under "Effect of Bend Orientation", in the section that follows.

Coil or strip stock less than about 0.010 in. thick sometimes presents special problems in handling. These difficulties and some techniques for overcoming them are described in Examples 578 and 579 in this article.

Bending and Flanging — Minimum Bend Radius

As a general rule, the bend radius should not be less than the thickness of the work metal. However, this does not take into account a number of factors that have a substantial effect on the severity of bend.

The bar graphs in Fig. 7 show the variation of the minimum bend radius with bend angle, alloy, temper, thickness, and orientation of bend. The following characteristics of minimum bend radius are shown in the graphs:

1 The minimum bend radius is substantially different for different alloys.
2 It increases with increasing hardness or temper, with increasing thickness of metal and with increasing angle of bend.
3 It varies with angle between bend axis and direction of rolling as follows:

90° to rolling: Small minimum bend radius
45° .... Intermediate radius
0° (parallel) .... Large radius

Values listed for minimum bend radius are approximate; actual results deviate from these values because of variation in material, tool condition and shop practice. Softer materials, in particular, will not necessarily fail by cracking if bent to a smaller radius. As bend radius is decreased, the first type of defect to appear is orange-peel roughening at the bend. This is characteristic of material of relatively large grain size. In these ratings, any significant amount of orange peel is unacceptable, because many bending operations are followed by plating or other finishing processes, and appearance is usually important. If appearance or subsequent operations are not factors, this type of defect need not be a cause for rejection.

Effect of Alloy. Some effects of alloy composition on minimum bend radius are described in the section on Effect of Alloying Elements on Formability, and comparative bend ratings are listed in Table 1, in this article.

Figure 7 shows minimum bend radius values for the three following alloys:

Alloy No. (and common name)	Characteristics
210 (gilding, 95%) ...	High bendability
260 (cartridge brass, 70%)	Intermediate bendability (most widely used brass)
353 (high-leaded brass, 62%)	Poor bendability (superior for machining and blanking)

The trends shown by these alloys are typical of the bending characteristics of copper alloys. The behavior of other alloys in bending can be predicted from these data and from the bend radii in Fig. 1 and 2.

In addition to alloy 210 (gilding, 95%), several high-copper brasses are outstanding in bending behavior. These include alloy 220 (commercial bronze, 90%); alloy 226 (jewelry bronze, 87.5%); and alloy 408 (gilding bronze, 95%). Of all the common copper alloys, only the high-strength alloys and those containing 2% or more lead are rated as mediocre or poor for bending.

Because of the wide variety of copper alloys available, there is usually more than one alloy that will meet product requirements. In the absence of other limitations, formability is sometimes the deciding factor in the selection of an alloy, as in the following example.

Example 577. Change in Alloy That Eliminated the Need for Intermediate Bending (Fig. 8)

Originally, a printed-circuit-board contact with a tail suitable for wire wrapping (Fig. 8) was formed from 0.012-in.-thick strip of quarter-hard alloy 172 (beryllium copper, 1.9%). With this material, the 72° bend (with axis parallel to the direction of rolling) could

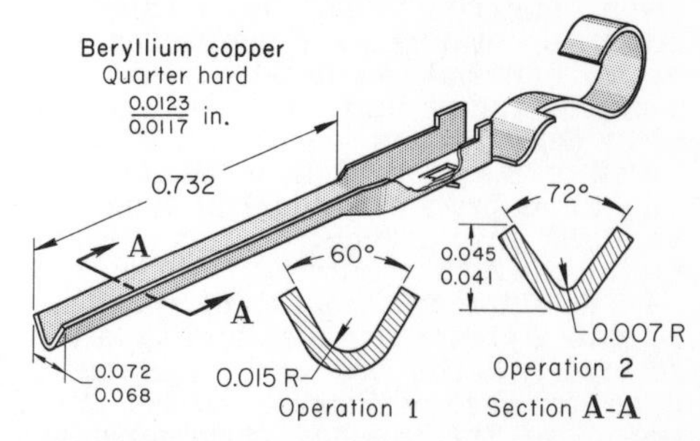

The bend in section A-A required two forming steps, shown as operations 1 and 2, when the original alloy 172 was used. The first step (operation 1) was eliminated when the more formable alloy 170 was substituted.

Fig. 8. Contact spring that was formed in a single operation by changing from alloy 172 (beryllium copper, 1.9%) to the more formable alloy 170 (beryllium copper, 1.7%) (Example 577)

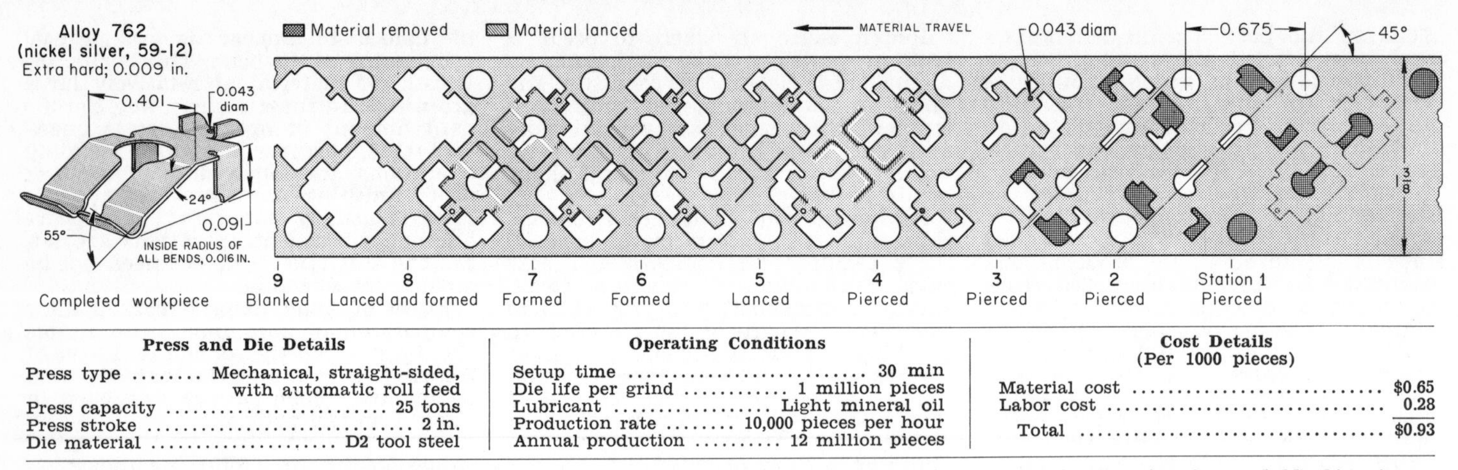

Press and Die Details	
Press type	Mechanical, straight-sided, with automatic roll feed
Press capacity	25 tons
Press stroke	2 in.
Die material	D2 tool steel

Operating Conditions	
Setup time	30 min
Die life per grind	1 million pieces
Lubricant	Light mineral oil
Production rate	10,000 pieces per hour
Annual production	12 million pieces

Cost Details (Per 1000 pieces)	
Material cost	$0.65
Labor cost	0.28
Total	$0.93

Fig. 9. Die layout for production of small electrical contacts from thin nickel silver strip by piercing, lancing, forming and blanking in a nine-station progressive die (Example 578)

not be formed to the required 0.007-in. radius in one step without cracking the strip. It was necessary first to make a 60° bend with a 0.015-in. radius, as shown in operation 1 in Fig. 8.

By changing to the more readily formable alloy 170 (beryllium copper, 1.7%) in the same temper, the preliminary operation was eliminated, and the 72° V-bend was formed directly from the flat material.

Effects of Temper and Thickness. Because they are interrelated, temper and thickness are treated together. General information is given in the section "Effect of Temper on Formability" in this article, and the relation between the annealed tempers and material thickness for bending applications for some of the common alloys is indicated in Table 3, also in this article.

Figure 7 shows the effects of temper and thickness on minimum bend radius of three copper alloys.

Minimum bend radius increases with increasing hardness or temper, and the effect of change in temper is usually greatest in the range from hard to spring temper. Extra-spring temper is nearly identical to spring temper in forming behavior and has slightly greater strength.

For a given alloy and temper, minimum bend radius is almost directly proportional to thickness. The relation:

$$\frac{\text{Minimum bend radius}}{\text{Thickness}} = \text{Constant}$$

can be used to estimate the minimum bend radii for other thicknesses of a given material when one value is known accurately. Low-temper or annealed material can usually be bent to a smaller radius than would be indicated by this equation.

Coil or strip less than 0.010 in. thick sometimes presents special problems in handling that are not related to bend radius. Such thin material is difficult to feed in automatic equipment (particularly in a progressive die) and to locate accurately in the dies, and it can readily be stretched or distorted by tool friction. Also, the finished parts must be handled with special care to avoid damage.

The following two examples describe the forming of hard-temper thin strip and foil into small parts and some of the methods used to overcome the special difficulties in handling and feeding presented by these materials.

Example 578. Maintaining a Stiff Skeleton in Forming Flexible, Thin Nickel Silver Strip (Fig. 9)

The snap-in lamp contact shown in Fig. 9 was made from alloy 762 (nickel silver, 59-12) in the extra-hard temper. Because of its flexibility, the 0.009-in.-thick coiled strip was difficult to feed and to locate accurately in the progressive die. Tolerances on all dimensions, except hole size and the 24° bend, were ±0.005 in.

The problem of maintaining as stiff a skeleton as possible was solved by (*a*) increasing the progression beyond that normally used for thicker strip, (*b*) retaining the tie-in to the part on three sides until the final forming operation, and (*c*) retaining the web between each pair of parts. The parts were made two at a time in a nine-station progressive die (see Fig. 9). In the lancing operation in station 5, the parts were cut at a slight angle, so that the portion to be formed was pulled into the wider opening, thus reducing interference between the part and the skeleton.

The 45° layout was used to economize on material and so that none of the 0.016-in.-radius bends would be made parallel to the direction of rolling. Production and cost details are given in the table with Fig. 9.

Even more stringent precautions are required in the handling of material that is less than 0.004 in. thick, particularly for soft and intermediate tempers. As shown in the example that follows, forming force must be closely controlled to avoid damaging the material, and friction against tool surfaces must be kept to a minimum to avoid stretching and loss of dimensional control. Location is usually by nesting rather than on pins, because of the low strength of the material.

Example 579. Accurate Control of Force in Forming Thin Beryllium Copper Foil (Fig. 10)

The alloy 172 (beryllium copper, 1.9%) spring clip shown in Fig. 10 was formed in two operations from half-hard 0.0015-in.-thick foil, using a 2-ton mechanical press with a 1¼-in. stroke. Special consideration was given in tool design for the ability to maintain close control over forming force. If a single forming punch had been used, the die could have been mounted in a hydraulic press with sensitive and precise control over the hydraulic pressure in the desired range.

The first operation was to form 110° V-bends simultaneously at each end of the part (see Fig. 10, operation 1). To control the force, the punches were spring loaded, with the springs selected so that small amounts of deflection would not result in a significant change in force.

In the forming of the two 90° bends in the second operation (see Fig. 10), the wiping cams were activated by adjustable springs. To reduce frictional force, which might have stretched the light-gage material and thus have caused dimensional inaccuracy, tool radii were polished at all points where bending action occurred. These polished tool radii are indicated by arrows in Fig. 10.

The workpieces were positioned by nesting against their edges (see Fig. 10), because pins fitting in holes in the blank would be likely to distort the area around the holes. No lubricant was used, because the adherence of even the smallest particles of grit to the lubricated die surfaces would have resulted in marking of the workpiece.

Tool life per grind was 100,000 pieces, and production was 500 pieces per hour for each operation. Setup time for operation 1 was 15 min; for operation 2, 20 min.

Effect of Bend Orientation. Figure 7 shows how minimum bend radius is affected by the orientation of the bend in relation to the direction of rolling. The behavior of the three alloys considered is typical of copper alloys in general. The minimum bend radius increases gradually as the angle between bend axis and rolling direction changes from 90° to 45° to 0° (or parallel). This effect results from the distortion of the grain structure of the metal during rolling, with individual grains becoming elongated in the direction of rolling. Fracture in bending takes place more readily along the elongated grain boundaries parallel to the direction of rolling. Sharper bends, therefore, can be made at right angles to the direction of rolling than parallel to it.

Consideration should be given in layout to the possibility of orienting the most severe bends at 90° to the rolling direction for maximum flexibility in material selection and for minimum tool maintenance. However, to avoid material-handling problems, or to use available standard widths of strip with minimum waste, the most suitable layout is often one that orients all critical bends at 30° to 60°.

Selection of a 45° layout to avoid making any bends parallel to the rolling direction and for efficient use of stock is shown in Example 578 (Fig. 9).

The example that follows describes a change from a 90° layout to a 45° layout to reduce material waste, while retaining adequate formability for severe bends in a hard material.

Example 580. Change From 90° to 45° Layout That Reduced Waste of Work Metal During Blanking (Fig. 11)

The spring retainer shown in Fig. 11 was made from 0.063-in.-thick strip of alloy 268 (yellow brass, 65%). It was originally blanked so that the 0.031-in.-radius bends for the T-

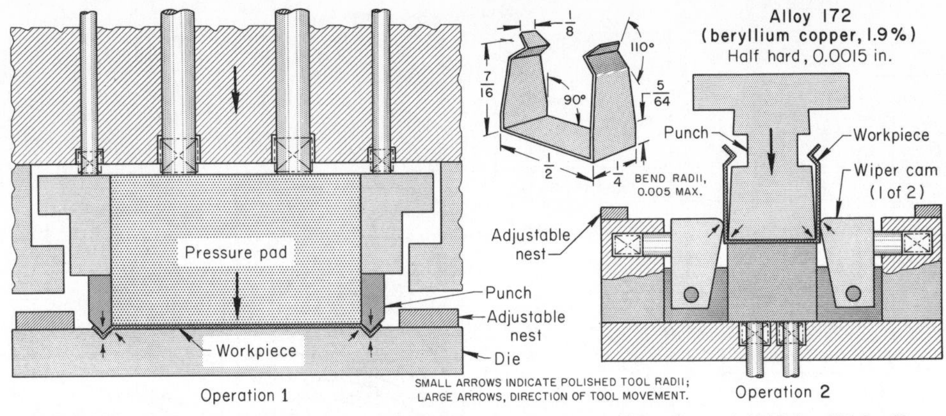

Fig. 10. Tooling setup for forming spring clips in two operations from 0.0015-in.-thick alloy 172 foil (Example 579)

lugs were at right angles to the direction of rolling. The bends were made in subsequent hand-feed operations.

The inefficient use of the strip with this arrangement was accepted at first, because of the smaller-than-normal bend radii. (The minimum bend radius for this alloy, thickness and temper is generally 0.062 in. at a 90° orientation and 0.125 in. at 45°.)

Production trials later showed that, with close control over the operation (minimum burr was required) and the raw material, the bending could be done at 45° to the direction of rolling. The tool layout was then redesigned to use the more economical layout shown in Fig. 11.

Production results with the 45° layout were good, and the waste of work metal was reduced by 35%. As shown in the table of production and cost details that accompanies Fig. 11, the change in layout lowered costs from $60.28 to $40.78 per 1000 pieces.

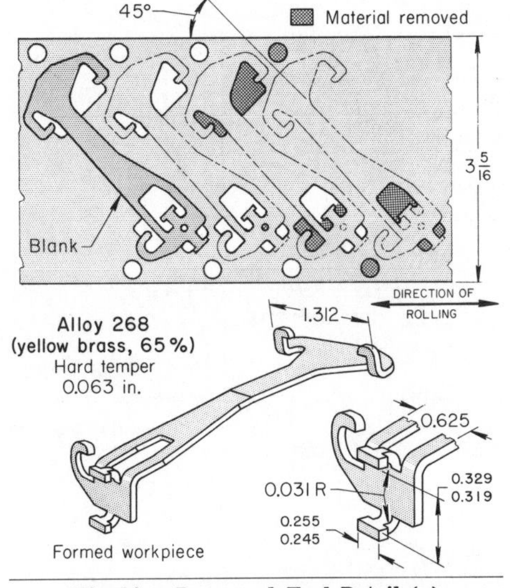

Blanking Press and Tool Details(a)

Press type	Mechanical, straight-sided(b)
Press capacity	50 tons
Press stroke	3 in.
Tool material	D2 tool steel

Operating Conditions

Setup time (blanking)	30 min
Tool life per grind (blanking)	70,000 pieces
Lubricant	Light mineral oil
Production rate:	
Blanking	3230 pieces per hour
First forming	1000 pieces per hour
Second forming	1000 pieces per hour
Annual production	150,000 to 300,000 pieces

Costs per 1000 Pieces

	90° layout	45° layout
Material	$55.00	$35.50
Direct labor:		
Blanking	0.78	0.78
Forming	4.50	4.50
Total costs	$60.28	$40.78

(a) Bending was done in a 35-ton mechanical gap-frame press. (b) With automatic roll feed.

Fig. 11. Spring retainer that was produced with less metal waste from a 45° layout than from a 90° layout (Example 580)

Effect of Surface Finish. Surface preparation can have a significant effect on minimum bend radius. The smooth surfaces obtained by buffing or polishing help to avoid fractures in bending. However, highly polished surfaces make orange-peel roughness more noticeable. Because of this, relatively small grain sizes and large bend radii may be needed, if appearance is critical.

Wire brushing or embossing before bending often produces scratches and irregularities that can concentrate stress in bending. Therefore, such treatments in the area to be bent usually require an increase in bend radius above the normal minimum.

On thin material, the amounts of metal removed by chemical etching or by chemical or electrolytic polishing may be significant, and the reduction in thickness should be considered.

Plated surfaces present a more complex situation. The effect of a plated coating on the formability of a metal involves not only the ductility of the coating, but also its thickness, strength and adhesion. There can be substantial differences in the formability of supposedly identical plated parts, because of differences in plating baths and operating conditions. An approximate guide to the usual effect of some individual electrodeposited coatings on the minimum bend radius of copper alloys is given in Table 6.

Table 6. Effect of Electrodeposited Coatings on the Bendability of Copper Alloys

Electrodeposit(a)	Effect of minimum bend radius
Tin or zinc	Little or no effect
Copper	Slight; may increase by one value(b)
Cadmium or silver	Increase by one or two values(b)
Chromium or nickel	Increase to more than ¼ in.

(a) Commercial deposits 0.2 to 0.3 mil thick; except 0.01 to 0.02 mil thick for chromium. (b) Over those shown in Fig. 7.

For composite coatings (such as copper-nickel-chromium), the combined effect is approximately that of the component shown in Table 6 as causing the greatest decrease in formability. The effect of a chemically produced deposit of a metal (such as electroless nickel) may differ greatly from the effect of the electrodeposited metal, depending on the purity and properties of the chemical deposit.

Copper alloys (and other metals with a face-centered cubic crystal structure) are not subject to hydrogen embrittlement from pickling or plating treatments. For clad materials, the minimum bend radius is determined by the least ductile component. Organic coatings usually require an increase of at least one level in the minimum bend radius.

Effect of Edge Finish. The importance of smooth edges in bending operations is mentioned under "Edge Condition", page 411 in this article. With rough edges, only the most ductile material can withstand sharp bends.

Effect of Bend Length. The distribution of strain in bending is affected by the bend length, as measured along the bend axis. In bends for which the width is greater than ten times the material thickness, the minimum bend radius can be decreased to one value below the applicable value in Fig. 7.

Effect of Bending Speed. For most bending operations with copper alloy flat stock, press speeds range from 70 to 120 in. per sec. Slow speeds, less than about 50 in. per sec, make it possible to use a minimum bend radius smaller than standard by one level. Excessive bending speed creates extremely high local stress that can result in failure.

Bending and Flanging — Springback

Springback must be taken into account in designing and constructing bending tools, so that the specified angle will be produced after bending and elastic recovery.

The curves in Fig. 12 and 13 show the springback behavior of the three copper alloys (210, 260 and 353) for which minimum bend radii are shown in Fig. 7. The curves indicate that the number of degrees of springback: (*a*) differs substantially for different alloys; (*b*) increases with increasing hardness (temper), bend angle, and bend radius; and (*c*) decreases with increasing thickness of the metal.

Effect of Workpiece Characteristics. The trends shown in Fig. 12 and 13 are typical of the springback behavior of copper alloys. If published values on springback are not available for an alloy, a rough approximation can be made from known values for most other alloys and a comparison of yield strengths (as a general rule, springback increases with increasing yield strength). Duplex alloys, such as leaded alloys, however, are notable exceptions to this rule. Also, springback varies directly with rate of work hardening.

Although the general effect of increasing temper is to increase springback, the magnitude of this effect varies, as shown in Fig. 12 and 13. The effect of thickness is consistent over the range shown in Fig. 12 and 13; the amount of springback encountered at a thickness of 0.018 in. is several times that at a thickness of 0.064 in.

Effect of Design Variables. The effect of bend radius is also shown in Fig. 12 and 13. Large differences in springback are observed for bend radii greater than

1/32 in. Springback increases as bend radius is increased, because the bending force is distributed over a larger area (unit stress is reduced) and the yield strength is not as greatly exceeded.

Bends at right angles to the rolling direction might be expected to show a greater amount of springback than bends parallel to the rolling direction. However, except in special applications, orientation of bends seldom has a significant effect on springback.

The V-die opening has some effect on springback, because it determines how much of the workpiece is confined between die surfaces in bending: the larger the die opening, the greater the springback.

Excessive clearance in closed dies should be avoided to minimize springback; inaccurate alignment will produce variable springback. If press speed is too fast, springback will be greater than normal. In addition, the bottom position of the press-ram stroke must be controlled closely for acceptable results. These variables are of importance mainly in keeping the amount of springback uniform and as low as possible.

Compensation for Springback. Three techniques are commonly used to compensate for springback: overbending, restriking, and the use of special dies.

Overbending by the exact amount of springback produces the desired angle. However, unavoidable fluctuations in thickness and properties, as well as in tool condition and other operating variables, necessitate constant adjustment. For precision work, the variation normally found in a coil may lead to unacceptable variation in springback, unless dies are checked and adjusted frequently during production.

Restriking in the original dies or in special fixtures will reduce springback and allow production to close tolerances on bend angle.

Special dies are sometimes used in bottoming techniques to exert a coining action and to stress most of the metal in the bend area beyond the elastic limit. In other die modifications, the metal is pinched slightly at the bend for a similar effect. In using these techniques, careful control must be exercised, because excessive thinning or overstressing of the bend area can cause the part to fail during bending, or can make it susceptible to early failure in service. Special procedures and equipment are also needed to prevent damage to tools from the accidental feeding of two blanks or of material that is too thick.

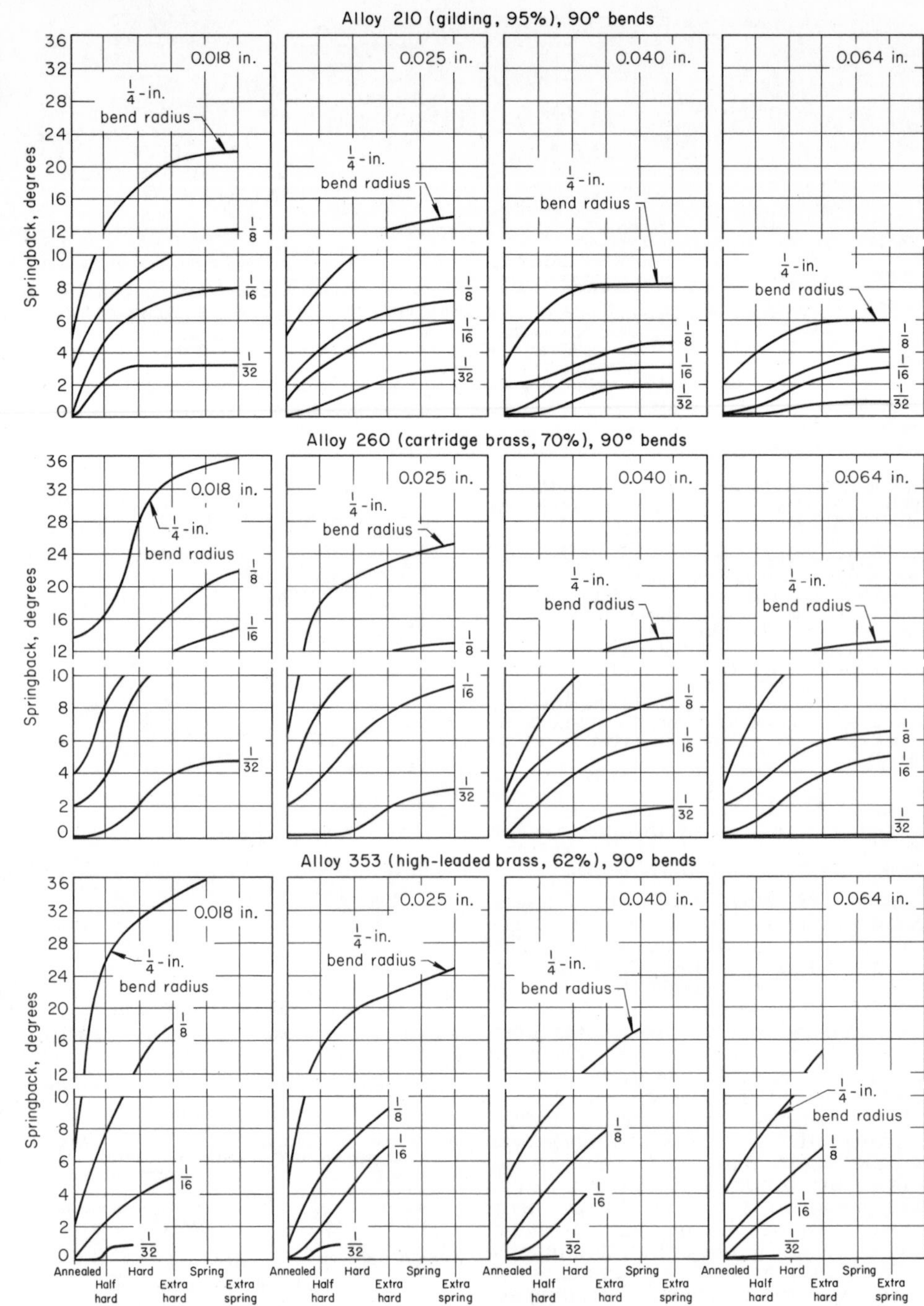

Fig. 12. Springback of three copper alloys in 90° bending, as a function of temper, sheet thickness, and bend radius. (Values can be interpolated for tempers or radii not shown.)

Forming

Forming differs from simple bending in that more severe deformation is required and appreciable changes in stock thickness by stretching or by upsetting are involved. In shallow drawing, the depth of draw is less than the diameter or smallest lateral dimension, and there is little or no ironing. Related operations include bulging, necking, curling, ribbing, and stretch forming.

With minor modifications, the discussion of bending and flanging in this article also applies to forming.

Bend Radius and Springback. The effects of workpiece characteristics and design variables on bending behavior are similar to those described for simple bending. However, because of the strain hardening produced by stretching and upsetting, the amount of springback and the limits on corner radius are usually developed by trial for specific forming applications.

Effect of Temper. The effect of temper on forming characteristics is shown in the three examples that follow.

Example 581. Change to Finer Grain Size That Reduced Finishing Costs

A 4½-in.-diam back for a rear-view mirror was originally drawn from 0.032-in.-thick alloy 260 (cartridge brass, 70%) that had a 0.035-mm grain size.

Changing to a 0.015-mm grain size, at no extra cost, made it possible to modify the subsequent finishing operations. Two mechanical finishing operations were eliminated, one was simplified, and a bright nickel plate of reduced thickness was used with the finer-grain material:

Sequence of Finishing Operations

0.035-mm grain	0.015-mm grain
1 Grease grind	1 Light buff
2 Buff	2 Copper strike
3 Copper strike	3 Bright nickel plate, 0.3 mil
4 Nickel plate, 0.45 mil	4 Chromium plate
5 Buff	
6 Chromium plate	

As a result, the finishing cost per piece was reduced from 27¢ to 12¢.

As shown in Table 2, the standard temper designations overlap to a considerable degree. Sometimes it is necessary not only to specify the temper, but also to specify a narrow hardness limit to minimize rejects, as for the part discussed in the following example.

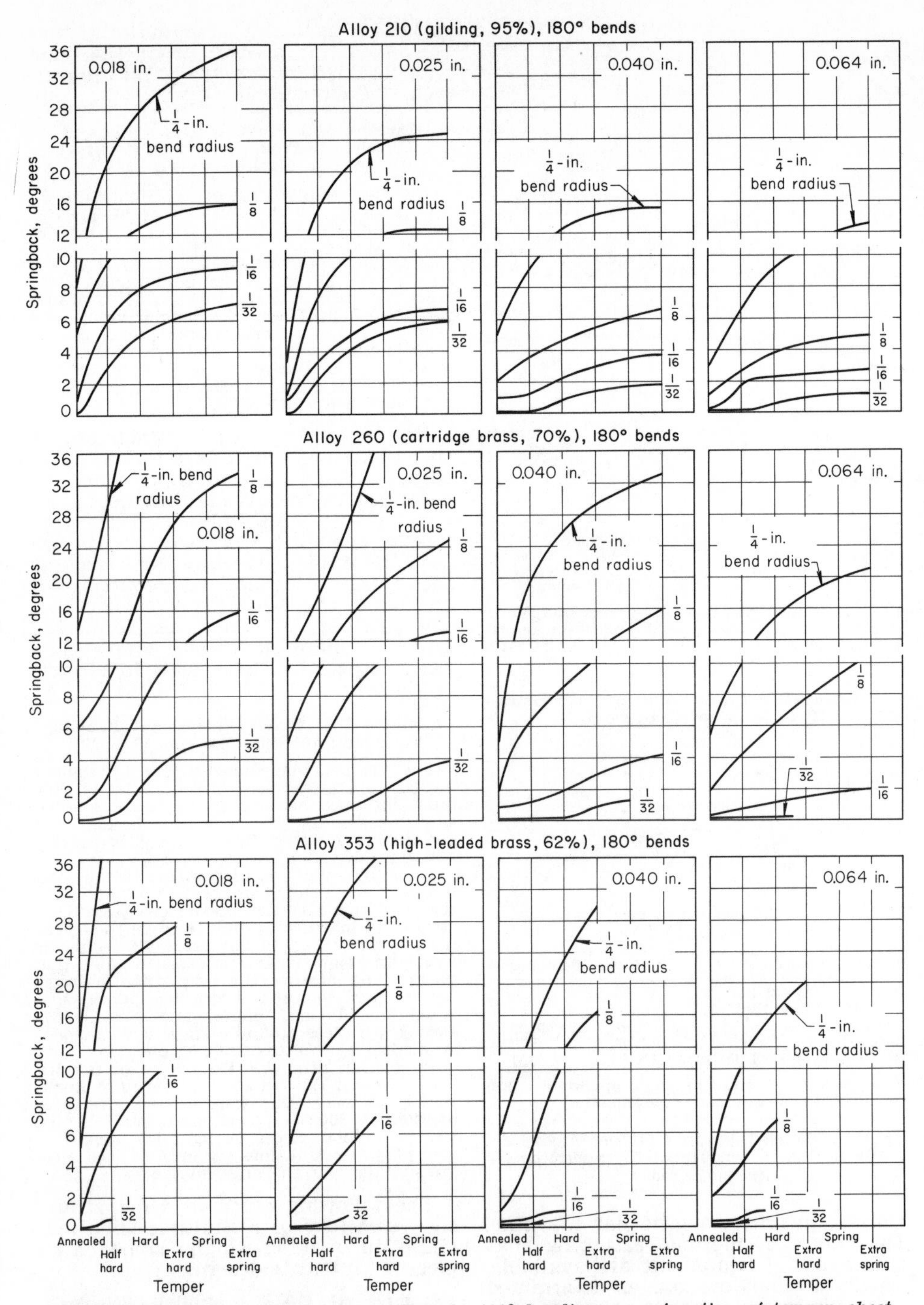

Fig. 13. Springback of three copper alloys in 180° bending, as a function of temper, sheet thickness, and bend radius. (Values can be interpolated for tempers or radii not shown.)

Example 582. Close Hardness Limits That Reduced Rejection Rate (Fig. 14)

A contact for a miniature-tube socket (Fig. 14) was produced in large quantities in a high-speed press, which formed two parts per stroke. Originally, these contacts were made from 0.0128-in.-thick alloy 510 (phosphor bronze, 5% – grade A) in the extra-hard temper (Rockwell 30-T 73 to 78). With this material, the rejection rate was high, because of orange peel and fractures in the stem of the part (see Fig. 14). Nearly all the failures were found to have occurred in material with hardness near the upper limit. The difficulty was eliminated by forming the socket from alloy 510 purchased to the special hardness range of Rockwell 30-T 75 to 76.

The softer annealed tempers (larger grain size) of low-strength alloys in thin gages sometimes have less formability than material of slightly greater hardness and smaller grain size. For instance, in one application cups ⅛ in. in diameter and depth were formed from annealed 0.010-in.-thick strip of alloy 260 (cartridge brass, 70%). Grain size of the material had to be maintained below 0.040 mm to avoid cracking during forming. Susceptibility to fracture in this thin-gage, relatively low-strength alloy was high when the grain size exceeded the 0.040-mm limit, because the workpiece then had only a few grains across its thickness of 0.010 in. (0.25 mm).

With alloys of inherently greater strength, such as beryllium copper, formability continues to improve as hardness decreases to the minimum commercial limits, and progressively softer tempers are usually required as depth of draw or severity of forming increases. When the limiting depth of draw in one operation has been reached for the softest annealed temper (or for the softest temper that is otherwise satisfactory for the part), the drawing can often be done in several steps, to obtain a greater depth of draw without intermediate annealing. The relation of formability to temper is illustrated in the next example.

Example 583. Formability vs Temper for Alloy 172 (Beryllium Copper, 1.9%) (Fig. 15)

The four parts shown in Fig. 15 required increasingly severe forming in their production, as shown by the ratios of depth and radius to thickness in the table with Fig. 15.

As a general rule, quarter-hard or half-hard alloy 172 is suitable for stretching applications in which depth of forming does not exceed four times the stock thickness, and in which forming radii are at least three times the stock thickness. These limits can sometimes be exceeded for thin material, such as that used for parts 1 and 2 in Fig. 15. For each of these two parts, however, only one of the rule-of-thumb limits was exceeded in forming between a mating punch and die.

The forming depth for part 3 was 18 times stock thickness, and the radius was only twice thickness. By using annealed material, this part was drawn from strip 0.005 in. thick.

In part 4, the extent of deformation was greater than could be drawn in one operation, even from annealed material. Accordingly, the part was drawn to the required shape in four operations, as shown in Fig. 15. It was trimmed to size, and slots, holes and center opening were pierced, in a final press operation.

Forming Dies. Copper alloys can be formed in any one of the four types of dies used in pressworking of metals (see page 113 and Table 1 in the article on Press Forming of Low-Carbon Steel in this volume). The type of die selected depends on several factors including the type and number of operations needed to make the part, the production rate and quantity, and the cost per piece.

General practice is to amortize the tool cost within one year unless other factors such as accuracy and safety have a greater influence. The part described in the following example could be produced by both single-operation and progressive dies. A progressive die was used, because the labor savings would pay for it in less than a year.

Example 584. Cost Savings by Change From Separate-Die to Progressive-Die Production (Fig. 16)

The part illustrated in Fig. 16 was originally produced in five separate operations in single dies: blanking and drawing, redrawing and trimming, trimming tab, piercing, and notching the end. The material was alloy 757 (nickel silver, 65-12), 0.024/0.025 in. thick. The cost comparison presented with Fig. 16

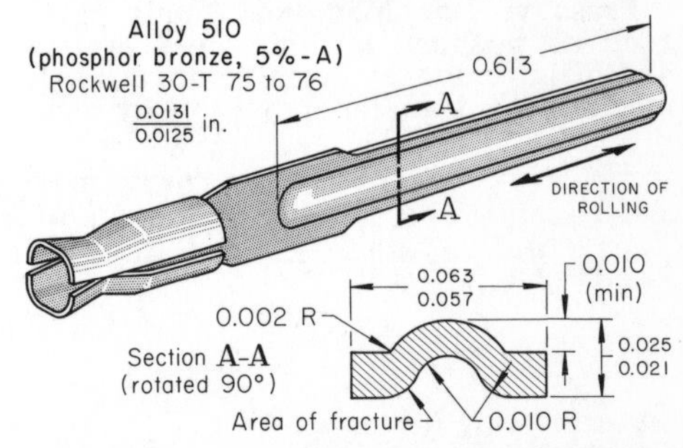

Fig. 14. Socket contact that was produced without fracture when formed from phosphor bronze purchased to special hardness limits (Example 582)

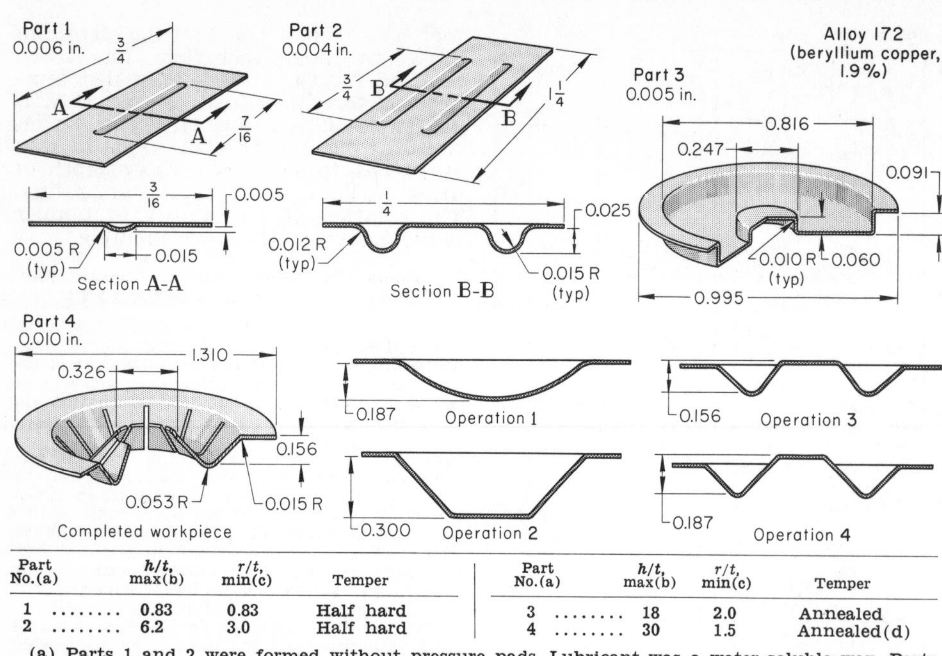

Part No.(a)	h/t, max(b)	r/t, min(c)	Temper
1	0.83	0.83	Half hard
2	6.2	3.0	Half hard
3	18	2.0	Annealed
4	30	1.5	Annealed(d)

(a) Parts 1 and 2 were formed without pressure pads. Lubricant was a water-soluble wax. Parts 3 and 4 were formed using pressure pads, which resulted in some stretching of the material. Lubricant was a fat-blended mineral oil. (b) Maximum ratio of depth to thickness. (c) Minimum ratio of inside bend radius to thickness. (d) Four-step progressive forming required.

Fig. 15. Four parts that illustrate the need for softer work-metal tempers and successive forming operations with gradually increasing severity of forming (Example 583)

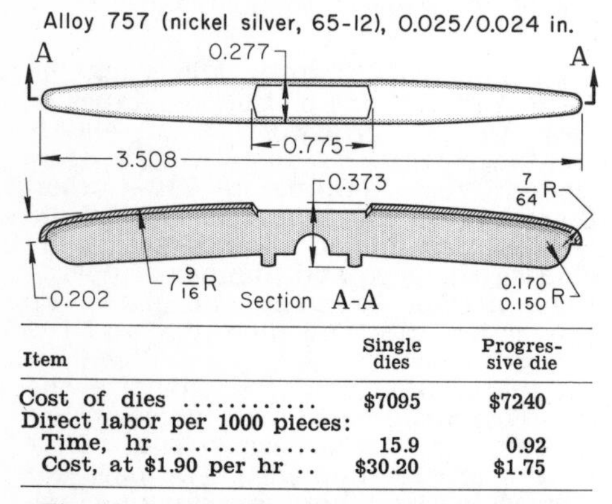

Item	Single dies	Progressive die
Cost of dies	$7095	$7240
Direct labor per 1000 pieces:		
Time, hr	15.9	0.92
Cost, at $1.90 per hr ..	$30.20	$1.75

Fig. 16. Part produced in a 12-station progressive die at lower labor cost than in five single dies (Example 584)

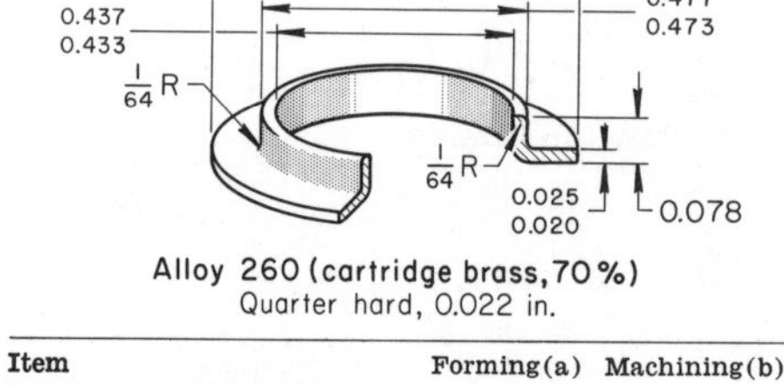

Item	Forming(a)	Machining(b)
Weight of metal per 1000 pieces, lb:		
Gross	5.16	15.00
Net	1.70	1.70
Production, pieces per hr ..	13,175	1100

(a) In a 9-ton transfer press, operated at 250 rpm. (b) In an automatic bar machine.

Fig. 17. Flanged washer that was produced by forming in preference to machining (Example 585)

shows that changing to a 12-station progressive die, which cost only $145 more than the five separate dies, resulted in a labor saving of $28.45 per thousand pieces. Thus, the extra die cost was paid for in making 5100 pieces, and the entire cost of the progressive die ($7240) was paid for in labor savings for 254,500 pieces (less than one year's production).

Two other costs in the five-die method were for degreasing after blanking and drawing and for handling; these are not shown with Fig. 16, since they were absorbed in indirect labor.

Press vs Bar Machine. Small parts such as washers, bushings and eyelets are often made by forming in a small mechanical transfer press or by machining in an automatic bar machine. The choice of method, assuming that both types of equipment are available, usually depends on cost, as determined primarily by the amount of metal consumed per part and by the production rate obtainable by each method. In most instances material consumption will be less for press forming; either method may have the advantage in speed, depending on the design and size of the part and on the particular type of press or bar machine available. The example that follows describes an application in which less material was consumed and greater production rate was obtained by the use of forming instead of machining.

Example 585. Production of a Flanged Washer by Press Forming in Preference to Machining (Fig. 17)

The small flanged washer shown in Fig. 17 was made in large quantities from quarter-hard alloy 260 (cartridge brass, 70%) strip, 25/32 in. wide by 0.022 in. thick.

Forming in a 9-ton transfer press was preferred over machining in an automatic bar machine, because only 35% as much material was needed in forming as in machining, and because production rate was 12 times that for the machining method — as shown in the table with Fig. 17. Tolerances on the inside and outside diameters of the flange on the finished part were held to ±0.002 in.

Use of Multiple-Slide Machines. A special kind of progressive forming machine, called a multiple-slide, is described in the article that begins on page 154 in this volume. The same type of machine and attachments are used to form copper alloy parts, such as the small electrical connections described in the following two examples. The intricacy of the pieces formed is typical of many such small copper alloy parts, especially those used in electric switchgear.

Example 586. Three-Dimensional Bending in a Multiple-Slide Machine (Fig. 18)

The terminal plug shown in Fig. 18 required bends in many different directions (to provide taper for easy insertion in the mating part), a spring clip on the side (for holding the connection together firmly), and bosses for added rigidity.

A multiple-slide machine with a 10-ton press ahead of the forming station was used to make the part from alloy 260 (cartridge brass, 70%) strip 0.019 in. thick by 1 in. wide, in the extra-hard temper. The 10-ton press was equipped with an eight-stage progressive die that pierced and notched the strip prior to forming. A cutoff tool at the forming station separated the finished blank, and three slides formed the piece around a stationary mandrel. A stripper ejected the finished piece.

Production rate was 150 plugs per minute. Tools were of D2 tool steel hardened to Rockwell C 60 to 61. Dies were ground after production of 300,000 pieces, and total die life was 20 million pieces. A light oil applied to the strip stock before it entered the progressive die was the only lubrication.

The following example demonstrates the versatility of a multiple-slide machine in making small copper alloy pieces of intricate design.

Example 587. Use of a Multiple-Slide Machine for Forming an Intricate Shape (Fig. 19)

The circuit-breaker terminal shown in Fig. 19 was formed in a multiple-slide machine from half-hard alloy 220 (commercial bronze, 90%) strip, 0.050 in. thick by 0.500 in. wide. There were two single-ram presses in the press station: a 20-ton press and a 12-ton press. Before entering the presses, the strip received a thin coat of light oil. Progressive dies in the two presses performed nine pierc-

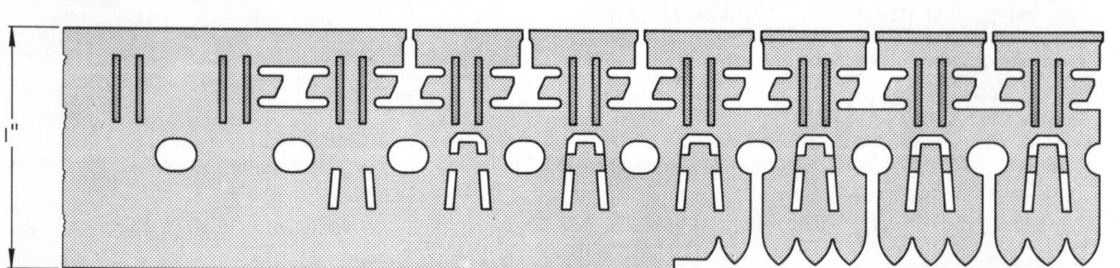

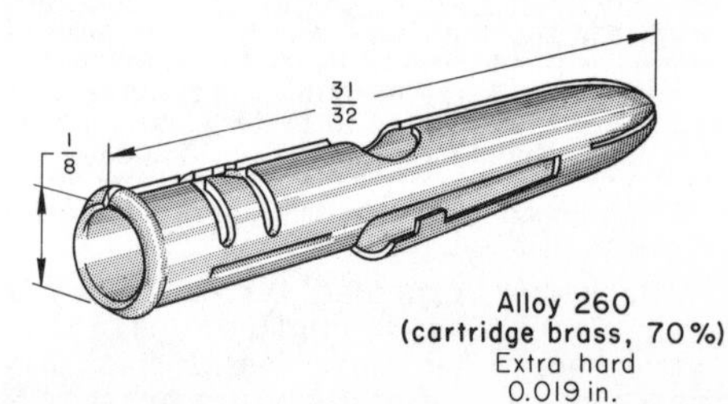

Fig. 18. Terminal plug (right) that was formed in a multiple-slide machine from strip developed as shown at left (Example 586)

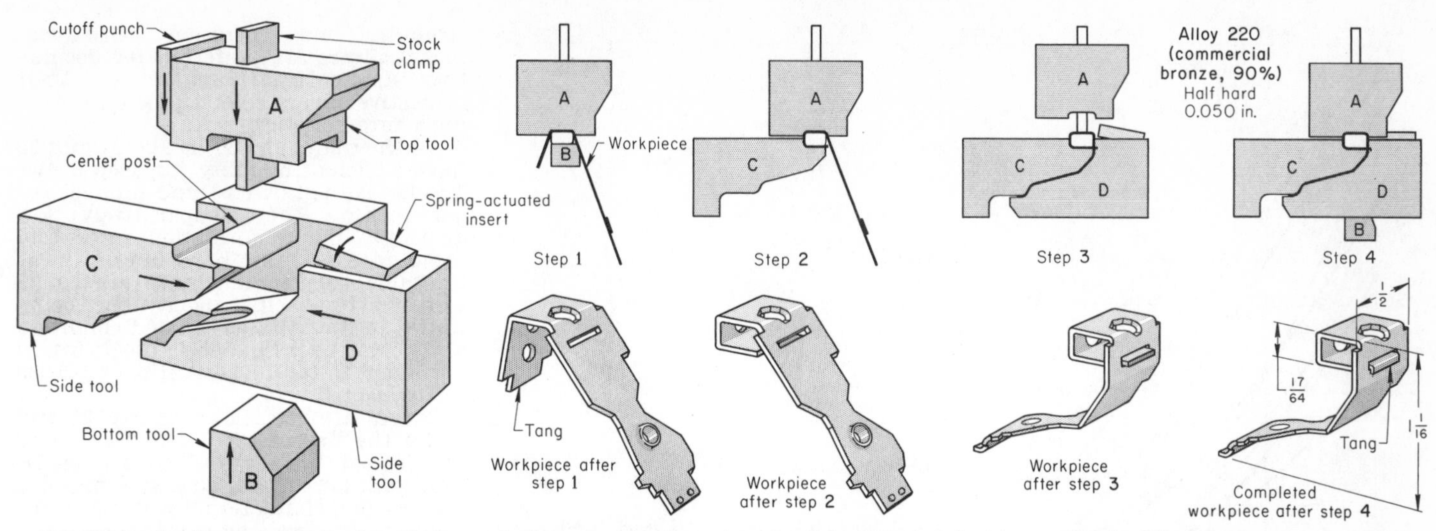

Fig. 19. Tool setup and progression of shapes in four-step forming of a circuit-breaker terminal in a multiple-slide machine (Example 587)

ing, notching or extruding operations before the strip passed to the forming station, where the blank was sheared off and formed into a hollow square over a center post, as shown by steps 1 and 2 in Fig. 19. The top tool formed the strip into an inverted "U" and the two side tools completed the square. To complete the terminal, the tang, blanked into the end of the short leg, was pressed through a slot on the long leg (step 3, Fig. 19). Finally, a cam on the top tool triggered the spring-actuated insert in the right-hand side tool, which turned over the tang to lock the hollow square (step 4, Fig. 19). This tang lock prevented any springback that could have opened the square, and provided rigid resistance against the jacking action of the terminal screw when it clamped an electric wire into place.

Tools were of D2 tool steel hardened to Rockwell C 60 to 61. Terminals were produced at the rate of 125 per minute. Die life per grind was 250,000 pieces.

Deep Drawing

Deep drawing, or drawing to a depth greater than the diameter or the smallest lateral dimension, can be done readily on nearly all copper alloys. In most applications of deep drawing, multiple draws are required. With a suitable alloy and temper, and with favorable processing conditions, several draws can be made in succession without intermediate annealing.

Drawing procedures, equipment and tools are generally the same as those used in the deep drawing of steel and aluminum. The emphasis is on mass production of relatively small articles, chiefly using eyelet presses. Deep drawing procedures for copper alloys emphasize ironing and thinning of sidewalls to a much greater degree than for steels, in order to minimize the number of draws and annealing operations and to improve the surface finish of the sidewall.

Tool design is described in the article on Deep Drawing, page 162 in this volume; the selection of tool materials is discussed in the article that begins on page 194. The selection, application and removal of lubricants are treated in the section on Lubrication in the present article (see page 408).

Alloy Selection. The selection of an alloy for a particular application usually involves other considerations, in addition to deep drawing characteristics. The major factors are dealt with in the section "Alloys" at the beginning of this article, and are also discussed in the article that begins on page 960 in Volume 1 of this Handbook.

The following example describes an application for which susceptibility to stress-corrosion cracking necessitated a change in alloy.

Example 588. Change in Work Metal for a Deep Drawn Part That Eliminated Stress-Corrosion Cracking in Service (Fig. 20)

When made from alloy 260 (cartridge brass, 70%) strip, the automotive taillight socket shown in Fig. 20 was subject to early failure in service by stress-corrosion cracking, unless stress relieved after forming. By changing to alloy 230 (red brass, 85%) strip, satisfactory parts were produced without the final anneal.

Selection of Alloy for Depth of Draw. The behavior of any given alloy in deep drawing depends on its original properties in the annealed condition and the changes in properties that result from cold reduction. Figure 21 shows the variation of ductility (percentage elongation) with extent of cold reduction in thickness by rolling (temper) for single-phase copper alloys. The elongation values show the remaining capacity for stretching after varying degrees of cold reduction and hence are a measure of depth of draw obtainable in a single operation. The deepest draws can be made with alloy 521 (phosphor bronze, 8% – grade C), followed by the brasses, in order of decreasing zinc content, and by copper. Alloy 172 (beryllium copper, 1.9%) has the lowest capacity for making deep draws in a single operation.

Selection of Alloy for Redrawing. Figure 22 shows the variation of tensile strength with extent of cold reduction for the same alloys. In general, the curves with flatter slope indicate a lower rate of work hardening and hence a capacity for being redrawn several times without intermediate annealing. (Redrawability, however, is more accurately indicated by reduction of area in the standard tension test.) The curves of tensile strength in Fig. 22 also indicate the amount of force needed for deformation of a given alloy after varying degrees of cold reduction.

Figure 22 shows that alloy 110 (ETP copper), and other coppers of similar purity, are unrivaled in capacity for re-

Original alloy: 260 (cartridge brass, 70%)
Changed to: alloy 230 (red brass, 85%)

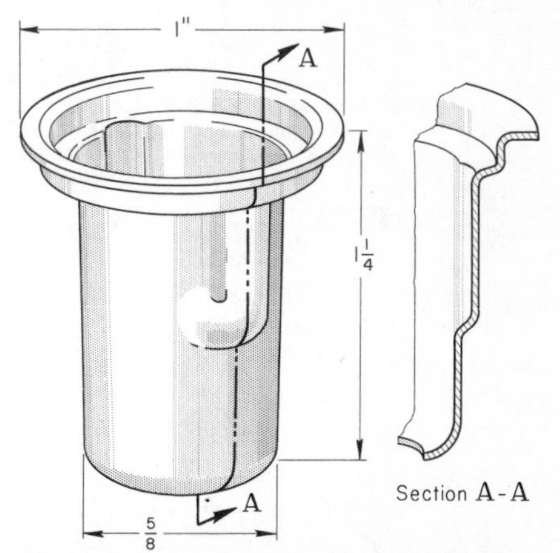

Fig. 20. Deep drawn taillight socket for which alloy reselection eliminated stress-corrosion cracking in service (Example 588)

drawing. This capacity falls off progressively, and the deformation force increases, with the increasing zinc content of the brasses, leveling off as the solubility limit of zinc is approached (alloys 110, 210, 220, 230, 240, 260 and 268).

The general trend among brasses of higher rates of work hardening (steeper slopes) with increasing tensile strength is continued with high-strength alloys such as the phosphor bronzes, silicon bronzes, and beryllium coppers. These alloys have little capacity for redrawing.

Copper nickels and nickel silvers, in contrast, show slopes, rates of work hardening, and a redrawing capacity comparable to those of the intermediate brasses, alloys 220 and 230.

Over-All Comparison of Alloys. The curves of elongation and tensile strength of Fig. 21 and 22 show the compromises in properties that must be made in selecting copper alloys for deep drawing capability. Although alloy 521 (phosphor bronze, 8% – grade C) permits the deepest draw in a single operation, it is not widely used for deep drawing, because it has only limited redrawing capacity and requires high deformation forces. If a deep drawn part must be made from this alloy or a

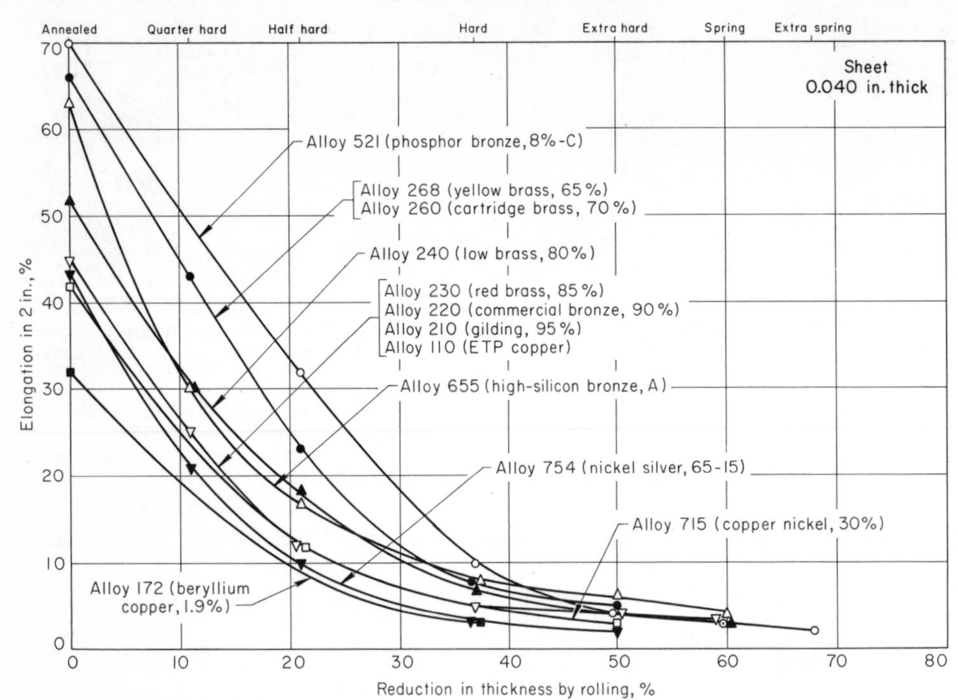

Fig. 21. Elongation of single-phase copper alloys as affected by percentage reduction in thickness by rolling (temper). The elongation values for a given percentage of cold reduction indicate the remaining capacity for deep drawing in a single operation.

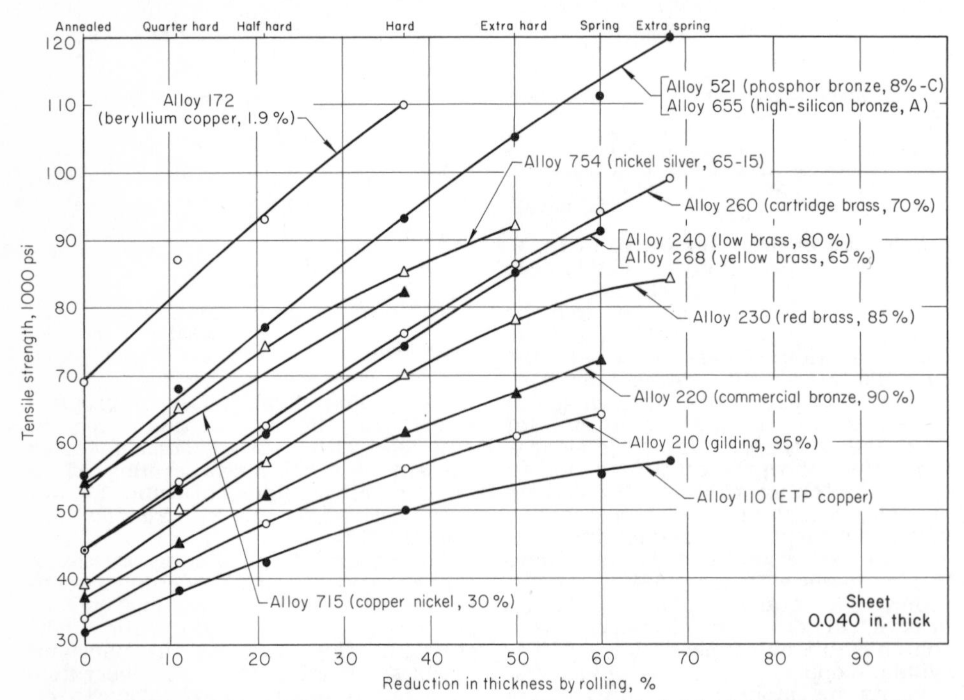

Fig. 22. Tensile strength of single-phase copper alloys as affected by percentage reduction in thickness by rolling (temper). Curves of lesser slope indicate a lower rate of work hardening and a higher capacity for redrawing.

silicon bronze for high strength, the material usually is first bright annealed to remove the abrasive oxides of tin and silicon.

The more highly alloyed brasses rate next in ductility and depth of draw. Because of this and their relatively good redrawing capacity and intermediate deformation force, they are favored for deep drawing applications. Alloy 260 (cartridge brass, 70%) is the copper alloy most commonly used for deep drawing, because of its excellent balance of mechanical properties, in addition to its good corrosion resistance, pleasing yellow color, and relatively low cost. Alloy 268 (yellow brass, 65%) also has many of these properties.

Copper and brasses with at least 85% copper show a balance of properties best suited for applications in which redrawing capacity is more important than strength or depth of single draw. Nickel silvers and copper nickels, although slightly less ductile and slightly lower in redrawing capacity and requiring a greater deformation force, are used in deep drawing applications. Both have the disadvantage of high cost, but have the advantages of excellent strength and corrosion resistance; nickel silvers are preferred for decorative applications because of their attractive silvery color and good finishing characteristics.

All the alloys shown in Fig. 21 and 22 have sufficient ductility for deep drawing, if justified by cost and product requirements. The comparatively low ductility, high deformation force and rapid rate of work hardening of heat treatable beryllium coppers are counteracted by their capacity for being drawn in the solution-treated condition and being subsequently precipitation hardened to tensile strengths of 185,000 to 200,000 psi.

Curves are not shown in Fig. 21 and 22 for the tin brasses (0.5 to 2% tin) or the leaded brasses (0.5 to 3% lead). The addition of tin does not improve the drawing characteristics of the corresponding brasses; the reason for adding it is to improve the strength and weldability of the brasses.

The addition of lead (two-phase structure) progressively reduces both ductility and capacity for redrawing, with amounts above about 1% producing alloys that cannot practically be deep drawn. Alloys containing about 40% or more zinc, such as alloy 280 (Muntz metal, 60%) or alloy 464 (naval brass), also have a two-phase structure and, therefore, very poor deep drawing characteristics.

The relationships shown in Fig. 21 and 22 are valid only for single-phase alloys; they do not apply to Muntz metal, naval brass, leaded alloys, and most other multiphase alloys.

Temper and Thickness. The section on Effect of Temper on Formability in this article reviews the general effects of temper on forming behavior. Because deep drawing, by its nature, involves severe cold working, only soft, annealed, or solution treated tempers are ordinarily used.

Considering only drawing to maximum depth without fracturing, the softest available annealed temper (largest grain size) would be desired for its high ductility. However, the roughness and orange-peel effects often associated with severe stretching of large-grain material may require the selection of a harder annealed temper (finer grain size) when appearance or quality of surface finish is important, as on parts to be electroplated or on other decorative items (see Example 581). Polishing a roughened surface can be prohibitively expensive. Another situation that sometimes requires the use of finer grain size is the drawing of very thin-gage material, in which strip of the softest temper would have only a few large grains across its thickness (see the discussion that follows Example 582, on page 415).

General recommendations on the selection of annealed tempers for deep drawing different thicknesses of some of the common copper alloys are given in Table 3.

Effect of Part Design. Part design is a major factor in determining production procedures and details of press equipment and tools.

Simple circular shells or cups can be drawn in one operation from the more ductile brasses to depths somewhat greater than diameter, provided the bottom radius is generous and quality of finish is not critical. Most deep drawn parts, however, require several successive draws, and may require intermediate annealing, depending on complexity of shape and severity of draw.

Procedures. For copper alloys, reduction in diameter in a single draw (cupping) usually ranges from 35 to 50%, with a 50% reduction corresponding to ideal conditions. Drawing procedures vary widely in commercial practice, as shown in several examples in this article. Reductions for successive draws of the commonly formed brasses, under favorable operating conditions and without intermediate annealing, are usually 45% for cupping; 25% for first redraw; and 20, 16, 13 and 10% for succeeding redraws. Greater reductions are usually obtained with blank thicknesses greater than about 0.064 in.; for blank thicknesses less than about 0.015 in., reductions are usually about 80% of the percentages shown.

With an annealing operation before each succeeding redraw, reduction of 35 to 45% in each successive redraw can be obtained under favorable operating conditions, assuming that the accompanying reduction in wall thickness is acceptable.

Die radius usually varies from about twenty times the metal thickness for material 0.005 in. thick, to about five times the metal thickness for material 0.125 in. thick. Radii of this size prevent high stress concentrations at the die opening, which can lead to tearing in subsequent draws. Sharper radii are needed for flanged shells and for meeting special design requirements.

Punch radius, except for the final stages of drawing, is usually less than one third of the punch diameter, or four to ten times the metal thickness. Clearance between punch and die is maintained at values that produce at least a slight amount of ironing of the sidewalls.

Examples of Practice. The five examples that follow describe the relation between part design and deep drawing procedure.

Example 589. Deep Drawing Alloy 230 (Red Brass, 85%) Strip in an Automatic Transfer Press (Fig. 23)

A small housing was originally to be machined from rod in an automatic bar machine. Instead, the part was produced from flat strip in an automatic transfer press (eyelet machine) because of higher production rate and savings in material and maintenance costs. Annealed alloy 230 (red brass, 85%), having a nominal grain size of 0.025 mm, was selected because of severe ironing in drawing the part.

As shown in Fig. 23, eight operations were performed. Starting with a 0.490-in.-diam blank, successive reductions in the five drawing operations were 49, 23, 22, 10 and 0.8%. In the third redraw (operation 4 in Fig. 23), the upper portion of the wall was reduced 67% in thickness. Final inside diameters were identical with the diameter of the sizing punch, but final outside diameter was 0.001 in. larger than the diameter of the sizing die, because of springback — evidence of the high compressive forces due to ironing of the wall.

Lubricant was of the oil-base type, given as No. 8 in Table 5. Draw-die bushings were made of carbide; punches were made of D2 tool steel, hardened to Rockwell C 61 to 63 and highly polished. Average production rate was 7000 pieces per hour. For 1 million pieces, costs averaged $3.97 per thousand. For 500,000 pieces, costs were $4.37 per thousand.

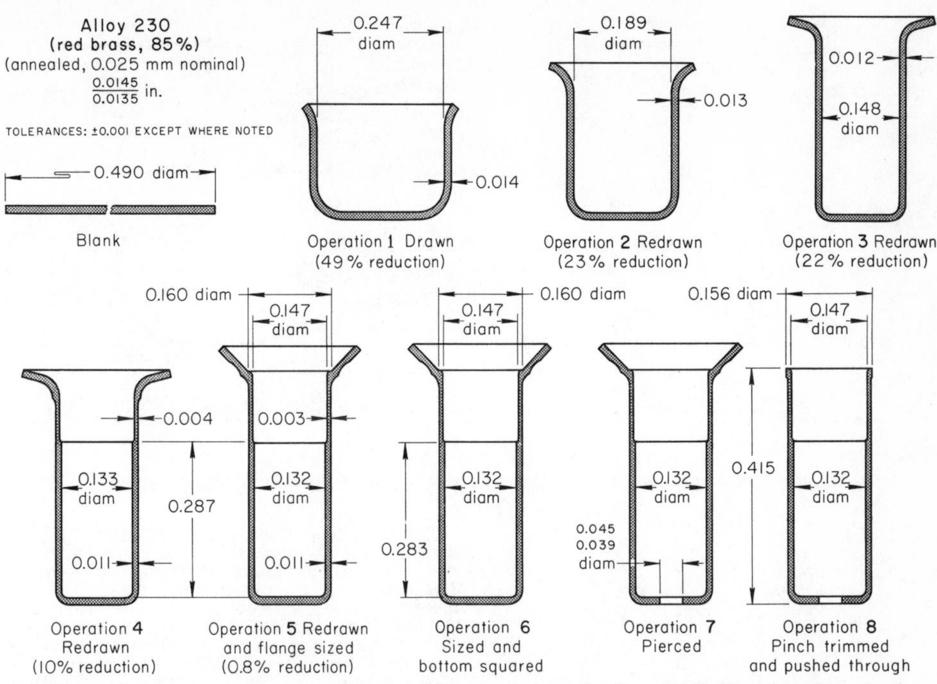

Fig. 23. Progression of shapes in the eight-operation production (including five draws) of a stepped-wall housing in an automatic transfer press (Example 589)

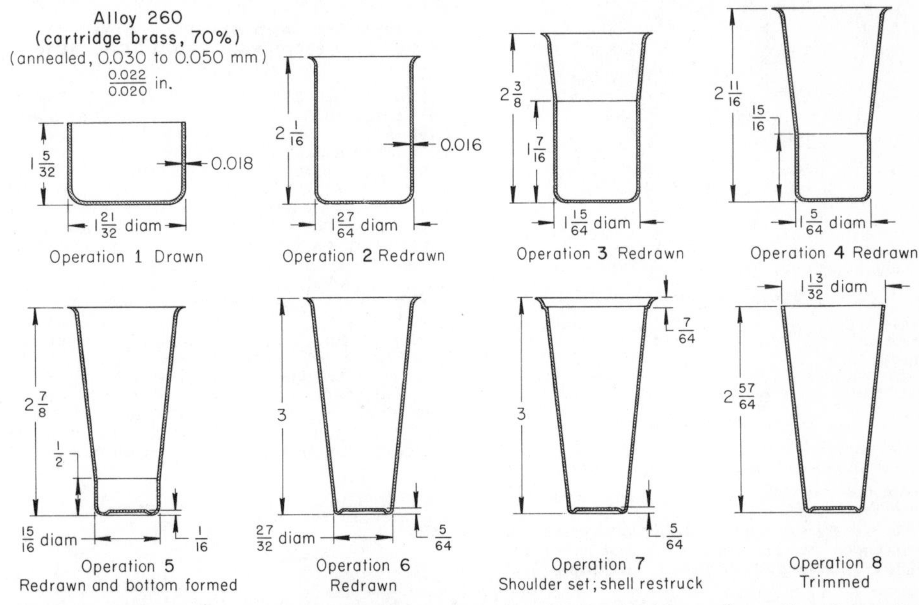

Fig. 24. Production of a tapered ferrule by deep drawing in eight operations. Cup drawn in operation 1 was annealed before being redrawn. (Example 590)

Example 590. Deep Drawing a Tapered Shell With Intermediate Annealing (Fig. 24)

The eight stages in the deep drawing of a tapered ferrule from a 3.384-in.-diam blank of 0.022/0.020-in.-thick coiled strip are shown in Fig. 24. The work metal was annealed alloy 260 (cartridge brass, 70%), having a grain size of 0.030 to 0.050 mm, a minimum elongation of 52% and a minimum tensile strength of 46,000 psi. Alloy 260 was selected because of its deep drawing characteristics and for longer tool life. A smooth surface finish, free from draw marks, was required.

Blanking and cupping were done in a 55-ton double-action mechanical press with a 2.5-in. blankholder stroke and a 5-in. punch stroke. In cupping, the blank was reduced 52%, and the sidewall was ironed to a thickness of 0.018 in. As much of the necessary work as possible was done on the workpiece before annealing in order to minimize work hardening in subsequent operations. After annealing to a grain size of 0.020 to 0.040 mm, the cups were pickled and washed.

The seven remaining operations (Fig. 24) were done in a multiple-station horizontal transfer press with a capacity of 6 tons per station and a 14-in. stroke. In the straight redraw (operation 2 in Fig. 24), the diameter was reduced 14% (almost to final top diameter) and the wall thickness was ironed 0.002 in. to the finished thickness of 0.016 in. Maximum reductions in the four taper draws that followed were 13%, 13%, 13% and 10%, producing a smooth profile.

Punch sleeves were used for alignment on the first three taper draws. The dies of highly polished and chromium plated W1 tool steel (Rockwell C 60 to 62) gave an average life of 30,000 pieces before plating. To avoid rings on the finished part, tool clearance was controlled closely at 0.018 in. for cupping and at 0.014 in. for redrawing and tapering.

Water-base lubricants, mixed 1-to-30 with water, were used. For the relatively severe cupping operation, the lubricant consisted of a diluted soap-plus-fat paste (No. 6 in Table 5); for the less severe redraws, an emulsion of soluble oils (No. 4 in Table 5).

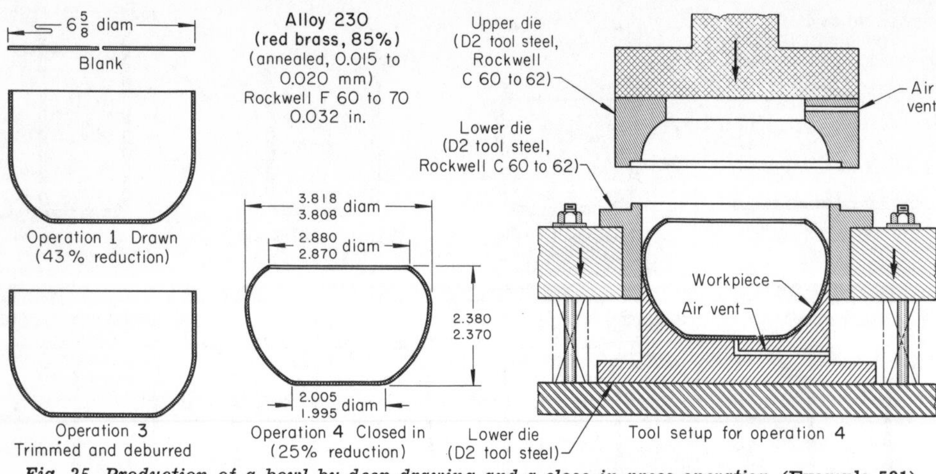

Fig. 25. Production of a bowl by deep drawing and a close-in press operation (Example 591)

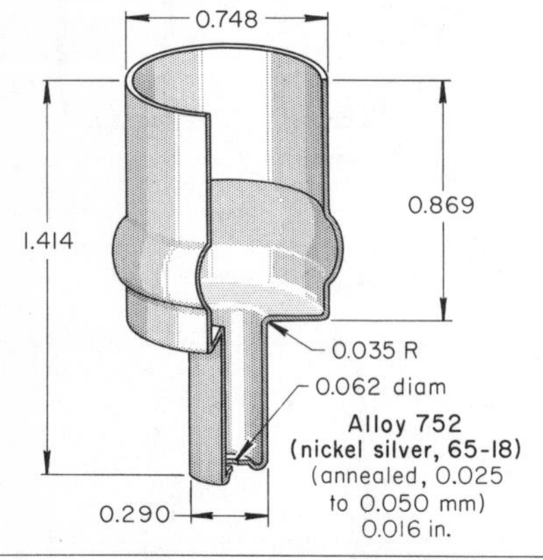

Sequence of Operations

1	Cup	5 to 8	Four redraws
2	Bright anneal	9	Bright anneal
3	First redraw	10 to 14	Five redraws
4	Bright anneal	15	Pierce and trim

Operating Conditions

Press type	Mechanical
Press capacity	22 to 40 tons
Setup time	2 hr
Production rate	1140 to 4860 pieces per hour
Tool life	250,000 pieces

Costs per 1000 Pieces

Material (17.4 lb per 1000 pieces)	$18.90
Labor plus overhead	5.60
Total cost per 1000 pieces	$24.50

Fig. 26. Nickel silver synchro-converter case that was produced in 11 drawing operations with intermediate anneals (Example 592)

Example 591. Production of a Sugar Bowl From Alloy 230 (Red Brass, 85%) by Deep Drawing and a Close-In Press Operation (Fig. 25)

The brass sugar bowl shown in Fig. 25 was produced in quantities of 5000 from alloy 230. This alloy was chosen for its color, redrawing capacity and ease of finishing.

The annealed blank, 6⅝ in. in diameter and 0.032 in. thick, had a grain size of 0.015 to 0.020 mm and a hardness of Rockwell F 60 to 70.

The single deep draw for a 43% reduction was designed to maintain the uniform wall thickness required for the subsequent close-in and to maintain a smooth finish. Draw-die radius was four to eight times the stock thickness. After the part was washed with an amine soap in a wetting agent, the top edge of the part was trimmed and deburred on a lathe, to control height to ±0.005 in. and to avoid edge irregularities that might cause buckling of the sidewalls during the close-in.

Reduction in diameter during the close-in was a maximum of 25%. This technique produced the final shape with a minimum of grain breakdown or orange peel, and gave a bright finish when the bowl was buffed. The die for the close-in operation was made in two sections, as shown in Fig. 25.

The drawing tools were mounted on an elevated die shoe, so that the parts could be handled without being scratched or dented. The tools were repolished after making 10,000 pieces. A No. 7 water-base lubricant (see Table 5) was applied by dipping for the drawing operation and was then removed. For the close-in operation, a lard-oil lubricant was used, applied by hand. Hourly production rates for the four operations were: drawing, 345 pieces; washing, 800 pieces; trimming and deburring, 220 pieces; closing-in, 300 pieces.

Example 592. Deep Drawing a Small Complex Part From Thin Nickel Silver Strip (Fig. 26)

The synchro-converter case shown in Fig. 26 was deep drawn from an annealed blank, 1.789 in. in diameter by 0.016 in. thick, of alloy 752 (nickel silver, 65-18) in 11 drawing operations, using three intermediate anneals. Grain size of the starting material was 0.025 to 0.050 mm. Alloy 752 was specified because it is one of the most ductile of the nickel silvers and has about the same redrawing capacity as the intermediate brasses. However, it is more restricted in depth of a single draw.

The parts were produced in lots of about 50,000 pieces to an accuracy of ±0.0015 to ±0.005 in. and a surface finish of 16 micro-in.

Tools for all operations were made of W1 tool steel hardened to Rockwell C 58 to 60. The lubricant used was water-base No. 6 (see Table 5); it was applied by immersion before cupping and redrawing, and was removed by hot water before each anneal.

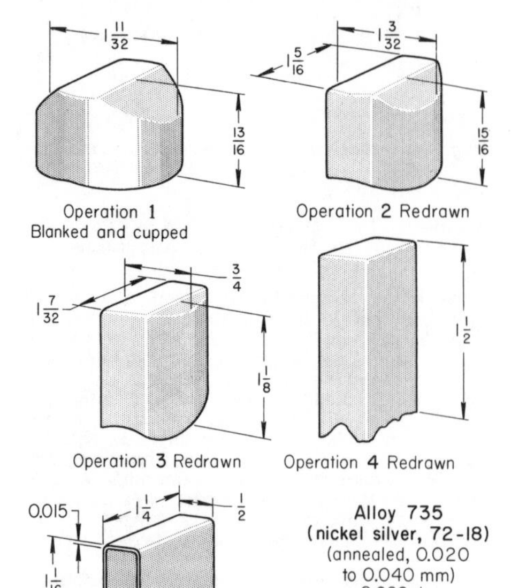

Fig. 27. Progression of shapes in five-operation production of a relay body by deep drawing and trimming. Workpiece was annealed before each redraw. (Example 593)

Additional production details are given in the table that accompanies Fig. 26.

Example 593. Forming a Rectangular Box From Nickel Silver in Four Draws, With Intermediate Anneals (Fig. 27)

A relay body was produced from 0.022-in.-thick alloy 735 (nickel silver, 72-18) in four drawing operations, as shown in Fig. 27. The strip had an initial grain size of 0.020 to 0.040 mm and was bright annealed to this grain size and cleaned before each redraw.

This alloy was selected for its strength and excellent finishing characteristics. It has an elongation of 37 to 41% as annealed, and has about the same rate of work hardening as the intermediate brasses.

The first operation was to blank and cup in a 55-ton double-action mechanical press with a 2.5-in. blankholder stroke and a 5-in. punch stroke. The end of the round cupping punch was ground to the approximate shape of the bottom of the finished shell, to avoid excess material that could cause wrinkles in later draws.

Redrawing was done in a vertical mechanical press rated at 30 tons and with a 10-in. stroke. Wall thickness was not reduced in the first redraw, in which the workpiece was drawn through an elliptical die to prevent gathering of metal in the corners. The second redraw produced a flattened oval shape and reduced the wall thickness to a minimum of 0.017 in. The final shape was produced in the third redraw, with a reduction of sidewall thickness to 0.015 in.; the shell was then cut to length in an oscillating trim die.

The redrawing dies, except for the final die, were made of S1 tool steel hardened to Rockwell C 54 to 56 and plated with 0.0002 in. of chromium. The final die was made of tungsten carbide. Tool life averaged 100,000 pieces for the tool steel dies and 250,000 pieces for the carbide die, when used with a No. 6 water-base lubricant for cupping and a No. 4 water-base for the redraws (see Table 5).

Effect of Cost on Selection of Method or Tool Material. When other production methods are available, the choice is usually made primarily on the basis of cost. The three examples that follow illustrate the effect of cost on the selection of method and equipment.

Example 594. Deep Drawing vs Machining of Alloy 230 (Red Brass, 85%) (Fig. 28)

Originally, the part shown in Fig. 28 (a plunger used to actuate the switch of a small flashlight) was machined from half-hard alloy 230 (red brass, 85%) wire in an automatic bar machine. Turnings accounted for over 90% of the material.

By changing to deep drawing, substantial savings resulted. As shown in the table with Fig. 28, the part was formed in an eyelet press from alloy 230 coiled strip (special non-earing grade produced by careful rolling and annealing). Red brass was desired for its rich color when lacquered and for its workability.

Sequence of operations consisted of blanking, cupping, six drawing passes, clipping and piercing with a side piercing attachment. As indicated in Fig. 28, deep drawing saved more than 84% in weight of material and produced parts at 10 times the machining rate.

Example 595. Carbide Inserts vs Solid Tool Steel Inserts for Cupping

Cartridge-case blanks for 7.62-mm ammunition were cupped and ironed in a 150-ton double-action cam press, before annealing and redrawing. Production rate was 48,000 pieces per hour for an annual production of about 154 million pieces. The starting material was 8.84-in.-wide by 0.166-in.-thick strip of alloy 260 (cartridge brass, 70%), annealed to a grain size of 0.050 to 0.100 mm.

By changing from water-hardening, chromium-plated tool steel to carbide inserts for cupping and ironing, tool life was increased from 275,000 to 1,600,000 pieces per grind. The change also resulted in a reduction in cost for regrinding tools, from $35 to $10, so that for every ten million pieces produced, tool-maintenance cost dropped from $1300 to $63.

The initial cost of about $90 for a chromium-plated tool steel die was increased by only $125 for carbide inserts. This added cost was recovered quickly by the savings in tool-maintenance cost; production rate was increased to 60,000 pieces per hour, and efficiency of press utilization was increased.

Example 596. Use of Carbide Drawing Tools That Avoided Costly Finishing Operations (Fig. 29)

Carbide tools were used for drawing the alloy 110 (ETP copper) cup shown in Fig. 29, to reduce over-all cost by eliminating the need for expensive finishing operations. A No. 7 water-base lubricant (see Table 5) was used.

Wall thickness was reduced about 13% in the second draw, producing a highly burnished finish that could be polished readily to a mirror finish for silver plating. Additional processing details are given in the table with Fig. 29. Yearly production rate was 300,000 pieces, in lots averaging 20,000 pieces.

Spinning

Nearly all commercial copper alloys can be formed by manual or power spinning, using the equipment, tooling and techniques described in the article "Spinning", in this volume.

Spinnability of Alloys. The rate of work hardening or the redrawing capacity of copper alloys (as shown in Fig. 22) is an approximate guide to their suitability for spinning, a low rate of work hardening being preferred. The correlation with deep drawing behavior is reasonably close, because the type and degree of deformation in the two processes are similar. A more accurate criterion of capacity for severe deformation by spinning (except for multiphase alloys) is a high reduction of area in the tension test, even after high drawing reductions (see Fig. 3).

Empirical spinnability tests, as described on page 207, have shown that metals that can undergo a 45% reduction of area in the tension test before failure can usually be reduced about 80% in thickness by spinning.

Tough pitch copper (alloy 110, ETP) is easier to spin than any of the copper alloys and usually does not require intermediate annealing. Brasses, except for Muntz metal (a multiphase alloy), are readily spun, although the harder ones sometimes require intermediate annealing. Tin brasses containing at least 87% copper require higher spinning pressure and more frequent annealing than brasses. Nickel silvers that contain at least 65% copper, as well as the copper nickels, are also well suited for spinning. Phosphor bronzes, aluminum bronzes and silicon bronzes are hard to spin, but can be spun into shallow shapes under favorable conditions.

Copper alloys not suited for spinning include Muntz metal, nickel silvers containing 55% or less copper, beryllium coppers, alloys containing more than about 0.5% lead, naval brass, and other multiphase alloys.

The single-phase high-strength copper alloys may be heated for spinning, to reduce the force required, to permit the spinning of thicker material, or to permit more severe deformation, provided the increased cost for heating is justified. The forming characteristics of Muntz metal, extra-high-leaded brass, and naval brass are also improved at elevated temperature, but special precautions must be taken to avoid even unintentional heating of the workpiece in spinning brasses that contain 0.5% or more lead and more than 64% copper.

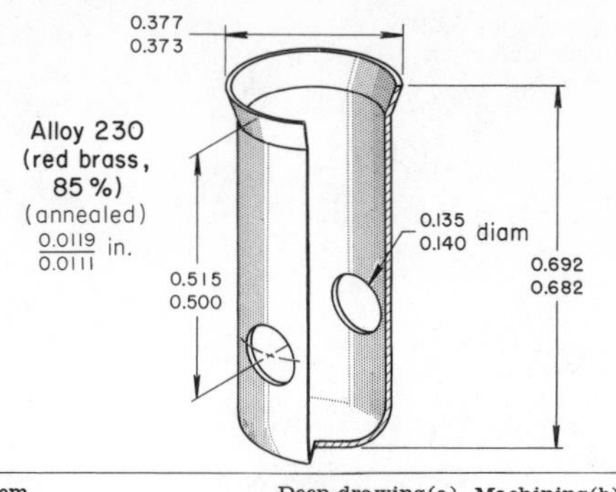

Item	Deep drawing(a)	Machining(b)
Work-Metal Details		
Type	Coiled strip(c)	Wire(d)
Size, in.	1³⁄₃₂ by 0.0115	⅜ diam
Weight per 1000 pcs, lb:		
Gross	4.43	28.30
Net	2.40	2.50
Operating Conditions		
Setup time, hr	10 to 14	3 to 4
Tool life (max), pcs	1 million	200,000
Production, pcs/hr	5000	500

(a) In an eyelet press. (b) In an automatic bar machine. (c) Annealed; grain size, 0.015 to 0.035 mm. (d) Half hard.

Fig. 28. Small brass part that was produced faster and with less material by deep drawing than by machining (Example 594)

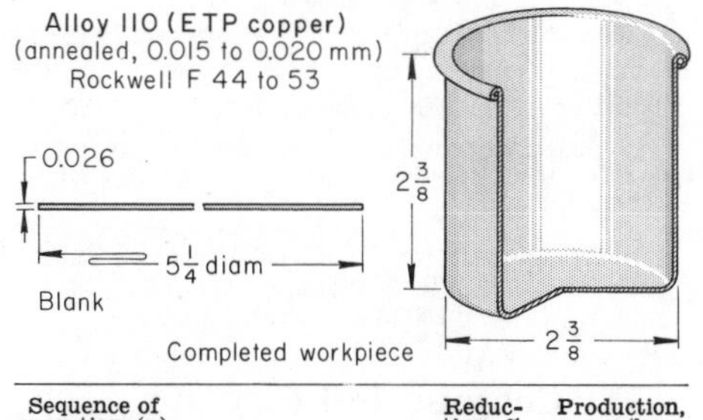

Sequence of operations(a)	Reduction, %	Production, pcs/hr
1 Blank and draw	40	400
2 Redraw	24	400
3 Wash	...	800
4 Lathe trim	...	650
5 Curl	...	600

(a) One operator did both operations 1 and 2.

Fig. 29. Cup that was drawn with tools made of carbide in preference to tool steel, to eliminate expensive finishing operations (Example 596)

Temper. Annealed tempers are almost always used in spinning copper alloys. Table 3 gives an approximate guide to the selection of tempers for spinning some of the more commonly used copper alloys in various thicknesses. Larger grain sizes (lower hardness) than those shown in Table 3 are easier to spin; finer grain sizes may be needed to meet surface-finish requirements.

Although stock as thin as 0.004 in. can be hand spun under special conditions, manual spinning is usually restricted to thicknesses of 0.020 to 0.250 in., with powered equipment being used in the upper part of this range.

Thicker stock is power spun, and thicknesses in excess of 1 in. can be shaped by hot power spinning.

Operating Conditions. Surface speed in spinning is usually in the range of 1000 to 2000 sfm and is rarely less than about 400 sfm. Feed is ordinarily about 0.010 to 0.080 in. per revolution or 1.5 to 6 in. per minute, depending on the material and on requirements of surface finish and dimensional accuracy.

Lubrication is normally required for spinning; the materials used are listed in the last two groups in Table 5. Particular attention must be paid to avoiding unacceptable tarnishing or chemical attack by active lubricants, and spun articles sometimes must be washed shortly after spinning to remove lubricant residues. For cold power spinning under high pressure, a water-base coolant may be required in addition to an adherent lubricant (see the section on Lubrication in this article).

Applications. Typical products spun from copper alloys include bell-mouth shapes for musical instruments, lighting-fixture components, vases, tumblers, decorative articles, pressure-vessel parts, and other circular parts with bulged or recessed contours.

Spinning is sometimes combined with preliminary deep drawing operations to produce bulged or concave contours in round shells, as shown in the two examples that follow.

Example 597. Production of a Copper Body for a Water Pitcher by Deep Drawing and Spinning (Fig. 30)

The water-pitcher body shown in Fig. 30 was produced from 13½-in.-diam by 0.036-in.-thick annealed blanks of alloy 110 (ETP cop-

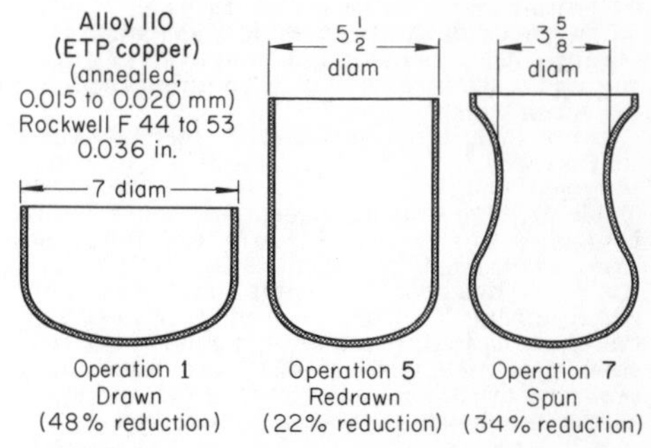

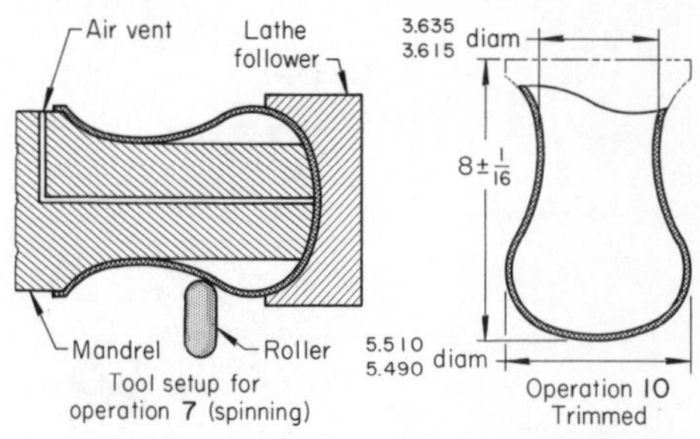

Sequence of operations	Production, pcs/hr(a)
1 Draw(b)	250
2 Wash	400
3 Anneal at 950 F	200
4 Pickle	200
5 Redraw(b)	200
6 Wash	400
7 Manual spin(c)	17
8 Emery polish, automatic	65
9 Buff, automatic	75
10 Chop trim	110

(a) Typical production run was 1000 pieces. (b) Dies were of D2 tool steel, hardened to Rockwell C 60 to 62, and ground and polished to a finish of 5 to 8 micro-in. Lubricant was a No. 7 water-base type (see Table 5). The radius on the draw dies was four to eight times the stock thickness. The tools were polished after 5000 pieces.

(c) Using a D2 tool steel roller (1-in. nose radius) at 1000 to 1200 sfm. No lubricant was used. The mandrel was made from A2 tool steel. Spinning tools were hardened to Rockwell C 60 to 62 and polished to 5 micro-in.

Fig. 30. Water-pitcher body that was produced in ten operations by deep drawing and manual spinning (Example 597)

per) having a grain size of 0.015 to 0.020 mm and a hardness of Rockwell F 44 to 53.

The straight-sided shell, which was drawn in two operations, was annealed before the second draw, and the part was formed to its final shape in a manual spinning lathe (see Fig. 30). The lower portion of the sidewall of the pitcher body was free-formed, while the upper portion was shaped to conform with the mandrel.

For the intended use of the part, the comparatively low strength of pure copper was satisfactory; copper was preferred to brass because its low rate of work hardening permitted a 34% reduction in diameter by spinning without the need for annealing the shell after the second draw.

Special precautions were taken in the drawing operations to avoid damaging the surface of the part, because it was to be buffed to a mirror finish and silver plated. The dies were polished to a finish of 5 to 8 micro-in., and the part was ejected from the top of the redraw die to avoid damage in handling. The finish of the drawn shell was improved by the planishing action of the spinning tool and by subsequent automatic polishing with emery and buffing. Additional processing details are given in the table with Fig. 30.

Example 598. Use of Drawing and Spinning to Produce a Thin-Wall Flared Pillar (Fig. 31)

The thin-wall flared pillar shown in Fig. 31 was made from a 7¾-in.-diam by 0.032-in.-thick blank of alloy 220 (commercial bronze, 90%) by deep drawing and manual spinning. Annealed blanks, with a grain size of 0.010 to 0.020 mm and a hardness of Rockwell F 70 to 75, were used. With them it was possible to obtain a 50% reduction in diameter in drawing and a 32% reduction in spinning, without an intermediate anneal.

Draw tools were of D2 tool steel hardened to Rockwell C 60 to 62 and polished to 5 to 7 micro-in. Lubricant was No. 7 water-base (see Table 5). The drawing operation was carefully controlled to maintain uniform wall thickness. The drawn shell was about ½ in. shorter than the final height of the pillar and was elongated during the first spinning passes. The two-piece spinning mandrel, made of A2 tool steel (Rockwell C 60 to 62), was designed to separate at the minor diameter of the spun shape, as shown in Fig. 31.

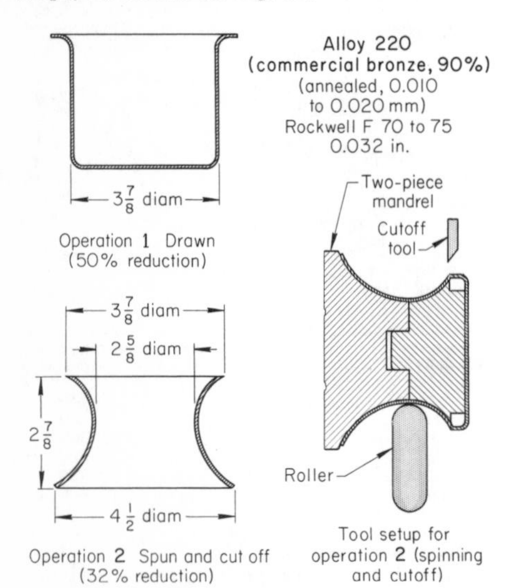

Fig. 31. Flared pillar that was produced in two operations by deep drawing and manual spinning (Example 598)

Before spinning, the part was washed with amine soap in a wetting agent. The spinning roller had a nose diameter about 25% of the mean diameter of the pillar, which reduced the shell diameter by about ⅛ in. in each pass at a speed of 1000 to 1200 sfm. A rough cutoff at the point of corner relief on the spinning chuck enabled the dismantling of the chuck and the removal of the spun workpiece, which was then lathe trimmed to its final height with a cutoff tool.

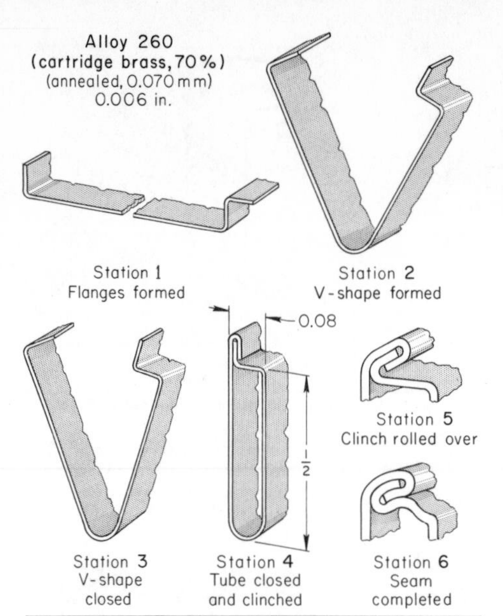

Processing Details

Machine	Automatic contour roll former
Roll material	D2 tool steel
Setup time	4 hr
Lubricant	Soluble oil
Tool life per grind	2 million pieces
Production rate	6860 pieces per hour(a)

Costs per 1000 Pieces

Material	$23.70
Labor	1.05
Total cost per 1000 pieces	$24.75

(a) Based on continuous production at 200 ft per min, with formed tube cut to length of 21 in. per piece.

Fig. 32. Production of a radiator-core tube by contour roll forming in six stations (Example 599)

Contour Roll Forming

Copper alloys are well suited for fabrication by contour roll forming. The techniques and equipment that are used on other metals, particularly low-carbon steel and aluminum alloys, can be used also on copper alloys (see the article on Contour Roll Forming, beginning on page 224 in this volume).

Alloy and Temper. The bendability ratings given in Table 1 provide an index of the relative suitability of the commonly used copper alloys for contour roll forming. Generally, alloys with ratings of less than 60 should not be selected for applications that require contour roll forming, although they can be formed in this way under favorable conditions — if the contour that is to be roll formed is not very severe.

Annealed tempers are needed for complicated shapes and extremely sharp bends that require severe forming. (See Table 3 for an approximate guide to the selection of annealed tempers of commonly used copper alloys in various thicknesses.)

To meet strength or rigidity requirements on simple shapes, such as angles and channels that do not have sharp radii, the tempers at the softer end of the scale of rolled (hard) tempers (see Table 2) are sometimes used.

Capabilities. Roll forming is basically a high-production process, operating at average linear speeds of about 80 to 100 ft per min. Machines are available that can handle extreme lengths and a wide range of stock thicknesses and widths and that are capable of producing varied and complex shapes.

Close tolerances on contour and dimensions, as well as excellent surface finish, are characteristic of the process. Auxiliary operations such as notching, slotting, punching and embossing can readily be combined with contour roll forming.

Minimum bend radii can be approximately half the normal values (see Fig. 7). Springback is counteracted by a gradual, stepwise decrease in radius as the strip passes through the machine, and by overforming at one of the final stations.

Limitations. Costs for equipment and tooling are high, and extremely close tolerances must be maintained on tool dimensions. Part design is limited to shapes having a uniform cross section.

Galling can readily occur in contour roll forming of copper and the lower-strength copper alloys at annealed tempers; to prevent galling, a high polish on the tools and effective lubrication are required.

Tooling. The design of rolls and related equipment and the selection of tool materials are discussed in the article "Contour Roll Forming" in this volume.

Lubricants. A lubricant from among the water-base compounds listed in Table 5 for the first two categories of forming operations is ordinarily used in contour roll forming of copper alloys, depending on the severity and speed of the operation. The work and rolls are often flooded with the lubricant, which also acts as a coolant.

Applications. Contour roll forming is used less extensively with copper alloys than with steel and aluminum alloys, because fewer copper alloy parts of suitable shapes and sizes are produced in large volume. Applications are mainly in the automotive and architectural industries.

The following example illustrates a high-production application of roll forming.

Example 599. Six-Station Roll Forming of a Radiator Tube (Fig. 32)

A core tube for an industrial radiator was roll formed in six stations, as shown in Fig. 32, from annealed alloy 260 (cartridge brass, 70%) coiled strip 0.006 in. thick. This application required excellent formability, moderate strength, good solderability and outstanding corrosion resistance.

Coil material of the desired width was formed into tube, dip soldered, and cut to length in one continuous sequence of operations. Production rate was 200 ft per min, or about one million parts, 21 in. long, per month per machine. To maintain this production rate, accumulators were used to permit the changing of coils without interrupting the operation. Additional processing and cost details are given in the table with Fig. 32.

Rubber-Pad Forming

Copper alloys are sometimes shaped or drawn by several related techniques that are classified as rubber-pad forming methods; these are described in the article "Rubber-Pad Forming", in this volume. The most important reasons for using rubber-pad forming in preference to conventional press techniques or other production methods are improved formability, low die costs and freedom from marring of workpiece surfaces.

In this process, the rubber pad usually serves as the female die, in conjunction with an inexpensive male punch. The pad is practically incompressible and transmits pressure in all directions in the same manner as hydraulic fluid. Selection of alloy and temper follows the same principles as for deep drawing with rigid dies. Rubber diaphragm forming uses hydraulic fluid behind the rubber pad.

Deep drawing by rubber-diaphragm or Marforming techniques often permits a 65% reduction of diameter in a single draw, without producing wrinkles or surface defects that could require expensive finishing operations. The following example illustrates the simplification of production procedures and reduction in cost for the rubber-diaphragm forming of copper, compared with conventional deep drawing with metal dies.

Example 600. Rubber-Diaphragm Forming vs Deep Drawing of Copper (Fig. 33)

The copper body for a coffee urn shown in Fig. 33 was produced by rubber-diaphragm forming in a single draw, in preference to multistage deep drawing with rigid dies. Three draws, one drop form and two anneal-and-pickle operations (see table with Fig. 33) were eliminated by using rubber-diaphragm forming. This was made possible by the higher formability that resulted from the multidirectional forming forces of the rubber diaphragm, the gradual increase in forming pressure and decrease in forming radius during the draw, and the absence of high local strains.

Tool and setup costs of rubber-diaphragm forming were about $1300 less than for conventional deep drawing. Also, in spite of a lower production rate for the single rubber-diaphragm drawing operation, the total production time per piece was 0.03055 hr, or about 20% less than the 0.0388 hr for drawing with rigid dies. Additional savings resulted from the freedom from wrinkles or surface defects in the drawn parts, which reduced the cost of subsequent finishing operations.

Hydraulic Forming

Copper alloys are sometimes formed by applying direct hydraulic pressure against the surface of the workpiece, which shapes the workpiece against a rigid die. The forming of grooves on large, thin flat sheets and the shaping of small parts to irregular contours can be done conveniently this way. Tool cost is low, but the method is ordinarily applicable only to small-lot production, because of comparatively low production rates.

The example that follows illustrates the production of an irregularly shaped small part by hydraulic forming.

Example 601. Use of Direct Hydraulic Forming in the Production of a Bellows From Tubing (Fig. 34)

Direct hydraulic forming was the first stage in making a bellows from ½-in.-OD alloy 510 (phosphor bronze, 5% – grade A) tube. The tube was bulged to conform to the shape of the die inserts (top view in Fig. 34) by internal water pressure. Axial pressure was exerted on the workpiece by an end ram, collapsing the material at the same time as it was expanded, to minimize thinning of the wall. Die inserts were of D2 tool steel; die wear was negligible.

The bulged part was then compressed axially to the final shape of the bellows (bottom view in Fig. 34). The production rate for this part, which was one of several similar parts produced by this method, was 500 pieces per hour. Typical lot size for parts of this type was about 4000 to 5000 pieces, for a total annual production of about six million of the various sizes of similar parts.

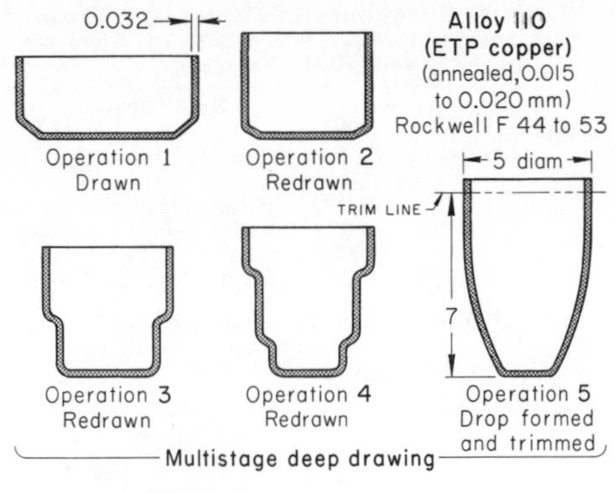

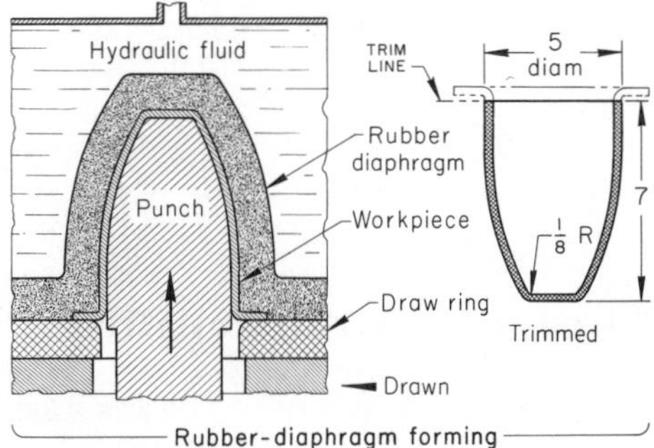

Sequence of operations	Pieces per hr
Multistage Deep Drawing	
Cup	250
Second draw	200
Anneal and pickle	210
Third draw	215
Fourth draw	250
Anneal and pickle	210
Drop form	165
Trim	180
Rubber-Diaphragm Forming	
Draw	40
Trim	180

Cost Details:	Tools	Setup
Deep drawing	$1696(a)	$38.60(b)
Rubber-diaphragm forming	$365(c)	$3.00(d)

(a) Deep-drawing tools were made of D2 tool steel; lubricant was No. 7 water-base type (see Table 5). (b) Five setups required. (c) Tools for rubber-diaphragm forming were made of A2 tool steel; lubricant was No. 8 oil-base type (see Table 5). (d) One setup required.

Fig. 33. Multistage deep drawing versus rubber-diaphragm forming (Example 600)

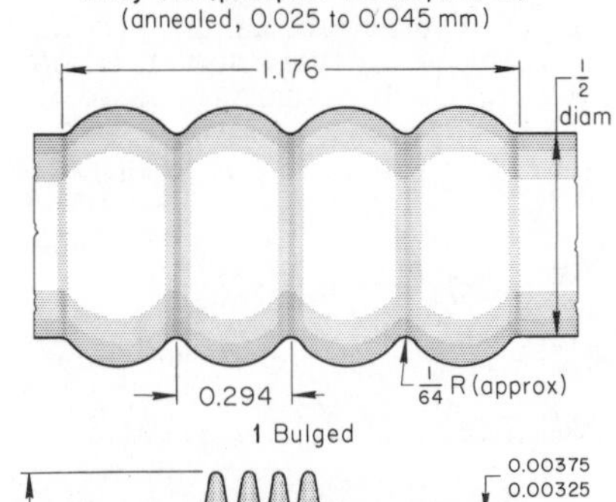

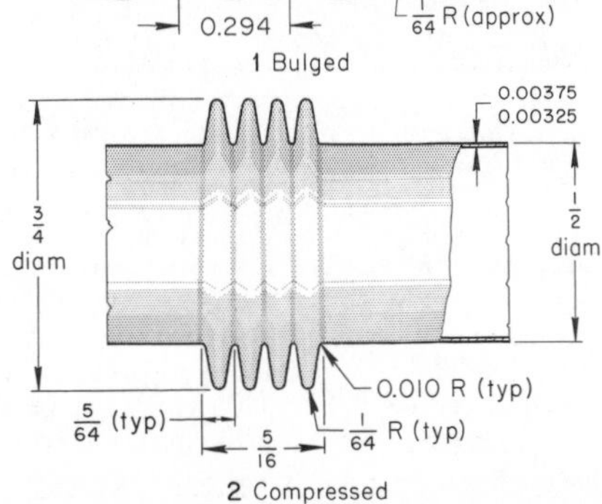

Fig. 34. Bellows formed by hydraulic bulging and axial compression (Example 601)

Coining

Copper alloys are frequently coined. The wide variety of parts coined includes medallions, buttons, coins, flatware, vanity cases, jewelry, key blanks, handles, nuts, rivets, washers, cover plates, nameplates, gear blanks, and electronic and small automotive components. For a detailed discussion of coining, and seven examples on copper (note tabulation below), see the article that begins on page 78.

Alloy and Temper. Coining, which is the most severe of the compressive cold forming operations, is applied mostly to the alloys with the lowest rate of work hardening or the highest capacity for redrawing, as indicated in Fig. 22. This includes, in order of decreasing formability, copper and brasses up to alloy 260 (cartridge brass, 70%). Nickel silvers that contain 65% copper, and copper nickels, can also be coined, but closer control of the forming conditions is required for these alloys, including close correlation between volume of metal and size of die cavity.

Annealed tempers are ordinarily required for coining (see Table 3), but the material is sometimes supplied in a hard temper for ease of blanking and is then annealed before coining.

Lubricants. Although the use of lubricants is generally avoided when possible in coining, particularly if a smooth finish and the reproduction of intricate detail are required, some lubrication is usually needed on copper alloys. For decorative items, the lubricant may be a water-base or oil-base type selected from the first or the second groups listed in Table 5, depending on the alloy and the amount of metal movement or the coining pressure. If a heavy-duty lubricant must be used, a nonpigmented type such as those listed in the third or the fourth groups contained in Table 5 is preferred, to avoid buildup on the die surfaces, which could cause a loss of definition.

Applications of coining of copper alloys are described in the article "Coining", which begins on page 78 in this volume. The following examples in that article describe methods of coining the products and alloys noted:

Product and alloy	Example No.
Fasteners, alloy 226(a)	70, 79, 81
Teaspoon, alloy 757(b)	90
Emblem, alloy 752(c)	95
Knife handle, alloy 757(b)	75
Small brass part, alloy 268(d)	91

(a) Jewelry bronze, 87.5%. (b) Nickel silver, 65-12. (c) Nickel silver, 65-18. (d) Yellow brass.

Stamping and swaging, which are closely related to coining (being compressive or squeezing operations), are also used frequently in the cold forming of copper alloys. The principles of alloy selection described for coining apply equally to stamping and swaging. However, stamping (impressing letters, numerals or designs into one surface by displacing metal to either side) can be done on any copper alloy, with special attention to tooling and selection of temper on the less formable alloys. Swaging is often used for the production of complicated electrical contacts from copper or brass.

Electromagnetic Forming

Electromagnetic forming has a number of important applications to copper and some brasses, because of the high electrical conductivity and excellent formability of these metals. The process is described in the article "Electromagnetic Forming", which begins on page 256 in this volume.

Metals having a resistivity greater than about 16 microhm-cm are formed by the use of a copper or aluminum electromagnetic "driver", one to three times the thickness of the work metal. Thermally or electrically conductive joints, torque joints and structural joints are produced in a single forming operation. Field shapers are frequently used to concentrate the forming force.

Table 7. Dimensions of Copper and Brass Terminal Connections Made by Electromagnetic Swaging

	Copper insert		Brass terminal		
AWG No.	OD before swaging	Wall thickness, in.	Outside diameter	Inside diameter	Wall thickness, in.
8	0.250	0.030	0.250	0.209	0.020
10	0.190	0.025	0.250	0.170	0.040
12	0.190	0.030	0.250	0.170	0.040
14	0.190	0.043	0.250	0.170	0.040

Electrical connections are made by electromagnetically swaging a copper band onto the end of stranded electrical conductor wire before insertion into a brass terminal. Optimum conductivity with 100% mechanical strength and long life under severe service conditions are obtained by using swaging forces great enough to compact the strands of the conductor so that a cross section of the joint appears to be essentially solid copper. The dimensions used with stranded wires of different sizes are listed in Table 7. The outside dimensions of the brass terminals are standardized for the range of wire sizes shown. The difference in wire size is compensated for by changing the inside diameter of the terminal to fit the wire that is applied.

Forming of Magnesium Alloys

*By the ASM Committee on Fabrication of Magnesium**

THE PRINCIPAL DIFFERENCE between forming magnesium alloys and forming steel, aluminum and copper is forming temperature. Although some forming of magnesium alloys can be done at room temperature, elevated temperatures are used in most applications.

Cold Forming

Cold forming of magnesium alloys is restricted to mild deformation with a generous bend radius. Alloys AZ31B-O (special bending sheet) and LA141A-O are exceptions; they have much better room-temperature formability than most other magnesium alloys.

Bend Radii. Cylinders and cones can be formed from magnesium alloys at room temperature by using standard power rolls. Simple flanges can be press formed at room temperature. Table 1 gives minimum radii for fast bending at room temperature, as in a press brake. Slightly smaller bend radii than given in Table 1 may be used when forming speeds are slower, as in a hydraulic press, or when proved by trial, as in the following example.

Table 1. Recommended Minimum Bend Radii for Fast Forming at Room Temperature

Alloy and temper	Min bend radius	Alloy and temper	Min bend radius
Sheet(a) (0.020 to 0.249 in. thick)		**Extruded Flat Strip** (0.875 in. by 0.090 in. thick)	
AZ31B-O, special bending sheet	3.0t	AZ31C-F	2.4t
		AZ31B-F	2.4t
AZ31B-O	5.5t	AZ61A-F	1.9t
AZ31B-H24	8.0t	AZ80A-F	2.4t
HK31A-O	6.0t	AZ80A-T5	8.3t
HK31A-H24	13.0t	HM31A-T5	11.0t
HM21A-T8	9.0t	ZK21A-F	15.0t
HM21A-T81 ...	10.0t	ZK60A-F	12.0t
LA141A-O	3.0t	ZK60A-T5	12.0t
ZE10A-O	5.5t	t = work-metal thickness	
ZE10A-H24	8.0t		

(a) Minimum bend radii are based on bending a 6-in.-wide specimen through 90°.

Example 602. Change in Alloy Grade That Permitted Use of Cold Instead of Hot Forming of Small Radii (Fig. 1)

A corner plate, shown in Fig. 1, was originally formed from standard-grade AZ31B-O sheet, 0.064 in. thick, at 500 F. Bend radii were required not to exceed twice the sheet thickness. Blanks were oven heated, and the die was heated by torch. Temperature was measured by temperature-indicating crayons.

By changing to special bending grade AZ31B-O sheet, the plates could be bent to the specified radius without heating. As shown in Fig. 1, bends were made across, parallel with, and at 45° to the direction of rolling. Although bend radii were 33% less than recommended (see Table 1), several hundred parts were made without defects.

Surface Protection. In low-production cold forming, a common method of preventing surface damage is to apply tape to critical areas of the work metal and, if feasible, to tool surfaces. It is especially important to keep the die clean and free from particles of foreign metal that can become embedded in the surface of the workpiece and impair its corrosion resistance.

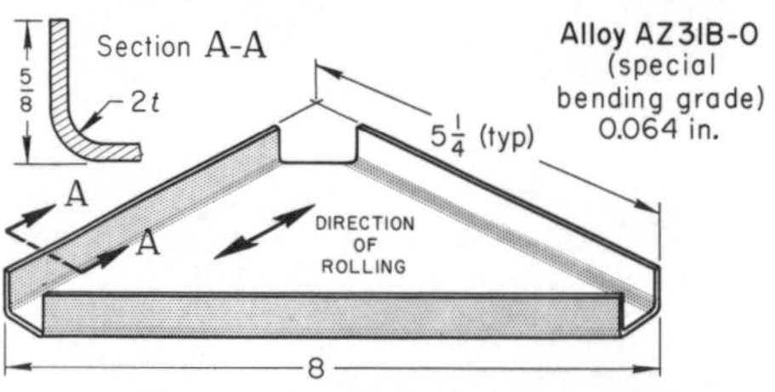

Fig. 1. Corner plate that was cold formed in a press brake to smaller than recommended bend radii (Example 602)

Table 2. Springback Allowances in Forming of 90° Bends in 0.016 to 0.064-In.-Thick Sheet

Forming temperature, F	Bend radius	Springback allowance for: AZ31B-O	AZ31B-H24
70	4t	8°	10°
	5t	11°	13°
	10t	17°	21°
	15t	25°	29°
200	3t	4°	5°
	5t	5°	7°
	10t	8°	12°
	15t	13°	17°
300	2t	1°	2°
	5t	3°	4°
	10t	5°	7°
	15t	8°	11°
450	2t	0°	0°
	5t	1°	1°
	10t	2°	2°
	15t	4°	4°
550	Up to 15t ..	0°	0°

t = thickness of sheet

Hard rubber inserts in dies are sometimes helpful in preventing damage to the work metal and in forming large radii. However, this practice is not recommended for high production, because the inserts wear rapidly, thus causing nonuniform workpieces.

Reworking of bends by straightening and rebending the same portion should not be done in cold forming, because metal fatigue can cause early failure.

*L. W. HUDSON, *Chairman,* Chief Metallurgist, Technical Service Dept., Goodyear Aerospace Corp.; ROBERT O. HUGHES, Supervisor of Production Engineering, AC Spark Plug Div., General Motors Corp.; C. E. LEHNHARDT, Contracts Manager, Aerospace America, Inc.

LLOYD F. LOCKWOOD, Metallurgical Laboratory, Metal Products Dept., Dow Chemical Co.; J. A. MALLEN, Materials Engineer, Materials and Components Engineering, Sperry Gyroscope Co. Div., Sperry Rand Corp.; EDWARD L. MOYER, Design Specialist, Lockheed-California Co.; JOHN R. POWERS, Section Head, Tool Engineering, Wheel and Brake Div., Goodyear Aerospace Corp.; STUART T. ROSS, Director of Engineering and Development, Wolverine Tube Div., Calumet & Hecla; FRANK SHEARA, Executive Vice President, Magnesium Elektron Inc.; V. M. TARDIFF, Project Engineer, Magline Inc.

GORDON VIVIAN, Chief Metallurgist, Outboard Marine Corp. of Canada Ltd.; ELLIOTT WILLNER, Specialist in Materials and Processes, Missiles and Space Co. Div., Lockheed Aircraft Corp.; J. P. YOUNG, Process and Equipment Engineering, Thomson Engineering Laboratory, Small Aircraft Engine Dept., General Electric Co.

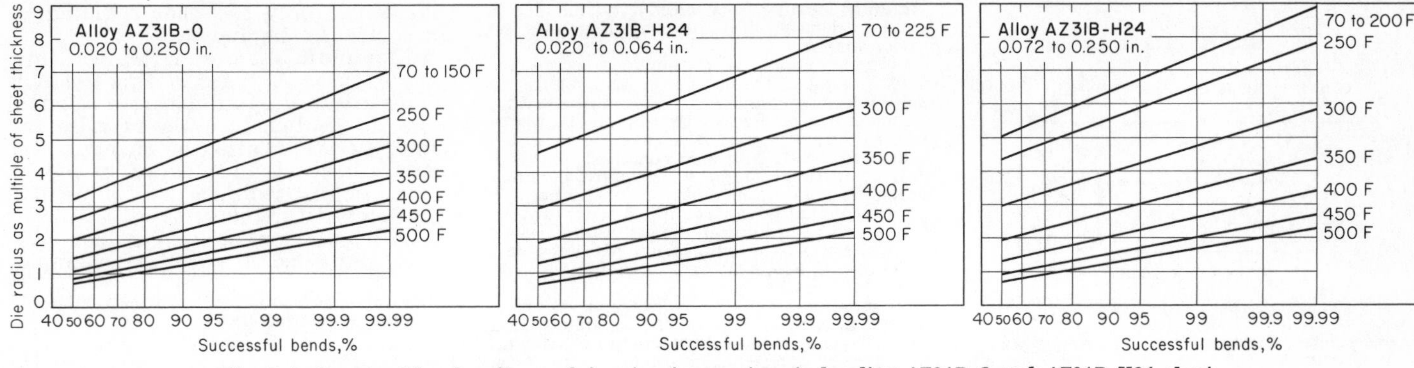

Fig. 2. Influence of bend radius and forming temperature in bending AZ31B-O and AZ31B-H24 sheet

Table 3. Temperature and Time at Temperature for Stress Relieving the Most Commonly Cold Formed Magnesium Alloys

Alloy and temper	Temp, F	Time, min	Alloy and temper	Temp, F	Time, min
Sheet			**Extruded Flat Strip**		
AZ31B-O	500	15	AZ31B-F, AZ61A-F, AZ80A-F	500	15
AZ31B-H24	300	60	AZ80A-T5	400	60
HK31A-H24	550	30	HM31A-T5	800	60
HM21A-T8, HM21A-T81(a)	700	30			

(a) 80 to 90% stress relief may be accomplished with a 30-min exposure at 750 F, but mechanical properties will be lower.

Springback can be as much as 30° for a 90° bend in cold forming of magnesium alloys. Springback allowances for alloy AZ31B sheet in two different tempers, and in thicknesses ranging from 0.016 to 0.064 in., are given in Table 2.

Effect of Bending on Length. Unlike aluminum alloys and steel, which lengthen in bending, magnesium alloys shorten, because the neutral axis moves slightly toward the tension side of the bend. For thin sheet, the extent of this shortening is small, because the axis shifts only 5 to 10%. However, in thicker sheet when several bends are made, the amount of shortening can be significant and must be allowed for in the development of the blank.

Stress Relieving. Magnesium-aluminum-zinc (AZ) alloys should be stress relieved after cold forming to prevent stress corrosion.

It may be desirable to stress relieve workpieces formed from the magnesium-thorium (HM, HK) alloys, particularly if they require straightening in fixtures. Recommended temperatures and times for stress relieving the magnesium alloys that are most commonly cold formed are given in Table 3.

Hot Forming

Magnesium alloys are hot formed at temperatures of 250 to 800 F. Tables 4 and 5 give minimum bend radii for forming magnesium alloys at various temperatures, and list minimum and maximum temperatures and total time of exposure to maximum temperatures. Total time, as shown in Tables 4 and 5, is the cumulative total of the time intervals during which the work is at the specified temperature for the particular alloy and temper. Exceeding the temperature-time relation usually reduces mechanical properties, thus increasing the probability that premature failure will occur in service.

Table 4. Minimum Bend Radii and Hot Forming Conditions for Sheet 0.020 to 0.249 In. Thick

Alloy and temper	Recommended minimum bend radius (t = sheet thickness) for forming at: 70 F	200 F	300 F	400 F	500 F	600 F	700 F	Minimum tempera-ture, F(a)	Maximum tempera-ture, F	Total time at maximum temperature, minutes(b)
AZ31B-O(c)	5.5t	5.5t	4t	3t	2t	..	..	250	550	60
AZ31B-H24(c)	8t	8t	6t	..	..	..	..	250	345	30
									300	60
HK31A-O	6t	6t	6t	5t	4t	3t	2t	400	750	60
HK31A-H24	13t	13t	13t	9t	8t	5t	3t	400	700	10
									650	60
HM21A-T8	9t	9t	9t	9t	9t	8t	6t	400	800	10
									750	60
HM21A-T81	10t	9t	9t	9t	9t	8t	6t	400	700	10
									650	60
LA141A-O	3t	2t	1t	..	..	..	..	..	300	60
ZE10A-O	5.5t	5.5t	4t	3t	2t	..	..	..	525	60
ZE10A-H24	8t	8t	6t	..	..	..	..	..	350	3
									300	60

(a) Alloy strength increases and ductility decreases sharply at forming temperatures lower than minimum. (b) Mechanical properties of completed parts are adversely affected if total time (including preheating, handling and press time) at maximum indicated temperature is exceeded. (c) AZ alloys formed at temperatures below the minimum hot forming temperature must be stress relieved.

Table 5. Minimum Bend Radii and Hot Forming Conditions for Extruded Flat Strip (a)

Alloy and temper	Minimum bend radius (t = strip thickness)	Minimum temperature, F(b)	Maximum temperature, F	Total time at maximum temperature, minutes(c)
AZ31C-F, AZ31B-F(d)	1.5t	250	550	60
AZ61A-F(d)	1.0t	400	550	60
AZ80A-F(d)	0.7t	285	550	30
AZ80A-T5(d)	1.7t	285	450	6
			380	60
ZK60A-F(e)	2.0t	300	550	30
ZK60A-T5(e)	6.6t	300	500	6
			400	30
HM31A-T5(e)	6.0t	550	800	60
			650	24 hr
ZK21A-F(e)	5.0t	300	600	30

(a) Applicable for 90° bends and for stretch forming. (b) Strength of the alloy increases and ductility decreases sharply at forming temperatures lower than minimum. (c) Mechanical properties of completed parts are adversely affected if total time (including preheating, handling and press time) at maximum indicated temperature is exceeded. (d) AZ alloys formed at temperatures below the minimum hot forming temperature must be stress relieved. (e) HM and ZK alloys should be stress relieved if straightening is required.

The forming temperatures given in Tables 4 and 5 can be exceeded and still produce satisfactory parts, as shown by Examples 604, 605, 606 and 607.

Bend radii smaller than the values suggested in Tables 4 and 5 can be used for some alloys, within the temperature and time restriction, if a slower-than-normal forming speed is used. Statistical data on 90° bends in AZ31B-O and AZ31B-H24 sheet formed at various temperatures and bend radii are plotted in the charts in Fig. 2.

Thermal Expansion. As shown in Table 6, magnesium alloys have a higher rate of thermal expansion than any other alloy listed, and more than twice that of steel. At 500 F, for example, each linear inch of magnesium alloy is 0.00692 in. greater than at room temperature (70 F), whereas each linear inch of steel at 500 F is only 0.00318 in. larger than at room temperature.

Therefore, when parts made of magnesium alloys are hot formed in tool steel or cast iron dies, the difference in the thermal expansion of the tool material and the work metal must be considered. The proper cold dimensions for the steel tools are calculated by multiplying the desired cold dimension of the magnesium alloy part by the appropriate dimensional factor shown in Table 7.

Table 6. Thermal Expansion of Four Metals Compared With Magnesium Alloys, in the Range From 70 to 750 F

Metal	Thermal expansion, micro-in./in./°F
Magnesium alloys	16.1
Zinc alloys	15.4
Aluminum alloys	14.4
Low-carbon steel	7.4
Cast iron (heat resistant)	6.8

Table 7. Dimensional Factors for Steel Dies Used in Hot Forming of Magnesium Alloys (a)

Forming temperature, F	Dimensional factor	Forming temperature, F	Dimensional factor
300	1.00187	600	1.00450
400	1.00270	700	1.00542
500	1.00359	800	1.00642

(a) To obtain the dimension of the steel die, multiply the desired workpiece dimension by the factor for the forming temperature to be used.

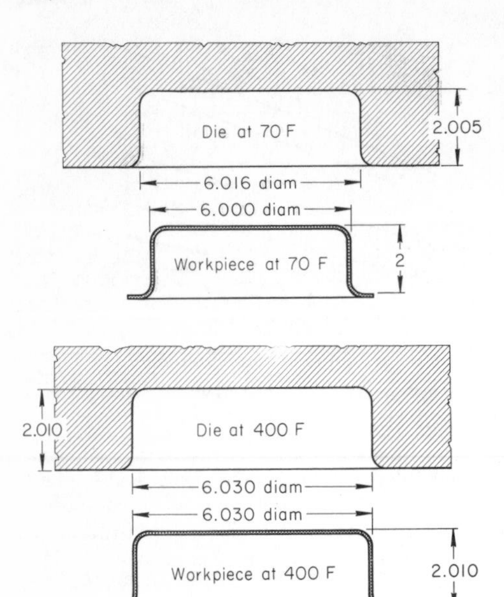

Room-temperature dimensions of steel die are found by multiplying design dimensions of magnesium alloy part by 1.00270, the factor indicated in Table 7 for forming at 400 F.

Fig. 3. Dimensional relations of a magnesium alloy workpiece and a steel die at room temperature, and at a forming temperature of 400 F

Figure 3 shows the relation between the size of a magnesium part and the size of a steel die at 70 F and at 400 F.

The dimensional factor need not be applied when the dies are made of zinc or aluminum alloys, because the coefficients of expansion of these alloys are similar to those of magnesium alloys.

Precautions. Magnesium alloy stock to be hot formed must be clean. Protective coatings, oil, dirt, moisture or other foreign matter must be removed.

Dies, punches and form blocks should be clean and free of scratches; tooling should be cleaned with solvent. Rust, scratches and minor imperfections can be removed by light polishing with fine-grit silicon abrasive cloth. Polishing must not alter the dimensions of the tool.

In forming, the possibility of fire due to ignition of magnesium is remote. However, an ample supply of suitable fire-extinguishing material, such as dry sand or proprietary powder, must be kept in the work area.

Methods of Heating

In most hot forming methods, both the tools and the magnesium alloy work metal must be heated. Heating equipment includes ovens, platen heaters, ring burners, electric heating elements, heat-transfer liquids, induction heaters, and lamps and other types of infrared heating. For small lots, tools and work may be heated by hand torches. Small dies that can be handled rapidly can be heated in ovens adjacent to the forming equipment.

Electric heating elements often are used for heating dies and other forming tools. Figure 4 shows the wiring diagram for an electric heating circuit for a draw die and the control circuit, including the thermocouple inserted into the die and the temperature control.

Electric-resistance heating can be used for heating some dies. Low-voltage, high-amperage current is passed into the die through conducting grips or clamps.

Radiant heating with electricity and gas is useful for heating dies and workpieces in some applications.

Radiant heating is particularly useful for rapid heating of the workpiece and for use in rapid-action presses. Also, with this heating method, cloth covers can be used on the workpiece to minimize heat loss.

Infrared heating is also commonly used. A bank of infrared lamps is the most common method, but gas-fired units are also used.

The principal advantage of infrared heating is that only the die and workpiece are heated and not the surrounding area. Also, the cost of heating is less, and working conditions are cooler and less hazardous.

Gas heating often is advantageous, because the installation of equipment is simple and fuel cost generally is low. Burners up to 75 in. long can be formed and welded from ¾-in. black iron pipe; 1-in. pipe is suggested for burners more than 75 in. long. Burner holes, spaced at ½-in. intervals, are made with a No. 40 drill. Burners are attached to the dies so that the flames touch the die surface. Hollow punches can be heated by a burner inside the punch.

Four gas-mixing systems are used for heating tools and dies:

1 Simple venturis, in which gas flows through a mixer that draws in air
2 Proportional mixers, which use compressed air flowing through a venturi (or an air injector) that pulls the gas into the burner at atmospheric pressure
3 A gas-air carburetor system, which uses a low-pressure turbocompressor to compress the gas-air mixture. The carburetor holds a constant fuel-to-air ratio regardless of the volume of flow
4 A venturi mixing system combined with turbocompressors, which gives accurate temperature control with minimum overshoot.

Heat-transfer fluids are used for heating platens, form blocks, drop hammer dies, and other forming tools large enough to have passages in the die. Heating by this method is rapid and permits good temperature control. Heat-transfer fluids with a working-temperature range of 300 to 750 F are available. Hot oils, natural and synthetic, that can withstand temperatures up to 650 F are commonly circulated in passages in the dies.

Commercially available equipment for use with heat-transfer fluids includes vapor generators, circulating mechanisms and means for temperature control.

Steam is readily available, but its maximum temperature usually is about 350 F. Steam is circulated through ducts in the tools or dies.

Temperature control is important. For forming a few pieces, contact pyrometers or temperature-sensitive crayons are satisfactory for determining temperature. Blue carpenter's chalk can sometimes be used. A streak of this chalk on a metal surface will turn white at approximately 600 F.

Automatic temperature controls are essential for most magnesium-forming operations. For heating methods similar to the one shown in Fig. 4, a conventional thermocouple can be used.

Radiant and infrared heat are more difficult to control than other kinds of heat. One type of infrared lamp has a control that extends or retracts the lamp when the tool or workpiece has reached the desired temperature. Another temperature control for infrared heating consists of a special radiometer

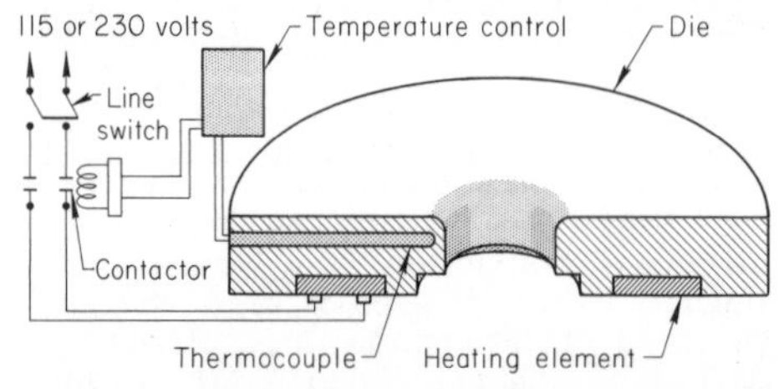

Fig. 4. Wiring diagram for heating and for temperature control of a draw die

that senses only the heat radiated by the surfaces being heated.

To maintain the desired temperature, controls used in gas heating systems usually operate by adjusting a solenoid valve in the line to lower or raise the flame. Electric heating by elements, resistance heating, and heating by means of heat-transfer fluids usually provide good temperature control.

The importance of temperature control is indicated in the next example:

Example 603. Die-Temperature Control That Prevented Cracking in Bending of Tubing

Tubing of alloy AZ31B-O, with a ⅜-in. OD and a wall thickness of 0.035 in., cracked when bent 6°, 52°, 59°, 89° and 92° to a radius of 1¹⁄₁₆ in. The cause was found to be poor control of die temperature. Cracking occurred when the die temperature was below 500 F, especially in the 92° bends if they were not made in one continuous motion. When an accurate temperature-control mechanism was provided for the dies, cracking was eliminated.

Bending was done in a standard draw bender, and a formed mandrel was used inside the tubing to improve the shape of the outer wall of the bend.

Lubricants

Generally, lubrication is more important in hot than in cold forming of magnesium alloys, because these alloys are more likely to gall as the forming temperature increases.

Lubricants for forming magnesium alloys include mineral oil, grease, tallow, soap, wax, molybdenum disulfide, colloidal graphite in a volatile vehicle, colloidal graphite in tallow, and thin sheets of paper or fiber glass.

Selection of lubricant depends primarily on forming temperature. For temperatures up to 250 F, oil, grease, tallow, soap and wax are generally used. These lubricants are similar to those discussed in the article on Lubricants, which begins on page 23.

In spinning, it is essential that the lubricant cling to the work metal; otherwise the lubricant will be thrown off by centrifugal force. This is not a problem when drawing in a die, or bending in a press brake.

Frequently, a lubricant that is used for other operations in the plant can be used, up to a forming temperature of 250 F. Common practice is to use the lubricant that can be most easily removed after forming and to apply it by roller coating or swabbing. Sometimes, the lubricant is applied to both the work metal and the tools.

When forming is done at temperatures higher than 250 F, the selection of lubricant is narrowed; ordinary oil, grease and wax are eliminated. Colloidal graphite can be applied at any temperature that is used for forming magnesium alloys, but because graphite is difficult to remove and interferes with subsequent surface treatments, it is used as little as possible.

A soap lubricant is acceptable for temperatures as high as 450 F. This compound is an aqueous solution and is applied to the work metal by dipping, brushing or roller coating. After coating, the work-metal blanks are dried in still or forced air. After drying, the blanks can be stored an indefinite period for future processing, because the dried lubricant is stable. Lubricant that remains after forming can be completely removed by cleaning in hot water.

When forming temperatures are higher than 450 F, the choice of lubricant is restricted to colloidal graphite or molybdenum disulfide.

Graphite in a vehicle such as spirits (2% graphite) is widely used; for spinning, the graphite is mixed with tallow to improve adherence.

Lubricants should be cleaned from parts as soon as possible after forming, to prevent corrosion or to avoid difficulty in their removal. Colloidal graphite is particularly difficult to remove if allowed to remain on parts for any length of time.

For some work, lubricants cannot be tolerated at any forming temperature, and thin sheets of paper or fiber glass (depending on temperature) are placed between the work metal and the tools instead of a conventional lubricant.

Press-Brake Forming

Press-brake forming of magnesium alloys is the same as for other metals, except that the work metal and the dies are usually heated.

Top and bottom dies can be made of steel, or if the workpiece permits cold forming, the steel punch can be bottomed in a rubber die held in a retaining box (for more on dies using a rubber pad, see page 106 in the article on Press-Brake Forming). Metal punches and dies should be highly polished, to prevent marking of workpiece surfaces.

A preferred method of heating the punch and die for hot forming is shown in Fig. 5. When only a few workpieces are to be formed, heating with a gas torch is satisfactory.

If the press-brake die is not heated, the workpiece should be heated to the maximum allowable temperature and formed quickly before the tools can cool the work metal too much.

Bend radii for cold forming should seldom be less than the minimum given in Table 1. However, for slow forming, smaller radii may sometimes be used. In press-brake forming of magnesium alloys, maximum springback can be expected, because of the high speed; in fast forming, there is no time for relaxation of the work metal.

Drawing in Presses

Mechanical presses are used less than hydraulic presses in drawing of magnesium alloys, because the ram stroke of a hydraulic press is longer than that of a mechanical press. The speed and length of stroke, and the shut height, are easily adjusted in a hydraulic press. These features are desirable for deep drawing operations.

Because of the need for higher production rates for parts with moderate depth of draw, considerable work has been done to establish the drawing limits for magnesium alloys in mechanical presses. Single-stage draws up to 59% reduction at a draw speed of 20 ft per min, and reductions up to 54% at a speed of 80 ft per min, are possible in hot drawing of magnesium alloys.

Draw Tools. For cold drawing of magnesium alloys, punches and dies are similar to those used for other metals.

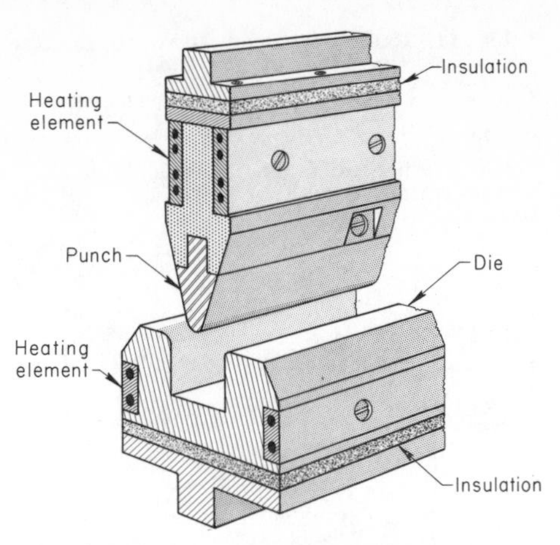

Fig. 5. Preferred method of heating a punch and die for hot forming in a press brake

For hot drawing, however, provision must be made for heating the draw ring, blankholder and pressure pad. Punches are often heated, but temperatures are lower than for other tool components. For example, usual punch temperatures for AZ31 alloys and ZE10A alloy are 225 to 325 F.

For hot forming, low-carbon steel is commonly used for punches, draw rings, pressure pads, and blankholders. It may be necessary to stress-relieve low-carbon steel tools before final machining, by heating at 1200 F for 1 hr, followed by air cooling. Stress relieving is especially important if welding is involved in the construction of the tools. Heat-resistant cast iron also is used. Magnesium, aluminum and zinc alloys often can be used for punches, on short runs.

Minimum thicknesses of low-carbon steel plate for draw rings and blankholders are given in Table 8 for blanks of various dimensions.

Draw-ring radii of four to seven times sheet thickness (4 to $7t$) provide maximum drawability. Radii as small as $1t$ and larger than $7t$ have been used in draws when flanges are made, although radii of less than $4t$ increase the resistance to drawing and can limit the depth of draw. Draw-ring radii larger than $7t$ will increase puckering.

Table 8. Minimum Thicknesses of Low-Carbon Steel Plate for Draw Rings and Blankholders in Forming Magnesium Alloy Blanks

Maximum blank dimensions, in.	Minimum plate thickness, in.
Up to 14	1.5
14 to 22	2.0
22 to 30	2.5
30 and over	3.0

Vertical corner radii are expressed in terms of the depth of draw, with 1/12 and 1/20 of the depth considered practical and minimum limits, respectively. Bottom radii usually are larger than $3t$; however, flat-bottom parts with radii as small as $1t$ have been drawn. In best practice the punch bottom radius is not less than $10t$.

Clearance between the punch and die is governed to some extent by the depth of draw. For draws of maximum depth, a clearance of 0.005 to 0.010 in. should be allowed in addition to stock thickness. Allowance for expansion caused by heating should be made in the tool (see Fig. 3).

Heating the Dies. Electric heating elements usually are used for heating the tools (see the section "Methods of Heating" and Fig. 4), although when intricate parts are drawn, gas-ring burners provide more flexibility, particularly if the work metal is likely to pucker. The base of the punch sometimes can be heated.

Another type of differential heating is used in the production of workpieces that have a slight crown. When the crown must be held to close tolerance, burners with separate controls are provided inside and outside the die. For more crown, the outside of the mating die is heated to a higher temperature than the inside. When the workpiece reaches die temperature and the outside of the sheet is hotter than the inside, the work metal retracts upon removal of the die, thus causing the crown to form. Alternatively, to eliminate crowning and obtain flatness, the inside of the die is heated to a higher temperature than the outside.

Blankholder pressures for magnesium alloys vary from the lowest obtainable to as much as 700 psi. In average draws, the blankholder pressure usually is 50 to 200 psi.

To secure proper wall thinning, blankholder pressures are obtained by trial. On most hydraulic presses, these figures are read off as tons of force, rather than being converted to pressure in pounds per square inch. An example of the blankholder and draw forces that were required for deep drawing a magnesium alloy part at various temperatures is given in Table 9.

Drawability. Annealed magnesium alloy sheet can be cold drawn to 25% reduction (blank diameter to cup diameter). With heat, drawability is greatly improved and up to 70% reduction is possible.

Drawability is also influenced by the shape of the workpiece. A maximum drawability of 70% is for drawing a round cup. Square and rectangular boxes, for example, seldom are drawn so severely. The maximum temperatures shown in Table 4 should be observed, in order to avoid decreasing the mechanical properties.

Effect of Speed on Drawability. Drawability at any temperature varies with the speed of drawing, which ranges from 1½ to 960 in. per minute. Large reductions (70%, for example) require slower speeds than moderate reductions (up to 55%).

Table 9. Blankholder and Draw Forces for Drawing a 1½-In.-Diam Cup to a 63% Reduction in a Hydraulic Press(a)

Drawing tempera-ture, F	Force, tons, for: Blankholder	Draw
400	0.28	3.12
425	0.21	2.87
450	0.17	2.62
475	0.15	2.40
500	0.12	2.25
525	0.10	2.10
550	0.09	1.90
575	0.08	1.80
600	0.06	1.70

(a) Forces are based on the use of AZ31B-O alloy sheet 0.064 in. thick at a drawing speed of 1¼ in. per min. Draw ring radius = $6t$.

Reductions up to about 55% can often be made on high-speed hydraulic or mechanical presses. Also, milder draws permit lower forming temperatures, and costs can be reduced, because strip feeding, blanking, lubrication, trimming and cleaning can be simplified.

In the following example, production rate for a moderately drawn part was greatly increased by changing from a hydraulic press to a mechanical press.

Example 604. Change From Conventional to High-Speed Drawing (Table 10)

As shown in Table 10, a cylindrical shell was originally conventionally drawn to a 55% reduction in a hydraulic press at a drawing temperature of 600 F and a drawing speed of 15 in. per minute.

However, because the reduction was moderate, the machine was changed for a faster (mechanical) press and the drawing speed was increased 16 times. The drawing temperature was lowered by 200 F, which made it simpler to heat the work metal and to feed strip stock, instead of the previously used precut blanks, into the heated dies. With a lower drawing temperature, it was also possible to use a soap lubricant, instead of graphite, which shortened the cleaning time.

With high-speed drawing, production rate increased by a factor of 60.

A comparison of the two methods is given in Table 10.

Table 10. Comparison of Conventional and High-Speed Deep Drawing to a 55% Reduction in a Cylindrical Shell (Example 604)

Item	Conventional drawing	High-speed drawing
Press Details		
Type	Hydraulic	Mechanical
Capacity, tons	300	100
Stroke, in.	24	9
Operating Conditions		
Drawing temp, F	600	400
Drawing speed, ipm	15	240
Preparation of blank	Precut	Strip
Lubricant	Graphite	Soap
Trimming	(a)	(b)
Time per pc, min(c)	18	0.3
Production, pcs/hr	3.3	200

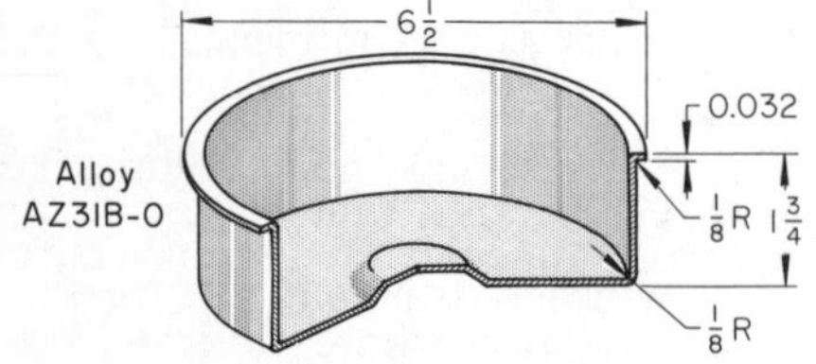

(a) Separate operation. (b) Shear at bottom of draw. (c) Includes all operations.

Drawing Radii. Vertical corner radius (R_1), bottom corner radius (R_2), and draw ring radius (R_3), which are shown on the sketch in Table 11, and reduction in blank diameter, are more important factors than depth of draw. Radii for deep drawing in one operation at a die and work-metal temperature of 600 F, are given in Table 11.

Examples. The three examples that follow are typical applications of production drawing of magnesium alloys.

Examples 605 and 606. Deep Drawing Rectangular Boxes at Elevated Temperature

Example 605 (Fig. 6). For the rectangular box shown in Fig. 6, the ratio of depth of draw to vertical corner radius was approximately nine (8 in./0.937 in.). Using the typical limit of $h/12$ (see Table 11), this workpiece could have been drawn to a height of 11 in.

Blanks, 0.051 in. thick, were coated with graphite and preheated to 600 F, then loaded into the die and clamped, using a blankholder pressure of 40 tons. Drawing was done at 15 in. per minute in a 300-ton double-action hydraulic press, using low-carbon steel dies and a cast iron punch. The operating temperature of the draw ring was 600 F, the pressure pad 650 F, and the punch 450 F.

Table 11. Radii for Deep Drawing in One Operation at 600 F(a)

Item(b)	Radii for drawn rectangular shape: Minimum	Typical
Vertical corner radius (R_1)	$h/20$	$h/12$
Bottom corner radius (R_2)	$3t$	$4t$
Draw ring radius (R_3)	$4t$	$6t$

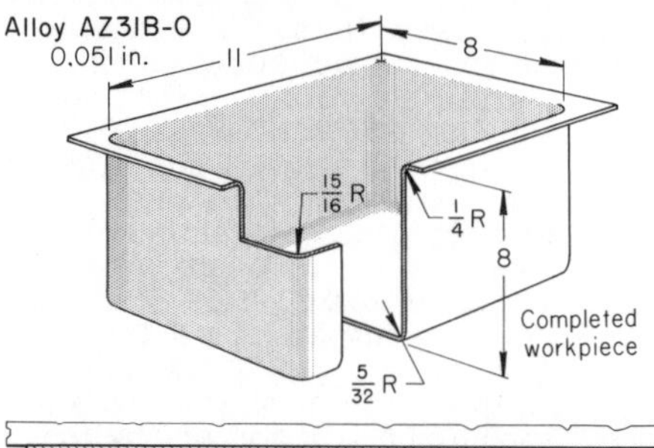

t = thickness of sheet; h = depth of draw.

(a) Draw ring 600 F, pressure ring 650 F, and punch 450 F. (b) Reduction in diameter of a cylindrical blank is 70% maximum, 65% typical. R_2 and R_3 minimum and typical radii are the same for a cylindrical shape.

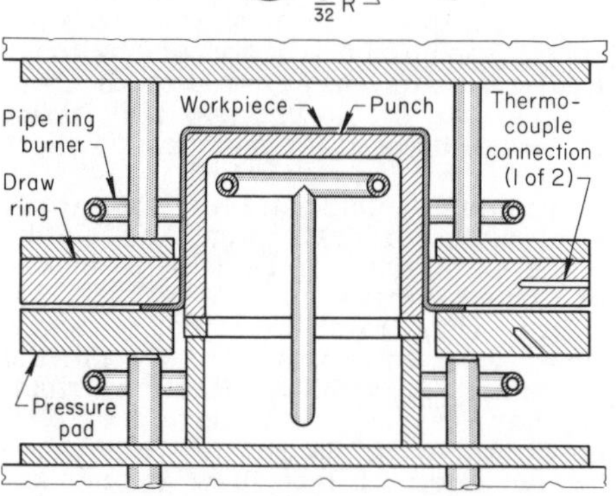

Fig. 6. Flanged rectangular box that was hot drawn in the setup shown, in a double-action hydraulic press (Example 605)

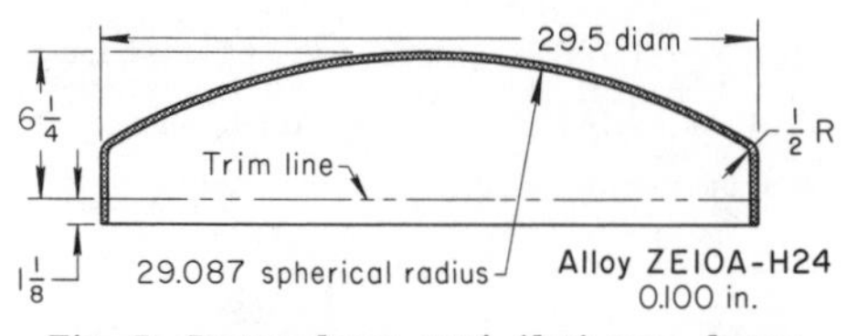

Fig. 7. Dome-shape part that was drawn successfully at 400 F but could not be drawn at 275 F (Example 607)

Example 606. Rectangular boxes, 9⅜ in. long by 6⅛ in. wide by 9½ in. deep were drawn from 0.081-in.-thick LA141A alloy, in a 350-ton hydraulic press. Temperature of the pressure pad was 540 F, the draw ring 440 F, and the punch 300 F. Clamp pressure was 75 psi. Drawing speed was about 2 ft per min.

Using the same press, boxes of the same size were drawn from the same thickness of alloy AZ31B or AZ31C. Ring and punch temperatures were 750 F, clamp pressure was 100 psi, and drawing speed was 1 ft per min. A graphite lubricant was used in both operations.

Example 607. Drawing a Dome-Shape Part From 0.100-In.-Thick Sheet (Fig. 7)

The dome-shape part shown in Fig. 7 was drawn from a ZE10A-H24 alloy blank 0.100 in. thick and 38 in. in diameter. The blank was graphite coated and heated to 400 F. Tools were heated by gas to 400 F; temperature was controlled by pyrometer. Clamping force varied from 1500 to 2000 lb. The punch had a spherical radius of 29.087 in. and traveled 7⅜ in. to form the dome.

Attempts to form this dome from this alloy at 275 F were unsuccessful. Tearing occurred at the bottom corner radius, and wrinkles formed on the crown of the dome.

Manual Spinning

Various conical and hemispherical shapes can be produced from magnesium alloys by manual spinning. Because tooling is inexpensive, manual spinning is often more economical than press forming for small quantities. When press tooling would be complex, manual spinning may be used for medium to large-production quantities.

Equipment and tooling for manual spinning of magnesium alloys are essentially the same as for other metals (see the article "Spinning" in this volume), except that when magnesium alloys are to be heated the mandrels (spin blocks) should be made of metal, with provision for controlled heating of the work metal.

For spinning a few pieces, common practice is to heat the blanks with a hand torch, using temperature-sensitive crayons to indicate the temperature. For production spinning, however, preferred practice is to use a thermostatically controlled burner on the lathe.

Procedure. Annealed sheet is usually used in spinning. Manual spinning depends to a large extent on operator skill, especially when spinning magnesium alloys, which are more temperature sensitive than most metals.

Many shapes can be spun from unheated blanks by a skilled operator, especially when thin sheet is used, because friction between the spinning tool and workpiece generates a substantial amount of heat. As severity or sheet thickness increases, the work metal must be heated. Temperatures of 500 to 600 F are common (see Table 4). If the work metal is in the H24 temper, the temperature must not exceed the value given in Table 4.

Whether spinning is done hot or cold, a lubricant should be used (see the section on Lubricants, in this article). Spindle speed should be such that the speed of the edge of the blank is about 2000 sfm when spinning begins.

Sizing. Spinning is sometimes used for the final sizing of parts that are impractical or impossible to form completely by other methods, as in the following example.

Example 608. Spinning a Die-Formed and Welded Part to Size (Fig. 8)

The conical shape shown in Fig. 8 was produced to rough size by welding together two die-formed half sections. Blanks of HK31A-H24 alloy, 0.180 in. thick, were die-formed at 650 F using graphite lubricant. The edges were then chamfered for welding. After welding, the welds were ground flush.

To remove the distortion caused by welding, the parts were sized by hot spinning on a suitably contoured cast iron mandrel. Workpiece and mandrel were heated by gas to 650 F, and temperature was controlled by a pyrometer. Spinning was done using a hard maple pole with graphite as lubricant. The workpiece was then cleaned and stress relieved at 500 F for 1 hr.

Tolerances. Typical tolerances that can be maintained in manual spinning of magnesium alloys are as follows:

Workpiece diam less than 18 in. ...	±1/32 in.
18 to 36 in. ...	±1/16
36 in. and over ...	±1/8

Spinning Extrusions. Manual spinning can be used either to close or flare the ends of extruded round tubing.

Closing the ends of tubes is done by slowly forcing a rotating hemispherical cup over the end of the tube until the end is closed and has assumed the hemispherical shape of the cup (spinning tool). This can be done on almost any machine that can hold the workpiece and rotate the cuplike tool. A drill press is frequently used. The use of grease or soap as a lubricant is helpful in producing better workpiece finish and prolonging the life of spinning tools. In most applications, tube ends can be closed without the use of heat.

Tube flaring is done either by inserting a stationary mandrel into the tube and pushing it out against a stationary die on the outside, or by spinning or rolling the flare against a stationary outside die with a conical rotating inside mandrel. The shape required for the flare usually determines the preferred procedure.

Tube-flaring machines have a stationary outside die and conical inside rotating spindle with adjustable eccentricity, the axis of which rotates off center at approximately 1600 rpm. The eccentric spindle forces the tube against the outer die to form the flare. In the flaring of magnesium alloy tubes, the outer die should be heated, preferably by electric heating elements in the die holder, to a preferred temperature of about 500 F. The tube to be flared is preheated to 500 F in an oven.

Lubrication may be required during tube flaring. The lubricants recommended for spinning can be used.

Power Spinning

Power spinning (shear spinning) can be used for magnesium alloys. Both cone spinning (spinning in accordance with the sine law) and tube spinning (spinning in which metal displacement is strictly volumetric) are used for magnesium alloys.

Equipment and Tooling. Special machines are used in cone and tube spinning of magnesium alloys. However, the equipment used in power spinning is the same as for other metals (see the article on Spinning, in this volume), except when hot spinning is done; then, torches or other heating equipment must be added to the machine. Consequently, the mandrels and rollers must be made from an alloy tool steel that will not be softened by heat. Tool steels such as H12 or H13 hardened to Rockwell C 54 to 58 are used in many applications.

Procedure. Magnesium alloys are sometimes power spun without heat, but more often the major portion of the reduction is performed hot and finished cold, or is rough worked hot and then finished at a somewhat lower temperature (warm). For the most successful results, a definite procedure of alternate spinning and heating should be followed, whether the metal is finished cold or warm. Table 12 presents recommended procedures for the two methods often used for alloys HK31A and HM21A. The use of the procedures outlined in Table 12 has resulted in total wall reductions as high as 80%.

Weld (1 of 2) — Alloy HK31A-H24 0.180 in. — 16.91 diam — 12.49 — 7.88 — 3.745 / 3.674 diam

Fig. 8. Conical shape that was sized by spinning after die-formed half sections were welded (Example 608)

Table 12. Procedures for Power Spinning Alloys HK31A and HM21A to Obtain Acceptable Properties (a)

HK31A	HM21A
Cold Finishing	
Hot work roughly to shape at 800 ± 50 F.	Hot work roughly to shape at 850 ± 50 F.
Heat treat for 45 ± 15 min at 850 to 900 F(b).	Heat treat for 45 ± 15 min at 900 to 950 F(c).
Cold work to a total reduction in thickness of at least 25%, using low reductions per pass.	Cold work to a total reduction in thickness of 15 to 25%, using low reductions per pass.
Heat 1 hr at 600 to 625 F.	Heat 1 hr at 675 to 725 F.
Warm Finishing	
Hot work roughly to shape at 800 ± 50 F, if necessary.	Hot work roughly to shape at 850 ± 50 F, if necessary.
Heat treat for 45 ± 15 min at 850 to 900 F(b).	Heat treat for 45 ± 15 min at 900 to 950 F(c).
Warm work at 600 to 700 F to a total reduction in thickness of greater than 50% with a minimum number of passes.	Warm work at 600 to 700 F to a total reduction in thickness of greater than 50% with a minimum number of passes.
Heat 16 hr at 400 F.	Heat 16 hr at 450 F.

(a) The properties obtained will approach those of the H24 temper for HK31A and T8 for HM21A. (b) Fairly rapid cooling is desirable but less critical than for HM21A. (c) Should be cooled from the heat treating temperature to 600 F or below within 5 min.

Rubber-Pad Forming

Hydraulic presses are generally used for the rubber-pad forming of magnesium alloys. Tooling is simple because only a form block is used (see Fig. 9). A conventional die is not needed.

For forming at room temperature, particularly for limited use, form blocks can be made of wood or masonite; or for higher production runs, of aluminum, zinc, or magnesium, which are more durable than wood or masonite. However, large radii must be used in cold forming, except for alloys AZ31B-O (special bending grade) or LA141A.

When rubber-pad forming at elevated temperature, form blocks must be made from metal that will not creep excessively at the working temperature and pressure; magnesium, aluminum or zinc can be used up to about 450 F. However, forming at temperatures higher than 450 F requires steel form blocks, and the factors given in Table 7 must be applied in their production.

Specially compounded grades of solid rubber or laminated sheets are used for the rubber pad when forming at temperatures up to 600 F. Hardness of the rubber is important — Durometer A 40 to 70 is the common range.

Heating. As shown in Fig. 9, the heating elements heat the steel platen and the heat is transferred to the form block, which is not fastened to the platen, by conduction. Alternatively, the form block can be heated separately in an oven and then placed on the platen. In this method, an asbestos blanket often is placed between the heated form block and the cold platen for insulation. Blanks usually are heated in ovens situated near the press to minimize loss of heat.

Forming Pressure. Pressure for rubber-pad forming is a function of sheet thickness and forming temperatures; 900 psi is adequate for most work.

Rubber-pad forming is generally done by shaping the blank around a form block by pressure from the rubber pad. However, when pressure must be concentrated at one point, or metal flow must start before general pressure is applied, deflector bars are used (see the article "Rubber-Pad Forming", page 209 in this volume).

Some severe forming is done in two operations: the workpiece is partly formed, is removed from the press for hand smoothing of wrinkles, and then is returned to the press for final forming under full pressure. In one-operation forming, thin throw sheets of heat-resistant rubber can be placed over the blank, or attached to the pad, to protect the rubber.

Shrink flanges that are wrinkle-free can be made with a higher percentage of compression from magnesium alloys than from other metals, such as aluminum, of the same gage. Maximum shrink limits are given in Table 13.

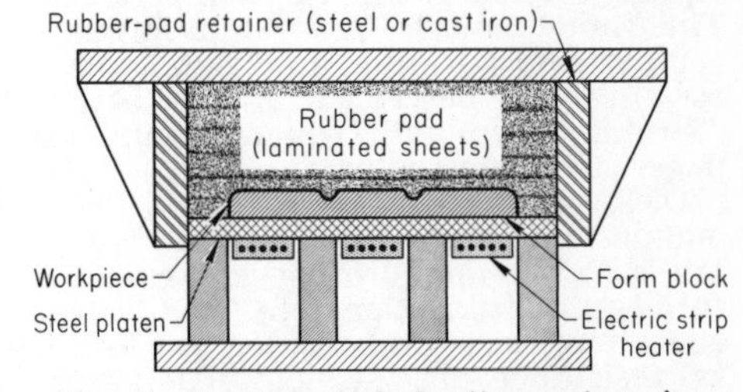

Fig. 9. Tooling and heating setup for rubber-pad forming of magnesium alloys at elevated temperature

Table 13. Maximum Compression Obtainable in Shrink Flanges Without Relief in Rubber-Pad Forming

Alloy and temper	Thickness of sheet, in.	Forming temperature, F	Maximum compression, %
AZ31B-H24	0.025	325	2.5
	0.040	325	4
AZ31B-O	0.025	550	3
	0.040	550	5

Higher compression is possible if wrinkles can be prevented. Minor wrinkles can be hand corrected after flanging. If the part is likely to wrinkle severely, scalloped cutouts or recesses in the form blocks may correct this condition. A draw plate to iron out wrinkles during forming often is helpful.

Stretch flanges of up to 40% stretch in hard rolled magnesium alloy sheet (H24 temper) and 70% in annealed sheet (O temper) can be made by rubber-pad forming. The ranges of stretch-flange limits for various thicknesses of AZ31B-O and AZ31B-H24 alloy sheet rubber-pad formed at 300 F are shown in Fig. 10.

A minimum flange radius of 5t is suggested for alloy AZ31B-H24 at 325 F. The radius of the die should be approximately ½t less to compensate for springback.

Beads. In rubber-pad forming, both internal and external beads can be formed in magnesium alloy sheet. External beads usually are easier to produce, although wrinkling is slight in both types.

Severity of forming internal and external beads is expressed as the ratio w/h (w = width of bead, h = height of bead). Beading is essentially a stretching operation, and this w/h ratio is related to the maximum percentage of stretch obtained in a given bead.

The effect of forming temperature on the w/h ratio in forming internal beads on alloys AZ31B-O and AZ31B-H24 is shown in Fig. 11. External beads are easier to form and can be made to equal or more severe ratios; minimum bead margin should be 0.38 in., and beads should be separated by a minimum centerpoint distance of 0.76 in.

Hand forming can slightly improve the definition of a part after rubber-pad forming, while the form block and the workpiece are still hot. A leather or plastic forming tool can be used to correct minor irregularities, or to improve flange angles. To avoid damage to the form block, do not use hard tools.

Stretch Forming

Stretch forming of magnesium alloys is the same as for other metals, except that magnesium alloys are generally stretch formed at elevated temperature. The fundamentals of stretch forming, compression forming and radial draw forming are described in the article "Stretch Forming", which begins on page 239 in this volume.

Dies, or form blocks, made from magnesium, aluminum, or zinc alloys are suitable for forming at temperatures up to 450 F. Concrete form blocks, containing wire mesh heated by electrical resistance, may also be used at temperatures up to 450 F. For temperatures higher than 450 F, cast iron form blocks are used.

Grippers used in the forming of magnesium alloys should not have serrated jaws, or the work metal may tear. Coarse emery paper or cloth can be placed between the work metal and the jaws to prevent tearing.

Tools and work metal can be heated by electric heating elements, or by radiant heat. Proper distribution of heat is important, and units should be placed at critical forming areas (see Table 4 for forming temperatures).

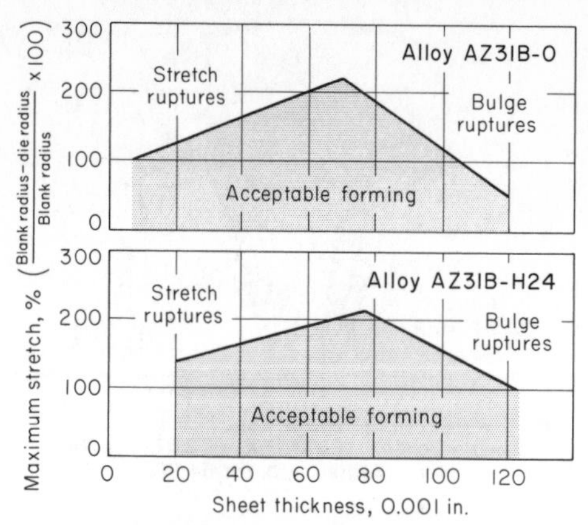

Fig. 10. Stretch-flange limits for various thicknesses of alloys AZ31B-O and AZ31B-H24 rubber-pad formed at 300 F

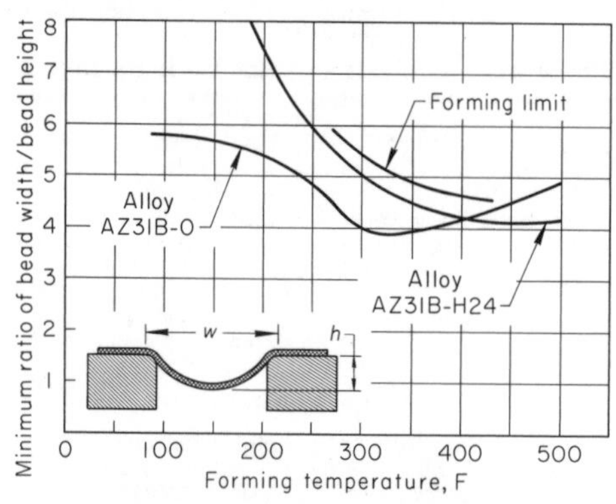

Fig. 11. Effect of rubber-pad forming temperature on the minimum ratio of bead width (w) to bead height (h) for forming internal beads on alloys AZ31B-O and AZ31B-H24

For differential stretching of sheet over forms of low curvature, the practical maximum stretch is about 15%. Twelve percent is the maximum if allowance (overstretch) is made for springback; however, little springback is normally encountered at elevated temperature, and usually an addition of 1% to the total stretch compensates for any springback that may occur.

Although freedom from wrinkles is an advantage of stretch forming in most applications, wrinkles can be a problem when making asymmetrical low-curvature parts. Wrinkles can be controlled by including proper restraints in the die. The skill of the operator largely determines where such restraints are needed.

Drop Hammer Forming

Drop hammer forming is used for producing shallow depths and asymmetrical shapes in magnesium alloys when quantities are small and for applications requiring minimum springback. Successful results depend on operator skill. Except for heating, drop hammer forming of magnesium alloys is the same as for other metals.

Zinc alloy can be used for both punch and die. Lead punches sometimes are used, but lead pickup can cause corrosion of the sheet. For production quantities greater than about 50 pieces, however, cast iron punches and dies are recommended, because zinc alloy tools would lose their shape.

Annealed sheet is preferred for drop hammer forming. Blanks should be heated (see Table 4) near the hammer, because the work cools rapidly — usually 30 to 45 F in 5 sec. Ten blows may be needed to form a part, with reheating between blows — 5 min for metal thicknesses up to 0.051 in. and 9 min for thicknesses of 0.051 to 0.125 in.

Heat-resistant rubber pads often are used in the dies for preliminary forming, and removed before final forming.

Dies can be heated in an oven near the hammer, or by torches or ring burners during operation. Small dies can be used on an electrically heated cast iron platen on the hammer bed, but this method is not practical for large dies. Heating of the punch and die by electric heating elements or by a heat-transfer fluid is also used. Working temperatures should be maintained at the levels given in Table 4.

The elevated temperatures used in drop hammer forming of magnesium alloys can reduce or eliminate springback; therefore, the maximum practical temperature should always be used. The rate of deformation must be carefully controlled, especially when deformation of the work metal is severe, or when the metal is in the H24 temper. For workpieces that require severe forming, the punch is lowered slowly and forming completed with subsequent blows. Tolerances of ±0.030 in. can be maintained in production.

Impact Extrusion

Impact extrusion is used for producing symmetrical tubular workpieces, especially those with thin walls or irregular profiles for which other methods are not practical. Application of this process to magnesium is described in the article on page 496.

The following example describes an application involving a reduction in area of about 42%.

Example 609. Impact Extruding a Cylindrical Container From Alloy AZ31B (Fig. 12)

The dry-cell battery container shown in Fig. 12 was impact extruded from a 0.245-in.-thick slug of alloy AZ31B in a mechanical press. Estimated punch force was 25 tons. Extruding temperature was 500 F. Principal dimensions of punch, die and slug shown in Fig. 12 were at room temperature. At operating temperature of 500 F, die and punch expanded approximately 0.003 in. in diameter, but the slug expanded 0.0067 in. in diameter. The die was tapered 0.002 in. per inch to allow easy removal of the part, although no taper would have been needed if a bottom knockout had been provided. Slugs were graphite lubricated.

Seventy extrusions were produced per minute. At a weight of 0.012 lb per slug, 83 containers were made per pound of slug metal.

Tolerances of extrusions are influenced by size and shape of part, length-to-diameter ratio and press alignment. Table 2, page 496, gives typical tolerances for a magnesium part with a length-to-diameter ratio of 6 to 1.

Joggling

Room-temperature joggling of magnesium alloy sheet and extrusions is done only on alloys AZ31B-O (special bending sheet) and LA141A-O, because of the high formability of these alloys at room temperature.

Displacement of metal in the joggled area differs from that produced by flange bending or rolling operations. Consequently, in this article, data for joggling operations have been developed primarily on the basis of transition length-to-depth ratio and secondarily on bend radius.

Transition Length-to-Depth Ratio. Actual shop practice has shown that a transition length-to-depth ratio of at least 4 to 1 is practical. This ratio sets a maximum limit on transition depth for any transition length. Minimum limits must be set on transition length because, as the length decreases to a small multiple of material thickness, joggling becomes more difficult.

Table 14 gives minimum transition lengths for various alloys, assuming the above 4-to-1 ratio. The data in this table were based on the joggling of angle shapes (across the grain) but can be used for other extruded shapes, as well as sheet. Test coupons of the same material and condition should be used when making the preliminary setup for equipment adjustment, temperature control, and technique.

Bend Radii. In general, the minimum bend radii shown in Tables 4 and 5 can be used as a guide when transition length is sufficiently large. When transition lengths approach the minimums of Table 14, however, smaller bend radii may be necessary. The reason is that, as the sum of the two bend radii approaches or exceeds the transition length, the material becomes pinched between the opposing joggle blocks, and the full depth of the intended joggle may never be reached.

To avoid marking heavier material (1/8 in. thick, or over) bend radii should be approximately one-quarter the transition length. If possible, they should be even larger.

For standard joggling of magnesium alloy extrusions, in thicknesses of 0.062 to 0.100 in., to a transition length and depth of $6t$ and $1.5t$, respectively, bend radii as small as 1/16 to 1/8 in. can be used. These radii produce good definition, but careful handling is needed to avoid excessive marking of the workpiece in the vicinity of the bend radii.

Joggling of magnesium alloys is usually done in a standard universal joggle tool, which is a multiple-use die holder with self-contained heating elements and controls. The workpiece is heated in an oven and joggled in the heated die, with minimum loss of time and temperature.

Joggle blocks of various shapes and sizes are assembled in die holders to form, hold and support the workpiece. The forming radii of the block determine the bend radii of the joggle. Other surfaces of the block must be carefully shaped to fit the surfaces of the workpiece, to prevent buckling. This applies to vertical legs of extruded shapes, such as angles or tees. For example, if the fillets between the stem and flange of a tee have a larger radius than the supporting block, the tee will hang up on the fillets. The tee can be adequately supported only if the radius of the block is equal to, or larger than, the fillet radius.

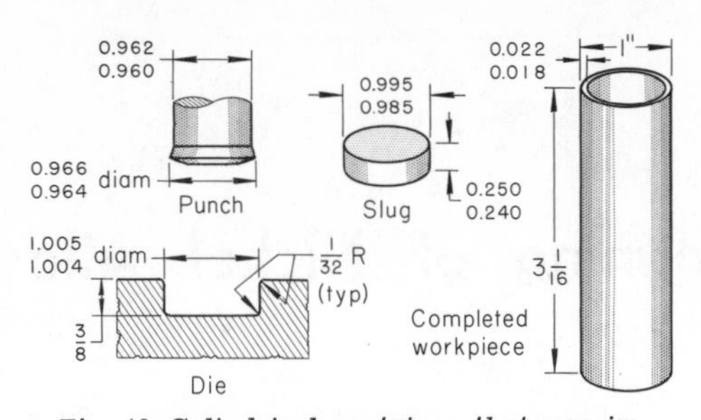

Fig. 12. Cylindrical container that was impact extruded from alloy AZ31B in a mechanical press (Example 609)

Table 14. Conditions for Joggling Magnesium Alloy Sheet and Extrusions Across the Grain

Alloy and temper(a)	Minimum joggle transition length(b)	Forming temperature, F	Max total time at max temp, minutes(c)
AZ31B-O	$3t$	400 to 550	60
AZ31B-H24	$5t$	250 to 345	30
AZ31B-F	$3t$	400 to 550	60
AZ61A-F	$2t$	400 to 550	60
AZ80A-F	$1.5t$	400 to 550	30
AZ80A-T5	$2t$	325 to 450	6
	$3t$	285 to 380	60
HK31A-O	$2t$	550 to 750	60
HK31A-H24	$5t$	525 to 700	10
HM21A-T8	$5t$	600 to 800	10
HM31A-T5	$5t$	550 to 750	60
ZK60A-F	$3t$	400 to 550	30
ZK60A-T5	$5t$	375 to 500	6
	$8t$	300 to 400	30
LA141A-O	$0.5t$	225 to 300	60
	$1t$	70	...

(a) AZ alloys and LA141A-O, to be subsequently welded, are joggled at 50 F less than the maximum with the same exposure time. (b) Joggle transition length must be at least four times joggle depth, but not less than the minimum values shown. These limits apply to the forming temperatures given in column 3 and are for "slow" forming equipment; "fast-action" equipment, such as a single-action punch press, may be too severe, when using minimum transition and maximum depth. (c) Time at temperature per joggle varies with stock thickness, as follows: 2 min for stock up to 0.095 in. thick, 3 min for stock 0.095 to 0.188 in. thick, and 4 min for stock 0.189 to 0.250 in. thick. The preceding times per joggle apply if die has heating elements in both upper and lower units, and if work is not preheated to maximum temperature.

Dimpling

Dimpling of magnesium alloys is generally done at elevated temperature, because cracking can occur during cold forming. In preferred practice, the area to be dimpled is heated rapidly and dimpling is done immediately.

Equipment and Tooling. For low-production dimpling, the work metal and dies are preheated and the dimpling is done in a manually operated, or in an air or hydraulic-actuated, arbor press.

Compression-squeeze dimple machines are available with electric heating devices and automatic feeds. Portable pneumatic dimplers with heating devices are frequently used on high-production assembly lines.

Two basic methods of heating the work metal are (*a*) by conduction from the die, which is heated with electric elements (the preferred method); and (*b*) resistance heating of the metal through electrodes and dimpling tools. Arcing problems and the need for extreme care in precleaning the metal surfaces are disadvantages of resistance heating.

Table 15. Temperatures of Electrically Heated Dies for Hot Dimpling of Sheet

Alloy and temper	Die temperature, F(a)
AZ31B-H24	575
AZ31B-O	575
HK31A-H24	825
HK31A-O	825
HM21A-T8	850

(a) The die must not be in contact with the sheet for a total elapsed time of more than 5 sec including the preheat dwell. If sheet is exposed to temperature for a longer period, as when using preheated sheet and dies, follow time and temperature limits given in Table 4.

Standard dimpling dies used on other metals are satisfactory for magnesium alloys, although sometimes modifications are necessary for maximum efficiency. Dies should have the same angle as the rivet head. Diameter of the dimple-forming portion of dies should be 10 to 15% larger than the diameter of the head of the rivet. If holes in the work metal are drilled undersize, the use of a pilot pin in the male die is desirable.

Procedure. The first step in dimpling is drilling or punching the holes. The usual practice with most metals is to make the hole in one operation. In magnesium sheet, however, fatigue life of the metal surrounding the rivet hole may be improved if the hole is punched 50% undersize or drilled one size smaller than the diameter of the rivet to be used. After forming the dimple, the hole is drilled to size. This procedure will insure the concentricity necessary for the best rivet bearing.

Magnesium alloy sheet to be dimpled usually does not exceed 0.050-in. thickness, and the time at highest temperature is so short that dimpling temperatures higher than those for other methods of hot forming can be used. A dwell time of 2 or 3 sec is sufficient for the dimpling tool. By establishing 5 sec as the total time the sheet is at its highest temperature, including the time for preheat and dwell, the die temperatures given in Table 15 can be relied upon.

For best results, it is sometimes necessary to experiment with the temperature, pressure and forming rate of the dimpling machine to establish the most satisfactory procedure. For example:

1 Too low a dimpling temperature can cause cracking.
2 The orange-peel effect sometimes observed on dimples in HK31A often has been eliminated by raising die temperature slightly above that shown in Table 15.
3 Warpage sometimes can be eliminated by reducing the forming rate.

Dimpling pressure can be regulated by using an inch-wide test strip of the sheet to be dimpled and adjusting the pressure so that the strip remains flat while a line of dimples is being made. When dimpling is done at higher temperatures (825 or 850 F), oxides are likely to build up on the dies, so that frequent cleaning of the die faces with wire brushes or steel wool is absolutely essential.

Forming of Nickel Alloys

By R. William Breitzig*

THE DUCTILITY of nickel alloys in the annealed condition makes them adaptable to virtually all methods of cold forming. Within this group of alloys (see Table 1 for compositions), other engineering properties vary sufficiently to cause the alloys to range from moderately easy to moderately difficult to form, in comparison with other materials.

Strain Hardening. Because strain hardening is related to the solid-solution strengthening afforded by alloying elements, strain-hardening rate generally increases with the complexity of the alloy. Accordingly, strain-hardening rates range from moderately low for nickel and nickel-copper alloys to moderately high for the nickel-chromium and nickel-iron-chromium alloys. Similarly, the age-hardenable alloys have higher strain-hardening rates than their solid-solution equivalents. Figure 1 compares the strain-hardening rates of six nickel alloys, in terms of the increase in hardness with increasing cold reduction, with those of four other materials. Note that the strain-hardening rates of the nickel alloys are greater than that of 1020 steel and most are less than that of 304 stainless steel.

Because the modulus of elasticity of the high-nickel alloys is relatively high (similar to that of steel), a small amount of springback in cold forming operations might be expected. However, springback is also a function of proportional limit, which can increase greatly during cold working of strain-hardenable materials. For instance, a yield strength of 25,000 psi of an alloy in the annealed condition might increase to 75,000 psi during a drawing operation. Therefore, the amount of springback for this alloy must be computed from the 75,000-psi yield strength, rather than from the initial value.

Strain-rate sensitivity, a property similar to strain-hardening rate, also affects cold forming practices.

Nickel alloys are sensitive to rate of strain. Therefore, rapidly operating forming equipment will produce a higher yield strength and lower ductility than would be indicated by a standard tension test. If a material having a yield strength of 50,000 psi at a strain rate of 0.1 in. per minute has an indicated yield strength of 150,000 psi at a strain rate of 200 ft per minute, tooling or equipment of marginal capacity might fail at the higher operating speed. Furthermore, the indicated ductility of the workpiece might decrease during forming and cause rupturing of the material. For these reasons, relatively slow operating speeds are recommended for cold forming of nickel alloys. (This rule does not apply in high-energy-rate forming, in which forming rates of several thousand feet per second at extremely high pressures are achieved with no apparent loss of ductility.)

Temper. Most cold forming operations require the use of annealed material. However, the softer alloys, such as Nickel 200 and Monel 400, are frequently used in skin-hard, ⅛-hard and ¼-hard tempers for improved shearing and piercing. For similar reasons, Monel 400 for fastener applications is usually cold headed in No. 1 or 0 temper.

Galling. Because nickel alloys do not readily develop an oxide film that would present a barrier to diffusion bonding, they cold weld (gall) easily to materials of similar atomic diameter. When a cold weld is formed, the high shear strength and ductility of the alloys prevent the weld from being broken easily. For these reasons, the coefficient of friction between nickel alloys and other metals, including most die materials, is usually high.

Alloying with highly reactive elements that form oxide films readily, such as chromium, reduces the galling or cold welding propensity of nickel alloys. Accordingly, the nickel-chromium and nickel-iron-chromium alloys are less likely to gall than are the nickel and nickel-copper alloys. However, the chromium oxide films are thin and brittle and provide only limited protection because they are easily broken when the substrate is deformed. The use of heavy-duty lubricants will minimize galling in most cold forming.

Lubricants

Heavy-duty lubricants are required in most cold forming of nickel alloys.

Although sulfur and chlorine can improve lubricants, they can also have harmful effects if not completely removed after forming. Sulfur will embrittle nickel alloys at elevated temperatures such as might be encountered in annealing or age hardening, and chlorine can cause pitting of the alloys after long exposure. Therefore, sulfurized and chlorinated lubricants should not be used if any difficulty is anticipated in cleaning the formed part. These lubricants are not recommended for use in spinning, as this operation may burnish the lubricant into the surface of the metal. Similarly, molybdenum disulfide is seldom recommended for use with nickel alloys because of the difficulty in removing it.

Pigmented oils and greases should be selected with care as the pigment might be white lead (lead carbonate), zinc oxide, or similar metallic compounds that have low melting points. These elements can embrittle nickel alloys if the compounds are left on the metal during heat treatment. Inert fillers such as talc or flour can be used safely.

Maximum film strength can be obtained by using a coating of copper. However, because application and removal are expensive, metallic coatings are used as lubricants only in severe cold forming operations and then only when they can be properly removed.

Ordinary petroleum greases are seldom used in forming nickel alloys. These greases do not necessarily have the film strength indicated by their viscosity, and they do not have a strong polar attraction for metals.

Phosphates do not form usable surface compounds on nickel alloys and cannot be used as lubricant carriers.

Light-bodied mineral oils and water-base lubricants have limited film strength and lubricity and can be used only in light forming operations.

Tools and Equipment

Nickel alloys do not require special equipment for cold forming. However, the physical and mechanical properties

Table 1. Nominal Compositions of Nickel Alloys (a)

Designation	Ni+Co	C	Mn	Fe	S	Si	Cu	Cr	Al	Ti	Mo	Cb+Ta
Nickel 200	99.5	0.08	0.18	0.2	0.005	0.18	0.13	...	...	...	...	...
Nickel 201	99.5	0.01	0.18	0.2	0.005	0.18	0.13	...	...	...	...	...
Duranickel 301	96.5	0.15	0.25	0.30	0.005	0.5	0.13	...	4.38	0.63	...	...
Monel 400	66.5	0.15	1.0	1.25	0.012	0.25	31.5	...	...	...	...	...
Monel K-500	66.5	0.13	0.75	1.00	0.005	0.5	29.5	...	3.00	0.63	...	...
Inconel 600	76.0	0.08	0.5	8.00	0.008	0.25	0.25	15.5	...	...	...	...
Inconel 625	61.0	0.05	0.25	2.5	0.008	0.25	...	21.5	0.2	0.2	9.0	3.65
Inconel 702	79.5	0.05	0.50	1.0	0.005	0.35	0.25	15.5	3.25	0.63	...	...
Inconel 718	52.5	0.04	0.18	18.5	0.008	0.18	0.15	19.0	0.50	0.90	3.05	5.13
Inconel 721	71.0	0.04	2.25	4.0	0.005	0.08	0.10	16.0	...	3.05	...	...
Inconel 722	75.0	0.04	0.50	7.0	0.005	0.35	0.25	15.5	0.70	2.38	...	...
Inconel X-750	73.0	0.04	0.50	7.00	0.005	0.25	0.25	15.5	0.70	2.50	...	0.95
Inconel 751	72.5	0.05	0.5	7.00	0.005	0.25	0.25	15.5	1.20	2.30	...	0.95
Incoloy 800	32.5	0.05	0.75	46.0	0.008	0.50	0.38	21.0	0.38	0.38	...	...
Incoloy 801	32.0	0.05	0.75	44.5	0.008	0.50	0.25	20.5	...	1.13	...	...
Incoloy 802	32.5	0.35	0.75	46.0	0.008	0.38	...	21.0	0.58	0.75	...	...
Incoloy 804	41.0	0.25	0.75	25.4	0.008	0.38	0.25	29.5	0.30	0.60	...	...
Incoloy 825	42.0	0.03	0.50	30.0	0.015	0.25	2.25	21.5	0.10	0.90	3.0	...

(a) Compositions reflect midrange percentages for some elements; hence, totals may exceed 100%.

*Technical Service Representative, Huntington Alloy Products Div., International Nickel Co.

of nickel alloys frequently necessitate modification of tools and dies used for cold forming other metals. These modifications are discussed in this section. Information applying to specific cold forming operations is presented in the sections covering those operations.

Die materials used in forming austenitic stainless steel are suitable for similar operations on nickel alloys.

Soft die materials such as aluminum bronze, nickel-aluminum bronze, and zinc alloy are used when superior surface finishes are desired. However, these materials have a relatively short service life. Parts formed with zinc alloy dies should be flash-pickled in dilute nitric acid to remove any traces of zinc picked up from the dies during forming. Zinc can cause embrittlement of nickel alloys during heat treatment or high-temperature service. For similar reasons, parts formed with brass or bronze dies should be pickled if the dies impart a bronze color to the workpiece.

Tool Design. Because nickel alloys are likely to gall, and because of the high pressures developed in forming, tooling should be designed with liberal radii, fillets and clearances. The radii and clearances used in cold forming nickel alloys are usually larger than those used for brass and low-carbon steel, and about equal to those used for the austenitic stainless steels.

Because nickel alloys, particularly the nickel-chromium alloys, have higher yield strengths and strain-hardening rates, they require stronger and harder dies and more powerful equipment than does low-carbon steel. Generally, 30 to 50% more power is required for nickel alloys than for low-carbon steel.

Equipment Operation. The strain-rate sensitivity and frictional characteristics of nickel alloys dictate that all forming operations, exclusive of high-energy-rate operations, be performed at relatively slow speeds. For instance, the slide speed in shearing, deep drawing, and press-brake bending is usually 30 to 50 ft per minute. Cold heading, piercing and similar operations are normally done at speeds of 60 to 100 strokes per minute.

Shearing, Blanking and Piercing

The optimum temper of nickel alloys for shearing, blanking and piercing varies from skin hard to full hard, depending on the alloy and thickness. For instance, thin strip of Nickel 200 should be blanked in full-hard temper for maximum die life and minimum edge burr, but Inconel 600 usually gives best results in skin-hard temper. Annealed temper is usually suitable for blanking of the precipitation-hardenable alloys such as Inconel X-750.

Punch-to-die clearance per side should be 3 to 5% of stock thickness for thin material and 5 to 10% of stock thickness for thick (⅛ in. and over) material. The clearance between the punch and the stripper plate should be as little as is practicable.

Shears should have a low-carbon steel rating of 50% greater than the size of the nickel alloy material to be sheared. For example, a shear with a low-carbon steel rating of ⅜ in. should be used to cut ¼-in.-thick Monel 400 plate.

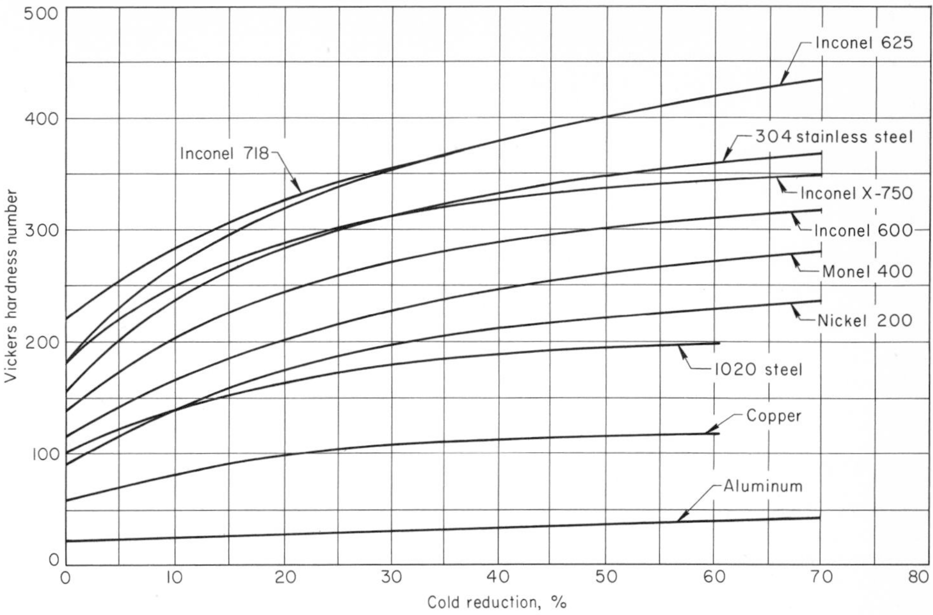

Fig. 1. Effect of cold work on the hardness of sheet metals

Table 2. Minimum Hole Diameters for Piercing Quarter-Hard Sheet of Nickel 200, Monel 400 and Inconel 600

Sheet thickness, in.	Minimum hole diameter
0.018 to 0.034	1.5 × thickness
0.037 to 0.070	1.3 × thickness
0.078 to 0.140	1.2 × thickness
5/32 and thicker	1.0 × thickness

Lubricants are usually omitted in shearing but should be used in blanking and piercing. A light mineral oil fortified with lard oil can be used for material less than ⅛ in. thick. A heavier sulfurized oil should be used for material that is thicker than ⅛ in.

Procedure. In piercing, the minimum hole diameter is usually equal to or greater than the thickness of the material, depending on the thickness, temper and specific alloy. Table 2 is a guide for establishing minimum hole diameters for given thicknesses of Monel 400, Nickel 200, and Inconel 600. Hole diameters equal to the thickness of the sheet have been produced in material as thin as 0.018 in., but only after considerable experience and with proper equipment.

The softer alloys, such as Nickel 200, have greater impact strength than have the harder, chromium-containing alloys. Consequently, the softer alloys are more sensitive to the condition of dies and equipment. Shear knives may penetrate 65 to 75% of the material thickness before separation occurs in shearing Nickel 200, whereas penetration may be only 20 to 30% in shearing the harder alloys.

Laboratory tests have indicated that the shear strength of nickel alloys in double shear averages about 65% of the tensile strength (see Table 3). However, these values were obtained under essentially ideal conditions using laboratory testing equipment having sharp edges and controlled clearances. The relationship of shear loads on nickel to those on low-carbon steel in production shearing is shown in Table 4; these data were derived using a power shear with a rake of $\frac{5}{16}$ in. per foot of blade length.

Deep Drawing

Nickel alloys can be drawn into any shape that is feasible with deep drawing steel. Nickel alloys have physical characteristics different from those of deep drawing steel, but not sufficiently so as to require different manipulation of dies for the average deep drawing operation.

Most simple shapes can be deep drawn in nickel alloys using dies and tools designed for use on steel or copper alloys. However, when intricate shapes

Table 3. Strength of Four Nickel Alloys in Double Shear (Results of Laboratory Tests)

Condition	Strength, psi — Shear	Strength, psi — Tensile	Rockwell hardness
Nickel 200			
Annealed	52,000	68,000	B 46
Half hard	58,000	79,000	B 84
Full hard	75,000	121,000	B 100
Monel 400			
Hot rolled, annealed	48,750	73,000	B 65
Cold rolled, annealed	49,500	76,800	B 60
Inconel 600			
Annealed	60,800	85,000	B 71
Half hard	66,250	98,800	B 98
Full hard	82,400	152,200	C 31
Inconel X-750			
Aged 1300 F, 20 hr	112,500	171,000	C 36

Table 4. Production Shear Loads for Nickel Alloy Sheet and Strip

Condition	Shear load, % of mild steel of same thickness	Tensile strength of sheet, psi	Rockwell B hardness
Nickel 200			
Annealed	113	68,500	43
Half hard	119	75,200	78
Full hard	127	113,000	100
Monel 400			
Annealed	116	81,150	67
Half hard	128	87,500	86
Full hard	130	136,450	104
Inconel 600			
Annealed	119	91,700	74
Half hard	127	115,000	99
Full hard	131	145,000	109

with accurate finished dimensions are required, minor die alterations are necessary. These alterations usually involve increasing clearances and enlarging the radius of the draw ring or of the punch nose.

Double-Action Drawing. In drawing and redrawing of thin stock (1/16 in. and under) into cylindrical shells with no ironing, the diameter reduction should be 35 to 40% on the first, or cupping, operation, and 15 to 25% on redraws. If the walls are held to size, the first and second operations may be the same as suggested above, but on further redrawing, the amount of reduction should be diminished about 5% on each successive redraw.

Although reductions of up to 50% can be made in one operation, this is not advisable because of the possibility of excessive shell breakage. Also, large reductions may open the surface of the metal and cause difficulty in finishing.

The number of redraws that can be made before annealing is necessary depends on the alloy being drawn. The alloys with the lower rates of work hardening (Fig. 1) can often undergo more than one redraw without an intermediate anneal. Trial runs may be needed to determine when annealing is necessary.

Single-Action Drawing. As with all metals, the depth to which nickel alloys can be drawn in single-action presses without hold-down mechanisms is controlled by the ratio of blank thickness to blank or workpiece diameter. For single-action drawing without hold-down pressure, the blank thickness should be at least 2% of the blank or workpiece diameter for reductions of up to 35%. With properly designed dies and sufficiently thick material, the reduction on the first (cupping) operation with a single-action setup may be made equal to those recommended for double-action dies — that is, 35 to 40%. Redraws should not exceed 20% reduction.

If the shell wall is to be ironed, the increased pressure on the bottom of the shell usually necessitates a decrease in the amount of reduction to prevent shell breakage. With reductions of 5% or less, the shell wall may be thinned as much as 30% in one draw. With medium reductions of about 12%, the thickness of the shell wall can be decreased about 15%. If the wall is to be reduced a large amount, the shell should first be drawn to the approximate size with little or no wall thinning and the ironing done last. If a good surface finish is desired, the final operation should have a burnishing effect with only a slight change in wall thickness.

Clearances. Because nickel alloys have higher mechanical properties than low-carbon steel of drawing quality, nickel alloys have greater resistance to the wall thinning caused by the pressure of the punch on the bottom of the shell. Consequently, greater die clearance is required than for steel if the natural flow of the metal is not to be resisted. However, the clearances required for nickel alloys are only slightly greater than those required for steel, and if dies used for steel have greater-than-minimum clearances, they are usually satisfactory for drawing nickel alloys, depending primarily on the mechanical properties of the alloy.

Table 5. Maximum Blank Thickness and Hardness for Manual Spinning of Nickel Alloys With Hand or Compound-Lever Tools

Alloy	Maximum Rockwell B hardness	Maximum thickness, in.
Nickel 200	64	0.062
Nickel 201	55	0.078
Monel 400	68	0.050
Inconel 600	80	0.037
Inconel 722	94	0.037
Inconel X-750	94	0.037
Incoloy 801	88	0.037

For ordinary deep drawing of cylindrical shells, a clearance per side of 120 to 125% of the blank thickness is sufficient, and will prevent the formation of wrinkles. In the drawing of sheet thicker than 1/16 in., it is a general practice to have the inside diameter of the draw ring larger than the diameter of the punch by three times the thickness of the blank (150% of stock thickness per side).

Draw-Ring and Punch Radii. Because nickel alloys work harden rapidly, relatively large draw-ring and punch radii should be used, especially for the early operations in a series of draws. Nickel alloys require more power to draw than does steel, and, consequently, the punch imposes a greater stress on the bottom corner of the shell. Small punch radii cause thinning of the shell at the line of contact, and if such a shell is further reduced, the thinned areas will appear farther up the shell wall, and may result in visible necking or rupture. Also, buffing a shell having thinned areas will cause the shell wall to have a wavy appearance. For redraws, it is preferable to draw over a beveled edge and to avoid round-edged punches except for the final draw.

The draw-ring radius for a circular die is governed principally by the thickness of the material to be drawn and the amount of reduction to be made. A general rule for light-gage material is to have the draw-ring radius from five to twelve times the thickness of the metal. Insufficient draw-ring radius may result in galling and excessive thinning of the wall.

Rectangular Shells. As with other materials, the depth to which nickel-alloy rectangular shapes can be drawn in one operation is governed principally by the corner radius. To permit drawing to substantial depths, the corner radii should be as large as possible. Even with large corner radii, the depth of draw should be limited to from two to five times the corner radius for Monel 400, Nickel 200 and Nickel 201, and to four times the corner radius for Inconel 600. The depth permissible also depends on the dimensions of the shape, and on whether the shape has straight or tapered sides. The depth of draw for sheet less than 0.025 in. thick should not exceed an amount equal to three times the corner radius for Monel 400, Nickel 200 and Nickel 201, and less for Inconel 600.

The corner radius on the drawing edge of the die should be as large as possible — approximately four to ten times the thickness of the material. To avoid wrinkles around the top corner of the shape, it is essential that the blank not be released too soon.

In redrawing for the purpose of sharpening the corners or smoothing out wrinkles along the sides, only a small amount of metal should be left in the corners.

Frequently, it is necessary to draw shapes on dies designed to make a deeper single draw than is practical for nickel alloys. With such dies, the general practice is to draw about two thirds of the full depth, to anneal the shape after this draw, and to complete the draw to full depth on the same dies. This same practice can be used to avoid wrinkling in drawing to lesser depths.

Spinning

Power spinning is preferred over manual spinning for nickel alloys. However, thin material, particularly of Nickel 200 and Monel 400, can be manually spun with no difficulty. Table 5 gives practical limits on blank thickness for manual spinning of seven nickel alloys.

Tools. Except for small, light shapes, the required pressure cannot be exerted with the ordinary bar or hand tool pivoted on a fixed pin. Most shapes require the use of a tool that is mechanically adapted for the application of greater force, such as a compound-lever tool or roller tools that are operated by a screw. For small jobs, a ball-bearing assembly can be used on the end of a compound lever to make a good roller tool. Roller tools should be used whenever practicable in order to keep friction at a minimum and exert maximum pressure. Roller tools should also be used to perfect the contour in the spinning of press-drawn shapes.

When possible, tools used for spinning nickel alloys should be broader and flatter than those used for softer materials. The broader tool distributes plastic flow over a greater area and reduces overstraining. Except for this consideration, bar and roller tools should be designed the same as those used for spinning copper or brass.

Correct tool materials are essential for successful spinning. The most suitable material for bar tools is a highly polished, hard alloy bronze. Hardened tool steels are preferred for roller and beading tools. Hard-chromium-plated hardened tool steel is recommended as it decreases metal pickup by the tool. Tools of common brass and carbon steel, which are used for spinning softer materials, are unsatisfactory for use with nickel alloys.

Rotary cutting shears are preferred for edge trimming. If rotary shears are not available, hand trimming bars hard faced with cobalt-base alloy may be used, but the trimming speed must be reduced. Hand trimming bars should be ground so that they have a back-rake angle of 15° to 20° from the cutting edge, and the edge must be kept sharp. A tool shaped like a thread-cutting lathe tool can be used for trimming. This tool also has a back rake from the cutting edge. With this type of tool, the material is not sheared off the edge; instead, the tool is fed into the side of the workpiece and a narrow ring is cut from the edge. The workpiece should be

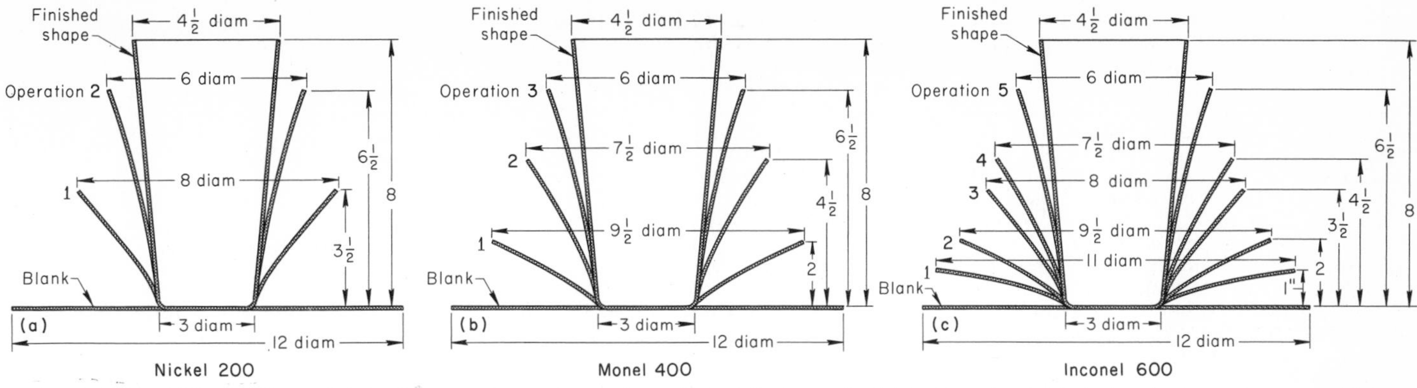

Fig. 2. Spinnability of three nickel alloys, as shown by number of operations required for manual spinning of a deep cup from a 0.037-in.-thick blank of each alloy. Annealing followed each numbered operation.

supported at the back during all trimming operations.

Chucks. Hardened alloy cast iron and steel chucks give longer life and better results than wood chucks. Hard maple or birch chucks may be used for intermediate operations if quantities are small and tolerances are liberal.

Spinning nickel alloys over chucks that are the same as those used for copper will not necessarily result in spun shapes of exactly the same dimensions as those of the softer metal. Most shapes of nickel alloy will have slightly larger peripheries than those of softer metals spun over the same chuck. This is caused by the difference in springback of the nickel alloys.

Lubricants. Heavy-bodied, solid lubricants, such as yellow laundry soap, beeswax and tallow, are recommended for spinning. These lubricants can be manually applied to the blank as it rotates. Blanks can be electroplated with 0.0002 to 0.0007 in. of copper to improve lubrication on difficult shapes.

Procedure for spinning nickel alloys is essentially the same as that used for other metals (see the article "Spinning", which begins on page 201).

As a general rule in laying out a spinning sequence for Monel 400, an increase in height of 1 to 1½ in. on the article being spun constitutes an operation if spinning is being done in the usual way with a bar tool. Approximately twice that depth per operation may be obtained with a compound-lever or roller tool. The workpiece should be trimmed and annealed before it is spun to greater depths.

In the early stages of spinning, shapes of Nickel 200 and Nickel 201 can usually be spun to two and occasionally three times the depth of a Monel 400 operation before annealing is required.

A hard-surfaced chuck should be provided for each operation so that the metal can always be pushed firmly against the surface of the chuck. This procedure keeps the surface of the work smooth and dense, and ensures the best results in annealing. With an insufficient number of intermediate chucks, the material is subjected to an excessive amount of cold working. This may result either in spinning a buckle into the material or in pulling it and forming a pebbled surface. It is virtually impossible to smooth out the former by additional cold work, or to correct the latter by annealing.

Figure 2 illustrates the number of chucks and annealing operations necessary for spinning deep cups from 0.037-in.-thick blanks of Nickel 200, Monel 400 and Inconel 600 using hand tools. This illustration also shows the amount of forming that can be done before annealing and between intermediate anneals. The spinnability of other alloys can be estimated from their relative work-hardening rates, shown in Fig. 1, and from their tensile properties.

In spinning, the optimum speed of the rotating blank is governed by its diameter and thickness. Small, thin blanks can be spun at greater speeds than larger or thicker pieces. Most operators spin nickel alloys at speeds of one half to three fourths those normally used in spinning the same shape from softer metals. Lathe speeds of 250 to 1000 rpm are usually satisfactory. Trimming speeds must necessarily be slow; ordinarily, trimming is done at the minimum speed of the lathe.

Bending Tube and Pipe

All common forming operations such as bending, coining and expanding can be performed readily on nickel alloy tube and pipe, using the same type of equipment as for other metals. (For information on tube-bending equipment, see the article on Bending and Forming of Tubing, which begins on page 308 in this volume.) In general, material in the annealed condition is recommended. Monel 400, Nickel 200 and Nickel 201 can be formed in the stress-relieved temper; however, the amount of deformation will be limited by the higher tensile strength and lower ductility. In bending, the minimum radius to which stress-relieved tubing can be bent is 25 to 50% greater than for annealed tubing of the same size.

The minimum radii to which nickel alloy tubing can be bent by various methods are given in Table 6. Depending on equipment design, tube size, and quality of the finished bend, it is possible to bend to smaller radii than those listed in Table 6; however, trial bends should be made to determine if the smaller radii are practicable.

Bending Without Mandrels or Fillers. When bending with no internal support, the dies should be slightly smaller than those used for bending with a mandrel or filler. Bending without use of a mandrel or filler is suitable only for tube and pipe that have a wall thickness greater than 7% of the outside diameter, or for bends of large radii. Nickel alloy tube in sizes within the

Table 6. Minimum Bend Radii for Nickel Alloy Tube

Method of bending	Minimum mean bend radius(a)	Maximum included angle of bend
Press bending, unfilled tube	6*D*	120°
Roll bending, filled tube ...	4*D*	360°
Compression bending:		
Unfilled tube	2½*D*	180°
Filled tube(b)	2*D*	180°
Draw bending:		
Unfilled tube	3*D*	180°
Filled tube(b)	2*D*	180°

(a) *D* = tube OD. (b) Or using mandrel.

above ratio can be bent with no mandrel or filler to a minimum mean radius of three times the outside diameter of the tube (3*D*) through 180°.

Bending With Mandrels or Fillers. Thin-wall tubing can be bent to small radii with freedom from wrinkles by use of a mandrel or filler. Thin-wall tubing of nickel alloys can be mandrel-bent through 180° to a minimum mean radius of 2*D*.

To minimize galling of the inside surface of the tube, mandrels should be made of hard alloy bronze rather than of steel. If steel mandrels are used, they should be chromium plated to reduce galling.

Mandrels must be lubricated before use. Lubricants of extreme-pressure, chlorinated oil are best for severe bending. For less severe bending or for ease of removal, water-soluble lubricants are used.

Any conventional filler material, like sand, resin, and low-melting alloys, can be used. Sand is the least desirable because it is difficult to pack tightly and hence can lead to the formation of wrinkles or kinks during bending.

Low-melting-alloy fillers produce the best bends. The expansion characteristics of these fillers insure that voids are eliminated and a sound center is created.

Alloy fillers are removed by heating the bent tube in steam or hot water. Metallic fillers must not be removed by direct torch heating, because they contain elements such as lead, tin and bismuth that will embrittle nickel alloys at elevated temperatures. It is imperative that all traces of metallic fillers be removed if the tube is to be subjected to elevated temperatures during subsequent fabrication or during service.

Press Bending. Press or ram bending, in which the tube is held by two supporting dies and a force applied between the dies, is normally used only for heavy-wall tubing where some flattening is tolerable. This method does not provide close tolerances and is applicable only to large-radius bends. The bend is limited to 120°, and the radius of the bend should not be less than six times the outside diameter of the tube (*6D*) if a smooth bend is desired. A filler material should be used for bends of radii less than *6D*.

Pressure dies used in press bending should be at least two times the outside diameter of the tube in length. Press bending with wing dies is used for unfilled, thin-wall, large-diameter tube.

Annealed tubing is not always preferred for press bending. Annealed tubing of low base hardness is not stiff enough to withstand deformation without excessive flattening. Consequently, nickel and nickel-copper alloys are usually press-bent in the stress-relieved temper. The chromium-containing Incoloy and Inconel alloys have higher mechanical properties in the annealed condition than nickel and nickel-copper alloys and should be press-bent in the annealed temper. Ideally, the choice of temper for a specific bend should be determined from the results of several trial bends.

Roll bending is the principal method of producing helical coils, spirals and circular configurations since an included angle of 360° can be obtained. Bending may be done on either unfilled or filled tube. The minimum bend radius that can be attained on unfilled tube is approximately six times the outside diameter of the tube.

Compression bending utilizes a stationary bending form and a movable wiper shoe. This method is unsuitable for thin-wall tubing and is generally used with no mandrel support.

Compression bending can produce bend radii down to 2½*D* but is normally used only for large-radius bends. The maximum included angle that can be produced is 180°.

Draw bending is the most common bending process and the preferred method for bending nickel alloy tube. The process is similar to compression bending, except that the bending form revolves and the pressure die either remains stationary or slides along a straight line. The sliding pressure die is preferred, because it distributes the applied stresses more evenly.

Bends of up to 180° with a minimum radius of *2D* can be produced by draw bending. Bending can be done with or without a mandrel. In general, a mandrel is preferred and must be used when the ratio of tube diameter to wall thickness is above the limit suitable for bending without tube wrinkling or collapsing. Various types of mandrels are used, including ball and plug types.

Hot Bending. When possible, tube and pipe should be formed by cold bending. If hot bending is necessary, it is performed by standard hot bending methods. Temperatures for hot bending of nickel alloys are the same as those in Fig. 1 in the article on Forging of Nickel, in Volume 5 of this Handbook.

Hot bending is normally limited to tube and pipe larger than 2-in. schedule 80. Thin-wall tubing should not be bent hot, because it is difficult to retain sufficient heat to make the bend.

Hot bending should be done on filled tube only. Sand is the normal filler material. The sand must be free of sulfur, because contamination of nickel alloy by sulfur will cause cracking of the tube during bending. Sulfur can be removed from sand by heating it to about 2100 F in an oxidizing atmosphere.

Tubing must be cleaned thoroughly before filling or heating.

Sand-filled tube and pipe in small sizes (2 to 2½-in. pipe size) can be bent hot to a minimum mean radius of two times the outside diameter of the tube. Larger sizes require greater bend radii.

In hot bending, the metal should be worked as soon as possible after removal from the furnace, to avoid cooling before bending is completed.

Expanding Heat-Exchanger Tube

Nickel alloy tubing can be expanded into tube sheets by any conventional method. The oversize allowance on tube-sheet holes to the nominal outside diameter of the tube should be kept to a minimum. The tube-sheet hole should be 0.004 to 0.008 in. larger than the nominal outside diameter of the tube for tubing less than 1½ in. in outside diameter. For tubing 1½ in. or larger in outside diameter, the oversize allowance should be 0.009 to 0.010 in.

Procedure. Expanding may be done by drifting with sectional expanders or by rolling with three-roll expanders. Three-roll expanders are preferred. The ends of rolled-in tubing are flared in the conventional manner.

The tube-sheet hole and both the outside and inside surfaces of the tube must be free of all foreign matter such as oxide, dirt and oil. The ends of the tube should also be deburred before rolling.

Lubrication should be provided between the rollers of the tool and the inside surface of the tube. Any sulfur-free mineral oil or lard oil, either diluted or straight, can be used. Lubricants that contain embrittling or contaminating elements such as sulfur or lead should be avoided, because of the difficulty in cleaning the finished assembly.

Controlled rolling equipment should be used to prevent overexpanding the tubes. Overexpanding may distort the tube sheet and plastically deform the tube-sheet ligaments, causing loose-fitting tubes. This is particularly true when the tube has a higher hardness than the tube sheet or a significantly higher rate of work hardening.

Temper. The tube sheet should be harder than the tube being rolled into it. Otherwise, springback in the tube may be greater than in the tube sheet, causing a gap between the two when the expanding tool is removed. For this reason, tube sheets are usually supplied in the as-rolled or as-forged temper and tube in the annealed temper. The need for the tube sheet to be harder than the tube is greatest when the thickness of the tube sheet is less than the outside diameter of the tube, and when the center-to-center spacing of the tubes (tube pitch) is less than 1¼ times the outside diameter of the tube, or the outside diameter plus ¼ in., whichever is greater.

Stress-relieved tubing may be slightly harder than the tube sheet but can be expanded to form a satisfactory connection if greater care is exercised in expanding. For greater assurance of pressure tightness, a seal weld may be placed around the end of the tube after expanding. The stress-relieved temper is suitable for either welding or silver brazing.

If rolling of stress-relieved tube appears to be a marginal operation, the problem can often be remedied by using annealed tube or stress-relieved tube with the ends annealed. Stress-relieved, end-annealed tubing combines the strength advantage of stress-relieved material with the ease of fabrication of annealed material.

Tubing in the annealed condition is used when optimum rolling or expanding characteristics are desired or for severe cold bending and flaring.

Forming of Rod and Bar

Rod and bar in the annealed condition are preferred for cold forming. Material in other tempers may be required for some forming operations or when properties that cannot be obtained by heat treatment after forming are desired in the end product.

Bending. Rod and bar may be bent in the same manner as tubing. The possibility of collapsing or wrinkling is eliminated, as the solid section provides its own internal support.

Most nickel alloys have suitable mechanical properties in the hot finished condition for moderate bending. The annealed temper should always be used for extremely short bend radii or low radius-to-thickness ratios. Cold drawn, annealed material should be used if surface roughening (orange peeling) related to coarse grain structure is undesirable.

Coiling of rod and bar is limited almost entirely to the production of springs. Nickel alloy springs for high-temperature service are usually annealed or solution treated and age hardened after forming. Consequently, they may be produced from annealed material (or even produced by hot coiling) with no adverse effect on final properties.

If the desired properties cannot be obtained by heat treating after forming, the spring must be coiled from tempered, cold worked material. The use of tempered material will greatly increase the minimum radius to which the rod or bar can be coiled.

Pressures and speeds encountered in production coiling usually require the use of high-grade lubricants with good film strength. Wire rod is often coated with copper to reduce friction and improve retention of organic lubricants.

The severe cold forming involved in producing coils and the severe service conditions in which these products are often used demand a high-grade starting product. Centerless-ground or ground and cold drawn material is used to obtain the necessary quality.

Cold Heading and Cold Extrusion

Cold heading and cold extrusion are most often used in the production of fasteners and similar cold upset parts. Cold extrusion is rarely done except in conjunction with cold heading.

The high strength and galling characteristics of the nickel alloys require slow operating speeds and high-alloy die materials. Cold heading machines should be operated at a ram speed of about 35 to 50 ft per minute. These ram speeds correspond to operating speeds of 60 to 100 strokes per minute on medium-size equipment.

Tools should be made of oil-hardening or air-hardening die steel. The air-hardening types, such as D2, D4 or high speed steel (M2 or T1), tempered to Rockwell C 60 to 63, are preferred.

Material. Rod stock (usually less than 1 in. in diameter) in coils is used for starting material, as cold heading is done on high-speed automatic or semiautomatic equipment. Although Monel 400 is sometimes cold headed in larger sizes, ⅞ in. is the maximum diameter in which Monel 400 and K-500 can be cold headed by most equipment. Limiting sizes in harder alloys are proportionately smaller, depending on their hardness and yield strength in the annealed condition. Stock sizes in excess of these limits are normally hot headed.

Cold heading equipment requires wire rod with diameter tolerances in the range of 0.003 to 0.005 in. Because Monel 400 should be cold headed in the 0 or No. 1 temper to provide resistance to crushing and buckling during forming, these tolerances can normally be obtained with the drawing pass used to develop this temper. For tighter tolerances or harder alloys, fully cold drawn material must be used.

The surface quality of regular hot rolled wire rod, even with a cold sizing pass, may not be adequate for cold heading. Consequently, a special cold-heading-quality wire rod is usually recommended. Configurations that are especially susceptible to splitting, such as rivets, flat-head screws and socket-head bolts, require shaved or centerless-ground material.

Lubricants. To prevent galling, high-grade lubricants must be used in cold heading nickel alloys.

Lime and soap are usually used as a base coating on Monel 400. Better finish and die life can be obtained by using copper plating (0.0003 to 0.0007 in. thick) as a lubricant carrier. Copper plating may be used also on the chromium-containing alloys such as Inconel 600 and Incoloy 800, but oxalate coatings serve as an adequate substitute.

Regardless of the type of carrier, a base lubricant is best applied by drawing it on in a light sizing pass to obtain a dry film of the lubricant. Any of the high-titre, dry soap powders of the sodium, calcium or aluminum stearate types can be applied this way.

If the wire rod is to be given a sizing or tempering pass before the cold heading operations, the heading lubricant should be applied during drawing.

Lubrication for cold heading is completed by dripping a heavy, sulfurized mineral oil or a sulfurized and chlorinated paraffin on the blank as it passes through the heading stations.

Straightening

Rod and bar in straight lengths are usually straightened by conical rolls, stretchers or punch presses. Material in coil form is straightened with staggered-roll straighteners or rotating-die straighteners.

Like other forming equipment, straighteners require about 50% more power for nickel alloys than for low-carbon steel; a straightener having a capacity of ½-in. diameter in steel will be limited to about ⅜-in. diameter in nickel alloys.

A lubricant should be used with rotating-die straighteners to reduce scratching and scoring, and to improve die life. Spiral scoring may become quite severe on large sizes of harder alloys. If scoring cannot be held to an acceptable level by using lubricants, material in the softest available temper should be used.

Staggered-roll straightening involves lower contact velocities than rotating-die types, and lubrication is less critical. Coil stock is often straightened without lubricant, for better grip on rolls.

Dies for rotary-die straighteners may be either bronze or cast iron. Cast iron dies must be used if contamination from bronze rubbing off occurs in the end product, and no pickling is done after straightening.

Forming of Titanium Alloys

*By the ASM Committee on Fabrication of Titanium**

TITANIUM ALLOYS can be formed in standard machines to tolerances similar to those obtained in the forming of stainless steel. However, in order to lessen the effect of springback variation on accuracy and to gain the advantage of increased ductility, the great majority of formed titanium parts are made by hot forming or by cold preforming and then hot sizing.

Characteristics of titanium and titanium alloys that must be considered in forming are:

1 Variation in mechanical properties from heat to heat
2 Notch sensitivity, which may cause cracking and tearing, especially in cold forming
3 Galling (worse than with stainless steel)
4 Poor ability to shrink (a disadvantage in some flanging operations)
5 Embrittlement from overheating and from absorption of gases, principally hydrogen (Scale and the surface layer adversely affected by the slower penetration of oxygen can be removed readily.)
6 Narrow spread (workability range) between yield strength and tensile strength.

The formability of annealed titanium alloys in six forming operations, at room temperature or at elevated temperatures, is given in Table 1.

Mechanical properties of titanium and its alloys vary widely. For example, the tensile strength of different grades of commercially pure titanium ranges from 35,000 to 80,000 psi, with correspondingly large differences in the minimum bend radius at room temperature. The tensile strength and ductility of commercially pure titanium are largely dependent on its oxygen content. Various grades of commercially pure titanium are available; the purer grades have lower oxygen content and are more formable.

Springback. In general, springback in forming titanium and titanium alloys varies directly with the ratio of bend radius to work-metal thickness, and inversely with forming temperature. These effects are illustrated for press-brake forming of alloy Ti-6Al-4V, in Fig. 4. Springback generally is reduced by increasing the forming pressure, as illustrated in the discussion of rubber-pad forming in this article.

The usual relation between springback and forming temperature does not hold true for all titanium alloys in rubber-pad forming, as illustrated in the data on stretch and shrink flanging in Table 10.

Springback in titanium alloys is more difficult to predict than springback in steel, although it depends on the same principles. Differences in the yield strength of various heats of titanium

*FRANCIS W. BOULGER, *Chairman,* Senior Technical Advisor, Columbus Laboratories, Battelle Memorial Institute; N. F. BRATKOVICH, Section Chief, Allison Div., General Motors Corp.; S. R. CARPENTER, Design Specialist, Astronautics Div., General Dynamics; JAMES E. COYNE, JR., Director of Research, Wyman-Gordon Co.; ERNEST DELL, Vice President, Tri-D Corp.

V. V. DONALDSON, Senior Application Engineer, Forge and Spring Div., Alco Products, Inc.; GENE F. ERBIN, General Manager, Technical Service and Development, Titanium Metals Corp. of America; GLENN FAULKNER, Aerojet General Corp.; REX A. FORD, Manufacturing Research Project Engineer, Vought Aeronautics Div., LTV Aerospace Corp.; GERALD GARFIELD, Assistant Director of Materials and Methods, Research and Engineering, Douglas Aircraft Co., Inc.; LARRY S. KLASS, Staff Engineer, Aerostructures Div., Avco Corp.; W. F. OSTERLOH, Manufacturing Engineering Coordinator, McDonnell Douglas Aircraft Co.

G. PFANNER, Chief of Manufacturing Research and Processes, Republic Aviation Div., Fairchild Hiller; R. M. POTTER, Research Engineer, Metallurgical Material and Process Laboratory, Columbus Div., North American Rockwell, Inc.; I. J. STEWART, Physical Research Laboratory, Cincinnati Milling Machine Co.; VERNON R. THOMPSON, Crucible Steel Co.; THOMAS L. WILE, Project Chief, Manufacturing Development and Research Section, Airplane Div., Boeing Co.

Table 1. Formability of Annealed Titanium Alloys in Six Forming Operations at Room Temperature or Elevated Temperature(a)

Press brake (minimum bend radius), 70 F	Guerin rubber-pad process(b): Stretch (maximum stretch), 600 to 700 F	Guerin rubber-pad process(b): Shrink (maximum shrink), 600 to 700 F	Stretch wrap (maximum stretch), 70 F	Skin stretch (maximum stretch), 850 to 950 F	Drop hammer (max stretch), 900 to 1450 F	Joggle (Length/depth ratio), 70 F	Joggle (Length/depth ratio), 600 to 700 F
Ti-13V-11Cr-3Al (1.5t)	Ti-13V-11Cr-3Al (10%)	Ti-13V-11Cr-3Al (6%)	Ti-8Mn (8%)	Ti-8Mn (18%)	Ti-13V-11Cr-3Al (16%)	Ti-13V-11Cr-3Al (1.25)	Ti-13V-11Cr-3Al (1)
Ti-8Mn (3t)	Ti-8Mn (7.5%)	Ti-8Mn (5%)	Ti-5Al-2.5Sn (8%)	Ti-6Al-4V (17%)	Ti-8Mn (16%)	Ti-8Mn (4)	Ti-8Mn (3)
Ti-5Al-2.5Sn (3.5t)	Ti-6Al-4V (5%)	Ti-6Al-4V (4%)	Ti-13V-11Cr-3Al (5.5%)	Ti-13V-11Cr-3Al (13.5%)	Ti-5Al-2.5Sn (13%)	Ti-5Al-2.5Sn (4)	Ti-6Al-4V (3)
Ti-8Al-2Cb-1Ta (4t)	Ti-5Al-2.5Sn (<5%)	Ti-5Al-2.5Sn (3%)	Ti-6Al-4V (3.5%)	Ti-5Al-2.5Sn (12.5%)	Ti-6Al-4V (13%)	Ti-6Al-4V (4.5)	Ti-5Al-2.5Sn (4.5)
Ti-4Al-3Mo-1V(c) (4.5t)							
Ti-2.5Al-16V(c) (4.5t)							
Ti-6Al-4V (4.5t)							
Ti-5Al-2.75Cr-1.25Fe (6.2t)							

(a) Alloys are listed in order of forming ease, the most formable alloy being at the top of the list. Numbers in parentheses following alloy designations are laboratory test values for the indexes of formability shown in parentheses at the top of each list. Laboratory index values shown should be relaxed at least 25% when designing for production. (b) The rubber-pad process is the least suitable of all processes listed for forming at elevated temperature. (c) Solution treated condition.

can cause differences in springback; higher ratios of yield strength to tensile strength generally result in greater springback. Accordingly, properties of titanium and titanium alloy stock must be specified carefully for critical forming applications.

Preparation of Sheet for Forming

Before titanium sheet is formed, it should be inspected for flatness, uniformity and thickness. Some plants test incoming material for hardness, strength and bending behavior.

Critical regions of titanium sheet should not be nicked, scratched or marred by tool or grinding marks, because the metal is notch sensitive. All scratches deeper than the finish produced by 180-grit emery should be removed by sanding the surface. Edges of the workpieces should be smooth, and scratches, if any, should be parallel to the edge of the blank, to prevent any concentration of stress that could cause the workpiece to break. To prevent difficulty in forming, as by increased notch sensitivity, surface oxide or scale should be removed before the titanium is formed.

Blanks and workpieces of titanium should be interleaved with paper or otherwise protected, to keep dirt and moisture from the metal. Holding the stock at room temperature for a period before forming helps to prevent condensation of water on metal that has been stored in a cold place.

Cleaning. Grease, oil, stencils, fingerprints, dirt, and all chemicals or residues that contain halogen compounds must be removed from titanium before any heating operation. Salt residues on the surface of the workpiece can cause stress corrosion in service or in heat treating; even the salt from a fingerprint can cause trouble. For this reason, titanium is often handled with clean cotton gloves after it has been cleaned, and before hot forming, hot sizing, or heat treatment.

Ordinary cleaners and solvents such as isopropyl alcohol and methyl-ethyl ketone are used on titanium. Halogen compounds, such as trichlorethylene, should not be used, unless the titanium is pickled in acid after cleaning.

Titanium that has been straightened or formed with tools made of lead or of low-melting alloy should be cleaned in nitric acid. Detailed information on the cleaning of titanium is given in the article "Cleaning and Finishing of Titanium Alloys", pages 664 to 668 in Volume 2 of this Handbook.

Table 2. Guide to the Amount of Metal That Should Be Removed After Heat Treatment of Titanium Alloys

Heat treating temperature, F	Thickness (in.) to be removed after heat treating for: Up to 10 min	10 to 30 min	30 min to 2 hr	2 to 10 hr	10 to 20 hr
Up to 1025	None	None	None	0.0005	0.001
1025 to 1200	0.0002	0.0005	0.001	0.001	0.002
1200 to 1350	0.0005	0.0005	0.001	0.002	0.003
1350 to 1500	0.001	0.001	0.002	0.003	0.005
1600 to 1750	0.003	0.004	0.005	...	...
1900 to 1950	0.005	0.008	0.012	...	...

Removal of Marks. Tool and grinding marks can be removed from titanium in an aqueous acid bath containing (by volume) 30% concentrated nitric acid and not more than 3% hydrofluoric acid. Failure to keep the ratio of nitric to hydrofluoric acid at 10 to 1 or greater (to suppress the formation of hydrogen gas during pickling), or the use of any pickling bath that produces hydrogen, can result in hydrogen embrittlement. The acid bath should remove 0.001 to 0.003 in. of thickness from each surface to eliminate the marks made by abrasives. Titanium should be washed or cleaned before it is immersed in acid.

Removal of Scale. Heavy gray and black scale and similar hard oxides that form on titanium at temperatures of 1000 F and higher, can be removed chemically or by wet or dry mechanical methods that use fine abrasives. Wire brushing and coarse abrasives generally are not used, because they can leave stress-raising marks; if these techniques are used, the damaged surface layer can be removed by pickling the titanium in nitric-hydrofluoric acid, as described above.

Thin oxides that form at temperatures below 1000 F can be removed by acid pickling. Blue oxide, which forms at 700 to 800 F, can be removed in 1 to 5 min; purple oxide, which forms in more severe oxidation, can be removed in 5 to 10 min. The colors of the oxides may differ, depending on the alloy and on previous treatment.

Table 2 can be used as a guide for judging the amount of metal that should be removed to eliminate the surface layer contaminated during heating.

Tool Materials and Lubricants

Tool materials for forming titanium are chosen to suit the forming operation, forming temperature, and expected quantity of production. The cost of tool material generally is only a small fraction of the cost of tools.

Cold forming can be done with epoxy-faced aluminum or zinc tools; hot forming, with ceramic, cast iron, tool steel, stainless steel, and nickel alloy tools.

Galling is the severest problem to be overcome in hot forming. Lubricants may react unfavorably with titanium when it is heated. Molybdenum disulfide suspended in a volatile carrier has been used successfully. If the lubricant reacts with oxidation products to produce a tenacious surface soil, it must be removed by sand blasting with garnet grit or 120-mesh aluminum oxide.

Temperature-resistant lubricants for hot forming have a graphite or molybdenum disulfide base. Zinc phosphate conversion coatings are sometimes first produced on the work-metal surface to aid in the retention of lubricants during severe forming.

Lubricants for cold forming of titanium are generally similar to those used for severe forming of aluminum alloys.

Tool materials and lubricants for cold and hot forming of titanium alloys are given in Table 3.

Preparation of Blanks

Most blanking of titanium alloy sheet ¼ in. thick or less is done in a punch press. As with other metals, maximum blank size depends on stock thickness, shear strength and available press tonnage. (See pages 33 and 34 in the article "Blanking of Low-Carbon Steel" in this volume for methods of calculating force requirements.)

Dies must be rigid and sharp to prevent cracking of the work metal; hardened tool steel must be used for adequate die life.

In one application, holes 0.25 in. in diameter were punched in 0.040 to 0.140-in.-thick annealed alloy Ti-6Al-4V sheet to within ±0.002 in. of diameter and with surface roughness less than 50 micro-in. The best holes were produced with flat-point punches having 0.001-in. die clearance.

Shearing. Titanium sheet up to 0.140 in. thick generally can be sheared without difficulty; with extra care, titanium sheet as thick as 0.187 in. can be sheared. Shears intended for low-carbon steel may not have enough hold-down force to prevent titanium sheets from slipping. A sharp shear blade in

Table 3. Tool Materials and Lubricants for Cold and Hot Forming of Titanium Alloys

Operation	Tool material	Lubricant
	Cold Forming	
Press forming, drawing, drop hammer forming	Cast zinc die or lead punch, with stainless steel caps	Graphite suspension(a)
Press-brake forming	4340 steel (R_C 36 to 40)	Graphite suspension(a)
Contour roll forming, three-roll forming	O2 tool steel	SAE 60 oil
Stretch forming:		
Sheet	Cast aluminum with epoxy face	Grease-oil mixture or wax
Sections	Cast zinc, cast bronze	Wax and graphite(b)
Extrusions	Low-carbon steel, 4130 steel	Molybdenum disulfide or graphite suspension(a)
	Hot Forming	
Press forming, drawing, drop hammer forming	High-silicon cast iron, RA-330 stainless steel, Inconel X-750, Incoloy 802	Graphite suspension(a)
Sizing	Low-carbon steel, high-silicon gray or ductile iron, H13 tool steel, 310 or RA-330 stainless steel, Inconel X-750, Hastelloy X, Incoloy 802	Graphite suspension(a)
Press-brake forming	H11, H13 tool steel; Incoloy 802	Graphite suspension(a)
Contour roll forming, three-roll forming	H11 or H13 tool steel	Graphite suspension(a)
Stretch forming:		
Sheet	Cast ceramic	Graphite suspension(a)
Sections	H11 or H13 tool steel, high-silicon gray iron	Wax and graphite(b)
Extrusions	4130 steel, 310 stainless steel	Molybdenum disulfide or graphite suspension(a)

(a) In a suitable volatile solvent. (b) Ten parts wax to one part graphite, by volume.

good condition with a capacity for cutting 3/16-in.-thick low-carbon steel can cut 1/8-in.-thick titanium sheet. Cutters should be kept sharp, to prevent edge cracking of the blank.

Sheared edges, especially on thicker work metal, can have straightness deviations of 0.01 to 0.20 in., usually because the shear blade is not stiff enough. Shearing can cause cracks at the edges of some titanium sheet thicker than 0.080 in. If cracks or other irregularities develop in a critical portion of the workpiece, an alternative method of cutting should be used, such as band sawing.

Slitting of titanium alloy sheet can be done with conventional slitting equipment and also with draw-bench equipment. Slitting shears are capable of straight cuts only; rotary shears can cut gentle contours (approximately 10-in. minimum radius). The process is usable in thicknesses up to 0.100 in. However, an individual machine must be restricted to titanium thicknesses no greater than 40% of the thickness of low-carbon steel for which the machine is rated.

Band sawing prevents cracking at the edges of titanium sheet but causes large burrs. Ordinarily, band sawing is used to cut titanium sheet that is 0.125 in. or more in thickness. The selection of a band-sawing method (semifriction, friction, or conventional) depends chiefly on the thickness of the sheet to be cut, as shown below:

Sheet up to 0.1 in. thick .....Semifriction
Sheet 0.1 to 1.0 in. thick ....Friction
Sheet 0.1 to 4.0 in. thick ....Conventional

The conventional method has the greatest range of applicability, but is by far the slowest. The band saw should have automatic positive feed and band tensioning. Sharp high speed steel bands, and coolants, preferably applied as a spray mist, are necessary for reasonable cutting life. Bands with tungsten carbide cutting edges are used in sawing exceptionally thick material

Table 4. Stress-Relieving Treatments for Titanium Alloys

Alloy	Temperature, F (±25°)	Time at temperature, min(a)
Commercially pure Ti	900 to 1000	30 to 60
Ti-8Mn	1000	30 to 60
Ti-5Al-2.5Sn	1175	30 to 60
Ti-6Al-4V, annealed	1175	30 to 60
Ti-8Al-1Mo-1V, duplex annealed	1175	30 to 60
Ti-13V-11Cr-3Al, annealed	1325	15

(a) When hot-sizing fixtures are used, add 60 minutes per inch of maximum cross-section thickness of fixture. Cool in still air.

and to minimize burr height and the depth of the heat-affected zone. For recommended band speeds and other aspects of band sawing, see the article "Contour Band Sawing" in Volume 3 of this Handbook, and Table 17 on page 505 of Volume 3.

Friction band sawing is done with blade speeds of 7,000 to 14,000 sfm. The edge produced by friction band sawing is rough and has a heavy burr. The small heat-affected zone (0.010 in.) produced must be removed by subsequent milling or belt sanding. No coolant is used, and inexpensive carbon steel blades (3/4 in. wide, 8 to 10 pitch) will suffice.

Semifriction band sawing is done at blade speeds of 1000 to 1400 sfm with a 1/4-in.-wide, 12 to 18-pitch carbon steel blade. This process permits rapid cutting of stock thinner than 0.01 in. with no resulting heat-affected zone or discoloration near the cut edge. The burr produced is small and easily removed.

Nibbling can be used to cut irregular blanks of titanium, but most blanks need filing or grinding after nibbling.

Edge Preparation. All visual evidence of a sheared or broken edge on a part should be removed by machining, sanding or filing before final deburring or polishing. All rough projections, scratches and nicks must be removed. Extra material must be allowed at the edges of titanium blanks so that shear cracks and other defects can be removed. On sheared parts a minimum of 0.010 in. must be removed from the edge, and on punched holes 0.014 in. On parts cut by friction band sawing or abrasive sawing, 0.25 in. or one thickness of sheet should be removed, whichever is the smaller.

The lay of the finish on the edges of sheet-metal parts should be parallel to the edge surface of the blank, and sharp edges should be removed. Edges of shrink flanges and stretch flanges must be polished before forming. To prevent scratching the forming dies, edges of holes and cutouts should be deburred on both sides, and should be polished where they are likely to stretch during forming.

Cold Forming

Commercially pure titanium and the most ductile titanium alloys can be formed cold to a limited extent. Alloy Ti-8Al-1Mo-1V sheet can be cold formed to shallow shapes by standard methods, but the bends must be of larger radii than in hot forming and must have shallower stretch flanges. Cold forming of other alloys generally results in excessive springback, requires stress relieving between operations, and requires more power. Titanium and titanium alloys are commonly stretch formed without being heated, although sometimes the die is warmed to 300 F.

For cold forming of all titanium alloys, formability is best at low forming speeds.

To improve accuracy, cold forming is generally followed by hot sizing. Hot sizing and stress relieving are ordinarily needed to reduce stress and to avoid delayed cracking and stress corrosion. Stress relief also is needed to restore compressive yield strength after cold forming. Hot sizing often is combined with stress relieving, with the workpiece being held in fixtures to prevent distortion. Stress-relieving treatments for commercially pure titanium and titanium alloys are given in Table 4. (For detailed information on heat treatment, see the article "Heat Treating of Titanium and Titanium Alloys", page 301 in Volume 2 of this Handbook.)

Hot Forming

Heating titanium increases the formability, reduces springback, takes advantage of a lesser variation in yield strength and allows for maximum deformation with minimum annealing between forming operations. Hot sizing is used in almost 90% of the products made of titanium and its alloys. Severe forming must be done in hot dies, generally with preheated stock.

The greatest improvement in the ductility and uniformity of properties for most titanium alloys is at temperatures above 1000 F. However, contamination is also more severe at the higher temperatures.

Effect of Alloy. In hot forming, some titanium alloys (such as Ti-6Al-4V) are easier to form at fast speeds than at slow speeds, but other alloys (such as Ti-13V-11Cr-3Al) are less formable at fast speeds.

As shown in Table 5, most hot forming operations, depending on their severity, are done at 400 to 600 F, or at temperatures above 900 F. For applications in which the utmost in ductility is required, temperatures of 600 to 800 F usually are avoided.

Table 5. Temperatures for Hot Forming of Titanium Alloys

Alloy	Temperature, F: Mild forming	Severe forming
Commercially pure Ti	400-600	900-1300
Alpha Alloys		
Ti-5Al-2.5Sn	400-600	900-1300(a)
Ti-8Al-1Mo-1V(b)	650	1200-1450
Alpha-Beta Alloys		
Ti-8Mn	400-600	900-1100
Ti-6Al-4V	400-600	900-1450(c)

(a) 1600 F may be needed for power spinning. (b) Duplex annealed Ti-8Al-1Mo-1V can be hot formed with no loss in mechanical properties, if heat treated after forming, at 1450 F for 15 min and rapidly cooled. (c) 1600 F may be needed for drop hammer forming, power spinning, and some press forming.

Stronger alloys, such as Ti-8Al-1Mo-1V, may need to be heated to 1475 F. Temperatures generally must be kept below 1500 F to avoid marked deterioration in mechanical properties. Heating temperature and time at temperature must be controlled, so that the titanium is hot for the shortest time practical and the metal temperature is in the correct range.

Scaling and Embrittlement. Titanium is scaled and embrittled by oxygen-rich surface layers formed at temperatures higher than 1000 F. Generally, for heating in air, 2 hr is the longest time at 1300 F that should be permitted and 20 min at 1600 F should be the limit; these times are cumulative and include all time that the metal is at that temperature for all the operations on a given workpiece. The subsequent removal of scale and embrittled surface, or a protective atmosphere, should be considered for any heating above 1000 F.

When titanium is to be heated in air, a scale-inhibiting coating is sometimes used to minimize surface contamination. After the metal has cooled to room temperature, the protective coating must be removed before the part is ready for assembly.

Aging. Some hot forming temperatures are high enough to age a titanium alloy. Heat treatable beta and alpha-beta alloys generally must be reheat treated after hot forming. (Alpha-beta alloys should not be formed above the beta transus temperature.)

Because of aging, scaling and embrittlement, as well as the greater cost of working at elevated temperatures, hot forming is ordinarily done at the lowest temperature that will permit the required deformation. When maximum formability is required, the forming should be done at the highest temperature practical that will retain the mechanical properties and serviceability required of the workpiece.

Advantages and disadvantages of hot forming are given in Table 6, and are compared with those of cold forming that is followed by hot sizing.

Table 6. Advantages and Disadvantages of Hot Forming, and of Cold Forming Followed by Hot Sizing, of Titanium Alloys

Hot forming	Cold forming followed by hot sizing
Advantages	**Advantages**
Single operation	More types of machines can be used
Less force needed than for cold forming	Less dwell time required
Heat is needed for a shorter period	Work is stress relieved during sizing
Disadvantages	**Disadvantages**
Heat-resistant tools are required	Needs more equipment (hot sizing press)
Tools must be designed with provision for heating the workpiece	30-min dwell time required (for sizing)
Slow press with 5-min dwell is needed	Workpiece needs heating for longer time
Suited only to work done in heated tools	Two sets of dies are required (one set must be made of heat-resisting steel)

Tools. Titanium alloys are often formed hot, in heated dies in presses that have a slow, controlled motion and that can dwell in the position needed during the press cycle. Hot forming is sometimes done in dies that include heating elements or in dies that are heated by the press platens. Press platens heated to 1200 F can transmit enough heat to keep the working faces of the die at 800 to 900 F. Other methods of heating include electrical-resistance heating and the use of quartz lamps and portable furnaces.

To withstand the high temperatures used in hot forming, dies are often made of ceramic materials. A castable ceramic may contain heating elements, and the working faces may be capped with stainless steel or another heat-resisting metal.

Accuracy. Hot forming (or sizing) has the advantage of improved uniformity in yield strength, especially when the forming or sizing temperature is above 1000 F. However, care must be taken to limit the accumulation of dimensional errors resulting from:

1 Differences in thermal expansion
2 Variations in temperature
3 Dimensional changes from scale formation
4 Changes in dimensions of tools
5 Reduction in thickness from chemical pickling operations.

Single-Stage Forming. Hot pressing can sometimes form in one operation a part that would require several operations in an alternative method, as described in the example that follows.

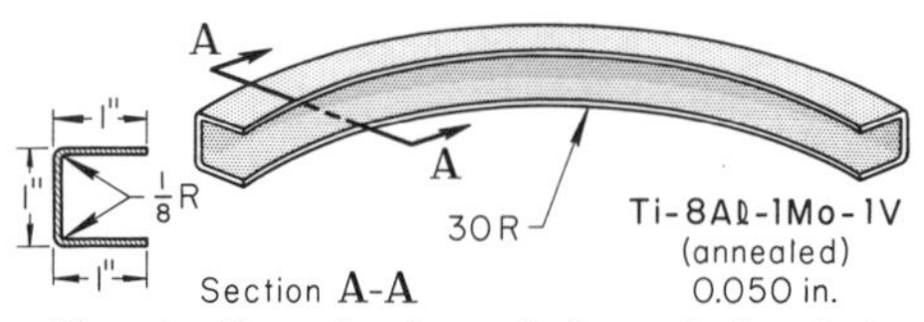

Fig. 1. Curved channel formed by hot pressing in one operation (Example 610)

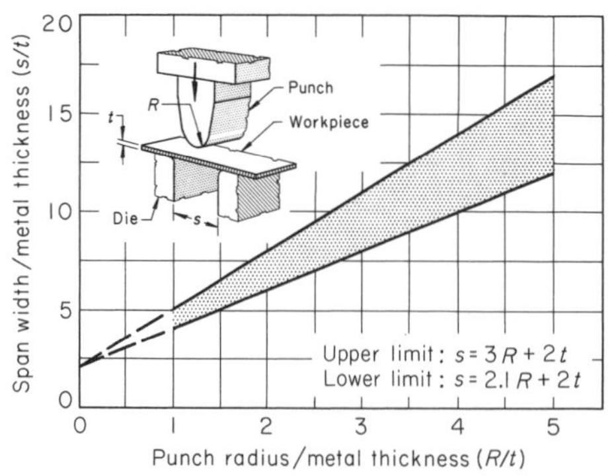

Fig. 2. Optimum relations among span width of die, punch radius and work-metal thickness in press-brake forming of titanium alloys. Shaded area of graph indicates acceptable forming limits.

Example 610. Hot Pressing a Curved Channel in One Operation (Fig. 1)

The curved channel shown in Fig. 1 was formed from sheet in one operation in a press with electrically heated platens, 36 by 54 in., and with 200-ton side rams. The die was machined from a gray iron casting. The workpiece was annealed alloy Ti-8Al-1Mo-1V, 0.050 in. thick. The sequence of operations was:

1 Shear to developed width, by 30-in. length
2 Deburr and smooth edges
3 Clean, water rinse, acid dip, water rinse, dry
4 Press form at 1325 F, using 2 min dwell with gradually increasing pressure (total time in the press, 10 min)
5 Repeat operations in step 3.

The above single-operation hot forming replaced an alternative method that needed more operations and used more equipment. The operations in the previous method were:

1 Shear to developed width, with length added to the 30 in. for holding at both ends
2 Clean with methyl-ethyl ketone
3 Form channel at room temperature in a press brake, with flanges bent 60° to a 3/16-in. radius
4 Clean in alkaline bath, water rinse, acid dip, water rinse and air dry
5 Hot size at 1325 F, to bend the flanges to 90° with 1/8-in. radius
6 Repeat operation 4
7 Sand blast the ends for gripping with stretch jaws
8 Stretch wrap at room temperature to a 30-in. radius
9 Trim the ends and deburr.

Two-Stage Forming. Hot forming of titanium is also done by using two sets of dies, as described in this example:

Example 611. Hot Forming and Sizing

A rectangular blank of commercially pure titanium sheet, 28 by 48 in. and 0.090 in. thick, was hot formed lengthwise to a 30-in. radius. At each end, near the center of the width were two oblong cups that tapered to a depth of 3½ in. at one end. One cup was 11½ in. long, the other 8½ in. long. The part was formed in two operations. The first operation was in a 7000-ton hydraulic press using an H11 steel die that had beryllium copper inserts for the draw rings and integral heating elements for heating the blank to 550 F. The forming was completed by heating the preform to 1000 F and sizing in a drop hammer using zinc alloy dies. Dies in the press and the drop hammer were lubricated with soap. After being formed, the part was trimmed to 24 by 36 in. The sequence of operations was:

1 Heat the press die to 550 F
2 Load the blank into the die, and because of variation in blank thickness, shim around the edge of the blank to 0.010 in. greater than nominal blank thickness, to insure even blankholding pressure on the work metal
3 Close the press on the blank, using light pressure, and allow to dwell for 4 min, to heat the blank
4 Apply the forming pressure slowly, taking 3 min to reach full load of 7000 tons; apply full force for 4 min
5 Unload workpiece; clean, rinse and dry
6 Stress relieve the workpiece
7 Heat the workpiece to 1000 F
8 In a drop hammer, size the workpiece (at 900 F) to +0, −0.010 in. on cups, ±0.010 in. on other dimensions
9 Trim the formed piece to 24 by 36 in.
10 Pickle the trimmed part.

Hot Sizing

Hot sizing is used to correct inaccuracies in shape and dimensions in preformed parts. Advantages and disadvantages of hot sizing after cold forming are listed in Table 6, along with those of hot forming.

The creep-forming principle is used to force irregularly shaped parts to assume correct shape against a heated die by the controlled application of horizontal and vertical forces over a period of time. Buckles and wrinkles can be removed from preforms in this way. A combination of creep and compression forming is used when reducing bend radii by hot sizing.

Springback is removed by restraining the parts against a heated die of the correct configuration, on the principle of stress relaxation forming, at stress relieving temperature.

Effect of Alloy. Although heat is helpful in the working of most titanium alloys, it is generally better to form alloy Ti-4Al-3Mo-1V at room temperature and hot size for any additional forming that may be needed. This alloy ages at 950 to 975 F, with some aging effect in less than 5 min. The ductility of this aged alloy does not improve with heating from room temperature to the aging temperature, so that heating is of no value. Ductility improves at temperatures higher than the aging temperature, but overaging decreases strength.

Solution-treated alloy Ti-5Al-2.75Cr-1.25Fe is more ductile at 750 to 800 F than at room temperature. Heat treatment is needed after forming, to relieve residual stress and to develop greater strength by aging.

Effect of Operating Conditions. Hot sizing is used to correct for springback in parts formed by other methods. The correction of springback depends on time and temperature; the higher the temperature, the shorter the time for processing. However, the effect of temperature on the properties of the metal limits the maximum useful temperature. The pressure applied to the part during hot sizing should be high enough to keep the part firmly against the fixture or die. Any additional pressure above the clamping requirement has no effect on the part and can cause deformation of the tooling.

Hot platen presses are commonly used for hot sizing of titanium. The tooling is designed for hot sizing of preforms; that is, it must only hold the workpiece to the required shape for the necessary time at temperature. Hot sizing in hot platen presses is done in the following sequence of operations:

1. The preformed parts are loaded on hot form blocks that are heated by the platen in the press.
2. The press is closed and heats the parts without applying the forming force.
3. Force is applied by the upper platen and auxiliary rams, and is held as long as necessary to complete the forming.

Press-Brake Forming

When formed in a press brake, titanium alloys behave like work-hardened stainless steel, except that springback is considerably greater. If bend radii are large enough, forming can be done cold. However, if bend radii are small enough to cause cracking in cold forming, hot forming must be used.

The setup and tooling for press-brake air bending are relatively simple, since the ram stroke determines the bend angle. The only tooling adjustments are the span width of the die and the radius of the punch. The span width of the die affects the formability of bend specimens, and is determined by the punch radius and the work-metal thickness as shown in Fig. 2. Acceptable conditions for dies in press-brake forming are shown as the shaded area between the upper and lower limits in Fig. 2.

The formability of four titanium alloys is shown in Fig. 3. With the exception of Ti-6Al-4V, which is given at room temperature only, curves are given for both room and elevated temperatures. Bends that plot above the curve for the alloy, condition and temperature, are expected to be successful. Bending under conditions that plot below the curve is expected to cause failure by splitting. These curves were developed from theory and verified by experiments. The limits are based on the formation of cracks that begin in the outside of the bend, and that can be seen at a magnification of ten diameters. The curves are for workpieces in which the bend length is more than eight times the metal thickness.

Minimum bend radius depends on the alloy, work-metal thickness, and forming temperature, as shown in Table 7.

Springback in press-brake forming depends on the ratio of punch radius (bend radius) to stock thickness and on forming temperature, as shown in Fig. 4 for alloy Ti-6Al-4V. (Figure 4 is not to be used for minimum bend radii.)

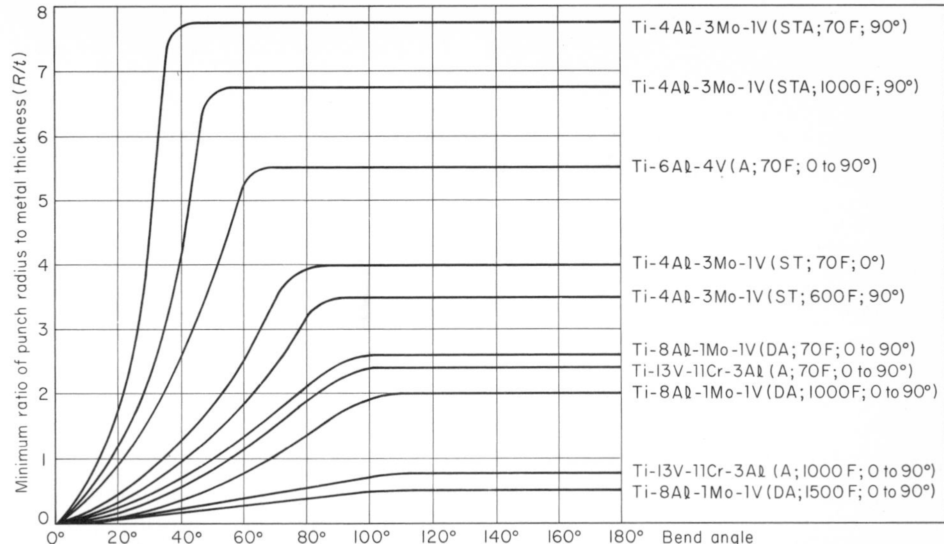

In parenthetical notes following alloy designations at right ends of curves: A = annealed; ST = solution treated; STA = solution treated and aged; DA = duplex annealed; temperatures are those at which alloy is formed; angles indicate orientation of bend axis from final rolling direction. Safe R/t ratios are those above each of the limiting curves.

Fig. 3. Forming limits of R/t ratios for safe bending of four titanium alloys in a press brake at various temperatures

Table 7. Minimum Bend Radii in Relation to Sheet Thickness for Press-Brake Forming of Titanium and Its Alloys at Various Temperatures(a)

Alloy	Condition(b)	Sheet thickness, in.	Minimum bend radius (t = sheet thickness) at a forming temperature of: 70 F	400 F	800 F
Commercially pure Ti	Ann	Thru 0.070	$3t$	...	...
		Over 0.070	$3.5t$	...	...
Ti-8Mn	Ann	Thru 0.080	$4t$	$2.5t$	$2.1t$
		Over 0.080	$5t$	...	...
Ti-5Al-2.5Sn	Ann	Thru 0.080	$5.5t$	$4.5t$	$4t$
		Over 0.080	$6t$	...	...
Ti-6Al-4V	Ann	Thru 0.070	$4.5t$	$4.3t$	$3.5t$
		Over 0.070	$5t$	...	...
	ST	All gages	$7t$	...	...
Ti-6Al-6V-2Sn	Ann	All gages	$4t$	...	...
Ti-8Al-1Mo-1V	Ann	All gages	$4.3t$	...	...
Ti-4Al-3Mo-1V	Ann	Thru 0.070	$3.5t$	...	...
		Over 0.070	$4t$	...	...
	ST	Thru 0.080	$5.5t$	...	...
		Over 0.080	$6t$	...	...
Ti-13V-11Cr-3Al	ST	Thru 0.070	$3t$	...	...
		Over 0.070	$3.5t$	...	...

(a) Data for forming at 70 F are all from the same source; data for elevated-temperature forming are from other sources. (b) Ann = annealed; ST = solution treated.

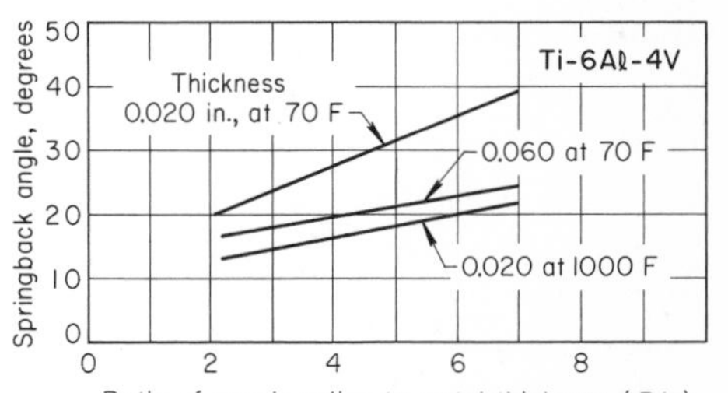

Fig. 4. Effect of ratio of punch radius to work-metal thickness on springback in press-brake forming alloy Ti-6Al-4V at 70 F and 1000 F

Deep Drawing

General rules for deep drawing of titanium alloy dome shapes at room temperature are:

1 The edges of the blank should be smooth, to prevent cracking during forming.
2 The flange radius should be at least 3/8 to 1/2 in.
3 The workpiece should be clean before each forming operation.
4 An overlay can be used to prevent wrinkles.
5 Severe forming and localized deformation should be avoided; forming pressure should be applied slowly.
6 The punch should be polished to prevent galling, regardless of lubrication.

Deep drawing of dome and hemisphere shapes in two different titanium alloys at room temperature in a rubber-diaphragm press is described in the two examples that follow.

Examples 612 and 613. Deep Drawing Dome-Shape Parts at Room Temperature

Example 612. A rubber-diaphragm press was used for drawing 8-in.-diam hemispheres from 16-in.-diam blanks sheared from Ti-8Al-1Mo-1V and Ti-6Al-4V sheet 0.050 in. thick. Before forming, the edges of the blanks were deburred on a grinding wheel and smoothed wth 400-grit abrasive paper; then the blanks were wiped clean with methyl-ethyl ketone.

A disk of 1018 steel, 16 in. in diameter, 1/8 in. thick, and with a 0.1935-in.-diam center hole, was used as an overlay to protect the diaphragm and to prevent wrinkles in the workpiece. Using a wax lubricant, the hemispheres were drawn in one operation with a ball-end punch 8 in. in diameter. The punch rose against the titanium blank, pressing the steel overlay up against the diaphragm under hydraulic pressure of 2000 psi. The pressure was gradually increased to 14,000 psi max.

After forming, the hemisphere was separated from the overlay by a blast of air through the center hole. The workpiece was cleaned in an alkaline bath, rinsed, pickled in an acid bath, rinsed, and dried in an oven. The hemispheres were annealed for 1 hr at 1300 F in air, followed by cooling in air.

Example 613. Hemispheres 16 in. in diameter were deep drawn in a hydraulic press (punch-and-diaphragm type) having a capacity for blanks 26 in. in diameter and 12-in. depth of draw, from blanks of alloy Ti-6Al-4V, 0.050 in. thick and sheared to 26-in. diam. The edges were deburred by grinding, then smoothed with 400-grit paper; the blanks were wiped clean with methyl-ethyl ketone.

A disk of 1018 steel, 26 in. in diameter and 1/8 in. thick, with a 0.1935-in.-diam center hole, was used as an overlay to protect the diaphragm and to prevent wrinkles in the work. Using a wax lubricant, the workpiece was drawn in two operations by a ball-end punch 16 in. in diameter. The punch rose against the titanium blank, pressing the steel overlay up against the flexible pad, as a hydraulic forming pressure of 2000 psi was applied. The pressure was increased gradually to 12,000 psi, to form the hemisphere, which had a flange radius of 1/2 in.

The workpiece was separated from the overlay by a blast of air in the center hole, then cleaned in an alkaline bath, rinsed, pickled in an acid bath, rinsed, and dried in an oven. The workpiece was annealed for 1 hr at 1300 F in an air-atmosphere furnace, and cooled in air; cleaning, rinsing, pickling and drying were then repeated. The overlays were wiped clean with methyl-ethyl ketone and replaced on the workpiece for further forming in the same setup.

Using 13,000 psi to press the punch deeper into the work, the ball end formed a short cylinder as an extension of the hemisphere, thus completing the draw. The completed workpiece was again separated from the overlay, and cleaned and annealed as before.

For a description of rubber-diaphragm forming, the reader is referred to the article on Rubber-Pad Forming, which begins on page 209 in this volume.

Table 8. Effect of Forming Temperature and Composition on Maximum Depth Obtainable in Deep Drawing of a Flat-Bottom Cup

Alloy	Tensile strength, 1000 psi(a)	Forming temperature, F	Maximum depth of draw, in.(b)
Ti-8Mn	120	80	0.80
	120	750	1.63
Ti-6Al-4V	140	1000	2.69

(a) Measured at room temperature. (b) Using molybdenum disulfide lubricant.

Table 9. Effect of Forming Temperature and Alloy on Maximum Depth of Draw for Deep Drawing a Rectangular Box

Alloy	Forming temperature, F	Maximum depth of draw, in.
Ti-8Mn	800	1.00
	1000	3.12
Ti-13V-11Cr-3Al	400	1.00
	1150	2.00
Ti-5Al-2.75Cr-1.25Fe	400	1.00
	1000	1.50
	1150	2.00
Ti-2.5Al-16V	1000	2.75

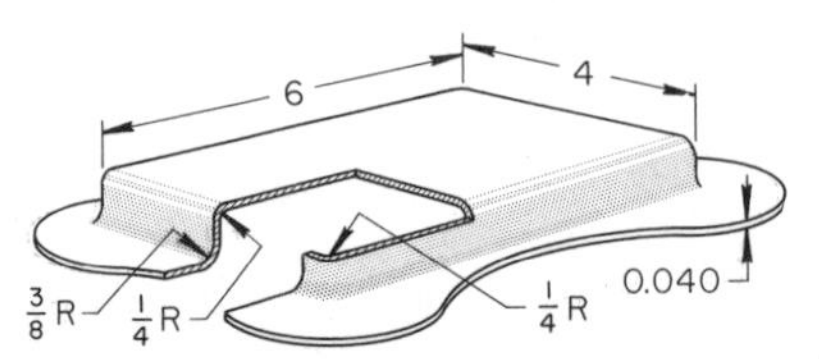

Hot Drawing. Titanium can be drawn deeper when hot, and more difficult forming can be done, than at room temperature. Table 8 shows the maximum depths of draw obtainable for a 4-in.-diam cup drawn from alloy Ti-8Mn at 80 and 750 F, and from alloy Ti-6Al-4V at 1000 F.

Generally, depth of draw depends on composition, workpiece shape, required radii, forming temperature, die design, die material, and lubricant. Table 9 shows the effect of forming temperature and alloy on maximum depth of draw for drawing a rectangular box.

Power Spinning

Most titanium alloys are difficult to form by power spinning. Alloys Ti-6Al-4V and Ti-13V-11Cr-3Al and some grades of commercially pure titanium are the most responsive to forming by this method. Conditions used in production power spinning are described in the three examples that follow.

Examples 614, 615 and 616. Power Spinning of Conical and Cylindrical Parts for Aircraft Engines

Example 614. Alloy Ti-6Al-4V sheet, 0.080 in. thick, was spun at room temperature, using a roller feed of 1/2 in. per min and mandrel speed of 150 rpm, to a 50% reduction in one pass. The same alloy, 0.152 in. thick, was power spun at 800 F, using a roller feed of 2 in. per min and mandrel speed of 400 rpm. The workpiece was 5.7 in. in diameter, and thickness was reduced 38% in one pass.

Example 615. Alloy Ti-13V-11Cr-3Al sheet, 0.130 in. thick, was power spun at room temperature, using a roller feed of 3½ in. per min and mandrel speed of 280 rpm. The 9.6-in.-diam part was reduced 53% in one pass.

Example 616. Cylinders 14 in. in diameter were power spun at room temperature from alloy Ti-13V-11Cr-3Al rolled ring blanks, in two passes. A roller feed of 4 in. per min and mandrel speed of 200 rpm were used. Annealing at 1400 F was required between passes.

In the first pass, the cylinder was spun to a diameter of 14.138 in., reducing the thickness by 51% (from 0.301 in. to 0.147 in.). The second pass reduced the thickness to 0.075 in. — a reduction of 49%. All cylinders that were power spun at room temperature had to be sized to minimize out-of-roundness.

Most tools for power spinning of titanium are made of high speed steel and hardened to Rockwell C 60.

Mandrels are heated for hot spinning, although the work metal may also be heated by torches. Tube preforms can be heated by radiation. Hot power spinning of titanium is done at 400 to 1800 F, depending on the alloy and operation. Typical power spinning temperatures are:

Commercially pure Ti	800 to 1000 F
Ti-5Al-2.5Sn	1200 to 1400 F
Ti-6Al-4V	1100 to 1200 F
Ti-13V-11Cr-3Al	1600 to 1800 F

Lubricants for power spinning of titanium are as follows:

Operating temperature, F	Lubricant
Up to 400 F(a)	Heavy drawing oils; graphited greases; colloidal graphite
400 to 800 F(b)	Bentonite greases with graphite; colloidal graphite or molybdenum disulfide
800 to 1800 F(b)	Bentonite greases with graphite; colloidal graphite; powdered mica

(a) Commercially pure titanium. (b) Commercially pure titanium, and titanium alloys.

Rubber-Pad Forming

Forming of titanium in a press with tooling that includes a rubber pad is used mostly for flanging thin stock and for forming beads and shallow recesses. The capacity of the press controls the range in size, strength and thickness of blanks that can be formed. Within this range, however, additional limits will be set by buckling and splitting.

Auxiliary devices, such as overlays, wiper rings, and sandwiches, usually are needed in rubber-pad forming, to improve the forming and to reduce the amount of wrinkling and buckling. Rubber-pad forming generally is done at room temperature or with only moderate heat. Usually, the forming must be followed by hot sizing to remove springback, smooth out wrinkles and buckles, and complete the forming. Sometimes hand work is needed to complete the forming. The cold formed workpiece should be stress relieved within 24 hr after forming.

Sharper bends can be made at higher forming pressures (see Fig. 5, which shows the effect of pad pressure on bend radius for two titanium alloys).

Springback behavior of titanium and its alloys in rubber-pad forming differs somewhat from that observed in other methods of forming. In general, springback in forming titanium varies directly with the ratio of bend radius to work-metal thickness, and inversely with forming temperature, as illustrated in Fig. 4 for press-brake forming of alloy Ti-6Al-4V.

Table 10 gives springback data for the rubber-pad forming of stretch and shrink flanges in five titanium alloys at four different temperatures. For some of the alloys listed, the data show a reversal of the usual relation between 70 and 1100 F. The effect of work-metal thickness and bend radius was not significant in this comparison.

Springback is affected also by forming pressure, as shown by the springback angles given below for the cold forming of 0.020-in.-thick sheets of two alloys at different pressures:

Pressure, psi	Ti-6Al-4V	Ti-13V-11Cr-3Al
10,000	17°	15°
50,000	13°	12°

These data were obtained for the forming of shrink flanges in a small part at room temperature by the rubber-pad forming process. The pressures were measured by a device placed in the rubber pad.

The following example describes a typical application of rubber-pad forming titanium sheet using the Verson-Wheelon process. (For a description of the Verson-Wheelon and other processes, see the article "Rubber-Pad Forming", page 209 in this volume.)

Example 617. Forming of Sheet by the Verson-Wheelon Rubber-Pad Process (Fig. 6)

The part shown in Fig. 6 was produced from a blank of annealed alloy Ti-6Al-4V sheet, 0.050 in. thick, by the Verson-Wheelon process.

Before forming, the edges of the blank were smoothed and the blank and form block cleaned with methyl-ethyl ketone. The form block was made of aluminum and was undercut, as shown in Fig. 6, to allow for springback, but hand work was still necessary. A lead overlay, ¼ in. thick, was placed over the flange areas only. The convex (shrink) flange was formed at 89° to 93°, and the concave (stretch) flange at 92°. The joggles needed hand work for better definition.

Beading. Beads can be formed to a limited extent in titanium alloy sheet by rubber-pad forming. Table 11 shows the limits of room-temperature formability of two titanium alloys in beading by the rubber-pad process. Because of the limited resistance of rubber to heat, practical commercial methods of hot forming titanium alloys by rubber-pad processes have not been developed. As shown in Table 11, the controlling variables in the forming of beads in titanium alloy sheet by the rubber-pad process are inside radius of bead (r), thickness of sheet (t), and spacing between beads (s). The spacing is important, because there must be enough room between beads for the rubber to flow down between them and make well-defined beads.

Stretch Forming

Generally, tooling that is used for stretch forming of stainless steel is also suitable for cold stretch forming of titanium, when used with a high clamping force that will prevent slipping and tearing. Stretch-forming machines can stretch wrap a sheet of alloy Ti-8Al-1Mo-1V that is 0.090 in. by 40 in. by 120 in., and bars that have section areas of 0.75 sq in. and are 144 in. long.

Titanium may show irregular incremental stretch under tension loads;

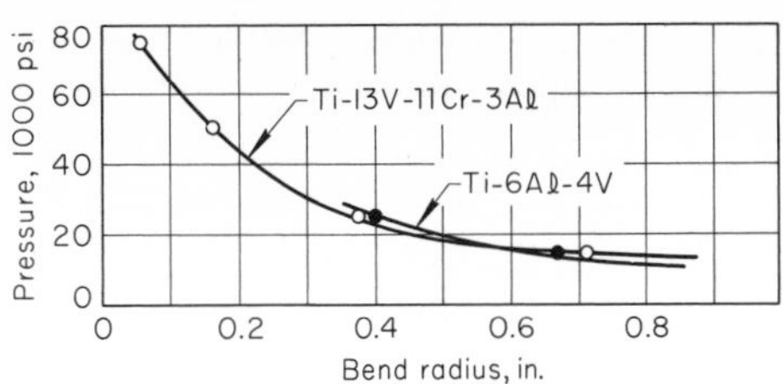

Fig. 5. Effect of pad pressure on radii formed on 0.063-in.-thick titanium alloy sheets by rubber-pad forming at 70 F

Table 10. Springback in Rubber-Pad Forming of Stretch and Shrink Flanges in Five Titanium Alloys at Four Temperatures (a)

	Springback angle at forming temperature of:							
	70 F		1100 F		1200 F		1500 F	
Alloy	Stretch	Shrink	Stretch	Shrink	Stretch	Shrink	Stretch	Shrink
Ti-3Mn-1.5Al	8°	10°	11°	11°	9°	13°	7°	8°
Ti-2Fe-2Cr-2Mo	12°	13°	11°	11°	9°	8°	0°	1°
Ti-8Mn	14°	13°	10°	11°	8°	10°	8°	9°
Ti-6Al-4V	11°-15°	12°-13°	13°-14°	13°-14°	12°-13°	11°-12°	6°-8°	4°-7°
	Fractured		14°-21°	13°-14°	13°-20°	12°-13°	9°-11°	10°-11°
Ti-5Al-2.5Sn	14°	14°	18°	14°	14°	14°	12°	12°

(a) Based on stock thickness of about 0.025 to 0.090 in. and bend radii of approximately $3t$ to $5t$

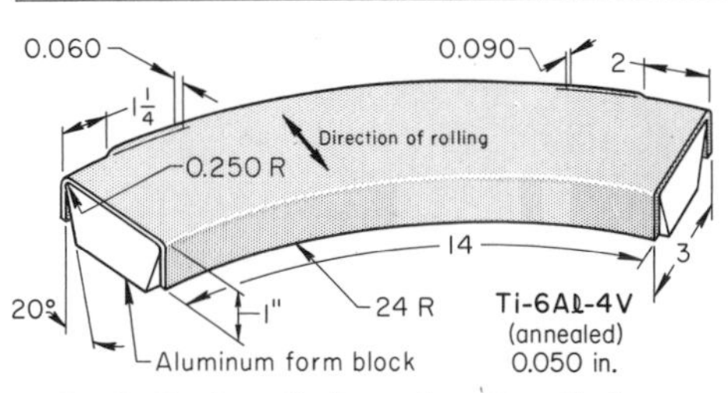

Fig. 6. Contoured channel section that was rubber-pad formed by the Verson-Wheelon process (Example 617)

Table 11. Limits on Room-Temperature Forming of Beads by the Guerin Rubber-Pad Process at a Pad Pressure of 3000 Psi

r/t ratio(a)	Forming limits r/s	s/t
Ti-8Al-1Mo-1V		
2	0.093	21.5
5	0.123	40.6
15	0.178	84.3
Ti-13V-11Cr-3Al		
7	0.12	60
15	0.14	104
30	0.17	173

(a) The r/t ratio cannot be higher than 40 to 50, or tearing of the metal will occur.

thus best results are obtained when titanium is stretch formed at slow strain rates. The rate of wrapping around a die should be about 8 in. per min.

In the stretch forming of angles, channels and hat-shape sections, deformation occurs mainly by bending at the fulcrum point of the die surface; compression buckling is avoided by applying enough tensile load to produce about 1% elongation in the inner fibers. The outer fibers elongate more, depending on the curvature of the die and on the shape of the workpiece. It is sometimes preferable or required (especially if sufficient forming power is not available) to stretch wrap at elevated temperature. Again, the wrapping speed must be slow, to prevent local overheating or necking.

The formability limits can be extended by permitting small compression buckles to occur at the inner fibers and removing them later by hot sizing. The buckled region represents a condition of overforming and should be limited to the amount that can be effectively removed by hot sizing.

Compression buckling is not a problem when sheet is stretch formed to produce single or compound curves. The ductility of sheet varies with orientation and is generally better in the direction of rolling. In the stretch forming of compound curves, the stretching force should be applied in the direction of the smaller radius. The rate of wrapping around the die should be about 8 in. per min.

Titanium parts that are stretch formed at room temperature should be stress relieved to minimize residual stress and reduction in compressive yield strength (see Table 4). A permanent stretch of 1% has been reported to cause a loss in compressive yield strength of up to 20%.

Depending on facilities and production quantities, the preformed workpiece can be placed over forms having the desired final contour and subjected to heat and pressure from a hot sizing platen press. Alternatively, the preforms can be clamped in a fixture, and the assembly heated in a furnace. Time and temperature for stress relieving of titanium alloys are given in Table 4.

Stress relieving may be combined with hot sizing, which can correct many faults in the workpiece at the same time (for example, wrinkles and buckles, and springback). Proper stress relieving can completely eliminate residual stress and Bauschinger effects on yield strength in some alloys, such as annealed alloy Ti-6Al-4V, and in commercially pure titanium. In other alloys, such as Ti-8Mn and Ti-5Al-2.5Sn, yield strength in compression is reduced 3% by stress relieving.

One large quantity of hat-shape sections of Ti-5Al-2.5Sn, stretch formed at room temperature, was slowed in production because there was not enough furnace capacity for stress relieving. The problem was solved by combining hot forming and stress relieving.

With heated blanks, the force needed in stretching is reduced. Another method is to reduce tension in stretch forming by the use of a wiper tool, as on radial draw machines. This can be effective in smoothing the workpiece and in fitting it to the form with less stretch, which results in less reduction in thickness of the metal and in the width of flanges.

Titanium is ordinarily stretch formed in the solution treated or annealed condition. Cold stretch forming is preferred, but the work metal may be

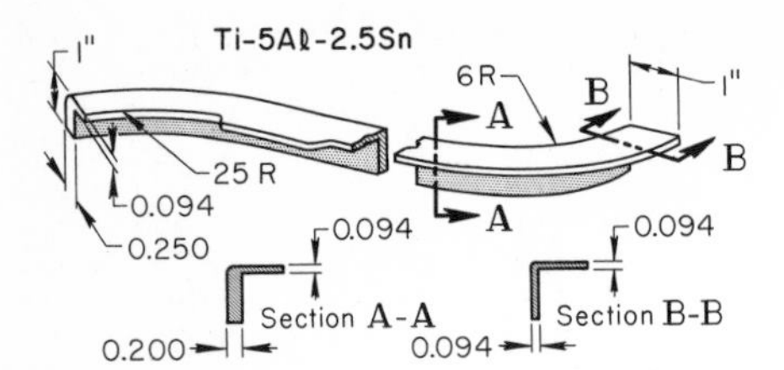

Fig. 7. Angle section, 37½ in. long, in which a compound curve was produced in two stages by cold and then hot stretch forming (Example 618)

heated if the available force is not sufficient for cold stretch forming. Titanium alloy shapes generally can be hot stretched up to 20% of their original length; commercially pure titanium can be hot or cold stretched 20%. Alloy Ti-8Mn can be cold stretched 15%; Ti-5Al-2.5Sn, 8%; and Ti-6Al-4V, 6%. Titanium sheet can be stretch formed cold to 60% of the maximum elongation determined in tension tests under comparable conditions.

Simple cold stretch forming of alloy Ti-6Al-4V sheet is done to 9% stretch, and compound forming to 4%. In compound stretch forming, alloy Ti-8Al-1Mo-1V sheet is cold stretched 5%. In compound forming of titanium sheet, the transverse stretch should be not more than half the major stretch.

An extruded angle, machined to vary the width and thickness, was stretch formed at room temperature, and then stretch formed hot to the final configuration, as described in the next example.

Example 618. Stretch Forming an Angle in Two Operations (Fig. 7)

The part shown in Fig. 7 was produced by machining an annealed extrusion of alloy Ti-5Al-2.5Sn, tapering the thickness of the vertical leg from 0.250 in. at one end to 0.094 at the other. The machined workpiece was then stretch formed at room temperature in a machine having a capacity of 35,000 lb, using a die of low-carbon steel, and finally restretched hot in the same die. The sequence of operations was:

1 Machine to remove the contaminated surface and to taper
2 Stress relieve, 2 hr at 1200 F
3 Stretch form, at room temperature, to develop required contour
4 Stress relieve, 2 hr at 1200 F
5 Hot size, by stretch forming at 1200 F
6 Trim to final size
7 Descale in nitric-hydrofluoric acid bath.

Because stretch forming is slow (average forming time is about 5 min), blanks are often heated on the form tools to save production time. The form tools should be at 1000 to 1200 F. Radiant heating of the blank can be used throughout the operation.

Proper speed for stretch forming depends on many factors, so that generally it must be determined by trial. Too fast a speed, like too much tension, causes needless reduction in thickness.

Hot stretch forming of commercially pure titanium and alloy Ti-8Mn should be done at 800 to 850 F. Alloys Ti-5Al-2.5Sn and Ti-6Al-4V should be hot stretch formed at 1125 to 1200 F.

Three-Roll Forming

The most economical method of forming titanium alloy sheet into aircraft skins, cylinders, or parts of cylinders is by three-roll forming. The sheet should be flat within 0.006 in. for each 2 in. of length. The corners of the sheet should be chamfered to prevent marking of the rolls.

The upper roll of the three-roll assembly can be adjusted vertically. The radius of the bend is controlled by the roll adjustment. Premature failure will occur if the contour radius is decreased too rapidly; however, too many passes through the rolls may cause excessive work hardening of the work metal. Several trial parts must sometimes be made in a new material or shape to establish suitable operating conditions.

Three-roll forming is also used to form curves in channels that have flanges of 1.5 in. or less. Figure 8 shows the use of the process for curving a channel with the heel in. Transverse buckling and wrinkling are common failures in the forming of channels.

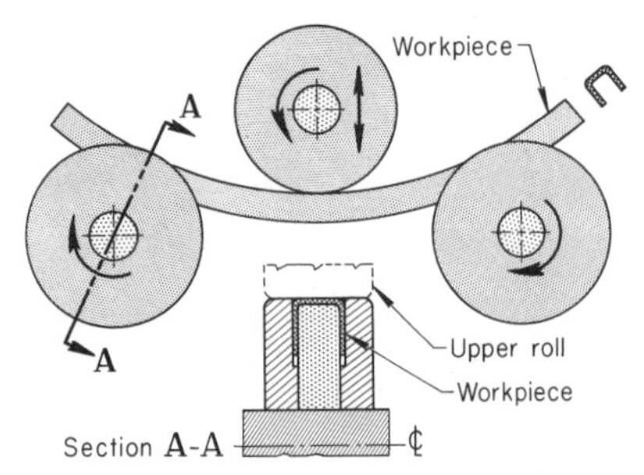

Fig. 8. Use of three-roll forming for producing a curve in a U-section channel, in heel-in position

Contour Roll Forming

Titanium sheet can be contour roll formed like any other sheet metal, but with special consideration for allowable bend radius and for the greater springback that is characteristic of titanium. Springback is affected to some extent by the pressure of the rolls.

In a series of tests, hat-shape sections with 90° bends were contour roll formed from two titanium alloys. The seven stands of high-chromium tool steel rolls were supplied with 50 hp to roll the titanium alloy sheets at 125 ft per min at room temperature. The alloys, sheet thicknesses, bend radii and springback are shown in Table 12. Springback was affected by the pressure applied to the workpiece.

In alloy Ti-4Al-3Mo-1V, bends can be made as sharp as $2.2t$ at 90° to the direction in which the sheet was rolled.

Hot rolling must be done on heated work metal with heated rolls.

Table 12. Results of Tests of Contour Roll Forming of Solution Heat Treated Alloys at Room Temperature

Sheet thickness (t), in.	Minimum bend radius	Average springback	Sheet thickness (t), in.	Minimum bend radius	Average springback
Ti-4Al-3Mo-1V(a)			0.063 ..	$3t$	10.8°
				$4t$	15.6°
0.020 ..	$3t$	11.2°	0.090 ..	$3t$	14.0°
	$4t$	14.6°			
0.040 ..	$3t$	10.4°	**Ti-2.5Al-16V(c)**		
	$4t$	17.8°			
	$3t$	3.5°	0.040 ..	$2t$	2.0°
	$1t$(b)	0.0°	0.060 ..	$2t$	7.0°
0.060 ..	$3t$	8.5°	0.090 ..	$3t$	15.0°
	$1t$(b)	0.0°			

(a) Seven-roll machine. (b) Formed at 1100 ± 25 F. (c) Six-roll machine.

Creep Forming

In creep forming, heat and pressure are combined to cause slow forming of titanium sheet into various shapes, such as double-curve panels, large rings, and small joggles. The metal flows plastically at a stress below its yield strength. At low temperature, creep rates are ordinarily very slow (for example, 0.1% elongation in 1000 hr), but the creep rate of titanium accelerates sharply with a rise in temperature.

Creep forming may be done by three different methods:

1 A blank is clamped at the edges, as for stretch forming, and a heated male tool is loaded to press against the unsupported portion of the blank; the metal yields under the combination of heat and pressure and slowly creeps to fit the tool.
2 A set of dies containing heating elements or coils is used in a hydraulic press in a manner similar to hot sizing.
3 A heated female die is used with a vacuum diaphragm, as in vacuum forming. (See the section on Vacuum Forming, which begins on this page.)

Temperatures for creep forming are the same as those used in hot forming (Table 5). Generally, titanium must be held at the creep-forming temperature for 3 to 20 min per operation. Sometimes creep forming takes 2 hr.

Four experimental applications of creep forming of titanium alloys are described below.

Application 1. A Y-ring of alloy Ti-8Al-1Mo-1V was creep formed to curve a lip and to form the ring to a radius of 16.5 ft. The die used was 6 ft long, in a hot-sizing press 24 ft long. The die was heated to 1450 F by the press platen. The ring moved through the die in indexed advances of 6 in., so that the metal was creep formed as it passed through the 6-ft length of die.

Application 2. Parts made of alloy Ti-6Al-4V, as large as 9⁄16 in. thick by 10 in. wide by 22 ft long, were creep formed in large ceramic fixtures. Each of the four fixtures was 3 ft wide, 12 ft high and 26 ft long. The steel support structure was faced with blocks of foamed ceramic. The ceramic surface of the fixtures contained resistance heaters that provided a temperature of 1250 F. Parts were clamped in the fixtures and submitted to a creep forming load for 1½ to 2 hr.

Application 3. Panels of alloy Ti-6Al-4V, 0.400 in. thick, 35 in. wide and 11 ft long, were shaped by creep forming to a 9⁄16-in. crown across the width. The creep forming was done in a pair of heated ceramic dies. Forming time was 1 hr at 1200 F.

Application 4. Thick-wall extrusions in T-sections and J-sections of alloy Ti-8Al-1Mo-1V were formed and sized in a pair of dies at 1450 F. The dies were cast of Hastelloy X or of other suitable material.

Vacuum Forming

Large panels (some as much as 60 ft long) for aircraft are vacuum formed from titanium alloy sheet. For vacuum forming, the blank is laid on a die of heated concrete, ceramic or metal, and a somewhat larger flexible diaphragm is laid on top of the blank to provide a seal around its edges. After the blank has been heated to forming temperature, the air is pumped out from between the blank and the die, so that the atmospheric pressure is used to form the work. This method, a kind of creep forming, cannot bend the work to sharp radii.

A production application of vacuum forming of titanium alloy is described in the example that follows.

Example 619. Vacuum Forming a Large Panel

A panel was vacuum formed from a Ti-6Al-4V sheet 14 ft long, 4 ft wide and 0.35 in. thick. The sheet was sculptured in thickness, some portions being 0.25 in. thick and some only 0.050 in. thick; the thinned portions were padded with honeycomb material. Before forming, the panel was cleaned with an alkaline detergent, to prevent hydrogen embrittlement. Cleaning was followed by a nitric-hydrofluoric acid dip and a deionized-water rinse.

The cleaned panel was laid on the die, which was made of cast iron and heated by electric-resistance heaters, and the work was covered by a diaphragm of stainless steel, 0.010 in. thick. The die and workpiece were heated to 1000 F and the air was exhausted from between the blank and the die. The temperature was held at 1000 F for 4 hr, and then raised to 1250 F for 30 min. Temperatures were controlled within ±25 F.

Drop Hammer Forming

Titanium should not be permitted to rub against lead, zinc or other low-melting metals that contaminate titanium. Drop hammer tools may be capped with sheet steel, stainless steel, or nickel alloy, depending on expected tool life. Nickel alloy, in thicknesses of 0.025 to 0.032 in., has the longest life.

As shown in Table 5, severe forming of most titanium alloys, which includes drop hammer forming, is done at 900 to 1450 F; alloy Ti-6Al-4V is formed at 1600 F by this method. Thermal expansion of the dies must be considered in the design. The approximate rate of expansion for steel dies is 0.006 in. per inch as temperature is increased from 70 to 1000 F.

Two-stage tools may be used if the shape cannot be formed in one blow, but more commonly the part is finished by hot sizing.

The minimum thickness of titanium sheet for drop hammer forming is 0.025 in.; thicker sheet is used for complex shapes. Tolerance on parts formed in drop hammers usually is 1/16 in.

Joggling

Joggling is frequently done on titanium alloy sheet. A joggle is an offset in a flat plane, consisting of two parallel bends in opposite directions at the same angle, as shown in Fig. 9. Generally, the joggle angle is less than 45°.

Joggles can be formed completely at room temperature or at elevated temperature in press brakes and mechanical or hydraulic presses. Common practice is to preform at room temperature and then hot size in a heated die. The sizing operation is usually done under conditions that result in stress relieving or aging.

Preforming can be done in the joggle die illustrated in Fig. 10. Shims are used for adjusting the offset; side plates prevent wrinkling in the flange.

In press-brake-formed or stretch-formed angles and channels, and in machined extrusions, joggles with radii smaller than the minimum bend radii for the metal at room temperature, or joggles with length-to-depth ratios of less than 5 to 1, are more successfully formed at elevated temperature. The forming temperature varies between 600 and 1200 F, depending on the alloy and its heat treated condition. Annealed alloys are joggled at 600 to 800 F. Heat treated or partly heat treated alloys are joggled at, or near, their aging temperature.

Details of joggling four solution treated titanium alloys of various thicknesses are given in Table 13.

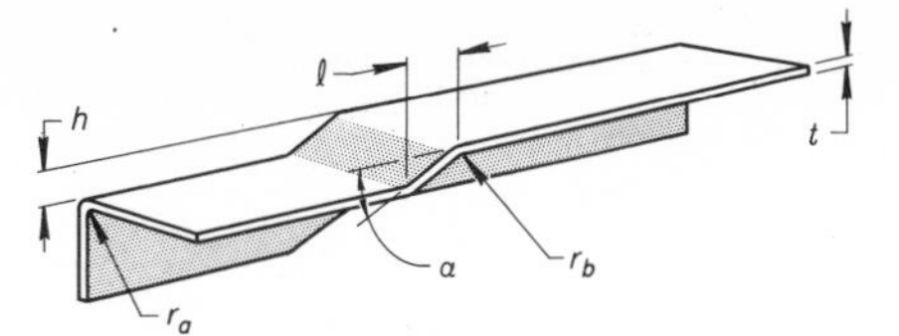

α = joggle-bend angle; h = joggle depth; l = joggle length; t = work-metal thickness; r_a = radius of preformed angle; r_b = joggle-bend radius on leading edge of joggle block.

Fig. 9. Details of a joggle

Table 13. Joggling of Solution Treated Sheets at Room Temperature

Sheet thickness, in.	Minimum joggle ratio, l/h(a)	Springback at minimum joggle ratio, %
Ti-4Al-3Mo-1V		
0.040(b)	...	35
0.063	3.50	35
0.090	4.25	50(c)
0.063(d)	3.00	...
0.090(d)	3.50	...
Ti-2.5Al-16V		
0.040	...	45 to 50(c)
0.063	3.50	45 to 50(c)
0.090	4.25	60 to 65(c)
Ti-13V-11Cr-3Al		
0.025	1.50	13
0.040	1.70	32
0.063	1.70	40
0.090	3.40	50
Ti-5Al-2.75Cr-1.25Fe		
0.025	...	32.5
0.040	...	46.8
0.063	...	46.5

(a) l = joggle length, h = joggle depth (see Fig. 9). (b) Forming temperature not available. (c) Approximate. (d) Joggled at 600 F.

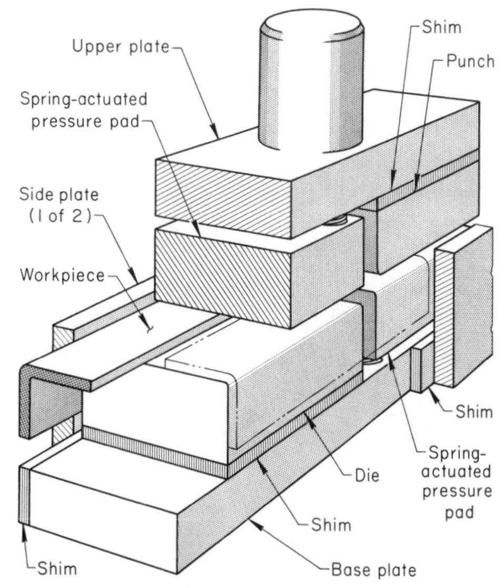

Fig. 10. Adjustable joggle die for angle sections of different thicknesses and offsets

Dimpling

Dimpling produces a small conical flange around a hole in sheet-metal parts that are to be assembled with flush or flat-head fasteners. Dimpling is most commonly applied to sheets that are too thin for countersinking. Sheets are always dimpled in the condition in which they are to be used, because subsequent heat treatment may cause distortion of the holes.

The ram-coin dimpling process is generally used, although dimples have been produced at room temperature by swaging. In ram-coin dimpling, force in excess of that required for forming is applied to coin the dimpled area and to reduce the amount of springback.

Titanium is dimpled at up to 1200 F with tool steel dies. If higher temperatures are required, tooling made of a high-strength heat-resisting alloy, or of a ceramic material, is required to prevent deformation of the dies during dimpling. Ordinarily, the work metal is heated by the dimpling tools, rather than being preheated.

The pilot holes must be drilled, rather than punched, and must be smooth, round, cylindrical and free of burrs. Because of the notch sensitivity of titanium, care must be taken in deburring the holes.

The amount of stretch required to form a dimple varies with the head and body diameters of the fastener and the bend angle. If the metal is not ductile enough to withstand forming to the required shape, cracks will occur radially in the edge of the stretch flange, or circumferentially at the bend radius. Circumferential cracks are more common in thin sheet; radial cracks are more common in thick stock.

Explosive Forming

Titanium can be explosive formed like other metals within limits set by its mechanical properties. Because of the limited ductility of titanium alloys at room temperature, it is better to form them at high temperature, but then water cannot be the transfer medium. Solids such as sand and talc may be used as the transfer medium, but these damp the energy of the explosion, reducing the efficiency of forming.

Bending of Extruded Shapes

Titanium extrusions usually are bent with heated tools. Extruded shapes can be bent hot to produce as much as 28% stretch in the extreme fiber of the tension leg, and to 10% shrink when one leg is in compression.

Extrusions of alloys Ti-6Al-4V and Ti-5Al-2.5Sn should be stress relieved before bending. The amount of stretch and shrink in bending is similar to that in stretch-wrap forming.

Most bending is done in a hydraulic press of at least 60-ton capacity, using a die or form blocks made of tool steel and hardened to Rockwell C 53. The tools can be heated by radiation or by the use of resistance-heating inserts. The press is partly closed on the workpiece until the workpiece heats to 600 to 800 F. Then the forming pressure is applied slowly, and the dies are allowed to dwell for 2 or 3 min when fully closed, to prevent springback.

Room-temperature bending and elevated-temperature bending of extruded angles and T-shapes are described in the following two examples.

Examples 620 and 621. Bending of Extruded Structural Shapes

Example 620 — Bending at Room Temperature. An extruded structural angle of alloy Ti-5Al-2.5Sn, 20 in. long by 1⅛ by 1⅛ by ⅛ in., was machined to a depth of 0.030 in. on each surface to remove the extruded surface, and then machined again to remove part of one leg. After machining, the workpiece was bent in a press with a die of H11 tool steel (hardened to Rockwell C 56), which formed the angle into an S-curve with 6-in. radii. No lubricant was used.

After bending, the workpiece was cleaned, and stress relieved for 2 hr at 1200 F to prevent stress corrosion, and was then descaled in a nitric-hydrofluoric pickling bath.

No hand work was needed. Die life was 300 pieces per regrind.

Example 621 — Bending in a Heated Die. An extruded structural T-shape of alloy Ti-5Al-2.5Sn, 20 in. long and with legs 1½ in. wide by ⅛ in. thick, was machined to a depth of 0.030 in. on each surface to remove the contaminated surface. The workpiece then was bent in a 60-ton press with a die of H11 tool steel (hardened to Rockwell C 53), which formed one end into an arc with a 5½-in. radius. The die was heated to 600 to 800 F by the heated platens of the press. The workpiece was loaded into the press, which was partly closed to heat the workpiece to 600 F before forming pressure was applied. The bend caused the extreme fiber to stretch 28%, with too much reduction of section in some workpieces. After forming, the part was stress relieved, pickled, and inspected with a dye penetrant. Some hand work was needed.

Bending of Tubing

Round tubing of commercially pure titanium and alloy Ti-6Al-4V can be formed at room temperature in ordinary draw bending machines. When hot bending is required, the equipment is modified by adding some means of heating the tools.

Minimum and preferred conditions for bending tubing of commercially pure (99.2%) titanium at room temperature and at elevated temperatures are given in Table 14. As shown in Table 14, tubing 2.5 in. or less in diameter ordinarily is bent at room temperature, while larger sizes are bent at elevated temperatures (350 to 400 F). In both cold and hot bending, bend radius is limited chiefly by tubing diameter, but maximum bend angle is affected by both diameter and wall thickness.

Commercially pure (99.2%) titanium deforms locally if the tension is not applied evenly. Bending should be slow; ¼° to 4° per minute is suitable. A recommended lubricant should be used.

Table 15 gives minimum bend radii and amount of springback observed in making 120° bends in annealed seamless tubing of Ti-6Al-4V.

Tools used in bending titanium and titanium alloy tubing are shown in Fig. 11. These tools are similar to those shown for bending bars and tubing in Fig. 1 on page 305, but include also a wiper die, a pressure-die boost cylinder, a cleat insert in the clamp, a cleated plug and a multiball mandrel. The mandrel and the wiper die are made of aluminum bronze to minimize galling; the pressure die, rotating form block and clamp are made of L6 or a similar tool steel. The tubing forms to the bend centerline radius around the rotating form block, which is case hardened to Rockwell C 55.

The tubing is gripped between the clamp and the straight portion of the rotating form block tightly enough to prevent axial slipping while the tubing is being bent. The clamped end of the tubing is supported by a plug. The cleat insert in the clamp and that attached to the end of the plug (see Fig. 11) are used only in bending the larger sizes of tubing that have thin walls, for which greater gripping power is needed.

The stationary wiper die helps to prevent the formation of wrinkles as the inner fibers of the tubing are compressed during bending. The wiper die is made of aluminum bronze to prevent galling during bending.

Table 14. Limits for Radii and Angles in Bending of Commercially Pure (99.2%) Titanium Tubing

Tube OD, in.	Wall thickness, in.	Bending conditions: Minimum — Bend radius, in.	Minimum — Max angle(a)	Preferred — Bend radius, in.	Preferred — Max angle(a)
Room-Temperature Bending					
1.5	0.016	2.25	90°	3	120°
	0.020	2.25	100°	3	160°
2.0	0.016	3.00	80°	4	110°
	0.020	3.00	100°	4	150°
2.5	0.016	3.75	70°	5	100°
	0.020	3.75	90°	5	140°
	0.035	3.75	110°	5	180°
Elevated-Temperature Bending (350 to 400 F)					
3.0	0.016	4.50	90°	6	120°
	0.020	4.50	110°	6	160°
	0.035	4.50	130°	6	180°
3.5	0.016	5.25	90°	7	120°
	0.020	5.25	110°	7	160°
	0.035	5.25	130°	7	180°
4.0	0.020	6.00	110°	8	160°
	0.035	6.00	120°	8	180°
4.5	0.020	6.75	130°	9	140°
	0.035	6.75	140°	9	140°
5.0	0.020	10.00	...	10	110°
6.0	0.020	12.00	...	12	100°

(a) Maximum bend angles are based on the use of a clamp section three times as long as the diameter of the tubing and on maximum mandrel-ball support of the tubing.

Table 15. Minimum Bend Radii, and Springback, in Making 120° Bends in Annealed Ti-6Al-4V Seamless Tubing

Tube OD, in.	Wall thickness, in.	Minimum bend radius, in.	Springback
½	0.016	2½	8°
	0.028	2	14°
⅝	0.016	2½(a)	8°
	0.035	2	12°
1	0.023	4(a)	8°
	0.057	3½	14°
1½	0.035	5(a)	12°
	0.085	4(a)	12°

(a) Using a pressure-die boost cylinder on the pressure-die carriage (see Fig. 11)

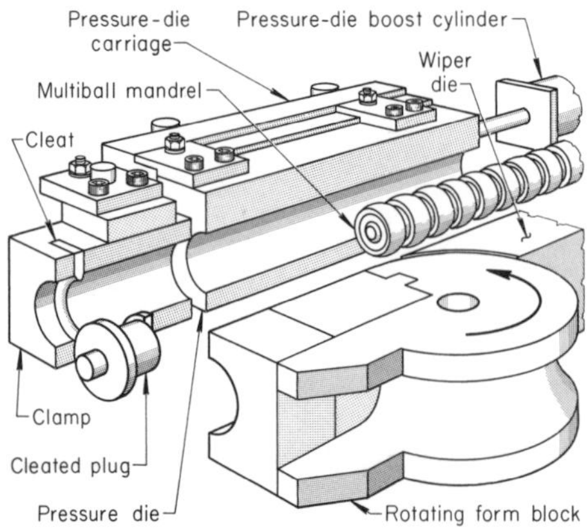

The cleats shown on the clamp and plug are used only in bending large tubing with thin walls. For hot bending, the pressure die and the mandrel are integrally heated.

Fig. 11. Tools and setup used in bending titanium and titanium alloy tubing

The moving pressure die holds the tubing against the rotating form block at the tangent point during bending, and also against the wiper die, thus confining the workpiece on all sides. The force applied by the pressure die determines the frictional drag for controlling the position of the neutral axis of the tubing during bending. The pressure die is ordinarily hardened to Rockwell C 45.

The mandrel used to provide internal support during bending is generally of the multiball type, as in Fig. 11. (For information on multiball mandrels, see page 310 in the article on Bending of Tubing, in this volume.)

Generally, when bending titanium alloys, it is necessary to use a pressure-die boost cylinder, as shown in Fig. 11, to apply a thrust force to the rear end of the pressure-die carriage as it moves with the unbent portion of the tubing into the bending area. By exerting a thrust force on the pressure die, the boost cylinder counteracts the drag of the pressure die, mandrel and wiper die. Pushing the tube into the bending area shifts the neutral axis of the tube toward the centerline, thus reducing wall thin-out and decreasing the bend severity by reducing the amount of stretching in the outer fibers of the bend area.

Tolerances. For commercially pure titanium tubing such as that used on low-pressure aircraft-duct systems, tube diameters should be within the tolerance range of +0.0025, −0.007 in. for tubing under 6 in. in diameter. For Ti-6Al-4V tubing, which is used for high-pressure hydraulic lines, and where ovality limits are placed on the finished formed bend, tube diameters up to 1½ in. should be controlled to a tolerance of +0.005, −0.000 in.

The straightness of tubes for bending is usually specified to be within 0.030 in. per foot. If tubes are straightened before bending, the limits of elongation of the tubes may be reduced as much as 20%. Annealing may not help, because the straightened tube may warp during annealing.

Forming Temperature. Commercially pure titanium tubing in the smaller sizes can be bent at room temperature, as shown in Table 14, but the larger sizes are generally formed at elevated temperatures, the best forming temperature being 350 to 400 F. In hot forming commercially pure titanium, the only tool components heated are the mandrel and the pressure die. Hot bending of Ti-6Al-4V tubing requires much higher temperatures (1300 to 1400 F), and problems with equipment and lubrication can be expected.

Lubrication. Drawing oils are used as lubricants for forming commercially pure titanium tubing at room temperature. High-viscosity deep drawing lubricants are used to cold form alloy Ti-6Al-4V. Grease with graphite is used as a lubricant for the hot bending of commercially pure titanium tubing, but is not recommended for temperatures above 600 F. Phosphate conversion coatings are sometimes used on tubing that is to be bent hot.

Working of Platinum Metals

By J. C. CHASTON*

FOUR of the platinum metals — platinum, palladium, rhodium and iridium — have the face-centered cubic crystal structure, which is usually associated with ductility. Yet only platinum and palladium can be cold worked from the cast condition. Rhodium must be broken down at a high temperature before it can be cold worked, and iridium can be cold worked, with difficulty, only after a fibrous structure has been imparted by careful hot working.

Ruthenium and osmium have a close-packed hexagonal structure. Osmium is completely unworkable and ruthenium very nearly so.

In general, the only problems special to working of the platinum metals are those resulting from surface contamination derived from rolls, swaging dies, and other tools. Base-metal impurities such as iron, which may be smeared on the surface or picked up as slivers or fine dust during hot working or annealing, will alloy with the surface layers and diffuse inward. Thus, physical characteristics such as electrical resistivity are affected and surface cracking may develop.

During hot working none of the platinum metals scale. Nevertheless, cracks usually are not easily welded or healed, probably on account of slight inevitable contamination by iron, iron oxide, or even films of adsorbed gas.

In the following sections, working procedures for each of the platinum metals are considered separately.

Platinum

Hot Working. Platinum ingots are normally broken down by hot forging or rolling. Ingots are heated to 2200 to 2750 F (1200 to 1500 C), usually in a gas-fired furnace, supported on high-grade alumina.

When forging, particular care is taken to keep the anvil surfaces smooth and bright. After the first few blows, the forging is cooled and carefully "overhauled" by gouging out with a chisel any surface cracks or folds. The work is then reheated and forging is continued to the finished size. The freedom of platinum from scaling is not without disadvantages: surface imperfections do not oxidize and flake away, but persist.

Platinum is hot rolled to sheet in simple slab rolls. Rod is hot rolled between grooved rolls, which may be provided with half-round sections throughout or, more frequently, with half-round sections for the finishing passes only, the early passes being formed with gothic sections alternating with oval sections.

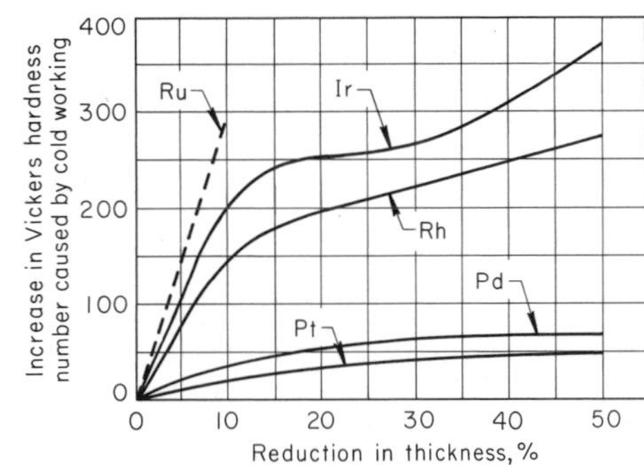

Fig. 1. Effect of cold work in increasing the hardness of the platinum metals

Cold Working. Platinum responds readily to cold working and can be reduced 98% or more by rolling or wiredrawing. The rate of work hardening is slow, as shown in Fig. 1, and in Table 1 (see the next page).

In cold rolling, the response of platinum is similar to that of copper and similar rolling programs are followed. It is seldom desirable to interpose annealing stages.

Foil thinner than about 0.0015 in. is sometimes made in small amounts by book rolling. A sheet of copper about 1/16 in. thick is folded back on itself, a platinum sheet about 0.01 in. thick is slipped into the fold, and the "book" is then rolled down as far as required, the copper and platinum being reduced together. The finish of book-rolled strip (when separated) is poor, but the method requires no special equipment. For good surfaces, direct rolling in a Sendzimir-type mill is preferred.

In wiredrawing, platinum is handled almost exactly like copper. Solid lubricants are used for drawing to about 3/32 in.; for smaller diameters, water-base lubricants of the soluble-oil type are suitable. Diamond dies, with profiles similar to those used for drawing copper wire are used below about 1/8 in., and platinum wires are drawn direct to sizes down to 0.0004 in. in diameter.

Wires smaller in diameter than 0.0004 in. can be made by the Wollaston process, by first sheathing a platinum rod with a thick-walled closely-fitting cylinder of silver, about ten times its diameter. The composite is drawn without annealing. In the finished wire, the average diameter of the platinum core is nearly in the same ratio to that of the outer silver coating as in the original assembly, although the platinum core is not quite round or uniform. Wollaston wire is usually supplied without removing the silver coating, which is dissolved in dilute nitric acid after the wire has been mounted for use.

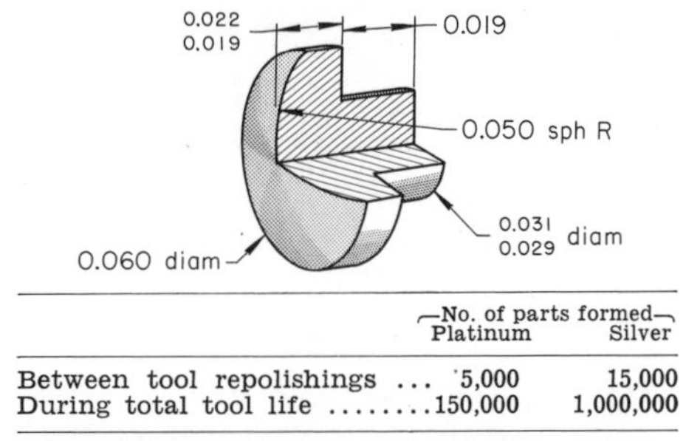

	No. of parts formed — Platinum	Silver
Between tool repolishings ...	5,000	15,000
During total tool life	150,000	1,000,000

Fig. 2. Electrical contact that was produced from platinum wire and silver wire by cold heading using steel punches (Example 622)

The usual press operations of blanking, piercing, bending and deep drawing are used for forming platinum, palladium, and their commercial alloys, using techniques and tools similar in all respects to those used for cartridge brass or silver. (Production methods have not been used for forming the other platinum metals. They are more difficult to fabricate, and the demand for press formed parts is small.)

When steel tools are used, tool life may be shortened by cold welding between the platinum metal and the working surface of the tool. In blanking and cutting operations, the cold welding impairs tool edges and makes frequent regrinding necessary. In cold heading operations, it may cause pickup on the hammer heads, which must be removed by grinding, as shown in the following example.

Example 622. Life of Steel Hammers for Cold Heading Silver and Platinum (Fig. 2)

The electrical contact shown in Fig. 2 was formed from both platinum and silver wires in the same cold heading machine, using identical heading tools made from a conventional die steel containing 2% carbon and 12% chromium, and hardened to Rockwell C 62 to 63. The platinum was lubricated with a smear of kerosine; the silver was run dry. About 15,000 parts could be headed from silver between tool regrinds and only 5000 could be headed from platinum, because the steel tools picked up platinum, which had to be removed by grinding. Total tool life was 150,000 parts from platinum and one million from silver.

Pickling. Platinum is often pickled *before* annealing to remove surface contaminants that might otherwise alloy with and diffuse into the metal. A hot 10% solution of sulfuric acid in water is usually employed. Occasionally, a 10% solution of hydrochloric acid is preferred if iron contamination alone is suspected. More rarely, hot aqua regia solution is used, particularly if slight surface alloying is suspected.

Annealing needs no protective atmosphere and is done at about 1830 F (1000 C). The platinum should be supported on clean refractories. Silica refractories may be used, provided fully oxidizing conditions are maintained in the heating chamber, but alumina is preferred.

Flash annealing techniques are commonly employed for platinum wire and sheet, to minimize grain growth.

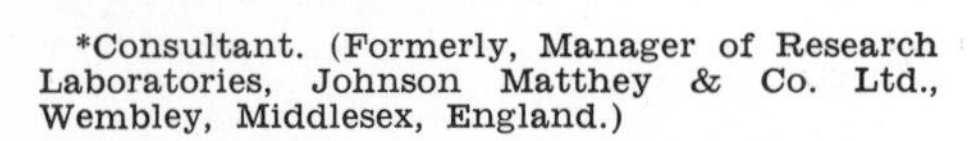

*Consultant. (Formerly, Manager of Research Laboratories, Johnson Matthey & Co. Ltd., Wembley, Middlesex, England.)

Table 1. Influence of Cold Work on the Hardness of Platinum, Palladium, and the More Important Platinum Alloys, With Recommended Annealing Temperatures (a)

Reduction of area, %	Pt	Pd	10 Rh 90 Pt	20 Rh 80 Pt	40 Rh 60 Pt	10 Ir 90 Pt	20 Ir 80 Pt	25 Ir 75 Pt	10 Ru 90 Pt
Brinell Hardness									
0	53	48	110	128	130	116	192	220	190
10	70	80	145	176	236	136	226	270	242
20	80	88	165	190	264	154	242	286	265
30	86	96	178	200	284	168	252	298	280
40	93	100	185	212	292	176	259	308	286
50	99	106	190	222	308	180	264	316	295
60	103	110	195	234	320	182	272	324	310
70	112	120	200	244	334	185	284	332	325
80	122	135	220	260	356	195	300	339	335
Recommended Annealing Temperature									
°F	1830	1560	2010	2010	2280	2010	2010	2190	2010
°C	1000	850	1100	1100	1250	1100	1100	1200	1100

(a) Values for hardness and annealing temperature will vary, because of differences in working procedures and in degree of purity of the alloy.

Palladium

Hot Working. Palladium can be hot forged or rolled at 2190 to 2550 F (1200 to 1400 C). It deforms less readily than platinum but appreciably more readily than low-carbon steel. It should be quenched in water from above 1500 F (850 C) in order to retain a bright surface. A tarnish film of PdO forms on palladium in air between 750 and 1560 F (400 to 850 C), and is thus found on metal that has cooled slowly through this temperature range. The oxide decomposes above 1560 F (850 C); metal can be cleaned from tarnish by heating above 1560 F and quenching.

Palladium is readily cold worked, and indeed small ingots are frequently reduced to the finished size by this means, although larger ingots are usually broken down by hot working.

Cold Working. In cold rolling and wiredrawing, palladium behaves much like platinum, although the rate of work hardening of palladium is slightly higher, as shown in Fig. 1 and Table 1.

Annealing. Palladium may be annealed in air at about 1560 F (850 C), but to retain a bright surface, it must be quenched in water, as described above. More usually, it is annealed in a protective atmosphere.

It is, perhaps surprisingly, practicable to use hydrogen as a protective atmosphere. Although palladium absorbs very large quantities of hydrogen at room temperature, with a notable increase in volume, the solubility at 1560 F (850 C) is low and remains low if the metal is quenched from the annealing temperature. A 95:5 nitrogen:hydrogen mixture is, however, equally effective in preventing tarnish and is usually preferred. Vacuum annealing of palladium is done to a limited extent, and flash annealing techniques are used to minimize grain growth.

Pickling. Tarnish films of PdO on palladium that has been slowly cooled or slack quenched can be removed by a hot 10% solution of sulfuric acid or by a 10% tartaric acid solution. Hot dilute sulfuric acid dissolves palladium slowly and thus can be used to remove contaminated surface layers.

Rhodium

Hot Working. Ingots cast from melted rhodium, as well as sintered powder metallurgy compacts, can be worked by hot forging at high temperature. Above 2370 F (1300 C) the metal is soft and malleable. It is usual to heat the small ingots to about 2730 F (1500 C), either in an electric resistance furnace in an atmosphere of hydrogen, as in a gas-fired furnace, or even in a blowpipe, and to reheat frequently during the early stages of reduction. A tarnish film of RhO_2 begins to form on rhodium when it is heated above about 930 F (500 C) and persists to much higher temperatures than does the film on palladium; the metal must be quenched from above about 2550 F (1400 C) to be entirely bright and free from oxide.

After preliminary forging, rhodium may be hot rolled to sheet or hot swaged to rod.

Cold Working. Once the cast structure of polycrystalline rhodium has been broken down by hot working, it becomes amenable to further reduction by cold working, although the rate of hardening by cold work is high, as shown in Fig. 1.

In both cold rolling and wiredrawing, it is necessary to anneal frequently. For the first few reductions, annealing should follow each reduction in area of 10 to 20%; as the workpiece size decreases, the reduction in area between anneals can be gradually increased to 30 to 40%. Single crystals of rhodium, made by vertical floating-zone melting, can be readily cold swaged, rolled, or drawn — responding as readily as pure nickel. However, if this cold worked rhodium is then recrystallized by full annealing, intercrystalline brittleness develops and further cold working becomes as difficult as with normal polycrystalline rhodium. Partial softening, with reasonable ductility, may be secured by stress-relief annealing at 1100 to 1500 F, and is sometimes helpful.

Annealing. Rhodium is usually annealed in hydrogen at about 2200 F (1200 C) and cooled to below about 390 F (200 C) in hydrogen so as to keep it bright. Rhodium wire is preferably continuously annealed in a tube furnace provided with a cooling extension and fed with hydrogen. Rhodium must always be bright annealed; no satisfactory method of chemical or electrochemical pickling is available.

Iridium

Hot Working. Iridium, either as argon-arc cast ingots or as powder metallurgy compacts, can be hot forged like rhodium, but with greater difficulty. The tarnish film of IrO_2 forms at about 750 F (400 C) and persists in the temperature region of 750 to 2050 F (400 to 1120 C). Above 2050 F (1120 C) it dissociates. The surface remains bright when the metal is quenched from temperatures above 2050 F (1120 C).

Ingots that have been broken down by forging can be hot rolled by small reductions to sheet or hot swaged to rod if precautions are taken to keep the material hot until it enters the swaging die. After hot forging, iridium can be hot drawn through heated dies, like tungsten, the wire being heated to about 1290 F (700 C) just before it enters each die. After working has started, iridium is embrittled if it is heated above its recrystallization temperature of 2460 F (1350 C).

Cold Working. Iridium that has been broken down by hot working to a fibrous structure and not recrystallized will withstand only a very small amount of cold work, such as is imparted by a planishing pass.

Single crystals of iridium, made by vertical zone melting, can be worked cold, like single crystals of rhodium, to reductions of about 50%. They cannot then be softened by annealing, because upon recrystallization, intercrystalline brittleness is developed.

Ruthenium

Hot Working. Small ingots of ruthenium can be deformed by small amounts by careful hot working at about 2730 F (1500 C), but dense fumes of the oxide are evolved and cracks invariably develop. Ruthenium powder compacts and cast ingots have been successfully hot rolled at 2200 F (1200 C) after enclosure in an envelope of stainless steel. The resulting sheet has little ductility.

For additional information on working of ruthenium, see D. W. Rhys, The Fabrication and Properties of Ruthenium, *Journal of the Less-Common Metals*, **1**, 1959, 269-291.

Platinum Alloys

The alloys of platinum with up to about 40% rhodium, 30% iridium, or 10% ruthenium comprise those of chief industrial use. All are worked by the same general methods as are used for platinum, allowance being made for the greater stiffness and hardness of the alloys.

Hot Working. The alloys can be forged, hot rolled, and hot swaged, usually at temperatures higher than for platinum. The platinum-ruthenium alloys give off fumes of ruthenium oxide above about 2000 F (1100 C) in air, and are preferably heated in a protective atmosphere.

Cold Working. All the alloys respond to cold working by rolling, swaging, and wiredrawing. The effects of cold work on the hardness of some typical alloys are given in Table 1.

Annealing. The alloys can be annealed in air, but all need to be quenched to prevent tarnishing by the oxide film of the alloying metal. Wires are usually continuously annealed and cooled in a hydrogen atmosphere. Annealing temperatures for the alloys are shown in Table 1.

POWDER METALLURGY

CONTENTS

Production of Powder Metallurgy Parts

*By the ASM Committee on Powder Metallurgy**

POWDER METALLURGY, in its simplest form, consists of compressing metal powder in a shaped die to produce green compacts, and then sintering (diffusion bonding) the compacts at elevated temperature in a furnace with a protective atmosphere. During sintering, the compacts become consolidated and strengthened.

The density of sintered compacts may be increased by re-pressing. When re-pressing is performed primarily to improve the dimensional accuracy of the compact, it is usually termed "sizing"; when performed to improve configuration, it is termed "coining". Re-pressing may be followed by resintering, which relieves stress due to cold work in re-pressing and may further consolidate the compacts.

Alloy compacts can be formed from mixtures of metal powders that are diffused during sintering. Usually, pre-alloyed powders are used. Consolidation is sometimes accelerated by sintering at a temperature at which one of the constituent metals is molten (as in copper-iron mixtures). Metals of relatively high melting point (such as iron or tungsten) are sometimes pressed to a skeleton, which is then infiltrated by a molten metal (such as copper or silver) having a melting point lower than that of the skeleton.

Process Capabilities. By pressing and sintering only, parts of over 80% theoretical density can be produced in iron and in many other metals and alloys. By re-pressing, with or without resintering, parts of 90% theoretical density or over can be produced. The density attainable is limited by the size and shape of the compact (see the section on Production Cycles, page 457).

Iron, copper, iron-copper, iron-carbon, iron-copper-carbon, brass, bronze, stainless steel, nickel silver, nickel and nickel alloys are among the materials used for powder metallurgy parts. In addition, mixtures of metals with nonmetallic materials (such as refractory oxides) — which cannot be formed except by powder metallurgy — are used for many applications. Parts made from many of the above materials respond to heat treatment, and iron compacts can be carburized.

In evaluating the cost of producing parts by powder metallurgy, savings that result from the absence of scrap and the elimination of machining and forming operations are important. Although powder is usually more costly per unit of weight or volume than other product forms of metal (average cost of transforming most metals to powder is 15¢ per pound), the saving achieved by minimizing waste from machining often results in lower metal cost for parts made from powder than for those machined from other forms.

Cost of tools for producing parts from powder must be distributed over the number of parts produced, as in any other process. In some applications, the cost of tools for producing parts by powder metallurgy is lower than the cost of tools for a competitive process if the run is short.

Successful production by powder metallurgy depends on proper selection and control of the following process variables: (*a*) powder characteristics, (*b*) powder preparation, (*c*) type of compacting press, (*d*) design of compacting tools and dies, (*e*) type of sintering furnace, (*f*) composition of sintering atmosphere, and (*g*) choice of production cycle.

Metal Powder Characteristics and Control

Powder particle size and shape have important effects on pressing and sintering characteristics, but the performance of each type of powder can be determined only empirically.

To insure uniformity in the handling and press performance of powders from batch to batch and in the strength of the compacts formed from them, laboratory tests are usually made on samples of powder from each batch. Results of quality-control tests can be applied only to samples of the same basic composition made by the same method. This limitation is illustrated in Fig. 1, which shows typical compressibility curves for three types of iron powders: electrolytic, reduced (low and high manganese), and atomized. Typical mechanical properties of sintered com-

*W. A. STADTLER, *Chairman,* Director of Technical Services, International Business Machines Corp.; NORBERT A. ARNOLD, Manager of Metal Powder Engineering, Keystone Carbon Co.; LOUIS W. BAUM, JR., Research Metallurgist, Hi-Dense Parts Div., Remington Arms Co., Inc.; W. J. DOELKER, Head of Metallurgical Research Department, National Cash Register Co.

FRANK EMLEY, Research Laboratory, C. K. Williams Div., Pfizer & Co., Inc.; E. G. GIBSON, Vice President, Zenith Sintered Products, Inc.; W. A. IRVINE, Manager of Production Engineering, Maytag Co.; J. K. LANGFITT, JR., Divisional Superintendent, Link-Belt Co.; PETER V. SCHNEIDER, Manager of Powdered Metals Engineering, Systems Manufacturing Div., International Business Machines Corp.

PAUL J. SHIPE, Supervisor, Physical Science Laboratory, Delco Moraine Div., General Motors Corp.; E. F. SWAZY, President, Qualimet (formerly with Mallory Metallurgical Div., P. R. Mallory & Co., Inc.); FRANK I. ZALESKI, Frankford Arsenal, Department of the Army.

The assistance of Kempton H. Roll, Executive Director, Metal Powder Industries Federation; and of the Technical Committee of the Powder Metallurgy Parts Manufacturers Association, Metal Powder Industries Federation, in preparing part of this article is gratefully acknowledged.

pacts made from each type of iron powder are also shown in Fig. 1.

Test procedures are commonly specified for sampling and determination of particle size distribution, flow rate, apparent density, weight loss in hydrogen, compressibility, green strength, sintering characteristics, and chemical composition. A cross index of standards for metal powders and powder metallurgy products is given in Table 1.

Sampling. Containers of metal powders are usually sampled by turning a specially designed auger-type sampler called a "sampling thief" vertically to the bottom of the container and removing the column of powder. A hollow tube is not suitable for sampling. One or more of these samples are taken from each drum of powder, the number of samples taken depending on the drum size. Samples taken in this manner are combined and reduced to the required size by means of a "sample splitter", or by rolling, coning and quartering.

Particle Size Distribution. A complete screen analysis of the particle size distribution is determined by placing a weighed sample of powder in the top screen of a "nest" of standard sieves having successively smaller openings — usually 100, 150, 200 and 325-mesh. The assembly is shaken mechanically for a standard period of time. The powder that is retained on each mesh size and the powder that passes through the finest sieve are both reported as weight percentages of the sample.

The powder passing 325-mesh can be further analyzed for its subsieve particle size distribution by use of an optical or electron microscope, by elutriation, or with a turbidimeter. Weight percentages are reported for decreasing micron sizes.

Flow Rate. The standard flowmeter for metal powders is a funnel-shaped apparatus having a calibrated orifice. The time required for a given amount of powder to flow unaided through the orifice is reported as the flow rate of the powder. For powders that do not flow, a special funnel is used or a zero value is reported.

Apparent Density. The standard flowmeter is used also for determining the apparent density of free-flowing powders. For nonflowing powders use is made of a baffled rectangular tower fed by a funnel having a large orifice. Both instruments serve to supply a controlled flow of powder into a cup of known volume. The content of the full cup is weighed, and the apparent density is reported as grams per cubic centimeter.

Weight Loss in Hydrogen. A fairly accurate indication of the oxide content of most metal powders is obtained by reducing a weighed sample of the powder in hydrogen under standard time-temperature conditions. The sample must be cooled to room temperature in an atmosphere of dry hydrogen.

Loss in weight caused by reduction of the oxides present is expressed as a percentage of the initial sample weight.

Compressibility. A given weight of metal powder is compacted at a definite pressure in a test die under accurately controlled conditions. The ratio of the density of the green compact to the theoretical density of the component

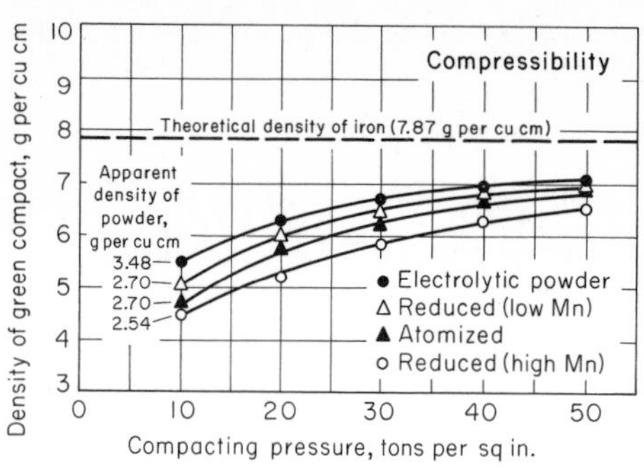

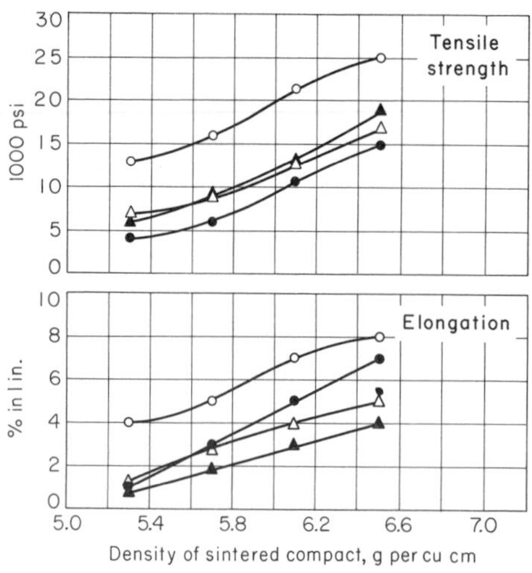

Item	Type of powder: Atomized	Reduced(a): Low Mn	Reduced(a): High Mn	Electrolytic
Composition, %				
Carbon	0.06	0.05	0.02	0.02
Manganese	0.15	0.05	0.50	0.03
Phosphorus	0.011	0.015	0.012	0.015
Sulfur	0.022	0.010	0.005	0.02
Acid insolubles	0.04	0.25	0.30	0.01
Hydrogen loss (oxygen)	0.65	0.48	0.9	0.40
Total iron	98.7	98.1	98.0	99.5
Sieve Analysis, Wt %				
On 80-mesh screen	1.0	...	...	...
Thru 80 on 100	6.1	0.3	0.5	0.8
Thru 100 on 150	16.2	8.2	15.3	22.3
Thru 150 on 200	20.1	23.2	17.9	34.1
Thru 200 on 250	13.7	17.8	11.2	16.1
Thru 250 on 325	18.0	21.9	15.2	13.7
Thru 325	24.6	28.1	39.9	12.9
Apparent density, g/cu cm	2.70	2.70	2.54	3.48
Flow rate, sec/50 g	25	24	30	21

(a) Low manganese is near 0.05%; high manganese, near 0.60%.

Fig. 1. Effect of compacting pressure on density and mechanical properties of iron powder compacts after sintering at 2050 F for 1 hr in dissociated ammonia

powders is a measure of the compressibility of the powder.

Green Strength. The strength of a green compact (unsintered metal powder specimen) is ordinarily determined by pressing a given weight of powder to a specified density in the shape of a rectangular bar of standard size. This test bar is supported at both ends as a simple beam and loaded transversely to fracture. The modulus of rupture (in pounds per square inch) is reported as the green strength of the powder undergoing evaluation.

Sintering Characteristics. A weighed quantity of a powder is compacted under controlled conditions and the dimensions of the green specimen are recorded. After sintering under controlled conditions dimensional measurements are again taken. The specimen is finally tested for mechanical properties. Sintering characteristics are generally reported in terms of dimensional changes, density changes, final density, and mechanical properties.

Chemical Composition. In addition to the above tests, routine chemical analyses are usually run on all powders to determine the amount of the major metal present, such as the total copper content in copper powder, plus such impurities as might normally be expected in the material and which, if present in excess, could cause unusual and undesirable behavior in processing.

Powder Preparation

Powders are often mixed or blended before use. This is done to obtain specific properties in the finished product. Mixing or blending must be carefully controlled. Also, it is important to use equipment that mixes rapidly and produces a uniform distribution of the powders in the desired proportions in minimum time.

Excessive blending, especially in an overloaded blender, may work harden the powder, making it less compressible and thus more difficult to compact. The cascading of powder inside the blender will gradually round the edges of the particles, thereby changing their shape. As a result, the powder exhibits different molding characteristics.

The double-cone blender is probably the most extensively used of the various types available. The final operation before compaction is to mix the powders with a lubricant, such as zinc stearate or stearic acid. The lubricant not only minimizes die friction and wear but also reduces interparticle friction, thus allowing the particles to pack more closely, resulting in higher density in the green compact.

Small percentages of alloying additives such as graphite, copper or nickel powders, as may be required, are also introduced during the final mixing.

Presses

Presses used for making powder metallurgy parts are similar to those used for other pressworking operations (see the article that begins on page 1 in this volume). However, several press requirements should be given specific consideration when a press is being selected. These requirements include: (*a*) sufficient length of stroke to compress fully the greatest depth of powder to be handled; (*b*) ability to apply sufficient pressure in both directions of pressing to provide density as nearly uniform as possible from top to bottom of the compact; (*c*) ability to control length and speed of the pressure and ejection strokes; (*d*) ability to adjust die fill; and (*e*) in multiple-action presses, ability to synchronize press strokes and to control the strokes for powder transfer and other automatic operations.

Presses used for compacting metal powders may be either mechanically or hydraulically actuated; or sometimes a combination of both may be used. Compacts can be pressed to a predetermined thickness in a mechanical press

Table 1. Cross Index of Standards for Metal Powders and Metal Powder Products (a)

Title	Designation (b) ASTM	MPIF	Other
METAL POWDERS			
Specifications			
Aluminum Powder, Flaked, Grained and Atomized	...	...	MIL-A-512
Brass Powder (For Sintered Parts)	...	...	MIL-B-11552
Magnesium-Aluminum Alloy, Powdered	...	...	JAN-M-454
Powders, Metal, Atomized (Aluminum, Magnesium, Magnesium-Aluminum)	...	...	MIL-P-14067
Titanium, Powdered	...	...	MIL-T-13405
Tungsten, Powdered	...	...	MIL-T-13827
Methods of Testing			
Bending Strength, Green Density, Hardness and Shrinkage of Compacted, Sintered Metal Powder Specimens	...	13-62	...
Compressibility of Metal Powders	B331	...	...
Compression Testing of Metallic Materials	E9	...	...
Density, Apparent, of Metal Powders	B212	4-45	...
Density, Apparent, of Non-Free-Flowing Metal Powders	B417	28-59	...
Density, Apparent, of Refractory Metals and Compounds by Scott Volumeter	B329	...	...
Determining the Cast Hardness of Powder Metallurgy Parts	...	37-65	...
Flow Rate of Metal Powders	B213	3-45	...
Green Strength of Compacted Metal Powder Specimens	B312	15-62	...
Hydrogen Loss of Metal Powders	E159	2-64	...
Insoluble Matter in Iron and Copper Powders	E194	6-64	...
Iron Content of Iron Powder	...	7-61	...
Particle Distribution of Tungsten Metal Powder by Turbidimetry	B430	...	...
Particle Size, Average, of Metal Powders by Fisher Subsieve Sizers	...	28-59	...
Particle Size, Average, of Refractory Metals and Compounds by Fisher Subsieve Sizers	B330	32-60	...
Particle Size Characteristics of Pigments	D1366	...	...
Particle Size Distribution of Particulate Substances of Subsieve Sizes by Microscopic Methods	E20	...	...
Procedures for Determining Particle Size Distribution, and Packed Density of Metal Powders	...	...	MIL-STD-1233
Sampling and Testing Aluminum Powder and Paste	D480	...	...
Sampling Finished Lots of Metal Powders	B215	1-61	...
Sieve Analysis of Granular Metal Powders	B214	5-62	...
Subsieve Analysis of Granular Metal Powders by Air Classification	B293	12-51	...
Tension Test Specimens for Pressed and Sintered Metal Powders	E8	10-63	...
METAL POWDER BEARINGS			
Specifications			
Copper-Base Sintered Metal Powder Bearings (Oil-Impregnated)	B438	35	SAE J471C
Iron-Base Sintered Metal Powder Bearings (Oil-Impregnated)	B439	35	SAE J471C
Materials Standards and Specifications for Powder Metallurgy Mechanical Components and Oil-Impregnated Bearings Plus Code Designations and Coding Systems	B438 B439	35	SAE J471C
Bearing and Bushing Alloys, Steel-Backed Metal Powder	B377	..	...
Bearings, Sintered, Metal Powder (Oil-Impregnated), Aircraft	...	...	MIL-B-5687
METAL POWDER BEARINGS: Methods of Testing			
Density and Interconnected Porosity of Sintered Powder Metal Structural Parts and Oil-Impregnated Bearings	B328	...	...
METAL POWDER STRUCTURAL PARTS			
Specifications			
Brass Sintered Metal Powder Structural Parts	B282	35	SAE 890, 891 MIL-B-12128
Bronze Sintered Metal Powder Structural Parts	B255	35	SAE 840, 841, 842, 843
Copper-Infiltrated Iron-Sintered Metal Powder Structural Parts	B303	35	SAE 870, 872
Iron-Copper-Carbon, Sintered Metal Powder Structural Parts	B426	35	SAE 864A, 864B, 865A, 865B, 866A, 866B, 867A, 867B
Iron-Copper Sintered Metal Powder Structural Parts	B222	35	SAE 861, 862, 863
Iron, Low and Medium Density, Sintered Metal Powder Structural Parts	B310	35	SAE 850, 851, 852, 853, 855
Sintered Metal Powder Bearings and Structural Parts	...	...	SAE J471C
Sintered Nickel Steel Structural Parts	B484	...	...
Tungsten Base, High Density Metal (Sintered or Hot Pressed)	B459	...	MIL-T-21014
Methods of Testing			
Bending Strength, Green Density, Hardness and Sintering Change of Sintered Metal Powder Specimens	...	13-62	...
Density and Interconnected Porosity	B328	35	...
Density of Sintered Metal Friction Materials	B376	...	...
Hardness of Sintered Metal Friction Materials	B347	...	...
Tension Test Specimens for Pressed and Sintered Metal Powders	E8	10-63	...
Transverse Rupture Strength of Sintered Metal Friction Materials	B378	...	...
CEMENTED CARBIDES			
Specifications			
Tungsten Carbide, Crystalline	...	...	MIL-T-13366
Methods of Testing			
Compression Testing for Cemented Carbides	...	...	CCPA P-104
Density of Cemented Carbides	B311	...	CCPA P-101
Diametral Compression Testing of Cemented Carbides	B485	...	CCPA P-115
Grain Size, Apparent, and Distribution of Cemented Tungsten Carbides	B390	...	CCPA P-107
Hardness Testing of Cemented Carbides	B294	...	CCPA P-103
Linear Thermal Expansion for Cemented Carbides	...	...	CCPA P-108
Porosity, Apparent, of Cemented Carbides	B276	...	CCPA M-201
Tension Testing of Cemented Carbides	B437	...	CCPA P-113
Transverse Rupture Strength of Cemented Carbides	B406	...	CCPA P-102
ELECTRICAL CONTACTS			
Specifications			
Brushes, Electrical Contacts, and Carbon Stock, Electrical Contact Brush	...	...	MIL-B-3743
MISCELLANEOUS			
Glossary for Metal Powder Compacting Presses and Tooling	...	31-59	...
Metal Powders Directory of Commercially Available Grades and Types	...	DS-3	...
Precision Micromesh Sieves	E161	...	...
Wire-Cloth Sieves for Testing	E11	...	...
Definitions of terms	B243	9-62	...

(a) Source: Part 7, ASTM Book of Standards, "Cross Index of Standards for Metal Powders and Metal Powder Products", revised January, 1969; ASTM index lists standards in addition to those given here. (b) Standards referenced include those of the American Society for Testing and Materials (ASTM), Metal Powder Industries Federation (MPIF), Society of Automotive Engineers (SAE), Cemented Carbide Producers Association (CCPA), and federal agencies, including the military (MIL, JAN).

by adjusting the stroke, or in a hydraulic press by the use of limit switches. When it is required to press to a predetermined pressure, hydraulic presses are usually used, although mechanical presses are adaptable to this requirement if they are equipped with hydraulic equalizers.

Part size, configuration and required density are the most important factors in selecting a press for a given powder metallurgy application.

Mechanical Presses. Presses operated by means of a crank or an adjustable eccentric are widely used for making small parts at high speed, especially when the press is fitted with a tableting machine or rotating die table such as is used in the pharmaceutical industry. Generally, the basic design of the press is simple, with a single upper punch, adjustable through the eccentric to control pressure and the thickness of compact. Stationary core rods can be used to produce holes in the direction of pressing. The die cavity is usually filled automatically, and the amount of powder is controlled by the position of a cam-operated lower punch when it is at the bottom of its travel.

In most presses, the lower punch remains stationary during filling and until the compact is almost pressed, at which time the lower punch exerts pressure and ejects the compact.

Eccentric presses are most commonly used for pressing powder compacts that require a force of no more than 30 tons, when the maximum horizontal dimension of the compact is about 3 in., and required depth of fill is about 2⅝ in. As many as 2000 compacts per hour can be produced with this type of mechanical press.

For exerting pressure up to about 500 tons, toggle or knuckle-joint presses are widely used for pressing metal powders. The toggle action, in addition to being more powerful than that of an eccentric or cam, is particularly suited to the needs of powder metallurgy. The fast motion of the punches at the start of their travel assists in accelerating the rate of operation. In addition, the slow squeezing action with which the press completes its stroke facilitates the flow of metal particles into all sections of the compact. Further, as the punches approach final compression, the toggle intensifies the applied pressure without increasing power consumption. Variable-speed drives permit adjustment of press speed to suit the flow characteristics of the powder being pressed and the mechanical requirements of the green compact.

In cam presses the movements of upper and lower punches are controlled independently in relation to each other. This capability permits production of a wide variety of different shapes. Cam presses are less powerful than toggle presses, usually not exceeding 85 tons in capacity. The multiple motions that cam presses provide make it possible to press complicated parts of irregular cross section.

In these presses cams can be adjusted or inserts can be fitted so that the motions of each punch can be changed in any way desired. Pressure can be applied from both top and bottom simultaneously, or independently. Moreover,

Table 2. Effect of Location of Specimen and Pressing Technique on Uniformity of Density in Pressed Compacts

Location of specimen	Density, g per cu cm — Single punch	Dual punch
Top of ring	6.46	6.08
Center of ring	6.33	5.93
Bottom of ring	6.14	6.10
Average	6.31	6.04

the timing can be adjusted so that the powder can be compressed a predetermined amount by the upper punch, then by the lower punch, and again by the upper punch. This flexibility permits the best combination of movements to obtain uniform density in compacts of varying thickness and complex shape.

Hydraulic presses having capacities up to about 5000 tons are used for compacting large powder metallurgy parts. Because of the long stroke needed when pressing large compacts and the relatively slow transmission of fluid, hydraulic presses are slower than mechanical presses. For pressing large parts, however, slow speeds are preferable, because a comparatively long time period is required to permit the escape of entrapped air from the compact while it is being compressed.

The high pressures that can be developed by hydraulic presses make them particularly suitable for re-pressing and coining. Because only a short stroke is needed for these applications, relatively high operating speeds are possible. Pressure-multiplying units have been developed to economize oil consumption during the final stages of pressing and to increase the speed of operation in normal pressing.

Combination Presses. Many of the presses used in powder metallurgy combine two or more operating principles. Nearly all eccentric presses, for example, have cam-operated motions for many auxiliary operations. Combined mechanical and hydraulic presses frequently are custom-designed and built for specific duties.

Press and Tooling Systems for Compacts of Varying Complexity

Metal powders do not behave like liquids. Friction between particles and die walls and among particles prevents an applied force from being transmitted uniformly throughout the mass. Friction and particle bonding increase with pressure, particularly with very small particles and those of irregular shape. Consequently, compacts pressed in a die with a single moving punch are the most dense in the immediate area of this punch face, with the density decreasing with increasing distance toward the opposite stationary punch. The rate of decrease in density depends on the length-to-diameter ratio of the compact and the nature of the powder. Although this effect may not be significant when pressing thin single-level compacts, such as disks or washers, special techniques must be employed for thicker compacts and for multiple-level compacts of complex contour. The more common press and tooling procedures are outlined below.

Single-action pressing uses a single upper punch to compress powder into a die, which is closed by a fixed lower punch that forms the bottom surface of the compact. One or more core rods supported beneath the lower punch may be used to form through-holes. After compaction, the part (compact) may be ejected by raising the lower punch.

Single-punch pressing is suitable only for making thin compacts of uniform cross section.

Floating-die pressing in its simplest form makes use of a single-action press provided with a floating die table held in its top position by a yieldable support such as a spring, or by air or oil pressure. As the upper punch descends, the friction between the powder and the inside surfaces of the die moves the die table down over the lower punch. The effect is to compress the powder by two opposed punches, both penetrating the die cavity, thus producing a compact of much more uniform density than is possible by single-action pressing. This type of press is suitable for pressing flanged parts by using a stepped die. Straight-through or stepped holes may be formed by the use of core rods.

Use of a floating die makes it possible to produce a reasonably uniform density in cylinders having a length-to-diameter ratio as great as 3 to 1.

The extent to which a compact made by this procedure may vary in density throughout its section is shown in Table 2 by data derived from tests made on specimens from a single production lot. The specimens were cut transversely from rings (4.145-in. ID, 4.545-in. OD, 0.865 in. thick) that were pressed from a hydrogen-reduced iron powder. Table 2 compares uniformity of density obtained in single-punch and dual-punch pressing. As shown in Table 2, density variation between the top and bottom of the specimens was much greater when the specimens were pressed with a single punch. Density was greatest in the portions of the specimens adjacent to the punches.

Density was determined by measuring each specimen in air and in water (ASTM B328-60).

Even better control of pressure distribution in the product is achieved with the use of mechanically actuated dies than with floating dies.

Double-action pressing provides an alternative means of exerting pressure on both top and bottom of the compact. This is achieved by moving both the lower punch and the upper punch under pressure, using a fixed die. The effect is similar to that of using a floating die with a single-action press. An advantage of double-action pressing, however, is that longer compacts can be pressed because of the two moving punches.

Pressing with multiple-motion punches is used for making complex multiple-level compacts in which a more uniform density is needed in both thick and thin sections. The presses employed are provided with separate punches for each level of the compact.

The individual punches serve two purposes: (*a*) they can be set so that the powder in all sections can be compacted at the same rate to obtain uniform density throughout the compact, and (b) they can provide support to all sections during ejection of the compact from the die. These two features are essential for the production of high-density compacts. During compaction, density must be built up uniformly throughout the compact, to avoid shear planes between the various sections, and all sections must be ejected positively at a uniform rate. In the production of high-density compacts, very little clearance between punch and die can be tolerated; otherwise, metal powder is forced between punch and die surfaces, which results in binding between the punch and die walls and galling of the punch or die, or both.

The example that follows describes a typical application of multiple-motion punches for production of a high-density complex shape.

Example 623. Production of a Multiple-Level Compact in a Mechanical Press (Fig. 2)

The safety-lock thumbpiece shown in Fig. 2 was more than twice as thick at one end as in its body, the transition being made through a short taper. A uniform green density of 7.0 to 7.1 g per cu cm was secured throughout the compact by using two lower punches, one for each level of thickness, and an upper punch with controlled travel to insure that the compact, when fully compressed, was at the correct level of the die to locate the tapered region. (With parallel-side dies, it is unnecessary to control the level of the compact in the die.) A mechanical press was used in preference to a hydraulic press to attain the required production rate. The stages involved in compacting this part are shown in Fig. 2. Press, tool and processing details are given in the table with Fig. 2.

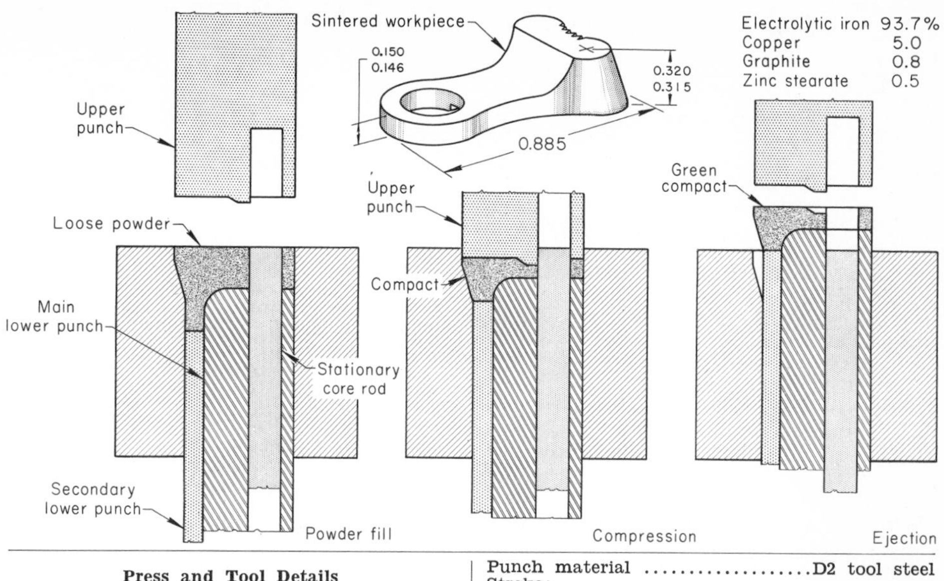

Press and Tool Details

Type of press	Mechanical
Maximum pressure:	
Upper punch	50 tons
Lower outer punch	50 tons
Lower inner punch	30 tons
Stationary core rod	10 tons
Workpiece-diameter capacity	4 in. max
Fill adjustment, lower punches	0 to 3½ in.
Die material	Carbide
Punch material	D2 tool steel
Stroke:	
Lower punches	0 to 1⅞ in.
Upper punch	5½ in. max
Die entrance	1⅝ in. max

Processing Details

Compacting pressure	40 tons per sq in.
Sintering treatment	1 hr at 2050 F(a)
Green density	7.0 to 7.1 g per cu cm
Sintered density	7.20 to 7.25 g per cu cm

(a) In dissociated or burned ammonia (dew point, 5 F max) at 450 cu ft per hr

Fig. 2. Pressing a multiple-level compact in three stages in a mechanical press (Example 623)

When equipment is not available for multiple punches, the use of stepped punches is sometimes an alternative procedure for pressing stepped compacts, particularly for thin compacts. Considerable experimentation, however, is usually necessary in setting up the die assembly. Control of the press operation is critical also. A procedure that was successful for pressing a multiple-level compact is described in the following example.

Example 624. Use of Stepped Punches to Produce a Multiple-Level Compact (Fig. 3)

Figure 3 (left) shows the die used in producing a flat-stepped workpiece, also shown in Fig. 3. A die cell was made with a periphery of the same contour as that of the finished workpiece. This die cell was used with a flat-faced upper punch and a stepped lower punch corresponding to the steps in the finished part. The top surface of the cell was hollowed out in varying amounts, as shown in Fig. 3, to allow some powder to be splashed out (where the part design calls for thinner sections). Depth of the powder on the predominating level of the lower punch was just sufficient to produce a finished thickness of 0.075 in. Step A on the lower punch received less powder, and step B received more powder, than the rest of the punch. As the detail of the unsintered compact shows, the three steps in the compact were pressed to three densities: 6.0, 6.5 and 7.0 g per cu cm. The thicknesses of the various steps were adjusted to yield densities of 7.5 and 7.65 g per cu cm when re-pressed. (This method of providing for variations in section thickness requires considerable adjustment by trial and error and strict control of all variables. In operation, the speed with which the upper punch hits the powder controls the amount of powder that is splashed out.)

The fit of the punches to the die cell was kept at about 0.0005 in. With looser fits, powder was extruded from regions of high density to regions of low density and caused rapid tool wear. It was necessary, moreover, to keep burrs to a minimum to meet the corner-break requirements.

The compacts were pressed in a 100-ton mechanical press with a floating die table, using zinc stearate as a die lubricant. Because the green compact was fragile in regions of lower density, the press was made to pause at the ejection point to allow the compact to be lifted off the lower punch. The re-pressed compact was resintered to relieve stress that resulted from the extreme cold work in the more heavily worked areas and to increase density. The compacts were fixtured on edge in the sintering furnace, and separated to allow the dissociated ammonia sintering atmosphere to reach all surfaces and to remove the zinc stearate lubricant used in re-pressing. Fixturing also helped to maintain flatness. Additional manufacturing details are tabulated with Fig. 3.

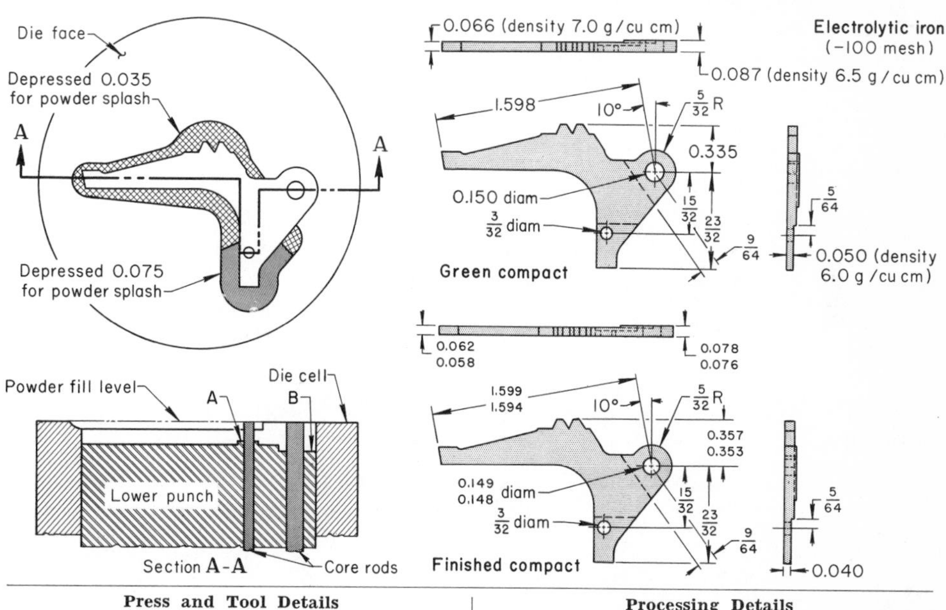

Press and Tool Details

Type of press used:	
Compacting	100-ton mechanical
Re-pressing	50-ton hydraulic
Die material	Carbide (9% Co)
Punch material	D2 tool steel
Core-rod material	Carbide (13% Co)
Punch-to-die clearance	0.0005 in.

Processing Details

Sintering treatment	45 min at 2070 F
Sintering atmosphere	Dissociated ammonia
Sintering rate	3800 compacts per hour
Resintering	20 min at 2050 F(a)
Production rate:	
Pressing compacts	400 per hour
Re-pressing compacts	600 per hour

(a) In dissociated ammonia

Fig. 3. Die and stepped lower punch used for pressing a multiple-level green compact. Finished compact shown is after re-pressing and resintering. (Example 624)

Dies and Tooling

Dies for powder metallurgy are commonly designed on the basis of experience rather than stress analysis. As a general rule, the forces developed in the die wall during pressing can be approximately calculated on the basis that full hydraulic pressure is exerted.

The complete tooling for making a given part is often assembled in a die set before being fitted in the press. This practice insures greater accuracy of setting, which reduces wear between punch and die. In addition, by using two sets of dies, downtime for die changing is decreased.

Dies are commonly constructed by using inserts held in a case by clamping or shrink fitting. For shrink fitting, interference limits should be about 0.0015 in. per inch of diameter for steel inserts and steel cases and about 0.0010 in. per inch of diameter for shrinking carbide inserts into steel cases.

Dies (or die insert portions) for medium-production requirements are usually made from an air-hardening or oil-hardening grade of high-carbon high-chromium tool steel such as D2 or D3 and heat treated to Rockwell C 60 to 64. For long runs or where abrasion is severe, tungsten carbide with 6 to 9% of cobalt binder is generally preferred. For simple dies the amount of cobalt may be as low as 3% to obtain better wear resistance at the expense of shock resistance. For multiple-level dies with vulnerable projections, carbide with as much as 20 to 30% cobalt is often used.

When inserts are used, cases are usually made of a medium-carbon alloy steel, heat treated to obtain strength and toughness (for example, 4140 steel heat treated to Rockwell C 35 to 40).

The mouth of the dies should be beveled to provide a 15° lead for a depth of 1/32 in. to guide the punches into the dies. Draft is sometimes needed in a die, to facilitate ejection of the compact, as in counterbored dies used for forming parts having thin flanges. By providing gradual relief of horizontal forces, damage to the compact during ejection is prevented.

Punches for severe use are commonly made from D2 or D3 tool steel heat treated to about Rockwell C 60. For extremely long runs, punches are often made from (or tipped with) carbide that contains 9 to 12% cobalt.

For some small-diameter fragile punches, the above materials are too brittle. Under these conditions, the best practice is to sacrifice some wear resistance by using a shock-resisting tool steel (such as S1) heat treated to about Rockwell C 55. Punches made from shock-resisting tool steel are sometimes carburized or carbonitrided to improve wear resistance.

Punches are usually relieved with a back taper of 0.005 to 0.010 in. on the diameter and 0.0025 and 0.005 in. around all profiles, to permit the escape of powder passing down beyond the punch faces. The close-fitting length at the tip is made as short as possible. Because punches sometimes chip at the edges, they may require regrinding several times before being replaced.

Core rods are usually made from carbide with a binder of 6 to 13% cobalt. A carbide coating applied to steel by a flame or by plasma has also been successful for core rods. For short-run production, core rods can be of hardened tool steel, such as D2, or sometimes a low-alloy tool steel is satisfactory, as in Example 630 where a core rod of O6 produced 50,000 pieces.

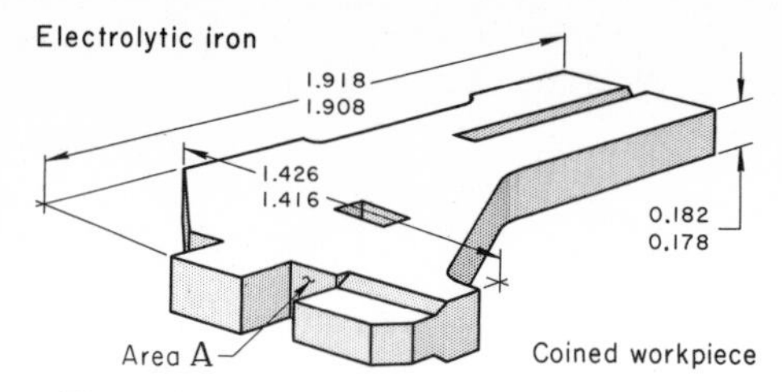

Fig. 4. Actuator base that was pressed and coined (after sintering) in the same die (Example 625)

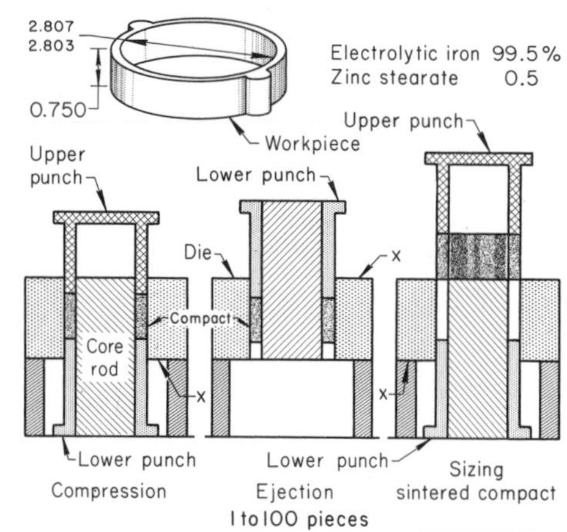

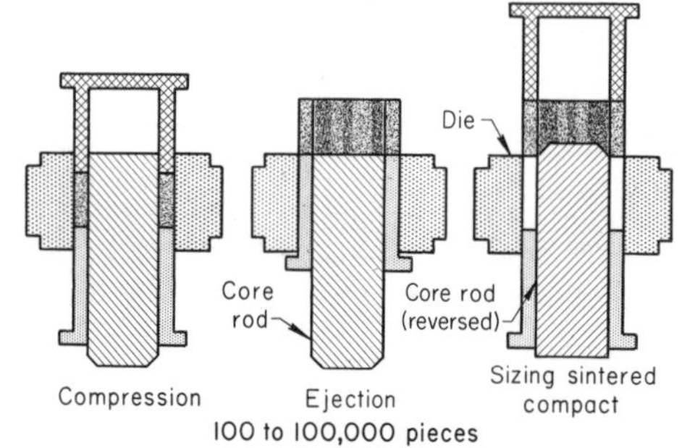

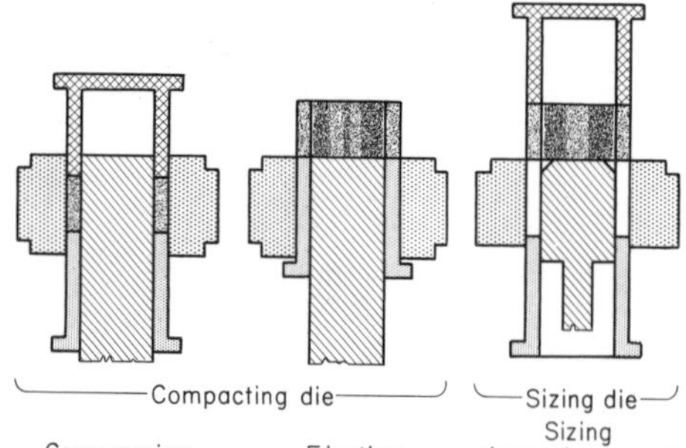

Production details	Pieces required: 1 to 100	100 to 100,000	Over 100,000
Production rate, pcs/hr:			
Compacting	5 to 15	600	600
Coining	10 to 20	300	1000
Feeding method:			
Compacting	Hand	Automatic	
Coining	Hand	Hand	Hand

Fig. 5. Tooling setups for compacting and coining a retainer ring in various production quantities (Example 626)

Core rods, like punches, are usually relieved with a back taper of 0.005 to 0.010 in. on the diameter, and the close-fitting portions should be kept as short as possible. When core rods are used to form blind or shoulder holes, the column loadings that are imposed must be taken into account in the design of the core rods.

Clearance and Finish. In making press tools for powder metallurgy processes, punches and dies should be fitted individually so that they can operate together within a specified clearance. Fitting must be closest when producing compacts for bearings; for such applications diametral clearance may be less than 0.0002 in. If a larger clearance is allowed, any slight variation in powder will push the core rod to one side, which will produce eccentric compacts. For most applications, clearances are 0.0005 to 0.001 in. on diametral dimensions of punches and dies.

Die cavities and core rods should be lapped or polished to a finish of 5 micro-in. or better, and the last lapping should be parallel to the longitudinal axis of the tools. Punch faces and punch lands should have an equally good polish. Poorly finished punches wear faster than punches that are well polished.

Coining Dies. The dies used for coining are the same as those used for pressing, but they may need renewal more frequently, because there are usually close limits on the permissible amount of wear. Costs are reduced whenever the same tooling is used for both pressing and coining. Sometimes, as in the following example, this is made possible by a modification in die design and material.

Example 625. Die Modification That Eliminated Breakage in Pressing and Coining (Fig. 4)

The actuator base shown in Fig. 4 was specified to have a uniform density of 7.5 g per cu cm to meet electrical requirements. Because density after pressing varied from 7.1 in the thin section to 5.8 in the thick section, coining was necessary.

Originally, a carbide die was used for both pressing and coining. Pressing, using a stepped upper and lower punch, presented no problem; but during coining, the section of carbide used for coining the junction between the two metal thicknesses (area A in Fig. 4) became highly stressed and frequently broke. The problem was solved by removing this carbide section and replacing it with a stationary core rod made of tool steel. This change not only made it possible to continue using the same die set, but also decreased the cost of tooling, and indirectly increased production by reducing downtime.

Tooling for Various Production Quantities. Tooling for making a powder metallurgy product often depends on the production quantity. Usually, complex dies can be justified only if a large number of parts are to be made. The following example gives details of the tooling used for compacting and coining a retainer ring in various production quantities.

Example 626. Tooling for Short, Medium and Long Runs (Fig. 5)

Three progressively more costly tooling setups are shown in Fig. 5 for producing a retainer (also shown in Fig. 5). For a quantity up to 100 pieces, a hand-operated press with a simple die made from tool steel and a spacer made from low-carbon steel was sufficient. (Note that in using this simple tooling, the upper punch is removed and the die is inverted to eject the compact.) For medium quantities (100 to 100,000 pieces), a mechanical press was used with a carbide die having a reversible core rod. Compacting and sizing were done successively in the same die. For high-production quantities (over 100,000 pieces), two carbide dies were used, one in a compacting press and the other in a coining press. Details of production rates and feeding methods are given in the table with Fig. 5.

Sintering

Sintering is the process by which the compressed metal powders are bonded by heating at temperatures below their melting points. Densification may or may not occur. If powders of two or more different metals are heated together to a sufficiently high temperature, alloying may take place simultaneously with sintering. Sometimes a liquid phase forms and assists in consolidation, or a compact may be sintered for a short time and then infiltrated with a molten metal of lower melting point.

The processes operative in sintering may be plastic flow, vapor transport and diffusion. A green compact becomes a sintered part in a series of continuous stages. On reaching a specific temperature, which depends on the powder composition, the compact shows increased strength, thermal conductivity and electrical conductivity. The particle surface contacts formed in pressing become larger. As the temperature or time is increased, the strength increases. The bonds between the particles grow and become stronger, and isolated pores appear. As time progresses, the rate of densification slows down and the larger pores increase in size even though the total porosity decreases. By holding at temperature for long periods the pore size may then decrease, but it is virtually impossible to obtain full density by sintering alone.

When the highest possible density is required, the compacts may be re-pressed and then resintered. Re-pressing closes up the larger pores mechanically, and in resintering, fresh bonds are formed. The improvement obtainable by these operations is illustrated by the following example.

Example 627. Re-pressing and Resintering for Increased Density (Fig. 6)

Densities of compacts 1 in. in diameter and 1 in. high were measured after pressing at pressures varying from 30 to 60 tons per sq in. and sintering for 1 hr in dissociated ammonia at 2050 F. The relation of compacting pressure and density, after sintering, is shown graphically in Fig. 6. Also shown in Fig. 6 is the increase in density effected by re-pressing at 50 tons per sq in. and resintering for 1 hr in dissociated ammonia at 2050 F.

Sintering Furnaces

Furnaces used for sintering powder metallurgy compacts are generally similar to the protective atmosphere furnaces used in the copper brazing of steel. However, some design principles incorporated in a sintering furnace are not required for brazing. For example, in brazing, the parts are held at temperature only long enough for the brazing material to flow. In contrast, powder metallurgy compacts must be held at the sintering temperature long enough to obtain the properties desired,

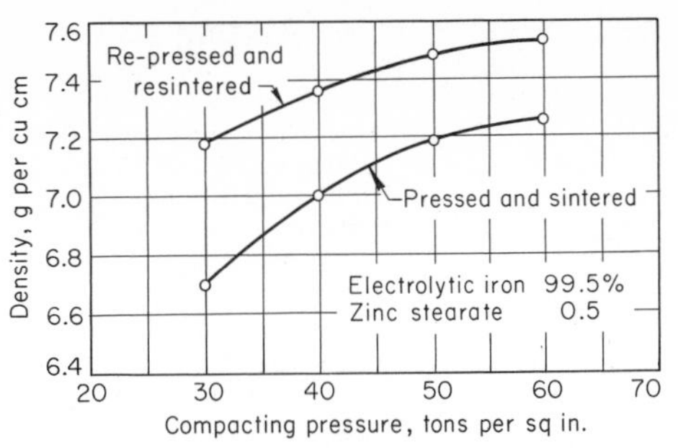

Fig. 6. Effect of re-pressing at 50 tons per sq in. and resintering on density of powder metallurgy compacts (Example 627)

such as density, strength and elongation. Furthermore, a "burn-off" chamber is required in which the compact can be heated slowly to expel air and trapped lubricants.

Large sintering furnaces are usually constructed with a gastight shell and electrical-resistance heating elements or gas-fired radiant tubes exposed to the heating chambers. Large muffles are expensive, costly to maintain, and introduce thermal losses. Full muffle construction, however, is normally essential when the dew point of hydrogen or dissociated ammonia atmospheres must be kept below about −20 F. This is because the hydrogen reacts with oxide refractories at sintering temperatures, producing water vapor and raising the dew point. By using high-purity alumina refractories, muffle-free furnaces with exposed molybdenum heating elements have been operated successfully. Full muffle furnaces have one further advantage — they purge faster, because there is no porous brickwork in the chamber and because less protective gas is required.

Production sintering furnaces are supplied throughout with a protective atmosphere and are divided into: (*a*) a burn-off chamber, which serves also for preheating; (*b*) a high-temperature heating chamber; and (*c*) a cooling chamber.

The burn-off chamber is usually controlled to heat the compacts to about 800 F, but provision should be made for the temperature to be raised to at least 1600 F should this be required. It is most important that all lubricants, including zinc stearate, stearic acid and waxes, should be volatilized and expelled from the furnace before the compacts enter the high-temperature zone, and both the flow of gas and the time of heating should be sufficient to insure that this is done. If hydrocarbons derived from lubricants pass into the heating chamber they will be cracked, and the liberated carbon will deposit on heating elements and refractories; in addition, the workpieces may be discolored and sintering will be impaired. Zinc compounds will contaminate the elements and may pass into the cooling chamber, condense on the walls, and reduce heat transfer.

The high-temperature heating chamber must be long enough to allow sufficient time for the compacts to be heated to temperature and maintained at temperature long enough for adequate sintering. Multiple-control zones are frequently used to obtain a suitable temperature gradient.

The cooling chamber often consists of a short insulated zone in which the compacts can partly cool slowly enough to avoid thermal shock. This is followed by a water-jacketed extension, which may be quite long. Automatic temperature control of the cooling water is most desirable. If the temperature of the walls should fall below the dew point of the protective gas, condensed water may collect on the workpieces and cause staining. If cooling time is insufficient, the compacts will oxidize when they emerge into the air.

Compacts are commonly conveyed through the furnace by mesh belts, roller hearths or pusher mechanisms.

Mesh-belt conveyors can handle low to medium production quantities and are suited particularly for small lightweight compacts. Stretch of the alloy belt limits the length of the furnace and the size of the furnace load. It is desirable to keep the temperature below 2100 F when using a mesh belt. Because each end of this type of furnace usually remains open during operation, the consumption of protective gas is high and ample gas capacity must be provided. Flame curtains may be used to assist in atmosphere control. A variable-speed drive gives flexibility in adjusting time and temperature cycles.

Roller-hearth furnaces are similar in arrangement to mesh-belt furnaces except that in place of the belt, a series of driven rollers is fitted along the entire length of the hearth. These rollers are spaced to support and carry trays loaded with compacts. Maximum operating temperature is limited by the properties of the alloy rolls and is usually about 2100 F. Depending on roll spacing, loads four to seven times greater than can be handled by a mesh furnace of equal length can be conveyed on a roller hearth. Furnace doors are provided and are opened only to charge or discharge the trays. Thus, consumption of protective gas is less and heat losses are lower than for mesh-belt furnaces.

Pusher-type furnaces are suitable for sintering compacts that are too heavy to be carried by a mesh belt or those requiring higher sintering temperatures. With this type of equipment compacts are fed into the furnace on trays, which are advanced by mechanical pushers. Alternatively, for small batches, the trays may be pushed through manually.

Sintering Atmospheres

Protective atmospheres are used in powder metallurgy (*a*) to prevent oxidation and reduce oxides when sintering copper, bronze, nickel, molybdenum, and tungsten compacts; and (*b*) to control the carburization and decarburization of iron and iron-rich compacts.

Oxidation and decarburization of iron compacts are caused by oxygen, water vapor, and carbon dioxide when present in improper proportions with respect to hydrogen and carbon monoxide content. Iron oxides are reduced by hydrogen, carbon monoxide and carbon. Carburization is caused by carbon monoxide, and by hydrocarbons such as methane.

Copper and bronze compacts are susceptible to general oxidation and to scaling or discoloring by oxygen. These compacts are not adversely affected by hydrogen, carbon monoxide, or carbon. Selective attack on zinc in brass compacts is caused by carbon dioxide, oxygen, sulfur, and water vapor.

Vacuum is used mainly for sintering compacts of stainless steel and refractory metals such as tantalum, titanium, zirconium and uranium, which react with most of the usual protective gases including hydrogen.

When the moisture content of any atmosphere must be kept very low (as in the sintering of alloys containing chromium), the furnace must be operated and maintained with special care, to eliminate all leakage or back-diffusion of air that would contaminate the furnace atmosphere. One factor is often overlooked: the dew point of the gas fed into the furnace may be different from the moisture content of the gas in contact with the workpieces.

The atmospheres most commonly used for sintering are: hydrogen, dissociated ammonia, burned ammonia, exothermic gas, purified rich exothermic gas, endothermic gas, and vacuum. Each is discussed individually in the sections that follow. (Details on the properties, generation, uses and cost of the various protective atmospheres will be found on pages 67 to 84 of Volume 2 of this Handbook.)

The characteristics and applications of gas atmospheres for sintering are summarized in Table 3. Most of the examples in this article demonstrate the use of a sintering atmosphere according to the recommendations of Table 3; Examples 628 and 629, in which dissociated or burned ammonia was used in the sintering of an iron-copper-carbon powder, are exceptions.

Hydrogen in cylinders is often the most economical gas for small installations, because the cost of gas-generating equipment is eliminated.

The explosiveness of hydrogen-oxygen mixtures demands that hydrogen be handled with extreme care. Its high thermal conductivity (seven times that of air) helps in increasing the rate of heat transfer in the heating and cooling chambers. Its low density causes it to diffuse rapidly outward. However, the use of hydrogen gas allows back diffusion of air through small openings and cracks — which results in a contaminated atmosphere.

Hydrogen delivered from bottles, cells, or catalytic conversion units may contain up to 0.5% impurities, including moisture, oxygen, carbon monoxide and methane. This atmosphere may be used for sintering most nonferrous metals, but it is usually decarburizing to iron and will oxidize chromium-containing alloys. When dried and purified efficiently, hydrogen may be rendered inert to iron and to chromium-containing alloys such as stainless steel. The purest hydrogen is that derived from palladium diffusion cells, but few furnaces are built tightly enough for effective use of hydrogen having this degree of purity.

Dissociated Ammonia. Cracked or dissociated ammonia is made by passing ammonia gas (from large cylinders or tanks) over a heated catalyst, and consists of a mixture of 75% hydrogen and 25% nitrogen by volume. It is remarkably dry and can be used as a substitute for pure hydrogen for nearly all sintering applications, including stainless steel, iron, brass, copper and tungsten. Its use, particularly when sintering molybdenum or ferrous materials, is sometimes avoided because of the danger of nitriding by traces of undissociated ammonia, which are nearly always present and dissociate on contact with hot metal. This residual ammonia may be removed almost completely by passing the gas through water (and subsequently drying it), or through activated alumina, or a molecular sieve.

Burned Ammonia. Mixtures of nitrogen with 0.5 to 24% hydrogen are made either by burning dissociated ammonia premixed with air (which contains 78% nitrogen) in a reaction chamber, or by direct catalytic oxidation of ammonia in air, and drying the reaction products. The hydrogen-nitrogen ratio is controlled by the proportion of air supplied to the burners. Burned ammonia constitutes the least costly source of nitrogen-hydrogen mixtures when large volumes are required. However, the capital cost of the installation is relatively high.

Exothermic gas is made by burning natural gas or coke-oven gas, methane, butane, or a similar hydrocarbon gas, in a refractory-lined combustion chamber with controlled amounts of air. A large amount of heat is given off in the reaction. Depending on the amount of air used, the gas may contain up to about 14% hydrogen by volume, up to 10% carbon monoxide, 5 to 12% carbon dioxide and, usually, small amounts of methane; the remainder is nitrogen. This atmosphere is ordinarily cooled to about 70 F, at which temperature its moisture content approaches saturation level. The principal advantages of exothermic gas are low flammability and low cost — it is the most economical gas available.

Like all gases derived from hydrocarbons, exothermic gas may have a carburizing or a decarburizing action on ferrous parts, depending on the carbon content of the work and the temperature. Details of reactions will be found on pages 67 to 84 of Volume 2 of this Handbook.

Rich or medium-rich exothermic gases are those most commonly used for sintering. The richest gas is formed from a 6-to-1 ratio of air to hydrocarbon gas and contains about 14% hydrogen, 10% carbon monoxide, 1% methane, 5% carbon dioxide and 70% nitrogen. It has a dew point of about 80 F and is useful for sintering compacts of copper, bronze, silver, iron, and iron-copper. It is usually strongly decarburizing to ferrous metals. A medium-rich gas, made by reacting air with natural gas in a ratio of 6.75 to 1, has been used for sintering nonferrous compacts.

Purified Rich Exothermic Gas. By removing water and carbon dioxide, a stable and mildly reactive gas with a dew point below −50 F may be produced. It has virtually no carburizing or decarburizing action on iron-graphite compacts. Purified rich exothermic gas is widely used for sintering com-

Table 3. Characteristics of Sintering Atmospheres for Powder Metallurgy Products

Gas atmosphere	Typical dew point, F	Gas characteristic at sintering temperature for:(a) Cu	Brass	Bronze	Ni	Ag	Mo	W	Iron	Iron-copper	Iron-carbon	Iron-Cu-carbon	Carbon steel	Stainless steel	Relative cost per cu ft(b)
Hydrogen, from:															
Bottles	−30 to +20	R	...	R	R	R	...	...	D1	D1	...	...	...	...	90
Cells	+70 to +90	R	...	R	R	R	...	...	D3	D3	...	...	...	...	16
Catalytic conversion units	+70 to +90	R	...	R	R	R	...	...	D3	D3	...	...	...	...	10
Hydrogen, dried, from:															
Cells	−60 to −100	Y	R	Y	Y	Y	R	R	X	X	X	X	X	R	16
Catalytic conversion units	−60 to −100	Y	R	Y	Y	Y	R	R	X	X	X	X	X	R	10
Diffusion units	−100	Y	R	Y	Y	Y	R	R	X	X	X	X	X	R	40
Hydrogen-nitrogen:															
Dissociated NH_3	−40 to −60	R	R	R	R	R	R	R	N	N	...	...	N	R	28
Burned NH_3, rich	+70 to +90(c)	R	...	R	R	R	...	...	D3	D3	...	...	...	...	20
Exothermic gas:															
Rich, saturated	+70 to +90	R	...	R	R	R	...	...	D3	D3	...	...	...	...	1
Medium rich, saturated	+70 to +90	...	...	R	R	R	...	...	...	...	...	...	...	...	1
Purified exothermic gas:															
Rich	<−40	R	R	R	R	R	...	...	C1	C1	C1	C1	C1	...	1.5
Medium rich	<−40	R	R	R	R	R	...	...	C1	C1	C1	C1	C1	...	1.5
Endothermic gas:															
Rich, dry	−10 to +10	R	R	R	R	R	...	C3	C3	C3	C3	C3	C3	...	1.9
Fairly rich, dry	+20 to +30	R	R	R	R	R	...	C2	C2	C2	C2	C2	C2	...	1.9
Medium rich, saturated	+70 to +90	R	...	R	R	R	...	...	D1	...	...	...	...	...	1.7
Lean, saturated	+70 to +90	R	...	R	R	R	...	...	D3	D3	...	...	...	...	1.7

(a) R, reducing; Y, recommended; C1, mildly carburizing; C2, carburizing; C3, strongly carburizing; N, neither carburizing nor decarburizing; X, not recommended; D1, mildly decarburizing; D2, decarburizing; D3, strongly decarburizing. (b) Costs are approximate and relative to exothermic gas = 1. (c) Dew point may be reduced by refrigeration or by adsorbent-tower dehydration.

pacts of iron, iron-copper, iron-carbon and iron-copper-carbon; and also for copper infiltration of iron or iron-carbon compacts.

Endothermic Gas. In making exothermic gas, the minimum ratio of air to natural gas that will allow combustion to be sustained is about 6 to 1, whereas endothermic gas producers allow lower ratios to be reacted by providing heated catalyst-filled combustion chambers. These combustion chambers are usually made of silicon carbide or heat-resisting alloy. The leanest endothermic gas has an air-gas ratio of about 4.5 to 1 and contains 21% hydrogen, 13.8% carbon monoxide, 3.0% carbon dioxide, and 61.7% nitrogen. The dew point is about 80 F. This gas is decarburizing to ferrous metals and is used to sinter compacts of iron, iron-copper, and nonferrous metals, and to infiltrate iron parts.

An endothermic gas such as AGA type 302 is richer. It usually has an air-gas ratio of 2.4 to 1 and contains about 20% carbon monoxide, virtually no carbon dioxide, about 38% hydrogen, 0.8% methane; the remainder is nitrogen. The dew point of this gas is usually about 0 F as it leaves the reactor. Close control of reactor operation is necessary to take full advantage of the special characteristics of this gas. It is carburizing and is used to sinter and copper infiltrate compacts of iron-graphite, as well as to sinter most nonferrous compacts.

Vacuum has been used for sintering some metals for which none of the prepared atmospheres discussed above is suitable. Sintering in a vacuum has been particularly successful for stainless steel, tantalum, titanium, uranium, zirconium, and other refractory metals that react with both hydrogen and carbon-containing gases. Inert gases are seldom satisfactory for sintering these metals, because of the difficulty of purging work chambers to expel all air.

Green compacts of refractory metals are sometimes heated at low temperatures in a separate unit, using pure argon or some other protective atmosphere to drive off volatiles before the compacts are placed in the vacuum sintering furnace. This practice minimizes the possibility of contamination.

Sintering Practice

Time and temperature cycles must be carefully chosen to develop the properties required in sintered compacts. The major causes of low density or low strength are too low a temperature or insufficient time at temperature. Of the two, low temperature is usually the more critical condition. When the compact is pressed from a mixture of two or more constituents, longer time at the sintering temperature is required for diffusion than is required for sintering a similar compact that is composed of a single metal.

Time and Temperature. The optimum values of time and temperature for sintering any given compact are invariably determined empirically. The sintering temperature should be as high as possible but below the melting point of the metal used. Optimum holding time is more difficult to predict.

Table 4. Typical Sintering Temperatures and Holding Times for Various Metals and Pre-Alloyed Powders

Material being sintered	Temperature, F	Time at temperature, minutes
Bronze	1400 to 1600	10 to 20
Brass	1550 to 1650	10 to 45
Copper	1550 to 1650	12 to 45
Iron, iron-carbon	1850 to 2100	8 to 45
Nickel	1850 to 2100	30 to 45
Stainless steel	2000 to 2350	30 to 60
Alnico magnets	2200 to 2375	120 to 150
Ferrites	2200 to 2700	10 to 600
Tungsten-nickel-copper, 90:6:4	2450 to 2900	12 to 120
Tungsten carbide	2600 to 2700	20 to 30
Molybdenum	3730	120 approx
Tungsten	4250	480 approx
Tantalum	4350	480 approx

Table 5. Nominal Compositions and Sintering Temperatures of Some Pre-Alloyed Metal Powders

Alloy composition	Sintering temperature, F: Hydrogen-base atmosphere	Sintering temperature, F: Nitrogen-base atmosphere
Copper-Base Alloys		
90 Cu, 0.5 P, 9.5 Zn	1725	...
90 Cu, 1.5 Pb, 8.5 Zn	1635	1650
90 Cu, 10 Zn	1615	1635
85 Cu, 15 Zn	1635	1650
78.5 Cu, 1.5 Pb, 0.3 P, 19.7 Zn	1650	...
78.5 Cu, 1.5 Pb, 20 Zn	1615	1650
70 Cu, 0.3 P, 29.7 Zn	1600	...
70 Cu, 30 Zn	1615	1600
60 Cu, 40 Zn	...	1490
64 Cu, 18 Ni, 18 Zn	1795	1760
64 Cu, 1.5 Pb, 18 Ni, 16.5 Zn	1615	1725
70 Cu, 10 Ni, 20 Zn	1725	...
Iron-Base Alloys		
17 Cr, 12 Ni, 2.5 Mo	...	2210
12.5 Cr	...	2210
50 Fe, 50 Ni	...	2150
97 Fe, 3 Si	...	2210
1.8 Ni, 0.5 Mo, add 0.6 graphite, rem Fe	...	2075
1.75 Ni, 1.5 Cu, 0.5 Mo, rem Fe	...	2030
0.4 Ni, 0.7 Mo, 2 Cu, rem Fe	...	2050
1 Mo, 0.4 Mn, rem Fe	...	2050

Once the maximum temperature is reached, the greatest consolidation in the compact generally takes place within a relatively short time. As sintering is prolonged, the measurable increase in density continues at a slower rate, until diminishing returns do not justify the expense involved. The ranges of time and temperatures most widely used are given in Table 4.

The sintering times and temperatures used in the examples in this article are within the ranges listed in Table 4. In Example 641, a temperature of 2350 F — substantially above the typical sintering temperature listed for iron — was used in a resintering operation, to increase the elongation of an iron compact.

Alloying in Iron-Base Compacts. Carbon is the most common alloying addition to iron. It may be added as graphite to the original blend of powders so as to alloy during sintering, or it may be added from a carburizing furnace atmosphere. The reaction between iron and graphite, and between iron, graphite, and the furnace atmosphere, is fairly rapid at the soaking temperature. For this reason it is necessary that the atmosphere be maintained at the desired carbon potential. The depth of carburization depends not only on time and temperature but also on the density of the compact at any particular location. Thus, a compact that varies in density from one section to another will also show a variation in the effect of the sintering atmosphere.

Copper is often alloyed with iron in the sintering furnace. It has a solid solubility in iron of 8 to 9% at normal sintering temperatures. Because the solubility of copper in iron decreases as temperature decreases, some precipitation hardening is likely to occur, depending on cooling rate. Additions of copper cause compacts to expand, which often results in difficulty of controlling dimensions. For consistent compact size, it is necessary to maintain close control over raw materials, and over sintering temperature, atmosphere and time.

Iron-copper-carbon alloys also can be easily formed in the sintering furnace. The solubility of copper in iron is lowered by the addition of carbon, and the presence of copper seems to decrease the sensitivity of the compacts to variations in the sintering atmospheres. Iron-copper-carbon alloys have good mechanical properties, and dimensions of compacts made from these materials are generally easier to control than are those of similar compacts made from iron and copper.

To obtain the maximum possible strength and density, post operations such as re-pressing and resintering may be employed. When the compact is to be re-pressed and resintered, it is not given a thorough sintering until the last pass through the furnace. The initial pass (or passes, when resintering is done more than once) is mainly for annealing the compact and burning off the lubricant. It is desirable that alloying be kept to a minimum during initial sintering so that the compact will not be strengthened sufficiently to resist compaction in subsequent re-pressing operations. As the density of the compact approaches that of a solid material and interconnecting porosity disappears, reaction of the compact to the atmosphere also approaches that of solid material.

Pre-Alloyed Powders. The use of pre-alloyed powders allows shorter time periods at sintering temperature. In addition, pre-alloyed powders provide a means of obtaining compacts with a more uniform structure than that of compacts produced by diffusing particles of the constituent metals. Sometimes, complex alloy compacts, such as those made of high-chromium heat-resisting alloys, are pressed from pre-alloyed powders mixed with elemental metal powders. Table 5 lists nominal compositions of some pre-alloyed metal powders, and gives sintering temperatures for these materials.

Production Cycles

The simplest cycle in making completed parts by powder metallurgy, and the most commonly used, involves two operations — pressing and sintering.

When greater strength and higher density are needed, or when closer control of dimensional tolerances is required, the compacts may, after sintering, be re-pressed or coined. (The two latter terms are synonymous in this context.) This operation increases hardness of a compact, as a result of the cold working.

Re-pressing closes up pores, but produces discontinuities rather than removing them, as in sintered iron having minimum density of 7.35 g per cu cm. During resintering, closed edges of pores weld together, and at the same time strains from cold working are relieved and the compact is restored to its soft condition.

Single Pressing and Sintering. The maximum density that can be obtained by single pressing and sintering depends

Table 6. Manufacturing Details for Producing Floor-Plate Latches by Single Pressing and Sintering (Example 628)

Press and Tool Details	
Type of press	Mechanical
Pressure	50 tons max
Workpiece diameter	4 in. max
Fill adjustment	0 to 3½ in.
Stroke length	5½ in. max
Stroke die entrance	1⅝ in. max
Die material	Carbide (9 to 12% Co)
Punch material	D2 tool steel
Processing Details	
Compacting pressure	42 to 48 tons per sq in.
Sintering treatment	1 hr at 2050 F(a)
Green density	7.15 g per cu cm
Sintered density	7.20 g per cu cm

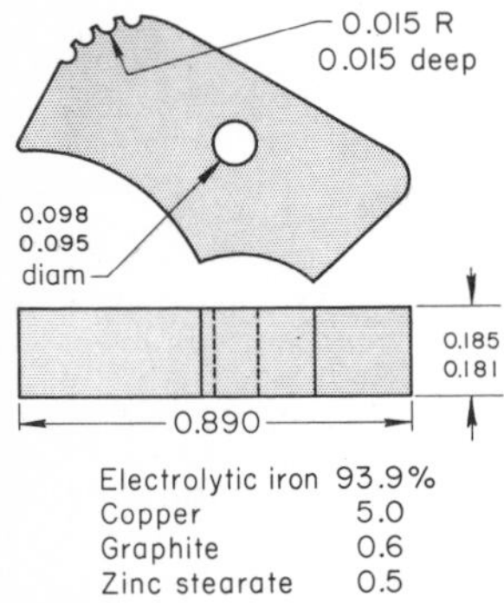

(a) In dissociated or burned ammonia (dew point, 5 F max)

Table 7. Processing and Cost Details for Producing Valve Guides by Single Pressing and Sintering (Example 629)

Processing Details	
Pressure required	10 tons
Fill height	2.23 in.(a)
Die material	Carbide (6% Co)
Core rod	D2 tool steel, flame sprayed
Punch material	D2 tool steel
Sintering treatment	25 min at 2050 F
Sintering atmosphere	Dissociated ammonia
Production rate:	
Pressed compacts	1000 per hour
Sintered compacts	2000 per hour
Cost per 1000 Compacts (Excluding burden)	
Material at $0.135 per lb	$ 2.16
Tooling (original cost, $750) (b)	1.00
Pressing	6.00
Sintering	1.20
Total cost	$10.36

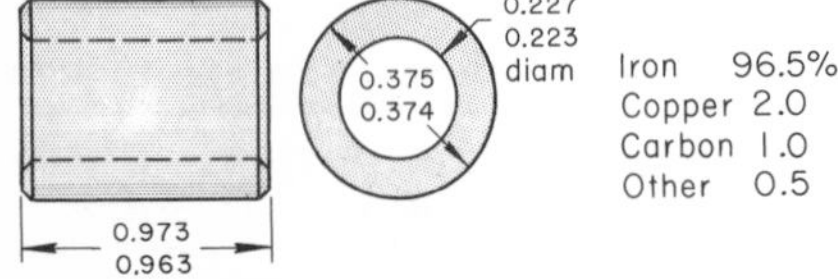

(a) Computed by dividing required compact density (6.6 g per cu cm) by apparent density (2.85 g per cu cm) and multiplying by height of finished compact (0.968 in.). (b) Assumes production of 1 million compacts before tools are replaced. Punch was refaced after each 100,000 compacts.

Table 8. Manufacturing and Cost Details for Producing Porous Bearings by Single Pressing and Sintering (Example 630)

Press and Tool Details	
Type of press	Mechanical(a)
Capacity	12 tons max
Die material	Carbide (6% Co)
Punch material	D2 tool steel
Core-rod material	O6 (mod) tool steel
Tool life, number of compacts pressed before reconditioning:	
Die	500,000
Punches	20,000
Core rod	50,000
Processing Details	
Compacting pressure	25 tons per sq in.
Preheating treatment	15 min at 2040 F
Sintering treatment	15 min at 2040 F(b)
Sintering atmosphere	Endothermic
Production rate:	
Pressed compacts	1000 per hour
Sintered compacts	4160 per hour
Cost per 1000 Pieces(c)	
Number of compacts:	
1,000	$36.75
5,000	29.70
10,000	24.40

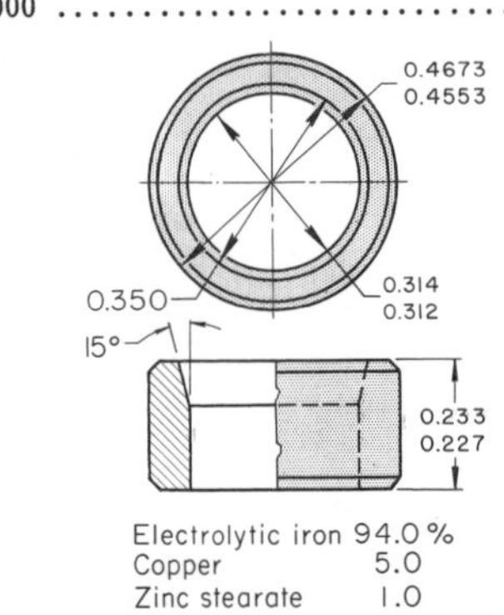

(a) Incorporating, as a special feature, top and bottom movable rams. (b) The furnace heat zone was 5 ft long, and parts were passed through in trays 10 by 12 in. (c) Includes labor, burden and material; tooling not included.

on surface area of the die wall, thickness and shape of the compact, compacting pressure, type and composition of powder, and time and temperature of sintering. Generally, the simple pressing and sintering cycle can produce high density only in small compacts of relatively simple shape. Many parts are not exposed to severe conditions in service and need not be particularly dense or strong. In other parts porosity is an advantage, because the voids provide a reservoir for oil that functions as a built-in lubricant in service.

The following three examples illustrate the use of the simple cycle of pressing and sintering for producing powder metallurgy parts.

Examples 628, 629 and 630. Parts Suited to Single Pressing and Sintering

Example 628 — Small High-Density Part (Table 6). Manufacturing details for producing floor-plate latches weighing 5.6 grams are given in Table 6. A sketch of the workpiece is also included in Table 6. Single pressing and sintering produced green compacts having a density of 7.15 g per cu cm, which increased to 7.20 during sintering.

Example 629 — Low-Density Valve Guide (Table 7). Processing and cost details for producing iron-copper-carbon valve guides are given in Table 7. A sketch of the workpiece is also included in Table 7. Requirements were: pearlitic structure, 100%; minimum density, 6.5 g per cu cm; and minimum tensile strength, 50,000 psi. These requirements were obtained consistently in mass production by single pressing and sintering. Some porosity in parts of this type is usually beneficial in service applications, because the pores retain lubricant.

Example 630 — Porous Bearing (Table 8). Manufacturing and cost details for making bearings by the single pressing and sintering technique are given in Table 8. A sketch of the bearing is also included with Table 8. Open porosity was intended for these compacts to permit subsequent impregnation with oil. This porosity was obtained mainly by the use of a comparatively low compacting pressure (25 tons per square inch).

Pressing, Sintering and Re-pressing. Re-pressing, or coining, is added as a final operation to: (*a*) increase dimensional accuracy, (*b*) increase density, or (*c*) eliminate surface porosity to prevent absorption of electrolyte during electroplating. The following example illustrates all three of these benefits of re-pressing a compact.

Example 631. Re-pressing for High Density, Dimensional Accuracy and Dense Surfaces (Table 9)

Specifications for an iron compact required: (*a*) a minimum density of 7.3 g per cu cm, (*b*) a nonporous surface suitable for chromium plating, and (*c*) close dimensional limits (two principal dimensions had to be within ±0.0005 in. and a third dimension within ±0.001 in., as shown in the illustration of the compact included in Table 9). These requirements were met by re-pressing the previously pressed and sintered compact. Processing details are given in Table 9.

Pressing, Sintering, Re-pressing and Resintering. A second sintering operation relieves the effects of cold work and assists in further consolidating the compact. The results are greater strength, improved magnetic properties, and better dimensional stability in the compacts after heat treatment. Resintering is sometimes effective in healing tears developed during re-pressing. Size changes in resintering are generally in-

Table 9. Manufacturing Details for the Production of a Rail Mounting Block Having Critical Dimensions by Pressing, Sintering and Re-pressing (Example 631)

Press and Tool Details	
Type of press	Mechanical
Capacity	100 tons
Die material	Carbide (6% Co)
Punch material	D2 tool steel
Tool life, number of compacts pressed before reconditioning:	
Die	500,000
Punches	20,000
Core pin	50,000
Processing Details	
Compacting pressure(a)	50 tons per sq in.
Preheating treatment	15 min at 2040 F
Sintering treatment	15 min at 2040 F
Sintering atmosphere	Dissociated ammonia
Production rate:	
Pressed compacts	600 per hour
Sintered compacts	280 per hour
Re-pressed compacts	800 per hour
Total cost per 1000 compacts	$112(b)

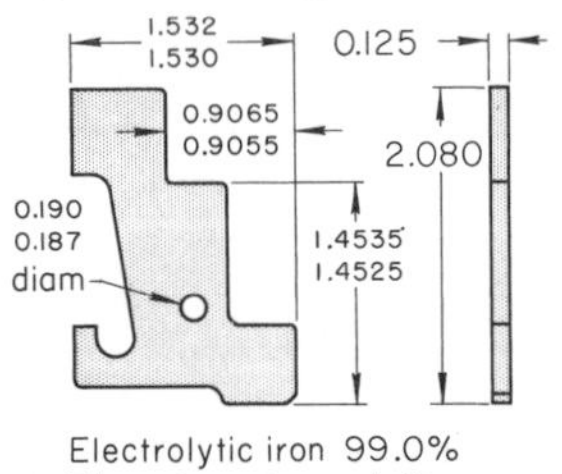

(a) Pressing and re-pressing. (b) In lots of 10,000 compacts; includes labor, burden and material; tool cost not included.

Table 10. Manufacturing Details for the Production of Armatures by Pressing, Sintering, Re-pressing and Resintering (Example 632)

Press and Tool Details

Type of press	Mechanical
Capacity	50 tons max
Die material	Carbide
Punch material	D2 tool steel
Workpiece diameter	4 in. max
Fill adjustment	0 to 3½ in.
Stroke length	5½ in. max
Stroke die entrance	1⅝ in. max
Tool life, number of compacts pressed before reconditioning:	
Die	1 million
Punches	50,000

Processing Details

Compacting pressure	50 tons per sq in.
Sintering treatment	1 hr at 2050 F(a)
Re-pressing pressure	50 tons per sq in.
Resintering treatment	2 hr at 2050 F(a)
Production rate:	
Pressed compacts	900 per hour
Sintered compacts	1000 per hour
Re-pressed compacts	900 per hour
Resintered compacts	500 per hour

Relative Cost vs Density(b)

	Density, g per cu cm	Relative cost per compact
Pressing	7.0	1.00
Pressing and sintering	7.0+	1.24
Pressing, sintering and re-pressing	7.5	1.96
Pressing, sintering, re-pressing and resintering	7.5+	2.24

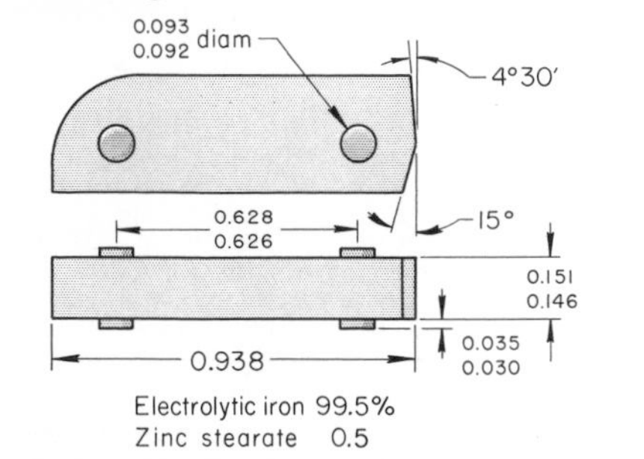

(a) In burned ammonia with dew point of 30 F; flow rate, 700 cfh. (b) These figures are for cost of operation only and do not include material cost, tool cost, or burden.

significant. Examples 632 and 633, which follow, demonstrate the value of resintering to improve magnetic properties. Example 634 describes the production of compacts that were subsequently case hardened.

Examples 632 and 633. Resintering to Improve Magnetic Properties

Example 632 — Resintered Armatures (Table 10). Manufacturing details for producing magnetic armatures are presented in Table 10 (a sketch of the armature is also included). Pressing, sintering, re-pressing and resintering were required in order to obtain the specified magnetic properties.

As noted in Table 10, this procedure yielded compacts with a density of 7.5+ g per cu cm, which is 95% of theoretical maximum for the material. Relative costs for compacts processed through progressive steps are included in Table 10.

Example 633 — Resintered Magnetic Armatures (Table 11). Manufacturing details for producing magnetic armatures to a density of 7.5 g per cu cm by re-pressing and resintering are given in Table 11. (An illustration of the armature is included in Table 11; a statement of the magnetic requirements is presented in the first footnote to that table.) A subsequent chromium-plating operation was made possible by re-pressing and resintering.

The relative costs given in Table 11 for making these armatures by three methods show that cost increases by 60% in progressing from simple pressing and sintering to re-pressing and resintering.

Example 634. Resintered Compacts for Dimensional Stability in Case Hardening (Fig. 7)

The upper views of Fig. 7 show a relatively complex powder metallurgy compact prepared by pressing, sintering, re-pressing and resintering. This part serves as a double cam after being case hardened to Rockwell C 60 to 61 and plated with 0.0001 in. of chromium. The compacts had to be dimensionally stable after case hardening and dense enough to resist absorption of plating solution.

The tool setup for pressing the compact is illustrated in the lower view of Fig. 7. As shown, the compact was pressed with the smaller of the two cam sections (0.687-in. diam) at the bottom. The 45° taper between the two cam sections permitted the iron powder to flow freely, thus providing uniformity of fill. Working faces of the upper and lower punches were shaped to the dimensions of the finished compact, except that the core rod for pressing was made 0.003 in. oversize. This was done to allow the compact (after sintering) to fit the 0.5025-in.-diam core rod that was used for re-pressing.

During sintering, these compacts registered a linear shrinkage of about 0.3%. After sintering, the compacts were tumbled to remove burrs and to develop radii of about 0.010 in. on the edges. They were then lubricated with zinc stearate and re-pressed to a minimum density of 7.5 g per cu cm. Adjacent coordinates of all cam surfaces were within 0.0002 in. The compacts were resintered, using the same procedure as that used for initial sintering. There were no significant dimensional changes during resintering. Additional processing details are given in the table accompanying Fig. 7.

Table 11. Manufacturing Details and Relative Cost for Producing Magnetic Armatures by Pressing, Sintering, Re-pressing and Resintering (Example 633) (a)

Press and Tool Details

Type of press	Mechanical(b)
Capacity	100 tons max
Die material	Carbide (7% Co)
Punch material	D2 tool steel
Core-rod material	Carbide (6% Co)
Tool life, number of compacts pressed before reconditioning:	
Die	500,000
Punch	30,000
Core rod	50,000

Processing Details

Compacting pressure	50 tons per sq in.
Preheating treatment	20 min at 2040 F(c)
Sintering and resintering treatment	20 min at 2040 F(c)
Production rate:	
Pressed compacts	700 per hour
Sintered compacts	800 per hour
Re-pressed compacts	1000 per hour
Resintered compacts	800 per hour
Total cost per 1000 compacts(d)	$93.91

Relative Cost
(Tooling not included)

	Press and sinter	Press, sinter and re-press	Press, sinter, re-press and resinter
Material	1	1	1
Machine operations	3	4	5
Setting up	2	3	4
Transporting	3	4	5
Inspection	1	1	1
Total units	10	13	16

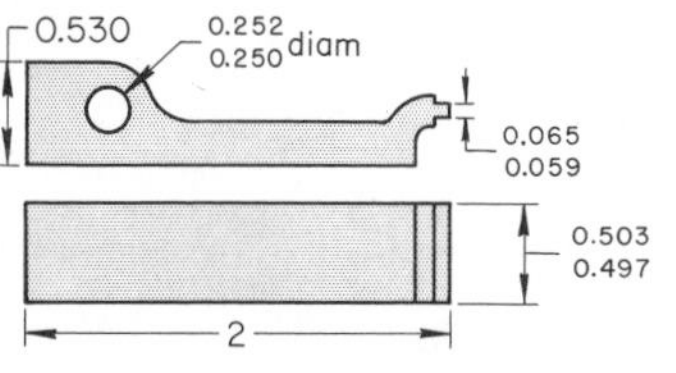

(a) Data are for producing shunts to a density of 7.5 g per cu cm, B_r of 11,000 gausses, and H_c of 2.6 oersteds (typical B_{max} is 13,000 gausses). (b) Press provided with a movable top ram and a floating table for bottom motion. (c) In dissociated ammonia. (d) In lots of 10,000 compacts; includes labor, burden and material; tool cost not included.

Limitations on Size and Shape of Compacts

Most powder metallurgy parts weigh no more than a few ounces. Compacts as small as one milligram in weight have been produced at the rate of hundreds per minute. Maximum size is limited mainly by availability of equipment (see "Maximum Size", page 460).

Minimum Weight. The minimum weight of a powder metallurgy compact that can be produced successfully depends primarily on the characteristics of the metal powder used and on the shape of the part.

Freedom of flow is the most important characteristic of a metal powder. A powder with poor flow will fill the die unevenly. Powders of some metals such

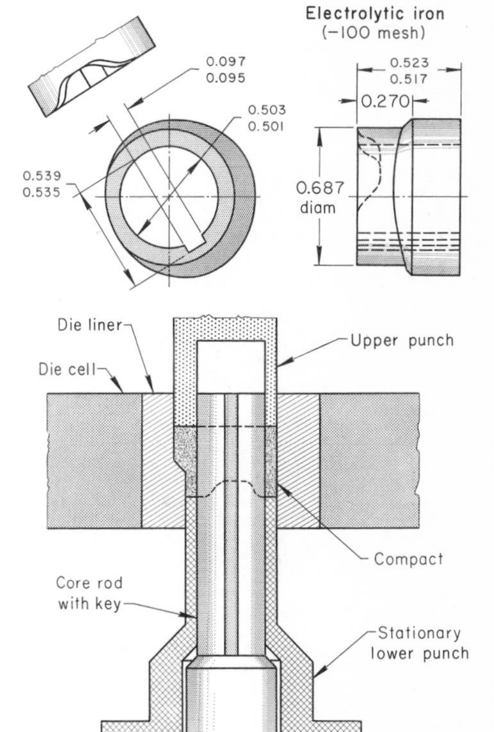

Press and Tool Details

Type of press:	
First pressing	60-ton mechanical(a)
Re-pressing	50-ton hydraulic
Die material	Carbide (9% Co)
Punch material	D2 tool steel
Core-rod material	Carbide (12% Co)
Tool life, number of compacts pressed before reconditioning:	
Die	200,000(b)
Punch	15,000(b)
Core rod	50,000(b)

Processing Details

Compacting pressure	50 tons per sq in., approx.
Sintering and resintering treatment	45 min at 2075 F
Sintering atmosphere	Dissociated ammonia
Production rate, compacts per hour:	
Pressed and re-pressed	700
Sintered and resintered	3600

(a) Using a dual punch action provided by a floating die table and a stationary lower punch. (b) Tools for re-pressing needed reconditioning about twice as often as those for first pressing.

Fig. 7. Tooling setup for complex cams produced by pressing, sintering, re-pressing and resintering (Example 634)

as aluminum adhere to the walls of the die during pressing and impair ejection. It is especially important to keep atmospheric humidity to a minimum when metal powders are being pressed into small parts, because high humidity impairs flow. The amount of lubricant normally incorporated in the powder mix to help in compacting and in ejecting the green part from the die also should be kept to a minimum to avoid sluggish flow.

The simplest form to press is a solid cylinder having its length equal to its diameter. The minimum weight for this configuration, when using iron, copper or silver powder, can be as low as 1 mg. However, when the same powders are used to produce compacts such as flat washers, or (going to the opposite extreme) sleeve bearings, their weight should be at least four times greater than that of the solid cylinder described above. For compacts with more complicated cross sections, the minimum practical weight may have to be increased even more. The following two examples describe procedures for producing small compacts (see also Examples 638 and 639).

Examples 635 and 636. Small Silver and Iron Compacts

Example 635 — Compacts Weighing up to 37 Mg (Fig. 8). The silver contact button (upper left in Fig. 8) had a diameter only slightly greater than its height and weighed 1.02 mg. It was pressed to nearly full density (7.0 g per cu cm).

The compact shown at the lower left in Fig. 8 weighed 14 mg and was pressed from iron powder to a density of 6.0 g per cu cm. The embossed triangular compact shown at the right in Fig. 8 weighed 37 mg and was pressed from iron powder to a density of 7.0 g per cu cm.

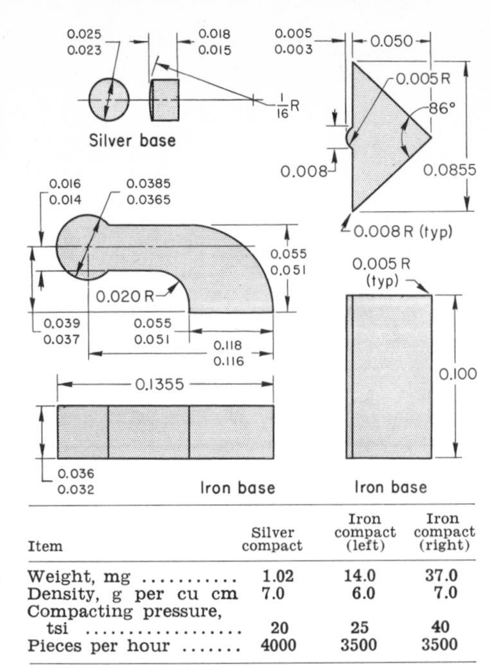

Item	Silver compact	Iron compact (left)	Iron compact (right)
Weight, mg	1.02	14.0	37.0
Density, g per cu cm	7.0	6.0	7.0
Compacting pressure, tsi	20	25	40
Pieces per hour	4000	3500	3500

Fig. 8. Small silver and iron compacts that were produced by powder metallurgy (Example 635)

Example 636 — Porous Washer Weighing 220 Mg (Fig. 9). The small porous iron washer shown in Fig. 9, weighing approximately 220 mg, was required to act both as a spacer and a bearing, and was therefore made to have an interconnecting porosity of 20% by volume to serve as an oil reservoir. Processing details are given in the table accompanying Fig. 9. By sintering in endothermic gas, 0.3 to 0.4% of combined carbon was introduced into the compact, contributing to dimensional stability, strength and hardness. After sintering, the compacts were lubricated with zinc stearate and sized to the dimensions shown in Fig. 9 (raising the density from 5.9 to 6.2 g per cu cm) by re-pressing in a hydraulic press, using stops to control the thickness within ±0.001 in. It was originally intended to hold the tolerance on thickness to ±0.0002 in., but this was not possible. Final dimensions were, therefore, achieved by grinding. The chamfers shown in Fig. 9 prevented formation of any significant burrs during grinding.

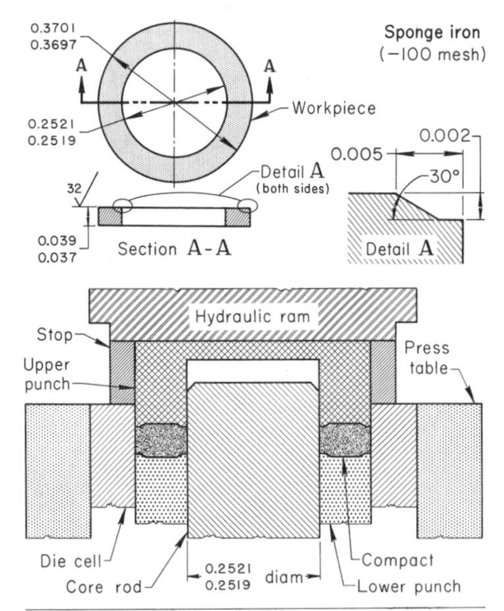

Press and Tool Details

Type of press (first pressing) ....Mechanical(a)
Press capacity (first pressing) ....4 tons
Type of press (re-pressing) ....Hydraulic(b)
Die material ....Carbide (9% Co)
Punch material ....D2 tool steel(c)
Core-rod material ....Carbide (12% Co)
Tool life, number of compacts pressed before reconditioning:
Die .... 500,000(d)
Punches .... 35,000(d)
Core rod .... 250,000(d)

Processing Details

Compacting pressure ....20 tons per sq in.
Sintering treatment ....30 min at 2075 F
Sintering atmosphere ....Endothermic(e)
Production rate:
Pressed compacts ....1,200 per hour
Sintered compacts ....30,000 per hour
Re-pressed compacts ....700 per hour

(a) Using dual-motion punches. (b) Using stops to maintain thickness within ±0.001 in. (c) Rockwell C 60 to 61. (d) In re-pressing operation, tool life before reconditioning was decreased to 125,000, 8750 and 62,500 compacts for die, punches and core rod, respectively. (e) Dew point, 30 F.

Fig. 9. Tool setup for producing porous washers (Example 636)

Maximum Size. The maximum size of workpiece that is practical for manufacturing by conventional powder metallurgy depends on the characteristics of the powder, required density, and press capacity. Bronze rods 8.125 in. in diameter and 6.5 in. long, weighing 80 lb, are being made on a production basis at a rate of eight pieces per hour. Automotive parts weighing 1¼ lb each are being produced commercially from iron-copper-carbon alloys at rates of 500 pieces per hour.

Each material has a different compressibility. For instance, bronze (ASTM B202-60T, Grade I, Class A) pressed to a density of 6.4 g per cu cm requires 15 tons per sq in. Assuming the availability of a 600-ton press, a compact having 40 sq in. of surface area could be pressed. However, pre-alloyed steel powder may require 60 tons per sq in. to press a desirable density. Under these conditions the largest surface area (perpendicular to the direction of pressing) would be only 10 sq in.

The length of part (in the direction of pressing) has not been taken into account, because this is primarily a function of die fill and press stroke. Presses are available for making compacts up to 10 in. long. Compacts longer than 10 in. normally present a problem of low density in the center section. Thus, the length of the compact also contributes to limiting the ultimate size obtainable using the powder metallurgy process.

The following example describes the production of one of the largest and most difficult compacts that can be produced by this process. In its production, it was necessary to vary the powder distribution at the various levels so that the density of each step would be the same. Special means also had to be provided to prevent damage to the green compacts as they were removed from the die setup. This was accomplished by applying controlled pressure as the cores were removed.

Example 637. Automotive Turbine Component (Fig. 10)

The automotive turbine component shown in Fig. 10(a) was a difficult part to produce by powder metallurgy, because of variations in thickness of the three different levels. A 530-ton mechanical press with a maximum fill depth of 4½ in., an upper ram stroke of 8 in., a shuttle-type feeder, and a 40-hp variable-speed drive unit was used. The press had three die platens; the two lower ones had adjustable mechanical stops, each capable of resisting a force of 400 tons. It was thus possible to press to a fixed dimension on all three levels of the compact. Three ejection motions, for each of which a force of 200 tons was available, were built into the lower part of the press, as well as an ejection motion in the dual upper punch assembly.

The iron powder used for this part was a soft powder having very good compressibility. The composition was 3% copper, 0.75% carbon and the remainder iron. It was required that the sintered part have a tensile strength of 65,000 psi.

The sequence of operations for producing this compact is shown in Fig. 10. In Fig. 10(b), the fill shoe of the shuttle-type feeder is shown over the die cavity in the fill position, which allowed the powder to be deposited in the die cavity. It was necessary for the shuttle feeder to dwell over the die long enough for the displaced air to escape from the cavity, thus insuring a uniform fill of powder. As the shuttle feeder returned to the rear of the press, it leveled the powder, as shown in Fig. 10(c). The dual upper punch assembly, mounted on the upper ram of the press (Fig. 10c), approached the die, and as soon as the outer upper punch compacted the powder in the amount of approximately 0.030 in., a feature of the press known as die control was put into motion. Die control forced the outer lower punch and intermediate lower punch to move downward without further compression of the powder. This operation transferred the loose powder from the area immediately over the stationary lower punch into the cavity created by the relative motions of the two upper punches (Fig. 10d). This powder-transfer operation was necessary, because the powder did not flow under pressure. The compact was then fully pressed as shown in Fig. 10(e).

The independent fill adjustments built into the press made it possible to get the right amount of powder into the right place; the adjustable position of the die control kept the powder in place; and the motions built into the press made it possible to press simultaneously in both directions on each level.

After pressing, the compact was ejected from the die (Fig. 10f). The core pins that formed the holes around the periphery of the compact fit into the outer lower punch. In effect, the pins became an integral part of this punch, because there was no motion between the pins and the punch at any time during the cycle. As the compact was ejected from the die it would normally expand, and because these pins were an integral part of the outer punch, the expansion of the compact against the pins would cause the compact to crack. Thus it was necessary either to control or to eliminate expansion of the compact during ejection. This was done by holding a reduced pressure on the compact through the dual upper punch assembly. Pressure was obtained by an air cylinder built into the press, and an adjustable pressure control eliminated the danger of crushing the compact.

Holding reduced pressure on the compact controlled expansion in such a manner that the pins could be removed without cracking the compact. The flanges of the compact were fully supported while the compact was ejected as follows: The die cell was pushed down from the compact; then the outer lower punch was pushed down; the die cell was pushed down to the level of the outer lower punch; the die cell and outer lower punch were then pushed on down to the level of the intermediate lower punch, and finally all three were pushed down to the level of the stationary lower punch. The compact was then in the ejected position, so that it could be lifted by fingers attached to the feeder as it moved forward to fill the die cavity again.

Minimum core-rod diameter is usually about 0.040 in. Core rod diameters smaller than 0.040 in. have been successfully used, although the danger of breakage is high. In one plant, rectangular parts 0.110 by 0.125 in. and 0.250 in. high requiring a cored hole 0.025 ± 0.001 in. through the 0.250-in. dimension were successfully produced. These parts were sintered to a density of 7.50 g per cu cm. The first of the two examples that follow describes the use of a smaller than minimum-size core rod, and the second the use of a minimum-size core rod.

Example 638. Small Pinion That Was Cored With a 0.0263-In.-Diam Rod (Fig. 11)

The pinion illustrated in Fig. 11 was pressed from type 316L stainless steel powder using a 0.0263-in.-diam core rod to form the 0.0261 to 0.0266-in.-diam hole. The rod was considerably smaller than is usually considered practical for coring. However, the depth of the hole was less than twice the diameter, thus minimizing deflection of the core rod. Additional details of the pinion are given in the table with Fig. 11.

The pinion was measured with oversize wires, so that the dimension over the wires would be greater than the major diameter of the gear.

Example 639. Interposer That Was Pressed With a 0.040-In.-Diam Cored Hole (Fig. 12)

The 0.040-in.-diam hole in the compact illustrated in Fig. 12 was produced with a carbide core rod to a tolerance of ±0.005 in. By re-pressing, it was possible to meet the dimensional requirements given in Fig. 12, and a density of 7.5 g per cu cm was achieved. The re-pressed compacts were case hardened to a depth of 0.004 to 0.008 in. All surfaces of the arm required file hardness; other surfaces did not. After heat treating, the compacts were plated with a minimum thickness of 0.00005 in. of chromium.

Maximum Thickness Variation. Compacts having section thicknesses that vary greatly in the direction of pressing can be produced successfully on presses capable of actuating more than one punch. The production of powder metallurgy products having wide variations in thickness by the use of multiple-punch setups is discussed in the two examples that follow.

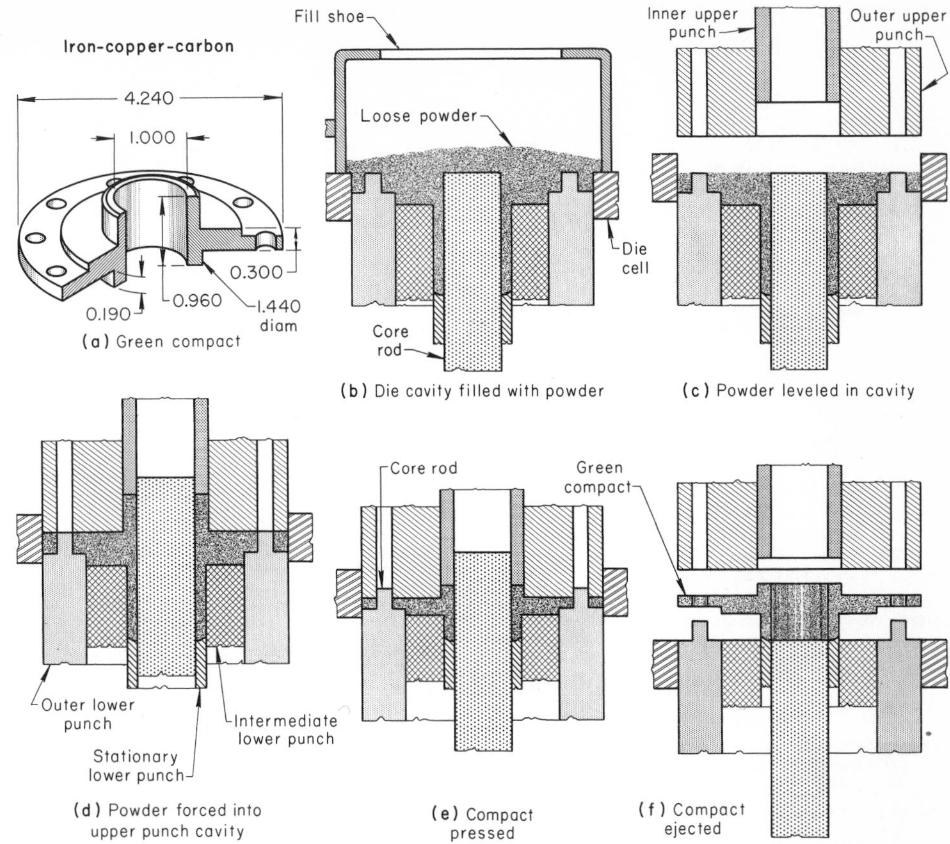

Fig. 10. Sequence of operations for pressing a large, difficult-to-produce flanged compact in a multiple-motion press (Example 637)

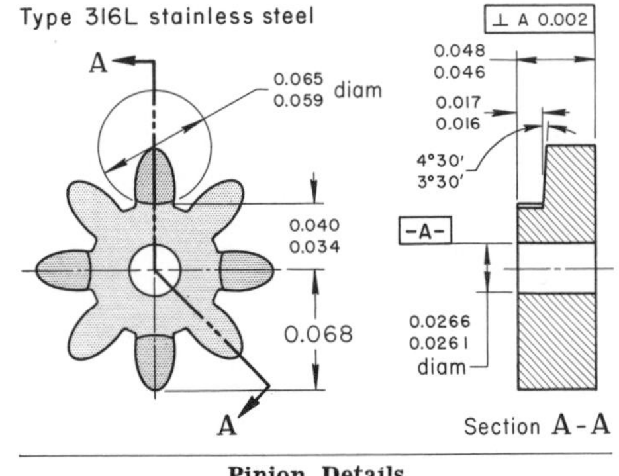

Pinion Details

Class (AGMA)	Commercial No. 4
Number of teeth	8
Diametral pitch	80
Pressure angle	20°
OD over two 0.024-in. wires	0.14237/0.14313 in.
Concentricity (all diameters with PD)	Within 0.0015 in. TIR

Fig. 11. Small pinion that was produced from metal powder using a core rod of less than the usual minimum diameter (Example 638)

Example 640. Section-Thickness Variation of 6 to 1 (Fig. 13)

A gear shape having two long teeth and a hub, and varying from 5/64 to 1/2 in. in section thickness, was produced in a three-step sequence as shown in Fig. 13. The compacts were required to have a minimum density of 7.20 g per cu cm, a weight variation of not more than 1% over minimum prescribed weight, and a thickness within ±0.001 in. of prescribed dimensions. These requirements were met by the use of several punches that separately controlled the pressure applied to each section (see Fig. 13). The finished parts were carburized, hardened and tempered to produce a surface hardness of Rockwell C 62. Processing details are given in the table that accompanies Fig. 13.

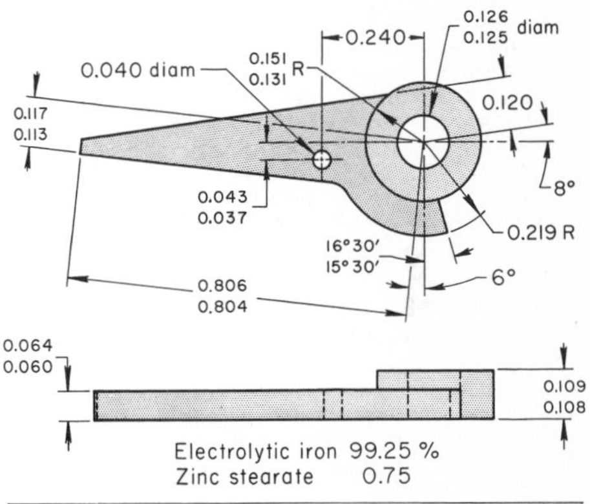

Press and Tool Details

Type of press	Mechanical(a)
Press capacity	50 tons
Die material	Carbide (6% Co)
Punch material	D2 tool steel
Core-rod material	Carbide (6% Co)
Tool life, number of compacts pressed before reconditioning:	
Die	250,000
Punches	20,000
Core rod	40,000

Processing Details

Compacting pressure	50 tons per sq in.
Preheating treatment	15 min at 1000 F
Preheating atmosphere	Dissociated ammonia
Sintering treatment	15 min at 2040 F
Sintering atmosphere	Dissociated ammonia
Production rate:	
Pressed compacts	1000 per hour
Sintered compacts	6000 per hour
Re-pressed compacts(b)	1200 per hour

(a) Press had multiple top and bottom action. (b) Re-pressing was necessary to meet the dimensional tolerances shown in the illustration.

Fig. 12. An interposer compact that was pressed with a 0.040-in.-diam cored hole. The 0.040-in.-diam carbide rod used is the minimum size that is ordinarily used for coring parts made by powder metallurgy. (Example 639)

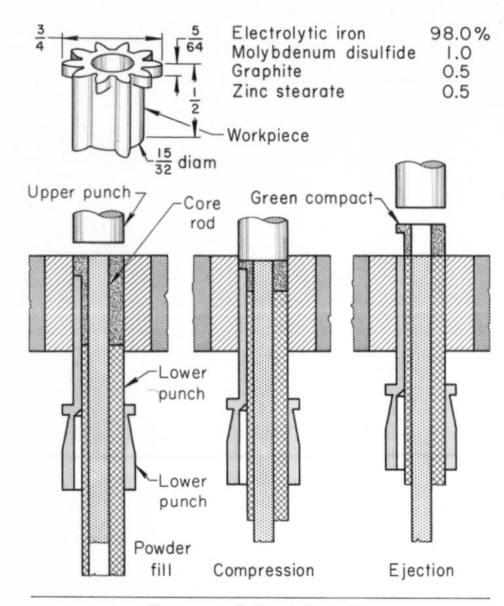

Press and Tool Details

Type of press	Mechanical and hydraulic(a)
Press capacity	50 tons
Die material	Carbide
Punch material	D2 tool steel(b)
Core rod material	Carbide
Tool life	50,000 compacts(c)

Processing Details

Compacting pressure	50 tons per sq in.
Re-pressing pressure	50 tons per sq in.
Sintering treatment	45 min at 2040 F
Resintering treatment	45 min at 2040 F
Sintering atmosphere	Endothermic
Production rate:	
Pressed compacts	600 per hour
Re-pressed compacts	1200 per hour

(a) Multiple-action, two above and three below. (b) Hardened to Rockwell C 62 minimum. (c) Number of compacts pressed between reconditionings. Normal wear was 0.003 to 0.005 in. for 50,000 pieces. When alignment was near perfect, 150,000 pieces could be obtained with little wear. Life of carbide core rods and dies was almost infinite.

Fig. 13. Three-step production of a compact having six-to-one variation in section thickness (Example 640)

Example 641. Angular Compact Having Abrupt Changes of Thickness (Fig. 14)

Regardless of its orientation in the die, the margin-stop slider illustrated in Fig. 14 exhibits large and abrupt changes in cross section in the direction of pressing. These differences in thickness are close to the maximum for producibility by powder metallurgy techniques. This compact required a minimum density of 7.5 g per cu cm and an elongation of 30 to 35% to permit subsequent forming, piercing and lancing. It was made by pressing, sintering, re-pressing and resintering. The resintered compacts were then case hardened to a depth of 0.003 to 0.007 in. and nickel plated. Processing details are given in the table accompanying Fig. 14.

Dimensional Accuracy

Dimensional accuracy in powder metallurgy parts depends mainly on: (*a*) control of powder composition, (*b*) amount of tool wear permitted before reconditioning, (*c*) precision used in controlling the amount of powder fed with each stroke, (*d*) control of press and die variables, and (*e*) control of variables in sintering.

Single Pressing and Sintering. For compacts that are not re-pressed, the following tolerances are practical: Horizontal dimensions, ±0.0015 in. per in.; vertical dimensions, ±0.004 in. per in.; and concentricity of cored holes, 0.003 in. up to 1-in. diam (add 0.001 in. to tolerance for each additional inch of hole diameter).

Pressing, Sintering, Re-pressing and Resintering. Re-pressing usually cannot improve the concentricity of cored holes, but other horizontal dimensions ordinarily can be controlled within ±0.0005 in. per in. by re-pressing.

The three examples that follow illustrate normal variations in production runs of typical ferrous powder metallurgy parts, all of which were pressed, sintered, re-pressed, resintered, carburized and hardened.

Example 642. Variations in Width Dimensions of Side Blocks (Fig. 15)

Figure 15 shows the results of measuring a critical die-controlled dimension on 225 parts of identical design pressed from 100-mesh electrolytic iron powder. These high-density parts were re-pressed to a minimum density of 7.49 g per cu cm, then resintered, carburized and hardened. The tolerance on the dimension measured was 0.001 in.; as Fig. 15 shows, total variance was only 0.0006 in.

Example 643. Variations in Position of a Cored Hole in a Pinion (Fig. 16)

In a high-density compact pressed from 100-mesh electrolytic iron powder, it was specified that tne distance from the center of a cored hole to a point on the die-formed periphery should be 0.731 to 0.733 in. (Fig. 16). In production, the compacts were re-pressed to a minimum density of 7.4 g per cu cm, resintered, carburized and hardened. The results of measuring this dimension on 200 parts are shown in Fig. 16. All were within the specified tolerance; total variation was 0.001 in.

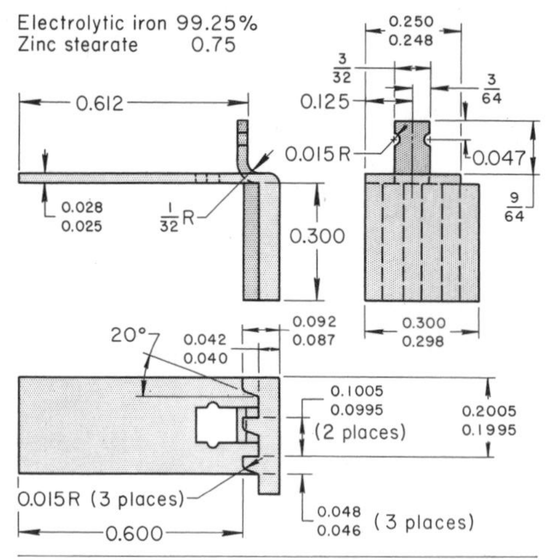

Press and Tool Details

Type of press	Mechanical(a)
Press capacity	50 tons
Die material	Carbide
Punch material	D2 tool steel
Tool life, number of compacts pressed before reconditioning:	
Die	500,000
Punches	20,000

Processing Details

Compacting pressure	50 tons per sq in.(b)
Re-pressing pressure	50 tons per sq in.
Preheating treatment	15 min at 1000 F
Sintering treatment	15 min at 2040 F
Resintering treatment	2 hr at 2350 F
Sintering atmosphere	Dissociated ammonia
Production rate:	
Pressed compacts	800 per hour
Sintered compacts	6000 per hour
Re-pressed compacts	1000 per hour
Resintered compacts	6000 per hour

(a) With manual control of top and bottom movements. (b) No die lubricant used; parts tumbled in molybdenum disulfide and steel shot.

Fig. 14. Compact that represents nearly the practical limit in section-thickness variation (Example 641)

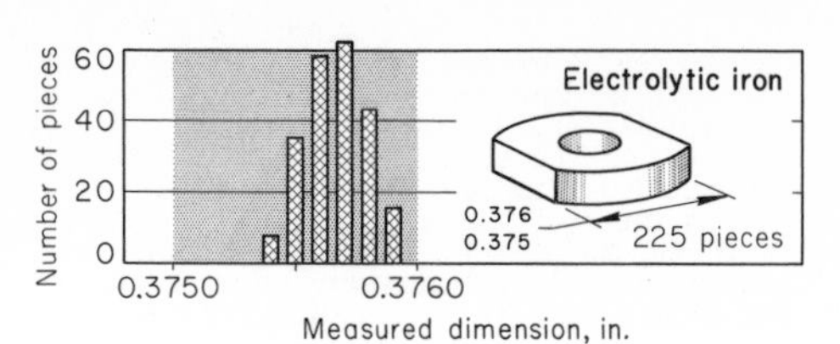

Fig. 15. Variations in width of side blocks after pressing, sintering, re-pressing, resintering, carburizing and hardening (Example 642)

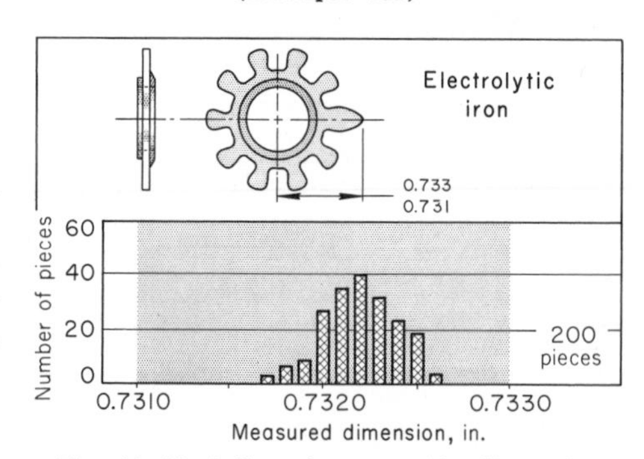

Fig. 16. Variations in a specific dimension among gearlike parts after pressing, sintering, re-pressing, resintering, carburizing and hardening (Example 643)

Example 644. Dimensional Variation at Different Production Stages (Fig. 17)

Figure 17 shows measurements taken at three stages during the production of compacts for four-point latch armatures: (*a*) after re-pressing, (*b*) after annealing for 20 min at 1600 F, and (*c*) after case hardening to a depth of 0.004 to 0.008 in. Figure 17 shows that some shrinkage took place during annealing, after which expansion occurred during case hardening. All of the measured dimensions were within the prescribed limits of 0.912 to 0.914 in.

Infiltration

Metal infiltration is an effective means for producing an essentially pore-free powder metallurgy compact having increased strength and density and improved machinability. In this process, the pores of the compact are filled with a metal or alloy having a melting point lower than that of the metal compact. Slugs of an infiltrant material are placed in contact with the part (usually underneath, although this is optional and in some plants the infiltrant slug is placed on top) and the two components are then passed through a furnace heated to a temperature slightly above the melting point of the infiltrant. The infiltrant melts and is drawn into the pores of the compact by capillary action. This method, compared with double pressing techniques, permits the use of lower compacting pressures; thus, smaller, less expensive presses and simplified tooling can be utilized.

The following requirements are essential for successful infiltration: (*a*) the infiltrant must have a melting point below that of the compact, (*b*) it must be fluid enough to wet the skeleton compact thoroughly at or below the infiltrating temperature, and (*c*) mutual solubility of the infiltrant with the compact must be low or zero.

The infiltration process is most frequently used in iron-base compacts; the most commonly used infiltrants are copper and copper alloys. The melting

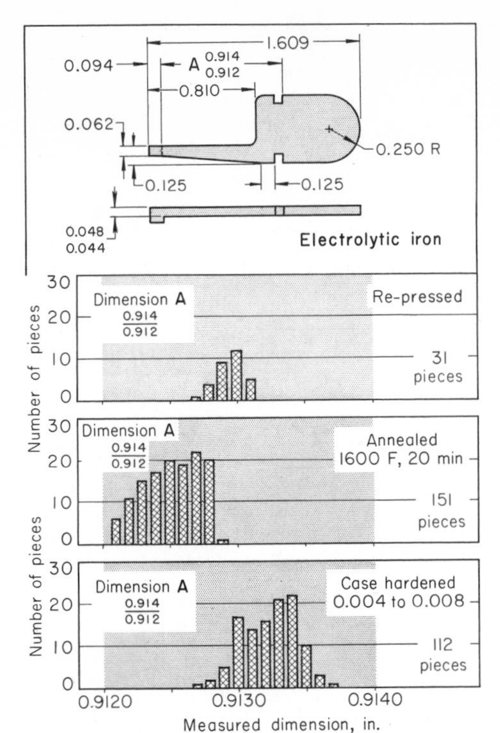

Fig. 17. Variations in a critical dimension on four-point latch armatures after re-pressing, after annealing, and after case hardening (Example 644)

point of pure copper is 1981 F, which is increased to about 2000 F by the small amount of iron it is able to dissolve. About 8% copper is soluble in gamma iron at 2010 F, and 4% iron can dissolve in the molten copper. This mutual solubility is low enough for successful infiltration and causes a desirable increase in hardness and strength. Another advantage of using copper as an infiltrant is that temperatures, times and atmospheres necessary for copper infiltration are so close to those used in sintering that the equipment required is usually the same for both operations.

In addition to pure copper, copper with a small amount of manganese or cobalt can be used for infiltrating iron compacts. Sometimes brass containing 10% zinc is used because of its lower melting point; infiltration can then be accomplished at temperatures lower than those required for copper. A disadvantage of this practice is the damage to furnace interiors resulting from volatilization of the zinc.

Infiltration of iron compacts can be done in two ways. Originally, a two-step process was used in which the iron compact was first pressed and sintered and then passed through the furnace again with the copper in contact with it in the form of solid, powder or compact. In a more recent technique, sintering and infiltration are accomplished simultaneously. Using this method, the unsintered compact and the copper are placed together and passed through the furnace, where they are held long enough to sinter the compact and allow the molten copper to fill the pores. The principal disadvantage of this simultaneous method is difficulty in maintaining dimensional control.

Maximum mechanical properties are obtained by filling the pores completely with infiltrant. However, because any excess will remain on the outside of the compact, a slight deficiency rather than an excess of infiltrant metal is customary, to guard against over-infiltration. Spot infiltration techniques can be used when only certain areas need infiltration. Infiltrated compacts can be readily electroplated because they are free from porosity; they do not retain plating solution below the surface. Copper-infiltrated compacts can be readily copper-brazed to each other or to wrought steel components. However, they are not self-brazing; extra copper must be added.

The two examples that follow illustrate the use of copper infiltration to produce strong iron-base compacts free from porosity. Example 645 shows the older, two-step technique. Example 646 shows the one-step technique.

Example 645. Infiltrating for Density, Machinability and Plateability (Fig. 18)

Figure 18 shows a small foot holder that required strength, machinability for tapping a thread, and plateability. These characteristics were achieved by infiltrating a sintered iron-rich skeleton (7% copper) with a copper-rich alloy containing 5% manganese and 5% iron. The compacts were infiltrated under furnace conditions similar to those used for sintering, using infiltrating slugs previously pressed. The infiltrated parts were electroplated with chromium to a satin finish. Processing details for the two-step procedure are given in the table with Fig. 18.

Example 646. Simultaneous Sintering and Infiltration for High Density (Fig. 19)

The iron-graphite-manganese compact (latch dog for a seat belt) shown in Fig. 19 was pressed to a density of 6.5 g per cu cm by means of the tool setup shown. It was simultaneously sintered and infiltrated with a 96.5% copper - 3.5% cobalt alloy to obtain a final minimum density of 7.8 g per cu cm, tensile strength of 140,000 psi, and a hardness of Rockwell C 40. The infiltrant material was pressed into a ⅜-in.-diam compact having a projection 3⁄16 in. in diameter by 0.015 in. high to hold it in place over the 0.250-in.-diam hole in the skeleton compact.

The skeletons with the infiltrant compacts in place were passed through a three-zone furnace. They were heated in the first zone at 1380 F to remove the zinc stearate and then to 1900 F in the second zone to alloy the iron and carbon, and finally to 2050 F for final sintering and infiltrating.

After the sintering-infiltration treatment, the parts were reheated to 1800 F, furnace cooled to 400 F, reheated to 1550 F, oil quenched, and tempered at 350 F.

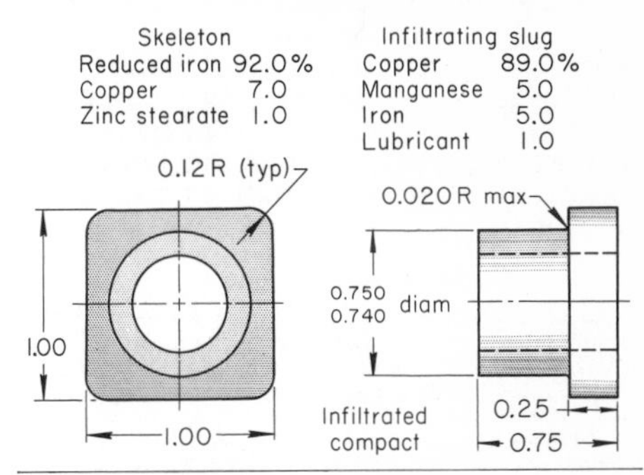

Press and Tool Details

Type of press	Mechanical(a)
Press capacity	50 tons
Die material	Carbide (6% Co)
Punch material	D2 tool steel
Core-rod material	Carbide (6% Co)
Tool life, number of compacts pressed before reconditioning:	
Die	500,000
Punches	50,000
Core rod	25,000

Processing Details

Compacting pressure:	
Skeleton	30 tons per sq in.
Infiltrating slugs	20 tons per sq in.
Preheating treatment	15 min at 2040 F
Sintering treatment	15 min at 2040 F
Infiltrating treatment	15 min at 2040 F
Atmosphere for sintering and infiltrating	Endothermic
Production rate:	
Skeletons pressed	800 per hour
Infiltrating slugs pressed	1500 per hour
Sintered compacts	1800 per hour
Infiltrated compacts	1800 per hour
Cost per 1000 infiltrated compacts	$92.15(b)

(a) Two movements above and three below. (b) Cost of material and burden is included; tooling cost is not included.

Fig. 18. Small compact infiltrated with copper alloy to provide machinability, strength and plateability (Example 645)

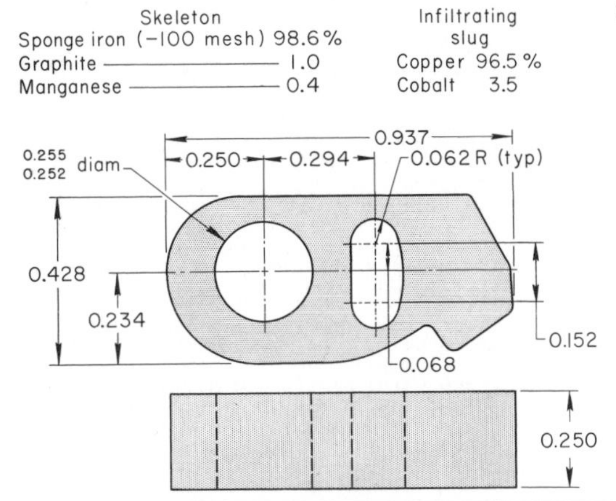

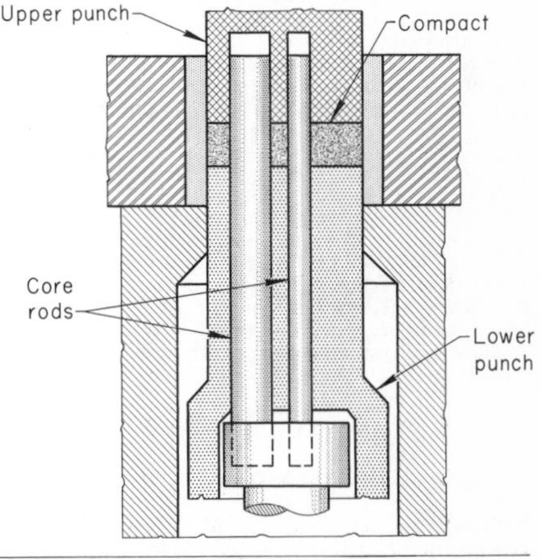

Press and Tool Details

Type of press	Dual-motion mechanical
Press capacity	12 tons
Die material	Carbide (9% Co)
Punch material	D2 tool steel(a)
Core-rod material	Carbide (12% Co)
Tool life, number of compacts pressed before reconditioning	50,000

Processing Details

Compacting pressure	50 tons per sq in.(b)
First preheating treatment	30 min at 1380 F
Second preheating treatment	40 min at 1900 F
Sintering and infiltrating treatment	20 min at 2050 F
Furnace atmosphere	Endothermic
Production rate, compacts per hour:	
Pressed	1500
Sintered and infiltrated	4000
Tool life(c):	
Die cell	1 million pieces
Core rods	80,000 pieces

(a) Rockwell C 60 to 61. (b) Zinc stearate used as lubricant. (c) Punch faces and core-rod diameters were lapped after every 20,000 pieces. Die cell was lapped after each 100,000 pieces.

Fig. 19. Tool setup for pressing skeletons (compacts) from iron-cobalt alloy (Example 646)

After the sintering-infiltration treatment the parts were reheated to 1800 F, furnace cooled to 400 F, reheated to 1550 F, oil quenched, and tempered at 350 F. The heat treated parts were then wet tumbled to remove burrs and finally were cadmium plated.

Disadvantages of infiltration include the following: (*a*) tolerances cannot be held as close with infiltration as with double pressing or the use of higher pressures to obtain high density; and (*b*) to get one compact, two compacts must be made. In most applications, it is more expensive to use infiltration to obtain high density than to use other methods.

Table 12. Ignition and Explosibility of Metal Powders (U. S. Bureau of Mines RI 6516)

Material	Ignition temperature, C: Cloud	Ignition temperature, C: Layer	Minimum explosive concentration, oz/cu ft	Minimum energy for igniting dust cloud, millijoules(a)	Maximum pressure, psig	Maximum rate of pressure rise, psi/sec	Size distribution of powder tested — Particle size, per cent passing through opening with size (microns) of: 149	104	74	53	44	Subsieve, microns
Severely Explosive												
Aluminum, atomized	650	760	0.045	50	73	20000+	...	...	...	...	100	..
Al-Mg alloy	430	480	0.020	80	86	10000	...	...	...	...	100	..
Magnesium	620	490	0.040	40	90	9000	...	...	100	...	...	..
Thorium hydride	260	20	0.080	3	60	6500	...	...	...	...	...	3
Zirconium	20	190	0.045	15(b)	55	6500	...	...	...	...	...	3
Uranium hydride	20	20	0.060	5(b)	43	6500	...	...	...	...	...	3
Titanium	330	510	0.045	25	70	5500	...	94	...	...	...	10
Uranium	20	100(b)	0.060	45(b)	53	3400	...	...	...	...	...	10
Thorium	270	280	0.075	5	48	3300	...	...	...	...	...	7
Strongly Explosive												
Al-Si alloy	670	...	0.040	60	74	7500	...	...	...	...	93	..
Calcium silicide	540	540	0.060	150	73	13000	...	...	...	...	...	2
Iron, carbonyl	320	310	0.105	20	41	2400	...	...	100	99	...	..
Ferrotitanium	370	400	0.140	80	53	9500	...	...	100	...	85	..
Moderately Explosive												
Silicon	...	790	0.110	100	82	12000	100	...	100	...	...	..
Boron	470	400	<0.100	60	90	2400	100	...	100	...	100	..
Al-Ni alloy	950	540	0.190	80	79	10000	...	...	...	...	85	..
Al-Li alloy	470	400	<0.100	140	96	3700	100	...	...	...	...	..
Al-Co alloy	950	570	0.180	100	78	8500	...	...	...	...	89	..
Ferromanganese	450	290	0.130	80	47	4200	100	...	100	...	...	..
Al-Cu alloy	...	830	0.100	100	68	2600	...	...	...	...	100	..
Chromium	580	400	0.230	140	55	4000	100	...	100	99	98	3
Manganese	460	240	0.125	305	48	2800	...	...	100	...	100	..
Tantalum	630	300	<0.200	120	50	2600	100	...	100	...	100	..
Tin	630	430	0.190	80	37	1300	100	...	97	96	...	..
Zirconium alloy	420	340	...	30	43	300	...	...	50	...	...	29
Weakly Explosive												
Al-Fe alloy	870	750	...	720	62	1800	...	...	...	...	80	..
Zinc	680	460	0.500	960	48	1800	100	...	100	...	...	..
Ferrosilicon	860	...	0.425	400	50	700	...	...	100	...	92	..
Vanadium	500	490	0.220	60	48	600	...	...	100	...	...	..
Antimony	420	330	0.420	1920	8	100	...	...	91	88	...	..
Cadmium	570	250	...	4000	7	100	...	...	100	82	...	..
Ferrovanadium	440	400	1.300	400	..	...	...	...	100	...	92	..
Ferrochromium	790	670	2.000	...	..	...	...	...	100	...	95	..

(a) These data apply to relatively coarse dust (through a No. 200 sieve) but not to submicron powder. (b) In this test, less than 1 gram of powder was used. Larger quantities of the powder ignited spontaneously.

Selected References

Claus G. Goetzel, "Treatise on Powder Metallurgy", Interscience Publishers, Inc., New York, Vol I, 1949, 778 pages; Vol II, 1950, 910 pages; Vol III, 1952, 899 pages; Vol IV, Parts 1 and 2, 1963, 1649 pages. [A comprehensive account of all aspects of powder metallurgy, with 12,851 references to the literature and world patents up to 1963.]

George H. de Groat, "Tooling for Metal Powder Parts", ASTE Technical Publications Committee, McGraw-Hill Book Co., New York, 1958; 242 pages. [Principles of press operation and die design.]

W. D. Jones, "Fundamental Principles of Powder Metallurgy", Edward Arnold (Publishers) Limited, London, 1960; 1032 pages.

"Materials Standard and Specifications for P/M Parts and Oil Impregnated Bearings", Powder Metallurgy Parts Manufacturers Assoc., Metal Powder Industries Federation, New York, 1965, 13 pages. [Mechanical, physical and chemical specifications for mechanical components and oil-impregnated bearings manufactured by the powder metallurgy process. Includes test methods, coding system and code designations.]

"The Powder Metallurgy Design Guidebook", Powder Metallurgy Parts Manufacturers Assoc., Metal Powder Industries Federation, New York, 1962; 24 pages. [Fundamentals of pressing powder metallurgy parts. Gives tolerances that can be maintained in production.]

"Powder Metallurgy Equipment Manual. Part I. Sintering Furnaces and Atmospheres", Powder Metallurgy Equipment Assoc., Metal Powder Industries Federation, New York, 1963; 88 pages. [Functions and general features of the commercially available types of sintering furnaces, sintering atmospheres, and temperature-control equipment.]

"Powder Metallurgy Equipment Manual. Part II. Compacting Presses and Tooling", Powder Metallurgy Equipment Assoc., Metal Powder Industries Federation, New York, 1965; 64 pages. [Constructional features and methods of operation of presses and tooling systems. Touches on die design, materials and construction, and tolerances.]

Roland P. Koehring, The Role of Powder Metallurgy in the Automotive Industry — Present and Future, *Progress in Powder Metallurgy*, 19, 7 to 23 (1963). [Applications of powder metallurgy are illustrated and the characteristics obtainable from iron-base parts are discussed.]

Hugh G. Taylor, A Critical Review of the Effect of Press and Tool Design upon the Economics of Sintered Structural Components, *Powder Metallurgy*, 8 (No. 16), 285 to 318 (1965). [A review of the fields of application of powder metallurgy. Lists the main features and costs of 56 powder metallurgy presses manufactured by American and German companies.]

APPENDIX

Explosiveness of Metal Powders

Industrial explosions have been caused by the ignition of clouds of metal powders. On the basis of test data accumulated by the U. S. Bureau of Mines, the metal powders ordinarily manufactured can be grouped approximately into five classes: severely explosive, strongly explosive, moderately explosive, weakly explosive, and nonexplosive. Data on the ignition and explosibility of a number of commercial powders in the first four groups are presented in Table 12.

Explosibility Factors. The ignition temperature, and the minimum energy necessary for ignition of a dust cloud have an important bearing on the probability of its exploding. The ignition temperatures of metal powders range from about 20 to over 1000 C (68 to over 1830 F). The minimum energy necessary for igniting metal powders ranges from a few millionths of a joule to several joules. The rate of oxidation of several metal powders, including powders of noble metals, is so small that their suspensions in air are incapable of propagating dust explosions. Some metal powders are ignited most readily by direct heat; others, notably aluminum, are ignited more readily by electric sparks. Reportedly, all metal and alloy powders in submicron size are pyrophoric.

The nature and violence of dust explosions are influenced principally by:

1. **Properties of the dust,** including: ease of oxidation; amount of oxygen needed for complete combustion; specific heat; purity of powder; presence of oxide film; shape, size and porosity of the particles; and affinity for nitrogen. Explosibility increases with decrease in particle size.
2. **Concentration of Dust Cloud.** To propagate an explosion, the concentration of dust in the air must be within certain upper and lower limits. The strongest explosion occurs at concentrations that are slightly higher than stoichiometric.
3. **Composition of Atmosphere.** A decrease in oxygen content of the atmosphere reduces violence of explosion and makes the suspension more difficult to ignite.
4. **Explosion Space.** Volume, shape and venting of the chamber in which the explosion occurs determine to a large extent the damage that results.

Severely Explosive Powders. Dust clouds composed of powders of the metals listed under "Severely Explosive" in Table 12 can be ignited readily by weak electric sparks, and layers of some of these powders can even be ignited by warm surfaces. All of the powders will explode in an atmosphere of commercial carbon dioxide. Magnesium and some Al-Mg powders will ignite in air-nitrogen mixtures containing as little as 3% oxygen. Such powders are processed in helium.

Zirconium can be ignited by more feeble electric sparks than any other dust tested. When it is dispersed in air at ordinary temperatures, the dust clouds ignite spontaneously under certain conditions.

Strongly Explosive Powders. The metal powders in this class present about the same dust-explosion hazard as pulverized bituminous coal. Ignition temperatures range from 310 to 670 C (590 to 1240 F). Minimum explosion concentrations in air range from 0.040 to 0.140 oz per cu ft. Atmospheres with sufficiently low oxygen content can inhibit these explosions.

Moderately Explosive Powders. Explosions of some powders in this category are nearly as strong as those in the strongly explosive group. Silicon, for example, develops 82 psig with a pressure rise of 12,000 psi per sec. Ignition temperatures are from 240 to 950 C (465 to 1740 F); minimum explosive concentrations are from 0.100 to 0.230 oz per cu ft.

Weakly Explosive Powders. Copper, impure iron, molybdenum, tungsten, cobalt and probably all noble-metal powders do not explode readily in air. Most of these powders have ignition temperatures above 700 C (1290 F). They are not easily ignited by sparks.

Nonexplosive Powders. This group (not represented in Table 12) includes nickel, stainless steel, aluminum bronze, beryllium copper, and manganese bronze.

Good housekeeping is the best way to avoid the hazards of dust explosion. Powder-processing equipment should be dust-tight. Dust should not be allowed to accumulate on beams, ledges, floors and other flat surfaces. The dust must be removed without raising it in a potentially explosive cloud. The dusting should be performed on a periodic basis and should be included as a separate item in plant maintenance schedules.

Electrical equipment and wiring should conform to the National Electrical Code for hazardous and dusty environment. Open lights and smoking should be prohibited in the affected areas. Repair work with torches and welding equipment should be performed during shutdown. Powder-processing equipment should be grounded to avoid static buildup.

COLD HEADING AND COLD EXTRUSION

CONTENTS

Cold Heading

*By the ASM Committee on Cold Heading**

COLD HEADING is a cold forging process in which the force developed by one or more strokes (blows) of a heading tool is employed to upset, or displace, the metal in a portion of a wire or rod blank to form a section of different contour or, more commonly, of larger cross section than the original. The process is widely used to produce a variety of small and medium-size hardware items — for example, bolts and rivets. However, the process is not limited to the cold deformation of the ends of a workpiece nor to conventional upsetting; metal displacement may be imposed at any point, or at several points, along the length of the workpiece and may incorporate extrusion in addition to upsetting. Advantages of the process over machining of the same parts from suitable bar stock include:

1 Almost no waste material
2 Increased tensile strength from cold work
3 Controlled grain flow.

Although the principal use of cold heading is for the production of heads on rivets or on blanks for threaded fasteners, a variety of other shapes can also be successfully and economically formed by the process. One application — forming a serrated collar at a considerable distance from the end of a preform — is described in the example that follows. In this application, the collar was developed by the back extrusion of a tapered shoulder previously formed by forward extrusion. (See also Examples 650 and 657 for other forms of center upsetting, and Example 649 for a description of the use of cold heading to produce a complex shape.)

Example 647. Cold Heading a Serrated Collar in One Blow (Fig. 1)

The serrated collar on the workpiece shown at the right in Fig. 1 was produced in a single blow on the extruded preform shown at the left in Fig. 1. The material was 1527 (formerly 1027) steel that was process annealed at 1600 F. Stock in the 20° extruded angle was forced to flow back and fill the toothed section of the heading punch. The metal was sheared for the depth of the tooth, and the diameter of the collar was filled by upsetting. The diameter of the collar was restricted by the punch to that of the shaft. Because this was a closed-die operation, there could be no allowance for flash, and it was important that the volume of metal being worked be accurately controlled. Too little metal caused underfilling; overfilling caused tool breakage. Additional production details are given with Fig. 1.

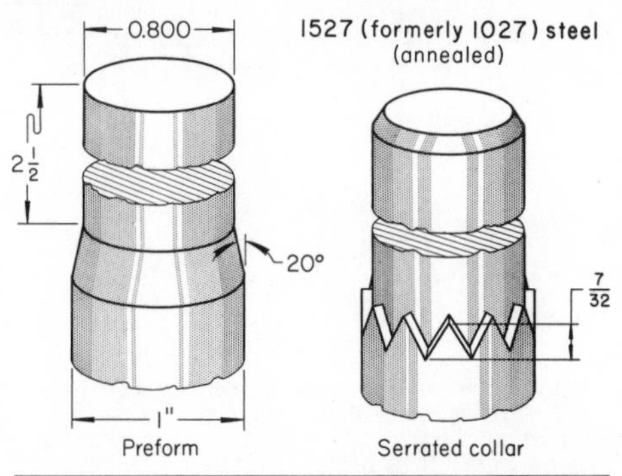

Machine	Modified double-stroke, double-end spoke header
Tool material (inserts)	M2 tool steel, at Rockwell C 62 to 64
Lubricant	Stearate, on rod only
Production rate	33 pieces per minute
Tool life	15,000 to 25,000 pieces

Fig. 1. Serrated collar cold headed on an extruded preform (Example 647)

Suitable Work Metals

Most cold heading is done on low-carbon steel wire with hardness ranging from Rockwell B 75 to 87. This is the type of material for which the machines are rated. Copper, aluminum, stainless steel, and some nickel alloys are also cold headed. Titanium, beryllium, magnesium, and refractory metals are less formable at room temperature and are likely to crack when cold headed; these metals are sometimes warm headed (see "Warm Heading", page 474).

Most wire used to head screws of SAE grades 3, 5 and 8 is of a low-carbon, medium-carbon, or low-alloy steel, the most commonly used being 1018, 1030, 1033, 1038, 1039, 1541 (formerly 1041), 4037, 4140 and 8640. These steels are selected for their strength after heat treatment.

Headability decreases as carbon and manganese content increase. Many head splits can be attributed directly to high carbon or high manganese, or both. Carbon steel wire that contains 0.25 to 0.44% carbon should be process annealed or spheroidize annealed, or both (see the section on Preparation of Work Metal in this article). Steels with medium carbon and high manganese contents, such as 1541 (formerly 1041), are sometimes difficult to head and may require a dual annealing treatment, as shown in the following example.

Example 648. Annealing Before Spheroidizing, to Avoid Bolt-Head Fracture (Fig. 2)

The head of a 4¾-in.-long cylinder-head bolt (7/16–14 UNC thread) was formed in an open die from spheroidize-annealed hot rolled

*ROBERT L. SPROAT, *Chairman,* Director of Engineering and Development, Standard Pressed Steel Co.; C. V. ANDERSON, Supervisor of Resident Engineering, Highland Park Machining Plant, Chrysler Corp.; RUDOLF K. F. BAUMLE, Chief Manufacturing Engineer, Shakeproof Div., Illinois Tool Works Inc.; ROBERT L. CALLAGHAN, Director of Sales, National Machinery Co.

RAY J. GATZ, Plant Manager, Lamson & Sessions Co.; LOUIS HRUSOVSKY, Chief Metallurgist of Research and Development, Rockwell-Standard Corp.; JOHN W. KEEGAN, Senior Metallurgist of Cold Heading Products, Carpenter Steel Co.; DAVID S. LAMBIE, Supervisor of Tool Manufacturing, Screw and Bolt Corp. of America; R. E. MCFARLAND, Director of Quality Control, Engineered Fasteners Div., Townsend Co. (Textron); M. O. NEWBY, Supervisor of Quality Control, Bolt and Forged Products, Sheffield Div., Armco Steel Corp.

C. VINCENT SCIULLO, Manager of Heading Machinery Sales, Waterbury Farrell (Textron); JOSEPH A. TABOR, Chief Machine Development Engineer, Russell, Burdsall & Ward Bolt and Nut Co.; ANTHONY R. TIRONE, President, Production Engineering Corp. (formerly with Production Cold Forming Div., Avis Industrial Corp.); A. V. WETZEL, Chief Metallurgist, Cleveland Cap Screw Div., Standard Pressed Steel Co.

1541 (formerly 1041) steel rod, which is satisfactory for most heading operations. Because of the severity of the upset, however, there was a high incidence of fractured heads (see Fig. 2). No defects could be tolerated.

Rod stock on hand was salvaged and acceptable bolt heads were produced when the spheroidized stock was conventionally annealed and then respheroidized. Cost of the additional heat treatments was $10 per ton.

Quality Levels of Steel. Steel wire for cold heading is generally available in five quality levels (pertaining to surface quality), which are listed below, in order of increasing quality and cost:

1 Industrial quality
2 Cold heading quality
3 Recessed head or scrapless nut quality
4 Special head quality
5 Coil-turned, ground, or shaved wire (seam-free).

The difference in cost between items 1 and 5 above is usually about 30%.

Selection of quality level depends largely on severity of the upset and the magnitude and number of defects that can be tolerated in the headed product. When quality requirements are extremely rigorous, the use of coil-turned or ground material is almost mandatory, as demonstrated in Example 655. In cold heading of commercial products, common practice is to begin with a lower quality and to upgrade only as is necessary (or is more economical).

Sometimes a change in processing procedure permits the use of steel of lower quality, as in the next example:

Example 649. Larger Stock Diameter That Eliminated Need for Cold Heading Quality Steel (Fig. 3)

A valve-spring retainer was originally produced from a 0.650-in.-diam by 0.75-in.-long slug in five blows (Fig. 3). With this size of slug, crack-free parts were obtained only by the use of cold heading quality wire.

By an improved procedure tooling was modified to accommodate 0.750-in.-diam wire and to shorten the slug length to 0.56 in. (Fig. 3). This change decreased the severity of heading, so that sound parts could be produced from industrial quality wire instead of the more expensive cold heading quality.

For both procedures, a ½-in. nut former equipped with a wire drawer, a shearing device, and five heading stations was used. For both diameters, the pickled and lime-coated rod was cold drawn at the machine from about 0.030 in. oversize to the cutoff diameter.

Stainless Steels. Austenitic steels 302, 304, 305, 316 and 321, and the ferritic and martensitic grades 430, 410 and 431, can be cold headed. However, because these steels work harden more rapidly than carbon steels, they are more difficult to cold head. More power is required and cracking of the headed or upset portion is more likely than when cold heading carbon or low-alloy steels. These difficulties are overcome by preheating the work metal to the temperatures recommended for warm heading (see the section on Warm Heading, page 474 in this article).

Length of Upset. Metals are rated for cold heading on the basis of the length of stock, in terms of diameter, that can be successfully upset (compressed into a head). Using flat-end punches, most cold headers can upset up to approximately two diameters of low-carbon steel wire per stroke. If this unsupported length is increased, the stock is likely to fold on itself, as shown in Fig. 4. With more formable metals such as copper alloys, the length of upset per stroke may be three or more diameters — except for the leaded copper alloys, which are usually limited to 1½ diameters because of the danger of splitting. Punches and dies can be designed to increase the headable length of any stock. For example, with a coning punch (Fig. 5) or a bulbing punch, it is possible to head as much as six diameters of low-carbon steel in two strokes.

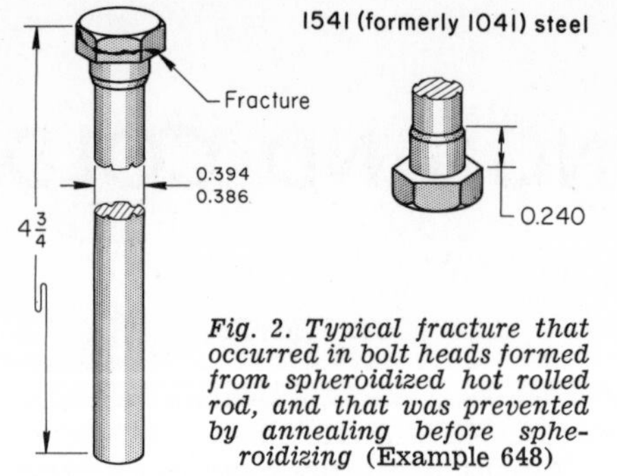

1541 (formerly 1041) steel

Fracture

0.394
0.386

$4\frac{3}{4}$

0.240

Fig. 2. Typical fracture that occurred in bolt heads formed from spheroidized hot rolled rod, and that was prevented by annealing before spheroidizing (Example 648)

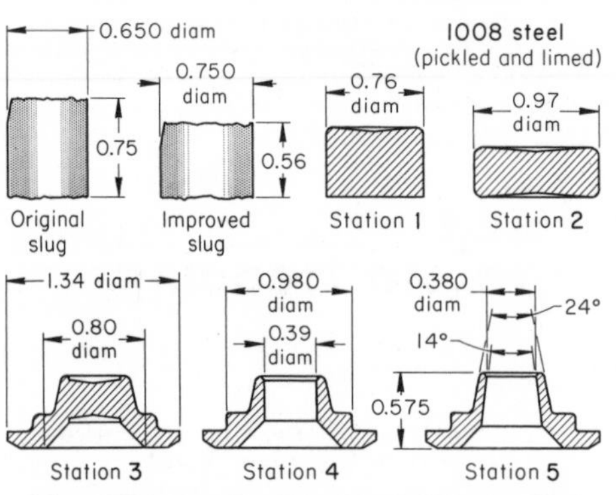

Fig. 3. Change in slug size that permitted use of lower-quality wire by decreasing heading severity in five-station production of a valve-spring retainer (Example 649)

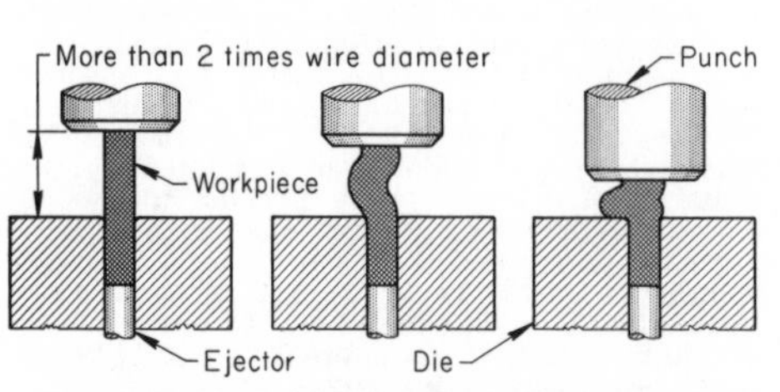

Fig. 4. Typical folding effect obtained with a flat-end punch when heading low-carbon steel wire with unsupported length of more than two diameters

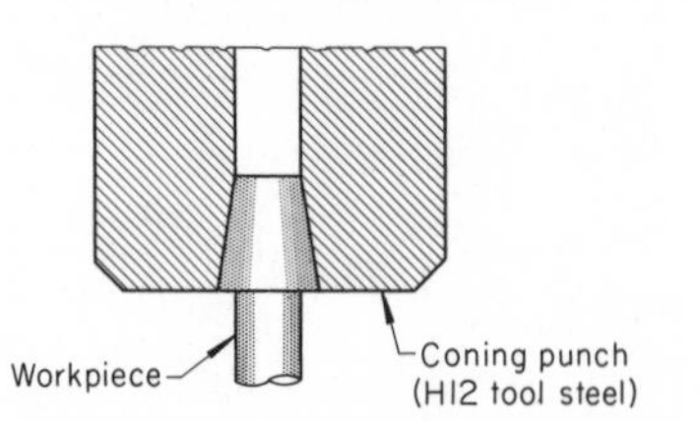

Fig. 5. Use of a coning punch in the first blow of a two-blow heading operation, which enables a low-carbon steel workpiece to be upset to a length of up to six diameters in two strokes

Machines

Standard cold headers are classified according to whether the dies open and close to admit the work metal or are solid, and according to the number of strokes (blows) the machine imparts to the workpiece during each cycle. The die in a single-stroke machine has one mating punch; in a double-stroke machine, the die has two punches. The two punches usually reciprocate, so that each contacts the workpiece during a machine cycle. Figure 6 shows a double-stroke header with a reciprocating punch holder.

Single-stroke solid-die headers are made in sizes of ⅛, 3/16, ¼, 5/16, ⅜, ½, ⅝, ¾, and 1 in. These sizes refer to the approximate diameter of stock that can be headed. Since they are single-stroke machines, product design should not call for more than two diameters of stock to form the head. Single-stroke extruding can also be done in this type of machine.

These machines are used to make rivets, rollers and balls for bearings, single-extruded studs, and clevis pins.

Double-stroke solid-die headers (Fig. 6) are available in the same sizes as single-stroke solid-die headers. These machines can make short to medium-length products (usually 8 to 16 diameters long), and can make heads that are as large as five times the stock diameter. Some of these machines are equipped for relief heading, which is a process for filling out sharp corners on the shoulder of a workpiece, or a square under the head.

Some extruding can also be done in these machines. Because of their versatility, double-stroke solid-die headers are used extensively in the production of fasteners.

Single-stroke open-die headers are made for smaller-diameter parts of medium and long lengths, and are limited to heading two diameters of stock because of their single stroke. Extruding cannot be done in this type of machine, but small fins or a point can be produced by pinching in the die, if desired. Similar machines are used for producing nails.

Double-stroke open-die headers are made in a wider range of sizes than single-stroke open-die headers, and can produce heads as large as five times stock diameter. They cannot be used for extrusion, but they can pinch fins on the workpiece, when required. (They will generally pinch fins or small lines under the head of the workpiece when these are *not* required; if these fins or lines are objectionable, they must be removed by another operation.)

Triple-stroke headers, using either solid or open dies, are classed as special machines. They are used when heads as large as five to eight times stock diameter are required, or when an unusual shape of head is required.

Transfer and progressive headers are solid-die machines with two or more separate stations for various steps in the operation. The workpiece is automatically transferred from one station to the next. These machines can perform one or more extrusions, or upset and extrude in one operation, or finish head and extrude in one operation. Maximum lengths of stock of various diameters headed in these machines are 6 in. (⅜-in. diam), 8 in. (½-in. diam), 9 in. (⅝-in. diam), and 10 in. (¾-in. diam). These machines can produce heads of five times stock diameter or more.

Boltmaking machines are solid-die headers similar to transfer and progressive headers, but they can trim, point, and roll threads, and usually have a blanking station, two heading stations and one trimming station served by the transfer mechanism. An ejector pin drives the blank through the hollow trimming die to the pointing station. The trimming station can be used as a third heading station, or for extruding. Boltmaking machines are made for bolt diameters of 3⁄16, 1⁄4, 5⁄16, 3⁄8, 1⁄2, 5⁄8, 3⁄4, 1 and 1 1⁄4 in.

Rod headers are open-die headers having either single or double stroke. They are used for extremely long work (from 8 to 160 times stock diameter). The workpiece is cut to length in a separate operation in another machine and fed into the rod header either manually or automatically.

Reheaders are used when the workpiece must be annealed before heading is completed — as, for example, when the amount of cold working needed would cause the work metal to fracture before heading was complete.

Reheaders are made as either open-die or solid-die machines, single or double stroke, and can be fed by hand or hopper. Punch presses are also used for reheading.

Nut formers generally have five forming dies and a transfer mechanism that rotates the blank 180° between one or two dies. Thus, both ends of the blank are worked, producing workpieces with close dimensions, a fine surface finish, and improved mechanical characteristics. A small slug of metal is pierced from the center of the nut, which amounts to 5 to 15% waste, depending on the design of the nut.

Operation. Most cold heading machines used in high production are fed by coiled wire stock. The stock is fed into the machine by feed rolls and passes through a stationary cutoff quill. In front of the quill is a combination shear-and-transfer mechanism. When the wire passes through the quill, the end butts against a wire stop or stock gage to determine the length of the slug to be headed. The shear-and-transfer mechanism grips the stock and with one motion shears it and transfers the slug to a position usually in front of the heading die. The heading punch moves forward and pushes the slug into the die; at the same time, the transfer mechanism releases the slug and moves back into position for another slug.

In the die, the slug is stopped by the ejector pin, which acts as a backstop and positions the slug with the correct amount protruding for heading. In a single-stroke or double-stroke header, the heading operation is completed in this die, and the ejector pin advances to eject the finished piece. In a progressive header or a boltmaking machine, the transfer mechanism has fingers in front of each of several dies. After each stroke, the ejector pin pushes the workpiece out of the die. The transfer mechanism grips it and advances it to the next station. In boltmaking machines, the last station in the heading area is a trimming station. The trimming die (which is on the punch side) is hollow, and the die ejector pin drives the trimmed workpiece completely through the die and, by an air jet or other means, through a tube to the pointing station.

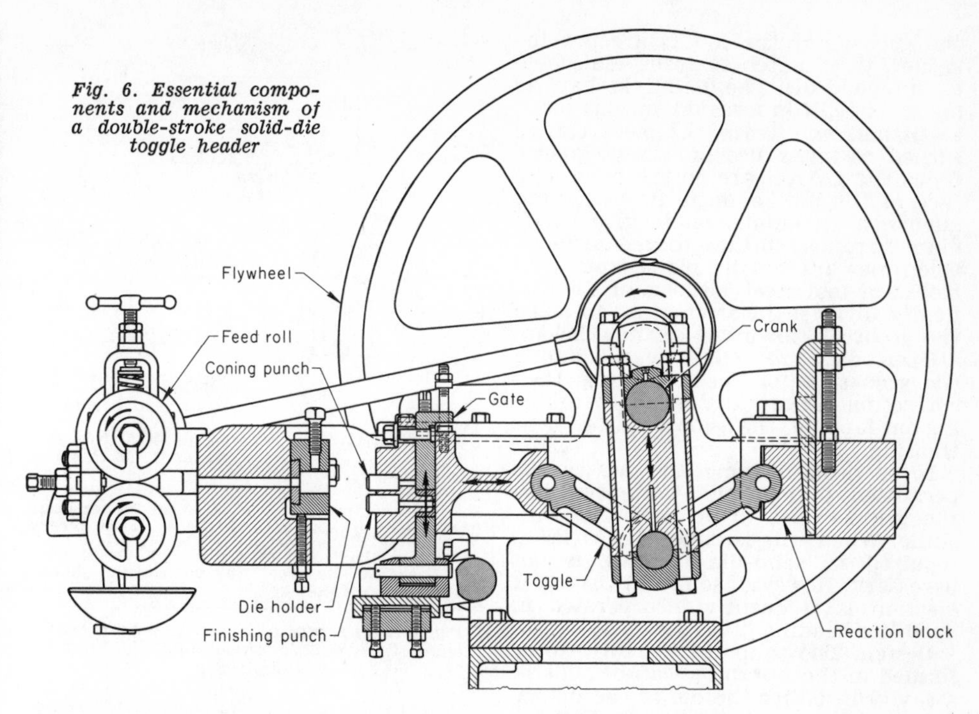

Fig. 6. Essential components and mechanism of a double-stroke solid-die toggle header

Pointers are of two types. Some have a set of cutters that operate much like a pencil sharpener in putting a point on the workpiece (thereby producing some scrap); others have a swaging or extruding device that forms the point by cold flow of the metal.

From the pointer the workpiece is placed in a thread roller. A boltmaking machine has a thread roller incorporated in it. The rolling dies are flat pieces of tool steel with a conjugate thread form on their faces. As the workpiece rolls between them the thread form is impressed on its shank, and it drops out of the dies at the end, often as a finished bolt. (Details of the equipment and techniques used in thread rolling are presented in the article "Thread Rolling", which begins on page 130 in Volume 3 of this Handbook.)

Tools

Tools used in cold heading consist principally of punches or hammers and dies. The dies can be made as one piece (solid dies) or as two pieces (open dies), as shown in Fig. 7.

Solid dies (known also as closed dies) consist of a cylinder of metal with a hole through the center (Fig. 7a). Solid dies may be made entirely from one material, or may be made with the center portion surrounding the hole as an insert of a different material. The choice of construction depends largely on the length of production run. For extremely long runs, it is sometimes desirable to use carbide inserts, but it may be more economical to use hardened tool steel inserts in a holder of less expensive and softer steel.

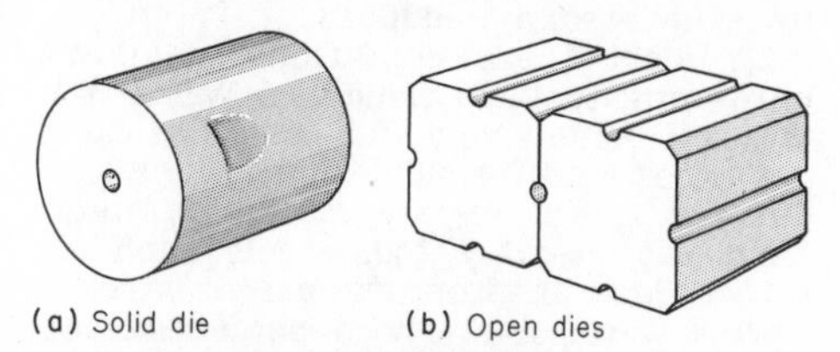

Fig. 7. Solid (one-piece) and open (two-piece) cold heading dies

When a solid die is made in one piece, common practice is to drill and ream the hole to within 0.003 to 0.005 in. of finish size before heat treatment. After heat treatment the die is ground or honed to the desired size.

Solid dies are usually quenched from the hardening temperature by forcing the quenching medium through the hole, making no particular attempt to quench the remainder of the die. By this means, maximum hardness is attained inside the hole; the outer portion of the die is softer and therefore more shock-resistant.

Because the work metal is not gripped in a solid die, the stock is cut to length in one station of the header, and the cut-to-length slug is then transferred by mechanical fingers to the heading die. In the heading die, the slug butts against a backstop as it is headed. Ordinarily, the backstop also serves as an ejector.

In general, solid dies are preferred for the heading of complex shapes. The next example describes a typical application in which a solid die was used.

Example 650. Centered Hexagon Made in a Double-Stroke Header (Fig. 8)

A stud blank with a centered hexagon head was produced in two blows in a double-stroke solid-die header, as shown in Fig. 8. A 3⁄8-in. header was used, because of its long stroke and the size of tools it could accommodate. The header had a built-in punch-ejector mechanism. The operation was planned so that the larger portion of the workpiece was in the die and would thus develop enough friction to pull the remaining portion out of the punch after each stroke. Choice of lubricant was more critical for this part than for producing a simple bolt head.

Additional operating conditions are given in the table with Fig. 8.

Open dies (also called two-piece dies) consist of two blocks with matching grooves in their faces (Fig. 7b). When the grooves in the blocks are put together, they match to form a die hole as in a solid die. The die blocks have as many as eight grooves on various faces, so that as one wears, the block can be turned to make use of a new groove. Since the grooves are on the outer surface of the blocks, open-die blocks are quenched by immersion to give maximum hardness to the grooved surfaces. Open dies are usually made from solid blocks of tool steel, because of the difficulty involved in attempting to make the groove in an insert set in a holder.

Open dies are made by machining the grooves before heat treating, then correcting for any distortion by grinding or lapping the grooves after heat treating.

In open-die heading, the dies can be permitted to grip the workpiece, like the gripper dies in an upsetting machine. When this is done, the backstop required in solid-die heading is not necessary. However, some provision for ejection is frequently incorporated in open-die heading.

Design. The shape of the head to be formed in the workpiece can be sunk in a cavity in either the die or the punch, or sometimes partly in each. Decision on the location of the cavity often depends on possible locations of the parting line on the head. It must be possible to extract the workpiece from both the punch and the die. It is generally useful, but not entirely necessary, to design some draft in the workpiece head for ease of ejection.

An important consideration in the design of cold heading tools is that the part should stay in the die and not stick in the punch. For this reason midshaft upsets are particularly difficult to design tooling for. Where possible, the longest part of the shank is left in the die. With open dies that use a special die-closing mechanism there is less of a problem. Some punches are equipped with a special synchronized ejector mechanism to make sure the workpiece comes free.

At best, cold heading imposes severe impact stress in both punches and dies. Minor changes in tool design often register large differences in tool life, as described in the example that follows.

Example 651. Improvements in Design of Heading Tool That Eliminated Tool Failure (Fig. 9)

The recessed-head screw (7/16–20 UNF–2A) shown in Fig. 9(a) was originally headed by the heading tool shown in Fig. 9(b). After producing only 500 pieces, the tool broke at the nib portion indicated as "Point of failure" in Fig. 9(b).

Design of the heading tool was improved by adding a radius and a slight draft to the nib as shown in Fig. 9(c). The entire nib was then highly polished. The redesigned tools produced 12,000 to 27,000 pieces before breakage occurred, but this tool life was still unacceptable.

A final design improvement is shown at the right in Fig. 9(c). The nib was made to fit a split holder, using a slight taper to prevent the nib insert from being pulled from the split holder as the header withdrew from the workpiece. Tools of this design did not break, and produced runs of more than 100,000 pieces before the nib was replaced because of wear.

Tool Materials

The shock loads imposed upon cold heading tools must be considered in selecting tool materials. For optimum tool

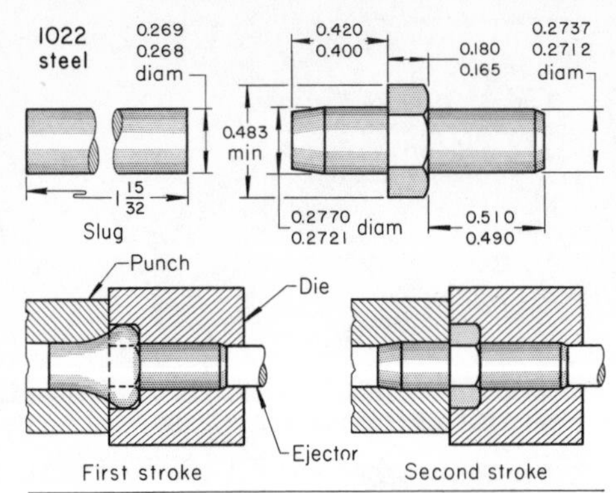

Machine	5/8-in. cold header(a)
Tool steels:	
Dies (inserts)	D2, at R_C 58 to 60(b)
Punches	S1, at R_C 56 to 58(c)
Setup time	2 hr
Lubricant	Extrusion oil
Production rate	4500 pieces per hour
Tool life	10,000 to 15,000 pieces

(a) Double-stroke solid-die. (b) Or similar cold heading die steel. (c) Or similar shock-resisting tool steel.

Fig. 8. Production of a hexagon-head stud blank in a double-stroke solid-die header (Example 650)

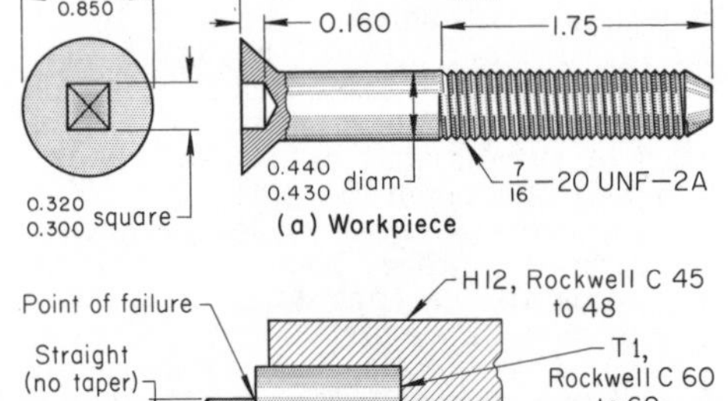

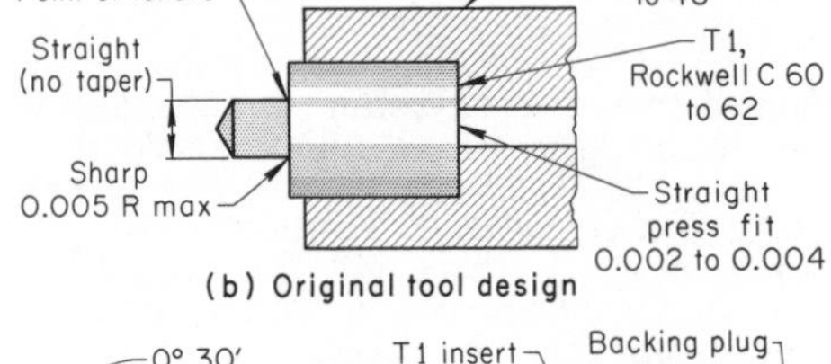

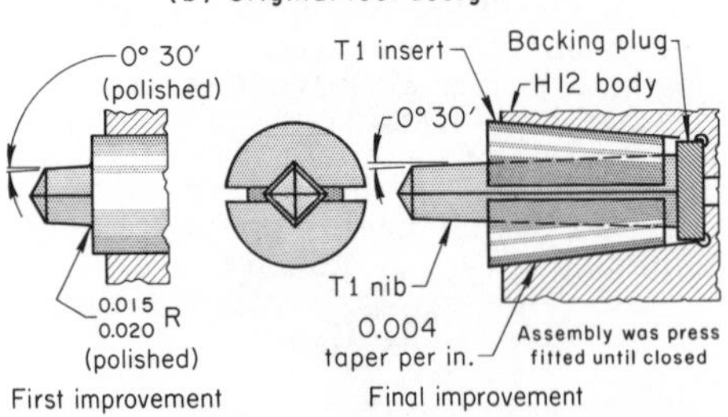

Fig. 9. Two improvements in the original design of a heading tool to eliminate tool failure in the production of recessed-head screws (Example 651)

life it is essential that both punches and dies have hard surfaces (preferably Rockwell C 60 or higher). However, except for heading hard materials, the interior portions of the tools must be softer (Rockwell C 40 to 50, and sometimes as low as Rockwell C 35 for larger tools) or breakage is likely.

To meet these conditions, shallow-hardening tool steel such as W1 or W2 is used extensively for punches and open dies, and for solid dies made without inserts. Inserts are commonly made from higher-alloy tool steels such as D2 or M2, or from tungsten carbide having a relatively high percentage of cobalt (13 to 25%). (More complete details on tool materials for cold heading are presented in the article "Selection of Material for Cold Heading Tools", page 725, Volume 1 of this Handbook.)

Shock-resisting tool steel such as S1 is also used for cold heading tools, especially for the heading of intricate shapes when a tool steel like W1 has failed by cracking. The shock-resisting steels are generally lower in hardness than preferred for maximum resistance to wear, but sacrifice of some wear resistance is often necessary to gain resistance to cracking.

Producing bolts that have square portions under the heads, or dished heads, or both, can result in tool failure. Under these conditions a change in grade of steel for the tools is sometimes mandatory, as described in the following example.

Example 652. Change From W1 to a Shock-Resisting Tool Steel (Fig. 10)

Open-die heading was required for the production of the dish-shape head on the bolt shown in Fig. 10. Originally, the dies were made of W1 (0.70 to 0.85% C) tool steel, at Rockwell C 48 to 52. With these dies only 2000 to 7000 pieces were produced before the dies fractured at the location shown in Fig. 10.

By changing to dies made from shock-resisting tool steel (0.55 C, 0.55 Mn, 0.65 Cr, 0.35 Mo), at Rockwell C 46 to 50, 80,000 to 120,000 pieces were headed before fracturing occurred in the same location on the dies (see Fig. 10). Because the dies would normally be replaced at this point from wear, no further improvement was attempted.

Preparation of Work Metal

Operations required for preparing stock for cold heading may include heat treating, drawing to size, machining, descaling, cutting to length, and lubricating.

Heat Treating. The cold heading properties of most steels are improved by process annealing, spheroidizing, or stress relieving. In general, process annealing is done at the steel mill on steels with low to medium carbon content. Additional heat treatment is not used unless required, for at least two reasons: (*a*) the process could cost more than any saving realized in cold heading; and (*b*) cold headed products often depend for their final strength on work hardening prior to and during the heading process, and if reannealed before cold heading they may lose much of their potential strength.

Carbon steels (1000 series) with up to about 0.25% carbon are usually cold headed in the mill-annealed condition as received from the steel supplier. If the heading is severe, they can be reannealed at some stage in the heading operations, but they are rarely given a full anneal before cold heading. Carbon steels (1000 series) with 0.25 to 0.44% carbon are also mill annealed. However, because higher carbon content decreases workability, they are sometimes normalized or annealed above the upper transformation temperature, and more frequently a spheroidizing treatment is used. Carbon steels that contain more than 0.44% carbon, most modified carbon steels (1500 series), and all alloy steels are fully spheroidized. (Heat treating methods for steels and nonferrous metals are described in Volume 2 of this Handbook.)

In practice, experience often indicates the need for annealing or spheroidizing, either to prevent cracking of the work metal or to obtain acceptable tool life, or both. In the first of the two examples that follow, an intermediate annealing treatment was incorporated in the sequence of operations, because severe heading was required. In the second example, annealing was rescheduled in the sequence of operations, to provide the work metal with lower tensile and yield strengths for heading.

Example 653. Intermediate Annealing for High-Severity Heading (Fig. 11)

An elevator bolt (1/4–20 UN thread) with a 31/32-in.-diam flat head was produced from cold heading quality 1010 steel wire in three separate operations as shown in Fig. 11. The first two upsets were done in a 3/8-in. double-stroke header. The workpiece was then annealed and coated with zinc phosphate and stearate soap before final heading in a 1/2-in. trimmer.

Because of the volume of metal in the bolt head, the high ratio of head diameter to shank diameter, and the severity of the blow required for forming the square under the head, production of this part in a triple-stroke header without annealing would more than likely have resulted in fracture of the workpiece, and in excessive tool wear or even tool breakage.

Example 654. Change in Annealing Sequence That Resulted in Reduced Tool Wear

Cap screws (3/8–16 NC thread) were originally headed from 25/64-in.-diam 1038 steel rod in the following sequence of operations:

1 Pickling to remove mill scale
2 Annealing to tensile strength of 72,000 psi and yield strength of 43,000 psi
3 Pickling and lime coating
4 Cold drawing to 0.364/0.361-in. diam (resulting in tensile strength of 90,000 psi and yield strength of 66,000 psi)
5 Heading in two blows in a multiple-stroke header.

By an improved method, 15/32-in.-diam 1038 steel rod was used, and the sequence of operations was revised to the following:

1 Pickling to remove mill scale, and lime coating
2 Cold drawing to 0.380-in. diam
3 Annealing to tensile strength of 70,000 psi and yield strength of 42,000 psi
4 Pickling and lime coating
5 Cold drawing to 0.364/0.361-in. diam (resulting in tensile strength of 80,000 psi and yield strength of 54,000 psi)
6 Heading in one blow.

Despite the increased processing cost for the additional drawing operation, the improved method yielded an over-all saving of $6 per ton of steel processed, by providing a softer metal for heading and thereby reducing tool wear and downtime for changing tools.

Drawing to size produces stock of uniform cross section that will perform as predicted in dies that have been carefully sized to fill out corners without flash or die breakage. Drawing to size also improves strength and hardness when these properties are to be developed by cold work and not by subsequent heat treatment.

Headability is sometimes expressed as the "heading limit", which is the ratio of the diameter of the largest possible headed portion to the diameter of the stock. There is usually a direct relationship between reduction of area in a tensile test, and heading limit as defined above.

Turning and Grinding. Drawn wire can have defects that carry over into the finished workpiece, exaggerated in the form of breaks and folds. Seams in the raw material that cause these defects may not be deep enough to be objectionable in the shank or body of a bolt, but can cause cracks in the head during cold heading or subsequent heat treatment.

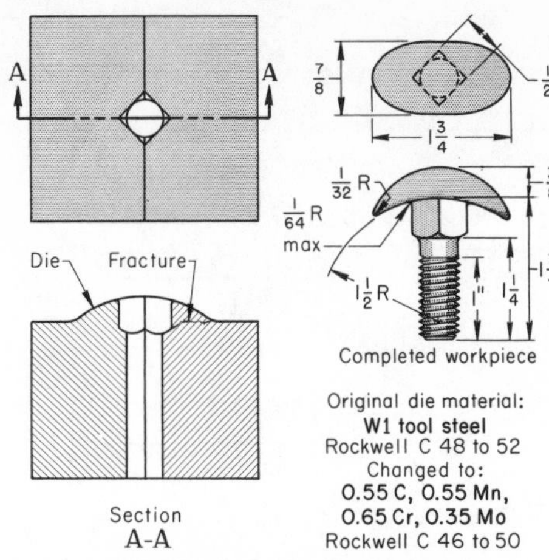

Fig. 10. Change in die material that increased die life (Example 652)

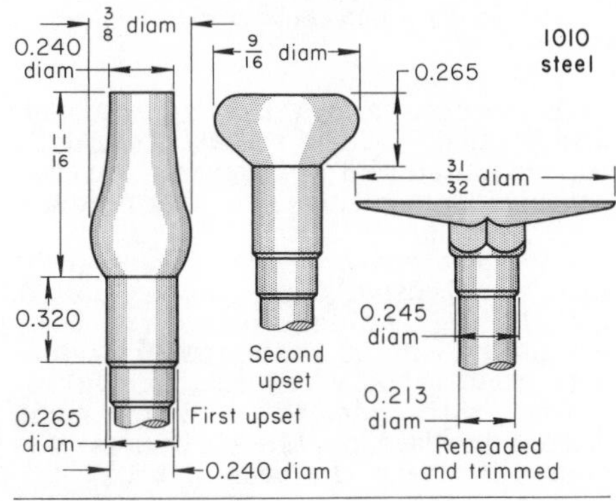

Machines:
Upsets 1 and 2(a): 3/8-in. double-stroke header
Reheading and trimming ...... 1/2-in. trimmer
Work metal .... Cold heading quality wire
Dimensional tolerance .... USASI B18.5
Tool materials:
Die and punch inserts ...... T1, Rc 60 to 62
Insert holders .... H12, Rockwell C 50
Production rate(b) ...... 4000 pieces per hour
Die life, avg(b) .... 50,000 pieces

(a) Workpiece was annealed after second upset. (b) In double-stroke header only.

Fig. 11. Production of an elevator bolt in three operations (Example 653)

Surface seams and laps can be removed by turning, grinding or shaving at the wire mill or by machining the headed product, but the former procedure often is less costly:

Example 655. Cost Saving by Heading Bolt Blanks From Turned Wire Instead of Grinding Bolt Blanks Headed From As-Drawn Wire

Hexagon-head bolts, 5/16 in. in diameter, 2 in. long and made from 8740 steel, for use in an aerospace application, had to be completely free of surface defects. This specification could be met either by grinding bolt blanks headed from as-drawn wire or by heading the bolt blanks from coil-turned wire. The use of turned wire, despite the higher initial cost of that material, was the more economical method, as shown by the following comparison of costs per 100 bolts:

	Turned wire	As-drawn wire
Material	$1.00	$0.77
Heading	0.26	0.26
Grinding	...	0.97
Total	$1.26	$2.00

Descaling. Work metal that has been heat treated usually needs to be descaled before cold heading. Scale can cause lack of definition, defects on critical surfaces, and dimensional inaccuracy of the workpiece.

Methods of descaling include abrasive blasting, use of water jets, pickling, wire brushing, and scraping. Selection of method depends largely on the amount of scale present and on the required quality of the surfaces on the headed workpieces. Acid pickling is usually the lowest-cost method for complete removal of heavy scale (see the article "Pickling of Iron and Steel", and the articles on cleaning and finishing of specific metals in Volume 2 of this Handbook).

Cutting to Length. In a header that has a shear-type cutoff device as an integral part of the machine, cutting to length by shearing is a part of the sequence. In applications where cutting to length is done separately, shearing is the method most commonly used for bars up to about 2-in. diam (see the article "Shearing of Bars" in this volume). For larger diameters, sawing is generally used. Gas cutting and cutting with abrasive wheels are less often used than shearing and sawing. For details on the advantages and disadvantages of the various methods used for cutting to length, see Table 8 in the article "Cold Extrusion", on page 482.

Lubrication. Although some of the more ductile metals can be successfully cold headed to moderate severity without a lubricant, most metals to be cold headed are lubricated to prevent galling of the work metal or the dies, sticking in the dies, and excessive die wear.

Lubricants used include lime coating, phosphate coating, stearates and oils, and plating with softer metals such as copper, tin or cadmium.

The ultimate in lubrication for steel to be cold headed is a coating of zinc phosphate with stearate soap — the same as is used for cold extrusion of steel (see the article "Cold Extrusion" in this volume). A similar treatment is often used for aluminum. However, for workpieces produced entirely by cold heading, this treatment is seldom necessary except for extremely severe heading (such as that described in Example 653).

In cold heading of carbon and alloy steel wire, common practice is to coat the work metal with a dry lubricant during the last draw. The lubricants most often used are calcium stearate or aluminum stearate. First, the wire is pickled to remove scale, dirt and any previous coatings. Then it is coated with lime, phosphate or borax, which acts as a base coating. Calcium or aluminum stearate is added as a dry lubricant. The lubricant sticks to the base coating and is fused by the heat developed when the wire passes through the drawing die.

For severe heading, extrusion oils are sometimes used (often in addition to the treatments given above), particularly when experience has proved that oil will improve results (see Examples 650 and 656).

Stainless steel is usually electroplated with copper and then lubricated with oil or molybdenum disulfide. Oxalates are sometimes used instead of the copper plating.

In cold heading of nonferrous metals, the need for lubrication varies from metal to metal. Nickel-base alloys need very good lubrication — especially the

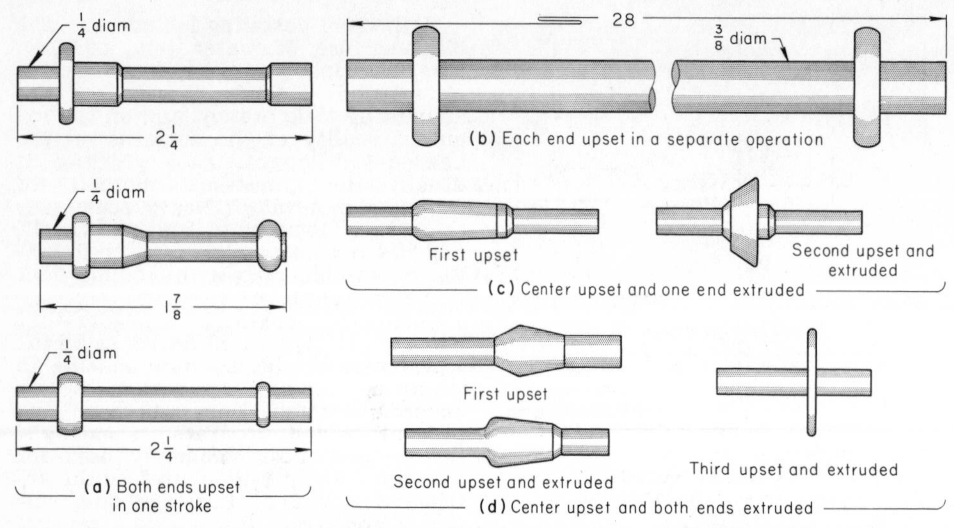

Fig. 12. Typical parts with upsets at both ends or with center upsets, illustrating production methods based on complexity

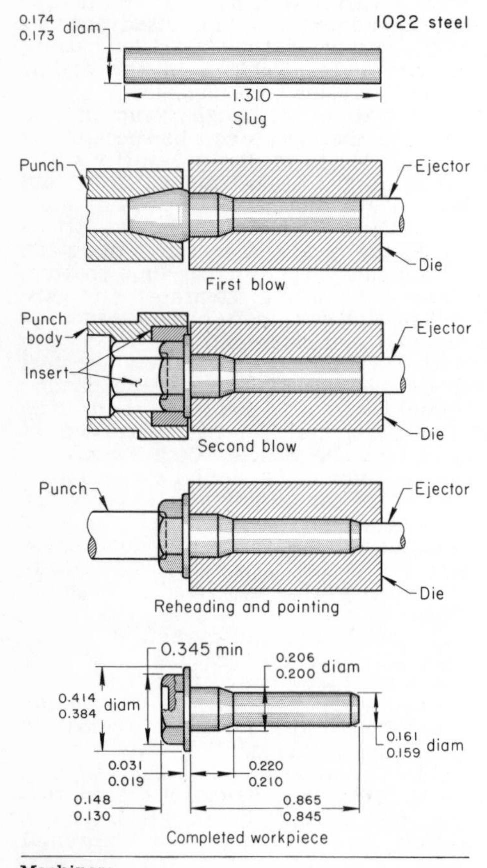

Machines:
First two blows ...... ¼-in. two-stroke header
Reheading and pointing .... No. 1 bolt-head trimmer
Tool materials:
Dies (all) .... Cold header tool steel(a)
Punches .... Shock-resisting tool steel(b)
Setup time .... 1.5 hr per machine
Lubricant .... Extrusion oil
Production rate ....6000 pieces per hour(c)
Tool life:
Heading .... 10,000 to 15,000 pieces
Reheading .... 100,000 pieces (approx)

(a) W1 at Rockwell C 60 to 62. (b) S1 or similar at Rockwell C 56 to 58 except for the finishing (second blow) punch, which was a high speed steel insert at Rockwell C 60 to 62 pressed into a hot work die steel (H12 or similar) body. (c) Each machine produced at approximately the same rate.

Fig. 13. Production of a complex, pointed screw blank in three blows in two machines (Example 656)

high-strength alloys like the Inconels and Waspaloy. These metals are usually copper plated and then given a stearate coating. The coatings are later removed with nitric acid.

The more formable nickel-base alloys like Monel usually are copper plated, also. If the heading is not severe, however, they can be headed with a stearate coating only, which can be removed with hot water. Nitric acid cannot be used on Monel, because the acid will attack the base metal.

Copper-base alloys have the least need for lubrication. For normal heading operations, oil or drawing compound is added at the header. For severe heading, a stearate coating can be added during the last draw of the wire. Sulfurized oil should not be used for cold heading of copper-base alloys unless some staining can be tolerated.

Aluminum header wire is generally coated with stearate. Aluminum needs more lubrication for cold heading than copper, but much less than nickel.

In all cold heading, best practice is to use the simplest and the least lubricant that will provide acceptable results, for two reasons: (*a*) excessive amounts of lubricant may load up the dies, resulting in scrapped workpieces or damaged dies; and (*b*) removal of lubricant is costly (the cost of removing lubricant usually increases in proportion to the effectiveness of the lubricant).

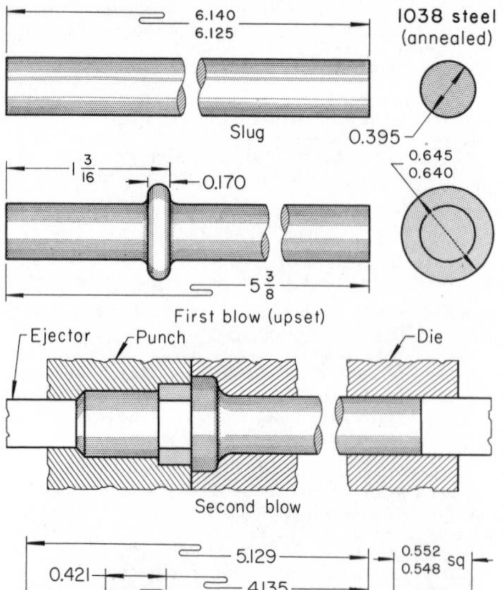

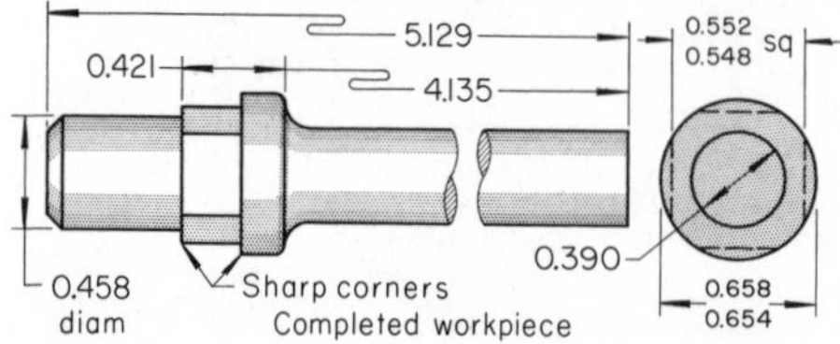

Machine ....½-in. boltmaking machine
Tool material ....M2 inserts, Rc 62 to 64
Lubricant ....Stearate on stock
Production rate ....4200 pieces per hour(a)
Tool life .... 10,000 to 15,000 pieces

(a) At 100% efficiency

Fig. 14. Two-blow production of a blank for a bicycle-pedal bolt with a complex center upset (Example 657)

Complex Workpieces

Cold headed products that have more than one upset portion need not be formed in two heading operations; many can be made in one operation of a double-stroke header. The length of stock that may be partly upset is generally limited to five times the diameter of the wire. The only other limitation is that the header must be able to accommodate the diameter and length of wire required for the workpiece.

Three pieces, each with two end upsets, that were made completely in one operation in a double-stroke open-die header are shown in Fig. 12(a). These parts were made at a rate of 80 pieces per minute. (Production rate is limited only by the speed of the machine used and not by the item being produced.)

The product becomes more expensive when the upsetting operation has to be performed twice — as in production of the 28-in.-long axle bolt shown in Fig. 12(b). This part required two upsetting operations because the die in a standard double-stroke cold header was not long enough to form both upsets in the machine at the same time.

One or more extra operations may be needed for workpieces that not only require a complex upset, but also require pointing, as in the next example.

Example 656. Production of a Complex Screw Blank in Three Blows in Two Machines (Fig. 13)

The indented-hexagon washer-head screw blank shown in Fig. 13 was produced in three blows — two blows in a header and one blow in a bolt-head trimmer. Successful heading of these complex parts in three blows depended largely on selecting a header having adequate capacity (a ¼-in. two-stroke header was used) and a built-in ejector. Operating details are given in the table with Fig. 13.

Center Upsetting. Although most cold heading involves forming an upset at the end of a section of rod or wire, forming of upsets at some distance from the end is common practice (see Example 647, and Fig. 1 and 12, in this article).

The trailer-hitch-ball stud shown in Fig. 12(c) is representative of an upset performed midway between the ends of the wire blank. This stud was upset and extruded in two strokes in a ¾-in. solid-die machine. The diameter of one end section is smaller than that of the original wire, and the round center collar is flared out to more than 2½ times the wire diameter. The center-collar stud shown in Fig. 12(d) is another example of a center upset. Both ends of the stud were extruded below wire size, while the center collar was expanded to more than three times the original wire diameter. This stud was formed in three strokes in a progressive header.

Control of the volume of work metal to prevent formation of flash, and to prevent excessive loads on the tools, is important in most cold heading operations. In center upsetting, control of metal volume is usually even more important, not only to prevent flash and tool overload but also to prevent folds. A technique used successfully in one application of center upsetting is described in the following example.

Example 657. Production of a Complex Center Upset in Two Blows (Fig. 14)

A blank for a bicycle-pedal bolt (Fig. 14) required sharp corners on the edges and corners of the square portion and complete absence of burrs or fins in the collar area. In heading, any excess pressure applied on the collar portion to fill the corners and edges of the square resulted in flash or overfill on the collar portion. To make this part successfully, it was necessary to upset the collar portion in one blow and form the square in a second blow (Fig. 14). The folds generally produced by this technique were avoided by careful control of size. By forming the collar completely during the first blow and almost completely confining it during the second blow, the remainder of the metal was controlled so that it could be directed into filling the square. Therefore, the pressure needed to form and fill the square was confined to this area and not allowed to cause further upsetting in any other portion. Accurate control of the headed volume depended on the accuracy of the cut blank and of the collar formed in the first blow.

Selection of Method on the Basis of Quantity and Cost

Cold heading is a high-production process. Generally, die life ranges from 50,000 to 500,000 pieces; carbide dies can usually last for a million or more pieces. However, a run of 5000 pieces or less can often be made economically, depending on the cost of the competitive process.

Location of the break-even point in the over-all cost of cold heading and of a competitive process, or a competitive procedure for cold heading, is often affected significantly by the cost of the work metal. As the cost of the work metal increases, the quantity required to justify tool cost for cold heading decreases (see Example 668).

Size and shape of the workpiece also have a significant effect on the choice of procedure for a given quantity of parts. Thus, each application must be studied individually to determine the most economical processing procedure for the quantity to be produced. The first two of the four examples that follow describe methods used for producing various quantities of bolts and cap screws. The last two of the following four examples compare quantity-cost relations for alternative methods of producing struts and bolts.

Examples 658 and 659. Effect of Quantity on Method Used for Producing Bolts and Cap Screws

Example 658 — Bolts (Fig. 15). The special shoulder-bolt blank shown in Fig. 15 was produced by four different methods, depending on production quantity. When no more than

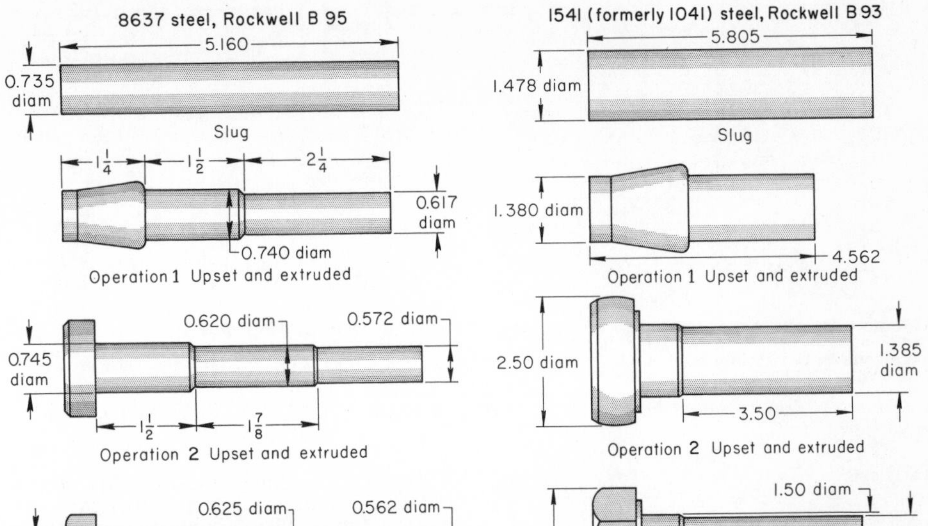

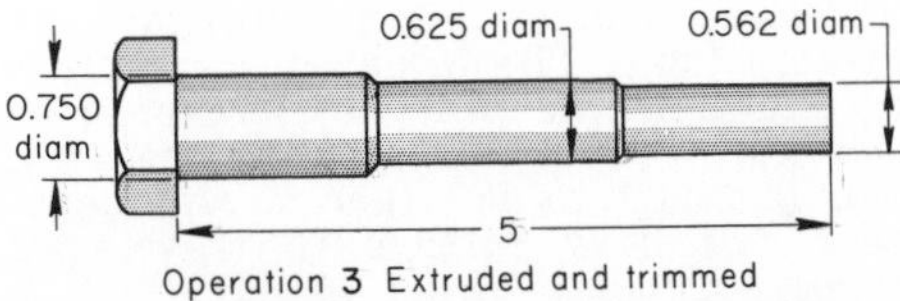

Fig. 15. Sequence of operations for producing shoulder-bolt blanks in quantities of more than 5000 in a ¾-in. boltmaking machine (Example 658)

Fig. 16. Upsetting, extruding and trimming sequence in the production of cap screws in a boltmaking machine. Method was used for 1000 pieces or more (Example 659)

100 bolts were required, the lowest-cost method was to machine completely from hexagonal bars, including cutting the threads, in a turret lathe or similar machine.

For quantities of over 100 to 999 bolts the most economical procedure was to hot head round blanks slightly over ¾ in. in diameter and then to complete the bolt by machining.

For quantities of 1000 to 5000, the head was upset, and the body and shank diameters were extruded, in a ¾-in. double-stroke header, and then head trimming and final extrusion of the small end to thread-pitch diameter were performed in a trimmer. By this procedure, separate operations were still required for pointing and thread rolling.

For quantities of more than 5000, all operations were completed in a ¾-in. boltmaking machine. This included the operations shown in Fig. 15 plus pointing and thread rolling.

Example 659 — Cap Screws (Fig. 16). The hexagon-head cap screw shown in Fig. 16 was produced by three different methods, depending on quantity requirements. In quantities up to 100, the screws were completely machined from hexagonal bar stock.

For quantities of over 100 to 999, the most economical method was to hot head blanks 1½ in. (or slightly smaller) in diameter, machine under the head, chamfer a point, and cut the 3½-in. length of thread.

Quantities of more than 999 screws were produced in a 1¼-in. boltmaking machine, by upsetting, extruding and trimming as shown in Fig. 16. Screw blanks were pointed and threads were rolled in the same machine.

Examples 660 and 661. Quantity vs Cost for Producing Struts and Place Bolts

Example 660 — Struts (Fig. 17). Costs for the use of three different methods of producing various quantities of automobile front-suspension struts prior to swaging are compared in Fig. 17. Because of its length, the strut was formed in a rod header, in the sequence of operations shown in Fig. 17. For quantities up to 30 pieces, the lowest-cost method was to use a single-pass rod header, temporary tools and manual operation (method 1 in Fig. 17); dies were changed for each operation until the production run was completed, and holes were produced by drilling.

For quantities of 30 to 2500, a multiple-pass hot header was used, but with the work at typical cold heading temperature (method 2 in Fig. 17). Feeding was manual, and the holes were drilled.

For quantities greater than 2500, a multiple-pass hot header was again used (method 3 in Fig. 17), but feeding and transfer from station to station were automatic, and the holes were punched.

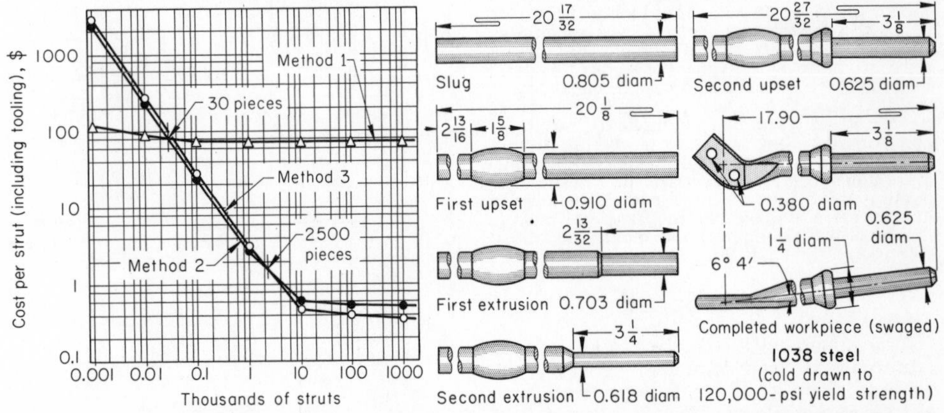

Method 1: Single-pass rod header, temporary tools, manual operation; holes drilled. **Method 2:** Multiple-pass hot header (work not heated), manual feed; holes drilled. **Method 3:** Multiple-pass hot header (work not heated), automatic feed and transfer; holes punched.

Fig. 17. Effect of quantity on cost of producing struts by three different methods, in the sequence of operations shown (Example 660)

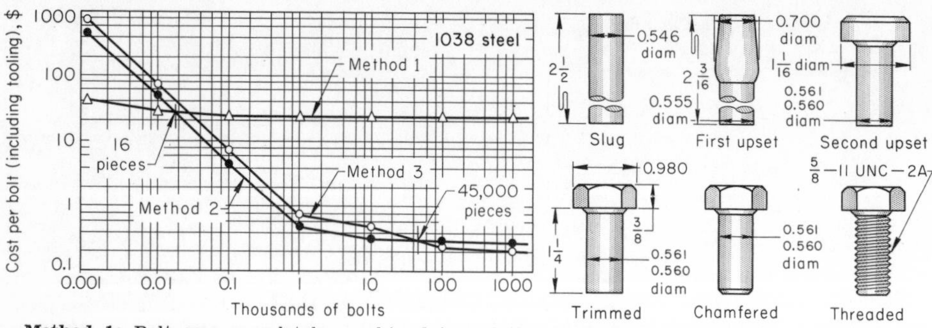

Method 1: Bolt was completely machined in a lathe. **Method 2:** In sequence shown at right, above, bolt was upset in a double-stroke header, then trimmed, chamfered and threaded in separate operations in a trimmer and a thread roller. **Method 3:** All operations in sequence shown above were done in a boltmaking machine.

Fig. 18. Effect of quantity on cost of producing place bolts by three different methods (Example 661)

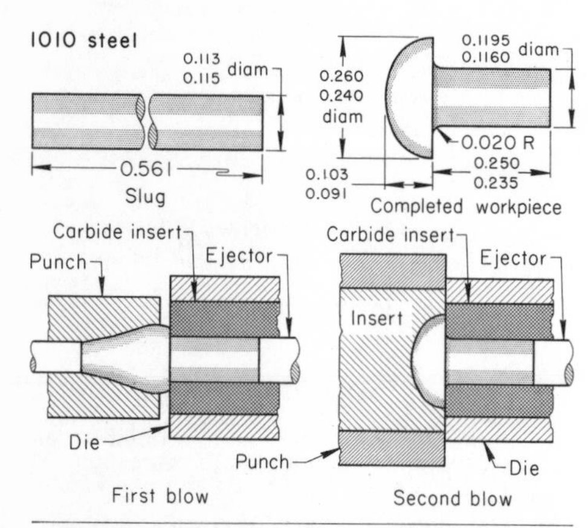

Machine	High-speed double-stroke header
Tool materials:	
Die (insert)	Carbide
Punch, 1st blow	Shock-resisting tool steel(a)
Punch, 2nd blow	High speed steel(b)
Setup time	1.5 hr
Production rate (approx)	15,000 pcs/hr(c)
Tool life (avg):	
Carbide die	4 million pieces
Punch, first blow	1 million pieces
Punch, finish blow	1 million pieces

(a) S1 or similar at Rockwell C 56 to 58. (b) M2 or similar insert at Rockwell C 60 to 62 pressed into hot work tool steel (H11 at Rockwell C 54 to 56) holder. (c) At 96.5% machine efficiency; 145 hr for 2,100,000 screw blanks.

Fig. 19. Two-blow production of a machine-screw blank in a high-speed header (Example 662)

The hole punching and swaging operations were performed in a crank press.

Example 661 — Place Bolts (Fig. 18). The relation of cost to quantity for three methods of producing hexagon-head place bolts is shown in Fig. 18. For producing up to 16 bolts, the lowest-cost method was machining (method 1 in Fig. 18), in which the threads were produced by cutting. For quantities of 17 to 45,000, the cheapest method consisted of making the two upsets in a double-stroke header, then trimming, chamfering (pointing) and thread rolling in separate operations in a trimmer and a thread roller (method 2 in Fig. 18; sequence shown at right of graph). For making quantities of more than 45,000 bolts, it was more economical to use a boltmaking machine for all operations, including thread rolling (method 3 in Fig. 18).

Header Speed

The speed with which a cold header can operate is a function of stock diameter, length of workpiece, and machine mechanism. All of these reflect the effects of inertia in limiting the cycle time of the machine. For instance, for larger stock diameter, more force will be needed to produce the upset; consequently, the machine members will have to be larger to transmit the greater force. The larger moving parts in the machine will accelerate more slowly; the dimensions of the machine will also have to be larger, so the members will have farther to travel per stroke.

Longer workpieces mean more stock to be fed into the machine, and therefore an appreciable increase in cycle time. A ¼-in. double-stroke toggle header (Fig. 6) can head about 125 1½-in.-long bolts per minute. A faster type of double-stroke machine drives the ram directly from the flywheel crank without an interposed toggle. This type of machine could head the same bolt at the rate of 250 per minute. Special high-speed machines might be able to head as many as 500 bolts per minute, provided the head is no more than medium in severity. In contrast, similarly designed ½-in. headers might have less than a third of these speeds.

In one operation, a ¼-in. double-stroke header was estimated to be able to produce 1½-in.-long pieces at the rate of about 9000 pieces per hour. But for 2½-in.-long pieces, production in the same machine was estimated to be around 8000 per hour. The reduction is attributable entirely to the greater amount of time required for feeding the additional stock.

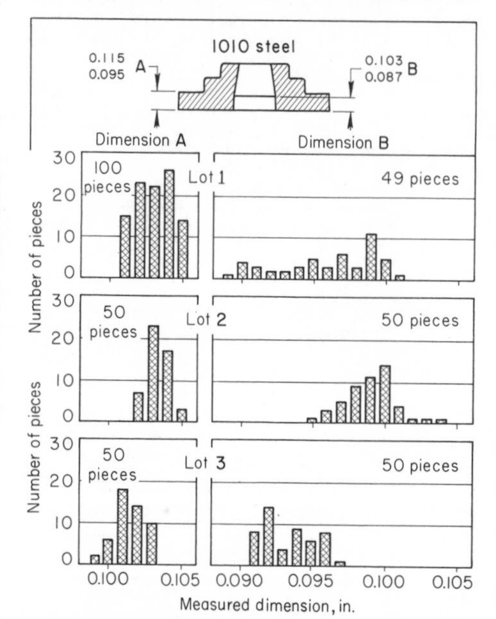

Fig. 20. Variations in two dimensions of valve-spring retainers selected from lots produced from three different coils in a five-station progressive nut former (Example 663)

High-Speed Heading. Many hardware items, such as rivets and blanks for threaded fasteners, are produced in continuous high production, or at least in runs of a million or more pieces. For this type of operation high-speed headers are available that produce as many as 350 headed pieces per minute (21,000 per hour) from coil stock. The following example describes a method used for producing small machine-screw blanks in mass-production quantities in a high-speed header.

Example 662. Use of High-Speed Header for a Long Production Run of Machine-Screw Blanks (Fig. 19)

Machine-screw blanks (6–32 NC thread) were made by two blows in a high-speed header as shown in Fig. 19. This header was capable of producing blanks at a rate of approximately 250 per minute (15,000 per hour). Operating conditions are given in the table with Fig. 19.

Small quantities of these parts (5000 or fewer) were usually produced in a toggle-type header, because it was easily set up; production rate was about 125 pieces per minute. For extremely long runs, headers were used that produced the screw blanks at the rate of 350 per minute (21,000 per hour).

Dimensional Accuracy

In general, work can be produced to much closer tolerances in cold headers than in hot headers. Tolerances on parts produced by single-stroke headers need to be wider than on parts given two or more blows. Rivets, often formed in single-stroke machines, have tolerances of ±0.015 in. except where otherwise specified. Shanks for rolled threads are allowed only ±0.0015 in. Generally, small parts can have closer tolerances than large parts. Tolerances can sometimes be maintained as close as ±0.001 in., although maintenance of a tolerance this close increases product cost, requires careful control of machines, tools and work metal, and is unusual in practice.

The three examples that follow demonstrate tolerance capabilities and show dimensional variations obtained in production runs of specific cold headed products.

Example 663. Variation in Dimensions of a Valve-Spring Retainer Produced in a Nut Former (Fig. 20)

The valve-spring retainer shown in Fig. 20 was produced from fine-grained, aluminum-killed 1010 steel (No. 2 bright annealed, cold heading quality), in a five-station progressive nut former. To determine the capabilities of the machine and tools for long-run production, several thousand pieces were made from three separate coils. Distribution charts were prepared for two critical dimensions on randomly selected parts made from each coil. Results are plotted in Fig. 20. Lots 1, 2 and 3 include parts made from the three different coils. As a further test of machine and tool capabilities, the tooling was set to a mean taper dimension for lot 1, high side for lot 2, and low side for lot 3.

The accuracy that could be maintained on thickness of a flat surface is demonstrated in Fig. 20. Although specifications permitted a total variation of 0.020 in. on seat thickness, actual spread did not exceed 0.005 in. for parts made from the three coils. A greater total variation was experienced for the taper-depth dimension. When the tools were set for mean, the total variation was 0.013 in., which was still within the 0.016 in. allowable (lot 1).

With tools set for high side, total variation was only 0.010 in., although one part was 0.001 in. out of the allowable range (lot 2). Best results were obtained on the taper dimension when tools were set for the low side (lot 3); total spread was only 0.007 in.

Examples 664 and 665. Variations in Dimensions of Rivets and Bolts

Example 664 — Rivets (Fig. 21). Variations in body and head diameters, head height, and shank length of 5⁄16-by-5⁄8-in. pan-head rivets made from 1008 steel is shown in Fig. 21. Dimensions plotted were obtained by measuring 100 random samples from each of two 2000-lb production runs (total of 200 samples representing 4000 lb or 182,000 rivets). Although all rivets measured were well within the prescribed tolerances, it is obvious that close tolerances were easier to maintain on some dimensions than on others. For instance, in lot 1, body diameter for the 100-piece sample was within 0.002 in. whereas 0.012 in. was allowed. Conversely, head diameter for the samples from lot 1 varied a total of 0.019 in. within an allowable variation of 0.034 in. Rivets were headed from lime-coated rod cold drawn to size. A single-stroke solid-die header was used for making the rivets.

Example 665 — Bolts (Fig. 22). Variations in body diameter, washer diameter, and shoulder length for a wheel bolt (3⁄8–24 NF thread) with an indented-hexagon washer head are plotted in Fig. 22. These bolts were headed from lime-coated cold drawn 1018 steel wire in a 1⁄2-in. boltmaking machine; the 100 pieces measured were selected at random from a production run of about 150,000 pieces. Although all dimensions were well within the tolerances specified, washer diameter had the widest spread whereas body diameter was uniform within 0.002 in.

The sequence of operations to form this bolt was: upset head, extrude, bump back shoulder, point, and roll thread.

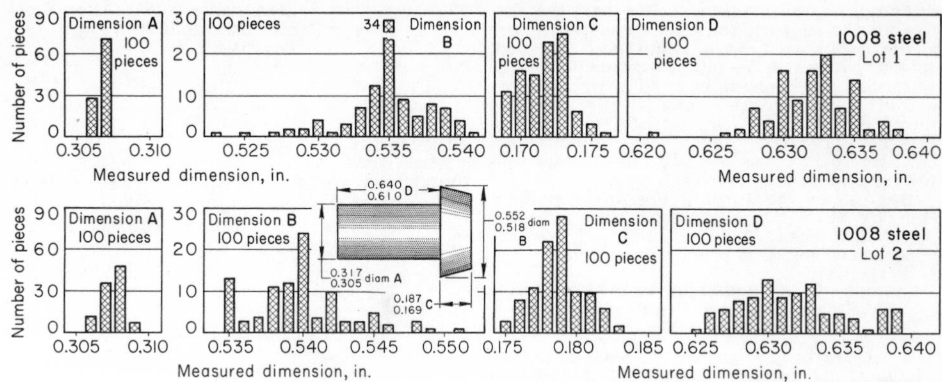

Fig. 21. Variations in four dimensions of pan-head rivets that were selected at random from two 2000-lb production lots (Example 664)

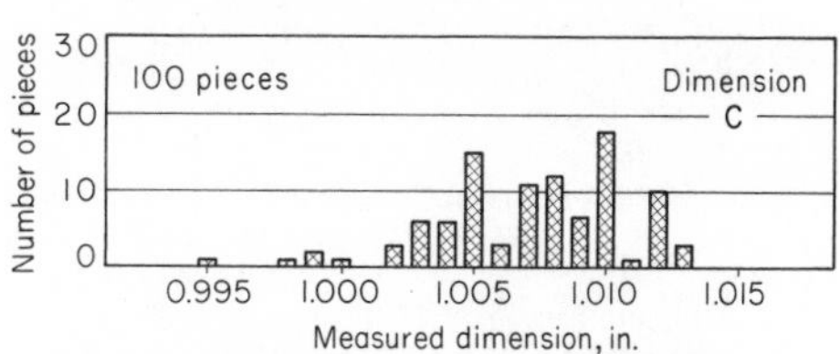

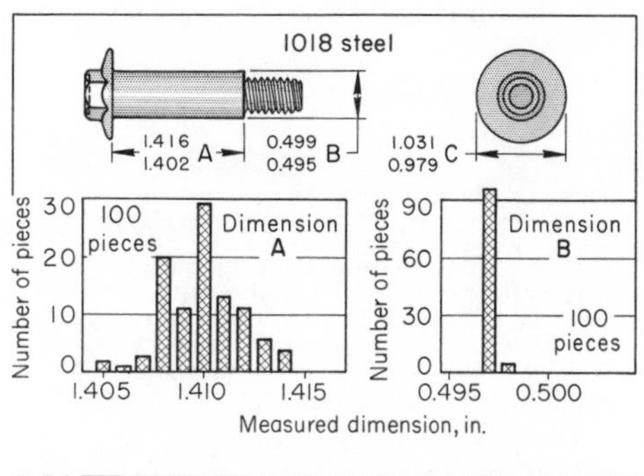

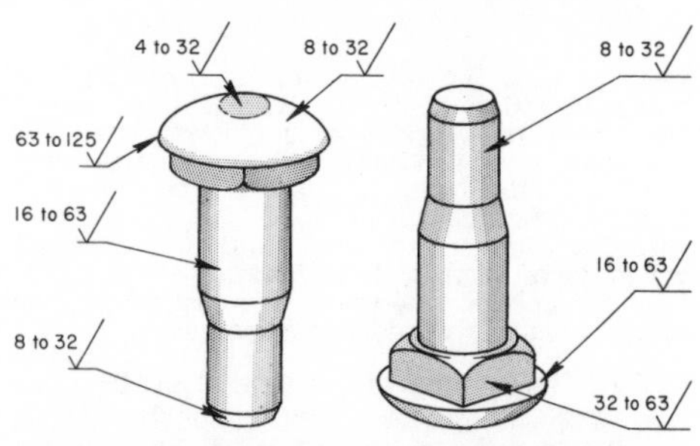

Fig. 22. Variations in three dimensions of 100 wheel bolts selected at random from a 150,000-piece run (Example 665)

Fig. 23. Typical ranges of surface roughness, in micro-inches, at various locations on a square-necked bolt headed from cold drawn steel with ground and polished tools

Surface Finish

Surfaces produced by cold heading are generally smooth and seldom need secondary operations for improving the finish. The surface roughness, however, can vary considerably among different workpieces, or among different areas of the same workpiece, depending on:

1 Surface of the wire or bar before heading
2 Amount of cold working in the particular area
3 Lubricant used
4 Condition of the tools.

Cold drawing of the wire before cold heading will improve the final surface finish. The best finish on any given workpiece is usually where direct contact has been made with the tools, such as on the top of a bolt head or on an extruded shank portion where cold working is severe.

The lubricant is likely to have a greater effect on the appearance of a headed surface than on surface roughness as measured by instruments. For instance, heavily limed or stearate-coated wire produces a dull finish, whereas a high-luster finish is produced when grease or oil is used.

Condition of the tools is most important in controlling the workpiece finish. Rough surfaces on punches or dies are registered on the workpiece. Thus, the best surface finish is produced only from tools that are kept polished.

The ranges of finish shown on the square-necked bolt in Fig. 23 are typical for such a part when headed from cold drawn steel, using ground and polished tools. Note that the best finish is on the top of the head and on the extruded shank, whereas the poorest is on the outer periphery of the round head.

Combined Heading and Extrusion

Combining cold heading with cold extrusion is common practice, and often permits the selection of a work-metal size that greatly lessens forming severity and prolongs tool life (see Example 667 in this article, and also Examples 681 to 685 in the article "Cold Extrusion"). Two parts shown in Fig. 12, a trailer-hitch-ball stud and a center-collar stud, reflect the flexibility in design obtained by combining center upsetting and extrusion.

In addition to increased tool life, other advantages sometimes can be obtained by combining cold heading and cold extrusion, as shown in the two examples that follow.

Example 666. Combined Heading and Extrusion That Eliminated Machining (Fig. 24)

As shown in Fig. 24, lawnmower wheel bolts were originally produced by: (*a*) heading the slug, and simultaneously extruding the opposite end to 0.525-in. diam; (*b*) coining and trimming the round head to hexagon shape; and (*c*) turning the bolt blank to 0.331-in. diam in a secondary operation prior to rolling a 3⁄8–16 NC thread for 3⁄8 in.

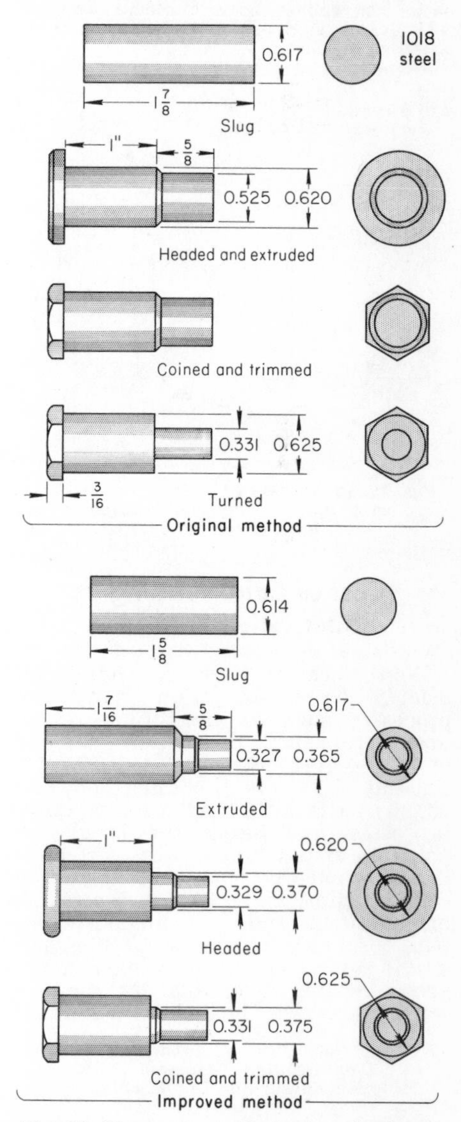

Fig. 24. Change in method of producing a bolt for a lawnmower wheel, in which a turning operation was eliminated by cold extruding the diameter to be thread rolled (Example 666)

By an improved method (Fig. 24), the slug was first extruded to form *two* diameters on the shank end, then headed, coined and trimmed. By this procedure the minor extruded diameter was ready for thread rolling; no turning was required. The improved method not only reduced cost 40%, by eliminating the secondary turning operation, but also produced a stronger part, because flow lines were not interrupted at the shoulder.

Because of the turning operation, production by the original method was only 300 pieces per hour. By the improved method, 3000 pieces could be produced per hour.

Example 667. Combining Extrusion With Heading to Decrease Heading Severity (Fig. 25)

A socket-head cap screw was originally produced by heading 0.915-in.-diam wire in four blows, using four dies.

By an improved method (Fig. 25), the screw was produced by starting with a larger wire (0.990-in. diam), then combining forward extrusion with a heading operation in a first blow and completing the head by backward extrusion in a second blow. Thus, one die and two punches replaced four dies and four punches for a reduction in tool cost of about 50%. The improved method also permitted the part to be processed in a ¾-by-8-in. double-stroke header.

The 0.990-in. starting diameter was cold drawn at the header from hot rolled, lime-coated 4037 steel with soap applied for a drawing lubricant. Molybdenum disulfide paste was applied as a lubricant when the cold drawn stock entered the machine for shearing to length.

Fig. 25. Production of a large socket-head cap screw by extruding and heading in two blows (Example 667)

Cost of Cold Heading vs Alternative Processes

Cold heading, when applicable, usually costs less than competitive processes such as machining or hot heading, for large production quantities or for continuous high production. Tooling for cold heading, however, usually costs more than for competitive processes, and hence the break-even point in quantity depends largely on the difference between tooling cost for cold heading and other processes. In one plant, a study was made to compare costs of producing a specific shape in the same quantity by three different processes. Results of this cost comparison are given in the following example.

Example 668. Cost of Producing Pins by Cold Heading Compared With Machining and Hot Heading (Table 1)

Costs of producing 25,000 pins from 8740 steel by three different methods — machining, hot heading and cold heading — are compared in Table 1. Although tool and setup costs

Table 1. Cost of Producing 25,000 Alloy Steel Pins by Three Different Methods (Example 668)

Item	Machining	Hot heading	Cold heading
Material cost	$295.00	$212.50	$192.50
Tooling cost(a) ...	60.00	90.00	150.00
Setup cost	30.00	35.00	50.00
Production cost ...	382.50	432.50	65.00
Total, 25,000 pcs	$767.50	$770.00	$457.50
Cost per piece	$0.0307	$0.0308	$0.0183
Production, pcs/hr	285	430	5000

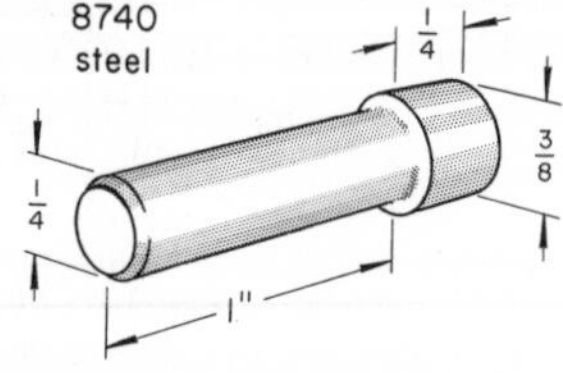

(a) Amortization of machines not included

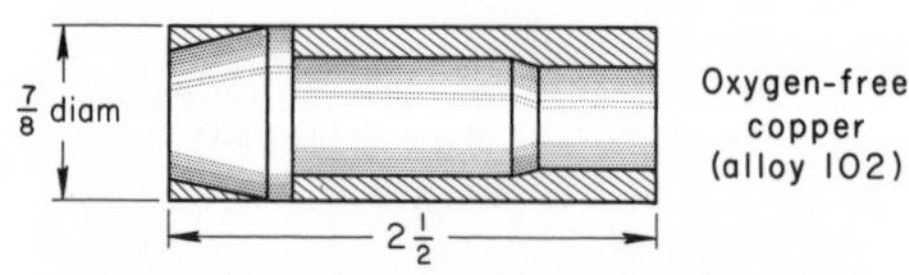

Fig. 26. Nozzle-component blank that was originally produced by machining, but was later cold headed in preference to machining because of the saving in work metal, indicated by shaded area (Example 669)

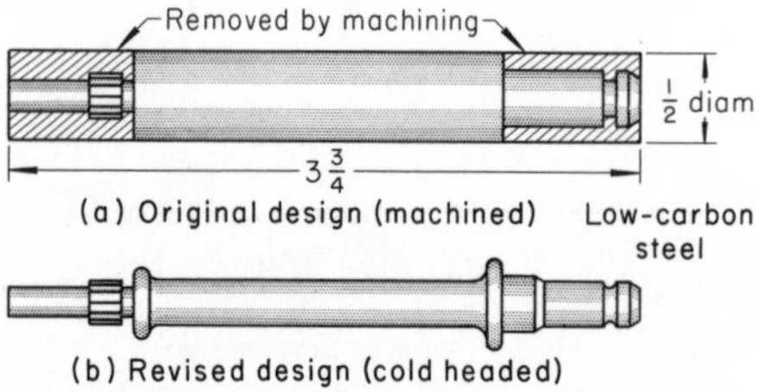

Fig. 27. Spacer stud that was redesigned to permit production by cold heading instead of machining (Example 670)

were greater for cold heading than for the two competitive methods, these higher initial costs were outweighed by the lower costs for material and production when using cold heading. The lower production cost for cold heading resulted from the high production rate. For larger quantities, the cost differential would have increased in favor of cold heading; for smaller quantities, the cost advantage of cold heading would have decreased.

With the more expensive metals, cold heading is often less costly than machining because of the saving in work metal. In the first of the two examples that follow, nozzle components were produced by cold heading with less than half the metal required for machining.

It is sometimes possible to reduce cost by replacing machining with cold heading, provided some change in workpiece design can be tolerated. The second of the two examples that follow describes one such application, in which elimination of some nonworking sections actually resulted in saving material (and weight) without adversely affecting the function of the part.

Example 669. Machining Replaced by Cold Heading, to Save Material (Fig. 26)

A blank for a threaded copper nozzle component (Fig. 26) was originally machined from bar stock. A saving in material of more than 50% (19¢ per piece) was realized by producing the component by cold heading instead of machining. The same shape and dimensional accuracy were produced by both methods. On both the machined and the headed component blanks, threads were rolled in a separate operation.

Example 670. Redesign of a Stud for Cold Heading, to Reduce Costs (Fig. 27)

The spacer stud shown in Fig. 27(a) was produced from bar stock in an automatic bar machine. To reduce costs (production and material), the stud was redesigned for cold heading as shown in Fig. 27(b). This change did not adversely affect the function of the part. The cold headed stud was produced at a saving of $10 per thousand studs.

Warm Heading

In warm heading, a variation of the cold heading process, the work metal is heated to a temperature high enough to increase its ductility. A rise in work-metal temperature usually results in a marked reduction in the energy required for heading the material. Temperatures for warm heading range from 350 to 1000 F, depending on the characteristics of the work metal.

Applications. Although warm heading is occasionally used for producing an upset that would have required a larger machine if the upsetting were done cold, by far the largest use of warm heading is for processing difficult-to-head metals such as austenitic stainless steel. Because they work harden rapidly, austenitic stainless steels are best headed at slow ram speeds.

Table 2 compares tensile and yield strengths and ductility of three austenitic stainless steels and the relatively easy-to-head 1335 alloy steel. Although 1335 steel has higher yield strength and lower ductility (as measured by reduction of area), it is by far the easiest of the four steels listed to cold head, because of its low work-hardening rate compared with that of stainless steel. Data shown in Fig. 28 suggest that speed of the heading punch greatly affects the headability of these stainless steels. According to investigations, 80% of the loss in ductility caused by heading speed can be recovered if the metal is heated to between 350 and 550 F. The increase in headability with increasing temperature is indicated in Fig. 29.

Machines and Heating Devices. Warm heading machines are essentially the same as cold heading machines, except that they are designed to withstand the elevated temperature of the work metal. Auxiliary heating equipment can be a furnace, induction heating coils, or resistance heating elements.

Typically, in furnace-heated warm heading, gas-fired furnaces are used to bring the work metal to the pre-established heading temperature. This type of furnace heating is the simplest method of heating and requires a minimum investment in equipment. Furnaces must be positioned so they can deliver heated stock directly to the stock-feeding side of the header.

By induction heating, the work is heated while being passed through an induction coil. The heated work metal is fed into the machine in the usual way. At least two advantages may be obtained in the use of induction heating for warm heading: (*a*) the work metal never comes in contact with the heating apparatus, and (*b*) induction equipment is readily adaptable to con-

Table 2. Comparison of Room-Temperature Mechanical Properties of Four Annealed Steels

Material	Tensile strength, psi	Yield strength, psi	Reduction of area, %
304 stainless steel	85,000	35,000	70
305 stainless steel	82,000	35,000	73
316 stainless steel	85,000	30,000	70
1335 low-alloy steel ..	75,000	50,000	62

tinuous heating, as for the heating of work metal as it is uncoiled.

The main disadvantage of induction heating is the high initial cost of vacuum-tube or motor-generator equipment. Thus, its use is generally restricted to continuous high production.

Resistance heating has the advantages of simplicity of equipment; accuracy of control; safety, because voltage is low; and adaptability to heating of a continuous length of work metal.

The usual setup for resistance heating employs a second feeder-roll stand similar to that already on the header. The second stand is positioned about 5 ft behind the first, and the wire stock (work metal) is fed through both sets of rolls. Leads from the electrical equipment are attached to the two sets of rolls, and the circuit is completed by the portion of the wire that passes between them. The wire (work metal) then becomes the resistance heater in the circuit. The electrical equipment consists of a transformer, a saturable reactor, a magnetic amplifier, and suitable controls. A sliding thermocouple on the work metal near the feeder rolls controls the current flow in the circuit. After the temperature of the wire stabilizes, it can be held within ±5 F.

Tools. Whether or not the same tools can be used for warm heading as for cold heading depends entirely on the temperature of the tools during operation. Although the tools usually operate at a temperature considerably lower than that of the work metal, it is important that the tool temperature be known. Tool temperature can be checked with sufficient accuracy by means of temperature-sensitive crayons. Under no circumstances should the tool be allowed to exceed the temperature at which it was tempered after hardening. This tempering temperature is usually 300 F for carbon tool steel such as W1 or W2. Tools made from a high-alloy tool steel, such as D2, ordinarily should not be permitted to operate above 500 F.

When tool temperatures exceed those discussed above, the use of tools made from a hot work tool steel, such as H12, is appropriate. However, the lower maximum hardness of such a steel somewhat limits its resistance to wear.

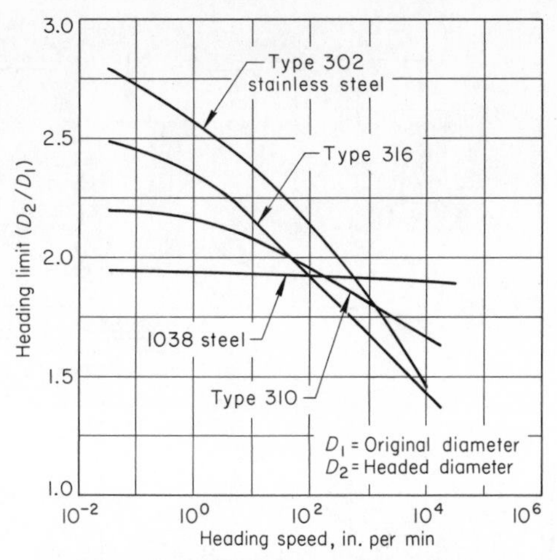

Fig. 28. Effect of heading speed on heading limit for three stainless steels and 1038 carbon steel

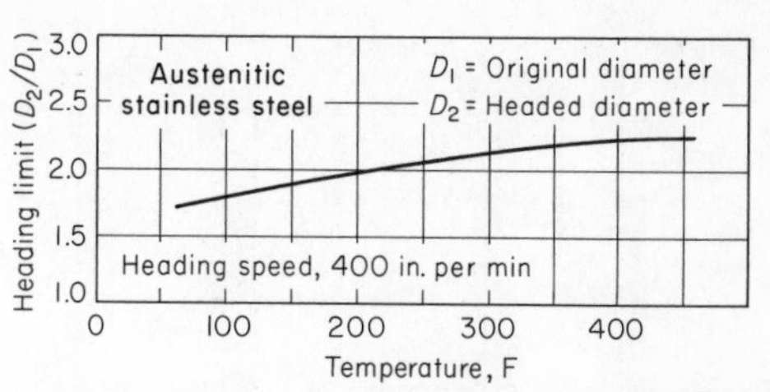

Fig. 29. Effect of work-metal temperature on the heading limit of austenitic stainless

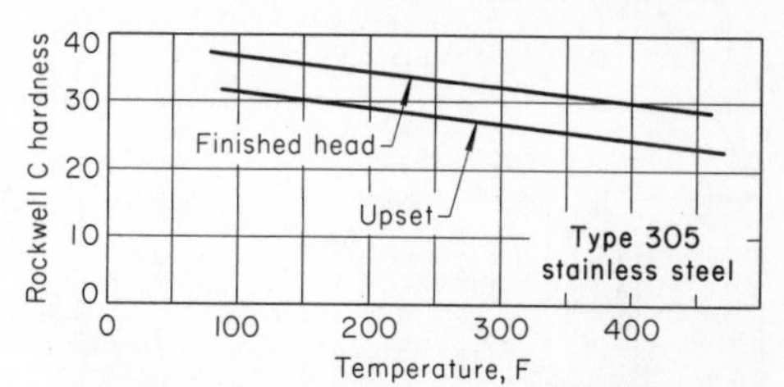

Fig. 30. Effect of heading temperature on hardness of upset portion and finished head of type 305 stainless steel flat-head machine screws

A high speed tool steel such as M2 will provide the high hardness and the resistance to tempering needed for long tool life.

Other Advantages of Warm Heading. As heading temperature of a work-hardenable material increases, the resulting hardness decreases, as shown in Fig. 30. Therefore, if a material is headed warm, the hardness will remain low enough to permit secondary operations like thread rolling, trimming, drilling and slotting.

In cold heading, the upset head of a work-hardening metal is very hard, a rolled thread is moderately hard, and the undeformed shoulder is relatively soft. By warm heading, these differences can be minimized.

Cold Extrusion

*By the ASM Committee on Cold Extrusion**

COLD EXTRUSION is so called because the slug or preform enters the die at room temperature or at a temperature appreciably below the recrystallization temperature. Any subsequent rise in temperature, which may amount to several hundred degrees Fahrenheit, is caused by friction during deformation. Cold extrusion involves backward or forward, or combined backward-and-forward, displacement of metal by plastic flow under steady, though not uniform, pressure. Backward displacement from a closed die is in the direction opposite to punch travel, as shown in Fig. 1(a). Workpieces are often cup-shaped and have wall thickness equal to the clearance between the punch and die. In forward extrusion, the work metal is forced in the direction of the punch travel, as shown in Fig. 1(b). Sometimes these two basic methods of extrusion are combined so that some of the work metal flows backward and some forward, as shown in Fig. 1(c).

In cold extrusion, a punch applies pressure to the slug or preform, causing the work metal to flow in the required direction. The relative motion between punch and die is obtained by attaching either one (almost always the die) to the stationary bed and the other to the reciprocating ram. The axis of the machine can be vertical or horizontal. The pressure may be applied rapidly as a sharp blow, as in a crank press or header (impact extrusion), or more slowly by a squeezing action, as in a hydraulic press.

The pressure exerted by the punch may be as low as 5000 psi, for soft metals, or as high as 450,000 psi, for severe extrusion of alloy steel.

Work Hardening of Metals. Metals are work hardened when deformed at temperatures below their recrystallization temperatures. This can be an advantage if the service requirements of a part allow its use in the as-formed condition. (Under some conditions, heat

*D. A. WILKINSON, *Chairman,* Chief Metallurgist, Saginaw Steering Gear Div., General Motors Corp.; C. R. BRADLEE, Chief Engineer – Press Machinery, Waterbury Farrel, a Textron Co.; A. G. FORREST, Chief Metallurgist, Republic Steel Corp.

ROBERT D. GOODWIN, Superintendent – Tool Manufacturing, Delco Products Div., General Motors Corp.; ROBERT D. HARGESHEIMER, Supervisor – Manufacturing Research, Saginaw Steering Gear Div., General Motors Corp.; G. S. HAUSER, Supervisor, Metal Forming Section, Mechanical Engineering Dept., Ford Motor Co.; H. G. JOHNSTIN, Chief Metallurgist, Vasco, a Teledyne Co.

H. N. MEYER, Assistant Chief Metallurgical Engineer, Bethlehem Steel Corp.; R. W. PERRY, Manager – Cold Forming, Parker Rust Proof Div., Hooker Chemical Corp.; N. L. WARD (formerly Chief Process Engineer, Sintered Products and Cold-Prest Div., Mueller Brass Co.).

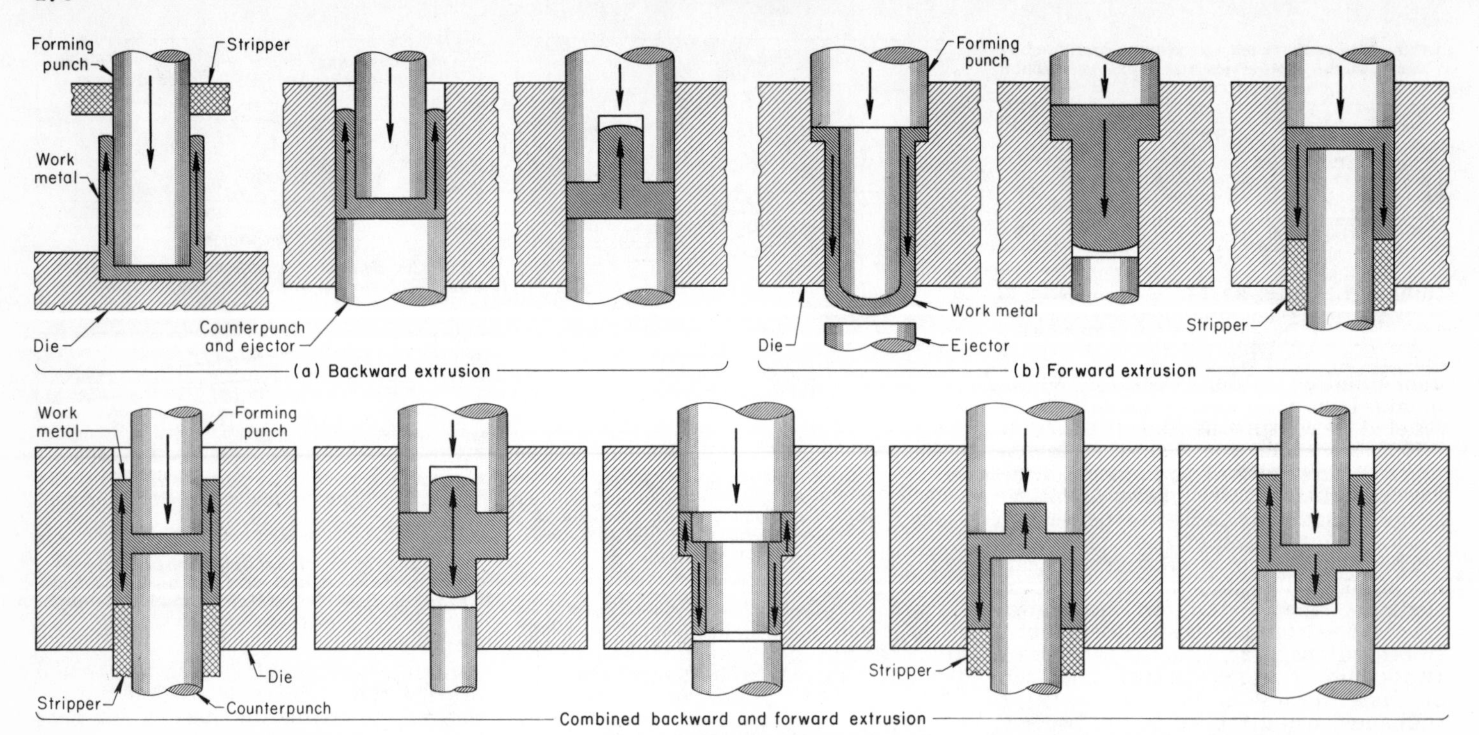

Fig. 1. Displacement of metal in cold extrusion: (a) *backward,* (b) *forward, and* (c) *combined backward and forward*

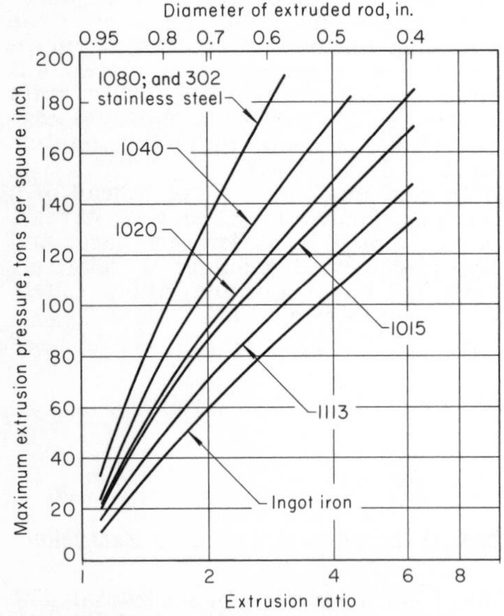

Conditions. Slug size, 1 in. in diameter by 1 in. long; slug condition, annealed; die profile, square entry, 0.050-in. radius; speed, 10 strokes per minute; lubricant, zinc phosphate and molybdenum disulfide in alcohol. (Extrusion pressures based on long tons — 2240 lb.)

Source of Data. H. Ll. D. Pugh, M. T. Watkins and J. McKenzie, *Sheet Metal Industries,* 38, Apr 1961, 253-279.

Fig. 2. Effect of reduction (extrusion ratio) on maximum pressure required for extruding rods from ingot iron and six steels

treatment is not needed.) Work hardening, however, raises the ratio of yield strength to tensile strength and lowers ductility. Therefore, when several severe cold extrusion operations follow one another, ductility must be restored between operations by annealing. Scale formed during annealing must be removed by blasting or pickling before subsequent extrusion.

The effect of cold extrusion on the hardness across a section of extruded steel is described in the section on Extrusion Ratio in this article.

In spite of the high pressure applied to it, the metal being extruded is not compressed to any measurable amount. Except for scale losses in annealing or the inadvertent formation of flash, constancy of volume throughout a sequence of operations is assured. For all practical purposes, volumetric calculations can be based on the assumption that there is no loss of metal.

Metals Cold Extruded. Aluminum and aluminum alloys, copper and copper alloys, low-carbon and medium-carbon steels, modified carbon steels, low-alloy steels, and stainless steels are the metals most commonly cold extruded. The above listing is in the order of decreasing extrudability.

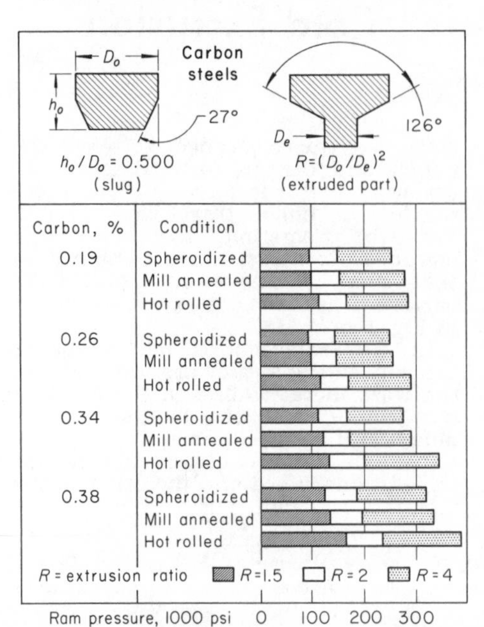

Fig. 3. Effect of carbon content, type of annealing treatment, and extrusion ratio on maximum ram pressure in forward extrusion of the carbon steel part shown from the preformed slug shown

Equipment and tooling are basically the same regardless of the metal being extruded (see relevant sections on equipment and tooling in this article). However, processing data given in this article are confined mainly to the cold extrusion of steel. Processing information on aluminum and copper is given in the articles on Cold Extrusion of Aluminum Alloy Parts, and Cold Extrusion of Copper and Copper Alloy Parts, both in this volume. For an application of cold extrusion of a cylindrical container from a magnesium alloy, see Example 609 on page 430.

Cold Extrusion vs Alternative Processes. Cold extrusion competes with other metal forming processes such as hot forging, hot extrusion, and machining, and sometimes with casting. Cold extrusion is used when the process is economically attractive because of:

1. Savings in material
2. Reduction or elimination of machining and grinding operations, because of good surface finish and dimensional accuracy of cold extruded parts
3. Elimination of heat treating operations, because of increase in the mechanical properties of cold extruded parts.

Although cold extrusion sometimes is used for producing only a few parts of a kind, it usually is confined to mass production — mainly because of the high cost of tools and equipment.

Extrusion Ratio

Extrusion ratio is determined by dividing the original area undergoing deformation by the final deformed area. The following calculations show how the ratio is determined for both backward and forward extrusion.

Calculation 1. If a 1-in.-diam slug is forward extruded into a ½-in.-diam product, the extrusion ratio is determined by dividing the area of a 1-in. diameter (0.7854 sq in.), which is the area undergoing deformation, by the area of a ½-in. diameter (0.1963 sq in.), which is the deformed area, thus giving an extrusion ratio of 4 to 1 (usually expressed as 4).

Calculation 2. In backward extruding a 1-in.-diam solid cylindrical slug to produce a tubular section having 1-in. OD and ½-in. ID (¼-in. wall), the extrusion ratio is calculated by dividing the area of the 1-in. OD (0.7854 sq in.) by the annular area of the 1-in. OD (the area undergoing deformation), which is determined by subtracting the area of a ½-in. ID (0.1963 sq in.) from the area of the 1-in. OD, or 0.5891 sq in. Thus, the extrusion ratio is 1.33 to 1 (0.7854 sq in. divided by 0.5891 sq in.).

Calculation 3. Assuming that a tubular section of 1-in. OD and ½-in. ID (¼-in. wall) is to be extruded to a section having ½-in. OD and ¼-in. ID (⅛-in. wall), the extrusion ratio is calculated by dividing the annular area of the 1-in.-OD tube (0.7854 sq in. minus 0.1963 sq in., or 0.5891 sq in.) by the annular area of the ½-in. tubular section (0.1963 sq in. minus 0.0492 sq in., or 0.1471 sq in.). The extrusion ratio is thus 4 to 1.

In all of the above calculations relating to cylindrical sections, the squares of the respective diameters may be substituted for areas, when convenient (see Fig. 3 and 4).

Because volume remains constant during extrusion, the extrusion ratio may also be calculated by increase in length. An extrusion ratio of 4 to 1 indicates that the length has increased by a factor of four.

The metal being extruded has a large effect on the maximum ratio that is practical. Some typical approximate maximum extrusion ratios are: 40 for 1100 aluminum alloy, 5 for 1018 steel, and 3.5 for type 305 stainless steel.

Extrusion pressure increases with extrusion ratio, as shown for six steels and ingot iron in Fig. 2. The data presented in Fig. 3 show that extrusion ratio has a larger effect on ram pressure than either carbon content or type of annealing treatment, in forward extrusion of carbon steel. The charts in Fig. 4 show the effect of tensile strength on extrudability in terms of ram pressure for both backward and forward extrusion of low-carbon and medium-carbon steels of the 1000, 1100, and 1500 series at different extrusion ratios.

Extrusion Ratio vs Work Hardening. Because an increase in extrusion ratio results in a corresponding increase in the amount of cold deformation, the effects of work hardening normally will vary directly with extrusion ratio.

The data in Fig. 5 illustrate the increase in hardness that resulted from the forward extrusion of three annealed slugs, two of 5120 steel and one of 8620 steel, varying in diameter and length, to form three steering gear components. In general, the hardness of these steels increased from approximately Rockwell 15-T 85 to 86 to Rockwell 15-T 92.5 for extrusion ratios ranging from 1.82 to 3.03. Within this range, the effect of an increase in extrusion ratio on hardness was slight, and the distribution of hardness across the sections of extruded parts (from surface to center) was notably uniform for all extrusion ratios and both materials. As Fig. 5(b) shows, an increase in section from slug to finished part, although small, entailed enough cold working to produce some increase in hardness. Although the total alloy content of 8620 steel exceeds that of 5120 steel, differences in their response to cold working, based on hardness, were not significant.

For data on the changes in tensile properties of the work metal during cold extrusion, see Example 679.

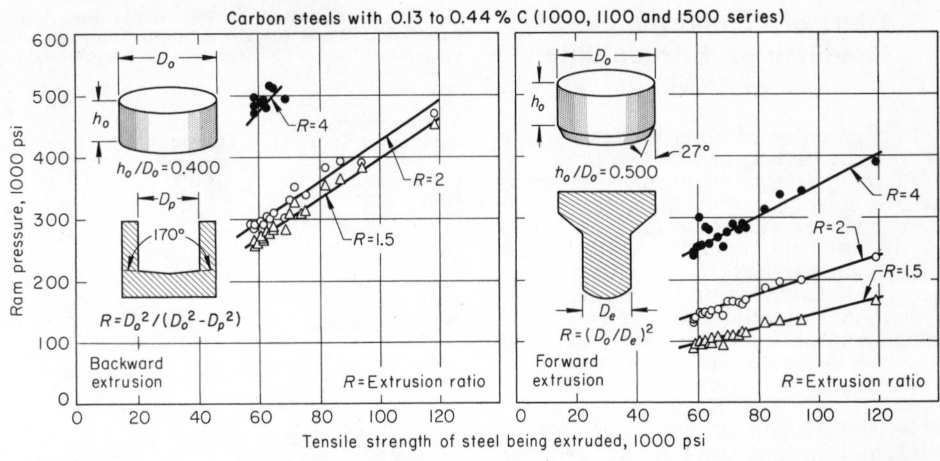

Fig. 4. Effect of tensile strength of steel being extruded on ram pressure required for backward and forward extrusion at different ratios

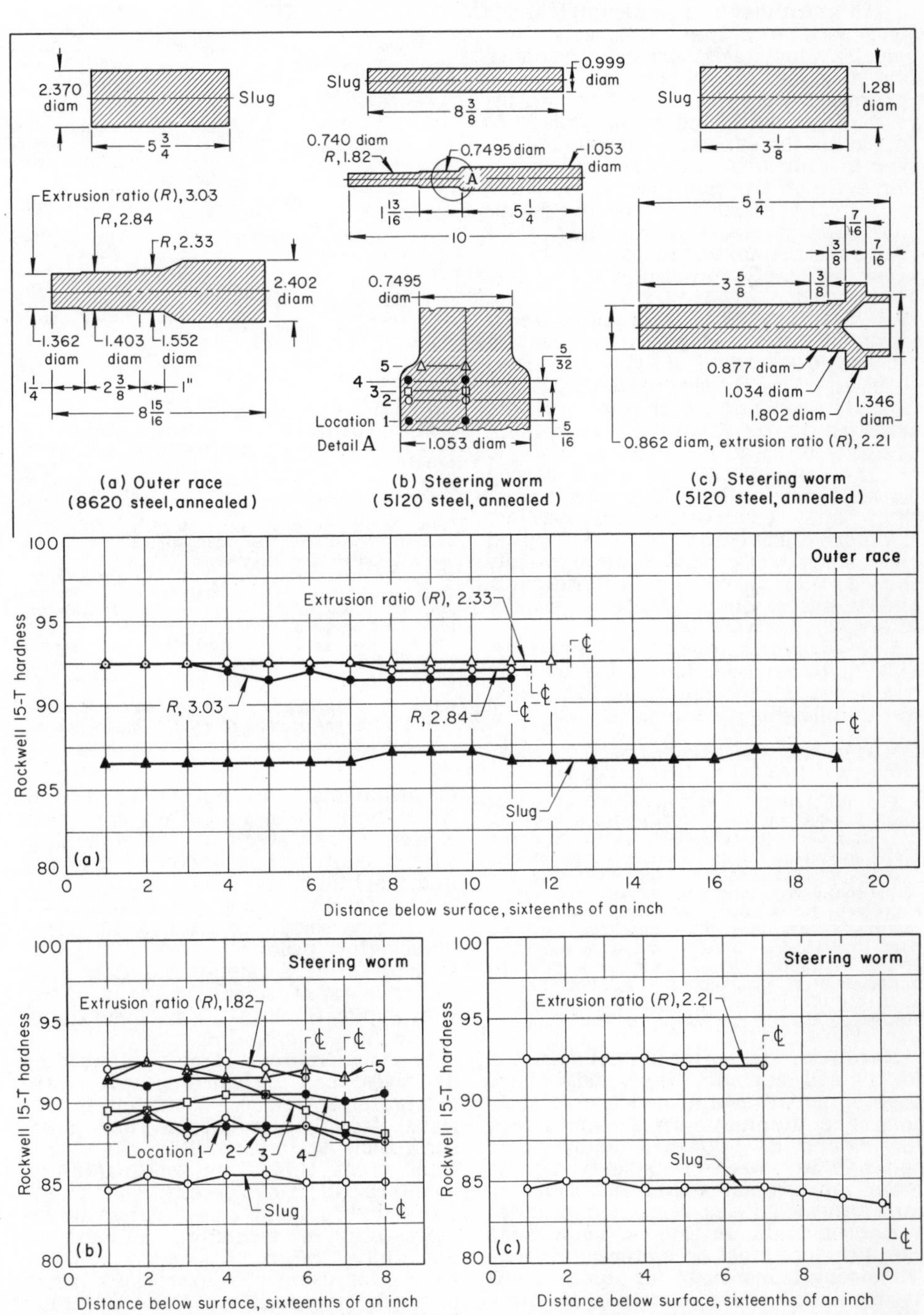

Fig. 5. Effects of forward extrusion at several extrusion ratios on the hardness and distribution of hardness in three cold extruded steering-gear components

Effect of Composition and Condition on Extrudability of Steel

Extrudability of steel decreases with increasing carbon or alloy content. Extrudability is also adversely affected by greater hardness. Free-machining additives such as sulfur or lead are likely to impair extrudability. Nonmetallic inclusions, particularly the silicate type, are also detrimental to extrudability.

Carbon Content. Cold extruding of steels containing up to 0.45% carbon is common practice, and steels with even higher carbon content have been successfully extruded. However, it is advisable to use steels of the lowest carbon content that will meet service requirements. Most carbon and alloy steels extruded have a carbon content of 0.10 to 0.25%. Although in some applications steels with more than 0.45% carbon (especially alloy steels) are cold extruded, this is seldom practical.

Figure 3 shows the results of an investigation conducted in one plant to determine the effects of carbon content, type of annealed structure, and extrusion ratio on the ram pressure required to forward extrude a specific shape from carbon steels. These data show that ram pressures are essentially the same for steels containing 0.19% and 0.26% carbon, regardless of the other variables, but that ram pressure is markedly increased as carbon content reaches 0.34% and 0.38%. The steel slugs (see Fig. 3) were coated with zinc stearate over zinc phosphate and were extruded under laboratory conditions, at a rate of 25 in. per minute.

Alloy Content. For a given carbon content, most alloy steels are harder than plain carbon steels and therefore are more difficult to extrude. Also, most alloy steels work harden more rapidly than do their carbon steel counterparts, and therefore they sometimes require intermediate annealing.

Low-carbon stainless steels are more difficult to extrude than plain low-carbon steels. This is shown in Fig. 2 and in the following example:

Example 671. Extrudability of 1022 Steel vs 305 Stainless Steel (Table 1)

The difference in extrudability between a plain low-carbon steel (1022) and a low-carbon stainless steel (type 305, with 0.12% max C) is shown in Table 1 by the comparison of punch pressure required for extruding the same shape from the two metals. The shape, a preform for a headed fastener, was forward extruded from 0.340-in.-diam stock in one blow to 0.240-in. diam, for an area reduction of approximately 50%. Extrusions of both materials were produced in the same header at a rate of 150 pieces per minute. Additional processing details are given in Table 1.

Hardness. The softer a steel, the easier it will extrude. Steels that have been spheroidize-annealed are in their softest condition and are thus preferred for extrusion. Figure 3 shows that spheroidized steels were extruded at lower ram pressures than hot rolled or mill-annealed steels, regardless of other variables. Data in Fig. 4 show that ram pressure must be increased as tensile strength increases for steels of low to medium carbon content, at three different extrusion ratios. However, operations that precede or that follow

Table 1. Comparison of Punch Pressure and Other Conditions for Extruding a Shape From 1022 Steel and 305 Stainless (Example 671)

Item	1022 steel	305 stainless
Steel hardness	R_B 70	R_B 93
Coating	Lime and soap(a)	Flash copper(a)
Punch load, lb	14,280	18,700
Punch pressure, psi	162,000	213,000
Punch material	M2	M2
Die material	Carbide	Carbide
Tool life, pieces	1,000,000	600,000

1022 steel or type 305 stainless steel; 1.18; 0.340 diam; 0.240; 0.40

(a) A water-soluble lubricant with extreme-pressure additives was applied at the header.

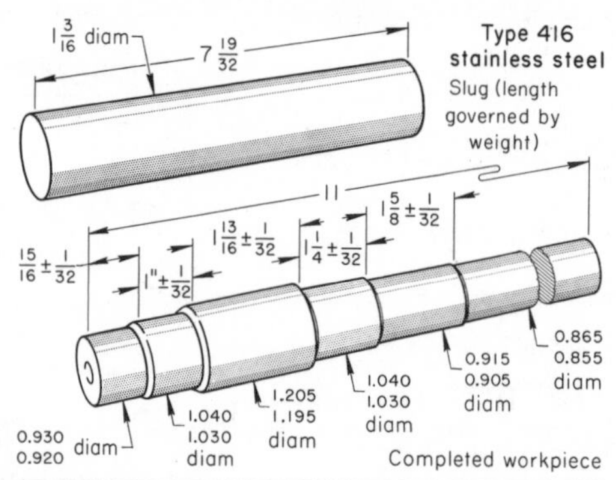

Press	Hydraulic, 140-ton(a)
Die	Two-station
Tool material	H21 or 6H2 steel(b)
Slug	Sawed and phosphated(c)
Lubricant	Soap
Tool life	15,000 to 20,000 pieces(d)
Production rate	160 pieces per hour

(a) Equipped with two hydraulic cylinders — one small cylinder for fast approach and one large cylinder for extrusion. (b) Inserts only. Main die parts were made of 4147 steel or resulfurized 4150. Carbide inserts were used for runs of 50,000 to 75,000 pieces. (c) Proprietary phosphating bath used. (d) For H21 or 6H2 inserts; average life of carbide inserts ranged from 50,000 to 75,000 pieces.

Fig. 6. Propeller shaft that was cold extruded in preference to machining because of less metal waste (Example 672)

extrusion may make it impractical to have the steel in its softest condition. Extremely soft steels of low to medium carbon content have poor shearability and machinability, and thus, for practical reasons, some extrudability is sometimes sacrificed. Annealing techniques that produce a partly pearlitic structure, with a corresponding increase in hardness, are ideal for many extrusion applications in which shearability or machinability is important.

Free-machining steels, containing additives such as lead and sulfur, are not preferred for cold extrusion. Extrusions from these steels are more susceptible to defects than are extrusions from their non-free-machining counterparts. Also, because parts produced by cold extrusion generally require only a minimum amount of machining (often, this is the primary reason for using cold extrusion), there is much less need for free-machining additives than when parts are produced entirely by machining.

Whether or not free-machining steels can be successfully extruded depends on the amount of upset, the flow of metal during extrusion, and quality requirements of the extruded part. Free-machining steels, as a rule, can withstand only the mildest upset without defects developing. If it is under compression at all times during flow, a free-machining steel probably will extrude without defects. However, if compressive force is suddenly changed to tensile force, rupture is likely.

The amount or nature of the machining operations following extrusion sometimes makes it desirable to extrude free-machining steels. One plant reports the use of leaded 1045 for a forward extruded part that includes a mild upset; 1106 steel also has been cold extruded with considerable success. The next example describes extrusion of a free-machining stainless steel.

Example 672. Cold Extrusion of a Propeller Shaft From Free-Machining Stainless Steel (Fig. 6)

Production of the 416 stainless steel propeller shaft shown in Fig. 6 by cold extrusion followed by partial machining cost less than machining the shaft from bar stock, because of the saving in metal used. The bar stock used when each piece was completely machined weighed 3.51 lb; the extrusion weighed 2.32 lb.

The shafts were extruded from slugs sawed from hot rolled bar stock of forging quality. The extrusions had a surface finish of less than 50 micro-in. Diameters were held to ±0.005 in. and straightness to 0.010 in. TIR. (All shafts were inspected for straightness.)

Final machining and spline rolling were done before the shafts were heat treated. Only 6.7 oz of metal was machined from each extrusion. Heat treatment developed a minimum hardness of Rockwell C 40.

Some shafts cracked during extrusion because of the sulfur content of the steel, which made it free-machining. However, the rejection rate was kept below 0.2% by close control of the process, including annealing practice. Additional processing details are given in the table that accompanies Fig. 6.

Nonmetallic Inclusions. The fewer the inclusions, the more desirable the steel for cold extrusion. Silicate inclusions have been found to be the most harmful. Therefore, some steels have been deoxidized with aluminum rather than silicon in an attempt to keep the number of silicate inclusions at a minimum. The aluminum-killed steels have better extrudability in severe applications.

Extrusion Quality

Carbon steel bars are available at extra cost in two classes of extrusion quality — cold extrusion quality A and cold extrusion quality B. Mill preparation of cold extrusion quality A is by the same procedure as used for special quality bars; cold extrusion quality B is a still higher quality.

Higher quality refers primarily to fewer external and internal defects. Hot scarfing and more rigorous inspection of the billets are additional operations performed at the mill to prepare cold extrusion quality B material.

Alloy steel without a quality extra is used in applications similar to those of cold extrusion quality A for carbon steel. Alloy steels are also available as cold heading quality, which parallels cold extrusion quality B for carbon steel. Boron-modified steels for heading and extrusion are also available.

Whether or not it is advisable to pay the extra cost for cold extrusion quality B or cold heading quality steel depends on the severity of extrusion, quality requirements of the extruded part, and the cost of rejected parts in comparison with the extra cost for these steels.

Severity of extrusion refers mainly to the extrusion ratio. If the ratio is low and the work metal is kept under compression during flow, it is unlikely that cold extrusion quality B steel will be beneficial. On the other hand, if the ratio is high (as in Fig. 21 and 22) or the work metal is in tension at times during metal flow, cold extrusion quality B steel should be considered.

The cold extrusion of many parts entails both extrusion and upsetting. Of the two operations, upsetting is the more critical, and the severity of the upset should determine the quality of steel required.

The over-all quality requirements of the finished part must be considered. Sometimes minor defects are acceptable in the finished part, or they may be removable in normal machining.

Presses and Headers

Hydraulic presses, mechanical presses, special knuckle-joint presses for cold extrusion, special cold forging machines, and cold heading machines are employed for cold extrusion. Most presses used for cold extrusion are essentially the same as those used for sheet metal forming (see the article beginning on page 1 in this volume).

Most cold extrusion operations are performed on mechanical presses or cold heading machines. Of the two, mechanical presses are used more often, because of their adaptability to other types of operations. Mechanical presses are generally less costly and are capable of higher speeds than are hydraulic presses of similar capacity. Also, in many applications, the sharp blow of a mechanical press is preferred to the slower squeezing action of a hydraulic press. A disadvantage of a mechanical press is its limited length of stroke.

A cold heading machine combines the essential features of a mechanical press with mechanisms that feed in bar stock, shear slugs, and transfer the slugs to the die and then to other dies if required. Disadvantages of a cold heading machine are limited capacity and the higher degree of skill required for tooling.

Although representing only a small fraction of the total number of presses used for cold extrusion, hydraulic presses are especially well suited to the production of parts requiring long working strokes. For example, the 20-in.-long aluminum alloy part shown in Fig. 7 was extruded in an 800-ton hydraulic press.

Proper selection of the press is important for successful cold extrusion and to prevent excessive maintenance charges. Mechanical presses must have (*a*) adequate horsepower; (*b*) sufficient flywheel energy (insufficient energy results in overloading and heating of the motor); (*c*) sufficient torque capacity in the drive mechanism to deliver the necessary force at the required point above the bottom of the stroke; and (*d*) rigid structural members to prevent excessive deflection under concentrated loading.

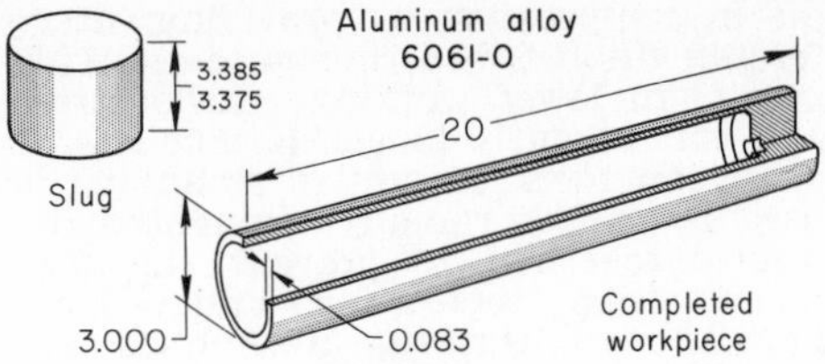

Aluminum alloy 6061-O

Slug 3.385 3.375

20

3.000 0.083 Completed workpiece

Fig. 7. Long slender part that was extruded in a hydraulic press because of the long working stroke required

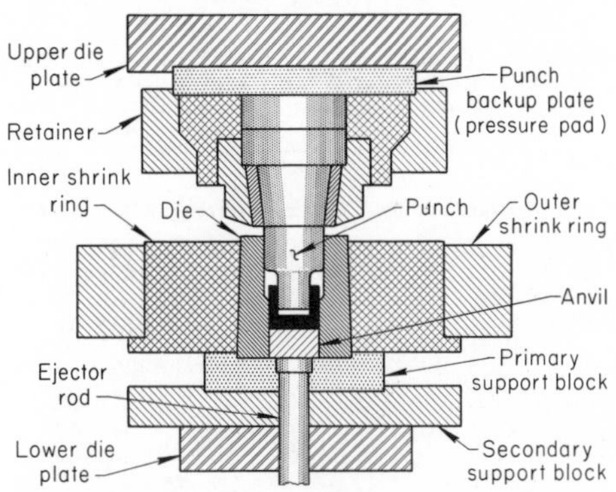

Fig. 8. Nomenclature of tools comprising a typical setup for backward extrusion of steel parts

Power Requirements. Because of work-metal and tool variables, data resulting from laboratory studies of power requirements for cold extrusion are not generally applicable to shop practice. The following rules can be used as guides in estimating pressure, force and horsepower requirements:

1. Determine the effective contact area of the forming tool. In backward extrusion, this area is the cross-sectional area of the punch tip. For forward extrusion, the effective contact area is the annular area of the die shoulder.
2. Determine the extrusion ratio and ascertain that the ratio is within practical limits (see the section on Extrusion Ratio in this article).
3. Consider the tool materials used. Properly supported punches and dies made of tool steel can be operated at peak pressures as high as 350,000 psi. Carbide punches can be operated at peak pressures up to 400,000 psi and carbide dies at 450,000 psi.
4. Extrusion forces can be safely estimated as the product of effective contact area, as determined in item 1 above, and the peak allowable stress, as indicated in item 3 above. The condition of the press equipment, tools, and work material, the design of the tools, and the lubricant used, all affect the maximum extrusion ratio obtainable in a particular operation.
5. The energy required is calculated as the product of extrusion force and distance over which it must act to form the part. The horsepower required can be calculated from this energy and the frequency at which the energy is to be delivered.
6. At operating speed, flywheel energy must be four to ten times that required per stroke for extrusion; the exact multiple depends on cycle time and type of motor.

The estimation of power requirements on the basis of extrusion ratio is one of several methods. Other methods, generally more complex, consider the influence of several interrelated variables, including properties of the metal to be extruded, size and shape of the part, thickness of the wall to be produced (or reduction of area), temperature, effect of lubrication, blank shape and thickness, and grain size and orientation. For a discussion of alternate methods, see especially references 1, 2, 4 and 5 at the end of this article.

Tooling*

Knowledge of the forces acting on tool components is not always a matter of certainty, and the design of tools is more often dictated by the dimensions of the part to be formed than by considerations of metal flow, lubrication, and other processing variables. Knowledge of the mechanical properties and load-carrying abilities of tool steels is limited, and safety factors for many items of tooling are often unknown.

Although many engineering components are, or can be, designed to last indefinitely, this is seldom true in the design of highly-stressed, "consumable" tools for cold extrusion, where a tool life of 100,000 pieces is likely to be considered above average. On the other hand, conventional design criteria are applicable to the less highly stressed, "nonconsumable" tools for extrusion. Accordingly, it is convenient to distinguish between consumable tooling components, such as punches and dies, and nonconsumable ones, such as shrink rings, ejectors, and pressure pads.

Estimation of Load. Knowledge of the forces or pressures required for forward or backward extrusion is essential in design, both with regard to determining tool stresses and in selecting suitable press equipment. Methods for estimating these requirements, including a method based on extrusion ratio, are discussed in the section of this article on Power Requirements. The pressure to be applied is a function of the deformation resistance and degree of deformation. Deformation resistance, in turn, is affected by the composition, mechanical properties, and condition of the work material, the external frictional forces applied, and the size and shape of both the initial slug and the finished workpiece. According to H. D. Feldmann and H. K. F. Honnens (reference 6), practical experience has shown that for the tool steels and carbides now in use, the specific forming pressure at the punch should not exceed about 344,000 psi and the die internal pressure should not exceed about 275,000 psi. If the estimated pressures exceed these limits, either the degree of deformation must be reduced or a considerably shorter tool life must be accepted.

The consumable tools — namely, the punch, die, and ejector — make direct contact with the metal to be extruded. These tools are exposed to a specific load and to wear. Their design should incorporate features that will conform to the design requirements of the workpiece, while minimizing specific load and wear. It is usually possible to design tools that will satisfy both objectives by facilitating the flow of metal and reducing losses due to internal and external friction.

Tool-Assembly Components. The components of a typical tool assembly used for backward extrusion of steel parts are identified in Fig. 8. There is considerable variation in tooling prac-

*This section is based, in part, on tooling recommendations given in references 6 and 13, listed at the end of this article.

tice and in the design details of tool-assembly components. Some of the principal factors affecting the design of punches and dies for backward and forward extrusion are discussed below, and in references 4, 5, 6, 9, 10, 12, 13, 14, and 15 at the end of this article.

Punch Design. A major problem in punch design lies in assessing the nature and magnitude of the stresses to which the punch is subjected in service. Because the stresses are dynamic, fatigue effects will arise, and these, in conjunction with the inherently brittle nature of hardened tool steels, necessitate care in avoiding design features likely to give rise to stress concentrations. Stability problems that may arise when slender punches are used will be affected by the accuracy of alignment provided by the tool set or by the press itself, or by factors in the extrusion operation, such as punch wander, initial centering, and use of distorted slugs. The ratio of punch length to punch diameter is also a factor affecting stability, and for the cold extrusion of steel with tool steel punches, a ratio of about 3 to 1 is probably the maximum. The ratio can be increased somewhat by using a punch material that has a high modulus of elasticity, such as tungsten carbide.

Design of the punch nose has a significant effect on extrusion pressures and tool life. In backward extrusion, a nose profile consisting of a truncated cone having an included angle of 170° to 180°, with an edge radius of 0.020 to 0.100 in., and a land length of 0.050 to 0.075 in. with the shank relieved 0.004 to 0.008 in. on the diameter gives acceptable results. Although they reduce initial punch stresses, small cone angles or large radii are undesirable because of rapid lubricant depletion and the risk of metal-to-metal contact. Design of the punch nose to properly distribute the lubricant during extrusion is essential for minimizing the pressures developed.

The area ratio between punch shank and head is also an important design factor. A large ratio will have the effect of spreading the punch load over a large area of pressure pad. On the other hand, it will require a wider block of metal for its fabrication with consequent increase in cost and inferior metallurgical properties, unless the punch is forged to shape. Because pressure pads are less expensive than punches, it is generally advisable to favor the smaller ratios. The pressure pad, which transmits the load from the back of the punch to the die set, should be designed for economy, ease of replacement, and efficiency in reducing the number of punch failures.

Die Design. In reducing and forward extrusion, the die is under maximum pressure, and this pressure is not distributed uniformly. Thus, the tool designer must calculate what the tensile stresses on the inner die wall will be and provide adequate reinforcement. Ordinarily, pressures of less than about 138,000 psi do not require reinforcement, while those in excess of about 220,000 psi do.

To provide reinforcement, extrusion dies are usually inserted in one or more shrink rings. These rings prestress the die in compression by providing interference fits between rings and die. This results in lower working tensile stress and consequently longer fatigue life of extrusion tools. A similar technique is used to shrink radially segmented die inserts together, to prevent the segments from separating under load. Permanent shrink-fit assemblies are sometimes made by heating the outer ring to facilitate assembly. Interchangeable die inserts are usually force fitted mechanically, using a tapered

Table 2. Recommended Tool Materials for Backward Extrusion of Parts 1 and 2(a)

Tool	Number of parts to be extruded: 5,000	50,000
Carbon Steel, to 0.40 C; Carburizing Alloy Steels		
Punch	M2, M3, M4	M3, M4
Die	M2, M3, M4	M4, carbide
Ejector rod	A2	A2, D2
Anvil	M2, M3	M2, M3
Aluminum Alloys		
Punch	A2	A2, D2
Die	W1(c)	W1(d)
Ejector rod	A2	D2

NOTE — Where more than one tool material is recommended for the same conditions, the materials are given in the order of ascending cost, with the least expensive material being presented first.

Part 1 Part 2

(a) For part 1, starting with a solid slug; for part 2, starting with part 1. In aluminum, part 2 can be made directly from a cylindrical blank. (b) For longer runs, see discussion of carbide in text. (c) Liquid nitrided. (d) The 1.00% C grade is recommended.

press fit and molybdenum disulfide as a lubricant. Of the two methods, shrinking-on by heating is generally preferred, because a cylindrical hole and shaft are easier to fabricate than a tapered hole and shaft. However, a taper fit has several advantages, notably:

1 The hardness and yield strength of the various die components are not affected by heating and can be measured with dependable accuracy.
2 The prestress value is assured by strict control of the input measurements.
3 Release and exchange of the inner die bushings is quick, easy and inexpensive.
4 Die parts can be standardized.
5 Hot working die steels are not required.
6 A die reinforced by taper fit has optimum load capacity.

The most commonly used taper angle is ½° to 1°. Conditions for obtaining the specified advantages of the taper force fit are careful preparation of the

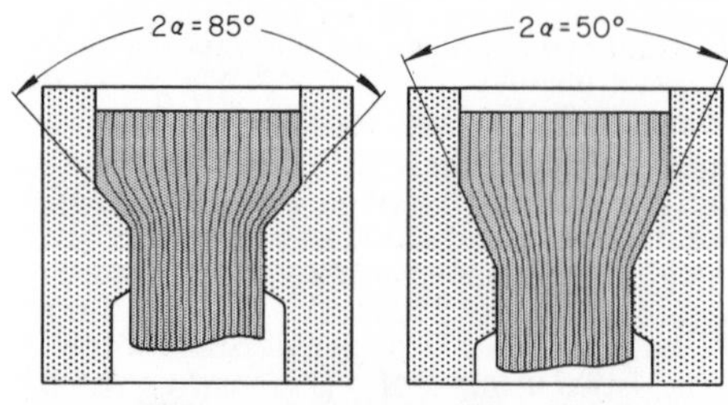

Fig. 9. Measurement of die angle in dies for forward extrusion

Table 3. Recommended Tool Materials for Forward Extrusion of Part 3(a)

Tool	Number of parts to be extruded: 5,000	50,000	Extruded part
Carbon Steel, to 0.40 C; Carburizing Alloy Steels			
Punch	M2, M3, M4	M4	
Die	M4	Carbide	
Aluminum Alloys			
Punch	A2	D2	
Die	W1(b)	A2, D2	

(a) Starting with part 2 (Table 2) for steel, or with a cylindrical slug for aluminum alloys. (b) The 1.00% C grade is recommended.

Table 4. Recommended Tool Materials for Forward Extrusion of Part 4

Tool	Number of parts to be extruded: 5,000	50,000	Extruded part
Carbon and Alloy Steels, to 0.40 C			
Punch	M2, M3, M4	M4	
Die	M2, M3, M4	Carbide	
Ejector	A2, T15	A2, T15	
Aluminum Alloys			
Punch	A2	D2	
Die	A2	A2	

Table 5. Recommended Tool Materials for Forward Extrusion of Part 5 From a Ring-Shape Blank

Tool	Number of parts to be extruded: 5,000	50,000	Extruded part
Carbon and Alloy Steels, to 0.40 C; Series 300 Stainless Steels			
Punch	M2, M3, M4	M4	
Die	M2, M3, M4	Carbide	
Ejector rod	S1, T15	S1, T15	
Aluminum Alloys			
Punch or die	A2	D2	
Ejector rod	S1, T15	S1, T15	

taper shell surfaces and exact agreement between taper angles of corresponding contact faces. If the shell surfaces do not provide uniform support over the entire die length, the prestresses will be unequal and the reinforcement will not be fully effective.

In some setups, the first reinforcement is applied by taper force fit and the second (outer) reinforcement by shrinking-on. It is advisable to standardize on the size of reinforcing elements. In general, no further advantage is gained by making the outer diameter of a reinforcement more than four to five times the die diameter.

Because notch effect adversely influences die life, effort should be made to eliminate or lessen it by die design, steel selection, and heat treatment. If some notch effect is unavoidable, dies should be divided into two or more parts. Dies must be firmly seated and supported to eliminate bending stresses.

In forward extrusion, die angles are determined by the shape of the workpiece and by the operating sequence. In general, an angle of $2\alpha = 24°$ to $70°$ (see Fig. 9) is selected for the forward extrusion of solids, and an angle of $2\alpha = 60°$ to $126°$ is preferred for extruding hollow parts, the angle varying inversely with wall thickness. Ejection pressure on the work increases with decreasing die angle, because greater friction must be overcome. This pressure also increases

Table 6. Recommended Steels for Secondary Tooling Components Used in Extruding the Five Parts Shown in Tables 2 to 5(a)

Part number	Type of extru-sion	Inner shrink ring	Outer shrink ring	Primary support block	Secondary support block	Upper die plate	Lower die plate	Punch backup plate
1, 2 (Table 2)	Bwd ..	S4, S5	1040	W2	W2	1040	1040	S1
3 (Table 3)	Fwd ..	S4, S5	1040	W2	W2	1040	1040	S1
4 (Table 4)	Fwd ..	4340(b), H12	W2, H12	S4, S5	D4	W2	W2	8620(b)
5 (Table 5)	Fwd ..	4340(b), H12	W2, H12	S4, S5	D4	W2	W2	8620(b)

(a) See Table 7 for nominal compositions of the steels, and Fig. 8 for identification of the various tooling components. (b) Or other alloy steel having sufficient hardenability for the component.

Table 7. Nominal Compositions of Steels Used for Cold Extrusion Tools

Steel	Composition
Tool Steels	
W1	0.60 to 1.40 C(a)
W2	0.60 to 1.40 C(a), 0.25 V
W3	0.60 to 1.40 C(a), 0.50 V
S1	0.50 C, 1.50 Cr, 2.50 W
S2	0.50 C, 1.00 Si, 0.50 Mo
S4	0.55 C, 0.80 Mn, 2.00 Si
S5	0.55 C, 0.80 Mn, 2.00 Si, 0.40 Mo
O1	0.90 C, 1.00 Mn, 0.50 Cr, 0.50 W
A2	1.00 C, 5.00 Cr, 1.00 Mo
D2	1.50 C, 12.00 Cr, 1.00 Mo
D4	2.25 C, 12.00 Cr, 1.00 Mo
M2, class 1	0.85 C, 4.00 Cr, 2.00 V, 6.25 W, 5.00 Mo
M3, class 1	1.05 C, 4.00 Cr, 2.50 V, 6.25 W, 5.75 Mo
M4	1.30 C, 4.00 Cr, 4.00 V, 5.50 W, 4.50 Mo
T15	1.55 C, 4.50 Cr, 5.00 V, 12.50 W, 5.00 Co
H12	0.35 C, 5.00 Cr, 0.40 V, 1.50 W, 1.50 Mo
H21	0.35 C, 3.50 Cr, 9.50 W
6F3 mod(b)	0.55 C, 1.0 Cr, 2.70 Ni, 0.45 Mo, 0.10 V
6F5(b)	0.55 C, 1.0 Mn, 1.0 Si, 0.50 Cr, 2.70 Ni, 0.50 Mo, 0.10 V
6G mod(b)	0.35 C, 0.75 Cr, 0.45 Mo, 0.45 W
6H2(b)	0.55 C, 1.10 Si, 5.0 Cr, 1.50 Ni, 1.50 Mo, 1.0 V
L6	0.70 C, 0.75 Cr, 1.50 Ni, 0.25 Mo
Carbon and Alloy Steels	
1040	0.40 C, 0.75 Mn
4340	0.40 C, 1.80 Ni, 0.80 Cr, 0.25 Mo
8620	0.20 C, 0.50 Ni, 0.50 Cr, 0.20 Mo

(a) Various carbon contents are available in 0.10% ranges between 0.60 and 1.40%C. (b) Not an AISI designation.

with an increase in the length of the part. Extrusion pressure causes elastic expansion of the die, which shrinks when the pressure is discontinued. Accordingly, very high wall pressures are developed, and these require correspondingly high ejection pressures.

Tooling Setups. Metals may be cold extruded by different tooling setups, depending mainly on the size and shape of the workpiece, composition of the work metal, and quantity requirements. Principal types of tooling employed and examples of products formed by each type are as follows:

Single-station tooling forms the part in one stroke of the press. Additional operations may be required for finishing. Closed-end containers, such as toothpaste tubes, are formed in this manner.

Multiple-station tooling involves a series of separate dies so arranged that the rough blank is made into a preform, which then proceeds through successive operations (usually, but not necessarily, in separate presses) until the required form is produced.

Multiple-station tooling is often used for semicontinuous operations, because of the need for annealing, pickling and lubrication between operations, although it is also adaptable to continuous operations utilizing a transfer mechanism (as in Example 679). This procedure has also been used in cold forming of 75-mm and 155-mm shell bodies involving backward and forward extrusion.

Transfer presses are similar to multiple-station tooling. For instance, a transfer press may shear, preform, extrude, and finish draw the part in consecutive operations. Mechanical fingers transfer the workpiece from one operation to the next. Pole pieces for alternator rotors have been produced in transfer presses. (See Examples 674 and 685.)

Upsetters or headers are used for continuous operation, frequently incorporating both backward and forward extrusion, and cold heading. Fasteners such as hexagonal socket-head cap screws are typical examples of parts produced in upsetters. (See Examples 671, 673, 681 and 682.)

Rotating dial or indexing can be applied for manual or automatic production. In operation, the table of the press holding the dies indexes and the head containing the punches remains stationary except for vertical movement. Slugs may be fed automatically, and one or more parts may be formed with each stroke of the press. Instrumentation stops the operation immediately in the event of misalignment, punch breakage, or a wrong-size slug. Gear extrusions are representative examples of parts produced in this type of tooling, at the rate of two extrusions for each press stroke. (See Example 675.)

Tool Materials

Compressive strength of the punch and tensile strength of the die are important considerations when selecting material for cold extrusion tools. Because the die is invariably prestressed in compression by the pressure of the inner and outer shrink rings, the principal requirement for a satisfactory die is a combination of tensile yield strength and prestressing that will prevent failure. Punches must have enough compressive strength to resist upsetting without being hazardously brittle. Thus, almost without exception, and particularly for extruding steel, the primary tools in contact with the workpiece must be made of steels that will harden through the section in the sizes involved. (This is notably different from cold heading tools, for which a hard case and soft core are usually desired.) Among the relatively few exceptions are small dies made of a water-hardening tool steel and bore quenched. As the bore hardens, the remainder of the die cools and shrinks, placing the bore in compression.

The degree of strength required for the tools is influenced by workpiece shape, composition and hardness of the metal being extruded, and production requirements.

Punches, Dies and Ejectors. Tables 2 through 5 list tool materials recommended for punches, dies, ejector rods, and anvils for several typical parts. In Table 2, the extrusion operations are similar in severity when part 1 is made from a cylindrical slug and part 2 is made from part 1. (In aluminum, part 2 can be made in a single step directly from a cylindrical blank.) The recommendations for dies to extrude these parts from steel are conservative.

In one application, there was a marked difference in punch wear in extruding steel parts similar to parts 1 and 2, with as much as four times greater wear for part 2. In this application, carbide punches lasted for as many as 300,000 pieces. Also, steel rocket heads have been extruded with carbide punches greater than 3 in. in diameter. Quantity of parts to be produced and the dimensional tolerances are more important than tool size in making a decision to use a carbide, instead of a tool steel, punch, provided the punch can be suitably supported.

Table 3 lists the materials recommended for tooling for the forward extrusion of part 3 from part 2 in Table 2. (In aluminum, part 3 could be made directly from a solid cylindrical slug.) In forward extrusion, the work metal moves over the die much farther than over the punch, and normal wear of the die is more rapid. In this operation, no ejector is required, because the part is stripped from the punch on the return stroke.

Table 4 recommends tool materials for forward extruding part 4. The shape of the die for this part may cause several problems: Because of residual stress from heat treatment, there may be local stress at corners; because of the corners, there may be discontinuity of loading stress; and because of extra frictional surface, more pressure may be required for extruding the part.

Table 5 recommends tool materials to forward extrude part 5 from a ring-shape blank. Thin-wall parts such as this require extremely high extrusion pressure, and dies are made of M2, M3 or M4 tool steel, or of carbide, for extruding such parts from steel.

Rings, Blocks and Plates. Typical constructional and tool steels used for secondary die components for extruding parts shown in Tables 2 through 5 are given in Table 6.

Inner shrink rings have a highly finished (8 to 10 micro-in.), slightly tapered bore into which the die is press fitted and thereby subjected to compressive prestressing, which counteracts the subsequent tensile stress during extrusion. Inner shrink rings are made from low-alloy or medium-alloy steels, or H12 tool steel, quenched and tempered to about Rockwell C 50 to withstand service stress without permanent deformation.

Outer shrink rings are usually made of a medium-carbon steel, such as 1040 or 1045, or of H12 or a high-carbon tool steel, depending on workpiece shape and method of extrusion (backward or forward).

Design and material for support blocks depend on the severity of the operation and the type of press equipment. Tool steels or alloy steels of sufficient hardenability to resist service stress without permanent deformation are required for this purpose.

Materials for upper and lower die plates are selected to resist the deforming pressures involved in the tooling design for a particular operation. Table 6 reflects the moderate severity of die-plate requirements involved in extruding parts 1, 2 and 3 and the higher severity involved in producing parts 4 and 5.

Compositions of constructional and tool steels recommended in Tables 2 through 6 are given in Table 7.

Preparation of Slugs

Preparation of slugs often represents a substantial fraction of the cost in producing cold extruded parts.

Producing the Slug Shape. Table 8 lists the methods commonly used for cutting or otherwise producing the slug, and gives the advantages and disadvantages of each method. Despite the loss of metal, sawing and cutting off in a machine such as an automatic bar machine are extensively used for producing slugs, because of the need for dimensional accuracy, freedom from distortion, and minimum work hardening.

Shearing is an economical means of producing slugs, and is often used when its disadvantages (Table 8) can be tolerated. Variation in size of the slugs is a major disadvantage of shearing. If slugs are allowed to vary in size, die design must be such as to allow escape of excess metal in the form of flash. An alternative to die adjustment that is feasible in some applications is to compensate for the distortion and other discrepancies in sheared slugs by coining the slugs to desired dimensions.

Hot rolled bar is usually the least costly form of steel for making slugs, but hot rolled bars are likely to have deeper surface seams and greater depth of decarburized layers than some other product forms. Also, the variation in the outside diameter of hot rolled bars will cause considerable variation in weight or volume of the slug, despite close control in cutting to length. Whether or not the surface seams and decarburization can be tolerated depends largely on the severity of extrusion and the quality requirements of the extruded part. In many applications, acceptable extrusions can be produced with slugs cut from hot rolled bars.

Variation in outside diameter of slugs cut from hot rolled bars can be compensated for by (*a*) grading the bars for size, and varying the length of cut inversely with the square of the diameter; or (*b*) grading the cut slugs by weight, and adjusting tools accordingly.

Cold finished bars cost more than hot rolled bars. Variation in size of cold finished bars is considerably less, and they undergo less distortion in shearing. However, some seams and decarburization will also be present in cold finished bar stock unless they are removed by grinding, turning, or other means. Some plants gain the advantage of cold drawn bars by passing hot rolled bars or rods through a cold drawing attachment immediately ahead of the slug-cutting operation.

Machined or ground bars are more costly than cold drawn bars, but eliminate the difficulties caused by decarburization, seams and variation in outside diameter. For some extrusions, especially those subjected to surface treatments that cannot tolerate a decarburized layer, requirements are such that previously machined bars or machined slugs must be used.

Surface Preparation of Steel Slugs. Phosphate coating for cold extrusion is almost universal practice. The main purposes of this coating are to form a nonmetallic separating, or antiflux, layer between the tools and workpiece and, by reaction with or absorption of the lubricant, to prevent its migration from bearing surfaces under high unit pressures. During extrusion, the coating flows with the metal as a tightly adherent layer.

Table 8. Advantages and Disadvantages of Commonly Used Methods for Producing Slugs for Cold Extrusion

Method of producing	Advantages	Disadvantages
Sawing from bar stock	Ends are square Outside diameter is symmetrical Work hardening is nominal	Loss of metal Burrs must be removed Operation is slow Much floor space required
Cutting off in an automatic bar machine	Ends are square Outside diameter is symmetrical Work hardening is nominal	Loss of metal Burrs must be removed Operation is slow Much floor space required
Blanking from plate	Useful when ratio of length to diameter is small	Metal loss is high Some work hardening occurs
Using a cast preform	Desired shape can be cast	Generally less extrudable than wrought metals
Shearing in a press	No loss of metal Operation is fast	Size is difficult to control Slug is distorted Ends are work hardened Length must exceed diameter (for minimum distortion)
Shearing and upsetting in a press	No loss of metal Operation is fast	Slug is work hardened Slug is imperfectly filled out
Shearing and heading in a header	No loss of metal Operation is fast Wire or cold drawn bars usable	Slug is work hardened Diameter is limited to 1¼ in.

The recommended preparation of steel slugs for extrusion consists of the following steps:

1. **Alkaline cleaning,** to remove oil, grease and soil from previous operations, so that subsequent pickling will be effective. Alkaline cleaning may be done by spraying the slugs with a heated solution (150 to 160 F) for 1 to 2 min or by immersing them in solution at 190 to 210 F for 5 to 10 min.
2. **Water rinsing,** to remove residual alkali and prevent neutralizing of acid pickling solution. Normally, slugs are rinsed by being dipped in overflowing hot water, but they may also be sprayed with hot water.
3. **Acid Pickling.** Most commercial installations use a sulfuric acid solution (10% by volume) at 140 to 190 F. Pickling may be by spraying for 2 to 15 min or by immersion for 5 to 30 min, depending on surface conditions (generally, the amount of scale). These time cycles usually are sufficient to remove all scale and permit a good phosphate coating. The use of bright annealing or mechanical scale removal, such as shot blasting, as a substitute for pickling has proved unsatisfactory for severe extrusion. However, the use of a mechanical scale-removing method prior to pickling can reduce pickling time, and for producing extrusions of mild severity, the mechanical (or bright annealing) methods have often been used without subsequent pickling.
4. **Cold and hot water rinsing** may be by immersion or spraying for ½ to 1 min for each rinse. Two rinses are used to insure complete removal of residual pickling acid and of iron salts. Cold water rinsing is usually of short duration, with heavy overflow of water to remove most of the residual acid. Hot water at about 160 F increases the temperature of the workpiece and insures complete rinsing.
5. **Phosphate coating** is by immersion in zinc phosphate at 160 to 180 F for 3 to 5 min. (See the article "Phosphate Coating", page 531 in Volume 2 of this Handbook.)
6. **Rinsing** with cold water, applied by spraying for ½ min or by immersion for 1 min, removes the major portion of residual acids and acid salts left over from the phosphating solution. This rinse is followed by a neutralizing rinse, applied by spraying or immersion for ½ to 1 min, using a well-buffered solution (such as sodium carbonate), which must be compatible with the lubricant. In the second rinse, the remaining residual acid and acid salts in the porous phosphate coating are neutralized so that absorption of, or reaction with, the lubricant is complete.

Direct cold extrusion of coiled steel wire or rod, a procedure similar to cold heading, is sometimes used for producing small parts. The coils of wire or rod can be prepared in a manner similar to that discussed above. A lime coating on the coil stock has been used instead of the zinc phosphate coating, but it is less effective. Lubricants for zinc phosphated coil stock may be applied by immersion or may be drawn onto the coated surface during sizing.

Stainless steels are not amenable to conventional phosphate coating (which is one reason why stainless steels are more difficult to extrude than carbon steels); copper plating of stainless steel slugs is preferred. Lime coating is sometimes substituted successfully for copper plating. In extreme cases, the stainless steel can be zinc plated, then coated with zinc phosphate and a suitable soap lubricant.

Methods of surface preparation that apply to copper and aluminum slugs are referred to on page 494 in the article "Cold Extrusion of Copper and Copper Alloy Parts" and on page 491 in the article "Cold Extrusion of Aluminum Alloy Parts" in this volume.

Lubricants for Steel

For extruding of steel, a soap lubricant gives best results. Slugs are immersed in a dilute (6 to 16 oz per gallon) soap solution at 145 to 190 F for 3 to 5 min. Some soaps are formulated to react chemically with the zinc phosphate coating, resulting in a layer of water-insoluble metal soap (zinc stearate) on the surfaces of the slugs. This coating has a high degree of lubricity and maintains a film between the work metal and tools at the high pressures and temperatures developed during extrusion.

Other soap lubricants, such as high-titer sodium tallow soaps, with or without filler additives, can be used effectively for mild extrusion of steel. This type of lubricant is absorbed by the phosphate coating, rather than reacting with it.

Although the lubricant obtained by reaction of soap and zinc phosphate is best for extruding steel, its use demands precautions. If soap builds up in the dies, workpieces will not completely fill out. Best practice is to vent all dies so that the soap can escape, and also to keep a coating of mineral seal oil (applied as an air-oil mist) on the dies to prevent adherence of the soap.

When steel extrusions are produced directly from coiled wire (similar to cold heading), the usual practice is to coat the coils with zinc phosphate, using the procedure outlined in the section on Preparation of Slugs. This practice, however, has one deficiency; because only the outside diameter of the work metal is coated, the sheared ends are uncoated at the time of extrusion. This deficiency is partly compensated for by constantly flooding the work with sulfochlorinated oil. Because the major axis of a heading machine is usually horizontal, there is less danger of entrapping lubricant than when extruding in a vertical press.

Cleaning the extruded parts can be a significant item in the cost of cold extrusion. In general, the more effective the lubricant, the more difficult it is to remove. Methods used for removing pigmented drawing compounds are usually effective for removing lubricants used for cold extrusion (see the article "Selection of Cleaning Process", which begins on page 307 in Volume 2 of this Handbook).

Selection of Procedure

Shape of the part is usually the major factor that determines the procedure used for extrusion. For instance, many cuplike parts are produced by backward extrusion, whereas shaftlike parts and hollow shapes can usually be produced more easily by forward extrusion. For many shapes both forward and backward extrusion are used.

Other factors influencing procedure are composition and condition of the steel, required dimensional accuracy, quantity, and cost.

Simpler procedures can be used for extruding a given shape from steels that have maximum extrudability than from steels that are more difficult to extrude. For difficult steels, it may be necessary to incorporate more passes and one or more annealing operations in the process. Some shapes may not be completely extrudable from a difficult-to-extrude steel; one or more machining operations may be required.

Normal extrusion procedures are associated with certain ranges of dimensional accuracy (see the section on Dimensional Accuracy, page 488 in this article). Special procedures and controls can provide greater-than-normal accuracy at higher cost.

Cold extrusion ordinarily is not considered unless a large quantity of identical parts must be produced. The process is seldom used for fewer than 100 parts, and more often it is used for hundreds of thousands of parts or continuous high production. Quantity requirements determine the degree of automation that can be justified and often determine whether the part will be completed by cold extrusion (assuming it can be if tooling is sufficiently elaborate) or whether, for low quantities, a combination of extruding and machining will be more economical.

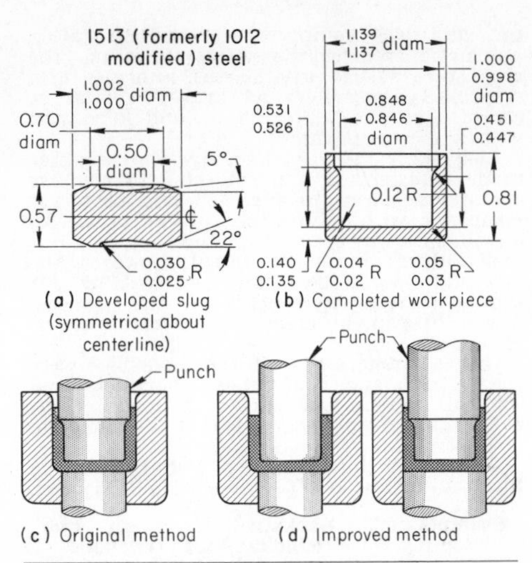

Press	Two-point mechanical, 500-ton(a)
Die	Dial type
Slug	Sheared, headed and phosphated
Lubricant	Soap
Tool material(b)	Carbide
Punch strokes per minute	30
Production rate	2 pieces per stroke
Punch life:	
Original method	75,000 pieces
Improved method	1 million pieces
Die life	2 million pieces

(a) Press had a 30-ton air cushion. (b) Punch and die insert.

Fig. 10. (a) Slug for producing a cup for a universal-joint bearing. (b) Extruded cup. (c) Original method (one operation). (d) Improved method (two operations). (Example 673)

Cost per part extruded usually decides (*a*) the degree of automation that can be justified; (*b*) whether a combination of extruding and machining should be used for low-quantity production; and (*c*) whether it is more economical to extrude parts for which better-than-normal dimensional accuracy is specified or to attain the required accuracy with secondary operations. Sometimes it is possible to extrude a given shape by two or more different procedures (see Example 678). Under these conditions, cost is usually the deciding factor.

Several procedures for extruding specific steel parts, categorized mainly by part shape, are discussed in the six sections that follow.

Cuplike Parts

The basic shape of a simple cup is often produced by backward extrusion, although one or more operations such as piercing or coining are frequently included in the operations sequence. For cuplike parts that are more complex in shape, a combination of backward and forward extrusion is more often used.

The four examples that follow describe applications in which various techniques were used for producing cuplike parts by cold extrusion.

Example 673. Increase in Punch Life by Extruding in Two Operations Instead of One (Fig. 10)

The bearing cup shown in Fig. 10(b) was originally produced by machining from 1117 steel in an automatic bar machine. Machining was replaced by cold extrusion, because the quantity requirements for these cups (continuous high-volume production) warranted the capital expenditure for cold extrusion tooling — which lowered the cost per piece.

The developed slug, shown in Fig. 10(a), was produced from cold extrusion quality 1513 (formerly, 1012 modified) steel coiled rod, drawn to 0.755-in. diam in a cold drawing attachment to the heading machine.

Slugs were sheared from the rod and headed in one blow to the shape shown, at a rate of 180 per minute. Slugs were then washed and grit blasted, and annealed in a controlled atmosphere at 1325 F for 4 to 5 hr; they were then treated in zinc phosphate and lubricated with a soap compound. Slugs were fed from a hopper equipped with an elevating feeder through an automatic weighing device and into the press.

Original extrusion tooling included a carbide punch designed to form the part in one operation, as indicated in Fig. 10(c). This punch had an average life of 75,000 pieces; the punch failed by breaking at the counterbore diameter. To increase the life of the punch, extrusion was done in two operations, as shown in Fig. 10(d). The first punch extruded the cup, after which a second punch formed the counterbore. Service life of each carbide punch thereby increased to about one million pieces. Additional processing details are given in the table that accompanies Fig. 10.

Example 674. Production of Ball-Joint Housings by Backward Extrusion, Drawing, Piercing, Coining and Restriking (Fig. 11)

The ball-joint housing shown in Fig. 11 was made from 1513 (formerly, 1012 modified) steel of cold extrusion quality. Slugs were sheared from hot rolled bars 1⅜ in. in di-

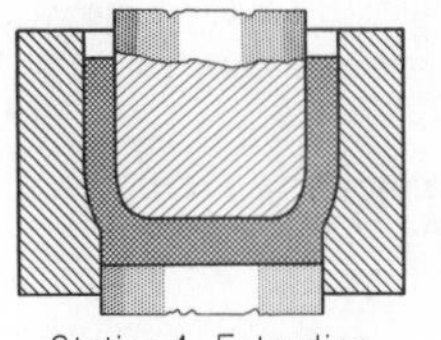

Station 2 Draw wiping

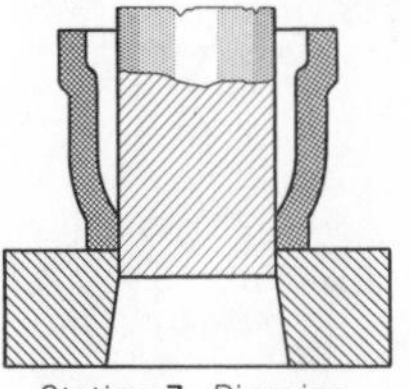

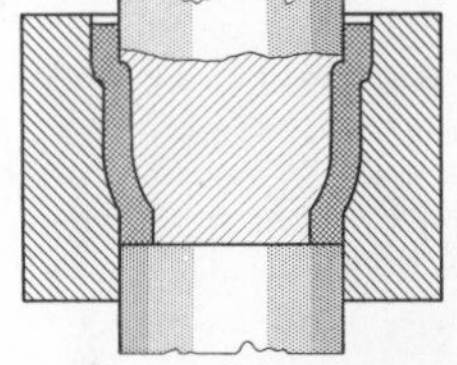

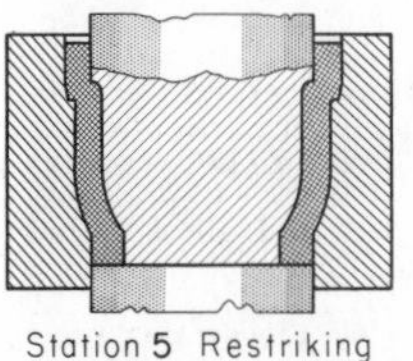

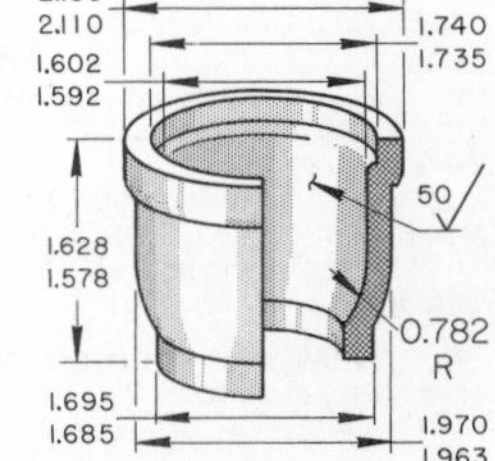

1513 (formerly 1012 modified) steel

Press	Two-point mechanical, 1000-ton(a)
Die	Five-station transfer
Tool material	(See punch and die life, below)
Slug	Sheared and phosphate coated
Lubricant	Soap
Extrusion pressure	700 tons
Punch strokes per minute	26
Setup time	8 hr
Production rate	1560 pieces per hour
Punch life, pieces:	
Station 1 (carbide)	200,000
Station 2 (M4)	500,000
Station 3 (M2)	1,000,000
Station 4 (M4)	400,000
Station 5 (M4)	1,000,000
Die life, pieces:	
Station 1 (carbide)	500,000
Station 2 (carbide)	500,000
Station 3 (D2)	1,000,000
Station 4 (M4)	1,000,000
Station 5 (M4)	1,000,000

(a) Bolster, 84 by 48 by 10 in.; 12-in. stroke

Fig. 11. Production of a ball-joint housing in five operations (Example 674)

ameter and 15 ft long that had been shot blasted, cold drawn, and machine straightened.

The slugs were sheared in a 150-ton single-point mechanical press operating at 40 strokes per minute. An automatic scale checked the slugs for correct weight of 260 ± 2 grams each, after which they were transferred from a hopper equipped with an elevating feeder into a 1000-ton knuckle-joint press, where they were upset. This press had a 50-ton air ejector, and was equipped with a two-station automatic transfer die. After upsetting, the slugs were washed, grit blasted, annealed in a controlled atmosphere at 1325 F for 5 hr, cooled, zinc phosphate coated, and lubricated with a soap compound.

Slugs were then fed to a five-station automatic transfer die and subjected to the five operations shown in Fig. 11; one part was completed with each stroke of the press. An air-oil mist was sprayed on the dies to minimize buildup of soap lubricant; however, the dies still had to be cleaned every 8 hr. Air sensing devices were used on the transfer fingers to stop the press when a part was out of position.

Critical dimensions of the housings were the outside and counterbore diameters and the ball radius. The surface formed by the ball radius required a finish of 50 micro-in. or better.

Previously, these housings had been made in an automatic bar machine from 1117 steel.

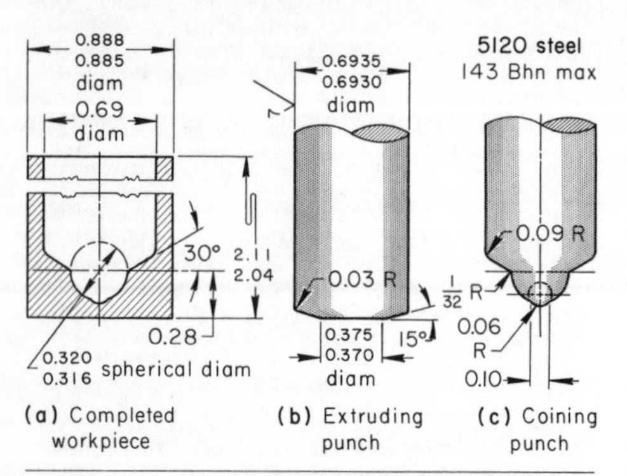

Press	Double crank; straight-sided mechanical, 400-ton
Die	Revolving dial transfer type
Tool material(a)	Carbide (13% cobalt)
Slug	Sawed, tumbled and phosphated
Lubricant	Soap
Punch strokes per minute	25
Production rate, avg	2000 pieces per hour(b)
Punch life	40,000 pieces
Die life	300,000 pieces

(a) Punch and die. (b) 3000 per hour at 100% efficiency.

Fig. 12. Valve tappet produced by extrusion and coining with punches shown (Example 675)

Example 675. Backward Extrusion and Coining for Producing Valve Tappets (Fig. 12)

The valve tappet shown in Fig. 12(a) was made from fine-grained, cold heading quality 5120 steel. Slugs were prepared by sawing to a length of 1.020 to 1.025 in. from bar stock 0.867 to 0.871 in. in diameter. Slugs were tumbled to round the edges, then phosphated and lubricated with soap.

The slugs were fed automatically into the two loading stations of the eight-station dial, then extruded, coined and ejected; one part was produced in each set of four stations (two parts per stroke). This technique helped to keep the ram balanced, thus avoiding tilting of the press ram, prolonging punch life, and reducing eccentricity between the outside and inside diameters of the extruded part. An eccentricity of less than 0.010 in. TIR was required. The cup could not be extruded to finished shape in one hit, because a punch of conelike shape would pierce rather than meter-out the phosphate coating. Therefore, two hits were used, the first to extrude and the second to coin. Punches are shown in Fig. 12(b) and (c). Pressure on the punch (axial) was about 320,000 psi. Additional processing details are given with Fig. 12.

Saving material is often a major reason for using cold extrusion instead of an alternative process such as machining, particularly for cuplike parts:

Example 676. Stock Saving of 84% by Changing From Machining to Cold Extrusion (Fig. 13)

The switch body shown in Fig. 13 was originally produced in an automatic bar machine from cold drawn hexagonal bars of 1116 steel. For each part, 0.404 lb of steel was used. At $0.12 per pound for the 1116 steel bar stock, material cost per piece was $0.048.

By cold extruding the switch body from hot rolled 1008 rimmed steel, only 0.064 to 0.065 lb of steel per piece was required; the steel cost only $0.08 per lb, and so material cost per piece was $0.005. Thus, the change in method resulted in a steel saving of 84% by weight and an 89% reduction in steel cost.

The slug used for cold extruding was formed in a heading machine to the shape shown in Fig. 13. After forming, the slug was annealed at 1320 F for 4 hr and cooled rapidly; it was then zinc phosphate treated and lubricated with soap before being backward and forward extruded in a mechanical press in one stroke. Conditions for extrusion are given in the table that accompanies Fig. 13.

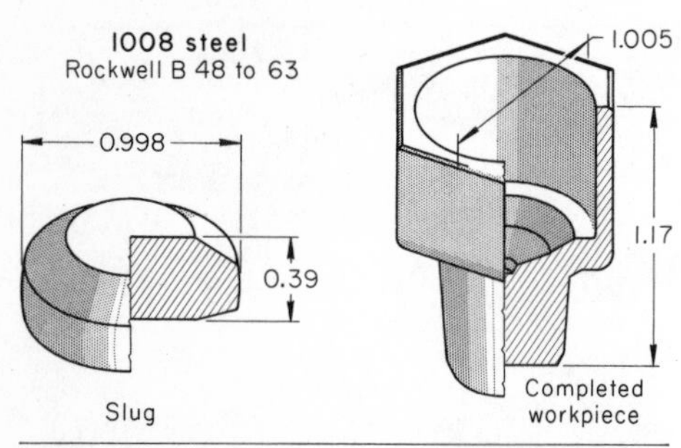

Press	Mechanical, 125-ton(a)
Die	Two-station transfer die
Punch material	Carbide (13% cobalt)
Die material	M2
Slug	Sheared, headed and phosphated
Lubricant	Soap
Punch strokes per minute	30
Production rate	2000 pieces per hour

(a) Press was equipped with devices for complete automation.

Fig. 13. Stoplight-switch body produced by combined backward and forward extrusion (Example 676)

Tubular Parts

Backward and forward extrusion, drawing, piercing and sometimes upsetting are frequently combined in a sequence of operations to produce various tubular parts. The following example describes a procedure for extruding a part having a long tubular section.

Example 677. Producing Axle-Housing Spindles in Five Operations (Fig. 14)

An axle-housing spindle was produced from a slug by backward extruding, piercing, and three forward extruding operations, as shown in Fig. 14.

The 22.5-lb slug was prepared by sawing, and then annealing in a protective atmosphere at 1250 to 1350 F for 2 hr, followed by air cooling. The slug was then cleaned, phosphate treated, and coated with soap. After backward extruding and piercing, and again after the first forward extruding operation, the workpiece was reannealed and recoated.

A 5500-ton crank press operated at 14 strokes per minute was used. Punches were made of D2, and die inserts of A2, tool steel.

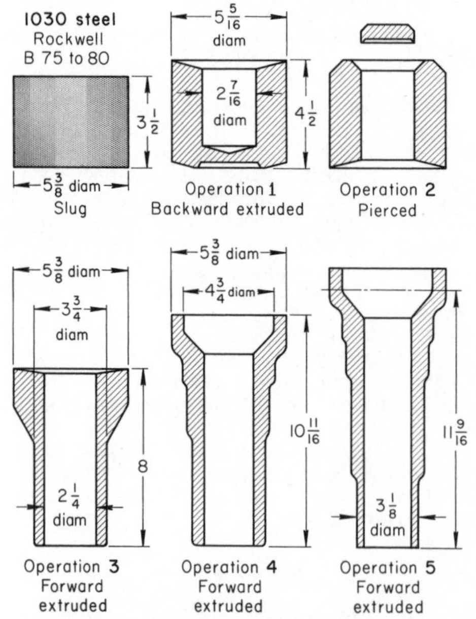

Fig. 14. Production of an axle-housing spindle by extruding and piercing in five operations (Example 677)

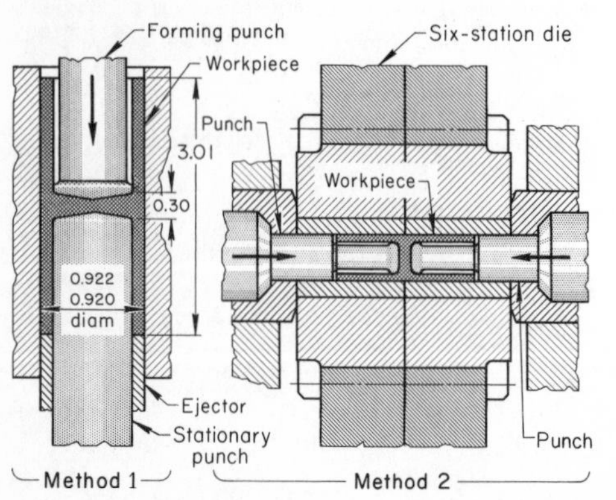

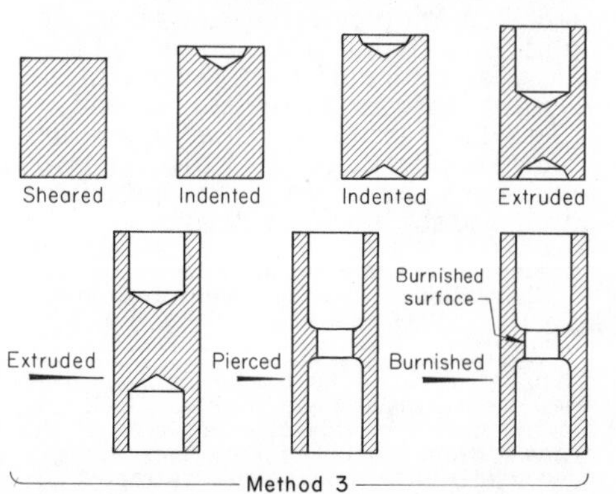

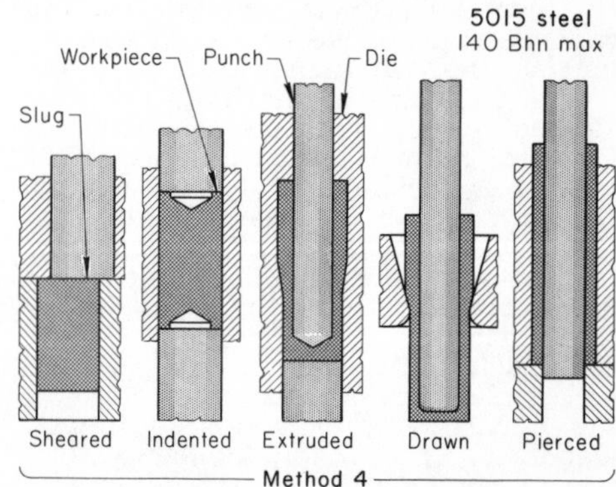

Fig. 15. Four different methods of producing automotive piston pins (Example 678)

Alternative Procedures. Often, acceptable results can be obtained by two or more procedures. Under these conditions available equipment and production requirements usually determine which method is used. The following example describes four methods for producing automotive piston pins.

Example 678. Four Different Methods of Producing Piston Pins (Fig. 15)

Figure 15 shows four methods used for producing piston pins from fine-grained, cold heading quality 5015 steel that was magnetically inspected and annealed in a controlled atmosphere to a maximum hardness of 140 Bhn. For methods 1 and 2, slugs were cut to a length of 1.975/1.970 in. from 0.919/0.916-in.-diam bars. Slugs were then chamfered in a four-spindle automatic machine, after which they were washed, phosphate coated, and lubricated with soap.

Method 1. Slugs were extruded in one stroke by simultaneous backward and forward extrusion, using one moving and one stationary punch, as shown in Fig. 15. This operation was performed in a 50-ton mechanical press. Tooling was carbide. The center web was removed by drilling. Output by this method was low — 700 pieces per hour.

Method 2 was a modification of method 1. The slugs were automatically fed into a dual-slide mechanical press (Fig. 15), the two horizontal rams of which were each rated at 150 tons. The dial carrying the six die stations rotated about a horizontal axis and indexed with the punch stations, which were permanently located on the rams. Tooling was carbide. Output by method 2 was about 2500 pins per hour. As in method 1, the 0.30-in.-thick center web was removed by drilling. The drilled area was then deburred prior to heat treating and grinding.

Method 3 was used for producing the piston pins in still larger quantities. For this seven-operation method (Fig. 15), hot rolled bars were annealed, cold drawn, phosphate coated, and lubricated with soap prior to being fed into a seven-station heading machine. The workpiece was transferred from station to station by means of spring clamps. Between stations 2 and 3, the workpiece was rotated as well as transferred, to permit indenting both ends. In method 3, not only was production rate greater than in method 2 (3500 vs 2500 pins per hour), but also the center web was removed in the sequence, eliminating the need for drilling and deburring.

Method 4 represents an alternative procedure for producing the piston pins in rather large quantities. In this five-operation method (Fig. 15), the steel was annealed and phosphate coated after it was indented in the second operation. An advantage of method 4 was that the web section was at one end of the workpiece rather than in the middle; this facilitated clean piercing of the web, and the pierced hole was at a point where the bending moment (and therefore the working stress) was lower. Another advantage was that the entire slug could be phosphate coated prior to extrusion. A disadvantage was that the extrusion punches had a greater length-to-diameter ratio than in the three other methods, which made the extrusion operation more difficult.

This method used a 100-ton crank press, and produced 2000 pieces per hour.

Stepped Shafts

Three methods are commonly used to cold form stepped shafts. If the head of the shaft is relatively short (length little or no greater than the headed diameter), it can be produced by upsetting (heading). For a head more than about 2½ diameters long, however, upsetting is not advisable, because buckling will result, caused by the excessive length-to-diameter ratio of the unsupported portion of the slug. Under these conditions forward extrusion should be considered.

Forward extrusion can be done in a closed die or an open die (Fig. 16). In a closed die, the slug is completely supported, and the cross-sectional area can be reduced by as much as 70%. However, if the length-to-diameter ratio of the slug is more than about 4 to 1, friction along the walls of the die is so high that the closed-die method is not feasible, and an open die must be used. In an open die, reduction must be limited to about 30%, or the unsupported portion of the slug will buckle. Stepped shafts can, however, be extruded in open dies using several consecutive operations, as described in the following example.

Example 679. Transmission Output Shaft Forward Extruded in Four Passes in an Open Die (Fig. 17)

A transmission output shaft was forward extruded from a sheared slug in four passes through a four-station open die, as shown in Fig. 17. Extrusion took place in two directions simultaneously. Transfer from station to station was accomplished by a walking-beam mechanism.

Air-actuated V-blocks (not shown in Fig. 17) were used to clamp the large diameter of the shaft to prevent buckling. A hydraulic cushion (Fig. 17) contacted the slug at the start of the stroke and remained in contact with the workpiece throughout the cycle. Thus, extrusion into the stationary tool holder took place first, assuring that variation in finished length, caused by variation in stock diameter, was always in the movable tool holder. Each station of the die was occupied by a workpiece at all times; a finished piece was obtained with each stroke of the press. Amount of area reduction was about the same for each pass, and totaled 65% for the four passes.

The cold working caused a marked change in mechanical properties:

	Before extrusion	After extrusion
Tensile strength, psi	85,000	137,000
Yield strength, psi	53,000	125,000
Elongation, %	26	7
Reduction of area, %	57	25

Additional processing details are presented in the table accompanying Fig. 17.

Closed-Die Extrusion. When required dimensional accuracy or surface finish is stringent, the closed-die technique is often used. The following example describes the extruding of worm blanks that required dimensional accuracy and a specific surface finish.

Example 680. Steering-Worm Blanks Forward Extruded in Three Operations in a Closed Die (Fig. 18)

Blanks 6.29 in. long for steering worms (Fig. 18) were forward extruded from 1¹⁄₁₆-in.-diam cold heading quality 5120 steel. Slugs, maintained to a weight of 718 ± 2 grams, were annealed in a controlled atmosphere at 1375 F for 5 hr prior to phosphating and applying soap as a lubricant.

Slugs were fed to the press by an elevating feeder that included an automatic weighing device. Extrusion was done in three operations, as shown in Fig. 18. Because of their length, workpieces were ejected from each die station by a combination of a die-cushion lift-out and a transfer mechanism.

Because surface finish was critical, the smallest section was ironed to the extent of 0.002 to 0.003 in., which resulted in a finish of 50 micro-in. or better. The distance between the two angles at the ends of the worms was also critical (±0.0075 in.). Some difficulty was encountered in maintaining this distance, because of temperature changes in the press and the tools. Additional processing details are given with Fig. 18.

Extrusion Combined With Cold Heading

Combining cold extrusion with cold heading is often the most economical means of producing hardware items and machinery parts that require two or more diameters that are widely dif-

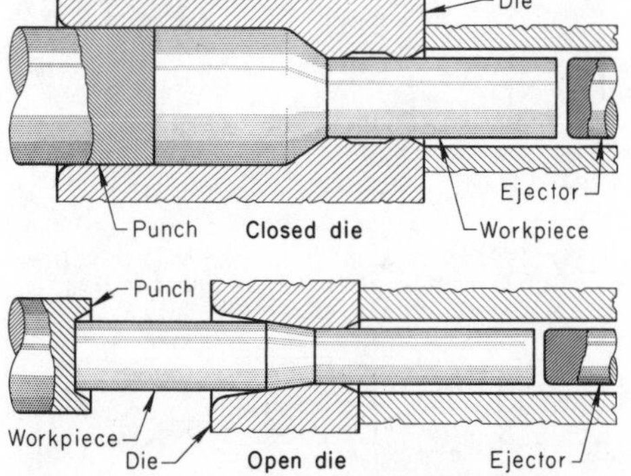

Fig. 16. End of stroke when forward extruding a stepped shaft in a closed die and an open die

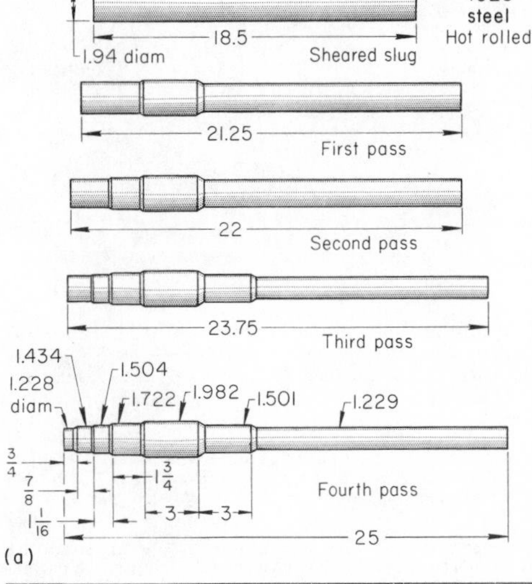

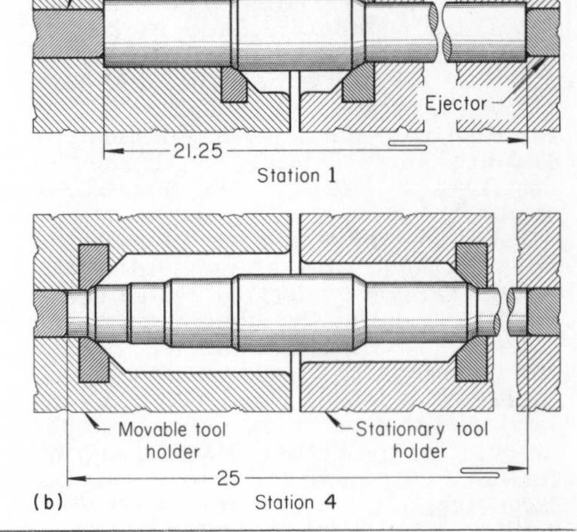

Press .... Horizontal mechanical, 250-ton	Lubricant .... Soap
Die .... Four-station	Production rate:
Tool material .... Carbide (20 to 21% cobalt)	Pieces per stroke 1
Slug .... Sheared and phosphated	Pieces per hour, approx 350

Fig. 17. (a) Shapes progressively produced in four-pass forward extrusion of a transmission shaft in a four-station open die. (b) Two of the die stations. (Example 679)

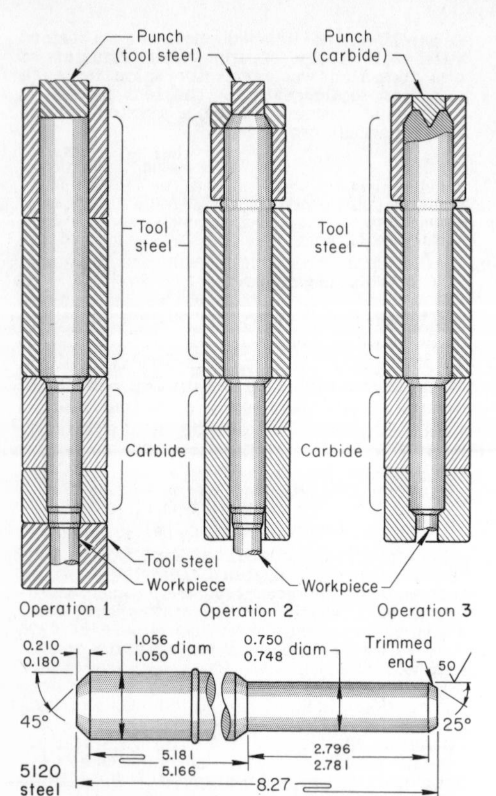

Press	Mechanical, two-point, 800-ton(a)
Die	3-station transfer on 10-in. centers(b)
Tool material	See illustration
Slug	Sheared, annealed and phosphated
Lubricant	Soap
Extrusion pressure	250 tons
Press speed	20 strokes per min
Setup time	6 hr
Production rate	1200 pieces per hour
Tool life, avg	100,000 pieces(c)

(a) Bolster size 84 by 48 by 9 in.; 18-in. stroke. Special feature was a 45-ton air cushion for lift-out. The press was also equipped with an elevating-type feeder and an automatic weighing device.

(b) Compression rings were 8⅞ in. in diameter, and were made from 4340 steel and hardened to Rockwell C 45 to 48. (c) Polishing was required after production of 25,000 pieces.

Fig. 18. Three-operation forward extrusion of steering-worm blanks in closed dies (Example 680)

ferent (see also the article "Cold Heading", page 465 in this volume). Such parts are commonly made in two or more passes in some type of heading machine (as in Examples 681 and 683), although presses are sometimes used for relatively small parts. For heading and extruding of larger parts, such as described in Example 685, presses are required.

Parts that have a large difference in cross-sectional area and weight distribution cannot be formed economically from material of size equivalent to the smallest or largest diameter of the completed part. The most economical procedure is to select material of an intermediate size, to effect a practical amount of reduction of area during forward extrusion, and to form the large sections of the part by heading. This practice is demonstrated in Examples 681 to 685, which follow. These examples describe procedures for producing parts requiring extruding and heading in as many as five operations or blows; the heading operations varied from extremely mild to severe.

Example 681. Wheel-Nut Blanks Produced by Five Blows in Two Headers (Fig. 19)

A blank for a truck-wheel nut (Fig. 19) was produced from 1³⁄₃₂-in.-diam phosphate-coated rod, in two heading machines. After the rod had been drawn to a 1-in. diam, it was fed into the first header, sheared into slugs 2 in. long, and headed in two blows to the shapes shown in Fig. 19. This header had a single die station, but two punches. The second punch swiveled into line with the die for the second blow, but the ejector was cammed to operate only once for every two strokes of the machine.

The preforms resulting from the second blow were annealed, phosphate coated, and lubricated with soap. Then they were fed from a hopper into a ¾-in. progressive header with three die and punch stations. The workpieces were carried from station to station by transfer fingers. Three blows in the second header completed the part, as shown in Fig. 19.

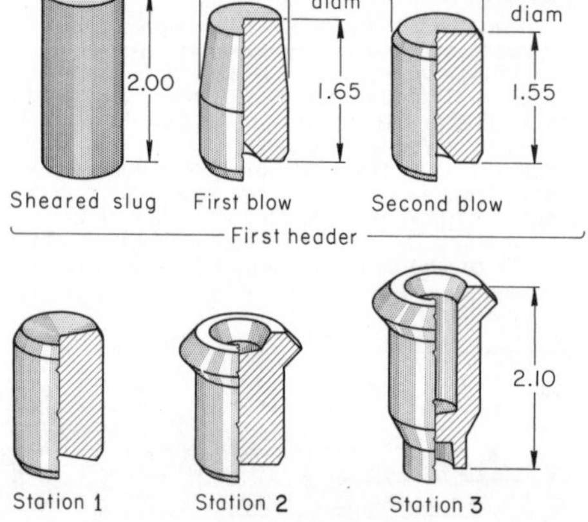

Fig. 19. Progression of shapes in production of a wheel-nut blank in two heading machines (Example 681)

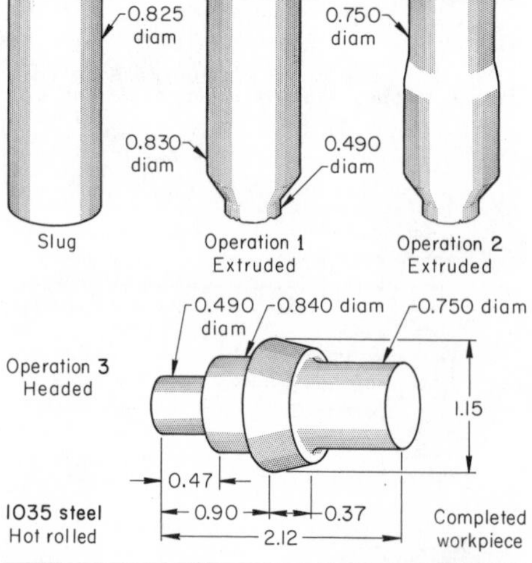

Machine	Progressive header(a)
Die	Three-station
Tool material	Tool steel(b)
Slug	Pickled and lime-coated wire(c)
Lubricant	Proprietary oil-base
Production rate	40 pieces per minute
Tool life	(d)

(a) With 1⅛-in. capacity. Special machine features were wire drawer and shear. (b) Carbide die for extruding the 0.490-in. diam. (c) Sheared to length in the header. (d) From 5000 to 500,000 pieces per tool for the eight major tool elements involved.

Fig. 20. Production of a brake anchor pin by extrusion and heading in a progressive header (Example 682)

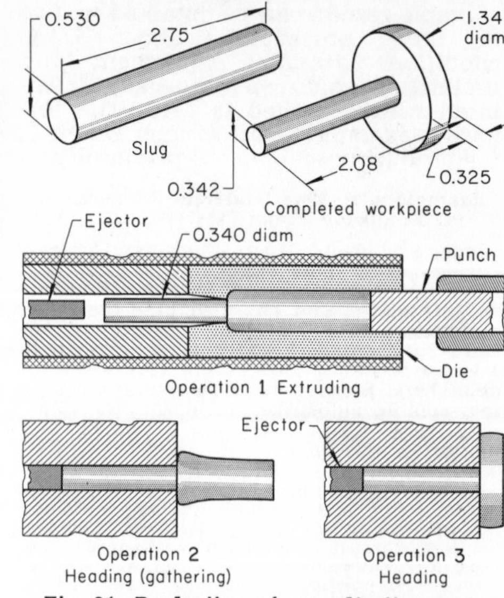

Fig. 21. Production of an adjusting-screw blank by forward extruding and severe cold heading (Example 683)

Example 682. Three-Operation Production of Brake Anchor Pins in a Progressive Header (Fig. 20)

Brake anchor pins were produced in a progressive header by extrusion followed by heading, as shown in Fig. 20. Slugs were made from hot rolled, pickled and lime-coated bars, which were drawn to size and sheared to length in the header. Slugs were then transferred to the die, where the parts were completed.

The workpiece had several diameters, as shown in Fig. 20. The ratio of maximum to minimum cross-sectional area was 5.5 to 1 (1.15-in. and 0.490-in. diameters). Under these conditions, forward extrusion of a diameter intermediate to the two extremes is normal procedure, and in this instance an intermediate diameter (0.840 in.) near slug diameter (0.825 in.) was chosen. Forward extrusion of the 0.490-in. diameter required a carbide die, a proprietary oil-base lubricant, and an extrusion load of 138,600 lb at the punch. This force produced a pressure of 256,000 psi on the punch and 387,000 psi on the die shoulder. An additional forward extrusion on the end opposite to that of the first formed the 0.750-in. diameter. Because reduction of area was small, the extrusion force was supported by the workpiece. The part was completed by cold heading, as shown in Fig. 20. Additional processing details are given with Fig. 20.

Example 683. Part Produced by Forward Extrusion and Severe Heading in Three Operations (Fig. 21)

The blank for a knurled-head adjusting screw, shown in the upper sketch of Fig. 21, was made from annealed and cold drawn rod that was coated with lime and a soap lubricant at the mill. In this condition, the rod was fed to a heading machine, where it was first cut to slug lengths. The slugs were then lubricated with an oil or a water-soluble lubricant containing extreme-pressure additives. As shown in Fig. 21, the slug was extruded in one die, then the workpiece was transferred to a second die, where it was cold headed in two operations — the first for stock-gathering, the second for completing the head (which represents severe cold heading). Except for the extrusion die, which was made from carbide, all dies and punches were made from M2 and D2 steels hardened to Rockwell C 60 to 62. Tool life for the carbide components was one million pieces; for the tool steel components, 250,000 pieces. Production rate was 6000 pieces per hour.

Example 684. Change in Slug Diameter and Processing to Accommodate Large Head Volume (Fig. 22)

Carbon steel fastener blanks (Fig. 22) were originally produced in a single die of shank diameter by forward extruding a 0.330-in.-

diam rod slug and partially gathering material for the head with one punch blow, and completing the gathering and upsetting with a second punch blow. Although it required only one die, this method suffered the limitation of attempting to fill the large volume required in the head of the blank from a rod size that was borderline, depending on length of shank and other design variables.

In an improved method, a greater volume of metal for heading was obtained by selecting a rod slug of larger diameter (0.485 in.). In a first die operation, the slug was forward extruded to provide a given length of desired shank size (0.330-in.-diam) and an adequate volume of metal for the head (see Fig. 22). The extruded blank was then transferred to a second die to complete the head. As a result of better die filling, this method provided an improved product and greater design flexibility.

Carbide dies, tool steel punches, and lime-coated rod stock were used for both methods. An extreme-pressure lubricant was applied generously to the slugs as they entered the dies. Production rate and tool life were essentially the same for both methods.

Example 685. Steering-Worm Blanks Extruded and Headed in Three Operations (Fig. 23)

Blanks for power-steering worms (Fig. 23) were produced from 1⁹⁄₃₂-in.-diam cold heading quality 5120 steel. Slug weight was maintained within ±2 grams. Slugs were annealed in a controlled atmosphere at 1375 F for 5 hr prior to phosphating and application of the soap lubricant.

Slugs were fed to the press by an elevating automatic feeder that included an automatic weighing device. Transfer fingers controlled by an air sensing device transferred the workpieces between stations.

An indent was made in the workpiece in operation 1 to improve concentricity and punch life during backward extrusion in operation 2 (Fig. 23). Also, the chamfer on the end in operation 1 was designed to match the lead angle for forward extrusion in operation 2. The combination forward and backward extrusion in operation 2 was well balanced so that the shoulder on the workpiece was not subjected to an excessive load. Dies used in operation 3 had to be well vented

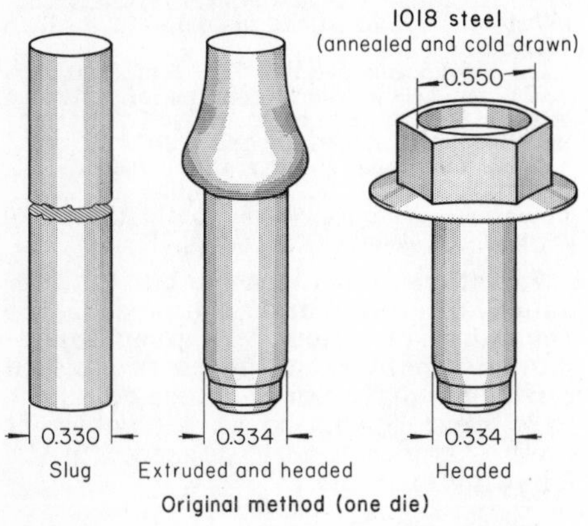

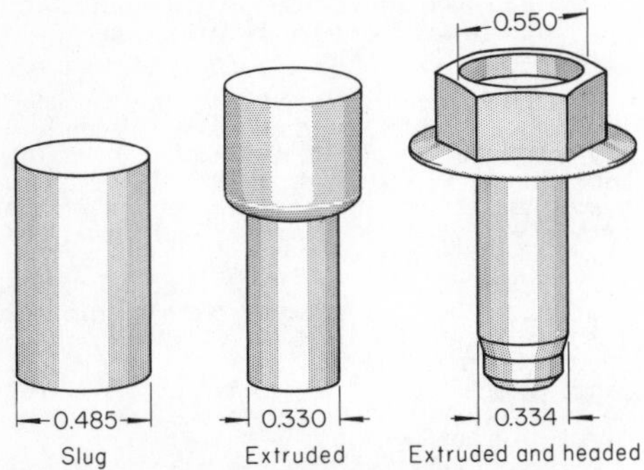

Fig. 22. Original and improved method for producing a fastener blank by extruding and heading (Example 684)

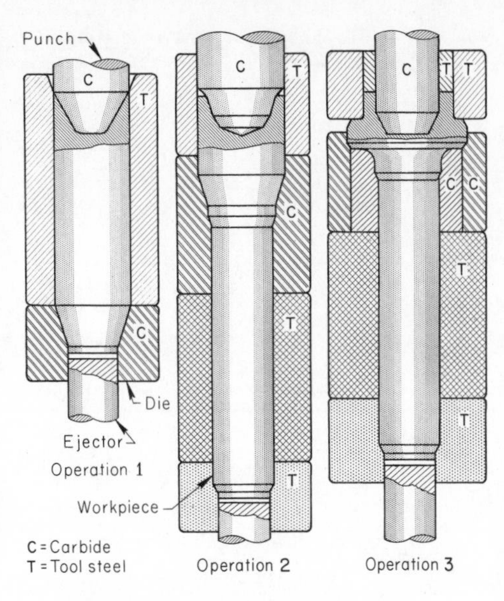

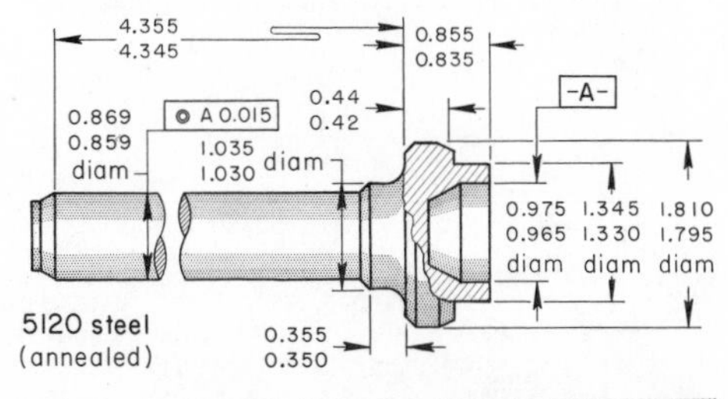

Press	Mechanical, two-point, 800-ton(a)
Die	Three-station transfer on 10-in. centers
Tool material	Carbide inserts (see drawing)
Slug	Sheared, annealed and phosphated
Lubricant	Soap
Extrusion pressure (total)	525 tons
Press speed	20 strokes per min
Setup time	8 hr
Production rate	1200 pieces per hour
Tool life (punch and die inserts):	
First station	100,000 pieces
Second station	50,000 pieces
Third station	75,000 pieces

(a) Bolster size, 84 by 48 by 9 in. Compression rings were 8⅞ in. in diameter and made from 4340 steel hardened to Rockwell C 45 to 48. Press had a 45-ton air cushion for lift-out, an elevating automatic feeder, and an automatic weighing device.

Fig. 23. Extruding and heading of a blank for a power-steering worm in three operations (Example 685)

to prevent buildup of lubricant, which would have prevented fillout of the workpiece in the flange area. An air-oil mist was sprayed on the dies to help prevent this buildup. Additional processing details are given with Fig. 23.

Extrusion of Hot Upset Preforms

Although the use of symmetrical slugs as the starting material for extruding is common practice, other shapes are often used as the starting slugs or blanks.

Sometimes one or more machining operations precede extrusion, to produce a shape that can be more easily extruded. The use of hot upset forgings as the starting material is also common practice. Hot upsetting followed by cold extrusion is often more economical than alternative procedures for producing a specific shape. Axle shafts for cars and trucks are regularly produced by this practice; advantages are not limited to cost but include improved grain flow. A typical application is described in the following example.

Example 686. Hot Forging and Cold Extrusion of Rear-Axle Drive Shafts to Improve Properties and Simplify Production (Fig. 24)

Producing rear-axle drive shafts (Fig. 24) for passenger cars and trucks by three-operation cold extrusion improved surfaces (and consequently fatigue resistance), maintained more uniform diameters and closer dimensional tolerances, increased strength and hardness, and simplified production.

The drive shafts were hot upset forged to form the flange and rough the shaft, and were cold extruded to lengthen the shaft. (The flange could have been upset as a final operation after the shaft had been cold extruded to length. However, this would have required more passes in the extrusion press than space allowed.)

Hot upsetting and cold extrusion replaced a hammer forging and machining sequence after which the flange, a separate piece, had been attached.

Steel was extrusion quality 1039 in 1¹¹⁄₁₆-in.-diam bars. The bars were sheared to lengths of 29¹³⁄₁₆ or 36⁹⁄₁₆ in., and then hot forged and shot blasted. A continuous conveyor took the hot upset preforms through a hot alkaline spray cleaner, a hot spray rinse, a zinc phosphating bath (165 F for 5 min), a cold spray rinse, a hot spray rinse, and finally a soap tank (190 F for 5 min).

As shown in Fig. 24, cold extrusion was a three-operation process that increased the length of the shaft and reduced the smallest diameter to 1.308 in.

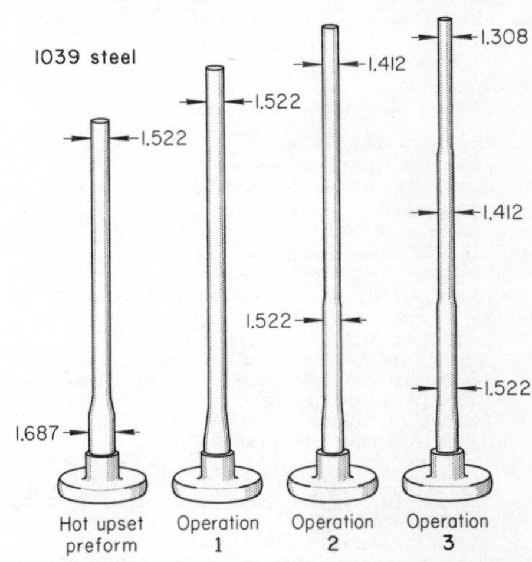

Press	Hydraulic, 175-ton
Tool material	Carbide inserts(a)
Slug (preform)	Hot upset forged, blast cleaned, and phosphated
Lubricant	Soap
Tool life	150,000 pieces(b)
Production rate	176 pieces per hour

(a) In H11 or H12 tool steel holders. (b) Total number extruded.

Fig. 24. Production of a rear-axle drive shaft by cold extruding an upset forging in three operations (Example 686)

Extruding of Large Parts

Although most cold extrusion of steel is confined to relatively small parts (starting slugs seldom weigh more than 25 lb), much larger parts have been successfully cold extruded. For press operations, the practical extremes of part size are governed by the availability of machinery and tool materials, the plasticity of the work material, and economical production quantities. Bodies for large-caliber ordnance shells have been produced successfully by both hot and cold extrusion processes. The procedure used in the production of these large parts by cold extrusion is described in Example 687, which follows.

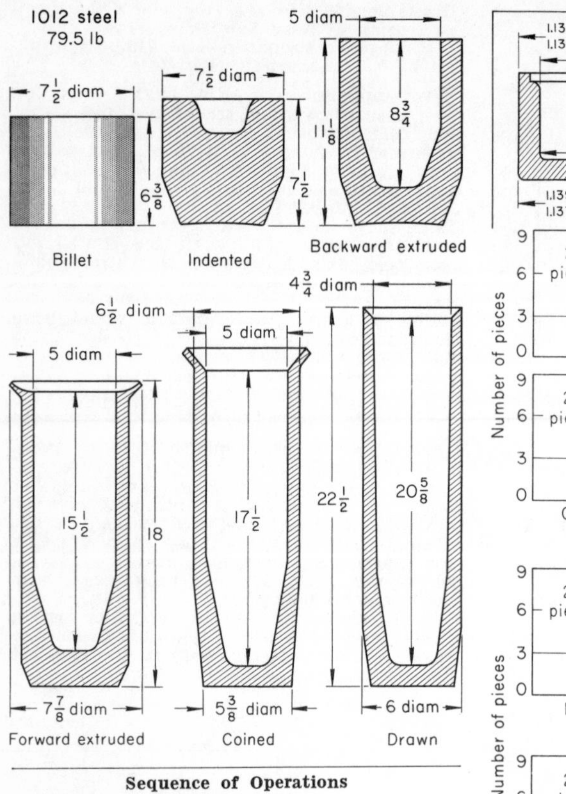

Sequence of Operations

1. Cold saw 79.5-lb billet
2. Chamfer sawed edges
3. Apply lubricant as follows:
   - Degrease in boiling caustic; rinse
   - Pickle in sulfuric acid; rinse
   - Apply zinc phosphate
   - Apply zinc stearate
4. Cold size indent (see drawing above), in No. 1 (3500-ton) press
5. Induction normalize (1700 to 1800 F)
6. Apply lubricant as in step 3
7. Backward extrude (see drawing above), in No. 2 (3000-ton) press
8. Induction normalize (1700 to 1800 F)
9. Apply lubricant as in step 3
10. Forward extrude, in two stages (to shape in drawing above), in No. 3 (3000-ton) press
11. Anneal lip by localized induction heating (1500 to 1525 F)
12. Apply lubricant as in step 3
13. Coin base and form boat tail to finish dimension and coin bottom (see drawing above), in No. 4 (3000-ton) press
14. Final draw (see drawing above), in No. 5 (1500-ton) press
15. Turn and recess lip
16. Induction anneal nose (1450 to 1500 F)
17. Apply lubricant as in step 3
18. Expand bourrelet, in No. 6 press
19. Form nose
20. Anneal for relief of residual stress.

Fig. 25. Progression of shapes in production of a 155-mm shell body by a multiple-method procedure that included cold extrusion (Example 687)

Example 687. Use of Extrusion in Multiple-Method Production of Shell Bodies From 79.5-Lb Billets (Fig. 25)

Figure 25 shows the progression of shapes resulting from extrusion, coining and drawing, in a multiple-method procedure for producing bodies for 155-mm shells from descaled 1012 steel billets 7½ in. in diameter that weighed 79.5 lb each. The sequence of operations is listed with Fig. 25.

Production of these shell bodies was designed for semicontinuous operation that included annealing, cleaning and application of lubricant between press operations.

Dimensional Accuracy

In cold extrusion, shape and size of the workpiece are determined by rigid tools that change dimensionally only from wear. Because tool wear is generally slow, successive parts made by cold extrusion are nearly identical.

The accuracy that can be achieved in cold extrusion depends largely on the size and shape of the given section.

Tolerances for cold extrusion are commonly denoted as close, medium, loose and open. Definitions of these tolerances, and applicability to specific types of extrusions, are as follows:

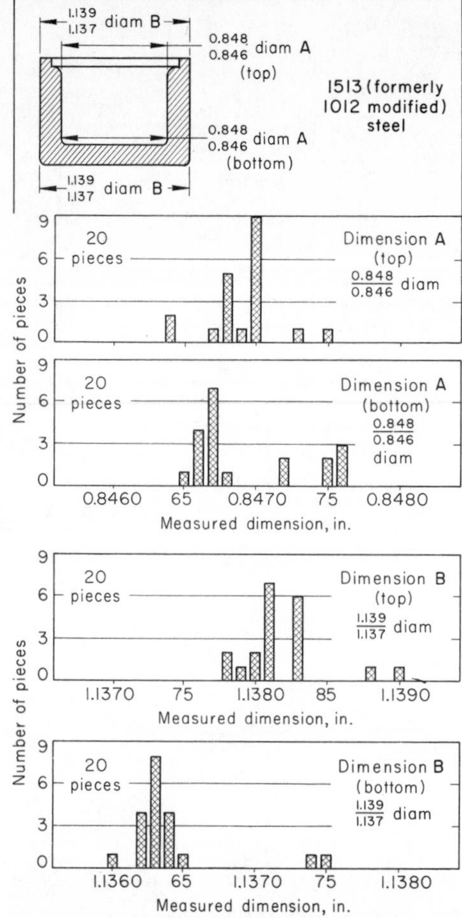

Fig. 26. Variation in inside and outside diameters at top and bottom of backward extruded bearing cups (Example 688)

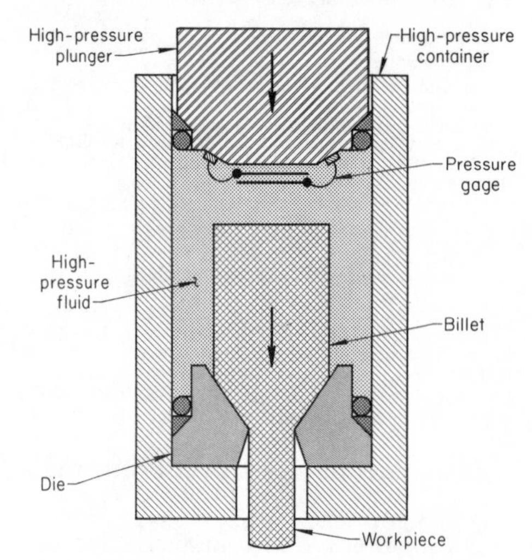

Fig. 27. Setup for hydrostatic extrusion

Close tolerance is generally considered to be ±0.001 in. or less. Close tolerances are usually restricted to small (under 1 in.) extruded diameters. For instance, the 0.846-in. diam in Example 673, the 0.920-in. diam in Example 678, and the 0.748-in. diam in Example 680 are typical of diameters on which close tolerance can be obtained.

Medium tolerance denotes ±0.005 in. Extruded diameters of larger parts (up to 4 in.), headed diameters of small parts, and concentricity of outside and inside diameters in backward extruded parts are typical of dimensions on which it is practical to maintain medium tolerance.

Loose tolerance denotes ±0.015 in., and generally applies to short lengths of extruded sections and sometimes to over-all lengths of extruded parts less than about 3½ in. long.

Open tolerance is generally considered as greater than ±0.015, and applies to length dimensions of long, slender parts (up to 20 in., and sometimes longer).

Table 9. Cold Extrusion Problems and Some Common Causes

Tool Breakage
Slug not properly located in the die
Slug material not completely annealed
Slug not symmetrical or not properly shaped
Improper selection or improper heat treatment of tool material
Misalignment and/or excessive deflection of tools and press equipment
Incorrect preloading of dies
Damage caused by double slugging or by overweight slugs
Galling or Scoring of Tools
Improper lubrication of slugs
Improper surface finish of tools
Improper selection or improper heat treatment of tool material
Improper edge or blend radii on punch or extrusion die
Workpieces Sticking to Dies
No back relief on punch or die
Incorrect nose angle on punch and incorrect extrusion angle of die
Galled or scored tools
Workpieces Splitting on Outside Diameter or Forming Chevrons in Inside Diameter
Slug material not completely annealed
Reduction of area either too great or too small
Excessive surface seams or internal defects in work material
Incorrect die angles
Excessive Buildup of Lubricant in Dies
Inadequate vent holes in die
Excessive amount of lubricant used
Lack of a means of removal of lubricant, or failure to prevent lubricant buildup by spraying the die with an air-oil mist

Variation. With reasonable maintenance of tools and equipment, the amount of variation for a given dimension is usually small for a production run. Some drift can be expected as the tools wear. Variation in diameters of small extruded cups is described in the following example.

Example 688. Variation in Diameter of Backward Extruded Bearing Cups (Fig. 26)

The bar charts in Fig. 26 show the variation in inside and outside diameters at the top and the bottom of 20 out of a run of 200 bearing cups that were backward extruded in two passes. As shown on the cross section of the part in Fig. 26, both diameters had a specified tolerance of ±0.001 in.

The data in Fig. 26 show that all inside diameters (top and bottom) were within the specified range of 0.846 to 0.848 in. All outside diameters were also within the prescribed range at the top, but at the bottom, 18 of the 20 cups were out of range on the low side by 0.0005 to 0.001 in.

In accounting for this discrepancy, it was noted that the outside diameter was kept undersize intentionally after the first extrusion to provide clearance for loading into the second die. In forming the counterbore in the second die, the forming pressure expanded the top portion of the outside diameter but did not affect the bottom portion. Consequently, the dimension in the bottom portion remained on the low side.

Causes of Problems

The problems most commonly encountered in cold extrusion are:

Tool breakage
Galling or scoring of tools
Workpieces sticking to dies
Workpieces splitting on outside diameter or cupping in inside diameter
Excessive buildup of lubricant in dies.

Table 9 lists the most likely causes of these problems.

APPENDIX

Hydrostatic Extrusion*

Hydrostatic extrusion is essentially a method of extruding a billet through a die by pressurized fluid instead of by the ram used in the conventional process; the pressurized fluid acts on the sides of the billet as well as on its back face, as illustrated in Fig. 27, which shows the nosed billet sitting on a conical die. This apparently slight change in principle results in significant technical advantages over the conventional process. The absence of contact between billet and container means that the billet-container friction is virtually eliminated, and consequently that the extrusion pressure, which is thus almost unaffected by length of billet, can be expected to be lower than that for conventional extrusion under comparable conditions. Also, because of the support given by the liquid to the sides of the billet, long billets (such as those required for coils of wire) can be extruded without buckling and without an increase in the extrusion pressure.

Equipment. Processing equipment, including that used for basic research and development work, has been constructed in several countries, including the United Kingdom, Sweden, the USSR and the United States. The pressures developed by this equipment range from 81,000 to 500,000 psi, and the container bores from 3¾ to ½ in. Although most equipment operates at room temperature, some can be used at elevated temperatures.

In the types of equipment used by Pugh and his co-workers (Fig. 27), the containers are made from a low-alloy steel and the plungers from a high speed tool steel. Extrusion fluids are selected on the basis of the pressure range employed and include mixtures of mineral oil – molybdenum disulfide, castor oil – methylated spirits, glycerine – ethylene glycol, and isopentane – white gasoline. When the extrusion fluid is a poor lubricant, the billet is covered with a solid lubricant such as molybdenum disulfide, graphite-containing greases, or latex rubber.

Tooling. For the extrusion of rod, only a die is required. For hollow products, a mandrel that fits the bore of the hollow billet is also needed. The mandrel initially must protrude below the die aperture and can be fixed with respect to the die or to the back face of the billet. The dies are made from the same tool steel as the plungers. Placing the high-pressure seal at the bottom of the die (Fig. 27) allows the pressurized fluid to give radial support to the die. This simplifies the construction of the die by eliminating the heavy shrink rings used in conventional dies and allows thin-wall dies to be used. Further advantage can be taken of the support provided by the pressurized fluid in the construction of dies for the extrusion of complex sections. These dies can be made in sections split either at right angles to the axis or into sectors, or both.

Extrusion Pressure. Because friction at the container walls is eliminated and lubrication at the interface of the billet and the die is improved, the pressure required in hydrostatic extrusion is less than that required in conventional extrusion under comparable conditions of tooling. Furthermore, in hydrostatic forward extrusion, pressure is not affected by billet length. However, when conical-entry dies are employed in hydrostatic forward extrusion, extrusion pressure is markedly affected by die angle, as shown in Fig. 28.

Pending attainment of an optimum die angle, extrusion pressure decreases with a decrease of the included angle of the conical-entry die. To some extent, the optimum die angle (about 45° in Fig. 28) depends on the properties of the metal being extruded. At an optimum die angle, minimum extrusion pressure is required; however, a further reduction in die angle results in an increase in required extrusion pressure.

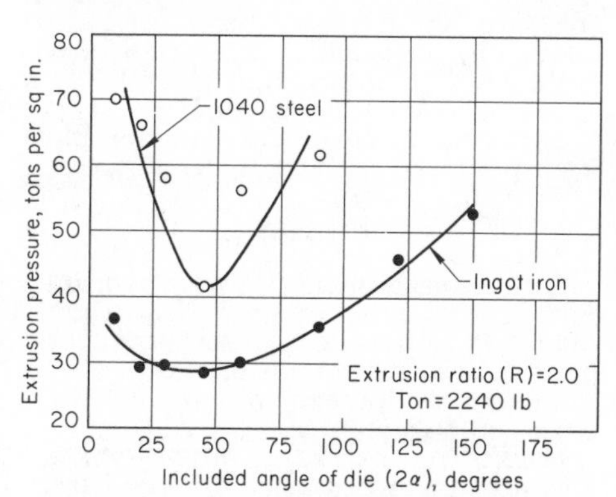

Fig. 28. Effect of die angle on extrusion pressure for 1040 steel and ingot iron

Results. In addition to the practical advantages cited previously, hydrostatic extrusion is able to extrude high-strength steels, titanium alloys, heat-resisting alloys, metal composites, and several refractory metals known to be difficult, or impossible, to extrude by conventional cold extrusion techniques. On a limited basis, it has been demonstrated that by altering certain key variables in hydrostatic extrusion, notably die angle, extrusion pressure, and extrusion ratio, it is possible to effect improvements in the mechanical properties and characteristics of some metals.

*Information for this appendix was abstracted from NEL Report 196, Oct 1965, National Engineering Laboratory, East Kilbride, Glasgow, and "Applications of Static High Pressure to the Forming of Metals — Hydrostatic Extrusion", by H. Ll. D. Pugh, in DMIC Report 226, July 7, 1966.

Selected References

1. Winfried Beisel, "Graphical Determination of Press Force and Deformation Work in Upsetting and Cold Extrusion" (in German), *Bander Bleche Rohre,* 7, Dec 1966, 854-860. [Presents two nomograms for determination of press force and work of deformation for upsetting and forward and backward extrusion.]

2. P. J. M. Boes and H. P. Pouw, "A Practical Calculation Method for Extrusion Pressures", *Sheet Metal Industries,* 43, May 1966, 377-390. [A practical method is described for making a rough calculation of forces in cold forming and cold extrusion to determine required press capacity and specific pressures and stresses in tools. The theories of deformation and deformation forces are discussed, as are the factors that influence these forces, such as the properties of the work material, cross-sectional area, extrusion ratio, tool design, friction, and extrusion speeds. Data compiled from existing literature show the relationship of the "*n*-factor" to the extrusion rate for selected ferrous and nonferrous alloys.]

3. A. W. F. Comley, "Tool Material for the Cold Extrusion Process", *Sheet Metal Industries,* 38, Mar 1961, 190-207. [Provides a selection of tool steels suitable for use in punches and dies for cold extrusion, together with a review of their heat treatment. Compares these tool steels with tungsten carbide.]

4. John L. Everhart, Impact and Cold Extrusion of Metals, Chemical Publishing Co., New York, 1964, 199 p. [A comprehensive review of the cold extrusion process and its products. Six chapters deal with the fundamentals of cold extrusion, extrusion pressure, tooling for extrusion, tool materials, lubrication, and high-energy-rate forming. Five concluding chapters cover factors in the design of extrusions and the metals that can be extruded. The book contains an extensive bibliography and index.]

5. H. D. Feldmann, Cold Forging of Steel, Hutchinson Scientific and Technical, London, 1961, 268 p. [Fourteen chapters cover areas of general interest, including fundamental theory of cold extrusion, steels for extrusion, heat treatment, effects of steel structure and mechanical properties, grain patterns, industrial application of cold forging, examples of cold forged parts, tools for extrusion, surface treatments, presses and equipment, and applications in munitions manufacture. Translated from the German edition first published in 1959.]

6. H. D. Feldmann and H. K. F. Honnens, "Development of Tools for the Cold Forging Process", *Sheet Metal Industries,* 43, Feb 1966, 95-110. [Calculates the pressure-stroke characteristics and maximum pressures required in cold upsetting, drawing, and extrusion, applying these values to tool design. Designs of dies and punches to minimize specific load and wear through proper tool geometry are recommended. Discussion includes control of forces during deformation, prestressing of dies and punches, tool selection, and heat treatment of tools.]

7. J. B. Haddow and W. Johnson, "Experiments in the Piercing of Soft Metals", *Machine Tool Design and Research,* 2, Jan-Mar 1962, 1-18. [Reviews experiments on annealed and work-hardened lead-base alloys, using flat-headed and conical-tipped punches. Deformation, cavitation, punch pressures, and punch penetration are correlated with uniaxial yield stress, lubrication, and punch velocity.]

8. F. Howard, H. A. J. Dennison, and N. Angus, "Some Investigations into the Cold Extrusion of Steel", *Sheet Metal Industries,* 38, June 1961, 403-425. [Reviews forward and backward extrusion, with calculations of load test forces. Also discusses heat treatment and lubrication of billets and slugs, component design, and commercial application.]

9. J. McKenzie, "Factors in the Design of Cold Extrusion Tooling", *Sheet Metal Industries,* 41, May 1964, 378-392. [Examines in detail the effects of each process variable and its influence on extrusion pressure and tool design. Relevant data are incorporated into design charts to present the information to tool designers in convenient form. Other methods of determining extrusion loads are considered.]

10. Walter Pohlmann, "Cold Extrusion of Steel" (in German), *Neue Hütte,* 10, Oct 1965, 602-606. [Reviews cold extrusion properties of steel and applications for extruded steel parts. Steels are classified as to extrudability. Also reviews types of dies that can be used in cold extrusion. Provides examples of backward extrusion, indicating dimensional tolerances that can be maintained.]

11. H. Ll. D. Pugh and M. T. Watkins, "Experimental Investigation of the Extrusion of Metals", *Production Engineer,* 40, April 1961, 256-282. [Reviews effects of extrusion method, billet dimensions, ram speed, extrusion ratio, tool design, and lubrication on the pressure required to extrude sample shapes from aluminum and copper alloys, columbium and titanium, and carbon, low-alloy and stainless steels.]

12. Karl Sieber, "Tooling Design for Cold Forging", *Sheet Metal Industries,* 43, Feb 1966, 111-129. [Outlines forming limitations for bolt-type parts and hollow components. Various production examples are provided. Tool load limitations are analyzed for dies, taking into account the danger of transverse fatigue fractures in highly stressed pressing dies. Cites steels that have proved most successful in cold extrusion punches. Design examples of complete tool sets are also provided.]

13. R. H. Spikes, "Tooling for the Cold Extrusion of Steel", *Sheet Metal Industries,* 43, Feb 1966, 131-145. [Gives recommendations for punch and die design for forward and backward extrusion, including the nature and magnitude of stresses, failure by fracture, distortion, or wear, and design of shrink rings to develop high compressive stresses at the die bore. The mechanical properties of tool steels for cold extrusion are also compared. Causes of tool failure are discussed, and acceptance standards for tool materials are provided.]

14. "The Design and Performance of Tooling for the Cold Extrusion of Steel", *Sheet Metal Industries,* 43, Feb 1966, 146-162. [The performance of punches made from various high-carbon, high-chromium steels and high speed tool steels is assessed in terms of their dimensional stability and buckling tendency in backward extrusion. Punches made of high speed tool steels are preferred. Discussion includes effects of preforming on punch performance and cites specific dimensions and tolerances for tools used in cold extrusion.]

15. "Tool Design Tips for Cold Extrusion", *Machinery* (U.S.), 74, May 1968, 104–110. [In addition to a general review of punch and die design principles, provides specific information for designing tools for forward and backward extrusion. Strength and hardness data are given for tool materials, including M4 for die nibs and anvils, M3 for extrusion punches, M2 for nibs, S5 for heading punches and anvils, A2 for transition structures, T1 and 1020 for upper and lower die shoes, H11 for shrink rings, and carbide for extrusion punches.]

Cold (Impact) Extrusion of Aluminum Alloy Parts

By N. L. WARD

ALUMINUM ALLOYS are well adapted to cold extrusion (often called impact extrusion). The lower-strength, more ductile alloys such as 1100 and 3003 are easiest to extrude. When higher mechanical properties are required in the final product, heat treatable grades are used, but extrusions from these metals are more susceptible to defects, such as laps or cracks, than are those from the lower-strength alloys.

Although nearly all aluminum alloys can be cold extruded, the five alloys listed in Table 1 are most commonly used. The alloys in Table 1 are listed in the order of decreasing extrudability based on pressure requirements. The easiest-to-extrude alloy (1100) has been assigned an arbitrary value of 1.0 in this comparison.

Temper of Work Metal. The softer an alloy is, the more easily it extrudes. Many extrusions are produced directly from slugs purchased in the O (annealed, recrystallized) temper. In other applications, especially when slugs are machined from bars, the slugs are annealed after machining and before surface preparation, even though the bars were purchased in the O temper. Sometimes the raw material is purchased in the F (as-fabricated) temper, and then the cut or punched slugs are annealed before being extruded.

Table 1. Relative Pressure Requirements for Cold Extruding Annealed Slugs of Five Aluminum Alloys (Alloy 1100 = 1.0)

Alloy	Relative extrusion pressure
1100	1.0
3003	1.2
6061	1.6
2014	1.8
7075	2.3

When extruding alloys that will be heat treated, such as 6061, common practice is to extrude the slug in the O temper, solution treat the preform to the T4 temper, and then size or finish extrude. This procedure has two advantages: (*a*) after solution treatment, the metal is reasonably soft, and will permit sizing or additional working; and (*b*) distortion caused by solution treatment can be corrected in final sizing. After sizing, the part can be aged to the T6 temper, if required.

Size of Extrusions. Equipment is readily available that can produce backward and forward extrusions up to 16 in. in diameter. Backward extrusions can be up to 60 in. long. The length of forward extrusions is limited only by the cross section of the part and the capacity of the press — unless a flange necessitates backing the extrusion out of the die, in which case the maximum length is about 60 in.

Hydraulic extrusion and forging presses, suitably modified, are used for making very large extrusions. Parts up to 33 in. in diameter have been produced by backward extrusion from high-strength aluminum alloys in a 14,000-ton extrusion press. Similar extrusions up to 40 in. in diameter have been produced in large forging presses.

Presses

Both mechanical and hydraulic presses are used in extruding aluminum. For detailed information on presses, see the article on Presses and Auxiliary Equipment, which begins on page 1 in this volume.

Presses for extruding aluminum alloys are not necessarily different from those used for extruding steel. There are, however, two considerations that enter into the selection of a press for aluminum: (*a*) because aluminum extrudes easily, the process is often applied to the forming of deep cuplike or tubular parts, and for this the press should have a long stroke; and (*b*) also because aluminum extrudes easily, the process is often used for mass production, which requires that the press be capable of high speeds.

The press must have a stroke long enough to permit removal of the longest part to be produced. Except for single-purpose equipment for relatively short extrusions, a stroke of at least 24 in. is required in large mechanical presses. A stroke of 36 in. or more is desirable in intermediate and large hydraulic presses. Long shells are sometimes cold extruded in short-stroke, knuckle-type presses, in which the punch is tilted forward or backward for removal of the workpiece.

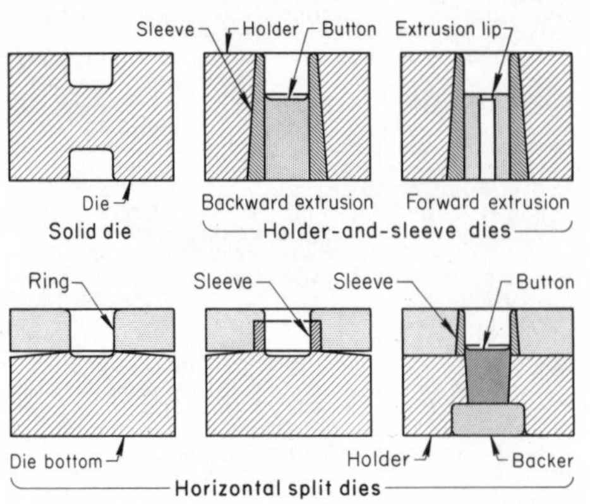

Fig. 1. Three types of dies used in the cold extrusion of aluminum alloy parts

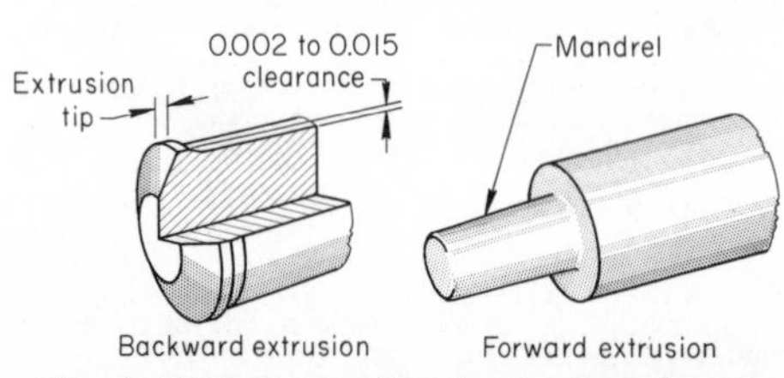

Fig. 2. Typical punches for backward and forward extrusion of aluminum alloy parts

Because of their high speeds, mechanical crank presses generally are preferred for producing parts requiring up to about 1200 tons of force. Production of as many as 70 extrusions per minute (4200 per hour) is not unusual, and higher production rates are often obtained. For this reason, auxiliary press equipment is usually designed for a high degree of automation when aluminum is to be extruded.

Cold heading machines also are used for cold extruding aluminum parts. Hollow aluminum rivets are formed and extruded in cold headers in mass-production quantities. In general, the extruded parts are small and usually require an upsetting operation that can be done economically in a cold header.

Tooling

Tools designed especially for extruding aluminum may be different from those used for steel, because aluminum extrudes more easily. For instance, a punch used for backward extrusion of steel should not have a length-to-diameter ratio greater than about 3 to 1, whereas this ratio, under favorable conditions, can be as high as 17 to 1 for aluminum (although a 10-to-1 ratio is usually the practical maximum).

Dies. Three basic types of dies for extruding aluminum are shown in Fig. 1. Solid dies are usually the most economical to make. Generally, a cavity is provided in each end, so that the die can

Table 2. Typical Steels for Tools Used in Extruding Aluminum (a)

Tool	AISI steel	Rockwell C hardness
Die, solid	W1	65 to 67
Die sleeve (b)	D2	60 to 62
	L6	56 to 62
	H13	48 to 52
Die button (c)	H11	48 to 50
	H13	48 to 50
	L6	50 to 52
	H21	47 to 50
	T1	58 to 60
Ejector	D2	55 to 57
	S1	52 to 54
Punch	S1	54 to 56
	D2	58 to 60
	H13	50 to 52
Stripper	L6	56 to 58
Mandrel, forward	S1	52 to 54
	H13	50 to 52
Holder	H11	42 to 48
	H13	42 to 48
	4130	36 to 44
	4140	36 to 44

(a) See also the article "Cold Extrusion", page 475 in this volume. (b) Sintered carbide is sometimes used for die sleeves. (c) Maraging steel is sometimes used for die buttons.

be reversed when one end becomes cracked or worn.

Holder-and-sleeve dies are used when extrusion pressures are extremely high. This type of die consists of a shrink ring or rings (the holder), a sleeve, and an insert (button). The die sleeve is prestressed in compression in the shrink ring to match the tension stress expected during extrusion.

Horizontal split dies are composed of as many as four parts: a shrink ring; a sleeve, or insert; and a one-piece or two-piece base. (Figure 1 identifies the one-piece base as a die bottom, and the components of the two-piece base as a holder and a backer.)

Compared to the die cavities used in the backward extrusion of steel (see the article "Cold Extrusion", page 475 in this volume), the die cavities for aluminum shown in Fig. 1 are notably shallow, reflecting a major difference in the extrusion characteristics of the two metals. Steel is more difficult to extrude, requiring higher pressures and continuous die support of the workpiece throughout the extrusion cycle. In contrast, aluminum extrudes readily, and when the punch strikes the slug in backward extrusion, the metal squirts up the sides of the punch, following the punch contours without the external restraint or support afforded by a surrounding die cavity.

Punches. Typical punches for forward and backward extrusion are shown in Fig. 2. In backward extruding of deep cuplike parts, specially designed punches may be used to facilitate stripping, as described in Example 693.

Tool Materials. Typical steels and their working hardnesses for extrusion of aluminum are given in Table 2. For further details on tool materials, see the article "Cold Extrusion", page 475.

Stock for Slugs

Slugs for extrusions are obtained by blanking from plate; sawing, shearing or machining from bars; or by casting. In general, the methods for preparing aluminum slugs are similar to those for preparing slugs from other metals and are thus subject to the same advantages and limitations (see Table 8 in "Cold Extrusion", page 482).

Rolled aluminum alloy plate is widely employed as a source of cold extrusion stock. The high speed at which slugs can be prepared is the major advantage of blanking from rolled plate. Hot rolled plate is suitable for high-quantity production of slugs when tolerance on the volume of the slug is not close (up to ±10%, for example). When closer tolerances are required, the plate must be cold rolled after hot rolling. When slug thickness is greater than about 2 in., or the thickness-to-diameter ratio is greater than about one-to-one, blanking from plate is uneconomical, if not impossible. Blanking is also excessively wasteful of metal, which negates a principal advantage of the cold extrusion process.

Sawing from bars is widely used as a method of obtaining slugs. Aluminum alloys are easily sawed by several methods, but the fastest uses a circular saw with inserted carbide tips. More accurate slugs are produced by sawing than by blanking; however, as in blanking, a considerable amount of metal is lost.

The properties of aluminum and its alloys that provide high extrudability likewise cause low shearability; thus, shearing generally results in severely distorted slugs. Consequently, shearing is used less in producing aluminum slugs than steel slugs.

When "doughnut" slugs are required, they can be sawed from tubing, or they can be punched, drilled or extruded. Machined slugs (such as those produced in an automatic bar machine) are generally more accurate but cost more than those produced by other methods.

Cast slugs can also be used; the choice of cast slugs is made on a basis of adequate quality at lower fabricating cost. Sometimes compositions that are not readily available in plate or bar stock can be successfully cast and extruded. Often there is a saving in metal when a preform can be cast to shape.

Tolerance on volume of the slug may vary from ±2% to ±10%, depending on design and economic considerations. When extrusions are trimmed, as most are, slug tolerance in the upper part of the above range can be tolerated. When extrusions are not trimmed and dimensions are critical, volume tolerance of the slugs must be held close to the bottom of the range. In high-quantity production of parts such as thin-wall containers, the degree to which slug volume must be controlled is often dictated by metal cost.

Surface Preparation

Slugs of the more extrudable aluminum alloys, such as 1100 and 3003, are often given no surface preparation before a lubricant is applied prior to extrusion. For slugs of the less extrudable aluminum alloys or for maximum extrusion severity, or both, preparation of the surface for retention of lubricant may be required. One method is to etch the slugs in a heated caustic solution, followed by water rinsing, nitric acid desmutting, and a final rinse in water. For the most severe extrusion, slug surfaces are given a phosphate coating before the lubricant is applied.

For details of alkaline etching, acid desmutting, and phosphate coating, see pages 619, 620 and 627 in the article "Cleaning and Finishing of Aluminum and Aluminum Alloys", in Volume 2 of this Handbook.

Lubricants. Aluminum and aluminum alloys can be successfully extruded with lubricants such as high-viscosity oil, grease, wax, tallow, and sodium-tallow soap. Zinc stearate, applied by dry tumbling, is an excellent lubricant for extruding aluminum.

The lubricant should be applied to clean metal surfaces, free from foreign oil, grease and dirt. Preliminary etching of the surfaces (see above) increases the effectiveness of the lubricant.

For the most difficult aluminum extrusions (less extrudable alloys or greater severity, or both), the slugs should be given a phosphate treatment followed by application of a soap that reacts with the surface to form a lubricating layer similar to that formed when extruding steel.

Shallow Cuplike Parts

Simple, shallow cuplike parts can be extruded from most of the wrought aluminum alloys without difficulty. If the wall thickness is uniform and the bottom is nearly flat, shallow cups can be produced in one hit (blow) at high production rates; but if the shape is more complex, at least two hits are often needed. In the three examples that follow, two hits were required. In the first example, an internal boss prevented completion of the extrusion in one hit; in Examples 690 and 691, the extrusions had stepped walls.

Example 689. Use of a Preform for Producing a Complex Bottom (Fig. 3)

The housing shown in Fig. 3 required two extrusion operations because of the internal boss, which was formed by backward extru-

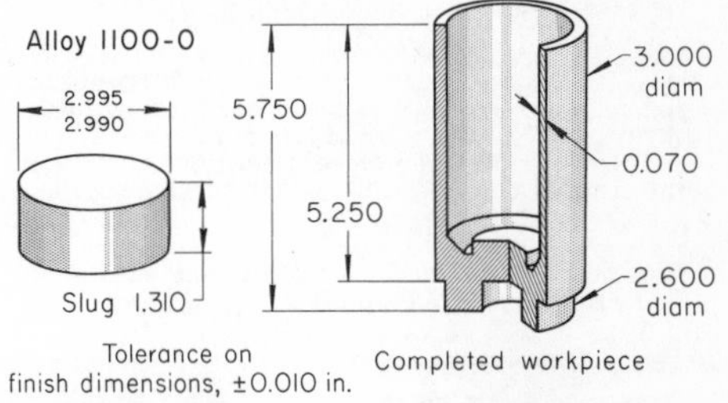

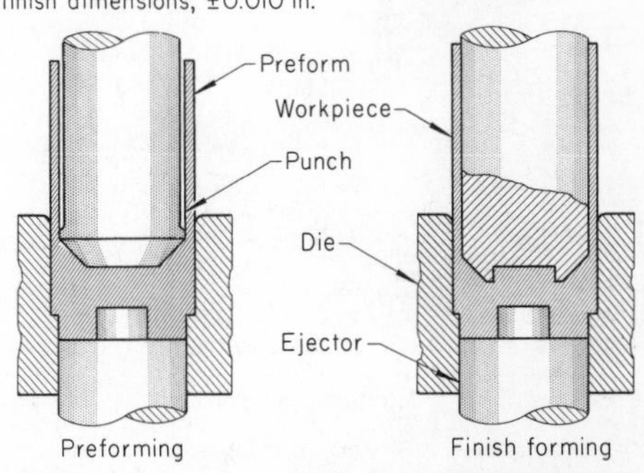

Press	Hydraulic, 350-ton
Die	Two-station
Type of slug	Sawed from bar, and annealed
Lubricant	Zinc stearate
Production rate:	
First operation	350 pieces per hour
Second operation	250 pieces per hour
Tool life, minimum	100,000 pieces

Fig. 3. Housing that was extruded in two operations because of an internal boss (Example 689)

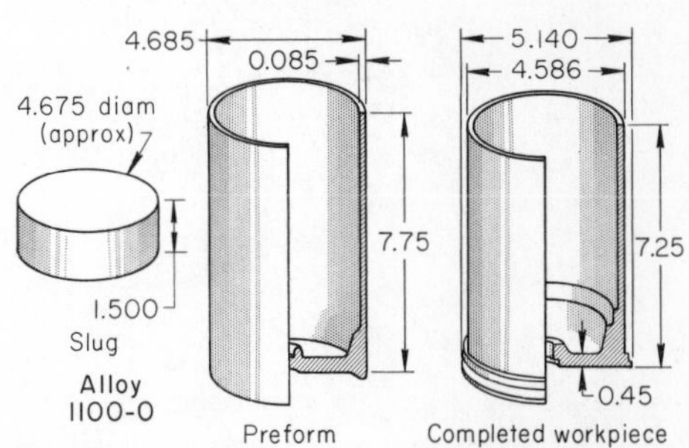

Press	Hydraulic, 2500-ton(a)
Die	Two-station
Type of slug	Sawed from bar, and annealed
Lubricant	Zinc stearate
Production rate	60 to 75 pieces per hour
Tool life, minimum	50,000 pieces

(a) 900 tons required for extruding and 1350 tons for sizing.

Fig. 4. Cartridge case that was completed in two press operations because of a stepped wall (Example 690)

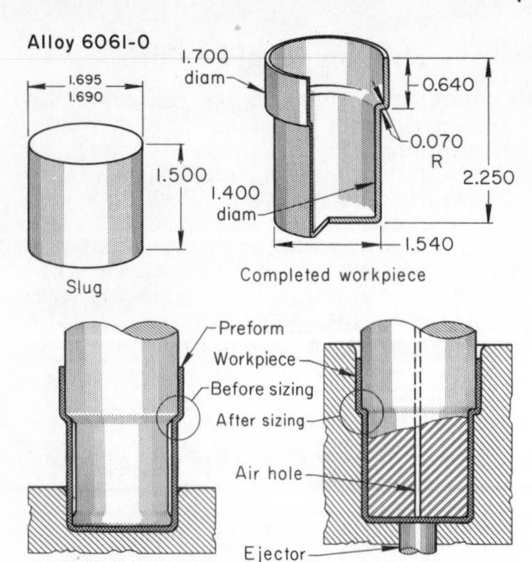

Press .... Mechanical, crank-type, 90-ton
Die .... Two-station
Type of slug .... Sawed from bar, and annealed
Lubricant .... Zinc stearate (first operation); liquid wax, dip (second operation)
Production rate .... 700 to 750 pieces per hour
Tool life, minimum .... 500,000 pieces

Fig. 5. Stepped-wall cup that was extruded and then sized to set 0.070-in. radii (Example 691)

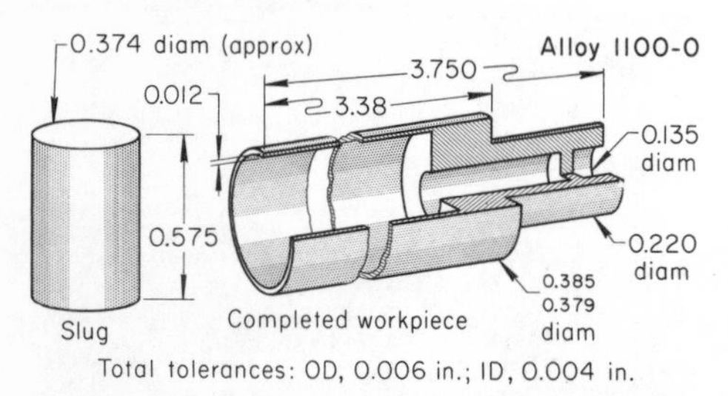

Press .... Mechanical, horizontal, 150-ton
Die .... Single-station
Type of slug .. Sawed or machined from bar, and annealed
Lubricant .... Zinc stearate
Production rate .. 4200 pcs/hr (100% efficiency)
Tool life, minimum .... 1 million pieces

Fig. 6. Long part that was extruded in one hit. Ratio of length to diameter (10 to 1) is about maximum for one-hit extrusion of alloy 1100-O. (Example 692)

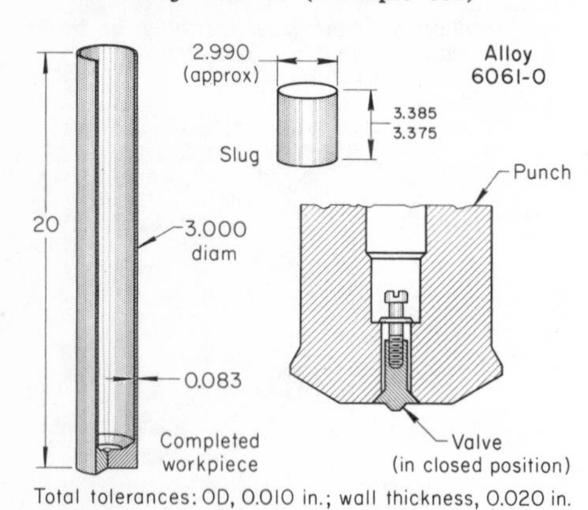

Press .... Hydraulic, 800-ton(a)
Die .... Single-station
Type of slug .... Sawed from bar, and annealed
Lubricant .... Zinc stearate
Production rate .... 300 pieces per hour
Tool life, minimum .... 50,000 pieces

(a) Workpiece was sized in a 30-ton hydraulic press after solution treatment and before aging.

Fig. 7. Long part that was extruded in one hit, and valved punch used for ease in stripping (Example 693)

sion in a second operation, as shown in Fig. 3. The blended angle in the preform functioned as a support for the finishing punch during extrusion of the internal boss. This counteracted the side pressure that was created as the metal flowed into the cavity of the finishing punch.

Additional processing details are given in the table that accompanies Fig. 3.

Example 690. Double Backward Extruding, Piercing and Finish Forming in Two Hits (Fig. 4)

The cartridge case shown in Fig. 4 was completed in two press operations. The preform, also shown in Fig. 4, was extruded in one operation. A stepped punch permitted the metal to fill the thicker wall portion first, after which wall thickness was reduced to 0.085 in. After being trimmed to length and pierced, the preform was upset (stepped flange) and finish formed in a second operation. Stamping of identification numbers on the bottom, tapering of the tubular section 0.0165 in. per inch, and forming of the primer seat were also done in the second operation. Additional manufacturing details are given in the table that accompanies Fig. 4.

Example 691. Extrusion and Sizing of Stepped-Wall Cups (Fig. 5)

A stepped-wall cup was made in two operations as shown in Fig. 5. The preform was extruded from a slug of solution-annealed 6061 alloy using a stepped punch with back relief on the smaller diameter, as shown in Fig. 5. The preform was then solution treated at 970 F, relubricated and finish formed as shown. A steady stream of air through the punch helped to keep the extrusion in the die during finish forming and also facilitated stripping it from the punch. Additional processing details are given in the table with Fig. 5.

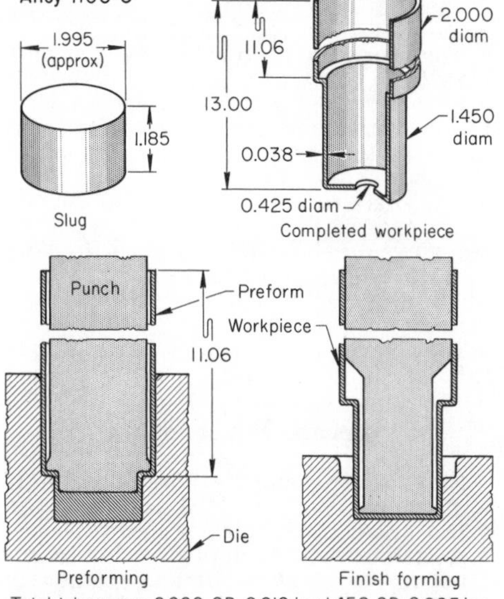

Press .... Mechanical, 190-ton
Die .... Two-station
Type of slug .... Sawed from bar, and annealed
Lubricant .... Zinc stearate
Production rate .... 1500 pieces per hour
Tool life, minimum .... 250,000 pieces

Fig. 8. Flare case that was extruded in two operations (Example 694)

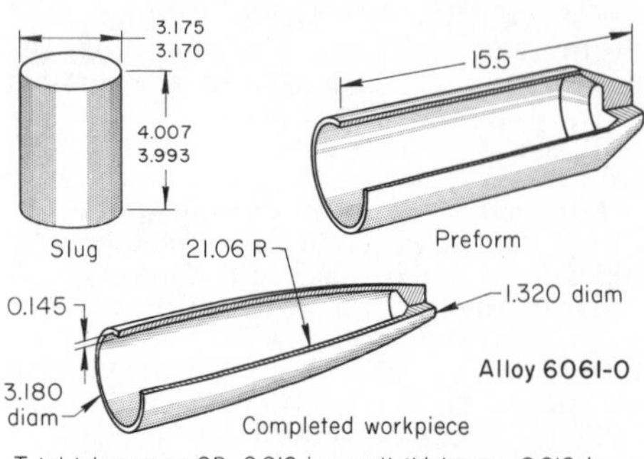

Press .... Hydraulic, 800-ton(a)
Die .... Two-station
Type of slug .... Sawed from bar, and annealed
Lubricant .... Zinc stearate(b)
Production rate .... 300 pieces per hour
Tool life, minimum .... 75,000 pieces

(a) Pressure set at 450 tons. (b) For extrusion of preform. Preform was lubricated with a solution of lanolin, zinc stearate, and trichlorethylene before finish forming.

Fig. 9. Motor housing that was extruded in two operations (Example 695)

Deep Cuplike Parts

Although cups having a length as great as 17 times the diameter have been produced, this extreme condition is seldom found in practice because a punch this slender is likely to deflect and cause nonuniform wall thickness in the backward extruded product.

In the four examples that follow, the lengths of the cuplike parts range from nearly ten diameters (Example 692) to about five (Example 695). This is a typical range of length-to-diameter ratios used in backward extruding deep cups.

Length of cup and number of operations (use of preform) are not necessarily related. Whether or not a preform is required depends mainly on the shape, particularly of the closed end. This is evident in Examples 692 and 693, in which two long parts were produced with only one hit each.

When forming deep cups from heat treatable alloys such as 6061, if the amount of reduction is 25% or more in the preform, the workpiece should be reannealed and relubricated between preforming and finish extruding (see Example 695).

Example 692. One-Hit Extrusion of a Part Ten Diameters Long (Fig. 6)

The hypodermic syringe shown in Fig. 6 was produced in one hit in a high-speed horizontal press. The 10-to-1 length-to-diameter ratio of this part was close to the practical maximum for extrusion in one hit, because of the high probability of lateral deflection of a long, slender punch. Processing details are given in the table with Fig. 6.

Example 693. Use of a Valved Punch for Ease in Stripping a Part Seven Diameters Long Extruded in One Hit (Fig. 7)

The part shown in Fig. 7 was extruded in one hit from an annealed 6061 alloy slug. It was then solution heat treated, relubricated, sized (ironed) in another press, and aged to the T6 temper.

In extruding straight-wall parts like the one in Fig. 7, stripping can be a problem because the punch creates a vacuum. In this application, the problem was solved by the use of a punch that incorporated a valve (shown in Fig. 7). The valve was closed when the punch moved down, and opened as the punch withdrew. Additional processing details are given with Fig. 7.

Example 694. Extruding a Deep, Two-Diameter Cup in Two Operations (Fig. 8)

The flare case shown in Fig. 8 was produced in two extrusion operations. The first hit formed the 11.06-in. tubular section shown as the preform in Fig. 8. In the second hit, the small-diameter bottom section was formed from the heavy section of the preform. Slugs were annealed before the first extrusion operation, but intermediate annealing and relubrication were not required. After extrusion, the

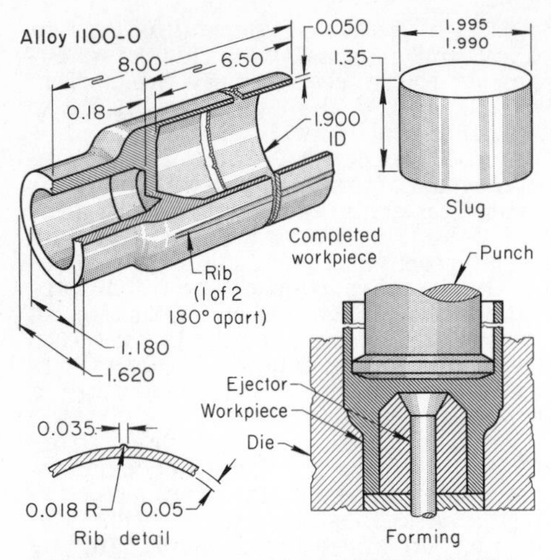

Total tolerances: OD, 0.004 in.; wall thickness, 0.005 in.

Press	Mechanical, crank-type, 190-ton
Die	Single-station
Type of slug	Sawed from bar, and annealed
Lubricant	Zinc stearate
Production rate	1500 pieces per hour
Tool life, minimum	75,000 pieces

Fig. 10. Flare casing with two outside ribs that was produced in one hit by backward-forward extrusion (Example 696)

workpiece was trimmed to length and the bottom hole was pierced. Processing details are given in the table with Fig. 8.

Example 695. Extrusion of a Tapered-Wall Motor Housing in Two Operations (Fig. 9)

Two extrusion operations were needed to form the motor housing shown in Fig. 9. This part was made of annealed 6061 alloy and required reannealing and relubricating between the two extrusion operations. After finish forming, the housing was solution heat treated and aged to the T6 temper. Additional processing details are given with Fig. 9.

Parts With Complex Shapes

Producing extrusions from aluminum and aluminum alloys in a single hit is not necessarily confined to simple shapes. The extrusions described in Examples 696 to 700, which follow, were all produced in a single hit despite their relatively complex shapes. For extrusions with longitudinal flutes, stems or grooves, the use of one of the most extrudable alloys, such as 1100, is helpful in minimizing difficulties. Sometimes, however, a less extrudable alloy can be used to form a complex shape in one hit, as in Example 700.

Successful extrusion of complex shapes, especially in a single hit, depends greatly on tool design and slug design. Ordinarily, some development work is required for each new job before it can be put into production.

Example 696. One-Hit Extrusion of a Casing With Outside Ribs (Fig. 10)

Figure 10 shows a flare casing with two longitudinal locating ribs on its outside diameter that was produced in one hit by backward-forward extrusion. The tool setup is also shown in Fig. 10, and processing details are given in the accompanying table.

Example 697. Use of a Tubular Slug and Punch for Double Backward Extrusion (Fig. 11)

The container shown in Fig. 11 was extruded by the double backward technique in one hit by using the tubular slug and hollow punch also shown in Fig. 11. Considerable development in tooling and slug dimensions was required before uniform wall thickness could be obtained for both the large and small diameters. Processing details are given in the table that accompanies Fig. 11.

Example 698. Maximum Extrudability for a Complex Shape (Fig. 12)

The hydraulic cylinder body shown in Fig. 12 was extruded from a solid slug in one hit. Alloy 1100, which has maximum extrudability, was required for this part because of the abrupt changes in section of the cylinder body. Surface cracks and laps resulted when more difficult-to-extrude alloys were used. The different wall thicknesses and steps in this design represent near-maximum severity for extruding in one hit, even with the most extrudable alloy. During development of this part, it was necessary to change the face angles, shorten the steps, and blend the outside ribs more gradually to insure complete fillout. Additional processing details are given in the table with Fig. 12.

Example 699. Use of a Doughnut Slug in Backward-Forward Extrusion in One Hit (Fig. 13)

The housing shown in Fig. 13 was extruded by the backward-forward technique in a single hit from a drilled (or pierced) slug. The tooling setup used in this operation is also shown in Fig. 13. The eight splines were formed in the small diameter by forward extrusion, using the serrated portion of the punch. At the same time, the ribbed cup portion of the workpiece was formed by backward extrusion with the

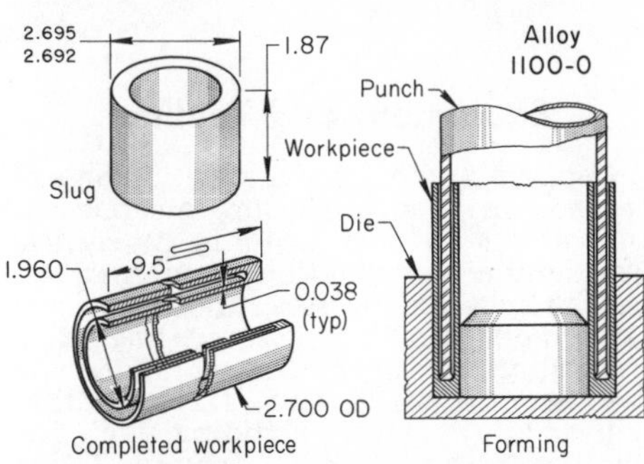

Total tolerances: diameters, ±0.004 in.; wall thickness, ±0.007 in. (held to ±0.003 in.)

Press	Hydraulic, 350-ton
Die	Single-station
Type of slug	Sawed from tubing(a)
Lubricant	Liquid wax (dip)
Production rate	300 pieces per hour
Tool life, minimum	50,000 pieces

(a) An alternate method was to extrude a cup-shaped slug to the same dimensions in a header, then machine square the open end and remove the closed end by machining. Slugs were annealed after sawing or heading.

Fig. 11. Double-wall container produced by extruding a tubular slug with a hollow punch (Example 697)

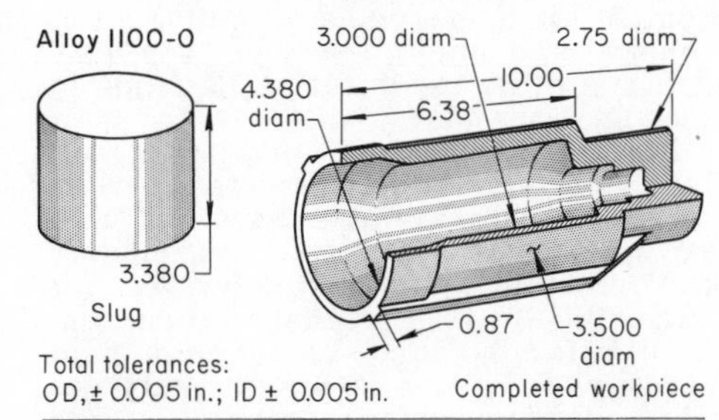

Total tolerances: OD, ± 0.005 in.; ID ± 0.005 in.

Press	Hydraulic, 800-ton (set at 500 tons)
Die	Single-station
Type of slug	Sawed from bar, and annealed
Lubricant	Zinc stearate
Production rate	300 pieces per hour
Tool life, minimum	70,000 pieces

Fig. 12. Hydraulic cylinder body extruded in one hit. Complexity of configuration is about the maximum producible by one-hit extrusion of alloy 1100-O. (Example 698)

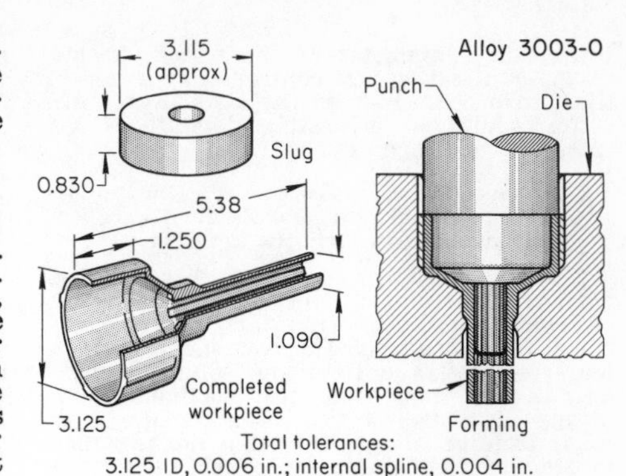

Total tolerances: 3.125 ID, 0.006 in.; internal spline, 0.004 in.

Press	Mechanical, horizontal, 1000-ton(a)
Die	Single-station
Type of slug	Sawed from bar(b)
Lubricant	Liquid wax (dip)
Production rate	1500 pieces per hour
Tool life, minimum	200,000 pieces

(a) 375 tons required. (b) Hole was drilled or pierced; slugs were then annealed.

Fig. 13. Splined housing extruded in one hit from a doughnut slug (Example 699)

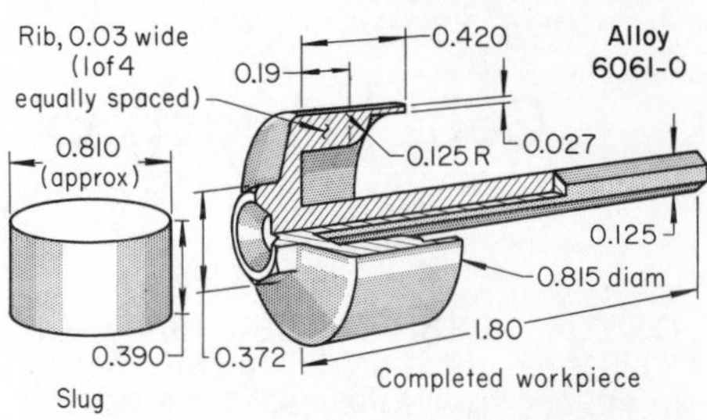

Total tolerances: Hexagonal pin, 0.004 in.; OD, 0.010 in.

Press	Mechanical, horizontal, 150-ton
Die	Single-station
Type of slug	Stamped wafer
Lubricant	Zinc stearate
Production rate	3900 pcs/hr (100% efficiency)
Tool life, minimum	300,000 pieces

Fig. 14. Striker with ribs and a center column that was extruded from a wafer slug in one hit (Example 700)

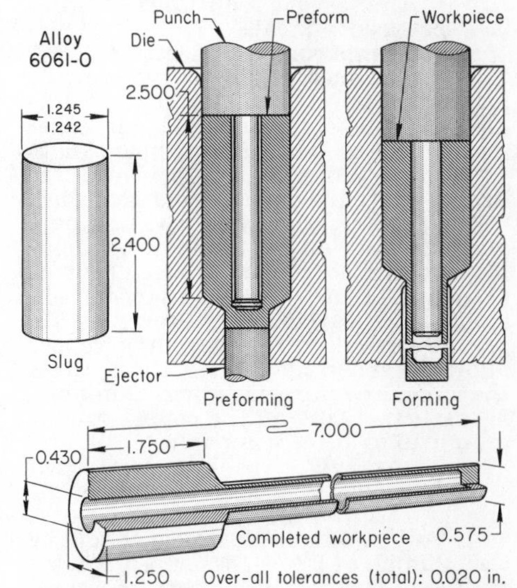

Press	Mechanical, crank-type, 190-ton
Dies	Two
Type of slug	Sawed from bar, and annealed
Lubricant	Zinc stearate(a)
Production, first hit	1200 pieces per hour
Production, second hit	700 pieces per hour
Tool life, minimum	150,000 pieces

(a) For extruding the preform; dipped in a solution of lanolin, zinc stearate, and trichlorethylene before finish forming.

Fig. 15. Burster tube that was extruded in two operations (Example 701)

intermediate diameter of the punch. Length of the cup section was controlled by a step in the punch that confined the metal in the die.

For additional processing details, see the table that accompanies Fig. 13.

Example 700. Production of Ribs and Center Column by Double Backward Extrusion in One Hit (Fig. 14)

The striker shown in Fig. 14 was extruded from a wafer slug in one hit by the double backward technique. This part, which incorporated a hexagonal boss on the outside, a four-rib tubular section, and an inside hexagonal stem, represents near-maximum complexity of shape for one hit, especially when made from an alloy (6061) that has less than maximum extrudability (see Table 1). Despite its complexity, this part was produced at a rate of 65 per minute in a horizontal press. Other processing details are given with Fig. 14.

Example 701. Two-Operation Extrusion of a Complex Shape From Alloy 6061 (Fig. 15)

A burster tube was produced by forward extrusion in two operations, as shown in Fig. 15. The preform was extruded from an annealed slug, after which the preform was reannealed, relubricated and finish formed in a second extrusion operation. After the second extrusion, the part was solution treated and aged to the T6 temper. Additional processing details are given in the table that accompanies Fig. 15.

Dimensional Accuracy

In general, aluminum extrusions are manufactured to close tolerances. The closeness depends on size, shape, alloy, wall thickness, type of tooling, and press equipment. Lubrication and slug fit in the die are also important.

Wall-thickness tolerances range from ±0.001 to ±0.005 in. for relatively thin-wall cylindrical shapes of moderate size extruded from low-strength alloys, but may be as great as ±0.010 to ±0.015 in. for large parts of high-strength alloys. Wall-thickness tolerances for rectangular shells range from ±0.005 to ±0.015 in., depending on size, alloy and nominal wall thickness. Diameter tolerances typically range from ±0.001 in. for small parts to ±0.010 to ±0.015 in. for large, high-strength alloy parts. Closer control of diameter can be achieved on small, heavy-wall parts by centerless grinding the extrusions (provided the alloy is one that can be ground satisfactorily). Dimensional tolerances in the forged portion of the impact are influenced by the same variables as those listed above, but a range of ±0.005 to ±0.015 in. is typical. Variations in extruded length usually necessitate a separate trimming operation.

Surface finish typically ranges from 20 to 70 micro-in. Smoother surfaces can sometimes be obtained by using extreme care in surface preparation and lubrication of the work metal, and by paying close attention to the surface condition of the tools.

Cold (Impact) Extrusion of Copper and Copper Alloy Parts

By N. L. WARD

OXYGEN-FREE COPPER (alloy 102) is the most extrudable of the coppers and copper-base alloys. Other grades of copper and most of the copper-base alloys can be cold (impact) extruded, although there are wide differences in extrudability among the different compositions. For example, the harder copper alloys, such as aluminum-silicon bronze and nickel silver, are far more difficult to extrude than are the softer, more ductile alloys, such as cartridge brass (alloy 260), which can satisfactorily withstand cold reductions of up to 90% between anneals.

Alloys containing as much as 1.25% lead can be successfully extruded if the amount of upset is mild and the workpiece is in compression at all times during metal flow. But copper alloys containing more than 1.25% lead are likely to crumble when cold extruded.

The pressure required for extruding a given area for one of the more extrudable coppers or copper alloys (such as alloy 102 or 260) is less than for extruding low-carbon steel. However, the pressure required for extruding copper alloys is generally two to three times that required for extruding aluminum alloys (depending on the copper or aluminum alloy being compared).

The length of a backward-extruded section is limited by the length-to-diameter ratio of the punch, and varies with unit pressure. This ratio should be a maximum of 5 to 1 for copper, whereas 10 to 1 is common for extruding aluminum and as high as 17 to 1 has been used. The total reduction in area for copper or copper alloys, under the best conditions, should not exceed 93%.

Fundamentals of the cold extrusion process that are applicable to various extrudable metals are discussed in the article "Cold Extrusion", page 475 in this volume. Also described are applications combining extrusion and cold heading — common in fastener production.

Equipment and Tooling

Coppers and copper alloys can be extruded in hydraulic or mechanical presses, or in cold heading machines. For detailed information on presses, see the article on Presses and Auxiliary Equipment, which begins on page 1.

Tooling procedures and tool materials are essentially the same for extruding copper alloys as for extruding steel. For detailed information on tools and tool materials, see the article "Cold Extrusion", and references appended thereto, pages 475 to 489 in this volume.

Preparation of Slugs

Sawing, shearing and machining are the methods used in preparing copper and copper-alloy slugs. Each method has advantages and limitations, as shown in Table 8 in the article "Cold Extrusion" (page 482). Sawing or shearing is generally used for producing solid slugs (see Examples 702, 703 and 705). Machining (as in a lathe) or cold forming in auxiliary equipment is seldom used unless a hole in the slug, or some other modification, is required (see Example 704).

Surface Preparation. In applications involving minimum to moderate severity, copper slugs are often extruded with no special surface preparation before the lubricant is applied. However, for extruding the harder alloys (aluminum bronze, for instance) or for maximum severity, or both, best practice includes the following surface preparation before the lubricant is applied:

1 Cleaning in an alkaline cleaner to remove oil, grease and soil
2 Rinsing in water
3 Pickling in 10% (by vol) sulfuric acid at 70 to 150 F to remove metal oxides
4 Rinsing in cold water
5 Rinsing in a well-buffered solution, such as carbonate or borate, to neutralize residual acid or acid salts.

Lubrication. Zinc stearate is an excellent lubricant for extruding copper alloys. Common practice is to etch the slugs as described above, and then to coat them by dry tumbling in zinc stearate. An alternative procedure is to dip the slugs (preferably, etched slugs) in a solution of lanolin, zinc stearate, and trichlorethylene.

Examples of Practice

The four examples that follow describe typical production practice for extruding parts from copper and brass. The parts described in Examples 702 and 703 could have been made by forging, casting or machining; however, cold extrusion produced more accurate dimensions than forging or casting, consumed less material than machining, and was the lowest-cost method.

Example 702. Shearing, Heading, Piercing, Extruding and Upsetting in a Header (Fig. 1)

The plumbing fitting shown in Fig. 1 was made of electrolytic tough pitch copper rod cold drawn (about 15% reduction of area) to a diameter of 1.06 in. The pipe-taper diameter and the 0.875-in. diameter of the tube socket were critical, being specified within 0.0025 in.

Manufacture of the fitting consisted of feeding the rod stock into the cold heading machine, which cut it into slugs 0.80 in. long and transferred the slugs progressively to dies for heading, backward extruding, piercing, forward extruding, and upsetting (Fig. 1). Only trimming on each end and tapping were required for completing the parts. Extrusion equipment consisted of a No. 4 cold heading machine and a five-station die.

The final cross-sectional area of the thin end after extrusion was 16.4% of the 1.21-in.-diam headed preform from which the fitting was made. A reduction of this magnitude could have been made in one operation if a cylindrical rod were being extruded from the 1.21-in.-diam preform. The shape, however, was not suitable for production in one operation. Therefore, the fitting was made by backward and forward extrusion and mild upsetting. Additional manufacturing details are given in the table with Fig. 1.

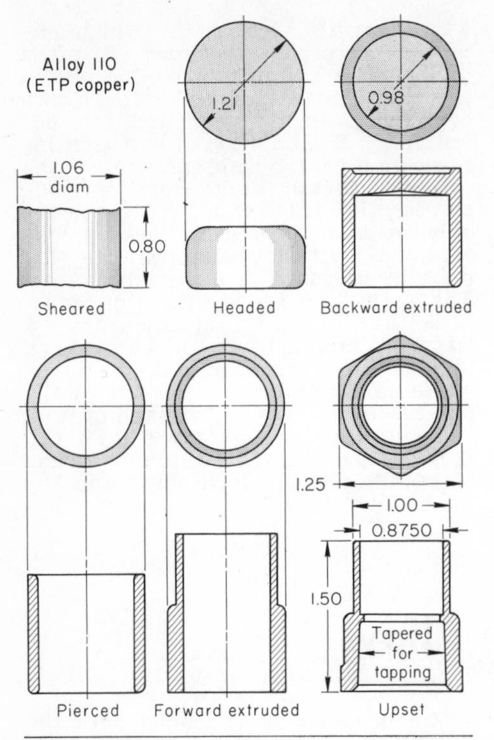

Press	No. 4 header
Die	Five-station (including heading)
Tool material	D2 tool steel(a)
Backward-extrusion pressure	200,000 psi
Forward-extrusion pressure	136,000 psi
Lubricant	Proprietary EP type
Type of slug	Sheared
Production rate	3600 pcs/hr (100% efficiency)
Tool life, minimum	200,000 pieces

(a) Hardness varied from Rockwell C 58 for tools having fragile sections to Rockwell C 62 for heavily loaded and more massive sections.

Fig. 1. Intermediate stages in production of a fitting from rod stock (Example 702)

Example 703. Extruding Instead of Machining, to Save Metal (Fig. 2)

The part shown in Fig. 2 originally was machined from bar stock in automatic equipment. To reduce cost by saving metal, the part was extruded in one blow from sawed slugs. The costs of machining and extruding were about the same, but extruding saved about 6 lb of metal per part. Processing details for extruding are given in the table with Fig. 2.

The two examples that follow give details for backward-forward extrusion of parts having long slender sections.

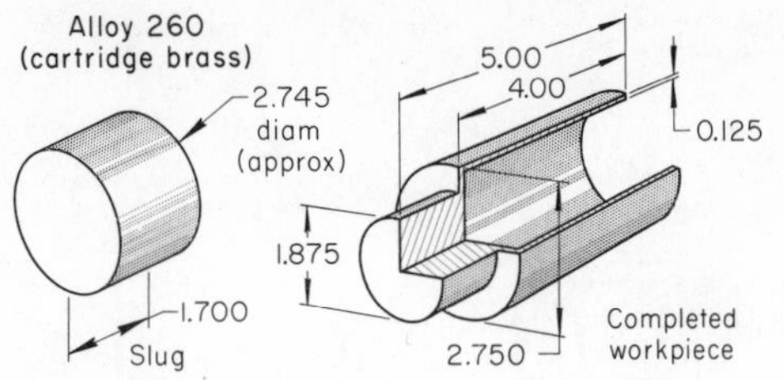

Press	Hydraulic, 800-ton
Die	Single-station
Lubricant	Zinc stearate
Type of slug	Sawed and annealed
Production rate	200 pieces per hour
Tool life, minimum	100,000 pieces

Fig. 2. Brass part extruded from a solid slug in one blow (Example 703)

Example 704. Extruding a Tubular Part From a Drilled Slug (Fig. 3)

The part illustrated in Fig. 3 was backward-forward extruded from a slug made in an automatic bar machine. The drilled hole in the slug permitted close control in forward extruding the 0.280-in.-OD tube section with a punch that incorporated a slender projection beyond the punch nose.

As shown in Fig. 3, a sliding sleeve guided the punch at the beginning of the cycle. The sleeve moved upward as the 0.937-in.-OD cup was formed, until it came to rest against the shoulder of the punch. This action terminated the backward-extrusion portion of the cycle and controlled the length of the cup. The sleeve and punch completed the down stroke to produce the proper thickness at the bottom of the cup and to complete the extrusion of the tube section. Thickness of the tube section was determined by the clearance at the orifice between the punch-nose projection and the neck of the die cavity. During the backward stroke of the press, the part was pulled out of the die, and the sleeve stripped the part from the punch. Additional processing details are given in the table with Fig. 3.

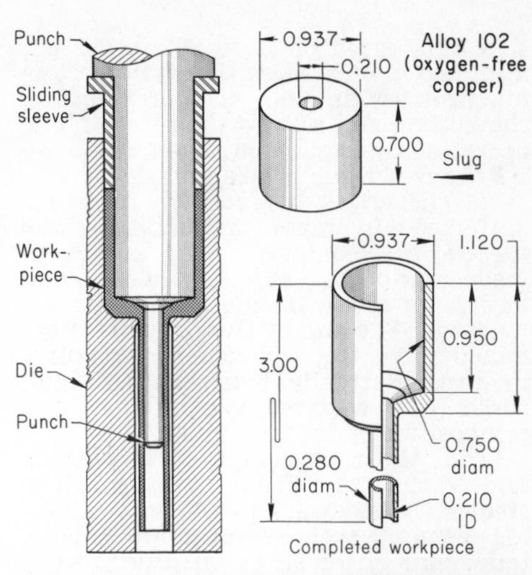

Press	Mechanical, crank-type, 65-ton
Die	Single-station
Lubricant	Lanolin – zinc stearate – trichlorethylene
Type of slug	Machined and annealed
Production rate	700 pieces per hour
Tool life, minimum	100,000 pieces

Fig. 3. Backward-forward extrusion of a machined slug (Example 704)

The part described in the following example represents a difficult extrusion for two reasons: (*a*) the metal (tellurium copper, alloy 145) is one of the more difficult-to-extrude copper alloys, and (*b*) the configuration (12 internal flutes and 12 external ribs) is difficult to extrude regardless of the metal used.

Example 705. Extrusion vs Brazed Assembly for Lower Cost (Fig. 4)

The rotor shown in Fig. 4 was originally produced by brazing a machined section into a drawn ribbed and fluted tubular section.

By an improved method this rotor was extruded from a sawed slug in one hit. The extruded rotor was produced at less cost and had better dimensional accuracy than the brazed assembly, and there were fewer rejects. For additional processing details, including production rate, see Fig. 4.

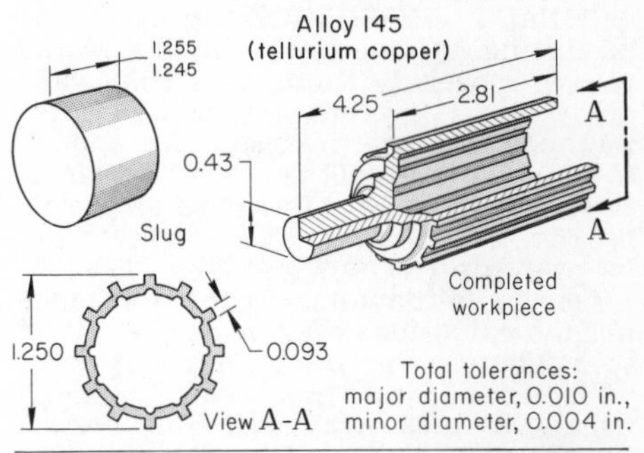

Press	Mechanical, crank-type, 190-ton
Die	Single-station
Lubricant	Lanolin – zinc stearate – trichlorethylene
Type of slug	Sawed and annealed
Production rate	1800 pieces per hour
Tool life, minimum	50,000 pieces

Fig. 4. Rotor produced by backward-forward extrusion (Example 705)

Impact Extrusion of Lead Alloys

THE METHOD of producing collapsible tubes and other containers by impact extrusion involves plastic deformation of a flat blank by forcing it through an orifice under hydrostatic pressure. Extrusion time in a mechanical press is about 1/20 sec; average production rate is 60 tubes per minute.

Tube Extrusion. Blanks for collapsible tubes are stamped from rolled sheet. After the blank has been lubricated by tumbling, it is placed in an extrusion die having an inside diameter (D) equal to the outside diameter of the tube to be extruded (see Fig. 1a). A punch is centered above the die. This punch has an outside diameter (d) equal to the inside diameter of the tube. The press moves the punch downward to deform the slug, until all the void below the punch and die has been filled and the metal is completely trapped. As the punch descends farther, an annular orifice between the punch and die will be formed. The width of the orifice is equivalent to the desired thickness of the wall of the tube, conventionally 0.004 to 0.005 in. The punch descends still farther, displacing the metal as in an ordinary squirt gun, and since the annular opening between the punch and the die is the only place through which the metal can escape, the metal is forced to climb up the punch, as shown in Fig. 1(b). The tube is completed when the punch has descended to the desired depth, leaving a predetermined bottom thickness. After the first part of the cycle has been completed, the punch withdraws, the knockout pushes the tube out of the die, and the tube stays on the punch until removed by hand or by an automatic stripper. The tube is thus extruded in one stroke of the press. Trimming and threading, if required, can be done in a second operation.

Caps and stoppers used in collapsible tubes are also produced by impact extrusion. A threaded cap for collapsible tubes can be completed in one operation at a speed of 80 to 90 strokes per minute. Other articles that have lettering, protrusions, slots, or depressions on the bottom can also be produced in one operation by impact extrusion.

Presses. Ordinary straight-side presses of the crank or eccentric type are preferred. In mass production, these presses are equipped with automatic feeds, strippers, safety devices, and means for removing the tubes from the machine. The size of the press is determined by the extrusion pressures involved. Normally, between 30,000 and 50,000 psi is required, depending on the composition of the lead alloy.

Lead Alloys. Although it is possible and feasible to extrude pure lead, it is frequently necessary to add some alloying element, such as antimony, copper, tellurium, tin or silver, in order to obtain the required stiffness. Alloying

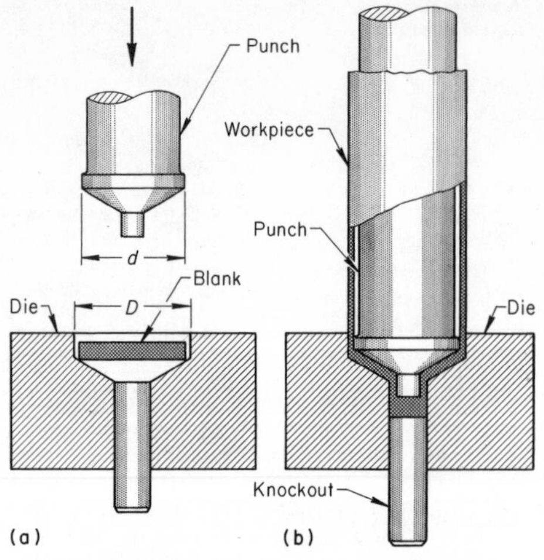

Fig. 1. Impact extruding a collapsible tube

with elements such as tin, which improves corrosion resistance, is often indicated. A common alloy for use in the manufacture of collapsible tubes contains 97 to 98% lead and 2 to 3% antimony. The addition of less than 1% silver improves its appearance.

Duplex Metal. Under some circumstances, tin-coated lead tubes are desirable. In order to produce these by conventional extrusion methods, the slug must be prepared in a special manner. The method used is to wrap a previously rolled, thin sheet of tin around a lead slab and then to roll them down together in a standard rolling mill by conventional procedure. Because of the difference in the cost of tin and of lead, it is customary to use only 3 to 7% tin. Slugs prepared in this manner extrude as readily as pure lead slugs, and the tin coating is distributed evenly.

Impact Extrusion of Magnesium Alloys

IMPACT EXTRUSION is used for producing symmetrical tubular workpieces, especially those with thin walls or irregular profiles for which other methods are not practical. As applied to magnesium alloys, the extrusion process cannot be referred to as "cold", because both blanks and tooling must be preheated to not less than 350 F.

Length-to-diameter ratios for magnesium extrusions may be as high as 15 to 1. There is no lower limit, but parts with ratios of less than about 2 to 1 can usually be press drawn at lower cost. A typical ratio is 8 to 1, and parts with higher length-to-diameter ratios are more amenable to forward extrusion than to backward extrusion. At all ratios, the mechanical properties of magnesium extrusions normally exceed those of the blanks from which they are made, because of the beneficial effects of mechanical working.

Equipment and Tooling. Because mechanical presses are faster, they are more widely used for impact extrusion than are hydraulic presses, except when long strokes are needed.

Presses with a capacity of 100 tons and a stroke of 6 in. are adequate for most extrusion applications. Up to 100 extrusions per minute have been produced. Extrusion rate is limited only by press speed.

Dies for impact extruding magnesium alloys differ from those used for other metals, because magnesium alloys are extruded at elevated temperature (usually 500 F). Common practice is to heat the die with tubular electric heaters. The die is insulated from the press by asbestos cloth, and an insulating shroud is built around the die. The top of the die is also covered, except for punch entry and the feeding and ejection devices. The punch is not heated, but during continuous operation becomes hot, so that the punch should be insulated from the ram by asbestos.

Punches and dies usually are made of a hot work tool steel, such as H12 or H13, heat treated to Rockwell C 48 to 52. In one application, tools made of heat treated H13 produced 200,000 extrusions. Carbide dies can be used and can extrude up to ten million pieces.

Table 1. Pressures Required at Various Temperatures to Impact Extrude Four Magnesium Alloys to a Reduction in Area of 85%

Alloy	Extrusion pressure (tons/sq in.) at: 450 F	500 F	550 F	600 F	650 F	700 F	750 F
AZ31B ...	33	33	30	27	26	25	23
AZ61A ...	35	34	33	32	31	30	29
AZ80A ...	36	35	34	33	32	31	30
ZK60A ...	34	33	32	31	29	27	26

Table 2. Typical Tolerances for a Magnesium Alloy Impact Extrusion With a Length-to-Diameter Ratio of 6 to 1

Dimension	Tolerance, in.
Diameter	±0.002 (a)
Bottom thickness	±0.005 (b)
Wall thickness, in.:	
0.020 to 0.029	±0.002
0.030 to 0.044	±0.003
0.045 to 0.059	±0.004
0.060 to 0.100	±0.005

(a) Per inch of diameter. (b) All thicknesses.

Sidewalls of the die cavity should have a draft of approximately 0.002 in. per inch of depth, which prevents the extrusion from sticking in the cavity. In normal operation, the part stays on the punch and is stripped from it on the upward stroke.

Procedure. Magnesium alloy slugs are prepared by the same methods as other metals — sawing from bar stock or blanking from plate, if rough edges can be tolerated. Slugs can also be made by casting. Slugs must be uniform in size and shape for centering in the die, to insure uniform wall thickness on the extrusion, which in turn depends on the clearance between die and punch.

Slugs are lubricated by tumbling in a graphite suspension for 10 min until a dry coat develops.

For automatic impact extrusion of magnesium parts, the lubricated slugs are loaded into a hopper feed. The slugs are heated by an electric heater as they pass along the track between the hopper and the die.

The heated slug is loaded onto the heated die, and the press is activated to produce the extrusion. Operating temperatures for extruding magnesium alloys range from 350 to 700 F, depending on composition and operating speed. The operating temperature should be held constant, to maintain tolerances.

In practice, slugs and dies usually are heated to 500 F for feeding by tongs, because the rate of operation is slow. In automatic feeding, the slug and die temperature can be as low as 350 F, because speed is greater; dies absorb heat during operation and can increase in temperature by as much as 150 F. Example 609 (page 430) describes extrusion of a magnesium alloy part at 500 F.

When a decrease in properties is not important, operating temperatures can be higher than those shown in Table 5 on page 425. However, temperatures above recommended limits should be used with discretion.

Pressures for impact extruding magnesium alloys are about half those required for aluminum and depend mainly on alloy composition, amount of reduction, and operating temperature. Table 1 shows the pressures required to extrude several magnesium alloys to a reduction in area of 85% at seven temperatures from 450 to 750 F.

Thermal Expansion. Magnesium has a relatively high coefficient of thermal expansion compared to steel. Thus, in order to insure that the magnesium extrusion, when cooled to room temperature, will be within dimensional tolerance, it is necessary to multiply room-temperature dimensions of steel tools by a compensatory factor for the temperature at which the magnesium alloy is to be extruded. Factors for temperatures from 300 to 800 F are given in Table 7 of the article "Forming of Magnesium Alloys", on page 425.

Tolerances of extrusions are influenced by size and shape of part, length-to-diameter ratio, and press alignment. Table 2 gives typical tolerances for a magnesium part with a length-to-diameter ratio of 6 to 1.

Index

The letter E, F, or T (in parentheses) following an index entry means that information is in an Example, Figure or Table, and the letter A following an entry means that the topic is the subject of an article.

The major entries in this index are forming operations (for example, **Cold extrusion; Press forming; Spinning**); forming equipment (for example, **Drop hammers; Headers; Presses**); tools (for example, **Deep drawing dies; Form blocks; Mandrels**); tool materials (such as **Aluminum bronze; Nylon tools; Tool steels, specific types**); lubricants; metals being formed; and the items formed (for example, **Angle sections; Eyebolts; Stator laminations; Zippers**). Page references for a forming process for a specific metal are given both under the metal and under the process; for example, see the subordinate entry of "coining" under **Stainless steel** and the subordinate entry of "stainless steel" under **Coining of.** Where no material is given for a process, the entries usually refer to low-carbon steel.

Specific numbered alloys and those designated by composition are listed under the basis metal, such as **Aluminum alloys, specific types; Steels, AISI-SAE specific types; Titanium alloys, specific types.** The heat-resisting alloys, copper alloys, nickel alloys, and refractory metal alloys are listed alphabetically; for example, **A-286** is in the A's, **Yellow brass, 65%** is in the Y's, **Incoloy 801** is in the I's, and columbium alloy **FS-80** is in the F's.

A

I

M

R

Some Abbreviations and Symbols Used in This Volume

α	angle
A	area
ac	alternating current
AISI	American Iron and Steel Institute
amp	ampere
AMS	Aeronautical Materials Specification
ann	annealed
approx	approximately
ASTM	American Society for Testing and Materials
ASTME	American Society of Tool and Manufacturing Engineers
avg	average
Bhn	Brinell hardness number
Btu	British thermal unit
C	Centigrade
cap'y	capacity
CCPA	Cemented Carbide Producers Association
cfh	cubic feet per hour
cm	centimeter
cps	cycles per second
CQ	commercial quality
CR	cold rolled
cu	cubic
d	inside diameter
D	diameter; outside diameter
dc	direct current
diam	diameter
DQ	drawing quality
EHF, EHF	electrohydraulic forming
EMF, EMF	electromagnetic forming
EP, EP	extreme pressure (lubricant)
est	estimated
ETP	electrolytic tough pitch (copper)
Ex.	Example
F	Fahrenheit
fpm	feet per minute
fps	feet per second
ft	foot
g	gram
gal	gallon
gpm	gallons per minute
$>$	greater than
h	height; depth
HERF	high-energy-rate forming
hp	horsepower
hr	hour
HR	hot rolled
ID	inside diameter
in.	inch
ipm	inches per minute
JIC	Joint Industry Conference
k	constant
kv	kilovolt
kw	kilowatt
l	length
L	load; force
lb	pound
$<$	less than
LPG, LPG	liquefied petroleum gas
max	maximum
mfd	microfarad
mg	milligram
microamp	microampere
micro-in.	micro-inch
microsec	microsecond
min	minimum; minute
mm	millimeter
neg	negative (−)
No.	number
OBI	open-back inclinable (press)
OD	outside diameter
oz	ounce
P	pressure
pcs/hr	pieces per hour
pos	positive (+)
psi	pounds per square inch
r	inside radius
R	radius; outside radius
R_B	Rockwell B scale
R_C	Rockwell C scale
rem	remainder
rpm	revolutions per minute
s	distance
S	stress
SAE	Society of Automotive Engineers
sec	second
sfm	surface feet per minute
spm	strokes per minute
sq	square
SUS	Saybolt universal second
t	stock thickness
temp	temperature
TIR	total indicator reading
tsi	tons per square inch
typ	typical
v	volt
vol	volume
w	watt
w	width
wt	weight

Geometric Characteristic Symbols

Characteristic	Symbol	Characteristic	Symbol
Flatness	⏥	Perpendicularity (squareness)	⊥
Straightness	—	Angularity	∠
Roundness (circularity)	○	Runout	↗
Cylindricity	⌭	True position	⌖
Profile of any line	⌒	Concentricity	◎
Profile of any surface	⌓	Symmetry	⌯
Parallelism	∥	Surface roughness, micro-in.	√